# LIST OF SECTIONS

## Alphabetic

# FORESTRY HANDBOOK

*Edited for the Society of American Foresters*

by

## REGINALD D. FORBES

CONSULTING FORESTER

NEW YORK

THE RONALD PRESS COMPANY

1961

Copyright, ©, 1955, by
THE RONALD PRESS COMPANY

5A

Library of Congress Catalog Card Number: 55–6815

PRINTED IN THE UNITED STATES OF AMERICA

# EDITORIAL COMMITTEES

## COMMITTEE ON MATERIALS, STRUCTURES, AND FACILITIES

Rex E. Melton, *Chairman*. Pennsylvania State Forest School, Mont Alto, Pa.
Arthur K. Roberts, West Coast Lumbermen's Association, Portland, Ore.
William C. Sechrist, Mont Alto, Pa.

## COMMITTEE ON UTILIZATION AND WOOD TECHNOLOGY

R. R. Blumenstein, *Chairman*. Timber Engineering Company, Washington, D. C.
C. C. Bell, Forest Products Laboratory, Madison, Wis.
T. A. Carlson (deceased, formerly of Forest Products Laboratory).
Roy M. Carter, School of Forestry, North Carolina State College, Raleigh, N. C.
Clarence W. Dietterich, Darlington Veneer Co., Inc., Darlington, S. C.
O. H. Schrader, Jr., U. S. Plywood Corporation, Seattle, Wash.
Lawrence W. Smith, U. S. Forest Service, Washington, D. C.
Joseph L. Stearns, Insular Lumber Co., Philadelphia, Pa.
Herman Work, West Virginia Pulp and Paper Company, Staunton, Va.
Lenthall Wyman, School of Forestry, North Carolina State College, Raleigh, N. C.

## COMMITTEE ON ECONOMICS AND FINANCE

Henry J. Vaux, *Chairman*. School of Forestry, University of California, Berkeley, Calif.
H. R. Josephson, U. S. Forest Service, Washington, D. C.
L. A. Nix, Consulting Forester, Port Credit, Ontario, Canada.
Raymond E. Stevens, Consulting Forester, Duluth, Minn.
Robert H. Van Voorhis, University of Alabama, University, Ala.

## COMMITTEE ON LOGGING

A. M. Koroleff, *Chairman*. Pulp and Paper Research Institute of Canada, Montreal, Canada.
Ralph C. Bryant, Jr., School of Forestry, North Carolina State College, Raleigh, N. C.
E. W. Fobes, Department of State, Monrovia, Liberia.
John D. Gilmour, Consulting Forester, Montreal, Canada.
F. M. Knapp, Faculty of Forestry, University of British Columbia, Vancouver, B. C., Canada.
C. H. Niederhof, West Virginia Pulp and Paper Company, Charleston, S. C.
J. Kenneth Pearce, College of Forestry, University of Washington, Seattle, Wash.
Charles R. Silversides, Abitibi Power and Paper Company, Toronto, Canada.
Frederick C. Simmons, Northeastern Forest Experiment Station, Upper Darby, Pa.
A. E. Wackerman, School of Forestry, Duke University, Durham, N. C.

## COMMITTEE ON SURVEYING AND FOREST ROAD ENGINEERING

Anthony P. Dean, *Chairman*. U. S. Forest Service, Washington, D. C.
Thomas P. Bixby, Bureau of Reclamation, Stockton, Kan.
M. Albert Bourget, Laval University, Quebec, Canada.
Ralph G. DeMoisy, U. S. Plywood Corporation, Mapleton, Ore.
James F. Dubuar, New York State Ranger School, Wanakena, N. Y.
Harold P. Miller, Crown Zellerbach Corporation, Portland, Ore.

## COMMITTEE ON AERIAL PHOTOGRAPHY

Stephen H. Spurr, *Chairman*. School of Natural Resources, University of Michigan, Ann Arbor, Mich.
Clarence D. Chase, Lake States Forest Experiment Station, Minneapolis, Minn.
Robert N. Colwell, School of Forestry, University of California, Berkeley, Calif.
Karl E. Moessner, Central States Forest Experiment Station, Columbus, Ohio.
Earl J. Rogers, U. S. Forest Service, Washington, D. C.

MYLES STANDISH, Brown Company, Berlin, N. H.

RICHARD C. WILSON, U. S. Forest Service, Washington, D. C.

## COMMITTEE ON COMMUNICATIONS

ELMER L. SURDAM, *Chairman*. National Forest Industries Communications, Eugene, Ore.

RAY L. ATKINSON, Florida Forest Service, Shalimar, Fla.

WILLARD S. BROMLEY, American Pulpwood Association, New York, N. Y.

## COMMITTEE ON CHEMISTRY AND PHYSICS OF WOOD

EDWIN C. JAHN, *Chairman*. College of Forestry, State University of New York, Syracuse, N. Y.

IRVING H. ISENBERG, Institute of Paper Chemistry, Appleton, Wis.

GEORGE KITAZAWA, College of Forestry, State University of New York, Syracuse, N. Y.

## COMMITTEE ON MATHEMATICS

HOWARD H. MORGAN, *Chairman*. U. S. Tariff Commission, Washington, D. C.

LEWIS R. GROSENBAUGH, Southern Forest Experiment Station, New Orleans, La.

MERTON HENRY, Operations Research Office, Johns Hopkins University, Baltimore, Md.

CLEMENT MESAVAGE, Southern Forest Experiment Station, Ozark Branch, Harrison, Ark.

ARTHUR D. READ, Consulting Forester, West Monroe, La.

In addition to the members of the committees the following are cited for the active part they have played in the preparation of this book:

Lowell S. Besley, C. A. Bickford, John G. Broughton, Arthur A. Brown, W. R. Chapline, David B. Cook, J. M. Cultice, William A. Dayton, E. J. Eliason, Bernard Frank, Warden Gano, Merle A. Gee, W. H. Larrimer, Carl E. Ostrom, Joseph F. Pechanec, Clifford C. Presnall, Jack S. Rothacher, Arnold M. Schultz, David M. Smith, Richard D. Taber, H. H. Tryon, M. L. Upchurch, G. K. Voight, Harold G. Wilm, and C. T. Youngberg.

# PREFACE

The FORESTRY HANDBOOK is a reference work designed for the use of all who have a professional or commercial interest in the forest lands and crops of North America. It presents the working methods and techniques, formulas, tables, converting factors, and related data most commonly used in the practice of on-the-ground forestry in the United States and Canada. In addition, it brings together the information which, in our best judgment, is most generally useful in such allied specializations as watershed management, forest recreation, forest wildlife management, and forest range management. Young men preparing for careers in forestry and its related fields and educators charged with their training will find in the Handbook an indispensable reference work and a valuable teaching aide.

A great deal of thought has gone into the organization of the material, which has been grouped under 23 descriptive headings. Every effort has been made to provide easy access to the facts needed by the general practitioner or the specialist, whether in the field or at his desk.

The compilation of material for the Handbook was undertaken by an editorial committee and 19 subject matter committees the memberships of which represent the important forest regions of the United States and Canada. The committees were further diversified and strengthened by the appointment of technicians, research workers, teachers, and administrators from all types of private and public organizations.

The task of preparing the manuscript was a prodigious one, involving the review of virtually all current literature in the field, the selection of material for inclusion and, in many cases, the preparation of original data. Special mention is made here of the preliminary committee headed by Ralph R. Hill and consisting of D. A. Anderson, S. R. Gevorkiantz, L. W. R. Jackson, and D. G. McKeever, whose survey and subsequent report gave rise to this project.

Six years in preparation, the Handbook literally represents the work and ideas, not only of the more than one hundred members of the editorial committees, but of at least a hundred others whose publications have been cited or who have contributed or reviewed the material. To all of these, many of whom have chosen to remain anonymous, the Society of American Foresters, on behalf of the profession of forestry, expresses its sincerest gratitude.

No less a task than the preparation of the manuscript was that of editing for publication. For this the Society is indebted to Reginald D. Forbes and Arthur B. Meyer.

THE SOCIETY OF AMERICAN FORESTERS

# CONTENTS

# CONTENTS

# FOREST MEASUREMENTS

## CONTENTS

## CONTENTS (*Continued*)

# FOREST MEASUREMENTS

---

## Measurement of Trees

**DIAMETER. Diameter at Breast Height.** In the United States and Canada the diameter of standing trees is most commonly measured at breast height (d.b.h.)—4½ ft. above the ground. Excepted from this custom are (1) turpentined trees, the diameter of which is measured 10 ft. above the ground (d.b.n., "diameter above bottleneck"); and (2) swell-butted species, such as baldcypress, tupelo, and other species of deep swamps, which should be measured about 18 in. above the pronounced swell, or as much as 7 to 11 ft. above the ground.

Height above ground is nearly always measured from the average ground level, though National Forest practice is to measure from the highest ground. Unless otherwise specified (i.e., d.b.h.i.b.), d.b.h. measurements are invariably outside bark. Methods of diameter measurement at points above breast height are described below.

The three instruments used for measuring diameters are calipers, the diameter tape, and the Biltmore stick.

The Biltmore stick is, at best, a rough tool for measuring tree diameters. Its precision is increased by observing the following rules:

1. On approaching the tree, estimate its diameter, and grasp the stick about midway between the corresponding diameter on the stick and the zero end.
2. Hold the stick against the tree at breast height, and read it (with one eye closed) from that height, and at the proper distance from the hand.

The geometry of the procedure is shown in Fig. 1.

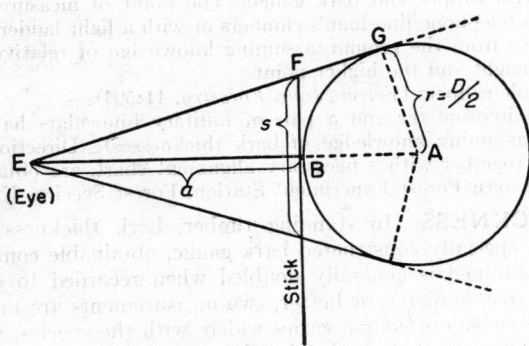

Fig. 1. Geometry of the Biltmore stick.

Most Biltmore sticks are made for a "reach" of 25 in. between the eye and tree —(*EB* in the figure). The graduations for such a stick are as given in Table 1.

**Table 1. Graduations for 25-in. "Reach" Biltmore Stick**

| D.b.h. (in.) | Graduation (in.) | D.b.h. (in.) | Graduation (in.) | D.b.h. (in.) | Graduation (in.) | D.b.h. (in.) | Graduation (in.) |
|---|---|---|---|---|---|---|---|
| 3 | 2.83 | 15 | 11.86 | 27 | 18.72 | 39 | 24.37 |
| 4 | 3.72 | 16 | 12.50 | 28 | 19.23 | 40 | 24.81 |
| 5 | 4.57 | 17 | 13.12 | 29 | 19.73 | 41 | 25.23 |
| 6 | 5.39 | 18 | 13.72 | 30 | 20.23 | 42 | 25.66 |
| 7 | 6.19 | 19 | 14.32 | 31 | 20.71 | 43 | 26.07 |
| 8 | 6.96 | 20 | 14.91 | 32 | 21.20 | 44 | 26.49 |
| 9 | 7.72 | 21 | 15.48 | 33 | 21.67 | 45 | 26.89 |
| 10 | 8.45 | 22 | 16.04 | 34 | 22.16 | 46 | 27.29 |
| 11 | 9.17 | 23 | 16.60 | 35 | 22.59 | 47 | 27.70 |
| 12 | 9.87 | 24 | 17.14 | 36 | 23.05 | 48 | 28.09 |
| 13 | 10.54 | 25 | 17.68 | 37 | 23.50 | 49 | 28.48 |
| 14 | 11.21 | 26 | 18.20 | 38 | 23.94 | 50 | 28.87 |

Graduations for sticks designed for other than 25-in. reaches may be calculated from the formula $S = \sqrt{\dfrac{aD^2}{a + D}}$, derived from the solution of the similar triangles $EGA$ and $EFB$ in Fig. 1. Biltmore stick graduations are often combined with those for a Merritt hypsometer, a log stick, and a yardstick to make a cruiser stick. A tree scale stick combines the Biltmore graduations with a complete volume table so that tree volumes may be estimated directly from readings on the stick.

**Diameter above Breast Height.** Diameter measurements of standing trees at points above breast height, as at the top of the first 16-ft. log for Girard Form Class (G.F.C.), may be made in several ways. (Ocular estimates are not recommended. A cruiser checking his judgment of G.F.C. makes no attempt to estimate either the top diameter inside bark or the d.b.h., but simply the ratio between them. He later measures both instrumentally.):

1. Directly with caliper and bark gauge. The point of measurement is reached either with telephone linesman's climbers or with a light ladder.
2. By estimate from the ground, assuming knowledge of relative bark thickness at breast height and the higher point.
   a. With pole calipers (Ferree, *Jour. Forestry*, 44:594).
   b. With a hypsometer and a pair of military binoculars having a mil-scale (again assuming knowledge of bark thicknesses). Directions for this procedure, together with a necessary alignment chart, are obtainable from the Northeastern Forest Experiment Station, Forest Service, Upper Darby, Pa.

**BARK THICKNESS.** In standing timber, bark thickness is most easily determined by a specially constructed bark gauge, obtainable commercially. The thickness thus obtained is generally doubled when recorded to conform to the measurement of tree diameter, or better, two measurements are taken and added.

Bark thickness, which of course varies widely with the species, varies also with the diameter of the tree and the height above ground of the point of measurement. It increases rapidly below breast height, and decreases more slowly above it. For most northeastern species the double bark thickness at breast height is 5 to 10 percent of d.b.h., but for the hard pines of the Southeast the percentage is much higher (see Table 2).

#### Table 2. Average Double Bark Thickness, in Inches, at Breast Height
New York State softwoods and hardwoods; * North Carolina loblolly pine †

| D.b.h. (in.) | New York | | | | | | | | | | N. C. Loblolly pine |
| --- | --- | --- | --- | --- | --- | --- | --- | --- | --- | --- | --- |
| | White pine | Red spruce | Eastern hemlock | Beech | Yellow birch | Paper birch | Sugar maple | Red maple | White ash | Basswood | |
| 2 | 0.14 | 0.12 | 0.20 | 0.08 | 0.14 | 0.14 | 0.16 | 0.10 | 0.20 | 0.20 | |
| 4 | .22 | .24 | .38 | .12 | .26 | .26 | .32 | .20 | .50 | .40 | 1.2 |
| 6 | .30 | .34 | .56 | .18 | .36 | .40 | .44 | .30 | .74 | .56 | 1.3 |
| 8 | .42 | .46 | .72 | .24 | .44 | .54 | .56 | .38 | .94 | .72 | 1.5 |
| 10 | .54 | .56 | .92 | .30 | .52 | .66 | .66 | .48 | 1.14 | .86 | 1.7 |
| 12 | .66 | .66 | 1.10 | .34 | .60 | .80 | .78 | .58 | 1.34 | 1.02 | 1.8 |
| 14 | .84 | .74 | 1.28 | .38 | .70 | .94 | .90 | .68 | 1.54 | 1.14 | 1.9 |
| 16 | 1.02 | .80 | 1.46 | .44 | .82 | 1.06 | 1.02 | .78 | 1.74 | 1.26 | 2.0 |
| 18 | 1.26 | .88 | 1.64 | .48 | .94 | 1.20 | 1.12 | .86 | 1.94 | 1.38 | 2.2 |
| 20 | 1.50 | .94 | 1.82 | .52 | 1.02 | | 1.22 | .96 | 2.16 | 1.48 | 2.3 |
| 22 | 1.76 | 1.00 | 2.00 | .56 | | | 1.30 | 1.06 | 2.36 | | 2.4 |
| 24 | 2.04 | 1.08 | 2.18 | .60 | | | 1.34 | 1.16 | 2.58 | | 2.5 |
| 26 | 2.28 | | 2.36 | .64 | | | 1.38 | | 2.78 | | 2.6 |
| 28 | 2.54 | | 2.54 | .68 | | | | | 3.00 | | 2.8 |
| 30 | 2.80 | | 2.72 | .72 | | | | | 3.22 | | 3.0 |
| 32 | 3.06 | | | | | | | | | | 3.1 |
| 34 | 3.28 | | | | | | | | | | 3.3 |
| 36 | 3.52 | | | | | | | | | | |

* C. H. Nims, quoted by H. C. Belyea, Forester's tables for N. Y. State, *Bull. No. 14*, The New York State College of Forestry, Syracuse University.

† W. W. Ashe, Loblolly or North Carolina pine, *Bull. No. 24*, North Carolina Geological and Economic Survey.

Double bark thickness **at the top of the first 16-ft. log** has been expressed by V. A. Clements, C. W. Stevens, and D. F. Roy, working with California species, as a percentage of d.b.h., varying with species and tree diameter (Table 3).

#### Table 3. Double Bark Thickness at Top of First 16-Ft. Log as a Percentage of D.B.H.

| D.b.h (in.) | Sugar pine | Red fir | Ponderosa pine | Douglas-fir | White fir |
| --- | --- | --- | --- | --- | --- |
| 12 | 10 | 11 | 13 | 11 | 10 |
| 16 | 10 | 11 | 12 | 11 | 11 |
| 20 | 10 | 12 | 10 | 11 | 12 |
| 24 | 10 | 12 | 10 | 12 | 11 |
| 28 | 10 | 12 | 9 | 12 | 11 |
| 32 | 10 | 12 | 9 | 12 | 11 |
| 36 | 10 | 12 | 8 | 12 | 11 |
| 40 | 9 | 13 | 8 | 12 | 10 |
| 50 | 9 | 13 | 7 | 12 | 10 |
| 60 | 8 | 12 | 6 | 12 | 9 |
| 70 | 7 | 12 | 6 | 12 | 8 |
| 80 | 7 | | 5 | 12 | 8 |
| 90 | 6 | | | | |

Walter H. Meyer found for western hemlock that the "ratio of bark volume to volume of bole inside bark was remarkably constant; it showed no consistent variation either with height or with diameter. . . . It averaged 13.8 percent. . . .

### Table 4. Proportion of Bark, in Percent, to Total Cubic Volume of Trees, Outside Bark—Lake States Species

| Species | Pole timber (4–10 in.) | Saw timber (12 in. and larger) | |
|---|---|---|---|
| | | Second growth | Old growth |
| **CONIFERS** | | | |
| Balsam fir | 12 | 12 | ... |
| White-cedar, N. | 14 | 14 | 14 |
| Hemlock | 17 | 17 | 19 |
| Pine | | | |
|   Jack | 17 | 14 | 10 |
|   Red | 16 | 13 | 11 |
|   White | 14 | 16 | 18 |
| Spruce | | | |
|   Black | 12 | 11 | ... |
|   White | 15 | 12 | 10 |
| Tamarack | 12 | 11 | |
| **HARDWOODS** | | | |
| Ash | | | |
|   Black | 16 | 15 | 14 |
|   Green | 17 | 16 | 19 |
|   White | 17 | 16 | 19 |
| Aspen | 13 | 13 | ... |
| Basswood | 18 | 20 | 20 |
| Beech | 8 | 8 | 7 |
| Birch | | | |
|   Paper | 11 | 12 | |
|   Yellow | 13 | 15 | 15 |
| Cottonwood | 17 | 17 | 18 |
| Elms | 17 | 18 | 19 |
| Hickories | 15 | 16 | ... |
| Maple | | | |
|   Red | 15 | 15 | 14 |
|   Sugar | 15 | 17 | 18 |
| Oaks | | | |
|   Red | 18 | 20 | 20 |
|   White | 20 | 20 | 22 |

Source: U. S. Forest Service, Lake States Forest Exp. Sta., Bark percent in Lake States trees, *Tech. Note No. 362*, 1951.

**Table 5. Proportion of Bark to Total and Merchantable Cubic Volume of Trees, Inside Bark—Eastern Spruces and Balsam Fir, Canada**

| D.b.h. (in.) | Black spruce | | | White and red spruce | | | Balsam fir | | |
|---|---|---|---|---|---|---|---|---|---|
| | D.b.t.* (in.) | Bark percent | | D.b.t.* (in.) | Bark percent | | D.b.t.* (in.) | Bark percent | |
| | | Total | Merch.† | | Total | Merch.† | | Total | Merch.† |
| 5 | 0.3 | 13 | 15 | 0.3 | 10 | 12 | 0.2 | 11 | 13 |
| 6 | .4 | 13 | 15 | .3 | 10 | 12 | .3 | 11 | 13 |
| 7 | .4 | 13 | 15 | .4 | 10 | 12 | .4 | 11 | 13 |
| 8 | .4 | 13 | 14 | .4 | 9 | 11 | .4 | 12 | 13 |
| 9 | .5 | 12 | 14 | .4 | 9 | 11 | .5 | 12 | 13 |
| 10 | .5 | 12 | 14 | .5 | 9 | 11 | .6 | 12 | 13 |
| 11 | .6 | 12 | 13 | .5 | 9 | 10 | .6 | 12 | 13 |
| 12 | .6 | 11 | 13 | .5 | 9 | 10 | .7 | 12 | 13 |
| 13 | .6 | 11 | 13 | .5 | 9 | 10 | .7 | 12 | 12 |
| 14 | .7 | 11 | 12 | .6 | 8 | 10 | .8 | 12 | 12 |
| 15 | .7 | 11 | 12 | .6 | 8 | 9 | .9 | 12 | 12 |
| 16 | .8 | 10 | 12 | .6 | 8 | 9 | .9 | 12 | 12 |
| 17 | .8 | 10 | 11 | .6 | 8 | 9 | 1.0 | 13 | 12 |
| 18 | .8 | 10 | 11 | .7 | 8 | 8 | 1.0 | 13 | 12 |
| 19 | .9 | 9 | 10 | .7 | 8 | 8 | 1.1 | 13 | 12 |
| 20 | .9 | 9 | 10 | .7 | 8 | 8 | 1.2 | 13 | 12 |

* D.b.t. = Double bark thickness.
† Merch. = Merchantable volume: 1·5-ft. stump, 4-in. top.
Source: Dept. of Mines and Resources, Dominion Forest Service, Canada, Form-class volume tables, 1948.

**Table 6. Volume Table for Bark of Eastern Hemlock in Vermont \***

| D.b.h. (in.) | Cords of bark | D.b.h. (in.) | Cords of bark |
|---|---|---|---|
| 8 | 0.03 | 20 | 0.22 |
| 10 | .06 | 22 | .28 |
| 12 | .08 | 24 | .34 |
| 14 | .10 | 26 | .40 |
| 16 | .14 | 28 | .46 |
| 18 | .18 | | |

* Assumes that there are 50 cu. ft. per cord of bark.
Source: Compiled by A. F. Hawes.

### Table 7. Multiple Table of Basal Areas in Square Feet

| Diam. (in.) | \multicolumn{10}{c}{Number of trees} |
|---|---|---|---|---|---|---|---|---|---|---|

| Diam. (in.) | 1 | 2 | 3 | 4 | 5 | 6 | 7 | 8 | 9 | 10 |
|---|---|---|---|---|---|---|---|---|---|---|
| 2 | 0.02 | 0.04 | 0.07 | 0.09 | 0.11 | 0.13 | 0.15 | 0.17 | 0.20 | 0.22 |
| 3 | .05 | .10 | .15 | .20 | .25 | .29 | .34 | .39 | .44 | .49 |
| 4 | .09 | .17 | .26 | .35 | .44 | .52 | .61 | .70 | .79 | .87 |
| 5 | .14 | .27 | .41 | .55 | .68 | .82 | .95 | 1.09 | 1.23 | 1.36 |
| 6 | .20 | .39 | .59 | .79 | .98 | 1.18 | 1.37 | 1.57 | 1.77 | 1.96 |
| 7 | .27 | .53 | .80 | 1.07 | 1.34 | 1.60 | 1.87 | 2.14 | 2.41 | 2.67 |
| 8 | .35 | .70 | 1.05 | 1.40 | 1.75 | 2.09 | 2.44 | 2.79 | 3.14 | 3.49 |
| 9 | .44 | .88 | 1.33 | 1.77 | 2.21 | 2.65 | 3.09 | 3.53 | 3.98 | 4.42 |
| 10 | .55 | 1.09 | 1.64 | 2.18 | 2.73 | 3.27 | 3.82 | 4.36 | 4.91 | 5.45 |
| 11 | .67 | 1.32 | 1.98 | 2.64 | 3.30 | 3.96 | 4.62 | 5.28 | 5.94 | 6.60 |
| 12 | .79 | 1.57 | 2.36 | 3.14 | 3.93 | 4.71 | 5.50 | 6.28 | 7.07 | 7.85 |
| 13 | .92 | 1.84 | 2.77 | 3.69 | 4.61 | 5.53 | 6.45 | 7.37 | 8.30 | 9.22 |
| 14 | 1.07 | 2.14 | 3.21 | 4.28 | 5.35 | 6.41 | 7.48 | 8.55 | 9.62 | 10.69 |
| 15 | 1.23 | 2.45 | 3.68 | 4.91 | 6.14 | 7.36 | 8.59 | 9.82 | 11.04 | 12.27 |
| 16 | 1.40 | 2.79 | 4.19 | 5.59 | 6.98 | 8.38 | 9.77 | 11.17 | 12.57 | 13.96 |
| 17 | 1.58 | 3.15 | 4.73 | 6.31 | 7.88 | 9.46 | 11.03 | 12.61 | 14.19 | 15.76 |
| 18 | 1.77 | 3.53 | 5.30 | 7.07 | 8.84 | 10.60 | 12.37 | 14.14 | 15.90 | 17.67 |
| 19 | 1.97 | 3.94 | 5.91 | 7.88 | 9.84 | 11.81 | 13.78 | 15.75 | 17.72 | 19.69 |
| 20 | 2.18 | 4.36 | 6.54 | 8.73 | 10.91 | 13.09 | 15.27 | 17.45 | 19.63 | 21.82 |
| 21 | 2.41 | 4.81 | 7.22 | 9.62 | 12.03 | 14.43 | 16.84 | 19.24 | 21.65 | 24.05 |
| 22 | 2.64 | 5.28 | 7.92 | 10.56 | 13.20 | 15.84 | 18.48 | 21.12 | 23.76 | 26.40 |
| 23 | 2.89 | 5.77 | 8.66 | 11.54 | 14.43 | 17.31 | 20.20 | 23.08 | 25.97 | 28.85 |
| 24 | 3.14 | 6.28 | 9.42 | 12.57 | 15.71 | 18.85 | 21.99 | 25.13 | 28.27 | 31.42 |
| 25 | 3.41 | 6.82 | 10.23 | 13.64 | 17.04 | 20.45 | 23.86 | 27.27 | 30.68 | 34.09 |
| 26 | 3.69 | 7.37 | 11.06 | 14.75 | 18.44 | 22.12 | 25.81 | 29.50 | 33.18 | 36.87 |
| 27 | 3.98 | 7.95 | 11.93 | 15.90 | 19.88 | 23.86 | 27.83 | 31.81 | 35.78 | 39.76 |
| 28 | 4.28 | 8.55 | 12.83 | 17.10 | 21.38 | 25.66 | 29.93 | 34.21 | 38.48 | 42.76 |
| 29 | 4.59 | 9.17 | 13.76 | 18.35 | 22.93 | 27.52 | 32.11 | 36.70 | 41.28 | 45.87 |
| 30 | 4.91 | 9.82 | 14.73 | 19.63 | 24.54 | 29.45 | 34.36 | 39.27 | 44.18 | 49.09 |

Source: Adapted by E. T. Hawes, U. S. Forest Service, from H. H. Chapman and D. B. Demeritt, *Elements of forest mensuration*, J. B. Lyon Co., 1936.

To find the bark volume for any tree size . . . the cubic-foot volume (inside bark) . . . should be multiplied by 0.138. For conversion into cords the result should be divided by 50, since that is approximately the number of cubic feet of bark in a stacked standard cord." Table 4 shows the proportion of bark to total cubic volume, outside bark, for 24 Lake States species. Variation with size of tree is not great, nor is it always in the same direction. The Dominion Forest Service in eastern Canada found the volume of bark, in percentage of peeled wood in trees, generally to decrease with increasing diameter of spruce and fir, particularly for the merchantable portion of the trees (see Table 5).

**BASAL AREA.** To find the basal area in square feet from a diameter measurement in inches, use the formula:

$$\text{B.A.} = \frac{\pi D^2}{4 \times 144} = 0.00545415 \, D^2$$

Table 7 may be used to compute (1) the basal area in square feet of one or more trees of specified d.b.h. (breast height rather than stump diameters are customarily used for this purpose), or (2) the volume in cubic feet of single cylinders whose height, in feet, corresponds to the "number of trees."

**HEIGHT.** Direct measurement of tree heights is possible if the trees are short. A graduated length of ¼ round molding, or similar light material, if held by an assistant, can be used to measure heights up to about 20 ft. Black friction tape may be used for graduations. For indirect measurements there is a great variety of instruments. Use of the commoner kinds should be fairly plain from a study of the diagrams.

Fig. 2 illustrates the trigonometric principles involved in the use of a transit, the Abney level, and the Forest Service hypsometer to determine tree heights. Except when the base or top of the tree is at precisely eye-height, two measurements are always required with these instruments. They are angular measurements, either from the horizontal as determined by the level bulb on transit and Abney, or from the vertical as determined by plumb bob (or free-swinging

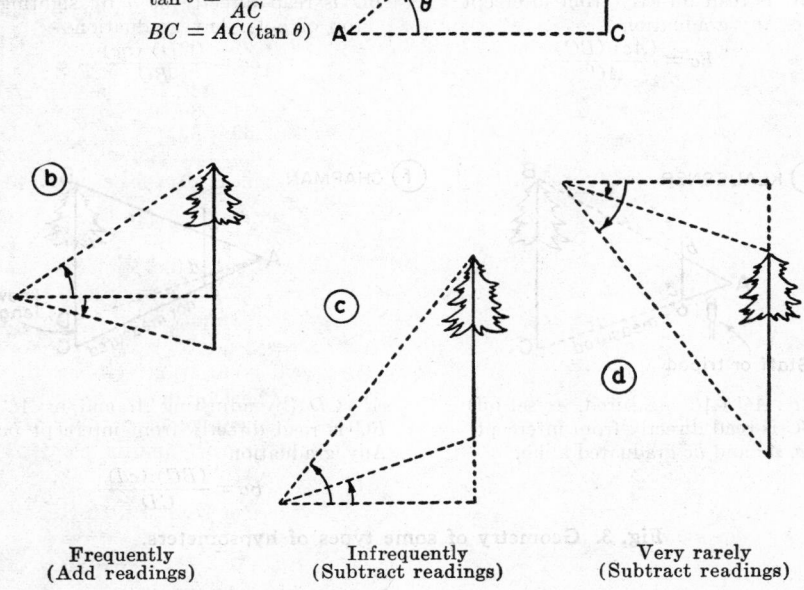

$$\tan \theta = \frac{BC}{AC}$$
$$BC = AC(\tan \theta)$$

| Frequently | Infrequently | Very rarely |
|---|---|---|
| (Add readings) | (Subtract readings) | (Subtract readings) |

**Fig. 2. Trigonometry of tree height measurement and conditions to be met.**

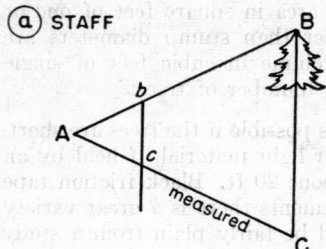

**(a) STAFF**

$$bc = Ac \text{ (set; } AC \text{ adjusted)}$$
$$BC = AC \text{ (}AC \text{ is paced)}$$

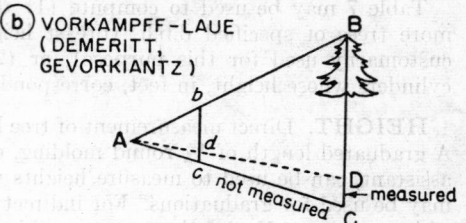

**(b) VORKAMPFF-LAUE (DEMERITT, GEVORKIANTZ)**

$$cd : bc = 1 : k \text{ (}k \text{ usually } = 10)$$
$$bc : BC \text{ (by adjusting } Ac \text{ and/or } AC)$$
$$BC = (k) \text{ } (CD) \text{ } (DC \text{ is measured)}$$

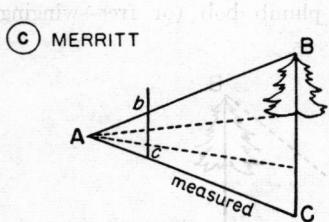

**(c) MERRITT**

$Ac : AC$ (both set, $AC$ paced)
$BC$ is read directly from intercept
$bc$. Any graduation—

$$bc = \frac{(Ac) \text{ } (BC)}{AC}$$

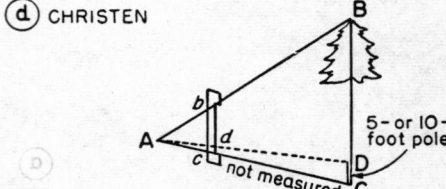

**(d) CHRISTEN**

$bc : BC$ (by adjusting $Ac$ and/or $AC$)
$BC$ is read directly at $d$ by sighting a
top of pole. Any graduation—

$$cd = \frac{(CD) \text{ } (bc)}{BC}$$

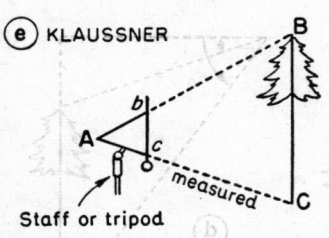

**(e) KLAUSSNER**

$Ac : AC$ ($AC$ measured, $Ac$ set off)
$BC$ is read directly from intercept
$bc$. $Ac$ and $bc$ graduated alike.

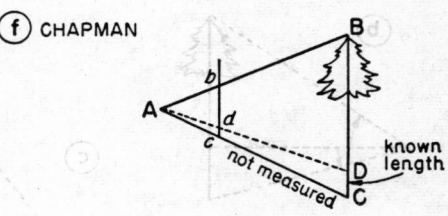

**(f) CHAPMAN**

$cd : CD$ (by adjusting $Ac$ and/or $AC$)
$BC$ is read directly from intercept $bc$.
Any graduation—

$$bc = \frac{(BC) \text{ } (cd)}{CD}$$

**Fig. 3. Geometry of some types of hypsometers.**

weight) in the hypsometer. They must be added or subtracted, as is shown in Fig. 2.

Use of the Abney hand level, if graduated in **degrees**, parallels that of a transit. If graduated in **percentages** (the number of feet rise or drop in 100 ft. of horizontal distance), which correspond to natural tangents, the only computation it requires is adding (or subtracting) the two readings, pointing off two places, and multiplying by the horizontal distance from the tree. If the observer can stand exactly 100 ft. (horizontally) from the tree, all multiplication can be avoided. If the Abney has a "topographic arc," direct readings are possible only at a distance of 66 ft.; at 33 ft. the readings must be halved, at 132 ft. doubled, etc. No Abney can be accurately used unless the observer is able to stand at least as far away from the tree being measured as its height; its use should not be attempted in dense stands of very tall timber.

**Hypsometers.** Hypsometers, the use of which is illustrated in Fig. 3, require only **one** reading for each tree.

The staff (Fig. 3) is simply a straight stick 4 or 5 ft. long. The observer holds it lightly at arm's length so that the heavy end swings it to a vertical, and the length of the stick above his hand equals the distance from hand to eye. He moves forward or back until the top of the tree is in line with the top of the stick and the base is in line with his hand. The distance to the base of the tree then equals the tree height.

The Merritt hypsometer, like the Biltmore stick, is graduated for a specified "reach" ($Ac$) and distance from the tree ($AC$) to be measured for height. These are most frequently 25 in. and 66 ft. With these distances, 3.79 in. on the hypsometer corresponds to 10 ft. of height of the tree. The instrument is so graduated and is read at the point where the line of sight crosses it to the top of the tree.

The vertical arm, with counterweight, of the Klaussner hypsometer is movable and is set to correspond with the distance at which the instrument is set up from the tree. The instrument is supported on a tripod; a setscrew raises or lowers the arm $Ab$, which is sighted to the top of the tree, while the base of the instrument is sighted to the base. Readings on the vertical arm are direct.

The remaining hypsometers shown in Fig. 3 do not require any measurement from the observer to the tree, but they do require the measurement of a fixed distance on the trunk of the tree above the base.

The Demeritt hypsometer is a stick divided into equal parts, usually 10. It is held vertically in such a position that the tip of the tree may just be seen over the upper end of the instrument and the base of the tree just below the lower end. The observer accomplishes this either by walking toward or away from the tree, or by moving the hypsometer toward or away from his eye, or both. An assistant holds a target against the tree near its base, and moves it up or down as directed by the observer until it is in line between the observer's eye and one of the lower graduations on the hypsometer. The distance of the target above the base of the tree is accurately measured, and bears the same relation to the total tree height as this graduation on the hypsometer bears to its over-all length.

The Christen hypsometer similarly intercepts the tree from tip to base, but the assistant holds a 10-ft. pole at the base of the tree and the observer reads the graduation on his instrument, which is in line between his eye and the top of the pole. If a 5-ft. pole is used, the graduations must be numbered to correspond. The graduations are necessarily read from the top down, and become very fine and difficult to read above 100 ft.

To use a Chapman hypsometer the observer stands at such a distance from the tree, or holds the hypsometer at such a distance from his eye, that the bottom of the hypsometer is in line with the base of the tree and a graduation on the hypsometer through which his line of sight passes to the top of a pole held at the base of the tree corresponds numerically with the length of the pole. The height of the tree is read from the graduation through which his line of sight passes to the top of the tree.

The Faustman hypsometer (not illustrated), although constructed on geometric principles like the instruments in Fig. 3, requires **two** readings. It may be used at any distance from the tree, without computation, by setting off this distance **in the instrument** by means of a slide between two scales. The observer sights (through peep sights) at the top of the tree and reads its vertical distance directly in a narrow mirror attached to the instrument on the right; he obtains a similar measurement for the base of the tree. The two measurements are added or subtracted in accordance with the principles illustrated in Fig. 2. The slide on a Faustman hypsometer has two index marks (I and II) and is reversible. For short distances from the tree it should be used with the II down, and set for distances on the right-hand scale; for longer distances, the II should be up, and it should be set against the left-hand scale.

Observance of the following points will insure increased accuracy in measurements:

1. Whatever the instrument to be used, first give it a thorough trial on a flagpole, open-grown tree, or other object of known height.
2. If it is graduated to read directly only at a fixed distance from the tree, know this distance (topographic Abney, 66 ft.; percent Abney, 100 ft.); if it is used at a greater distance, increase the readings; if used at a shorter distance, decrease them.
3. If the instrument is graduated for a specified "reach" and distance from the tree (Merritt), or height of measuring stick at base of tree (Christen), know and observe these specifications.
4. If the instrument requires two readings (transit, Abney level, Forest Service, and Faustman hypsometers) be sure whether they should be added or subtracted; the closer the base of the tree is to eye-height, the more difficult this determination is.
5. If measurement to the tree is required, pacing is sufficiently accurate with staff or the Merritt hypsometer.
6. All points sighted at base of tree (Demeritt, Gevorkiantz, Chapman) should be clearly visible to the observer, and carefully measured by his assistant.
7. With all instruments observe tip and base of tree by movement of the eyeball, not of the head.
8. With all instruments:
   a. Avoid leaning trees.
   b. Measure flat- or round-topped trees from a sufficient distance to be sure of the tallest branch or main stem.
   c. In dense stands be sure to observe the tip and base of the right tree; surprisingly large trees may be sufficiently jarred (by an assistant) at the base to identify the tip on a calm day.

**Merchantable Height.** Measurement of merchantable heights requires knowledge of the minimum size to which various products may be taken and the defects, chiefly knots and crook, which are allowable. In measuring timber for immediate local consumption, specifications furnished by local buyers should be understood and strictly observed (typical specifications are given in Section **14** on Utilization). For low-grade products such as pulpwood or mine props, the limitation is largely in diameter, except that excessive limbiness may so increase the cost of limbing and peeling that utilization to the minimum diameter is not feasible from a practical standpoint.

For trees producing saw logs, veneer bolts, and similar high-grade products, not upper diameter alone but also straightness of stem, and size and number of knots, determine the limit of merchantability. As a broad generalization, in old-growth saw timber the top diameter of the merchantable log is commonly 50 percent of the d.b.h., but it may run as high as 70 percent for 10-in. trees and drop to 40 percent for trees 30 to 80 in. d.b.h.

Early volume tables (see Section **2**) were generally based on a fixed top diameter somewhat below average utilization; more recent tables, on flexible limits reflecting actual utilization, in no case below a specified minimum. Volume tables based on the number of logs or bolts reflect the usual range of merchantable length, particularly if the extent of basic data is shown. Logs currently on the log decks of efficient local mills are of course the best guide to merchantability.

**FORM AND TAPER. Definitions.** The following definitions are based on Fig. 4. Small $d$ indicates diameters inside bark, large $D$ those outside bark. Subscripts indicate the point of measurement, as $d_B$ (diameter inside bark at top of first 16-ft. log), or $D_D$ (diameter outside bark at 4.5 ft., or breast height). The quotients are obviously decimals, but they are commonly multiplied by 100 and written as percentages.

(1) Form quotient $= \dfrac{d_G}{d_D}$

(2) Normal form quotient (for swell-butted trees) $=$

$\dfrac{d_G}{d_D - s}$  where $s =$ swell at breast height. Normal diameter of such trees is diameter at breast height minus bark and swell.

(3) Absolute form quotient (for normal-butted trees) $=$

$\dfrac{d_H}{d_D}$ or $\dfrac{D_H}{D_D}$ (differences are slight). Form quotients are grouped in **form classes**, with class intervals usually of **5** percent.

(4) Girard's form class $= \dfrac{d_B}{D_D}$

(5) Girard's form diameter $= \dfrac{d_B}{T}$  where $T$ is rate of taper above first 16-ft. log, varying with d.b.h. and log height.

(6) Girard's form point $= \dfrac{D_F}{D_D}$  (Not to be confused with Swedish form point.)

**Taper Between Stump Height and Breast Height.** The ratio between diameters at these two points is important in designating diameter limits for cutting where more refined methods of regulating the cut are not practicable. Table 10, prepared for this purpose, is based on measurements throughout the State of Maine; stump as well as breast-height diameters are outside bark, and stumps were of the height prevalent in the pulp and paper industry (1950).

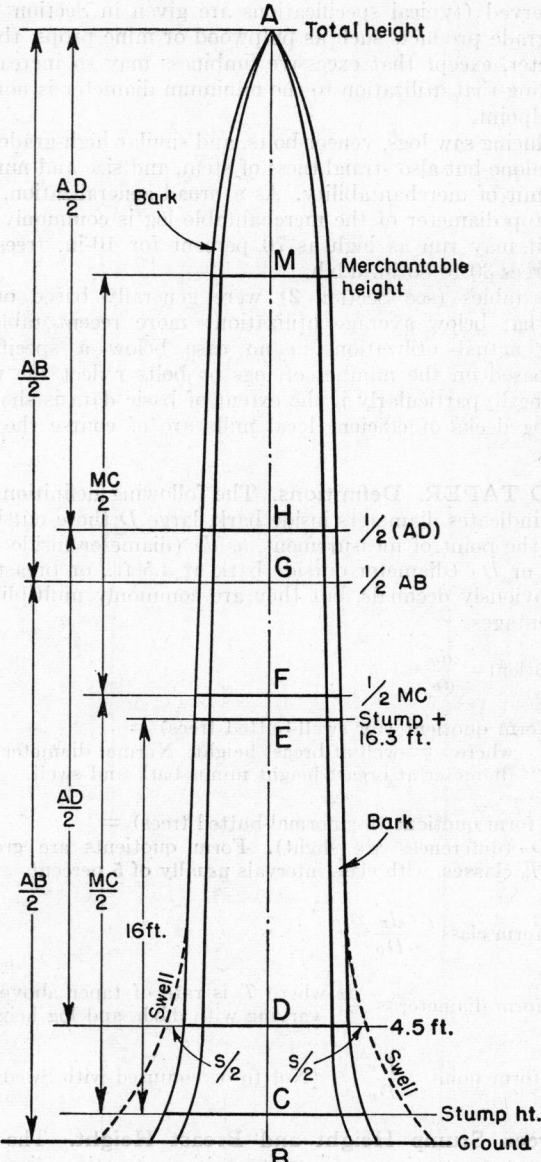

**Fig. 4. Diagram of tree, showing common points of diameter measurement.**

Table 8. D.B.H. in Relation to Stump Diameter, in Inches—Northeastern Hardwoods
0.5-Ft. Stumps

| Stump (d.i.b.) | Yellow poplar | Black cherry | Red & sugar maple | Black & yellow birch | Beech | Aspen | White oak | Red oak | Chestnut oak | White ash | Basswood |
|---|---|---|---|---|---|---|---|---|---|---|---|
| 5 | 5 | 5 | 4 | 4 | 4 | 5 | 4 | 4 | 5 | 4 | 5 |
| 6 | 6 | 6 | 5 | 5 | 5 | 6 | 5 | 5 | 5 | 5 | 6 |
| 7 | 7 | 7 | 6 | 5 | 6 | 7 | 5 | 6 | 6 | 6 | 6 |
| 8 | 7 | 7 | 7 | 6 | 6 | 8 | 6 | 6 | 7 | 7 | 7 |
| 9 | 8 | 8 | 8 | 7 | 7 | 9 | 7 | 7 | 8 | 8 | 8 |
| 10 | 9 | 9 | 8 | 8 | 8 | 10 | 7 | 8 | 9 | 9 | 9 |
| 11 | 10 | 10 | 9 | 8 | 9 | 10 | 8 | 8 | 10 | 9 | 10 |
| 12 | 11 | 11 | 10 | 9 | 9 | 11 | 8 | 9 | 11 | 10 | 11 |
| 13 | 12 | 11 | 11 | 10 | 10 | 12 | 9 | 10 | 12 | 11 | 11 |

Source: U. S. Forest Service, Northeastern Forest Exp. Sta., Relation of tree-stump diameter to diameter breast high, *Note No. 1,* 1947.

Table 9. D.B.H. in Relation to Stump Diameter, in Inches—Northeastern Hardwoods
1.0-Ft. Stumps

| Stump (d.i.b.) | Yellow-poplar | Black cherry | Red & sugar maple | Black & yellow birch | Beech | Aspen | White oak | Red oak | Chestnut oak | White ash | Bass-wood |
|---|---|---|---|---|---|---|---|---|---|---|---|
| 11 | 11 | 11 | 10 | 9  | 10 | 11 | 9  | 10 | 11 | 10 | 11 |
| 12 | 12 | 11 | 11 | 10 | 11 | 12 | 9  | 10 | 12 | 11 | 11 |
| 13 | 13 | 12 | 12 | 11 | 11 | 13 | 10 | 11 | 12 | 12 | 12 |
| 14 | 14 | 13 | 13 | 12 | 12 | 14 | 11 | 12 | 13 | 13 | 13 |
| 15 | 14 | 14 | 14 | 13 | 13 | 15 | 12 | 13 | 14 | 14 | 14 |
| 16 | 15 | 15 | 14 | 13 | 14 | 16 | 12 | 14 | 15 | 15 | 15 |
| 17 | 16 | 16 | 15 | 14 | 15 | :  | 13 | 15 | 16 | 16 | 16 |
| 18 | 17 | 17 | 16 | 15 | 15 | :  | 14 | 16 | 17 | 17 | 16 |
| 19 | 18 | 18 | 17 | 16 | 16 | :  | 15 | 17 | 18 | 17 | 17 |
| 20 | 19 | 19 | 18 | 17 | 17 | :  | 15 | 18 | 18 | 18 | 18 |
| 21 | 20 | 20 | 19 | 17 | 18 | :  | 16 | 18 | 19 | 19 | 19 |
| 22 | 21 | 21 | 20 | 18 | 19 | :  | 17 | 19 | 20 | 20 | 20 |
| 23 | 21 | 22 | 20 | 19 | 19 | :  | 18 | 20 | 21 | 21 | 21 |
| 24 | 22 | 23 | 21 | 20 | 20 | :  | 18 | 21 | 22 | 22 | 22 |
| 25 | 23 | 24 | 22 | 21 | 21 | :  | 19 | 21 | 23 | 23 | 23 |
| 26 | 24 | :  | 23 | :  | 21 | :  | 20 | 22 | 24 | 24 | 24 |
| 27 | :  | :  | 24 | :  | 22 | :  | 21 | 23 | :  | :  | :  |
| 28 | :  | :  | :  | :  | 23 | :  | 21 | 24 | :  | :  | :  |
| 29 | :  | :  | :  | :  | 24 | :  | 22 | :  | :  | :  | :  |
| 30 | :  | :  | :  | :  | :  | :  | 23 | :  | :  | :  | :  |

Source: *Ibid.*

#### Table 10. Relationship of Stump Diameter to D.B.H. for Spruce-Fir Regions

| D.b.h. (in.) | Stump (in.) | D.b.h. (in.) | Stump (in.) | Stump (in.) | D.b.h. (in.) | Stump (in.) | D.b.h. (in.) |
|---|---|---|---|---|---|---|---|
| 5 | 6.4 | 13 | 15.9 | 7 | 5.6 | 15 | 12.3 |
| 6 | 7.5 | 14 | 17.1 | 8 | 6.5 | 16 | 13.1 |
| 7 | 8.7 | 15 | 18.3 | 9 | 7.3 | 17 | 14.0 |
| 8 | 9.9 | 16 | 19.5 | 10 | 8.2 | 18 | 14.8 |
| 9 | 11.1 | 17 | 20.7 | 11 | 9.0 | 19 | 15.6 |
| 10 | 12.3 | 18 | 22.0 | 12 | 9.8 | 20 | 16.5 |
| 11 | 13.5 | 19 | 23.1 | 13 | 10.7 | 21 | 17.2 |
| 12 | 14.7 | 20 | 24.2 | 14 | 11.5 | 22 | 18.0 |

Source: U. S. Forest Service, Northeastern Forest Exp. Sta., *Northeastern Res. Notes No. 4*, 1951.

The relationship between stump d.i.b. and d.b.h. is useful in reconstructing stand tables, expressed in number of trees by d.b.h., from stumps, as in trespass cases. Tables 8, 9, 11, and 12 give this relationship for 18 species of northeastern United States and eastern and central Canada.

#### Table 11. D.B.H. in Relation to Stump Diameter, in Inches—Northeastern Conifers
0.5-Ft. Stumps

| Stump (d.i.b.) | White pine [a] | Jack pine [b] | Pitch pine [a] | Hemlock [c] |
|---|---|---|---|---|
| 2 | ... | 2 | ... | ... |
| 3 | ... | 3 | ... | ... |
| 4 | ... | 4 | ... | ... |
| 5 | 4 | 5 | 5 | 4 |
| 6 | 5 | 6 | 6 | 5 |
| 7 | 6 | 6 | 6 | 6 |
| 8 | 7 | 7 | 7 | 7 |
| 9 | 8 | 8 | 8 | 8 |
| 10 | 9 | 9 | 9 | 9 |
| 11 | 10 | 10 | 10 | 9 |
| 12 | 10 | 11 | 11 | 10 |
| 13 | 11 | 12 | 11 | 11 |
| 14 | ... | 12 | ... | ... |
| 15 | ... | 13 | ... | ... |

[a] U. S. Forest Service, Northeastern Forest Exp. Sta., Relation of tree-stump diameter to diameter breast high, *Note No. 1*, 1947.
[b] Canadian Forest Service, 1930.
[c] R. S. Johnson (unpublished information), Mersey Paper Co., Ltd., Liverpool, Nova Scotia, 1950.

**Taper of Butt Logs.** Measurement of the ratio (Girard form class) between d.b.h. and the top d.i.b. of the first 16-ft. log has now been made for many thousand trees. Wide variations between and within species have been noted. Many factors are probably involved. An obvious cause of difference between

## Table 12. D.B.H. in Relation to Stump Diameter, in Inches—Northeastern Conifers

### 1.0-Ft. Stumps

| Stump (d.i.b.) | White pine Canada [a] | White pine Penn. [b] | Red pine [a] | Jack pine [a] | Pitch pine [b] | Hemlock Canada [c] | Hemlock Penn. [b] |
|---|---|---|---|---|---|---|---|
| 2 | ... | ... | 2 | ... | ... | ... | ... |
| 3 | ... | ... | 3 | ... | ... | ... | ... |
| 4 | ... | ... | 4 | ... | ... | ... | ... |
| 5 | 5 | ... | 5 | ... | ... | 5 | ... |
| 6 | 6 | ... | 6 | ... | ... | 6 | ... |
| 7 | 7 | ... | 6 | ... | ... | 7 | ... |
| 8 | 7 | ... | 7 | 8 | ... | 8 | ... |
| 9 | 8 | ... | 8 | 9 | ... | 8 | ... |
| 10 | 9 | ... | 9 | 9 | ... | 9 | ... |
| 11 | 10 | 11 | 10 | 10 | 11 | 10 | 10 |
| 12 | 11 | 12 | 11 | 11 | 12 | 11 | 11 |
| 13 | 12 | 13 | 12 | 12 | 13 | 12 | 12 |
| 14 | 12 | 13 | 13 | 12 | 14 | 13 | 13 |
| 15 | 13 | 14 | 14 | ... | 15 | 14 | 14 |
| 16 | 14 | 15 | 16 | ... | 15 | 15 | 15 |
| 17 | 15 | 16 | 17 | ... | 16 | 16 | 15 |
| 18 | 16 | 17 | 18 | ... | 17 | 17 | 16 |
| 19 | 17 | 18 | ... | ... | 18 | 18 | 17 |
| 20 | 18 | 19 | ... | ... | ... | 19 | 18 |
| 21 | ... | 20 | ... | ... | ... | 20 | 19 |
| 22 | ... | 20 | ... | ... | ... | 21 | 19 |
| 23 | ... | 21 | ... | ... | ... | 22 | 20 |
| 24 | ... | 22 | ... | ... | ... | 23 | 21 |
| 25 | ... | 23 | ... | ... | ... | 24 | 22 |
| 26 | ... | 23 | ... | ... | ... | 25 | 22 |
| 27 | ... | 24 | ... | ... | ... | 26 | 23 |
| 28 | ... | ... | ... | ... | ... | 27 | 24 |
| 29 | ... | ... | ... | ... | ... | 27 | ... |
| 30 | ... | ... | ... | ... | ... | 28 | ... |

[a] Dominion Forest Service, 1930.
[b] U. S. Forest Service, Northeastern Forest Exp. Sta., Relation of tree-stump diameter to diameter breast high, *Note No. 1*, 1947.
[c] R. S. Johnson (unpublished information), Mersey Paper Co., Ltd., Liverpool, Nova Scotia, 1950.

### Table 13. Girard Form-Class Averages by Species and Regions— Eastern United States

| Species | North-east | Appa-lachian | Missis-sippi delta | South | Central States | Lake States |
|---|---|---|---|---|---|---|
| **SOFTWOODS** | | | | | | |
| Southern pines (second growth) ........ | ... | ... | 78 | ... | ... | |
| Southern pines (old growth) ........... | ... | ... | 84 | ... | ... | |
| White pine ........................ | 80 | 79 | ... | ... | 80 | 78 |
| Hemlock ......................... | 78 | 78 | ... | ... | 78 | 77 |
| Spruces .......................... | 78 | 82 | ... | ... | 78 | 80 |
| Balsam fir ........................ | 80 | ... | ... | ... | ... | 80 |
| Cypress ........................... | | 78* | 78* | 78* | ... | ... |
| **HARDWOODS** | | | | | | |
| White oak (second growth) ......... | 78 | 78 | 78 | 78 | 78 | 78 |
| White oak (old growth) ........... | 82 | 82 | 80 | 80 | 82 | 80 |
| Red oaks ......................... | 78 | 78 | 78 | 78 | 78 | 78 |
| Yellow-poplar (second growth) ...... | 78 | 78 | 77 | 77 | 78 | 78 |
| Yellow-poplar (old growth) ......... | 80 | 82 | 80 | 81 | 82 | 80 |
| Cherry ........................... | 80 | 82 | ... | ... | 82 | 80 |
| Basswood ........................ | 80 | 80 | ... | 79 | 78 | 78 |
| Walnut .......................... | 78 | 78 | ... | 78 | 78 | 78 |
| Beech ........................... | 84 | 84 | 82 | 82 | 82 | 82 |
| Maples .......................... | 79 | 79 | 78 | 77 | 79 | 78 |
| Birches .......................... | 78 | 78 | 78 | 78 | 78 | 78 |
| Upland ashes ..................... | 80 | 82 | 80 | 78 | 82 | 82 |
| Sweetgum and blackgum ............ | 78 | 78 | ... | 77 | 80 | 80 |
| Hickories ........................ | 78 | 78 | 76 | 77 | 78 | 78 |
| Swamp ash ....................... | | ... | 80* | ... | ... | ... |
| Cottonwood and willow ............. | 78 | 78 | 76 | 78 | 78 | 78 |
| Tupelo ........................... | | ... | 80* | ... | ... | ... |
| Other common hardwoods .......... | 78 | 78 | 76 | 78 | 78 | 78 |

* Form class of cypress, tupelo, and swamp ash based on tree diameter measured at about 18 in. above pronounced swell.

Source: U. S. Forest Service, Tables for estimating board-foot volume of timber (for administrative use), 1946.

### Table 14.  Relationship of D.B.H. to D.O.B. at 20 Ft.—Redwood (Old Growth)

| Mendocino, Sonoma, Santa Cruz, San Mateo | | Humboldt, Del Norte | |
|---|---|---|---|
| D.b.h. (in.) | D.o.b. at 20 ft. (in.) | D.b.h. (in.) | D.o.b. at 20 ft. (in.) |
| 24 | 17 | 32 | 26 |
| 28 | 21 | 36 | 28 |
| 32 | 24 | 40 | 30 |
| 36 | 27 | 44 | 33 |
| 40 | 30 | 48 | 36 |
| 44 | 33 | 52 | 39 |
| 48 | 36 | 56 | 42 |
| 52 | 39 | 60 | 46 |
| 56 | 42 | 64 | 49 |
| | | 68 | 50 |
| 60 | 45 | 72 | 56 |
| 64 | 48 | 76 | 59 |
| 68 | 52 | 80 | 63 |
| 72 | 54 | 84 | 66 |
| 76 | 57 | | |
| 80 | 60 | | |
| 84 | 63 | | |
| 88 | 66 | | |
| 92 | 72 | | |

Source: R. G. Wagner, *Redwood forest handbook,* State Div. of Forestry, California Dept. of Natural Resources.

species is variation in bark thickness.  Of the environmental factors, degree of stocking (stand density) during the main period of stand development is unquestionably a principal one.  But a single indicator, such as d.b.h., is unreliable; the Forest Survey in Missouri, Kentucky, and Illinois rather generally found the Girard form class to increase with tree diameter, at least up to a certain point, while in the Lake States the survey found it to decrease.  In the absence of valid generalizations, the need is clear for local determination of the ratio by diameter classes.

Table 13 is based principally on measurements in stands of above-average stocking.  Measurements made by the United States Forest Service in the course of its surveys of all forest land in several states average consistently lower, almost certainly because many of the trees measured, although merchantable, were in open-grown stands where limbiness and taper are at a maximum.  Table 14 gives the relationship between d.b.h. and d.o.b. at 20 ft. for redwood, a species in which butt swell extends above breast height.  The influence of excessive butt swell on what is essentially a Girard form class of Sitka spruce is shown in Table 15, prepared from measurements of representative stands.

**Form Point.**  Form point is a point representing the center of wind pressure, or geometric center, in the tree crown.  It is ocularly determined from standing trees, and its position above ground is expressed as a percentage of total tree height.  Swedish studies indicate that it may be useful in estimating form class when felled trees are not available for the purpose.  Assume that wind pressure on the bole below the crown is negligible and that the crown alone is therefore to be considered.  Remember that when the tree crown approximates a cone, its geometric center is at ⅓ the distance from the base of the crown to the top of the tree; correct for irregularities.  A Christen hypsometer is a convenient means for

Table 15. D.I.B., in Inches, at 18 Ft. in Relation to D.B.H., Representative
Stands—Sitka Spruce, Alaska, British Columbia, Oregon, Washington

| D.b.h. (in.) | Second-growth under 100 yr. | 120-yr.-old stand on fair site | 170-yr.-old stand on good site | Old growth Brit. Col. | Old growth with heavy butt swell | Old growth with light butt swell |
|---|---|---|---|---|---|---|
| 4 | 2.8 | ... | ... | ... | ... | ... |
| 6 | 4.6 | ... | ... | ... | ... | ... |
| 8 | 6.4 | ... | ... | ... | ... | ... |
| 10 | 8.2 | ... | ... | ... | ... | ... |
| 12 | 10.0 | 10.0 | ... | 10.0 | ... | ... |
| 14 | 11.7 | 11.5 | ... | 11.8 | ... | ... |
| 16 | 13.4 | 12.8 | 13.9 | 13.5 | ... | ... |
| 18 | 15.1 | 14.4 | 15.2 | 15.3 | ... | ... |
| 20 | 16.7 | 16.0 | 16.7 | 17.0 | ... | ... |
| 22 | 18.3 | 17.5 | 18.4 | 18.7 | ... | ... |
| 24 | 19.8 | 19.0 | 20.2 | 20.4 | ... | ... |
| 26 | 21.3 | 20.6 | 22.0 | 22.1 | ... | ... |
| 28 | 22.8 | 22.0 | 24.0 | 23.9 | ... | ... |
| 30 | 24.3 | 23.5 | 26.0 | 25.6 | ... | ... |
| 32 | 25.7 | 25.0 | 28.2 | 27.3 | 20.0 | ... |
| 34 | 27.1 | 26.3 | 30.4 | 29.0 | 21.2 | ... |
| 36 | 28.5 | 27.6 | 32.6 | 30.7 | 22.2 | ... |
| 38 | 29.9 | 28.9 | 34.8 | 32.3 | 23.3 | ... |
| 40 | 31.2 | 30.2 | 37.1 | 33.9 | 24.4 | ... |
| 44 | 33.9 | 32.6 | ... | 36.9 | 26.6 | ... |
| 48 | 36.7 | 34.9 | ... | 39.8 | 28.9 | 39.0 |
| 52 | 39.3 | 37.2 | ... | 42.6 | 31.0 | 42.4 |
| 56 | 42.0 | 39.4 | ... | 45.3 | 33.2 | 45.2 |
| 60 | 44.5 | 41.6 | ... | 48.0 | 35.6 | 48.0 |
| 64 | ... | ... | ... | 50.7 | 37.8 | 50.6 |
| 68 | ... | ... | ... | ... | 39.9 | 53.3 |
| 72 | ... | ... | ... | ... | 42.1 | 56.0 |
| 76 | ... | ... | ... | ... | 44.3 | 58.8 |
| 80 | ... | ... | ... | ... | 46.5 | 61.5 |

Source: U. S. Forest Service, Pacific Northwest Forest Exp. Sta., Volume tables for Sitka spruce, 1935.

estimating the proportion of total tree height below the form point, once it has been located.

**Stem Taper. 1.** The **Höjer formula** for tree taper is:

$$\frac{d}{D} = C \log \frac{c + l}{c}$$

in which $D$ = d.b.h., $d$ = the diameter at distance $l$ from the tip, and $C$ and $c$ are constants varying with the form quotient (formula 3, page 1·11) of the timber. As $l$ is expressed as a percentage of the total height above breast height, the equation is general and applicable to trees of any size class.

**2.** The **Behre formula** for tree taper is:

$$y = \frac{x}{a + bx}$$

### Table 16A. Average Upper-Log (Above Butt Log) Taper (In.) in 16-Ft. Logs— Southern Conifers and Eastern Hardwoods

| D.b.h. (in.) | 2-log tree 2d log | 3-log tree 2d log | 3-log tree 3d log | 4-log tree 2d log | 4-log tree 3d log | 4-log tree 4th log | 5-log tree 2d log | 5-log tree 3d log | 5-log tree 4th log | 5-log tree 5th log | 6-log tree 2d log | 6-log tree 3d log | 6-log tree 4th log | 6-log tree 5th log | 6-log tree 6th log |
|---|---|---|---|---|---|---|---|---|---|---|---|---|---|---|---|
| 10 | 1.4 | 1.2 | 1.4 | | | | | | | | | | | | |
| 12 | 1.6 | 1.3 | 1.5 | 1.1 | 1.4 | 1.9 | | | | | | | | | |
| 14 | 1.7 | 1.4 | 1.6 | 1.2 | 1.5 | 2.0 | | | | | | | | | |
| 16 | 1.9 | 1.5 | 1.7 | 1.2 | 1.6 | 2.1 | | | | | | | | | |
| 18 | 2.0 | 1.6 | 1.8 | 1.3 | 1.7 | 2.2 | | | | | | | | | |
| 20 | 2.1 | 1.7 | 1.9 | 1.4 | 1.8 | 2.4 | 1.1 | 1.6 | 2.2 | 2.9 | | | | | |
| 22 | 2.2 | 1.8 | 2.0 | 1.4 | 2.0 | 2.5 | 1.1 | 1.7 | 2.3 | 2.9 | | | | | |
| 24 | 2.3 | 1.8 | 2.2 | 1.5 | 2.2 | 2.6 | 1.1 | 1.8 | 2.4 | 3.1 | | | | | |
| 26 | 2.4 | 1.9 | 2.3 | 1.5 | 2.3 | 2.7 | 1.1 | 1.9 | 2.5 | 3.2 | | | | | |
| 28 | 2.5 | 1.9 | 2.5 | 1.6 | 2.4 | 2.8 | 1.2 | 1.9 | 2.6 | 3.3 | 0.9 | 1.4 | 2.1 | 3.2 | 4.4 |
| 30 | 2.6 | 2.0 | 2.6 | 1.7 | 2.5 | 3.0 | 1.2 | 2.0 | 2.7 | 3.5 | 0.9 | 1.4 | 2.1 | 3.2 | 4.5 |
| 32 | 2.7 | 2.0 | 2.7 | 1.7 | 2.5 | 3.1 | 1.2 | 2.1 | 2.9 | 3.7 | 1.0 | 1.4 | 2.1 | 3.2 | 4.6 |
| 34 | 2.8 | 2.1 | 2.7 | 1.8 | 2.5 | 3.3 | 1.3 | 2.1 | 3.0 | 3.8 | 1.0 | 1.4 | 2.2 | 3.3 | 4.7 |
| 36 | 2.8 | 2.1 | 2.8 | 1.8 | 2.6 | 3.4 | 1.3 | 2.2 | 3.0 | 3.9 | 1.1 | 1.5 | 2.2 | 3.3 | 4.9 |
| 38 | 2.9 | 2.1 | 2.8 | 1.9 | 2.6 | 3.4 | 1.3 | 2.2 | 3.1 | 3.9 | 1.1 | 1.5 | 2.3 | 3.4 | 5.1 |
| 40 | 2.9 | 2.2 | 2.8 | 1.9 | 2.7 | 3.4 | 1.4 | 2.3 | 3.2 | 4.0 | 1.2 | 1.5 | 2.4 | 3.5 | 5.3 |

Source: U. S. Forest Service, Tables for estimating board-foot volume of timber, 1946.

### Table 16B. Average Upper-Log Taper (In.) in 16-Ft. Logs—Northern Conifers

| D.b.h. (in.) | Top logs | Second-from-top logs | Third-from-top logs | Fourth-from-top logs |
|---|---|---|---|---|
| 10 | 1.57 | | | |
| 12 | 2.03 | 1.56 | | |
| 14 | 2.49 | 1.85 | | |
| 16 | 2.96 | 2.14 | 1.75 | |
| 18 | 3.42 | 2.44 | 1.98 | |
| 20 | 3.88 | 2.74 | 2.21 | |
| 22 | 4.35 | 3.04 | 2.44 | 2.14 |
| 24 | 4.81 | 3.33 | 2.67 | 2.34 |
| 26 | 5.28 | 3.63 | 2.88 | 2.53 |
| 28 | 5.74 | 3.93 | 3.11 | 2.72 |
| 30 | 6.20 | 4.22 | 3.34 | 2.92 |

Source: U. S. Forest Service, Northeastern Forest Exp. Sta., Form-class volume tables for estimating board-foot content of northern conifers, *Sta. Paper No. 38*, 1951.

in which $y = d/D$, $x =$ the percentage of the length from tip to breast height, and $a$ and $b$ are constants varying with the form quotient and $a + b = 1$. $D = $ d.b.h. and $d =$ diameter at distance $x$ from the tip. The variable $y$ may, therefore, be defined as the ratio of the diameter at distance $x$ (in percent) from the tip to the normal d.b.h.

3. **Percentile taper** is the relative taper of a tree in terms of diameters at regular intervals along the stem, expressed in percent of d.b.h.

4. **Upper-log tapers.** Table 16A gives the average taper, in inches, of upper logs of southern conifers and eastern hardwoods. Table 16B gives the same

**Table 17. Percentage of Total Taper [a] Applicable to Each Log [b] in a Tree—Southern Conifers**

| Merchantable length of tree (logs) | 1st log | 2d log | 3d log | 4th log | 5th log |
|---|---|---|---|---|---|
| 1½ | 70 | 30 | | | |
| 1¾ | 66 | 34 | | | |
| 2 | 63 | 37 | | | |
| 2¼ | 56 | 34 | 10 | | |
| 2½ | 50 | 30 | 20 | | |
| 2¾ | 48 | 25 | 27 | | |
| 3 | 45 | 25 | 30 | | |
| 3¼ | 44 | 23 | 24 | 9 | |
| 3½ | 44 | 21 | 22 | 13 | |
| 3¾ | 42 | 20 | 21 | 17 | |
| 4 | 40 | 19 | 19 | 22 | |
| 4¼ | 39 | 18 | 18 | 18 | 6 |
| 4½ | 39 | 16 | 17 | 17 | 11 |
| 4¾ | 37 | 16 | 16 | 17 | 15 |
| 5 | 36 | 15 | 15 | 15 | 19 |

[a] Total taper is the d.b.h. (o.b.) minus the merchantable top d.i.b.
[b] 16-ft. logs.
Source: F. J. Lemieux, Log rules, taper tables, and volume tables for use in the South, *Jour. Forestry* (1936), 34:970–974.

**Table 18. Percentage of Total Taper [a] Applicable to Each Log [b] in a Tree—Southern Hardwoods**

| Merchantable length of tree (logs) | 1st log | 2d log | 3d log | 4th log | 5th log |
|---|---|---|---|---|---|
| 1½ | 77 | 23 | | | |
| 1¾ | 74 | 26 | | | |
| 2 | 70 | 30 | | | |
| 2¼ | 68 | 24 | 8 | | |
| 2½ | 65 | 23 | 12 | | |
| 2¾ | 63 | 21 | 16 | | |
| 3 | 59 | 20 | 21 | | |
| 3¼ | 56 | 18 | 18 | 8 | |
| 3½ | 53 | 18 | 18 | 11 | |
| 3¾ | 49 | 17 | 17 | 17 | |
| 4 | 50 | 15 | 15 | 20 | |
| 4¼ | 48 | 14 | 14 | 15 | 9 |
| 4½ | 46 | 14 | 14 | 14 | 12 |
| 4¾ | 43 | 14 | 14 | 14 | 15 |
| 5 | 41 | 14 | 14 | 14 | 17 |

[a] Total taper is the d.b.h. (o.b.) minus merchantable top d.i.b.
[b] 16-ft. logs.
Source: *Ibid.*

information for northern conifers. Table 17 expresses upper-log taper of southern conifers, and Table 18 of southern hardwoods, in percent of total taper from breast height to the limit of saw-log merchantability in the top.

Table 19. Log Diameter in Percentage of Diameter Inside Bark at End of First 16-Ft. Log—Conifers, Western Species[a]

| Merchantable length of tree in number of 16-ft. logs[b] | 1 | 1½ | 2 | 2½ | 3 | 3½ | 4 | 4½ | 5 | 5½ | 6 | 6½ | 7 | 7½ | 8 | 8½ | 9 | 9½ | 10 | 10½ | 11 |
|---|---|---|---|---|---|---|---|---|---|---|---|---|---|---|---|---|---|---|---|---|---|
| 1-log height | 1.00 | | | | | | | | | | | | | | | | | | | | |
| 1½-log height | 1.00 | 0.50 | | | | | | | | | | | | | | | | | | | |
| 2-log height | 1.00 | | 0.50 | | | | | | | | | | | | | | | | | | |
| 2½-log height | 1.00 | | .74 | 0.50 | | | | | | | | | | | | | | | | | |
| 3-log height | 1.00 | | .82 | | 0.50 | | | | | | | | | | | | | | | | |
| 3½-log height | 1.00 | | .87 | | .66 | 0.50 | | | | | | | | | | | | | | | |
| 4-log height | 1.00 | | .89 | | .74 | | 0.50 | | | | | | | | | | | | | | |
| 4½-log height | 1.00 | | .91 | | .79 | | .62 | 0.50 | | | | | | | | | | | | | |
| 5-log height | 1.00 | | .92 | | .82 | | .69 | | 0.50 | | | | | | | | | | | | |
| 5½-log height | 1.00 | | .93 | | .85 | | .74 | | .59 | 0.50 | | | | | | | | | | | |
| 6-log height | 1.00 | | .94 | | .87 | | .77 | | .66 | | 0.50 | | | | | | | | | | |
| 6½-log height | 1.00 | | .95 | | .88 | | .80 | | .70 | | .58 | 0.50 | | | | | | | | | |
| 7-log height | 1.00 | | .95 | | .89 | | .82 | | .74 | | .63 | | 0.50 | | | | | | | | |
| 7½-log height | 1.00 | | .95 | | .90 | | .84 | | .77 | | .68 | | .57 | 0.50 | | | | | | | |
| 8-log height | 1.00 | | .96 | | .91 | | .85 | | .79 | | .71 | | .62 | | 0.50 | | | | | | |
| 8½-log height | 1.00 | | .96 | | .91 | | .87 | | .81 | | .74 | | .66 | | .56 | 0.50 | | | | | |
| 9-log height | 1.00 | | .96 | | .92 | | .88 | | .82 | | .76 | | .69 | | .60 | | 0.50 | | | | |
| 9½-log height | 1.00 | | .96 | | .93 | | .88 | | .84 | | .78 | | .71 | | .64 | | .55 | 0.50 | | | |
| 10-log height | 1.00 | | .97 | | .93 | | .89 | | .85 | | .80 | | .74 | | .67 | | .59 | | 0.50 | | |
| 10½-log height | 1.00 | | .97 | | .94 | | .89 | | .86 | | .81 | | .75 | | .70 | | .63 | | .55 | 0.50 | |
| 11-log height | 1.00 | | .97 | | .94 | | .90 | | .87 | | .82 | | .77 | | .72 | | .66 | | .58 | | 0.50 |

[a] In the Pacific Northwest the conventional scaling practice makes special tables based on 32-ft. logs necessary. (See below.)

[b] Merchantable length is defined by a minimum diameter equal to 50 percent of the diameter at the small end of the first log.

Source: J. W. Girard and D. Bruce, *Tables for estimating board foot volume of trees in 16-foot logs.* Mason, Bruce & Girard, Portland, Ore.

**Table 20. Log Diameter in Percentage of Diameter Inside Bark at End of First 32-Ft. Log**

| Merchantable length of tree in number of 32-ft. logs * | 1 | 2 | 2½ | 3 | 3½ | 4 | 4½ | 5 | 5½ | 6 |
|---|---|---|---|---|---|---|---|---|---|---|
| 1-log tree......... | 1.000 | | | | | | | | | |
| 2-log tree......... | 1.000 | 0.600 | | | | | | | | |
| 2½-log tree....... | 1.000 | .760 | 0.600 | | | | | | | |
| 3-log tree......... | 1.000 | .829 | | 0.600 | | | | | | |
| 3½-log tree....... | 1.000 | .867 | | .700 | 0.600 | | | | | |
| 4-log tree......... | 1.000 | .891 | | .760 | | 0.600 | | | | |
| 4½-log tree....... | 1.000 | .910 | | .800 | | .673 | 0.600 | | | |
| 5-log tree......... | 1.000 | .920 | | .829 | | .723 | | 0.600 | | |
| 5½-log tree....... | 1.000 | .929 | | .850 | | .760 | | .657 | 0.600 | |
| 6-log tree......... | 1.000 | .937 | | .867 | | .788 | | .700 | | 0.600 |

* Merchantable length is defined by a minimum diameter equal to 60 percent of the diameter at the small end of the first log.

Source: J. W. Girard and D. Bruce, *Tables for estimating board foot volume of trees in 32-foot logs*. Mason, Bruce & Girard, Portland, Oregon.

**TREE QUALITY OR GRADE.** Classifying or grading standing trees for various purposes is a practice which is finding increased use among foresters. Two common criteria are silvicultural condition and the value of products obtainable from the tree. There is no standard procedure for either kind of classification; they are occasionally combined.

**Vigor and Risk Groups.** These are based on such silvicultural factors as position (crown class in even-aged stands—dominant, codominant, etc., with modifications to fit all-aged stands), density, and general health of the crown; soundness of bole and visible roots; lean, crook, and excessive forking. An example of four classes for northern hardwoods appears in Table 21. It is commonly known as Stott's classification.

Other vigor classifications for trees are described in Section 6, Silvics and Silviculture section.

**Value Groups—Tree Grades.** Value of the products which may be cut from a tree is most simply judged from the proportion of its merchantable length which is free of all visible defect. For example, the following tree grades for southern pine were developed by the U. S. Forest Service at Franklin, Va.:

| Tree Grade | Proportion of merchantable length that is free from all visible defects |
|---|---|
| 1 | 60 percent or more. |
| 2 | 40–60 percent. |
| 3 | Less than 40 percent but containing at least one 16-ft. saw log. |
| 4 | Less than one saw log, or with a cull section of 10 ft. or more. |

Source: M. Martinelli, Jr., The conversion of flat-rate stumpage value to specific rate for individual tree grade. *Jour. Forestry* (1948), 46:844.

Employed in a valuation of several North Carolina woodlands in which stumpage was actually selling at an **average** rate per M bd. ft. of $14 to $28, these grades

## Table 21. Northern Hardwood Tree Vigor and Risk Classes *

| Vigor and risk class* | General vigor and crown position | Rot and frost cracks | Dead branches | Risk |
|---|---|---|---|---|
| **A** (excellent growing stock) | Crown dominant or codominant. Dense silhouette. | No rot or frost cracks in the main trunk. Permits sound burls on lower trunk. | Permits natural pruning and an occasional dead branch in crown. | Firmly rooted, no recent mechanical damage to roots, trunk or crown. (Withstands almost any kind of selective cut.) |
| **B** (good growing stock) | Crown dominant, codominant, or intermediate | Moderate rot or open frost cracks permitted in first 8′ of the bole. A few limb swells or blind knots may be permitted above 8′. | Permits a few large dead limbs within the crown and a few large branch stubs on the upper bole. Some branches may be dying back. | Firmly rooted, no serious recent damage to roots, trunk, or crown. (Withstands moderate selective cutting.) |

Trees not meeting the above specifications are *Class C*. One or more of the characteristics listed below will definitely throw a tree into Class C.

| | | | | |
|---|---|---|---|---|
| **C** (poor growing stock) | Crown suppressed. Open silhouette. | Heavy rot. Moderate rot above first 8′ of the bole. Numerous rot pockets and blind knots. | Many large dead limbs in the crown or many large branch stubs on the upper bole. Many branches dying back. | Sprung roots. Serious recent mechanical damage to roots, trunk, or crown. Large weak crotches in upper trunk. (Subject to definite deterioration or loss after moderate selective cutting). |

| **4D** (Cull) | Trees less than 40% sound in saw-log volume. | | | |

* The judgment of the estimator in deciding vigor and risk classes must not be influenced by the site quality or by the location of the individual tree in relation to topographic or physical features.

Source: U. S. Forest Service, Region 9, The woodlot forester's tool kit, 1945.

resulted in values per M of $28.89 for Grade 1 trees, $16.06 for Grade 2, $10.61 for Grade 3, and a **negative** value of $11.32 for Grade 4; corresponding numbers of trees per M were 4.06, 4.41, 5.18, and 10.46.

Tree value classes are more commonly based on the grade (see below for a description of log grades) of logs (generally the butt log, or the first cut above a culled portion left in the woods) in the tree, which in turn depends on freedom from visible defect.

Examples of tree grades based on butt log alone are:

### NORTHERN HARDWOOD TREE GRADES
#### Value Groups

1. Trees the first log of which is Grade 1.
2. Trees the first log of which is Grade 2.
3. Trees the first log of which is Grade 3.
4. Trees containing a net of less than 40 percent of their gross log scale.

Source: U. S. Forest Service, Region 9, Guide to stand structure analysis for the old growth northern hardwood and hemlock forest, 1942.

### APPALACHIAN HARDWOOD TREE GRADES
#### Butt log [a] specifications

| Tree grade | Minimum D.b.h. (in.) | Log grade | Minimum total clear length (ft.) | Maximum number of sections | Maximum allowed defect, percent |
|---|---|---|---|---|---|
| A | 20 | Select | 12 | 1 | 10 |
|  | 30 | Select | 14 [b] | 2 | 25 |
| B | 18 | No. 1 | 13 [c] | 3 | 25 |
| C | Any tree with a No. 2 or No. 3 butt log | | | | |

[a] Normally the first 16 ft. above stump. Jump butts up to 6 ft. permitted; any longer jump butt considered a part of butt log, and the log and tree graded accordingly.
[b] Each section must have at least 7 ft. clear. Thus a centered knot or similar defect is permissible.
[c] Each section need have only 5 ft. between defects.
Source: U. S. Forest Service, Southeastern Forest Exp. Sta., Tree grades, yields and values for some Appalachian hardwoods, *Sta. Paper No. 9*, 1951.

Tests of the Appalachian hardwood grades indicate that there is an orderly decline in grade of logs up the tree and that the butt log therefore provides a reasonably good estimate of tree value.

Examples of more elaborate tree grades are as follows:

### SANTEE TREE GRADES FOR LOBLOLLY AND SHORTLEAF PINE

| Tree grade | Description |
|---|---|
| 1–2 | Butt log Grade 1 and second log Grade 2 or better. |
| 1–3 | Butt log Grade 1 and second log Grade 3. |
| 2 | Butt log Grade 2. |
| 3 | Butt log Grade 3. |

Source: U. S. Forest Service, Southeastern Forest Exp. Sta., Tree grades for loblolly and shortleaf pine, *Tech. Note No 69*, 1948.

### Joint Tree Grades for Southern Pine*

A.  Any tree with Grade 1 log.
    Any 1-log tree with a Grade 2 log.
    Any 2-(or more) log tree with a 2-log grade-sum of 4 or less.
B.  Any 1-log tree with a Grade 3 log.
    Any 2-(or more) log tree with a 2-log grade-sum of 5 or 6.
C.  Any 1-log tree with a Grade 4 log.
    Any 2-(or more) log tree with a 2-log grade-sum of 7 or 8.

* Grade the first two logs by Interim Log Grades (see p. 1·39), jump-butting where advisable, and cutting logs 12 to 20 ft. long to get best possible recovery. Then sum the grade numbers of the two logs.
    Source: U. S. Forest Service, unpublished report of Southern Pine Log and Tree Grade Committee, November 1, 1950.

**Log Grades.** Log grades, which are the basis for most tree value grades, are in turn based on the quality, and ultimately the value, of the products obtainable from the log. Log grading, like tree grading, has not been standardized, and the practicing forester should check locally on the log grades recognized for the species of his region.

A number of trade associations have adopted and published specifications for grading logs. The Western Pine Association, Portland, Oregon, publishes those for Pacific Northwest species, including Douglas-fir, ponderosa pine, western white pine, sugar pine, and associated species. The Columbia River (Portland, Oregon), Puget Sound (Seattle, Wash.), and Grays Harbor (Aberdeen, Wash.) Log Scaling and Grading Bureaus also cover Pacific Northwest species. Log-grading rules for other species are published by the California Redwood Association, San Francisco; Hemlock and Northern Hardwood Manufacturers Association, Oshkosh, Wis.; and American Walnut Manufacturers Association, Chicago, Ill.

Log grades are sometimes established by law, as is the case in British Columbia (Table 22).

Public agencies, notably the Forest Products Laboratory of the U. S. Forest Service, have developed log grades based on (1) size of log, and (2) location and amount of visible defects. For hardwoods the Laboratory recognizes three use classes: (1) factory lumber, (2) ties and timbers (structural), and (3) local use, such as blocking and dunnage. The hardwood log grades it recommends for factory lumber are described in Table 23.

**Application of factory grade specifications.** Grading of logs is not as difficult as it appears to the novice.

1. Note whether the log is a butt or an upper log. Second, measure its average diameter inside bark at the small end, and its length, dropped to a full foot.

2. Scrutinize the log for hidden defects (Table 24 lists surface and end abnormalities which might figure in this examination). After some practice the examiner will find that the examination of most logs in the process of scaling suffices for grading also. Even in logs where the grade is not immediately apparent, it is seldom necessary to lay out the actual cuttings. Usually measurements to see whether the cuttings conform to the minimum size will be enough to determine the grade.

3. Faces. The diagram (Fig. 5) accompanying Table 23 defines log faces. Taking into account surface and end defects, first square the log, full length, into four faces so oriented as to give the largest possible number of good faces. This

## Table 22. Official British Columbia Log Grades

| Log Grade | Minimum Length (ft.) | Minimum Diam. (in.) | Straightness | Soundness | Surface clarity | Other specifications |
|---|---|---|---|---|---|---|
| | | | | CEDAR AND CYPRESS* | | |
| 1 | 16 | 20 | ............ | ............ | ............ | Will cut 50% of scale in clear inch lumber. |
| 2 | 16 | 16 | ............ | ............ | ............ | Better than No. 3 Grade, but did not grade No. 1. |
| 3 | ... | ... | ............ | ............ | Rough | Suitable only for shiplap or dimension. |
| Culls | ... | ... | ............ | ............ | ............ | Lower in grade than No. 3. |
| | | | | DOUGLAS-FIR | | |
| 1 | 20 | 30 | Reasonably straight | Sound | Clear | Grain straight enough to insure strength. |
| 2 { | 24 | 14 | | | No rotten knots or bunch knots | |
| | 24 | 12 | | | | |
| 3 | ... | ... | Bad crooks | Bad knots | ............ | Lumber grade is below merchantable. |
| Culls | ... | ... | ............ | ............ | ............ | Lower in grade than No. 3. |

*(Continued on following page.)*

* Alaska-cedar.

## Table 22. Official British Columbia Log Grades (Continued)

| Log Grade | Minimum Length (ft.) | Minimum Diam. (in.) | Straightness | Soundness | Surface clarity | Other specifications |
|---|---|---|---|---|---|---|
| **HEMLOCK** | | | | | | |
| 1 | 16 | 26 | ......... | ......... | ......... | Will cut out 50% or more of scaled contents in No. 2 clear, B, or better lumber. Maximum spiral grain: Logs 35 in. and under—1 in. per lineal ft. Logs 36 in. and over—1½ in. per lineal ft. |
| 2 | 16 | 20 | ......... | ......... | ......... | Will cut out 65% or more of scaled contents in merchantable or better lumber, or 20% or more of clear lumber. Maximum spiral grain: Logs 20–25 in.—slight. Logs 26–35 in.—1 in. per lineal ft. Logs 36 in. and over—1½ in. per lineal ft. |
| 3 | ... | ... | ......... | Less than 50% of gross scale | ......... | Lower in grade than No. 2, but suitable for pulp and lumber. |
| Culls | ... | ... | ......... | Less than ⅓ of gross scale | | |
| **SPRUCE, PINE, AND COTTONWOOD** | | | | | | |
| 1 | 12–32 / 32 / 24 | 30 / 24 / 14 | Reasonably straight | ......... | Clear | Free from such defects as would impair the value of clear lumber. |
| 2 | 24 | 12 | Reasonably straight | Sound | No rotten knots or bunch knots | Grain straight enough to insure strength. |
| 3 | ... | ... | Bad crooks | Bad knots | ......... | Lumber grade is below merchantable. |
| Culls | ... | ... | ......... | ......... | ......... | Lower in grade than No. 3. |

Source: Adapted from Chap. 128, Revised Statutes of British Columbia, 1948, and amendments.

### Table 23. Hardwood Log Grades for Factory Lumber

| Grade factors | Log grade F-1 | | Log grade F-2 | Log grade F-3 |
|---|---|---|---|---|
| | Butts only | Butts and uppers | Butts and uppers | Butts and uppers |
| Diameter (minimum) . . . . . . . . | 13″–15″ | 16″–19″; 20″+ | 11″ | 8″+ |
| Length (minimum). . . . . . . . . . | 10′+ | 10′+ | 8′–11′; 12′+ | 8′+ |
| Clear cuttings (on the 3 best faces) | | | | |
|    Length (minimum). . . . . . . . | 7′ | 5′; 3′ | 3′ | 2′ |
|    Number on face (maximum). . | 2 | 2 | 2; 3 | Unlimited |
|    Yield in face length (minimum) | $\frac{5}{6}$ | $\frac{5}{6}$ | $\frac{4}{6}$ | $\frac{3}{6}$ |
| Sweep and crook deduction (maximum). . . . . . . . . . . . . . | 15% | 15% | 30% | 50% |
| Cull deduction, including sweep (maximum). . . . . . . . . . . . . . . | 40% | 40% | 50% | 50% |
| Sound end defects, area (maximum). . . . . . . . . . . . . . | See instructions | | | |

Exceptions. In ash and basswood 12″ d.i.b. for Grade 1 butts.
Grade 2 10″ d.i.b. must be Grade 1 surface quality.
Grade 2 11″ d.i.b. limited to two cuttings.
Grade 2 8′ and 9′ lengths limited to 12″ d.i.b.; ¾ yield in not more than two 3′+ cuttings.
Sweep and crook allowance reduced ⅛ in logs with more than ¼ diameter in sound end defects.
Sixty percent cull deduction permitted in Grade 2 if otherwise of Grade 1 quality.
Sixty percent cull deduction permitted in Grade 3 if otherwise of Grade 2 quality.

requires concentrating the maximum number of defects in one face, and so far as possible confining any defect to a single face.

4. Clear cuttings. The next step is to establish the grade of the best three faces, on the basis of the clear cutting requirements. The portions of any face that lie between surface defects, or between the ends of the log and defects, and which extend the full width of the face, are clear cuttings. They are permitted to include the trimming allowance, or overlength, of the log. Only when two of the best three faces grade higher than the third is it necessary to examine the fourth face in order to be sure that the best faces have been selected. The grade of the log is finally determined from the "grading face," which is the poorest of the three best faces—in other words, the next-to-the-poorest face.

5. Knots, bark-covered defects such as bumps, overgrown knots, grub holes, etc., either projecting or recessed, are excluded from clear cuttings. However, no feature such as shallow fire and other scars, seams, and frost cracks whose maximum depth is one-fifth or less of the diameter of the log at that point, is considered a defect.

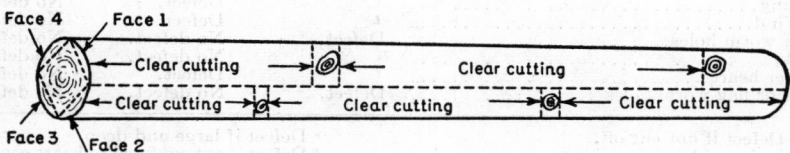

Fig. 5. Log faces.

## Table 24. Classification of Log Abnormalities

### Log Surface Abnormalities

| Abnormalities | Factory logs | Tie and timber logs | Local-use logs |
|---|---|---|---|
| Adventitious bud clusters.............. | Defect. | No defect. | No defect. |
| Bulges: | | | |
|   Butt............................. | a | a | No defect. |
|   Stem............................. | a | a | No defect. |
| Bumps: | | | |
|   High............................. | Defect. | b | b |
|   Low.............................. | c | c | b |
| Burl................................. | Defect. | Defect. | b |
| Butt scar........................... | a   d | a   d | No defect. |
| Butt swell........................... | No defect. | No defect. | No defect. |
| Canker.............................. | a | a | No defect. |
| Conk................................ | Defect. | Defect. | No defect. |
| Flanges............................. | No defect. | No defect. | No defect. |
| Flutes.............................. | d | d | No defect. |
| Fork................................ | a | a | No defect. |
| Holes: | | | |
|   Large............................ | Defect. | e | b |
|   Medium: | | | |
|     Ant, fresh...................... | No defect. | No defect. | No defect. |
|     Ant, old....................... | Defect. | No defect. | No defect. |
|     Birds, light.................... | No defect. | No defect. | No defect. |
|     Birds, heavy.................... | Defect. | No defect. | No defect. |
|     Grub........................... | Defect. | No defect. | No defect. |
|     Increment borer................. | Defect. | No defect. | No defect. |
|     Tap............................ | Defect. | No defect. | No defect. |
|   Small............................ | d | No defect. | No defect. |
| Knots: | | | |
|   Sound............................ | Defect. | b | b |
|   Unsound.......................... | Defect. | e | b |
| Limbs............................... | Defect. | b | b |
| Overgrowths: | | | |
|   Knots and bark pockets............. | Defect. | b | No defect. |
|   Insects.......................... | Defect. | No defect. | No defect. |
|   Bird peck........................ | Defect. | No defect. | No defect. |
|   Bark distortions................. | Defect. | No defect. | No defect. |
| Seams............................... | d | d | No defect. |
| Splits.............................. | d | d | No defect. |
| Surface rise........................ | No defect. | No defect. | No defect. |
| Wounds: | | | |
|   New.............................. | No defect. | No defect. | No defect. |
|   Old.............................. | d | d | No defect. |

### Log End Abnormalities

| | | | |
|---|---|---|---|
| Dote................................ | f | Defect. | No defect. |
| Double pith......................... | a | a | No defect. |
| Grease spots........................ | g | No defect. | No defect. |
| Grub channels....................... | g | g | No defect. |
| Gum spots........................... | g | No defect. | No defect. |
| Loose heart......................... | f | Defect. | No defect. |
| Mineral streak and stain............ | g | No defect. | No defect. |
| Pin worm holes...................... | Defect. | No defect. | No defect. |
| Rot................................. | f | Defect. | No defect. |
| Shake: | | | |
|   Ring............................. | f | Defect. | No defect. |
|   Wind............................. | f | Defect. | No defect. |
| Shot worm holes..................... | Defect. | No defect. | No defect. |
| Soak................................ | g | No defect. | No defect. |
| Spider heart........................ | f | Defect. | No defect. |
| Spot or flag worm holes............. | Defect. | No defect. | No defect. |

a Defect if not cut off.
b Defect if large.
c Defect if certain species involved.
d Defect if not superficial.

e Defect if large and deep.
f Defect if not confined to heart center.
g Defect if concentrated.

Source: U. S. Dept. Agr., Log defects in southern hardwoods, *Agr. Handbook No. 4*, 1950.

6. Sweep, crook, and cull. Logs reduced in scale by these defects a percentage greater than that allowed for a particular grade are dropped one grade. All deductions made by enclosing an end defect in a rectangle are computed, according to the U. S. Forest Service National Forest Scaling Handbook (1940), by multiplying width, height, and length of defect together and dividing by 15 to obtain percentage. Because this handbook prescribes scaling by the Scribner Rule, the percentage deduction thus arrived at should be multiplied by the factors given on page 1·62 when gross scale of the log is computed by the Doyle or International Rules.

For sweep, the rule-of-thumb given in the Scaling Handbook is replaced by the provision that the percentage deduction is taken as the maximum sweep minus 2, divided by log diameter.

7. End defects. **Sound** end defects, such as medium to heavy mineral stain in hard maple and yellow-poplar, and slight dote in yellow birch on the small end of the log, shall not exceed one-half the log diameter for Grade 1 logs, and for Grade 2 logs under 16 in., or three-fifths the log diameter on Grade 2 logs 16 in. and larger. Excess will lower the log one grade. When the defect is not concentrated in one spot, its extent is taken as the sum of the individual occurrences. Slight stain is not a defect.

**Unsound** end defect, such as decay and heavy shake, outside the heart zone (taken as one-fifth of the diameter from the pith), when extending more than one-half the distance between the heart zone and the bark, prevents taking clear cuttings on the face surface overlying it. When it extends less than the full log length, cuttings can be taken over one-third of its estimated length from the end tapering out.

**Specific end defects,** such as bird peck, worm holes, spot wormhole stain, mineral spots or streaks, and such unsound defects as grub holes and bark pockets are considered when outside the heart zone (as previously defined). When these defects affect one-half the radial distance between the heart zone and the bark under three faces of the log at one end, or two faces at both ends, a log of Grade 1 or 2 shall be dropped one grade. When there is less than 3 in. either between the heart zone and the defect, or between defects, the portion will be included with the defect.

8. For seams, frost cracks, and fire or other scars which exceed in depth one-fifth the diameter, but not extending the full length of the log, clear cuttings can be taken over one-third of its length from the end tapering out.

9. Bird pecks are considered defects in cuttings of Grade 1 and Grade 2 logs when the area contains more than four bird pecks per square foot. However, when the depth of the bird peck on the end of the log is less than one-tenth of the log diameter, it is not considered a defect.

The application of the foregoing grades to factory logs is shown graphically in Figs. 6–8.

The results obtained by region-wide application of these log grades are shown in Table 25.

Specifications for the Forest Service standard hardwood construction log (tie and timber logs), two of which are illustrated in Fig. 9, and those proposed for local-use logs, are given in Tables 26A and 26B.

**Veneer and plywood log grades.** The hardwood factory log grades of the Forest Products Laboratory, in its opinion, "give workable results when using the F–1 grade specifications as a veneer grade. There is no provision, however, for

A 16-ft. butt log 13 in. in diameter at the small end. More than ⅚ of its grading-face length is clear in two sections 7 and 8 ft. long. Less than 40 percent deduction for cull or sweep.

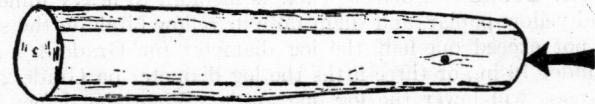

A 10-ft. log 16 in. in diameter at the small end. More than ⅚ of its grading-face length is clear in one section 8 ft. long. Less than 15 percent deduction for sweep; total cull deduction is less than 40 percent.

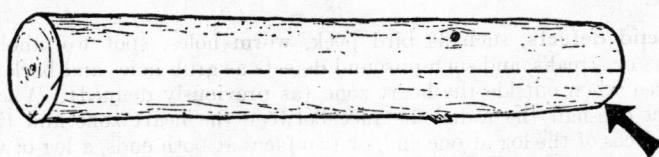

A 12-ft. log 20 in. in diameter at the small end. Five-sixths of its grading-face length is clear in two sections 8 and 3 ft. long. Deduction for cull and sweep is less than 40 percent.

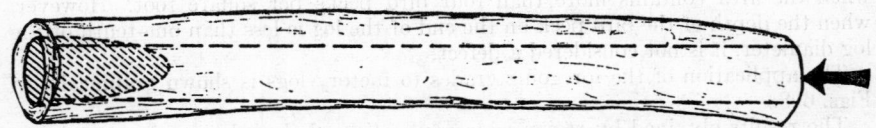

A 16-ft. log 20 in. in diameter at the small end. Less than 15 percent deduction for sweep. Total deduction for sweep and rot is less than 40 percent. There are no surface indications of defect.

**Fig. 6. Four examples of Grade F-1 hardwood logs.**
(U. S. Forest Service, Northeastern Forest Exp. Sta., *Sta. Paper No. 42,* 1951.)

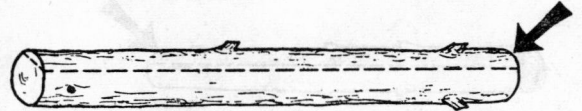

A 10-ft. log 11 in. in diameter at the small end. More than ⅔ of its grading-face length is clear in two sections each 4 ft. long. Less than 50 percent deduction for cull and sweep.

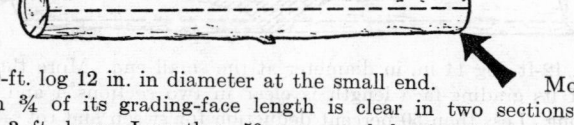

A 9-ft. log 12 in. in diameter at the small end. More than ¾ of its grading-face length is clear in two sections 4 and 3 ft. long. Less than 50 percent deduction for cull and sweep.

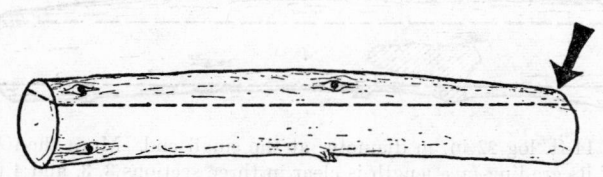

An 11-ft. log 18 in. in diameter at the small end. More than ⅔ of its grading-face length is clear in two sections 5 and 4 ft. long. Deduction for sweep is 30 percent. Total deduction is less than 50 percent.

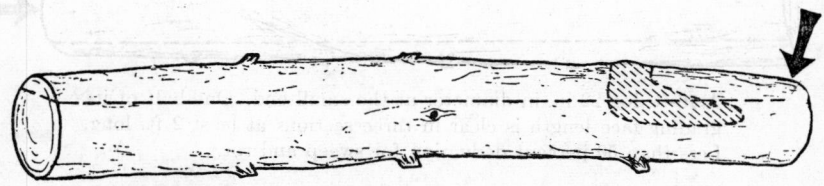

A 16-ft. log 22 in. in diameter at the small end. More than ⅔ of its grading-face length is clear in three sections 4, 3, and 4 ft. long. Less than 30 percent deduction for sweep. Total deduction is less than 50 percent.

**Fig. 7. Four examples of Grade F-2 hardwood logs.**

(U. S. Forest Service, Northeastern Forest Exp. Sta., *Sta. Paper No. 42*, 1951.)

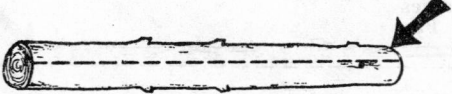

An 8-ft. log 8 in. in diameter at the small end. More than ½ of
its grading-face length is clear in two sections of 2 ft. or longer.
Less than 50 percent deduction for cull and sweep.

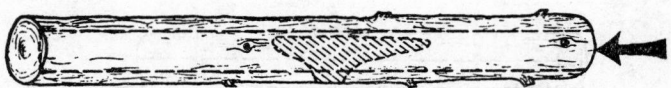

A 12-ft. log 14 in. in diameter at the small end. More than ½
of its grading-face length is clear in two sections 4 and 2 ft.
long. Less than 50 percent deduction for sweep and rot.

A 14-ft. log 22 in. in diameter at the small end. More than ½
of its grading-face length is clear in three sections 3, 3, and 4 ft.
long. Less than 50 percent deduction for sweep and rot.

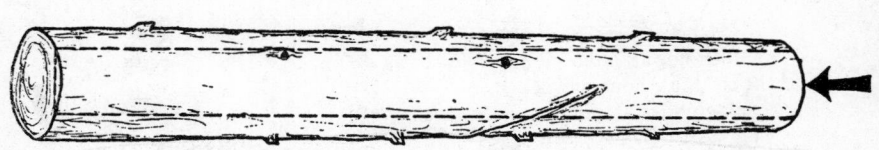

A 16-ft. log 22 in. in diameter at the small end. One-half of its
grading-face length is clear in three sections at least 2 ft. long.
Less than 50 percent deduction for sweep and rot.

**Fig. 8. Four examples of Grade F-3 hardwood logs.**
(U. S. Forest Service, Northeastern Forest Exp. Sta., *Sta. Paper No. 42*, 1951.)

log end conditions affecting the chuckability of a log. The Northern Hemlock and
Hardwood Manufacturers' Association has adopted a set of log grading rules,
based primarily on the Forest Products Laboratory grades, with the F-1 grade
modified to serve as a veneer grade. These specifications perform favorably when
compared to our specifications."

**Table 25. Yields and Values of No. 1 Common and Better Hardwood Lumber, by Factory Log Grades and Species**

| Lumber | Yield, in percent, of No. 1 common and better lumber [a] | | | Comparative value of lumber, in percent, with Log Grade 1 taken as 100 | |
|---|---|---|---|---|---|
| | Log grade | | | Log grade | |
| | F–1 | F–2 | F–3 | F–2 | F–3 |
| Ash .................... | 80 | 57 | 30 | 77 | 54 |
| Basswood .............. | 72 | 53 | 30 | 81 | 67 |
| Birch, yellow ........... | 70 | 42 | 13 | 69 | 41 |
| Gum, sap ............. | 72 | 49 | 24 | 78 | 58 |
| Maple, hard ........... | 68 | 41 | 15 | 71 | 48 |
| Oak, black ............ | 68 | 32 | 20 | 64 | 54 |
| Oak, chestnut [b] ........ | 65 | 42 | 36 | 70 | 60 |
| Oak, red (upland)....... | 72 | 44 | 18 | 72 | 51 |
| Oak, red (lowland)....... | 67 | 44 | 23 | 76 | 61 |
| Oak, white (upland)...... | 72 | 43 | 15 | 67 | 46 |
| Oak, white (lowland) ..... | 68 | 42 | 18 | 73 | 56 |
| Poplar, yellow .......... | 73 | 47 | 20 | 80 | 65 |
| Beech .................. | 67 | 47 | 19 | 83 | 63 |
| Cottonwood ............. | 72 | 52 | 33 | 87 | 77 |
| Elm, soft ............. | 67 | 45 | 20 | 81 | 66 |
| Gum, black ............. | 76 | 60 | 32 | 84 | 63 |
| Hickory ................ | 65 | 40 | 14 | 78 | 62 |
| Maple, soft ............ | 73 | 64 | 25 | 89 | 64 |
| Sycamore .............. | 67 | 50 | 31 | 84 | 66 |

[a] These columns consist of the actual yield of FAS, Selects, and No. 1 Common.
[b] Combined grading WHND (worm holes no defect) and WHAD (worm holes a defect).
Source: U. S. Forest Service, Forest Products Laboratory, Hardwood log grades for standard lumber, proposals and results, *Report D1737, 1949*.

A 10-ft. log 18 in. in diameter at the small end. It has numerous knots, but none with a knot collar exceeding ⅓ of the log diameter at the point where it occurs. No unsound defect. The log is straight; so there is no problem of sweep.

A 12-ft. log 22 in. in diameter at the small end. This is a rough log with numerous knots and some sweep. However, the knots are within permissible limits and sweep does not exceed ¼ of the diameter of the small end of the log.

**Fig. 9. Two examples of hardwood logs in the tie and structural grade.**

### Table 26A. Hardwood Construction Log Specifications (Tie and Timber Logs)

| Grading factors | Specifications |
|---|---|
| Position in tree | Butt and upper. |
| D.i.b., small end | 8 in. or larger. |
| Length without trim | 8 ft. or longer. |
| Clear cuttings | No requirements. Not graded on cutting basis. |
| Sweep allowance, maximum | ¼ d.i.b. of small end each 8 ft. of length ½ d.i.b. for 16 ft. logs. |
| Sound surface defects permitted: | |
| Single knots | Any number, if none has an average collar diameter in excess of ⅓ of log diameter at point of occurrence. [a] |
| Whorled knots [b] | Any number, provided the sum of the collar diameter does not exceed ⅓ the log diameter at point of occurrence. |
| Holes | Any number, not exceeding knot size specifications, if they do not extend over 3 in. into the contained tie or timber. |
| Unsound defects permitted: | |
| Surface | Any number and size if they do not extend into contained tie or timber. If they extend into contained tie and timber, they shall not exceed size, number, and depth of limits of sound knots. |
| Interior | None permitted except one shake not more than ⅓ the width of the contained tie or timber and one split not over 5 in. long. |

[a] Knot collar is the average of the vertical and horizontal diameters of the limb or knot swelling as measured flush with the surface of the log.
[b] Those occurring less than 6 in. apart vertically.

### Table 26B. Proposed Specifications for Local-Use Logs

| Grading factors | Specifications |
|---|---|
| Position in tree | Butt and upper |
| D.i.b., small end | 8 in. or larger |
| Length without trim | 8 ft. or longer |
| Sweep allowance, maximum | ½ diameter of small end |
| Total cull allowed | 50 percent |
| Clear cuttings | No requirements |
| Surface defects | Only requirement is that diameter of knots, holes, rot, etc., shall not exceed ½ diameter of log at point of occurrence |
| End defects | No requirements |

Grades for plywood logs are published by the western trade associations cited previously in this section.

Among the log grades developed by state agencies are the following for Indiana hardwoods:

### Purdue Hardwood Log Grades

**Prime.** Practically (90 percent) surface clear on three visible faces. Must be 16 in. or larger in d.i.b.

**No. 1.** At least three-fourths (75 percent) of length on three visible faces must be surface clear in one cutting. Must be at least 14 in. in d.i.b.

**No. 2.** At least one-half (50 percent) of length on three visible faces must be surface clear in two cuttings, neither of which is less than three ft. long. Must be at least 10 in. in d.i.b.

**No. 3.** Will not meet No. 2 specifications.

Source: A. M. Herrick, How to grade hardwood sawlogs, Purdue University, *Ext. Bull. No. 346,* 1949.

The effect of log diameter on the grade, under the above rules, of some 861 logs is shown in Table 27.

**Table 27. Average Percentage Lumber Grade Recovery by Log Diameters and Grades, Indiana Hardwoods**

| Log grade | Lumber grade | Diameter of log | | | | | | | | | | | All sizes |
|---|---|---|---|---|---|---|---|---|---|---|---|---|---|
| | | 8 | 10 | 12 | 14 | 16 | 18 | 20 | 22 | 24 | 26 | 28 | |
| Prime | FAS | | | | | 43 | 43 | 43 | 43 | 43 | 44 | 48 | 43 |
| | No. 1C | | | | | 33 | 33 | 33 | 33 | 33 | 36 | 40 | 33 |
| | No. 2C | | | | | 14 | 9 | 7 | 7 | 8 | 7 | 5 | 7 |
| | No. 3C | | | | | 10 | 15 | 17 | 17 | 16 | 13 | 7 | 17 |
| No. 1 | FAS | | | | 20 | 20 | 21 | 22 | 24 | 26 | 29 | 32 | 21 |
| | No. 1C | | | | 36 | 38 | 40 | 43 | 46 | 50 | 53 | 57 | 40 |
| | No. 2C | | | | 23 | 22 | 19 | 15 | 12 | 9 | 6 | 4 | 19 |
| | No. 3C | | | | 21 | 20 | 20 | 20 | 18 | 15 | 12 | 7 | 20 |
| No. 2 | FAS | | 7 | 7 | 7 | 8 | 9 | 11 | 14 | 18 | 22 | 27 | 8 |
| | No. 1C | | 31 | 33 | 35 | 37 | 40 | 44 | 48 | 51 | 54 | 56 | 36 |
| | No. 2C | | 30 | 29 | 28 | 26 | 24 | 21 | 17 | 13 | 9 | 6 | 27 |
| | No. 3C | | 32 | 31 | 30 | 29 | 27 | 24 | 21 | 18 | 15 | 11 | 29 |
| No. 3 | FAS | 0 | 0 | 0 | 1 | 1 | 2 | 4 | 6 | 9 | 12 | 17 | 1 |
| | No. 1C | 14 | 15 | 18 | 23 | 31 | 38 | 44 | 50 | 55 | 60 | 63 | 25 |
| | No. 2C | 34 | 37 | 38 | 36 | 32 | 28 | 24 | 20 | 16 | 12 | 8 | 35 |
| | No. 3C | 52 | 48 | 44 | 40 | 36 | 32 | 28 | 24 | 20 | 16 | 12 | 39 |
| All grades | FAS | 0 | 5 | 10 | 15 | 19 | 22 | 25 | 28 | 30 | 33 | 36 | 20 |
| | No. 1C | 15 | 20 | 25 | 30 | 34 | 37 | 40 | 42 | 44 | 45 | 45 | 35 |
| | No. 2C | 40 | 37 | 33 | 28 | 23 | 19 | 15 | 12 | 10 | 8 | 6 | 22 |
| | No. 3C | 45 | 38 | 32 | 27 | 24 | 22 | 20 | 18 | 16 | 14 | 13 | 23 |

Source: Allyn M. Herrick, Grade yields and overrun from Indiana hardwood sawlogs, Purdue Univ. Agr. Exp. Sta., *Ext. Bull. No. 516,* 1946.

Grades for Southern pines developed by the United States Forest Service include:

LOG GRADES FOR SECOND-GROWTH LOBLOLLY AND SHORTLEAF PINES
AND ASSOCIATED HARDWOODS WEST OF THE
MISSISSIPPI RIVER

No. 1. Surface-clear logs 10 in. d.i.b. or over, and logs over 16 in. d.i.b. with not more than three 2- to 4-in. knots; length 10 ft. or over.

No. 2. Logs 8 in. d.i.b. or over containing numerous small knots (any knot less than 2 in. in diameter) ; or logs more than 14 in. d.i.b. containing four to six 2-to 4-in. knots; length 10 ft. or over.

No. 3. Knotty or crooked merchantable logs 8 in. d.i.b. or over that do not fall in either No. 1 or No. 2 grade; length 10 ft. or over.

No. 4. Logs that are extremely crooked, or less than one-third sound.

Source: U. S. Dept. Agr., Financial aspects of selective cutting in the management of second-growth pine-hardwood forests west of the Mississippi River, *Tech. Bull. No. 861,* 1944.

The above grades, modified chiefly by omission of requirements for log length, are the basis for the "Santee Tree Grades," p. 1·25. Similar grades to those shown in Table 28 were the basis for the proposed "Joint Tree Grades for Southern Pine," p. 1·26.

Log grades developed in the Northeast by the U. S. Forest Service for eastern white pine, spruce, balsam, eastern hemlock, and red pine are given in Table 29.

**GROWTH. Diameter.** Volume and other characteristics of the standing tree are expressed in terms of diameter at breast height outside bark. Changes in volume, basal area, height, etc., due to growth can therefore be calculated from the observed changes in diameter at breast height, as determined from periodic measurements of the same tree, or from increment borings. Repeated measurements of the same tree at intervals of several years give directly the diameter growth of the tree, including bark growth. Increment borings show diameter growth excluding bark growth. As explained below, diameter growth excluding bark growth can easily be converted to diameter growth including bark growth. Similarly, growth measurements made at some point other than at breast height can and must be converted to diameter growth at breast height.

**Bark.** Bark growth is determined on the basis of the ratio ($K$) between diameter o.b. and diameter i.b. If $I$ is an annual or a periodic increment in diameter, including bark, and $i$ is the increment without bark, at the end of the growth period the diameter o.b. is $D + I$, and the diameter i.b. is $d + i$. Then, from $D = K \cdot d$, we have

$$D + I = K (d + i)$$

or, substituting $K \cdot d$ for $D$,

$$I = K \cdot i$$

In other words, to obtain the diameter growth including bark growth, the diameter growth excluding bark growth, as measured on a core, must be multiplied by $K$.

Bark growth itself is equal to

$$I - i = K \cdot i - i = i(K - 1)$$

## Table 28. Interim Log Grades for Southern Pine (1953)
(Based on unit value of yard lumber)

| | |
|---|---|
| Log | Any approximately cylindrical tree section. Common usage excludes pieces with length less than 8 ft. or with average scaling diameter inside bark at small end smaller than 4½ in. Logs longer than 20 ft. are beyond the scope of this table unless graded as several shorter logs. |
| Face | Any quarter-cylindrical surface running full log length. |
| Overgrown knot | Any invisible branch or stub buried beneath the log surface but indicated by a surface bump or disturbance of bark pattern. |
| Sound knot | Any visible branch, stub, or socket which contains neither advance decay extending to log heart nor any hole larger than ¼ in. penetrating more than 2 in. (excludes defects defined in 1948 SPIB Rules paragraph 12d and 12e). |
| Unsound knot | Any visible branch, stub, or socket not conforming to definition of sound knot. |
| D | Average diameter of log inside bark at small end to nearest whole inch. |
| K | Number of overgrown knots plus sum of diameters of sound knots plus twice sum of diameters of unsound knots. Average diameter of knots should be measured to nearest whole inch at point where limb would normally be trimmed. |
| Sweep | Greatest deviation of longitudinal log axis from straight line connecting centers of each end of log. It should be measured to nearest whole inch, and is analogous to the middle ordinate of an arc. |
| Bad knot | Any visible knot which is so large that D is less than 6 times knot diameter, or any unsound knot. |

### INTERIM SOUTHERN PINE YARD LUMBER LOG GRADE CRITERIA

| Log grade | Minimum diameter and maximum aggregate knot criteria | | |
|---|---|---|---|
| | With 4 visible faces | With 3 visible faces | With 2 visible faces |
| 1 | $D \geqq 17$ and $5K \leqq D$ | $D \geqq 17$ and $7K \leqq D$ | $D \geqq 17$ and $10K \leqq D$ |
| 2 | $D \geqq 10$ and $2K \leqq D < 5K$ | $D \geqq 10$ and $3K \leqq D < 7K$ | $D \geqq 10$ and $4K \leqq D < 10K$ |
| 3 | $D \geqq 5$ and $D < 2K$ | $D \geqq 5$ and $D < 3K$ | $D \geqq 5$ and $D < 4K$ |
| 4 | $D \geqq 5$, but not qualified for higher grade after compliance with following degrade rules: | | |

(A) Degrade any log one grade if $D$ equals or is less than 3 times sweep of at least 3 in.

(B) Then degrade any non-Grade 4 log one grade if massed heart-rot hyphae visible on circumferential log surface suggest that fruiting has occurred or is imminent.

(C) Then degrade any Grade 3 log to Grade 4 if "bad knots" are too dispersed for containment in a 90 degree radial sector extending ¼ of log length.

Table 29. Log Grades for Some Eastern Softwoods

| Species | Log grade | Minimum sizes Diameter (in.) | Minimum sizes Length (ft.) | Maximum defect permitted (percent) | Surface requirements on visible faces |
|---|---|---|---|---|---|
| Eastern white pine.... | 1 | 13+ | 8+ | 10 | Surface clear. |
| | | 13+ | 10+ | 30 | Must be 50 percent clear in cuttings at least 8 ft. long or one face clear full length. |
| | 2 | 9+ | 10+ | 30 | Sound, tight knots not larger than 2½ in. in diameter. Occasional larger knots permitted if others are not larger than 2 in. |
| | | 17+ | 8+ | 40 | Tight knots not over 3 in. in diameter. Occasional larger knots permitted if others are tight and not over 2½ in. in diameter. |
| | 3 | 6+ | 8+ | 50 | Any log below No. 2 generally sawed. Logs with knots 4 in. or more in diameter in whorls less than 2 ft. apart not accepted unless ¼ full length has knots 2 in. or less in diameter. |
| Spruce and balsam.... | 1 | 8+ | 12+ | 20 | Sound, tight knots not over 2 in. in diameter or in whorls not closer together than 2 ft. |
| | 2 | 8+ | 10+ | 50 | Sound, tight knots not over 3 in. in diameter in whorls not closer together than 2 ft. unless ¼ full length has knots only 2 in. in diameter. |
| Eastern hemlock...... | 1 | 8+ | 10+ | 25 | Sound, tight knots not over 2½ in. in diameter or in groups not less than 2 ft. apart. Shake not over 15 percent of gross scale. |
| | 2 | 8+ | 10+ | 50 | Sound knots; no size limitation. Shake not over 25 percent gross scale. Logs generally sawed for lumber. |
| Red pine.......... | 1 | 13+ | 8+ | 10 | Surface clear; no shake. |
| | | 13+ | 10+ | 20 | Must be at least 50 percent clear in cuttings 8 ft. or longer, or clear one face for full length. No shake. |
| | 2 | 9+ | 10+ | 30 | Sound, tight knots not over 2½ in. in diameter. Occasional larger knots if other knots not over 2 in. in diameter. |
| | | 17+ | 10+ | 40 | Sound, tight knots not over 3 in. in diameter. Occasional larger knots if other knots not over 2½ in. in diameter. |
| | 3 | 8+ | 10+ | 50 | Any log below No. 2 generally sawed. Logs with knots 4 in. or more in diameter in whorls less than 2 ft. apart not accepted unless ¼ full length has knots 2 in. or less in diameter. |

Source: U. S. Dept. Agr., Small sawmill operators' manual, *Agr. Handbook No. 27*, 1952.

## Table 30. Rules for Grading American (Black) Walnut Stumps

Minimum Specifications for Walnut Stumps Fresh Cut from Live Timber

| Grade | Length | Minimum diameter | | Average height of figure | | No. of pieces allowed in entire stump | Intensity of figure (must be true stump figure) |
|---|---|---|---|---|---|---|---|
| | | Longer than 30″ | 24″–30″ | Longer than 30″ | 24″–30″ | | |
| A | 24″ and up | 22″ and up | 22″ and up | ⅔ | ¾ | 2 pieces; except those 23 in. and up may be 3 pieces. | Must be close, heavy, dense figure. |
| B | 24″ and up | 18″ and up | 20″ and up | ½ | ⅔ | 2 pieces; except those 21 in. and up may be 3 pieces. | Must be heavy close figure. |
| C | 24″ and up | 18″ and up | 18″ and up | ⅓ | ½ | 2 pieces; except those 20 in. and up may be 3 pieces. Any stump under 20 in. having more than 3 pieces, must have "B" height of figure. | Medium to heavy stump figure permitted. |

Source: American Walnut Manufacturers Assn., Chicago, 1947.

**Conversion of Diameter Growth Measured at Stump Height to Diameter Growth at Breast Height.** Measurements of annual rings made on the stump of felled trees, or borings taken at stump height, can be converted to diameter growth at breast height if the relationship between diameter at breast height o.b. ($D$) to stump diameter o.b. ($D_s$) is known. By plotting measurements of $D$ against the corresponding measurements of $D_s$ (using average values for 1- or 2-in. diameter classes) it is usually found that a straight line expresses adequately the relationship between $D$ and $D_s$. The equation of this straight line determined from a line fitted to the data by free hand or calculated by the method of least squares may be written in the form

$$D = a + b \cdot D_s$$

where $a$ and $b$ are constants which depend on species, stump height, and other factors. For an increment in stump height diameter ($I_s$) there will be a corresponding increment in diameter at breast height ($I$), and we find by a process analogous to the previous one that the diameter growth at breast height including bark growth is equal to $b \cdot I_s$. The diameter growth at stump height ($I_s$) is obtained from the corresponding diameter growth excluding bark ($i_s$) by the expression $I_s = K \cdot i_s$, so that

$$I = b \cdot K \cdot i_s$$

In an upland oak forest in central Pennsylvania, the following numerical data have been obtained:

$$D = a + bD_s = -0.175 + 0.801 D_s$$

$$D = K \cdot d = 1.09 \cdot d$$

so that

$$I = b \cdot K \cdot i_s = 0.801 \cdot 1.09 \cdot i_s = 0.873 \cdot i_s$$

**Basal Area and Volume.** Growth in basal area and volume can be computed from growth in diameter if the relationship of basal area to diameter, or volume to diameter, is known. The former relationship is given by the formula

$$B = \frac{\pi}{4} D^2$$

and the latter is given in the form of a local volume table.

Basal area growth ($I_B$) per tree is obtained by subtracting the initial basal area ($B$) from the basal area corresponding to a diameter $D + I$ (where $I$ is the annual or periodic diameter growth):

$$I_B = \frac{\pi}{4}(D + I)^2 - \frac{\pi}{4}D^2$$

$$= \frac{\pi}{4}2DI + \frac{\pi}{4}I^2$$

The term $\frac{\pi}{4}I^2$ is small compared to the term $\frac{\pi}{4}2D \cdot I$, and we have with sufficient approximation

$$I_B = \frac{\pi}{2}DI$$

Volume growth per tree can be expressed by formula only if the local volume table is given in mathematical form. A formula which adequately expresses average volume per tree $(V)$ as a function of diameter at breast height $(D)$, and which has been successfully used in practice, is

$$V = k \cdot D^b \quad \text{(for cubic foot volume)}$$

and

$$V - \gamma = k \cdot (D - \delta)^b \quad \text{(for board foot volume)}$$

In these formulas $k$ and $b$ are the constants which define a given volume table. Their values depend on the definition of volume, on species, average tree height, tree form, etc. In the formula for board foot volmue, $\delta$ is the minimum merchantable diameter o.b. (such as 6, 8, or 10 in.) and $\gamma$ is the volume of a bolt of wood reaching from stump height up to breast height, with a diameter o.b. measured at the small end equal to $\delta$. With these formulas volume growth can be calculated in the same manner as basal area growth. After neglecting all terms containing second and higher powers of $I$, we obtain the useful expressions:

$$I_V = k \cdot bD^{b-1} \cdot I \quad \text{(for cubic feet)}$$
$$I_V = k \cdot b (D - \delta)^{b-1} \cdot I \quad \text{(for board feet)}$$

The formula expressing growth per tree in cubic feet is of particular importance for the calculation of growth percent as shown below.

**Growth Percent Formulas.** Growth per tree in diameter $(I_D)$, basal area growth $(I_B)$, or volume growth $(I_V)$ may be expressed in percent of diameter $(D)$, basal area $(B)$, or volume $(V)$, respectively, as follows:

$$I_{D(\text{percent})} = \frac{I_D}{D} \cdot 100$$

$$I_{B(\text{percent})} = \frac{I_B}{B} \cdot 100$$

$$I_{V(\text{percent})} = \frac{I_V}{V} \cdot 100$$

The quotients $p_D$, $p_B$, and $p_V$ represent the **growth rates** in diameter, basal area, and volume. The corresponding **growth percentages** are $p_D(\%) = 100p_D$, $p_B(\%) = 100p_D$, and $p_V(\%) = 100p_V$.

The relation between corresponding growth rates in diameter and basal area is

$$p_B = 2p_D$$

that is, the percentage growth in basal area is twice the corresponding percentage growth in diameter. If volume per tree in terms of diameter is expressed by the formula $V = k \cdot D^b$ (see above for nature of $k$ and $b$), then

$$p_V = b \cdot p_D = b \cdot \frac{I_D}{D}$$

For cubic foot volume $b$ varies between 2.2 and 2.6. For example, in constructing a local cubic foot volume table by plotting average volume per tree on logarithmic paper and fitting a straight line to the data, one may find that the slope of the line $(= b)$ is 2.45. With respect to **this** volume table, volume growth in percent of volume may be computed by the simple formula

$$I_D(\%) = 245\frac{I_D}{D}$$

It is important to keep in mind that the value of the constant $b$ varies from one volume table to another. For the special value $b = 2.28$ the above formula becomes what is known in American literature as Gevorkiantz's formula.

For an observed periodic growth, as for example an increment in d.b.h. of 1.0 in., **annual growth rates** can be computed from initial volume $(v)$, $n$ years ago, and present volume $(V)$ by using either simple or compound interest formulas. These are (for volume):

**Simple growth rate**

$$r = \frac{V - v}{n \cdot v}, \text{ or } r \text{ (in percent)} = 100r$$

**Compound growth rate**

$$p = \sqrt[n]{\frac{V}{v}} - 1, \text{ or } p \text{ (in percent)} = 100p$$

**Pressler's formula:**

$$P = \frac{V - v}{V + v} \times \frac{200}{n}$$

in which $P$, $V$, $v$, and $n$ have the same meaning as in the compound interest formula, is an attempt to approximate that formula with first-degree quantities. It has been widely used.

**Kunze's formula:**

$$P = \frac{(V - v)\,200}{V(n - 1) + v(n + 1)}$$

in which $n$ again = number of years between measurements, more closely approximates the compound interest formula than does Pressler's.

**Schneider's formula:**

$$P = \frac{400}{nd}$$

in which $n =$ the number of rings in the last inch of radius, and $d =$ present d.b.h. in inches, is simple but inaccurate, unless applied only to **basal area growth** (it disregards the height and form factor).

## Volumes of Trees and (Primary) Forest Products

**UNITS OF VOLUME AND EQUIVALENTS. Cubic Foot.** Formulas for computing volumes of geometric solids are given below:

Cylinder: $\qquad\qquad V = BL$

Paraboloid: $\qquad\qquad V = \dfrac{BL}{2}$

Cone: $\qquad\qquad\quad V = \dfrac{BL}{3}$

Neiloid: $\qquad\qquad\; V = \dfrac{BL}{4}$

Frustum of Paraboloid

Smalian's formula

$$V = \frac{B + b}{2} L$$

Huber's formula:

$V = B_{\frac{1}{2}} \, L$ where $B_{\frac{1}{2}}$ is area of cross section half-way between the two bases

Newton's formula:

$$V = (B + 4B_{\frac{1}{2}} + b) \frac{L}{6}$$

Frustum of Cone:

$$V = \frac{1}{3} (B + b + \sqrt{B \cdot b}) L$$

in which $V$ = volume in cubic feet
$B$ and $b$ = areas of lower and upper bases, respectively, in square feet
$L$ = height or length in feet

A table of log volumes, computed in cubic feet by Smalian's formula from diameters in inches and lengths in feet, will be found in Table 37.

**Board Foot.** This unit is equal to $\frac{1}{12}$ of a cubic foot; it represents a board 1 ft. square and 1 in. thick, and refers to rough lumber. In finished or surfaced lumber, width and thickness are based on measurements before surfacing or other finishing.

Table 31 gives the number of board feet contained in lumber or timbers of some common dimensions and lengths. The number of board feet contained in saw logs is considered in detail under log rules, page **1 · 52**.

Board foot–cubic foot and board foot–cord ratios are subject to so many variables that generalizations are almost valueless. Table 32 shows how the number of board feet to the cubic foot increases as the size of the log increases. Canadian measurements (Technical Committee, Governing Council, Assn. of Forest Engineers for the Province of Quebec, Report of Nov. 30, 1927) of the board-foot content of nearly 100 cords of 4-ft. spruce, fir, and jack pine pulpwood similarly reflect the influence of bolt size: where the number of bolts was 40 per cord, the board footage was nearly 400, and where the number was 110, the footage decreased to about 325. The average was 349, or markedly less than the 500 board foot commonly used by the U. S. Forest Service as the equivalent of a standard cord.

The largest square timber which may be cut from a straight log measures 0.7071 × d.i.b. of the log at the small end.

**Cords.** A **standard cord** is generally accepted in the United States and Canada as 4 by 4 by 8 ft. It most commonly consists of sticks 4 ft. long, in a pile 4 ft. high and 8 ft. long. It contains 128 cu. ft. of wood, bark, and air space, or of wood and air space if the wood is peeled. In some regions the term "rick" is substituted for "pile"; it does not define stick length.

The vertical face of a cord is 4 by 8 ft., or 32 sq. ft. Such a **face cord** is sometimes used in the Northeast in the sale of short-length fuelwood.

The length of stick has been more or less arbitrarily varied for use by different industries, but there is some tendency toward regional standardization. A 4 by 8-ft. stack of over-length sticks is called a **long cord.** Frequently these long cords, or even a standard cord, have been given the name "unit." The term, however, should not be used except locally, and then only after careful definition.

To measure stacked cordwood or pulpwood, multiply the length by the height of the stack, both in feet, and divide by 32. The result is the number of units or cords, depending on the length of the stick. On sloping ground the length and the height of the stack or rick should always be taken at right angles to each other.

Table 31. Board-Foot Contents of Sawn Lumber

BOARD TABLE—LENGTH IN FEET

| Size in Inches | 6 | 8 | 10 | 12 | 14 | 16 | 18 | 20 | 22 | 24 |
|---|---|---|---|---|---|---|---|---|---|---|
| 1x2 | 1 | 1⅓ | 1⅔ | 2 | 2⅓ | 2⅔ | 3 | 3⅓ | 3⅔ | 4 |
| 1x3 | 1½ | 2 | 2½ | 3 | 3½ | 4 | 4½ | 5 | 5½ | 6 |
| 1x4 | 2 | 2⅔ | 3⅓ | 4 | 4⅔ | 5⅓ | 6 | 6⅔ | 7⅓ | 8 |
| 1x5 | 2½ | 3⅓ | 4⅙ | 5 | 5⅚ | 6⅔ | 7½ | 8⅓ | 9⅙ | 10 |
| 1x6 | 3 | 4 | 5 | 6 | 7 | 8 | 9 | 10 | 11 | 12 |
| 1x8 | 4 | 5⅓ | 6⅔ | 8 | 9⅓ | 10⅔ | 12 | 13⅓ | 14⅔ | 16 |
| 1x10 | 5 | 6⅔ | 8⅓ | 10 | 11⅔ | 13⅓ | 15 | 16⅔ | 18⅓ | 20 |
| 1x12 | 6 | 8 | 10 | 12 | 14 | 16 | 18 | 20 | 22 | 24 |
| 1½x6 | 3¾ | 5 | 6¼ | 7½ | 8¾ | 10 | 11¼ | 12½ | 13¾ | 15 |
| 1½x8 | 5 | 6⅔ | 8⅓ | 10 | 11⅔ | 13⅓ | 15 | 16⅔ | 18⅓ | 20 |
| 1½x10 | 6¼ | 8⅓ | 10⅓ | 12½ | 14½ | 16⅔ | 18¾ | 20⅚ | 23 | 25 |
| 1½x12 | 7½ | 10 | 12½ | 15 | 17½ | 20 | 22½ | 25 | 27½ | 30 |
| 1½x2 | 1½ | 2 | 2½ | 3 | 3½ | 4 | 4½ | 5 | 5½ | 6 |
| 1½x3 | 2¼ | 3 | 3¾ | 4½ | 5¼ | 6 | 6¾ | 7½ | 8¼ | 9 |
| 1½x4 | 3 | 4 | 5 | 6 | 7 | 8 | 9 | 10 | 11 | 12 |
| 1½x5 | 3¾ | 5 | 6¼ | 7½ | 8¾ | 10 | 11¼ | 12½ | 13¾ | 15 |
| 1½x6 | 4½ | 6 | 7½ | 9 | 10½ | 12 | 13½ | 15 | 16½ | 18 |
| 1½x8 | 6 | 8 | 10 | 12 | 14 | 16 | 18 | 20 | 22 | 24 |

Dimension Table—Length in Feet

| Size in Inches | 12 | 14 | 16 | 18 | 20 | 22 | 24 | 26 | 28 | 30 | 32 | 34 | 36 | 38 | 40 |
|---|---|---|---|---|---|---|---|---|---|---|---|---|---|---|---|
| 2x4 | 8 | 9 | 11 | 12 | 13 | 15 | 16 | 17 | 19 | 20 | 21 | 23 | 24 | 25 | 27 |
| 2x6 | 12 | 14 | 16 | 18 | 20 | 22 | 24 | 26 | 28 | 30 | 32 | 34 | 36 | 38 | 40 |
| 2x8 | 16 | 19 | 21 | 24 | 27 | 29 | 32 | 35 | 37 | 40 | 43 | 45 | 48 | 51 | 53 |
| 2x10 | 20 | 23 | 27 | 30 | 33 | 37 | 40 | 43 | 47 | 50 | 53 | 57 | 60 | 63 | 67 |
| 2x12 | 24 | 28 | 32 | 36 | 40 | 44 | 48 | 52 | 56 | 60 | 64 | 68 | 72 | 76 | 80 |
| 2x14 | 28 | 33 | 37 | 42 | 47 | 51 | 56 | 61 | 65 | 70 | 75 | 79 | 84 | 89 | 93 |
| 3x6 | 18 | 21 | 24 | 27 | 30 | 33 | 36 | 39 | 42 | 45 | 48 | 51 | 54 | 57 | 60 |
| 3x8 | 24 | 28 | 32 | 36 | 40 | 44 | 48 | 52 | 56 | 60 | 64 | 68 | 72 | 76 | 80 |
| 3x10 | 30 | 35 | 40 | 45 | 50 | 55 | 60 | 65 | 70 | 75 | 80 | 85 | 90 | 95 | 100 |
| 3x12 | 36 | 42 | 48 | 54 | 60 | 66 | 72 | 78 | 84 | 90 | 96 | 102 | 108 | 114 | 120 |
| 3x14 | 42 | 49 | 56 | 63 | 70 | 77 | 84 | 91 | 98 | 105 | 112 | 119 | 126 | 133 | 140 |
| 4x4 | 16 | 19 | 21 | 24 | 27 | 29 | 32 | 35 | 37 | 40 | 43 | 45 | 48 | 51 | 53 |
| 4x6 | 24 | 28 | 32 | 36 | 40 | 44 | 48 | 52 | 56 | 60 | 64 | 68 | 72 | 76 | 80 |
| 6x6 | 36 | 42 | 48 | 54 | 60 | 66 | 72 | 78 | 84 | 90 | 96 | 102 | 108 | 114 | 120 |
| 6x8 | 48 | 56 | 64 | 72 | 80 | 88 | 96 | 104 | 112 | 120 | 128 | 136 | 144 | 152 | 160 |
| 8x8 | 64 | 75 | 85 | 96 | 107 | 117 | 128 | 139 | 149 | 160 | 171 | 181 | 192 | 203 | 213 |
| 8x10 | 80 | 93 | 107 | 120 | 133 | 147 | 160 | 173 | 187 | 200 | 213 | 227 | 240 | 253 | 267 |
| 10x10 | 100 | 117 | 133 | 150 | 167 | 183 | 200 | 217 | 233 | 250 | 267 | 283 | 300 | 317 | 333 |
| 10x12 | 120 | 140 | 160 | 180 | 200 | 220 | 240 | 260 | 280 | 300 | 320 | 340 | 360 | 380 | 400 |
| 12x12 | 144 | 168 | 192 | 216 | 240 | 264 | 288 | 312 | 336 | 360 | 384 | 408 | 432 | 456 | 480 |
| 12x14 | 168 | 196 | 224 | 252 | 280 | 308 | 336 | 364 | 392 | 420 | 448 | 476 | 504 | 532 | 560 |
| 14x14 | 196 | 229 | 261 | 294 | 327 | 359 | 392 | 425 | 457 | 490 | 523 | 555 | 588 | 621 | 653 |

Table 32. Board Foot–Cubic Foot Ratio for 16-Ft. Logs of Various Diameters

| Diameter at small end (in.) | Volume in cubic feet [a] | Volume in board feet [b] | Board feet per cubic foot |
|---|---|---|---|
| 4 | 2.27 | 6.64 | 2.93 |
| 5 | 3.23 | 13.04 | 4.04 |
| 6 | 4.36 | 21.2 | 4.86 |
| 7 | 5.67 | 31.1 | 5.49 |
| 8 | 7.16 | 42.8 | 5.98 |
| 9 | 8.81 | 56.2 | 6.38 |
| 10 | 10.64 | 71.4 | 6.71 |
| 12 | 14.8 | 107.1 | 7.22 |
| 14 | 19.7 | 150. | 7.60 |
| 16 | 25.3 | 200. | 7.89 |
| 18 | 31.6 | 256. | 8.12 |
| 20 | 38.6 | 320. | 8.30 |
| 25 | 59.1 | 511. | 8.64 |
| 30 | 84.0 | 745. | 8.87 |
| 35 | 113.2 | 1,023. | 9.04 |
| 40 | 146.8 | 1,346. | 9.17 |

[a] Smalian's formula, assumed taper ½ in. per 4 ft.
[b] International ⅛-In. Rule.
Source: D. Bruce and Frances X. Schumacher, *Forest mensuration*, McGraw-Hill Book Co., Inc., New York, 1942.

A **pen** of wood stacked in layers is used in the South as a pulpwood unit. It consists of two pulpwood sticks to a layer, each layer being stacked at right angles to the one beneath. Five pens, 6 ft. high, are considered equal to a cord (if of 4-ft. wood), or to a unit (if of longer wood—generally 5 ft., 3 in.).

A **cunit** in the Province of Quebec is a stack of wood containing 100 cu. ft. of solid wood; in volume calculations each stick is measured separately at both ends, and the sum is divided by 2. (In the Pacific Northwest a "cunit" describes 100 cu. ft. of hogged mill waste).

**Solid Content of a Stacked Cord.** (By "solid content" is meant both wood and bark, in the case of unpeeled wood. The term "wood content" will later be used to indicate wood alone.) To determine the solid content of a stacked cord or rick, photograph the face. Along equally spaced lines on the print, measure the proportion of each line crossing solid wood (or wood and bark), and average. Or superimpose on the print a transparent template of equally spaced dots, and count the dots falling on wood or bark in relation to the total number of dots; this method is particularly well adapted to unpeeled wood.

Because the area of **any** circle is 0.785 (approximately) of that of the square in which it is inscribed, the solid content of a cord of sticks, all perfect cylinders, and of a **single diameter**, would be the same whether the sticks were large or small. (Staggering the rows—hexagonal piling—increases the ratio to 0.8.) A mixture of sizes would, however, give a larger solid content, because small sticks, down to the minimum size for cordwood, could be inserted in the spaces between the larger. It is because even unsplit cordwood sticks are never uniform in size and shape, and are never perfect cylinders, that the solid content varies. Roughness, crook —anything which causes cordwood sticks to vary from perfect cylinders—increase the air space in a stacked cord. Hence:

1. A stacked cord of hardwood has less solid content than one of conifers.
2. A stacked cord of long sticks has less solid content than one of short sticks. In an experiment with northern hardwoods, bucking 4-ft. sticks—many of them split—into stovewood lengths reduced the stacked volume by 19 percent.
3. A stacked cord of small sticks has less solid content than one of large sticks (evidence, however, is somewhat conflicting on this point; Canadian measurements earlier referred to showed an average solid content of 77.5 cu. ft. to a cord of 30 to 50 sticks, and 83.5 to a cord of 100 or more sticks).
4. A stacked cord of split wood has less solid content than one of round wood.
5. A stacked cord of unpeeled wood has less solid content than one of peeled wood.
6. A stacked cord of wood cut from open-grown, limby trees has less solid content than wood from well pruned trees. Comparison of forest-grown and open-grown spruce by a Canadian pulp company gave this differential as nearly 7 percent.
7. A stacked cord of tops and branches has less solid content than one of bole or stem wood.

**Table 33. Solid Content, in Cubic Feet, of Stacked Cord * of Unpeeled Wood by Dimension and Condition of Bolts—Lake States**

| Condition of bolts | Middle diameter and length of bolts | | | | | |
| --- | --- | --- | --- | --- | --- | --- |
| | Diameter less than 6 in. | | Diameter 6 to 12 in. | | Diameter more than 12 in. | |
| | Length 4 ft. | Length 8 ft. | Length 4 ft. | Length 8 ft. | Length 4 ft. | Length 8 ft. |
| **Softwoods** | | | | | | |
| **Straight** | | | | | | |
| Smooth...... | 90 | 88 | 95 | 93 | 100 | 98 |
| Slightly rough.. | 88 | 85 | 93 | 91 | 98 | 96 |
| Slightly rough and knotty... | 84 | 80 | 91 | 88 | 96 | 94 |
| **Not straight** | | | | | | |
| Slightly crooked and rough.... | 80 | 76 | 88 | 84 | 93 | 91 |
| Considerably crooked..... | 76 | 72 | 85 | 80 | 90 | 87 |
| Crooked, rough, and knotty... | 70 | 65 | 79 | 75 | 83 | 80 |
| Top and branches. | 67 | 60 | | | | |
| **Hardwoods** | | | | | | |
| **Straight** | | | | | | |
| Smooth........ | 85 | 82 | 91 | 88 | 98 | 95 |
| Slightly rough.. | 82 | 78 | 89 | 86 | 96 | 93 |
| Slightly rough and knotty.. | 78 | 73 | 85 | 82 | 92 | 90 |
| **Not straight** | | | | | | |
| Slightly crooked and rough...... | 75 | 70 | 82 | 79 | 89 | 86 |
| Considerably crooked..... | 70 | 65 | 79 | 75 | 85 | 82 |
| Crooked, rough, and knotty... | 67 | 60 | 75 | 70 | 78 | 75 |
| Tops and branches | 58 | 50 | | | | |

* 4 by 4 by 8 ft.
Source: U. S. Forest Service. Lake States Forest Exp. Sta., *Forest Res. Digest*, May, 1935.

Careless piling, with sticks not parallel, may obviously be a major factor in reducing solid content—perhaps up to 10 percent. The influence of some of the above factors, for unpeeled wood in the Lake States, is shown in Table 33. In the South converting factors commonly used per stacked cord of unpeeled wood are 90 cu. ft. for softwoods and 80 for hardwoods.

**Bark volume in cordwood** (see previous information on bark thickness). Bark volume in cordwood depends on relative bark thickness as determined by the average ratio $k$ of diameter inside bark to diameter outside bark. For a given species and locality the value of $k$ may be determined by measuring double bark thickness of 20 to 30 pulpwood bolts with a bark gauge. After obtaining the middle diameter inside bark of each bolt, the sum of these diameters is divided by the sum of the corresponding diameters outside bark to find $k$. The bark volume in percent of the cordwood volume including bark is then obtained by the formula (E. B. Chamberlain and H. A. Meyer, *Tappi* 33:554–555):

$$\text{Bark volume } (\%) = 80(1 - k^2)$$

The bark factor $k$ varies from about 0.85 for thick-barked species such as chestnut oak to about 0.95 for thin-barked species such as beech. One and the same species may have different bark factors when growing on different sites and in different localities. The bark volume in cordwood corresponding to different values of $k$ is as follows:

| Bark factor or ratio d.i.b./d.o.b. | Bark volume in percent of unpeeled wood |
|:---:|:---:|
| 0.85 | 22.2 |
| .86 | 20.8 |
| .87 | 19.4 |
| .88 | 18.0 |
| .89 | 16.6 |
| .90 | 15.2 |
| .91 | 13.8 |
| .92 | 12.3 |
| .93 | 10.8 |
| .94 | 9.3 |
| .95 | 7.8 |

**Volume loss from seasoning.** In the Lake States shrinkage of 2.2 to 2.6 percent—the greater loss with wood from small trees—was observed in jack pine pulpwood peeled and left in the stack 150 days.

**Wood Content of a Stacked Cord.** Measurements in Ontario, Canada, indicate that there are about 95 cu. ft. of solid wood in the average cord of peeled spruce and fir, with a range of 84 to 103 cu. ft.; for unpeeled wood, the average is about 84 cu. ft., with a range of 79 to 87. With these and other northeastern species Mountain in a year's test obtained the results shown in Table 34. In southern United States the solid content of the average stacked cord of unpeeled pine varies from 73 to 78 cu. ft.; hardwoods from 65 to 70. Table 35 gives the factors recommended for converting cubic-foot volumes inside bark to rough, or unpeeled, cords.

**Cull wood.** Where deductions in the content of stacked cords must be made for rot, unacceptable species, etc., Table 36 is useful. It assumes a solid content of 85 cu. ft. in a standard cord.

### Table 34. Average Contents of Wood, Bark, and Space in Gross Cords, 4-Ft. Pulpwood *—Northeastern Species

| Species | Pcs. per cd. | Solid wood (%) | Solid wood (cu. ft.) | Bark (%) | Bark (cu. ft.) | Space (%) | Space (cu. ft.) |
|---|---|---|---|---|---|---|---|
| Pine, hemlock, larch, cedar ... | 83 | 65.35 | 83.65 | 12.91 | 16.52 | 21.74 | 27.83 |
| Spruce and fir.... | 100 | 67.63 | 86.57 | 13.23 | 16.93 | 19.14 | 24.50 |
| Mixed hardwoods | 87 | 62.27 | 79.71 | 12.73 | 16.29 | 25.00 | 32.00 |

* Tests made in northeastern United States, and eastern Canada show a range in bark percentage from 9 to 15 percent.
Source: H. S. Mountain, Determining the solid wood volume of four-foot pulpwood sticks, *Jour. Forestry* (1949), 47:630.

### Table 35. Average Wood Content per Stacked Cord of Unpeeled Wood— Southern Pines and Hardwoods

| Locality | Pines (cu. ft.) | Hardwoods (cu. ft.) |
|---|---|---|
| Alabama | | |
| Naval stores region | 74.9 | 65.1 |
| Remainder of state | 75.9 | 65.4 |
| Arkansas | | |
| Delta region | 73.4 | 66.7 |
| Southern pine-hardwood region | 76.7 | 65.6 |
| Florida | 74.1 | 67.0 |
| Georgia | | |
| Northern pine-hardwood region | 76.1 | 65.5 |
| Naval stores region | 74.2 | 65.5 |
| Louisiana | | |
| Delta region | 74.1 | 67.5 |
| Western pine-hardwood region | 76.3 | 66.3 |
| Naval stores region | 75.3 | 66.0 |
| Mississippi | | |
| Delta region | ... | 69.9 |
| Central pine-hardwood region | 75.5 | 65.6 |
| Naval stores region | 75.1 | 65.0 |
| Oklahoma | 78.0 | 64.9 |
| Texas | 76.3 | 65.5 |

Source: U. S. Forest Service, Southern Forest Exp. Sta., Tables for estimating cubic-foot volume of timber, *Occ. Paper No. 111,* 1947.

### Table 36. Cull Table for Cordwood

| Diameter of stick (in.) | Basal area per stick (sq. ft.) | Number of sticks for 32-sq. ft. face | Number of sticks for 32 sq. ft. stacked surface, ratio 85/128 = 0.664 | Percentage of stacked cord in one stick |
|---|---|---|---|---|
| 4 | 0.087 | 367.8 | 244 | 0.41 |
| 6 | 0.196 | 163.2 | 108 | 0.93 |
| 8 | 0.349 | 91.6 | 61 | 1.64 |
| 10 | 0.545 | 58.7 | 39 | 2.56 |
| 12 | 0.785 | 40.8 | 27 | 3.70 |

Source: H. H. Chapman and W. H. Meyer, *Forest mensuration,* McGraw-Hill Book Co., Inc., New York, 1949.

**LOG VOLUMES. Cubic Feet.** For volumes computed by Smalian's formula, see Table 37. For volumes calculated by Huber's formula, multiply basal areas given in Table 7 corresponding to diameter in the middle of log by length of log in feet. Sorenson's Log Rule:

$$V = \left[ 0.0054 \left( d + \frac{L}{20} \right)^2 \right] L$$

where $V$ = volume in cubic feet
$d$ = diameter at the small end, in inches
$L$ = length in feet

### Table 37. Cubic-Foot Volume of Logs by Smalian's Formula

| Top diameter of log * (in.) | Log length in feet | | | | | | | | | | |
|---|---|---|---|---|---|---|---|---|---|---|---|
| | 8 | 10 | 12 | 14 | 16 | 18 | 20 | 22 | 24 | 26 | 28 |
| 6 | 2 | 2 | 3 | 4 | 4 | 5 | 6 | 7 | 8 | 9 | 10 |
| 7 | 2 | 3 | 4 | 5 | 6 | 7 | 8 | 9 | 10 | 11 | 12 |
| 8 | 3 | 4 | 5 | 6 | 7 | 8 | 10 | 11 | 12 | 14 | 15 |
| 9 | 4 | 5 | 6 | 8 | 9 | 10 | 12 | 13 | 15 | 16 | 18 |
| 10 | 5 | 6 | 8 | 9 | 11 | 12 | 14 | 16 | 18 | 20 | 22 |
| 11 | 6 | 7 | 9 | 11 | 13 | 15 | 17 | 19 | 21 | 23 | 25 |
| 12 | 7 | 9 | 11 | 13 | 15 | 17 | 19 | 22 | 24 | 27 | 29 |
| 13 | 8 | 10 | 12 | 15 | 17 | 20 | 22 | 25 | 28 | 31 | 34 |
| 14 | 9 | 12 | 14 | 17 | 20 | 23 | 26 | 29 | 32 | 35 | 38 |
| 15 | 10 | 13 | 16 | 19 | 22 | 26 | 29 | 32 | 36 | 40 | 43 |
| 16 | 12 | 15 | 18 | 22 | 25 | 29 | 33 | 36 | 40 | 44 | 49 |
| 17 | 13 | 17 | 21 | 24 | 28 | 32 | 37 | 41 | 45 | 50 | 54 |
| 18 | 15 | 19 | 23 | 27 | 32 | 36 | 41 | 45 | 50 | 55 | 60 |
| 19 | 17 | 21 | 26 | 30 | 35 | 40 | 45 | 50 | 55 | 61 | 66 |
| 20 | 18 | 23 | 28 | 33 | 39 | 44 | 49 | 55 | 61 | 67 | 73 |
| 21 | 20 | 26 | 31 | 37 | 42 | 48 | 54 | 60 | 67 | 73 | 80 |
| 22 | 22 | 28 | 34 | 40 | 46 | 53 | 59 | 66 | 73 | 80 | 87 |
| 23 | 24 | 30 | 37 | 44 | 50 | 57 | 64 | 72 | 79 | 86 | 94 |
| 24 | 26 | 33 | 40 | 47 | 55 | 62 | 70 | 77 | 85 | 93 | 102 |
| 25 | 28 | 36 | 43 | 51 | 59 | 67 | 75 | 84 | 92 | 101 | 110 |
| 26 | 31 | 39 | 47 | 55 | 64 | 72 | 81 | 90 | 99 | 109 | 118 |
| 27 | 33 | 42 | 50 | 59 | 69 | 78 | 87 | 97 | 107 | 117 | 127 |
| 28 | 35 | 45 | 54 | 64 | 73 | 83 | 93 | 104 | 114 | 125 | 136 |
| 29 | 38 | 48 | 58 | 68 | 79 | 89 | 100 | 111 | 122 | 133 | 145 |
| 30 | 41 | 51 | 62 | 73 | 84 | 95 | 107 | 118 | 130 | 142 | 154 |
| 31 | 43 | 55 | 66 | 78 | 89 | 101 | 114 | 126 | 139 | 151 | 164 |
| 32 | 46 | 58 | 70 | 83 | 95 | 108 | 121 | 134 | 147 | 161 | 174 |
| 33 | 49 | 62 | 75 | 88 | 100 | 114 | 128 | 142 | 156 | 170 | 185 |
| 34 | 52 | 65 | 79 | 93 | 107 | 121 | 136 | 150 | 165 | 180 | 196 |
| 35 | 55 | 69 | 84 | 98 | 113 | 128 | 144 | 159 | 175 | 191 | 207 |
| 36 | 58 | 73 | 88 | 104 | 120 | 135 | 152 | 168 | 184 | 201 | 218 |
| 37 | 61 | 77 | 93 | 110 | 126 | 143 | 160 | 177 | 194 | 212 | 230 |
| 38 | 65 | 81 | 98 | 115 | 133 | 150 | 168 | 186 | 205 | 223 | 242 |
| 39 | 68 | 86 | 103 | 121 | 140 | 158 | 177 | 196 | | | |
| 40 | 72 | 90 | 109 | 128 | 147 | | | | | | |

* Taper allowance: 0.5 in. in 4-ft. of length. Volumes listed are subject to correction for other tapers.

Source: U. S. Forest Service, Northern Rocky Mountain Forest & Range Exp. Sta., The cubic foot as a national log scaling standard (mimeo.).

## Table 37. Cubic-Foot Volume of Logs by Smalian's Formula (Continued)

| Top diameter of log (in.) | Log length in feet | | | | | | | |
|---|---|---|---|---|---|---|---|---|
| | 30 | 32 | 34 | 36 | 38 | 40 | 42 | 44 |
| 6 | 11 | 12 | 13 | 14 | 16 | 17 | 19 | 20 |
| 7 | 13 | 15 | 16 | 18 | 19 | 21 | 23 | 25 |
| 8 | 17 | 18 | 20 | 22 | 23 | 25 | 27 | 30 |
| 9 | 20 | 22 | 24 | 26 | 28 | 30 | 33 | 35 |
| 10 | 24 | 26 | 28 | 30 | 33 | 35 | 38 | 41 |
| 11 | 28 | 30 | 33 | 35 | 38 | 31 | 44 | 47 |
| 12 | 32 | 35 | 38 | 41 | 44 | 47 | 51 | 54 |
| 13 | 37 | 40 | 43 | 47 | 50 | 54 | 58 | 61 |
| 14 | 42 | 45 | 49 | 53 | 57 | 61 | 65 | 69 |
| 15 | 47 | 51 | 55 | 59 | 64 | 68 | 73 | 77 |
| 16 | 53 | 57 | 62 | 66 | 71 | 76 | 81 | 86 |
| 17 | 59 | 64 | 69 | 74 | 79 | 84 | 90 | 95 |
| 18 | 65 | 71 | 76 | 82 | 87 | 93 | 99 | 105 |
| 19 | 72 | 78 | 84 | 90 | 96 | 102 | 109 | 115 |
| 20 | 79 | 85 | 92 | 98 | 105 | 112 | 119 | 126 |
| 21 | 86 | 93 | 100 | 107 | 114 | 122 | 129 | 137 |
| 22 | 94 | 101 | 109 | 116 | 124 | 132 | 140 | 149 |
| 23 | 102 | 110 | 118 | 126 | 135 | 143 | 152 | 161 |
| 24 | 110 | 119 | 127 | 136 | 145 | 155 | 164 | 174 |
| 25 | 119 | 128 | 137 | 147 | 156 | 166 | 176 | 187 |
| 26 | 128 | 138 | 148 | 158 | 168 | 179 | 189 | 200 |
| 27 | 137 | 147 | 158 | 169 | 180 | 191 | 203 | 214 |
| 28 | 147 | 158 | 169 | 181 | 192 | 204 | 216 | 229 |
| 29 | 157 | 168 | 181 | 193 | 205 | 218 | 231 | 244 |
| 30 | 167 | 179 | 192 | 205 | 218 | 232 | 245 | 259 |
| 31 | 177 | 191 | 204 | 218 | 232 | 246 | 261 | 275 |
| 32 | 188 | 202 | 217 | 231 | 246 | 261 | 276 | 292 |
| 33 | 200 | 215 | 230 | 245 | 261 | 276 | 292 | 309 |
| 34 | 211 | 227 | 243 | 259 | 275 | 292 | 309 | 326 |
| 35 | 223 | 240 | 256 | 273 | 291 | 308 | 326 | 344 |
| 36 | 235 | 253 | 270 | 288 | 306 | 325 | 343 | 362 |
| 37 | 248 | 266 | 285 | 303 | 322 | | | |
| 38 | 261 | | | | | | | |
| 39 | | | | | | | | |
| 40 | | | | | | | | |

**Board Feet. Log rules.** See Tables 38 to 43B.

## Table 38. International Log Rule, Board Feet

(Saw kerf ¼ in.) *

| Top diameter, i.b. (in.) | Length of log in feet | | | | | | |
|---|---|---|---|---|---|---|---|
| | 8 | 10 | 12 | 14 | 16 | 18 | 20 |
| 4 | . . . | 5 | 5 | 5 | 5 | 5 | 10 |
| 5 | 5 | 5 | 10 | 10 | 10 | 15 | 15 |
| 6 | 10 | 10 | 15 | 15 | 20 | 25 | 25 |
| 7 | 10 | 15 | 20 | 25 | 30 | 35 | 40 |
| 8 | 15 | 20 | 25 | 35 | 40 | 45 | 50 |
| 9 | 20 | 30 | 35 | 45 | 50 | 60 | 70 |
| 10 | 30 | 35 | 45 | 55 | 65 | 75 | 85 |
| 11 | 35 | 45 | 55 | 70 | 80 | 95 | 105 |
| 12 | 45 | 55 | 70 | 85 | 95 | 110 | 125 |
| 13 | 55 | 70 | 85 | 100 | 115 | 135 | 150 |
| 14 | 65 | 80 | 100 | 115 | 135 | 155 | 175 |
| 15 | 75 | 95 | 115 | 135 | 160 | 180 | 205 |
| 16 | 85 | 110 | 130 | 155 | 180 | 205 | 235 |
| 17 | 95 | 125 | 150 | 180 | 205 | 235 | 265 |
| 18 | 110 | 140 | 170 | 200 | 230 | 265 | 300 |
| 19 | 125 | 155 | 190 | 225 | 260 | 300 | 335 |
| 20 | 135 | 175 | 210 | 250 | 290 | 330 | 370 |
| 21 | 155 | 195 | 235 | 280 | 320 | 365 | 410 |
| 22 | 170 | 215 | 260 | 305 | 355 | 405 | 455 |
| 23 | 185 | 235 | 285 | 335 | 390 | 445 | 495 |
| 24 | 205 | 255 | 310 | 370 | 425 | 485 | 545 |
| 25 | 220 | 280 | 340 | 400 | 460 | 525 | 590 |
| 26 | 240 | 305 | 370 | 435 | 500 | 570 | 640 |
| 27 | 260 | 330 | 400 | 470 | 540 | 615 | 690 |
| 28 | 280 | 355 | 430 | 510 | 585 | 665 | 745 |
| 29 | 305 | 385 | 465 | 545 | 630 | 715 | 800 |
| 30 | 325 | 410 | 495 | 585 | 675 | 765 | 860 |
| 31 | 350 | 440 | 530 | 625 | 720 | 820 | 915 |
| 32 | 375 | 470 | 570 | 670 | 770 | 875 | 980 |
| 33 | 400 | 500 | 605 | 715 | 820 | 930 | 1,045 |
| 34 | 425 | 535 | 645 | 760 | 875 | 990 | 1,110 |
| 35 | 450 | 565 | 685 | 805 | 925 | 1,050 | 1,175 |
| 36 | 475 | 600 | 725 | 855 | 980 | 1,115 | 1,245 |
| 37 | 505 | 635 | 770 | 905 | 1,040 | 1,175 | 1,315 |
| 38 | 535 | 670 | 810 | 955 | 1,095 | 1,245 | 1,390 |
| 39 | 565 | 710 | 855 | 1,005 | 1,155 | 1,310 | 1,465 |
| 40 | 595 | 750 | 900 | 1,060 | 1,220 | 1,380 | 1,540 |
| 41 | 625 | 785 | 950 | 1,115 | 1,280 | 1,450 | 1,620 |
| 42 | 655 | 825 | 995 | 1,170 | 1,345 | 1,525 | 1,705 |
| 43 | 690 | 870 | 1,045 | 1,230 | 1,410 | 1,600 | 1,785 |
| 44 | 725 | 910 | 1,095 | 1,290 | 1,480 | 1,675 | 1,870 |
| 45 | 755 | 955 | 1,150 | 1,350 | 1,550 | 1,755 | 1,960 |
| 46 | 795 | 995 | 1,200 | 1,410 | 1,620 | 1,835 | 2,050 |
| 47 | 830 | 1,040 | 1,255 | 1,475 | 1,695 | 1,915 | 2,140 |
| 48 | 865 | 1,090 | 1,310 | 1,540 | 1,770 | 2,000 | 2,235 |
| 49 | 905 | 1,135 | 1,370 | 1,605 | 1,845 | 2,085 | 2,330 |
| 50 | 940 | 1,185 | 1,425 | 1,675 | 1,920 | 2.175 | 2,425 |
| 51 | 980 | 1,235 | 1,485 | 1,745 | 2,000 | 2,265 | 2,525 |
| 52 | 1,020 | 1,285 | 1,545 | 1,815 | 2,080 | 2,355 | 2,625 |
| 53 | 1,060 | 1,335 | 1,605 | 1,885 | 2,165 | 2,445 | 2,730 |
| 54 | 1,100 | 1,385 | 1,670 | 1,960 | 2,245 | 2,540 | 2,835 |
| 55 | 1,145 | 1,440 | 1,735 | 2,035 | 2,330 | 2,640 | 2,945 |
| 56 | 1,190 | 1,495 | 1,800 | 2,110 | 2,420 | 2,735 | 3,050 |
| 57 | 1,230 | 1,550 | 1,865 | 2,185 | 2,510 | 2,835 | 3,165 |
| 58 | 1,275 | 1,605 | 1,930 | 2,265 | 2,600 | 2,935 | 3,275 |
| 59 | 1,320 | 1,660 | 2,000 | 2,345 | 2,690 | 3,040 | 3,390 |
| 60 | 1,370 | 1,720 | 2,070 | 2,425 | 2,785 | 3,145 | 3,510 |

* Scale for seasoned lumber with ¹⁄₁₆-in. shrinkage per 1-in. board, and saws cutting a ¼-in. kerf, or for green lumber, for saws cutting a ⁵⁄₁₆-in. kerf. For saws cutting a ⅛-in. kerf add 10.5 percent. Formula: $[(D^2 \times 0.22) - 0.71D] \times 0.904762$ for 4-ft. sections. Taper allowance: ½-in. per 4-ft. lineal.

Source: U. S. Dept. Agr., Converting factors and tables of equivalents used in forestry, *Misc. Publ. No. 225*, 1949.

### Table 39. Scribner Decimal C Log Rule, Board Feet *

| Top diameter, i.b. (in.) | Length of log in feet | | | | | | | | | |
|---|---|---|---|---|---|---|---|---|---|---|
| | 6 | 8 | 10 | 12 | 14 | 16 | 18 | 20 | 22 | 24 |
| 6 | 0.5 | 0.5 | 1 | 1 | 1 | 2 | 2 | 2 | 3 | 3 |
| 7 | .5 | 1 | 1 | 2 | 2 | 3 | 3 | 3 | 4 | 4 |
| 8 | 1 | 1 | 2 | 2 | 2 | 3 | 3 | 3 | 4 | 4 |
| 9 | 1 | 2 | 3 | 3 | 3 | 4 | 4 | 4 | 5 | 6 |
| 10 | 2 | 3 | 3 | 3 | 4 | 6 | 6 | 7 | 8 | 9 |
| 11 | 2 | 3 | 4 | 4 | 5 | 7 | 8 | 8 | 9 | 10 |
| 12 | 3 | 4 | 5 | 6 | 7 | 8 | 9 | 10 | 11 | 12 |
| 13 | 4 | 5 | 6 | 7 | 8 | 10 | 11 | 12 | 13 | 15 |
| 14 | 4 | 6 | 7 | 9 | 10 | 11 | 13 | 14 | 16 | 17 |
| 15 | 5 | 7 | 9 | 11 | 12 | 14 | 16 | 18 | 20 | 21 |
| 16 | 6 | 8 | 10 | 12 | 14 | 16 | 18 | 20 | 22 | 24 |
| 17 | 7 | 9 | 12 | 14 | 16 | 18 | 21 | 23 | 25 | 28 |
| 18 | 8 | 11 | 13 | 16 | 19 | 21 | 24 | 27 | 29 | 32 |
| 19 | 9 | 12 | 15 | 18 | 21 | 24 | 27 | 30 | 33 | 36 |
| 20 | 11 | 14 | 17 | 21 | 24 | 28 | 31 | 35 | 38 | 42 |
| 21 | 12 | 15 | 19 | 23 | 27 | 30 | 34 | 38 | 42 | 46 |
| 22 | 13 | 17 | 21 | 25 | 29 | 33 | 38 | 42 | 46 | 50 |
| 23 | 14 | 19 | 23 | 28 | 33 | 38 | 42 | 47 | 52 | 57 |
| 24 | 15 | 21 | 25 | 30 | 35 | 40 | 45 | 50 | 55 | 61 |
| 25 | 17 | 23 | 29 | 34 | 40 | 46 | 52 | 57 | 63 | 69 |
| 26 | 19 | 25 | 31 | 37 | 44 | 50 | 56 | 62 | 69 | 75 |
| 27 | 21 | 27 | 34 | 41 | 48 | 55 | 62 | 68 | 75 | 82 |
| 28 | 22 | 29 | 36 | 44 | 51 | 58 | 65 | 73 | 80 | 87 |
| 29 | 23 | 31 | 38 | 46 | 53 | 61 | 68 | 76 | 84 | 91 |
| 30 | 25 | 33 | 41 | 49 | 57 | 66 | 74 | 82 | 90 | 99 |
| 31 | 27 | 36 | 44 | 53 | 62 | 71 | 80 | 89 | 98 | 106 |
| 32 | 28 | 37 | 46 | 55 | 64 | 74 | 83 | 92 | 101 | 110 |
| 33 | 29 | 39 | 49 | 59 | 69 | 78 | 88 | 98 | 108 | 118 |
| 34 | 30 | 40 | 50 | 60 | 70 | 80 | 90 | 100 | 110 | 120 |
| 35 | 33 | 44 | 55 | 66 | 77 | 88 | 98 | 109 | 120 | 131 |
| 36 | 35 | 46 | 58 | 69 | 81 | 92 | 104 | 115 | 127 | 138 |
| 37 | 39 | 51 | 64 | 77 | 90 | 103 | 116 | 129 | 142 | 154 |
| 38 | 40 | 54 | 67 | 80 | 93 | 107 | 120 | 133 | 147 | 160 |
| 39 | 42 | 56 | 70 | 84 | 98 | 112 | 126 | 140 | 154 | 168 |
| 40 | 45 | 60 | 75 | 90 | 105 | 120 | 135 | 150 | 166 | 181 |
| 41 | 48 | 64 | 79 | 95 | 111 | 127 | 143 | 159 | 175 | 191 |
| 42 | 50 | 67 | 84 | 101 | 117 | 134 | 151 | 168 | 185 | 201 |
| 43 | 52 | 70 | 87 | 105 | 122 | 140 | 157 | 174 | 192 | 209 |
| 44 | 56 | 74 | 93 | 111 | 129 | 148 | 166 | 185 | 204 | 222 |
| 45 | 57 | 76 | 95 | 114 | 133 | 152 | 171 | 190 | 209 | 228 |
| 46 | 59 | 79 | 99 | 119 | 139 | 159 | 178 | 198 | 218 | 238 |
| 47 | 62 | 83 | 104 | 124 | 145 | 166 | 186 | 207 | 228 | 248 |
| 48 | 65 | 86 | 108 | 130 | 151 | 173 | 194 | 216 | 238 | 260 |
| 49 | 67 | 90 | 112 | 135 | 157 | 180 | 202 | 225 | 247 | 270 |
| 50 | 70 | 94 | 117 | 140 | 164 | 187 | 211 | 234 | 257 | 281 |
| 51 | 73 | 97 | 122 | 146 | 170 | 195 | 219 | 243 | 268 | 292 |
| 52 | 76 | 101 | 127 | 152 | 177 | 202 | 228 | 253 | 278 | 304 |
| 53 | 79 | 105 | 132 | 158 | 184 | 210 | 237 | 263 | 289 | 316 |
| 54 | 82 | 109 | 137 | 164 | 191 | 218 | 246 | 273 | 300 | 328 |
| 55 | 85 | 113 | 142 | 170 | 198 | 227 | 255 | 283 | 312 | 340 |
| 56 | 88 | 118 | 147 | 176 | 206 | 235 | 264 | 294 | 323 | 353 |
| 57 | 91 | 122 | 152 | 183 | 213 | 244 | 274 | 304 | 335 | 365 |
| 58 | 95 | 126 | 158 | 189 | 221 | 252 | 284 | 315 | 347 | 379 |
| 59 | 98 | 131 | 163 | 196 | 229 | 261 | 294 | 327 | 359 | 392 |
| 60 | 101 | 135 | 169 | 203 | 237 | 270 | 304 | 338 | 372 | 406 |

* In tens of bd. ft. (0's omitted).
Source: *Ibid*.

## Table 40. Doyle Log Rule, Board Feet *

| Diameter of log (small end. inside bark) (in.) | Length of log in feet | | | | | | | | | | | | |
|---|---|---|---|---|---|---|---|---|---|---|---|---|---|
| | 6 | 7 | 8 | 9 | 10 | 11 | 12 | 13 | 14 | 15 | 16 | 17 | 18 |
| | Contents of log in board feet | | | | | | | | | | | | |
| 6 | 1 | 2 | 2 | 2 | 2 | 3 | 3 | 3 | 3 | 4 | 4 | 4 | 4 |
| 7 | 3 | 4 | 4 | 5 | 5 | 6 | 7 | 7 | 8 | 8 | 9 | 10 | 10 |
| 8 | 6 | 7 | 8 | 9 | 10 | 11 | 12 | 13 | 14 | 15 | 16 | 17 | 18 |
| 9 | 9 | 11 | 12 | 14 | 16 | 17 | 19 | 20 | 22 | 23 | 25 | 27 | 28 |
| 10 | 13 | 16 | 18 | 20 | 22 | 25 | 27 | 29 | 31 | 34 | 36 | 38 | 40 |
| 11 | 18 | 21 | 24 | 28 | 31 | 34 | 37 | 40 | 43 | 46 | 49 | 52 | 55 |
| 12 | 24 | 28 | 32 | 36 | 40 | 44 | 48 | 52 | 56 | 60 | 64 | 68 | 72 |
| 13 | 30 | 35 | 40 | 46 | 51 | 56 | 61 | 66 | 71 | 76 | 81 | 86 | 91 |
| 14 | 37 | 44 | 50 | 56 | 62 | 69 | 75 | 81 | 87 | 94 | 100 | 106 | 112 |
| 15 | 45 | 53 | 60 | 68 | 76 | 83 | 91 | 98 | 106 | 113 | 121 | 129 | 136 |
| 16 | 54 | 63 | 72 | 81 | 90 | 99 | 108 | 117 | 126 | 135 | 144 | 153 | 162 |
| 17 | 63 | 74 | 84 | 95 | 106 | 116 | 127 | 137 | 148 | 158 | 169 | 180 | 190 |
| 18 | 73 | 86 | 98 | 110 | 122 | 135 | 147 | 159 | 171 | 184 | 196 | 208 | 220 |
| 19 | 84 | 98 | 112 | 127 | 141 | 155 | 169 | 183 | 197 | 211 | 225 | 239 | 253 |
| 20 | 96 | 112 | 128 | 144 | 160 | 176 | 192 | 208 | 224 | 240 | 256 | 272 | 288 |
| 21 | 108 | 126 | 144 | 163 | 181 | 199 | 217 | 235 | 253 | 271 | 289 | 307 | 325 |
| 22 | 121 | 142 | 162 | 182 | 202 | 223 | 243 | 263 | 283 | 304 | 324 | 344 | 364 |
| 23 | 135 | 158 | 180 | 203 | 226 | 248 | 271 | 293 | 316 | 338 | 361 | 384 | 406 |
| 24 | 150 | 175 | 200 | 225 | 250 | 275 | 300 | 325 | 350 | 375 | 400 | 425 | 450 |
| 25 | 165 | 193 | 220 | 248 | 276 | 303 | 331 | 358 | 386 | 413 | 441 | 469 | 496 |
| 26 | 181 | 212 | 242 | 272 | 302 | 333 | 363 | 393 | 423 | 454 | 484 | 514 | 544 |
| 27 | 198 | 231 | 264 | 298 | 331 | 364 | 397 | 430 | 463 | 496 | 529 | 562 | 595 |
| 28 | 216 | 252 | 288 | 324 | 360 | 396 | 432 | 468 | 504 | 540 | 576 | 612 | 648 |
| 29 | 234 | 273 | 312 | 352 | 391 | 430 | 469 | 508 | 547 | 586 | 625 | 664 | 702 |
| 30 | 253 | 296 | 338 | 380 | 422 | 465 | 507 | 549 | 591 | 634 | 676 | 718 | 760 |
| 31 | 273 | 319 | 364 | 410 | 456 | 501 | 547 | 592 | 638 | 683 | 729 | 775 | 820 |
| 32 | 294 | 343 | 392 | 441 | 490 | 539 | 588 | 637 | 686 | 735 | 784 | 833 | 882 |
| 33 | 315 | 368 | 420 | 473 | 526 | 578 | 631 | 683 | 736 | 788 | 841 | 894 | 946 |
| 34 | 337 | 394 | 450 | 506 | 562 | 619 | 675 | 731 | 787 | 844 | 900 | 956 | 1,012 |
| 35 | 360 | 420 | 480 | 541 | 601 | 661 | 721 | 781 | 841 | 901 | 961 | 1,021 | 1,081 |
| 36 | 384 | 448 | 512 | 576 | 640 | 704 | 768 | 832 | 896 | 960 | 1,024 | 1,088 | 1,152 |
| 37 | 408 | 476 | 544 | 613 | 681 | 749 | 817 | 885 | 953 | 1,021 | 1,089 | 1,157 | 1,225 |
| 38 | 433 | 506 | 578 | 650 | 722 | 795 | 867 | 939 | 1,011 | 1,084 | 1,156 | 1,228 | 1,300 |
| 39 | 459 | 536 | 612 | 689 | 766 | 842 | 919 | 995 | 1,072 | 1,148 | 1,225 | 1,302 | 1,378 |
| 40 | 486 | 567 | 648 | 729 | 810 | 891 | 972 | 1,053 | 1,134 | 1,215 | 1,296 | 1,377 | 1,458 |

* Formula: $\dfrac{(D - 4)^2 \times L}{16}$

Source: U. S. Dept. Agr., Measuring and marketing farm timber, *Farmer's Bull. No. 1210.*

## Table 41. British Columbia Log Rule, Board Feet

Legal rule in the province of British Columbia

| Diameter i.b. at small end of log* (in.) | Length of log in feet | | | | | | | | | | | | | | | |
|---|---|---|---|---|---|---|---|---|---|---|---|---|---|---|---|---|
| | 10 | 12 | 14 | 16 | 18 | 20 | 22 | 24 | 26 | 28 | 30 | 32 | 34 | 36 | 38 | 40 |
| 10 | 34 | 41 | 48 | 55 | 62 | 69 | 76 | 83 | 89 | 96 | 103 | 110 | 117 | 124 | 131 | 138 |
| 11 | 43 | 52 | 60 | 69 | 77 | 86 | 94 | 103 | 112 | 120 | 129 | 137 | 146 | 155 | 163 | 172 |
| 12 | 53 | 63 | 73 | 84 | 94 | 105 | 115 | 126 | 136 | 147 | 157 | 168 | 178 | 189 | 199 | 210 |
| 13 | 63 | 76 | 88 | 101 | 113 | 126 | 138 | 151 | 164 | 176 | 189 | 201 | 214 | 227 | 239 | 252 |
| 14 | 74 | 89 | 104 | 119 | 134 | 149 | 164 | 178 | 193 | 208 | 223 | 238 | 253 | 268 | 283 | 297 |
| 15 | 87 | 104 | 121 | 139 | 156 | 173 | 191 | 208 | 226 | 243 | 260 | 278 | 295 | 312 | 330 | 347 |
| 16 | 100 | 120 | 140 | 160 | 180 | 200 | 220 | 240 | 260 | 280 | 300 | 320 | 340 | 360 | 380 | 400 |
| 17 | 114 | 137 | 160 | 183 | 206 | 229 | 252 | 274 | 297 | 320 | 343 | 366 | 389 | 412 | 435 | 457 |
| 18 | 130 | 155 | 181 | 207 | 233 | 259 | 285 | 311 | 337 | 363 | 389 | 415 | 441 | 466 | 492 | 518 |
| 19 | 146 | 175 | 204 | 233 | 262 | 292 | 321 | 350 | 379 | 408 | 437 | 466 | 496 | 525 | 554 | 583 |
| 20 | 163 | 195 | 228 | 261 | 293 | 326 | 358 | 391 | 424 | 456 | 489 | 521 | 554 | 586 | 619 | 652 |
| 21 | 181 | 217 | 253 | 290 | 326 | 362 | 398 | 434 | 471 | 507 | 543 | 579 | 615 | 652 | 688 | 724 |
| 22 | 200 | 240 | 280 | 320 | 360 | 400 | 440 | 480 | 520 | 560 | 600 | 640 | 680 | 720 | 760 | 800 |
| 23 | 220 | 264 | 308 | 352 | 396 | 440 | 484 | 528 | 572 | 616 | 660 | 704 | 748 | 792 | 836 | 880 |
| 24 | 241 | 289 | 337 | 386 | 434 | 482 | 530 | 578 | 626 | 675 | 723 | 771 | 819 | 867 | 916 | 964 |
| 25 | 263 | 315 | 368 | 421 | 473 | 526 | 578 | 631 | 683 | 736 | 789 | 841 | 894 | 946 | 999 | 1,051 |
| 26 | 286 | 343 | 400 | 457 | 514 | 571 | 629 | 686 | 743 | 800 | 857 | 914 | 971 | 1,028 | 1,086 | 1,143 |
| 27 | 309 | 371 | 433 | 495 | 557 | 619 | 681 | 743 | 805 | 867 | 928 | 990 | 1,052 | 1,114 | 1,176 | 1,238 |
| 28 | 334 | 401 | 468 | 535 | 602 | 668 | 735 | 802 | 869 | 936 | 1,003 | 1,070 | 1,136 | 1,203 | 1,270 | 1,337 |
| 29 | 360 | 432 | 504 | 576 | 648 | 720 | 791 | 864 | 936 | 1,008 | 1,080 | 1,152 | 1,224 | 1,296 | 1,368 | 1,440 |
| 30 | 387 | 464 | 541 | 619 | 696 | 773 | 850 | 928 | 1,005 | 1,082 | 1,160 | 1,237 | 1,314 | 1,392 | 1,469 | 1,546 |
| 32 | 443 | 531 | 620 | 708 | 797 | 886 | 974 | 1,063 | 1,151 | 1,240 | 1,328 | 1,417 | 1,505 | 1,594 | 1,682 | 1,771 |

## Table 41. British Columbia Log Rule, Board Feet (Continued)

| Diameter i. b. at small end of log* (in.) | Length of log in feet | | | | | | | | | | | | | | | |
|---|---|---|---|---|---|---|---|---|---|---|---|---|---|---|---|---|
| | 10 | 12 | 14 | 16 | 18 | 20 | 22 | 24 | 26 | 28 | 30 | 32 | 34 | 36 | 38 | 40 |
| 34 | 503 | 603 | 704 | 804 | 905 | 1,005 | 1,106 | 1,207 | 1,307 | 1,408 | 1,508 | 1,609 | 1,709 | 1,810 | 1,910 | 2,011 |
| 36 | 567 | 680 | 793 | 906 | 1,020 | 1,133 | 1,246 | 1,360 | 1,473 | 1,586 | 1,700 | 1,813 | 1,926 | 2,039 | 2,153 | 2,266 |
| 38 | 634 | 761 | 888 | 1,015 | 1,141 | 1,268 | 1,395 | 1,522 | 1,649 | 1,775 | 1,902 | 2,029 | 2,156 | 2,283 | 2,410 | 2,536 |
| 40 | 705 | 847 | 988 | 1,129 | 1,270 | 1,411 | 1,552 | 1,693 | 1,834 | 1,975 | 2,116 | 2,258 | 2,399 | 2,540 | 2,681 | 2,822 |
| 42 | 781 | 937 | 1,093 | 1,249 | 1,405 | 1,561 | 1,717 | 1,874 | 2,030 | 2,186 | 2,342 | 2,498 | 2,654 | 2,810 | 2,967 | 3,123 |
| 44 | 860 | 1,032 | 1,204 | 1,376 | 1,547 | 1,719 | 1,891 | 2,063 | 2,235 | 2,407 | 2,579 | 2,751 | 2,923 | 3,095 | 3,267 | 3,439 |
| 46 | 943 | 1,131 | 1,320 | 1,508 | 1,697 | 1,885 | 2,074 | 2,262 | 2,451 | 2,639 | 2,828 | 3,016 | 3,205 | 3,393 | 3,582 | 3,770 |
| 48 | 1,029 | 1,235 | 1,441 | 1,647 | 1,852 | 2,058 | 2,264 | 2,470 | 2,676 | 2,882 | 3,087 | 3,293 | 3,499 | 3,705 | 3,911 | 4,117 |
| 50 | 1,120 | 1,343 | 1,567 | 1,791 | 2,015 | 2,239 | 2,463 | 2,687 | 2,911 | 3,135 | 3,359 | 3,583 | 3,807 | 4,030 | 4,254 | 4,478 |
| 52 | 1,214 | 1,457 | 1,699 | 1,942 | 2,185 | 2,428 | 2,670 | 2,913 | 3,156 | 3,399 | 3,641 | 3,884 | 4,127 | 4,370 | 4,612 | 4,855 |
| 54 | 1,312 | 1,574 | 1,837 | 2,099 | 2,361 | 2,624 | 2,886 | 3,148 | 3,411 | 3,673 | 3,936 | 4,198 | 4,460 | 4,723 | 4,985 | 5,247 |
| 56 | 1,414 | 1,696 | 1,979 | 2,262 | 2,545 | 2,827 | 3,110 | 3,393 | 3,676 | 3,958 | 4,241 | 4,524 | 4,807 | 5,089 | 5,372 | 5,655 |
| 58 | 1,519 | 1,823 | 2,127 | 2,431 | 2,735 | 3,039 | 3,343 | 3,646 | 3,950 | 4,254 | 4,558 | 4,862 | 5,166 | 5,470 | 5,774 | 6,077 |
| 60 | 1,629 | 1,955 | 2,280 | 2,606 | 2,932 | 3,258 | 3,583 | 3,909 | 4,235 | 4,561 | 4,886 | 5,212 | 5,538 | 5,864 | 6,190 | 6,515 |
| 62 | 1,742 | 2,091 | 2,439 | 2,787 | 3,136 | 3,484 | 3,833 | 4,181 | 4,529 | 4,878 | 5,226 | 5,575 | 5,923 | 6,272 | 6,620 | 6,968 |
| 64 | 1,859 | 2,231 | 2,603 | 2,975 | 3,347 | 3,718 | 4,090 | 4,462 | 4,834 | 5,206 | 5,578 | 5,949 | 6,321 | 6,693 | 7,065 | 7,437 |
| 66 | 1,980 | 2,376 | 2,772 | 3,168 | 3,564 | 3,960 | 4,356 | 4,752 | 5,148 | 5,444 | 5,950 | 6,336 | 6,732 | 7,128 | 7,577 | 7,920 |
| 68 | 2,105 | 2,526 | 2,947 | 3,368 | 3,789 | 4,210 | 4,631 | 5,051 | 5,472 | 5,893 | 6,314 | 6,735 | 7,156 | 7,577 | 7,998 | 8,419 |
| 70 | 2,233 | 2,689 | 3,127 | 3,573 | 4,020 | 4,467 | 4,913 | 5,360 | 5,807 | 6,253 | 6,700 | 7,146 | 7,593 | 8,040 | 8,486 | 8,933 |

* The point of division between diameter-classes is one-half inch, i.e., logs over 8.5 inches would be scaled as 9.0 inch logs. Interpolate for values of logs of odd lengths.
Source: Dept. of Mines and Resources, Dominion Forest Service, Canada, Form-class volume tables, 1948.

Table 42. Comparison of Log Rules, Board Feet, 16-Ft. Logs

| Top diameter i.b. (in.) | International ¼″ kerf | Scribner | Scribner Decimal C | Spaulding | Doyle | Doyle and Scribner | Holland or Maine | Blodgett or New Hampshire | Humphrey or Vermont |
|---|---|---|---|---|---|---|---|---|---|
| 4 | 5 | (10) | (1) | ... | ... | ... | (3) | 13 | 11 |
| 5 | 10 | (13) | (1) | ... | 1 | 1 | (11) | 19 | 16 |
| 6 | 20 | 18 | 2 | ... | 4 | 4 | 20 | 26 | 24 |
| 7 | 30 | 24 | 3 | ... | 9 | 9 | 31 | 35 | 32 |
| 8 | 40 | 32 | 3 | ... | 16 | 16 | 44 | 43 | 43 |
| 9 | 50 | 42 | 4 | ... | 25 | 25 | 52 | 54 | 53 |
| 10 | 65 | 54 | 6 | 50 | 36 | 36 | 68 | 66 | 67 |
| 11 | 80 | 64 | 7 | 63 | 49 | 49 | 83 | 78 | 80 |
| 12 | 95 | 79 | 8 | 77 | 64 | 64 | 105 | 92 | 96 |
| 13 | 115 | 97 | 10 | 94 | 81 | 81 | 120 | 106 | 112 |
| 14 | 135 | 114 | 11 | 114 | 100 | 100 | 142 | 123 | 131 |
| 15 | 160 | 142 | 14 | 137 | 121 | 121 | 161 | 139 | 149 |
| 16 | 180 | 159 | 16 | 161 | 144 | 144 | 179 | 157 | 171 |
| 17 | 205 | 185 | 18 | 188 | 169 | 169 | 205 | 176 | 192 |
| 18 | 230 | 213 | 21 | 216 | 196 | 196 | 232 | 197 | 216 |
| 19 | 260 | 240 | 24 | 245 | 225 | 225 | 271 | 217 | 240 |
| 20 | 290 | 280 | 28 | 276 | 256 | 256 | 302 | 240 | 267 |
| 21 | 320 | 304 | 30 | 308 | 289 | 289 | 336 | 262 | 293 |
| 22 | 355 | 334 | 33 | 341 | 324 | 324 | 363 | 287 | 323 |
| 23 | 390 | 377 | 38 | 376 | 361 | 361 | 401 | 313 | 352 |
| 24 | 425 | 404 | 40 | 412 | 400 | 400 | 439 | 339 | 384 |
| 25 | 460 | 459 | 46 | 449 | 441 | 441 | 477 | 367 | 416 |
| 26 | 500 | 500 | 50 | 488 | 484 | 484 | 507 | 397 | 451 |
| 27 | 540 | 548 | 55 | 528 | 529 | 530 | 546 | 426 | 485 |
| 28 | 585 | 582 | 58 | 569 | 576 | 582 | 614 | 457 | 523 |
| 29 | 630 | 609 | 61 | 612 | 625 | 609 | 657 | 489 | 560 |
| 30 | 675 | 657 | 66 | 656 | 676 | 657 | 706 | 514 | 600 |
| 31 | 720 | 710 | 71 | 701 | 728 | 710 | 755 | 557 | 640 |
| 32 | 770 | 736 | 74 | 748 | 784 | 736 | 792 | 592 | 683 |
| 33 | 820 | 784 | 78 | 796 | 841 | 784 | 848 | 628 | 725 |
| 34 | 875 | 800 | 80 | 845 | 900 | 800 | 900 | 666 | 771 |
| 35 | 925 | 876 | 88 | 897 | 961 | 876 | 949 | 704 | 816 |
| 36 | 980 | 923 | 92 | 950 | 1,024 | 923 | 1,026 | 744 | 864 |
| 37 | 1,040 | 1,029 | 103 | 1,006 | 1,089 | 1,029 | 1,089 | 785 | 912 |
| 38 | 1,095 | 1,068 | 107 | 1,064 | 1,156 | 1,068 | 1,135 | 827 | 963 |
| 39 | 1,155 | 1,120 | 112 | 1,124 | 1,225 | 1,120 | 1,209 | 870 | 1,013 |
| 40 | 1,220 | 1,204 | 120 | 1,185 | 1,296 | 1,204 | 1,261 | 914 | 1,067 |

**Table 43A. Conversion Factors Between International ¼-In. Rule and Scribner and Doyle Rules—Lake States Species**

| Tree d.b.h. (in.) | Doyle volume [a] as compared with International ¼-in. (%)[b] | Scribner volume [a] as compared with International ¼-in. (%)[b] |
|---|---|---|
| 10 | 39 | 77 |
| 12 | 49 | 82 |
| 14 | 57 | 87 |
| 16 | 64 | 89 |
| 18 | 70 | 90 |
| 20 | 75 | 91 |
| 22 | 79 | 92 |
| 24 | 82 | 93 |
| 26 | 85 | 94 |
| 28 | 88 | 94 |
| 30 | 91 | 95 |
| 32 | 93 | 95 |
| 34 | 95 | 95 |
| 36 | 96 | 95 |
| 38 | 98 | 95 |
| 40 | 99 | 95 |
| 42 | ... | 95 |

[a] Stump height is 1 ft. Trees of average height scaled in 16-ft. logs for average saw-log utilization to a variable top not smaller than 8 in. inside bark.
[b] To convert volumes from International scale, multiply by the appropriate factor; to convert from Doyle or Scribner to International scale, divide by the appropriate factor.
Adapted from: Lake States Forest Exp. Sta., *Tech. Notes 283* and *287*.

**Table 43B. Relationship of Scale by International ¼-In. Rule to Scribner Rule Scale \*—Douglas-Fir (Second Growth), Pacific Northwest**

| D.b.h. average tree (in.) | Relationship of scale by International ¼-in. to Scribner scale (%) |
|---|---|
| 12 | 120.7 |
| 14 | 117.7 |
| 16 | 114.7 |
| 18 | 112.8 |
| 20 | 111.3 |
| 22 | 110.3 |
| 24 | 109.5 |
| 26 | 108.7 |
| 28 | 108.1 |
| 30 | 107.5 |
| 32 | 106.9 |
| 34 | 106.4 |
| 36 | 106.0 |
| 38 | 105.7 |
| 40 | 105.0 |

\* Logs scaled in 16-ft. lengths to 8-in. top.
Source: U. S. Forest Service, Pacific Northwest Forest & Range Exp. Sta., The yield of Douglas-fir in the Pacific Northwest measured by International ¼-in. kerf log rule, *Res. Note No. 46,* 1948.

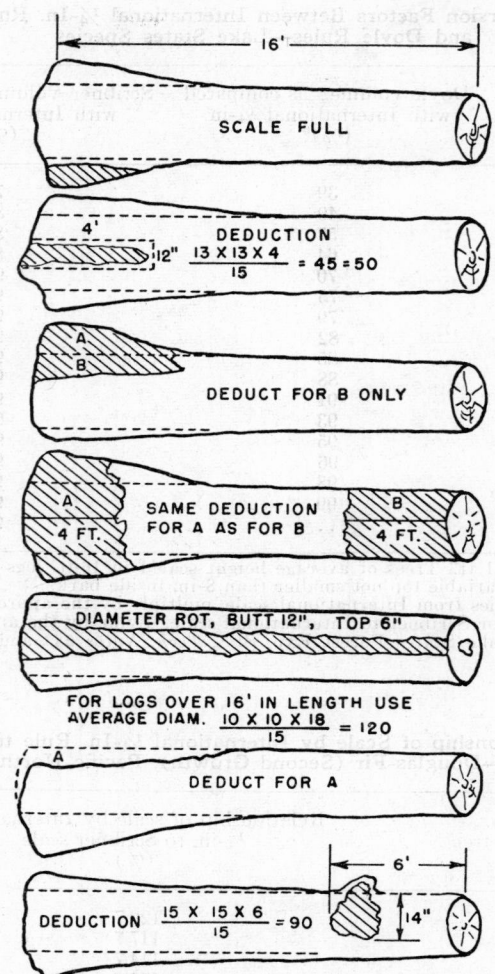

**Fig. 10. Common defects in logs and methods of deducting for them.**
(*National forest scaling handbook*, U. S. Forest Service.)

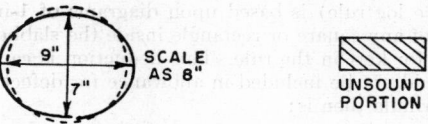

**Fig. 10. Common defects in logs and methods of deducting for them** (Continued).
*(National forest scaling handbook, U. S. Forest Service.)*

**LOG SCALING PRACTICES.** Log scaling practices differ according to the locality and to the final product to be made from the log (see "Scaling" in Section **16**). They should be governed by local custom unless otherwise specified in timber sale contracts.

The practices of cutting a log back to the next merchantable length and scaling the log to the next lowest diameter are common and are acceptable with the possible exception of large logs in the West. Defects can also be scaled out with the log rule, the difference between the scale of the defect and the gross scale being the estimated amount of merchantable wood in the log.

**Deduction for Defects.** The following discussion of practices in deducting for defects is adapted from instructions to scalers contained in the National Forest Scaling Handbook of the United States Forest Service.

Fig. 10 shows the more common defects in saw logs and the general methods of deducting for them.

**Classification of defects.** The effect of rot and other defects upon the merchantable volume of logs of different species and in different regions varies so greatly that no rules for making deductions can be applied inflexibly. Scalers must constantly exercise good judgment, based upon knowledge of local timber obtained by watching defective logs "opened up" under the saw. Defects are classified in the following manner:

    a. Interior defects, which cause waste in the interior of logs.
    b. Side defects, which cause waste on the outside of logs.
    c. Defects from curve or sweep.
    d. Defects from crotches.
    e. Defects from an excessive number of knots in top logs.

**The right cylinder.** Fig. 11 illustrates the right cylinder of a log. A defect which occurs outside the right cylinder will not be taken into consideration in making deductions.

Fig. 11. Right cylinder of a log.

**Standard rule.** The most accurate method of mathematically reducing the scale for the interior defects showing in one or both ends of the log is to treat the defects as sawed out in square or rectangular cross-section. The Scribner Decimal C Rule (the standard Forest Service log rule) is based upon diagrams of 1-in. boards with ¼-in. kerf. Twenty percent of any square or rectangle inside the slabbed surfaces of the log is, therefore, deducted for kerf in the rule. This deduction is carried in scaling sound timber, and hence should not be included in allowance for defect when scaling by the Scribner Rule. The formula then is:

$$\text{Net allowance for defect (bd. ft.)} = \left(\frac{W \times H \times L}{12}\right) 0.8 = \frac{W \times H \times L}{15},$$

where $W$ = the width and $H$ = the height of the cross-section of the defect, both in inches, and $L$ = the length in feet. The 12 in the denominator of the first fraction converts to board feet.

When scaling by the Doyle or International Rule, allowances for defect computed by the above formula should be multiplied by the following factors:

| Doyle Rule | Factor | International Rule | Factor |
|---|---|---|---|
| Logs  8 to 11 in. . . . . . . . . . . | 0.6 | Logs  8 to 14 in. . . . . . . . . . . | 1.2 |
| Logs 12 to 13 in. . . . . . . . . . . | 0.8 | Logs 15 to 19 in. . . . . . . . . . . | 1.1 |
| Logs 14 to 20 in. . . . . . . . . . . | 0.9 | Logs 20 to 36 in. . . . . . . . . . . | 1.05 |
| Logs 21 to 31 in. . . . . . . . . . . | 1.0 | Logs 37 in. and up . . . . . . . . . | 1.0 |
| Logs 32 to 40 in. . . . . . . . . . . | 1.1 | | |

**Dimension of defects.** Always add 1 in. to both dimensions of the cross-section to allow for loss of sound wood surrounding the unsound. When defect shows in both ends of a 16-ft. or shorter log, the larger visible defect is ordinarily measured, whether on the large or small end of the log. On a log longer than 16 ft., or on any log if lumber shorter than 8 ft. is merchantable, average the widths and heights of the defect on the two ends of the log.

When the defect shows on only one end of a log, determine its length by a close inspection of the surface of the log. Interior rots, with the exception of butt rots, can usually be detected by punks, punk scars, or rotten knots. If none is evident, use the diameter of the visible defect as a guide to its length. It may help to know that stem rot usually extends farther down the tree than up from the point of infection. If the estimated length leaves a portion of the log shorter than the minimum merchantable board, use the length of the log.

Where logs are bucked in the woods in long lengths merely for convenience in logging and are cut into shorter lengths at the mill before sawing, consider separately the logs into which the long log will be divided. For instance, if one of the 16-ft. logs which goes to make up a 32-ft. stick is a cull log under the merchantability clause of the sale agreement, the net scale of the other 16-ft. log only will be considered in

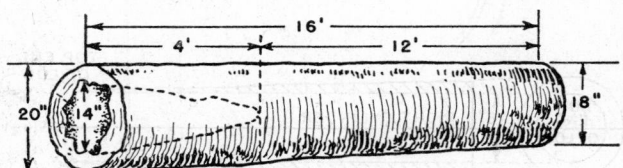

Fig. 12. Deduction for defect caused by stump rot.

recording the scale of the 32-ft. log. In other words, ignore any net scale which it may be possible to obtain in the cull log.

**Ground or stump rot.** Ground or stump rot in butt logs seldom extends far into the log, and usually tapers to a point. Fig. 12 illustrates a 16-ft. log scaling 210 bd. ft. gross, with a 4-ft. stump rot in the butt having an average diameter of 14 in. Deduct

4 ft. from the length of the log, giving the log the scale of a 12-ft. log, 18 in. in diameter: 160 bd. ft. The amount of deduction is then 210 minus 160, or 50 bd. ft.

In this case the standard rule would give a deduction greater than the actual scale of a 4-ft. section of the log: viz., $14 + 1 = 15$, and $(15 \times 15 \times 4)/15 = 60$ bd. ft. In cases where the deduction obtained by the standard rule is greater than the deduction obtained by reducing the length of the log (for the same length of defect) the latter method will be used.

**Bole or stem rots.** Wood-rotting fungi vary widely in their behavior as between species and regions. In learning how to deduct for rot in scaling, there is no substitute for observing how logs "open up" at the local sawmill. For given dimensions of defect (width, height, and length) the amount of defect is calculated by applying the standard rule as explained above.

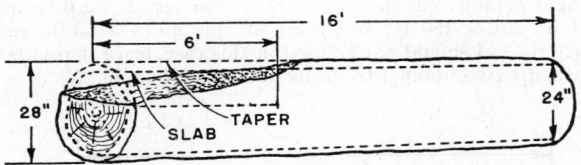

Fig. 13. Deduction for defect caused by fire scar.

**Sapwood.** In certain species with pronounced differences between sapwood and heartwood, the sapwood may have started to decay while the heartwood is unaffected and fully as merchantable as if the sapwood were sound. This may be particularly true of logs cut from dead trees. In such cases, the net scale of the log is obtained by scaling the sound heart.

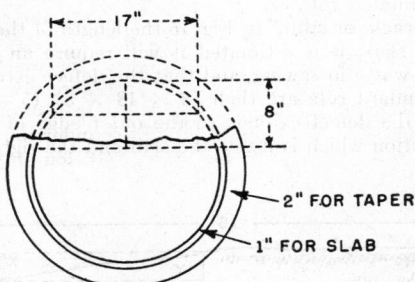

Fig. 14. Application of standard rule for determining defect caused by fire scar, Fig. 13.

**Cat face or fire scar** (see Figs. 13 and 14). The scar is 7 in. deep, inside the slab, at the end of the log, but tapers out within 6 ft. The average depth of the defect is $\frac{(7 + 1) + (0 + 1)}{2} = 4.5 = 5$ in. Seventeen in. is the average width of the defective portion, inside slab (Fig. 14). By the standard rule the deduction is then $\frac{5 \times 17 \times 6}{15}$ $= 34$ bd. ft. It will be noted that this solution of the problem allows for the utiliza-

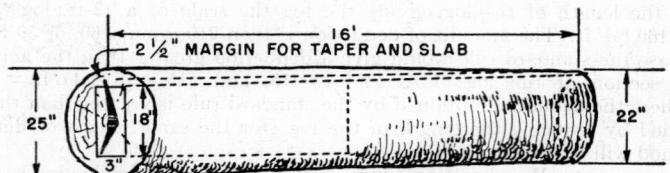

Fig. 15. Deduction for defect caused by heart check.

tion of some boards 10, 12, and 14 ft. long; otherwise a somewhat larger deduction would be made.

A rule-of-thumb solution might have been to estimate that one-third of the cross section of the right cylinder (24-in. diameter) is affected. A log 6 ft. long with a top diameter of 24 in. scales 150 ft; one-third of this gives a 50-ft. deduction. This method is inaccurate and should not be used in this case, since it results in a net scale which is lower than that obtained by using the standard rule.

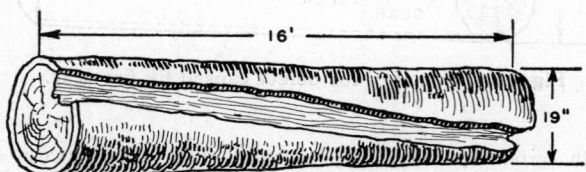

Fig. 16. Deduction for defect caused by lightning.

**Circular shake or pitch ring.** Apply the standard rule as in the case of any other circular defect, but if there is a central core of sound wood, scale it as a log and deduct it from the estimated rot.

**Heart check, frost crack, or split.** In Fig. 15 the length of the check is 18 in. inside the right cylinder and slab; it is estimated it will require an allowance of 3 in. in width to eliminate the waste in sawing, and that the defect extends into the log 8 ft. Deductions by the standard rule are then $(3 \times 18 \times 8)/15 = 29$ bd. ft. It will be noticed that although the defect extends to the outer edge of the log, deduction is made only for that portion which is inside the slab and the right cylinder.

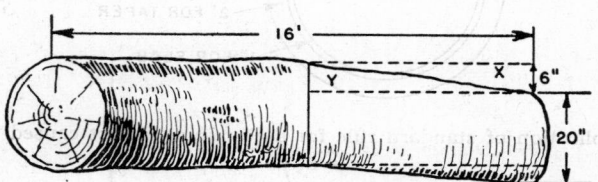

Fig. 17. Deduction for crook or sweep.

Heart check is often twisted, and when it passes through the log and comes out at a different angle, the deduction will necessarily have to be increased to allow for the loss of lumber due to short lengths.

**Lightning defect.** The log shown in Fig. 16 has a severe lightning scar extending along its entire length, spiraling one-fourth of the way around the log. Its depth is 4 in. (that is, 3 in. inside the right cylinder and slab), and it is 4 in. wide. If the scar were straight instead of spiraling, the standard rule could be applied. Adding 1 in. to each dimension of the defect, the deduction would be $(4 \times 5 \times 16)/15 = 21$ bd. ft.

Because the scar spirals, however, one-fourth of the surface of the log will be affected to a depth of 3 in. inside the slab. (If there is considerable taper in the log, the average depth may be less than 3 in.) The log is 19 in. in diameter, therefore approximately 60 in. in circumference. Using one-fourth of this, apply the standard rule: $(4 \times 15 \times 16)/15 = 60$ bd. ft. deduction. But an estimated one-half of the part of the log affected by the defect is sound and will produce boards 8 ft. long, or longer. The allowance is therefore $60/2 = 30$ bd. ft.

**Crook or sweep** (see Fig. 17). If crook or sweep occurs in long logs which are scaled as two or more logs, allowance will be made only for so much of the defect as cannot be eliminated when dividing the log into shorter sections for scaling. Half of the log in Fig. 17 is not affected by the crook. One-third of the other half of the log will not produce full scale because the portion marked $X$ is lost; none of portion $Y$ will produce 16-ft. lumber. Altogether it is estimated that two-thirds of $X$ plus $Y$ are lost. If they are figured to contain one-third of the scale of the 8-ft. section, the deduction is $\frac{2}{3} \times \frac{1}{3}$ of the scale of the section, or $\frac{2}{9}$ of 140 (the scale of a 20-in log 8 ft. long) $= 31$ bd. ft.

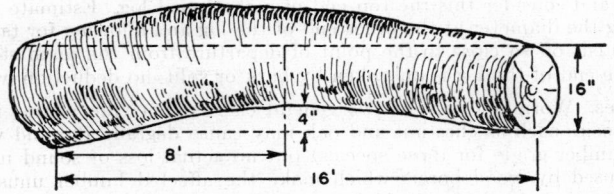

Fig. 18. Method of deducting for sweep.

It is common practice to make deductions for crook by merely reducing the length of the log. In this case the log would probably have been scaled as a 14-ft. log, 20 in. in diameter, which would make the deduction 40 bd. ft., or 9 ft. more than by the method used above.

Another method of deducting for sweep is illustrated in Fig. 18. In this case the sweep extends the whole length of the log and will evidently cause some waste when the log is sawed. If the sweep causes a deviation not exceeding the taper of the log, no loss occurs and no deduction will be made.

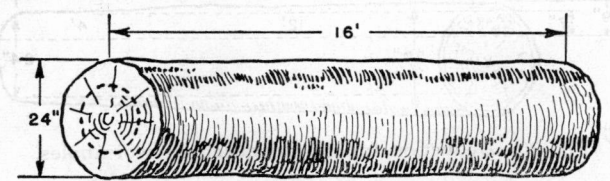

Fig. 19. Deduction for defect caused by wind checks.

A rule-of-thumb given by Chapman is, "Add $\frac{1}{3}$ to the percent of sweep as expressed in terms of the diameter of the log to obtain percent of cull." Applied to the log shown in Fig. 18, this rule gives:

$$\frac{4}{3} \times \frac{4}{16} = \frac{16}{48} = \frac{1}{3} = 33\frac{1}{3} \text{ percent deduction}$$

**Wind or sun check.** Fig. 19 illustrates a log with wind checks over its entire length. The checks on the ends of the log extend from the surface 6 in. toward the center. The common method of deducting for this defect is to consider it as a shell having a radial thickness of half the depth of the checks. The sound scale for this 24-in. log then is that of a log 24 minus 6 in., or 18 in., in diameter. The reason for not using the full radial depth of the checks in computing the defective shell is that the checks are deeper at the exposed ends of the logs than they are throughout its length.

**Stains.** Blue stain in itself is not a wood-destroying fungus, but it offers an entrance to other fungi which break down the structure of the sapwood. Deduction for defective sapwood will be made by scaling to the average diameter inside the sap. No deduction will be made for sound blue stain.

Red stain may be an early stage of red rot, and treatment in scaling should be governed by the principle that deduction for defect is made only where the defect causes a reduction in the sound material contained in the log.

Mineral stain and firm blackheart in hardwoods ordinarily do not involve actual breakdown of the wood fibers, but may ruin a log for the manufacture of specific products such as turnery stock. It is preferable to sell timber of this character on a log-grade basis, considering sound defects in defining log grades, rather than deducting for them in scaling.

**Crotch or fork.** Drop back to a point just below the swelling (in one plane) caused by the fork, and consider this the top end of a shortened log. Estimate its diameter by measuring the diameter at the other end of the log and allowing for taper. In case the crotch is cut off so close to the point of departure from the main stem that the surface of the end of the log is unbroken by bark or split, no deduction will be made.

**Wormholes.** Wormholes are of two general classes: (1) "pin worm" holes, which in certain species such as chestnut and oak may cause degrade ("sound wormy" is a recognized lumber grade for these species) but no actual loss of sound material, and (2) holes caused by wood borers which make the affected lumber unusable. Obviously, no deduction should be made for class (1) wormholes in species and localities where such lumber is salable. Defect caused by class (2) wormholes requires deductions in scaling.

Fig. 20 represents a 16-ft. log, 24 in. in diameter, having wormholes to a depth of 9 in. on one side of the butt end, and extending from the butt to within 4 ft. of the top. Because the 4-ft. lumber at the end beyond the defect is not merchantable, deduction must be made for the entire length of the log.

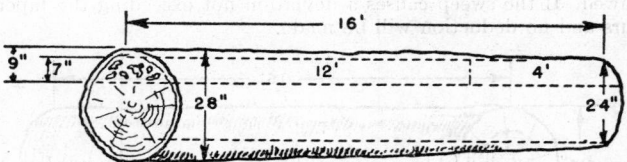

**Fig. 20. Deduction for defect caused by wormholes.**

The diameter of the right cylinder is 24 in. The zone of loss due to the wormholes is confined to a cross-sectional area measuring 6 in. by an average of 15 in. within the right cylinder and slab. By the standard rule the deduction is then $(7 \times 16 \times 16)/15 = 119$ bd. ft.

**International ¼-In. Rule Deduction for Defects.** For square or rectangular defects, the deduction is

$$\text{Bd. ft.} = \frac{W \times H \times L}{16}$$

## Table 44. Forest Service Assumed Taper for Scaling Long Logs

| Total length (ft.) | Butt log Length (ft.) | Butt log Diameter increase (in.) | Second log Length (ft.) | Second log Diameter increase (in.) | Third log Length (ft.) | Third log Diameter increase (in.) | Top log Length (ft.) |
|---|---|---|---|---|---|---|---|
| | | **For scaling in maximum lengths of 16 ft.** | | | | | |
| 18 | 10 | 1 | ... | ... | ... | ... | 8 |
| 20 | 10 | 1 | ... | ... | ... | ... | 10 |
| 22 | 12 | 1 | ... | ... | ... | ... | 10 |
| 24 | 12 | 1 | ... | ... | ... | ... | 12 |
| 26 | 14 | 1 | ... | ... | ... | ... | 12 |
| 28 | 14 | 2 | ... | ... | ... | ... | 14 |
| 30 | 16 | 2 | ... | ... | ... | ... | 14 |
| 32 | 16 | 2 | ... | ... | ... | ... | 16 |
| 34 | 12 | 3 | 12 | 1 | ... | ... | 10 |
| 36 | 12 | 3 | 12 | 1 | ... | ... | 12 |
| 38 | 14 | 3 | 12 | 1 | ... | ... | 12 |
| 40 | 16 | 3 | 12 | 1 | ... | ... | 12 |
| 42 | 14 | 3 | 14 | 1 | ... | ... | 14 |
| 44 | 16 | 3 | 16 | 1 | ... | ... | 12 |
| 46 | 16 | 4 | 16 | 2 | ... | ... | 14 |
| 48 | 16 | 4 | 16 | 2 | ... | ... | 16 |
| 50 | 14 | 4 | 12 | 3 | 12 | 1 | 12 |
| 52 | 16 | 4 | 12 | 3 | 12 | 1 | 12 |
| 54 | 16 | 5 | 14 | 3 | 12 | 1 | 12 |
| 56 | 16 | 5 | 16 | 3 | 12 | 1 | 12 |
| 58 | 16 | 5 | 16 | 3 | 14 | 2 | 12 |
| 60 | 16 | 5 | 16 | 3 | 14 | 2 | 14 |
| | | **For scaling in maximum lengths of 40 ft.** | | | | | |
| 42 | 22 | 2 | ... | ... | ... | ... | 20 |
| 44 | 22 | 2 | ... | ... | ... | ... | 22 |
| 46 | 24 | 2 | ... | ... | ... | ... | 22 |
| 48 | 24 | 3 | ... | ... | ... | ... | 24 |
| 50 | 26 | 3 | ... | ... | ... | ... | 24 |
| 52 | 26 | 3 | ... | ... | ... | ... | 26 |
| 54 | 28 | 3 | ... | ... | ... | ... | 26 |
| 56 | 28 | 3 | ... | ... | ... | ... | 28 |
| 58 | 30 | 4 | ... | ... | ... | ... | 28 |
| 60 | 30 | 4 | ... | ... | ... | ... | 30 |
| 62 | 32 | 4 | ... | ... | ... | ... | 30 |
| 64 | 32 | 4 | ... | ... | ... | ... | 32 |
| 66 | 34 | 5 | ... | ... | ... | ... | 32 |
| 68 | 34 | 5 | ... | ... | ... | ... | 34 |
| 70 | 36 | 5 | ... | ... | ... | ... | 34 |
| 72 | 36 | 5 | ... | ... | ... | ... | 36 |
| 74 | 38 | 6 | ... | ... | ... | ... | 36 |
| 76 | 38 | 6 | ... | ... | ... | ... | 38 |
| 78 | 40 | 6 | ... | ... | ... | ... | 38 |
| 80 | 40 | 6 | ... | ... | ... | ... | 40 |
| 82 | 28 | 7 | 28 | 5 | ... | ... | 26 |
| 84 | 28 | 8 | 28 | 5 | ... | ... | 28 |
| 86 | 30 | 8 | 28 | 5 | ... | ... | 28 |
| 88 | 30 | 8 | 30 | 5 | ... | ... | 28 |
| 90 | 30 | 8 | 30 | 6 | ... | ... | 30 |
| 92 | 32 | 8 | 30 | 6 | ... | ... | 30 |
| 94 | 32 | 8 | 30 | 6 | ... | ... | 30 |
| 96 | 32 | 8 | 32 | 6 | ... | ... | 32 |
| 98 | 34 | 9 | 32 | 6 | ... | ... | 32 |
| 100 | 34 | 9 | 34 | 6 | ... | ... | 32 |

Source: U. S. Forest Service, *National forest scaling handbook.*

where $W$ = width and $H$ = thickness, both in inches, and $L$ = length in feet, of the defect. For circular defects, deduct

$$\text{Bd. ft.} = \frac{D^2 L}{16}$$

where $D$ = diameter in inches and $L$ = length in feet.

**Scaling Long Logs.** U. S. Forest Service practice in scaling long logs, in the absence of actual information on taper, is to divide the logs and assume the taper, as shown in Table 44.

In parts of the East long logs are scaled at the mid-point, inside bark, by the Doyle Rule. For details see "Scaling" in Section **16**.

**TREE VOLUMES. Volume Tables.** There are many ways of constructing a volume table. Probably the most accurate is by the use of logarithmic equations. The type equations for volume of the entire stem, or of the stem to any desired merchantable limit, in both cubic and board feet, are as follows:

For the cubic volume of the entire stem:

$$(1) \quad V = D^{b_1} H^{b_2} C$$

For cubic feet to a merchantable limit:

$$(2) \quad V - v = (D - d)^{b_1} (H - 4.5)^{b_2} C$$

For board foot volume to a fixed top diameter and total height:

$$(3) \quad V - v = (D - d)^{b_1} (H - 17)^{b_2} C$$

For board foot volume to a variable top diameter:

$$(4) \quad V - v = D^{b_1} (H - h)^{b_2} C$$

For board feet to a fixed top and merchantable height:

$$(5) \quad V - v = (D^2 - d^2)^{b_1} (H' - 17)^{b_2} C$$

Any of the formulas (1) to (5) expressed in logarithms will be quickly recognized as a multiple regression equation. Expression (1) given in terms of logarithms, for example, is

$$\log V = b_1 \log D + b_2 \log H + \log C$$

where $b_1$ and $b_2$ are regression coefficients and $\log C$ is the $\log V$ intercept value. They are all obtained by the regular least-squares procedure.

In any expression,

$V$ = volume in cubic or board feet, as the case may be
$D$ = diameter at breast height, inside bark
$H$ = total height
$H'$ = merchantable height
$d$ = diameter at merchantable or top limit
$v$ = in (2) the cubic volume of a bolt of a diameter equal to the merchantable limit and a length equal to the distance from stump height to breast height. For a 4.0-in. top limit and a 1-ft. stump, the dimensions of the bolt are 4.0 in. diameter and 3.5 ft. in length, with a volume of 0.30 cu. ft.
$v$ = in (3) the board-foot volume of a log with a top diameter equal to the merchantable limit and $\frac{3.5}{16}$ ft. in length. For Scribner bd. ft. volume to an

$$\text{8.0 in. top limit } v = 35 \times \frac{3.5}{16} = 7.7 \text{ bd.ft.}$$

$v$ = in (4) the board-foot volume of a log of $h$ length (distance from stump to breast height) and ½$D$. Height in this expression is not total height but distance from stump to point of ½$D$ on stem

$v$ = in (5) the board-foot volume of a 16-ft. log with a diameter equal to the merchantable limit

The logarithmic volume equation lends itself well to the construction of volume tables by the method of least squares (see Section **23**). Many other equations expressing tree volume in terms of diameter, height, and form factor have been proposed and used with varying degrees of success. Board-foot form-class volume tables are usually constructed on the basis of taper tables as given in Tables 16 to 18.

Local volume tables may be based upon data collected for a restricted area, but more often they are derived from a standard volume table or a form-class volume table by interpolating the average volume per tree for each diameter and corresponding balanced values of tree height and form class (see Section **2**).

**Form Factors.** Form factors are used in the construction of volume tables. The **absolute form factor** is the ratio between the volume of a tree and that of a cylinder having the same diameter as the tree at its base (ground level), and the same height:

$$f = \frac{V}{Bh}$$

where $B$ = basal area of cylinder and tree    $V$ = volume of tree
$h$ = height of cylinder and tree    $f$ = form factor
$Bh$ = volume of cylinder

In using form factors to calculate the volume of trees it is helpful to remember that a cone has a form class of 50, and that the volume of a cone is one-third that of a cylinder having the same base and height. For basal areas in square feet, from diameter measurements in inches, see Table 7.

In the **breast-height form factor** or **cubic form factor** the formula is the same as above except that $B$ = basal area at breast height.

Form factors are occasionally computed as the ratio of the volume of the stem of a tree (inside bark) to that of a cylinder of the same height and of a diameter equal to its d.b.h. (outside bark).

In the **normal form factor** the diameter (and hence the basal area) is measured at a distance above ground having a fixed ratio to the height of the tree.

The **frustum form factor** formula is:

$$f = \frac{V}{V'} \text{ and } V = V' f$$

in which $V$ = volume in tree, $V'$ = volume in frustum of cone, and $f$ = form factor. This is a practical method of determining volumes of trees which do not have abnormal butt swell and is preferable where utilization is to a fixed top diameter. Frustum form factors may be computed from volumes expressed in any unit.

**Distribution of Volume in Trees.** When estimating high-quality timber, the estimator can use Table 45 in log-by-log estimates of high-quality or defective material.

**Table 45. Percent of Board-Foot Volume in Logs According to Their Position in the Tree—Southern Conifers and Eastern Hardwoods**

| Usable length, in No. of 16-ft. logs | Position of log in tree | | | | | |
|---|---|---|---|---|---|---|
| | Butt | 2d | 3d | 4th | 5th | 6th |
| 1 | 100 | | | | | |
| 2 | 58 | 42 | | | | |
| 3 | 42 | 33 | 25 | | | |
| 4 | 34 | 29 | 22 | 15 | | |
| 5 | 29 | 25 | 21 | 15 | 10 | |
| 6 | 24 | 23 | 20 | 16 | 11 | 6 |

Source: U.S. Forest Service, *Tables for estimating board-foot volume of timber, 1946.*

**Table 46. Percentage of Tree Volume in Each 16-Ft. Log—Western Species**

| Tree height | 1 | 2 | 3 | 4 | 5 | 6 | 7 | 8 | 9 | 10 | 11 |
|---|---|---|---|---|---|---|---|---|---|---|---|
| 1 log | 100 | | | | | | | | | | |
| 2 log | 85 | 15 | | | | | | | | | |
| 3 log | 55 | 35 | 10 | | | | | | | | |
| 4 log | 41 | 31 | 20 | 8 | | | | | | | |
| 5 log | 32 | 27 | 21 | 14 | 6 | | | | | | |
| 6 log | 27 | 23 | 19 | 15 | 11 | 5 | | | | | |
| 7 log | 23 | 20 | 17 | 15 | 12 | 8 | 5 | | | | |
| 8 log | 20 | 18 | 16 | 14 | 12 | 9 | 7 | 4 | | | |
| 9 log | 17 | 16 | 15 | 13 | 11 | 10 | 8 | 6 | 4 | | |
| 10 log | 16 | 15 | 13 | 12 | 11 | 10 | 8 | 7 | 5 | 3 | |
| 11 log | 14 | 13 | 13 | 11 | 11 | 10 | 8 | 7 | 6 | 4 | 3 |

Source: J. W. Girard and D. Bruce, *Tables for estimating board foot volume of trees in 16-foot logs,* Mason, Bruce & Girard, Portland, Ore.

**Table 47. Percentage of Tree Volume in Each 32-Ft. Log—Western Species**

Log Position

| Tree height | 1 | 1½ | 2 | 2½ | 3 | 3½ | 4 | 4½ | 5 | 5½ | 6 |
|---|---|---|---|---|---|---|---|---|---|---|---|
| 1   log | 100 | | | | | | | | | | |
| 1½ log | 86 | 14 | | | | | | | | | |
| 2   log | 75 | | 25 | | | | | | | | |
| 2½ log | 62 | | 28 | 10 | | | | | | | |
| 3   log | 50 | | 33 | | 17 | | | | | | |
| 3½ log | 46 | | 31 | | 15 | 8 | | | | | |
| 4   log | 37 | | 29 | | 21 | | 13 | | | | |
| 4½ log | 37 | | 28 | | 19 | | 10 | 6 | | | |
| 5   log | 30 | | 25 | | 20 | | 15 | | 10 | | |
| 5½ log | 30 | | 25 | | 19 | | 13 | | 8 | 5 | |
| 6   log | 25 | | 22 | | 18 | | 15 | | 12 | | 8 |

Note: The percentages vary slightly with the diameter of the tree. The above average figures are therefore not precise but are accurate enough for all practical purposes.

Source: J. W. Girard and D. Bruce, *Tables for estimating board foot volume of trees in 32-foot logs,* Mason, Bruce & Girard, Portland, Ore.

Fig. 21 shows the distribution of cubic-foot and board-foot volume in Lake States trees (average of all merchantable trees of all species in Forest Survey).

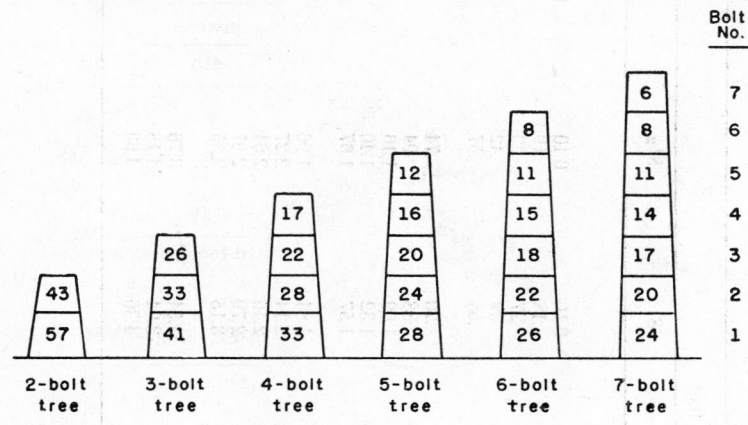

POLE-TIMBER TREES
(Showing percentage of cubic-foot volume in various 8-ft. bolts.)

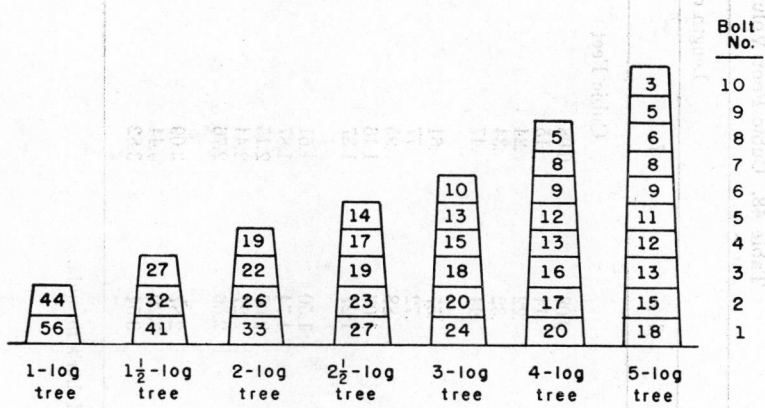

SAW-TIMBER TREES
(Showing percentage of saw-timber volume International ¼-in. in various 8-ft. bolts.)

**Fig. 21. Distribution of volume in Lake States trees.**
(U.S. Forest Service, Lake States Forest Exp. Sta., *Tech. Note No. 347*, 1943.)

**PIECE PRODUCT VOLUMES.** Table 48 shows the volume of small posts, such as fence posts, in cubic feet.

**Posts and Poles.** Volumes of larger poles may be computed by measuring the diameters at both ends and the length of the pole. Volume can then be calculated by applying either Smalian's formula or the cone-frustum formula. Table 49 is based on the cone-frustum formula. The factors listed in this table multiplied by the length of the pole give its volume in cubic feet.

## Table 48. Cubic-Foot Volume of Posts

| Average diameter (in.) | Length of post in feet | | | | | | |
|---|---|---|---|---|---|---|---|
| | 6 | 6½ | 7 | 7½ | 8 | 8½ | 9 |
| | Cubic Feet | | | | | | |
| 1.5 | 0.07 | 0.08 | 0.08 | 0.09 | 0.10 | 0.10 | 0.11 |
| 2.0 | .13 | .14 | .15 | .16 | .18 | .19 | .20 |
| 2.5 | .20 | .22 | .24 | .26 | .27 | .29 | .31 |
| 3.0 | .29 | .32 | .34 | .37 | .39 | .42 | .44 |
| 3.5 | .40 | .44 | .47 | .50 | .54 | .57 | .60 |
| 4.0 | .52 | .57 | .61 | .65 | .70 | .74 | .78 |
| 4.5 | .66 | .72 | .77 | .82 | .88 | .94 | .99 |
| 5.0 | .82 | .88 | .95 | 1.02 | 1.09 | 1.16 | 1.22 |
| 5.5 | .99 | 1.07 | 1.16 | 1.24 | 1.32 | 1.40 | 1.48 |
| 6.0 | 1.18 | 1.27 | 1.37 | 1.47 | 1.57 | 1.67 | 1.76 |
| 6.5 | 1.38 | 1.50 | 1.61 | 1.72 | 1.84 | 1.96 | 2.07 |
| 7.0 | 1.60 | 1.74 | 1.87 | 2.00 | 2.14 | 2.27 | 2.40 |
| 7.5 | 1.84 | 2.00 | 2.15 | 2.30 | 2.46 | 2.61 | 2.76 |
| 8.0 | 2.09 | 2.27 | 2.44 | 2.62 | 2.79 | 2.97 | 3.14 |
| 8.5 | 2.36 | 2.56 | 2.76 | 2.96 | 3.15 | 3.35 | 3.55 |
| 9.0 | 2.65 | 2.87 | 3.09 | 3.32 | 3.54 | 3.76 | 3.98 |
| 9.5 | 2.95 | 3.20 | 3.44 | 3.69 | 3.94 | 4.18 | 4.43 |
| 10.0 | 3.27 | 3.54 | 3.82 | 4.09 | 4.36 | 4.63 | 4.90 |

Note: Volumes computed by Huber's formula.

## Table 49. Calculating Cubic Contents of Poles, Piling, and Small Round Products

Find the average diameter at each end of the piece to the nearest half inch. Multiply the number in the table corresponding to these two diameters by the length of the piece in feet. The result is in cubic feet. The formula is:

$$V = 0.2618L\left(\frac{D^2+d^2+dD}{144}\right)$$

| Diameter of large end (in.) | Diameter of small end (in.) | | | | | | | | | | | | | |
|---|---|---|---|---|---|---|---|---|---|---|---|---|---|---|
| | 2½ | 3 | 3½ | 4 | 4½ | 5 | 5½ | 6 | 6½ | 7 | 7½ | 8 | 8½ | 9 |
| 2½ | 0.034 | | | | | | | | | | | | | |
| 3 | .041 | 0.049 | | | | | | | | | | | | |
| 3½ | .050 | .058 | 0.067 | | | | | | | | | | | |
| 4 | | | | 0.087 | | | | | | | | | | |
| 4½ | | | | .099 | 0.110 | | | | | | | | | |
| 5 | | | | .111 | .123 | 0.136 | | | | | | | | |
| 5½ | | | | .124 | .137 | .150 | 0.165 | | | | | | | |
| 6 | | | | .138 | .151 | .165 | .180 | 0.196 | | | | | | |
| 6½ | | | | .153 | .167 | .181 | .197 | .213 | 0.230 | | | | | |
| 7 | | | | .169 | .183 | .198 | .214 | .231 | .249 | 0.267 | | | | |
| 7½ | | | | .186 | .200 | .216 | .232 | .250 | .268 | .287 | 0.307 | | | |
| 8 | | | | .204 | .219 | .235 | .251 | .269 | .288 | .307 | .328 | 0.349 | | |
| 8½ | | | | .222 | .238 | .254 | .271 | .290 | .309 | .329 | .350 | .371 | 0.394 | |
| 9 | | | | .242 | .258 | .275 | .292 | .311 | .330 | .351 | .372 | .395 | .418 | 0.442 |
| 9½ | | | | .262 | .279 | .296 | .314 | .333 | .353 | .374 | .396 | .419 | .442 | .467 |
| 10 | | | | .284 | .300 | .318 | .337 | .356 | .377 | .398 | .420 | .444 | .468 | .493 |
| 10½ | | | | .306 | .323 | .341 | .360 | .380 | .401 | .423 | .446 | .470 | .494 | .520 |
| 11 | | | | .329 | .347 | .365 | .385 | .405 | .427 | .449 | .472 | .496 | .521 | .547 |
| 11½ | | | | .353 | .371 | .390 | .410 | .431 | .453 | .476 | .500 | .524 | .550 | .576 |
| 12 | | | | .378 | .397 | .416 | .437 | .458 | .480 | .504 | .528 | .553 | .579 | .605 |
| 12½ | | | | .404 | .423 | .443 | .464 | .486 | .509 | .532 | .559 | .582 | .609 | .636 |
| 13 | | | | .431 | .450 | .471 | .492 | .515 | .538 | .562 | .587 | .613 | .640 | .667 |
| 13½ | | | | | .479 | .500 | .521 | .544 | .568 | .592 | .618 | .644 | .671 | .700 |
| 14 | | | | | | | .551 | .575 | .599 | .624 | .650 | .676 | .704 | .733 |
| 14½ | | | | | | | | .606 | .630 | .656 | .682 | .710 | .738 | .767 |
| 15 | | | | | | | | | .663 | .689 | .716 | .744 | .772 | .802 |
| 15½ | | | | | | | | | | .723 | .750 | .779 | .808 | .838 |
| 16 | | | | | | | | | | | .786 | .815 | .844 | .875 |
| 16½ | | | | | | | | | | | | .851 | .881 | .912 |
| 17 | | | | | | | | | | | | | .920 | .951 |
| 17½ | | | | | | | | | | | | | | .990 |

*(Continued on following page.)*

## Table 49. Calculating Cubic Contents of Poles, Piling, and Small Round Products (Continued)

| Diameter of large end (in.) | Diameter of small end (in.) | | | | | | | | | | | |
|---|---|---|---|---|---|---|---|---|---|---|---|---|
| | 9½ | 10 | 10½ | 11 | 11½ | 12 | 12½ | 13 | 13½ | 14 | 14½ | 15 |
| 9½ | 0.492 | | | | | | | | | | | |
| 10 | .519 | 0.545 | | | | | | | | | | |
| 10½ | .546 | .573 | 0.601 | | | | | | | | | |
| 11 | .574 | .602 | .630 | 0.660 | | | | | | | | |
| 11½ | .603 | .631 | .660 | .690 | 0.721 | | | | | | | |
| 12 | .633 | .662 | .691 | .722 | .753 | 0.785 | | | | | | |
| 12½ | .664 | .693 | .723 | .754 | .786 | .819 | 0.852 | | | | | |
| 13 | .696 | .725 | .756 | .787 | .819 | .853 | .887 | 0.922 | | | | |
| 13½ | .729 | .759 | .790 | .821 | .854 | .888 | .922 | .958 | 0.994 | | | |
| 14 | .762 | .793 | .824 | .856 | .890 | .924 | .959 | .994 | 1.031 | 1.069 | | |
| 14½ | .797 | .828 | .860 | .892 | .926 | .960 | .996 | 1.032 | 1.069 | 1.108 | 1.147 | |
| 15 | .832 | .864 | .896 | .929 | .963 | .998 | 1.034 | 1.071 | 1.109 | 1.147 | 1.187 | 1.227 |
| 15½ | .869 | .900 | .933 | .967 | 1.001 | 1.037 | 1.073 | 1.110 | 1.149 | 1.188 | 1.228 | 1.269 |
| 16 | .906 | .938 | .971 | 1.005 | 1.040 | 1.076 | 1.113 | 1.151 | 1.189 | 1.229 | 1.269 | 1.311 |
| 16½ | .944 | .977 | 1.010 | 1.045 | 1.080 | 1.117 | 1.154 | 1.192 | 1.231 | 1.271 | 1.312 | 1.354 |
| 17 | .983 | 1.016 | 1.050 | 1.085 | 1.121 | 1.158 | 1.196 | 1.234 | 1.274 | 1.314 | 1.356 | 1.398 |
| 17½ | 1.023 | 1.057 | 1.091 | 1.127 | 1.163 | 1.200 | 1.239 | 1.278 | 1.318 | 1.359 | 1.400 | 1.443 |
| 18 | 1.064 | 1.098 | 1.133 | 1.169 | 1.206 | 1.244 | 1.282 | 1.322 | 1.362 | 1.404 | 1.446 | 1.489 |
| 18½ | | 1.140 | 1.176 | 1.212 | 1.249 | 1.288 | 1.327 | 1.367 | 1.408 | 1.449 | 1.492 | 1.530 |
| 19 | | | | 1.256 | 1.294 | 1.333 | 1.372 | 1.413 | 1.454 | 1.496 | 1.539 | 1.584 |
| 19½ | | | | | 1.339 | 1.379 | 1.419 | 1.459 | 1.501 | 1.544 | 1.588 | 1.632 |
| 20 | | | | | | 1.425 | 1.466 | 1.507 | 1.549 | 1.593 | 1.637 | 1.682 |
| 20½ | | | | | | | 1.514 | 1.556 | 1.599 | 1.642 | 1.687 | 1.732 |
| 21 | | | | | | | | 1.605 | 1.649 | 1.693 | 1.738 | 1.784 |
| 21½ | | | | | | | | | 1.699 | 1.744 | 1.789 | 1.836 |
| 22 | | | | | | | | | | 1.796 | 1.842 | 1.889 |
| 22½ | | | | | | | | | | | 1.896 | 1.943 |
| 23 | | | | | | | | | | | | 1.998 |

### Table 50. Cubic-Foot Volume of Poles, by Classes [a]—Southern Yellow Pine and Douglas-Fir
(For lodgepole pine see footnote [b])

| Length | Class | | | | | | | | | |
|---|---|---|---|---|---|---|---|---|---|---|
| | 1 | 2 | 3 | 4 | 5 | 6 | 7 | 8 | 9 | 10 |
| Minimum top diam. (in.)... | 8.6 | 8.0 | 7.3 | 6.7 | 6.1 | 5.4 | 4.8 | 5.7 | 4.8 | 3.8 |
| 16 | | | | | 4.25 | 3.67 | 3.00 | 3.42 | 2.50 | 2.00 |
| 18 | | | 6.92 | 5.92 | 5.00 | 4.25 | 3.42 | 3.83 | 2.75 | 2.42 |
| 20 | 12.91 | 10.25 | 8.50 | 7.17 | 6.00 | 5.17 | 4.25 | 4.75 | 3.67 | 2.92 |
| 22 | 15.00 | 12.25 | 10.17 | 8.42 | 7.25 | 6.17 | 5.17 | 5.58 | 4.25 | 3.42 |
| 25 | 18.00 | 14.75 | 12.25 | 10.42 | 8.92 | 7.67 | 6.25 | 7.08 | 5.25 | 4.25 |
| 30 | 23.25 | 19.67 | 16.75 | 14.25 | 12.00 | 10.00 | 8.25 | 9.33 | 6.75 | |
| 35 | 28.50 | 24.42 | 21.00 | 18.25 | 15.67 | 13.50 | 11.75 | 12.67 | | |
| 40 | 34.25 | 29.50 | 25.50 | 22.17 | 19.25 | 16.75 | 14.67 | | | |
| 45 | 40.41 | 34.75 | 30.25 | 26.25 | 23.17 | 20.25 | 17.75 | | | |
| 50 | 47.00 | 40.25 | 35.00 | 30.67 | 27.17 | 24.17 | 21.25 | | | |
| 55 | 54.42 | 46.67 | 40.00 | 35.17 | 31.25 | 28.42 | | No butt requirement | | |
| 60 | 62.75 | 53.50 | 45.67 | 39.75 | 35.50 | 32.75 | | | | |
| 65 | 73.00 | 60.75 | 51.17 | 44.67 | 40.67 | | | | | |
| 70 | 84.00 | 68.75 | 57.17 | 49.67 | 45.25 | | | | | |
| 75 | 94.50 | 77.00 | 63.75 | 54.92 | | | | | | |
| 80 | 106.67 | 86.17 | 70.67 | 60.25 | | | | | | |
| 85 | 120.00 | 95.75 | 78.17 | | | | | | | |
| 90 | 135.67 | 106.75 | 86.00 | | | | | | | |

[a] American Standards Assn. specifications.
[b] For lodgepole pine add 4 percent to these volumes.

### Table 51. Contents of Poles in Board Feet, by Classes [a]
International ¼-Inch Rule

| Length (ft.) | Pole class [b] | | | | | | |
|---|---|---|---|---|---|---|---|
| | 1 | 2 | 3 | 4 | 5 | 6 | 7 |
| | Average top d.i.b. in inches | | | | | | |
| | 8.9 | 8.3 | 7.6 | 7.0 | 6.4 | 5.7 | 5.1 |
| 16 | | | | | 19 | 19 | 12 |
| 18 | | | 45 | 33 | 22 | 22 | 14 |
| 20 | 66 | 50 | 50 | 36 | 31 | 25 | 16 |
| 22 | 74 | 57 | 57 | 42 | 37 | 29 | 19 |
| 25 | 87 | 78 | 67 | 49 | 43 | 34 | 21 |
| 30 | 123 | 97 | 84 | 75 | 55 | 44 | 37 |
| 35 | 135 | 126 | 117 | 89 | 74 | 57 | 47 |
| 40 | 184 | 164 | 147 | 115 | 86 | 74 | 62 |
| 45 | 236 | 191 | 161 | 152 | 117 | 93 | 66 |
| 50 | 280 | 229 | 203 | 159 | 153 | 113 | 90 |
| 55 | 320 | 262 | 253 | 202 | 167 | 132 | |
| 60 | 384 | 300 | 272 | 228 | 180 | 155 | |
| 65 | 417 | 347 | 347 | 283 | 208 | | |
| 70 | 483 | 405 | 365 | 315 | 238 | | |
| 75 | 511 | 441 | 428 | 353 | | | |
| 80 | 609 | 517 | 517 | 432 | | | |
| 85 | 629 | 548 | 532 | 456 | | | |
| 90 | 739 | 630 | 630 | 532 | | | |

[a] American Standards Assn. specifications.
[b] All poles scaled in 16-ft. lengths or less, inside bark, to nearest full inch. Average rather than minimum diameter used for each class.

Source: U. S. Forest Service, Region 8, 1941.

# Table 52. Contents of Poles in Board Feet, by Classes [a]
## Scribner Decimal C Rule

| Length (ft.) | Pole class [b] | | | | | | |
|---|---|---|---|---|---|---|---|
| | 1 | 2 | 3 | 4 | 5 | 6 | 7 |
| | Average top d.i.b. in inches | | | | | | |
| | 8.9 | 8.3 | 7.6 | 7.0 | 6.4 | 5.7 | 5.1 |
| 16 | | | | | 2 | 2 | 2 |
| 18 | | | 4 | 3 | 2 | 2 | 2 |
| 20 | 6 | 5 | 5 | 3 | 3 | 2 | 2 |
| 22 | 6 | 5 | 5 | 3 | 3 | 3 | 2 |
| 25 | 7 | 5 | 5 | 4 | 3 | 3 | 2 |
| 30 | 10 | 8 | 6 | 6 | 4 | 4 | 4 |
| 35 | 11 | 10 | 9 | 6 | 6 | 5 | 4 |
| 40 | 16 | 13 | 12 | 10 | 9 | 6 | 5 |
| 45 | 20 | 16 | 13 | 13 | 10 | 8 | 6 |
| 50 | 23 | 19 | 16 | 14 | 11 | 9 | 7 |
| 55 | 26 | 22 | 20 | 16 | 13 | 11 | |
| 60 | 32 | 24 | 22 | 19 | 14 | 13 | |
| 65 | 35 | 28 | 28 | 24 | 18 | | |
| 70 | 41 | 35 | 29 | 26 | 20 | | |
| 75 | 44 | 40 | 37 | 29 | | | |
| 80 | 53 | 44 | 44 | 38 | | | |
| 85 | 55 | 47 | 46 | 40 | | | |
| 90 | 65 | 55 | 55 | 45 | | | |

[a] American Standards Assn. specifications.
[b] All poles scaled in 16-ft. lengths or less inside bark to nearest full inch. Average rather than minimum diameter used for each class.
Source: U. S. Forest Service, Region 8, 1941.

# Table 53. Contents of Poles in Board Feet, by Classes [a]
## Doyle Rule

| Length (ft.) | Pole class [b] | | | | | | |
|---|---|---|---|---|---|---|---|
| | 1 | 2 | 3 | 4 | 5 | 6 | 7 |
| | Average top d.i.b. in inches | | | | | | |
| | 8.9 | 8.3 | 7.6 | 7.0 | 6.4 | 5.7 | 5.1 |
| 16 | | | | | 4 | 4 | 1 |
| 18 | | | 24 | 14 | 7 | 7 | 3 |
| 20 | 38 | 26 | 26 | 15 | 12 | 7 | 3 |
| 22 | 43 | 37 | 29 | 17 | 14 | 9 | 4 |
| 25 | 48 | 41 | 32 | 20 | 16 | 10 | 4 |
| 30 | 71 | 50 | 39 | 33 | 19 | 12 | 10 |
| 35 | 81 | 75 | 67 | 45 | 34 | 22 | 16 |
| 40 | 112 | 97 | 82 | 60 | 36 | 27 | 21 |
| 45 | 150 | 113 | 87 | 81 | 55 | 37 | 21 |
| 50 | 191 | 158 | 124 | 89 | 85 | 53 | 39 |
| 55 | 216 | 180 | 158 | 117 | 87 | 61 | |
| 60 | 267 | 190 | 166 | 130 | 91 | 72 | |
| 65 | 276 | 222 | 222 | 169 | 105 | | |
| 70 | 347 | 286 | 231 | 195 | 132 | | |
| 75 | 361 | 313 | 287 | 222 | | | |
| 80 | 445 | 360 | 360 | 285 | | | |
| 85 | 461 | 384 | 371 | 292 | | | |
| 90 | 556 | 455 | 455 | 365 | | | |

[a] American Standards Assn. specifications.
[b] All poles scaled in 16-ft. lengths or less, inside bark, to the nearest full inch. Average rather than minimum diameters for each class have been used.
Source: U. S. Forest Service, Region 8, 1941.

**Table 54. Minimum D.B.H. of Trees Producing Poles of Specified Classes and Lengths [a]—Lodgepole Pine and Southern Pines [b]**

| Length (ft.) | Pole classes [b] | | | | | | | | | |
|---|---|---|---|---|---|---|---|---|---|---|
| | 1 | 2 | 3 | 4 | 5 | 6 | 7 | 8 | 9 | 10 |
| | Minimum top d.i.b. in inches | | | | | | | | | |
| | 8.6 | 8.0 | 7.3 | 6.7 | 6.1 | 5.4 | 4.8 | 5.7 | 4.8 | 3.8 |
| | Minimum d.b.h. outside bark (in.) | | | | | | | | | |
| 16 [b] | | | | | 7.8 | 7.3 | 6.8 | No butt requirement | | |
| 18 [b] | | | 9.8 | 9.1 | 8.4 | 7.6 | 7.1 | | | |
| 20 [b] | 11.6 | 10.8 | 10.1 | 9.4 | 8.7 | 8.0 | 7.5 | | | |
| 25 | 12.6 | 11.8 | 10.9 | 10.2 | 9.5 | 8.8 | 8.1 | | | |
| 30 | 13.6 | 12.8 | 11.9 | 11.1 | 10.2 | 9.5 | 8.8 | | | |
| 35 | 14.5 | 13.5 | 12.6 | 11.8 | 10.9 | 10.0 | 9.3 | | | |
| 40 | 15.4 | 14.3 | 13.3 | 12.4 | 11.6 | 10.7 | 9.9 | | | |
| 45 | 16.1 | 15.0 | 14.0 | 13.0 | 12.1 | 11.2 | 10.4 | | | |
| 50 | 16.7 | 15.7 | 14.7 | 13.6 | 12.6 | 11.8 | 10.9 | | | |
| 55 | 17.3 | 16.2 | 15.2 | 14.2 | 13.1 | 12.1 | | | | |
| 60 | 17.9 | 16.7 | 15.7 | 14.7 | 13.5 | | | | | |
| 65 | 18.5 | 17.3 | 16.1 | 15.0 | | | | | | |
| 70 | 19.0 | 17.8 | 16.6 | | | | | | | |
| 75 | 19.5 | 18.3 | | | | | | | | |

[a] American Standards Assn. specifications.

[b] For southern pines most of the above minima may be reduced by 0.1 or 0.2 in. (Data computed by E. T. Hawes, U. S. Forest Service, Region 8, by formula:

$$\text{D.b.h.} = \frac{\text{Minimum circumference, 6 ft. from butt, of specified pole}}{0.88 \, \pi}$$

Hawes found the ratio between d.b.h. and d.i.b. at 6 ft. from butt to vary from 0.85 to 0.92, depending on bark thickness. He supplied values in this table for 16-, 18-, and 20-ft. poles by using 0.895 as the ratio for lodgepole pine.)

Source: U. S. Forest Service, Northern Rocky Mt. Forest and Range Exp. Sta., Conversion of standard pole classes to tree diameters in lodgepole pine, *Res. Note No. 39*, 1946.

**Piles.** Because of the great variation in specifications for this forest product and the wide spread between minimum and maximum dimensions within a single specification, it is impracticable to develop general tables of cubic-foot and board-foot contents.

Rules-of-thumb. After scaling a number of piles meeting a given buyer's specifications, a rule-of-thumb may be developed. Extreme caution must be exercised in using any rule-of-thumb outside the range of conditions for which it was devised.

**Cross Ties.** See Tables 55 and 56.

**Cooperage Bolts.** Frequently stave and heading bolts and/or billet blocks are scaled differently from any other forest product. Piles of bolts are often scaled in terms of linear feet of diameter inside bark. In this method of scaling, the diameter of each piece is measured with a flexible tape, as illustrated in Fig. 22.

**Table 55. Number and Grades of Ties and Additional Products per 100 Hardwood Tie Bolts of Different Top Diameters**

| Top diameter of tie bolt i.b. (in.) | Number of ties per 100 bolts * | | | | | Side lumber (bd. meas.) | Slab wood and edgings (standard cords) |
|---|---|---|---|---|---|---|---|
| | Grade No. 1 (6"x6") | Grade No. 2 (6"x7") | Grade No. 3 (6"x8") | Grade No. 4 (7"x8") | Grade No. 5 (7"x9") | | |
| 9 | 100 | ... | ... | ... | ... | 405 | 1.8 |
| 10 | 20 | 80 | ... | ... | ... | 495 | 2.2 |
| 11 | ... | ... | 60 | 40 | ... | 594 | 2.6 |
| 12 | ... | ... | 10 | 70 | 20 | 702 | 3.1 |
| 13 | ... | ... | 5 | 35 | 60 | 819 | 3.6 |
| 14 | ... | ... | 5 | 30 | 65 | 945 | 4.2 |
| 15 | ... | ... | 80 | 30 | 30 | 1,080 | 4.8 |
| 16 | ... | ... | 110 | 26 | 26 | 1,224 | 5.4 |
| 17 | ... | ... | 110 | 45 | 25 | 1,377 | 6.1 |
| 18 | ... | ... | 40 | 120 | 30 | 1,539 | 6.8 |
| 19 | ... | ... | ... | 120 | 80 | 1,710 | 7.6 |
| 20 | ... | ... | ... | 210 | 60 | 1,890 | 8.4 |
| 21 | ... | ... | ... | 170 | 120 | 2,079 | 9.2 |
| 22 | ... | ... | ... | 150 | 150 | 2,277 | 10.1 |
| 23 | ... | ... | ... | 140 | 180 | 2,484 | 11.0 |
| 24 | ... | ... | ... | 160 | 200 | 2,700 | 12.0 |
| 25 | ... | ... | ... | 150 | 250 | 2,925 | 13.0 |

* Grades Nos. 1 and 2, and "pole" ties are sawed on two sides only; grades Nos. 3, 4, and 5 are "square" ties and are sawed on four sides. The expected yield of tie sides will consist of lumber in random widths (4 in. and wider) and of various grades (No. 3 Common and better). Lumber is sawed 1⅛ in. in thickness when green.
Source: U. S. Forest Service, Lake States Forest Exp. Sta., *Tech. Note No. 194.*

**Table 56. Board-Foot Contents * of Sawed Railroad Ties**

| Grade | End dimensions (in.) | Length (ft.) | | |
|---|---|---|---|---|
| | | Narrow gauge 6½ | Standard gauge | |
| | | | 8 | 8½ |
| 1 | 6 x 6 | 20 | 24 | 26 |
| 2 | 6 x 7 | 23 | 28 | 30 |
| 3 | 6 x 8 | 26 | 32 | 34 |
| 3 | 7 x 7 | 27 | 33 | 35 |
| 4 | 7 x 8 | 30 | 37 | 40 |
| 5 | 7 x 9 | | 42 | 45 |

* To the nearest whole foot, board measure.

The measurements from piece to piece are carried successively on the tape and the tape is not read until the whole pile is scaled. Thus, the reading on the tape after the pile is scaled shows the total number of feet of d.i.b. in the pile. For 32-in. billets, 48 lin. ft. of diameter are taken as one cord. For any other length of billet, divide the length into 1,536, or 32 × 48, to obtain the number of linear feet equal to a cord (U. S. Forest Service, Region 9).

## Measurement of Forests

**LAND MEASUREMENTS.** For land measurements, see Section 17.

**SITE QUALITY.** For a discussion of site quality, see Section 6.

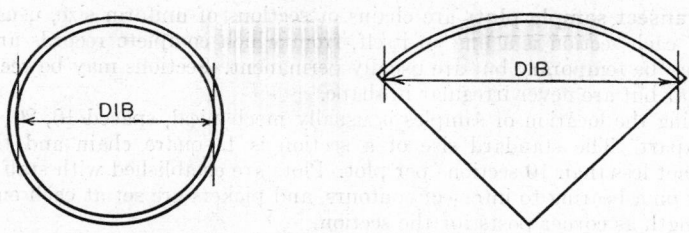

Fig. 22. Methods of measuring cooperage bolts.

## SAMPLING METHODS. Types of Samples.

1. **A random sample** is a sample chosen in such a way that each item or individual in the population has an equal and independent chance of being included.

2. **A representative sample** is a sample which represents all the essential variations existing in the population.

3. **A stratified sample** is a randomized sample composed of two or more sets of random samples, each drawn from a single homogeneous unit of a heterogeneous population.

4. **Permanent sample plots** are small representative areas on which developments are followed by means of repeated measurements or examinations continuing through a period usually exceeding 10 yr. Sometimes as small as 1 square chain for studies in dense sapling stands, permanent plots should generally be not less than a half-acre; a full acre is preferable.

For simplicity and accuracy rectangular plots are preferable to circular plots. Long, narrow plots are not recommended as they are likely to include too many variations in the factors under observation.

In studies of effect of treatment, one or more control plots should be included in each series of permanent plots and the number of plots requisite for any given experiment is three or more, depending on the number of degrees of variation to be sampled. Sample areas should be selected to represent, as nearly as possible, the **average** of the condition being investigated.

Boundaries of permanent plots should be run with staff compass or transit and linear measurements made with steel tape. The error of closure should not be greater than 1 in 300.

Trees are usually numbered with metal tags and often mapped as to location in the plot. For this purpose and for tallying, the plot should be subdivided into 20-ft. strips by means of string run from permanent pickets on two opposite boundaries.

5. **Control plots** are plots established in untreated or undisturbed areas to form a base or norm with which the response of treated plots may be compared and are not required in studies of development of untreated stands.

6. **The surround** is the area immediately surrounding a permanent sample plot, treated in the same way as the plot proper, to ensure like conditions throughout the plot area.

7. **Raunkiaer plots** are areas of 1/10 of a meter, delimited by a metal ring sub-divided internally. The ring is dropped at fixed intervals for vegetation sampling.

8. **Transect sample plots** are chains of sections of uniform size, usually contiguous; each section is a unit in itself, from which complete records are taken. They may be temporary but are usually permanent. Sections may be rectangular or circular but are never irregular in shape.

Selecting the location of samples is usually mechanical, spaced 10, 20, or more chains apart. The standard size of a section is 1 square chain and there are usually not less than 10 sections per plot. Plots are established with staff or hand compass on a bearing to intersect contours, and pickets are set at each end of the chain length as corner posts for the section.

9. **Line plots** are plots of uniform size, either rectangular or circular, distributed at regular intervals along parallel compass lines spaced at regular intervals over a forested area.

### Table 57. Circular Plot Dimensions

| Plot area | Radius in: | | |
|---|---|---|---|
| (acres) | Feet | Chains | Rods |
| 1/160 | 9.31 | 0.141 | 0.564 |
| 1/40 | 18.62 | .282 | 1.13 |
| 1/10 | 37.24 | .564 | 2.26 |
| 1/5 | 52.66 | .798 | 3.19 |
| 1/4 | 58.88 | .892 | 3.57 |
| 1/2 | 83.26 | 1.262 | 5.05 |
| 1 | 117.75 | 1.784 | 7.14 |

### Table 58. Square Plot Dimensions

| Plot area | Side of square in: | | |
|---|---|---|---|
| (acres) | Feet | Chains | Rods |
| 1/160 | 16.5 | 0.25 | 1.0 |
| 1/40 | 33.0 | 0.5 | 2.0 |
| 1/10 | 66.0 | 1.0 | 4.0 |
| 1/5 | 93.34 | 1.414 | 5.66 |
| 1/4 | 104.35 | 1.581 | 6.32 |
| 1/2 | 147.57 | 2.236 | 8.94 |
| 1 | 208.71 | 3.162 | 12.65 |

10. **Triangular one-quarter-acre plots** have been used with considerable success. An equilateral triangle of this area can be laid out quickly with less liability of error than in the case of rectangular or circular plots. The only chance for error is in getting the altitude perpendicular to the base and here an error of locating the apex as much as 6.5 ft. to one side or the other makes a difference of only 0.04 percent in area. The sides are 158.58 ft. and the altitude 137.34 ft. In laying out the plot, a braided copper line is used, carried on a reel, and exactly the length of a side. The half length of a side is marked by a piece of red cloth, and the altitude by orange cloth, wired to the line.

On reaching the point in the cruise line where the plot is to begin, a picket is set and the head chainman goes forward along the line until the red flannel is in

**Table 59. Rectangular Plot (Intermittent Strip) Dimensions**

| Plot area (acres) | Length (chains) | Width (chains) |
|---|---|---|
| 1/20 | 2.0 | 0.25 |
| 1/10 | 2.0 | 0.5 |
| 1/5 | 2.0 | 1.0 |
| 1/5 | 4.0 | 0.5 |
| 1/4 | 2.5 | 1.0 |
| 1/4 | 5.0 | 0.5 |
| 1/2 | 5.0 | 1.0 |

the hands of the rear chainman. He sets a picket and continues until the end of the base is reached, where he sets another picket. He then returns to the center point and goes out at right angles until the orange flannel is in the hands of the rear chainman, and sets a picket for the apex of the triangle. The caliper men are kept inside the plot by the tallyman sighting from one corner picket to another. The line lying on the ground marks the base of the triangle. If the timber is very dense, a cord stretched between the pickets marking the angles will outline the plot.

11. A **sample strip** is a long narrow strip used as a sampling unit in surveys. Widths of sample strips commonly used vary from ¼ to 2 chains.

12. **Subplots or quadrats** are small divisions laid out within sample plots for the purpose of recording reproduction or plants too abundant to be tallied for the whole plot. Quadrats are frequently 1 square meter or 1 milacre (generally square, 10 links on a side) in size.

**Layout of Samples, Standard Procedure.** 1. **Line plots** are usually spaced at regular intervals on cruise lines or compass lines, the size of the plot, the spacing of the lines, and the spacing of the plots varying with the intensity of the cruise required. Circular plots may not be spaced closer together between centers than a distance equal to their diameter. For plots of ¼ acre, a location at intervals of 2½ chains is about as close as is usually attempted and spacing of 5 or 10 chains between centers is common. Cruise lines should be run at right angles to the drainage or other natural features to obtain representative samples by intersecting belts, types, or stands of timber rather than traversing them lengthwise.

With the use of air photos to delineate forest types, plot locations are often arbitrarily selected on the photos and then located on the ground by compass and chain lines (see Table 60). With this system less sampling is required for the same degree of accuracy, provided all the areas of each type sampled as a single classification have reasonable homogeneity.

Besides being numerous, samples should be distributed over the area so as to "catch" all conditions and in such a way as to give every part of the tract an equal and independent chance of being represented. Any particular timber condition should be represented in the sampling in the proportion in which it occurs over the entire area.

2. In laying out **circular line plots** the center is usually marked by a stake or blazed tree. The radii in the direction of the compass line and at right angles thereto are then measured and the boundary or the circumference of the plot is

marked at these four points. In tallying trees on the plot, line trees or trees concerning which there is uncertainty as to whether they are in or out should be measured from the center. This measuring of the radius is laborious if conscientiously done with a pocket tape and accurate results have been obtained by stadia, using a small pocket telescope and paper stadia "rod."

3. In **rectangular line plots,** the chain used for measuring the cruise line is generally used as a center line or one side of the plot. The length of the plot is measured by this chain and the width is determined by means of a pocket tape with an end fastener. The distance from the center line of the plot to line trees is measured by inserting the end fastener of the pocket tape in the bark of the tree on the side in which the cruise line is being run and stretching the tape back to the cruising tape.

4. **Sample strips** are laid out in the same manner as rectangular plots, using the cruising tape to measure the length of the strip for the sample within a forest type or for the length of the sample as tallied. Tallies on strips should usually be changed at 5- or 10-chain intervals if the same type continues for a greater distance.

5. The **intensity of sampling** required to give an acceptable sampling error is discussed on page 1·84. Table 60 shows a number of commonly used spacings of samples to give various required intensities.

6. **Errors in area measurement** of samples arise from inaccuracy in determining the perimeters of sample areas. Lengths and widths of rectangular plots and radii of circular plots should be measured carefully and frequently. The probability of error increases with the size of the sample area and with the presence of underbrush. Trees on the boundary of the sample area should be included only if the center of the tree is within the boundary line.

**THE SAMPLING ERROR OF A FOREST CRUISE.** A partial cruise of a forest is affected by sampling errors which depend essentially on the variation in volume between sampling units and on the intensity of the cruise. The variation between sampling units is numerically expressed as a **coefficient of variation** ($s\%$), which is the standard deviation between sampling units in percent of average volume. Since this standard deviation varies with the size of the sampling unit, the coefficient of variation must be specifically defined as the standard deviation between observations of volume measured on **one acre** (observation of weight one) expressed in percent of volume per acre. A coefficient of variation so defined varies from about 10 percent to 60 percent and more, depending on the homogeneity of the forest or compartment cruised. The **intensity of a cruise** is expressed as a percentage, namely the area in plots or strips actually measured in relation to the total area of the forest. By increasing the cruising intensity, the sampling error can be reduced to any desired level.

**Calculation of sampling error.** For a given coefficient of variation

$$s(\%) = \frac{s}{\overline{X}} \cdot 100,$$

where $s$ is the standard deviation of an observation of weight one, calculated by the formula

$$s^2 = \frac{\Sigma w(X - \overline{X})^2}{N - 1}$$

## Table 60. Commonly Used Spacing of Samples (in Chains) for Various Cruise Intensities

### PLOT CRUISE

| ⅕-acre plots | | ¼-acre plots | | ½ acre plots | | 1-acre plots | |
|---|---|---|---|---|---|---|---|
| Distance between plots | Distance between cruise lines | Distance between plots | Distance between cruise lines | Distance between plots | Distance between cruise lines | Distance between plots | Distance between cruise lines |
| | | | 10% Intensity | | | | |
| 4 | 5 | 5 | 5 | 5 | 10 | 10 | 10 |
| | | | 5% Intensity | | | | |
| 4 | 10 | 5 | 10 | 5 | 20 | | |
| 5 | 8 | | | 10 | 10 | 10 | 20 |
| | | | 2½% Intensity | | | | |
| 5 | 16 | 5 | 20 | | | 10 | 40 |
| 8 | 10 | 10 | 10 | 10 | 20 | 20 | 20 |
| | | | 1% Intensity | | | | |
| 5 | 40 | 5 | 50 | 10 | 50 | | |
| 10 | 20 | 10 | 25 | 20 | 25 | 20 | 50 |
| | | | | | | 25 | 40 |
| | | | | | | 30 | 33 |

### STRIP CRUISE

| Width of strip in chains | Distance (in chains) between strips for cruise intensities | | | | | |
|---|---|---|---|---|---|---|
| | 30% | 20% | 10% | 5% | 2½% | 1% |
| ¼ | | | 2.5 | 5 | 10 | 25 |
| ½ | | 2.5 | 5 | 10 | 20 | 50 |
| 1 | 3.3 | 5 | 10 | 20 | 40 | |
| 1½ | 5 | 7.5 | 15 | | | |
| 2 | 6.6 | 10 | 20 | | | |

Note: All distances are given in chains and reckoned from center to center of cruise lines or plots.

the percentage standard deviation of the average volume per acre is equal to

$$s_{\bar{x}}(\%) = \frac{s(\%)}{\sqrt{\Sigma w}}$$

With cruising intensities of more than about 5 percent, a correction factor for limited population ($\sqrt{1 - \text{proportion cruised}}$) should be applied to the standard deviation of the arithmetic average. The symbols used in the above formulas are:

$X$ = volume per acre of a sampling unit

$w$ = area of a sampling unit in acres. This area is taken as the weight of the per acre volume of a given sampling unit ($\Sigma w$ = total area in plots or strips).

$wX$ = total volume on a sampling unit

$\bar{X}$ = weighted arithmetic average of sample. This is identical with the average volume per acre of all sampling units measured ($\bar{X} = \Sigma wX/\Sigma w$).

$N$ = number of sampling units. This is the number of strips or cruise lines.

The calculation of the sampling error of a cruise is shown in Table 61. The example worked out in detail refers to a line plot cruise of a single tract of 54 acres which has been cruised as one unit. If large tracts are subdivided into blocks, compartments, or types, and if each unit is cruised separately, the sampling error must likewise be calculated separately by units. Knowing the volume in each subdivision of a forest and its sampling error, the sampling error of the total volume of the forest is equal to the square root of the sum of the squared sampling errors of each subdivision; for example:

| Compartment | Area (acres) | Total volume (M bd. ft.) | Standard error of total volume (M bd. ft.) |
|---|---|---|---|
| 1 | 400 | 2,200 | ±110 |
| 2 | 500 | 2,800 | ±130 |
| 3 | 420 | 3,000 | ±150 |
| 4 | 600 | 1,200 | ± 60 |
| 5 | 380 | 1,800 | ±100 |
| Total | 2,300 | | $11,000 \pm \sqrt{110^2 + 130^2 + 150^2 + 60^2 + 100^2}$ |
| | | | $11,000 \pm 255$ |

$$\text{Average volume per acre} = \frac{1}{2,300}(11,000 \pm 255)$$
$$= 4.78 \pm 0.11 \text{ M bd. ft.}$$

The method of cruising applied to each tract of land that is not further subdivided into relatively more homogeneous stands, types, age classes, or size classes must be such that the coefficient of variation, and hence the sampling error of the cruise, be as small as possible. With stratification present, the cruise lines should run at more or less right angles to the main stratification, which in hilly country usually means at right angles to the contour lines. In each cruise line or strip all strata are then represented in the approximate proportion of their occurrence and the variation among the per acre averages of each line will be reduced to a minimum. The calculation of the cruising error from the individual plot volumes, which vary considerably in the presence of pronounced stratification, would lead to greatly exaggerated sampling errors. With different numbers of plots per line or different lengths of the strips, the use of weighted observations and weighted averages in the calculation of sampling error as explained in Table 61 cannot be avoided.

**Estimation of required cruising intensity.** Attempts have been made to estimate the coefficient of variation of a cruise on the basis of prevailing forest conditions. Obviously, in homogeneous stands with uniform density, the variation in volume between sampling units will be small. In open stands with a patchy distribution of volume, the variation will be large. Other factors being constant, the coefficient of variation is relatively large in forests with a low volume per acre and small in forests with a high volume per acre. The coefficient of variation also changes with the size and shape of the sampling units, and with the particular type of cruising design applied. Working within a given forest type, it is necessary to determine the coefficient of variation from a number of trial cruises before a reliable appraisal of the probable accuracy of a cruise can be made in advance. To cite an example, in the application of ¼-chain-wide strips in upland oak forests in Pennsylvania in tracts up to about 300 acres in size, the coefficient of variation was found to vary between 8 and 25 percent, the average being 15 percent. With such factual information available, it is possible to estimate in advance the probable accuracy of a cruise for a given sampling intensity by applying the formula

$$s_{\bar{x}}(\%) = \frac{s\%}{\sqrt{\Sigma w}}$$

## Table 61. Calculation of Coefficient of Variation and Standard Error of Volume of Line Plot Cruise

Area of tract 54 acres. Cruising intensity 25.2 percent.

| Line No. | No. of plots on line | Area of plots on line * $w$ (acres) | Volume per acre $X$ (M bd.ft.) | Volume on plots $wX$ (M bd.ft.) | $(X - \overline{X})$ | $w(X - \overline{X})$ | $w(X - \overline{X})^2$ |
|---|---|---|---|---|---|---|---|
| 1 | 3 | 0.6 | 0.4 | 0.24 | −0.80 | −0.48 | 0.384 |
| 2 | 8 | 1.6 | 1.7 | 2.72 | 0.50 | 0.80 | 0.400 |
| 3 | 7 | 1.4 | 0.6 | 0.84 | −0.60 | −0.84 | 0.504 |
| 4 | 7 | 1.4 | 1.0 | 1.40 | −0.20 | −0.28 | 0.056 |
| 5 | 15 | 3.0 | 1.4 | 4.20 | 0.20 | 0.60 | 0.120 |
| 6 | 10 | 2.0 | 0.6 | 1.20 | −0.60 | −1.20 | 0.720 |
| 7 | 9 | 1.8 | 2.4 | 4.32 | 1.20 | 2.16 | 2.592 |
| 8 | 5 | 1.0 | 0.8 | 0.80 | −0.40 | −0.40 | 0.160 |
| 9 | 4 | 0.8 | 0.8 | 0.64 | −0.40 | −0.32 | 0.128 |
| | | 13.6 | | 16.36 | | −3.52 3.56 | 5.064 |

$$\overline{X} = \frac{\Sigma wX}{\Sigma w} = \frac{16.36}{13.6} = 1.20 \qquad (\overline{X} = \text{volume per acre})$$

$$s^2 = \frac{\Sigma w(X - \overline{X})^2}{N - 1} = \frac{5.064}{9 - 1} = 0.633 \qquad \begin{array}{l}(N = \text{number of sampling units;} \\ \text{number of strips or lines})\end{array}$$

$$s = \sqrt{0.633} = \pm 0.80 \qquad \begin{array}{l}(s = \text{standard error of observa-} \\ \text{tion of weight 1})\end{array}$$

$$s(\%) = \frac{s}{\overline{X}} \cdot 100 = \frac{0.80}{1.20} \cdot 100 = 67\% \qquad (s(\%) = \text{coefficient of variation})$$

$$(s_{\overline{x}})^2 = \frac{s^2}{\Sigma w} = \frac{0.633}{13.6} = 0.0465$$

$$(s_{\overline{x}})^2 \text{ (corrected)} = (s_{\overline{x}})^2 (1 - \text{proportion cruised})$$

$$= 0.0465 \left(1 - \frac{13.6}{54.0}\right) = 0.0348$$

$$s_{\overline{x}} \text{ (corrected)} = \sqrt{0.0348} = \pm 0.19 \qquad \begin{array}{l}(s_{\overline{x}} \text{ (corrected)} = \text{standard error} \\ \text{of arithmetic average, cor-} \\ \text{rected for limited population})\end{array}$$

$$\text{Volume per acre} = 1.20 \pm 0.19 \text{ M bd.ft.}$$
$$\text{Total volume} = 54(1.20 \pm 0.19)$$
$$= 64.8 \pm 10.3 \text{ M bd.ft.}$$

---

* When cruising by strips, $w$ is equal to the area of the strip in acres. If all observations are of equal weight, $w$ becomes a constant factor and the calculation can be slightly simplified. It is recommended, however, to retain the above form in order to obtain the correct value for the coefficient of variation of an observation of weight 1.

or, considering the correction factor for limited population:

$$s_{\overline{x}}(\%) = \frac{s\%}{\sqrt{\Sigma w}} \sqrt{1 - \text{proportion cruised}}$$

It is clear from the above formulas that for a given coefficient of variation the percentage standard error of the calculated volume per acre depends essentially on the area in sample plots or strips ($\Sigma w$). The required cruising intensity will differ greatly with the size of the forest to be cruised. Table 62 shows the required cruising intensity (cruising percent) for different percentage standard errors of the cruise for tracts of different size and coefficients of variation of 15, 30, and 60 percent. For correct use of this table refer to the accompanying footnote.

**Interpretation of cruising errors; limit of error.** With cruise lines or strips laid out at random and at right angles to the main stand stratification, sampling errors will be normally distributed, and the actual error of a cruise will on the average be smaller than the calculated standard error two times out of three. The probability of the actual sampling error being larger than 2 or $2\frac{1}{2}$ times the standard error is 0.05 and 0.01 respectively, and it is customary to consider such multiples of the standard error as the **limit of error** to be expected in any particular cruise. If the calculation of the standard error is based on relatively few observations, the limit of error corresponding to certain probability levels is obtained more accurately with the help of the $t$-distribution. The value of $t$ by which the standard error must be multiplied in order to obtain the limit of error depends on the number of **degrees of freedom**, which in an ordinary line plot or strip cruise is equal to the number of randomly selected lines or strips minus one. Table 63 shows the values of $t$ for different degrees of freedom corresponding to probabilities 0.05 and 0.01. In the cruising example worked out in Table 61, the number of cruise lines is equal to 9 and the number of degrees of freedom is $9 - 1 = 8$. The limit of error which will be exceeded with a probability of 0.05 is

$$s \cdot t = 0.19 \cdot 2.3 = 0.44M \text{ bd. ft.}$$

The calculated volume per acre with its upper and lower limit of error is thus equal to $1.20 \pm 0.44M$ bd. ft.

When using Table 62 to determine the desired cruising intensity for an acceptable **limit of error**, this error must be divided by 2 or $2\frac{1}{2}$ (or by the proper value of $t$) in order to find the corresponding percentage **standard error**.

In a **systematic cruise**, as contrasted to a random cruise, strips or cruise lines are evenly spaced. The accuracy of such a cruise is likely to be somewhat higher than that of a random cruise of the same intensity. Consequently, if the standard error of a systematic cruise is calculated as if it were a random cruise, it cannot be interpreted in the usual way. As indicated in the footnote to Table 62, the somewhat higher accuracy of the systematic cruise may be taken into account by using a smaller multiplier (2 instead of $2\frac{1}{2}$ or 3) when computing the limit of error that corresponds to a given standard error. By subdividing a forest into relatively homogeneous blocks, and by applying a cruising design which will ensure that each sampling unit cuts across the main stand stratification, the sampling errors of a systematic cruise will be distributed like those of a random cruise and they can be interpreted as usual. On the other hand, the most serious errors in estimating the accuracy of a systematic cruise occur when these precautions are neglected, as for example, when computing the standard deviation

**Table 62. Required Cruising Percent for Certain Standard Errors of Estimated Volume in Forests or Tracts of Different Size**

| Size of tract or forest (acres) | Allowable standard error in percent of volume | | | | | | |
|---|---|---|---|---|---|---|---|
| | 1% | 2% | 4% | 6% | 8% | 10% | 12% |

Required cruising percent

(i) for coefficient of variation of 15 percent *

| | | | | | | | |
|---|---|---|---|---|---|---|---|
| 50 | | | 22.0 | 11.1 | 6.6 | 4.3 | 3.0 |
| 100 | | 36.0 | 12.3 | 5.9 | 3.4 | 2.2 | 1.5 |
| 200 | | 18.4 | 6.6 | 3.0 | 1.7 | 1.1 | 0.8 |
| 500 | 31.0 | 10.1 | 2.7 | 1.2 | 0.7 | 0.4 | 0.3 |
| 1,000 | 18.4 | 5.3 | 1.4 | 0.6 | 0.4 | 0.2 | 0.2 |
| 2,000 | 10.1 | 2.7 | 0.7 | 0.3 | 0.2 | 0.1 | 0.1 |
| 5,000 | 4.3 | 1.1 | 0.3 | 0.1 | 0.1 | 0.04 | 0.03 |
| 10,000 | 2.2 | 0.6 | 0.1 | 0.1 | 0.04 | 0.02 | 0.02 |

(ii) for coefficient of variation of 30 percent *

| | | | | | | | |
|---|---|---|---|---|---|---|---|
| 50 | | | 52.9 | 33.3 | 22.0 | 15.3 | 11.1 |
| 100 | | | 36.0 | 20.0 | 12.3 | 8.3 | 5.9 |
| 200 | | 52.9 | 22.0 | 11.1 | 6.6 | 4.3 | 3.0 |
| 500 | | 31.0 | 10.1 | 4.8 | 2.7 | 1.8 | 1.2 |
| 1,000 | 47.4 | 18.4 | 5.3 | 2.4 | 1.4 | 0.9 | 0.6 |
| 2,000 | 31.0 | 10.1 | 2.7 | 1.2 | 0.7 | 0.4 | 0.3 |
| 5,000 | 15.3 | 4.3 | 1.1 | 0.5 | 0.3 | 0.2 | 0.1 |
| 10,000 | 8.3 | 2.2 | 0.56 | 0.2 | 0.1 | 0.1 | 0.1 |

(iii) for coefficient of variation of 60 percent *

| | | | | | | | |
|---|---|---|---|---|---|---|---|
| 50 | | | | 52.9 | 41.9 | 33.3 | |
| 100 | | | | 50.0 | 36.0 | 26.5 | 20.0 |
| 200 | | | 52.9 | 33.3 | 22.0 | 15.3 | 11.1 |
| 500 | | | 31.0 | 16.7 | 10.1 | 6.7 | 4.8 |
| 1,000 | | 47.4 | 18.4 | 9.1 | 5.3 | 3.5 | 2.4 |
| 2,000 | 64.3 | 31.0 | 10.1 | 4.8 | 2.7 | 1.8 | 1.2 |
| 5,000 | 41.9 | 15.3 | 4.3 | 2.0 | 1.1 | 0.7 | 0.5 |
| 10,000 | 26.5 | 8.3 | 2.2 | 1.0 | 0.6 | 0.4 | 0.2 |

* Coefficient of variation is here defined as the standard error of observations of volume measured on one acre (observation of weight 1) expressed in percent of volume per acre. For stands of high uniformity and normal density this coefficient may be as low as 15 percent, provided an efficient cruising design is applied which will eliminate as much as possible the effect of visible stand stratification. A coefficient of 30 percent corresponds to average conditions of forest cruising. Values of 60 percent are characteristic of irregular stands with a patchy distribution of volume. Estimates of the actual value of the coefficient of variation are best determined from trial cruises.

The figures of this table are strictly applicable only if the sampling units are selected independently and at random. The accuracy of a systematic cruise is generally higher than that of a random cruise of the same intensity. This may be taken into consideration by using a somewhat smaller multiplier (2 instead of 2½ or 3) when computing the limit of error that corresponds to a given standard error.

between individual plots evenly spaced over an area with a heterogeneous distribution of volume. The calculation of the cruising error can be determined from the variation between individual plots only when these plots are laid out in homogeneous blocks or stands previously segregated on the ground or on aerial photographs.

## Stand and Stock Data

**TALLY SYSTEMS AND SHEETS.** The tally system and sheets used for recording stand and stock data vary with the method of compiling the estimate. Where trees are recorded by diameter classes, or diameter and height classes, for instance, the dot tally system is used. Where only the total number of trees in the sample is obtained, the use of a single or multiple tally register is often more convenient. Direct volume estimates may be tallied on paper with cross-section rulings, or on a special multiple volume table form.

**Table 63. Values of _t_ for Probabilities 0.05 and 0.01 and Different Numbers of Degrees of Freedom**

| Degrees of freedom | Probability 0.05 | Probability 0.01 |
|:---:|:---:|:---:|
| 4 | 2.8 | 4.6 |
| 6 | 2.4 | 3.7 |
| 8 | 2.3 | 3.4 |
| 10 | 2.2 | 3.2 |
| 15 | 2.1 | 2.9 |
| 20 | 2.1 | 2.8 |
| 30 | 2.0 | 2.8 |
| ∞ | 2.0 | 2.6 |

Source: Adapted from R. A. Fisher, _Statistical methods for research workers,_ 11th ed., Oliver & Boyd, 1950.

Before recording any information in the field, plan very carefully the computations to be made from it. If all that is needed is the present volume on an entire area—board feet from a 100-percent cruise, for example—all trees (in this case of saw timber size only) can be recorded on a single sheet of the field book. But if it is planned to sample the present volume and estimate the growth of a large tract, each sample should be recorded separately (for analysis of accuracy) and must record enough trees below present saw-log size to calculate ingrowth. If the decision as to methods of computation must wait until conditions in the field are known, remember that it is easy to throw separate tallies together but impossible to subdivide a total.

Tally sheets should provide adequate space for the recording of all essential information in an orderly fashion, yet should be compact and of convenient size. For intensive surveys the letterhead size may be desirable as a standard in order to accommodate all the information to be collected. For extensive surveys tally sheets should be designed for use with common noteholders which fit in the cruiser's pocket.

Where wet weather or other difficult field conditions may be encountered, tally sheets, map sheets, air photos, reference tables, etc., are conveniently protected by sheets of transparent cellulose acetate, about 0.03 in. thick, joined together with ordinary medical waterproof adhesive tape. Forms are sometimes printed on celluloid for use in heavy rain. Data from them must be transferred nightly to regular tally sheets, and the celluloid cleaned with water and a household cleanser before being used again. Acetate and sheet celluloid are obtainable from scientific supply houses, or from large stationery stores.

**VOLUME ESTIMATES. Rules-of-Thumb.** A multitude of so-called "rules-of-thumb" for the rapid estimation of the volume in a tree or stand have been put forward from time to time, but none has won universal acceptance. They resemble local volume tables in that most of them are applicable only in specific regions for given species and volume units.

**Tree Tally.** The most common method of determining the volume of a forest stand is by a tree tally, or stand table, converted to volume by the use of a local, standard, or form class volume table. The basic requirement of this method is that all trees in the sample be tallied by diameter classes, and sufficient additional information be gathered so that the appropriate volume may be assigned to each tree. Where a local volume table is available, the volume of the tree may be estimated from diameter alone. Otherwise one or more independent variables must be used in addition to diameter—total height, merchantable length in feet or number of standard log lengths, and form class. Because of the difficulty of estimating total height, particularly in dense or tall stands, merchantable height is much more commonly used, except in parts of Canada.

**Log Tally.** Where the merchantable volume of a stand is to be estimated, particularly for saw logs in board feet, tree tally may be replaced by log tally. If the log length is standardized, for instance at 16 ft. for conifers and 8 ft. for hardwoods, merchantable saw logs may be tallied by their top diameters. A rule-of-thumb, expressing upper log diameter in percentage of d.b.h., is extremely useful as an aid to estimating top diameters of successive logs in the standing tree. Where the timber is uniform and the range of log diameters small, this method may be reduced, with little error, to a count of the number of merchantable logs and the estimation of average top diameter. The total merchantable volume is then the computed product of the number of logs and the volume of the log of average top diameter.

**Direct Tree Scale.** Where the cruiser has had considerable experience in the estimation of log diameters and the number of merchantable saw logs, as through the use of Girard's Form Class method, it becomes possible to estimate the merchantable volume of a tree directly without carrying out the intermediate steps of estimating tree and log diameters and computing and summing the volumes of the individual logs. Experienced cruisers use this method, recording only their estimates of merchantable tree volumes. This method cannot be used by inexperienced estimators; it yields results which are difficult to check for accuracy, and as it provides no stand table, only by translating volumes into corresponding diameters can a mental picture of the stand be obtained.

**Cumulative Tally.** The method of tallying which employs cumulative tally sheets was originated by Macon and Gevorkiantz for use in the Lake States. It is predicated on the use of a "composite volume table," a single volume table applicable to many species provided the same standards of utilization are employed. Sheets may be constructed to give volumes in cubic feet, cords, or in board feet by any log rule, and for any desired standards of utilization.

The principal advantage of this method is its ease of application, providing a quick and fairly reliable estimate of volume on the ground. Chief limitations are that where numerous species are encountered, several sheets must be used per plot, and some species cannot be combined for volume computation owing to differences in form and bark thickness.

## Growth and Mortality

**DEFINITIONS.** The following concepts and definitions refer to the growth of a specific forest area, which may be a single stand, a forest, or the total forest area, of a district, state, or county (compare F.A.O. 1948).

1. **Gross growth.** The total volume of wood produced by all trees in the forest (usually computed as an average for a 10-yr. period); often referred to as current annual gross growth, or current periodic gross growth. The terms **growth** and **increment** are used synonymously.

2. **Mortality.** The volume of trees rendered unusable periodically or annually by forest fire, insects, tree diseases, and climatic factors such as windstorm, ice, etc. Annual mortality is computed as an average of periodic mortality.

3. **Net growth.** The net volume remaining after subtracting natural losses or mortality, as defined above, from gross growth.

4. **Net increase.** The net volume remaining after subtracting mortality and yield from gross growth; net increase is equal also to net growth minus yield. A negative net increase is the same as a net loss in volume.

5. **Yield.** The volume of the trees felled annually or periodically, whether removed from the forest or not.

6. **Ingrowth.** The trees (their number or volume) which during a given period grow into measurable size.

The relationships between the first five quantities can be conveniently written as follows:

$$\text{Gross growth} = \text{Net growth} + \text{Mortality}$$
$$\text{Net growth} = \text{Net increase} + \text{Yield}$$
$$\text{Net increase} = \text{Difference in volume of forest in}$$
$$\text{two successive inventories}$$

When using any of these terms it must be clearly distinguished as to whether ingrowth is included or not included. This is particularly important with regard to gross growth. Net growth, net increase, and yield usually include ingrowth.

The terms **growth determination** and **growth prediction** are often used interchangeably.

**PREDICTION FROM INCREMENT CORES.** Increment cores are taken from trees selected at random along cruise lines, on sample plots, or in randomly selected clusters of 5 to 10 trees. Complete randomness of selection may be properly restricted so that roughly the same number of trees is measured in each diameter class. A reliable estimate of average diameter growth by diameter classes cannot usually be obtained from less than 100 tree measurements for each species (or group of species) which is investigated separately. The data obtained for each tree should include d.b.h. ($D$), double bark thickness ($2B$), and the width of the last 10 rings of the core ($L$). The average annual diameter growth inside the bark ($i$) is then $2L/10$. It must be multiplied by $K$ (see page $1 \cdot 38$) for the species or species group to give diameter growth including bark ($I$):

$$I = K \cdot i$$

Diameter growth, including bark growth, is best related to tree diameter at the middle of the 10-yr. period, which is obtained simply by subtracting the length of the core ($L$)—a radial measurement—from the **diameter** inside bark ($d$); it is designated by $x$. The corresponding diameter outside bark is then

$$X = K \cdot x$$

Having computed for each tree the diameter $X$ and the diameter growth including bark growth ($I$), group the data by 1- or 2-inch diameter classes. The number of trees in each diameter class represents the weight of the calculated average diameter growth. After plotting the calculated average diameter growth ($I$) as a function of diameter at breast height ($X$), fit a straight line or curve to the data. The method of least squares is highly recommended for this work.

**Calculation of Current Annual Volume Growth; Interpolation Method.** One procedure for the calculation of current annual volume growth is shown in Table 64. The data, including number of trees and their diameter growth, both by d.b.h., are for an average acre of oak saw timber in Pennsylvania.

1. The volume per tree (local volume table) listed in Column 2 should be given for one diameter class above and below the range of trees measured.
2. The difference in volume per tree for successive diameter classes is written in Column 3 **between** the lines of the preceding column.
3. Successive volume differences of Column 3 are averaged [for example, $(3.90 + 5.41)/2 = 4.66$ for 8-in. d.b.h.] and the averages are again written in line with the midpoints of the various diameter classes (adjusted volume difference, Column 4).
4. Average annual diameter growth is listed in Column 5.
5. Average annual volume growth per tree (Column 6) is obtained by dividing the adjusted volume difference by 2 (= width of diameter class) and multiplying the quotient by the average annual diameter growth.
6. Multiply the number of trees, Column 7, by volume growth per tree and obtain volume growth by d.b.h. classes, Column 8.
7. Add the values in Column 8 to obtain volume growth per acre.

The current annual volume growth obtained by this method represents **gross increment** of initial volume; it does not include ingrowth. **Net growth** can be obtained by reducing the number of trees by diameter classes in accordance with estimated mortality.

**Calculation of Growth Percentage.** The volume growth per tree, in percent of volume per tree, is readily calculated from Table 64 by dividing Column 6 by Column 2. The percentages are given in Column 9. By multiplying them by the stand volume of each diameter class (Column 2 times Column 7), and dividing by 100, the same figures for volume growth (Column 8) are obtained as before.

Special methods for the calculation of total volume growth in percent of volume can be devised if the relationship between volume per tree and its diameter at breast height can be expressed by a mathematical function.

The formula

$$V = k \cdot D^b$$

is a satisfactory expression of average cubic foot volume per tree ($V$) in terms of

**Table 64.  Calculation of Annual Volume Growth (Interpolation Method)—Average Acre, Pennsylvania Oak**

| (1)<br>D.b.h.<br>(in.) | (2)<br>Volume<br>per<br>tree<br>(cu. ft.) | (3)<br>Volume<br>differ-<br>ence<br>(cu. ft.) | (4)<br>Adjusted<br>volume<br>differ-<br>ence<br>(cu. ft.) | (5)<br>Annual<br>diameter<br>growth<br>per<br>tree<br>(in.) | (6)<br>Annual<br>volume<br>growth<br>per<br>tree<br>(cu. ft.) | (7)<br>Number<br>of<br>trees<br>per<br>acre | (8)<br>Volume<br>growth<br>per<br>acre<br>(cu. ft.) | (9)<br>Volume<br>growth<br>percent-<br>age |
|---|---|---|---|---|---|---|---|---|
| 6 | 4.16 | ... | ... | ... | ... | ... | ... | ... |
|  |  | 3.90 |  |  |  |  |  |  |
| 8 | 8.06 |  | 4.66 | 0.123 | 0.28 | 16.6 | 4.6 | 3.5 |
|  |  | 5.41 |  |  |  |  |  |  |
| 10 | 13.47 |  | 6.21 | .130 | .40 | 14.5 | 5.8 | 3.0 |
|  |  | 7.01 |  |  |  |  |  |  |
| 12 | 20.48 |  | 7.86 | .137 | .54 | 10.3 | 5.6 | 2.6 |
|  |  | 8.72 |  |  |  |  |  |  |
| 14 | 29.20 |  | 9.61 | .144 | .69 | 12.2 | 8.4 | 2.4 |
|  |  | 10.50 |  |  |  |  |  |  |
| 16 | 39.70 |  | 11.42 | .152 | .87 | 10.8 | 9.4 | 2.2 |
|  |  | 12.35 |  |  |  |  |  |  |
| 18 | 52.05 |  | 13.32 | .159 | 1.06 | 7.3 | 7.7 | 2.0 |
|  |  | 14.28 |  |  |  |  |  |  |
| 20 | 66.33 |  | 15.26 | .166 | 1.27 | 4.0 | 5.1 | 1.9 |
|  |  | 16.25 |  |  |  |  |  |  |
| 22 | 82.58 |  | 17.22 | .173 | 1.49 | 1.2 | 1.8 | 1.8 |
|  |  | 18.2 |  |  |  |  |  |  |
| 24 | 100.8 |  | 19.3 | .180 | 1.74 | 0.9 | 1.6 | 1.7 |
|  |  | 20.4 |  |  |  |  |  |  |
| 26 | 121.2 |  | 21.5 | .188 | 2.02 | 0.9 | 1.8 | 1.7 |
|  |  | 22.6 |  |  |  |  |  |  |
| 28 | 143.8 |  | ... | ... | ... | ... | ... | ... |
| Totals | ... | ... | ... | ... | ... | 78.7 | 51.8 |  |

d.b.h. (*D*); *k* and *b* are constants. The volume table listed in the second column of the preceding table conforms to this equation, the constants being $k = 0.0675$ and $b = 2.3$. Volume growth in percent of volume is given by the formula

$$\text{Growth percent} = \frac{I \times b \times 100}{D}$$

where $I =$ average annual diameter growth, and $D =$ diameter at breast height. Taking the 8-in. diameter class as an example, substitute $b = 2.3$ and $D = 8$:

$$\text{Growth percent} = 3.5 \text{ percent}$$

which is the figure already listed in Table 64.

**Calculation of periodic volume growth; prediction.** The prediction of future volume by determining the movement of trees from one diameter class into the next is again based on the calculated average diameter growth by diameter classes. The periodic diameter growth, usually for a 10-yr. period, is obtained by multiplying the average annual diameter growth by the length of the period in years. This periodic diameter growth may possibly be adjusted for estimated trends in growth, if reliable data for making such an adjustment are available. The usual procedure for determining the movement of trees into the upper diameter classes is based on the assumption that the trees are evenly distributed throughout a diameter class and that all trees within a diameter class grow at an identical rate, equal to the calculated average diameter growth. Often diameter growth is expressed in terms of tree diameter 10 yr. ago ($d - 2L$, see above) rather than in terms of tree diameter at the middle of the period covered by the core.

Table 65 illustrates the calculation of the future inventory by the stand table method, known also as the step-up or movement factor method.

1. Basic data are entered in Columns 1, 2, 3.
2. The number of trees rising from one class into the next higher class is obtained by multiplying the number of trees in a given class by the estimated diameter growth ($I$) and by dividing the result by the width of the diameter class ($= 2$ in.). $I/2$ is called the movement factor. For the 8-in. diameter class the number of trees rising is equal to

$$\frac{16.6 \times 1.23}{2} = 10.2$$

The trees rising are written in between the lines of the various diameter classes.
3. Obtain trees stationary by subtracting trees rising from the trees in a given class, e.g., $16.6 - 10.2 = 6.4$, for the 8-in. class.
4. Obtain a future stand table by adding for each diameter class the number of trees rising into the class to the trees stationary in the class, e.g., for the 10-in. class: $10.2 + 5.1 = 15.3$.
5. Calculate the present and future stock table and periodic growth as indicated in Columns 7, 8, and 9.

Gross growth calculated for a period of 10 yr. (567 cu. ft.) is somewhat larger than 10 times the annual volume growth determined by the interpolation method ($10 \times 51.8 = 518$), Table 64. The discrepancy is mainly due to the fact that trees are not evenly distributed throughout a diameter class. A correction might be made also for the slope of the diameter distribution within diameter classes.

**Estimation of Ingrowth.** Ingrowth is determined by extrapolation from the number of trees rising into the various upper diameter classes. Accurate results are obtained only when dealing with data from a large forest area with a more or less balanced distribution of trees by diameter classes. For large forests in which the number of trees decreases with increasing diameter, the number of trees rising will plot along a straight line when using semilogarithmic paper. In this case, extrapolation is fairly accurate. In the previous example, ingrowth cannot be determined with a high degree of accuracy; it may lie between 10 and 12 trees per acre.

Ingrowth in volume is obtained by multiplying the number of trees estimated to rise into the lowest diameter class by the volume per tree of this same class. If the periodic diameter growth is larger than the width of a diameter class, the number of trees which move into the second higher class must be multiplied by the volume per tree of that second class.

**Estimation of Mortality.** Estimates of future mortality for a specified period of years are uncertain since mortality may be high or low, depending on weather conditions during that period. For the same reason, actual mortality determinations for a short period of the immediate past may be of relatively little value as a basis for estimating future mortality. Despite these shortcomings, estimates of future mortality are often based on observations collected from permanent sample plots or on the count of trees estimated to have died during the last 3 to 5 yr. However, only the aggregate information of many series of observations of this type can be used with any degree of confidence for predictions of future mortality.

**Table 65. Calculation of Periodic Volume Growth (Movement Factor Method)**

| (1) | (2) | (3) | (4) | (5) | (6) | (7) | (8) | (9) |
|---|---|---|---|---|---|---|---|---|
| | | Present | | Trees | Pre-dicted | Volume | Present | Future |
| | 10-yr. | stand | | station- | stand | per | stock | stock |
| | diameter | table | Trees | ary | table | tree | table | table |
| D.b.h. | growth (in.) | per acre (no.) | rising (no.) | (no.) | (no.) | (cu. ft.) | (cu. ft.) | (cu. ft.) |
| 28 | ... | ... | | ... | 0.8 | 143.8 | ... | 115 |
| | | | 0.8 | | | | | |
| 26 | 1.88 | 0.9 | | 0.1 | .9 | 121. | 109 | 109 |
| | | | .8 | | | | | |
| 24 | 1.80 | .9 | | .1 | 1.1 | 100.8 | 91 | 111 |
| | | | 1.0 | | | | | |
| 22 | 1.73 | 1.2 | | .2 | 3.5 | 82.58 | 99 | 289 |
| | | | 3.3 | | | | | |
| 20 | 1.66 | 4.0 | | .7 | 6.5 | 66.33 | 265 | 431 |
| | | | 5.8 | | | | | |
| 18 | 1.59 | 7.3 | | 1.5 | 9.7 | 52.05 | 380 | 505 |
| | | | 8.2 | | | | | |
| 16 | 1.52 | 10.8 | | 2.6 | 11.4 | 39.70 | 429 | 453 |
| | | | 8.8 | | | | | |
| 14 | 1.44 | 12.2 | | 3.4 | 10.5 | 29.20 | 356 | 307 |
| | | | 7.1 | | | | | |
| 12 | 1.37 | 10.3 | | 3.2 | 12.6 | 20.48 | 211 | 258 |
| | | | 9.4 | | | | | |
| 10 | 1.30 | 14.5 | | 5.1 | 15.3 | 13.47 | 195 | 206 |
| | | | 10.2 | | | | | |
| 8 | 1.23 | 16.6 | | 6.4 | 6.4* | 8.06 | 134 | 52 |
| Totals | ... | 78.7 | 55.4 | 23.3 | 78.7 | ... | 2,269 | 2,836 |
| | | | | | | | | 2,269 |
| | | | | | | 10-yr. volume growth per acre | | 567 |

* Does not include ingrowth.

Mortality also depends greatly on the intensity of the silvicultural management applied. With frequent thinnings and improvement cuttings, that is, with the application of a cutting cycle of not over 10 yr., mortality becomes unimportant. In determining the allowable cut of a forest, a flat 10 to 20 percent reduction of the proposed gross cut is frequently made as compensation for a natural loss through mortality.

**DETERMINATION FROM SUCCESSIVE MEASUREMENTS. Continuous Inventory.** Table 66 illustrates the French method, as applied to a permanent sample plot by the Dominion Forest Service, in a 10-yr. period. Again the stand table is inverted for convenience in calculation. Columns 2, 3, and 4 show initial stand table, trees dead and removed (measured at the time of marking or removal), and the final stand table. If the trees removed were cut immediately after taking the first inventory, they should be subtracted from it to enable calculation of the growth of trees left standing. If the trees were removed shortly before taking the second inventory, they should be added to the second inventory so that their growth during the period under consideration is included in the total growth of the stand. With these special cases in mind, it is logical to divide the trees removed at the middle of the growth period into equal groups, one group to be subtracted from the first inventory, the other to be added to the second inventory. This implies that the total growth of the trees removed for one-half the length of the growth period is equivalent to the growth of one-half the trees for the entire growth period. Similarly, trees removed after 3 yr. in a 10-yr. growing period should be divided so as to subtract $\frac{7}{10}$ from the first inventory and to add $\frac{3}{10}$ to the second inventory. The 18 dead trees in Table 66 are assumed to have died at the middle of the period; consequently 9 are subtracted from the first inventory, and 9 added to the second. Computations in Table 66 are as follows:

1. Divide the trees dying or removed so that, as nearly as possible, equal numbers fall in the same diameter classes in each column (Columns 3 and 4); thus, these trees are treated as living for one-half of the period.
2. In Column 5 enter the number of trees in each diameter class at the end of the period.
3. Column 6 is the difference between Columns 2 and 3. It is the 1928 inventory, adjusted for mortality.
4. Column 7 is the sum of Columns 4 and 5. It is the 1938 inventory, adjusted for mortality.
5. Trees rising (Column 8) and trees stationary (Column 9). In calculating the number of trees rising out of a diameter class and those remaining stationary, the calculation has to begin with the highest diameter class; this class is therefore put at the top of the table. In this plot the 1938 adjusted inventory shows that no trees have risen above the 16-in. class; this is indicated by a zero in Column 8 **between** the 16- and 17-in. classes. As there were no 16-in. trees in 1928, none was stationary, and zero is recorded in Column 9 for the 16-in class. One tree was found in the 16-in. class at the second inventory. This tree must have risen from a lower class, presumably the 15-in. class (Column 6); therefore 1 is recorded in Column 8 between Classes 15 and 16. As this tree has risen from the 15-in. class, none remained stationary and zero is recorded in Column 9 opposite Class 15. The computation proceeds down the table in this manner. Had any trees grown through one entire diameter class, a **negative** number of trees would have been stationary.
6. Because the entries in Column 8 are mid-class, it is necessary to get the computations back on a full-inch basis. The next three steps accomplish this. Column 10 (Double rising) is the sum of the figures in the two adjacent diameter classes in Column 8. This is double the average number of trees rising in and out of every diameter class.
7. Column 11 (Double effective) is the sum of the figures in Columns 6 and 7. It is double the average number of trees contained in each diameter class during the period.
8. Column 12 is the diameter increment obtained by dividing values in Column 10 by those in Column 11. If 2-in. diameter classes were used, this quotient would be multiplied by 2.
9. Column 13. Values of Column 12 are smoothed by curve.
10. Column 14. The average annual increment is obtained by dividing values in Column 13 by the length of the period, in this case 10 yr.

**Calculation of volume growth and ingrowth.** An example, using the data obtained from a 33.4-acre woodland, is shown in Table 67; the volume per tree by diameter classes (local volume table) is shown in Column 5. Number of trees removed, plus number of trees in the second inventory, minus number of trees in the first inventory is equal to ingrowth:

$$\text{Ingrowth (number of trees)} = 622 + 3{,}392 - 2{,}641 = 1{,}373$$

Because the number of trees removed plus the number of trees of the second inventory, found in the 8-in. diameter class $(425 + 1{,}908 = 2{,}333)$, is larger than the number of trees grown into measurable size, it is reasonable to suppose that

Table 66. Computation of Diameter Growth, French Method (Continuous Inventory)

| (1) D.b.h. class (in.) | (2) Inventory 1928 | (3) Half of mortality | (4) Half of mortality | (5) Inventory 1938 | (6) Difference Col. 3 from Col. 2 | (7) Sum of Cols. 4 & 5 | (8) Trees rising | (9) Trees stationary | (10) Double rising | (11) Double effective Col. 6+7 | (12) Increment Cols. 10/11 | (13) Curved (in.) | (14) Average annual increment (in.) |
|---|---|---|---|---|---|---|---|---|---|---|---|---|---|
| 17 | ... | 9 | ... | ... | ... | ... | ... | ... | ... | ... | ... | ... | ... |
| 16 | ... | ... | ... | 1 | 0 | 1 | 0 | 0 | 1 | 1 | 1.00 | 1.00 | 0.10 |
| 15 | ... | ... | ... | 0 | 0 | 0 | 0 | 0 | 0 | 1 | 1.00 | 1.00 | .10 |
| 14 | ... | ... | ... | 0 | 0 | 0 | 0 | 0 | 0 | 0 | 1.00 | 0.97 | .10 |
| 13 | 11 | ... | ... | 9 | 12 | 8 | 8 | 0 | 8 | 20 | 0.70 | .92 | .09 |
| 12 | 8 | ... | ... | 9 | 12 | 13 | 6 | 6 | 14 | 17 | .76 | .85 | .08 |
| 11 | 11 | ... | ... | 13 | 19 | 7 | 8 | 8 | 13 | 25 | .60 | .77 | .08 |
| 10 | 12 | ... | ... | 7 | 8 | 17 | 4 | 4 | 15 | 18 | .67 | .70 | .07 |
| 9 | 11 | ... | ... | 17 | ... | 10 | 11 | 6 | 12 | 27 | .56 | .63 | .06 |
| 8 | 11 | ... | ... | 10 | ... | 10 | 2 | 6 | 15 | 29 | .45 | .55 | .05 |
| 7 | 19 | ... | ... | 8 | ... | 7 | 1 | 6 | 13 | 22 | .09 | .43 | .04 |
| 6 | 13 | ... | ... | 4 | ... | 6 | 0 | 0 | 2 | 13 | .08 | .14 | .01 |
| 5 | 4 | ... | ... | 2 | ... | ... | ... | ... | 1 | 13 | .08 | ... | .01 |
| 4 | 10 | ... | ... | ... | ... | ... | ... | ... | ... | ... | ... | ... | .01 |
| Total | 106 −9 / 97 | 9 | ... | 88 +9 / 97 | 97 | 97 | 48 | 49 48 / 97 | 96 | 194 | 0.49 | ... | 0.05 |

Source: Dept. of Mines and Resources, Dominion Forest Service, Sample plot methods, 1946.

the trees representing ingrowth are in the 8-in. class. In order to find ingrowth in terms of volume, the 1,373 trees are multiplied by the volume of an 8-in. tree (7.53 cu. ft.):

$$\text{Ingrowth (volume)} = 1{,}373 \times 7.53 = 10{,}339 \text{ cu. ft.}$$

**Volume growth by diameter classes; growth percent** (Table 68). The number of trees rising was computed as before. However, it was not necessary to allocate the trees removed to the first and second inventories; they were simply added to the second inventory. Because a tree rising into the next higher diameter class increases its volume by an amount equal to the difference of volume per tree

**Table 67. Example of Growth Determination on 33.4 Acres**

| D.b.h. (in.) | Number of trees | | | Volume | | | |
|---|---|---|---|---|---|---|---|
| | Inventory 9/38 | Trees removed | Inventory 3/46 | Volume per tree (cu. ft.) | Inventory 9/38 (cu. ft.) | Trees removed (cu. ft.) | Inventory 3/46 (cu. ft.) |
| 26 | 1 | . . . | 1 | 131.7 | 132 | . . . | 132 |
| 24 | . . . | . . . | . . . | 108.5 | . . . | . . . | . . . |
| 22 | . . . | . . . | 4 | 87.81 | . . . | . . . | 351 |
| 20 | 4 | 2 | 7 | 69.67 | 279 | 139 | 488 |
| 18 | 11 | . . . | 31 | 53.95 | 594 | . . . | 1,672 |
| 16 | 56 | 10 | 78 | 40.53 | 2,270 | 405 | 3,161 |
| 14 | 111 | 10 | 180 | 29.31 | 3,254 | 293 | 5,276 |
| 12 | 266 | 44 | 349 | 20.16 | 5,362 | 887 | 7,036 |
| 10 | 589 | 131 | 834 | 12.95 | 7,628 | 1,696 | 10,800 |
| 8 | 1,603 | 425 | 1,908 | 7.53 | 12,072 | 3,200 | 14,367 |
| Total | 2,641 | 622 | 3,392 | . . . | 31,591 | 6,620 | 43,283 |
| Per acre | 79 | 19 | 102 | . . . | 946 | 198 | 1,296 |
| Gross increment. . . . | . . . | . . . | . . . | . . . | 18,312 | . . . |
| Ingrowth. . . . . . . . . | 1,373 x 7.53 | | . . . | . . . | 10,339 | . . . |
| Total growth of initial volume (7 growing seasons). . . . . . . . . . . | | | | | 7,973 | . . . |
| Annual growth of initial volume. . . . . . . . . . . . . . . . . . . . . . . . . | | | | | 1,139 | . . . |
| Annual growth of initial volume, per acre. . . . . . . . . . . . . . . . . . | | | | | 34.1 | . . . |

between two successive diameter classes, its growth is obtained by subtraction (note that inversion of the stand table facilitates this process), and multiplied by the number of trees to obtain class growth. The growth so calculated may be expressed as a percent of the initial volume in each diameter class.

**Example.** The difference in volume between an 8- and a 10-in. tree is 12.95 − 7.53 = 5.42 cu. ft. This amount multiplied by the number of trees rising into the 10-in. diameter class gives 5.42 × 643 = 3,485 cu. ft. This expressed as a percent of the initial volume in the 8-in. class is

$$\frac{3{,}485}{12{,}072} \cdot 100 = 28.9 \text{ percent}$$

Because 7 yr. elapsed between inventories, growth per year = 28.9/7 = 4.1 percent.

The use of the continuous inventory system is not restricted to contiguous areas inventoried on a 100 percent basis as illustrated above. It can also be applied to a series of permanent sample plots distributed over a large forest area, but the combined area of such plots should not be smaller than 10–20 acres.

Table 68. Calculation of Volume Growth by Diameter Classes and in Percent of Initial Volume

| D.b.h. (in.) | Inventory 1938 | Inventory 1945 plus trees removed | Trees rising | Trees stationary | Volume per tree (cu. ft.) | Initial volume 1938 (cu. ft.) | Volume difference (cu. ft.) | Volume growth for 7-yr. period (cu. ft.) | Volume growth in percent of initial volume (percent) | Average annual growth (percent) |
|---|---|---|---|---|---|---|---|---|---|---|
| 26 | 1 | 1 | 0 | 1 | 131.7 | 132 | 23.2 | ... | ... | ... |
| 24 | ... | ... | 0 | 0 | 108.5 | ... | 20.7 | ... | ... | ... |
| 22 | ... | 4 | 0 | 0 | 87.81 | ... | 18.14 | ... | ... | ... |
| 20 | 4 | 9 | 4 | 0 | 69.67 | 279 | 15.72 | 73 | 26.2 | 3.7 |
| 18 | 11 | 31 | 9 | 2 | 53.95 | 594 | 13.41 | 141 | 23.7 | 3.4 |
| 16 | 56 | 88 | 29 | 27 | 40.53 | 2,270 | 11.22 | 389 | 17.1 | 2.4 |
| 14 | 111 | 190 | 61 | 50 | 29.31 | 3,254 | 9.15 | 684 | 21.0 | 3.0 |
| 12 | 266 | 393 | 140 | 126 | 20.16 | 5,362 | 7.21 | 1,290 | 24.0 | 3.4 |
| 10 | 589 | 965 | 267 | 322 | 12.95 | 7,628 | 5.42 | 1,925 | 25.2 | 3.6 |
| 8 | 1,603 | 2,333 | 643 | 960 | 7.53 | 12,072 | ... | 3,485 | 28.9 | 4.1 |
| 6 | ... | ... | 1,373 | ... | ... | ... | ... | ... | ... | ... |
| Totals | | | | | | 31,591 | | 7,986 | | 3.6 |

Annual volume growth on 33.4 acres .............. 1,141

Average annual volume growth per acre .............. 34.1

Ingrowth = 1,373 trees or 1,373×7.53 = 10,339 cu. ft.

## BIBLIOGRAPHY

BELYEA, H. C. 1931. *Forest measurement.* John Wiley & Sons, Inc., New York.

BELYEA, H. C. 1933. Forester's tables for New York State. N. Y. State College of Forestry, *Bull. 14.* 206 pp.

BESLEY, LOWELL. 1937. *Introduction to forest measurements.* Brownell Photo-Lithograph Co., Philadelphia.

BRUCE, DONALD, and F. X. SCHUMACHER. 1950. *Forest mensuration.* 3d ed. McGraw-Hill Book Co., Inc., New York.

CHAPMAN, H. H., and D. B. DEMERITT. 1936. *Elements of forest mensuration.* J. B. Lyon Co., Albany, N. Y.

CHAPMAN, H. H., and W. H. MEYER. 1949. *Forest mensuration.* McGraw-Hill Book Co., Inc., New York.

GIRARD, J. W., and D. BRUCE. 1947. *Tables for estimating board foot volumes of trees in 16-foot logs.* Mason, Bruce & Girard, Portland, Ore.

GIRARD, J. W., and D. BRUCE. 1948. *Tables for estimating board foot volumes of trees in 32-foot logs.* Mason, Bruce & Girard, Portland, Ore.

GIRARD, J. W., and S. R. GEVORKIANTZ. 1939. *Timber cruising.* U. S. Forest Service. (Mimeo.)

HARRISON, J. D. B. 1950. *National forest inventory.* Forest and Agriculture Organization of the United Nations.

HERRICK, A. M. 1949. How to grade hardwood sawlogs. Purdue Univ. *Extension Bull. 346.*

MEYER, H. ARTHUR. 1953. *Forest mensuration.* Penns Valley Publishers, Inc., State College, Pa.

ROBERTSON, W. M., and G. A. MULLOY. 1946. Sample plot methods. Dominion Forest Service of Canada.

SCHUMACHER, F. X., and HALL FRANCISCO DAS SANTOS. 1933. Logarithmic expression of timber-tree volumes. *Jour. Agr. Research* 47:719–734.

SCHUMACHER, F. X., and R. A. CHAPMAN. 1942. Sampling methods in forestry and range management. Duke Univ. School of Forestry, *Bull. 7.*

SPURR, S. H. 1952. *Forest inventory.* The Ronald Press Co., New York.

U. S. DEPT. AGR. 1941. *National forest scaling handbook.* U. S. Forest Serv., Washington, D. C.

U. S. FOREST SERV., Forest Products Lab. 1949. Hardwood log grades for standard lumber.

U. S. FOREST SERV., Northeastern Forest Exp. Sta. 1948. Hardwood log grading and lumber value. *Sta. Paper No. 14.*

U. S. FOREST SERV., Southeastern Forest Exp. Sta. 1948. Tree grades for loblolly and shortleaf pine. *Tech. Note No. 69.*

---

NOTE: In the interest of brevity the Editorial Committees have been selective rather than comprehensive in preparing the bibliographies for their respective sections. To conserve further space many publications of public or semipublic agencies, such as those of the experiment stations of the U. S. Forest Service, have not been listed separately by author.

# FOREST MANAGEMENT—VOLUME TABLES

## CONTENTS

# FOREST MANAGEMENT—VOLUME TABLES

The section on Forest Measurements describes the **methods** of measuring trees and stands. The **results** of such measurements—volume, stand, and yield tables and such supplementary information as current and periodic growth—are given in this and the following two sections. Some data preliminary to the preparation of these tables are given in the Forest Measurements section.

## Volume Tables

The following volume tables are largely form-class tables. They were selected from a much greater number of tables, covering individual species principally in the United States, because of the ease with which form-class tables can be adapted to local use, or regional use such as for the Forest Survey in a single state or group of states. Mensurational practices differ between the United States and Canada— the Girard form class and merchantable length being favored south of the Inter- national Boundary, and the older mid-tree form class and total height north of it. This has resulted in some duplication of tables. Even without it, space is not available to print all desirable tables in a size of type adapted to day-after-day use. The practicing forester will undoubtedly copy into his field notebooks the tables he uses daily or will prepare cumulative tally sheets and have them printed for his convenience in the field. For continued office use he will make his own multiple-tree tables.

**SELECTING A VOLUME TABLE.** To select from form-class tables the volumes to be used in estimating a given stand requires information on taper. For saw timber of southern conifers and eastern hardwoods (Tables 1 to 4), Mesavage and Girard recommended measurement of Girard form class on "about 50 trees of assorted diameter in each usable length class . . . well distributed over the area." For cubic-foot volumes, Mesavage suggests measurement of about 150 trees (all diameters combined) if errors greater than $2\frac{1}{2}$ percent are to be avoided in cruising tracts of less than 50 acres. For areas up to 500 acres, he increases the number of trees to be measured for form class to 300. In large tracts Mesavage recommends the intensity of sampling previously cited for saw timber.

To select the Girard form-class table appropriate for board-foot estimates of northern hardwoods (Table 5), Bickford says: "Where moderate precision is acceptable . . . measure about 30 trees of assorted diameters for form-class; if greater precision is needed, a larger sample should be measured, say 100 to 150 trees."

In using Girard form-class tables (Tables 36 and 38) for California saw timber, Clements, Stevens, and Roy state: "If it is desired that volume estimates be within 2 or 3 percent of the true volume 19 out of 20 times, the form-class average must be within one class of the true average. If the standard deviation of form class is 6 classes, which is about the average value for several locality groups of our data, 144 sample trees will be necessary. . . . It would be desirable to estimate the form class of every tree in small sales of 150 trees or less, particularly for valuable timber."

In 1948, the Dominion Forest Service of Canada stated, with reference to its form-class tables (Tables 49 to 85):

> While it was formerly recommended that the average form-class of a species in each type in a district should be determined by measuring 50 trees in all diameter classes, it has since been found that form-class decreases with diameter in most stands. . . . Error can be avoided by averaging form-class by diameter-classes and smoothing off the average form-class for each diameter-class by plotting the values and drawing a curve.

**LOCAL VOLUME TABLES.** Once the average form class and the range of average heights over diameter for trees in a given stand or forest have been determined, it is often convenient to prepare from the general volume table a local table for repeated measurements in that stand or forest. If differences in utilization are consequential, allowance must be made for them in preparing local tables. Where site affects form, site-class volume tables are sometimes worth the labor of preparation.

**USE OF MERCHANTABLE-HEIGHT VOLUME TABLES.** Regardless of the volume table selected for use, certain principles must be followed in applying it to an individual tree. Meyer has stated them succinctly in the following words:

> Proper use of merchantable-height tables demands that these heights be estimated as the tables stipulate and not as limbiness or quality of the bole indicates. To reduce the merchantable height of the tree because of a poor top and to look up this dimension in the volume table leads to gross underestimate. To illustrate: a tree with a dry top is 36 in. at breast height outside bark and measures four 32-ft. logs to what would be a 12-in. top inside bark were it alive at this point. Because of the dead top the estimator calls the height only 3½ logs. Table 29 gives for 36 in. and 4 logs a volume of 2,640 bd. ft., and for 36 in. and 3½ logs 2,200 bd. ft., a difference of 440 bd. ft. Actually the top cull log has only 80 bd. ft. in it. In this instance the arbitrary reduction of merchantable height leads to an error five and one half times the error of exact interpretation of the table. **This rule is general for all volume tables:** Use the tables as the limits of utilization stipulate in the table headings. The resulting error will be far smaller than if the personal factor is introduced.

**ADJUSTMENT OF VOLUMES BETWEEN FORM CLASSES.** Space limitations prevent including published values for all form classes. A footnote to each form-class table indicates the percentage increase in volume corresponding to one point change in form class. In computing volumes of several species, with known differences in form class in a tally or stand table, it is time-saving to use one form-class table for all species and adjust the total volume for each species by the appropriate percentage.

## Volume Tables for the United States

**EASTERN SPECIES.** See Tables 1 to 14.

# SOUTHERN CONIFERS AND EASTERN HARDWOODS

## Table 1. Volumes in Merchantable Cubic Feet*

### Girard Form Class 77

Cordwood volume (cu. ft., inside bark) by length (feet) of merchantable stem

| Tree diameter (in.) | 12 | 16 | 20 | 24 | 28 | 32 | 36 | 40 | 44 | 48 | 52 | 56 | 60 |
|---|---|---|---|---|---|---|---|---|---|---|---|---|---|
| 5 | 1.3 | 1.6 | 1.9 | 2.2 | 2.5 | 2.7 | 3.0 | 3.3 | 3.6 | 3.9 | 4.2 | 4.4 | 4.7 |
| 6 | 1.8 | 2.3 | 2.7 | 3.0 | 3.4 | 3.8 | 4.1 | 4.5 | 4.9 | 5.2 | 5.6 | 6.0 | 6.3 |
| 7 | 2.4 | 3.0 | 3.5 | 4.0 | 4.4 | 4.9 | 5.4 | 5.9 | 6.4 | 6.8 | 7.3 | 7.8 | 8.3 |
| 8 | 3.0 | 3.9 | 4.5 | 5.1 | 5.7 | 6.3 | 7.0 | 7.6 | 8.2 | 8.8 | 9.4 | 10.0 | 10.6 |
| 9 | 3.7 | 4.8 | 5.5 | 6.3 | 7.0 | 7.7 | 8.5 | 9.2 | 9.9 | 10.7 | 11.4 | 12.1 | 12.9 |
| 10 | 4.5 | 5.9 | 6.7 | 7.6 | 8.4 | 9.3 | 10.1 | 10.9 | 11.8 | 12.6 | 13.5 | 14.3 | 15.1 |

Saw-log volume (cu. ft., inside bark) and scaling diameter (in.) of top saw log, by number of 16-ft. logs

| Tree diameter (in.) | 1 | 1½ | 2 | 2½ | 3 | 3½ | 4 | 4½ | 5 | 5½ | 6 |
|---|---|---|---|---|---|---|---|---|---|---|---|
| 10 | 5.9—8" | 8.0—8" | 10.2—6" | 11.8—6" | 13.3—5" | | | | | | |
| 11 | 7.2—8 | 9.8—8 | 12.4—7 | 14.4—6 | 16.3—6 | | | | | | |
| 12 | 8.4—9 | 11.5—8 | 14.6—7 | 17.0—7 | 19.3—6 | | | | | | |
| 13 | 10.0—10 | 13.7—9 | 17.4—8 | 20.3—8 | 23.2—7 | | | | | | |
| 14 | 11.5—11 | 15.8—10 | 20.2—9 | 23.6—8 | 27.0—7 | 29.5—7" | 32.0—6" | | | | |
| 15 | 13.2—12 | 18.2—11 | 23.2—10 | 27.2—9 | 31.2—8 | 34.2—8 | 37.3—7 | | | | |
| 16 | 15.0—12 | 20.6—11 | 26.3—10 | 30.8—10 | 35.4—9 | 39.0—8 | 42.6—7 | | | | |
| 17 | 17.0—13 | 23.5—12 | 30.0—11 | 35.2—10 | 40.4—9 | 44.6—9 | 48.8—8 | | | | |
| 18 | 19.1—14 | 26.4—13 | 33.7—12 | 39.6—11 | 45.5—10 | 50.3—10 | 55.1—9 | | | | |
| 19 | 21.3—15 | 29.4—14 | 37.6—13 | 44.2—12 | 50.9—11 | 56.2—10 | 61.6—9 | | | | |
| 20 | 23.5—15 | 32.6—14 | 41.6—13 | 49.0—13 | 56.3—12 | 62.2—11 | 68.1—10 | 73.0—9" | 77.9—8" | | |
| 21 | 26.0—16 | 36.0—15 | 46.0—14 | 54.2—13 | 62.4—12 | 69.0—11 | 75.6—10 | 81.2—9 | 86.8—8 | | |
| 22 | 28.6—17 | 39.6—16 | 50.5—15 | 59.5—14 | 68.5—13 | 75.8—12 | 83.2—11 | 89.5—10 | 95.8—9 | | |
| 23 | 31.6—18 | 43.7—17 | 55.8—15 | 65.8—15 | 75.8—14 | 83.8—13 | 91.8—12 | 99.0—11 | 106.3—9 | | |
| 24 | 34.6—18 | 47.8—17 | 61.0—16 | 72.0—15 | 83.0—14 | 91.7—13 | 100.4—12 | 108.6—11 | 116.8—10 | | |
| 25 | 37.6—19 | 52.0—18 | 66.4—17 | 78.4—16 | 90.3—15 | 100.0—14 | 109.6—13 | 118.6—12 | 127.6—11 | | |
| 26 | 40.7—20 | 56.2—19 | 71.7—18 | 84.6—17 | 97.6—16 | 108.2—15 | 118.9—13 | 128.7—12 | 138.5—11 | | |
| 27 | 44.4—20 | 61.2—20 | 78.1—18 | 92.2—17 | 106.4—16 | 118.0—15 | 129.5—14 | 140.3—13 | 151.1—12 | | |
| 28 | 48.2—22 | 66.4—20 | 84.5—19 | 99.9—18 | 115.3—17 | 127.7—16 | 140.1—15 | 151.9—14 | 163.7—13 | 174.6—11" | 185.4—10" |
| 29 | 52.0—22 | 71.5—21 | 91.0—20 | 107.6—19 | 124.2—18 | 137.4—17 | 150.7—15 | 163.6—14 | 176.6—13 | 188.8—12 | 201.0—10 |
| 30 | 55.9—23 | 76.7—22 | 97.5—20 | 115.2—19 | 133.0—18 | 147.2—17 | 161.3—16 | 175.4—15 | 189.6—14 | 203.2—12 | 216.7—11 |
| 31 | 60.0—24 | 82.2—22 | 104.4—21 | 123.6—20 | 142.7—19 | 158.0—18 | 173.4—17 | 188.3—15 | 203.2—15 | 218.0—13 | 232.8—12 |
| 32 | 64.1—25 | 87.8—23 | 111.4—22 | 131.9—21 | 152.4—20 | 169.0—19 | 185.6—17 | 201.2—16 | 216.9—15 | 232.9—14 | 248.9—12 |
| 33 | 68.8—25 | 94.0—24 | 119.3—23 | 141.2—22 | 163.2—21 | 181.1—19 | 199.0—18 | 215.8—17 | 232.6—16 | 250.1—14 | 267.6—13 |
| 34 | 73.4—26 | 100.3—25 | 127.2—23 | 150.6—22 | 174.0—21 | 193.2—20 | 212.3—19 | 230.2—17 | 248.2—16 | 267.2—15 | 286.2—14 |
| 35 | 78.1—27 | 106.6—26 | 135.2—24 | 160.1—23 | 185.0—22 | 205.4—21 | 225.9—19 | 245.2—18 | 264.4—17 | 284.2—15 | 304.0—14 |
| 36 | 82.8—28 | 113.0—26 | 143.3—25 | 169.7—24 | 196.1—23 | 217.8—21 | 239.5—20 | 260.0—19 | 280.5—17 | 301.1—16 | 321.7—15 |
| 37 | 88.0—28 | 120.1—27 | 152.2—25 | 180.4—25 | 208.7—24 | 231.7—22 | 254.7—21 | 276.8—19 | 299.0—18 | 320.9—17 | 342.8—15 |
| 38 | 93.3—29 | 127.2—28 | 161.2—26 | 191.2—25 | 221.3—24 | 245.6—23 | 269.9—21 | 293.8—20 | 317.6—19 | 340.7—17 | 363.8—16 |
| 39 | 98.3—30 | 134.2—29 | 170.0—27 | 201.6—26 | 233.2—25 | 259.1—24 | 285.0—22 | 309.7—21 | 334.4—19 | 359.0—18 | 383.5—16 |
| 40 | 103.3—31 | 141.0—29 | 178.7—28 | 211.9—27 | 245.1—26 | 272.6—24 | 300.2—23 | 325.8—21 | 351.3—20 | 377.2—18 | 403.2—17 |

* The increase in cubic-foot volumes in this table for each Girard form class is 3 percent.

Source: Clement Mesavage, Tables for estimating cubic-foot volume of timber, Southern Forest Exp. Sta., *Occ. Paper No. 111*, 1947.

## SOUTHERN CONIFERS AND EASTERN HARDWOODS

### Table 2. Girard Form-Class Volume Tables, 1946 [a]

Board feet, Doyle Log Rule—Form Class 78

| D.b.h. (in.) | Number of merchantable 16-ft logs [b] | | | | | | | | | | |
|---|---|---|---|---|---|---|---|---|---|---|---|
| | 1 | 1½ | 2 | 2½ | 3 | 3½ | 4 | 4½ | 5 | 5½ | 6 |
| 10 | 14 | 17 | 20 | 21 | 22 | | | | | | |
| 12 | 29 | 36 | 43 | 48 | 53 | 54 | 56 | | | | |
| 14 | 48 | 62 | 75 | 84 | 93 | 98 | 103 | | | | |
| 16 | 72 | 94 | 116 | 132 | 149 | 160 | 170 | | | | |
| 18 | 100 | 132 | 164 | 190 | 215 | 232 | 248 | | | | |
| 20 | 135 | 180 | 225 | 261 | 297 | 322 | 346 | 364 | 383 | | |
| 22 | 174 | 234 | 295 | 344 | 392 | 427 | 462 | 492 | 521 | | |
| 24 | 216 | 293 | 370 | 433 | 496 | 539 | 582 | 625 | 668 | | |
| 26 | 266 | 362 | 459 | 539 | 619 | 678 | 737 | 793 | 849 | | |
| 28 | 317 | 434 | 551 | 650 | 750 | 820 | 890 | 961 | 1,032 | 1,096 | 1,161 |
| 30 | 376 | 517 | 658 | 778 | 898 | 984 | 1,069 | 1,160 | 1,251 | 1,339 | 1,427 |
| 32 | 441 | 608 | 776 | 922 | 1,068 | 1,176 | 1,283 | 1,386 | 1,488 | 1,600 | 1,712 |
| 34 | 506 | 700 | 894 | 1,064 | 1,235 | 1,361 | 1,487 | 1,608 | 1,730 | 1,866 | 2,003 |
| 36 | 581 | 808 | 1,035 | 1,234 | 1,434 | 1,583 | 1,732 | 1,878 | 2,023 | 2,173 | 2,323 |
| 38 | 655 | 912 | 1,170 | 1,402 | 1,635 | 1,805 | 1,975 | 2,148 | 2,322 | 2,491 | 2,660 |
| 40 | 740 | 1,035 | 1,330 | 1,594 | 1,858 | 2,059 | 2,260 | 2,448 | 2,636 | 2,832 | 3,027 |

[a] The increase in board-foot volumes in this table for each Girard form class is 3 percent.
[b] To a flexible limit, but not less than 6 in. d.i.b.
Source for Tables 2 to 4: Clement Mesavage and James W. Girard, Tables for estimating board-foot volume of timber, U. S. Forest Service (for administrative use), 1946.

## SOUTHERN CONIFERS AND EASTERN HARDWOODS

### Table 3. Girard Form-Class Volume Tables, 1946 [a]

Board feet, Scribner Log Rule—Form Class 78

| D.b.h. (in.) | Number of merchantable 16-ft logs [b] | | | | | | | | | | |
|---|---|---|---|---|---|---|---|---|---|---|---|
| | 1 | 1½ | 2 | 2½ | 3 | 3½ | 4 | 4½ | 5 | 5½ | 6 |
| 10 | 28 | 36 | 44 | 48 | 52 | | | | | | |
| 12 | 47 | 61 | 75 | 85 | 95 | 100 | 106 | | | | |
| 14 | 69 | 92 | 114 | 130 | 146 | 156 | 166 | | | | |
| 16 | 95 | 127 | 159 | 185 | 211 | 229 | 247 | | | | |
| 18 | 123 | 166 | 209 | 244 | 280 | 306 | 331 | | | | |
| 20 | 157 | 214 | 270 | 317 | 364 | 398 | 432 | 459 | 486 | | |
| 22 | 194 | 266 | 338 | 398 | 458 | 504 | 549 | 588 | 626 | | |
| 24 | 234 | 322 | 409 | 484 | 558 | 611 | 665 | 718 | 770 | | |
| 26 | 281 | 388 | 494 | 585 | 676 | 745 | 814 | 880 | 945 | | |
| 28 | 327 | 452 | 578 | 686 | 795 | 877 | 959 | 1,040 | 1,120 | 1,190 | 1,261 |
| 30 | 382 | 530 | 678 | 806 | 933 | 1,028 | 1,124 | 1,224 | 1,325 | 1,421 | 1,517 |
| 32 | 440 | 612 | 784 | 936 | 1,089 | 1,206 | 1,322 | 1,432 | 1,543 | 1,661 | 1,779 |
| 34 | 498 | 695 | 892 | 1,066 | 1,239 | 1,373 | 1,507 | 1,636 | 1,766 | 1,906 | 2,046 |
| 36 | 563 | 789 | 1,015 | 1,216 | 1,416 | 1,572 | 1,728 | 1,877 | 2,026 | 2,182 | 2,338 |
| 38 | 629 | 882 | 1,135 | 1,366 | 1,596 | 1,769 | 1,942 | 2,118 | 2,295 | 2,466 | 2,637 |
| 40 | 703 | 988 | 1,274 | 1,532 | 1,791 | 1,993 | 2,195 | 2,384 | 2,574 | 2,768 | 2,961 |

[a] The increase in board-foot volumes in this table for each Girard form class is 3 percent.
[b] To a flexible limit, but not less than 6 in. d.i.b.
Source: *Ibid.*

## SOUTHERN CONIFERS AND EASTERN HARDWOODS

### Table 4. Girard Form-Class Volume Tables, 1946 [a]

Board feet, International ¼-In. Rule—Form Class 78

| D.b.h. (in.) | Number of merchantable 16-ft. logs [b] | | | | | | | | | | |
|---|---|---|---|---|---|---|---|---|---|---|---|
| | 1 | 1½ | 2 | 2½ | 3 | 3½ | 4 | 4½ | 5 | 5½ | 6 |
| 10 | 36 | 48 | 59 | 66 | 73 | | | | | | |
| 12 | 56 | 74 | 92 | 106 | 120 | 128 | 137 | | | | |
| 14 | 78 | 105 | 132 | 153 | 174 | 187 | 200 | | | | |
| 16 | 106 | 143 | 180 | 210 | 241 | 263 | 285 | | | | |
| 18 | 136 | 184 | 233 | 274 | 314 | 344 | 374 | | | | |
| 20 | 171 | 234 | 296 | 348 | 401 | 440 | 480 | 511 | 542 | | |
| 22 | 211 | 290 | 368 | 434 | 500 | 552 | 603 | 647 | 691 | | |
| 24 | 251 | 346 | 441 | 523 | 605 | 664 | 723 | 782 | 840 | | |
| 26 | 299 | 414 | 528 | 626 | 725 | 801 | 877 | 949 | 1,021 | | |
| 28 | 347 | 482 | 616 | 733 | 850 | 938 | 1,027 | 1,114 | 1,201 | 1,280 | 1,358 |
| 30 | 403 | 560 | 718 | 854 | 991 | 1,094 | 1,198 | 1,306 | 1,415 | 1,517 | 1,619 |
| 32 | 462 | 644 | 826 | 988 | 1,149 | 1,274 | 1,400 | 1,518 | 1,637 | 1,762 | 1,888 |
| 34 | 521 | 728 | 934 | 1,119 | 1,304 | 1,447 | 1,590 | 1,727 | 1,864 | 2,014 | 2,163 |
| 36 | 589 | 826 | 1,063 | 1,274 | 1,485 | 1,650 | 1,814 | 1,974 | 2,135 | 2,298 | 2,461 |
| 38 | 656 | 921 | 1,186 | 1,428 | 1,670 | 1,854 | 2,038 | 2,224 | 2,410 | 2,590 | 2,771 |
| 40 | 731 | 1,030 | 1,329 | 1,598 | 1,868 | 2,081 | 2,294 | 2,494 | 2,693 | 2,898 | 3,103 |

[a] The increase in board-foot volumes in this table for each Girard form class is 3 percent.
[b] To a flexible limit, but not less than 6 in. d.i.b.
Source: *Ibid.*

## NORTHERN CONIFERS

### Table 5. Girard Form-Class Volume Tables, 1951 [a]

Board feet, International ¼-In. Rule—Form Class 78

| D.b.h. (in.) | Estimated merchantable height, in 16-ft. logs [b] | | | | | | | | |
|---|---|---|---|---|---|---|---|---|---|
| | 1 | 1½ | 2 | 2½ | 3 | 3½ | 4 | 4½ | 5 |
| 10 | 36 | 48 | 56 | 63 | | | | | |
| 12 | 56 | 74 | 88 | 98 | 109 | | | | |
| 14 | 78 | 104 | 124 | 140 | 156 | 167 | | | |
| 16 | 106 | 141 | 168 | 192 | 212 | 231 | 247 | | |
| 18 | 136 | 182 | 217 | 248 | 276 | 300 | 321 | | |
| 20 | 171 | 229 | 275 | 313 | 348 | 379 | 407 | 431 | |
| 22 | 211 | 282 | 337 | 387 | 430 | 467 | 503 | 535 | |
| 24 | 252 | 338 | 406 | 463 | 517 | 563 | 606 | 644 | 681 |
| 26 | 299 | 400 | 480 | 550 | 614 | 672 | 722 | 768 | 814 |
| 28 | 347 | 464 | 560 | 642 | 716 | 783 | 844 | 898 | 948 |
| 30 | 403 | 540 | 648 | 744 | 830 | 909 | 980 | 1,045 | 1,104 |

[a] The increase in board-foot volumes in this table for each Girard form class is 3 percent.
[b] To a flexible limit, but not less than 6 in. d.i.b.
Source: C. A. Bickford, Form-class volume tables for estimating board-foot content of Northern conifers, Northeastern Forest Exp. Sta., *Sta. Paper No. 38,* 1951.

## NORTHEASTERN CONIFERS AND HARDWOODS

### Table 6.   Basic   Volume   Table

Merchantable Cords [a]

| D.b.h. (in.) | Height in number of 16-ft. logs [b] | | | | | | |
|---|---|---|---|---|---|---|---|
| | 1 | 1½ | 2 | 2½ | 3 | 3½ | 4 |
| 8 | 0.05 | 0.07 | 0.09 | 0.11 | | | |
| 10 | .08 | .11 | .14 | .16 | 0.17 | | |
| 12 | .12 | .17 | .20 | .24 | .26 | 0.28 | |
| 14 | .16 | .22 | .28 | .33 | .36 | .39 | |
| 16 | .21 | .29 | .36 | .43 | .48 | .52 | 0.53 |
| 18 | .26 | .36 | .46 | .54 | .60 | .65 | .67 |
| 20 | .32 | .44 | .56 | .66 | .74 | .80 | .82 |
| 22 | .38 | .54 | .67 | .79 | .89 | .96 | .99 |
| 24 | .45 | .63 | .79 | .93 | 1.05 | 1.13 | 1.17 |
| 26 | .53 | .73 | .92 | 1.09 | 1.22 | 1.32 | 1.36 |
| 28 | .61 | .84 | 1.06 | 1.26 | 1.41 | 1.51 | 1.56 |
| 30 | .69 | .96 | 1.20 | 1.41 | 1.59 | 1.71 | 1.76 |
| 32 | .78 | 1.07 | 1.34 | 1.59 | 1.79 | 1.91 | 1.97 |

[a] The following percentages are to be applied to the above volumes, for various northeastern species to correct for differences in form class: spruce, 97; balsam fir, 86; hemlock, 86; white and red pine, 97; beech, 100; paper and yellow birch, 92; sugar maple, 89; red maple, 94; white ash, 92 ; basswood, 94; red oak, 94. The beech, on which these volumes are based, was old growth.
[b] To a flexible limit, but not less than 6 in. d.i.b.
Source: L. H. Reineke, Northeastern Forest Exp. Sta., 1949.

## LAKE STATES PULPWOOD SPECIES

### Table 7.  Merchantable Volume * Table, Unpeeled Wood, 1945

Standard Cords

| D.b.h. (in.) | Usable height in number of 8-ft. bolts | | | | | | | |
|---|---|---|---|---|---|---|---|---|
| | 1 | 2 | 3 | 4 | 5 | 6 | 7 | 8 |
| 4 | 0.004 | 0.008 | | | | | | |
| 5 | .010 | .018 | 0.027 | | | | | |
| 6 | .018 | .030 | .043 | 0.058 | | | | |
| 7 | .025 | .039 | .056 | .074 | 0.093 | | | |
| 8 | .032 | .050 | .070 | .092 | .116 | 0.138 | | |
| 9 | .040 | .061 | .085 | .112 | .140 | .168 | | |
| 10 | .049 | .074 | .101 | .132 | .167 | .200 | 0.239 | 0.270 |
| 11 | .059 | .087 | .119 | .155 | .195 | .233 | .280 | .320 |
| 12 | .070 | .100 | .138 | .180 | .225 | .271 | .324 | .365 |
| 14 | .095 | .134 | .179 | .233 | .291 | .351 | .419 | .472 |
| 16 | | | .222 | .290 | .361 | .437 | .521 | .587 |
| 18 | | | .270 | .350 | .439 | .531 | .634 | .715 |
| 20 | | | .321 | .416 | .522 | .632 | .755 | .851 |
| 22 | | | | .490 | .612 | .739 | .883 | .995 |
| 24 | | | | | | .855 | 1.02 | 1.15 |

* In stem above 1-ft. stump to variable merchantable top diameter, but not less than 4 in. d.i.b.  For volumes of peeled wood, subtract 14 percent.
Source: S. R. Gevorkiantz, Lake States Forest Exp. Sta., *Tech Note No. 241,* 1945.

## LAKE STATES SAW TIMBER

### Table 8. Number of Standard Cords of Top Wood per M Board Feet, Scribner Rule

| Total height of tree (ft.) | Merchantable height (number of 8-ft. saw logs) | | | | | |
|---|---|---|---|---|---|---|
| | 1 (cords) | 2 (cords) | 3 (cords) | 4 (cords) | 5 (cords) | 6 (cords) |
| 30 | 1.2 | 0.45 | | | | |
| 40 | 2.2 | 0.85 | 0.40 | | | |
| 50 | 3.1 | 1.3 | 0.70 | 0.35 | | |
| 60 | 4.0 | 1.8 | 1.0 | 0.60 | 0.30 | |
| 70 | 5.0 | 2.4 | 1.4 | 0.80 | 0.50 | 0.35 |
| 80 | 6.1 | 2.9 | 1.8 | 1.2 | 0.80 | 0.60 |
| 90 | 7.1 | 3.5 | 2.3 | 1.5 | 1.1 | 0.80 |
| 100 | 8.2 | 4.1 | 2.8 | 1.9 | 1.4 | 1.0 |

**Example 1.** An individual tree 80 ft. in height with four 8-ft. logs scaling 450 bd. ft., Scribner rule, will yield fuel wood at the **rate** of 1.2 cords per M bd. ft., or, for this particular tree, 0.54 standard cord (450/1,000 × 1.2 = 0.54).

**Example 2.** A stand of hardwoods having an average height of 90 ft. contains 85 M bd. ft., Scribner rule. On the average, there are three 8-ft. logs per tree. This stand will yield at the **rate** of 2.3 cords per M bd. ft., or, for the entire stand, 196 cords of stovewood (85,000/1,000 × 2.3 = 196).

Source: Lake States Forest Exp. Sta., Volume of fuel wood in tree tops, *Tech. Note No. 184*, 1942.

## LAKE STATES NORTHERN WHITE-CEDAR

### Table 9. Cubic-Foot and Board-Foot Content of 8-Ft. Tie Cuts

| Unit of measure | Small-end diameter, inside bark, inches | | | | | | | | | | | |
|---|---|---|---|---|---|---|---|---|---|---|---|---|
| | 9 | 10 | 11 | 12 | 13 | 14 | 15 | 16 | 17 | 18 | 19 | 20 |
| In small tie stands (10- to 14-in. trees predominating) | | | | | | | | | | | | |
| Cubic feet ......... | 4.1 | 5.1 | 6.2 | 7.4 | 8.7 | 10.1 | 11.6 | 13.4 | 15.3 | 17.4 | 19.6 | 22.0 |
| In large tie stands (16-in and larger trees predominating) | | | | | | | | | | | | |
| Cubic feet ......... | 4.1 | 5.0 | 6.1 | 7.3 | 8.6 | 9.9 | 11.3 | 13.0 | 14.8 | 16.7 | 18.8 | 21.0 |
| In all stands | | | | | | | | | | | | |
| Board feet ......... | 21 | 27 | 35 | 43 | 52 | 61 | 72 | 83 | 94 | 108 | 121 | 136 |

Source: S. R. Gevorkiantz and W. A. Duerr, Volume and yield of northern white-cedar in the Lake States, Lake State Forest Exp. Sta., 1939.

**Rule-of-Thumb, Southern Pine, Cubic-Foot Volumes.** The United States Forest Service uses this rule-of-thumb in second-growth southern pine: to obtain the volume in cubic feet, including bark, of a forest-grown stem to a minimum top diameter of 4 in., take ½ the d.b.h. in inches, subtract 1, and square the remainder. Thus the volume of a 6-in. tree is 4 cu. ft., of an 8-in. tree is 9 cu. ft., etc. If the trees are tall and cylindrical, add about 10 percent to the total volume calculated by this rule; if short and tapering, subtract 10 percent; if the trees are very short boled, in old fields, subtract 15 to 30 percent. To convert cubic feet to standard 4 by 4 by 8-ft. cords of rough wood, divide by 90. For wood from trees predominantly 6-in., divide by 85, and for wood from trees 10 in. or larger divide by 95.

## SOUTHERN PINES

### Table 10. Volume of Merchantable Tops, Trees of Saw-Log Size, in Cubic Feet, Inside Bark

Gross volume (cubic feet inside bark) by length of merchantable top section in feet

| Scaling diam. top saw log (in.) | 4 | 8 | 12 | 16 | 20 | 24 | 28 | 32 | 36 | 40 | 44 |
|---|---|---|---|---|---|---|---|---|---|---|---|
| **TREES OF HIGH TOP FORM INDEX** | | | | | | | | | | | |
| 5 | 0.4 | 0.8 | 1.2 | 1.5 | 1.9 | 2.3 | 2.7 | 3.1 | 3.5 | 3.8 | 4.2 |
| 6 | 0.6 | 1.1 | 1.7 | 2.3 | 2.8 | 3.4 | 4.0 | 4.5 | 5.1 | 5.7 | 6.2 |
| 7 | 0.8 | 1.6 | 2.4 | 3.1 | 3.9 | 4.7 | 5.5 | 6.3 | 7.1 | 7.9 | 8.6 |
| 8 | 1.0 | 2.0 | 3.0 | 4.0 | 5.0 | 6.1 | 7.1 | 8.1 | 9.1 | 10.1 | 11.1 |
| 9 | 1.3 | 2.5 | 3.8 | 5.0 | 6.3 | 7.6 | 8.8 | 10.1 | 11.3 | 12.6 | 13.9 |
| 10 | 1.6 | 3.2 | 4.7 | 6.3 | 7.9 | 9.5 | 11.0 | 12.6 | 14.2 | 15.8 | 17.3 |
| 11 | 1.9 | 3.9 | 5.8 | 7.7 | 9.6 | 11.6 | 13.5 | 15.4 | 17.3 | 19.3 | 21.2 |
| 12 | 2.3 | 4.5 | 6.8 | 9.1 | 11.4 | 13.6 | 15.9 | 18.2 | 20.4 | 22.7 | 25.0 |
| 13 | 2.6 | 5.3 | 7.9 | 10.6 | 13.2 | 15.8 | 18.5 | 21.1 | 23.8 | 26.4 | 29.0 |
| 14 | 3.1 | 6.2 | 9.3 | 12.4 | 15.4 | 18.5 | 21.6 | 24.7 | 27.8 | 30.9 | 34.0 |
| 15 | 3.6 | 7.1 | 10.7 | 14.3 | 17.9 | 21.4 | 25.0 | 28.6 | 32.2 | 35.7 | 39.3 |
| 16 | 4.0 | 8.1 | 12.1 | 16.1 | 20.2 | 24.2 | 28.2 | 32.3 | 36.3 | 40.4 | 44.4 |
| 17 | 4.5 | 9.0 | 13.6 | 18.1 | 22.6 | 27.1 | 31.7 | 36.2 | 40.7 | 45.2 | 49.8 |
| 18 | 5.1 | 10.2 | 15.3 | 20.4 | 25.5 | 30.6 | 35.8 | 40.9 | 46.0 | 51.1 | 56.2 |
| 19 | 5.7 | 11.5 | 17.2 | 22.9 | 28.6 | 34.4 | 40.1 | 45.8 | 51.5 | 57.3 | 63.0 |
| 20 | 6.3 | 12.6 | 18.9 | 25.2 | 31.5 | 37.8 | 44.1 | 50.4 | 56.7 | 63.1 | 69.4 |
| **TREES OF AVERAGE TOP FORM INDEX** | | | | | | | | | | | |
| 5 | 0.3 | 0.6 | 0.9 | 1.3 | 1.6 | 1.9 | 2.2 | 2.5 | 2.8 | 3.2 | 3.5 |
| 6 | 0.4 | 0.9 | 1.3 | 1.8 | 2.2 | 2.6 | 3.1 | 3.5 | 4.0 | 4.4 | 4.9 |
| 7 | 0.6 | 1.2 | 1.8 | 2.5 | 3.1 | 3.7 | 4.3 | 4.9 | 5.5 | 6.1 | 6.7 |
| 8 | 0.8 | 1.6 | 2.4 | 3.1 | 3.9 | 4.7 | 5.5 | 6.3 | 7.1 | 7.9 | 8.6 |
| 9 | 1.0 | 2.0 | 3.0 | 4.0 | 5.0 | 6.1 | 7.1 | 8.1 | 9.1 | 10.1 | 11.1 |
| 10 | 1.2 | 2.5 | 3.7 | 4.9 | 6.1 | 7.4 | 8.6 | 9.8 | 11.0 | 12.3 | 13.5 |
| 11 | 1.5 | 3.0 | 4.5 | 6.0 | 7.5 | 9.0 | 10.5 | 12.0 | 13.5 | 15.0 | 16.5 |
| 12 | 1.8 | 3.5 | 5.3 | 7.1 | 8.8 | 10.6 | 12.4 | 14.1 | 15.9 | 17.7 | 19.4 |
| 13 | 2.1 | 4.2 | 6.3 | 8.4 | 10.5 | 12.6 | 14.7 | 16.8 | 18.9 | 21.0 | 23.0 |
| 14 | 2.4 | 4.8 | 7.2 | 9.6 | 12.0 | 14.4 | 16.8 | 19.2 | 21.6 | 24.1 | 26.5 |
| 15 | 2.8 | 5.6 | 8.4 | 11.1 | 13.9 | 16.7 | 19.5 | 22.3 | 25.1 | 27.9 | 30.6 |
| 16 | 3.1 | 6.3 | 9.4 | 12.6 | 15.7 | 18.8 | 22.0 | 25.1 | 28.3 | 31.4 | 34.6 |
| 17 | 3.6 | 7.1 | 10.7 | 14.3 | 17.9 | 21.4 | 25.0 | 28.6 | 32.2 | 35.7 | 39.3 |
| 18 | 4.0 | 8.0 | 11.9 | 15.9 | 19.9 | 23.9 | 27.8 | 31.8 | 35.8 | 39.8 | 43.7 |
| 19 | 4.5 | 8.9 | 13.4 | 17.8 | 22.3 | 26.8 | 31.2 | 35.7 | 40.2 | 44.6 | 49.1 |
| 20 | 4.9 | 9.8 | 14.7 | 19.6 | 24.5 | 29.5 | 34.4 | 39.3 | 44.2 | 49.1 | 54.0 |
| **TREES OF LOW TOP FORM INDEX** | | | | | | | | | | | |
| 5 | 0.3 | 0.5 | 0.8 | 1.0 | 1.3 | 1.5 | 1.8 | 2.0 | 2.3 | 2.5 | 2.8 |
| 6 | 0.3 | 0.7 | 1.0 | 1.4 | 1.7 | 2.1 | 2.4 | 2.8 | 3.1 | 3.5 | 3.8 |
| 7 | 0.5 | 1.0 | 1.4 | 1.9 | 2.4 | 2.9 | 3.4 | 3.8 | 4.3 | 4.8 | 5.3 |
| 8 | 0.6 | 1.3 | 1.9 | 2.5 | 3.2 | 3.8 | 4.5 | 5.1 | 5.7 | 6.4 | 7.0 |
| 9 | 0.8 | 1.6 | 2.4 | 3.1 | 3.9 | 4.7 | 5.5 | 6.3 | 7.1 | 7.8 | 8.6 |
| 10 | 1.0 | 2.0 | 2.9 | 3.9 | 4.9 | 5.9 | 6.9 | 7.8 | 8.8 | 9.8 | 10.8 |
| 11 | 1.2 | 2.4 | 3.6 | 4.8 | 6.0 | 7.2 | 8.4 | 9.6 | 10.8 | 12.0 | 13.2 |
| 12 | 1.4 | 2.8 | 4.2 | 5.6 | 7.0 | 8.4 | 9.8 | 11.2 | 12.6 | 14.0 | 15.4 |
| 13 | 1.7 | 3.3 | 5.0 | 6.6 | 8.3 | 9.9 | 11.6 | 13.2 | 14.9 | 16.5 | 18.2 |
| 14 | 1.9 | 3.9 | 5.8 | 7.7 | 9.6 | 11.6 | 13.5 | 15.4 | 17.4 | 19.3 | 21.2 |
| 15 | 2.2 | 4.4 | 6.5 | 8.7 | 10.9 | 13.1 | 15.3 | 17.4 | 19.6 | 21.8 | 24.0 |
| 16 | 2.5 | 5.0 | 7.5 | 10.0 | 12.5 | 15.0 | 17.5 | 20.0 | 22.5 | 25.0 | 27.5 |
| 17 | 2.8 | 5.7 | 8.5 | 11.3 | 14.2 | 17.0 | 19.9 | 22.7 | 25.5 | 28.4 | 31.2 |
| 18 | 3.2 | 6.4 | 9.6 | 12.8 | 16.0 | 19.2 | 22.4 | 25.6 | 28.8 | 32.0 | 35.2 |
| 19 | 3.5 | 7.0 | 10.6 | 14.1 | 17.6 | 21.1 | 24.6 | 28.2 | 31.7 | 35.2 | 38.7 |
| 20 | 3.9 | 7.8 | 11.7 | 15.7 | 19.6 | 23.5 | 27.4 | 31.3 | 35.2 | 39.2 | 43.1 |

Source: Clement Mesavage, Tables for estimating cubic-foot volume of timber, Southern Forest Exp. Sta., *Occ. Paper No. 111*, 1947.

## REDCEDAR TREE VOLUME TALLY CUMULATIVE BY TREES
### CEDAR INDUSTRY (2/3) LOG RULE.

| DBH inches | LOGS 8 Ft | CUT · VOLUME — 10 BOARD FEET | TOTAL | POSTS IN TOPS NUMBER | LEAVE VOLUME — 10 BOARD FEET | TOTAL | POSTS IN TOPS NUMBER |
|---|---|---|---|---|---|---|---|
| 5 | 1 | 0.4 1 1 1 2 2 3 3 4 / 4 4 5 5 5 6 6 6 7 7 | | | 0 1 1 1 2 2 3 3 4 / 4 4 5 5 5 6 6 6 7 7 | | |
| 6 | 1 | 0.6 1 2 2 3 4 4 5 5 6 / 7 7 8 8 9 10 10 11 11 12 | | | 1 1 2 2 3 4 4 5 5 6 / 7 7 8 8 9 10 10 11 11 12 | | |
| 6 | 2 | 1.1 2 3 4 6 7 8 9 10 11 / 12 13 14 15 16 18 19 20 21 22 | | | 1 2 3 4 6 7 8 9 10 11 / 12 13 14 15 16 18 19 20 21 22 | | |
| 7 | 1 | 1.0 2 3 4 5 6 7 8 9 10 / 11 12 13 14 15 16 17 18 19 20 | | | 1 2 3 4 5 6 7 8 9 10 / 11 12 13 14 15 16 17 18 19 20 | | |
| 7 | 2 | 1.5 3 4 6 8 9 10 12 14 15 / 16 18 20 21 22 24 26 27 28 30 | | | 2 3 4 6 8 9 10 12 14 15 / 16 18 20 21 22 24 26 27 28 30 | | |
| 7 | 3 | 2.2 4 7 9 11 13 15 18 20 22 / 24 26 29 31 33 35 37 40 42 44 | | | 2 4 7 9 11 13 15 18 20 22 / 24 26 29 31 33 35 37 40 42 44 | | |
| 8 | 1 | 1.5 3 4 6 7 8 10 11 13 14 | | | 1 3 4 6 7 8 10 11 13 14 | | |
| 8 | 2 | 2.0 4 6 8 10 12 14 16 18 20 | | | 2 4 6 8 10 12 14 16 18 20 | | |
| 8 | 3 | 2.8 6 8 11 14 17 20 22 25 28 | | | 3 6 8 11 14 17 20 22 25 28 | | |
| 9 | 2 | 2.5 5 8 10 12 | | | 2 5 8 10 12 | | |
| 9 | 3 | 3.5 7 10 14 18 | | | 4 7 10 14 18 | | |
| 9 | 4 | 4.7 9 14 19 24 | | | 5 9 14 19 24 | | |
| 10 | 2 | 3.1 6 9 12 16 | | | 3 6 9 12 16 | | |
| 10 | 3 | 4.2 8 13 17 21 | | | 4 8 13 17 21 | | |
| 10 | 4 | 5.6 11 17 22 28 | | | 6 11 17 22 28 | | |
| 11 | 3 | 5.0 10 15 20 25 | | | 5 10 15 20 25 | | |
| 11 | 4 | 6.5 13 20 26 32 | | | 6 13 20 26 32 | | |
| 12 | 3 | 5.8 12 17 23 29 | | | 6 12 17 23 29 | | |
| 12 | 4 | 7.5 15 22 30 38 | | | 8 15 22 30 38 | | |
| 12 | 5 | 9.6 19 29 38 48 | | | 10 19 29 38 48 | | |
| 13 | 3 | 6.7 13 20 27 34 | | | 7 13 20 27 34 | | |
| 13 | 4 | 8.5 17 26 34 42 | | | 8 17 26 34 42 | | |
| 13 | 5 | 10.8 22 32 43 54 | | | 11 22 32 43 54 | | |
| 14 | 3 | 7.7 15 23 31 38 | | | 8 15 23 31 38 | | |
| 14 | 4 | 9.6 19 29 38 48 | | | 10 19 29 38 48 | | |
| 14 | 5 | 12.2 24 37 49 61 | | | 12 24 37 49 61 | | |
| 15 | 3 | 8.8 18 26 35 44 | | | 9 18 26 35 44 | | |
| 15 | 4 | 10.7 21 32 43 54 | | | 11 21 32 43 54 | | |
| 15 | 5 | 13.6 27 41 54 68 | | | 14 27 41 54 68 | | |
| 16 | 3 | 9.9 20 30 40 50 | | | 10 20 30 40 50 | | |
| 16 | 4 | 11.9 24 36 48 60 | | | 12 24 36 48 60 | | |
| 16 | 5 | 15.1 30 45 60 76 | | | 15 30 45 60 76 | | |
| 17 | 3 | 11.0 22 33 44 55 | | | 11 22 33 44 55 | | |
| 17 | 4 | 13.1 26 39 52 66 | | | 13 26 39 52 66 | | |
| 17 | 5 | 16.6 33 50 66 83 | | | 17 33 50 66 83 | | |
| 18 | 4 | 14.4 29 43 58 72 | | | 14 29 43 58 72 | | |
| 18 | 5 | 18.1 36 54 72 90 | | | 18 36 54 72 90 | | |

Location: _____

Area: _____ A.

Plot: _____

Tallied by: _____

Date: _____

| DBH | TREES WITH POSTS, NO LOGS 0 | 1 | 2 | 3 | 4 | TOTAL TREES | POSTS | TREES WITH POSTS, NO LOGS 0 | 1 | 2 | 3 | 4 | TOTAL TREES | POSTS |
|---|---|---|---|---|---|---|---|---|---|---|---|---|---|---|
| 3 | | | | | | | | | | | | | | |
| 4 | | | | | | | | | | | | | | |
| 5 | | | | | | | | | | | | | | |
| 6 | | | | | | | | | | | | | | |
| ALL | | | | | | | | | | | | | | |

AHZ & SP/RD

TVA DIVISION OF FORESTRY RELATIONS    DECEMBER 1951

### Fig. 1. Redcedar cumulative volume tally.
(A. H. Zimmerman and W. H. Cummings, Redcedar cumulative volume tally, Jour. Forestry (1952) 50 (11), 867.)

## LOBLOLLY, LONGLEAF, AND SLASH PINES

### Table 11. Volume in Merchantable Cords (Standard)*

Coastal Plain, Georgia, and South Carolina

(With bark)

| Diameter (in.) | Number of 5.25-ft. bolts | | | | | | | | | | |
|---|---|---|---|---|---|---|---|---|---|---|---|
| | 2 | 3 | 4 | 5 | 6 | 7 | 8 | 9 | 10 | 11 | 12 |
| 4 | .0091 | .0144 | .0274 | .0337 | .0400 | | | | | | |
| 5 | .0148 | .0211 | .0361 | .0436 | .0511 | .0586 | | | | | |
| 6 | .0211 | .0286 | .0459 | .0549 | .0639 | .0729 | .0819 | .0909 | | | |
| 7 | | .0369 | .0569 | .0676 | .0783 | .0891 | .0998 | .1105 | .1213 | .1320 | .1427 |
| 8 | | .0461 | .0689 | .0816 | .0944 | .1071 | .1199 | .1326 | .1453 | .1581 | .1708 |
| 9 | | | .0821 | .0971 | .1121 | .1271 | .1421 | .1571 | .1721 | .1871 | .2021 |
| 10 | | | .0963 | .1139 | .1314 | .1489 | .1664 | .1839 | .2015 | .2190 | .2365 |
| 11 | | | .1117 | .1320 | .1523 | .1726 | .1929 | .2132 | .2335 | .2538 | .2741 |
| 12 | | | .1282 | .1516 | .1749 | .1982 | .2216 | .2449 | .2683 | .2916 | .3149 |
| 13 | | | .1458 | .1725 | .1991 | .2257 | .2524 | .2790 | .3057 | .3323 | .3590 |
| 14 | | | | | | .2552 | .2854 | .3156 | .3458 | .3760 | .4062 |
| 15 | | | | | | .2864 | .3205 | .3545 | .3885 | .4225 | .4566 |
| 16 | | | | | | | | | | | |

\* Prepared from measurements on 6,800 trees in 29 localities on the coastal plain of South Carolina and Georgia. Longleaf pine, whole merchantable stems, salvage of tops of saw-log trees, round and turpentined. Slash pine, whole merchantable stems, round and turpentined. Loblolly pine, salvage of tops of saw-log trees. Min. top diam. 4 in. d.i.b.

Source: F. X. Schumacher and A. E. Wackerman, Duke University (mimeo.), 1944.

**Purdue Rule-of-Thumb for Indiana Hardwoods.** "The average log in a hardwood tree has a scaling diameter equal to ¾ of the d.b.h." (Dept. of Agr. Ext., Purdue Univ.)

## BLACK LOCUST

### Table 12. Volume Table, 1938

| D.b.h. (in.) | 7-ft. posts | | |
| --- | --- | --- | --- |
| | Site I Number of posts | Site II Number of posts | Site III Number of posts |
| 6 | 2 | 2 | 1 |
| 8 | 5 | 4 | 3 |
| 10 | 8 | 7 | 4 |
| 12 | 11 | 10 | 7 |
| 14 | 14 | 12 | 8 |
| 16 | 17 | 14 | 9 |
| 18 | 20 | 16 | 10 |
| 20 | 22 | 18 | 11 |
| 22 | 24 | 21 | 12 |
| 24 | 27 | 23 | 13 |
| 26 | 31 | 26 | 15 |

Source: J. R. Hicks, U. S. Forest Service, George Washington National Forest.

## VIRGINIA PINE

### Table 13. Merchantable Volume in Cords, with Bark *

Monongahela National Forest, West Virginia

| D.b.h. (in.) | Total height in feet | | | | | |
| --- | --- | --- | --- | --- | --- | --- |
| | 20 | 30 | 40 | 50 | 60 | 70 |
| 6 | 0.027 | 0.033 | 0.039 | 0.045 | | |
| 8 | .037 | .047 | .058 | .070 | | |
| 10 | .047 | .066 | .085 | .103 | | |
| 12 | | .088 | .125 | .166 | | |
| 14 | | .115 | .180 | .260 | 0.35 | 0.44 |
| 16 | | .147 | .245 | .360 | .48 | .62 |
| 18 | | .184 | .320 | .480 | .67 | .85 |
| 20 | | | .410 | .610 | .85 | 1.08 |

* Stump height, 12 in. on uphill side. Minimum top diameter at limit of merchantability, 4 in. inside bark. Average deviation, volume of individual tree, 14.4 percent. Reduce volumes 15 percent for peeled wood.

Source: Roberts, Monongahela National Forest, 1937.

## BALSAM FIR

### Table 14. Number of Trees per Cord (Solid Content)
Maine and New York

| D.b.h. (in.) | Height of tree in feet | | | | | | |
|---|---|---|---|---|---|---|---|
| | 20 | 30 | 40 | 50 | 60 | 70 | 80 |
| 3 | 200.0 | 125.0 | | | | | |
| 4 | 111.1 | 62.5 | 45.5 | | | | |
| 5 | 62.5 | 41.7 | 30.3 | 23.8 | | | |
| 6 | | 29.4 | 22.2 | 17.5 | 14.7 | | |
| 7 | | 22.2 | 16.7 | 13.3 | 11.2 | 9.5 | |
| 8 | | | 12.8 | 10.4 | 8.8 | 7.3 | 6.0 |
| 9 | | | 10.1 | 8.4 | 7.0 | 5.8 | 4.9 |
| 10 | | | 8.3 | 6.4 | 5.8 | 4.9 | 4.2 |
| 11 | | | 6.8 | 5.6 | 4.9 | 4.1 | 3.6 |
| 12 | | | | 4.7 | 4.1 | 3.6 | 3.1 |
| 13 | | | | | 3.5 | 3.1 | 2.7 |
| 14 | | | | | | 2.7 | 2.4 |
| 15 | | | | | | 2.4 | 2.2 |

Source: Raphael Zon, U. S. Forest Service, *Bull. No. 55*, 1914.

## WESTERN HARDWOODS. See Table 15.

### RED ALDER

### Table 15. Volume in Board Feet, Scribner Log Rule *
British Columbia, Oregon, and Washington

| Tree diameter (in.) | Number of 8-ft. logs to merchantable top (8 in. minimum) | | | | | | | | | |
|---|---|---|---|---|---|---|---|---|---|---|
| | 1 | 2 | 3 | 4 | 5 | 6 | 7 | 8 | 9 | 10 |
| 10 | 18 | 35 | 53 | 71 | 89 | 107 | ... | ... | ... | ... |
| 11 | 21 | 42 | 63 | 85 | 106 | 127 | ... | ... | ... | ... |
| 12 | 24 | 49 | 74 | 99 | 125 | 150 | 175 | 200 | ... | ... |
| 13 | 28 | 57 | 86 | 115 | 144 | 173 | 203 | 232 | ... | ... |
| 14 | 33 | 66 | 99 | 132 | 165 | 199 | 232 | 266 | ... | ... |
| 15 | 37 | 75 | 112 | 150 | 188 | 226 | 264 | 302 | ... | ... |
| 16 | 42 | 84 | 126 | 169 | 212 | 255 | 297 | 340 | 383 | ... |
| 17 | 47 | 94 | 141 | 189 | 237 | 285 | 333 | 380 | 428 | ... |
| 18 | 52 | 104 | 157 | 210 | 263 | 316 | 370 | 423 | 476 | 530 |
| 19 | ... | 115 | 174 | 232 | 291 | 350 | 408 | 467 | 526 | 585 |
| 20 | ... | 127 | 191 | 257 | 320 | 384 | 449 | 514 | 578 | 643 |
| 21 | ... | 139 | 209 | 279 | 350 | 421 | 491 | 562 | 633 | 704 |
| 22 | ... | 151 | 228 | 304 | 381 | 458 | 535 | 613 | 690 | 767 |
| 23 | ... | 164 | 247 | 330 | 414 | 497 | 581 | 665 | 749 | 833 |
| 24 | ... | 178 | 267 | 358 | 448 | 538 | 629 | 719 | 810 | 901 |
| 25 | ... | ... | 288 | 385 | 483 | 594 | 678 | 775 | 873 | 971 |
| 26 | ... | ... | 310 | 414 | 519 | 624 | 729 | 834 | 939 | 1,040 |
| 27 | ... | ... | 332 | 444 | 557 | 669 | 782 | 894 | 1,007 | 1,120 |
| 28 | ... | ... | 355 | 475 | 595 | 716 | 836 | 956 | 1,077 | 1,198 |

* Basis: 415 trees, various sites and form classes. Standard error of an individual tree volume, 10.3 percent.
Source: Floyd A. Johnson, R. M. Kallander (Oregon State Board of Forestry), Paul G. Lauterbach (Weyerhaeuser Timber Co.), Volume tables for red alder. Pacific Northwest Forest and Range Exp. Sta., *Res. Note No. 55*, 1949.

# WESTERN SOFTWOODS. See Tables 16 to 48.

## DOUGLAS-FIR (OLD GROWTH)

### Table 16. Board-Foot Volume for Merchantable Heights by 16.3-Ft. Logs to an 8-In. Top,* Scribner Decimal C Rule

Site Qualities I, II, and III, or the coast form of the Pacific Northwest

Height in 16.3-ft. logs to 8-in. top inside bark

Board feet in tens

| D.b.h. (in.) | 2 | 3 | 4 | 5 | 6 | 7 | 8 | 9 | 10 | 11 | 12 | 13 | 14 | 15 | 16 | 17 | 18 |
|---|---|---|---|---|---|---|---|---|---|---|---|---|---|---|---|---|---|
| 16 | 11 | 19 | 26 | 33 | 40 | 47 | 53 | 59 | | | | | | | | | |
| 18 | 13 | 22 | 30 | 39 | 48 | 56 | 63 | 71 | | | | | | | | | |
| 20 | 15 | 25 | 35 | 46 | 56 | 65 | 74 | 83 | 92 | 102 | | | | | | | |
| 22 | 17 | 29 | 41 | 53 | 65 | 76 | 87 | 99 | 109 | 122 | | | | | | | |
| 24 | 19 | 33 | 47 | 61 | 74 | 87 | 101 | 115 | 128 | 143 | | | | | | | |
| 26 | 21 | 37 | 53 | 69 | 84 | 101 | 116 | 132 | 147 | 165 | | | | | | | |
| 28 | 23 | 41 | 59 | 77 | 96 | 115 | 132 | 150 | 168 | 188 | | | | | | | |
| 30 | 25 | 46 | 66 | 87 | 108 | 130 | 149 | 170 | 190 | 214 | 235 | 255 | | | | | |
| 32 | | 51 | 73 | 97 | 120 | 145 | 166 | 190 | 215 | 242 | 265 | 290 | | | | | |
| 34 | | 56 | 80 | 107 | 134 | 160 | 185 | 214 | 241 | 270 | 300 | 325 | | | | | |
| 36 | | 62 | 88 | 117 | 148 | 175 | 205 | 238 | 267 | 300 | 335 | 362 | 395 | 430 | 460 | 495 | 525 |
| 38 | | 67 | 96 | 129 | 163 | 193 | 227 | 262 | 295 | 333 | 365 | 400 | 435 | 470 | 505 | 540 | 580 |
| 40 | | 72 | 105 | 141 | 178 | 213 | 249 | 290 | 326 | 366 | 400 | 440 | 475 | 515 | 555 | 595 | 635 |
| 42 | | | 114 | 153 | 193 | 233 | 273 | 318 | 357 | 399 | 440 | 480 | 520 | 560 | 605 | 650 | 690 |
| 44 | | | 123 | 165 | 210 | 253 | 299 | 344 | 389 | 435 | 480 | 520 | 570 | 615 | 655 | 705 | 750 |
| 46 | | | 133 | 180 | 228 | 275 | 326 | 375 | 422 | 472 | 520 | 565 | 620 | 665 | 710 | 765 | 815 |
| 48 | | | 143 | 195 | 247 | 300 | 353 | 405 | 456 | 510 | 560 | 610 | 665 | 715 | 765 | 825 | 875 |
| 50 | | | 153 | 210 | 267 | 325 | 380 | 435 | 490 | 550 | 600 | 655 | 710 | 770 | 825 | 885 | 945 |
| 52 | | | 163 | 225 | 288 | 350 | 410 | 470 | 525 | 590 | 645 | 700 | 765 | 830 | 880 | 950 | 1,015 |
| 54 | | | 175 | 240 | 310 | 375 | 440 | 505 | 560 | 630 | 690 | 755 | 820 | 890 | 945 | 1,025 | 1,095 |
| 56 | | | 187 | 258 | 333 | 400 | 470 | 540 | 595 | 675 | 740 | 810 | 875 | 950 | 1,010 | 1,100 | 1,175 |
| 58 | | | 200 | 276 | 356 | 428 | 500 | 575 | 635 | 720 | 790 | 865 | 935 | 1,010 | 1,085 | 1,170 | 1,255 |
| 60 | | | 216 | 297 | 379 | 457 | 530 | 610 | 680 | 765 | 840 | 920 | 995 | 1,085 | 1,160 | 1,245 | 1,335 |
| 62 | | | | | 402 | 486 | 565 | 645 | 725 | 810 | 895 | 975 | 1,065 | 1,150 | 1,230 | 1,320 | 1,415 |
| 64 | | | | | 428 | 515 | 600 | 685 | 770 | 855 | 950 | 1,030 | 1,130 | 1,220 | 1,310 | 1,400 | 1,500 |
| 66 | | | | | 454 | 545 | 635 | 725 | 815 | 910 | 1,005 | 1,095 | 1,195 | 1,290 | 1,390 | 1,480 | 1,585 |
| 68 | | | | | 480 | 578 | 670 | 770 | 860 | 965 | 1,060 | 1,160 | 1,260 | 1,360 | 1,470 | 1,570 | 1,665 |
| 70 | | | | | 506 | 612 | 705 | 815 | 910 | 1,020 | 1,120 | 1,225 | 1,335 | 1,440 | 1,545 | 1,650 | 1,750 |
| 72 | | | | | 532 | 646 | 745 | 860 | 960 | 1,080 | 1,180 | 1,290 | 1,410 | 1,515 | 1,625 | 1,730 | 1,840 |
| 74 | | | | | 560 | 680 | 785 | 905 | 1,010 | 1,140 | 1,250 | 1,360 | 1,485 | 1,595 | 1,700 | 1,815 | 1,930 |
| 76 | | | | | 588 | 715 | 830 | 950 | 1,065 | 1,200 | 1,320 | 1,430 | 1,560 | 1,675 | 1,780 | 1,900 | 2,015 |
| 78 | | | | | 619 | 750 | 875 | 995 | 1,120 | 1,260 | 1,390 | 1,500 | 1,635 | 1,750 | 1,860 | 1,985 | 2,100 |
| 80 | | | | | 650 | 785 | 920 | 1,050 | 1,180 | 1,320 | 1,450 | 1,570 | 1,705 | 1,825 | 1,940 | 2,065 | 2,175 |
| 82 | | | | | | 815 | 965 | 1,105 | 1,240 | 1,380 | 1,510 | 1,630 | 1,775 | 1,900 | 2,020 | 2,145 | 2,250 |
| 84 | | | | | | 850 | 1,010 | 1,160 | 1,300 | 1,440 | 1,580 | 1,710 | 1,850 | 1,980 | 2,100 | 2,225 | 2,330 |
| 86 | | | | | | 890 | 1,055 | 1,215 | 1,360 | 1,500 | 1,650 | 1,790 | 1,925 | 2,060 | 2,180 | 2,300 | 2,420 |
| 88 | | | | | | 930 | 1,100 | 1,270 | 1,420 | 1,570 | 1,720 | 1,870 | 2,000 | 2,140 | 2,260 | 2,380 | 2,510 |
| 90 | | | | | | 970 | 1,150 | 1,325 | 1,480 | 1,640 | 1,790 | 1,930 | 2,075 | 2,210 | 2,320 | 2,460 | 2,600 |
| 92 | | | | | | | 1,200 | 1,380 | 1,540 | 1,710 | 1,860 | 1,990 | 2,145 | 2,280 | 2,400 | 2,550 | 2,700 |
| 94 | | | | | | | 1,250 | 1,440 | 1,600 | 1,780 | 1,930 | 2,070 | 2,215 | 2,350 | 2,490 | 2,640 | 2,800 |
| 96 | | | | | | | 1,300 | 1,500 | 1,660 | 1,850 | 2,000 | 2,140 | 2,285 | 2,420 | 2,580 | 2,740 | 2,890 |
| 98 | | | | | | | 1,355 | 1,560 | 1,720 | 1,920 | 2,070 | 2,210 | 2,355 | 2,510 | 2,670 | 2,830 | 2,980 |
| 100 | | | | | | | 1,410 | 1,620 | 1,780 | 1,980 | 2,125 | 2,280 | 2,430 | 2,600 | 2,750 | 2,920 | 3,070 |
| 102 | | | | | | | 1,470 | 1,660 | 1,840 | 2,040 | 2,180 | 2,340 | 2,500 | 2,690 | 2,830 | 3,010 | 3,170 |
| 104 | | | | | | | 1,500 | 1,710 | 1,900 | 2,100 | 2,240 | 2,410 | 2,590 | 2,770 | 2,920 | 3,100 | 3,270 |
| 106 | | | | | | | 1,570 | 1,780 | 1,960 | 2,160 | 2,300 | 2,480 | 2,680 | 2,840 | 3,010 | 3,190 | 3,360 |
| 108 | | | | | | | | 1,830 | 2,020 | 2,220 | 2,360 | 2,560 | 2,760 | 2,920 | 3,100 | 3,280 | 3,450 |
| 110 | | | | | | | | 1,900 | 2,080 | 2,280 | 2,420 | 2,640 | 2,840 | 3,000 | 3,190 | 3,370 | 3,540 |
| 112 | | | | | | | | | 2,130 | 2,330 | 2,480 | 2,710 | 2,920 | 3,070 | 3,280 | 3,450 | 3,630 |
| 114 | | | | | | | | | 2,180 | 2,390 | 2,530 | 2,780 | 3,000 | 3,150 | 3,370 | 3,540 | 3,720 |
| 116 | | | | | | | | | 2,240 | 2,450 | 2,590 | 2,850 | 3,080 | 3,220 | 3,460 | 3,630 | 3,810 |
| 118 | | | | | | | | | 2,300 | 2,500 | 2,650 | 2,930 | 3,160 | 3,300 | 3,550 | 3,720 | 3,910 |
| 120 | | | | | | | | | 2,360 | 2,560 | 2,710 | 3,000 | 3,240 | 3,370 | 3,650 | 3,820 | 4,000 |

* Prepared by alinement chart method. Stump height 2 ft. No allowance for defect. Basis, 2,643 trees. Actual volume, 0.25 percent above estimated volume. (W. H. Meyer, 1932.)

WESTERN SOFTWOODS. See Tables 16 to 19.

DOUGLAS-FIR (COAST TYPE)

## DOUGLAS-FIR
### Table 17. Cubic-foot Volume*
Mendocino and Trinity Counties, California

Total height in feet — Volume in cubic feet

| Diameter, breast height, inches | 30 | 40 | 50 | 60 | 70 | 80 | 90 | 100 | 110 | 120 | 130 | 140 | 150 | 160 | 170 | 180 | 190 | 200 |
|---|---|---|---|---|---|---|---|---|---|---|---|---|---|---|---|---|---|---|
| 3 | 0.55 | 0.80 | 1.04 | 1.29 | 1.55 | 1.80 | | | | | | | | | | | | |
| 4 | 0.97 | 1.38 | 1.79 | 2.23 | 2.68 | 3.10 | | | | | | | | | | | | |
| 5 | 1.49 | 2.08 | 2.70 | 3.39 | 4.02 | 4.70 | | | | | | | | | | | | |
| 6 | 2.07 | 2.90 | 3.82 | 4.75 | 5.63 | 6.28 | 7.18 | 8.09 | 8.98 | 9.75 | 10.05 | 11.1 | 12.22 | 13.0 | 13.9 | 14.7 | 15.5 | 16.3 |
| 7 | 2.76 | 3.90 | 5.03 | 6.32 | 7.58 | 8.72 | 9.80 | 11.0 | 12.0 | 13.0 | 14.0 | 15.3 | 16.3 | 17.5 | 18.6 | 19.7 | 20.8 | 22.0 |
| 8 | 3.57 | 5.02 | 6.53 | 8.18 | 9.80 | 11.30 | 12.6 | 14.0 | 15.5 | 16.8 | 18.1 | 19.7 | 21.0 | 22.4 | 23.8 | 25.2 | 26.7 | 28.2 |
| 9 | 4.43 | 6.24 | 8.08 | 10.0 | 12.1 | 14.1 | 15.9 | 17.8 | 19.2 | 21.0 | 22.7 | 24.8 | 26.1 | 27.9 | 29.9 | 31.3 | 33.2 | 35.0 |
| 10 | 5.33 | 7.58 | 9.92 | 12.4 | 14.9 | 17.0 | 19.2 | 21.5 | 23.4 | 25.5 | 27.6 | 29.8 | 32.0 | 34.0 | 36.1 | 38.3 | 40.3 | 42.7 |
| 11 | 6.35 | 9.00 | 12.0 | 14.9 | 17.7 | 20.5 | 23.1 | 25.8 | 28.0 | 30.3 | 33.0 | 35.8 | 37.9 | 40.3 | 43.4 | 45.7 | 48.5 | 51.6 |
| 12 | 7.48 | 10.7 | 14.0 | 17.4 | 20.8 | 24.0 | 27.0 | 30.0 | 32.9 | 35.9 | 39.0 | 42.0 | 45.0 | 47.8 | 50.7 | 54.0 | 56.9 | 60.4 |
| 13 | 8.56 | 12.4 | 16.2 | 20.0 | 24.0 | 27.8 | 31.6 | 35.0 | 38.3 | 41.6 | 45.4 | 49.0 | 52.2 | 55.5 | 59.3 | 62.4 | 66.0 | 70.0 |
| 14 | 9.87 | 14.1 | 18.6 | 23.0 | 27.5 | 31.9 | 36.4 | 40.3 | 44.0 | 47.8 | 52.3 | 56.2 | 60.0 | 64.2 | 68.0 | 71.6 | 76.1 | 80.4 |
| 15 | 11.2 | 16.0 | 21.0 | 26.2 | 30.9 | 36.10 | 40.8 | 45.6 | 50.0 | 54.4 | 59.0 | 63.7 | 68.0 | 72.4 | 76.7 | 81.5 | 86.0 | 90.8 |
| 16 | 12.7 | 17.9 | 23.6 | 29.5 | 35.0 | 40.8 | 46.4 | 51.5 | 56.4 | 61.5 | 66.7 | 71.8 | 77.0 | 80.9 | 86.8 | 91.0 | 96.8 | 102 |
| 17 | | 20.0 | 26.3 | 32.8 | 39.1 | 45.4 | 51.6 | 57.0 | 63.0 | 68.7 | 74.5 | 80.0 | 86.0 | 91.2 | 96.5 | 102 | 108 | 115 |
| 18 | | 22.0 | 29.1 | 36.3 | 43.2 | 50.5 | 57.4 | 63.5 | 69.7 | 75.8 | 82.6 | 88.3 | 95.2 | 101 | 108 | 113 | 120 | 128 |
| 19 | | 24.2 | 32.0 | 40.1 | 48.0 | 56.0 | 63.2 | 69.5 | 76.8 | 83.9 | 90.8 | 98.1 | 105 | 112 | 119 | 125 | 132 | 140 |
| 20 | | 26.7 | 35.2 | 44.3 | 52.6 | 61.0 | 68.7 | 76.3 | 84.0 | 91.4 | 99.0 | 108 | 115 | 122 | 130 | 138 | 145 | 153 |
| 21 | | 29.1 | 38.2 | 48.2 | 57.3 | 66.7 | 75.6 | 83.1 | 92.0 | 100 | 109 | 118 | 126 | 134 | 142 | 150 | 159 | 168 |
| 22 | | 31.3 | 41.4 | 52.3 | 62.2 | 72.8 | 81.8 | 90.0 | 100 | 109 | 118 | 127 | 137 | 146 | 154 | 162 | 171 | 180 |
| 23 | | 33.4 | 45.0 | 56.4 | 67.0 | 78.7 | 88.0 | 97.0 | 108 | 119 | 129 | 139 | 149 | 158 | 167 | 176 | 186 | 197 |
| 24 | | 36.1 | 48.5 | 61.8 | 72.2 | 84.0 | 95.0 | 104 | 117 | 128 | 138 | 149 | 160 | 170 | 180 | 190 | 200 | 211 |

* Prepared by [illegible] method. Should sample 2% [illegible] no allowable deductions. Basis, 2411 trees. Total volume: 0.3 percent minus [illegible] volume [illegible].

## Table 17. Cubic-foot Volume (Continued)

| Diameter, breast height, inches | Total height in feet | | | | | | | | | | | | | | | | | |
|---|---|---|---|---|---|---|---|---|---|---|---|---|---|---|---|---|---|---|
| | 30 | 40 | 50 | 60 | 70 | 80 | 90 | 100 | 110 | 120 | 130 | 140 | 150 | 160 | 170 | 180 | 190 | 200 |
| | | | | | | Volume in cubic feet | | | | | | | | | | | |
| 25 | | | 52.0 | 65.5 | 78.0 | 90.0 | 101 | 112 | 123 | 135 | 148 | 159 | 170 | 180 | 191 | 202 | 214 | 226 |
| 26 | | | 55.3 | 70.0 | 83.8 | 97.5 | 109 | 120 | 133 | 145 | 158 | 170 | 181 | 195 | 206 | 219 | 230 | 242 |
| 27 | | | 59.1 | 74.5 | 89.9 | 103 | 114 | 129 | 141 | 155 | 169 | 180 | 196 | 207 | 220 | 231 | 244 | 260 |
| 28 | | | 62.7 | 79.5 | 95.0 | 111 | 122 | 138 | 150 | 165 | 179 | 191 | 208 | 220 | 233 | 247 | 260 | 276 |
| 29 | | | 66.8 | 84.0 | 100 | 118 | 130 | 145 | 160 | 174 | 189 | 202 | 219 | 232 | 249 | 262 | 275 | 292 |
| 30 | | | 70.6 | 89.0 | 108 | 122 | 139 | 153 | 170 | 185 | 200 | 216 | 231 | 247 | 262 | 278 | 291 | 309 |
| 31 | | | 75.0 | 94.0 | 113 | 130 | 146 | 162 | 180 | 196 | 211 | 229 | 247 | 260 | 278 | 299 | 309 | 323 |
| 32 | | | 78.7 | 98.8 | 119 | 138 | 154 | 170 | 190 | 208 | 222 | 241 | 260 | 275 | 293 | 310 | 326 | 345 |
| 33 | | | 81.6 | 104 | 125 | 146 | 161 | 180 | 200 | 218 | 235 | 251 | 271 | 290 | 306 | 327 | 342 | 361 |
| 34 | | | 86.7 | 109 | 131 | 157 | 170 | 190 | 210 | 230 | 246 | 267 | 288 | 303 | 325 | 343 | 360 | 380 |
| 35 | | | 90.8 | 114 | 138 | 160 | 179 | 200 | 220 | 240 | 260 | 280 | 300 | 320 | 340 | 360 | 380 | 400 |
| 36 | | | 95.1 | 120 | 145 | 168 | 189 | 210 | 230 | 250 | 270 | 291 | 316 | 333 | 354 | 377 | 398 | 420 |
| 37 | | | 99.5 | 124 | 151 | 176 | 197 | 220 | 240 | 261 | 283 | 305 | 328 | 349 | 370 | 393 | 413 | 437 |
| 38 | | | 103 | 130 | 159 | 182 | 205 | 230 | 250 | 273 | 298 | 320 | 345 | 365 | 390 | 412 | 432 | 451 |
| 39 | | | 109 | 136 | 164 | 191 | 213 | 239 | 261 | 287 | 309 | 333 | 359 | 380 | 405 | 430 | 452 | 478 |
| 40 | | | 112 | 141 | 171 | 200 | 221 | 249 | 272 | 300 | 321 | 349 | 375 | 397 | 424 | 450 | 472 | 498 |
| 41 | | | 118 | 149 | 179 | 208 | 232 | 260 | 285 | 311 | 335 | 361 | 390 | 413 | 440 | 469 | 494 | 517 |
| 42 | | | 121 | 153 | 187 | 214 | 242 | 271 | 298 | 324 | 349 | 375 | 406 | 430 | 460 | 485 | 510 | 540 |
| 43 | | | 126 | 160 | 194 | 223 | 252 | 282 | 309 | 338 | 361 | 390 | 423 | 448 | 475 | 502 | 530 | 558 |
| 44 | | | 132 | 168 | 200 | 232 | 261 | 290 | 319 | 348 | 377 | 405 | 433 | 464 | 495 | 522 | 550 | 580 |

* Volume is total cubic volume of stem, including stump and top, but excluding bark. Basis: 267 trees, 30 to 110 yr. old on stump.
Source: Francis X. Schumacher, Yield, stand and volume tables for Douglas-fir in California, *Calif. Agr. Exp. Sta. Bull. No. 491*, 1930.

## DOUGLAS-FIR (OLD GROWTH)

**Table 18. Board-Foot Volume for Log Heights, by 32.6-Ft. Logs to a Variable Actual Top Diameter,\* Scribner Decimal C Rule**

Site Qualities I, II, and III or the coast form of the Pacific Northwest

| D.b.h. (in.) | Height in 32.6-ft. logs to variable top | | | | | | | | | | | | Av. top d.i.b. (in.) |
|---|---|---|---|---|---|---|---|---|---|---|---|---|---|
| | 1½ | 2 | 2½ | 3 | 3½ | 4 | 4½ | 5 | 5½ | 6 | 6½ | 7 | |
| | | | | | Board feet in tens | | | | | | | | |
| 16 | 15 | 21 | 28 | 36 | 45 | 53 | 63 | | | | | | 8 |
| 18 | 17 | 24 | 34 | 44 | 55 | 65 | 77 | | | | | | 8.5 |
| 20 | 19 | 28 | 40 | 52 | 65 | 78 | 93 | 107 | 123 | | | | 9 |
| 22 | 21 | 32 | 46 | 61 | 78 | 93 | 110 | 126 | 143 | | | | 10 |
| 24 | 24 | 37 | 53 | 71 | 91 | 110 | 127 | 145 | 165 | | | | 10.5 |
| 26 | 28 | 43 | 62 | 83 | 106 | 127 | 146 | 168 | 190 | | | | 11 |
| 28 | 32 | 50 | 74 | 98 | 123 | 144 | 169 | 194 | 220 | | | | 11.5 |
| 30 | 36 | 57 | 86 | 113 | 140 | 165 | 193 | 222 | 250 | 291 | 330 | | 12 |
| 32 | 41 | 66 | 98 | 127 | 157 | 186 | 218 | 252 | 280 | 328 | 370 | | 13 |
| 34 | 46 | 75 | 110 | 140 | 174 | 207 | 243 | 280 | 313 | 365 | 410 | | 13.5 |
| 36 | 52 | 84 | 122 | 152 | 192 | 228 | 268 | 310 | 346 | 402 | 450 | 495 | 14 |
| 38 | | 93 | 134 | 169 | 210 | 251 | 294 | 340 | 381 | 440 | 495 | 545 | 15 |
| 40 | | 103 | 146 | 186 | 231 | 275 | 320 | 372 | 418 | 480 | 540 | 600 | 15.5 |
| 42 | | 113 | 159 | 203 | 254 | 300 | 353 | 405 | 470 | 525 | 590 | 655 | 16 |
| 44 | | 126 | 177 | 226 | 280 | 330 | 390 | 450 | 520 | 585 | 650 | 725 | 17 |
| 46 | | 139 | 196 | 252 | 310 | 370 | 430 | 500 | 575 | 645 | 725 | 800 | 17.5 |
| 48 | | 153 | 216 | 278 | 345 | 410 | 475 | 550 | 630 | 705 | 800 | 875 | 18.5 |
| 50 | | 168 | 238 | 305 | 377 | 450 | 525 | 605 | 690 | 770 | 875 | 970 | 19.5 |
| 52 | | | 262 | 336 | 414 | 490 | 575 | 660 | 750 | 850 | 970 | 1,070 | 20.5 |
| 54 | | | 288 | 367 | 453 | 540 | 625 | 720 | 820 | 930 | 1,065 | 1,170 | 22 |
| 56 | | | 315 | 400 | 496 | 590 | 680 | 780 | 900 | 1,015 | 1,160 | 1,270 | 24 |
| 58 | | | 342 | 435 | 539 | 640 | 740 | 850 | 980 | 1,100 | 1,255 | 1,370 | 25.5 |
| 60 | | | 369 | 470 | 588 | 690 | 800 | 920 | 1,060 | 1,185 | 1,350 | 1,475 | 27 |
| 62 | | | 394 | 505 | 630 | 740 | 860 | 990 | 1,140 | 1,270 | 1,445 | 1,580 | 28 |
| 64 | | | 420 | 540 | 670 | 790 | 920 | 1,060 | 1,220 | 1,360 | 1,540 | 1,685 | 29.5 |
| 66 | | | 446 | 575 | 710 | 840 | 985 | 1,130 | 1,300 | 1,450 | 1,635 | 1,795 | 30.5 |
| 68 | | | 478 | 615 | 760 | 900 | 1,050 | 1,200 | 1,380 | 1,550 | 1,730 | 1,905 | 31.5 |
| 70 | | | 510 | 650 | 810 | 960 | 1,125 | 1,270 | 1,460 | 1,655 | 1,840 | 2,030 | 32.5 |
| 72 | | | 540 | 690 | 860 | 1,030 | 1,200 | 1,350 | 1,550 | 1,760 | 1,960 | 2,165 | 33.5 |
| 74 | | | 570 | 730 | 920 | 1,090 | 1,270 | 1,440 | 1,650 | 1,870 | 2,090 | 2,300 | 34 |
| 76 | | | 610 | 780 | 980 | 1,160 | 1,340 | 1,530 | 1,750 | 1,980 | 2,220 | 2,440 | 35 |
| 78 | | | 640 | 820 | 1,030 | 1,220 | 1,410 | 1,620 | 1,850 | 2,090 | 2,350 | 2,580 | 36 |
| 80 | | | 670 | 860 | 1,080 | 1,280 | 1,480 | 1,710 | 1,950 | 2,200 | 2,470 | 2,720 | 37 |
| 82 | | | | 910 | 1,130 | 1,340 | 1,560 | 1,800 | 2,050 | 2,310 | 2,590 | 2,860 | 37.5 |
| 84 | | | | 950 | 1,180 | 1,400 | 1,640 | 1,890 | 2,150 | 2,420 | 2,710 | 3,000 | 38.5 |
| 86 | | | | 1,000 | 1,240 | 1,460 | 1,710 | 1,980 | 2,250 | 2,530 | 2,840 | 3,140 | 39 |
| 88 | | | | 1,040 | 1,290 | 1,530 | 1,790 | 2,070 | 2,350 | 2,640 | 2,970 | 3,270 | 40 |
| 90 | | | | 1,090 | 1,340 | 1,600 | 1,860 | 2,160 | 2,450 | 2,750 | 3,110 | 3,400 | 41 |
| 92 | | | | 1,130 | 1,390 | 1,670 | 1,940 | 2,250 | 2,550 | 2,860 | 3,240 | 3,540 | 42 |
| 94 | | | | 1,180 | 1,450 | 1,740 | 2,020 | 2,340 | 2,660 | 3,000 | 3,370 | | 43 |
| 96 | | | | 1,230 | 1,510 | 1,820 | 2,120 | 2,430 | 2,780 | 3,140 | 3,500 | | 44 |
| 98 | | | | 1,290 | 1,580 | 1,900 | 2,220 | 2,530 | 2,900 | 3,280 | 3,660 | | 45 |
| 100 | | | | 1,340 | 1,660 | 2,000 | 2,330 | 2,650 | 3,050 | 3,430 | 3,830 | | 46 |
| 102 | | | | | 1,400 | 1,750 | 2,100 | 2,450 | 2,780 | 3,200 | 3,600 | | 47 |
| 104 | | | | | 1,470 | 1,840 | 2,200 | 2,560 | 2,920 | 3,350 | 3,780 | | 48 |
| 106 | | | | | 1,560 | 1,930 | 2,300 | 2,680 | 3,060 | 3,520 | 3,990 | | 49 |
| 108 | | | | | | 2,030 | 2,410 | 2,800 | 3,210 | 3,680 | 4,200 | | 50 |
| 110 | | | | | | 2,130 | 2,520 | 2,920 | 3,350 | 3,850 | 4,380 | | 51 |
| 112 | | | | | | 2,230 | 2,620 | 3,040 | 3,500 | 4,030 | | | 52 |
| 114 | | | | | | 2,340 | 2,730 | 3,170 | 3,650 | 4,200 | | | 53 |
| 116 | | | | | | 2,460 | 2,850 | 3,310 | 3,800 | 4,380 | | | 54 |
| 118 | | | | | | 2,580 | 2,970 | 3,450 | 3,970 | 4,570 | | | 55 |
| 120 | | | | | | 2,700 | 3,080 | 3,590 | 4,130 | 4,760 | | | 56 |

\* Prepared by alinement chart method. Stump height 2 ft. No allowance for defect. Basis, 2,583 trees. Actual volume, 0.03 percent below estimated volume. (W. H. Meyer, 1932.)

## DOUGLAS-FIR (OLD GROWTH)

**Table 19. Board-Foot Volume for Log Heights by 16.3-Ft. Logs to an 8-In. Top,***
**Scribner Decimal C Rule**

Site Qualities IV and V of inland form

| D.b.h. (in.) | Height in 16.3-ft. logs to 8-in. top inside bark | | | | | | | | | | |
|---|---|---|---|---|---|---|---|---|---|---|---|
| | 2 | 3 | 4 | 5 | 6 | 7 | 8 | 9 | 10 | 11 | 12 |
| | Board feet in tens | | | | | | | | | | |
| 10 | 6.6 | 10 | 13 | 17 | 21 | | | | | | |
| 12 | 8.1 | 12 | 16 | 22 | 26 | | | | | | |
| 14 | 9.6 | 14 | 20 | 27 | 33 | 38 | | | | | |
| 16 | 11.1 | 18 | 25 | 33 | 40 | 47 | | | | | |
| 18 | 12.6 | 21 | 30 | 39 | 48 | 56 | 66 | | | | |
| 20 | 14.2 | 24 | 35 | 46 | 57 | 67 | 78 | | | | |
| 22 | 16 | 28 | 41 | 54 | 67 | 79 | 93 | 106 | | | |
| 24 | 18 | 32 | 47 | 62 | 78 | 92 | 109 | 125 | | | |
| 26 | 20 | 36 | 53 | 71 | 89 | 106 | 126 | 145 | 162 | | |
| 28 | 22 | 41 | 60 | 81 | 101 | 122 | 144 | 166 | 188 | | |
| 30 | 24 | 46 | 68 | 91 | 115 | 138 | 163 | 190 | 214 | 237 | |
| 32 | | 51 | 76 | 101 | 129 | 155 | 185 | 214 | 240 | 269 | |
| 34 | | 56 | 84 | 113 | 144 | 174 | 207 | 239 | 270 | 300 | 333 |
| 36 | | 62 | 92 | 126 | 159 | 193 | 229 | 267 | 300 | 333 | 370 |
| 38 | | | 101 | 139 | 174 | 212 | 253 | 295 | 330 | 368 | 411 |
| 40 | | | 111 | 152 | 193 | 232 | 280 | 323 | 364 | 408 | 452 |
| 42 | | | 122 | 165 | 212 | 255 | 306 | 352 | 400 | 448 | 500 |
| 44 | | | | 180 | 231 | 280 | 332 | 387 | 439 | 490 | 548 |
| 46 | | | | 197 | 250 | 303 | 361 | 422 | 478 | 535 | 593 |
| 48 | | | | 215 | 270 | 328 | 393 | 456 | 518 | 580 | 645 |
| 50 | | | | 236 | 292 | 353 | 425 | 495 | 560 | 625 | 695 |
| 52 | | | | | 313 | 380 | 456 | 535 | 600 | 675 | 750 |
| 54 | | | | | 335 | 410 | 492 | 576 | 650 | 727 | 805 |
| 56 | | | | | 360 | 440 | 529 | 616 | 698 | 780 | 865 |
| 58 | | | | | 386 | 472 | 566 | 659 | 748 | 835 | 930 |
| 60 | | | | | 413 | 505 | 603 | 704 | 800 | 890 | 990 |
| 62 | | | | | 440 | 540 | 640 | 750 | 850 | 950 | 1,050 |
| 64 | | | | | 468 | 575 | 680 | 795 | 900 | 1,005 | 1,120 |
| 66 | | | | | 500 | 610 | 720 | 840 | 945 | 1,065 | 1,190 |
| 68 | | | | | 532 | 650 | 760 | 890 | 995 | 1,130 | 1,260 |
| 70 | | | | | 578 | 685 | 800 | 940 | 1,050 | 1,200 | 1,330 |

* Prepared by alinement chart method. Stump height 15 ft. No allowance for defect. Basis, 4,072 trees. Actual volume, 0.51 percent above estimated volume. (W. H. Meyer, 1932.)

# DOUGLAS-FIR (OLD GROWTH)

### Table 20. Cubic-Foot Volume
Inland Empire

| D.b.h. (in.) | 40 | 50 | 60 | 70 | 80 | 90 | 100 | 110 | 120 | 140 | 160 | 200 |
|---|---|---|---|---|---|---|---|---|---|---|---|---|
| | | | | | MEDIUM SITE | | | | | | | |
| 16 | 22.2 | 27.1 | 32.0 | 36.7 | 41.3 | 46.0 | 50.5 | 55.0 | 59.7 | 69.0 | 78.2 | 97.2 |
| 17 | 24.8 | 30.3 | 35.8 | 41.1 | 46.3 | 51.4 | 56.6 | 61.6 | 66.6 | 77.0 | 87.5 | 108.8 |
| 18 | 27.4 | 33.7 | 39.6 | 45.8 | 51.5 | 57.1 | 62.9 | 68.4 | 74.0 | 85.6 | 97.2 | 120.9 |
| 19 | 30.3 | 37.1 | 43.8 | 50.4 | 56.9 | 63.1 | 69.3 | 75.4 | 81.5 | 94.5 | 107.4 | 133.5 |
| 20 | 33.3 | 40.8 | 48.3 | 55.3 | 62.5 | 69.3 | 75.9 | 82.8 | 89.5 | 103.8 | 118.0 | 146.6 |
| 21 | 36.3 | 44.6 | 52.7 | 60.5 | 68.1 | 75.8 | 83.0 | 90.5 | 97.8 | 113.5 | 128.9 | 160.2 |
| 22 | 39.5 | 48.6 | 57.2 | 65.8 | 74.1 | 82.7 | 90.3 | 98.4 | 106.4 | 123.4 | 140.2 | 174.2 |
| 23 | 42.8 | 52.5 | 62.0 | 71.3 | 80.3 | 89.3 | 97.8 | 106.6 | 115.3 | 133.7 | 151.9 | 188.7 |
| 24 | 46.3 | 56.7 | 66.9 | 77.0 | 86.9 | 96.1 | 105.6 | 115.1 | 124.8 | 144.7 | 163.9 | 203.6 |
| 25 | 49.8 | 61.0 | 72.0 | 82.8 | 93.5 | 103.7 | 113.9 | 124.1 | 134.2 | 155.6 | 176.2 | 218.9 |
| 26 | 53.4 | 65.5 | 77.2 | 89.0 | 100.3 | 111.5 | 122.4 | 133.4 | 144.2 | 167.2 | 189.4 | 235.2 |
| 27 | 56.9 | 70.0 | 82.8 | 95.2 | 107.5 | 119.5 | 131.2 | 143.0 | 154.6 | 178.7 | 202.9 | 250.5 |
| 28 | 60.7 | 74.8 | 88.5 | 101.8 | 114.9 | 128.1 | 140.7 | 153.4 | 165.2 | 191.0 | 216.9 | 268.5 |
| 29 | 64.8 | 79.6 | 94.1 | 108.5 | 122.6 | 136.6 | 150.0 | 163.5 | 176.1 | 204.2 | 231.2 | 287.1 |
| 30 | 68.9 | 84.4 | 99.8 | 115.4 | 130.8 | 145.4 | 159.5 | 173.9 | 187.9 | 217.8 | 246.6 | 306.3 |
| 31 | | 89.6 | 106.0 | 122.5 | 138.8 | 154.7 | 169.8 | 185.1 | 200.0 | 231.9 | 262.5 | 326.0 |
| 32 | | 95.2 | 112.6 | 130.2 | 147.0 | 164.9 | 181.0 | 197.2 | 213.1 | 246.3 | 278.8 | 346.3 |
| 33 | | 101.0 | 119.4 | 137.6 | 155.9 | 174.3 | 191.9 | 209.1 | 226.0 | 261.1 | 295.5 | 367.1 |
| 34 | | 106.9 | 126.7 | 145.7 | 165.4 | 184.4 | 203.0 | 221.3 | 239.1 | 277.2 | 313.7 | 389.6 |
| 35 | | | 133.9 | 153.9 | 174.8 | 194.8 | 214.5 | 233.7 | 252.6 | 292.8 | 331.4 | 411.6 |
| 36 | | | 141.2 | 162.3 | 184.4 | 205.5 | 226.2 | 247.2 | 267.2 | 309.7 | 350.6 | 435.4 |
| 37 | | | 148.7 | 170.9 | 194.1 | 216.4 | 238.2 | 260.4 | 281.3 | 326.1 | 369.2 | 458.4 |
| 38 | | | 156.4 | 180.3 | 204.8 | 228.2 | 251.2 | 274.6 | 296.8 | 344.0 | 389.4 | 483.6 |
| 39 | | | | 189.3 | 215.0 | 239.7 | 263.8 | 288.4 | 311.6 | 361.2 | 408.8 | 509.4 |
| 40 | | | | 199.2 | 226.2 | 252.1 | 277.5 | 302.4 | 327.8 | 379.9 | 430.1 | 535.8 |
| 41 | | | | 208.6 | 236.9 | 264.1 | 290.6 | 317.7 | 344.4 | 397.9 | 450.3 | 561.1 |
| 42 | | | | 218.2 | 247.8 | 277.1 | 305.0 | 333.4 | 361.4 | 417.6 | 472.6 | 588.8 |
| 43 | | | | | 259.0 | 289.5 | 319.7 | 348.3 | 377.6 | 436.3 | 493.8 | 615.2 |
| 44 | | | | | 271.1 | 303.1 | 334.7 | 364.7 | 395.3 | 456.8 | 517.0 | 644.1 |
| 45 | | | | | 282.8 | 316.1 | 349.0 | 380.3 | 412.2 | 477.8 | 540.8 | 673.7 |
| 46 | | | | | 295.5 | 330.3 | 364.7 | 397.4 | 430.7 | 499.3 | 565.1 | 704.0 |
| 47 | | | | | 308.4 | 344.8 | 379.5 | 413.5 | 448.2 | 519.5 | 587.9 | 732.5 |
| 48 | | | | | 321.7 | 359.7 | 395.8 | 431.3 | 467.5 | 541.9 | 613.2 | 764.0 |
| 49 | | | | | 334.2 | 373.6 | 412.5 | 449.4 | 487.1 | 562.9 | 637.0 | 793.6 |
| 50 | | | | | 348.0 | 389.0 | 429.5 | 468.0 | 507.2 | 586.1 | 663.2 | 826.3 |

Source: U. S. Forest Service, Region 1.

## DOUGLAS-FIR (SECOND GROWTH)

### Table 21. Volume in Board Feet, Scribner Rule*

Western Oregon and Washington

| D.b.h. (in.) | Number of 16-ft. logs | | | | | | | | | | | | |
|---|---|---|---|---|---|---|---|---|---|---|---|---|---|
| | 1¼ | 2 | 3 | 4 | 5 | 6 | 7 | 8 | 9 | 10 | 11 | 12 | 13 |
| 12 | 62 | 80 | 133 | 183 | 235 | 286 | 338 | | | | | | |
| 14 | 64 | 88 | 147 | 210 | 274 | 338 | 400 | | | | | | |
| 16 | 67 | 96 | 163 | 242 | 320 | 399 | 478 | | | | | | |
| 18 | 71 | 109 | 190 | 280 | 370 | 459 | 550 | 640 | 729 | | | | |
| 20 | 75 | 123 | 221 | 330 | 435 | 543 | 651 | 758 | 865 | 970 | | | |
| 22 | 80 | 136 | 258 | 383 | 509 | 633 | 760 | 884 | 1,011 | 1,136 | 1,260 | | |
| 24 | | 151 | 292 | 438 | 584 | 728 | 882 | 1,035 | 1,188 | 1,340 | 1,495 | 1,641 | |
| 26 | | 170 | 333 | 500 | 666 | 832 | 1,013 | 1,190 | 1,368 | 1,546 | 1,724 | 1,895 | |
| 28 | | 188 | 371 | 560 | 750 | 941 | 1,144 | 1,346 | 1,551 | 1,752 | 1,956 | 2,152 | 2,361 |
| 30 | | | | 638 | 850 | 1,062 | 1,291 | 1,518 | 1,749 | 1,975 | 2,202 | 2,420 | 2,656 |
| 32 | | | | 716 | 955 | 1,195 | 1,449 | 1,700 | 1,954 | 2,211 | 2,462 | 2,707 | 2,968 |
| 34 | | | | 791 | 1,059 | 1,333 | 1,614 | 1,898 | 2,180 | 2,463 | 2,745 | 3,006 | 3,295 |
| 36 | | | | 882 | 1,175 | 1,494 | 1,782 | 2,095 | 2,410 | 2,721 | 3,025 | 3,318 | 3,630 |
| 38 | | | | 978 | 1,290 | 1,614 | 1,955 | 2,305 | 2,660 | 2,985 | 3,315 | 3,642 | 3,990 |
| 40 | | | | | 1,410 | 1,779 | 2,150 | 2,523 | 2,892 | 3,266 | 3,634 | 3,995 | 4,380 |
| 42 | | | | | 1,541 | 1,937 | 2,340 | 2,735 | 3,138 | 3,528 | 3,920 | 4,301 | 4,717 |
| 44 | | | | | 1,663 | 2,090 | 2,520 | 2,949 | 3,386 | 3,812 | 4,240 | 4,651 | 5,100 |
| 46 | | | | | 1,790 | 2,255 | 2,724 | 3,180 | 3,638 | 4,094 | 4,550 | 5,008 | 5,495 |
| 48 | | | | | 1,920 | 2,420 | 2,927 | 3,414 | 3,905 | 4,400 | 4,890 | 5,400 | 5,935 |
| 50 | | | | | | 2,606 | 3,130 | 3,660 | 4,190 | 4,725 | 5,259 | 5,774 | 6,330 |
| 52 | | | | | | 2,775 | 3,330 | 3,908 | 4,480 | 5,055 | 5,620 | 6,168 | 6,758 |
| 54 | | | | | | 2,944 | 3,550 | 4,153 | 4,760 | 5,389 | 6,010 | 6,610 | 7,240 |

*Stump height, 2.0 ft. Top d.i.b., 8 in. Basis, 1,434 trees, all sites. Average deviation of individual tree volumes, 23.1 percent.
Source: R. E. McArdle and W. H. Meyer, The yield of Douglas-fir in the Pacific Northwest, U. S. Dept. Agr., *Tech. Bull. No. 201*, 1930.

## DOUGLAS-FIR (SECOND GROWTH)

### Table 22. Cubic-Foot Volume*

Western foothills of Cascade Mountains, Washington and Oregon

Height of tree in feet — Volume in cubic feet

| D.b.h., Inches | 20 | 30 | 40 | 50 | 60 | 70 | 80 | 90 | 100 | 110 | 120 | 130 | 140 | 150 | 160 | 170 | 180 | 190 | 200 | 210 | 220 | 230 | 240 |
|---|---|---|---|---|---|---|---|---|---|---|---|---|---|---|---|---|---|---|---|---|---|---|---|
| 2 | 0.22 | 0.35 | 0.45 | 0.56 | 0.69 | | | | | | | | | | | | | | | | | | |
| 3 | .51 | .75 | .98 | 1.21 | 1.45 | 1.70 | | | | | | | | | | | | | | | | | |
| 4 | .88 | 1.30 | 1.70 | 2.06 | 2.55 | 2.88 | 3.1 | | | | | | | | | | | | | | | | |
| 5 | 1.39 | 1.99 | 2.61 | 3.18 | 3.80 | 4.30 | 4.89 | 5.50 | | | | | | | | | | | | | | | |
| 6 | 1.97 | 2.85 | 3.70 | 4.50 | 5.35 | 6.14 | 6.95 | 7.76 | | | | | | | | | | | | | | | |
| 7 | 2.61 | 3.86 | 4.96 | 6.02 | 7.15 | 8.22 | 9.30 | 10.40 | 11.2 | 12.2 | | | | | | | | | | | | | |
| 8 | 3.38 | 4.97 | 6.35 | 7.84 | 9.12 | 10.7 | 12.3 | 13.3 | 14.4 | 15.8 | 17.2 | 19.0 | | | | | | | | | | | |
| 9 | 4.24 | 6.19 | 7.95 | 9.98 | 11.6 | 13.5 | 15.2 | 16.6 | 18.1 | 20.0 | 21.7 | 23.5 | | | | | | | | | | | |
| 10 | 5.20 | 7.55 | 9.82 | 11.8 | 14.2 | 16.4 | 18.5 | 20.1 | 22.0 | 24.4 | 26.3 | 28.7 | 31.1 | | | | | | | | | | |
| 11 | 6.26 | 9.10 | 11.7 | 14.3 | 17.0 | 19.5 | 22.0 | 24.0 | 26.3 | 29.1 | 31.7 | 34.2 | 37.3 | 40.4 | 43.1 | | | | | | | | |
| 12 | | 10.8 | 13.8 | 16.8 | 20.0 | 22.8 | 25.9 | 28.3 | 31.1 | 34.6 | 37.4 | 40.5 | 44.0 | 47.9 | 51.3 | 54.2 | | | | | | | |
| 13 | | 12.4 | 16.0 | 19.5 | 23.2 | 26.5 | 30.2 | 33.3 | 36.7 | 40.3 | 43.7 | 47.3 | 51.4 | 55.8 | 59.6 | 63.0 | | | | | | | |
| 14 | | 14.2 | 18.4 | 22.4 | 26.6 | 30.4 | 34.7 | 38.5 | 42.3 | 46.1 | 50.0 | 54.2 | 58.8 | 63.8 | 68.2 | 72.5 | 78.0 | 82.9 | | | | | |
| 15 | | | 21.0 | 25.6 | 30.2 | 34.8 | 39.5 | 43.7 | 48.0 | 52.2 | 56.5 | 61.2 | 66.5 | 71.9 | 76.9 | 82.0 | 88.0 | 93.6 | 99.9 | | | | |
| 16 | | | 23.7 | 28.8 | 33.9 | 39.2 | 44.3 | 49.2 | 53.9 | 58.4 | 63.1 | 68.2 | 74.4 | 80.5 | 86.0 | 92.6 | 98.8 | 105.0 | 113.0 | | | | |
| 17 | | | 26.4 | 32.2 | 38.0 | 43.8 | 49.2 | 54.8 | 60.0 | 64.8 | 70.0 | 75.8 | 82.8 | 89.5 | 95.5 | 103.0 | 110.0 | 117.0 | 125.0 | 134 | 145 | | |
| 18 | | | 29.3 | 35.7 | 42.2 | 48.4 | 54.5 | 60.4 | 67.0 | 71.3 | 77.2 | 83.7 | 91.4 | 99.0 | 106.0 | 114.0 | 122.0 | 130.0 | 139.0 | 157 | 160 | | |
| 19 | | | | 39.5 | 46.5 | 53.3 | 59.8 | 66.1 | 72.4 | 77.8 | 84.7 | 91.6 | 100.0 | 108.0 | 116.0 | 125.0 | 134.0 | 143.0 | 153.0 | 162 | 176 | 186 | 195 |
| 20 | | | | 43.4 | 51.1 | 58.3 | 65.5 | 72.2 | 79.0 | 84.8 | 92.1 | 99.8 | 109.0 | 118.0 | 127.0 | 137.0 | 147.0 | 157.0 | 168.0 | 178 | 192 | 204 | 214 |
| 21 | | | | 47.5 | 55.6 | 63.5 | 71.2 | 78.3 | 85.7 | 92.0 | 100.0 | 108.0 | 118.0 | 128.0 | 138.0 | 148.0 | 159.0 | 170.0 | 183.0 | 194 | 208 | 222 | 234 |
| 22 | | | | 51.7 | 60.2 | 69.0 | 77.0 | 84.8 | 92.5 | 99.2 | 108.0 | 117.0 | 127.0 | 138.0 | 149.0 | 160.0 | 172.0 | 185.0 | 198.0 | 210 | 225 | 240 | 253 |
| 23 | | | | | 65.0 | 74.3 | 83.0 | 91.0 | 99.4 | 107.0 | 115.0 | 125.0 | 136.0 | 148.0 | 160.0 | 172.0 | 185.0 | 199.0 | 213.0 | 227 | 243 | 258 | 273 |
| 24 | | | | | 69.8 | 80.0 | 89.0 | 97.8 | 105.0 | 114.0 | 123.0 | 133.0 | 144.0 | 157.0 | 170.0 | 184.0 | 198.0 | 213.0 | 229.0 | 245 | 262 | 277 | 294 |
| 25 | | | | | | 85.7 | 95.0 | 104.0 | 113.0 | 122.0 | 131.0 | 142.0 | 154.0 | 168.0 | 182.0 | 196.0 | 212.0 | 228.0 | 245.0 | 262 | 282 | 297 | 315 |
| 26 | | | | | | 91.5 | 101.0 | 111.0 | 120.0 | 129.0 | 139.0 | 150.0 | 162.0 | 178.0 | 193.0 | 208.0 | 226.0 | 243.0 | 261.0 | 281 | 300 | 317 | 337 |
| 27 | | | | | | | 107.0 | 117.0 | 128.0 | 137.0 | 147.0 | 159.0 | 172.0 | 188.0 | 204.0 | 220.0 | 239.0 | 258.0 | 278.0 | 298 | 320 | 337 | 360 |
| 28 | | | | | | | | | 135.0 | 145.0 | 155.0 | 168.0 | 181.0 | 198.0 | 216.0 | 233.0 | 253.0 | 274.0 | 295.0 | 317 | 341 | 359 | 384 |
| 29 | | | | | | | | | 142.0 | 152.0 | 163.0 | 177.0 | 191.0 | 209.0 | 227.0 | 246.0 | 268.0 | 290.0 | 310.0 | 335 | 360 | 382 | 408 |
| 30 | | | | | | | | | 149.0 | 160.0 | 171.0 | 185.0 | 200.0 | 220.0 | 239.0 | 259.0 | 282.0 | 307.0 | 327.0 | 354 | 381 | 403 | 434 |
| 31 | | | | | | | | | 156.0 | 167.0 | 179.0 | 194.0 | 210.0 | 230.0 | 251.0 | 272.0 | 299.0 | 321.0 | 344.0 | 372 | 400 | 426 | 457 |

*The volume is total cubic volume of the stem, including stump and top, but excluding bark.

## DOUGLAS-FIR (SECOND GROWTH)

### Table 22. Cubic-Foot Volume * (Continued)

Western foothills of Cascade Mountains, Washington and Oregon

| D.b.h. inches | 20 | 30 | 40 | 50 | 60 | 70 | 80 | 90 | 100 | 110 | 120 | 130 | 140 | 150 | 160 | 170 | 180 | 190 | 200 | 210 | 220 | 230 | 240 |
|---|---|---|---|---|---|---|---|---|---|---|---|---|---|---|---|---|---|---|---|---|---|---|---|
| | | | | | | | | | | | | | | | | | | | Volume in cubic feet | | | | |
| 32 | | | | | | | | 151.0 | 163.0 | 175.0 | 188.0 | 203.0 | 220.0 | 241.0 | 263.0 | 285.0 | 312.0 | 336.0 | 362.0 | 391 | 421 | 449 | 482 |
| 33 | | | | | | | | 158.0 | 171.0 | 183.0 | 196.0 | 212.0 | 230.0 | 252.0 | 276.0 | 299.0 | 325.0 | 350.0 | 378.0 | 409 | 442 | 472 | 506 |
| 34 | | | | | | | | | | 191.0 | 204.0 | 221.0 | 240.0 | 263.0 | 289.0 | 310.0 | 338.0 | 365.0 | 395.0 | 428 | 462 | 496 | 532 |
| 35 | | | | | | | | | | 199.0 | 212.0 | 231.0 | 250.0 | 275.0 | 300.0 | 322.0 | 352.0 | 381.0 | 412.0 | 447 | 488 | 519 | 560 |
| 36 | | | | | | | | | | | 220.0 | 239.0 | 259.0 | 286.0 | 310.0 | 335.0 | 366.0 | 396.0 | 430.0 | 465 | 504 | 543 | 582 |
| 37 | | | | | | | | | | | 228.0 | 248.0 | 269.0 | 298.0 | 321.0 | 348.0 | 379.0 | 412.0 | 447.0 | 485 | 525 | 565 | 605 |
| 38 | | | | | | | | | | | 237.0 | 257.0 | 279.0 | 307.0 | 332.0 | 360.0 | 393.0 | 427.0 | 465.0 | 503 | 547 | 588 | 632 |
| 39 | | | | | | | | | | | | 266.0 | 289.0 | 316.0 | 343.0 | 372.0 | 407.0 | 443.0 | 482.0 | 523 | 567 | 612 | 657 |
| 40 | | | | | | | | | | | | 275.0 | 298.0 | 325.0 | 353.0 | 384.0 | 421.0 | 458.0 | 500.0 | 542 | 590 | 636 | 683 |
| 41 | | | | | | | | | | | | | | 334.0 | 365.0 | 398.0 | 435.0 | 475.0 | 518.0 | 562 | 610 | 660 | 708 |
| 42 | | | | | | | | | | | | | | 343.0 | 376.0 | 410.0 | 448.0 | 490.0 | 535.0 | 581 | 632 | 683 | 734 |
| 43 | | | | | | | | | | | | | | 353.0 | 387.0 | 422.0 | 462.0 | 506.0 | 553.0 | 601 | 653 | 707 | 760 |
| 44 | | | | | | | | | | | | | | 362.0 | 398.0 | 435.0 | 476.0 | 522.0 | 572.0 | 622 | 675 | 732 | 786 |
| 45 | | | | | | | | | | | | | | 372.0 | 409.0 | 448.0 | 489.0 | 537.0 | 589.0 | 642 | 696 | 754 | 812 |
| 46 | | | | | | | | | | | | | | 382.0 | 420.0 | 460.0 | 504.0 | 553.0 | 607.0 | 662 | 718 | 778 | 842 |
| 47 | | | | | | | | | | | | | | | 432.0 | 473.0 | 517.0 | 569.0 | 625.0 | 682 | 739 | 802 | 863 |
| 48 | | | | | | | | | | | | | | | 442.0 | 486.0 | 532.0 | 585.0 | 643.0 | 701 | 762 | 826 | 889 |
| 49 | | | | | | | | | | | | | | | 453.0 | 498.0 | 545.0 | 600.0 | 662.0 | 721 | 782 | 850 | 914 |
| 50 | | | | | | | | | | | | | | | 464.0 | 511.0 | 559.0 | 615.0 | 680.0 | 742 | 805 | 874 | 941 |
| 51 | | | | | | | | | | | | | | | 475.0 | 523.0 | 572.0 | 631.0 | 698.0 | 767 | 826 | 898 | 966 |
| 52 | | | | | | | | | | | | | | | 487.0 | 536.0 | 586.0 | 647.0 | 716.0 | 782 | 848 | 922 | 993 |
| 53 | | | | | | | | | | | | | | | 498.0 | 548.0 | 600.0 | 663.0 | 735.0 | 803 | 868 | 945 | 1,018 |
| 54 | | | | | | | | | | | | | | | 510.0 | 562.0 | 615.0 | 679.0 | 754.0 | 825 | 890 | 970 | 1,045 |

* The volume is total cubic volume of the stem, including stump and top, but excluding bark.
Source: R. E. McArdle and W. H. Meyer, The yield of Douglas-fir in the Pacific Northwest, U. S. Dept. Agr., Tech. Bull. No. 201, 1930.

# DOUGLAS-FIR (OLD GROWTH)

## Table 23. Volume in Board Feet, Scribner Rule [a]     New Mexico

| D.b.h. O.b. (in.) | D.b.h. I.b. (in.) | 1 [b] | 2 | 3 | 4 | 5 | 6 | 7 | 8 | 9 |
|---|---|---|---|---|---|---|---|---|---|---|
| 12 | 9.42 | 36 | 74 | 115 | | | | | | |
| 14 | 11.14 | 37 | 85 | 137 | 188 | | | | | |
| 16 | 12.87 | 39 | 98 | 162 | 226 | | | | | |
| 18 | 14.59 | 41 | 113 | 192 | 270 | | | | | |
| 20 | 16.31 | | 130 | 226 | 320 | 412 | 504 | | | |
| 22 | 18.03 | | 150 | 264 | 377 | 488 | 598 | | | |
| 24 | 19.75 | | | 307 | 440 | 571 | 701 | | | |
| 26 | 21.47 | | | 354 | 509 | 663 | 815 | 966 | | |
| 28 | 23.19 | | | 405 | 585 | 763 | 939 | 1,114 | | |
| 30 | 24.91 | | | | 668 | 873 | 1,076 | 1,276 | 1,477 | |
| 32 | 26.63 | | | | 758 | 992 | 1,223 | 1,452 | 1,681 | |
| 34 | 28.35 | | | | 855 | 1,119 | 1,382 | 1.641 | 1,900 | |
| 36 | 30.07 | | | | | 1,258 | 1,553 | 1.846 | 2,138 | |
| 38 | 31.79 | | | | | 1,404 | 1,734 | 2,062 | 2,388 | |
| 40 | 33.51 | | | | | 1,559 | 1,927 | 2,291 | 2,654 | |
| 42 | 35.23 | | | | | | 2,136 | 2.541 | 2,944 | 3.345 |
| 44 | 36.95 | | | | | | 2,351 | 2.797 | 3,242 | 3,684 |
| 46 | 38.67 | | | | | | 2,582 | 3,072 | 3,561 | 4,047 |
| 48 | 40.39 | | | | | | 2,822 | 3.358 | 3,892 | 4,424 |
| 50 | 42.11 | | | | | | 3,076 | 3.661 | 4,244 | 4,824 |
| 52 | 43.83 | | | | | | | 3.982 | 4,617 | 5,248 |
| 54 | 45.55 | | | | | | | 4,310 | 4,998 | 5,681 |

[a] Stump height, 1.2 ft. above highest ground. Top d.i.b., 8 in. Basis: 304 trees. Average percentage deviation, 7.99.
[b] 1⅓ logs.
Source: H. Krauch and G. Peterson, Two new board-foot volume tables for Douglas-fir, Southwestern Forest & Range Exp. Sta., *Res. Note No. 107,* 1943.

# GRAND FIR (OLD GROWTH)

## Table 24. Cubic-Foot Volume     Inland Empire

| D.b.h. (in.) | 40 | 50 | 60 | 70 | 80 | 90 | 100 | 110 | 120 | 140 | 160 | 200 |
|---|---|---|---|---|---|---|---|---|---|---|---|---|
| | | | | | | MEDIUM SITE | | | | | | |
| 16 | 26.9 | 32.8 | 38.7 | 44.4 | 50.0 | 55.7 | 61.1 | 66.6 | 72.2 | 83.5 | 94.6 | 117.6 |
| 18 | 33.2 | 40.8 | 47.9 | 55.4 | 62.3 | 69.1 | 76.1 | 82.8 | 89.5 | 103.6 | 117.6 | 146.3 |
| 20 | 40.3 | 49.4 | 58.4 | 66.9 | 75.6 | 83.9 | 91.8 | 100.2 | 108.3 | 125.6 | 142.8 | 177.4 |
| 22 | 47.8 | 58.8 | 69.2 | 79.6 | 89.7 | 100.1 | 109.3 | 119.1 | 128.7 | 149.3 | 169.6 | 210.8 |
| 24 | 56.0 | 68.6 | 80.9 | 93.2 | 105.1 | 116.3 | 127.8 | 139.3 | 151.0 | 175.1 | 198.3 | 246.4 |
| 26 | 64.6 | 79.3 | 93.4 | 107.7 | 121.4 | 134.9 | 148.1 | 161.4 | 174.5 | 202.3 | 229.2 | 284.6 |
| 28 | 73.4 | 90.5 | 107.1 | 123.2 | 139.0 | 155.0 | 170.2 | 185.6 | 199.9 | 231.1 | 262.4 | 324.9 |
| 30 | 33.4 | 102.1 | 120.8 | 139.6 | 158.3 | 175.9 | 193.0 | 210.4 | 227.4 | 263.5 | 298.4 | 370.6 |
| 32 | | 115.2 | 136.2 | 157.5 | 177.9 | 199.5 | 219.0 | 238.6 | 257.9 | 298.0 | 337.3 | 419.0 |
| 34 | | 129.3 | 153.3 | 176.3 | 200.1 | 223.1 | 245 6 | 267 8 | 289.3 | 335.4 | 379.6 | 471.4 |
| 36 | | | 170.9 | 196.4 | 223.1 | 248.7 | 273.7 | 299.1 | 323.3 | 374.7 | 424.2 | 526.8 |
| 38 | | | 189.2 | 218.2 | 247.8 | 276.1 | 304.0 | 332.3 | 359.1 | 416.2 | 471.2 | 585.2 |
| 40 | | | | 241.0 | 273.7 | 305.0 | 335.8 | 365.9 | 396.6 | 459.7 | 520.4 | 648.3 |
| 42 | | | | 264.0 | 299.8 | 335.3 | 369.0 | 403.4 | 437.3 | 505.3 | 571.8 | 712.4 |
| 44 | | | | | 328.0 | 366 8 | 405.0 | 441.3 | 478.3 | 552.7 | 625.6 | 779.4 |
| 46 | | | | | 357.6 | 399.7 | 441.3 | 480.9 | 521.1 | 604.2 | 683.8 | 851.8 |
| 48 | | | | | 389.3 | 435.2 | 478 9 | 521.9 | 565.7 | 655.7 | 742.0 | 924.4 |
| 50 | | | | | 421.1 | 470.7 | 519.7 | 566.3 | 613.7 | 709.2 | 802.5 | 999.8 |

Source: U. S. Forest Service, Region 1.

## WHITE FIR

### Table 25. Volume in Board Feet, Scribner Rule *
New Mexico

| O.b. (in.) | D.b.h. I.b. (in.) | Number of 16.3-ft. logs | | | | | | | |
|---|---|---|---|---|---|---|---|---|---|
| | | 1 | 2 | 3 | 4 | 5 | 6 | 7 | 8 |
| 12 | 9.7 | 60 | 117 | 182 | 254 | | | | |
| 14 | 11.5 | 60 | 124 | 202 | 288 | | | | |
| 16 | 13.3 | 60 | 134 | 226 | 326 | | | | |
| 18 | 15.1 | | 146 | 253 | 368 | 490 | | | |
| 20 | 16.9 | | 159 | 282 | 416 | 556 | 703 | | |
| 22 | 18.7 | | 174 | 314 | 467 | 628 | 796 | | |
| 24 | 20.5 | | | 349 | 522 | 706 | 897 | | |
| 26 | 22.3 | | | 386 | 582 | 789 | 1,004 | 1,227 | |
| 28 | 24.1 | | | 426 | 646 | 878 | 1,120 | 1,369 | |
| 30 | 25.8 | | | 466 | 710 | 967 | 1,235 | 1,512 | |
| 32 | 27.6 | | | | 781 | 1,066 | 1,364 | 1,671 | |
| 34 | 29.4 | | | | 856 | 1,171 | 1,499 | 1,838 | 2,186 |
| 36 | 31.2 | | | | 934 | 1,281 | 1,641 | 2,014 | 2,396 |
| 38 | 32.9 | | | | 1,012 | 1,389 | 1,782 | 2,187 | 2,603 |
| 40 | 34.7 | | | | 1,097 | 1,508 | 1,936 | 2,378 | 2,832 |

* Stump height, 1.2 ft. Top d.i.b. 10 in. Basis, 184 trees. Average percentage deviation, 5.96.
Source: B. R. Lexen and W. G. Thomson, White fir merchantable height volume table, Southwestern Forest & Range Exp. Sta., *Res. Note No. 27*, 1938.

## WESTERN HEMLOCK (OLD GROWTH)

### Table 26. Cubic-foot Volume
Inland Empire

| D.b.h. (in.) | Total height in feet | | | | | | | | | | | |
|---|---|---|---|---|---|---|---|---|---|---|---|---|
| | 40 | 50 | 60 | 70 | 80 | 90 | 100 | 110 | 120 | 140 | 160 | 200 |
| | MEDIUM SITE | | | | | | | | | | | |
| 16 | 23.9 | 29.4 | 34.9 | 40.3 | 45.8 | 51.4 | 57.3 | 63.3 | 69.7 | 83.1 | 95.4 | 120.3 |
| 18 | 29.9 | 36.9 | 43.8 | 51.0 | 57.8 | 64.9 | 72.6 | 80.2 | 88.2 | 104.5 | 120.3 | 151.9 |
| 20 | 36.7 | 45.2 | 54.0 | 62.3 | 71.2 | 80.0 | 89.0 | 98.7 | 108.3 | 128.7 | 148.0 | 186.3 |
| 22 | 43.9 | 54.4 | 64.6 | 75.0 | 85.4 | 96.7 | 107.3 | 118.9 | 130.6 | 154.9 | 177.9 | 223.7 |
| 24 | 51.9 | 64.0 | 76.2 | 88.6 | 101.2 | 113.6 | 126.9 | 140.8 | 155.0 | 183.6 | 210.0 | 263.7 |
| 26 | 60.3 | 74.5 | 88.6 | 103.2 | 117.8 | 133.0 | 148.6 | 164.7 | 180.7 | 213.7 | 244.7 | 306.9 |
| 28 | 68.9 | 85.6 | 102.1 | 118.9 | 135.9 | 154.0 | 172.2 | 191.3 | 208.5 | 246.0 | 282.0 | 352.3 |
| 30 | 78.5 | 97.1 | 115.8 | 135.6 | 155.7 | 175.9 | 196.7 | 218.4 | 238.6 | 282.1 | 322.6 | 403.7 |
| 32 | | 109.9 | 131.3 | 153.6 | 176.0 | 200.7 | 224.4 | 248.9 | 272.1 | 320.7 | 366.1 | 458.2 |
| 34 | | 123.8 | 148.1 | 172.7 | 198.8 | 225.5 | 253.1 | 280.6 | 307.0 | 362.3 | 413.5 | 517.4 |
| 36 | | | 165.5 | 193.0 | 222.4 | 252.4 | 283.2 | 314.2 | 343.9 | 405.7 | 463.5 | 579.5 |
| 38 | | | 183.8 | 214.6 | 247.4 | 280.9 | 315.5 | 350.1 | 382.9 | 452.0 | 516.0 | 645.1 |
| 40 | | | | 237.6 | 273.7 | 310.8 | 349.1 | 386.5 | 423.8 | 500.3 | 571.2 | 715.8 |
| 42 | | | | 260.5 | 300.3 | 342.2 | 384.3 | 426.8 | 468.4 | 551.2 | 628.6 | 787.2 |
| 44 | | | | | 328.8 | 374.6 | 422.4 | 467.5 | 513.1 | 603.9 | 688.6 | 861.8 |
| 46 | | | | | 359.0 | 408.6 | 461.0 | 510.3 | 559.9 | 661.1 | 753.8 | 942.0 |
| 48 | | | | | 391.2 | 445.3 | 501.1 | 554.7 | 608.7 | 718.6 | 818.6 | 1,023.0 |
| 50 | | | | | 423.5 | 482.0 | 544.6 | 602.8 | 661.4 | 777.8 | 886.0 | 1,106.4 |

Source: U. S. Forest Service, Region 1.

# WESTERN HEMLOCK

## Table 27. Cubic-Foot Volume*

Western Oregon and Washington

| D.b.h. (in.) | Total height in feet | | | | | | | | | | | | | | | | | | | | | | |
|---|---|---|---|---|---|---|---|---|---|---|---|---|---|---|---|---|---|---|---|---|---|---|---|
| | 40 | 50 | 60 | 70 | 80 | 90 | 100 | 110 | 120 | 130 | 140 | 150 | 160 | 170 | 180 | 190 | 200 | 210 | 220 | 230 | 240 | 250 | 260 |
| 6 | 3.0 | 4.0 | 5.1 | 6.2 | 7.5 | 7.7 | | | | | | | | | | | | | | | | | |
| 8 | 5.1 | 6.9 | 8.7 | 10.5 | 12.4 | 14. | 16 | 18 | | | | | | | | | | | | | | | |
| 10 | | 11. | 13. | 16. | 18. | 21. | 23 | 26 | 29 | 31 | 34 | | | | | | | | | | | | |
| 12 | | | 19 | 23 | 26 | 30 | 34 | 37 | 41 | 44 | 48 | 51 | 54 | 58 | | | | | | | | | |
| 14 | | | 26 | 31 | 36 | 41 | 45 | 50 | 54 | 59 | 64 | 68 | 73 | 78 | | | | | | | | | |
| 16 | | | 34 | 40 | 46 | 52 | 58 | 64 | 70 | 76 | 82 | 88 | 94 | 101 | 107 | 114 | 120 | | | | | | |
| 18 | | | 43 | 50 | 57 | 65 | 73 | 80 | 87 | 95 | 103 | 110 | 117 | 125 | 132 | 139 | 146 | | | | | | |
| 20 | | | | 61 | 70 | 80 | 89 | 98 | 107 | 117 | 126 | 133 | 142 | 151 | 159 | 167 | 175 | 183 | 191 | | | | |
| 22 | | | | | 84 | 95 | 106 | 117 | 128 | 138 | 148 | 158 | 168 | 178 | 188 | 197 | 206 | 215 | 225 | | | | |
| 24 | | | | | | 110 | 124 | 138 | 150 | 162 | 173 | 184 | 195 | 207 | 219 | 229 | 240 | 251 | 261 | | | | |
| 26 | | | | | | 125 | 144 | 158 | 172 | 185 | 198 | 210 | 223 | 237 | 250 | 262 | 275 | 288 | 300 | | | | |
| 28 | | | | | | | 164 | 180 | 195 | 210 | 225 | 239 | 254 | 270 | 284 | 298 | 312 | 326 | 340 | | | | |
| 30 | | | | | | | 185 | 202 | 219 | 236 | 252 | 268 | 285 | 303 | 320 | 335 | 350 | 366 | 382 | | | | |
| 32 | | | | | | | 208 | 238 | 245 | 263 | 281 | 299 | 319 | 338 | 356 | 373 | 391 | 410 | 425 | 450 | 470 | | |
| 34 | | | | | | | 231 | 251 | 270 | 291 | 312 | 332 | 353 | 375 | 395 | 415 | 435 | 455 | 475 | 500 | 520 | | |
| 36 | | | | | | | | | | 320 | 345 | 365 | 390 | 415 | 435 | 455 | 480 | 500 | 525 | 550 | 570 | | |
| 38 | | | | | | | | | | | 380 | 405 | 430 | 455 | 480 | 500 | 525 | 550 | 575 | 600 | 625 | | |
| 40 | | | | | | | | | | | 415 | 440 | 465 | 495 | 520 | 545 | 570 | 600 | 625 | 650 | 675 | 700 | 725 |
| 42 | | | | | | | | | | | | 475 | 505 | 540 | 565 | 590 | 620 | 650 | 675 | 700 | 730 | 760 | 790 |
| 44 | | | | | | | | | | | | 515 | 545 | 580 | 610 | 640 | 670 | 700 | 730 | 760 | 790 | 820 | 850 |
| 46 | | | | | | | | | | | | 550 | 590 | 625 | 660 | 690 | 720 | 750 | 780 | 810 | 845 | 880 | 910 |
| 48 | | | | | | | | | | | | 590 | 640 | 675 | 710 | 740 | 770 | 805 | 840 | 870 | 905 | 940 | 980 |
| 50 | | | | | | | | | | | | 630 | 675 | 720 | 755 | 790 | 820 | 860 | 895 | 930 | 970 | 1,010 | 1,045 |
| 52 | | | | | | | | | | | | | 725 | 770 | 810 | 840 | 875 | 915 | 955 | 995 | 1,035 | 1,075 | 1,110 |
| 54 | | | | | | | | | | | | | 770 | 820 | 860 | 895 | 930 | 975 | 1,015 | 1,055 | 1,095 | 1,135 | 1,175 |
| 56 | | | | | | | | | | | | | 815 | 865 | 910 | 945 | 985 | 1,030 | 1,070 | 1,110 | 1,155 | 1,195 | 1,235 |
| 58 | | | | | | | | | | | | | 860 | 915 | 960 | 1,005 | 1,045 | 1,085 | 1,125 | 1,170 | 1,215 | 1,255 | 1,300 |
| 60 | | | | | | | | | | | | | 900 | 960 | 1,015 | 1,055 | 1,095 | 1,140 | 1,180 | 1,225 | 1,275 | 1,320 | 1,370 |

* Gross volume including stump and tip but not bark. Basis, 1,572 trees. This table is for a Girard Form Class of 84. For trees with form class above 84, add 1⅔ percent to tabular volumes per form class; for trees below, subtract 1⅔ percent.
Source: W. H. Meyer, Volume tables for western hemlock, Pacific Northwest Forest Exp. Sta., 1933.

# WESTERN HEMLOCK

## Table 28.  Volume in Cords *

Volume by total height of trees

| Diameter at breast height (inches) | 40 feet Cords | 50 feet Cords | 60 feet Cords | 70 feet Cords | 80 feet Cords | 90 feet Cords | 100 feet Cords | 110 feet Cords | 120 feet Cords | 130 feet Cords | 140 feet Cords | 150 feet Cords | 160 feet Cords | 170 feet Cords | 180 feet Cords | 190 feet Cords | 200 feet Cords | 210 feet Cords | 220 feet Cords | 230 feet Cords | 240 feet Cords | 250 feet Cords | 260 feet Cords |
|---|---|---|---|---|---|---|---|---|---|---|---|---|---|---|---|---|---|---|---|---|---|---|---|
| 8  | 0.03 | 0.05 | 0.07 | 0.08 | 0.09 | 0.10 | 0.12 | 0.14 | .25 | .27 | .29 | .48 | .51 | .55 | | | | | | | | | |
| 10 | | .09 | .11 | .14 | .15 | .18 | .20 | .22 | .39 | .41 | .45 | .68 | .73 | .78 | | | | | | | | | |
| 12 | | | .18 | .22 | .24 | .28 | .32 | .35 | .54 | .59 | .64 | .91 | .97 | 1.04 | 1.10 | 1.18 | 1.24 | | | | | | |
| 14 | | | .26 | .31 | .36 | .41 | .45 | .50 | .72 | .79 | .85 | 1.16 | 1.24 | 1.32 | 1.40 | 1.47 | 1.54 | | | | | | |
| 16 | | | .35 | .41 | .48 | .54 | .60 | .66 | .92 | 1.01 | 1.09 | 1.42 | 1.51 | 1.61 | 1.69 | 1.78 | 1.86 | 1.95 | 2.03 | | | | |
| 18 | | | .46 | .53 | .60 | .69 | .77 | .85 | 1.14 | 1.25 | 1.34 | 1.67 | 1.78 | 1.88 | 1.99 | 2.08 | 2.18 | 2.28 | 2.38 | | | | |
| 20 | | | | .65 | .75 | .85 | .95 | 1.04 | 1.35 | 1.46 | 1.57 | 1.93 | 2.04 | 2.17 | 2.29 | 2.40 | 2.51 | 2.63 | 2.73 | | | | |
| 22 | | | | | .89 | 1.01 | 1.12 | 1.24 | 1.57 | 1.70 | 1.81 | 2.16 | 2.30 | 2.44 | 2.58 | 2.70 | 2.83 | 2.97 | 3.09 | | | | |
| 24 | | | | | | 1.15 | 1.30 | 1.44 | 1.77 | 1.91 | 2.04 | 2.45 | 2.60 | 2.76 | 2.91 | 3.05 | 3.19 | 3.34 | 3.48 | | | | |
| 26 | | | | | | 1.29 | 1.48 | 1.63 | 2.00 | 2.15 | 2.30 | 2.74 | 2.92 | 3.10 | 3.27 | 3.43 | 3.58 | 3.75 | 3.91 | | | | |
| 28 | | | | | | | 1.68 | 1.84 | 2.24 | 2.41 | 2.58 | 3.0 | 3.0 | 3.5 | 3.6 | 3.8 | 4.0 | 4.2 | 4.4 | 4.6 | 4.8 | | |
| 30 | | | | | | | 1.89 | 2.07 | 2.51 | 2.69 | 2.86 | 3.4 | 3.3 | 3.8 | 4.0 | 4.2 | 4.5 | 4.7 | 4.9 | 5.1 | 5.3 | | |
| 32 | | | | | | | 2.13 | 2.34 | 2.8 | 3.0 | 3.2 | 3.7 | 3.6 | 4.3 | 4.5 | 4.7 | 4.9 | 5.1 | 5.4 | 5.6 | 5.9 | | |
| 34 | | | | | | | 2.4 | 2.6 | | 3.3 | 3.5 | 4.1 | 4.0 | 4.7 | 4.9 | 5.1 | 5.4 | 5.6 | 5.9 | 6.1 | 6.4 | | |
| 36 | | | | | | | | | | | 3.9 | 4.5 | 4.4 | 5.1 | 5.3 | 5.6 | 5.8 | 6.1 | 6.4 | 6.7 | 6.9 | 7.2 | 7.4 |
| 38 | | | | | | | | | | | 4.2 | 4.9 | 4.8 | 5.5 | 5.8 | 6.0 | 6.4 | 6.7 | 6.9 | 7.2 | 7.5 | 7.8 | 8.1 |
| 40 | | | | | | | | | | | 4.6 | 5.3 | 5.2 | 5.9 | 6.2 | 6.5 | 6.9 | 7.2 | 7.5 | 7.8 | 8.1 | 8.4 | 8.7 |
| 42 | | | | | | | | | | | 5.0 | 5.6 | 5.6 | 6.4 | 6.8 | 7.0 | 7.4 | 7.7 | 8.0 | 8.3 | 8.6 | 9.0 | 9.3 |
| 44 | | | | | | | | | | | 5.3 | 6.0 | 6.0 | 6.9 | 7.3 | 7.6 | 7.9 | 8.2 | 8.6 | 8.9 | 9.3 | 9.6 | 10.0 |
| 46 | | | | | | | | | | | 5.7 | 6.4 | 6.5 | 7.4 | 7.7 | 8.1 | 8.4 | 8.8 | 9.2 | 9.5 | 9.9 | 10.3 | 10.7 |
| 48 | | | | | | | | | | | 6.1 | | 6.9 | 7.9 | 8.3 | 8.6 | 9.0 | 9.4 | 9.8 | 10.2 | 10.6 | 11.0 | 11.4 |
| 50 | | | | | | | | | | | | | 7.4 | 8.4 | 8.8 | 9.2 | 9.5 | 10.0 | 10.4 | 10.8 | 11.1 | 11.6 | 12.0 |
| 52 | | | | | | | | | | | | | 7.9 | 8.9 | 9.3 | 9.7 | 10.1 | 10.5 | 10.9 | 11.4 | 11.8 | 12.2 | 12.6 |
| 54 | | | | | | | | | | | | | 8.3 | 9.4 | 9.8 | 10.3 | 10.7 | 11.1 | 11.5 | 12.0 | 12.4 | 12.7 | 13.3 |
| 56 | | | | | | | | | | | | | 8.8 | 9.8 | 10.4 | 10.8 | 11.2 | 11.7 | 12.1 | 12.5 | 13.0 | 13.5 | 14.0 |
| 58 | | | | | | | | | | | | | 9.2 | | | | | | | | | | |
| 60 | | | | | | | | | | | | | | | | | | | | | | | |

* Volume of stacked wood, peeled and usually split, in standard cords 4 by 4 by 8 ft.
Source: W. H. Meyer, Yield of even-aged stands of Sitka spruce and western hemlock, U. S. Dept. Agr., *Tech. Bull. No. 544*, 1937.

# WESTERN HEMLOCK
## Table 29. Volume in Board Feet, Scribner Decimal C Log Rule *
Western Oregon and Washington
(Volume in Tens)

| D.b.h. (in.) | Height in 32.6-ft. logs to 12-in. top inside bark | | | | | | | | | |
|---|---|---|---|---|---|---|---|---|---|---|
| | 1½ | 2 | 2½ | 3 | 3½ | 4 | 4½ | 5 | 5½ | 6 |
| 14 | 26 | 39 | 45 | | | | | | | |
| 16 | 29 | 43 | 54 | 65 | | | | | | |
| 18 | 31 | 47 | 61 | 74 | 88 | | | | | |
| 20 | 33 | 51 | 68 | 84 | 99 | 117 | | | | |
| 22 | 36 | 57 | 76 | 95 | 113 | 137 | 154 | | | |
| 24 | 39 | 63 | 84 | 106 | 130 | 154 | 174 | 200 | 225 | |
| 26 | 41 | 68 | 92 | 117 | 144 | 170 | 191 | 220 | 250 | 285 |
| 28 | 44 | 74 | 101 | 129 | 158 | 186 | 211 | 244 | 275 | 315 |
| 30 | 47 | 80 | 110 | 141 | 172 | 203 | 232 | 267 | 300 | 345 |
| 32 | | 86 | 120 | 154 | 187 | 222 | 255 | 290 | 330 | 375 |
| 34 | | 93 | 131 | 168 | 203 | 243 | 278 | 316 | 360 | 410 |
| 36 | | 100 | 142 | 181 | 220 | 264 | 300 | 342 | 390 | 440 |
| 38 | | 108 | 153 | 195 | 238 | 286 | 325 | 370 | 420 | 475 |
| 40 | | 116 | 164 | 210 | 258 | 308 | 351 | 400 | 450 | 510 |
| 42 | | 125 | 176 | 226 | 278 | 332 | 378 | 430 | 485 | 550 |
| 44 | | 133 | 188 | 242 | 298 | 357 | 405 | 460 | 520 | 585 |
| 46 | | 140 | 199 | 258 | 317 | 379 | 430 | 490 | 555 | 625 |
| 48 | | 148 | 211 | 274 | 337 | 400 | 460 | 520 | 590 | 660 |
| 50 | | 157 | 224 | 291 | 356 | 425 | 485 | 550 | 625 | 700 |
| 52 | | | 236 | 304 | 375 | 450 | 510 | 580 | 650 | 730 |
| 54 | | | 247 | 318 | 390 | 470 | 530 | 605 | 680 | 760 |
| 56 | | | 256 | 333 | 405 | 490 | 555 | 630 | 705 | 790 |
| 58 | | | 265 | 345 | 420 | 505 | 575 | 650 | 730 | 820 |
| 60 | | | 274 | 355 | 440 | 520 | 595 | 670 | 750 | 845 |

* Stump height 2 ft. Basis, 1,293 trees. This table is for a Girard Form Class of 84. For trees with form class above 84, add 1⅔ percent to tabular volumes, per form class; for trees below 84, subtract 1⅔ percent, per form class.
Source: W. H. Meyer, Volume tables for western hemlock, Pacific Northwest Forest Exp. Sta., 1933.

## WESTERN LARCH (OLD GROWTH)

### Table 30. Cubic-Foot Volume          Inland Empire

| D.b.h. (in.) | Total height in feet | | | | | | | | | | | |
|---|---|---|---|---|---|---|---|---|---|---|---|---|
| | 40 | 50 | 60 | 70 | 80 | 90 | 100 | 110 | 120 | 140 | 160 | 200 |
| **MEDIUM SITE** | | | | | | | | | | | | |
| 16 | 21.5 | 26.0 | 31.0 | 35.6 | 40.1 | 44.6 | 49.0 | 53.4 | 57.9 | 66.9 | 75.9 | 94.3 |
| 18 | 26.4 | 32.5 | 38.2 | 44.2 | 49.7 | 55.1 | 60.7 | 66.0 | 71.4 | 82.6 | 93.8 | 116.7 |
| 20 | 32.0 | 39.2 | 46.4 | 53.1 | 60.0 | 66.5 | 72.9 | 79.5 | 85.9 | 99.6 | 113.3 | 140.7 |
| 22 | 37.6 | 46.3 | 54.5 | 62.6 | 70.5 | 78.7 | 86.0 | 93.7 | 101.3 | 117.5 | 133.5 | 165.8 |
| 24 | 43.6 | 53.4 | 63.0 | 72.5 | 81.9 | 90.5 | 99.5 | 108.4 | 117.6 | 136.3 | 154.4 | 191.8 |
| 26 | 49.6 | 60.8 | 71.6 | 82.6 | 93.1 | 103.5 | 113.6 | 123.8 | 133.8 | 155.2 | 175.8 | 218.3 |
| 28 | 55.5 | 68.4 | 80.9 | 93.0 | 105.0 | 117.1 | 128.6 | 140.2 | 151.0 | 174.6 | 198.2 | 245.4 |
| 30 | 61.9 | 75.8 | 89.6 | 103.6 | 117.5 | 130.6 | 143.2 | 156.2 | 168.7 | 195.6 | 221.4 | 275.1 |
| 32 | | 83.8 | 99.1 | 114.6 | 129.4 | 145.1 | 159.3 | 173.5 | 187.5 | 216.7 | 245.3 | 304.7 |
| 34 | | 92.4 | 109.5 | 125.9 | 142.9 | 159.3 | 175.4 | 191.2 | 206.6 | 239.5 | 271.0 | 336.6 |
| 36 | | | 120.0 | 138.0 | 156.7 | 174.7 | 192.3 | 210.1 | 227.1 | 263.2 | 298.0 | 370.1 |
| 38 | | | 130.8 | 150.7 | 171.2 | 190.8 | 210.0 | 229.6 | 248.1 | 287.6 | 325.5 | 404.3 |
| 40 | | | | 164.5 | 186.8 | 208.2 | 229.2 | 249.8 | 270.8 | 313.8 | 355.3 | 442.6 |
| 42 | | | | 178.5 | 202.7 | 226.7 | 249.5 | 272.7 | 295.6 | 341.6 | 386.6 | 481.6 |
| 44 | | | | | 220.1 | 246.1 | 271.8 | 296.1 | 321.0 | 370.9 | 419.8 | 523.0 |
| 46 | | | | | 238.8 | 266.9 | 294.7 | 321.1 | 348.0 | 403.4 | 456.6 | 568.8 |
| 48 | | | | | 258.3 | 288.8 | 317.8 | 346.3 | 375.4 | 435.1 | 492.4 | 613.5 |
| 50 | | | | | 278.4 | 311.2 | 345.6 | 374.4 | 405.8 | 468.9 | 530.6 | 661.0 |

Source: U. S. Forest Service, Region 1.

## PONDEROSA PINE (SECOND GROWTH)

### Table 31. Cubic-Foot Volume *          Entire Range

| D.b.h. (in.) | Total height in feet | | | | | | | | | | | | | |
|---|---|---|---|---|---|---|---|---|---|---|---|---|---|---|
| | 20 | 30 | 40 | 50 | 60 | 70 | 80 | 90 | 100 | 110 | 120 | 130 | 140 | 150 |
| 4 | 0.8 | 1.2 | 1.5 | 1.9 | 2.2 | | | | | | | | | |
| 6 | 1.7 | 2.3 | 2.9 | 3.6 | 4.2 | 4.8 | 5.5 | | | | | | | |
| 8 | | 3.7 | 4.9 | 6.0 | 7.1 | 8.3 | 9.5 | 11 | 12 | | | | | |
| 10 | | 5.8 | 7.7 | 9.5 | 11.5 | 12.5 | 15.5 | 17.5 | 20 | 22 | 24 | | | |
| 12 | | | 11 | 14 | 17 | 20 | 23 | 26 | 29 | 32 | 35 | 38 | | |
| 14 | | | 15 | 19 | 23 | 28 | 32 | 36 | 40 | 44 | 48 | 52 | 56 | |
| 16 | | | 20 | 26 | 31 | 36 | 42 | 47 | 52 | 58 | 63 | 68 | 72 | 76 |
| 18 | | | 26 | 33 | 40 | 46 | 53 | 60 | 66 | 74 | 80 | 86 | 92 | 98 |
| 20 | | | 32 | 41 | 50 | 58 | 66 | 74 | 83 | 91 | 99 | 107 | 114 | 121 |
| 22 | | | | 49 | 60 | 70 | 80 | 90 | 100 | 110 | 119 | 129 | 137 | 146 |
| 24 | | | | 59 | 71 | 83 | 96 | 107 | 119 | 130 | 141 | 151 | 162 | 171 |
| 26 | | | | 70 | 84 | 98 | 112 | 125 | 139 | 152 | 164 | 177 | 186 | 199 |
| 28 | | | | | 98 | 114 | 130 | 144 | 160 | 175 | 189 | 203 | 216 | 229 |
| 30 | | | | | 112 | 130 | 148 | 165 | 182 | 198 | 214 | 230 | 244 | 259 |
| 32 | | | | | 126 | 146 | 167 | 186 | 204 | 222 | 239 | 257 | 272 | 288 |
| 34 | | | | | 140 | 165 | 186 | 208 | 226 | 246 | 265 | 284 | 300 | 316 |
| 36 | | | | | | 182 | 206 | 230 | 250 | 271 | 290 | 311 | 328 | 344 |
| 38 | | | | | | 200 | 227 | 252 | 274 | 296 | 315 | 337 | 356 | 374 |
| 40 | | | | | | 220 | 248 | 274 | 298 | 321 | 341 | 364 | 384 | 404 |
| 42 | | | | | | | 269 | 296 | 322 | 346 | 367 | 391 | 412 | 433 |
| 44 | | | | | | | 290 | 318 | 346 | 371 | 393 | 418 | 440 | 462 |
| 46 | | | | | | | | 340 | 370 | 396 | 419 | 445 | 468 | 492 |
| 48 | | | | | | | | 362 | 394 | 421 | 445 | 472 | 496 | 521 |
| 50 | | | | | | | | 385 | 418 | 446 | 471 | 499 | 524 | 550 |

* Data collected in Oregon, California, Arizona, Colorado, New Mexico, and Montana. Basis, 2,947 trees. Volume includes peeled stump, stem, and top. Standard deviation 11.8 percent. Approximate Girard form class, 76.
Source: W. H. Meyer, Yield of even-aged stands of ponderosa pine, U. S. Dept. Agr., *Tech. Bull. No. 630*, 1938.

# PONDEROSA PINE (SECOND GROWTH)

## Table 32.  Volume in Board Feet, Scribner Rule *  Entire Range
### (Volume in Tens)

| D.b.h. (in.) | \_\_ | | | | | Total height in feet | | | | | | |
|---|---|---|---|---|---|---|---|---|---|---|---|---|
| | 40 | 50 | 60 | 70 | 80 | 90 | 100 | 110 | 120 | 130 | 140 | 150 |
| 10 | 1 | 1 | 2 | 2 | 3 | 3 | 4 | 4 | 5 | | | |
| 12 | 2 | 4 | 5 | 6 | 8 | 10 | 11 | 12 | 14 | 15 | | |
| 14 | 4 | 6 | 8 | 11 | 13 | 15 | 18 | 20 | 22 | 24 | 26 | |
| 16 | 6 | 10 | 12 | 16 | 18 | 21 | 24 | 27 | 30 | 34 | 36 | 40 |
| 18 | 9 | 13 | 17 | 21 | 24 | 29 | 34 | 37 | 41 | 46 | 50 | 54 |
| 20 | 12 | 17 | 22 | 27 | 32 | 37 | 44 | 48 | 53 | 58 | 64 | 69 |
| 22 | | 21 | 27 | 34 | 41 | 47 | 54 | 60 | 67 | 74 | 81 | 89 |
| 24 | | 26 | 33 | 42 | 50 | 58 | 66 | 74 | 83 | 91 | 100 | 109 |
| 26 | | | 41 | 51 | 60 | 69 | 79 | 90 | 100 | 109 | 119 | 129 |
| 28 | | | 48 | 59 | 70 | 82 | 94 | 106 | 117 | 127 | 138 | 148 |
| 30 | | | 56 | 69 | 81 | 96 | 109 | 122 | 134 | 145 | 157 | 167 |
| 32 | | | 64 | 80 | 95 | 110 | 124 | 138 | 151 | 163 | 175 | 186 |
| 34 | | | 74 | 91 | 109 | 124 | 140 | 154 | 168 | 181 | 194 | 206 |
| 36 | | | | 104 | 123 | 138 | 156 | 171 | 185 | 199 | 213 | 226 |
| 38 | | | | 117 | 137 | 152 | 172 | 188 | 203 | 218 | 232 | 247 |
| 40 | | | | 130 | 150 | 167 | 188 | 204 | 221 | 237 | 252 | 268 |
| 42 | | | | | 163 | 182 | 203 | 221 | 238 | 256 | 273 | 289 |
| 44 | | | | | 176 | 197 | 218 | 238 | 257 | 275 | 293 | 309 |
| 46 | | | | | | 211 | 234 | 255 | 275 | 294 | 313 | 329 |
| 48 | | | | | | 225 | 249 | 272 | 293 | 313 | 333 | 350 |
| 50 | | | | | | 240 | 264 | 289 | 311 | 332 | 353 | 371 |

* Data collected in Oregon, California, Montana, Colorado, Arizona, and New Mexico. Basis, 2,865 trees. Stump height, 1 to 2 ft. Trees scaled in 16.3-ft. log lengths to 8-in. top d.i.b. Standard deviation 17.8 percent. Approximate Girard form class, 76.
Source: *Ibid.*

## Table 33.  Volume in Board Feet, International ⅛-In. Rule †  Entire Range
### (Volume in Tens)

| D.b.h. (in.) | | | | | | Total height in feet | | | | | | |
|---|---|---|---|---|---|---|---|---|---|---|---|---|
| | 40 | 50 | 60 | 70 | 80 | 90 | 100 | 110 | 120 | 130 | 140 | 150 |
| 8 | 1 | 1 | 1 | 2 | 2 | | | | | | | |
| 10 | 2 | 3 | 4 | 6 | 7 | 9 | 10 | 12 | 13 | | | |
| 12 | 4 | 6 | 8 | 10 | 12 | 15 | 17 | 19 | 22 | 24 | | |
| 14 | 6 | 9 | 12 | 16 | 19 | 22 | 25 | 28 | 32 | 35 | 38 | |
| 16 | 9 | 13 | 17 | 22 | 26 | 30 | 34 | 38 | 43 | 47 | 52 | 56 |
| 18 | 12 | 17 | 22 | 28 | 34 | 39 | 44 | 50 | 55 | 61 | 66 | 72 |
| 20 | 15 | 22 | 28 | 35 | 42 | 49 | 56 | 62 | 70 | 76 | 84 | 91 |
| 22 | | 27 | 35 | 43 | 52 | 60 | 68 | 76 | 85 | 94 | 103 | 111 |
| 24 | | 33 | 42 | 52 | 62 | 72 | 82 | 93 | 102 | 112 | 122 | 131 |
| 26 | | | 50 | 62 | 74 | 86 | 98 | 110 | 121 | 132 | 142 | 152 |
| 28 | | | 59 | 73 | 87 | 101 | 114 | 127 | 139 | 151 | 162 | 173 |
| 30 | | | 69 | 85 | 101 | 117 | 131 | 144 | 158 | 170 | 182 | 194 |
| 32 | | | 79 | 98 | 116 | 133 | 148 | 161 | 176 | 190 | 202 | 216 |
| 34 | | | 90 | 112 | 130 | 149 | 164 | 179 | 194 | 210 | 224 | 238 |
| 36 | | | | 125 | 144 | 164 | 180 | 197 | 214 | 230 | 245 | 260 |
| 38 | | | | 138 | 158 | 179 | 197 | 215 | 234 | 250 | 266 | 283 |
| 40 | | | | 151 | 172 | 195 | 214 | 234 | 254 | 272 | 289 | 307 |
| 42 | | | | | 187 | 211 | 232 | 253 | 274 | 293 | 312 | 331 |
| 44 | | | | | 202 | 226 | 250 | 272 | 294 | 315 | 335 | 355 |
| 46 | | | | | | 243 | 268 | 291 | 314 | 337 | 359 | 380 |
| 48 | | | | | | 260 | 286 | 311 | 335 | 359 | 383 | 406 |
| 50 | | | | | | 278 | 306 | 331 | 357 | 382 | 407 | 432 |

† Data collected in Oregon, California, Montana, Arizona, Colorado, and New Mexico. Basis, 2,865 trees. Stump height 1 to 2 ft. Trees scaled in 16.3-ft. log lengths to 6-in. top d.i.b. Standard deviation 18.4 percent. Approximate Girard form class, 76.
Source: *Ibid.*

## PONDEROSA PINE (BLACKJACK AND IMMATURE)

### Table 34.  Volume in Board Feet, Scribner Rule [a]

Arizona

| D.b.h. O.b. (in.) | I.b. (in.) | Number of 16.3-ft. logs | | | | | |
|---|---|---|---|---|---|---|---|
| | | 1 [b] | 2 | 3 | 4 | 5 | 6 |
| 10 | 8.07 | 39 | 69 | 94 | | | |
| 12 | 9.83 | 42 | 82 | 117 | | | |
| 14 | 11.64 | 46 | 100 | 146 | 185 | | |
| 16 | 13.45 | 51 | 123 | 183 | 234 | | |
| 18 | 15.23 | | 150 | 227 | 294 | 354 | |
| 20 | 17.04 | | 182 | 281 | 366 | 443 | |
| 22 | 18.85 | | 221 | 344 | 451 | 548 | |
| 24 | 20.60 | | | 417 | 548 | 668 | 779 |
| 26 | 22.47 | | | 505 | 666 | 813 | 949 |
| 28 | 24.22 | | | 598 | 791 | 967 | 1,130 |
| 30 | 26.00 | | | 706 | 936 | 1,144 | 1,339 |
| 32 | 27.85 | | | | 1,104 | 1,351 | 1,582 |
| 34 | 29.60 | | | | | 1,568 | 1,837 |

[a] Basis, 219 trees. Stump height, 1 ft. Top d.i.b., 8 in. Average percentage deviation, 5.69.
[b] 1⅛ logs.
Source: Geraldine Peterson, Merchantable height volume table for immature ponderosa pine, Southwestern Forest & Range Exp. Sta., *Res. Note No. 73*, 1939.

## PONDEROSA PINE (MATURE)

### Table 35.  Volume in Board Feet, Scribner Rule [a]

Arizona

| D.b.h. O.b. (in.) | I.b. (in.) | Number of 16.3-ft. logs | | | | | | | |
|---|---|---|---|---|---|---|---|---|---|
| | | 1 [b] | 2 | 3 | 4 | 5 | 6 | 7 | 8 |
| 10 | 9.10 | 38 | 79 | | | | | | |
| 12 | 10.50 | 39 | 90 | 140 | | | | | |
| 14 | 12.08 | 42 | 104 | 167 | 227 | | | | |
| 16 | 13.80 | 44 | 123 | 202 | 277 | | | | |
| 18 | 15.65 | 48 | 146 | 246 | 340 | 430 | | | |
| 20 | 17.50 | 52 | 174 | 296 | 412 | 523 | 632 | | |
| 22 | 19.35 | | 205 | 355 | 496 | 632 | 765 | | |
| 24 | 21.30 | | 243 | 424 | 596 | 761 | 922 | 1,079 | |
| 26 | 23.25 | | 285 | 502 | 707 | 906 | 1,098 | 1,286 | |
| 28 | 25.10 | | 329 | 585 | 826 | 1,059 | 1,286 | 1,506 | 1,724 |
| 30 | 27.10 | | 383 | 684 | 968 | 1,243 | 1,510 | 1,770 | 2,026 |
| 32 | 29.00 | | | 788 | 1,118 | 1,436 | 1,746 | 2,048 | 2,345 |
| 34 | 31.00 | | | 907 | 1,288 | 1,656 | 2,014 | 2,363 | 2,707 |
| 36 | 32.90 | | | 1,028 | 1,462 | 1,880 | 2,288 | 2,685 | 3,076 |
| 38 | 34.80 | | | 1,162 | 1,655 | 2,130 | 2,592 | 3,043 | 3,487 |
| 40 | 36.80 | | | | 1,869 | 2,407 | 2,930 | 3,440 | 3,943 |
| 42 | 38.80 | | | | 2,100 | 2,705 | 3,294 | 3,869 | 4,435 |

[a] Basis: 174 trees. Stump height, 1 ft. Top d.i.b., 8 in. Average percentage deviation, 5.69.
[b] 1⅛ logs.
Source: Geraldine Peterson, Merchantable height volume table for mature ponderosa pine, Southwestern Forest & Range Exp. Sta., *Res. Note No. 74*, 1939.

# PONDEROSA PINE, DOUGLAS-FIR, AND WHITE FIR IN CALIFORNIA *

## Table 36. Volume in Board Feet, Scribner Decimal C Rule
### Girard Form Class 80

| D.b.h. and number of logs to 10-inch d.i.b | Log number and volume (board feet in tens) | | | | | | | | | | | | | Tree volume | | Utilized length 16-ft. logs |
|---|---|---|---|---|---|---|---|---|---|---|---|---|---|---|---|---|
| | 1 | 2 | 3 | 4 | 5 | 6 | 7 | 8 | 9 | 10 | 11 | 12 | 13 | 10-inch top | Utilized top | |
| 12 - 1 | 5 | | | | | | | | | | | | | 5 | 8 | 1.9 |
| 14 - 1 | 7 | | | | | | | | | | | | | 7 | 11 | 1.8 |
| 2 | 7 | 6 | | | | | | | | | | | | 13 | 14 | 2.5 |
| 16 - 1 | 10 | | | | | | | | | | | | | 10 | 12 | 1.5 |
| 2 | 10 | 6 | | | | | | | | | | | | 16 | 17 | 2.1 |
| 3 | 10 | 8 | 6 | | | | | | | | | | | 24 | 25 | 3.2 |
| 4 | 10 | 9 | 8 | 6 | | | | | | | | | | 33 | 34 | 4.3 |
| 18 - 1 | 13 | | | | | | | | | | | | | 13 | 15 | 1.5 |
| 2 | 13 | 6 | | | | | | | | | | | | 19 | 19 | 2.0 |
| 3 | 13 | 10 | 6 | | | | | | | | | | | 29 | 28 | 2.9 |
| 4 | 13 | 11 | 9 | 6 | | | | | | | | | | 39 | 38 | 3.9 |
| 5 | 13 | 12 | 10 | 8 | 6 | | | | | | | | | 49 | 48 | 4.9 |
| 20 - 2 | 17 | 6 | | | | | | | | | | | | 23 | 23 | 1.9 |
| 3 | 17 | 12 | 6 | | | | | | | | | | | 35 | 34 | 2.8 |
| 4 | 17 | 14 | 10 | 6 | | | | | | | | | | 47 | 46 | 3.7 |
| 5 | 17 | 15 | 12 | 9 | 6 | | | | | | | | | 59 | 58 | 4.7 |
| 6 | 17 | 15 | 14 | 11 | 9 | 6 | | | | | | | | 72 | 70 | 5.6 |
| 7 | 17 | 16 | 14 | 12 | 11 | 8 | 6 | | | | | | | 84 | 83 | 6.6 |
| 22 - 2 | 20 | 6 | | | | | | | | | | | | 26 | 27 | 1.8 |
| 3 | 20 | 14 | 6 | | | | | | | | | | | 40 | 40 | 2.7 |
| 4 | 20 | 17 | 12 | 6 | | | | | | | | | | 55 | 54 | 3.6 |
| 5 | 20 | 18 | 15 | 10 | 6 | | | | | | | | | 69 | 69 | 4.6 |
| 6 | 20 | 18 | 16 | 13 | 10 | 6 | | | | | | | | 83 | 81 | 5.5 |
| 7 | 20 | 19 | 17 | 15 | 12 | 9 | 6 | | | | | | | 98 | 95 | 6.4 |
| 8 | 20 | 19 | 18 | 16 | 14 | 12 | 9 | 6 | | | | | | 114 | 111 | 7.3 |
| 24 - 2 | 25 | 6 | | | | | | | | | | | | 31 | 29 | 1.8 |
| 3 | 25 | 16 | 6 | | | | | | | | | | | 47 | 47 | 2.7 |
| 4 | 25 | 20 | 13 | 6 | | | | | | | | | | 64 | 63 | 3.6 |
| 5 | 25 | 21 | 17 | 12 | 6 | | | | | | | | | 81 | 79 | 4.5 |
| 6 | 25 | 22 | 19 | 15 | 11 | 6 | | | | | | | | 98 | 95 | 5.4 |
| 7 | 25 | 23 | 20 | 17 | 14 | 10 | 6 | | | | | | | 115 | 112 | 6.3 |
| 8 | 25 | 23 | 21 | 19 | 16 | 13 | 9 | 6 | | | | | | 132 | 129 | 7.2 |
| 9 | 25 | 23 | 22 | 20 | 18 | 15 | 12 | 9 | 6 | | | | | 150 | 145 | 8.2 |
| 26 - 2 | 30 | 6 | | | | | | | | | | | | 36 | 34 | 1.8 |
| 3 | 30 | 18 | 6 | | | | | | | | | | | 54 | 54 | 2.7 |
| 4 | 30 | 23 | 15 | 6 | | | | | | | | | | 74 | 74 | 3.6 |
| 5 | 30 | 25 | 20 | 13 | 6 | | | | | | | | | 94 | 93 | 4.5 |
| 6 | 30 | 26 | 22 | 18 | 12 | 6 | | | | | | | | 114 | 112 | 5.4 |
| 7 | 30 | 27 | 24 | 20 | 16 | 11 | 6 | | | | | | | 134 | 131 | 6.3 |
| 8 | 30 | 27 | 25 | 22 | 18 | 15 | 10 | 6 | | | | | | 153 | 149 | 7.2 |
| 9 | 30 | 28 | 25 | 23 | 20 | 17 | 14 | 10 | 6 | | | | | 173 | 169 | 8.1 |
| 28 - 2 | 35 | 6 | | | | | | | | | | | | 41 | 40 | 1.8 |
| 3 | 35 | 21 | 6 | | | | | | | | | | | 62 | 63 | 2.7 |
| 4 | 35 | 27 | 17 | 6 | | | | | | | | | | 85 | 84 | 3.6 |
| 5 | 35 | 29 | 23 | 14 | 6 | | | | | | | | | 107 | 105 | 4.4 |
| 6 | 35 | 30 | 26 | 20 | 13 | 6 | | | | | | | | 130 | 128 | 5.3 |
| 7 | 35 | 31 | 28 | 23 | 18 | 12 | 6 | | | | | | | 153 | 150 | 6.2 |
| 8 | 35 | 32 | 29 | 25 | 21 | 16 | 11 | 6 | | | | | | 175 | 171 | 7.1 |
| 9 | 35 | 32 | 30 | 27 | 23 | 19 | 15 | 10 | 6 | | | | | 197 | 191 | 8.0 |
| 10 | 35 | 32 | 30 | 28 | 25 | 22 | 18 | 14 | 10 | 6 | | | | 220 | 213 | 8.9 |
| 30 - 3 | 40 | 23 | 6 | | | | | | | | | | | 69 | 71 | 2.7 |
| 4 | 40 | 31 | 18 | 6 | | | | | | | | | | 95 | 95 | 3.5 |
| 5 | 40 | 34 | 25 | 16 | 6 | | | | | | | | | 121 | 120 | 4.4 |
| 6 | 40 | 35 | 29 | 22 | 14 | 6 | | | | | | | | 146 | 145 | 5.3 |
| 7 | 40 | 36 | 31 | 26 | 20 | 13 | 6 | | | | | | | 172 | 170 | 6.2 |
| 8 | 40 | 37 | 33 | 29 | 24 | 18 | 12 | 6 | | | | | | 199 | 196 | 7.1 |
| 9 | 40 | 37 | 34 | 30 | 27 | 22 | 16 | 11 | 6 | | | | | 223 | 217 | 8.0 |
| 10 | 40 | 38 | 35 | 32 | 29 | 24 | 20 | 16 | 11 | 6 | | | | 251 | 244 | 8.9 |

* The increase in board-foot volumes in this table for each Girard form class is 3 percent.

## Table 36. Volume in Board Feet, Scribner Decimal C Rule (Continued)

| D.b.h. and number of logs to 10-inch d.i.b | Log number and volume (board feet in tens) | | | | | | | | | | | | | Tree volume | | Utilized length 16-ft. logs |
|---|---|---|---|---|---|---|---|---|---|---|---|---|---|---|---|---|
| | 1 | 2 | 3 | 4 | 5 | 6 | 7 | 8 | 9 | 10 | 11 | 12 | 13 | 10-inch top | Utilized top | |
| 32 - 3 | 46 | 26 | 6 | | | | | | | | | | | 78 | 81 | 2.6 |
| 4 | 46 | 35 | 20 | 6 | | | | | | | | | | 107 | 108 | 3.5 |
| 5 | 46 | 39 | 29 | 17 | 6 | | | | | | | | | 137 | 136 | 4.4 |
| 6 | 46 | 40 | 33 | 25 | 15 | 6 | | | | | | | | 165 | 163 | 5.3 |
| 7 | 46 | 41 | 36 | 29 | 22 | 14 | 6 | | | | | | | 194 | 191 | 6.2 |
| 8 | 46 | 42 | 38 | 32 | 27 | 20 | 12 | 6 | | | | | | 223 | 220 | 7.1 |
| 9 | 46 | 43 | 39 | 35 | 30 | 24 | 18 | 12 | 6 | | | | | 253 | 247 | 8.0 |
| 10 | 46 | 43 | 40 | 36 | 32 | 28 | 23 | 17 | 11 | 6 | | | | 282 | 275 | 8.8 |
| 11 | 46 | 43 | 40 | 37 | 34 | 30 | 26 | 21· | 16 | 11 | 6 | | | 310 | 301 | 9.7 |
| 34 - 3 | 53 | 29 | 6 | | | | | | | | | | | 88 | 92 | 2.6 |
| 4 | 53 | 40 | 22 | 6 | | | | | | | | | | 121 | 123 | 3.5 |
| 5 | 53 | 43 | 32 | 18 | 6 | | | | | | | | | 152 | 152 | 4.4 |
| 6 | 53 | 46 | 37 | 28 | 16 | 6 | | | | | | | | 186 | 185 | 5.3 |
| 7 | 53 | 47 | 40 | 33 | 24 | 15 | 6 | | | | | | | 218 | 216 | 6.2 |
| 8 | 53 | 48 | 43 | 36 | 30 | 22 | 13 | 6 | | | | | | 251 | 248 | 7.1 |
| 9 | 53 | 48 | 44 | 39 | 33 | 27 | 20 | 12 | 6 | | | | | 282 | 276 | 8.0 |
| 10 | 53 | 49 | 45 | 41 | 36 | 31 | 25 | 18 | 12 | 6 | | | | 316 | 309 | 8.8 |
| 11 | 53 | 49 | 46 | 42 | 38 | 34 | 29 | 23 | 17 | 11 | 6 | | | 348 | 341 | 9.7 |
| 36 - 3 | 59 | 32 | 6 | | | | | | | | | | | 97 | 101 | 2.6 |
| 4 | 59 | 44 | 24 | 6 | | | | | | | | | | 133 | 135 | 3.5 |
| 5 | 59 | 49 | 36 | 20 | 6 | | | | | | | | | 170 | 171 | 4.4 |
| 6 | 59 | 51 | 42 | 30 | 18 | 6 | | | | | | | | 206 | 205 | 5.3 |
| 7 | 59 | 53 | 45 | 37 | 27 | 16 | 6 | | | | | | | 243 | 240 | 6.2 |
| 8 | 59 | 53 | 48 | 41 | 33 | 24 | 14 | 6 | | | | | | 278 | 272 | 7.0 |
| 9 | 59 | 54 | 49 | 44 | 37 | 30 | 22 | 13 | 6 | | | | | 314 | 307 | 7.9 |
| 10 | 59 | 55 | 51 | 46 | 40 | 34 | 28 | 20 | 12 | 6 | | | | 351 | 345 | 8.8 |
| 11 | 59 | 55 | 51 | 47 | 43 | 38 | 32 | 25 | 18 | 12 | 6 | | | 386 | 379 | 9.7 |
| 12 | 59 | 55 | 52 | 48 | 44 | 40 | 35 | 30 | 23 | 17 | 11 | 6 | | 420 | 412 | 10.6 |
| 38 - 3 | 66 | 36 | 6 | | | | | | | | | | | 108 | 112 | 2.6 |
| 4 | 66 | 49 | 27 | 6 | | | | | | | | | | 148 | 150 | 3.5 |
| 5 | 66 | 54 | 39 | 22 | 6 | | | | | | | | | 187 | 188 | 4.4 |
| 6 | 66 | 57 | 46 | 33 | 19 | 6 | | | | | | | | 227 | 226 | 5.3 |
| 7 | 66 | 59 | 50 | 41 | 29 | 17 | 6 | | | | | | | 268 | 265 | 6.2 |
| 8 | 66 | 60 | 53 | 45 | 36 | 26 | 15 | 6· | | | | | | 307 | 301 | 7.0 |
| 9 | 66 | 61 | 55 | 49 | 41 | 32 | 23 | 14 | 6 | | | | | 347 | 340 | 7.9 |
| 10 | 66 | 62 | 56 | 51 | 45 | 38 | 30 | 22 | 13 | 6 | | | | 389 | 383 | 8.8 |
| 11 | 66 | 62 | 57 | 53 | 48 | 42 | 35 | 28 | 20 | 12 | 6 | | | 429 | 422 | 9.7 |
| 12 | 66 | 62 | 58 | 54 | 49 | 44 | 39 | 32 | 26 | 19 | 12 | 6 | | 467 | 458 | 10.6 |
| 40 - 3 | 74 | 39 | 6 | | | | | | | | | | | 119 | 124 | 2.6 |
| 4 | 74 | 54 | 29 | 6 | | | | | | | | | | 163 | 167 | 3.5 |
| 5 | 74 | 60 | 43 | 23 | 6 | | | | | | | | | 206 | 208 | 4.4 |
| 6 | 74 | .63 | 51 | 37 | 20 | 6 | | | | | | | | 251 | 251 | 5.3 |
| 7 | 74 | 66 | 55 | 45 | 32 | 18 | 6 | | | | | | | 296 | 294 | 6.2 |
| 8 | 74 | 66 | 59 | 50 | 40 | 28 | 16 | 6 | | | | | | 339 | 333· | 7.0 |
| 9 | 74 | 67 | 61 | 53 | 46 | 35 | 25 | 15 | 6 | | | | | 382 | ·375 | 7.9 |
| 10 | 74 | 68 | 62 | 56 | 49 | 41 | 33 | 23 | 14 | 6 | | | | 426 | 420 | · 8.8 |
| 11 | 74 | 69 | 64 | 58 | 53 | 46 | 39 | 30 | 21 | 13 | 6 | | | ·473 | 467 | 9.7 |
| 12 | 74 | 69 | 65 | 60 | 55 | 49 | 43 | 35 | 28 | 20 | 12 | 6 | | 516 | 508 | 10.6 |
| 42 - 4 | 82 | 60 | 31 | 6 | | | | | | | | | | 179 | 183 | 3.5 |
| 5 | 82 | 66 | 48 | 25 | 6 | | | | | | | | | 227 | 229 | 4.4 |
| 6 | 82 | 70 | 56 | 40 | 22 | 6 | | | | | | | | 276 | 276 | 5.3 |
| 7 | 82 | 72 | 61 | 49 | 34 | 19 | 6 | | | | | | | 323 | 322 | 6.2 |
| 8 | 82 | 74 | 65 | 55 | 44 | 30 | 17 | 6 | | | | | | 373 | 367 | 7.0 |
| 9 | 82 | 75 | 67 | 59 | 50 | 39 | 27 | 16 | 6 | | | | | 421 | 413 | 7.9 |
| 10 | 82 | 76 | 69 | 62 | 54 | 46 | 35 | 25 | 15 | 6 | | | | 470 | 461 | 8.8 |
| 11 | 82 | 76 | 70 | 64 | 58 | 51 | 42 | 33 | 23 | 14 | 6 | | | 519 | 509 | 9.7 |
| 12 | 82 | 77 | 71 | 66 | 60 | 54 | 47 | 39 | 30 | 21 | 13 | 6 | | 566 | 556 | 10.6 |
| 44 - 4 | 90 | 66 | 34 | 6 | | | | | | | | | | 196 | 200 | 3.5 |
| 5 | 90 | 73 | 52 | 27 | 6 | | | | | | | | | 248 | 251 | 4.4 |
| 6 | 90 | 77 | 62 | 44 | 23 | 6 | | | | | | | | 302 | 303 | 5.3 |
| 7 | 90 | 80 | 67 | 53 | 38 | 20 | 6 | | | | | | | 354 | 354 | 6.2 |
| 8 | 90 | 81 | 71 | 60 | 48 | 33 | 18 | 6 | | | | | | 407 | 401 | 7.0 |
| 9 | 90 | 82 | 74 | 65 | 54 | 42 | 29 | 17 | 6 | | | | | 459 | 451 | 7.9 |
| 10 | 90 | 83 | 76 | 68 | 59 | 49 | 39 | 27 | 16 | 6 | | | | 513 | 504 | 8.8 |
| 11 | 90 | 84 | 78 | 70 | 63 | 55 | 46 | 35 | 24 | 15 | 6 | | | 566 | 557 | 9.7 |
| 12 | 90 | 84 | 78 | 72 | 66 | 59 | 51 | 42 | 32 | 23 | 14 | 6 | | 617 | 606 | 10.6 |

## Table 36. Volume in Board Feet, Scribner Decimal C Rule (Continued)

| D.b.h. and number of logs to 10-inch d.i.b | Log number and volume (board feet in tens) | | | | | | | | | | | | | Tree volume | | Utilized length 16-ft. logs |
|---|---|---|---|---|---|---|---|---|---|---|---|---|---|---|---|---|
| | 1 | 2 | 3 | 4 | 5 | 6 | 7 | 8 | 9 | 10 | 11 | 12 | 13 | 10-inch top | Utilized top | |
| 46 - 4 | 99 | 71 | 36 | 6 | | | | | | | | | | 212 | 218 | 3.5 |
| 5 | 99 | 80 | 56 | 29 | 6 | | | | | | | | | 270 | 274 | 4.4 |
| 6 | 99 | 84 | 67 | 47 | 24 | 6 | | | | | | | | 327 | 329 | 5.3 |
| 7 | 99 | 87 | 73 | 58 | 40 | 22 | 6 | | | | | | | 385 | 384 | 6.2 |
| 8 | 99 | 89 | 78 | 65 | 51 | 35 | 19 | 6 | | | | | | 442 | 436 | 7.0 |
| 9 | 99 | 90 | 80 | 70 | 59 | 46 | 31 | 18 | 6 | | | | | 499 | 491 | 7.9 |
| 10 | 99 | 91 | 83 | 74 | 65 | 54 | 42 | 29 | 16 | 6 | | | | 559 | 550 | 8.8 |
| 11 | 99 | 92 | 85 | 77 | 69 | 60 | 50 | 38 | 26 | 15 | 6 | | | 617 | 608 | 9.7 |
| 12 | 99 | 93 | 86 | 79 | 72 | 64 | 55 | 46 | 35 | 24 | 14 | 6 | | 673 | 663 | 10.6 |
| 48 - 4 | 108 | 78 | 39 | 6 | | | | | | | | | | 231 | 238 | 3.5 |
| 5 | 108 | 87 | 61 | 31 | 6 | | | | | | | | | 293 | 297 | 4.4 |
| 6 | 108 | 92 | 73 | 51 | 26 | 6 | | | | | | | | 356 | 358 | 5.3 |
| 7 | 108 | 95 | 80 | 63 | 44 | 23 | 6 | | | | | | | 419 | 419 | 6.1 |
| 8 | 108 | 97 | 85 | 71 | 55 | 38 | 20 | 6 | | | | | | 480 | 474 | 7.0 |
| 9 | 108 | 98 | 88 | 77 | 64 | 49 | 33 | 18 | 6 | | | | | 541 | 534 | 7.9 |
| 10 | 108 | 99 | 90 | 80 | 70 | 58 | 45 | 31 | 17 | 6 | | | | 604 | 595 | 8.8 |
| 11 | 108 | 100 | 92 | 84 | 75 | 65 | 53 | 41 | 28 | 16 | 6 | | | 668 | 659 | 9.7 |
| 12 | 108 | 101 | 94 | 86 | 78 | 70 | 60 | 49 | 38 | 26 | 15 | 6 | | 731 | 721 | 10.5 |
| 13 | 108 | 102 | 95 | 88 | 81 | 74 | 64 | 55 | 45 | 35 | 24 | 14 | 6 | 791 | 779 | 11.4 |
| 50 - 5 | 118 | 94 | 66 | 33 | 6 | | | | | | | | | 317 | 322 | 4.4 |
| 6 | 118 | 100 | 78 | 55 | 28 | | | | | | | | | 385 | 387 | 5.2 |
| 7 | 118 | 103 | 86 | 68 | 47 | 24 | 6 | | | | | | | 452 | 452 | 6.1 |
| 8 | 118 | 105 | 92 | 77 | 60 | 40 | 21 | 6 | | | | | | 519 | 513 | 7.0 |
| 9 | 118 | 107 | 95 | 83 | 69 | 53 | 36 | 19 | 6 | | | | | 586 | 579 | 7.9 |
| 10 | 118 | 108 | 98 | 88 | 76 | 63 | 48 | 33 | 18 | 6 | | | | 656 | 647 | 8.8 |
| 11 | 118 | 109 | 100 | 91 | 81 | 70 | 58 | 44 | 30 | 17 | 6 | | | 724 | 714 | 9.6 |
| 12 | 118 | 110 | 102 | 94 | 85 | 76 | 65 | 53 | 40 | 28 | 16 | 6 | | 793 | 782 | 10.5 |
| 13 | 118 | 110 | 103 | 95 | 88 | 80 | 70 | 59 | 49 | 38 | 25 | 15 | 6 | 856 | 844 | 11.4 |
| 52 - 5 | 128 | 102 | 71 | 35 | 6 | | | | | | | | | 342 | 348 | 4.4 |
| 6 | 128 | 108 | 85 | 58 | 29 | 6 | | | | | | | | 414 | 418 | 5.2 |
| 7 | 128 | 112 | 93 | 73 | 50 | 25 | 6 | | | | | | | 487 | 489 | 6.1 |
| 8 | 128 | 114 | 99 | 82 | 64 | 43 | 22 | 6 | | | | | | 558 | 552 | 7.0 |
| 9 | 128 | 116 | 103 | 89 | 75 | 57 | 38 | 20 | 6 | | | | | 632 | 625 | 7.9 |
| 10 | 128 | 117 | 106 | 95 | 82 | 67 | 51 | 35 | 19 | 6 | | | | 706 | 697 | 8.8 |
| 11 | 128 | 118 | 108 | 98 | 87 | 76 | 62 | 47 | 31 | 18 | 6 | | | 779 | 770 | 9.6 |
| 12 | 128 | 119 | 110 | 101 | 92 | 81 | 69 | 57 | 43 | 29 | 16 | 6 | | 851 | 841 | 10.5 |
| 13 | 128 | 120 | 112 | 103 | 95 | 86 | 75 | 64 | 52 | 40 | 27 | 15 | 6 | 923 | 911 | 11.4 |
| 54 - 5 | 138 | 110 | 76 | 37 | 6 | | | | | | | | | 367 | 373 | 4.4 |
| 6 | 138 | 117 | 92 | 63 | 31 | 6 | | | | | | | | 447 | 451 | 5.2 |
| 7 | 138 | 120 | 100 | 78 | 53 | 27 | 6 | | | | | | | 522 | 524 | 6.1 |
| 8 | 138 | 123 | 107 | 89 | 69 | 46 | 23 | 6 | | | | | | 601 | 595 | 7.0 |
| 9 | 138 | 125 | 112 | 96 | 80 | 61 | 41 | 21 | 6 | | | | | 680 | 673 | 7.9 |
| 10 | 138 | 126 | 114 | 102 | 88 | 72 | 55 | 37 | 20 | 6 | | | | 758 | 749 | 8.8 |
| 11 | 138 | 127 | 117 | 106 | 94 | 81 | 66 | 50 | 33 | 18 | 6 | | | 836 | 827 | 9.6 |
| 12 | 138 | 129 | 119 | 109 | 99 | 87 | 75 | 61 | 46 | 31 | 17 | 6 | | 917 | 906 | 10.5 |
| 13 | 138 | 129 | 120 | 112 | 103 | 93 | 80 | 68 | 55 | 43 | 28 | 16 | 6 | 991 | 979 | 11.4 |
| 56 - 5 | 149 | 118 | 82 | 39 | 6 | | | | | | | | | 394 | 401 | 4.4 |
| 6 | 149 | 126 | 98 | 67 | 33 | 6 | | | | | | | | 479 | 483 | 5.2 |
| 7 | 149 | 130 | 108 | 84 | 57 | 28 | 6 | | | | | | | 562 | 564 | 6.1 |
| 8 | 149 | 132 | 115 | 95 | 74 | 49 | 24 | 6 | | | | | | 644 | 638 | 7.0 |
| 9 | 149 | 134 | 120 | 104 | 86 | 65 | 43 | 22 | 6 | | | | | 729 | 722 | 7.9 |
| 10 | 149 | 136 | 124 | 110 | 95 | 78 | 59 | 39 | 20 | 6 | | | | 816 | 808 | 8.8 |
| 11 | 149 | 138 | 126 | 114 | 101 | 87 | 71 | 53 | 35 | 19 | 6 | | | 899 | 890 | 9.6 |
| 12 | 149 | 138 | 128 | 117 | 106 | 94 | 80 | 65 | 48 | 32 | 18 | 6 | | 981 | 970 | 10.5 |
| 13 | 149 | 139 | 130 | 120 | 110 | 99 | 86 | 74 | 59 | 45 | 30 | 17 | 6 | 1064 | 1051 | 11.4 |
| 58 - 5 | 160 | 127 | 87 | 42 | 6 | | | | | | | | | 422 | 429 | 4.4 |
| 6 | 160 | 135 | 105 | 72 | 34 | 6 | | | | | | | | 512 | 518 | 5.2 |
| 7 | 160 | 139 | 116 | 90 | 60 | 30 | 6 | | | | | | | 601 | 603 | 6.1 |
| 8 | 160 | 142 | 124 | 102 | 79 | 52 | 26 | 6 | | | | | | 691 | 685 | 7.0 |
| 9 | 160 | 144 | 129 | 111 | 92 | 69 | 46 | 23 | 6 | | | | | 780 | 773 | 7.9 |
| 10 | 160 | 146 | 132 | 117 | 102 | 82 | 62 | 41 | 22 | 6 | | | | 870 | 861 | 8.8 |
| 11 | 160 | 148 | 135 | 122 | 108 | 93 | 76 | 57 | 37 | 20 | 6 | | | 962 | 953 | 9.6 |
| 12 | 160 | 148 | 138 | 126 | 114 | 100 | 85 | 69 | 51 | 34 | 18 | 6 | | 1049 | 1039 | 10.5 |
| 13 | 160 | 150 | 139 | 129 | 118 | 107 | 93 | 78 | 63 | 48 | 31 | 17 | 6 | 1139 | 1127 | 11.4 |

## Table 36. Volume in Board Feet, Scribner Decimal C Rule (Continued)

| D.b.h. and number of logs to 10-inch d.i.b | Log number and volume (board feet in tens) | | | | | | | | | | | | | Tree volume | | Utilized length 16-ft. logs |
| --- | --- | --- | --- | --- | --- | --- | --- | --- | --- | --- | --- | --- | --- | --- | --- | --- |
| | 1 | 2 | 3 | 4 | 5 | 6 | 7 | 8 | 9 | 10 | 11 | 12 | 13 | 10-inch top | Utilized top | |
| 60 - 6 | 172 | 144 | 112 | 76 | 36 | 6 | | | | | | | | 546 | 553 | 5.2 |
| 7 | 172 | 149 | 124 | 96 | 64 | 31 | 6 | | | | | | | 642 | 646 | 6.1 |
| 8 | 172 | 153 | 132 | 109 | 84 | 55 | 27 | 6 | | | | | | 738 | 732 | 7.0 |
| 9 | 172 | 155 | 138 | 119 | 98 | 73 | 48 | 24 | 6 | | | | | 833 | 827 | 7.9 |
| 10 | 172 | 157 | 142 | 126 | 108 | 88 | 66 | 44 | 22 | 6 | | | | 931 | 924 | 8.8 |
| 11 | 172 | 158 | 145 | 131 | 116 | 99 | 80 | 60 | 39 | 21 | 6 | | | 1027 | 1018 | 9.6 |
| 12 | 172 | 160 | 147 | 134 | 122 | 107 | 91 | 73 | 54 | 36 | 19 | 6 | | 1121 | 1110 | 10.5 |
| 13 | 172 | 160 | 149 | 138 | 127 | 114 | 99 | 84 | 67 | 51 | 33 | 18 | 6 | 1218 | 1206 | 11.4 |
| 62 - 6 | 184 | 154 | 120 | 81 | 38 | 6 | | | | | | | | 583 | 591 | 5.2 |
| 7 | 184 | 160 | 132 | 102 | 68 | 33 | 6 | | | | | | | 685 | 688 | 6.1 |
| 8 | 184 | 162 | 141 | 116 | 89 | 58 | 28 | 6 | | | | | | 784 | 778 | 7.0 |
| 9 | 184 | 165 | 147 | 127 | 104 | 78 | 51 | 25 | 6 | | | | | 887 | 881 | 7.9 |
| 10 | 184 | 168 | 151 | 134 | 116 | 94 | 70 | 46 | 23 | 6 | | | | 992 | 985 | 8.7 |
| 11 | 184 | 169 | 155 | 139 | 124 | 106 | 86 | 64 | 41 | 22 | 6 | | | 1096 | 1087 | 9.6 |
| 12 | 184 | 170 | 158 | 144 | 130 | 114 | 96 | 78 | 58 | 38 | 20 | 6 | | 1196 | 1186 | 10.5 |
| 13 | 184 | 171 | 160 | 147 | 135 | 121 | 105 | 89 | 71 | 53 | 35 | 18 | 6 | 1295 | 1283 | 11.4 |
| 64 - 6 | 196 | 165 | 127 | 86 | 40 | 6 | | | | | | | | 620 | 628 | 5.2 |
| 7 | 196 | 170 | 140 | 108 | 72 | 34 | 6 | | | | | | | 726 | 731 | 6.1 |
| 8 | 196 | 174 | 150 | 124 | 95 | 62 | 30 | 6 | | | | | | 837 | 831 | 7.0 |
| 9 | 196 | 176 | 156 | 134 | 111 | 82 | 54 | 27 | 6 | | | | | 942 | 935 | 7.9 |
| 10 | 196 | 179 | 161 | 143 | 123 | 100 | 75 | 49 | 24 | 6 | | | | 1056 | 1048 | 8.7 |
| 11 | 196 | 180 | 165 | 148 | 131 | 113 | 91 | 67 | 44 | 22 | 6 | | | 1163 | 1154 | 9.6 |
| 12 | 196 | 182 | 168 | 153 | 138 | 122 | 103 | 82 | 61 | 40 | 20 | 6 | | 1271 | 1261 | 10.5 |
| 13 | 196 | 183 | 170 | 157 | 144 | 129 | 112 | 94 | 75 | 56 | 36 | 19 | 6 | 1377 | 1366 | 11.4 |
| 66 - 6 | 209 | 175 | 135 | 91 | 42 | 6 | | | | | | | | 658 | 667 | 5.2 |
| 7 | 209 | 181 | 149 | 115 | 76 | 36 | 6 | | | | | | | 772 | 777 | 6.1 |
| 8 | 209 | 185 | 160 | 131 | 100 | 65 | 31 | 6 | | | | | | 887 | 881 | 7.0 |
| 9 | 209 | 188 | 166 | 143 | 117 | 87 | 56 | 28 | 6 | | | | | 1000 | 993 | 7.8 |
| 10 | 209 | 190 | 172 | 152 | 131 | 106 | 78 | 51 | 25 | 6 | | | | 1120 | 1112 | 8.7 |
| 11 | 209 | 192 | 176 | 158 | 140 | 119 | 96 | 71 | 46 | 23 | 6 | | | 1236 | 1228 | 9.6 |
| 12 | 209 | 193 | 179 | 163 | 147 | 129 | 109 | 87 | 64 | 42 | 21 | 6 | | 1349 | 1339 | 10.5 |
| 13 | 209 | 195 | 181 | 167 | 153 | 137 | 118 | 100 | 80 | 59 | 38 | 20 | 6 | 1463 | 1454 | 11.3 |
| 68 - 6 | 222 | 186 | 143 | 96 | 44 | 6 | | | | | | | | 697 | 707 | 5.2 |
| 7 | 222 | 192 | 158 | 122 | 80 | 38 | 6 | | | | | | | 818 | 823 | 6.1 |
| 8 | 222 | 196 | 170 | 139 | 106 | 68 | 32 | 6 | | | | | | 939 | 933 | 7.0 |
| 9 | 222 | 200 | 176 | 152 | 124 | 92 | 59 | 29 | 6 | | | | | 1060 | 1054 | 7.8 |
| 10 | 222 | 202 | 182 | 161 | 138 | 112 | 83 | 54 | 26 | 6 | | | | 1186 | 1179 | 8.7 |
| 11 | 222 | 204 | 186 | 168 | 148 | 126 | 102 | 75 | 48 | 24 | 6 | | | 1309 | 1301 | 9.6 |
| 12 | 222 | 206 | 189 | 173 | 156 | 136 | 115 | 92 | 67 | 44 | 22 | 6 | | 1428 | 1418 | 10.5 |
| 13 | 222 | 207 | 192 | 177 | 162 | 145 | 126 | 106 | 84 | 62 | 40 | 20 | 6 | 1549 | 1538 | 11.3 |
| 70 - 6 | 236 | 197 | 151 | 101 | 46 | 6 | | | | | | | | 737 | 748 | 5.2 |
| 7 | 236 | 204 | 168 | 129 | 85 | 39 | 6 | | | | | | | 867 | 873 | 6.1 |
| 8 | 236 | 208 | 180 | 147 | 112 | 72 | 33 | 6 | | | | | | 994 | 988 | 7.0 |
| 9 | 236 | 212 | 187 | 160 | 132 | 97 | 62 | 30 | 6 | | | | | 1122 | 1116 | 7.8 |
| 10 | 236 | 214 | 193 | 170 | 146 | 118 | 88 | 56 | 28 | 6 | | | | 1255 | 1247 | 8.7 |
| 11 | 236 | 217 | 198 | 177 | 157 | 134 | 107 | 79 | 50 | 25 | 6 | | | 1386 | 1378 | 9.6 |
| 12 | 236 | 218 | 201 | 183 | 165 | 144 | 122 | 97 | 71 | 46 | 23 | 6 | | 1512 | 1502 | 10.4 |
| 13 | 236 | 220 | 204 | 188 | 172 | 154 | 132 | 112 | 88 | 66 | 42 | 21 | 6 | 1641 | 1629 | 11.3 |
| 72 - 6 | 250 | 208 | 160 | 107 | 48 | 6 | | | | | | | | 779 | 791 | 5.2 |
| 7 | 250 | 216 | 177 | 136 | 89 | 41 | 6 | | | | | | | 915 | 922 | 6.1 |
| 8 | 250 | 221 | 190 | 156 | 118 | 76 | 35 | 6 | | | | | | 1052 | 1046 | 7.0 |
| 9 | 250 | 224 | 198 | 170 | 139 | 103 | 66 | 31 | 6 | | | | | 1187 | 1182 | 7.8 |
| 10 | 250 | 227 | 204 | 180 | 155 | 124 | 92 | 59 | 28 | 6 | | | | 1325 | 1319 | 8.7 |
| 11 | 250 | 229 | 209 | 188 | 165 | 141 | 113 | 83 | 53 | 26 | 6 | | | 1463 | 1454 | 9.6 |
| 12 | 250 | 231 | 213 | 194 | 174 | 153 | 129 | 103 | 75 | 48 | 24 | 6 | | 1600 | 1590 | 10.4 |
| 13 | 250 | 233 | 216 | 199 | 182 | 162 | 140 | 117 | 93 | 69 | 44 | 22 | 6 | 1733 | 1717 | 11.3 |
| 74 - 7 | 265 | 228 | 187 | 143 | 93 | 43 | 6 | | | | | | | 965 | 975 | 6.1 |
| 8 | 265 | 234 | 200 | 164 | 124 | 79 | 36 | 6 | | | | | | 1108 | 1102 | 7.0 |
| 9 | 265 | 237 | 209 | 180 | 146 | 108 | 69 | 32 | 6 | | | | | 1252 | 1247 | 7.8 |
| 10 | 265 | 240 | 216 | 190 | 163 | 131 | 97 | 62 | 30 | 6 | | | | 1400 | 1392 | 8.7 |
| 11 | 265 | 242 | 221 | 198 | 175 | 148 | 119 | 87 | 55 | 27 | 6 | | | 1543 | 1535 | 9.6 |
| 12 | 265 | 244 | 225 | 205 | 184 | 161 | 135 | 108 | 78 | 50 | 24 | 6 | | 1685 | 1671 | 10.4 |
| 13 | 265 | 246 | 228 | 210 | 192 | 171 | 147 | 124 | 98 | 72 | 46 | 23 | 6 | 1828 | 1811 | 11.3 |

Table 36. Volume in Board Feet, Scribner Decimal C Rule (Continued)

| D.b.h. and number of logs to 10-inch d.i.b | Log number and volume (board feet in tens) | | | | | | | | | | | | | Tree volume | | Utilized length 16-ft. logs |
|---|---|---|---|---|---|---|---|---|---|---|---|---|---|---|---|---|
| | 1 | 2 | 3 | 4 | 5 | 6 | 7 | 8 | 9 | 10 | 11 | 12 | 13 | 10-inch top | Utilized top | |
| 76 - 7 | 280 | 240 | 198 | 151 | 98 | 44 | 6 | | | | | | | 1017 | 1027 | 6.1 |
| 8 | 280 | 246 | 212 | 174 | 131 | 83 | 38 | 6 | | | | | | 1170 | 1164 | 7.0 |
| 9 | 280 | 249 | 221 | 189 | 154 | 113 | 72 | 33 | 6 | | | | | 1317 | 1313 | 7.8 |
| 10 | 280 | 254 | 228 | 201 | 171 | 138 | 102 | 65 | 30 | 6 | | | | 1475 | 1469 | 8.7 |
| 11 | 280 | 256 | 234 | 209 | 184 | 157 | 126 | 91 | 57 | 28 | 6 | | | 1628 | 1621 | 9.6 |
| 12 | 280 | 258 | 237 | 216 | 194 | 170 | 142 | 113 | 82 | 52 | 25 | 6 | | 1775 | 1761 | 10.4 |
| 13 | 280 | 260 | 240 | 221 | 202 | 181 | 156 | 130 | 103 | 76 | 47 | 23 | 6 | 1925 | 1910 | 11.3 |
| 78 - 7 | 295 | 254 | 208 | 158 | 103 | 46 | 6 | | | | | | | 1070 | 1080 | 6.1 |
| 8 | 295 | 259 | 222 | 182 | 138 | 87 | 39 | 6 | | | | | | 1228 | 1222 | 6.9 |
| 9 | 295 | 263 | 233 | 199 | 162 | 119 | 75 | 35 | 6 | | | | | 1387 | 1382 | 7.8 |
| 10 | 295 | 267 | 240 | 212 | 180 | 145 | 107 | 67 | 32 | 6 | | | | 1551 | 1545 | 8.7 |
| 11 | 295 | 270 | 246 | 220 | 194 | 165 | 132 | 95 | 60 | 29 | 6 | | | 1712 | 1700 | 9.6 |
| 12 | 295 | 272 | 250 | 228 | 204 | 179 | 149 | 119 | 86 | 54 | 26 | 6 | | 1868 | 1854 | 10.4 |
| 13 | 295 | 274 | 254 | 233 | 213 | 190 | 163 | 136 | 108 | 79 | 49 | 24 | .6 | 2024 | 2008 | 11.3 |
| 80 - 7 | 310 | 267 | 219 | 166 | 107 | 48 | 6 | | | | | | | 1123 | 1134 | 6.1 |
| 8 | 310 | 273 | 234 | 192 | 144 | 91 | 41 | 6 | | | | | | 1291 | 1285 | 6.9 |
| 9 | 310 | 277 | 245 | 209 | 170 | 124 | 78 | 36 | 6 | | | | | 1455 | 1447 | 7.3 |
| 10 | 310 | 281 | 253 | 222 | 189 | 152 | 112 | 71 | 33 | 6 | | | | 1629 | 1623 | 8.7 |
| 11 | 310 | 284 | 258 | 232 | 204 | 173 | 138 | 100 | 62 | 30 | 6 | | | 1797 | 1785 | 9.6 |
| 12 | 310 | 286 | 263 | 240 | 215 | 188 | 157 | 124 | 90 | 56 | 27 | 6 | | 1962 | 1948 | 10.4 |
| 13 | 310 | 288 | 267 | 245 | 224 | 200 | 171 | 143 | 113 | 82 | 51 | 25 | 6 | 2125 | 2109 | 11.3 |

Source: V. A. Clements, C. W. Stevens, and D. F. Roy, Form-class volume tables for ponderosa pine, Douglas-fir, and white fir in California, Calif. Forest & Range Exp. Sta., *Res. Note No. 60*, 1949.

## PONDEROSA PINE (OLD GROWTH)

### Table 37. Volume in Board Feet, Scribner Decimal C Rule *
Inland Empire
(Volume in Tens)

| D.b.h. (in.) | Number of 16-ft. logs | | | | | | | | | | | | D.i.b. top (in.) |
|---|---|---|---|---|---|---|---|---|---|---|---|---|---|
| | 1 | 2 | 3 | 4 | 5 | 6 | 7 | 8 | 9 | 10 | 11 | 12 | |
| 10 | 4 | 7 | | | | | | | | | | | 7 |
| 12 | 4 | 8 | 15 | | | | | | | | | | 8 |
| 14 | 5 | 10 | 17 | | | | | | | | | | 8 |
| 16 | 6 | 12 | 19 | 27 | | | | | | | | | 8 |
| 18 | 7 | 14 | 23 | 32 | 41 | | | | | | | | 8 |
| 20 | 9 | 18 | 29 | 38 | 48 | 58 | | | | | | | 9 |
| 22 | 11 | 24 | 35 | 46 | 58 | 71 | 84 | | | | | | 9 |
| 24 | 15 | 30 | 44 | 57 | 71 | 86 | 102 | | | | | | 9 |
| 26 | 20 | 39 | 55 | 70 | 87 | 104 | 123 | 143 | | | | | 10 |
| 28 | 26 | 48 | 68 | 86 | 106 | 126 | 146 | 169 | | | | | 10 |
| 30 | 35 | 60 | 83 | 105 | 128 | 150 | 172 | 196 | 230 | | | | 10 |
| 32 | | 72 | 100 | 125 | 152 | 176 | 201 | 230 | 260 | | | | 10 |
| 34 | | 86 | 119 | 148 | 176 | 200 | 230 | 260 | 290 | 330 | | | 11 |
| 36 | | 110 | 140 | 170 | 200 | 230 | 260 | 290 | 330 | 360 | | | 11 |
| 38 | | | 170 | 200 | 230 | 260 | 290 | 330 | 360 | 400 | 450 | | 11 |
| 40 | | | 200 | 230 | 260 | 290 | 330 | 370 | 400 | 450 | 500 | | 11 |
| 42 | | | 240 | 270 | 300 | 330 | 370 | 410 | 450 | 500 | 550 | | 11 |
| 44 | | | | 300 | 330 | 370 | 410 | 450 | 500 | 550 | 600 | 660 | 12 |
| 46 | | | | 330 | 370 | 420 | 460 | 500 | 560 | 610 | 660 | 710 | 12 |
| 48 | | | | 360 | 420 | 470 | 510 | 560 | 610 | 660 | 720 | 770 | 12 |
| 50 | | | | | 470 | 520 | 570 | 610 | 670 | 720 | 780 | 830 | 12 |
| 52 | | | | | 520 | 570 | 630 | 670 | 730 | 780 | 840 | 890 | 12 |
| 54 | | | | | 570 | 630 | 690 | 730 | 790 | 850 | 910 | 960 | 12 |
| 56 | | | | | | 690 | 750 | 790 | 850 | 920 | 980 | 1,040 | 12 |
| 58 | | | | | | 750 | 790 | 860 | 920 | 990 | 1,060 | 1,130 | 12 |
| 60 | | | | | | 790 | 860 | 920 | 990 | 1,070 | 1,150 | 1,230 | 13 |
| 62 | | | | | | | 920 | 980 | 1,060 | 1,150 | 1,240 | 1,340 | 13 |
| 64 | | | | | | | 980 | 1,060 | 1,130 | 1,230 | 1,340 | 1,450 | 13 |
| 66 | | | | | | | 1,060 | 1,130 | 1,210 | 1,320 | 1,440 | 1,570 | 13 |
| 68 | | | | | | | | 1,200 | 1,300 | 1,410 | 1,550 | 1,690 | 13 |
| 70 | | | | | | | | 1,280 | 1,390 | 1,500 | 1,660 | 1,820 | 14 |
| 72 | | | | | | | | 1,360 | 1,480 | 1,600 | 1,770 | 1,950 | |
| 74 | | | | | | | | | 1,580 | 1,700 | 1,880 | 2,090 | |
| 76 | | | | | | | | | 1,680 | 1,800 | 1,990 | 2,230 | |

* Average stump height 2.2 to 2.8 ft. Logs scaled in commercial lengths as cut.
Source: U. S. Forest Service.

# SUGAR PINE AND RED FIR IN CALIFORNIA *

## Table 38. Volume in Board Feet, Scribner Decimal C Rule
### Form Class 80

| D.b.h. and number of logs to 10-inch d.i.b | Log number and volume (board feet in tens) | | | | | | | | | | | | | Tree volume | | Utilized length 16-ft. logs |
|---|---|---|---|---|---|---|---|---|---|---|---|---|---|---|---|---|
| | 1 | 2 | 3 | 4 | 5 | 6 | 7 | 8 | 9 | 10 | 11 | 12 | 13 | 10-inch top | Utilized top | |
| 12 – 1 | 5 | | | | | | | | | | | | | 5 | 8 | 1.9 |
| 14 – 1 | 7 | | | | | | | | | | | | | 7 | 11 | 1.9 |
| 2 | 7 | 6 | | | | | | | | | | | | 13 | 16 | 2.8 |
| 3 | 7 | 7 | 6 | | | | | | | | | | | 20 | 23 | 3.8 |
| 16 – 1 | 10 | | | | | | | | | | | | | 10 | 12 | 1.5 |
| 2 | 10 | 6 | | | | | | | | | | | | 16 | 16 | 2.1 |
| 3 | 10 | 8 | 6 | | | | | | | | | | | 24 | 25 | 3.2 |
| 4 | 10 | 9 | 8 | 6 | | | | | | | | | | 33 | 34 | 4.2 |
| 18 – 1 | 13 | | | | | | | | | | | | | 13 | 14 | 1.5 |
| 2 | 13 | 6 | | | | | | | | | | | | 19 | 19 | 2.0 |
| 3 | 13 | 10 | 6 | | | | | | | | | | | 29 | 29 | 3.0 |
| 4 | 13 | 11 | 9 | 6 | | | | | | | | | | 39 | 39 | 4.0 |
| 5 | 13 | 12 | 10 | 8 | 6 | | | | | | | | | 49 | 48 | 4.9 |
| 20 – 1 | 17 | | | | | | | | | | | | | 17 | 19 | 1.5 |
| 2 | 17 | 6 | | | | | | | | | | | | 23 | 23 | 1.9 |
| 3 | 17 | 11 | 6 | | | | | | | | | | | 34 | 34 | 2.9 |
| 4 | 17 | 13 | 10 | 6 | | | | | | | | | | 46 | 45 | 3.8 |
| 5 | 17 | 14 | 12 | 9 | 6 | | | | | | | | | 58 | 57 | 4.8 |
| 6 | 17 | 15 | 13 | 11 | 9 | 6 | | | | | | | | 71 | 69 | 5.6 |
| 7 | 17 | 15 | 14 | 12 | 10 | 8 | 6 | | | | | | | 82 | 80 | 6.6 |
| 22 – 2 | 20 | 6 | | | | | | | | | | | | 26 | 27 | 1.9 |
| 3 | 20 | 13 | 6 | | | | | | | | | | | 39 | 39 | 2.8 |
| 4 | 20 | 16 | 11 | 6 | | | | | | | | | | 53 | 52 | 3.6 |
| 5 | 20 | 18 | 14 | 10 | 6 | | | | | | | | | 68 | 67 | 4.6 |
| 6 | 20 | 18 | 16 | 13 | 10 | 6 | | | | | | | | 83 | 81 | 5.5 |
| 7 | 20 | 18 | 17 | 15 | 12 | 9 | 6 | | | | | | | 97 | 94 | 6.4 |
| 8 | 20 | 19 | 17 | 16 | 14 | 11 | 8 | 6 | | | | | | 111 | 108 | 7.2 |
| 24 – 2 | 25 | 6 | | | | | | | | | | | | 31 | 32 | 1.9 |
| 3 | 25 | 15 | 6 | | | | | | | | | | | 46 | 46 | 2.8 |
| 4 | 25 | 19 | 13 | 6 | | | | | | | | | | 63 | 62 | 3.6 |
| 5 | 25 | 21 | 16 | 11 | 6 | | | | | | | | | 79 | 77 | 4.5 |
| 6 | 25 | 22 | 18 | 15 | 10 | 6 | | | | | | | | 96 | 94 | 5.4 |
| 7 | 25 | 22 | 20 | 17 | 14 | 10 | 6 | | | | | | | 114 | 111 | 6.4 |
| 8 | 25 | 23 | 20 | 18 | 16 | 12 | 9 | 6 | | | | | | 129 | 126 | 7.2 |
| 9 | 25 | 23 | 21 | 19 | 17 | 15 | 12 | 9 | 6 | | | | | 147 | 142 | 8.1 |
| 26 – 2 | 30 | 6 | | | | | | | | | | | | 36 | 38 | 1.9 |
| 3 | 30 | 17 | 6 | | | | | | | | | | | 53 | 54 | 2.8 |
| 4 | 30 | 22 | 14 | 6 | | | | | | | | | | 72 | 72 | 3.6 |
| 5 | 30 | 24 | 19 | 12 | 6 | | | | | | | | | 91 | 91 | 4.5 |
| 6 | 30 | 25 | 22 | 17 | 12 | 6 | | | | | | | | 112 | 110 | 5.4 |
| 7 | 30 | 26 | 23 | 19 | 15 | 11 | 6 | | | | | | | 130 | 127 | 6.2 |
| 8 | 30 | 27 | 24 | 21 | 18 | 14 | 10 | 6 | | | | | | 150 | 146 | 7.1 |
| 9 | 30 | 27 | 25 | 23 | 20 | 17 | 13 | 10 | 6 | | | | | 171 | 165 | 8.0 |
| 28 – 2 | 35 | 6 | | | | | | | | | | | | 41 | 44 | 1.9 |
| 3 | 35 | 19 | 6 | | | | | | | | | | | 60 | 62 | 2.8 |
| 4 | 35 | 25 | 16 | 6 | | | | | | | | | | 82 | ·83 | 3.6 |
| 5 | 35 | 28 | 22 | 14 | 6 | | | | | | | | | 105 | 105 | 4.5 |
| 6 | 35 | 30 | 25 | 19 | 12 | 6 | | | | | | | | 127 | 125 | 5.4 |
| 7 | 35 | 30 | 27 | 22 | 17 | 12 | 6 | | | | | | | 149 | 145 | 6.2 |
| 8 | 35 | 31 | 28 | 24 | 20 | 16 | 11 | 6 | | | | | | 171 | 167 | 7.1 |
| 9 | 35 | 31 | 29 | 26 | 23 | 19 | 15 | 10 | 6 | | | | | 194 | 188 | 8.0 |
| 10 | 35 | 32 | 30 | 27 | 24 | 21 | 18 | 14 | 10 | 6 | | | | 217 | 210 | 8.9 |
| 30 – 3 | 40 | 22 | 6 | | | | | | | | | | | 68 | 71 | 2.8 |
| 4 | 40 | 29 | 18 | 6 | | | | | | | | | | 93 | 93 | 3.6 |
| 5 | 40 | 32 | 24 | 15 | 6 | | | | | | | | | 117 | 117 | 4.5 |
| 6 | 40 | 34 | 28 | 21 | 14 | 6 | | | | | | | | 143 | 142 | 5.4 |
| 7 | 40 | 35 | 31 | 25 | 19 | 12 | 6 | | | | | | | 168 | 166 | 6.2 |
| 8 | 40 | 36 | 32 | 28 | 23 | 17 | 12 | 6 | | | | | | 194 | 190 | 7.1 |
| 9 | 40 | 36 | 33 | 30 | 26 | 21 | 16 | 11 | 6 | | | | | 219 | 213 | 8.0 |
| 10 | 40 | 37 | 34 | 31 | 28 | 24 | 19 | 15 | 10 | 6 | | | | 244 | 238 | 8.9 |

\* The increase in board-foot volumes in this table for each Girard form class is 3 percent.

## Table 38. Volume in Board Feet, Scribner Decimal C Rule (Continued)

| D.b.h. and number of logs to 10-inch d.i.b | 1 | 2 | 3 | 4 | 5 | 6 | 7 | 8 | 9 | 10 | 11 | 12 | 13 | Tree volume 10-inch top | Utilized top | Utilized length 16-ft. logs |
|---|---|---|---|---|---|---|---|---|---|---|---|---|---|---|---|---|
| 32 - 3 | 46 | 24 | 6 | | | | | | | | | | | 76 | 78 | 2.6 |
| 4 | 46 | 33 | 19 | 6 | | | | | | | | | | 104 | 105 | 3.5 |
| 5 | 46 | 37 | 28 | 17 | 6 | | | | | | | | | 134 | 132 | 4.4 |
| 6 | 46 | 39 | 32 | 24 | 15 | 6 | | | | | | | | 162 | 159 | 5.2 |
| 7 | 46 | 40 | 35 | 28 | 21 | 13 | 6 | | | | | | | 189 | 186 | 6.1 |
| 8 | 46 | 41 | 37 | 32 | 26 | 19 | 12 | 6 | | | | | | 219 | 216 | 7.1 |
| 9 | 46 | 41 | 38 | 34 | 29 | 23 | 18 | 12 | 6 | | | | | 247 | 241 | 8.0 |
| 10 | 46 | 42 | 39 | 35 | 31 | 27 | 22 | 16 | 11 | 6 | | | | 275 | 268 | 8.9 |
| 11 | 46 | 42 | 39 | 36 | 33 | 29 | 25 | 20 | 15 | 10 | 6 | | | 301 | 293 | 9.6 |
| 34 - 3 | 53 | 27 | 6 | | | | | | | | | | | 86 | 89 | 2.6 |
| 4 | 53 | 37 | 21 | 6 | | | | | | | | | | 117 | 119 | 3.5 |
| 5 | 53 | 42 | 30 | 18 | 6 | | | | | | | | | 149 | 149 | 4.4 |
| 6 | 53 | 44 | 36 | 26 | 16 | 6 | | | | | | | | 181 | 179 | 5.2 |
| 7 | 53 | 46 | 39 | 32 | 23 | 14 | 6 | | | | | | | 213 | 210 | 6.1 |
| 8 | 53 | 46 | 41 | 35 | 29 | 21 | 13 | 6 | | | | | | 244 | 241 | 7.1 |
| 9 | 53 | 47 | 43 | 38 | 32 | 26 | 19 | 12 | 6 | | | | | 276 | 270 | 8.0 |
| 10 | 53 | 48 | 44 | 40 | 35 | 30 | 24 | 18 | 12 | 6 | | | | 310 | 303 | 8.9 |
| 11 | 53 | 48 | 45 | 41 | 38 | 33 | 28 | 22 | 17 | 11 | 6 | | | 342 | 333 | 9.6 |
| 36 - 3 | 59 | 30 | 6 | | | | | | | | | | | 95 | 98 | 2.6 |
| 4 | 59 | 41 | 23 | 6 | | | | | | | | | | 129 | 131 | 3.5 |
| 5 | 59 | 47 | 34 | 19 | 6 | | | | | | | | | 165 | 166 | 4.4 |
| 6 | 59 | 49 | 40 | 29 | 17 | 6 | | | | | | | | 200 | 199 | 5.2 |
| 7 | 59 | 51 | 44 | 35 | 25 | 15 | 6 | | | | | | | 235 | 233 | 6.1 |
| 8 | 59 | 52 | 46 | 40 | 31 | 23 | 14 | 6 | | | | | | 271 | 265 | 7.0 |
| 9 | 59 | 53 | 48 | 43 | 36 | 29 | 21 | 13 | 6 | | | | | 308 | 301 | 7.9 |
| 10 | 59 | 53 | 49 | 45 | 39 | 33 | 26 | 19 | 12 | 6 | | | | 341 | 333 | 8.8 |
| 11 | 59 | 54 | 50 | 46 | 42 | 36 | 30 | 24 | 18 | 12 | 6 | | | 377 | 367 | 9.6 |
| 12 | 59 | 54 | 51 | 48 | 44 | 39 | 34 | 29 | 23 | 17 | 11 | 6 | | 415 | 405 | 10.5 |
| 38 - 3 | 66 | 32 | 6 | | | | | | | | | | | 104 | 109 | 2.6 |
| 4 | 66 | 46 | 25 | 6 | | | | | | | | | | 143 | 146 | 3.5 |
| 5 | 66 | 52 | 38 | 21 | 6 | | | | | | | | | 183 | 184 | 4.4 |
| 6 | 66 | 55 | 44 | 32 | 18 | 6 | | | | | | | | 221 | 220 | 5.2 |
| 7 | 66 | 57 | 49 | 39 | 27 | 16 | 6 | | | | | | | 260 | 258 | 6.1 |
| 8 | 66 | 58 | 52 | 44 | 35 | 25 | 15 | 6 | | | | | | 301 | 295 | 7.0 |
| 9 | 66 | 59 | 53 | 48 | 40 | 31 | 22 | 14 | 6 | | | | | 339 | 332 | 7.9 |
| 10 | 66 | 60 | 55 | 50 | 44 | 36 | 29 | 21 | 13 | 6 | | | | 380 | 372 | 8.8 |
| 11 | 66 | 60 | 56 | 51 | 46 | 40 | 34 | 27 | 19 | 12 | 6 | | | 417 | 408 | 9.6 |
| 12 | 66 | 61 | 57 | 53 | 49 | 43 | 38 | 31 | 25 | 18 | 12 | 6 | | 459 | 449 | 10.5 |
| 40 - 3 | 74 | 35 | 6 | | | | | | | | | | | 115 | 121 | 2.6 |
| 4 | 74 | 51 | 27 | 6 | | | | | | | | | | 158 | 162 | 3.5 |
| 5 | 74 | 58 | 41 | 23 | 6 | | | | | | | | | 202 | 203 | 4.4 |
| 6 | 74 | 61 | 49 | 35 | 19 | 6 | | | | | | | | 244 | 245 | 5.2 |
| 7 | 74 | 63 | 54 | 43 | 30 | 17 | 6 | | | | | | | 287 | 286 | 6.1 |
| 8 | 74 | 65 | 57 | 48 | 38 | 27 | 16 | 6 | | | | | | 331 | 325 | 7.0 |
| 9 | 74 | 66 | 59 | 52 | 44 | 34 | 24 | 15 | 6 | | | | | 374 | 367 | 7.9 |
| 10 | 74 | 66 | 61 | 55 | 48 | 40 | 31 | 22 | 14 | 6 | | | | 417 | 409 | 8.8 |
| 11 | 74 | 67 | 62 | 57 | 51 | 44 | 37 | 29 | 21 | 13 | 6 | | | 461 | 452 | 9.6 |
| 12 | 74 | 67 | 63 | 58 | 53 | 48 | 41 | 34 | 27 | 19 | 12 | 6 | | 502 | 493 | 10.5 |
| 42 - 4 | 82 | 55 | 29 | 6 | | | | | | | | | | 172 | 176 | 3.5 |
| 5 | 82 | 64 | 45 | 24 | 6 | | | | | | | | | 221 | 223 | 4.4 |
| 6 | 82 | 67 | 54 | 38 | 21 | 6 | | | | | | | | 268 | 268 | 5.2 |
| 7 | 82 | 70 | 59 | 47 | 33 | 18 | 6 | | | | | | | 315 | 314 | 6.1 |
| 8 | 82 | 71 | 63 | 53 | 41 | 29 | 17 | 6 | | | | | | 362 | 356 | 7.0 |
| 9 | 82 | 73 | 66 | 57 | 48 | 38 | 26 | 16 | 6 | | | | | 412 | 404 | 7.9 |
| 10 | 82 | 74 | 67 | 60 | 53 | 44 | 34 | 24 | 14 | 6 | | | | 458 | 450 | 8.8 |
| 11 | 82 | 74 | 68 | 63 | 56 | 49 | 40 | 31 | 22 | 14 | 6 | | | 505 | 495 | 9.6 |
| 12 | 82 | 75 | 69 | 65 | 59 | 53 | 45 | 37 | 29 | 20 | 13 | 6 | | 553 | 543 | 10.5 |
| 44 - 4 | 90 | 61 | 32 | 6 | | | | | | | | | | 189 | 194 | 3.5 |
| 5 | 90 | 70 | 49 | 26 | 6 | | | | | | | | | 241 | 243 | 4.4 |
| 6 | 90 | 74 | 59 | 41 | 22 | 6 | | | | | | | | 292 | 293 | 5.2 |
| 7 | 90 | 77 | 65 | 51 | 35 | 20 | 6 | | | | | | | 344 | 343 | 6.1 |
| 8 | 90 | 78 | 69 | 58 | 45 | 31 | 18 | 6 | | | | | | 395 | 389 | 7.0 |
| 9 | 90 | 80 | 72 | 63 | 53 | 41 | 28 | 16 | 6 | | | | | 449 | 442 | 7.9 |
| 10 | 90 | 80 | 74 | 66 | 58 | 48 | 37 | 26 | 15 | 6 | | | | 500 | 492 | 8.8 |
| 11 | 90 | 82 | 75 | 69 | 62 | 53 | 44 | 34 | 24 | 14 | 6 | | | 553 | 544 | 9.6 |
| 12 | 90 | 82 | 76 | 71 | 65 | 57 | 49 | 40 | 31 | 22 | 13 | 6 | | 602 | 592 | 10.5 |

## Table 38. Volume in Board Feet, Scribner Decimal C Rule (Continued)

| D.b.h. and number of logs to 10-inch d.i.b | Log number and volume (board feet in tens) | | | | | | | | | | | | | Tree volume | | Utilized length 16-ft. logs |
|---|---|---|---|---|---|---|---|---|---|---|---|---|---|---|---|---|
| | 1 | 2 | 3 | 4 | 5 | 6 | 7 | 8 | 9 | 10 | 11 | 12 | 13 | 10-inch top | Utilized top | |
| 46 – 4 | 99 | 66 | 34 | 6 | | | | | | | | | | 205 | 211 | 3.5 |
| 5 | 99 | 76 | 53 | 28 | 6 | | | | | | | | | 262 | 265 | 4.4 |
| 6 | 99 | 81 | 64 | 44 | 24 | 6 | | | | | | | | 318 | 319 | 5.2 |
| 7 | 99 | 84 | 71 | 55 | 38 | 21 | 6 | | | | | | | 374 | 373 | 6.1 |
| 8 | 99 | 86 | 76 | 63 | 49 | 34 | 19 | 6 | | | | | | 432 | 426 | 7.0 |
| 9 | 99 | 87 | 78 | 68 | 57 | 44 | 30 | 17 | 6 | | | | | 486 | 479 | 7.9 |
| 10 | 99 | 88 | 80 | 72 | 63 | 52 | 40 | 28 | 16 | 6 | | | | 544 | 535 | 8.8 |
| 11 | 99 | 89 | 82 | 75 | 67 | 58 | 48 | 36 | 25 | 15 | 6 | | | 600 | 591 | 9.6 |
| 12 | 99 | 90 | 84 | 78 | 70 | 62 | 53 | 44 | 33 | 23 | 14 | 6 | | 656 | 647 | 10.5 |
| 48 – 4 | 108 | 72 | 36 | 6 | | | | | | | | | | 222 | 229 | 3.5 |
| 5 | 108 | 83 | 57 | 30 | 6 | | | | | | | | | 284 | 287 | 4.4 |
| 6 | 108 | 88 | 70 | 48 | 25 | 6 | | | | | | | | 345 | 347 | 5.2 |
| 7 | 108 | 92 | 77 | 60 | 41 | 22 | 6 | | | | | | | 406 | 406 | 6.1 |
| 8 | 108 | 94 | 82 | 68 | 53 | 36 | 20 | 6 | | | | | | 467 | 461 | 7.0 |
| 9 | 108 | 95 | 86 | 75 | 62 | 47 | 32 | 18 | 6 | | | | | 529 | 522 | 7.9 |
| 10 | 108 | 96 | 88 | 78 | 68 | 56 | 43 | 29 | 17 | 6 | | | | 589 | 581 | 8.8 |
| 11 | 108 | 97 | 89 | 82 | 73 | 62 | 51 | 39 | 27 | 16 | 6 | | | 650 | 641 | 9.6 |
| 12 | 108 | 98 | 91 | 84 | 77 | 67 | 58 | 47 | 36 | 25 | 15 | 6 | | 712 | 702 | 10.5 |
| 13 | 108 | 99 | 92 | 86 | 80 | 72 | 63 | 53 | 44 | 33 | 23 | 14 | 6 | 773 | 761 | 11.4 |
| 50 – 5 | 118 | 90 | 62 | 32 | 6 | | | | | | | | | 308 | 312 | 4.4 |
| 6 | 118 | 96 | 76 | 51 | 27 | 6 | | | | | | | | 374 | 376 | 5.2 |
| 7 | 118 | 99 | 84 | 65 | 44 | 23 | 6 | | | | | | | 439 | 439 | 6.1 |
| 8 | 118 | 102 | 89 | 74 | 57 | 39 | 21 | 6 | | | | | | 506 | 500 | 7.0 |
| 9 | 118 | 103 | 93 | 80 | 67 | 51 | 34 | 19 | 6 | | | | | 571 | 564 | 7.9 |
| 10 | 118 | 105 | 95 | 85 | 74 | 60 | 46 | 31 | 17 | 6 | | | | 637 | 630 | 8.8 |
| 11 | 118 | 106 | 97 | 89 | 79 | 67 | 55 | 42 | 29 | 16 | 6 | | | 704 | 695 | 9.6 |
| 12 | 118 | 107 | 99 | 92 | 83 | 73 | 62 | 51 | 39 | 26 | 15 | 6 | | 771 | 762 | 10.5 |
| 13 | 118 | 107 | 100 | 94 | 86 | 78 | 68 | 58 | 47 | 35 | 24 | 14 | 6 | 835 | 824 | 11.4 |
| 52 – 5 | 128 | 97 | 66 | 34 | 6 | | | | | | | | | 331 | 336 | 4.4 |
| 6 | 128 | 104 | 81 | 55 | 28 | 6 | | | | | | | | 402 | 406 | 5.2 |
| 7 | 128 | 108 | 90 | 70 | 47 | 24 | 6 | | | | | | | 473 | 474 | 6.1 |
| 8 | 128 | 110 | 96 | 80 | 61 | 41 | 22 | 6 | | | | | | 544 | 538 | 7.0 |
| 9 | 128 | 112 | 100 | 87 | 72 | 54 | 36 | 20 | 6 | | | | | 615 | 608 | 7.9 |
| 10 | 128 | 114 | 103 | 92 | 80 | 65 | 49 | 33 | 18 | 6 | | | | 688 | 681 | 8.8 |
| 11 | 128 | 114 | 105 | 96 | 85 | 73 | 59 | 45 | 30 | 17 | 6 | | | 758 | 750 | 9.6 |
| 12 | 128 | 116 | 107 | 99 | 89 | 79 | 67 | 54 | 41 | 28 | 16 | 6 | | 830 | 820 | 10.5 |
| 13 | 128 | 116 | 108 | 101 | 93 | 84 | 74 | 62 | 50 | 38 | 26 | 15 | 6 | 901 | 890 | 11.4 |
| 54 – 5 | 138 | 105 | 71 | 36 | 6 | | | | | | | | | 356 | 361 | 4.4 |
| 6 | 138 | 112 | 87 | 59 | 30 | 6 | | | | | | | | 432 | 435 | 5.2 |
| 7 | 138 | 116 | 98 | 75 | 50 | 26 | 6 | | | | | | | 509 | 511 | 6.1 |
| 8 | 138 | 119 | 104 | 86 | 66 | 44 | 23 | 6 | | | | | | 586 | 580 | 7.0 |
| 9 | 138 | 121 | 108 | 94 | 77 | 58 | 39 | 21 | 6 | | | | | 662 | 655 | 7.9 |
| 10 | 138 | 122 | 112 | 99 | 86 | 69 | 52 | 35 | 19 | 6 | | | | 738 | 731 | 8.8 |
| 11 | 138 | 124 | 113 | 103 | 92 | 78 | 63 | 48 | 32 | 18 | 6 | | | 815 | 806 | 9.6 |
| 12 | 138 | 125 | 115 | 107 | 96 | 85 | 72 | 58 | 44 | 29 | 16 | 6 | | 891 | 882 | 10.5 |
| 13 | 128 | 126 | 117 | 109 | 100 | 90 | 79 | 66 | 53 | 40 | 27 | 16 | 6 | 967 | 955 | 11.4 |
| 56 – 5 | 149 | 113 | 77 | 38 | 6 | | | | | | | | | 383 | 389 | 4.4 |
| 6 | 149 | 120 | 94 | 63 | 31 | 6 | | | | | | | | 463 | 468 | 5.2 |
| 7 | 149 | 125 | 104 | 80 | 53 | 27 | 6 | | | | | | | 544 | 546 | 6.1 |
| 8 | 149 | 128 | 112 | 92 | 70 | 47 | 24 | 6 | | | | | | 628 | 622 | 7.0 |
| 9 | 149 | 130 | 116 | 100 | 82 | 62 | 41 | 22 | 6 | | | | | 708 | 701 | 7.9 |
| 10 | 149 | 132 | 120 | 107 | 92 | 75 | 55 | 37 | 20 | G | | | | 793 | 785 | 8.8 |
| 11 | 149 | 133 | 122 | 111 | 99 | 84 | 67 | 51 | 34 | 18 | 6 | | | 874 | 865 | 9.6 |
| 12 | 149 | 134 | 124 | 114 | 104 | 91 | 77 | 62 | 46 | 31 | 17 | 6 | | 955 | 945 | 10.5 |
| 13 | 149 | 135 | 126 | 117 | 108 | 97 | 85 | 71 | 57 | 43 | 28 | 16 | 6 | 1038 | 1024 | 11.2 |
| 58 – 5 | 160 | 121 | 82 | 40 | 6 | | | | | | | | | 409 | 416 | 4.4 |
| 6 | 160 | 129 | 100 | 67 | 33 | 6 | | | | | | | | 495 | 500 | 5.2 |
| 7 | 160 | 134 | 112 | 86 | 57 | 29 | 6 | | | | | | | 584 | 586 | 6.1 |
| 8 | 160 | 138 | 119 | 99 | 75 | 49 | 25 | 6 | | | | | | 671 | 665 | 7.0 |
| 9 | 160 | 140 | 125 | 108 | 88 | 66 | 44 | 23 | 6 | | | | | 760 | 753 | 7.9 |
| 10 | 160 | 142 | 129 | 114 | 98 | 80 | 59 | 39 | 20 | 6 | | | | 847 | 841 | 8.8 |
| 11 | 160 | 143 | 131 | 119 | 106 | 89 | 72 | 54 | 36 | 19 | 6 | | | 935 | 926 | 9.6 |
| 12 | 160 | 144 | 133 | 123 | 111 | 98 | 82 | 66 | 49 | 33 | 18 | 6 | | 1023 | 1013 | 10.5 |
| 13 | 160 | 145 | 135 | 126 | 116 | 104 | 90 | 76 | 61 | 45 | 30 | 17 | 6 | 1111 | 1096 | 11.2 |

## Table 38. Volume in Board Feet, Scribner Decimal C Rule (Continued)

| D.b.h. and number of logs to 10-inch d.i.b | Log number and volume (board feet in tens) | | | | | | | | | | | | | Tree volume | | Utilized length 16-ft. logs |
|---|---|---|---|---|---|---|---|---|---|---|---|---|---|---|---|---|
| | 1 | 2 | 3 | 4 | 5 | 6 | 7 | 8 | 9 | 10 | 11 | 12 | 13 | 10-inch top | Utilized top | |
| 60 - 6 | 172 | 138 | 107 | 71 | 35 | 6 | | | | | | | | 529 | 535 | 5.2 |
| 7 | 172 | 144 | 120 | 92 | 60 | 30 | 6 | | | | | | | 624 | 627 | 6.1 |
| 8 | 172 | 147 | 128 | 106 | 80 | 52 | 26 | 6 | | | | | | 717 | 711 | 7.0 |
| 9 | 172 | 150 | 134 | 115 | 94 | 70 | 46 | 24 | 6 | | | | | 811 | 805 | 7.9 |
| 10 | 172 | 152 | 138 | 122 | 105 | 85 | 63 | 41 | 22 | 6 | | | | 906 | 899 | 8.8 |
| 11 | 172 | 153 | 140 | 127 | 113 | 95 | 77 | 57 | 38 | 20 | 6 | | | 998 | 989 | 9.6 |
| 12 | 172 | 155 | 142 | 131 | 119 | 104 | 88 | 70 | 52 | 34 | 18 | 6 | | 1091 | 1079 | 10.4 |
| 13 | 172 | 156 | 144 | 134 | 124 | 111 | 96 | 80 | 64 | 48 | 31 | 17 | 6 | 1183 | 1169 | 11.2 |
| 62 - 6 | 184 | 148 | 114 | 76 | 37 | 6 | | | | | | | | 565 | 571 | 5.2 |
| 7 | 184 | 153 | 128 | 98 | 64 | 31 | 6 | | | | | | | 664 | 668 | 6.1 |
| 8 | 184 | 158 | 136 | 113 | 85 | 55 | 28 | 6 | | | | | | 765 | 759 | 7.0 |
| 9 | 184 | 160 | 142 | 123 | 100 | 75 | 49 | 24 | 6 | | | | | 863 | 858 | 7.9 |
| 10 | 184 | 162 | 147 | 131 | 112 | 90 | 66 | 44 | 22 | 6 | | | | 964 | 958 | 8.8 |
| 11 | 184 | 164 | 150 | 136 | 120 | 102 | 81 | 60 | 40 | 21 | 6 | | | 1064 | 1055 | 9.6 |
| 12 | 184 | 165 | 152 | 140 | 127 | 111 | 93 | 74 | 55 | 36 | 19 | 6 | | 1162 | 1149 | 10.4 |
| 13 | 184 | 166 | 154 | 144 | 132 | 118 | 103 | 86 | 68 | 50 | 33 | 18 | 6 | 1262 | 1248 | 11.2 |
| 64 - 6 | 196 | 158 | 122 | 80 | 39 | 6 | | | | | | | | 601 | 608 | 5.2 |
| 7 | 196 | 164 | 136 | 104 | 67 | 33 | 6 | | | | | | | 706 | 710 | 6.1 |
| 8 | 196 | 168 | 145 | 119 | 89 | 58 | 29 | 6 | | | | | | 810 | 804 | 7.0 |
| 9 | 196 | 170 | 152 | 131 | 107 | 79 | 51 | 26 | 6 | | | | | 918 | 912 | 7.9 |
| 10 | 196 | 174 | 156 | 138 | 119 | 95 | 70 | 46 | 23 | 6 | | | | 1023 | 1017 | 8.8 |
| 11 | 196 | 175 | 160 | 145 | 128 | 108 | 86 | 64 | 42 | 22 | 6 | | | 1132 | 1119 | 9.5 |
| 12 | 196 | 176 | 162 | 150 | 134 | 118 | 99 | 78 | 58 | 38 | 20 | 6 | | 1235 | 1222 | 10.4 |
| 13 | 196 | 177 | 165 | 153 | 140 | 126 | 109 | 91 | 72 | 53 | 35 | 19 | 6 | 1342 | 1327 | 11.2 |
| 66 - 6 | 209 | 168 | 129 | 85 | 41 | 6 | | | | | | | | 638 | 646 | 5.2 |
| 7 | 209 | 174 | 144 | 110 | 71 | 34 | 6 | | | | | | | 748 | 754 | 6.1 |
| 8 | 209 | 179 | 155 | 127 | 95 | 62 | 30 | 6 | | | | | | 863 | 857 | 7.0 |
| 9 | 209 | 182 | 162 | 139 | 113 | 84 | 54 | 27 | 6 | | | | | 976 | 970 | 7.9 |
| 10 | 209 | 184 | 166 | 147 | 126 | 101 | 74 | 48 | 24 | 6 | | | | 1085 | 1076 | 8.6 |
| 11 | 209 | 186 | 170 | 154 | 136 | 114 | 91 | 67 | 44 | 22 | 6 | | | 1199 | 1188 | 9.5 |
| 12 | 209 | 188 | 173 | 159 | 143 | 125 | 105 | 83 | 61 | 40 | 20 | 6 | | 1312 | 1300 | 10.4 |
| 13 | 209 | 189 | 175 | 163 | 149 | 133 | 116 | 96 | 76 | 56 | 36 | 19 | 6 | 1423 | 1409 | 11.2 |
| 68 - 6 | 222 | 178 | 136 | 89 | 43 | 6 | | | | | | | | 674 | 682 | 5.2 |
| 7 | 222 | 185 | 153 | 116 | 75 | 36 | 6 | | | | | | | 793 | 798 | 6.1 |
| 8 | 222 | 189 | 164 | 134 | 100 | 65 | 31 | 6 | | | | | | 911 | 905 | 7.0 |
| 9 | 222 | 193 | 171 | 147 | 120 | 88 | 57 | 28 | 6 | | | | | 1032 | 1027 | 7.9 |
| 10 | 222 | 196 | 176 | 156 | 134 | 107 | 78 | 51 | 25 | 6 | | | | 1151 | 1141 | 8.6 |
| 11 | 222 | 197 | 180 | 163 | 144 | 121 | 96 | 71 | 46 | 23 | 6 | | | 1269 | 1258 | 9.5 |
| 12 | 222 | 200 | 183 | 169 | 152 | 132 | 111 | 88 | 64 | 41 | 21 | 6 | | 1389 | 1378 | 10.4 |
| 13 | 222 | 200 | 186 | 173 | 158 | 142 | 122 | 102 | 80 | 58 | 38 | 20 | 6 | 1507 | 1493 | 11.2 |
| 70 - 6 | 236 | 189 | 144 | 94 | 44 | 6 | | | | | | | | 713 | 723 | 5.2 |
| 7 | 236 | 196 | 162 | 123 | 79 | 38 | 6 | | | | | | | 840 | 846 | 6.1 |
| 8 | 236 | 201 | 174 | 142 | 106 | 68 | 33 | 6 | | | | | | 966 | 960 | 7.0 |
| 9 | 236 | 204 | 182 | 156 | 127 | 93 | 59 | 29 | 6 | | | | | 1092 | 1087 | 7.9 |
| 10 | 236 | 208 | 187 | 165 | 141 | 113 | 82 | 53 | 26 | 6 | | | | 1217 | 1208 | 8.6 |
| 11 | 236 | 209 | 191 | 173 | 152 | 128 | 102 | 75 | 48 | 24 | 6 | | | 1344 | 1333 | 9.5 |
| 12 | 236 | 212 | 194 | 179 | 160 | 140 | 117 | 93 | 68 | 44 | 22 | 6 | | 1471 | 1458 | 10.4 |
| 13 | 236 | 213 | 197 | 183 | 168 | 150 | 129 | 107 | 85 | 62 | 40 | 21 | 6 | 1597 | 1582 | 11.2 |
| 72 - 6 | 250 | 200 | 153 | 99 | 47 | 6 | | | | | | | | 755 | 765 | 5.2 |
| 7 | 250 | 208 | 171 | 129 | 83 | 39 | 6 | | | | | | | 886 | 893 | 6.1 |
| 8 | 250 | 213 | 184 | 150 | 112 | 71 | 34 | 6 | | | | | | 1020 | 1014 | 7.0 |
| 9 | 250 | 217 | 192 | 165 | 134 | 98 | 62 | 30 | 6 | | | | | 1154 | 1146 | 7.8 |
| 10 | 250 | 220 | 198 | 175 | 149 | 119 | 87 | 55 | 27 | 6 | | | | 1286 | 1277 | 8.6 |
| 11 | 250 | 222 | 202 | 183 | 161 | 135 | 107 | 78 | 50 | 25 | 6 | | | 1419 | 1408 | 9.5 |
| 12 | 250 | 224 | 206 | 189 | 170 | 148 | 124 | 98 | 71 | 46 | 23 | 6 | | 1555 | 1542 | 10.4 |
| 13 | 250 | 225 | 208 | 194 | 177 | 158 | 136 | 113 | 89 | 65 | 41 | 21 | 6 | 1683 | 1669 | 11.2 |
| 74 - 7 | 265 | 219 | 181 | 136 | 87 | 41 | 6 | | | | | | | 935 | 943 | 6.1 |
| 8 | 265 | 225 | 194 | 158 | 117 | 75 | 35 | 6 | | | | | | 1075 | 1069 | 7.0 |
| 9 | 265 | 229 | 203 | 174 | 141 | 103 | 65 | 31 | 6 | | | | | 1217 | 1209 | 7.8 |
| 10 | 265 | 233 | 209 | 185 | 158 | 126 | 91 | 58 | 28 | 6 | | | | 1359 | 1349 | 8.6 |
| 11 | 265 | 234 | 213 | 193 | 170 | 142 | 113 | 82 | 53 | 26 | 6 | | | 1497 | 1485 | 9.5 |
| 12 | 265 | 237 | 218 | 200 | 180 | 156 | 130 | 103 | 75 | 48 | 24 | 6 | | 1642 | 1629 | 10.4 |
| 13 | 265 | 238 | 220 | 205 | 187 | 167 | 144 | 119 | 94 | 68 | 43 | 22 | 6 | 1778 | 1764 | 11.2 |

## Table 38. Volume in Board Feet, Scribner Decimal C Rule (Continued)

| D.b.h. and number of logs to 10-inch d.i.b | Log number and volume (board feet in tens) | | | | | | | | | | | | | Tree volume | | Utilized length 16-ft. logs |
|---|---|---|---|---|---|---|---|---|---|---|---|---|---|---|---|---|
| | 1 | 2 | 3 | 4 | 5 | 6 | 7 | 8 | 9 | 10 | 11 | 12 | 13 | 10-inch top | Utilized top | |
| 76 - 7 | 280 | 232 | 191 | 144 | 92 | 43 | 6 | | | | | | | 988 | 996 | 6.1 |
| 8 | 280 | 237 | 204 | 167 | 124 | 78 | 37 | 6 | | | | | | 1133 | 1125 | 6.9 |
| 9 | 280 | 241 | 214 | 183 | 148 | 108 | 68 | 32 | 6 | | | | | 1280 | 1273 | 7.8 |
| 10 | 280 | 245 | 221 | 195 | 165 | 132 | 96 | 61 | 29 | 6 | | | | 1430 | 1421 | 8.6 |
| 11 | 280 | 248 | 226 | 204 | 179 | 151 | 119 | 86 | 55 | 27 | 6 | | | 1581 | 1570 | 9.5 |
| 12 | 280 | 249 | 229 | 211 | 189 | 164 | 137 | 107 | 78 | 49 | 24 | 6 | | 1723 | 1711 | 10.4 |
| 13 | 280 | 252 | 233 | 216 | 197 | 176 | 152 | 126 | 98 | 71 | 45 | 23 | 6 | 1875 | 1860 | 11.2 |
| 78 - 7 | 295 | 244 | 201 | 151 | 96 | 44 | 6 | | | | | | | 1037 | 1047 | 6.1 |
| 8 | 295 | 250 | 215 | 176 | 130 | 82 | 38 | 6 | | | | | | 1192 | 1184 | 6.9 |
| 9 | 295 | 255 | 225 | 192 | 156 | 113 | 71 | 34 | 6 | | | | | 1347 | 1339 | 7.8 |
| 10 | 295 | 258 | 233 | 205 | 174 | 138 | 100 | 63 | 30 | 6 | | | | 1502 | 1493 | 8.6 |
| 11 | 295 | 261 | 238 | 214 | 188 | 158 | 124 | 90 | 57 | 28 | 6 | | | 1659 | 1648 | 9.5 |
| 12 | 295 | 263 | 241 | 222 | 199 | 173 | 144 | 113 | 82 | 51 | 25 | 6 | | 1814 | 1802 | 10.4 |
| 13 | 295 | 266 | 245 | 228 | 208 | 185 | 160 | 132 | 103 | 74 | 47 | 24 | 6 | 1973 | 1957 | 11.2 |
| 80 - 7 | 310 | 256 | 211 | 158 | 100 | 46 | 6 | | | | | | | 1087 | 1081 | 6.0 |
| 8 | 310 | 263 | 227 | 184 | 136 | 86 | 40 | 6 | | | | | | 1252 | 1244 | 6.9 |
| 9 | 310 | 268 | 237 | 203 | 163 | 119 | 75 | 35 | 6 | | | | | 1416 | 1408 | 7.8 |
| 10 | 310 | 272 | 245 | 216 | 183 | 145 | 105 | 66 | 31 | 6 | | | | 1579 | 1570 | 8.6 |
| 11 | 310 | 275 | 250 | 226 | 198 | 166 | 131 | 94 | 59 | 29 | 6 | | | 1744 | 1733 | 9.5 |
| 12 | 310 | 277 | 255 | 234 | 209 | 182 | 151 | 118 | 85 | 53 | 26 | 6 | | 1906 | 1894 | 10.4 |
| 13 | 310 | 280 | 257 | 240 | 218 | 194 | 168 | 138 | 108 | 78 | 49 | 24 | 6 | 2070 | 2055 | 11.2 |
| 82 - 7 | 326 | 270 | 222 | 166 | 105 | 48 | 6 | | | | | | | 1143 | 1137 | 6.0 |
| 8 | 326 | 277 | 238 | 193 | 142 | 89 | 41 | 6 | | | | | | 1312 | 1305 | 6.9 |
| 9 | 326 | 281 | 249 | 213 | 171 | 124 | 78 | 36 | 6 | | | | | 1484 | 1477 | 7.8 |
| 10 | 326 | 286 | 257 | 227 | 192 | 153 | 110 | 69 | 32 | 6 | | | | 1658 | 1650 | 8.6 |
| 11 | 326 | 289 | 263 | 237 | 208 | 174 | 136 | 99 | 62 | 30 | 6 | | | 1830 | 1819 | 9.5 |
| 12 | 326 | 291 | 267 | 245 | 219 | 190 | 158 | 124 | 89 | 56 | 27 | 6 | | 1998 | 1985 | 10.4 |
| 13 | 326 | 294 | 271 | 252 | 229 | 204 | 176 | 144 | 113 | 81 | 51 | 25 | 6 | 2172 | 2156 | 11.2 |
| 84 - 7 | 343 | 283 | 233 | 174 | 110 | 50 | 6 | | | | | | | 1199 | 1193 | 6.0 |
| 8 | 343 | 290 | 249 | 203 | 149 | 93 | 43 | 6 | | | | | | 1376 | 1368 | 6.9 |
| 9 | 343 | 296 | 261 | 222 | 180 | 130 | 81 | 38 | 6 | | | | | 1557 | 1549 | 7.8 |
| 10 | 343 | 301 | 270 | 238 | 201 | 160 | 115 | 72 | 33 | 6 | | | | 1739 | 1730 | 8.6 |
| 11 | 343 | 304 | 276 | 248 | 218 | 182 | 143 | 103 | 65 | 30 | 6 | | | 1918 | 1908 | 9.5 |
| 12 | 343 | 305 | 280 | 257 | 230 | 200 | 165 | 129 | 93 | 58 | 28 | 6 | | 2094 | 2082 | 10.4 |
| 13 | 343 | 308 | 284 | 264 | 240 | 214 | 184 | 151 | 118 | 84 | 53 | 26 | 6 | 2275 | 2260 | 11.2 |
| 86 - 7 | 360 | 297 | 244 | 182 | 114 | 51 | 6 | | | | | | | 1254 | 1248 | 6.0 |
| 8 | 360 | 304 | 262 | 213 | 156 | 98 | 44 | 6 | | | | | | 1443 | 1436 | 6.9 |
| 9 | 360 | 310 | 274 | 234 | 188 | 136 | 84 | 39 | 6 | | | | | 1631 | 1624 | 7.8 |
| 10 | 360 | 314 | 283 | 249 | 211 | 167 | 120 | 75 | 34 | 6 | | | | 1819 | 1811 | 8.6 |
| 11 | 360 | 317 | 289 | 260 | 228 | 191 | 149 | 107 | 67 | 31 | 6 | | | 2005 | 1996 | 9.5 |
| 12 | 360 | 320 | 294 | 269 | 241 | 208 | 174 | 135 | 97 | 60 | 29 | 6 | | 2193 | 2181 | 10.4 |
| 13 | 360 | 323 | 298 | 277 | 252 | 224 | 192 | 158 | 123 | 88 | 54 | 27 | 6 | 2382 | 2362 | 11.1 |
| 88 - 8 | 377 | 318 | 274 | 222 | 162 | 102 | 46 | 6 | | | | | | 1507 | 1500 | 6.9 |
| 9 | 377 | 324 | 287 | 244 | 196 | 142 | 88 | 40 | 6 | | | | | 1704 | 1697 | 7.8 |
| 10 | 377 | 330 | 296 | 260 | 221 | 174 | 125 | 78 | 36 | 6 | | | | 1903 | 1895 | 8.6 |
| 11 | 377 | 333 | 302 | 273 | 239 | 200 | 156 | 112 | 70 | 32 | 6 | | | 2100 | 2091 | 9.5 |
| 12 | 377 | 336 | 308 | 282 | 252 | 218 | 181 | 141 | 101 | 62 | 30 | 6 | | 2294 | 2276 | 10.2 |
| 13 | 377 | 339 | 312 | 290 | 264 | 234 | 201 | 165 | 128 | 92 | 56 | 28 | 6 | 2492 | 2471 | 11.1 |
| 90 - 8 | 395 | 334 | 286 | 232 | 170 | 106 | 48 | 6 | | | | | | 1577 | 1570 | 6.9 |
| 9 | 395 | 340 | 300 | 256 | 205 | 148 | 92 | 41 | 6 | | | | | 1783 | 1776 | 7.8 |
| 10 | 395 | 345 | 309 | 272 | 230 | 182 | 130 | 80 | 37 | 6 | | | | 1986 | 1979 | 8.6 |
| 11 | 395 | 348 | 316 | 285 | 249 | 208 | 162 | 117 | 72 | 33 | 6 | | | 2191 | 2182 | 9.5 |
| 12 | 395 | 351 | 322 | 296 | 264 | 228 | 189 | 147 | 105 | 65 | 30 | 6 | | 2398 | 2380 | 10.2 |
| 13 | 395 | 354 | 326 | 304 | 276 | 245 | 210 | 173 | 134 | 95 | 58 | 28 | 6 | 2604 | 2584 | 11.1 |

Source: V. A. Clements, C. W. Stevens, and D. F. Roy, Form-class volume tables for sugar pine and red fir in California, Calif. Forest & Range Exp. Sta., *Res. Note No. 61*, 1949.

## WESTERN WHITE PINE (OLD GROWTH)

### Table 39. Cubic-Foot Volume

Inland Empire

MEDIUM SITE

| D.b.h. (in.) | Total height in feet | | | | | | | | | | | |
|---|---|---|---|---|---|---|---|---|---|---|---|---|
| | 40 | 50 | 60 | 70 | 80 | 90 | 100 | 110 | 120 | 140 | 160 | 200 |
| 16 | 23.8 | 29.5 | 35.0 | 40.4 | 45.5 | 50.5 | 55.3 | 60.2 | 64.7 | 74.7 | 84.2 | 104.5 |
| 18 | 29.8 | 37.0 | 43.8 | 50.5 | 57.0 | 63.3 | 69.4 | 75.4 | 81.0 | 93.5 | 105.7 | 131.1 |
| 20 | 36.4 | 45.1 | 53.5 | 61.8 | 69.6 | 77.6 | 84.9 | 92.4 | 99.2 | 114.5 | 129.5 | 160.6 |
| 22 | 43.6 | 54.1 | 64.3 | 74.3 | 83.8 | 93.1 | 101.9 | 110.9 | 119.4 | 137.5 | 155.4 | 192.7 |
| 24 | 51.5 | 63.9 | 76.0 | 87.7 | 99.0 | 110.0 | 120.7 | 131.3 | 141.0 | 162.7 | 184.0 | 228.1 |
| 26 | | 74.5 | 88.5 | 102.5 | 115.6 | 128.7 | 140.8 | 153.3 | 164.6 | 190.0 | 215.3 | 266.9 |
| 28 | | 85.9 | 102.1 | 118.2 | 133.4 | 148.5 | 162.5 | 176.9 | 190.4 | 219.7 | 248.4 | 307.9 |
| 30 | | | 116.3 | 135.0 | 152.8 | 170.1 | 186.1 | 202.5 | 217.9 | 251.5 | 284.3 | 352.4 |
| 32 | | | 132.0 | 152.9 | 172.9 | 192.5 | 211.1 | 229.8 | 247.3 | 285.4 | 322.6 | 399.9 |
| 34 | | | | 172.1 | 194.7 | 216.8 | 237.7 | 258.7 | 278.4 | 321.3 | 364.2 | 450.2 |
| 36 | | | | 192.5 | 217.7 | 242.4 | 266.5 | 290.0 | 312.1 | 360.2 | 407.2 | 504.7 |
| 38 | | | | | 242.0 | 269.3 | 296.1 | 322.3 | 347.8 | 400.2 | 453.6 | 562.3 |
| 40 | | | | | 265.3 | 298.5 | 328.1 | 357.1 | 384.3 | 442.3 | 502.7 | 621.3 |
| 42 | | | | | 294.8 | 328.2 | 360.8 | 393.7 | 423.7 | 487.6 | 552.6 | 685.0 |
| 44 | | | | | 322.7 | 360.2 | 396.0 | 430.9 | 465.0 | 533.7 | 606.5 | 749.7 |
| 46 | | | | | | 392.6 | 431.6 | 471.0 | 508.3 | 583.3 | 661.1 | 819.4 |
| 48 | | | | | | 427.5 | 470.0 | 512.8 | 551.9 | 633.3 | 719.8 | 892.2 |
| 50 | | | | | | 462.7 | 509.9 | 555.0 | 598.8 | 687.2 | 778.9 | 965.4 |

Source: U. S. Forest Service, Region 1.

# WESTERN REDCEDAR

## Table 40. Volume in Board Feet, Scribner Decimal C Rule
### Puget Sound
(16 ft. logs—Volume in Tens)

| D.b.h. | No. logs | Bd. ft. | D.b.h. | No. logs | Bd. ft. | D.b.h. | No. logs | Bd. ft. |
|---|---|---|---|---|---|---|---|---|
| 16 | 1 | 8 | 34 | 5 | 110 | 46 | 6 | 242 |
|    | 2 | 11 |    | 6 | 138 |    | 7 | 291 |
|    | 3 | 18 |    | 7 | 167 |    | 8 | 339 |
|    | 4 | 26 |    | 8 | 196 |    | 9 | 386 |
| 18 | 1 | 9 |    | 9 | 224 |    | 10 | 435 |
|    | 2 | 12 | 36 | 5 | 122 |    | 11 | 480 |
|    | 3 | 21 |    | 6 | 155 | 48 | 6 | 262 |
|    | 4 | 30 |    | 7 | 185 |    | 7 | 314 |
| 20 | 2 | 14 |    | 8 | 217 |    | 8 | 365 |
|    | 3 | 25 |    | 9 | 250 |    | 9 | 420 |
|    | 4 | 35 |    | 10 | 281 |    | 10 | 470 |
|    | 5 | 45 | 38 | 6 | 170 |    | 11 | 515 |
| 22 | 2 | 16 |    | 7 | 204 | 50 | 7 | 338 |
|    | 3 | 28 |    | 8 | 240 |    | 8 | 392 |
|    | 4 | 40 |    | 9 | 275 |    | 9 | 450 |
|    | 5 | 53 |    | 10 | 310 |    | 10 | 500 |
| 24 | 3 | 32 | 40 | 6 | 185 |    | 11 | 550 |
|    | 4 | 47 |    | 7 | 224 | 54 | 7 | 386 |
|    | 5 | 62 |    | 8 | 262 |    | 8 | 445 |
|    | 6 | 77 |    | 9 | 300 |    | 9 | 510 |
| 26 | 4 | 53 |    | 10 | 338 |    | 10 | 565 |
|    | 5 | 70 | 42 | 6 | 203 |    | 11 | 622 |
|    | 6 | 86 |    | 7 | 244 | 58 | 8 | 508 |
|    | 7 | 104 |    | 8 | 286 |    | 9 | 570 |
| 28 | 4 | 60 |    | 9 | 327 |    | 10 | 630 |
|    | 5 | 78 |    | 10 | 368 |    | 11 | 697 |
|    | 6 | 99 | 44 | 6 | 222 | 62 | 8 | 565 |
|    | 7 | 119 |    | 7 | 268 |    | 9 | 635 |
| 30 | 5 | 90 |    | 8 | 312 |    | 10 | 705 |
|    | 6 | 112 |    | 9 | 355 |    | 11 | 775 |
|    | 7 | 135 |    | 10 | 399 | 66 | 8 | 623 |
|    | 8 | 159 |    |    |    |    | 9 | 700 |
| 32 | 5 | 98 |    |    |    |    | 10 | 770 |
|    | 6 | 124 |    |    |    |    | 11 | 848 |
|    | 7 | 151 |    |    |    |    |    |    |
|    | 8 | 177 |    |    |    |    |    |    |

Source: Adapted from H. B. Steer, New western redcedar volume table compiled, *Timberman* (1930) 32(2):20.

## Table 41. Cubic-Foot Volume
### Inland Empire

| D.b.h. (in.) | Total height in feet | | | | | | | | | | | |
|---|---|---|---|---|---|---|---|---|---|---|---|---|
| | 40 | 50 | 60 | 70 | 80 | 90 | 100 | 110 | 120 | 140 | 160 | 200 |

### MEDIUM SITE

| D.b.h. | 40 | 50 | 60 | 70 | 80 | 90 | 100 | 110 | 120 | 140 | 160 | 200 |
|---|---|---|---|---|---|---|---|---|---|---|---|---|
| 16 | 25.2 | 27.2 | 31.8 | 36.1 | 40.3 | 44.4 | 48.4 | 52.4 | 56.5 | 64.2 | 72.0 | 87.9 |
| 18 | 27.2 | 29.4 | 34.4 | 39.0 | 43.6 | 48.1 | 52.5 | 56.9 | 61.2 | 69.9 | 78.3 | 95.7 |
| 20 | 30.5 | 39.2 | 45.8 | 52.0 | 58.1 | 64.1 | 70.0 | 75.8 | 81.6 | 94.9 | 104.7 | 128.7 |
| 22 | 38.2 | 46.2 | 53.9 | 61.9 | 68.5 | 75.5 | 82.5 | 89.4 | 96.2 | 110.2 | 123.4 | 152.1 |
| 24 | 44.2 | 53.7 | 62.6 | 71.3 | 83.0 | 88.1 | 96.0 | 104.0 | 112.1 | 128.0 | 151.3 | 178.6 |
| 26 | 50.9 | 61.8 | 71.9 | 81.9 | 91.9 | 101.4 | 110.9 | 120.1 | 129.2 | 148.8 | 167.7 | 208.2 |
| 28 | 58.0 | 70.4 | 82.2 | 93.6 | 105.0 | 115.7 | 126.5 | 137.4 | 148.4 | 170.1 | 192.5 | 239.7 |
| 30 | 65.4 | 79.4 | 92.9 | 106.0 | 118.2 | 131.2 | 143.4 | 155.6 | 168.0 | 193.9 | 220.1 | 274.2 |
| 32 | 73.1 | 89.0 | 104.1 | 118.8 | 133.6 | 147.8 | 161.5 | 175.8 | 189.8 | 219.1 | 249.6 | 310.9 |
| 34 | 81.5 | 99.5 | 116.4 | 133.3 | 149.3 | 165.1 | 181.0 | 197.1 | 212.8 | 245.7 | 279.8 | 349.8 |
| 36 | 90.6 | 110.4 | 129.3 | 147.9 | 166.3 | 183.9 | 201.6 | 219.4 | 236.9 | 274.5 | 312.5 | 390.7 |
| 38 | 100.5 | 122.6 | 143.9 | 164.5 | 185.0 | 204.6 | 225.0 | 244.9 | 264.4 | 306.3 | 348.9 | 436.1 |
| 40 | 109.9 | 133.9 | 157.5 | 180.2 | 202.5 | 224.7 | 246.3 | 268.1 | 290.5 | 336.4 | 383.2 | 478.9 |
| 42 | 120.3 | 146.6 | 172.6 | 197.4 | 221.8 | 246.1 | 270.6 | 294.6 | 319.1 | 370.9 | 422.4 | 526.2 |
| 44 | 131.6 | 160.4 | 188.7 | 215.9 | 242.6 | 269.1 | 296.0 | 322.1 | 349.0 | 405.6 | 462.0 | 575.4 |
| 46 | 143.0 | 174.1 | 204.9 | 235.1 | 264.2 | 293.1 | 322.3 | 350.8 | 381.4 | 443.6 | 503.1 | 626.6 |
| 48 | 155.2 | 189.0 | 222.5 | 255.2 | 286.7 | 318.1 | 349.8 | 380.6 | 413.8 | 481.0 | 547.7 | 679.8 |
| 50 | 167.9 | 204.4 | 240.5 | 276.0 | 310.0 | 344.0 | 378.2 | 411.6 | 447.4 | 520.1 | 592.2 | 737.6 |

Source: U. S. Forest Service, Region 1.

## Table 42. Volume in Board Feet, Scribner Decimal C Rule *
### Kaniksu National Forest, Idaho

| D.b.h. (in.) | Number of 16-ft. logs | | | | | | | | | | |
|---|---|---|---|---|---|---|---|---|---|---|---|
| | 1 | 1½ | 2 | 2½ | 3 | 3½ | 4 | 4½ | 5 | 5½ | 6 |
| 8 | 15 | 25 | 30 | | | | | | | | |
| 9 | 20 | 30 | 40 | 50 | | | | | | | |
| 10 | 20 | 35 | 50 | 60 | 80 | | | | | | |
| 11 | 25 | 40 | 55 | 70 | 90 | 100 | | | | | |
| 12 | 30 | 45 | 65 | 80 | 100 | 115 | 130 | | | | |
| 13 | | 50 | 75 | 90 | 110 | 125 | 145 | | | | |
| 14 | | 55 | 80 | 105 | 125 | 140 | 165 | | | | |
| 15 | | 60 | 90 | 115 | 135 | 160 | 180 | 205 | | | |
| 16 | | 65 | 95 | 125 | 150 | 175 | 200 | 225 | 265 | 325 | |
| 17 | | | 100 | 140 | 165 | 195 | 225 | 250 | 295 | 350 | |
| 18 | | | | 155 | 185 | 220 | 245 | 275 | 325 | 375 | 435 |
| 19 | | | | 170 | 200 | 240 | 270 | 300 | 350 | 405 | 465 |
| 20 | | | | 190 | 220 | 265 | 295 | 330 | 380 | 440 | 500 |
| 21 | | | | | | 285 | 320 | 360 | 405 | 470 | 540 |
| 22 | | | | | | 310 | 345 | 385 | 435 | 505 | 575 |
| 23 | | | | | | 330 | 370 | 415 | 465 | 545 | 620 |
| 24 | | | | | | | 395 | 445 | 495 | 585 | 665 |
| 25 | | | | | | | 425 | 475 | 535 | 630 | 715 |
| 26 | | | | | | | 450 | 505 | 575 | 675 | 760 |
| 27 | | | | | | | 480 | 540 | 620 | 720 | 805 |
| 28 | | | | | | | | 575 | 665 | 765 | 850 |
| 29 | | | | | | | | 605 | 715 | 805 | 900 |
| 30 | | | | | | | | | | 850 | 950 |
| 31 | | | | | | | | | | | 1,005 |

* Height of stump, 2.0 ft. Diameter inside bark of top, 6 to 7 in. Density of stand 0.5. Basis, 1,890 trees.
Source: Millar, U. S. Forest Service, Region 1, 1910.

## REDWOOD (SECOND GROWTH)

### Table 43. Volume in Board Feet, Scribner Rule *

Del Norte, Humboldt, Mendocino. and Sonoma Counties, California
Form Class 70

| D.b.h. (in.) | Height in number of 16.3-ft. logs utilized | | | | | | | | | | Minimum top d.i. utilized |
|---|---|---|---|---|---|---|---|---|---|---|---|
| | 1 | 2 | 3 | 4 | 5 | 6 | 7 | 8 | 9 | 10 | |
| 12 | 37 | 72 | 105 | ... | ... | ... | ... | ... | ... | ... | 8 |
| 14 | 50 | 97 | 142 | ... | ... | ... | ... | ... | ... | ... | 9 |
| 16 | 65 | 125 | 183 | 240 | ... | ... | ... | ... | ... | ... | 10 |
| 18 | 82 | 157 | 230 | 302 | 372 | ... | ... | ... | ... | ... | 10 |
| 20 | 101 | 193 | 282 | 370 | 456 | 541 | ... | ... | ... | ... | 11 |
| 22 | 121 | 232 | 340 | 445 | 549 | 651 | ... | ... | ... | ... | 11 |
| 24 | 143 | 275 | 402 | 526 | 649 | 770 | 890 | ... | ... | ... | 12 |
| 26 | ... | 321 | 469 | 615 | 758 | 900 | 1,040 | ... | ... | ... | 12 |
| 28 | ... | 370 | 542 | 710 | 875 | 1,038 | 1,200 | 1,360 | ... | ... | 13 |
| 30 | ... | 423 | 619 | 811 | 1,000 | 1,187 | 1,372 | 1,555 | ... | ... | 13 |
| 32 | ... | 479 | 701 | 919 | 1,133 | 1,345 | 1,554 | 1,762 | ... | ... | 14 |
| 34 | ... | 539 | 789 | 1,033 | 1,274 | 1,512 | 1,748 | 1,981 | ... | ... | 14 |
| 36 | ... | 602 | 881 | 1,154 | 1,423 | 1,689 | 1,952 | 2,213 | 2,472 | 2,729 | 15 |
| 38 | ... | 668 | 978 | 1,282 | 1,580 | 1,875 | 2,168 | 2,457 | 2,745 | 3,030 | 15 |
| 40 | ... | 738 | 1,080 | 1,415 | 1,745 | 2,071 | 2,394 | 2,714 | 3,031 | 3,346 | 15 |
| 42 | ... | ... | 1,187 | 1,556 | 1,918 | 2,276 | 2,631 | 2,983 | 3,331 | 3,678 | 16 |
| 44 | ... | ... | 1,299 | 1,702 | 2,099 | 2,491 | 2,879 | 3,264 | 3,645 | 4,025 | 16 |
| 46 | ... | ... | 1,416 | 1,855 | 2,288 | 2,715 | 3,138 | 3,557 | 3,973 | 4,386 | 17 |
| 48 | ... | ... | ... | 2,014 | 2,484 | 2,948 | 3,407 | 3,863 | 4,314 | 4,763 | 17 |
| 50 | ... | ... | ... | 2,180 | 2,688 | 3,190 | 3,687 | 4,180 | 4,669 | 5,155 | 18 |
| 52 | ... | ... | ... | 2,352 | 2,900 | 3,442 | 3,978 | 4,510 | 5,037 | 5,561 | 18 |
| 54 | ... | ... | ... | 2,530 | 3,120 | 3,703 | 4,280 | 4,852 | 5,419 | 5,983 | 18 |
| 56 | ... | ... | ... | 2,715 | 3,348 | 3,973 | 4,592 | 5,206 | 5,815 | 6,419 | 19 |
| 58 | ... | ... | ... | 2,906 | 3,583 | 4,253 | 4,915 | 5,572 | 6,223 | 6,871 | 19 |
| 60 | ... | ... | ... | 3,103 | 3,826 | 4,541 | 5,248 | 5,950 | 6,646 | 7,337 | 20 |

* Stump height, 18 in. on uphill side. Basis, 118 trees. Average deviation of individual tree volume. 3.9 percent. For other form classes, multiply tabular values by following factors:

| Form class (tens) | 0 | 1 | 2 | 3 | 4 (units) | 5 | 6 | 7 | 8 | 9 |
|---|---|---|---|---|---|---|---|---|---|---|
| 5 | 0.63 | 9.65 | 0.66 | 0.68 | 0.69 | 0.71 | 0.73 | 0.74 | 0.76 | 0.78 |
| 6 | 0.80 | 0.81 | 0.83 | 0.85 | 0.87 | 0.89 | 0.91 | 0.93 | 0.96 | 0.98 |
| 7 | 1.00 | 1.02 | 1.05 | 1.07 | 1.10 | 1.12 | 1.15 | 1.17 | 1.20 | 1.23 |
| 8 | 1.26 | 1.29 | 1.32 | 1.35 | 1.38 | 1.41 | 1.44 | 1.48 | 1.51 | 1.55 |

**Example:** Volume of 36-in., 5-log tree, form class 78 is $1,423 \times 1.20 = 1,708$.

Source: A. A. Hasel, Board-foot and cubic-foot volume tables for second-growth redwood, Calif. Forest & Range Exp. Sta. *Res. Note No. 66*, 1950.

## REDWOOD (OLD GROWTH)

### Table 44. Volume in Board Feet, Scribner Decimal C Rule
(Volume in Tens)

| D.o.b. at 20 ft. (in.) | D.b.h.[a] N[b] (in.) | S[c] (in.) | Number of 20-ft. logs[d] 2 | 3 | 4 | 5 | 6 | 7 | 8 | 9 | 10 |
|---|---|---|---|---|---|---|---|---|---|---|---|
| 16 | | | 23 | 31 | | | | | | | |
| 18 | | | 24 | 37 | 47 | 60 | | | | | |
| 20 | | | 28 | 43 | 57 | 74 | | | | | |
| 22 | | | 33 | 53 | 71 | 91 | | | | | |
| 24 | | 32 | | 67 | 88 | 110 | | | | | |
| 26 | 32 | | | 81 | 106 | 130 | | | | | |
| 28 | 36 | | | 95 | 127 | 153 | | | | | |
| 30 | 40 | 40 | | 110 | 147 | 179 | 218 | | | | |
| 32 | | | | 130 | 169 | 203 | 249 | 290 | | | |
| 34 | | | | 145 | 191 | 230 | 280 | 329 | 379 | | |
| 36 | 48 | 48 | | 175 | 215 | 259 | 318 | 368 | 423 | | |
| 38 | | | | 184 | 240 | 290 | 350 | 410 | 468 | | |
| 40 | | | | 205 | 269 | 322 | 386 | 450 | 520 | | |
| 44 | | | | 250 | 324 | 398 | 465 | 550 | 621 | | |
| 48 | | 64 | | | 381 | 470 | 558 | 658 | 742 | | |
| 52 | | 68 | | | 457 | 560 | 647 | 764 | 880 | | |
| 56 | 72 | | | | 530 | 650 | 796 | 895 | 1,045 | | |
| 60 | | 80 | | | | 742 | 912 | 1,033 | 1,203 | 1,335 | |
| 64 | | | | | | 845 | 1,039 | 1,173 | 1,368 | 1,515 | |
| 68 | | | | | | 960 | 1,157 | 1,377 | 1,536 | 1,756 | |
| 72 | 92 | | | | | 1,080 | 1,298 | 1,545 | 1,713 | 1,964 | |
| 76 | | | | | | 1,220 | 1,436 | 1,710 | 1,910 | 2,177 | 2,372 |
| 80 | | | | | | 1,380 | 1,587 | 1,796 | 2,103 | 2,399 | 2,615 |
| 86 | | | | | | 1,590 | 1,889 | 2,174 | 2,423 | 2,764 | 3,012 |
| 92 | | | | | | 1,810 | 2,089 | 2,479 | 2,865 | 3,153 | 3,437 |
| 98 | | | | | | 2,075 | 2,366 | 2,807 | 3,130 | 3,567 | 3,886 |
| 104 | | | | | | 2,325 | 2,662 | 3,161 | 3,524 | 4,016 | 4,375 |
| 110 | | | | | | 2,575 | 2,972 | 3,524 | 3,927 | 4,478 | 4,883 |

[a] Redwood Forest Handbook, Calif. Dept. of Natural Resources.
[b] Humboldt, Del Norte counties.
[c] Mendocino, Sonoma, Santa Cruz, San Mateo counties.
[d] To assumed top d.i.b. of ½ d.o.b. at 20 ft.
Source: W. E. Hallin, Calif. Forest & Range Exp. Sta., 1941.

# REDWOOD (OLD GROWTH)

## Table 45. Volume in Board Feet, Spalding Log Rule (in Tens)

### Humboldt County, California

Height in feet to a top d.i.b. 50% of 20-ft. d.i.b.[b]

| 20 ft. d.o.b.[a] | 50 | 60 | 70 | 80 | 90 | 100 | 110 | 120 | 130 | 140 | 150 | 160 | 170 | 180 | 190 | 200 | 210 | 220 | 230 | 240 | 250 |
|---|---|---|---|---|---|---|---|---|---|---|---|---|---|---|---|---|---|---|---|---|---|
| 16 | 14 | 19 | 23 | 28 | 33 | 38 | 44 | 49 | 55 | 61 | 66 | | | | | | | | | | |
| 18 | 18 | 24 | 30 | 37 | 44 | 51 | 58 | 66 | 73 | 81 | 89 | | | | | | | | | | |
| 20 | 24 | 32 | 40 | 48 | 57 | 67 | 76 | 86 | 95 | 104 | 113 | | | | | | | | | | |
| 22 | 30 | 40 | 51 | 62 | 73 | 85 | 96 | 107 | 118 | 129 | 139 | | | | | | | | | | |
| 24 | 36 | 49 | 62 | 75 | 89 | 102 | 115 | 128 | 141 | 154 | 167 | | | | | | | | | | |
| 26 | | | 76 | 92 | 107 | 123 | 138 | 153 | 168 | 183 | 198 | 213 | 227 | 242 | 256 | | | | | | |
| 28 | | | 91 | 109 | 127 | 144 | 162 | 180 | 197 | 214 | 231 | 248 | 266 | 282 | 299 | | | | | | |
| 30 | | | 106 | 127 | 148 | 168 | 188 | 208 | 228 | 248 | 267 | 287 | 306 | 325 | 344 | | | | | | |
| 32 | | | 123 | 146 | 170 | 192 | 215 | 238 | 260 | 283 | 305 | 327 | 348 | 370 | 392 | | | | | | |
| 34 | | | 140 | 167 | 193 | 219 | 244 | 270 | 295 | 320 | 345 | 369 | 394 | 418 | 442 | | | | | | |
| 36 | | | 159 | 188 | 217 | 246 | 274 | 302 | 330 | 358 | 386 | 413 | 440 | 467 | 493 | | | | | | |
| 38 | | | 178 | 211 | 243 | 275 | 306 | 338 | 368 | 399 | 429 | 460 | 489 | 519 | 548 | | | | | | |
| 40 | | | 198 | 234 | 270 | 305 | 340 | 374 | 408 | 442 | 475 | 508 | 541 | 574 | 606 | | | | | | |
| 42 | | | 220 | 260 | 298 | 337 | 375 | 413 | 450 | 487 | 524 | 560 | 596 | 632 | 667 | | | | | | |
| 44 | | | 243 | 286 | 328 | 369 | 411 | 452 | 493 | 533 | 573 | 613 | 652 | 691 | 730 | | | | | | |
| 46 | | | 266 | 312 | 358 | 403 | 448 | 492 | 537 | 580 | 624 | 667 | 710 | 753 | 795 | | | | | | |
| 48 | | | 291 | 340 | 390 | 438 | 487 | 535 | 583 | 631 | 678 | 726 | 772 | 819 | 865 | | | | | | |
| 50 | | | | | 422 | 474 | 527 | 579 | 630 | 682 | 733 | 784 | 835 | 885 | 935 | 985 | 1,035 | | | | |
| 52 | | | | | 457 | 512 | 567 | 622 | 678 | 733 | 788 | 843 | 898 | 954 | 1,009 | 1,064 | 1,119 | | | | |
| 54 | | | | | 493 | 552 | 612 | 671 | 730 | 790 | 849 | 908 | 968 | 1,027 | 1,086 | 1,146 | 1,205 | | | | |
| 56 | | | | | 528 | 592 | 656 | 719 | 783 | 847 | 911 | 975 | 1,039 | 1,102 | 1,167 | 1,230 | 1,294 | | | | |
| 58 | | | | | 567 | 636 | 704 | 773 | 841 | 910 | 978 | 1,047 | 1,116 | 1,184 | 1,253 | 1,321 | 1,390 | | | | |
| 60 | | | | | | 680 | 753 | 826 | 899 | 972 | 1,045 | 1,118 | 1,191 | 1,264 | 1,337 | 1,410 | 1,483 | 1,556 | | | |
| 62 | | | | | | 723 | 801 | 879 | 957 | 1,035 | 1,113 | 1,191 | 1,269 | 1,347 | 1,425 | 1,503 | 1,580 | 1,658 | | | |
| 64 | | | | | | 768 | 851 | 934 | 1,018 | 1,101 | 1,184 | 1,267 | 1,350 | 1,433 | 1,517 | 1,600 | 1,683 | 1,766 | | | |
| 66 | | | | | | 815 | 904 | 992 | 1,081 | 1,169 | 1,258 | 1,347 | 1,436 | 1,524 | 1,613 | 1,702 | 1,790 | 1,879 | | | |
| 68 | | | | | | 863 | 957 | 1,051 | 1,145 | 1,239 | 1,333 | 1,428 | 1,522 | 1,616 | 1,710 | 1,804 | 1,898 | 1,992 | | | |
| 70 | | | | | | | 1,016 | 1,114 | 1,214 | 1,312 | 1,412 | 1,510 | 1,610 | 1,708 | 1,806 | 1,906 | 2,004 | 2,114 | 2,202 | 2,302 | 2,400 |

a Redwood Forest, Humboldt, Del Norte, Mendocino, Sonoma, and Santa Cruz counties.
b To assumed top d.i.b. of 50% of 20-ft. d.i.b.

Source: W. E. Hallin, Calif. Forest & Range Exp. Sta., 1951.

Height in feet to a top d.i.b. 50% of 20-ft. d.i.b.[b]

| 20 ft. d.o.b.[a] | 50 | 60 | 70 | 80 | 90 | 100 | 110 | 120 | 130 | 140 | 150 | 160 | 170 | 180 | 190 | 200 | 210 | 220 | 230 | 240 | 250 |
|---|---|---|---|---|---|---|---|---|---|---|---|---|---|---|---|---|---|---|---|---|---|
| 72 | | | | | | | 1,072 | 1,176 | 1,280 | 1,386 | 1,490 | 1,594 | 1,698 | 1,804 | 1,908 | 2,012 | 2,116 | 2,220 | 2,326 | 2,430 | 2,534 |
| 74 | | | | | | | 1,130 | 1,240 | 1,350 | 1,462 | 1,572 | 1,682 | 1,792 | 1,902 | 2,014 | 2,124 | 2,234 | 2,344 | 2,456 | 2,566 | 2,676 |
| 76 | | | | | | | 1,190 | 1,306 | 1,422 | 1,540 | 1,656 | 1,772 | 1,888 | 2,004 | 2,122 | 2,238 | 2,354 | 2,470 | 2,588 | 2,704 | 2,820 |
| 78 | | | | | | | 1,250 | 1,374 | 1,498 | 1,620 | 1,744 | 1,868 | 1,992 | 2,114 | 2,238 | 2,362 | 2,486 | 2,609 | 2,732 | 2,856 | 2,980 |
| 80 | | | | | | | 1,320 | 1,450 | 1,580 | 1,708 | 1,838 | 1,968 | 2,098 | 2,226 | 2,356 | 2,486 | 2,616 | 2,746 | 2,874 | 3,004 | 3,134 |
| 82 | | | | | | | 1,386 | 1,522 | 1,660 | 1,796 | 1,932 | 2,068 | 2,206 | 2,342 | 2,478 | 2,616 | 2,752 | 2,888 | 3,024 | 3,162 | 3,298 |
| 84 | | | | | | | 1,454 | 1,596 | 1,740 | 1,882 | 2,026 | 2,168 | 2,312 | 2,454 | 2,596 | 2,740 | 2,882 | 3,028 | 3,168 | 3,312 | 3,454 |
| 86 | | | | | | | 1,520 | 1,670 | 1,820 | 1,970 | 2,120 | 2,270 | 2,420 | 2,570 | 2,720 | 2,870 | 3,020 | 3,170 | 3,320 | 3,470 | 3,620 |
| 88 | | | | | | | 1,584 | 1,742 | 1,898 | 2,056 | 2,212 | 2,370 | 2,526 | 2,684 | 2,842 | 2,998 | 3,156 | 3,312 | 3,470 | 3,626 | 3,784 |
| 90 | | | | | | | 1,656 | 1,820 | 1,984 | 2,148 | 2,312 | 2,476 | 2,640 | 2,802 | 2,966 | 3,130 | 3,294 | 3,458 | 3,622 | 3,786 | 3,950 |
| 92 | | | | | | | 1,732 | 1,902 | 2,074 | 2,244 | 2,414 | 2,584 | 2,756 | 2,926 | 3,096 | 3,268 | 3,438 | 3,608 | 3,778 | 3,950 | 4,120 |
| 94 | | | | | | | 1,806 | 1,984 | 2,160 | 2,338 | 2,516 | 2,694 | 2,870 | 3,048 | 3,226 | 3,402 | 3,580 | 3,758 | 3,936 | 4,112 | 4,290 |
| 96 | | | | | | | 1,886 | 2,070 | 2,256 | 2,440 | 2,624 | 2,808 | 2,994 | 3,178 | 3,362 | 3,548 | 3,732 | 3,916 | 4,100 | 4,286 | 4,470 |
| 98 | | | | | | | 1,962 | 2,154 | 2,346 | 2,538 | 2,730 | 2,922 | 3,114 | 3,306 | 3,498 | 3,690 | 3,882 | 4,074 | 4,266 | 4,458 | 4,650 |
| 100 | | | | | | | 2,036 | 2,236 | 2,436 | 2,636 | 2,838 | 3,038 | 3,238 | 3,438 | 3,638 | 3,838 | 4,038 | 4,240 | 4,440 | 4,640 | 4,840 |
| 102 | | | | | | | 2,122 | 2,330 | 2,538 | 2,746 | 2,952 | 3,160 | 3,368 | 3,576 | 3,784 | 3,992 | 4,200 | 4,406 | 4,614 | 4,822 | 5,030 |
| 104 | | | | | | | 2,206 | 2,422 | 2,636 | 2,852 | 3,068 | 3,282 | 3,498 | 3,714 | 3,928 | 4,144 | 4,358 | 4,574 | 4,790 | 5,004 | 5,220 |
| 106 | | | | | | | 2,286 | 2,510 | 2,734 | 2,958 | 3,182 | 3,406 | 3,630 | 3,854 | 4,076 | 4,300 | 4,524 | 4,748 | 4,972 | 5,196 | 5,420 |
| 108 | | | | | | | 2,374 | 2,606 | 2,838 | 3,070 | 3,304 | 3,536 | 3,768 | 4,000 | 4,232 | 4,464 | 4,696 | 4,930 | 5,162 | 5,394 | 5,626 |
| 110 | | | | | | | 2,456 | 2,696 | 2,938 | 3,178 | 3,418 | 3,660 | 3,900 | 4,140 | 4,382 | 4,622 | 4,864 | 5,104 | 5,344 | 5,586 | 5,826 |
| 112 | | | | | | | 2,546 | 2,794 | 3,044 | 3,292 | 3,542 | 3,790 | 4,040 | 4,288 | 4,536 | 4,786 | 5,034 | 5,284 | 5,532 | 5,782 | 6,030 |
| 114 | | | | | | | 2,630 | 2,888 | 3,144 | 3,402 | 3,658 | 3,916 | 4,172 | 4,430 | 4,688 | 4,944 | 5,202 | 5,458 | 5,716 | 5,972 | 6,230 |
| 116 | | | | | | | 2,720 | 2,988 | 3,254 | 3,522 | 3,788 | 4,056 | 4,322 | 4,590 | 4,858 | 5,124 | 5,392 | 5,658 | 5,926 | 6,192 | 6,460 |
| 118 | | | | | | | 2,810 | 3,086 | 3,362 | 3,638 | 3,914 | 4,190 | 4,466 | 4,742 | 5,018 | 5,294 | 5,570 | 5,846 | 6,122 | 6,398 | 6,674 |
| 120 | | | | | | | 2,906 | 3,192 | 3,476 | 3,762 | 4,048 | 4,332 | 4,618 | 4,904 | 5,188 | 5,474 | 5,758 | 6,044 | 6,330 | 6,614 | 6,900 |
| 122 | | | | | | | 3,006 | 3,300 | 3,594 | 3,888 | 4,182 | 4,476 | 4,770 | 5,064 | 5,356 | 5,650 | 5,944 | 6,238 | 6,532 | 6,826 | 7,120 |
| 124 | | | | | | | 3,104 | 3,408 | 3,710 | 4,014 | 4,318 | 4,620 | 4,924 | 5,228 | 5,530 | 5,834 | 6,136 | 6,440 | 6,744 | 7,046 | 7,350 |
| 126 | | | | | | | 3,206 | 3,518 | 3,830 | 4,142 | 4,452 | 4,764 | 5,076 | 5,388 | 5,700 | 6,012 | 6,324 | 6,634 | 6,946 | 7,258 | 7,570 |
| 128 | | | | | | | 3,316 | 3,636 | 3,958 | 4,278 | 4,598 | 4,920 | 5,240 | 5,560 | 5,882 | 6,202 | 6,524 | 6,844 | 7,164 | 7,486 | 7,806 |
| 130 | | | | | | | 3,426 | 3,756 | 4,086 | 4,414 | 4,744 | 5,074 | 5,404 | 5,732 | 6,062 | 6,392 | 6,722 | 7,052 | 7,380 | 7,710 | 8,040 |

[a] Diameters outside bark 20 ft. above upper ground line.
[b] Stump height 3.5 ft. Scaled in 16.4-ft. logs. Basis, 561 trees. Mean deviation ±7.2 percent.
Source: W. E. Hallin, Calif. Forest & Range Exp. Sta., 1940.

## ENGELMANN SPRUCE (OLD GROWTH)

### Table 46. Cubic-Foot Volume
Inland Empire—all sites

| D.b.h. (in.) | Total height in feet | | | | | | | | | | | |
|---|---|---|---|---|---|---|---|---|---|---|---|---|
| | 40 | 50 | 60 | 70 | 80 | 90 | 100 | 110 | 120 | 140 | 160 | 200 |
| 16 | 24.8 | 30.7 | 36.7 | 42.6 | 48.5 | 54.3 | 60.2 | 66.0 | 71.9 | 83.7 | 95.4 | 119.0 |
| 18 | 30.7 | 38.1 | 45.4 | 52.7 | 60.0 | 67.3 | 74.4 | 81.8 | 89.1 | 103.7 | 118.5 | 148.1 |
| 20 | 37.5 | 46.0 | 54.8 | 63.7 | 72.6 | 81.3 | 90.1 | 99.1 | 107.9 | 125.5 | 143.5 | 179.3 |
| 22 | 44.1 | 54.8 | 65.4 | 76.0 | 86.6 | 97.2 | 102.7 | 118.2 | 128.6 | 149.7 | 171.1 | 213.3 |
| 24 | 51.7 | 64.3 | 76.7 | 89.1 | 101.3 | 113.6 | 126.0 | 138.6 | 150.8 | 175.5 | 200.1 | 250.1 |
| 26 | 59.9 | 74.3 | 88.7 | 103.0 | 117.4 | 131.7 | 146.0 | 160.2 | 174.7 | 203.4 | 231.8 | 289.8 |
| 28 | 68.6 | 85.1 | 101.6 | 118.2 | 134.4 | 150.8 | 167.2 | 183.5 | 200.1 | 232.9 | 265.5 | 331.8 |
| 30 | 78.1 | 96.9 | 116.0 | 134.7 | 153.5 | 172.3 | 191.0 | 209.5 | 227.9 | 265.3 | 303.2 | 378.0 |
| 32 | 88.2 | 109.8 | 131.0 | 152.5 | 173.4 | 194.5 | 215.6 | 237.2 | 258.0 | 300.2 | 342.2 | 426.7 |
| 34 | 99.1 | 123.3 | 147.2 | 171.3 | 195.2 | 219.1 | 242.1 | 266.3 | 289.8 | 337.2 | 384.4 | 479.2 |
| 36 | 110.8 | 157.8 | 164.6 | 191.0 | 217.7 | 244.3 | 270.7 | 297.0 | 323.2 | 376.0 | 428.6 | 534.4 |
| 38 | 123.2 | 162.8 | 182.4 | 212.3 | 242.0 | 271.5 | 300.9 | 330.1 | 359.1 | 417.9 | 476.3 | 593.9 |
| 40 | 135.8 | 168.8 | 201.6 | 234.0 | 266.7 | 299.2 | 331.6 | 363.8 | 395.8 | 460.6 | 525.0 | 654.5 |
| 42 | | | | | | | | | 435.0 | 504.0 | 575.7 | 716.2 |

Source: U. S. Forest Service, Region 1.

## SITKA SPRUCE

### Table 47. Cubic-Foot Volume *
Alaska, British Columbia, Oregon, Washington

| D.i.b. at 18 ft. (in.) | Total height in feet | | | | | | | | | | | | |
|---|---|---|---|---|---|---|---|---|---|---|---|---|---|
| | 20 | 40 | 60 | 80 | 100 | 120 | 140 | 160 | 180 | 200 | 220 | 240 | 260 |
| 2 | 0.9 | 1.2 | | | | | | | | | | | |
| 4 | 1.8 | 3.0 | 4.2 | | | | | | | | | | |
| 6 | 3.3 | 5.9 | 8.7 | 11 | | | | | | | | | |
| 8 | | 10.9 | 14 | 18 | 22 | | | | | | | | |
| 10 | | 14.5 | 21 | 28 | 34 | | | | | | | | |
| 12 | | 20.0 | 29 | 39 | 47 | 55 | | | | | | | |
| 14 | | | 39 | 51 | 62 | 73 | 84 | | | | | | |
| 16 | | | 49 | 65 | 80 | 95 | 112 | 125 | | | | | |
| 18 | | | 61 | 81 | 101 | 120 | 139 | 155 | 172 | | | | |
| 20 | | | 74 | 99 | 124 | 144 | 166 | 185 | 202 | 225 | | | |
| 22 | | | 89 | 120 | 147 | 170 | 195 | 220 | 246 | 275 | | | |
| 24 | | | 108 | 140 | 170 | 198 | 227 | 260 | 291 | 320 | 350 | | |
| 26 | | | 126 | 160 | 195 | 231 | 265 | 302 | 338 | 370 | 410 | | |
| 28 | | | | 182 | 223 | 266 | 305 | 348 | 388 | 430 | 470 | 510 | |
| 30 | | | | 203 | 257 | 302 | 350 | 395 | 443 | 490 | 535 | 580 | |
| 32 | | | | 234 | 289 | 340 | 395 | 445 | 500 | 550 | 610 | 660 | 710 |
| 34 | | | | | 323 | 380 | 445 | 500 | 560 | 620 | 685 | 740 | 800 |
| 36 | | | | | 358 | 425 | 495 | 560 | 625 | 700 | 760 | 825 | 900 |
| 38 | | | | | 395 | 475 | 545 | 620 | 700 | 775 | 840 | 920 | 1,000 |
| 40 | | | | | 440 | 520 | 600 | 690 | 775 | 860 | 940 | 1,020 | 1,100 |
| 42 | | | | | | 570 | 660 | 760 | 850 | 945 | 1,030 | 1,120 | 1,200 |
| 44 | | | | | | 620 | 725 | 830 | 930 | 1,030 | 1,120 | 1,220 | 1,310 |
| 46 | | | | | | 680 | 790 | 900 | 1,010 | 1,115 | 1,220 | 1,320 | 1,430 |
| 48 | | | | | | 740 | 860 | 980 | 1,090 | 1,200 | 1,320 | 1,440 | 1,560 |
| 50 | | | | | | 800 | 930 | 1,060 | 1,180 | 1,300 | 1,430 | 1,570 | 1,690 |
| 52 | | | | | | | 1,000 | 1,130 | 1,270 | 1,410 | 1,550 | 1,700 | 1,830 |
| 54 | | | | | | | 1,070 | 1,210 | 1,370 | 1,520 | 1,680 | 1,830 | 1,990 |
| 56 | | | | | | | 1,150 | 1,300 | 1,480 | 1,630 | 1,810 | 1,970 | 2,150 |
| 58 | | | | | | | 1,220 | 1,400 | 1,590 | 1,750 | 1,940 | 2,120 | 2,300 |
| 60 | | | | | | | 1,300 | 1,500 | 1,700 | 1,880 | 2,080 | 2,270 | 2,450 |
| 62 | | | | | | | | 1,600 | 1,800 | 2,010 | 2,220 | 2,420 | 2,600 |
| 64 | | | | | | | | 1,710 | 1,920 | 2,140 | 2,360 | 2,550 | 2,750 |
| 66 | | | | | | | | 1,810 | 2,040 | 2,280 | 2,500 | 2,700 | 2,900 |
| 68 | | | | | | | | 1,930 | 2,170 | 2,410 | 2,640 | 2,850 | 3,060 |
| 70 | | | | | | | | 2,050 | 2,300 | 2,540 | 2,780 | 3,000 | 3,220 |
| 72 | | | | | | | | | 2,430 | 2,670 | 2,920 | 3,150 | 3,380 |
| 74 | | | | | | | | | 2,560 | 2,810 | 3,060 | 3,300 | 3,540 |
| 76 | | | | | | | | | 2,690 | 2,950 | 3,210 | 3,450 | 3,700 |
| 78 | | | | | | | | | 2,830 | 3,090 | 3,360 | 3,600 | 3,860 |
| 80 | | | | | | | | | 2,960 | 3,230 | 3,510 | 3,770 | 4,030 |

* Total volume inside bark including stump and tip. Basis: 599 old-growth and 680 young-growth trees. Standard error of single volume estimate, 9.6 percent.

Source for Tables 47 and 48: W. H. Meyer, Volume tables for Sitka spruce, Pacific Northwest Forest Exp. Sta., 1935.

## SITKA SPRUCE

### Table 48.  Volume in Board Feet, Scribner Decimal C Rule *
Alaska, British Columbia, Oregon, Washington
(Volume in Tens)

| D.i.b. at 18 ft. (in.) | Height in 32.6-ft. logs to 12-in. top | | | | | | | | | | | | |
|---|---|---|---|---|---|---|---|---|---|---|---|---|---|
| | 1 | 1½ | 2 | 2½ | 3 | 3½ | 4 | 4½ | 5 | 5½ | 6 | 6½ | 7 |
| 10 | 16 | 27 | 37 | | | | | | | | | | |
| 12 | 16 | 29 | 40 | 55 | | | | | | | | | |
| 14 | 16 | 31 | 43 | 55 | | | | | | | | | |
| 16 | 16 | 33 | 47 | 61 | 76 | 92 | | | | | | | |
| 18 | | 35 | 52 | 70 | 87 | 105 | 122 | | | | | | |
| 20 | | 38 | 58 | 79 | 100 | 120 | 140 | 160 | | | | | |
| 22 | | 41 | 64 | 90 | 113 | 136 | 160 | 185 | 215 | | | | |
| 24 | | 44 | 72 | 100 | 126 | 153 | 185 | 215 | 250 | 275 | | | |
| 26 | | 47 | 80 | 110 | 139 | 170 | 207 | 240 | 280 | 310 | 350 | | |
| 28 | | 49 | 87 | 120 | 153 | 190 | 230 | 270 | 310 | 345 | 390 | 430 | |
| 30 | | 52 | 95 | 130 | 176 | 210 | 253 | 295 | 340 | 380 | 430 | 475 | 515 |
| 32 | | 55 | 103 | 142 | 186 | 235 | 280 | 325 | 380 | 420 | 470 | 520 | 565 |
| 34 | | 59 | 111 | 155 | 206 | 265 | 310 | 360 | 415 | 460 | 510 | 570 | 620 |
| 36 | | 63 | 119 | 169 | 226 | 280 | 340 | 390 | 450 | 500 | 560 | 620 | 680 |
| 38 | | 66 | 128 | 185 | 246 | 305 | 370 | 425 | 490 | 550 | 610 | 670 | 740 |
| 40 | | 70 | 136 | 200 | 267 | 330 | 400 | 460 | 530 | 600 | 660 | 725 | 800 |
| 42 | | | 146 | 220 | 290 | 360 | 435 | 500 | 580 | 650 | 720 | 790 | 870 |
| 44 | | | 158 | 240 | 315 | 390 | 470 | 545 | 630 | 700 | 780 | 860 | 940 |
| 46 | | | 170 | 260 | 340 | 425 | 510 | 590 | 680 | 760 | 850 | 940 | 1,020 |
| 48 | | | 184 | 280 | 370 | 460 | 550 | 640 | 730 | 820 | 920 | 1,010 | 1,100 |
| 50 | | | 199 | 300 | 400 | 495 | 595 | 690 | 790 | 890 | 990 | 1,090 | 1,190 |
| 52 | | | | 322 | 425 | 530 | 640 | 740 | 850 | 950 | 1,060 | 1,170 | 1,270 |
| 54 | | | | 343 | 450 | 570 | 685 | 790 | 910 | 1,020 | 1,130 | 1,250 | 1,360 |
| 56 | | | | 364 | 480 | 600 | 725 | 840 | 970 | 1,080 | 1,200 | 1,330 | 1,450 |
| 58 | | | | 385 | 510 | 640 | 770 | 900 | 1,030 | 1,150 | 1,280 | 1,410 | 1,550 |
| 60 | | | | 405 | 540 | 675 | 815 | 950 | 1,080 | 1,220 | 1,350 | 1,500 | 1,660 |
| 62 | | | | | 570 | 715 | 860 | 1,000 | 1,140 | 1,280 | 1,420 | 1,600 | 1,770 |
| 64 | | | | | 600 | 750 | 910 | 1,050 | 1,210 | 1,350 | 1.510 | 1,700 | 1,870 |
| 66 | | | | | 630 | 790 | 960 | 1,110 | 1,270 | 1,430 | 1,620 | 1,810 | 1,980 |
| 68 | | | | | 665 | 840 | 1,010 | 1,170 | 1,340 | 1,520 | 1,720 | 1,920 | 2,100 |
| 70 | | | | | 730 | 890 | 1,060 | 1,240 | 1,410 | 1,610 | 1,820 | 2,030 | 2,230 |
| 72 | | | | | | 930 | 1,120 | 1,300 | 1,490 | 1,710 | 1,930 | 2,140 | 2,360 |
| 74 | | | | | | 970 | 1,180 | 1,360 | 1,580 | 1,810 | 2,030 | 2,260 | 2,490 |
| 76 | | | | | | 1,020 | 1,230 | 1,430 | 1,680 | 1,900 | 2,140 | 2,380 | 2,630 |
| 78 | | | | | | 1.070 | 1,280 | 1,500 | 1,770 | 2,000 | 2,240 | 2,510 | 2,760 |
| 80 | | | | | | 1,110 | 1,330 | 1,570 | 1,850 | 2,080 | 2,350 | 2,630 | 2,880 |

* Stump height 2 to 3 ft. Basis, 592 trees for old-growth and 402 trees for young-growth. Standard error of single volume estimate, 9.7 percent.
Source: *Ibid.*

# Volume Tables for Canada *

## EASTERN HARDWOODS. See Table 49.

### POPLAR, MATCHWOOD OR SPLINTWOOD
#### Table 49. Cubic-Foot Volume

| Diameter breast height (In.) | Total height of tree in feet | | | | | | Number of trees | Diameter inside bark at top (In.) |
|---|---|---|---|---|---|---|---|---|
| | 50 | 60 | 70 | 80 | 90 | 100 | | |
| | VOLUME (Cu. ft.) | | | | | | | |
| 7 | 4.84 | 5.30 | 5.75 | | | | 4 | 6.0 |
| 8 | 5.57 | 6.25 | 6.85 | 7.6 | | | 27 | 6.5 |
| 9 | 6.43 | 7.26 | 8.21 | 9.3 | | | 23 | 7.0 |
| 10 | 7.4 | 8.7 | 10.0 | 11.2 | 12.7 | | 37 | 7.5 |
| 11 | 8.7 | 10.3 | 11.7 | 13.7 | 16.7 | | 58 | 8.0 |
| 12 | 10.3 | 11.8 | 14.2 | 17.7 | 22.2 | 26.7 | 64 | 8.5 |
| 13 | 11.7 | 14.2 | 18.0 | 23.5 | 29.0 | 34.8 | 42 | 9.0 |
| 14 | | 17.3 | 22.4 | 29.0 | 35.7 | 41.0 | 38 | 9.0 |
| 15 | | 21.2 | 27.7 | 35.0 | 42.0 | 47.8 | 16 | 9.0 |
| 16 | | 26.0 | 34.0 | 41.0 | 48.0 | 55.0 | 10 | 9.0 |
| 17 | | | 38.2 | 46.0 | 54.0 | 62.0 | 3 | 9.0 |
| 18 | | | 43.7 | 52.0 | 61.0 | 69.5 | 3 | 9.0 |

Aggregate difference is 1.17 percent low. Average deviation is ± 12.2 percent. Stump height 1.5 ft. Basis of table 325 trees.

Data collected in 1921 at Petawawa Forest Experiment Station. Table prepared by alignment chart method.

Source for Tables 49 to 75: Dominion Forest Service, Dept. of Mines and Resources, Canada, Form-class-volume tables, 1948.

## EASTERN SOFTWOODS. See Tables 50 to 75.

### BALSAM FIR
#### Table 50. Cubic-Foot Volume, Form Class 65

| Diameter breast height (In.) | Total height of tree in feet | | | | | | | | Diameter inside bark at top (In.) | Double bark thickness at breast height (In.) |
|---|---|---|---|---|---|---|---|---|---|---|
| | 20 | 30 | 40 | 50 | 60 | 70 | 80 | 90 | | |
| | MERCHANTABLE VOLUME Stump height, 1.0 ft. (Cu. ft.) | | | | | | | | | |
| 4 | 0.3 | 0.5 | 0.7 | 0.9 | | | | | | 0.2 |
| 5 | 0.7 | 1.0 | 1.4 | 1.8 | 2.1 | | | | 4 | 0.2 |
| 6 | 1.3 | 1.8 | 2.4 | 3.0 | 3.5 | 4.1 | | | 4 | 0.3 |
| 7 | 2.0 | 2.8 | 3.6 | 4.4 | 5.2 | 6.0 | | | 5 | 0.4 |
| 8 | 2.9 | 3.9 | 5.0 | 6.1 | 7.2 | 8.3 | | | 5 | 0.4 |
| 9 | | 5.1 | 6.6 | 8.0 | 9.5 | 11.0 | | | 5 | 0.5 |
| 10 | | 6.4 | 8.3 | 10.2 | 12.1 | 14.0 | 16.0 | | 5 | 0.6 |
| 11 | | | 10.2 | 12.6 | 15.0 | 17.4 | 19.9 | | 6 | 0.6 |
| 12 | | | 12.4 | 15.3 | 18.2 | 21.1 | 24.0 | | 6 | 0.7 |
| 13 | | | 14.8 | 18.2 | 21.6 | 25.0 | 28.4 | | 6 | 0.7 |
| 14 | | | 17.4 | 21.4 | 25.3 | 29.2 | 33.2 | | 6 | 0.8 |
| 15 | | | 20.2 | 24.8 | 29.3 | 33.8 | 38.4 | 42.9 | 6 | 0.9 |
| 16 | | | | 28.4 | 33.6 | 38.7 | 43.9 | 49.1 | | 0.9 |
| 17 | | | | 32.2 | 38.1 | 43.9 | 49.8 | 55.7 | | 1.0 |
| 18 | | | | 36.2 | 42.8 | 49.4 | 56.0 | 62.6 | | 1.0 |
| 19 | | | | 40.4 | 47.7 | 55.1 | 62.4 | 69.7 | | 1.1 |
| 20 | | | | 44.8 | 52.9 | 60.9 | 69.0 | 77.0 | | 1.2 |

Table developed from one taper curve for all diameter classes, based on measurements of 368 trees in seven localities in Manitoba, Quebec, and New Brunswick.

Source: *Ibid.*

\* All volumes are wood volumes inside bark.

## BALSAM FIR

### Table 51. Volume in Board Feet, Doyle Log Rule

Saw Log Operation, Form Class 65

| Diameter breast height (In.) | Total height of tree in feet | | | | | | | | Diameter inside bark at top (In.) | Double bark thickness at breast height (In.) |
| | 30 | 40 | 50 | 60 | 70 | 80 | 90 | 100 | | |
| | VOLUME Stump height, 1.5 ft.; log length, 16.3 ft. (Bd. ft.) | | | | | | | | | |
|---|---|---|---|---|---|---|---|---|---|---|
| 7 | 5 | 5 | 5 | 5 | 5 | | | | 6 | 0.4 |
| 8 | 5 | 5 | 5 | 10 | 10 | | | | 6 | 0.4 |
| 9 | 5 | 10 | 10 | 15 | 15 | | | | 7 | 0.5 |
| 10 | 10 | 15 | 15 | 20 | 25 | 30 | | | 7 | 0.6 |
| 11 | | 20 | 25 | 30 | 40 | 45 | | | 7 | 0.6 |
| 12 | | 25 | 35 | 45 | 55 | 60 | | | 7 | 0.7 |
| 13 | | 30 | 45 | 60 | 70 | 80 | | | 7 | 0.7 |
| 14 | | 40 | 55 | 75 | 90 | 105 | | | 7 | 0.8 |
| 15 | | 50 | 70 | 90 | 110 | 130 | 150 | 170 | 7 | 0.9 |
| 16 | | | 85 | 110 | 135 | 160 | 185 | 210 | 8 | 0.9 |
| 17 | | | 100 | 130 | 160 | 195 | 225 | 255 | 8 | 1.0 |
| 18 | | | 120 | 155 | 190 | 230 | 265 | 305 | 8 | 1.0 |
| 19 | | | 140 | 180 | 220 | 265 | 310 | 355 | 8 | 1.1 |
| 20 | | | 160 | 210 | 255 | 305 | 355 | 405 | 8 | 1.2 |

Table developed from one taper curve for all diameter classes, based on measurements of 368 trees in seven localities in Manitoba, Quebec, and New Brunswick.

Source: *Ibid.*

### Table 52. Volume in Board Feet, Scribner Log Rule

Saw Log Operation, Form Class 65

| Diameter breast height (In.) | Total height of tree in feet | | | | | | | | Diameter inside bark at top (In.) | Double bark thickness at breast height (In.) |
| | 30 | 40 | 50 | 60 | 70 | 80 | 90 | 100 | | |
| | VOLUME Stump height, 1.5 ft.; log length, 16.3 ft. (Bd. ft.) | | | | | | | | | |
|---|---|---|---|---|---|---|---|---|---|---|
| 7 | 5 | 10 | 15 | 20 | | | | | 6 | 0.4 |
| 8 | 10 | 15 | 20 | 25 | | | | | 6 | 0.4 |
| 9 | 15 | 20 | 25 | 35 | 40 | | | | 7 | 0.5 |
| 10 | 20 | 25 | 35 | 45 | 55 | 65 | | | 7 | 0.6 |
| 11 | | 35 | 45 | 55 | 70 | 80 | | | 7 | 0.6 |
| 12 | | 45 | 55 | 70 | 85 | 100 | | | 7 | 0.7 |
| 13 | | 55 | 70 | 85 | 105 | 125 | | | 7 | 0.7 |
| 14 | | 65 | 85 | 105 | 125 | 150 | | | 7 | 0.8 |
| 15 | | 75 | 100 | 125 | 150 | 180 | 205 | 230 | 7 | 0.9 |
| 16 | | | 115 | 150 | 180 | 210 | 240 | 270 | 8 | 0.9 |
| 17 | | | 135 | 175 | 210 | 245 | 280 | 315 | 8 | 1.0 |
| 18 | | | 155 | 200 | 240 | 285 | 325 | 365 | 8 | 1.0 |
| 19 | | | 175 | 225 | 275 | 325 | 375 | 420 | 8 | 1.1 |
| 20 | | | 195 | 255 | 310 | 365 | 425 | 480 | 8 | 1.2 |

Table developed from one taper curve for all diameter classes, based on measurements of 368 trees in seven localities in Manitoba, Quebec, and New Brunswick.

Source: *Ibid.*

## BALSAM FIR

### Table 53. Volume in Board Feet, International ¼-In. Log Rule

Saw Log Operation, Form Class 65

| Diameter breast height (In.) | Total height of tree in feet | | | | | | | | Diameter inside bark at top (In.) | Double bark thickness at breast height (In.) |
|---|---|---|---|---|---|---|---|---|---|---|
| | 30 | 40 | 50 | 60 | 70 | 80 | 90 | 100 | | |
| | VOLUME Stump height, 1.5 ft.; log length, 16.3 ft. (Bd. ft.) | | | | | | | | | |
| 8 | 8 | 15 | 22 | 29 | 36 | | | | 6 | 0.4 |
| 9 | 12 | 22 | 31 | 41 | 51 | | | | 7 | 0.5 |
| 10 | | 30 | 42 | 55 | 68 | | | | 7 | 0.6 |
| 11 | | 40 | 55 | 71 | 87 | 103 | | | 7 | 0.6 |
| 12 | | 51 | 70 | 89 | 108 | 128 | | | 7 | 0.7 |
| 13 | | 63 | 86 | 109 | 132 | 156 | | | 7 | 0.7 |
| 14 | | 75 | 102 | 130 | 158 | 186 | | | 7 | 0.8 |
| 15 | | 88 | 120 | 153 | 186 | 219 | | | 7 | 0.9 |
| 16 | | | 139 | 178 | 216 | 254 | 292 | 330 | 8 | 0.9 |
| 17 | | | 159 | 204 | 248 | 292 | 336 | 380 | 8 | 1.0 |
| 18 | | | 180 | 231 | 281 | 331 | 381 | 431 | 8 | 1.0 |
| 19 | | | 202 | 259 | 316 | 373 | 430 | 487 | 8 | 1.1 |
| 20 | | | 225 | 288 | 352 | 416 | 480 | 544 | 8 | 1.2 |

Table developed from one taper curve for all diameter classes, based on measurements of 368 trees in seven localities in Manitoba, Quebec, and New Brunswick.

Source: *Ibid.*

## EASTERN HEMLOCK

### Table 54. Cubic-Foot Volume

| Diameter breast height (In.) | Total height of tree in feet | | | | | | Double bark thickness at breast height (In.) | Diameter inside bark at top (In.) | Number of trees |
|---|---|---|---|---|---|---|---|---|---|
| | 40 | 50 | 60 | 70 | 80 | 90 | | | |
| | MERCHANTABLE VOLUME (Cu. ft.) | | | | | | | | |
| 10 | 6.5 | 8.2 | 9.9 | 11.6 | | | 1.1 | 7.0 | 16 |
| 11 | 7.6 | 9.7 | 11.8 | 13.8 | | | 1.2 | 7.3 | 73 |
| 12 | 9.2 | 11.5 | 13.8 | 16.1 | | | 1.3 | 7.5 | 85 |
| 13 | 10.9 | 13.7 | 16.5 | 19.4 | | | 1.4 | 7.8 | 106 |
| 14 | 12.8 | 16.0 | 19.2 | 22.5 | 25.8 | | 1.5 | 8.1 | 104 |
| 15 | 14.7 | 18.4 | 22.2 | 26.0 | 29.8 | | 1.6 | 8.4 | 76 |
| 16 | | 21.5 | 25.7 | 29.9 | 34.1 | | 1.7 | 8.7 | 97 |
| 17 | | 24.5 | 29.4 | 34.3 | 39.2 | | 1.8 | 8.9 | 90 |
| 18 | | 27.6 | 33.1 | 38.6 | 44.2 | | 1.9 | 9.3 | 71 |
| 19 | | | 36.9 | 43.1 | 49.3 | 55.5 | 2.0 | 9.6 | 47 |
| 20 | | | 40.8 | 47.8 | 54.8 | 61.8 | 2.1 | 9.9 | 33 |
| 21 | | | 44.9 | 52.7 | 60.4 | 68.2 | 2.2 | 10.2 | 32 |
| 22 | | | 49.5 | 57.9 | 66.3 | 74.7 | 2.3 | 10.6 | 35 |
| 23 | | | 54.1 | 63.4 | 72.8 | 82.2 | 2.4 | 11.0 | 19 |
| 24 | | | 59.0 | 69.0 | 79.0 | 88.9 | 2.5 | 11.5 | 11 |
| 25 | | | 63.9 | 74.6 | 85.3 | 95.9 | 2.6 | 12.0 | 11 |

Aggregate difference 0.58 percent low. Average deviation ± 14.1 percent. Log lengths 8, 12, and 16 ft. Table based on 906 trees.
Data obtained from operation of James MacLaren Co., Ltd., Buckingham, P. Q.

Source: *Ibid.*

## EASTERN HEMLOCK
### Table 55.　Volume in Board Feet
Saw Log Operation

| Diameter breast height (In.) | Total height of tree in feet | | | | | | Diameter inside bark at top (In.) | Double bark thickness at breast height (In.) | Number of trees |
|---|---|---|---|---|---|---|---|---|---|
| | 40 | 50 | 60 | 70 | 80 | 90 | | | |
| | MERCHANTABLE VOLUME (Bd. ft.) | | | | | | | | |
| DOYLE LOG RULE [a] | | | | | | | | | |
| 10 | 12 | 19 | 26 | 34 | | | 7.0 | 1.1 | 10 |
| 11 | 16 | 24 | 32 | 40 | | | 7.3 | 1.2 | 50 |
| 12 | 22 | 30 | 39 | 48 | | | 7.5 | 1.3 | 60 |
| 13 | 29 | 39 | 49 | 59 | | | 7.8 | 1.4 | 70 |
| 14 | 40 | 51 | 62 | 73 | 85 | 97 | 8.1 | 1.5 | 65 |
| 15 | 51 | 64 | 78 | 92 | 106 | 120 | 8.4 | 1.6 | 40 |
| 16 | 63 | 80 | 97 | 114 | 131 | 149 | 8.7 | 1.7 | 53 |
| 17 | | 97 | 118 | 139 | 160 | 182 | 8.9 | 1.8 | 52 |
| 18 | | 115 | 140 | 165 | 192 | 219 | 9.3 | 1.9 | 36 |
| 19 | | | 165 | 195 | 226 | 257 | 9.6 | 2.0 | 27 |
| 20 | | | 190 | 226 | 262 | 299 | 9.9 | 2.1 | 15 |
| 21 | | | 218 | 259 | 301 | 343 | 10.2 | 2.2 | 16 |
| 22 | | | 247 | 294 | 341 | 388 | 10.6 | 2.3 | 14 |
| 23 | | | 279 | 330 | 382 | 434 | 11.0 | 2.4 | 5 |
| 24 | | | 312 | 368 | 424 | 481 | 11.5 | 2.5 | 7 |
| 25 | | | | 408 | 469 | 531 | 12.0 | 2.6 | 3 |
| 26 | | | | 450 | 517 | 584 | 12.5 | 2.7 | 1 |
| 27 | | | | 493 | 566 | 639 | 13.0 | 2.8 | 1 |
| 28 | | | | 536 | 615 | 694 | 13.7 | 2.9 | 1 |
| 29 | | | | 580 | 665 | 751 | 14.2 | 3.0 | |
| 30 | | | | 625 | 717 | 809 | 14.8 | 3.1 | |
| SCRIBNER LOG RULE [b] | | | | | | | | | |
| 10 | 24 | 36 | 48 | 61 | | | 7.0 | 1.1 | 14 |
| 11 | 30 | 43 | 57 | 71 | | | 7.3 | 1.2 | 50 |
| 12 | 37 | 53 | 69 | 85 | | | 7.5 | 1.3 | 63 |
| 13 | 46 | 64 | 82 | 99 | | | 7.8 | 1.4 | 72 |
| 14 | 56 | 76 | 96 | 115 | 135 | 155 | 8.1 | 1.5 | 68 |
| 15 | 67 | 89 | 112 | 135 | 158 | 181 | 8.4 | 1.6 | 42 |
| 16 | 79 | 104 | 130 | 156 | 182 | 208 | 8.7 | 1.7 | 56 |
| 17 | | 121 | 150 | 179 | 209 | 239 | 8.9 | 1.8 | 53 |
| 18 | | 138 | 172 | 206 | 240 | 274 | 9.3 | 1.9 | 38 |
| 19 | | | 197 | 236 | 275 | 314 | 9.6 | 2.0 | 26 |
| 20 | | | 225 | 269 | 313 | 357 | 9.9 | 2.1 | 15 |
| 21 | | | 254 | 302 | 351 | 400 | 10.2 | 2.2 | 16 |
| 22 | | | 284 | 337 | 390 | 443 | 10.6 | 2.3 | 15 |
| 23 | | | 315 | 372 | 429 | 487 | 11.0 | 2.4 | 7 |
| 24 | | | 347 | 409 | 471 | 533 | 11.5 | 2.5 | 7 |
| 25 | | | | 446 | 513 | 580 | 12.0 | 2.6 | 2 |
| 26 | | | | 485 | 557 | 629 | 12.5 | 2.7 | |
| 27 | | | | 524 | 602 | 680 | 13.0 | 2.8 | 1 |
| 28 | | | | 563 | 647 | 731 | 13.7 | 2.9 | 1 |
| 29 | | | | 602 | 692 | 783 | 14.2 | 3.0 | |
| 30 | | | | 643 | 740 | 838 | 14.8 | 3.1 | |

[a] Aggregate difference 0.3 percent high. Average deviation ± 17.4 percent. Log lengths 8, 12, and 16 ft. Table based on 526 trees.

[b] Aggregate difference 0.08 percent high. Average deviation ± 14.6 percent. Log lengths 8, 12, and 16 ft. Table based on 546 trees.

Data obtained from operation of James MacLaren Co., Ltd., Buckingham, P. Q.

Source: *Ibid.*

## JACK PINE
### Table 56. Cubic-Foot Volume
Form Class 65

| Diameter breast height (In.) | Total height of tree in feet | | | | | | | | Diameter inside bark at top (In.) | Double bark thickness at breast height (In.) |
|---|---|---|---|---|---|---|---|---|---|---|
| | 20 | 30 | 40 | 50 | 60 | 70 | 80 | 90 | | |
| | MERCHANTABLE VOLUME Stump height, 1.0 ft. (Cu. ft.) | | | | | | | | | |
| 3 | 0.3 | 0.4 | 0.5 | | | | | | | |
| 4 | 0.6 | 0.9 | 1.1 | 1.3 | | | | | | 0.4 |
| 5 | 1.1 | 1.5 | 1.9 | 2.3 | 2.8 | 3.3 | | | | 0.4 |
| 6 | 1.7 | 2.3 | 2.9 | 3.5 | 4.2 | 4.8 | | | | 0.5 |
| 7 | 2.4 | 3.2 | 4.0 | 4.9 | 5.8 | 6.7 | | | 4 | 0.5 |
| 8 | | 4.2 | 5.3 | 6.5 | 7.7 | 8.9 | | | 4 | 0.5 |
| 9 | | 5.3 | 6.8 | 8.4 | 9.9 | 11.5 | | | 5 | 0.6 |
| 10 | | 6.5 | 8.5 | 10.5 | 12.4 | 14.4 | 16.3 | | 5 | 0.6 |
| 11 | | | 10.5 | 12.9 | 15.3 | 17.7 | 20.0 | | 5 | 0.6 |
| 12 | | | 12.7 | 15.6 | 18.5 | 21.3 | 24.1 | | 6 | 0.7 |
| 13 | | | 15.1 | 18.5 | 21.9 | 25.2 | 28.5 | | 6 | 0.7 |
| 14 | | | 17.7 | 21.6 | 25.5 | 29.4 | 33.2 | | 6 | 0.8 |
| 15 | | | 20.4 | 24.9 | 29.4 | 33.8 | 38.2 | 42.6 | 7 | 0.8 |
| 16 | | | | 28.5 | 33.5 | 38.5 | 43.5 | 48.4 | 7 | 0.8 |
| 17 | | | | 32.3 | 37.9 | 43.5 | 49.1 | 54.6 | 7 | 0.9 |
| 18 | | | | 36.3 | 42.5 | 48.8 | 55.0 | 61.2 | 8 | 0.9 |
| 19 | | | | 40.4 | 47.4 | 54.4 | 61.3 | 68.2 | 8 | 0.9 |
| 20 | | | | 44.7 | 52.5 | 60.2 | 68.0 | 75.7 | 8 | 1.0 |

Table developed from one taper curve for all diameter classes, based on measurements of 858 trees in twelve localities in Saskatchewan, Manitoba, and Ontario.

Source: *Ibid.*

### Table 57. Volume in Board Feet, Doyle Log Rule
Saw Log Operation, Form Class 65

| Diameter breast height (In.) | Total height of tree in feet | | | | | | | Diameter inside bark at top (In.) | Double bark thickness at breast height (In.) |
|---|---|---|---|---|---|---|---|---|---|
| | 30 | 40 | 50 | 60 | 70 | 80 | 90 | | |
| | VOLUME Stump height, 1.5 ft.; log length, 16.3 ft. (Bd. ft.) | | | | | | | | |
| 7 | | | 5 | 5 | 5 | 5 | | 4 | 0.5 |
| 8 | | | 5 | 5 | 10 | 10 | | 4 | 0.5 |
| 9 | | | 5 | 10 | 15 | 15 | | 5 | 0.6 |
| 10 | | 5 | 10 | 15 | 20 | 25 | | 5 | 0.6 |
| 11 | | | 15 | 20 | 30 | 35 | 40 | 5 | 0.6 |
| 12 | | | 20 | 30 | 40 | 45 | 55 | 65 | 6 | 0.7 |
| 13 | | | 25 | 40 | 50 | 60 | 75 | 90 | 6 | 0.7 |
| 14 | | | 35 | 50 | 65 | 80 | 100 | 115 | 6 | 0.8 |
| 15 | | | 45 | 65 | 85 | 105 | 125 | 145 | 7 | 0.8 |
| 16 | | | | 80 | 105 | 130 | 155 | 180 | 7 | 0.8 |
| 17 | | | | 100 | 130 | 160 | 185 | 215 | 7 | 0.9 |
| 18 | | | | 120 | 155 | 190 | 220 | 255 | 8 | 0.9 |
| 19 | | | | 140 | 180 | 220 | 260 | 300 | 8 | 0.9 |
| 20 | | | | 165 | 210 | 255 | 300 | 350 | 8 | 1.0 |
| 21 | | | | 190 | 240 | 295 | 345 | 400 | 9 | 1.0 |
| 22 | | | | 215 | 275 | 335 | 395 | 455 | 9 | 1.1 |
| 23 | | | | 240 | 310 | 380 | 445 | 515 | 10 | 1.1 |
| 24 | | | | 270 | 350 | 425 | 500 | 580 | 10 | 1.1 |
| 25 | | | | 305 | 390 | 475 | 560 | 645 | 10 | 1.2 |

Table developed from one taper curve for all diameter classes, based on measurements of 858 trees in twelve localities in Saskatchewan, Manitoba, and Ontario.

Source: *Ibid.*

## JACK PINE

### Table 58. Volume in Board Feet

Saw Log Operation, Form Class 65

| Diameter breast height (In.) | Total height of tree in feet | | | | | | | Diameter inside bark at top (In.) | Double bark thickness at breast height (In.) |
|---|---|---|---|---|---|---|---|---|---|
| | 30 | 40 | 50 | 60 | 70 | 80 | 90 | | |
| | VOLUME Stump height, 1.5 ft.; log length, 16.3 ft. (Bd. ft.) | | | | | | | | |
| SCRIBNER LOG RULE | | | | | | | | | |
| 7 | 5 | 10 | 20 | 25 | 30 | | | 4 | 0.5 |
| 8 | 5 | 15 | 25 | 30 | 35 | | | 4 | 0.5 |
| 9 | 10 | 20 | 30 | 40 | 45 | | | 5 | 0.6 |
| 10 | 15 | 25 | 40 | 50 | 60 | 70 | | 5 | 0.6 |
| 11 | | 35 | 50 | 60 | 75 | 90 | 105 | 5 | 0.6 |
| 12 | | 45 | 60 | 75 | 90 | 110 | 125 | 6 | 0.7 |
| 13 | | 55 | 70 | 90 | 110 | 130 | 150 | 6 | 0.7 |
| 14 | | 65 | 85 | 110 | 130 | 155 | 180 | 6 | 0.8 |
| 15 | | 75 | 100 | 130 | 155 | 180 | 210 | 7 | 0.8 |
| 16 | | | 115 | 150 | 180 | 210 | 245 | 7 | 0.8 |
| 17 | | | 135 | 170 | 205 | 245 | 285 | 7 | 0.9 |
| 18 | | | 155 | 195 | 235 | 280 | 325 | 8 | 0.9 |
| 19 | | | 175 | 220 | 270 | 320 | 370 | 8 | 0.9 |
| 20 | | | 195 | 250 | 305 | 365 | 420 | 8 | 1.0 |
| 21 | | | 220 | 280 | 345 | 410 | 475 | 9 | 1.0 |
| 22 | | | 245 | 315 | 385 | 455 | 530 | 9 | 1.1 |
| 23 | | | 275 | 350 | 430 | 505 | 585 | 10 | 1.1 |
| 24 | | | 305 | 390 | 475 | 560 | 645 | 10 | 1.1 |
| 25 | | | 335 | 430 | 525 | 620 | 710 | 10 | 1.2 |
| INTERNATIONAL ¼-IN. LOG RULE | | | | | | | | | |
| 8 | 9 | 17 | 25 | 33 | 42 | | | 4 | 0.5 |
| 9 | 14 | 24 | 34 | 45 | 56 | | | 5 | 0.6 |
| 10 | 20 | 33 | 45 | 58 | 71 | | | 5 | 0.6 |
| 11 | | 43 | 58 | 74 | 90 | 106 | | 5 | 0.6 |
| 12 | | 53 | 72 | 92 | 112 | 132 | | 6 | 0.7 |
| 13 | | 63 | 86 | 110 | 134 | 158 | 182 | 6 | 0.7 |
| 14 | | 74 | 101 | 129 | 157 | 185 | 213 | 6 | 0.8 |
| 15 | | 87 | 119 | 151 | 184 | 218 | 251 | 7 | 0.8 |
| 16 | | 100 | 138 | 176 | 215 | 254 | 292 | 7 | 0.8 |
| 17 | | | 157 | 201 | 246 | 291 | 336 | 7 | 0.9 |
| 18 | | | 178 | 229 | 280 | 332 | 383 | 8 | 0.9 |
| 19 | | | 200 | 258 | 316 | 374 | 432 | 8 | 0.9 |
| 20 | | | 223 | 288 | 353 | 418 | 483 | 8 | 1.0 |
| 21 | | | 248 | 320 | 392 | 464 | 536 | 9 | 1.0 |
| 22 | | | 275 | 354 | 433 | 512 | 591 | 9 | 1.1 |
| 23 | | | 304 | 391 | 479 | 566 | 653 | 10 | 1.1 |
| 24 | | | 335 | 431 | 527 | 623 | 718 | 10 | 1.1 |
| 25 | | | 368 | 472 | 577 | 681 | 785 | 10 | 1.2 |

Table developed from one taper curve for all diameter classes, based on measurements of 858 trees in twelve localities in Saskatchewan, Manitoba, and Ontario.

Source: *Ibid.*

## RED PINE

### Table 59. Volume in Board Feet, Doyle Log Rule

Saw Log Operation, Form Class 70

| Diameter breast height (In.) | Total height of tree in feet VOLUME Stump height, 1.5 ft.; log length, 16.3 ft. (Bd. ft.) | | | | | | | | | Diameter inside bark at top (In.) | Double bark thickness at breast height (In.) |
|---|---|---|---|---|---|---|---|---|---|---|---|
| | 30 | 40 | 50 | 60 | 70 | 80 | 90 | 100 | 110 | | |
| **UNDER 120 YR.[a]** | | | | | | | | | | | |
| 7 | | | 5 | 5 | 5 | | | | | 5 | 0.5 |
| 8 | | 5 | 10 | 10 | 10 | | | | | 5 | 0.6 |
| 9 | 5 | 10 | 15 | 15 | 15 | | | | | 5 | 0.7 |
| 10 | 10 | 15 | 20 | 20 | 25 | 30 | | | | 6 | 0.8 |
| 11 | | 20 | 25 | 30 | 35 | 45 | 50 | | | 6 | 0.9 |
| 12 | | 25 | 30 | 40 | 50 | 60 | 70 | | | 7 | 1.0 |
| 13 | | 30 | 40 | 55 | 65 | 80 | 90 | | | 7 | 1.1 |
| 14 | | 40 | 55 | 70 | 85 | 100 | 115 | | | 7 | 1.2 |
| 15 | | 50 | 70 | 90 | 110 | 125 | 145 | | | 8 | 1.3 |
| 16 | | | 85 | 110 | 135 | 155 | 180 | | | 8 | 1.4 |
| 17 | | | 100 | 130 | 160 | 190 | 220 | | | 9 | 1.5 |
| 18 | | | 120 | 155 | 190 | 225 | 260 | | | 9 | 1.6 |
| 19 | | | 140 | 185 | 225 | 265 | 305 | | | 10 | 1.8 |
| 20 | | | 165 | 215 | 260 | 305 | 350 | | | 10 | 1.9 |
| **OVER 120 YR.[b]** | | | | | | | | | | | |
| 6 | 5 | 5 | 5 | 5 | 5 | | | | | 5 | |
| 7 | 5 | 5 | 5 | 5 | 5 | | | | | 6 | 0.4 |
| 8 | 5 | 5 | 5 | 5 | 10 | | | | | 6 | 0.5 |
| 9 | 5 | 5 | 10 | 10 | 15 | | | | | 6 | 0.6 |
| 10 | 5 | 10 | 15 | 20 | 25 | 25 | | | | 7 | 0.7 |
| 11 | | 15 | 20 | 30 | 35 | 40 | 45 | | | 7 | 0.8 |
| 12 | | 25 | 30 | 40 | 50 | 60 | 65 | 70 | | 8 | 0.9 |
| 13 | | 35 | 45 | 55 | 70 | 80 | 90 | 100 | | 8 | 1.0 |
| 14 | | 45 | 60 | 75 | 90 | 105 | 120 | 135 | | 8 | 1.0 |
| 15 | | 55 | 75 | 95 | 110 | 130 | 150 | 170 | | 9 | 1.1 |
| 16 | | | 90 | 115 | 135 | 160 | 185 | 210 | 230 | 9 | 1.2 |
| 17 | | | 105 | 135 | 160 | 190 | 220 | 250 | 280 | 9 | 1.3 |
| 18 | | | 125 | 160 | 190 | 225 | 260 | 295 | 330 | 9 | 1.4 |
| 19 | | | 145 | 185 | 225 | 265 | 305 | 345 | 385 | 10 | 1.5 |
| 20 | | | 165 | 210 | 260 | 305 | 350 | 400 | 445 | 10 | 1.6 |
| 21 | | | 185 | 240 | 295 | 345 | 400 | 455 | 510 | 10 | 1.8 |
| 22 | | | 210 | 270 | 330 | 390 | 450 | 510 | 575 | 10 | 2.0 |
| 23 | | | 235 | 300 | 365 | 435 | 500 | 570 | 640 | 10 | 2.2 |
| 24 | | | 265 | 335 | 405 | 480 | 555 | 630 | 705 | 10 | 2.4 |
| 25 | | | 295 | 370 | 450 | 530 | 610 | 695 | 775 | 10 | 2.6 |
| 26 | | | 410 | 495 | 585 | 670 | 760 | 850 | | 10 | 2.8 |
| 27 | | | 450 | 545 | 640 | 735 | 830 | 930 | | 10 | 3.0 |
| 28 | | | 490 | 595 | 695 | 800 | 905 | 1010 | | 10 | 3.2 |
| 29 | | | 535 | 645 | 755 | 865 | 980 | 1090 | | 11 | 3.4 |
| 30 | | | 580 | 700 | 815 | 935 | 1055 | 1175 | | 11 | 3.6 |

[a] Table developed from one taper curve for all diameter classes, based on measurements of 473 trees in three localities in Ontario and New Brunswick.

[b] Table developed from one taper curve for all diameter classes, based on measurements of 371 trees in five localities in Ontario and Quebec.

Source: *Ibid.*

## RED PINE
### Table 60. Volume in Board Feet, Scribner Log Rule
Saw Log Operation, Form Class 70

| Diameter breast height (In.) | Total height of tree in feet | | | | | | | | | Diameter inside bark at top (In.) | Double bark thickness at breast height (In.) |
|---|---|---|---|---|---|---|---|---|---|---|---|
| | 30 | 40 | 50 | 60 | 70 | 80 | 90 | 100 | 110 | | |
| | VOLUME — Stump height, 1.5 ft.; log length, 16.3 ft. (Bd. ft.) | | | | | | | | | | |
| UNDER 120 YR.[a] | | | | | | | | | | | |
| 6 | 8 | 12 | 15 | 18 | 22 | | | | | 4 | 0.4 |
| 7 | 10 | 15 | 20 | 25 | 30 | | | | | 5 | 0.5 |
| 8 | 14 | 20 | 26 | 32 | 38 | | | | | 5 | 0.6 |
| 9 | 18 | 26 | 34 | 42 | 50 | | | | | 5 | 0.7 |
| 10 | 23 | 33 | 43 | 53 | 63 | 73 | | | | 6 | 0.8 |
| 11 | | 40 | 52 | 64 | 76 | 88 | 99 | | | 6 | 0.9 |
| 12 | | 48 | 63 | 77 | 92 | 107 | 121 | | | 7 | 1.0 |
| 13 | | 58 | 75 | 93 | 110 | 127 | 145 | | | 7 | 1.1 |
| 14 | | 68 | 89 | 109 | 130 | 151 | 172 | | | 7 | 1.2 |
| 15 | | 80 | 104 | 128 | 152 | 177 | 202 | | | 8 | 1.3 |
| 16 | | | 121 | 149 | 177 | 206 | 234 | | | 8 | 1.4 |
| 17 | | | 141 | 173 | 206 | 238 | 270 | | | 9 | 1.5 |
| 18 | | | 161 | 198 | 236 | 273 | 310 | | | 9 | 1.6 |
| 19 | | | 181 | 224 | 266 | 308 | 350 | | | 10 | 1.8 |
| 20 | | | 203 | 253 | 302 | 351 | 400 | | | 10 | 1.9 |
| OVER 120 YR.[b] | | | | | | | | | | | |
| 6 | 5 | 7 | 9 | 11 | 13 | | | | | 5 | 0.3 |
| 7 | 8 | 11 | 14 | 17 | 20 | | | | | 6 | 0.4 |
| 8 | 11 | 16 | 21 | 25 | 30 | | | | | 6 | 0.5 |
| 9 | 15 | 22 | 29 | 35 | 42 | 49 | | | | 6 | 0.6 |
| 10 | 20 | 29 | 38 | 47 | 56 | 65 | 74 | | | 7 | 0.7 |
| 11 | | 37 | 48 | 59 | 70 | 81 | 92 | 103 | | 7 | 0.8 |
| 12 | | 46 | 60 | 74 | 87 | 101 | 115 | 129 | | 8 | 0.9 |
| 13 | | 56 | 73 | 90 | 107 | 124 | 141 | 158 | | 8 | 1.0 |
| 14 | | 68 | 89 | 110 | 130 | 151 | 172 | 193 | | 8 | 1.0 |
| 15 | | 80 | 105 | 130 | 154 | 179 | 204 | 229 | | 9 | 1.1 |
| 16 | | | 121 | 150 | 180 | 210 | 241 | 272 | 303 | 9 | 1.2 |
| 17 | | | 137 | 173 | 209 | 246 | 283 | 319 | 356 | 9 | 1.3 |
| 18 | | | 155 | 197 | 239 | 282 | 325 | 367 | 410 | 9 | 1.4 |
| 19 | | | 175 | 223 | 271 | 320 | 370 | 419 | 468 | 10 | 1.5 |
| 20 | | | 197 | 251 | 305 | 361 | 417 | 472 | 527 | 10 | 1.6 |
| 21 | | | 219 | 280 | 341 | 403 | 464 | 526 | 587 | 10 | 1.8 |
| 22 | | | 243 | 310 | 378 | 446 | 514 | 582 | 650 | 10 | 2.0 |
| 23 | | | 269 | 343 | 418 | 493 | 567 | 642 | 716 | 10 | 2.2 |
| 24 | | | 297 | 378 | 460 | 542 | 624 | 705 | 786 | 10 | 2.4 |
| 25 | | | 327 | 414 | 503 | 592 | 681 | 770 | 858 | 10 | 2.6 |
| 26 | | | 450 | 547 | 644 | 741 | 838 | 934 | | 10 | 2.8 |
| 27 | | | 489 | 594 | 699 | 804 | 909 | 1013 | | 10 | 3.0 |
| 28 | | | 531 | 644 | 758 | 871 | 984 | 1097 | | 10 | 3.2 |
| 29 | | | 574 | 696 | 818 | 940 | 1062 | 1185 | | 11 | 3.4 |
| 30 | | | 617 | 748 | 879 | 1010 | 1142 | 1274 | | 11 | 3.6 |

[a] Table developed from one taper curve for all diameter classes, based on measurements of 473 trees in three localities in Ontario and New Brunswick.
[b] Table developed from one taper curve for all diameter classes, based on measurements of 371 trees in five localities in Ontario and Quebec.

Source: *Ibid.*

## RED PINE

### Table 61. Volume in Board Feet, International ¼-In. Log Rule

Saw Log Operation, Form Class 70

| Diameter breast height (In.) | Total height of tree in feet | | | | | | | | | Diameter inside bark at top (In.) | Double bark thickness at breast height (In.) |
|---|---|---|---|---|---|---|---|---|---|---|---|
| | 30 | 40 | 50 | 60 | 70 | 80 | 90 | 100 | 110 | | |
| | VOLUME Stump height, 1.5 ft.; log length, 16.3 ft. (Bd. ft.) | | | | | | | | | | |
| **UNDER 120 YR.[a]** | | | | | | | | | | | |
| 6 | 5 | 10 | 15 | 20 | 25 | | | | | 4 | 0.4 |
| 7 | 5 | 15 | 20 | 25 | 35 | | | | | 5 | 0.5 |
| 8 | 10 | 20 | 30 | 35 | 45 | | | | | 5 | 0.6 |
| 9 | 15 | 25 | 40 | 50 | 60 | | | | | 5 | 0.7 |
| 10 | 25 | 35 | 50 | 65 | 75 | 90 | | | | 6 | 0.8 |
| 11 | | 45 | 60 | 80 | 95 | 115 | | | | 6 | 0.9 |
| 12 | | 55 | 75 | 95 | 115 | 140 | 160 | | | 7 | 1.0 |
| 13 | | 65 | 90 | 115 | 140 | 165 | 190 | | | 7 | 1.1 |
| 14 | | 75 | 105 | 135 | 165 | 195 | 225 | | | 7 | 1.2 |
| 15 | | 90 | 120 | 155 | 190 | 225 | 260 | | | 8 | 1.3 |
| 16 | | | 140 | 180 | 220 | 260 | 300 | | | 8 | 1.4 |
| 17 | | | 160 | 205 | 250 | 295 | 340 | | | 9 | 1.5 |
| 18 | | | 180 | 230 | 280 | 330 | 380 | | | 9 | 1.6 |
| 19 | | | 200 | 260 | 315 | 370 | 425 | | | 10 | 1.8 |
| 20 | | | 225 | 290 | 350 | 410 | 475 | | | 10 | 1.9 |
| **OVER 120 YR.[b]** | | | | | | | | | | | |
| 6 | 5 | 10 | 15 | 20 | 25 | | | | | 5 | 0.3 |
| 7 | 10 | 15 | 20 | 25 | 30 | | | | | 6 | 0.4 |
| 8 | 15 | 20 | 25 | 30 | 40 | | | | | 6 | 0.5 |
| 9 | 20 | 25 | 35 | 45 | 55 | | | | | 6 | 0.6 |
| 10 | 25 | 35 | 45 | 60 | 75 | 90 | | | | 7 | 0.7 |
| 11 | | 45 | 60 | 75 | 90 | 105 | 125 | | | 7 | 0.8 |
| 12 | | 60 | 75 | 90 | 110 | 130 | 150 | | | 8 | 0.9 |
| 13 | | 75 | 90 | 110 | 130 | 155 | 180 | | | 8 | 1.0 |
| 14 | | 90 | 105 | 130 | 155 | 180 | 210 | | | 8 | 1.0 |
| 15 | | 105 | 125 | 155 | 185 | 215 | 245 | 280 | | 9 | 1.1 |
| 16 | | 120 | 145 | 180 | 215 | 250 | 285 | 325 | 365 | 9 | 1.2 |
| 17 | | | 170 | 210 | 250 | 290 | 335 | 380 | 425 | 9 | 1.3 |
| 18 | | | 195 | 240 | 285 | 330 | 385 | 435 | 485 | 9 | 1.4 |
| 19 | | | 220 | 270 | 320 | 375 | 435 | 490 | 545 | 10 | 1.5 |
| 20 | | | 245 | 300 | 355 | 420 | 485 | 545 | 610 | 10 | 1.6 |
| 21 | | | 270 | 330 | 395 | 465 | 535 | 600 | 675 | 10 | 1.8 |
| 22 | | | 295 | 360 | 435 | 510 | 585 | 660 | 740 | 10 | 2.0 |
| 23 | | | 320 | 395 | 475 | 555 | 635 | 720 | 805 | 10 | 2.2 |
| 24 | | | 345 | 430 | 515 | 600 | 690 | 780 | 875 | 10 | 2.4 |
| 25 | | | 370 | 465 | 555 | 645 | 745 | 845 | 945 | 10 | 2.6 |
| 26 | | | | 500 | 600 | 700 | 805 | 910 | 1015 | 10 | 2.8 |
| 27 | | | | 535 | 645 | 755 | 865 | 980 | 1095 | 10 | 3.0 |
| 28 | | | | 575 | 690 | 810 | 930 | 1050 | 1175 | 10 | 3.2 |
| 29 | | | | 615 | 740 | 865 | 995 | 1125 | 1255 | 11 | 3.4 |
| 30 | | | | 660 | 795 | 930 | 1065 | 1200 | 1340 | 11 | 3.6 |

[a] Table developed from one taper curve for all diameter classes, based on measurements of 473 trees in three localities in Ontario and New Brunswick.
[b] Table developed from one taper curve for all diameter classes, based on measurements of 371 trees in five localities in Ontario and Quebec.

Source: *Ibid.*

## RED PINE (Under 120 yr.)

### Table 62. Cubic-Foot Volume
### Form Class 70

| Diameter breast height (In.) | Total height of tree in feet | | | | | | | | Diameter inside bark at top (In.) | Double bark thickness at breast height (In.) |
|---|---|---|---|---|---|---|---|---|---|---|
| | 20 | 30 | 40 | 50 | 60 | 70 | 80 | 90 | | |
| | MERCHANTABLE VOLUME Stump height, 1.5 ft. (Cu. ft.) | | | | | | | | | |
| 5 | | 1.2 | 1.6 | 2.0 | 2.4 | | | | | |
| 6 | | 1.9 | 2.5 | 3.1 | 3.7 | | | | 4.4 | 0.4 |
| 7 | | 2.9 | 3.8 | 4.7 | 5.6 | | | | 4.6 | 0.5 |
| 8 | | 4.0 | 5.2 | 6.4 | 7.6 | 8.8 | | | 4.8 | 0.6 |
| 9 | | 5.2 | 6.8 | 8.3 | 9.9 | 11.5 | | | 5.0 | 0.7 |
| 10 | | 6.5 | 8.5 | 10.4 | 12.4 | 14.4 | | | 5.3 | 0.8 |
| 11 | | 7.9 | 10.4 | 12.8 | 15.2 | 17.6 | 20.9 | | 5.6 | 0.9 |
| 12 | | | 12.5 | 15.3 | 18.2 | 21.0 | 23.9 | 26.8 | 5.8 | 1.0 |
| 13 | | | 14.8 | 18.1 | 21.4 | 24.7 | 28.0 | 31.4 | 6.0 | 1.1 |
| 14 | | | 17.2 | 21.1 | 24.9 | 28.8 | 32.7 | 36.7 | 6.2 | 1.2 |
| 15 | | | 19.8 | 24.3 | 28.9 | 33.5 | 38.1 | 42.7 | 6.4 | 1.3 |
| 16 | | | 22.4 | 27.7 | 33.0 | 38.3 | 43.6 | 48.8 | 6.6 | 1.4 |
| 17 | | | | 31.2 | 37.2 | 43.2 | 49.1 | 55.0 | 6.8 | 1.5 |
| 18 | | | | 34.9 | 41.5 | 48.1 | 54.7 | 61.3 | 7.0 | 1.6 |
| 19 | | | | 38.7 | 46.1 | 53.5 | 60.9 | 68.2 | 7.2 | 1.8 |
| 20 | | | | 42.7 | 50.9 | 59.1 | 67.3 | 75.5 | 7.4 | 1.9 |

Table developed from one taper curve for all diameter classes, based on measurements of 473 trees in three localities in Ontario and New Brunswick.

Source: *Ibid.*

## WHITE PINE (Under 120 yr.)

### Table 63. Cubic-Foot Volume
### Form Class 70

| Diameter breast height (In.) | Total height of tree in feet | | | | | | | | | | | Double bark thickness at breast height (In.) |
|---|---|---|---|---|---|---|---|---|---|---|---|---|
| | 10 | 20 | 30 | 40 | 50 | 60 | 70 | 80 | 90 | 100 | 110 | |
| | VOLUME Stump and top included (Cu. ft.) | | | | | | | | | | | |
| 1 | .03 | .05 | .08 | | | | | | | | | 0.1 |
| 2 | .14 | .22 | .31 | | | | | | | | | 0.2 |
| 3 | .31 | .49 | .70 | .89 | | | | | | | | 0.2 |
| 4 | .56 | .89 | 1.25 | 1.59 | 1.93 | | | | | | | 0.3 |
| 5 | | 1.39 | 1.97 | 2.50 | 3.02 | | | | | | | 0.4 |
| 6 | | | 2.85 | 3.61 | 4.38 | 5.22 | | | | | | 0.4 |
| 7 | | | 3.89 | 4.93 | 5.98 | 7.12 | | | | | | 0.5 |
| 8 | | | 5.10 | 6.47 | 7.84 | 9.34 | 10.7 | 12.1 | | | | 0.5 |
| 9 | | | | 8.20 | 9.98 | 11.8 | 13.6 | 15.4 | | | | 0.6 |
| 10 | | | | 10.2 | 12.3 | 14.6 | 16.7 | 18.9 | | | | 0.7 |
| 11 | | | | 14.9 | 17.7 | 20.3 | 23.1 | | | | | 0.7 |
| 12 | | | | 17.8 | 21.1 | 24.2 | 27.5 | | | | | 0.8 |
| 13 | | | | 21.0 | 24.7 | 28.4 | 32.3 | 36.1 | | | | 0.9 |
| 14 | | | | 24.3 | 28.8 | 33.0 | 37.8 | 41.9 | | | | 0.9 |
| 15 | | | | 28.0 | 33.1 | 38.0 | 43.1 | 48.2 | 53.3 | 58.3 | | 1.0 |
| 16 | | | | | 37.7 | 43.2 | 49.1 | 55.0 | 61.0 | 66.6 | | 1.0 |
| 17 | | | | | 42.5 | 48.9 | 55.5 | 62.2 | 69.0 | 75.2 | | 1.1 |
| 18 | | | | | 47.9 | 55.0 | 62.4 | 69.9 | 77.7 | 84.6 | | 1.2 |
| 19 | | | | | 53.2 | 61.3 | 69.7 | 78.0 | 86.7 | 94.6 | | 1.2 |
| 20 | | | | | 59.2 | 68.0 | 77.3 | 86.4 | 96.0 | 104.0 | | 1.3 |

Table developed from one taper curve for all diameter classes, based on measurements of 522 trees in five localities in Ontario and New Brunswick.

Source: *Ibid.*

## WHITE PINE

### Table 64. Volume in Board Feet, Doyle Log Rule

Saw Log Operation

| Diameter breast height (In.) | Total height of tree in feet | | | | | | | | | | Diameter inside bark at top (In.) | Double bark thickness at breast height (In.) |
|---|---|---|---|---|---|---|---|---|---|---|---|---|
| | 30 | 40 | 50 | 60 | 70 | 80 | 90 | 100 | 110 | .120 | | |
| | VOLUME Stump height, 1.5 ft.; log length, 16.3 ft. (Bd. ft.) | | | | | | | | | | | |

OVER 120 YR., FORM CLASS 65 [a]

| | | | | | | | | | | | | |
|---|---|---|---|---|---|---|---|---|---|---|---|---|
| 7 | 5 | 5 | 10 | 10 | 10 | | | | | | 6 | 0.6 |
| 8 | 5 | 5 | 10 | 10 | 15 | | | | | | 6 | 0.6 |
| 9 | 5 | 5 | 10 | 15 | 20 | | | | | | 6 | 0.7 |
| 10 | 5 | 10 | 15 | 20 | 25 | 30 | | | | | 6 | 0.8 |
| 11 | | 15 | 20 | 30 | 35 | 40 | 50 | 55 | | | 6 | 0.9 |
| 12 | | 20 | 30 | 40 | 45 | 55 | 65 | 75 | | | 7 | 1.0 |
| 13 | | 25 | 40 | 50 | 60 | 70 | 80 | 95 | | | 7 | 1.1 |
| 14 | | 35 | 50 | 60 | 75 | 85 | 100 | 115 | | | 7 | 1.1 |
| 15 | | 45 | 60 | 75 | 90 | 105 | 125 | 140 | 155 | 170 | 7 | 1.2 |
| 16 | | | 70 | 90 | 110 | 130 | 150 | 170 | 190 | 210 | 7 | 1.3 |
| 17 | | | 85 | 110 | 135 | 160 | 180 | 205 | 230 | 255 | 8 | 1.4 |
| 18 | | | 100 | 130 | 160 | 190 | 215 | 245 | 275 | 305 | 8 | 1.5 |
| 19 | | | 120 | 155 | 190 | 225 | 255 | 290 | 325 | 360 | 8 | 1.6 |
| 20 | | | 140 | 180 | 220 | 260 | 295 | 335 | 375 | 415 | 8 | 1.7 |
| 21 | | | 160 | 205 | 250 | 295 | 340 | 385 | 430 | 475 | 8 | 1.8 |
| 22 | | | 180 | 235 | 285 | 335 | 390 | 440 | 490 | 540 | 9 | 1.8 |
| 23 | | | 205 | 265 | 320 | 380 | 440 | 495 | 555 | 610 | 9 | 1.9 |
| 24 | | | 230 | 295 | 360 | 425 | 490 | 555 | 620 | 685 | 9 | 2.0 |
| 25 | | | 255 | 325 | 400 | 470 | 545 | 620 | 690 | 765 | 9 | 2.1 |
| 26 | | | | 360 | 440 | 520 | 605 | 685 | 765 | 850 | 9 | 2.2 |
| 27 | | | | 400 | 485 | 575 | 665 | 755 | 845 | 935 | 10 | 2.3 |
| 28 | | | | 440 | 535 | 635 | 730 | 830 | 930 | 1025 | 10 | 2.4 |
| 29 | | | | 485 | 590 | 695 | 800 | 910 | 1015 | 1120 | 10 | 2.5 |
| 30 | | | | 530 | 645 | 760 | 875 | 990 | 1105 | 1220 | 10 | 2.5 |

UNDER 120 YR., FORM CLASS 70 [b]

| | | | | | | | | | | | | |
|---|---|---|---|---|---|---|---|---|---|---|---|---|
| 7 | | 5 | 5 | 5 | | | | | | | 6 | 0.5 |
| 8 | | 5 | 5 | 10 | 10 | | | | | | 6 | 0.5 |
| 9 | | 5 | 10 | 15 | 20 | | | | | | 6 | 0.6 |
| 10 | 5 | 10 | 20 | 25 | 30 | | | | | | 6 | 0.7 |
| 11 | | 20 | 30 | 35 | 45 | 50 | | | | | 6 | 0.7 |
| 12 | | 30 | 40 | 50 | 60 | 70 | 80 | | | | 7 | 0.8 |
| 13 | | 40 | 50 | 65 | 75 | 90 | 105 | | | | 7 | 0.9 |
| 14 | | 50 | 65 | 80 | 95 | 115 | 135 | | | | 7 | 0.9 |
| 15 | | 60 | 80 | 100 | 120 | 145 | 170 | | | | 7 | 1.0 |
| 16 | | 70 | 95 | 120 | 150 | 175 | 205 | | | | 7 | 1.0 |
| 17 | | | 110 | 145 | 180 | 210 | 245 | | | | 8 | 1.1 |
| 18 | | | 130 | 170 | 210 | 250 | 290 | | | | 8 | 1.2 |
| 19 | | | 155 | 200 | 245 | 290 | 335 | | | | 8 | 1.2 |
| 20 | | | 180 | 235 | 285 | 335 | 385 | | | | 8 | 1.3 |

[a] Table developed from three taper curves, one for each of three diameter groups, namely, (1) below 15 in., (2) 15 to 19 in., and (3) over 19 in., based on measurements of 350 trees in four localities in Ontario.
[b] Table developed from one taper curve for all diameter classes, based on measurements of 522 trees in five localities in Ontario and New Brunswick.

Source: *Ibid.*

## WHITE PINE
### Table 65. Volume in Board Feet, Scribner Log Rule
Saw Log Operation

| Diameter breast height (In.) | 30 | 40 | 50 | 60 | 70 | 80 | 90 | 100 | 110 | 120 | Diameter inside bark at top (In.) | Double bark thickness at breast height (In.) |
|---|---|---|---|---|---|---|---|---|---|---|---|---|
| | | | | | VOLUME<br>Stump height, 1.5 ft.; log length, 16.3 ft.<br>(Bd. ft.) | | | | | | | |
| **Over 120 Yr., Form Class 65** [a] | | | | | | | | | | | | |
| 7 | 5 | 7 | 9 | 11 | 13 | | | | | | 6 | 0.6 |
| 8 | 9 | 13 | 16 | 19 | 23 | | | | | | 6 | 0.6 |
| 9 | 13 | 18 | 23 | 28 | 33 | | | | | | 6 | 0.7 |
| 10 | 19 | 25 | 31 | 37 | 44 | 51 | | | | | 6 | 0.8 |
| 11 | | 33 | 42 | 51 | 59 | 68 | 77 | | | | 6 | 0.9 |
| 12 | | 43 | 54 | 66 | 77 | 88 | 100 | 112 | | | 7 | 1.0 |
| 13 | | 53 | 67 | 82 | 97 | 111 | 126 | 141 | | | 7 | 1.1 |
| 14 | | 64 | 82 | 100 | 119 | 137 | 155 | 173 | | | 7 | 1.1 |
| 15 | | 75 | 97 | 119 | 141 | 163 | 184 | 205 | 226 | 248 | 7 | 1.2 |
| 16 | | | 112 | 138 | 163 | 189 | 213 | 237 | 262 | 287 | 7 | 1.3 |
| 17 | | | 125 | 155 | 185 | 215 | 245 | 274 | 303 | 333 | 8 | 1.4 |
| 18 | | | 138 | 174 | 210 | 245 | 280 | 315 | 350 | 385 | 8 | 1.5 |
| 19 | | | 152 | 194 | 236 | 278 | 319 | 360 | 401 | 443 | 8 | 1.6 |
| 20 | | | 168 | 216 | 265 | 313 | 361 | 409 | 457 | 504 | 8 | 1.7 |
| 21 | | | 185 | 240 | 295 | 349 | 404 | 458 | 513 | 567 | 8 | 1.8 |
| 22 | | | 205 | 268 | 331 | 393 | 455 | 517 | 579 | 641 | 9 | 1.8 |
| 23 | | | 227 | 297 | 367 | 437 | 506 | 576 | 645 | 715 | 9 | 1.9 |
| 24 | | | 252 | 328 | 404 | 481 | 558 | 635 | 712 | 789 | 9 | 2.0 |
| 25 | | | 278 | 360 | 442 | 525 | 610 | 695 | 780 | 865 | 9 | 2.1 |
| 26 | | | | 396 | 487 | 579 | 671 | 763 | 855 | 947 | 9 | 2.2 |
| 27 | | | | 435 | 534 | 633 | 733 | 833 | 932 | 1032 | 10 | 2.3 |
| 28 | | | | 474 | 581 | 687 | 795 | 903 | 1011 | 1119 | 10 | 2.4 |
| 29 | | | | 513 | 630 | 747 | 864 | 981 | 1098 | 1215 | 10 | 2.5 |
| 30 | | | | 561 | 688 | 815 | 942 | 1069 | 1196 | 1322 | 10 | 2.5 |
| **Under 120 Yr., Form Class 70** [b] | | | | | | | | | | | | |
| 6 | 5 | 8 | 12 | 16 | 19 | | | | | | 6 | 0.4 |
| 7 | 7 | 12 | 17 | 22 | 27 | | | | | | 6 | 0.5 |
| 8 | 10 | 17 | 23 | 30 | 37 | | | | | | 6 | 0.5 |
| 9 | 15 | 24 | 32 | 41 | 50 | | | | | | 6 | 0.6 |
| 10 | 20 | 31 | 42 | 54 | 65 | 76 | | | | | 6 | 0.7 |
| 11 | | 39 | 53 | 68 | 82 | 96 | 110 | | | | 6 | 0.7 |
| 12 | | 48 | 65 | 82 | 99 | 116 | 134 | | | | 7 | 0.8 |
| 13 | | 57 | 77 | 98 | 118 | 139 | 160 | | | | 7 | 0.9 |
| 14 | | 67 | 91 | 116 | 140 | 165 | 190 | | | | 7 | 0.9 |
| 15 | | 78 | 107 | 136 | 165 | 194 | 223 | | | | 7 | 1.0 |
| 16 | | | 125 | 159 | 193 | 227 | 261 | | | | 7 | 1.0 |
| 17 | | | 145 | 184 | 223 | 262 | 301 | | | | 8 | 1.1 |
| 18 | | | 167 | 212 | 256 | 301 | 345 | | | | 8 | 1.2 |
| 19 | | | 191 | 242 | 293 | 344 | 394 | | | | 8 | 1.2 |
| 20 | | | 216 | 274 | 332 | 389 | 446 | | | | 8 | 1.3 |

[a] Table developed from three taper curves, one for each of three diameter groups, namely, (1) below 15 in., (2) 15 to 19 in. (inclusive), and (3) over 19 in., based on measurements of 350 trees in four localities in Ontario.

[b] Table developed from one taper curve for all diameter classes, based on measurements of 522 trees in five localities in Ontario and New Brunswick.

Source: *Ibid.*

## WHITE PINE

### Table 66. Volume in Board Feet, International ¼-In. Log Rule

Saw Log Operation

| Diameter breast height (In.) | Total height of tree in feet | | | | | | | | | | Diameter inside bark at top (In.) | Double bark thickness at breast height (In.) |
|---|---|---|---|---|---|---|---|---|---|---|---|---|
| | 30 | 40 | 50 | 60 | 70 | 80 | 90 | 100 | 110 | 120 | | |
| | VOLUME Stump height, 1.5 ft.; log length, 16.3 ft. (Bd. ft.) | | | | | | | | | | | |

OVER 120 YR., FORM CLASS 65 [a]

| Diameter breast height (In.) | 30 | 40 | 50 | 60 | 70 | 80 | 90 | 100 | 110 | 120 | Diameter inside bark at top (In.) | Double bark thickness (In.) |
|---|---|---|---|---|---|---|---|---|---|---|---|---|
| 8 | | 15 | 20 | 30 | | | | | | | 6 | 0.6 |
| 9 | | 20 | 30 | 40 | 50 | | | | | | 6 | 0.7 |
| 10 | | 25 | 40 | 50 | 65 | | | | | | 6 | 0.8 |
| 11 | | 35 | 50 | 65 | 80 | | | | | | 6 | 0.9 |
| 12 | | 45 | 65 | 85 | 100 | 120 | | | | | 7 | 1.0 |
| 13 | | 60 | 80 | 105 | 125 | 145 | | | | | 7 | 1.1 |
| 14 | | 70 | 95 | 120 | 150 | 175 | 200 | 225 | | | 7 | 1.1 |
| 15 | | 80 | 110 | 140 | 170 | 200 | 230 | 265 | | | 7 | 1.2 |
| 16 | | 95 | 125 | 160 | 195 | 230 | 265 | 300 | | | 7 | 1.3 |
| 17 | | | 140 | 180 | 220 | 260 | 300 | 335 | 375 | 410 | 8 | 1.4 |
| 18 | | | 160 | 205 | 250 | 295 | 340 | 380 | 425 | 465 | 8 | 1.5 |
| 19 | | | 180 | 230 | 280 | 330 | 380 | 425 | 475 | 520 | 8 | 1.6 |
| 20 | | | 200 | 255 | 310 | 365 | 420 | 470 | 525 | 580 | 8 | 1.7 |
| 21 | | | 220 | 285 | 340 | 405 | 465 | 525 | 580 | 640 | 8 | 1.8 |
| 22 | | | 245 | 315 | 380 | 450 | 515 | 585 | 650 | 715 | 9 | 1.8 |
| 23 | | | 270 | 345 | 420 | 495 | 570 | 645 | 720 | 790 | 9 | 1.9 |
| 24 | | | 300 | 380 | 460 | 540 | 625 | 705 | 785 | 865 | 9 | 2.0 |
| 25 | | | 325 | 410 | 500 | 590 | 680 | 765 | 855 | 940 | 9 | 2.1 |
| 26 | | | 355 | 445 | 540 | 635 | 735 | 830 | 925 | 1020 | 9 | 2.2 |
| 27 | | | 385 | 480 | 580 | 685 | 790 | 895 | 995 | 1095 | 10 | 2.3 |
| 28 | | | 415 | 515 | 630 | 740 | 855 | 965 | 1080 | 1185 | 10 | 2.4 |
| 29 | | | | 560 | 680 | 800 | 930 | 1060 | 1180 | 1295 | 10 | 2.5 |
| 30 | | | | 605 | 735 | 870 | 1010 | 1155 | 1280 | 1410 | 10 | 2.5 |

UNDER 120 YR., FORM CLASS 70 [b]

| Diameter breast height (In.) | 30 | 40 | 50 | 60 | 70 | 80 | 90 | 100 | 110 | 120 | Diameter inside bark at top (In.) | Double bark thickness (In.) |
|---|---|---|---|---|---|---|---|---|---|---|---|---|
| 6 | 5 | 10 | 10 | 15 | 20 | | | | | | 6 | 0.4 |
| 7 | 10 | 10 | 15 | 20 | 25 | | | | | | 6 | 0.5 |
| 8 | 10 | 15 | 25 | 30 | 40 | | | | | | 6 | 0.5 |
| 9 | 15 | 25 | 35 | 45 | 55 | | | | | | 6 | 0.6 |
| 10 | 20 | 35 | 45 | 60 | 75 | 85 | | | | | 6 | 0.7 |
| 11 | | 45 | 60 | 75 | 95 | 110 | | | | | 6 | 0.7 |
| 12 | | 55 | 75 | 95 | 115 | 135 | 160 | | | | 7 | 0.8 |
| 13 | | 65 | 90 | 115 | 140 | 165 | 190 | | | | 7 | 0.9 |
| 14 | | 80 | 110 | 140 | 170 | 200 | 230 | | | | 7 | 0.9 |
| 15 | | 95 | 130 | 165 | 200 | 235 | 270 | | | | 7 | 1.0 |
| 16 | | | 150 | 190 | 230 | 275 | 315 | | | | 7 | 1.0 |
| 17 | | | 170 | 220 | 265 | 315 | 360 | | | | 8 | 1.1 |
| 18 | | | 195 | 250 | 300 | 355 | 410 | | | | 8 | 1.2 |
| 19 | | | 220 | 280 | 340 | 400 | 460 | | | | 8 | 1.2 |
| 20 | | | 245 | 315 | 380 | 450 | 515 | | | | 8 | 1.3 |

[a] Table developed from three taper curves, one for each of three diameter groups, namely, (1) below 15 in., (2) 15 to 19 in., and (3) over 19 in., based on measurements of 350 trees in four localities in Ontario.
[b] Table developed from one taper curve for all diameter classes, based on measurements of 522 trees in five localities in Ontario and New Brunswick.

Source: *Ibid.*

## BLACK SPRUCE

### Table 67. Cubic-Foot Volume

#### Form Class 65

| Diameter breast height (In.) | Total height of tree in feet | | | | | | | | Diameter inside bark at top (In.) | Double bark thickness at breast height (In.) |
|---|---|---|---|---|---|---|---|---|---|---|
| | 20 | 30 | 40 | 50 | 60 | 70 | 80 | 90 | | |
| | MERCHANTABLE VOLUME Stump height, 1.0 ft. (Cu. ft.) | | | | | | | | | |
| 4 | 0.1 | 0.2 | 0.4 | 0.5 | | | | | | 0.3 |
| 5 | 0.5 | 0.9 | 1.3 | 1.6 | 2.0 | | | | 4 | 0.3 |
| 6 | 1.1 | 1.8 | 2.4 | 3.0 | 3.6 | 4.2 | | | 4 | 0.4 |
| 7 | 1.9 | 2.8 | 3.7 | 4.6 | 5.5 | 6.4 | | | 5 | 0.4 |
| 8 | | 4.0 | 5.2 | 6.4 | 7.6 | 8.8 | | | 5 | 0.4 |
| 9 | | 5.4 | 6.9 | 8.4 | 9.9 | 11.4 | | | 5 | 0.5 |
| 10 | | 7.0 | 8.8 | 10.6 | 12.5 | 14.3 | 16.2 | | 5 | 0.5 |
| 11 | | | 10.8 | 13.0 | 15.3 | 17.5 | 19.7 | | 6 | 0.6 |
| 12 | | | 13.0 | 15.6 | 18.3 | 20.9 | 23.5 | | 6 | 0.6 |
| 13 | | | 15.4 | 18.5 | 21.6 | 24.6 | 27.7 | | 6 | 0.6 |
| 14 | | | 18.0 | 21.6 | 25.2 | 28.7 | 32.3 | | 6 | 0.7 |
| 15 | | | 20.7 | 24.9 | 29.0 | 33.1 | 37.3 | 41.5 | 6 | 0.7 |
| 16 | | | | 28.4 | 33.1 | 37.9 | 42.7 | 47.5 | | 0.8 |
| 17 | | | | 32.2 | 37.6 | 43.0 | 48.4 | 53.9 | | 0.8 |
| 18 | | | | 36.3 | 42.4 | 48.4 | 54.5 | 60.6 | | 0.8 |
| 19 | | | | 40.6 | 47.4 | 54.2 | 61.0 | 67.7 | | 0.9 |
| 20 | | | | 45.1 | 52.7 | 60.3 | 67.8 | 75.3 | | 0.9 |

Table developed from two taper curves, one for each of two diameter groups, namely, (1) 4.6 to 9.5 in. (inclusive), (2) over 9.5 in., based on measurements of 917 trees in ten localities in Manitoba, Ontario, Quebec, and New Brunswick.

Source: *Ibid.*

### Table 68. Cubic-Foot Volume

#### Pit Props, Form Class 65

| Diameter breast height (In.) | Total height of tree in feet | | | |
|---|---|---|---|---|
| | 30 | 40 | 50 | 60 |
| | MERCHANTABLE VOLUME (Cu. ft.) | | | |
| 4 | 0.85 | 0.93 | | |
| 5 | 1.60 | 1.90 | 2.30 | |
| 6 | 2.50 | 3.08 | 3.45 | |
| 7 | | 4.50 | 5.00 | 5.52 |
| 8 | | | 6.70 | 7.60 |
| 9 | | | 8.60 | 10.00 |

From measurements of 78 trees in New Brunswick. Length of pit props from 5 to 9 ft., with top diameters from 2½ to 8 in. Net deviation is 0.08 cu. ft.

Source: *Ibid.*

## WHITE SPRUCE AND RED SPRUCE

### Table 69. Cubic-Foot Volume *

Form Class 65

| Diameter breast height (In.) | 20 | 30 | 40 | 50 | 60 | 70 | 80 | 90 | 100 | Diameter inside bark at top (In.) | Double bark thickness at breast height (In.) |
|---|---|---|---|---|---|---|---|---|---|---|---|
| | | | MERCHANTABLE VOLUME Stump height, 1.0 ft. (Cu. ft.) | | | | | | | | |
| 4 | 0.2 | 0.3 | 0.4 | 0.5 | | | | | | | 0.3 |
| 5 | 0.7 | 1.1 | 1.4 | 1.6 | 1.9 | | | | | 4 | 0.3 |
| 6 | 1.4 | 2.0 | 2.5 | 3.0 | 3.6 | 4.2 | | | | 4 | 0.3 |
| 7 | 2.2 | 3.0 | 3.8 | 4.6 | 5.5 | 6.4 | | | | 5 | 0.4 |
| 8 | 3.1 | 4.2 | 5.3 | 6.4 | 7.6 | 8.8 | | | | 5 | 0.4 |
| 9 | | 5.5 | 7.0 | 8.5 | 10.0 | 11.5 | | | | 5 | 0.4 |
| 10 | | 7.0 | 8.9 | 10.8 | 12.6 | 14.5 | 16.3 | | | 5 | 0.5 |
| 11 | | | 10.9 | 13.2 | 15.4 | 17.7 | 19.9 | | | 6 | 0.5 |
| 12 | | | 13.1 | 15.8 | 18.5 | 21.2 | 23.9 | | | 6 | 0.5 |
| 13 | | | 15.5 | 18.7 | 21.9 | 25.0 | 28.2 | | | 6 | 0.5 |
| 14 | | | 18.2 | 21.9 | 25.6 | 29.2 | 32.9 | | | 6 | 0.6 |
| 15 | | | 21.2 | 25.4 | 29.6 | 33.8 | 38.0 | 42.3 | | 6 | 0.6 |
| 16 | | | | 29.1 | 33.9 | 38.7 | 43.5 | 48.3 | | | 0.6 |
| 17 | | | | 33.0 | 38.5 | 43.9 | 49.4 | 54.8 | | | 0.6 |
| 18 | | | | 37.2 | 43.4 | 49.5 | 55.7 | 61.8 | 68.0 | | 0.7 |
| 19 | | | | 41.6 | 48.6 | 55.5 | 62.5 | 69.4 | 76.4 | | 0.7 |
| 20 | | | | 46.2 | 54.0 | 61.8 | 69.7 | 77.6 | 85.5 | | 0.7 |
| 21 | | | | | | 68.4 | 77.4 | 86.4 | 95.4 | | |
| 22 | | | | | | 75.4 | 85.6 | 95.9 | 106.2 | | |
| 23 | | | | | | 82.7 | 94.4 | 106.1 | 117.8 | | |
| 24 | | | | | | 90.4 | 103.7 | 117.0 | 130.3 | | |
| 25 | | | | | | 98.6 | 113.6 | 128.5 | 143.4 | | |

### Table 70. Volume in Board Feet, Doyle Log Rule *

Saw Log Operation, Form Class 65

| Diameter breast height (In.) | 30 | 40 | 50 | 60 | 70 | 80 | 90 | 100 | Diameter inside bark at top (In.) | Double bark thickness at breast height (In.) |
|---|---|---|---|---|---|---|---|---|---|---|
| | | | VOLUME Stump height, 1.5 ft.; log length, 16.3 ft. (Bd. ft.) | | | | | | | |
| 7 | 5 | 5 | 5 | | | | | | 6 | 0.4 |
| 8 | 5 | 5 | 5 | 10 | | | | | 6 | 0.4 |
| 9 | 5 | 5 | 10 | 15 | 15 | | | | 7 | 0.4 |
| 10 | 10 | 10 | 15 | 20 | 25 | 30 | | | 7 | 0.5 |
| 11 | | 15 | 20 | 30 | 35 | 45 | | | 7 | 0.5 |
| 12 | | 20 | 30 | 40 | 50 | 60 | | | 7 | 0.5 |
| 13 | | 30 | 40 | 55 | 65 | 80 | | | 7 | 0.5 |
| 14 | | 40 | 55 | 70 | 85 | 105 | | | 7 | 0.6 |
| 15 | | 50 | 70 | 90 | 110 | 130 | 150 | 170 | 7 | 0.6 |
| 16 | | | 85 | 110 | 135 | 160 | 185 | 210 | 8 | 0.6 |
| 17 | | | 105 | 135 | 165 | 195 | 225 | 255 | 8 | 0.6 |
| 18 | | | 125 | 160 | 195 | 230 | 270 | 305 | 8 | 0.7 |
| 19 | | | 150 | 190 | 230 | 270 | 315 | 355 | 8 | 0.7 |
| 20 | | | 175 | 220 | 265 | 315 | 365 | 410 | 8 | 0.7 |

* Tables 69 and 70 developed from two taper curves, one for each of two diameter groups, namely, (1) 4.6 to 9.5 in. (inclusive), (2) over 9.5 in., based on measurements of 917 trees in ten localities in Manitoba, Ontario, Quebec, and New Brunswick.

Source: *Ibid.*

## WHITE SPRUCE AND RED SPRUCE

### Table 71. Volume in Board Feet

Saw Log Operation, Form Class 65

| Diameter breast height (In.) | Total height of tree in feet | | | | | | | | | | Diameter inside bark at top (In.) | Double bark thickness at breast height (In.) |
|---|---|---|---|---|---|---|---|---|---|---|---|---|
| | 30 | 40 | 50 | 60 | 70 | 80 | 90 | 100 | 110 | 120 | | |
| | VOLUME — Stump height, 1.5 ft.; log length, 16.3 ft. (Bd. ft.) | | | | | | | | | | | |
| **SCRIBNER LOG RULE** [a] | | | | | | | | | | | | |
| 7 | 5 | 10 | 15 | 15 | | | | | | | 6 | 0.4 |
| 8 | 10 | 15 | 20 | 20 | | | | | | | 6 | 0.4 |
| 9 | 15 | 20 | 25 | 30 | | | | | | | 7 | 0.4 |
| 10 | 20 | 25 | 35 | 45 | 55 | 65 | | | | | 7 | 0.5 |
| 11 | | 35 | 45 | 60 | 70 | 85 | | | | | 7 | 0.5 |
| 12 | | 45 | 60 | 75 | 90 | 105 | | | | | 7 | 0.5 |
| 13 | | 55 | 75 | 90 | 110 | 125 | | | | | 7 | 0.5 |
| 14 | | 65 | 90 | 110 | 130 | 150 | | | | | 7 | 0.6 |
| 15 | | 80 | 105 | 130 | 155 | 180 | 205 | 230 | | | 7 | 0.6 |
| 16 | | | 120 | 150 | 180 | 210 | 245 | 275 | | | 8 | 0.6 |
| 17 | | | 135 | 170 | 210 | 245 | 285 | 325 | | | 8 | 0.6 |
| 18 | | | 155 | 195 | 240 | 285 | 330 | 375 | | | 8 | 0.7 |
| 19 | | | 175 | 225 | 275 | 330 | 380 | 430 | | | 8 | 0.7 |
| 20 | | | 200 | 255 | 315 | 375 | 430 | 490 | | | 8 | 0.7 |
| **INTERNATIONAL ¼-IN. LOG RULE** [b] | | | | | | | | | | | | |
| 8 | 10 | 18 | 27 | 35 | 44 | | | | | | 5.4 | 0.4 |
| 9 | 15 | 26 | 37 | 48 | 60 | | | | | | 5.5 | 0.4 |
| 10 | 20 | 34 | 48 | 62 | 77 | 91 | | | | | 5.5 | 0.5 |
| 11 | | 43 | 60 | 78 | 95 | 113 | | | | | 5.6 | 0.5 |
| 12 | | 52 | 73 | 95 | 116 | 137 | | | | | 5.7 | 0.5 |
| 13 | | 63 | 88 | 114 | 139 | 164 | | | | | 5.8 | 0.5 |
| 14 | | 75 | 105 | 135 | 164 | 193 | | | | | 5.8 | 0.6 |
| 15 | | 88 | 123 | 157 | 190 | 225 | 260 | 293 | | | 5.9 | 0.6 |
| 16 | | | 142 | 181 | 220 | 260 | 299 | 338 | | | 6.0 | 0.6 |
| 17 | | | 163 | 208 | 253 | 298 | 343 | 388 | | | 6.1 | 0.6 |
| 18 | | | 186 | 237 | 288 | 339 | 390 | 440 | | | 6.2 | 0.7 |
| 19 | | | 211 | 268 | 325 | 382 | 440 | 498 | | | 6.3 | 0.7 |
| 20 | | | 238 | 300 | 363 | 425 | 493 | 559 | | | 6.4 | 0.7 |
| 21 | | | | | | 472 | 550 | 624 | 703 | | 6.5 | 0.7 |
| 22 | | | | | | 523 | 608 | 692 | 778 | | 6.6 | 0.8 |
| 23 | | | | | | 577 | 670 | 762 | 855 | | 6.6 | 0.8 |
| 24 | | | | | | 633 | 734 | 835 | 933 | | 6.7 | 0.9 |
| 25 | | | | | | 690 | 800 | 908 | 1015 | 1123 | 6.8 | 0.9 |
| 26 | | | | | | | 867 | 984 | 1100 | 1213 | 6.9 | 1.0 |
| 27 | | | | | | | 939 | 1062 | 1185 | 1307 | 7.0 | 1.1 |
| 28 | | | | | | | 1014 | 1145 | 1276 | 1406 | 7.1 | 1.1 |
| 29 | | | | | | | 1090 | 1230 | 1368 | 1505 | 7.1 | 1.2 |
| 30 | | | | | | | 1166 | 1315 | 1465 | 1615 | 7.2 | 1.3 |

[a] Table developed from two taper curves, one for each of two diameter groups, namely, (1) 4.6 to 9.5 in. (inclusive), (2) over 9.5 in., based on measurements of 917 trees in ten localities in Manitoba, Ontario, Quebec, and New Brunswick.

[b] Table developed from three taper curves for three diameter groups, (1) 4.6 to 9.5 in., (2) 9.6 to 20 in., and (3) 21 to 30 in., based on measurements of 1098 trees in 13 localities in Saskatchewan, Manitoba, Ontario, Quebec, and New Brunswick.

Source: *Ibid.*

# LODGEPOLE PINE

## Table 72. Linear Feet of Mine Props
### Form Class 65

| Diameter breast height (In.) | Total height of tree in feet | | | | | | | Double bark thickness at breast height (In.) |
|---|---|---|---|---|---|---|---|---|
| | 30 | 40 | 50 | 60 | 70 | 80 | 90 | |
| | | | | (Linear feet) | | | | |
| 5 | 4.7 | 5.3 | 5.9 | 6.5 | | | | 0.2 |
| 6 | 11.2 | 14.2 | 17.2 | 20.2 | | | | 0.3 |
| 7 | 15.5 | 20.3 | 25.1 | 30.0 | 35.0 | | | 0.3 |
| 8 | 18.5 | 24.3 | 30.2 | 36.1 | 42.0 | | | 0.3 |
| 9 | 20.5 | 27.0 | 33.5 | 40.1 | 46.7 | | | 0.4 |
| 10 | 21.8 | 28.8 | 35.9 | 43.0 | 50.1 | 57.2 | 64.4 | 0.4 |

Calculated from the taper curve F.C. 65 with 4.5-in. top (d.i.b.) and 1.0-ft. stump.
Source: *Ibid.*

## Table 73. Cubic-Foot Volume
### Form Class 65

| Diameter breast height (In.) | Total height of tree in feet | | | | | | | Diameter inside bark at top (In.) | Double bark thickness at breast height (In.) |
|---|---|---|---|---|---|---|---|---|---|
| | 20 | 30 | 40 | 50 | 60 | 70 | 80 | 90 | | |
| | MERCHANTABLE VOLUME Stump height, 1.0 ft. (Cu. ft.) | | | | | | | | | |
| 4 | .818 | 1.10 | | | | | | | 2.0 | 0.2 |
| 5 | 1.28 | 1.71 | 2.21 | 2.74 | 3.24 | | | | 2.5 | 0.2 |
| 6 | | 2.50 | 3.21 | 3.97 | 4.69 | | | | 3.0 | 0.3 |
| 7 | | 3.45 | 4.41 | 5.42 | 6.42 | 7.40 | | | 3.5 | 0.3 |
| 8 | | 4.56 | 5.81 | 7.11 | 8.42 | 9.72 | | | 4.0 | 0.3 |
| 9 | | 5.81 | 7.41 | 9.07 | 10.7 | 12.4 | | | 4.5 | 0.4 |
| 10 | | 7.20 | 9.26 | 11.3 | 13.3 | 15.4 | 17.5 | | 5.0 | 0.4 |
| 11 | | | 11.3 | 13.7 | 16.2 | 18.7 | 21.1 | 23.5 | 5.5 | 0.4 |
| 12 | | | 13.5 | 16.4 | 19.4 | 22.3 | 25.2 | 28.1 | 6.0 | 0.4 |
| 13 | | | 15.9 | 19.4 | 22.9 | 26.3 | 29.7 | 33.1 | 6.0 | 0.5 |
| 14 | | | 18.6 | 22.6 | 26.6 | 30.6 | 34.6 | 38.5 | 6.0 | 0.5 |
| 15 | | | 21.5 | 26.1 | 30.6 | 35.2 | 39.8 | 44.3 | 6.0 | 0.5 |
| 16 | | | | 29.9 | 35.0 | 40.2 | 45.4 | 50.6 | 6.0 | 0.6 |
| 17 | | | | 33.9 | 39.7 | 45.6 | 51.5 | 57.4 | 6.0 | 0.6 |
| 18 | | | | 38.1 | 44.7 | 51.4 | 58.0 | 64.7 | 6.0 | 0.6 |
| 19 | | | | 42.5 | 50.0 | 57.5 | 65.0 | 72.5 | 6.0 | 0.7 |
| 20 | | | | 47.2 | 55.6 | 64.0 | 72.4 | 80.8 | 6.0 | 0.7 |
| 21 | | | | 52.2 | 61.5 | 70.8 | 80.2 | 89.5 | 6.0 | 0.7 |
| 22 | | | | 57.5 | 67.7 | 78.0 | 88.3 | 98.6 | 6.0 | 0.7 |
| 23 | | | | 63.0 | 74.2 | 85.5 | 96.8 | 108.0 | 6.0 | 0.8 |
| 24 | | | | 68.8 | 81.0 | 93.3 | 106.0 | 118.0 | 6.0 | 0.8 |
| 25 | | | | 74.9 | 88.1 | 102.0 | 116.0 | 129.0 | 6.0 | 0.8 |

Table developed from one taper curve for all diameter classes, based on measurements of 243 trees in seven localities in British Columbia and Alberta.
Source: *Ibid.*

# LODGEPOLE PINE

### Table 74. Volume in Board Feet

Saw Log Operation

| Diameter breast height (In.) | Total height of tree in feet | | | | | | | Diameter inside bark at top (In.) | Double bark thickness at breast height (In.) |
|---|---|---|---|---|---|---|---|---|---|
| | 30 | 40 | 50 | 60 | 70 | 80 | 90 | | |
| | VOLUME Stump height, 1.5 ft.; log length, 16.3 ft. (Bd. ft.) | | | | | | | | |
| BRITISH COLUMBIA LOG RULE, FORM CLASS 65 | | | | | | | | | |
| 7 | 10 | 20 | 30 | 35 | 45 | | | 4 | 0.3 |
| 8 | 15 | 25 | 35 | 45 | 55 | | | 4 | 0.3 |
| 9 | 20 | 30 | 40 | 55 | 65 | | | 5 | 0.4 |
| 10 | 25 | 35 | 50 | 65 | 80 | 90 | | 5 | 0.4 |
| 11 | | 45 | 60 | 75 | 95 | 110 | 125 | 5 | 0.4 |
| 12 | | 55 | 70 | 90 | 110 | 130 | 145 | 6 | 0.4 |
| 13 | | 65 | 85 | 105 | 130 | 150 | 170 | 6 | 0.5 |
| 14 | | 75 | 100 | 125 | 150 | 175 | 200 | 6 | 0.5 |
| 15 | | 90 | 115 | 145 | 170 | 200 | 230 | 7 | 0.5 |
| 16 | | | 130 | 165 | 195 | 230 | 265 | 7 | 0.6 |
| 17 | | | 150 | 185 | 225 | 265 | 305 | 7 | 0.6 |
| 18 | | | 170 | 210 | 255 | 300 | 345 | 8 | 0.6 |
| 19 | | | 190 | 235 | 285 | 335 | 385 | 8 | 0.7 |
| 20 | | | 210 | 265 | 320 | 375 | 430 | 8 | 0.7 |
| 21 | | | 235 | 295 | 355 | 420 | 480 | 9 | 0.7 |
| 22 | | | 260 | 330 | 395 | 465 | 535 | 9 | 0.7 |
| 23 | | | 285 | 365 | 440 | 515 | 595 | 10 | 0.8 |
| 24 | | | 315 | 400 | 485 | 570 | 655 | 10 | 0.8 |
| 25 | | | 345 | 440 | 535 | 625 | 720 | 10 | 0.8 |
| SCRIBNER LOG RULE, FORM CLASS 60 | | | | | | | | | |
| 7 | 10 | 15 | 20 | 25 | 30 | | | 4 | 0.3 |
| 8 | 15 | 20 | 25 | 30 | 35 | | | 4 | 0.3 |
| 9 | 20 | 25 | 30 | 35 | 40 | | | 5 | 0.4 |
| 10 | 25 | 30 | 35 | 45 | 50 | 60 | | 5 | 0.4 |
| 11 | | 35 | 45 | 55 | 65 | 80 | 95 | 5 | 0.4 |
| 12 | | 40 | 55 | 70 | 85 | 100 | 115 | 6 | 0.4 |
| 13 | | 50 | 65 | 85 | 105 | 120 | 140 | 6 | 0.5 |
| 14 | | 60 | 80 | 100 | 125 | 145 | 165 | 6 | 0.5 |
| 15 | | 70 | 95 | 120 | 145 | 170 | 195 | 7 | 0.5 |
| 16 | | | 110 | 140 | 165 | 195 | 225 | 7 | 0.6 |
| 17 | | | 125 | 160 | 190 | 225 | 260 | 7 | 0.6 |
| 18 | | | 140 | 180 | 220 | 260 | 300 | 8 | 0.6 |
| 19 | | | 155 | 200 | 250 | 295 | 340 | 8 | 0.7 |
| 20 | | | 170 | 225 | 280 | 335 | 385 | 8 | 0.7 |
| 21 | | | 190 | 255 | 315 | 375 | 435 | 9 | 0.7 |
| 22 | | | 215 | 285 | 350 | 420 | 485 | 9 | 0.7 |
| 23 | | | 240 | 315 | 390 | 465 | 540 | 10 | 0.8 |
| 24 | | | 265 | 350 | 430 | 515 | 595 | 10 | 0.8 |
| 25 | | | 295 | 385 | 475 | 565 | 655 | 10 | 0.8 |

Table developed from one taper curve for all diameter classes, based on measurements of 243 trees in seven localities in British Columbia and Alberta.

Source: *Ibid.*

## LODGEPOLE PINE

### Table 75.　Volume in Board Feet, International ¼-In. Log Rule
#### Saw Log Operation, Form Class 65

| Diameter breast height (In.) | Total height of tree in feet | | | | | | | Diameter inside bark at top (In.) | Double bark thickness at breast height (In.) |
|---|---|---|---|---|---|---|---|---|---|
| | 30 | 40 | 50 | 60 | 70 | 80 | 90 | | |
| | VOLUME Stump height, 1.5 ft.; log length, 16.3 ft. (Bd. ft.) | | | | | | | | |
| 7 | 9 | 17 | 26 | 35 | 44 | | | 4 | 0.3 |
| 8 | 12 | 22 | 32 | 42 | 52 | | | 4 | 0.3 |
| 9 | 16 | 27 | 38 | 50 | 62 | | | 5 | 0.4 |
| 10 | 23 | 35 | 49 | 63 | 77 | 91 | | 5 | 0.4 |
| 11 | | 45 | 61 | 77 | 93 | 110 | 127 | 5 | 0.4 |
| 12 | | 56 | 75 | 94 | 113 | 133 | 153 | 6 | 0.4 |
| 13 | | 67 | 89 | 111 | 134 | 157 | 180 | 6 | 0.5 |
| 14 | | 80 | 106 | 133 | 160 | 187 | 214 | 6 | 0.5 |
| 15 | | 95 | 124 | 156 | 188 | 220 | 252 | 7 | 0.5 |
| 16 | | | 142 | 179 | 216 | 253 | 290 | 7 | 0.6 |
| 17 | | | 163 | 206 | 249 | 292 | 335 | 7 | 0.6 |
| 18 | | | 186 | 235 | 284 | 333 | 382 | 8 | 0.6 |
| 19 | | | 210 | 264 | 319 | 374 | 429 | 8 | 0.7 |
| 20 | | | 237 | 298 | 359 | 420 | 481 | 8 | 0.7 |
| 21 | | | 266 | 333 | 400 | 468 | 536 | 9 | 0.7 |
| 22 | | | 295 | 368 | 443 | 518 | 593 | 9 | 0.7 |
| 23 | | | 324 | 405 | 486 | 568 | 650 | 10 | 0.8 |
| 24 | | | 355 | 443 | 531 | 620 | 710 | 10 | 0.8 |
| 25 | | | 388 | 485 | 582 | 680 | 778 | 10 | 0.8 |

Table developed from one taper curve for all diameter classes, based on measurements of 243 trees in seven localities in British Columbia and Alberta.

Source: *Ibid.*

## BIBLIOGRAPHY

The bibliography for this section on Forest Management Volume Tables is combined with that of the following two sections because of the integration of the subject matter of the three sections. (See page **4·14**.)

# FOREST MANAGEMENT—YIELD TABLES AND STOCKING

## C O N T E N T S

# FOREST MANAGEMENT—YIELD TABLES
## AND STOCKING

### Yield Tables

A normal yield table is a tabulation of the volume, basal area, number of trees, etc., per acre found in full stands on specified sites at specified ages. Most normal yield tables have been prepared to apply strictly to even-aged, pure stands. Frequently they have been considered as a guide to the life history of the ideal stand for the species studied. Actually the theoretical normal stand seldom possesses this significance; it is merely a standard to which an actual forest may be compared. Because of this, several problems exist in the application of yield tables. Special types of tables have been devised to help meet the problems, but still other types may be needed for future management tasks.

### WHITE ASH
#### Table 1. Yields per Fully Stocked Acre
Massachusetts

| Age (yr.) | Trees per acre | Height (ft.) | D.b.h. (in.) | Basal area (sq. ft.) | Cubic ft. per acre | | Total yield | |
|---|---|---|---|---|---|---|---|---|
| | | | | | Saw logs | Cordwood | Cu. ft. | Bd. ft |
| 10 | 8,210 | 18 | 1.2 | 65 | ... | ... | 1,231 | |
| 20 | 2,052 | 36 | 2.7 | 82 | ... | 2,131 | 1,231 | |
| 30 | 912 | 53 | 4.8 | 115 | ... | 2,650 | 2,650 | |
| 40 | 513 | 68 | 6.9 | 133 | ... | 4,104 | 4,104 | |
| 50 | 328 | 77 | 8.8 | 139 | ... | 4,756 | 4,756 | |
| 60 | 228 | 81 | 10.6 | 140 | 4,332 | 912 | 5,244 | 25,000 |
| 70 | 168 | 82 | 12.4 | 141 | 4,036 | 1,344 | 5,380 | 28,000 |

Source: R. T. Patton, Red oak and white ash—a study of growth and yield, *Harvard Forest Bull. No. 4,* 1922.

## EASTERN COTTONWOOD

### Table 2. Yields per Fully Stocked Acre
Mississippi Valley

| Age. | Number of trees per acre. | | Average size. | | Yield per acre. | | | Average annual yield per acre. | | |
|---|---|---|---|---|---|---|---|---|---|---|
| | 14 inches and over. | All trees. | Diameter breast-high. | Height. | Stem wood. | Scribner decimal. | Doyle. | Stem wood. | Scribner decimal. | Doyle. |
| Years. | | | Inches. | Feet. | Cu.ft. | Bd.ft. | Bd.ft. | Cu.ft. | Bd.ft. | Bd.ft. |
| 5 | .. | ..... | 2.0 | 22 | 650 | ..... | ..... | 130 | ... | ... |
| 6 | .. | ..... | 2.8 | 29 | 875 | ..... | ..... | 146 | ... | ... |
| 7 | .. | 1,450 | 3.5 | 36 | 1,025 | ..... | ..... | 146 | ... | ... |
| 8 | .. | 1,163 | 4.2 | 43 | 1,250 | ..... | ..... | 156 | ... | ... |
| 9 | .. | 900 | 5.0 | 49 | 1,500 | ..... | ..... | 167 | ... | ... |
| 10 | .. | 699 | 5.7 | 56 | 1,800 | ..... | ..... | 180 | ... | ... |
| 11 | .. | 558 | 6.4 | 61 | 2,175 | ..... | ..... | 198 | ... | ... |
| 12 | 3 | 452 | 7.1 | 67 | 2,600 | ..... | 200 | 217 | ... | 17 |
| 13 | 8 | 375 | 7.8 | 72 | 3,050 | 800 | 700 | 235 | 62 | 54 |
| 14 | 15 | 320 | 8.5 | 76 | 3,500 | 1,600 | 1,300 | 250 | 114 | 93 |
| 15 | 22 | 276 | 9.2 | 81 | 3,850 | 2,400 | 1,900 | 257 | 160 | 127 |
| 16 | 29 | 243 | 9.8 | 85 | 4,150 | 3,200 | 2,600 | 259 | 200 | 163 |
| 17 | 34 | 217 | 10.5 | 88 | 4,400 | 4,000 | 3,300 | 259 | 235 | 194 |
| 18 | 37 | 195 | 11.1 | 92 | 4,575 | 4,900 | 4,100 | 254 | 272 | 228 |
| 19 | 40 | 178 | 11.7 | 95 | 4,750 | 5,800 | 4,900 | 250 | 305 | 258 |
| 20 | 43 | 163 | 12.3 | 97 | 4,900 | 6,600 | 5,700 | 245 | 330 | 285 |
| 21 | 45 | 150 | 12.8 | 100 | 5,025 | 7,600 | 6,500 | 239 | 362 | 310 |
| 22 | 47 | 140 | 13.4 | 102 | 5,125 | 8,600 | 7,500 | 233 | 391 | 341 |
| 23 | 49 | 130 | 13.9 | 104 | 5,250 | 9,600 | 8,400 | 228 | 417 | 365 |
| 24 | 50 | 121 | 14.5 | 106 | 5,350 | 10,700 | 9,500 | 223 | 446 | 396 |
| 25 | 52 | 114 | 15.0 | 108 | 5,450 | 11,900 | 10,700 | 218 | 476 | 428 |
| 26 | 53 | 106 | 15.5 | 109 | 5,525 | 13,200 | 12,000 | 213 | 508 | 462 |
| 27 | 54 | 99 | 16.0 | 111 | 5,600 | 14,700 | 13,400 | 207 | 544 | 496 |
| 28 | 55 | 92 | 16.5 | 112 | 5,675 | 16,300 | 15,100 | 203 | 582 | 540 |
| 29 | 55 | 86 | 16.9 | 114 | 5,750 | 18,100 | 17,100 | 198 | 624 | 590 |
| 30 | 55 | 80 | 17.4 | 115 | 5,825 | 20,300 | 19,200 | 194 | 677 | 640 |
| 31 | 55 | 75 | 17.9 | 116 | 5,875 | 22,700 | 21,400 | 190 | 732 | 690 |
| 32 | 55 | 70 | 18.3 | 117 | 5,950 | 24,900 | 23,500 | 186 | 778 | 734 |
| 33 | 55 | 66 | 18.8 | 119 | 6,025 | 26,800 | 25,300 | 183 | 812 | 767 |
| 34 | 54 | 62 | 19.3 | 120 | 6,075 | 28,300 | 26,600 | 179 | 832 | 782 |
| 35 | 53 | 59 | 19.7 | 121 | 6,160 | 29,400 | 27,500 | 176 | 840 | 786 |
| 36 | 52 | 57 | 20.2 | 123 | 6,200 | 30,100 | 28,200 | 172 | 836 | 783 |
| 37 | 51 | 53 | 20.6 | 124 | 6,275 | 30,400 | 28,700 | 170 | 822 | 776 |
| 38 | 50 | 51 | 21.1 | 125 | 6,325 | 30,700 | 29,100 | 166 | 808 | 766 |
| 39 | 49 | 50 | 21.5 | 126 | 6,375 | 30,900 | 29,300 | 163 | 792 | 751 |
| 40 | 48 | 49 | 22.0 | 127 | 6,425 | 31,000 | 29,300 | 161 | 775 | 733 |
| 41 | 46 | 48 | 22.4 | 128 | 6,475 | 31,000 | 29,400 | 158 | 756 | 717 |
| 42 | 45 | 45 | 22.9 | 129 | 6,525 | 31,100 | 29,400 | 155 | 740 | 702 |
| 43 | 44 | 44 | 23.4 | 130 | 6,575 | 31,000 | 29,500 | 153 | 721 | 686 |
| 44 | 43 | 43 | 23.8 | 131 | 6,625 | 31,000 | 29,500 | 151 | 705 | 670 |
| 45 | 42 | 42 | 24.2 | 132 | 6,675 | 30,900 | 29,500 | 148 | 687 | 656 |
| 46 | 40 | 40 | 24.7 | 133 | 6,725 | 30,800 | 29,500 | 146 | 670 | 641 |
| 47 | 38 | 38 | 25.1 | 134 | 6,775 | 30,700 | 29,500 | 144 | 653 | 628 |
| 48 | 37 | 37 | 25.6 | 135 | 6,825 | 30,600 | 29,500 | 142 | 638 | 615 |
| 49 | 34 | 34 | 26.0 | 136 | 6,875 | 30,500 | 29,500 | 140 | 622 | 602 |
| 50 | 32 | 32 | 26.5 | 136 | 6,900 | 30,300 | 29,400 | 138 | 606 | 588 |

Source: A. W. Williamson, Cottonwood in the Mississippi Valley, U. S. Dept. Agr., *Bull. No. 24,* 1913.

# DOUGLAS-FIR

## Table 3. Yield Tables per Fully Stocked Acre

Pacific Slope, California

Site index—height of average dominant at 50 years

| Age, years | NUMBER OF TREES TO THE ACRE [a] | | | | | BASAL AREA TO THE ACRE [b] | | | | | CUBIC VOLUME TO THE ACRE [c] | | | | |
|---|---|---|---|---|---|---|---|---|---|---|---|---|---|---|---|
| | 60 | 80 | 100 | 120 | 140 | 60 | 80 | 100 | 120 | 140 | 60 | 80 | 100 | 120 | 140 |
| | | | | | | sq.ft. | sq.ft. | sq.ft. | sq.ft. | sq.ft. | cu.ft. | cu.ft. | cu.ft. | cu.ft. | cu.ft. |
| 30 | | 1,060 | 672 | 485 | 394 | | 198 | 217 | 230 | 243 | | 3,300 | 4,900 | 6,500 | 7,700 |
| 40 | | 780 | 497 | 364 | 297 | | 223 | 243 | 267 | 285 | | 5,000 | 7,200 | 9,350 | 10,900 |
| 50 | 1,033 | 601 | 386 | 278 | 230 | 205 | 237 | 264 | 290 | 305 | 2,300 | 6,400 | 9,000 | 11,700 | 13,100 |
| 60 | 790 | 475 | 302 | 220 | 182 | 214 | 249 | 281 | 305 | 319 | 3,650 | 7,600 | 10,500 | 13,200 | 14,800 |
| 70 | 643 | 382 | 241 | 176 | 147 | 222 | 260 | 295 | 316 | 328 | 4,800 | 8,550 | 11,750 | 14,500 | 16,200 |
| 80 | 530 | 313 | 200 | 148 | 121 | 228 | 271 | 305 | 323 | 334 | 5,700 | 9,350 | 12,750 | 15,500 | 17,400 |
| 90 | 445 | 260 | 168 | 125 | 100 | 233 | 280 | 313 | 329 | 339 | 6,400 | 10,000 | 13,550 | 16,400 | 18,400 |
| 100 | 378 | 225 | 143 | 104 | 85 | 238 | 288 | 318 | 333 | 342 | 6,950 | 10,500 | 14,300 | 17,200 | 19,200 |
| 110 | 324 | 193 | 122 | 91 | | 242 | 294 | 322 | 336 | | 7,400 | 11,000 | 14,900 | 17,950 | |
| 120 | 282 | 170 | 107 | 80 | | 245 | 298 | 326 | 338 | | 7,700 | 11,400 | 15,400 | 18,600 | |
| 130 | 254 | 152 | 95 | 70 | | 248 | 302 | 328 | 340 | | 7,950 | 11,700 | 15,950 | 19,200 | |
| 140 | 230 | 138 | 87 | 62 | | 250 | 305 | 330 | 341 | | 8,150 | 12,000 | 16,400 | 19,800 | |
| 150 | 212 | 124 | 79 | 58 | | 251 | 308 | 331 | 342 | | 8,350 | 12,300 | 16,800 | 20,300 | |
| 160 | 198 | 113 | 75 | 54 | | 252 | 309 | 332 | 343 | | 8,600 | 12,500 | 17,200 | 20,800 | |

[a] At least 4.5 ft. tall.
[b] At breast height.
[c] Entire stem, including stump and tip, but without limbs or bark.

## Table 3. Yield Tables per Fully Stocked Acre (Continued)

Site index—height of average dominant at 50 years

| Age, years | Average Diameter, Breast High | | | | | Number of Trees Eight Inches and Over, to the Acre | | | | | Volume Board Measure to the Acre [d] | | | | |
|---|---|---|---|---|---|---|---|---|---|---|---|---|---|---|---|
| | 60 | 80 | 100 | 120 | 140 | 60 | 80 | 100 | 120 | 140 | 60 | 80 | 100 | 120 | 140 |
| | in. | in. | in. | in. | in. | | | | | | bd. ft. | bd. ft. | bd. ft. | bd. ft. | bd. ft. |
| 30 | | 5.9 | 7.7 | 9.3 | 10.6 | | 185 | 265 | 258 | 252 | | 7,760 | 17,050 | 27,900 | 37,000 |
| 40 | | 7.2 | 9.5 | 11.6 | 13.3 | | 252 | 278 | 251 | 230 | | 16,000 | 31,700 | 47,700 | 59,400 |
| 50 | 6.0 | 8.5 | 11.2 | 13.8 | 15.6 | 191 | 279 | 258 | 221 | 198 | 8,940 | 25,200 | 45,000 | 64,800 | 76,200 |
| 60 | 7.1 | 9.8 | 13.1 | 15.9 | 17.9 | 250 | 277 | 230 | 190 | 170 | 15,060 | 34,300 | 56,900 | 77,400 | 90,600 |
| 70 | 8.0 | 11.2 | 15.0 | 18.1 | 20.3 | 266 | 260 | 203 | 165 | 143 | 21,000 | 42,700 | 67,300 | 89,000 | 103,500 |
| 80 | 8.9 | 12.6 | 16.7 | 20.0 | 22.5 | 269 | 234 | 179 | 144 | 118 | 26,500 | 49,650 | 76,200 | 98,400 | 114,800 |
| 90 | 9.8 | 14.0 | 18.5 | 22.0 | 25.0 | 260 | 210 | 158 | 124 | 98 | 31,400 | 55,700 | 83,800 | 107,400 | 124,100 |
| 100 | 10.7 | 15.3 | 20.2 | 24.2 | 27.0 | 243 | 190 | 139 | 105 | 85 | 35,900 | 60,600 | 91,000 | 115,300 | 131,500 |
| 110 | 11.7 | 16.7 | 22.0 | 26.0 | | 225 | 174 | 122 | 91 | | 39,400 | 65,650 | 97,600 | 122,200 | |
| 120 | 12.6 | 17.9 | 23.6 | 27.2 | | 210 | 159 | 106 | 80 | | 42,200 | 68,200 | 102,700 | 127,600 | |
| 130 | 13.4 | 19.1 | 25.2 | 29.8 | | 199 | 146 | 94 | 70 | | 44,600 | 73,200 | 107,800 | 133,700 | |
| 140 | 14.1 | 20.2 | 26.3 | 31.8 | | 187 | 135 | 85 | 63 | | 46,750 | 76,400 | 111,800 | 139,000 | |
| 150 | 14.7 | 21.3 | 27.7 | 32.9 | | 178 | 124 | 79 | 58 | | 48,300 | 79,700 | 115,700 | 142,900 | |
| 160 | 15.3 | 22.4 | 28.5 | 34.1 | | 167 | 114 | 75 | 54 | | 49,600 | 82,400 | 119,000 | 146,600 | |

[d] By International ⅛-Inch Rule. Trees 8 in. and larger. Stump 1 ft. Top d.i.b. 5 in. Trees scaled in 16.3-foot logs.
Source: F. X. Schumacher, Yield, stand and volume tables for Douglas-fir in California, Calif. Agr. Exp. Sta., *Bull. No. 491*, 1930.

# DOUGLAS-FIR

## Table 4. Stand Table, Including All Trees, per Acre
### Pacific Slope, California

| D. b. h. class, inches | Age of stand in years | | | | | | | | | | | | | |
|---|---|---|---|---|---|---|---|---|---|---|---|---|---|---|
| | 30 | 40 | 50 | 60 | 70 | 80 | 90 | 100 | 110 | 120 | 130 | 140 | 150 | 160 |
| | Number of trees by diameter classes | | | | | | | | | | | | | |
| *Site index 60 feet at 50 years* | | | | | | | | | | | | | | |
| 0.0– 2.0 | | | 173 | 37 | 58 | 28 | 15 | 13 | 8 | 7 | 2 | 2 | 2 | |
| 2.0– 4.0 | | | 233 | 135 | 90 | 60 | 36 | 22 | 14 | 9 | 7 | 5 | 4 | 3 |
| 4.0– 6.0 | | | 251 | 177 | 127 | 89 | 62 | 44 | 31 | 21 | 16 | 12 | 9 | 8 |
| 6.0– 8.0 | | | 184 | 159 | 132 | 102 | 79 | 59 | 43 | 33 | 26 | 21 | 17 | 15 |
| 8.0–10.0 | | | 107 | 110 | 105 | 91 | 80 | 65 | 52 | 41 | 33 | 27 | 23 | 21 |
| 10.0–12.0 | | | 52 | 65 | 72 | 70 | 67 | 60 | 51 | 43 | 37 | 32 | 28 | 25 |
| 12.0–14.0 | | | 22 | 32 | 36 | 46 | 49 | 45 | 45 | 40 | 36 | 33 | 29 | 27 |
| 14.0–16.0 | | | 8 | 11 | 16 | 27 | 31 | 33 | 36 | 34 | 32 | 30 | 27 | 26 |
| 16.0–20.0 | | | | 2 | 6 | 16 | 24 | 32 | 36 | 40 | 42 | 44 | 43 | 42 |
| 20.0–24.0 | | | | | | 1 | 2 | 5 | 9 | 12 | 16 | 19 | 21 | 23 |
| 24.0–28.0 | | | | | | | | | | 2 | 4 | 5 | 6 | 7 |
| 28.0–32.0 | | | | | | | | | | | | | 1 | 1 |
| Total | | | 1030 | 788 | 642 | 530 | 445 | 378 | 325 | 282 | 251 | 230 | 210 | 198 |
| *Site index 80 feet at 50 years* | | | | | | | | | | | | | | |
| 0.0– 2.0 | 189 | 72 | 42 | 19 | 10 | 6 | 4 | 4 | | | | | | |
| 2.0– 4.0 | 240 | 134 | 71 | 39 | 21 | 13 | 6 | 5 | 3 | 2 | 1 | 1 | | |
| 4.0– 6.0 | 259 | 175 | 104 | 67 | 40 | 26 | 15 | 9 | 6 | 4 | 3 | 2 | 1 | 1 |
| 6.0– 8.0 | 183 | 157 | 119 | 85 | 55 | 37 | 25 | 16 | 11 | 7 | 5 | 4 | 3 | 2 |
| 8.0–10.0 | 105 | 122 | 101 | 85 | 65 | 46 | 32 | 23 | 17 | 13 | 9 | 6 | 5 | 4 |
| 10.0–12.0 | 53 | 69 | 77 | 70 | 60 | 48 | 36 | 28 | 21 | 16 | 12 | 10 | 7 | 6 |
| 12.0–14.0 | 21 | 36 | 48 | 52 | 50 | 43 | 37 | 31 | 24 | 19 | 15 | 12 | 9 | 8 |
| 14.0–16.0 | 5 | 14 | 26 | 33 | 37 | 37 | 32 | 29 | 25 | 21 | 17 | 14 | 11 | 9 |
| 16.0–20.0 | | 4 | 12 | 23 | 37 | 43 | 47 | 46 | 43 | 39 | 35 | 30 | 26 | 23 |
| 20.0–24.0 | | | | 2 | 7 | 13 | 22 | 25 | 28 | 29 | 28 | 27 | 25 | 23 |
| 24.0–28.0 | | | | | | 2 | 5 | 8 | 13 | 15 | 18 | 19 | 19 | 19 |
| 28.0–32.0 | | | | | | | | 1 | 3 | 6 | 8 | 10 | 12 | 12 |
| 32.0–36.0 | | | | | | | | | | 1 | 1 | 3 | 5 | 6 |
| 36.0–40.0 | | | | | | | | | | | | | | 1 |
| Total | 1055 | 783 | 600 | 475 | 382 | 314 | 261 | 225 | 194 | 172 | 152 | 138 | 123 | 114 |
| *Site index 100 feet at 50 years* | | | | | | | | | | | | | | |
| 0.0– 2.0 | 65 | 18 | 10 | 3 | 2 | 1 | | | | | | | | |
| 2.0– 4.0 | 101 | 47 | 20 | 10 | 5 | 3 | 1 | 1 | 1 | | | | | |
| 4.0– 6.0 | 139 | 73 | 41 | 22 | 11 | 6 | 3 | 2 | 1 | 1 | | | | |
| 6.0– 8.0 | 136 | 92 | 56 | 33 | 20 | 11 | 6 | 4 | 2 | 2 | 1 | 1 | | |
| 8.0–10.0 | 106 | 88 | 64 | 41 | 27 | 17 | 11 | 7 | 4 | 3 | 2 | 2 | 1 | 1 |
| 10.0–12.0 | 65 | 75 | 61 | 45 | 32 | 21 | 14 | 10 | 7 | 4 | 3 | 2 | 2 | 2 |
| 12.0–14.0 | 36 | 51 | 51 | 43 | 34 | 25 | 18 | 12 | 9 | 6 | 5 | 3 | 3 | 2 |
| 14.0–16.0 | 17 | 30 | 37 | 37 | 31 | 26 | 20 | 14 | 10 | 8 | 6 | 5 | 4 | 3 |
| 16.0–20.0 | 5 | 19 | 37 | 49 | 49 | 45 | 39 | 32 | 26 | 19 | 15 | 12 | 10 | 9 |
| 20.0–24.0 | | 2 | 7 | 16 | 26 | 30 | 31 | 28 | 25 | 20 | 18 | 15 | 13 | 11 |
| 24.0–28.0 | | | | 3 | 7 | 14 | 18 | 20 | 20 | 19 | 17 | 15 | 14 | 12 |
| 28.0–32.0 | | | | | 1 | 3 | 6 | 10 | 12 | 14 | 13 | 13 | 12 | 12 |
| 32.0–36.0 | | | | | | | 1 | 3 | 5 | 8 | 9 | 10 | 9 | 10 |
| 36.0–40.0 | | | | | | | | | 1 | 3 | 5 | 5 | 7 | 7 |
| 40.0–44.0 | | | | | | | | | | | 1 | 3 | 3 | 4 |
| 44.0–48.0 | | | | | | | | | | | | | 1 | 2 |
| 48.0–52.0 | | | | | | | | | | | | | | |
| Total | 670 | 495 | 384 | 302 | 245 | 202 | 168 | 143 | 123 | 107 | 95 | 86 | 79 | 75 |

Source: *Ibid.*

## Table 4. Stand Table, Including All Trees, per Acre (Continued)

| D. b. h. class, inches | Age of stand in years | | | | | | | | | | | | | |
|---|---|---|---|---|---|---|---|---|---|---|---|---|---|---|
| | 30 | 40 | 50 | 60 | 70 | 80 | 90 | 100 | 110 | 120 | 130 | 140 | 150 | 160 |
| | Number of trees by diameter classes | | | | | | | | | | | | | |
| *Site index 120 feet at 50 years* | | | | | | | | | | | | | | |
| 0.0– 2.0 | 26 | 14 | 2 | 1 | | | | | | | | | | |
| 2.0– 4.0 | 51 | 20 | 8 | 4 | 1 | 1 | 1 | | | | | | | |
| 4.0– 6.0 | 77 | 39 | 19 | 8 | 4 | 2 | 1 | 1 | | | | | | |
| 6.0– 8.0 | 92 | 52 | 29 | 16 | 8 | 4 | 2 | 1 | 1 | 1 | | | | |
| 8.0–10.0 | 86 | 60 | 37 | 21 | 13 | 7 | 4 | 2 | 2 | 1 | | | | |
| 10.0–12.0 | 67 | 56 | 41 | 26 | 17 | 10 | 6 | 4 | 3 | 2 | 1 | 1 | 1 | |
| 12.0–14.0 | 45 | 47 | 40 | 29 | 20 | 13 | 8 | 6 | 4 | 3 | 2 | 1 | 1 | 1 |
| 14.0–16.0 | 26 | 35 | 35 | 28 | 21 | 15 | 10 | 7 | 5 | 3 | 3 | 2 | 1 | 1 |
| 16.0–20.0 | 16 | 33 | 48 | 48 | 40 | 32 | 24 | 17 | 13 | 9 | 7 | 6 | 5 | 4 |
| 20.0–24.0 | | 7 | 18 | 28 | 31 | 28 | 24 | 20 | 16 | 13 | 10 | 8 | 6 | 5 |
| 24.0–28.0 | | | 3 | 10 | 16 | 21 | 20 | 19 | 16 | 14 | 12 | 10 | 8 | 7 |
| 28.0–32.0 | | | | 1 | 5 | 10 | 14 | 14 | 14 | 13 | 12 | 10 | 8 | 8 |
| 32.0–36.0 | | | | | 1 | 3 | 6 | 9 | 10 | 11 | 10 | 10 | 8 | 8 |
| 36.0–40.0 | | | | | | | 2 | 4 | 5 | 7 | 8 | 8 | 8 | 7 |
| 40.0–44.0 | | | | | | | | 1 | 3 | 3 | 5 | 5 | 6 | 6 |
| 44.0–48.0 | | | | | | | | | | 1 | 2 | 3 | 4 | 4 |
| 48.0–52.0 | | | | | | | | | | | | 1 | 2 | 2 |
| 52.0–56.0 | | | | | | | | | | | | | 1 | 1 |
| Total | 486 | 363 | 280 | 220 | 177 | 146 | 122 | 105 | 92 | 81 | 72 | 65 | 59 | 54 |
| *Site index 140 feet at 50 years* | | | | | | | | | | | | | | |
| 0.0– 2.0 | 12 | 10 | 2 | | | | | | | | | | | |
| 2.0– 4.0 | 26 | 10 | 3 | 1 | 1 | | | | | | | | | |
| 4.0– 6.0 | 48 | 22 | 8 | 4 | 2 | 1 | 1 | | | | | | | |
| 6.0– 8.0 | 63 | 33 | 16 | 7 | 4 | 2 | 1 | 1 | | | | | | |
| 8.0–10.0 | 69 | 42 | 22 | 13 | 7 | 3 | 2 | 1 | | | | | | |
| 10.0–12.0 | 62 | 45 | 28 | 17 | 10 | 6 | 3 | 2 | | | | | | |
| 12.0–14.0 | 49 | 43 | 31 | 20 | 12 | 8 | 5 | 3 | | | | | | |
| 14.0–16.0 | 34 | 37 | 30 | 23 | 14 | 9 | 6 | 4 | | | | | | |
| 16.0–20.0 | 29 | 44 | 49 | 44 | 32 | 23 | 16 | 11 | | | | | | |
| 20.0–24.0 | 3 | 13 | 29 | 31 | 29 | 24 | 18 | 14 | | | | | | |
| 24.0–28.0 | | 1 | 10 | 18 | 21 | 21 | 18 | 15 | | | | | | |
| 28.0–32.0 | | | 1 | 6 | 11 | 14 | 15 | 13 | | | | | | |
| 32.0–36.0 | | | | 1 | 3 | 7 | 10 | 11 | | | | | | |
| 36.0–40.0 | | | | | 1 | 3 | 5 | 7 | | | | | | |
| 40.0–44.0 | | | | | | | 1 | 3 | | | | | | |
| 44.0–48.0 | | | | | | | | 1 | | | | | | |
| 48.0–52.0 | | | | | | | | | | | | | | |
| Total | 395 | 300 | 229 | 183 | 147 | 121 | 101 | 86 | | | | | | |

# DOUGLAS-FIR

## Table 5. Yields per Fully Stocked Acre, Total Stand *
### Pacific Northwest

### TOTAL NUMBER OF TREES

| Age (years) | Site Class V | | Site Class IV | | | Site Class III | | | Site Class II | | | Site Class I | | |
|---|---|---|---|---|---|---|---|---|---|---|---|---|---|---|
| | Site index 80 | Site index 90 | Site index 100 | Site index 110 | Site index 120 | Site index 130 | Site index 140 | Site index 150 | Site index 160 | Site index 170 | Site index 180 | Site index 190 | Site index 200 | Site index 210 |
| | Number | Number | Number | Number | Number | Number | Number | Number | Number | Number | Number | Number | Number | Number |
| 20 | 6,920 | 5,500 | 4,150 | 3,069 | 2,324 | 1,815 | 1,460 | 1,210 | 1,012 | 880 | 756 | 654 | 571 | 490 |
| 30 | 2,700 | 2,200 | 1,800 | 1,472 | 1,219 | 1,030 | 865 | 735 | 640 | 555 | 483 | 408 | 350 | 300 |
| 40 | 1,530 | 1,275 | 1,090 | 927 | 798 | 680 | 585 | 510 | 445 | 385 | 335 | 282 | 240 | 203 |
| 50 | 1,050 | 890 | 764 | 659 | 572 | 496 | 430 | 377 | 331 | 290 | 248 | 208 | 176 | 150 |
| 60 | 790 | 670 | 580 | 500 | 439 | 380 | 337 | 296 | 261 | 228 | 195 | 164 | 138 | 116 |
| 70 | 625 | 537 | 468 | 405 | 352 | 310 | 274 | 242 | 214 | 186 | 160 | 135 | 113 | 95 |
| 80 | 525 | 455 | 394 | 345 | 303 | 266 | 232 | 207 | 182 | 159 | 136 | 115 | 97 | 81 |
| 90 | 451 | 398 | 347 | 304 | 266 | 235 | 205 | 180 | 158 | 138 | 118 | 100 | 84 | 71 |
| 100 | 403 | 352 | 311 | 271 | 239 | 209 | 184 | 161 | 142 | 123 | 106 | 89 | 75 | 64 |
| 110 | 362 | 319 | 281 | 247 | 217 | 188 | 166 | 146 | 128 | 111 | 95 | 81 | 69 | 58 |
| 120 | 331 | 292 | 259 | 224 | 197 | 173 | 152 | 134 | 116 | 101 | 87 | 74 | 63 | 53 |
| 130 | 305 | 271 | 240 | 209 | 184 | 161 | 141 | 124 | 108 | 94 | 80 | 69 | 59 | 49 |
| 140 | 284 | 252 | 224 | 195 | 171 | 149 | 131 | 115 | 101 | 88 | 75 | 64 | 55 | 45 |
| 150 | 266 | 238 | 211 | 184 | 160 | 141 | 123 | 108 | 95 | 82 | 71 | 60 | 51 | 42 |
| 160 | 250 | 225 | 200 | 175 | 152 | 133 | 117 | 102 | 90 | 78 | 67 | 57 | 48 | 40 |

### DIAMETER OF AVERAGE TREE AT BREASTHEIGHT

| Age (years) | Site index 80 | Site index 90 | Site index 100 | Site index 110 | Site index 120 | Site index 130 | Site index 140 | Site index 150 | Site index 160 | Site index 170 | Site index 180 | Site index 190 | Site index 200 | Site index 210 |
|---|---|---|---|---|---|---|---|---|---|---|---|---|---|---|
| | Inches | Inches | Inches | Inches | Inches | Inches | Inches | Inches | Inches | Inches | Inches | Inches | Inches | Inches |
| 20 | 1.3 | 1.5 | 1.8 | 2.2 | 2.6 | 3.0 | 3.4 | 3.8 | 4.2 | 4.5 | 4.9 | 5.3 | 5.7 | 6.2 |
| 30 | 2.6 | 3.0 | 3.4 | 3.9 | 4.4 | 4.9 | 5.5 | 6.0 | 6.5 | 7.0 | 7.6 | 8.3 | 9.0 | 9.8 |
| 40 | 3.8 | 4.4 | 4.9 | 5.5 | 6.1 | 6.8 | 7.4 | 8.0 | 8.7 | 9.4 | 10.2 | 11.2 | 12.2 | 13.3 |
| 50 | 4.9 | 5.6 | 6.3 | 7.0 | 7.7 | 8.5 | 9.3 | 10.1 | 10.9 | 11.8 | 12.8 | 14.0 | 15.3 | 16.7 |
| 60 | 6.0 | 6.8 | 7.6 | 8.5 | 9.3 | 10.2 | 11.1 | 12.0 | 12.9 | 14.0 | 15.2 | 16.6 | 18.2 | 19.9 |
| 70 | 7.0 | 7.9 | 8.8 | 9.8 | 10.8 | 11.8 | 12.8 | 13.8 | 14.8 | 16.0 | 17.5 | 19.1 | 20.9 | 22.8 |
| 80 | 7.9 | 8.9 | 9.9 | 10.9 | 12.0 | 13.1 | 14.3 | 15.4 | 16.6 | 17.9 | 19.6 | 21.4 | 23.3 | 25.5 |
| 90 | 8.7 | 9.7 | 10.8 | 11.9 | 13.1 | 14.3 | 15.6 | 16.9 | 18.2 | 19.6 | 21.4 | 23.3 | 25.6 | 28.0 |
| 100 | 9.4 | 10.5 | 11.6 | 12.7 | 14.2 | 15.5 | 16.9 | 18.2 | 19.7 | 21.6 | 24.1 | 25.1 | 27.6 | 30.1 |
| 110 | 10.1 | 11.3 | 12.4 | 13.7 | 15.2 | 16.6 | 18.0 | 19.5 | 21.0 | 22.6 | 24.6 | 26.9 | 29.4 | 32.2 |
| 120 | 10.7 | 11.9 | 13.2 | 14.6 | 16.1 | 17.6 | 19.1 | 20.7 | 22.3 | 24.0 | 26.1 | 28.5 | 31.1 | 34.2 |
| 130 | 11.3 | 12.5 | 13.9 | 15.3 | 16.9 | 18.5 | 20.1 | 21.7 | 23.5 | 25.3 | 27.5 | 30.0 | 32.7 | 36.0 |
| 140 | 11.9 | 13.1 | 14.5 | 16.0 | 17.7 | 19.4 | 21.1 | 22.8 | 24.5 | 26.5 | 28.8 | 31.4 | 34.8 | 37.8 |
| 150 | 12.4 | 13.7 | 15.1 | 16.7 | 18.4 | 20.2 | 22.0 | 23.8 | 25.6 | 27.7 | 30.0 | 32.8 | 35.8 | 39.4 |
| 160 | 12.9 | 14.2 | 15.7 | 17.4 | 19.1 | 21.0 | 22.8 | 24.7 | 26.6 | 28.9 | 31.2 | 34.1 | 37.2 | 41.0 |

# Table 5. Yields per Fully Stocked Acre, Total Stand * (Continued)

## TOTAL BASAL AREA

| Age | Sq. ft. | Sq. ft. | Sq. ft. | Sq. ft. | Sq. ft. | Sq. ft. | Sq. ft. | Sq. ft. | Sq. ft. | Sq. ft. | Sq. ft. | Sq. ft. | Sq. ft. | Sq. ft. |
|---|---|---|---|---|---|---|---|---|---|---|---|---|---|---|
| 20 | 64 | 70 | 76 | 81 | 86 | 89 | 92 | 95 | 97 | 98 | 99 | 100 | 101 | 102 |
| 30 | 96 | 105 | 114 | 122 | 129 | 135 | 140 | 144 | 147 | 150 | 152 | 153 | 154 | 155 |
| 40 | 121 | 132 | 143 | 153 | 162 | 170 | 177 | 182 | 186 | 189 | 191 | 193 | 195 | 196 |
| 50 | 140 | 153 | 165 | 177 | 187 | 196 | 204 | 210 | 214 | 217 | 220 | 222 | 224 | 226 |
| 60 | 154 | 169 | 182 | 195 | 207 | 217 | 226 | 232 | 237 | 241 | 244 | 246 | 248 | 250 |
| 70 | 166 | 183 | 197 | 211 | 224 | 235 | 244 | 251 | 256 | 260 | 264 | 266 | 268 | 270 |
| 80 | 177 | 194 | 210 | 224 | 238 | 249 | 259 | 266 | 271 | 276 | 280 | 283 | 285 | 287 |
| 90 | 185 | 204 | 220 | 235 | 249 | 262 | 272 | 279 | 285 | 290 | 294 | 297 | 299 | 301 |
| 100 | 193 | 212 | 229 | 245 | 260 | 273 | 283 | 291 | 297 | 302 | 306 | 309 | 312 | 314 |
| 110 | 200 | 220 | 238 | 254 | 269 | 282 | 293 | 301 | 307 | 313 | 317 | 320 | 323 | 325 |
| 120 | 206 | 226 | 245 | 261 | 277 | 290 | 301 | 310 | 316 | 322 | 326 | 329 | 332 | 335 |
| 130 | 213 | 233 | 251 | 268 | 284 | 298 | 309 | 318 | 325 | 331 | 335 | 338 | 341 | 344 |
| 140 | 218 | 238 | 257 | 275 | 291 | 305 | 317 | 326 | 333 | 338 | 343 | 347 | 350 | 353 |
| 150 | 223 | 243 | 263 | 281 | 298 | 312 | 324 | 333 | 340 | 346 | 351 | 354 | 357 | 360 |
| 160 | 227 | 248 | 268 | 287 | 304 | 318 | 331 | 340 | 347 | 353 | 357 | 361 | 364 | 367 |

## TOTAL YIELD IN CUBIC FEET **

| Age | Cu. ft. | Cu. ft. | Cu. ft. | Cu. ft. | Cu. ft. | Cu. ft. | Cu. ft. | Cu. ft. | Cu. ft. | Cu. ft. | Cu. ft. | Cu. ft. | Cu. ft. | Cu. ft. |
|---|---|---|---|---|---|---|---|---|---|---|---|---|---|---|
| 20 | 520 | 620 | 730 | 870 | 990 | 1,120 | 1,250 | 1,380 | 1,490 | 1,550 | 1,650 | 1,730 | 1,830 | 1,920 |
| 30 | 1,330 | 1,610 | 1,930 | 2,270 | 2,630 | 2,980 | 3,300 | 3,610 | 3,880 | 4,110 | 4,330 | 4,530 | 4,750 | 4,990 |
| 40 | 2,110 | 2,520 | 3,020 | 3,560 | 4,150 | 4,690 | 5,250 | 5,750 | 6,160 | 6,540 | 6,900 | 7,220 | 7,500 | 7,830 |
| 50 | 2,840 | 3,410 | 4,080 | 4,780 | 5,540 | 6,300 | 7,050 | 7,730 | 8,300 | 8,840 | 9,320 | 9,770 | 10,150 | 10,560 |
| 60 | 3,500 | 4,200 | 5,010 | 5,880 | 6,880 | 7,760 | 8,700 | 9,490 | 10,200 | 10,860 | 11,450 | 12,000 | 12,500 | 12,960 |
| 70 | 4,090 | 4,920 | 5,820 | 6,830 | 8,000 | 9,100 | 10,150 | 11,060 | 11,900 | 12,660 | 13,300 | 13,950 | 14,500 | 15,080 |
| 80 | 4,580 | 5,510 | 6,530 | 7,690 | 9,000 | 10,240 | 11,350 | 12,400 | 13,360 | 14,220 | 14,990 | 15,700 | 16,350 | 16,970 |
| 90 | 5,000 | 6,010 | 7,120 | 8,400 | 9,810 | 11,160 | 12,390 | 13,500 | 14,600 | 15,540 | 16,400 | 17,190 | 17,880 | 18,500 |
| 100 | 5,350 | 6,420 | 7,620 | 9,000 | 10,510 | 11,940 | 13,270 | 14,460 | 15,600 | 16,610 | 17,550 | 18,370 | 19,140 | 19,820 |
| 110 | 5,640 | 6,780 | 8,050 | 9,500 | 11,080 | 12,610 | 14,000 | 15,290 | 16,500 | 17,560 | 18,510 | 19,390 | 20,200 | 20,940 |
| 120 | 5,900 | 7,080 | 8,410 | 9,920 | 11,580 | 13,180 | 14,600 | 15,990 | 17,240 | 18,340 | 19,320 | 20,220 | 21,090 | 21,870 |
| 130 | 6,130 | 7,340 | 8,720 | 10,290 | 12,000 | 13,650 | 15,140 | 16,560 | 17,870 | 19,000 | 20,000 | 20,980 | 21,840 | 22,660 |
| 140 | 6,340 | 7,600 | 9,020 | 10,620 | 12,370 | 14,080 | 15,610 | 17,090 | 18,410 | 19,590 | 20,640 | 21,610 | 22,520 | 23,360 |
| 150 | 6,520 | 7,810 | 9,280 | 10,920 | 12,710 | 14,490 | 16,080 | 17,560 | 18,910 | 20,130 | 21,270 | 22,250 | 23,170 | 24,030 |
| 160 | 6,670 | 8,000 | 9,500 | 11,200 | 13,040 | 14,850 | 16,490 | 18,010 | 19,380 | 20,650 | 21,820 | 22,830 | 23,780 | 24,660 |

* All conifers (but not understory trees, if present) 1.5 in. in diameter and larger.

** Volume of entire stem including stump and top but excluding bark and limbs.

Source for Tables 5-7: R. E. McArdle, W. H. Meyer, and Donald Bruce, The yield of Douglas-fir in the Pacific Northwest, U. S. Dept. Agr., Tech. Bull. No. 201, 1949 (rev.).

## Table 6. Yields per Fully Stocked Acre, Trees 12 In. D.B.H. and Larger

Pacific Northwest

### NUMBER OF TREES

| Age (years) | Site Class V | | Site Class IV | | | Site Class III | | | Site Class II | | | Site Class I | | |
|---|---|---|---|---|---|---|---|---|---|---|---|---|---|---|
| | Site index 80 | Site index 90 | Site index 100 | Site index 110 | Site index 120 | Site index 130 | Site index 140 | Site index 150 | Site index 160 | Site index 170 | Site index 180 | Site index 190 | Site index 200 | Site index 210 |
| | Number | Number | Number | Number | Number | Number | Number | Number | Number | Number | Number | Number | Number | Number |
| 20 | 0 | 0 | 0 | 0 | 0 | 0 | 0 | 0 | 0 | 0 | 2 | 5 | 7 | 10 |
| 30 | 0 | 0 | 0 | 0 | 0 | 2 | 6 | 12 | 18 | 27 | 36 | 46 | 57 | 69 |
| 40 | 0 | 0 | 0 | 7 | 16 | 26 | 37 | 49 | 61 | 75 | 89 | 101 | 109 | 113 |
| 50 | 1 | 8 | 17 | 29 | 44 | 61 | 79 | 97 | 110 | 120 | 128 | 129 | 126 | 118 |
| 60 | 12 | 24 | 39 | 58 | 79 | 101 | 118 | 129 | 137 | 141 | 137 | 129 | 118 | 105 |
| 70 | 27 | 45 | 65 | 90 | 113 | 129 | 139 | 144 | 145 | 140 | 130 | 118 | 105 | 92 |
| 80 | 44 | 67 | 92 | 114 | 132 | 143 | 148 | 148 | 143 | 133 | 120 | 107 | 93 | 80 |
| 90 | 62 | 88 | 112 | 130 | 142 | 149 | 149 | 145 | 136 | 124 | 110 | 97 | 84 | 71 |
| 100 | 78 | 105 | 136 | 141 | 148 | 149 | 145 | 137 | 127 | 115 | 101 | 88 | 75 | 64 |
| 110 | 93 | 118 | 142 | 146 | 150 | 146 | 139 | 130 | 119 | 106 | 93 | 81 | 69 | 58 |
| 120 | 105 | 127 | 146 | 149 | 148 | 142 | 134 | 123 | 111 | 99 | 87 | 74 | 63 | 53 |
| 130 | 114 | 133 | 148 | 150 | 145 | 138 | 128 | 116 | 105 | 93 | 80 | 69 | 59 | 49 |
| 140 | 122 | 138 | 148 | 149 | 142 | 133 | 123 | 110 | 99 | 87 | 75 | 64 | 55 | 45 |
| 150 | 127 | 141 | 149 | 147 | 138 | 129 | 117 | 105 | 94 | 82 | 71 | 60 | 51 | 42 |
| 160 | 132 | 143 | 147 | 144 | 135 | 125 | 113 | 100 | 89 | 78 | 67 | 57 | 48 | 40 |

### DIAMETER OF AVERAGE TREE AT BREASTHEIGHT

| Age (years) | Site index 80 | Site index 90 | Site index 100 | Site index 110 | Site index 120 | Site index 130 | Site index 140 | Site index 150 | Site index 160 | Site index 170 | Site index 180 | Site index 190 | Site index 200 | Site index 210 |
|---|---|---|---|---|---|---|---|---|---|---|---|---|---|---|
| | Inches | Inches | Inches | Inches | Inches | Inches | Inches | Inches | Inches | Inches | Inches | Inches | Inches | Inches |
| 20 | 0 | 0 | 0 | 0 | 0 | 0 | 0 | 0 | 0 | 0 | 12.4 | 12.5 | 12.6 | 12.8 |
| 30 | 0 | 0 | 0 | 0 | 0 | 12.4 | 12.5 | 12.7 | 12.8 | 13.0 | 13.2 | 13.4 | 13.7 | 14.0 |
| 40 | 0 | 0 | 0 | 12.6 | 12.7 | 12.9 | 13.1 | 13.3 | 13.6 | 13.9 | 14.3 | 14.7 | 15.2 | 15.8 |
| 50 | 12.4 | 12.6 | 12.4 | 13.1 | 13.3 | 13.6 | 13.9 | 14.1 | 14.5 | 15.0 | 15.6 | 16.3 | 17.1 | 18.1 |
| 60 | 12.7 | 13.0 | 12.8 | 13.6 | 13.9 | 14.3 | 14.7 | 15.2 | 15.6 | 16.2 | 17.1 | 18.0 | 19.2 | 20.6 |
| 70 | 13.0 | 13.3 | 13.2 | 14.1 | 14.5 | 15.0 | 15.6 | 16.2 | 16.8 | 17.7 | 18.7 | 20.0 | 21.4 | 23.2 |
| 80 | 13.3 | 13.7 | 13.7 | 14.6 | 15.2 | 15.8 | 16.5 | 17.2 | 18.0 | 19.0 | 20.3 | 21.8 | 23.6 | 25.7 |
| 90 | 13.6 | 14.0 | 14.1 | 15.1 | 15.9 | 16.6 | 17.4 | 18.2 | 19.2 | 20.4 | 21.9 | 23.6 | 25.6 | 28.0 |
| 100 | 13.9 | 14.4 | 14.5 | 15.7 | 16.5 | 17.3 | 18.4 | 19.3 | 20.4 | 21.8 | 23.4 | 25.3 | 27.6 | 30.1 |
| 110 | 14.2 | 14.7 | 15.4 | 16.2 | 17.1 | 18.1 | 19.2 | 20.3 | 21.6 | 23.1 | 24.8 | 26.9 | 29.4 | 32.2 |
| 120 | 14.5 | 15.1 | 15.8 | 16.7 | 17.7 | 18.8 | 20.0 | 21.3 | 22.7 | 24.2 | 26.2 | 28.5 | 31.1 | 34.2 |
| 130 | 14.8 | 15.5 | 16.2 | 17.2 | 18.3 | 19.5 | 20.8 | 22.2 | 23.7 | 25.4 | 27.5 | 30.0 | 32.7 | 36.0 |
| 140 | 15.0 | 15.8 | 16.6 | 17.7 | 18.9 | 20.2 | 21.6 | 23.2 | 24.7 | 26.6 | 28.8 | 31.4 | 34.3 | 37.8 |
| 150 | 15.3 | 16.1 | 17.0 | 18.1 | 19.5 | 20.8 | 22.4 | 24.0 | 25.7 | 27.8 | 30.0 | 32.8 | 35.8 | 39.4 |
| 160 | 15.6 | 16.4 | 17.4 | 18.6 | 20.0 | 21.5 | 23.1 | 24.9 | 26.7 | 28.9 | 31.2 | 34.1 | 37.2 | 41.0 |

Source: Ibid.

## Table 6. Yields per Fully Stocked Acre, Trees 12 In. D.B.H. and Larger (Continued)

### BASAL AREA

| Age (years) | Site Class V | | Site Class IV | | | Site Class III | | | Site Class II | | | Site Class I | | |
|---|---|---|---|---|---|---|---|---|---|---|---|---|---|---|
| | Site index 80 | Site index 90 | Site index 100 | Site index 110 | Site index 120 | Site index 130 | Site index 140 | Site index 150 | Site index 160 | Site index 170 | Site index 180 | Site index 190 | Site index 200 | Site index 210 |
| | Sq. ft. | Sq. ft. | Sq. ft. | Sq. ft. | Sq. ft. | Sq. ft. | Sq. ft. | Sq. ft. | Sq. ft. | Sq. ft. | Sq. ft. | Sq. ft. | Sq. ft. | Sq. ft. |
| 20 | 0 | 0 | 0 | 0 | 0 | 0 | 0 | 0 | 0 | 0 | 2 | 4 | 6 | 9 |
| 30 | 0 | 0 | 0 | 0 | 0 | 1 | 6 | 10 | 16 | 24 | 33 | 44 | 58 | 74 |
| 40 | 0 | 0 | 2 | 7 | 14 | 23 | 34 | 48 | 62 | 80 | 100 | 120 | 139 | 155 |
| 50 | 1 | 7 | 15 | 27 | 42 | 61 | 83 | 106 | 127 | 149 | 170 | 187 | 200 | 211 |
| 60 | 11 | 21 | 37 | 59 | 84 | 113 | 140 | 164 | 183 | 202 | 217 | 229 | 238 | 244 |
| 70 | 25 | 44 | 67 | 98 | 130 | 160 | 186 | 207 | 224 | 238 | 249 | 257 | 264 | 268 |
| 80 | 42 | 69 | 100 | 133 | 166 | 197 | 220 | 238 | 251 | 263 | 272 | 278 | 283 | 287 |
| 90 | 62 | 95 | 129 | 162 | 196 | 224 | 245 | 261 | 273 | 283 | 289 | 294 | 298 | 301 |
| 100 | 82 | 119 | 155 | 188 | 219 | 244 | 264 | 279 | 289 | 297 | 303 | 308 | 311 | 314 |
| 110 | 102 | 140 | 176 | 208 | 238 | 262 | 280 | 293 | 302 | 309 | 314 | 319 | 323 | 325 |
| 120 | 120 | 158 | 194 | 225 | 253 | 276 | 293 | 305 | 313 | 319 | 324 | 329 | 332 | 335 |
| 130 | 136 | 173 | 209 | 239 | 266 | 287 | 304 | 314 | 322 | 329 | 334 | 338 | 341 | 344 |
| 140 | 150 | 187 | 221 | 251 | 277 | 297 | 313 | 323 | 331 | 337 | 343 | 347 | 350 | 353 |
| 150 | 163 | 199 | 233 | 261 | 286 | 306 | 320 | 330 | 339 | 346 | 351 | 354 | 357 | 360 |
| 160 | 175 | 210 | 242 | 271 | 295 | 313 | 328 | 338 | 346 | 353 | 357 | 361 | 364 | 367 |

### YIELD IN CUBIC FEET [a]

| Age (years) | Site Class V | | Site Class IV | | | Site Class III | | | Site Class II | | | Site Class I | | |
|---|---|---|---|---|---|---|---|---|---|---|---|---|---|---|
| | Site index 80 | Site index 90 | Site index 100 | Site index 110 | Site index 120 | Site index 130 | Site index 140 | Site index 150 | Site index 160 | Site index 170 | Site index 180 | Site index 190 | Site index 200 | Site index 210 |
| | Cu. ft. | Cu. ft. | Cu. ft. | Cu. ft. | Cu. ft. | Cu. ft. | Cu. ft. | Cu. ft. | Cu. ft. | Cu. ft. | Cu. ft. | Cu. ft. | Cu. ft. | Cu. ft. |
| 20 | 0 | 0 | 0 | 0 | 0 | 0 | 0 | 0 | 0 | 0 | 30 | 80 | 140 | 200 |
| 30 | 0 | 0 | 0 | 0 | 0 | 70 | 150 | 300 | 490 | 730 | 1,020 | 1,400 | 1,850 | 2,450 |
| 40 | 0 | 0 | 60 | 190 | 430 | 760 | 1,190 | 1,660 | 2,250 | 2,960 | 3,770 | 4,750 | 5,650 | 6,450 |
| 50 | 60 | 170 | 470 | 850 | 1,430 | 2,200 | 3,100 | 4,120 | 5,200 | 6,300 | 7,380 | 8,440 | 9,290 | 10,000 |
| 60 | 310 | 680 | 1,200 | 1,990 | 3,030 | 4,225 | 5,650 | 7,000 | 8,200 | 9,400 | 10,400 | 11,330 | 12,050 | 12,750 |
| 70 | 720 | 1,360 | 2,190 | 3,400 | 4,970 | 6,550 | 8,000 | 9,400 | 10,650 | 11,820 | 12,750 | 13,650 | 14,330 | 14,950 |
| 80 | 1,240 | 2,110 | 3,300 | 4,800 | 6,500 | 8,380 | 9,940 | 11,380 | 12,570 | 13,720 | 14,650 | 15,500 | 16,230 | 16,900 |
| 90 | 1,820 | 2,980 | 4,370 | 6,170 | 8,050 | 9,950 | 11,430 | 12,850 | 14,100 | 15,230 | 16,200 | 17,050 | 17,850 | 18,500 |
| 100 | 2,410 | 3,690 | 5,350 | 7,170 | 9,130 | 10,950 | 12,620 | 14,000 | 15,300 | 16,410 | 17,440 | 18,300 | 19,140 | 19,820 |
| 110 | 3,000 | 4,500 | 6,190 | 8,050 | 10,020 | 11,880 | 13,530 | 14,980 | 16,290 | 17,430 | 18,450 | 19,350 | 20,200 | 20,940 |
| 120 | 3,570 | 5,190 | 6,890 | 8,760 | 10,760 | 12,620 | 14,300 | 15,760 | 17,100 | 18,270 | 19,300 | 20,220 | 21,090 | 21,870 |
| 130 | 4,120 | 5,720 | 7,470 | 9,360 | 11,360 | 13,240 | 14,920 | 16,410 | 17,760 | 18,960 | 20,000 | 20,980 | 21,840 | 22,660 |
| 140 | 4,600 | 6,190 | 7,960 | 9,860 | 11,880 | 13,790 | 15,450 | 16,980 | 18,350 | 19,580 | 20,640 | 21,610 | 22,520 | 23,360 |
| 150 | 5,000 | 6,600 | 8,390 | 10,300 | 12,320 | 14,250 | 15,910 | 17,480 | 18,870 | 20,130 | 21,270 | 22,250 | 23,170 | 24,030 |
| 160 | 5,350 | 6,950 | 8,750 | 10,700 | 12,750 | 14,690 | 16,340 | 17,950 | 19,350 | 20,650 | 21,820 | 22,830 | 23,760 | 24,660 |

[a] Total cubic volume of trees above 12 in. d.b.h., including stump and top but excluding bark and limbs.

## Table 6. Yields per Fully Stocked Acre, Trees 12 In. D.B.H. and Larger (Continued)

### YIELD IN BOARD FEET, INTERNATIONAL RULE (⅛-INCH KERF) [b]

| | Bd. ft. | Bd. ft. | Bd. ft. | Bd. ft. | Bd. ft. | Bd. ft. | Bd. ft. | Bd. ft. | Bd. ft. | Bd. ft. | Bd. ft. | Bd. ft. | Bd. ft. | Bd. ft. |
|---|---|---|---|---|---|---|---|---|---|---|---|---|---|---|
| 30 | 0 | 0 | 0 | 0 | 0 | 0 | 0 | 1,200 | 2,300 | 4,400 | 6,700 | 9,100 | 12,500 | 16,400 |
| 40 | 0 | 0 | 0 | 900 | 2,400 | 4,300 | 7,200 | 10,500 | 14,300 | 19,300 | 24,400 | 31,000 | 37,500 | 43,600 |
| 50 | 0 | 800 | 2,500 | 5,400 | 9,000 | 13,800 | 19,800 | 26,600 | 33,900 | 41,900 | 49,600 | 57,600 | 64,600 | 71,100 |
| 60 | 1,800 | 4,200 | 7,800 | 12,800 | 19,300 | 27,400 | 37,400 | 46,500 | 55,500 | 64,200 | 72,600 | 81,000 | 88,400 | 95,000 |
| 70 | 4,400 | 8,600 | 14,500 | 22,100 | 32,600 | 43,300 | 54,100 | 64,200 | 74,000 | 83,600 | 92,500 | 100,900 | 108,400 | 115,000 |
| 80 | 7,600 | 14,200 | 21,800 | 31,800 | 44,600 | 56,800 | 68,800 | 79,700 | 90,000 | 99,900 | 109,200 | 117,000 | 124,700 | 131,000 |
| 90 | 11,200 | 19,200 | 28,900 | 40,200 | 54,600 | 67,800 | 81,000 | 92,400 | 103,500 | 113,500 | 122,800 | 130,800 | 137,700 | 144,000 |
| 100 | 15,200 | 24,800 | 35,400 | 48,000 | 63,100 | 77,000 | 90,700 | 102,900 | 114,400 | 124,200 | 133,400 | 141,500 | 148,900 | 155,400 |
| 110 | 19,600 | 29,600 | 41,500 | 55,000 | 70,200 | 85,100 | 98,900 | 111,300 | 123,000 | 133,000 | 142,000 | 150,100 | 157,900 | 164,900 |
| 120 | 23,800 | 34,000 | 47,000 | 60,800 | 76,300 | 91,900 | 105,600 | 118,400 | 130,000 | 140,500 | 149,400 | 157,500 | 165,500 | 172,700 |
| 130 | 27,200 | 38,000 | 51,400 | 65,800 | 81,600 | 97,400 | 111,300 | 124,400 | 136,000 | 146,500 | 155,700 | 164,000 | 172,000 | 179,500 |
| 140 | 30,400 | 41,700 | 55,100 | 70,000 | 86,300 | 102,300 | 116,500 | 129,700 | 141,300 | 152,000 | 161,300 | 169,900 | 178,000 | 185,400 |
| 150 | 33,200 | 45,000 | 58,600 | 74,000 | 90,900 | 106,600 | 121,000 | 134,300 | 146,300 | 156,700 | 166,500 | 175,300 | 183,300 | 190,900 |
| 160 | 35,900 | 48,100 | 61,900 | 77,600 | 94,500 | 110,400 | 125,000 | 138,700 | 150,200 | 161,100 | 171,400 | 180,300 | 188,100 | 196,000 |

### YIELD IN BOARD FEET, SCRIBNER RULE [c]

| | Bd. ft. | Bd. ft. | Bd. ft. | Bd. ft. | Bd. ft. | Bd. ft. | Bd. ft. | Bd. ft. | Bd. ft. | Bd. ft. | Bd. ft. | Bd. ft. | Bd. ft. | Bd. ft. |
|---|---|---|---|---|---|---|---|---|---|---|---|---|---|---|
| 30 | 0 | 0 | 0 | 0 | 0 | 0 | 300 | 900 | 1,500 | 2,600 | 4,000 | 6,000 | 8,000 | 10,500 |
| 40 | 0 | 0 | 0 | 200 | 1,200 | 2,600 | 4,500 | 6,500 | 9,000 | 11,900 | 15,500 | 19,600 | 24,400 | 29,400 |
| 50 | 30 | 200 | 1,600 | 3,300 | 5,500 | 8,400 | 12,400 | 17,000 | 22,200 | 27,400 | 32,700 | 38,400 | 44,100 | 50,000 |
| 60 | 1,100 | 2,600 | 4,800 | 8,100 | 12,500 | 18,000 | 23,800 | 29,600 | 36,200 | 42,800 | 49,300 | 55,900 | 62,000 | 68,300 |
| 70 | 2,400 | 5,300 | 9,000 | 14,000 | 20,600 | 27,000 | 35,200 | 42,500 | 50,100 | 57,200 | 64,400 | 71,500 | 78,200 | 85,000 |
| 80 | 4,400 | 8,000 | 13,900 | 20,100 | 28,600 | 37,000 | 45,700 | 54,300 | 62,100 | 70,000 | 78,000 | 85,400 | 92,500 | 99,800 |
| 90 | 6,900 | 12,000 | 18,600 | 26,000 | 35,700 | 45,200 | 55,000 | 64,000 | 72,900 | 81,200 | 89,200 | 97,100 | 104,800 | 112,300 |
| 100 | 9,600 | 15,400 | 22,800 | 31,400 | 42,000 | 52,400 | 62,800 | 72,400 | 81,800 | 90,400 | 98,900 | 107,100 | 115,100 | 122,900 |
| 110 | 12,400 | 18,900 | 26,700 | 36,300 | 47,500 | 58,500 | 69,400 | 79,800 | 89,200 | 98,300 | 107,000 | 115,200 | 123,700 | 131,200 |
| 120 | 14,700 | 21,800 | 30,400 | 40,700 | 52,400 | 63,900 | 75,000 | 85,500 | 95,500 | 105,100 | 114,100 | 122,500 | 131,100 | 139,000 |
| 130 | 17,100 | 24,600 | 33,800 | 44,700 | 56,700 | 68,600 | 80,000 | 91,000 | 101,100 | 111,000 | 120,000 | 128,900 | 137,700 | 146,100 |
| 140 | 19,200 | 27,200 | 36,700 | 48,300 | 60,600 | 72,900 | 84,500 | 95,900 | 106,200 | 116,300 | 125,300 | 134,500 | 143,500 | 152,000 |
| 150 | 21,300 | 29,600 | 39,700 | 51,600 | 64,000 | 76,600 | 88,600 | 100,300 | 111,000 | 121,200 | 130,700 | 139,500 | 148,700 | 157,200 |
| 160 | 23,300 | 31,900 | 42,200 | 54,600 | 67,100 | 80,100 | 92,400 | 104,400 | 115,400 | 125,700 | 135,400 | 144,400 | 153,500 | 162,000 |

b To minimum top d.i.b. of 5 in.
c To minimum top d.i.b. of 8 in., and for scaling in 16-ft. logs.

# DOUGLAS-FIR

## Table 7. Stand Table, per Acre
### Pacific Northwest

### SITE I

| 2-inch-diameter class | Number of trees by age classes | | | | | | | |
|---|---|---|---|---|---|---|---|---|
| | 20 years | 40 years | 60 years | 80 years | 100 years | 120 years | 140 years | 160 years |
| 2–3 | 131 | | | | | | | |
| 4–5 | 223 | 8 | | | | | | |
| 6–7 | 157 | 27 | | | | | | |
| 8–9 | 60 | 42 | 7 | | | | | |
| 10–11 | | 48 | 12 | 3 | | | | |
| 12–13 | | 43 | 16 | 4 | 2 | | | |
| 14–15 | | 36 | 18 | 8 | 2 | 2 | | |
| 16–17 | | 20 | 18 | 9 | 5 | 2 | 1 | |
| 18–19 | | 11 | 19 | 10 | 6 | 3 | 2 | |
| 20–21 | | 5 | 16 | 11 | 6 | 4 | 2 | |
| 22–23 | | | 13 | 10 | 7 | 4 | 3 | |
| 24–25 | | | 9 | 10 | 7 | 5 | 4 | |
| 26–27 | | | 5 | 9 | 6 | 6 | 4 | |
| 28–29 | | | 5 | 8 | 7 | 5 | 4 | |
| 30–31 | | | | 6 | 7 | 5 | 4 | |
| 32–33 | | | | 4 | 6 | 5 | 4 | |
| 34–35 | | | | 3 | 4 | 5 | 5 | |
| 36–37 | | | | 2 | 4 | 5 | 4 | |
| 38–39 | | | | | 2 | 4 | 4 | |
| 40–41 | | | | | 2 | 3 | 4 | |
| 42–43 | | | | | 2 | 2 | 3 | |
| 44–45 | | | | | | 1 | 2 | |
| 46–47 | | | | | | 1 | 2 | |
| 48–49 | | | | | | 1 | 1 | |
| 50–51 | | | | | | | 1 | |
| Over 50 | | | | | | | 1 | |
| Total | 571 | 240 | 138 | 97 | 75 | 63 | 55 | |

### SITE II

| 2-inch-diameter class | Number of trees by age classes | | | | | | | |
|---|---|---|---|---|---|---|---|---|
| | 20 years | 40 years | 60 years | 80 years | 100 years | 120 years | 140 years | 160 years |
| 2–3 | 398 | 9 | | | | | | |
| 4–5 | 363 | 60 | 3 | | | | | |
| 6–7 | 119 | 89 | 13 | 3 | | | | |
| 8–9 | | 90 | 33 | 6 | 3 | | | |
| 10–11 | | 77 | 35 | 16 | 4 | 3 | | |
| 12–13 | | 41 | 38 | 20 | 10 | 4 | | 2 |
| 14–15 | | 19 | 38 | 22 | 13 | 7 | 3 | 2 |
| 16–17 | | | 30 | 21 | 13 | 9 | 6 | 3 |
| 18–19 | | | 20 | 20 | 14 | 10 | 8 | 5 |
| 20–21 | | | 10 | 19 | 15 | 10 | 8 | 6 |
| 22–23 | | | 8 | 14 | 13 | 11 | 8 | 7 |
| 24–25 | | | | 8 | 13 | 11 | 9 | 7 |
| 26–27 | | | | 5 | 10 | 9 | 8 | 7 |
| 28–29 | | | | 5 | 6 | 9 | 8 | 7 |
| 30–31 | | | | | 4 | 6 | 7 | 6 |
| 32–33 | | | | | 3 | 5 | 7 | 6 |
| 34–35 | | | | | 2 | 3 | 4 | 6 |
| 36–37 | | | | | | 2 | 3 | 5 |
| 38–39 | | | | | | 2 | 3 | 3 |
| 40–41 | | | | | | | 2 | 2 |
| 42–43 | | | | | | | | 2 |
| 44–45 | | | | | | | | 2 |
| Total | 880 | 385 | 228 | 159 | 123 | 101 | 88 | 78 |

## Table 7. Stand Table, per Acre (Continued)

### SITE III

| 2-inch-diameter class | Number of trees by age classes | | | | | | | |
|---|---|---|---|---|---|---|---|---|
| | 20 years | 40 years | 60 years | 80 years | 100 years | 120 years | 140 years | 160 years |
| 2-3 | | 52 | | | | | | |
| 4-5 | | 159 | 22 | | | | | |
| 6-7 | | 175 | 54 | 14 | | | | |
| 8-9 | | 129 | 67 | 29 | 15 | 6 | 3 | |
| 10-11 | | 54 | 73 | 35 | 21 | 10 | 5 | 5 |
| 12-13 | | 16 | 55 | 39 | 24 | 16 | 10 | 6 |
| 14-15 | | | 39 | 37 | 26 | 19 | 14 | 9 |
| 16-17 | | | 18 | 32 | 26 | 19 | 14 | 12 |
| 18-19 | | | 9 | 22 | 23 | 20 | 16 | 12 |
| 20-21 | | | | 14 | 21 | 18 | 16 | 13 |
| 22-23 | | | | 10 | 13 | 15 | 14 | 13 |
| 24-25 | | | | | 8 | 13 | 13 | 12 |
| 26-27 | | | | | 7 | 7 | 10 | 11 |
| 28-29 | | | | | | 5 | 6 | 9 |
| 30-31 | | | | | | 4 | 5 | 6 |
| 32-33 | | | | | | | 5 | 4 |
| 34-35 | | | | | | | | 3 |
| 36-37 | | | | | | | | 2 |
| Total | | 585 | 337 | 232 | 184 | 152 | 131 | 117 |

### SITE IV

| 2-inch-diameter class | 20 years | 40 years | 60 years | 80 years | 100 years | 120 years | 140 years | 160 years |
|---|---|---|---|---|---|---|---|---|
| 2-3 | | 261 | 22 | | | | | |
| 4-5 | | 353 | 103 | 25 | | | | |
| 6-7 | | 234 | 129 | 58 | 33 | 13 | 7 | 3 |
| 8-9 | | 79 | 121 | 57 | 44 | 27 | 14 | 9 |
| 10-11 | | | 83 | 85 | 46 | 32 | 25 | 19 |
| 12-13 | | | 32 | 61 | 49 | 38 | 27 | 22 |
| 14-15 | | | 10 | 36 | 45 | 36 | 30 | 24 |
| 16-17 | | | | 16 | 27 | 30 | 28 | 24 |
| 18-19 | | | | 7 | 16 | 23 | 25 | 22 |
| 20-21 | | | | | 11 | 14 | 18 | 21 |
| 22-23 | | | | | | 7 | 10 | 13 |
| 24-25 | | | | | | 4 | 7 | 9 |
| 26-27 | | | | | | | 4 | 5 |
| 28-29 | | | | | | | | 4 |
| Total | | 927 | 500 | 345 | 271 | 224 | 195 | 175 |

### SITE V

| 2-inch-diameter class | 20 years | 40 years | 60 years | 80 years | 100 years | 120 years | 140 years | 160 years |
|---|---|---|---|---|---|---|---|---|
| 2-3 | | | 148 | 15 | 8 | | | |
| 4-5 | | | 305 | 90 | 57 | 26 | 11 | 6 |
| 6-7 | | | 214 | 125 | 92 | 57 | 37 | 21 |
| 8-9 | | | 91 | 132 | 97 | 69 | 51 | 41 |
| 10-11 | | | 22 | 100 | 85 | 73 | 57 | 45 |
| 12-13 | | | | 45 | 42 | 56 | 50 | 43 |
| 14-15 | | | | 18 | 22 | 32 | 43 | 42 |
| 16-17 | | | | | | 18 | 19 | 26 |
| 18-19 | | | | | | | 16 | 15 |
| 20-21 | | | | | | | | 11 |
| Total | | | 780 | 525 | 403 | 331 | 284 | 250 |

Source: *Ibid.*

## DOUGLAS-FIR

### Table 8. Yield of a Fully Stocked Acre, in Board Feet, International Rule (¼-Inch Kerf)

Pacific Northwest

| Age (yr.) | Site class V | | Site class IV | | | Site class III | | | Site class II | | | Site class I | | |
|---|---|---|---|---|---|---|---|---|---|---|---|---|---|---|
| | Site index 80 | Site index 90 | Site index 100 | Site index 110 | Site index 120 | Site index 130 | Site index 140 | Site index 150 | Site index 160 | Site index 170 | Site index 180 | Site index 190 | Site index 200 | Site index 210 |
| 30 | | | | | | | 400 | 1,100 | 1,800 | 3,100 | 4,800 | 7,100 | 9,500 | 12,400 |
| 40 | | | | 200 | 1,400 | 3,100 | 5,400 | 7,700 | 10,600 | 14,000 | 18,200 | 22,900 | 28,300 | 33,800 |
| 50 | 40 | 200 | 1,900 | 3,900 | 6,500 | 9,900 | 14,600 | 20,000 | 26,000 | 31,800 | 37,700 | 43,900 | 50,100 | 56,400 |
| 60 | 1,300 | 3,100 | 5,700 | 9,600 | 14,700 | 21,100 | 27,800 | 34,300 | 41,700 | 49,000 | 56,000 | 63,100 | 69,300 | 75,700 |
| 70 | 2,900 | 6,300 | 10,600 | 16,500 | 24,100 | 32,400 | 40,600 | 48,700 | 57,000 | 64,600 | 72,500 | 79,600 | 86,400 | 93,300 |
| 80 | 5,200 | 10,200 | 16,300 | 23,500 | 33,100 | 42,600 | 52,200 | 61,600 | 70,000 | 78,400 | 86,700 | 94,200 | 101,500 | 108,600 |
| 90 | 8,200 | 14,100 | 21,800 | 30,200 | 41,000 | 51,600 | 62,300 | 72,100 | 81,500 | 89,900 | 98,400 | 106,600 | 114,100 | 121,400 |
| 100 | 11,300 | 18,000 | 26,500 | 36,200 | 48,000 | 59,400 | 70,600 | 80,900 | 90,800 | 99,800 | 108,500 | 116,700 | 124,500 | 132,100 |
| 110 | 14,300 | 22,000 | 30,900 | 41,600 | 54,000 | 65,900 | 77,600 | 88,200 | 98,500 | 107,900 | 116,800 | 124,900 | 133,200 | 140,300 |
| 120 | 17,200 | 25,300 | 35,000 | 46,400 | 59,200 | 71,600 | 83,500 | 94,600 | 105,000 | 115,000 | 124,000 | 132,200 | 140,500 | 147,900 |
| 130 | 19,800 | 28,400 | 38,700 | 50,700 | 63,800 | 76,700 | 88,600 | 100,300 | 110,800 | 121,000 | 129,800 | 138,600 | 147,100 | 154,900 |
| 140 | 22,300 | 31,300 | 42,000 | 54,600 | 67,900 | 81,100 | 93,300 | 105,300 | 116,000 | 126,200 | 135,300 | 144,000 | 152,700 | 160,800 |
| 150 | 24,700 | 33,900 | 45,100 | 58,200 | 71,400 | 84,900 | 97,500 | 109,800 | 120,800 | 131,000 | 140,500 | 149,000 | 157,800 | 166,000 |
| 160 | 26,900 | 36,500 | 47,800 | 61,300 | 74,700 | 88,500 | 101,500 | 113,900 | 125,200 | 135,500 | 145,000 | 153,600 | 162,400 | 170,100 |

Source: P. A. Briegleb, The yield of Douglas-fir in the Pacific Northwest measured by International ¼-Inch Kerf Log Rule, Pacific Northwest Forest & Range Exp. Sta., *Res. Note No. 46*, 1948. (Derived by adjustment of Scribner volumes by R. E. McArdle and W. H. Meyer, The yield of Douglas Fir in the Pacific Northwest, U. S. Dept. Agr., *Tech. Bull. No. 201*, 1930.)

# DOUGLAS-FIR

## Table. 9. Revised Yields per Acre, Fully Stocked Stands, by Average Diameter of Stand, Instead of by Site and Age

### Pacific Northwest

| Average d.b.h.[a] of stand (in.) | Normal number[b] of trees per acre | Normal height of trees of average d.b.h. (ft.) | Volume per tree (cu. ft.) | | | | Volume per tree, 12 in. d.b.h. and over (bd. ft.) | |
|---|---|---|---|---|---|---|---|---|
| | | | Total stand[b] and entire stand | 5 in. d.b.h. and over to 4-in. top | 7 in. d.b.h. and over to 4-in. top | 12 in. d.b.h. and over to 4-in. top | International ⅛-in. Rule[c] | Scribner Rule[d] |
| 2 | 4,466 | 22 | | | | | | |
| 3 | 2,387 | 31 | | | | | | |
| 4 | 1,530 | 39 | 1.8 | 0.9 | 0.2 | | | |
| 5 | 1,084 | 47 | 3.2 | 2.1 | 1.1 | | | |
| 6 | 818 | 55 | 5.1 | 3.8 | 2.6 | 0.3 | | |
| 7 | 644 | 62 | 7.6 | 6.2 | 4.9 | 1.1 | 5 | 3 |
| 8 | 524 | 69 | 10.9 | 9.4 | 8.0 | 2.5 | 18 | 11 |
| 9 | 437 | 76 | 14.9 | 13.4 | 12.1 | 5.3 | 35 | 23 |
| 10 | 371 | 83 | 19.6 | 18.0 | 16.7 | 9.5 | 66 | 43 |
| 11 | 320 | 90 | 25.2 | 23.6 | 22.7 | 15.1 | 102 | 67 |
| 12 | 280 | 97 | 31.5 | 29.8 | 29.3 | 21.7 | 148 | 99 |
| 13 | 248 | 104 | 38.5 | 36.6 | 36.5 | 29.5 | 224 | 149 |
| 14 | 221 | 110 | 46.6 | 44.3 | 44.3 | 38.3 | 274 | 184 |
| 15 | 198 | 117 | 55.5 | 52.8 | 52.8 | 48.0 | 347 | 236 |
| 16 | 180 | 123 | 65 | 62 | 62 | 58 | 432 | 296 |
| 17 | 164 | 130 | 76 | 72 | 72 | 69 | 521 | 359 |
| 18 | 150 | 135 | 87 | 83 | 83 | 81 | 618 | 429 |
| 19 | 138 | 141 | 99 | 95 | 95 | 93 | 724 | 510 |
| 20 | 127 | 147 | 112 | 108 | 108 | 106 | 836 | 593 |
| 21 | 118 | 152 | 126 | 121 | 121 | 119 | 956 | 683 |
| 22 | 110 | 157 | 142 | 136 | 136 | 134 | 1,075 | 779 |
| 23 | 102 | 162 | 158 | 152 | 152 | 150 | 1,205 | 886 |
| 24 | 96 | 167 | 175 | 169 | 169 | 168 | 1,339 | 999 |
| 25 | 91 | 171 | 193 | 186 | 186 | 185 | 1,485 | 1,125 |
| 26 | 85 | 176 | 213 | 205 | 205 | 204 | 1,653 | 1,262 |
| 27 | 80 | 180 | 234 | 227 | 227 | 227 | 1,826 | 1,405 |
| 28 | 76 | 185 | 256 | 249 | 249 | 249 | 2,031 | 1,562 |
| 29 | 72 | 189 | 279 | 271 | 271 | 271 | 2,249 | 1,730 |
| 30 | 68 | 194 | 302 | 293 | 293 | 293 | 2,476 | 1,905 |

Cubic foot volumes exclude bark. Board foot volumes in tens.

a Weighted by basal area.
b Total stand; i e., trees over 1.5 in. in d.b.h.
c To 5-in. top.
d To 8-in. top.
Source: R. E. McArdle, W. H. Meyer, and Donald Bruce. The yield of Douglas-fir in the Pacific Northwest, U. S. Dept. Agr., *Tech. Bull. No. 201*, 1949 (rev.).

**Supplemental information concerning Table 9.** Yield tables based on average diameter, instead of age, are considered a promising tool in forest management.

The reader is urged to refer to Bruce's exposition in the indicated bulletin supplement for a full explanation of the use of average diameter as a basis for yield tables and an explanation of the use of this table. Bruce concludes his write-up with the following: "This is not an argument for the complete abandonment of the conventional form of yield table. Such tables are useful for making general determinations of the growth capacity of forest land as distinct from the growing stock that happens to be thereon. Most of the problems of forest management, however, are concerned with actual growing stock that is seldom normal. For these problems the new tables seem to have decided advantages. Their limitations can be determined only by further testing."

## BALSAM FIR

### Table 10. Yields per Fully Stocked Acre, Trees 7 In. D.B.H. and Larger *
#### Northeastern United States, Volume in Board Feet

| Total age (yr.) | Site index | | | |
|---|---|---|---|---|
| | 70 | 60 | 50 | 40 |
| 40 | 5,850 | 4,150 | 2,430 | 720 |
| 50 | 18,500 | 13,150 | 7,700 | 2,280 |
| 60 | 31,000 | 22,000 | 12,900 | 3,820 |
| 70 | 40,900 | 29,100 | 17,000 | 5,040 |
| 80 | 48,200 | 34,200 | 20,000 | 5,930 |
| 90 | 53,800 | 38,200 | 22,400 | 6,620 |

* International ⅛-Inch Rule.

Source: W. H. Meyer, Yields of second-growth spruce and fir in the Northeast, U. S. Dept. Agr., *Tech. Bull. No. 142, 1929.*

## RED FIR

### Table 11. Yield Tables for Fully Stocked Acre, All Trees
#### California, Site Index 40 Ft. at 50 Yr.

| Age (yr.) | Height of average tree (ft.) | Mean d.b.h. (in.) | Total number of trees per acre | Total basal area per acre (sq. ft.) | Volume per acre (cu. ft.) | Average annual growth (cu. ft.) |
|---|---|---|---|---|---|---|
| 30 | 13 | 1.7 | 3,240 | 125 | 1,000 | 34 |
| 40 | 18 | 2.5 | 2,510 | 195 | 2,050 | 51 |
| 50 | 24 | 3.6 | 1,990 | 248 | 3,200 | 64 |
| 60 | 31 | 4.7 | 1,580 | 289 | 4,350 | 73 |
| 70 | 38 | 6.1 | 1,250 | 323 | 5,700 | 81 |
| 80 | 47 | 7.7 | 990 | 352 | 7,200 | 90 |
| 90 | 56 | 9.4 | 762 | 378 | 8,800 | 98 |
| 100 | 67 | 11.1 | 580 | 400 | 10,550 | 106 |
| 110 | 77 | 12.8 | 442 | 422 | 12,700 | 115 |
| 120 | 87 | 14.4 | 350 | 440 | 15,100 | 126 |
| 130 | 96 | 16.0 | 289 | 455 | 17,150 | 132 |
| 140 | 103 | 17.4 | 246 | 469 | 18,950 | 135 |
| 150 | 109 | 18.6 | 211 | 481 | 20,100 | 134 |
| 160 | 114 | 19.6 | 185 | 490 | 21,000 | 131 |

Cubic foot volumes are inside bark.

## RED FIR

### Table 12. Yield Tables for Fully Stocked Acre, Trees 8 In. and Over
#### California, Site Index 40 Ft. at 50 Yr.

| Age (yr.) | Number of trees per acre | Volume per acre (bd. ft.) | Average annual growth (bd. ft.) | Logs per M. bd. ft. |
|---|---|---|---|---|
| 40 | 25 | 1,030 | 26 | 42 |
| 50 | 135 | 6,050 | 121 | 42 |
| 60 | 253 | 14,400 | 240 | 41 |
| 70 | 388 | 25,000 | 357 | 40 |
| 80 | 447 | 37,100 | 473 | 35 |
| 90 | 430 | 50,200 | 588 | 26 |
| 100 | 368 | 65,700 | 695 | 21 |
| 110 | 303 | 84,000 | 793 | 16 |
| 120 | 256 | 104,500 | 871 | 13 |
| 130 | 226 | 122,000 | 938 | 10 |
| 140 | 196 | 136,000 | 971 | 9 |
| 150 | 172 | 145,000 | 967 | 8 |
| 160 | 154 | 151,000 | 944 | 7 |

Board foot volumes are by International ⅛ in. rule.
Source for Tables 11 and 12: F. X. Schumacher, Yield, stand, and volume tables for red fir in California, Calif. Agr. Exp. Sta., *Bull. No. 456,* 1928.

# SWEETGUM (SECOND GROWTH)

## Table 13. Yields per Fully Stocked Acre

### Alluvial Lands, S. C. to La. and Ark.

| Age at breast-height (yr.) | Average height of dominant trees (ft.) | Merchantable trees (number) | Average d.b.h. of merchantable trees (in.) | Basal area of merchantable trees (sq. ft.) | Merchantable volume in board feet per acre | | | | | | | | | |
|---|---|---|---|---|---|---|---|---|---|---|---|---|---|---|
| | | | | | Scribner Log Rule [a] | | | | | Doyle Log Rule [a] | | | | |
| | | | | | Grade 1 | Grade 2 | Grade 3 | Grade 4 | Total [b] | Grade 1 | Grade 2 | Grade 3 | Grade 4 | Total |
| | | | | | MEDIUM SITE—(SITE INDEX 100) [b] | | | | | | | | | |
| 40 | 89 | 44 | 14.8 | 58 | | 370 | 1,700 | 2,190 | 4,260 | | 310 | 1,080 | 1,550 | 2,940 |
| 50 | 100 | 64 | 15.4 | 91 | 260 | 1,510 | 2,720 | 3,690 | 8,180 | 220 | 1,390 | 1,960 | 2,750 | 6,320 |
| 60 | 108 | 76 | 16.1 | 115 | 880 | 3,040 | 3,450 | 5,030 | 12,400 | 840 | 2,540 | 2,600 | 3,900 | 9,880 |
| 70 | 115 | 86 | 17.0 | 133 | 1,750 | 4,530 | 3,970 | 6,260 | 16,510 | 1,630 | 3,840 | 3,060 | 4,960 | 13,490 |
| 80 | 122 | 93 | 17.8 | 146 | 2,720 | 5,930 | 4,370 | 7,440 | 20,460 | 2,490 | 4,980 | 3,420 | 5,970 | 16,860 |
| 90 | 127 | 97 | 18.6 | 156 | 3,700 | 7,240 | 4,680 | 8,500 | 24,120 | 3,340 | 5,960 | 3,700 | 6,920 | 19,920 |
| 100 | 131 | 99 | 19.3 | 163 | 4,610 | 8,390 | 4,940 | 9,420 | 27,360 | 4,180 | 6,860 | 3,930 | 7,820 | 22,790 |

[a] Grades are defined as follows. (A sound log has at least ⅔ its volume in sound material.)
Grade 1. A sound log at least 12 ft. long and 16 in. in d.i.b. at the small end, from which at least 70 percent of the volume can be cut into number 1 common lumber or better (either sap gum or sweetgum).
Grade 2. A sound log at least 12 ft. long and 12 in. in d.i.b. at the small end, from which 35 to 69 percent of the volume can be cut into number 1 common lumber or better (either sap gum or sweetgum).
Grade 3. A sound log at least 12 ft. long and 9 in. in d.i.b. at the small end, which cannot be classified as grade 2 because of either size or sweep. A log of this grade is especially suitable for the production of barrel staves and small dimension stock.
Grade 4. A sound log at least 12 ft. long and 10 in. in d.i.b. at the small end, which cannot be classified as grade 3 or better because of size or quality. At least 50 percent of its volume must be suitable for ties, timbers, or rough structural material. Logs of this grade are usually rough and knotty, and may be of any diameter above the minimum specified.

[b] Total height, in feet, of dominant and codominant trees at 50 yr.

Source: R. K. Winters and J. G. Osborne, Growth and yield of second-growth red gum in fully stocked stands on alluvial lands in the South, Southern Forest Exp. Sta., Occ. Paper No. 54, 1935.

## HARDWOODS

### Table 14. Yields of Better Stocked Stands

Central New England

(All trees 2 in. and over
in diameter)

| Age in years | Trees per acre | Basal area sq. feet | Height in feet | D.B.H. in inches | Volume per acre cubic feet | Volume per acre cords | Forest form factor |
|---|---|---|---|---|---|---|---|
| 25 | 1360 | 59.8 | 27.8 | 2.84 | 982 | 14.65 | .593 |
| 30 | 1235 | 77.9 | 31.8 | 3.40 | 1380 | 20.40 | .557 |
| 35 | 1125 | 91.1 | 34.8 | 3.86 | 1798 | 25.48 | .567 |
| 40 | 1030 | 101.6 | 37.4 | 4.25 | 2180 | 29.53 | .574 |
| 45 | 940 | 110.3 | 39.8 | 4.66 | 2534 | 33.04 | .577 |
| 50 | 855 | 117.9 | 41.5 | 4.94 | 2828 | 35.98 | .580 |
| 55 | 775 | 124.6 | 42.8 | 5.43 | 3118 | 38.55 | .584 |
| 60 | 700 | 130.7 | 44.2 | 5.85 | 3375 | 41.08 | .584 |
| 65 | 630 | 136.6 | 45.3 | 6.31 | 3638 | 43.42 | .587 |
| 70 | 565 | 142.2 | 46.3 | 6.79 | 3895 | 45.61 | .592 |
| 75 | 500 | 147.7 | 47.0 | 7.36 | 4146 | 47.75 | .598 |
| 80 | 440 | 153.0 | 47.6 | 7.98 | 4390 | 49.80 | .601 |

(All trees 7 in. and over
in diameter)

| Age in years | Trees per acre | Basal area sq. ft. | Height in feet | D.B.H. in inches | Volume per acre cu. ft. | Volume per acre cords | Volume per acre board feet | additional cords | Forest form factor |
|---|---|---|---|---|---|---|---|---|---|
| 35 | 56 | 16.0 | 49.4 | 7.25 | 530 | 6.7 | 800 | 4.7 | .671 |
| 40 | 104 | 35.0 | 54.5 | 7.85 | 1010 | 14.0 | 1,920 | 9.1 | .529 |
| 45 | 133 | 51.3 | 56.7 | 8.41 | 1460 | 19.7 | 3,250 | 11.4 | .502 |
| 50 | 157 | 66.0 | 59.4 | 8.78 | 1870 | 24.6 | 4,780 | 12.3 | .477 |
| 55 | 175 | 79.9 | 61.6 | 9.15 | 2250 | 29.1 | 6,600 | 12.2 | .459 |
| 60 | 188 | 92.8 | 63.2 | 9.51 | 2620 | 32.8 | 8,660 | 10.2 | .447 |
| 65 | 197 | 105.7 | 64.4 | 9.90 | 2970 | 36.4 | 10,850 | 8.6 | .437 |
| 70 | 203 | 117.9 | 65.4 | 10.32 | 3310 | 39.7 | 12,710 | 7.1 | .429 |
| 75 | 206 | 130.0 | 66.2 | 10.75 | 3660 | 42.7 | 14,220 | 6.2 | .425 |
| 80 | 207 | 141.8 | 66.8 | 11.21 | 4020 | 46.0 | 15,380 | 6.1 | .424 |

Board foot volumes are by Clark's International Rule.

Source: J. Nelson Spaeth, Growth study and normal yield tables for second-growth hardwood stands in central New England, *Harvard Forest Bull. No 2,* 1920.

## NORTHERN HARDWOODS

### Table 15. Yields Per Acre of Well-Stocked Stands, by Main-Stand Age
Lake States. Typical areas: Upper Peninsula Mich. and parts western Wis.

| Main-stand [a] age (yr.) | Average main-stand diam. (in.) | No. of trees per acre | Basal area per acre (sq. ft.) | Volume per acre | | | |
|---|---|---|---|---|---|---|---|
| | | | | Saw timber (bd. ft.) | | Total volume | |
| | | | | Scrib. | Int. ¼″ | Cu. ft. | Cords |
| | | | Medium Site | | | | |
| 40 | 5.6 | 480 | 82 | 300 | 400 | 740 | 13 |
| 60 | 7.8 | 295 | 97 | 1,600 | 2,000 | 1,350 | 24 |
| 80 | 9.5 | 220 | 109 | 3,500 | 4,250 | 1,930 | 33 |
| 100 | 10.9 | 185 | 119 | 5,350 | 6,400 | 2,450 | 41 |
| 120 | 12.2 | 155 | 128 | 7,200 | 8,450 | 2,890 | 48 |
| 140 | 13.5 | 135 | 136 | 8,850 | 10,200 | 3,270 | 53 |
| 160 | 14.8 | 120 | 143 | 10,300 | 11,700 | 3,580 | 58 |
| 180 | 16.1 | 105 | 149 | 11,500 | 12,950 | 3,830 | 61 |
| 200 | 17.4 | 95 | 155 | 12,600 | 14,000 | 4,050 | 63 |
| 220 | 18.7 | 85 | 159 | 13,450 | 14,900 | 4,230 | 65 |
| 240 | 20.0 | 75 | 163 | 14,200 | 15,600 | 4,380 | 67 |

[a] Main-stand age may be determined with sufficient accuracy by averaging the ages of trees of the following diameter classes within each size class:

| Size class (in.) | Key diameter classes (in.) |
|---|---|
| 1–5 (small poles) | 2, 4 |
| 3–9 (cordwood) | 6, 8 |
| 9–15 (second-growth saw timber) | 10, 12, 14 |
| 15 (old-growth saw timber) | 14, 16, 18, 20 |

Cu. ft. and cordwood volumes are the gross volumes, excluding bark, of sound trees 5″ or larger d.b.h., to a top dia. of 4″ inside bark. Cordwood is assumed to be piled with the bark on.

Source: S. R. Gevorkiantz and W. A. Duerr, A yield table for northern hardwoods in the Lake States, *Jour. Forestry* 35:340–343, 1937.

## NORTHERN HARDWOODS (SECOND GROWTH)

### Table 16. Yields per Acre, Stands of Average Density
Vermont, Soil Quality II

| Age (yr.) | Average d.b.h. (in.) | Average height (ft.) | Total number of trees | Volume per acre expressed in cords alone | Volume per acre expressed in | |
|---|---|---|---|---|---|---|
| | | | | | Lumber* (bd. ft.) | And in additional cords |
| 20 | 2.5 | 33 | 1,650 | 14.4 | .... | ... |
| 25 | 2.9 | 37 | 1,520 | 17.6 | .... | ... |
| 30 | 3.3 | 41 | 1,380 | 20.8 | .... | ... |
| 35 | 3.7 | 45 | 1,230 | 24.0 | .... | ... |
| 40 | 4.1 | 48 | 1,070 | 26.7 | 2,000 | 21.2 |
| 45 | 4.6 | 51 | 910 | 29.5 | .... | ... |
| 50 | 5.0 | 54 | 750 | 32.8 | 4,500 | 22.9 |
| 55 | 5.5 | 56 | 630 | 34.4 | .... | ... |
| 60 | 5.9 | 58 | 540 | 36.5 | 8,200 | 22.6 |
| 65 | 6.3 | 59 | 470 | 38.2 | .... | ... |
| 70 | 6.6 | 60 | 420 | 40.0 | 10,900 | 20.6 |
| 75 | 6.9 | 61 | 390 | 41.4 | .... | ... |
| 80 | .. | .. | .... | 42.9 | 12,800 | 19.4 |
| 85 | .. | .. | .... | 44.2 | .... | ... |

* All logs 6 in. or over at the top were scaled, whether merchantable or not. New Hampshire Rule.

Source: A. F. Hawes and B. A. Chandler, The management of second-growth hardwoods in Vermont, Vermont Agr Exp Sta., *Bull. No. 176*, 1914.

## LARCH AND DOUGLAS-FIR

**Table 17. Yields per Fully Stocked Acre, in Board Feet, Scribner Decimal C Rule ***

Inland Empire

| Age (yr.) | Site I | Site II | Site III | Site IV | Site V |
|---|---|---|---|---|---|
| 40 | 50 | | | | |
| 50 | 340 | 120 | 10 | | |
| 60 | 800 | 380 | 140 | 4 | |
| 70 | 1,450 | 750 | 320 | 80 | |
| 80 | 2,290 | 1,220 | 540 | 170 | |
| 90 | 3,390 | 1,800 | 810 | 280 | 7 |
| 100 | 4,350 | 2,540 | 1,120 | 400 | 30 |
| 110 | 5,140 | 3,310 | 1,490 | 530 | 60 |
| 120 | 5,820 | 3,980 | 1,920 | 680 | 100 |
| 130 | 6,430 | 4,580 | 2,410 | 840 | 150 |
| 140 | 6,980 | 5,120 | 2,910 | 1,020 | 200 |
| 150 | 7,480 | 5,600 | 3,380 | 1,210 | 260 |
| 160 | 7,950 | 6,040 | 3,810 | 1,410 | 320 |
| 170 | 8,380 | 6,440 | 4,200 | 1,620 | 390 |
| 180 | 8,770 | 6,810 | 4,550 | 1,840 | 460 |
| 190 | 9,130 | 7,150 | 4,870 | 2,070 | 530 |
| 200 | 9,460 | 7,450 | 5,160 | 2,310 | 600 |
| 210 | 9,760 | 7,730 | 5,420 | 2,550 | 660 |
| 220 | 10,030 | 7,980 | 5,660 | 2,780 | 720 |
| 230 | 10,280 | 8,210 | 5,880 | 2,990 | 780 |
| 240 | 10,510 | 8,420 | 6,080 | 3,190 | 830 |
| 250 | 10,720 | 8,620 | 6,260 | 3,370 | 880 |
| 260 | 10,920 | 8,800 | 6,430 | 3,540 | 930 |
| 270 | 11,110 | 8,970 | 6,580 | 3,690 | 980 |
| 280 | 11,280 | 9,120 | 6,720 | 3,830 | 1,020 |
| 290 | 11,440 | 9,260 | 6,850 | 3,960 | 1,060 |
| 300 | 11,590 | 9,390 | 6,970 | 4,080 | 1,100 |

* Trees 13 in. d.b.h. and larger.
Source: L. J. Cummings, Larch—Douglas-fir board foot yield tables, Northern Rocky Mt. Forest & Range Exp. Sta., *Applied Forestry Note No. 78,* 1937 (adapted).

## RED OAK

### Table 18. Yields per Fully Stocked Acre

Massachusetts

| Age (yr.) | Trees per acre | Height (ft.) | D.b.h. (in.) | Basal area (sq. ft.) | Cu. ft. per acre | | Total yield | |
|---|---|---|---|---|---|---|---|---|
| | | | | | Saw logs | Cordwood | Cu. ft. | Bd. ft.* |
| 10 | 7,100 | 16 | 1.2 | 56 | ... | ... | ... | ... |
| 20 | 1,540 | 37 | 2.7 | 61 | ... | 924 | 924 | ... |
| 30 | 657 | 57 | 4.5 | 73 | ... | 1,840 | 1,840 | ... |
| 40 | 350 | 68 | 6.8 | 88 | ... | 2,660 | 2,660 | ... |
| 50 | 222 | 75 | 9.5 | 109 | ... | 3,760 | 3,760 | ... |
| 60 | 151 | 82 | 12.2 | 122 | 3,694 | 906 | 4,600 | 22,600 |
| 70 | 108 | 85 | 15.0 | 133 | 4,108 | 972 | 5,080 | 27,400 |

* Trees 11 in. d.b.h. and larger. International Rule.
Source: R. T. Patton, Red oak and white ash—a study of growth and yield, *Harvard Forest Bull. No. 4*, 1922.

## UPLAND OAKS (SECOND GROWTH)

### Table 19. Yield per Acre, Excluding Bark, of Trees 0.6 In. D.B.H. and Larger, by Stand Density Classes

Entire Range

| Age (yr.) | Yield per acre by density class * in cu. ft. | | | | | | | | |
|---|---|---|---|---|---|---|---|---|---|
| | 50 | 60 | 70 | 80 | 90 | 100 | 110 | 120 | 130 |
| | AVERAGE SITE—INDEX 60 | | | | | | | | |
| 10 | 0 | 0 | 30 | 145 | 245 | 330 | 422 | 540 | 650 |
| 15 | 0 | 95 | 228 | 340 | 445 | 540 | 635 | 755 | 880 |
| 20 | 140 | 288 | 419 | 540 | 648 | 748 | 855 | 985 | 1,135 |
| 25 | 305 | 460 | 604 | 728 | 850 | 955 | 1,080 | 1,225 | 1,385 |
| 30 | 475 | 635 | 790 | 928 | 1,070 | 1,180 | 1,320 | 1,478 | 1,670 |
| 35 | 650 | 825 | 990 | 1,148 | 1,300 | 1,425 | 1,570 | 1,740 | 1,925 |
| 40 | 840 | 1,030 | 1,220 | 1,380 | 1,540 | 1,675 | 1,840 | 2,015 | 2,210 |
| 45 | 1,020 | 1,230 | 1,430 | 1,615 | 1,775 | 1,925 | 2,085 | 2,275 | 2,470 |
| 50 | 1,215 | 1,435 | 1,645 | 1,835 | 2,010 | 2,170 | 2,335 | 2,525 | 2,720 |
| 55 | 1,390 | 1,630 | 1,855 | 2,050 | 2,240 | 2,390 | 2,565 | 2,755 | 2,985 |
| 60 | 1,555 | 1,795 | 2,030 | 2,240 | 2,425 | 2,580 | 2,755 | 2,975 | 3,220 |
| 65 | 1,695 | 1,950 | 2,195 | 2,400 | 2,590 | 2,750 | 2,945 | 3,170 | 3,420 |
| 70 | 1,845 | 2,110 | 2,350 | 2,565 | 2,750 | 2,930 | 3,130 | 3,370 | 3,635 |
| 75 | 1,970 | 2,240 | 2,485 | 2,690 | 2,910 | 3,100 | 3,305 | 3,555 | 3,850 |
| 80 | 2,085 | 2,360 | 2,610 | 2,820 | 3,045 | 3,240 | 3,455 | 3,725 | 4,020 |
| 85 | 2,190 | 2,465 | 2,710 | 2,955 | 3,175 | 3,370 | 3,600 | 3,890 | 4,205 |
| 90 | 2,305 | 2,585 | 2,840 | 3,080 | 3,320 | 3,530 | 3,770 | 4,055 | 4,390 |
| 95 | 2,410 | 2,675 | 2,960 | 3,210 | 3,450 | 3,665 | 3,920 | 4,235 | 4,580 |
| 100 | 2,495 | 2,785 | 3,070 | 3,330 | 3,580 | 3,820 | 4,070 | 4,400 | 4,775 |

* Density is percentage of average number of trees. Compute average diameter and number of trees per acre of the stand and refer to Fig. 2, page 3·58, to determine density class.
Source: G. Luther Schnur, Yield, stand, and volume tables for even-aged upland oak forests, U. S. Dept. Agr., *Tech. Bull. No. 560*, 1937.

# UPLAND OAKS (SECOND GROWTH)

## Table 20. Yields for Fully Stocked Acre, Trees 0.6 In. D.B.H. and Larger

### Entire Range

### SITE INDEX 60—AVERAGE SITE

| Age (years) | Total height, average dominant and co-dominant oak | Trees per acre | Basal area per acre | Average diameter breast high | Yield per acre — Entire stem inside bark | Yield per acre — Merchantable stem to a 4-inch top outside bark [a] | Yield per acre — Merchantable [a] | Yield per acre — International rule [b] | Yield per acre — Scribner rule [c] | Mean annual growth per acre — Entire stem inside bark | Mean annual growth per acre — Merchantable stem to a 4-inch top outside bark [a] | Mean annual growth per acre — Merchantable [a] | Mean annual growth per acre — International rule [b] | Mean annual growth per acre — Scribner rule [c] |
|---|---|---|---|---|---|---|---|---|---|---|---|---|---|---|
| | *Feet* | *Number* | *Square feet* | *Inches* | *Cubic feet* | *Cubic feet* | *Cords* | *Board feet* | *Board feet* | *Cubic feet* | *Cubic feet* | *Cords* | *Board feet* | *Board feet* |
| 10 | 17 | 4,060 | 41 | 1.4 | 345 | | | | | 34 | | | | |
| 20 | 30 | 1,945 | 68 | 2.5 | 805 | 170 | 2.00 | | | 40 | 8 | 0.10 | | |
| 30 | 41 | 965 | 84 | 4.0 | 1,265 | 880 | 10.35 | 850 | 50 | 42 | 29 | .34 | 28 | 2 |
| 40 | 51 | 611 | 93 | 5.3 | 1,725 | 1,580 | 18.59 | 3,200 | 500 | 43 | 40 | .46 | 80 | 12 |
| 50 | 60 | 482 | 100 | 6.3 | 2,165 | 2,230 | 26.24 | 6,300 | 1,400 | 43 | 45 | .52 | 126 | 28 |
| 60 | 67 | 390 | 108 | 7.2 | 2,590 | 2,800 | 32.94 | 9,700 | 3,150 | 43 | 47 | .55 | 162 | 52 |
| 70 | 71 | 326 | 115 | 8.0 | 2,970 | 3,290 | 38.71 | 12,800 | 5,650 | 42 | 47 | .55 | 183 | 81 |
| 80 | 75 | 292 | 123 | 8.8 | 3,325 | 3,730 | 43.88 | 15,650 | 8,250 | 42 | 47 | .55 | 196 | 104 |
| 90 | 77 | 268 | 130 | 9.4 | 3,655 | 4,120 | 48.47 | 18,300 | 11,050 | 41 | 46 | .54 | 203 | 123 |
| 100 | 79 | 248 | 138 | 10.1 | 3,970 | 4,480 | 52.71 | 20,900 | 13,700 | 40 | 45 | .53 | 209 | 137 |

[a] Converting factor, 85 cu. ft. per cord.
[b] ⅛-in. saw kerf to a 5-in. top inside bark.
[c] To an 8-in. top inside bark.

Source: *Ibid.*

3·22

# JACK PINE

## Table 21. Yields per Fully Stocked Acre

### Lake States

#### Medium site—Site index 53

| Age of stands (yr.) | Ave. ht. of dominants (ft.) | Ave. stand diameter (in.) | Ave. vol. per tree (cu. ft.)ᵃ | No. of trees per acre | Basal area (sq. ft.) | Average space per tree (sq. ft.) | Space per sq. ft. of B. A. | Yield per acre | | | Current annual growth in cu. ft. |
|---|---|---|---|---|---|---|---|---|---|---|---|
| | | | | | | | | Merch. cu. ft.ᵃ | Board feetᵇ | | |
| | | | | | | | | | Scribner Rule | Int. ¼" Rule | |
| 20 | 22 | 3.7 | 0.35 | 1,700 | 128 | 26 | 340 | 595 | ... | ... | 66 |
| 30 | 35 | 5.4 | 1.43 | 875 | 140 | 50 | 311 | 1,250 | 500 | 650 | 52 |
| 40 | 45 | 6.8 | 3.10 | 570 | 143 | 76 | 305 | 1,770 | 1,150 | 1,500 | 36 |
| 50 | 53 | 7.9 | 5.02 | 425 | 144 | 102 | 303 | 2,135 | 2,100 | 2,650 | 19 |
| 60 | 60 | 8.8 | 6.86 | 340 | 142 | 128 | 307 | 2,330 | 3,050 | 3,750 | 3 |
| 70 | 65 | 9.6 | 8.45 | 280 | 138 | 155 | 316 | 2,360 | 3,900 | 4,800 | −16 |
| 80 | 69 | 10.2 | 10.00 | 220 | 127 | 199 | 343 | 2,200 | 4,250 | 5,150 | |

ᵃ Volume, inside bark, of trees 5 in. d.b.h. and larger, to a 3-in. top d.i.b.
ᵇ Volume of trees 9 in. d.b.h. and larger, to variable top d.i.b., not less than 6 in.
Source: S. R. Gevorkiantz, Growth and yield of jack pine in the Lake States, Lake States Forest Exp. Sta., *Paper No. 7*, 1947.

## LOBLOLLY PINE (SECOND GROWTH)
### Table 22. Normal Yields, by Site Index

| Age [a] (yr.) | Total height, average of dominant and co-dominant trees | Trees 4 in. d.b.h. and larger | | | | | Trees 8 in. d.b.h. and larger | |
|---|---|---|---|---|---|---|---|---|
| | | | | | Rough wood [d] | | Yield per acre (Scribner Dec. C Rule) (bd. ft. in tens) | Growth per acre per year (Scribner Dec. C Rule) (bd. ft. in tens) |
| | | Stand per acre | Average diameter [b] | Basal area [c] per acre | Yield per acre | Growth per acre per year | | |
| | | | | **70-FT. SITE** | | | | |
| 15 | 29 | 580 | 4.8 | 74 | 12 | 0.80 | ... | ... |
| 20 | 38 | 675 | 5.2 | 107 | 17 | 0.85 | 10 | ... |
| 25 | 45 | 630 | 6.0 | 128 | 24 | 0.96 | 135 | 5 |
| 30 | 52 | 575 | 6.8 | 140 | 31 | 1.03 | 350 | 12 |
| 35 | 58 | 505 | 7.5 | 147 | 37 | 1.06 | 645 | 18 |
| 40 | 63 | 430 | 8.2 | 151 | 42 | 1.05 | 940 | 24 |
| 45 | 67 | 370 | 8.8 | 154 | 47 | 1.04 | 1,240 | 28 |
| 50 | 70 | 325 | 9.5 | 157 | 50 | 1.00 | 1,520 | 30 |
| 55 | 73 | 295 | 10.0 | 159 | 53 | 0.96 | 1,760 | 32 |
| 60 | 75 | 270 | 10.6 | 161 | 55 | 0.92 | 1,960 | 33 |
| | | | | **90-FT. SITE** | | | | |
| 15 | 37 | 640 | 5.1 | 92 | 18 | 1.20 | ... | ... |
| 20 | 48 | 630 | 6.1 | 126 | 27 | 1.35 | 160 | 8 |
| 25 | 58 | 510 | 7.2 | 143 | 37 | 1.48 | 525 | 21 |
| 30 | 67 | 415 | 8.2 | 152 | 46 | 1.53 | 1,070 | 36 |
| 35 | 74 | 345 | 9.3 | 157 | 54 | 1.54 | 1,585 | 45 |
| 40 | 81 | 290 | 10.2 | 161 | 61 | 1.52 | 2,055 | 51 |
| 45 | 86 | 250 | 11.1 | 165 | 67 | 1.49 | 2,470 | 55 |
| 50 | 90 | 220 | 12.0 | 167 | 71 | 1.42 | 2,825 | 56 |
| 55 | 93 | 195 | 12.7 | 169 | 75 | 1.36 | 3,085 | 56 |
| 60 | 96 | 175 | 13.4 | 171 | 78 | 1.30 | 3,310 | 55 |

[a] Average age of dominant trees in stand. If age determinations are made at breast height (4½ ft. from the ground), 3 yr. should be added to get total age. If they are made at a stump height of 1 ft., 2 yr. should be added.

[b] Diameter at breast height of the tree of average basal area.

[c] Cross-sectional area in square feet at the point of diameter measurement (4½ ft. from the ground).

[d] In cords. A cord equals 128 cu. ft. gross volume of stacked cordwood.

Source: This table was assembled from Tables 33, 41, 42, 43, 46, 47, 55, and 56, Volume, yield, and stand tables for second-growth southern pines, U. S. Dept. Agr., *Misc. Publ. No. 50*, 1929. Sites are designated by the height attained on each by the average dominant and codominant trees in a 50-yr.-old stand. This height is called the site index. Thus a site with an index of 70 ft. produces dominant and codominant trees averaging 70 ft. in height at 50 yr.

## LONGLEAF PINE (SECOND GROWTH)

### Table 23. Normal Yields, by Site Index

| | | | | | | | Trees 8 in. d.b.h. and larger | |
| Age [a] (yr.) | Total height, average of dominant and co-dominant trees | Trees 4 in. d.b.h. and larger | | | | | Yield per acre (Scribner Dec. C Rule) (bd. ft. in tens) | Growth per acre per year (Scribner Dec. C Rule) (bd. ft. in tens) |
| | | Stand per acre | Average diameter [b] | Basal area [c] per acre | Rough wood [d] | | | |
| | | | | | Yield per acre | Growth per acre per year | | |
| | | | | | | | | |
| **70-FT. SITE** | | | | | | | | |
| 15 | 26 | 250 | 4.6 | 29 | 7 | 0.47 | ... | ... |
| 20 | 36 | 500 | 5.2 | 75 | 14 | 0.70 | 20 | 1 |
| 25 | 45 | 550 | 5.7 | 92 | 21 | 0.84 | 85 | 3 |
| 30 | 52 | 540 | 6.2 | 105 | 28 | 0.93 | 200 | 7 |
| 35 | 57 | 495 | 6.7 | 115 | 33 | 0.94 | 390 | 11 |
| 40 | 62 | 450 | 7.2 | 124 | 39 | 0.98 | 610 | 15 |
| 45 | 66 | 415 | 7.6 | 132 | 43 | 0.96 | 880 | 20 |
| 50 | 70 | 380 | 8.1 | 137 | 48 | 0.96 | 1,140 | 23 |
| 55 | 74 | 355 | 8.5 | 141 | 52 | 0.95 | 1,400 | 25 |
| 60 | 77 | 330 | 8.9 | 145 | 55 | 0.92 | 1,640 | 27 |
| **90-FT. SITE** | | | | | | | | |
| 15 | 33 | 345 | 5.3 | 52 | 16 | 1.07 | 12 | 1 |
| 20 | 46 | 580 | 5.7 | 98 | 26 | 1.30 | 100 | 5 |
| 25 | 57 | 550 | 6.4 | 116 | 35 | 1.40 | 290 | 12 |
| 30 | 66 | 495 | 7.1 | 130 | 43 | 1.43 | 650 | 22 |
| 35 | 74 | 425 | 7.8 | 141 | 51 | 1.46 | 1,120 | 32 |
| 40 | 80 | 380 | 8.4 | 149 | 59 | 1.48 | 1,580 | 40 |
| 45 | 85 | 345 | 9.0 | 156 | 66 | 1.47 | 2,010 | 45 |
| 50 | 90 | 320 | 9.6 | 162 | 72 | 1.44 | 2,410 | 48 |
| 55 | 94 | 295 | 10.2 | 167 | 78 | 1.42 | 2,780 | 51 |
| 60 | 98 | 275 | 10.7 | 171 | 84 | 1.40 | 3,100 | 52 |

[a] Average age of dominant trees in stand. If age determinations are made at breast height (4½ ft. from the ground), 7 yr. should be added to get total age. If they are made at a stump height of 1 ft., 5 yr. should be added.
[b] Diameter at breast height of the tree of average basal area.
[c] Cross-sectional area in square feet at the point of diameter measurement (4½ ft. from the ground).
[d] In cords. A cord equals 128 cu. ft. gross volume of stacked cordwood.
Source: This table was assembled from Tables 65, 73, 74, 75, 78, 79, 87, and 88, Volume, yield, and stand tables for second-growth southern pines, U. S. Dept. Agr., *Misc. Publ. No. 50*, 1929. Sites are designated by the height attained on each by the average dominant and codominant trees in a 50-yr.-old stand. This height is called the site index. Thus a site with an index of 70 ft. produces dominant and codominant trees averaging 70 ft. in height at 50 yr.

## PONDEROSA PINE

### Table 24. Yield Tables for Fully Stocked Acre, Total Stand [a]

Entire Range

HEIGHT OF DOMINANT AND CODOMINANT TREES OF AVERAGE BREAST-HEIGHT DIAMETER, IN FEET

| Age (yr.) | Site index in feet | | | | | | | | | | | | |
|---|---|---|---|---|---|---|---|---|---|---|---|---|---|
| | 40 | 50 | 60 | 70 | 80 | 90 | 100 | 110 | 120 | 130 | 140 | 150 | 160 |
| 20 | 6 | 9 | 12 | 16 | 20 | 25 | 30 | 35 | 40 | 45 | 50 | 55 | 60 |
| 30 | 11 | 15 | 20 | 26 | 32 | 38 | 44 | 51 | 57 | 64 | 70 | 77 | 84 |
| 40 | 16 | 22 | 28 | 35 | 42 | 49 | 55 | 63 | 70 | 77 | 85 | 93 | 100 |
| 50 | 21 | 28 | 35 | 43 | 51 | 58 | 65 | 73 | 80 | 89 | 97 | 105 | 113 |
| 60 | 26 | 34 | 42 | 50 | 58 | 66 | 73 | 81 | 90 | 99 | 107 | 115 | 124 |
| 70 | 30 | 39 | 47 | 56 | 64 | 73 | 80 | 89 | 98 | 108 | 116 | 125 | 134 |
| 80 | 34 | 43 | 52 | 61 | 70 | 79 | 88 | 97 | 106 | 116 | 124 | 133 | 143 |
| 90 | 37 | 47 | 57 | 66 | 75 | 85 | 94 | 104 | 113 | 123 | 132 | 142 | 152 |
| 100 | 40 | 50 | 60 | 70 | 80 | 90 | 100 | 110 | 120 | 130 | 140 | 150 | 160 |
| 110 | 42 | 53 | 63 | 74 | 84 | 95 | 106 | 116 | 127 | 137 | 147 | 158 | 168 |
| 120 | 44 | 55 | 66 | 77 | 88 | 100 | 111 | 122 | 133 | 144 | 154 | 165 | 175 |
| 130 | 45 | 57 | 69 | 80 | 92 | 104 | 116 | 128 | 139 | 151 | 161 | 172 | 182 |
| 140 | 46 | 59 | 71 | 83 | 96 | 108 | 121 | 133 | 145 | 157 | 167 | 179 | 189 |
| 150 | 47 | 60 | 73 | 86 | 99 | 112 | 125 | 138 | 151 | 163 | 173 | 185 | 195 |
| 160 | 48 | 61 | 75 | 89 | 102 | 116 | 129 | 143 | 156 | 169 | 179 | 191 | 201 |
| 170 | 48 | 62 | 77 | 91 | 105 | 119 | 133 | 147 | 161 | 174 | 184 | 196 | 206 |
| 180 | 49 | 63 | 78 | 93 | 108 | 122 | 136 | 151 | 165 | 179 | 189 | 201 | 211 |
| 190 | 49 | 63 | 79 | 95 | 110 | 125 | 139 | 154 | 169 | 183 | 194 | 205 | 216 |
| 200 | 50 | 64 | 80 | 97 | 112 | 128 | 143 | 157 | 172 | 187 | 198 | 209 | 220 |

NUMBER OF TREES PER ACRE 0.6 IN. AND MORE IN DIAMETER

| Age (yr.) | Trees per acre, by site index | | | | | | | | | | | | |
|---|---|---|---|---|---|---|---|---|---|---|---|---|---|
| | 40 | 50 | 60 | 70 | 80 | 90 | 100 | 110 | 120 | 130 | 140 | 150 | 160 |
| 20 | ... | 7,600 | 4,600 | 3,000 | 2,250 | 1,700 | 1,280 | 970 | 779 | 650 | 561 | 470 | 394 |
| 30 | 9,440 | 5,710 | 3,678 | 2,328 | 1,750 | 1,318 | 1,000 | 800 | 649 | 556 | 476 | 409 | 353 |
| 40 | 6,960 | 4,020 | 2,700 | 1,712 | 1,270 | 994 | 785 | 642 | 539 | 462 | 405 | 358 | 316 |
| 50 | 4,400 | 2,660 | 1,732 | 1,188 | 905 | 725 | 574 | 498 | 425 | 373 | 332 | 298 | 266 |
| 60 | 2,800 | 1,780 | 1,145 | 850 | 662 | 540 | 445 | 389 | 340 | 301 | 269 | 244 | 224 |
| 70 | 1,840 | 1,235 | 831 | 632 | 502 | 415 | 352 | 310 | 272 | 244 | 220 | 204 | 189 |
| 80 | 1,300 | 875 | 634 | 490 | 393 | 329 | 286 | 252 | 225 | 204 | 185 | 174 | 162 |
| 90 | 955 | 674 | 495 | 390 | 316 | 272 | 236 | 210 | 189 | 173 | 159 | 149 | 140 |
| 100 | 744 | 532 | 400 | 318 | 266 | 228 | 199 | 179 | 162 | 150 | 139 | 130 | 123 |
| 110 | 612 | 433 | 329 | 269 | 225 | 197 | 172 | 154 | 141 | 131 | ... | ... | ... |
| 120 | 512 | 368 | 281 | 230 | 196 | 171 | 152 | 136 | 125 | 115 | ... | ... | ... |
| 130 | 435 | 314 | 247 | 203 | 173 | 151 | 134 | 121 | 110 | 102 | ... | ... | ... |
| 140 | 375 | 280 | 219 | 182 | 153 | 134 | 120 | 108 | 99 | 91 | ... | ... | ... |
| 150 | 334 | 248 | 198 | 165 | 138 | 120 | 108 | 98 | 89 | 83 | ... | ... | ... |
| 160 | 302 | 227 | 181 | 150 | 126 | 109 | 98 | 88 | 81 | 75 | ... | ... | ... |
| 170 | 274 | 208 | 165 | 137 | 115 | 100 | 89 | 81 | 74 | 69 | ... | ... | ... |
| 180 | 254 | 191 | 152 | 125 | 106 | 92 | 82 | 74 | 68 | 63 | ... | ... | ... |
| 190 | 234 | 176 | 140 | 115 | 99 | 85 | 76 | 69 | 63 | 58 | ... | ... | ... |
| 200 | 218 | 167 | 130 | 108 | 92 | 79 | 70 | 64 | 58 | 54 | ... | ... | ... |

[a] All trees 0.6-in. d.b.h. and larger.

Source for Tables 24 to 28: W. H. Meyer, Yield of even-aged stands of ponderosa pine, U. S. Dept. Agr., *Tech. Bull. No. 630*, 1938.

**Table 24. Yield Tables for Fully Stocked Acre, Total Stand** (Continued)

BASAL AREA IN SQUARE FEET

| Age (yr.) | Site index—in feet | | | | | | | | | | | | |
|---|---|---|---|---|---|---|---|---|---|---|---|---|---|
|  | 40 | 50 | 60 | 70 | 80 | 90 | 100 | 110 | 120 | 130 | 140 | 150 | 160 |
| 20 | ... | 32 | 46 | 58 | 70 | 82 | 93 | 104 | 115 | 126 | 137 | 148 | 159 |
| 30 | 74 | 90 | 106 | 122 | 138 | 152 | 165 | 177 | 189 | 201 | 213 | 225 | 237 |
| 40 | 123 | 137 | 151 | 165 | 180 | 195 | 210 | 224 | 238 | 252 | 264 | 276 | 287 |
| 50 | 138 | 153 | 167 | 182 | 196 | 211 | 226 | 240 | 255 | 269 | 283 | 296 | 308 |
| 60 | 141 | 155 | 169 | 184 | 198 | 213 | 228 | 243 | 258 | 273 | 288 | 303 | 317 |
| 70 | 141 | 155 | 169 | 184 | 198 | 213 | 228 | 243 | 258 | 273 | 288 | 303 | 318 |
| 80 | 141 | 155 | 169 | 184 | 198 | 213 | 228 | 243 | 258 | 273 | 288 | 303 | 318 |
| 90 | 141 | 155 | 169 | 184 | 198 | 213 | 228 | 243 | 258 | 273 | 288 | 303 | 318 |
| 100 | 141 | 155 | 169 | 184 | 198 | 213 | 228 | 243 | 258 | 273 | 288 | 303 | 318 |
| 110 | 141 | 155 | 169 | 184 | 198 | 213 | 228 | 243 | 258 | 273 | ... | ... | ... |
| 120 | 141 | 155 | 169 | 184 | 198 | 213 | 228 | 243 | 258 | 273 | ... | ... | ... |
| 130 | 141 | 155 | 169 | 184 | 198 | 213 | 228 | 243 | 258 | 273 | ... | ... | ... |
| 140 | 141 | 155 | 169 | 184 | 198 | 213 | 228 | 243 | 258 | 273 | ... | ... | ... |
| 150 | 141 | 155 | 169 | 184 | 198 | 213 | 228 | 243 | 258 | 273 | ... | ... | ... |
| 160 | 141 | 155 | 169 | 184 | 198 | 213 | 228 | 243 | 258 | 273 | ... | ... | ... |
| 170 | 141 | 155 | 169 | 184 | 198 | 213 | 228 | 243 | 258 | 273 | ... | ... | ... |
| 180 | 141 | 155 | 169 | 184 | 198 | 213 | 228 | 243 | 258 | 273 | ... | ... | ... |
| 190 | 141 | 155 | 169 | 184 | 198 | 213 | 228 | 243 | 258 | 273 | ... | ... | ... |
| 200 | 141 | 155 | 169 | 184 | 198 | 213 | 228 | 243 | 258 | 273 | ... | ... | ... |

AVERAGE DIAMETER BREAST HIGH IN INCHES

| Age (yr.) | Site index—in feet | | | | | | | | | | | | |
|---|---|---|---|---|---|---|---|---|---|---|---|---|---|
|  | 40 | 50 | 60 | 70 | 80 | 90 | 100 | 110 | 120 | 130 | 140 | 150 | 160 |
| 20 | ... | 0.9 | 1.3 | 1.9 | 2.4 | 3.0 | 3.6 | 4.4 | 5.2 | 6.0 | 6.7 | 7.6 | 8.6 |
| 30 | 1.2 | 1.7 | 2.3 | 3.1 | 3.8 | 4.6 | 5.5 | 6.4 | 7.3 | 8.2 | 9.1 | 10.1 | 11.1 |
| 40 | 1.8 | 2.5 | 3.2 | 4.2 | 5.1 | 6.0 | 7.0 | 8.0 | 9.0 | 10.0 | 10.9 | 11.9 | 12.9 |
| 50 | 2.4 | 3.2 | 4.2 | 5.3 | 6.3 | 7.3 | 8.5 | 9.4 | 10.5 | 11.5 | 12.5 | 13.5 | 14.6 |
| 60 | 3.0 | 4.0 | 5.1 | 6.3 | 7.4 | 8.5 | 9.7 | 10.7 | 11.8 | 12.9 | 14.0 | 15.1 | 16.1 |
| 70 | 3.7 | 4.8 | 6.0 | 7.3 | 8.5 | 9.7 | 10.9 | 12.0 | 13.2 | 14.3 | 15.5 | 16.5 | 17.6 |
| 80 | 4.5 | 5.7 | 7.0 | 8.3 | 9.6 | 10.9 | 12.1 | 13.3 | 14.5 | 15.7 | 16.9 | 17.9 | 19.0 |
| 90 | 5.2 | 6.5 | 7.9 | 9.3 | 10.7 | 12.0 | 13.3 | 14.6 | 15.8 | 17.0 | 18.2 | 19.3 | 20.4 |
| 100 | 5.9 | 7.3 | 8.8 | 10.3 | 11.7 | 13.1 | 14.5 | 15.8 | 17.1 | 18.3 | 19.5 | 20.7 | 21.8 |
| 110 | 6.5 | 8.1 | 9.7 | 11.2 | 12.7 | 14.1 | 15.6 | 17.0 | 18.3 | 19.6 | ... | ... | ... |
| 120 | 7.1 | 8.8 | 10.5 | 12.1 | 13.6 | 15.1 | 16.6 | 18.1 | 19.5 | 20.9 | ... | ... | ... |
| 130 | 7.7 | 9.5 | 11.2 | 12.9 | 14.5 | 16.1 | 17.7 | 19.2 | 20.7 | 22.2 | ... | ... | ... |
| 140 | 8.3 | 10.1 | 11.9 | 13.6 | 15.4 | 17.1 | 18.7 | 20.3 | 21.9 | 23.4 | ... | ... | ... |
| 150 | 8.8 | 10.7 | 12.5 | 14.3 | 16.2 | 18.0 | 19.7 | 21.4 | 23.1 | 24.6 | ... | ... | ... |
| 160 | 9.3 | 11.2 | 13.1 | 15.0 | 17.0 | 18.9 | 20.7 | 22.5 | 24.2 | 25.8 | ... | ... | ... |
| 170 | 9.7 | 11.7 | 13.7 | 15.7 | 17.8 | 19.8 | 21.7 | 23.5 | 25.3 | 27.0 | ... | ... | ... |
| 180 | 10.1 | 12.2 | 14.3 | 16.4 | 18.5 | 20.6 | 22.6 | 24.5 | 26.4 | 28.2 | ... | ... | ... |
| 190 | 10.5 | 12.7 | 14.9 | 17.1 | 19.2 | 21.4 | 23.5 | 25.5 | 27.5 | 29.4 | ... | ... | ... |
| 200 | 10.9 | 13.1 | 15.4 | 17.7 | 19.9 | 22.2 | 24.4 | 26.5 | 28.6 | 30.6 | ... | ... | ... |

### Table 24. Yield Tables for Fully Stocked Acre, Total Stand (Continued)
CUBIC-FOOT VOLUME [b] INCLUDING STUMP AND TIP BUT NOT BARK

| Age (yr.) | Site index—in feet | | | | | | | | | | | | |
|---|---|---|---|---|---|---|---|---|---|---|---|---|---|
| | 40 | 50 | 60 | 70 | 80 | 90 | 100 | 110 | 120 | 130 | 140 | 150 | 160 |
| 20 | ... | 200 | 400 | 700 | 1,000 | 1,350 | 1,700 | 2,100 | 2,400 | 2,750 | 3,350 | 3,750 | 4,350 |
| 30 | 500 | 800 | 1,100 | 1,450 | 1,950 | 2,450 | 3,000 | 3,600 | 4,200 | 4,850 | 5,500 | 6,150 | 6,850 |
| 40 | 1,050 | 1,350 | 1,750 | 2,150 | 2,750 | 3,400 | 4,100 | 4,900 | 5,650 | 6,650 | 7,500 | 8,400 | 9,350 |
| 50 | 1,450 | 1,850 | 2,300 | 2,750 | 3,400 | 4,200 | 5,050 | 6,050 | 7,000 | 8,200 | 9,300 | 10,500 | 11,700 |
| 60 | 1,800 | 2,250 | 2,750 | 3,250 | 3,950 | 4,850 | 5,850 | 7,000 | 8,150 | 9,500 | 10,900 | 12,300 | 13,700 |
| 70 | 2,100 | 2,600 | 3,100 | 3,700 | 4,450 | 5,400 | 6,500 | 7,800 | 9,100 | 10,650 | 12,300 | 13,850 | 15,450 |
| 80 | 2,400 | 2,900 | 3,400 | 4,100 | 4,900 | 5,900 | 7,100 | 8,500 | 9,950 | 11,650 | 13,500 | 15,150 | 16,950 |
| 90 | 2,650 | 3,150 | 3,650 | 4,450 | 5,300 | 6,350 | 7,650 | 9,100 | 10,700 | 12,550 | 14,550 | 16,250 | 18,250 |
| 100 | 2,900 | 3,400 | 3,900 | 4,750 | 5,650 | 6,750 | 8,100 | 9,650 | 11,350 | 13,350 | 15,450 | 17,200 | 19,350 |
| 110 | 3,100 | 3,600 | 4,150 | 5,000 | 5,950 | 7,100 | 8,500 | 10,100 | 11,900 | 14,050 | ... | ... | ... |
| 120 | 3,300 | 3,800 | 4,400 | 5,250 | 6,200 | 7,400 | 8,850 | 10,500 | 12,400 | 14,650 | ... | ... | ... |
| 130 | 3,450 | 4,000 | 4,600 | 5,500 | 6,450 | 7,700 | 9,150 | 10,850 | 12,850 | 15,150 | ... | ... | ... |
| 140 | 3,600 | 4,150 | 4,800 | 5,700 | 6,650 | 7,950 | 9,450 | 11,200 | 13,250 | 15,550 | ... | ... | ... |
| 150 | 3,700 | 4,300 | 4,950 | 5,900 | 6,850 | 8,200 | 9,750 | 11,500 | 13,600 | 15,900 | ... | ... | ... |
| 160 | 3,800 | 4,450 | 5,100 | 6,050 | 7,050 | 8,450 | 10,000 | 11,800 | 13,950 | 16,250 | ... | ... | ... |
| 170 | 3,900 | 4,550 | 5,250 | 6,200 | 7,250 | 8,650 | 10,250 | 12,100 | 14,250 | 16,600 | ... | ... | ... |
| 180 | 4,000 | 4,650 | 5,400 | 6,350 | 7,450 | 8,850 | 10,500 | 12,350 | 14,550 | 16,950 | ... | ... | ... |
| 190 | 4,100 | 4,750 | 5,500 | 6,500 | 7,650 | 9,050 | 10,750 | 12,600 | 14,850 | 17,300 | ... | ... | ... |
| 200 | 4,200 | 4,850 | 5,600 | 6,650 | 7,800 | 9,250 | 10,950 | 12,800 | 15,100 | 17,650 | ... | ... | ... |

[b] To nearest 50 cu. ft.

## PONDEROSA PINE

### Table 25. Yield Tables for Fully Stocked Acre, Trees 11.6 In. D.B.H. and Larger

Entire Range

NUMBER OF TREES

| Age (yr.) | Site index—in feet | | | | | | | | | | | | |
|---|---|---|---|---|---|---|---|---|---|---|---|---|---|
| | 40 | 50 | 60 | 70 | 80 | 90 | 100 | 110 | 120 | 130 | 140 | 150 | 160 |
| 20 | ... | ... | ... | ... | ... | ... | ... | 2 | 4 | 10 | 17 | 35 | 60 |
| 30 | ... | ... | ... | ... | ... | 3 | 9 | 20 | 37 | 66 | 92 | 116 | 133 |
| 40 | ... | ... | ... | 3 | 8 | 17 | 36 | 65 | 100 | 127 | 146 | 162 | 172 |
| 50 | ... | ... | 3 | 9 | 21 | 41 | 84 | 110 | 136 | 155 | 168 | 178 | 181 |
| 60 | ... | 2 | 6 | 18 | 42 | 79 | 109 | 132 | 151 | 164 | 171 | 174 | 174 |
| 70 | 1 | 6 | 14 | 36 | 73 | 103 | 126 | 143 | 155 | 161 | 163 | 162 | 160 |
| 80 | 3 | 11 | 27 | 63 | 94 | 117 | 134 | 146 | 152 | 154 | 151 | 149 | 145 |
| 90 | 7 | 18 | 47 | 85 | 107 | 125 | 137 | 143 | 145 | 143 | 138 | 135 | 131 |
| 100 | 11 | 31 | 68 | 96 | 115 | 128 | 135 | 136 | 134 | 131 | 127 | 122 | 118 |
| 110 | 16 | 47 | 81 | 104 | 118 | 126 | 129 | 127 | 123 | 120 | ... | ... | ... |
| 120 | 25 | 62 | 90 | 109 | 118 | 123 | 122 | 118 | 113 | 109 | ... | ... | ... |
| 130 | 35 | 73 | 95 | 110 | 117 | 118 | 114 | 109 | 104 | 100 | ... | ... | ... |
| 140 | 48 | 79 | 99 | 110 | 113 | 111 | 107 | 101 | 96 | 91 | ... | ... | ... |
| 150 | 57 | 84 | 101 | 109 | 108 | 104 | 100 | 93 | 88 | 83 | ... | ... | ... |
| 160 | 64 | 88 | 102 | 107 | 103 | 98 | 93 | 86 | 81 | 75 | ... | ... | ... |
| 170 | 68 | 90 | 101 | 104 | 98 | 92 | 86 | 80 | 74 | 69 | ... | ... | ... |
| 180 | 72 | 92 | 100 | 100 | 93 | 87 | 80 | 74 | 68 | 63 | ... | ... | ... |
| 190 | 76 | 93 | 98 | 96 | 89 | 82 | 75 | 69 | 63 | 58 | ... | ... | ... |
| 200 | 78 | 93 | 96 | 92 | 85 | 78 | 70 | 64 | 58 | 54 | ... | ... | ... |

## PONDEROSA PINE

### Table 25. Yield Tables for Fully Stocked Acre, Trees 11.6 In. D.B.H. and Larger (Continued)

Entire Range

#### BASAL AREA IN SQUARE FEET

| Age (yr.) | Site index—in feet | | | | | | | | | | | | |
|---|---|---|---|---|---|---|---|---|---|---|---|---|---|
| | 40 | 50 | 60 | 70 | 80 | 90 | 100 | 110 | 120 | 130 | 140 | 150 | 160 |
| 20 | ... | ... | ... | ... | ... | ... | ... | 2 | 4 | 9 | 16 | 33 | 60 |
| 30 | ... | ... | ... | ... | ... | 3 | 8 | 18 | 35 | 64 | 95 | 126 | 154 |
| 40 | ... | ... | ... | 3 | 7 | 15 | 34 | 63 | 102 | 138 | 168 | 199 | 228 |
| 50 | ... | ... | 3 | 8 | 19 | 39 | 83 | 115 | 153 | 186 | 217 | 246 | 272 |
| 60 | ... | 2 | 5 | 16 | 40 | 78 | 117 | 150 | 185 | 217 | 248 | 273 | 295 |
| 70 | 1 | 5 | 13 | 34 | 73 | 110 | 145 | 178 | 209 | 236 | 263 | 284 | 305 |
| 80 | 3 | 10 | 25 | 62 | 100 | 135 | 169 | 199 | 226 | 251 | 273 | 292 | 310 |
| 90 | 6 | 17 | 45 | 88 | 122 | 155 | 188 | 215 | 239 | 259 | 278 | 297 | 314 |
| 100 | 10 | 29 | 69 | 106 | 140 | 172 | 200 | 225 | 245 | 264 | 282 | 300 | 317 |
| 110 | 15 | 46 | 87 | 122 | 154 | 183 | 209 | 231 | 249 | 268 | ... | ... | ... |
| 120 | 23 | 62 | 101 | 136 | 165 | 192 | 215 | 235 | 252 | 270 | ... | ... | ... |
| 130 | 34 | 77 | 112 | 146 | 174 | 198 | 219 | 238 | 255 | 272 | ... | ... | ... |
| 140 | 47 | 87 | 122 | 154 | 180 | 202 | 222 | 240 | 257 | 273 | ... | ... | ... |
| 150 | 57 | 96 | 130 | 160 | 185 | 205 | 224 | 242 | 258 | 273 | ... | ... | ... |
| 160 | 66 | 103 | 137 | 165 | 188 | 207 | 226 | 243 | 258 | 273 | ... | ... | ... |
| 170 | 73 | 110 | 142 | 169 | 190 | 209 | 227 | 243 | 258 | 273 | ... | ... | ... |
| 180 | 79 | 116 | 146 | 172 | 192 | 211 | 228 | 243 | 258 | 273 | ... | ... | ... |
| 190 | 85 | 121 | 150 | 175 | 194 | 212 | 228 | 243 | 258 | 273 | ... | ... | ... |
| 200 | 90 | 125 | 154 | 177 | 195 | 213 | 228 | 243 | 258 | 273 | ... | ... | ... |

#### AVERAGE DIAMETER BREAST HIGH, IN INCHES

| Age (yr.) | Site index—in feet | | | | | | | | | | | | |
|---|---|---|---|---|---|---|---|---|---|---|---|---|---|
| | 40 | 50 | 60 | 70 | 80 | 90 | 100 | 110 | 120 | 130 | 140 | 150 | 160 |
| 20 | ... | ... | ... | ... | ... | ... | ... | 12.7 | 12.8 | 12.9 | 13.0 | 13.2 | 13.5 |
| 30 | ... | ... | ... | ... | ... | 12.7 | 12.8 | 12.9 | 13.2 | 13.4 | 13.7 | 14.1 | 14.6 |
| 40 | ... | ... | ... | 12.7 | 12.8 | 12.9 | 13.1 | 13.3 | 13.7 | 14.1 | 14.5 | 15.0 | 15.6 |
| 50 | ... | ... | 12.6 | 12.8 | 12.9 | 13.2 | 13.5 | 13.8 | 14.3 | 14.8 | 15.4 | 15.9 | 16.6 |
| 60 | ... | 12.6 | 12.7 | 12.9 | 13.2 | 13.5 | 14.0 | 14.4 | 15.0 | 15.6 | 16.3 | 16.9 | 17.6 |
| 70 | 12.6 | 12.7 | 12.9 | 13.1 | 13.5 | 14.0 | 14.6 | 15.1 | 15.7 | 16.4 | 17.2 | 17.9 | 18.7 |
| 80 | 12.7 | 12.8 | 13.1 | 13.4 | 13.9 | 14.5 | 15.2 | 15.8 | 16.5 | 17.3 | 18.2 | 18.9 | 19.8 |
| 90 | 12.8 | 13.0 | 13.3 | 13.8 | 14.4 | 15.1 | 15.8 | 16.6 | 17.4 | 18.2 | 19.2 | 20.0 | 21.0 |
| 100 | 12.9 | 13.2 | 13.6 | 14.2 | 14.9 | 15.7 | 16.5 | 17.4 | 18.3 | 19.2 | 20.2 | 21.2 | 22.2 |
| 110 | 13.0 | 13.4 | 14.0 | 14.6 | 15.5 | 16.3 | 17.2 | 18.3 | 19.2 | 20.2 | ... | ... | ... |
| 120 | 13.1 | 13.6 | 14.4 | 15.1 | 16.0 | 16.9 | 18.0 | 19.1 | 20.2 | 21.3 | ... | ... | ... |
| 130 | 13.2 | 13.9 | 14.7 | 15.6 | 16.5 | 17.6 | 18.8 | 20.0 | 21.2 | 22.4 | ... | ... | ... |
| 140 | 13.4 | 14.2 | 15.0 | 16.0 | 17.1 | 18.3 | 19.5 | 20.9 | 22.2 | 23.5 | ... | ... | ... |
| 150 | 13.6 | 14.4 | 15.4 | 16.4 | 17.7 | 19.0 | 20.3 | 21.8 | 23.2 | 24.6 | ... | ... | ... |
| 160 | 13.8 | 14.6 | 15.7 | 16.8 | 18.3 | 19.7 | 21.1 | 22.7 | 24.2 | 25.8 | ... | ... | ... |
| 170 | 14.0 | 14.9 | 16.0 | 17.3 | 18.9 | 20.4 | 22.0 | 23.6 | 25.3 | 27.0 | ... | ... | ... |
| 180 | 14.2 | 15.2 | 16.4 | 17.8 | 19.5 | 21.1 | 22.8 | 24.5 | 26.4 | 28.2 | ... | ... | ... |
| 190 | 14.4 | 15.5 | 16.8 | 18.3 | 20.0 | 21.7 | 23.6 | 25.5 | 27.5 | 29.4 | ... | ... | ... |
| 200 | 14.6 | 15.7 | 17.1 | 18.8 | 20.5 | 22.4 | 24.4 | 26.5 | 28.6 | 30.6 | ... | ... | ... |

Source: *Ibid.*

## Table 25. Yield Tables for Fully Stocked Acre, Trees 11.6 In. D.B.H. and Larger (Continued)

### CUBIC-FOOT VOLUME,[a] INCLUDING STUMP AND TIP BUT NOT BARK

| Age (yr.) | Site index—in feet | | | | | | | | | | | | |
| --- | --- | --- | --- | --- | --- | --- | --- | --- | --- | --- | --- | --- | --- |
|  | 40 | 50 | 60 | 70 | 80 | 90 | 100 | 110 | 120 | 130 | 140 | 150 | 160 |
| 20 | ... | ... | ... | ... | ... | ... | ... | 40 | 120 | 280 | 530 | 1,060 | 1,880 |
| 30 | ... | ... | ... | ... | ... | 60 | 200 | 470 | 970 | 1,860 | 2,750 | 3,760 | 4,910 |
| 40 | ... | ... | ... | 30 | 120 | 340 | 820 | 1,740 | 2,770 | 3,990 | 5,230 | 6,580 | 7,950 |
| 50 | ... | ... | 30 | 150 | 410 | 970 | 2,060 | 3,230 | 4,600 | 6,170 | 7,670 | 9,260 | 10,780 |
| 60 | ... | 30 | 120 | 400 | 990 | 2,040 | 3,280 | 4,710 | 6,320 | 8,080 | 9,830 | 11,520 | 13,140 |
| 70 | ... | 90 | 310 | 870 | 1,870 | 3,090 | 4,440 | 6,110 | 7,910 | 9,730 | 11,590 | 13,380 | 15,080 |
| 80 | 50 | 220 | 710 | 1,650 | 2,720 | 4,110 | 5,540 | 7,310 | 9,210 | 11,100 | 13,030 | 14,880 | 16,640 |
| 90 | 110 | 470 | 1,310 | 2,400 | 3,520 | 5,010 | 6,520 | 8,310 | 10,280 | 12,230 | 14,200 | 16,110 | 17,940 |
| 100 | 240 | 870 | 1,960 | 3,100 | 4,270 | 5,790 | 7,310 | 9,130 | 11,140 | 13,140 | 15,160 | 17,430 | 19,020 |
| 110 | 460 | 1,370 | 2,560 | 3,710 | 4,890 | 6,420 | 7,950 | 9,780 | 11,800 | 13,900 | ... | ... | ... |
| 120 | 780 | 1,820 | 3,060 | 4,220 | 5,410 | 6,950 | 8,490 | 10,330 | 12,360 | 14,540 | ... | ... | ... |
| 130 | 1,140 | 2,210 | 3,460 | 4,640 | 5,850 | 7,400 | 8,950 | 10,800 | 12,840 | 15,070 | ... | ... | ... |
| 140 | 1,450 | 2,550 | 3,810 | 5,000 | 6,230 | 7,780 | 9,340 | 11,200 | 13,250 | 15,500 | ... | ... | ... |
| 150 | 1,720 | 2,840 | 4,110 | 5,320 | 6,560 | 8,120 | 9,680 | 11,550 | 13,600 | 15,850 | ... | ... | ... |
| 160 | 1,950 | 3,080 | 4,360 | 5,600 | 6,840 | 8,420 | 9,990 | 11,850 | 13,950 | 16,200 | ... | ... | ... |
| 170 | 2,160 | 3,300 | 4,590 | 5,840 | 7,090 | 8,680 | 10,270 | 12,150 | 14,250 | 16,550 | ... | ... | ... |
| 180 | 2,360 | 3,510 | 4,810 | 6,060 | 7,320 | 8,920 | 10,500 | 12,400 | 14,550 | 16,900 | ... | ... | ... |
| 190 | 2,550 | 3,710 | 5,020 | 6,270 | 7,530 | 9,140 | 10,750 | 12,650 | 14,850 | 17,250 | ... | ... | ... |
| 200 | 2,730 | 3,900 | 5,220 | 6,470 | 7,730 | 9,340 | 10,950 | 12,850 | 15,100 | 17,600 | ... | ... | ... |

### BOARD-FOOT VOLUME,[b] SCRIBNER RULE

| Age (yr.) | Site index—in feet | | | | | | | | | | | | |
| --- | --- | --- | --- | --- | --- | --- | --- | --- | --- | --- | --- | --- | --- |
|  | 40 | 50 | 60 | 70 | 80 | 90 | 100 | 110 | 120 | 130 | 140 | 150 | 160 |
| 20 | ... | ... | ... | ... | ... | ... | ... | 100 | 400 | 900 | 1,900 | 3,800 | 7,300 |
| 30 | ... | ... | ... | ... | ... | 200 | 1,000 | 2,500 | 5,100 | 8,400 | 11,800 | 16,000 | 21,400 |
| 40 | ... | ... | ... | 100 | 600 | 1,900 | 4,300 | 7,500 | 12,100 | 17,600 | 23,100 | 29,200 | 36,500 |
| 50 | ... | ... | 100 | 700 | 2,300 | 5,000 | 9,200 | 14,000 | 20,300 | 27,400 | 34,600 | 42,500 | 51,300 |
| 60 | ... | ... | 600 | 2,200 | 5,100 | 9,100 | 14,800 | 21,000 | 28,400 | 37,000 | 45,800 | 55,300 | 65,400 |
| 70 | ... | 300 | 1,800 | 4,300 | 8,500 | 13,800 | 20,500 | 27,800 | 36,400 | 46,200 | 56,500 | 67,300 | 78,800 |
| 80 | 100 | 900 | 3,500 | 7,000 | 12,200 | 18,500 | 26,000 | 34,200 | 43,900 | 54,800 | 66,500 | 78,600 | 91,300 |
| 90 | 200 | 2,000 | 5,500 | 10,000 | 16,000 | 23,000 | 31,200 | 40,200 | 50,800 | 62,700 | 75,800 | 89,200 | 103,000 |
| 100 | 400 | 3,400 | 7,800 | 13,100 | 19,700 | 27,200 | 36,100 | 45,800 | 57,100 | 70,000 | 84,400 | 99,100 | 113,900 |
| 110 | 800 | 5,000 | 10,200 | 16,200 | 23,100 | 31,100 | 40,600 | 50,800 | 62,900 | 76,700 | ... | ... | ... |
| 120 | 1,500 | 7,000 | 12,500 | 19,000 | 26,200 | 34,700 | 44,600 | 55,400 | 68,200 | 82,800 | ... | ... | ... |
| 130 | 2,500 | 8,900 | 14,700 | 21,500 | 29,000 | 38,000 | 48,300 | 59,600 | 73,000 | 88,300 | ... | ... | ... |
| 140 | 3,800 | 10,700 | 16,700 | 23,700 | 31,500 | 40,900 | 51,700 | 63,400 | 77,400 | 93,200 | ... | ... | ... |
| 150 | 5,200 | 12,400 | 18,500 | 25,700 | 33,800 | 43,600 | 54,800 | 66,900 | 81,400 | 97,600 | ... | ... | ... |
| 160 | 6,600 | 13,900 | 20,100 | 27,500 | 35,900 | 46,100 | 57,600 | 70,100 | 84,900 | 101,500 | ... | ... | ... |
| 170 | 7,900 | 15,300 | 21,600 | 29,200 | 37,800 | 48,400 | 60,100 | 73,000 | 88,000 | 105,000 | ... | ... | ... |
| 180 | 9,000 | 16,600 | 23,100 | 30,900 | 39,600 | 50,500 | 62,400 | 75,600 | 90,900 | 108,200 | ... | ... | ... |
| 190 | 10,000 | 17,800 | 24,500 | 32,500 | 41,300 | 52,400 | 64,600 | 78,000 | 93,600 | 111,200 | ... | ... | ... |
| 200 | 11,000 | 19,000 | 25,800 | 34,000 | 43,000 | 54,200 | 66,700 | 80,200 | 96,100 | 114,100 | ... | ... | ... |

[a] To nearest 10 cu. ft.
[b] In 16-ft. logs above 2-ft. stump to 8-in top; volumes to nearest 100 bd. ft.

## PONDEROSA PINE
### Table 26. Increment of Fully Stocked Acre in Cubic Feet,* Trees 0.6-In. D.B.H. and Larger
#### Entire Range
##### PERIODIC ANNUAL INCREMENT

| Age (yr.) | Site index—in feet | | | | | | | | | | | | |
|---|---|---|---|---|---|---|---|---|---|---|---|---|---|
| | 40 | 50 | 60 | 70 | 80 | 90 | 100 | 110 | 120 | 130 | 140 | 150 | 160 |
| 25 | ... | 60 | 70 | 75 | 95 | 110 | 130 | 150 | 180 | 210 | 215 | 240 | 250 |
| 35 | 55 | 55 | 65 | 70 | 80 | 95 | 110 | 130 | 145 | 180 | 200 | 225 | 250 |
| 45 | 40 | 50 | 55 | 60 | 65 | 80 | 95 | 115 | 135 | 155 | 180 | 210 | 235 |
| 55 | 35 | 40 | 45 | 50 | 55 | 65 | 80 | 95 | 115 | 130 | 160 | 180 | 200 |
| 65 | 30 | 35 | 35 | 45 | 50 | 55 | 65 | 80 | 95 | 115 | 140 | 155 | 175 |
| 75 | 30 | 30 | 30 | 40 | 45 | 50 | 60 | 70 | 85 | 100 | 120 | 130 | 150 |
| 85 | 25 | 25 | 25 | 35 | 40 | 45 | 55 | 60 | 75 | 90 | 105 | 110 | 130 |
| 95 | 25 | 25 | 25 | 30 | 35 | 40 | 45 | 55 | 65 | 80 | 90 | 95 | 110 |
| 105 | 20 | 20 | 25 | 25 | 30 | 35 | 40 | 45 | 55 | 70 | ... | ... | ... |
| 115 | 20 | 20 | 25 | 25 | 25 | 30 | 35 | 40 | 50 | 60 | ... | ... | ... |
| 125 | 15 | 20 | 20 | 25 | 25 | 30 | 30 | 35 | 45 | 50 | ... | ... | ... |
| 135 | 15 | 15 | 20 | 20 | 20 | 25 | 30 | 35 | 40 | 40 | ... | ... | ... |
| 145 | 10 | 15 | 15 | 20 | 20 | 25 | 30 | 30 | 35 | 35 | ... | ... | ... |
| 155 | 10 | 15 | 15 | 15 | 20 | 25 | 25 | 30 | 35 | 35 | ... | ... | ... |
| 165 | 10 | 10 | 15 | 15 | 20 | 20 | 25 | 30 | 30 | 35 | ... | ... | ... |
| 175 | 10 | 10 | 15 | 15 | 20 | 20 | 25 | 25 | 30 | 35 | ... | ... | ... |
| 185 | 10 | 10 | 10 | 15 | 20 | 20 | 25 | 25 | 30 | 35 | ... | ... | ... |
| 195 | 10 | 10 | 10 | 15 | 15 | 20 | 20 | 20 | 25 | 35 | ... | ... | ... |

##### MEAN ANNUAL INCREMENT

| Age (yr.) | Site index—in feet | | | | | | | | | | | | |
|---|---|---|---|---|---|---|---|---|---|---|---|---|---|
| | 40 | 50 | 60 | 70 | 80 | 90 | 100 | 110 | 120 | 130 | 140 | 150 | 160 |
| 20 | ... | 10 | 20 | 35 | 50 | 68 | 85 | 105 | 120 | 138 | 168 | 188 | 218 |
| 30 | 17 | 27 | 37 | 48 | 65 | 82 | 100 | 120 | 140 | 162 | 183 | 205 | 228 |
| 40 | 26 | 34 | 44 | 54 | 69 | 85 | 102 | 122 | 141 | 166 | 188 | 210 | 234 |
| 50 | 29 | 37 | 46 | 55 | 68 | 84 | 101 | 121 | 140 | 164 | 186 | 210 | 234 |
| 60 | 30 | 38 | 46 | 54 | 66 | 81 | 98 | 117 | 136 | 158 | 182 | 205 | 228 |
| 70 | 30 | 37 | 44 | 53 | 64 | 77 | 93 | 111 | 130 | 152 | 176 | 198 | 221 |
| 80 | 30 | 36 | 42 | 51 | 61 | 74 | 89 | 106 | 124 | 146 | 169 | 189 | 212 |
| 90 | 29 | 35 | 41 | 49 | 59 | 71 | 85 | 101 | 119 | 139 | 162 | 181 | 203 |
| 100 | 29 | 34 | 39 | 48 | 56 | 68 | 81 | 96 | 114 | 134 | 154 | 172 | 194 |
| 110 | 28 | 33 | 38 | 45 | 54 | 65 | 77 | 92 | 108 | 128 | ... | ... | ... |
| 120 | 28 | 32 | 37 | 44 | 52 | 62 | 74 | 88 | 103 | 122 | ... | ... | ... |
| 130 | 27 | 31 | 35 | 42 | 50 | 59 | 70 | 83 | 99 | 117 | ... | ... | ... |
| 140 | 26 | 30 | 34 | 41 | 48 | 57 | 68 | 80 | 95 | 111 | ... | ... | ... |
| 150 | 25 | 29 | 33 | 39 | 46 | 55 | 65 | 77 | 91 | 106 | ... | ... | ... |
| 160 | 24 | 28 | 32 | 38 | 44 | 53 | 62 | 74 | 87 | 102 | ... | ... | ... |
| 170 | 23 | 27 | 31 | 36 | 43 | 51 | 60 | 71 | 84 | 98 | ... | ... | ... |
| 180 | 22 | 26 | 30 | 35 | 41 | 49 | 58 | 69 | 81 | 94 | ... | ... | ... |
| 190 | 22 | 25 | 29 | 34 | 40 | 48 | 57 | 66 | 78 | 91 | ... | ... | ... |
| 200 | 21 | 24 | 28 | 33 | 39 | 46 | 55 | 64 | 76 | 88 | ... | ... | ... |

Source: *Ibid.*
* Including stump and tip but not bark or branches.

## PONDEROSA PINE

### Table 27. Increment of Fully Stocked Acre, in Board Feet, Scribner Rule, Trees 11.6 In. D.B.H. and Larger

Entire Range

PERIODIC ANNUAL INCREMENT

| Age (yr.) | 40 | 50 | 60 | 70 | 80 | 90 | 100 | 110 | 120 | 130 | 140 | 150 | 160 |
|---|---|---|---|---|---|---|---|---|---|---|---|---|---|
| 25 | ... | ... | ... | ... | ... | ... | ... | 240 | 470 | 750 | 990 | 1,220 | 1,410 |
| 35 | ... | ... | ... | ... | ... | 170 | 330 | 500 | 700 | 920 | 1,130 | 1,320 | 1,510 |
| 45 | ... | ... | ... | 60 | 170 | 310 | 490 | 650 | 820 | 980 | 1,150 | 1,330 | 1,480 |
| 55 | ... | ... | 50 | 150 | 280 | 410 | 560 | 700 | 810 | 960 | 1,120 | 1,280 | 1,410 |
| 65 | ... | ... | 120 | 210 | 340 | 470 | 570 | 680 | 800 | 920 | 1,070 | 1,200 | 1,340 |
| 75 | ... | 60 | 170 | 270 | 370 | 470 | 550 | 640 | 750 | 860 | 1,000 | 1,130 | 1,250 |
| 85 | 10 | 110 | 200 | 300 | 380 | 450 | 520 | 600 | 690 | 790 | 930 | 1,060 | 1,170 |
| 95 | 20 | 140 | 230 | 310 | 370 | 420 | 490 | 560 | 630 | 730 | 860 | 990 | 1,090 |
| 105 | 40 | 160 | 240 | 310 | 340 | 390 | 450 | 500 | 580 | 670 | ... | ... | ... |
| 115 | 70 | 200 | 230 | 280 | 310 | 360 | 400 | 460 | 530 | 610 | ... | ... | ... |
| 125 | 100 | 190 | 220 | 250 | 280 | 330 | 370 | 420 | 480 | 550 | ... | ... | ... |
| 135 | 130 | 180 | 200 | 220 | 250 | 290 | 340 | 380 | 440 | 490 | ... | ... | ... |
| 145 | 140 | 170 | 180 | 200 | 230 | 270 | 310 | 350 | 400 | 440 | ... | ... | ... |
| 155 | 140 | 150 | 160 | 180 | 210 | 250 | 280 | 320 | 350 | 390 | ... | ... | ... |
| 165 | 130 | 140 | 150 | 170 | 190 | 230 | 250 | 290 | 310 | 350 | ... | ... | ... |
| 175 | 110 | 130 | 150 | 170 | 180 | 210 | 230 | 260 | 290 | 320 | ... | ... | ... |
| 185 | 100 | 120 | 140 | 160 | 170 | 190 | 220 | 240 | 270 | 300 | ... | ... | ... |
| 195 | 100 | 120 | 130 | 150 | 170 | 180 | 210 | 220 | 250 | 290 | ... | ... | ... |

MEAN ANNUAL INCREMENT

| Age (yr.) | 40 | 50 | 60 | 70 | 80 | 90 | 100 | 110 | 120 | 130 | 140 | 150 | 160 |
|---|---|---|---|---|---|---|---|---|---|---|---|---|---|
| 20 | ... | ... | ... | ... | ... | ... | ... | 5 | 20 | 45 | 95 | 190 | 365 |
| 30 | ... | ... | ... | ... | ... | 7 | 33 | 83 | 170 | 280 | 393 | 533 | 713 |
| 40 | ... | ... | ... | 2 | 15 | 48 | 108 | 188 | 302 | 440 | 578 | 730 | 912 |
| 50 | ... | ... | 2 | 14 | 46 | 100 | 184 | 280 | 406 | 548 | 692 | 850 | 1,026 |
| 60 | ... | ... | 10 | 37 | 85 | 152 | 247 | 350 | 473 | 617 | 763 | 922 | 1,090 |
| 70 | ... | 4 | 26 | 61 | 121 | 197 | 293 | 397 | 520 | 660 | 807 | 961 | 1,126 |
| 80 | 1 | 11 | 44 | 88 | 152 | 231 | 325 | 428 | 549 | 685 | 831 | 982 | 1,141 |
| 90 | 2 | 22 | 61 | 111 | 178 | 256 | 347 | 447 | 564 | 697 | 842 | 991 | 1,144 |
| 100 | 4 | 34 | 78 | 131 | 197 | 272 | 361 | 458 | 571 | 700 | 844 | 991 | 1,139 |
| 110 | 7 | 45 | 93 | 147 | 210 | 283 | 369 | 462 | 572 | 697 | ... | ... | ... |
| 120 | 12 | 58 | 104 | 158 | 218 | 289 | 372 | 462 | 568 | 690 | ... | ... | ... |
| 130 | 19 | 68 | 113 | 165 | 223 | 292 | 372 | 458 | 562 | 679 | ... | ... | ... |
| 140 | 27 | 76 | 119 | 169 | 225 | 292 | 369 | 453 | 553 | 666 | ... | ... | ... |
| 150 | 35 | 83 | 123 | 171 | 225 | 291 | 365 | 446 | 543 | 651 | ... | ... | ... |
| 160 | 41 | 87 | 126 | 172 | 224 | 288 | 360 | 438 | 531 | 634 | ... | ... | ... |
| 170 | 46 | 90 | 127 | 172 | 222 | 285 | 354 | 429 | 518 | 618 | ... | ... | ... |
| 180 | 50 | 92 | 128 | 172 | 220 | 281 | 347 | 420 | 505 | 601 | ... | ... | ... |
| 190 | 53 | 94 | 129 | 171 | 217 | 276 | 340 | 411 | 493 | 585 | ... | ... | ... |
| 200 | 55 | 95 | 129 | 170 | 215 | 271 | 334 | 401 | 480 | 570 | ... | ... | ... |

Source: *Ibid.*

# PONDEROSA PINE

## Table 28. Stand Table for Fully Stocked Acre

### Entire Range

#### SITE INDEX 40

| Diameter class (inches) | Trees per acre, by age class | | | | | | | | | |
|---|---|---|---|---|---|---|---|---|---|---|
| | 20 years | 40 years | 60 years | 80 years | 100 years | 120 years | 140 years | 160 years | 180 years | 200 years |
| | Number | Number | Number | Number | Number | Number | Number | Number | Number | Number |
| 1 | | 4,072 | 532 | 146 | 41 | 19 | 9 | 4 | 2 | 1 |
| 2–3 | | 2,645 | 1,568 | 504 | 190 | 89 | 43 | 26 | 16 | 9 |
| 4–5 | | 223 | 588 | 396 | 216 | 128 | 68 | 47 | 32 | 24 |
| 6–7 | | 20 | 98 | 177 | 156 | 115 | 82 | 58 | 44 | 36 |
| 8–9 | | | 14 | 61 | 89 | 79 | 75 | 57 | 49 | 40 |
| 10–11 | | | | 16 | 37 | 47 | 48 | 48 | 43 | 37 |
| 12–13 | | | | | 11 | 22 | 27 | 30 | 30 | 28 |
| 14–15 | | | | | 4 | 9 | 14 | 17 | 20 | 22 |
| 16–17 | | | | | | 2 | 6 | 9 | 13 | 11 |
| 18–19 | | | | | | 2 | 2 | 5 | 3 | 6 |
| 20–21 | | | | | | | 1 | 1 | 1 | 3 |
| 22–23 | | | | | | | | | 1 | 1 |
| Total | | 6,960 | 2,800 | 1,300 | 744 | 512 | 375 | 302 | 254 | 218 |

#### SITE INDEX 60

| Diameter class (inches) | 20 years | 40 years | 60 years | 80 years | 100 years | 120 years | 140 years | 160 years | 180 years | 200 years |
|---|---|---|---|---|---|---|---|---|---|---|
| 1 | 3,359 | 486 | 96 | 23 | 7 | 2 | 1 | | 1 | 1 |
| 2–3 | 1,168 | 1,457 | 350 | 110 | 42 | 15 | | 3 | | 1 |
| 4–5 | 64 | 608 | 358 | 159 | 70 | 33 | 16 | 8 | 4 | 2 |
| 6–7 | 9 | 130 | 217 | 149 | 81 | 49 | 28 | 17 | 10 | 6 |
| 8–9 | | 19 | 90 | 98 | 78 | 53 | 37 | 24 | 17 | 11 |
| 10–11 | | | 26 | 56 | 58 | 45 | 39 | 31 | 22 | 16 |
| 12–13 | | | 8 | 25 | 32 | 37 | 34 | 31 | 24 | 20 |
| 14–15 | | | | 10 | 19 | 24 | 25 | 25· | 24 | 19 |
| 16–17 | | | | 4 | 8 | 13 | 16 | 18 | 19 | 18 |
| 18–19 | | | | | 3 | 6 | 10 | 12 | 14 | 15 |
| 20–21 | | | | | 2 | 3 | 5 | 7 | 9 | 11 |
| 22–23 | | | | | | 1 | 2 | 3 | 5 | 6 |
| 24–25 | | | | | | | 1 | 1 | 2 | 3 |
| 26–27 | | | | | | | | 1 | 1 | 1 |
| 28–29 | | | | | | | | | | 1 |
| Total | 4,600 | 2,700 | 1,145 | 634 | 400 | 281 | 219 | 181 | 152 | 130 |

#### SITE INDEX 80

| Diameter class (inches) | 20 years | 40 years | 60 years | 80 years | 100 years | 120 years | 140 years | 160 years | 180 years | 200 years |
|---|---|---|---|---|---|---|---|---|---|---|
| 1 | 810 | 103 | 22 | 4 | | | | | | |
| 2–3 | 1,171 | 399 | 97 | 32 | 8 | 4 | 1 | | | |
| 4–5 | 238 | 394 | 158 | 57 | 21 | 6 | 3 | 2 | 1 | |
| 6–7 | 27 | 235 | 149 | 75 | 36 | 17 | 7 | 4 | 2 | 2 |
| 8–9 | 4 | 99 | 116 | 75 | 46 | 25 | 13 | 7 | 4 | 3 |
| 10–11 | | 30 | 64 | 65 | 47 | 31 | 18 | 12 | 7 | 5 |
| 12–13 | | 10 | 33 | 39 | 39 | 32 | 22 | 14 | 10 | 7 |
| 14–15 | | | 15 | 25 | 31 | 29 | 24 | 19 | 14 | 10 |
| 16–17 | | | 6 | 12 | 19 | 21 | 21 | 18 | 15 | 11 |
| 18–19 | | | 2 | 6 | 11 | 15 | 17 | 17 | 15 | 12 |
| 20–21 | | | | 2 | 5 | 9 | 13 | 13 | 13 | 12 |
| 22–23 | | | | 1 | 2 | 4 | 7 | 10 | 11 | 11 |
| 24–25 | | | | | 1 | 2 | 4 | 6 | 7 | 9 |
| 26–27 | | | | | | 1 | 2 | 3 | 4 | 6 |
| 28–29 | | | | | | | 1 | 1 | 2 | 3 |
| 30–31 | | | | | | | | | 1 | 1 |
| Total | 2,250 | 1,270 | 662 | 393 | 266 | 196 | 153 | 126 | 106 | 92 |

Source: *Ibid.*

## Table 28. Stand Table for Fully Stocked Acre (Continued)

### SITE INDEX 100

| Diameter class (inches) | Trees per acre, by age class | | | | | | | | | |
|---|---|---|---|---|---|---|---|---|---|---|
| | 20 years | 40 years | 60 years | 80 years | 100 years | 120 years | 140 years | 160 years | 180 years | 200 years |
| | Number | Number | Number | Number | Number | Number | Number | Number | Number | Number |
| 1 | 211 | 29 | 4 | | | | | | | |
| 2-3 | 634 | 137 | 35 | 7 | 2 | | | | | |
| 4-5 | 320 | 196 | 63 | 19 | 5 | 2 | 1 | | | |
| 6-7 | 95 | 181 | 85 | 34 | 12 | 5 | 2 | 1 | | |
| 8-9 | 20 | 121 | 85 | 49 | 22 | 9 | 4 | 2 | 1 | 1 |
| 10-11 | | 68 | 71 | 50 | 27 | 15 | 8 | 4 | 2 | 1 |
| 12-13 | | 35 | 47 | 44 | 31 | 20 | 11 | 7 | 4 | 2 |
| 14-15 | | 13 | 32 | 36 | 32 | 23 | 14 | 9 | 6 | 3 |
| 16-17 | | 5 | 13 | 23 | 25 | 22 | 17 | 11 | 8 | 5 |
| 18-19 | | | 6 | 13 | 19 | 20 | 17 | 13 | 9 | 6 |
| 20-21 | | | 4 | 7 | 12 | 16 | 16 | 13 | 10 | 8 |
| 22-23 | | | | 3 | 7 | 10 | 13 | 12 | 11 | 9 |
| 24-25 | | | | 1 | 3 | 6 | 9 | 10 | 10 | 9 |
| 26-27 | | | | | 2 | 3 | 5 | 8 | 8 | 8 |
| 28-29 | | | | | | 1 | 2 | 5 | 6 | 7 |
| 30-31 | | | | | | | 1 | 2 | 4 | 6 |
| 32-33 | | | | | | | | 1 | 2 | 3 |
| 34-35 | | | | | | | | | 1 | 1 |
| 36-37 | | | | | | | | | | 1 |
| Total | 1,280 | 785 | 445 | 286 | 199 | 152 | 120 | 98 | 82 | 70 |

### SITE INDEX 120

| Diameter class (inches) | 20 years | 40 years | 60 years | 80 years | 100 years | 120 years | 140 years | 160 years | 180 years | 200 years |
|---|---|---|---|---|---|---|---|---|---|---|
| 1 | 62 | 9 | | | | | | | | |
| 2-3 | 234 | 51 | 10 | 2 | | | | | | |
| 4-5 | 242 | 92 | 28 | 6 | 2 | | | | | |
| 6-7 | 148 | 108 | 44 | 14 | 4 | 3 | 1 | | | |
| 8-9 | 65 | 108 | 61 | 23 | 9 | 4 | 2 | 1 | 1 | |
| 10-11 | 21 | 75 | 58 | 32 | 15 | 7 | 3 | 2 | 1 | 1 |
| 12-13 | 7 | 48 | 51 | 37 | 19 | 10 | 5 | 3 | 1 | 1 |
| 14-15 | | 28 | 39 | 35 | 23 | 13 | 7 | 4 | 2 | 1 |
| 16-17 | | 13 | 25 | 28 | 24 | 16 | 10 | 6 | 4 | 3 |
| 18-19 | | 5 | 14 | 22 | 22 | 18 | 12 | 8 | 5 | 4 |
| 20-21 | | 2 | 6 | 14 | 19 | 17 | 14 | 9 | 6 | 4 |
| 22-23 | | | 3 | 7 | 13 | 14 | 12 | 11 | 7 | 5 |
| 24-25 | | | 1 | 3 | 7 | 11 | 11 | 10 | 9 | 6 |
| 26-27 | | | | 2 | 4 | 7 | 9 | 9 | 8 | 7 |
| 28-29 | | | | | 1 | 4 | 7 | 8 | 7 | 8 |
| 30-31 | | | | | | 1 | 4 | 6 | 6 | 7 |
| 32-33 | | | | | | | 2 | 3 | 5 | 6 |
| 34-35 | | | | | | | | 1 | 4 | 5 |
| 36-37 | | | | | | | | | 2 | 2 |
| Total | 779 | 539 | 340 | 225 | 162 | 125 | 99 | 81 | 68 | 58 |

## Table 28.  Stand Table for Fully Stocked Acre (Continued)

### SITE INDEX 140

| Diameter class (inches) | Trees per acre, by age class | | | | | | | | | |
|---|---|---|---|---|---|---|---|---|---|---|
| | 20 years | 40 years | 60 years | 80 years | 100 years | 120 years | 140 years | 160 years | 180 years | 200 years |
| | Number | Number | Number | Number | Number | Number | Number | Number | Number | Number |
| 1 | 24 | 2 | | | | | | | | |
| 2–3 | 111 | 17 | 2 | | | | | | | |
| 4–5 | 146 | 44 | 8 | 3 | | | | | | |
| 6–7 | 129 | 65 | 19 | 6 | 3 | | | | | |
| 8–9 | 81 | 75 | 32 | 13 | 4 | | | | | |
| 10–11 | 42 | 67 | 39 | 16 | 8 | | | | | |
| 12–13 | 19 | 55 | 45 | 22 | 11 | | | | | |
| 14–15 | 7 | 38 | 42 | 26 | 14 | | | | | |
| 16–17 | 2 | 23 | 32 | 27 | 17 | | | | | |
| 18–19 | | 11 | 24 | 26 | 19 | | | | | |
| 20–21 | | 5 | 14 | 18 | 18 | | | | | |
| 22–23 | | 3 | 7 | 14 | 17 | | | | | |
| 24–25 | | | 3 | 8 | 13 | | | | | |
| 26–27 | | | 2 | 4 | 8 | | | | | |
| 28–29 | | | | 1 | 4 | | | | | |
| 30–31 | | | | 1 | 2 | | | | | |
| 32–33 | | | | | 1 | | | | | |
| Total | 561 | 405 | 269 | 185 | 139 | | | | | |

### SITE INDEX 160

| Diameter class (inches) | 20 years | 40 years | 60 years | 80 years | 100 years | 120 years | 140 years | 160 years | 180 years | 200 years |
|---|---|---|---|---|---|---|---|---|---|---|
| 1 | 9 | | | | | | | | | |
| 2–3 | 42 | 5 | | | | | | | | |
| 4–5 | 75 | 15 | 4 | 1 | | | | | | |
| 6–7 | 83 | 32 | 9 | 3 | 2 | | | | | |
| 8–9 | 74 | 46 | 16 | 6 | 3 | | | | | |
| 10–11 | 53 | 54 | 23 | 10 | 4 | | | | | |
| 12–13 | 32 | 53 | 31 | 14 | 6 | | | | | |
| 14–15 | 15 | 43 | 35 | 19 | 9 | | | | | |
| 16–17 | 7 | 30 | 32 | 21 | 12 | | | | | |
| 18–19 | 3 | 20 | 28 | 24 | 15 | | | | | |
| 20–21 | 1 | 11 | 21 | 21 | 18 | | | | | |
| 22–23 | | 5 | 13 | 17 | 15 | | | | | |
| 24–25 | | 2 | 7 | 13 | 13 | | | | | |
| 26–27 | | | 3 | 8 | 11 | | | | | |
| 28–29 | | | 2 | 4 | 8 | | | | | |
| 30–31 | | | | 1 | 4 | | | | | |
| 32–33 | | | | | 3 | | | | | |
| Total | 394 | 316 | 224 | 162 | 123 | | | | | |

**Supplementary information concerning Tables 24–28.** "It is seldom appreciated that the volume lost by a forest stand through **normal mortality** is such a large portion of the total production" (Meyer). Volumes in the following table are uncurved, and are approximate only; they include all trees 0.6-in. and larger dying in 20-yr. periods.

PERIODIC VOLUME LOSS PER ACRE * BY MORTALITY IN CUBIC FEET

| Age period (yr.) | Site index 40 | Site index 60 | Site index 80 | Site index 100 | Site index 120 | Site index 140 | Site index 160 |
|---|---|---|---|---|---|---|---|
| 20–40 | ... | 194 | 101 | 130 | 106 | 99 | 73 |
| 40–60 | 391 | 556 | 552 | 613 | 601 | 741 | 868 |
| 60–80 | 499 | 507 | 605 | 601 | 893 | 1,267 | 1,719 |
| 80–100 | 322 | 427 | 465 | 722 | 1,095 | 1,344 | 1,700 |
| 100–120 | 221 | 307 | 409 | 727 | 865 | ... | ... |
| 120–140 | 179 | 248 | 427 | 710 | 1,088 | ... | ... |
| 140–160 | 144 | 189 | 425 | 767 | 1,224 | ... | ... |
| 160–180 | 88 | 225 | 490 | 699 | 1,073 | ... | ... |
| 180–200 | 107 | 217 | 347 | 765 | 961 | ... | ... |

CUMULATIVE VOLUME LOSS PER ACRE * IN CUBIC FEET

| Age period (yr.) | Site index 40 | Site index 60 | Site index 80 | Site index 100 | Site index 120 | Site index 140 | Site index 160 |
|---|---|---|---|---|---|---|---|
| 20–40 | ... | 194 | 101 | 130 | 106 | 99 | 73 |
| 20–60 | 391 | 750 | 653 | 743 | 707 | 840 | 941 |
| 20–80 | 890 | 1,257 | 1,258 | 1,344 | 1,600 | 2,107 | 2,660 |
| 20–100 | 1,212 | 1,684 | 1,723 | 2,066 | 2,695 | 3,451 | 4,360 |
| 20–120 | 1,433 | 1,991 | 2,132 | 2,793 | 3,560 | ... | ... |
| 20–140 | 1,612 | 2,239 | 2,559 | 3,503 | 4,648 | ... | ... |
| 20–160 | 1,756 | 2,428 | 2,984 | 4,270 | 5,872 | ... | ... |
| 20–180 | 1,844 | 2,653 | 3,474 | 4,969 | 6,945 | ... | ... |
| 20–200 | 1,951 | 2,870 | 3,821 | 5,734 | 7,906 | ... | ... |

* In understocked stands volume loss by mortality is less than in normal stands, absolutely and perhaps relatively.

Cubic-foot and board-foot rotations suggested by the increments shown (disregarding the economic aspect) are as follows:

ROTATION AGES FOR EVEN-AGED STANDS IN YEARS

| Site index | Cubic-foot measure | Board-foot measure | | Site index | Cubic-foot measure | Board-foot measure | |
|---|---|---|---|---|---|---|---|
| | | International Rule | Scribner Rule | | | International Rule | Scribner Rule |
| 40 | 70 | ... | ... | 120 | 39 | 76 | 107 |
| 60 | 54 | 161 | 196 | 140 | 41 | 70 | 97 |
| 80 | 42 | 107 | 148 | 160 | 45 | 64 | 87 |
| 100 | 40 | 90 | 124 | | | | |

Financial considerations will probably dictate much shorter rotations than the above.

Footnotes for Table 29 (opposite):
[a] Mature heights, 151 + feet; yellow pine 80 + percent.
[b] Age at breast height is 20 years less than total age.
[c] Mature heights, 131 to 150 feet; yellow pine 80 + percent.
[d] Mature heights, 111 to 130 feet; yellow pine 80 + percent.
[e] Mature heights, 91 to 110 feet; yellow pine 80 + percent.
[f] Mature heights, 71 to 90 feet; yellow pine 80 + percent.
Source: S. B. Show, Yield capacities of the pure yellow pine type on the east slope of the Sierra Nevada Mountains in California, *Jour. Agr. Research* 51 (12), 1925.

### Table 29. Yields per Acre, Cubic Feet, and Board Feet, International $\frac{1}{8}$-In. Rule
Lassen National Forest, California

SITE 1[a]

| Total age (years) | Number of trees per acre | Basal area per acre | Height of dominant | Average diameter at breast height | Volume per acre | | Periodic annual growth | Mean annual growth | Board-feet per cubic foot |
|---|---|---|---|---|---|---|---|---|---|
| | | Sq. ft. | Feet | Inches | M. bd. ft. | Cu. ft. | M. bd. ft. | M. bd. ft. | |
| 60 | 356 | 168 | 53.0 | 9.3 | 3.5 | 2,320 | 0.35 | 0.06 | 1.51 |
| 70 | 251 | 197 | 64.0 | 12.0 | 13.5 | 4,300 | 1.00 | .19 | 3.14 |
| 80 | 202 | 225 | 75.0 | 14.3 | 27.5 | 6,480 | 1.40 | .34 | 4.24 |
| 90 | 174 | 252 | 86.0 | 16.3 | 43.5 | 8,500 | 1.60 | .48 | 5.12 |
| 100 | 158 | 276 | 95.0 | 17.9 | 58.5 | 10,250 | 1.50 | .58 | 5.71 |
| 110 | 146 | 297 | 103.0 | 19.3 | 67.5 | 11,680 | .90 | .61 | 5.78 |
| 120 | 138 | 314 | 109.0 | 20.4 | 74.0 | 12,800 | .65 | .62 | 5.78 |
| 130 | 134 | 328 | 113.5 | 21.2 | 79.0 | 13,650 | .50 | .61 | 5.79 |
| 140 | 133 | 342 | 117.0 | 21.7 | 83.0 | 14,350 | .40 | .59 | 5.78 |
| 150 | 132 | 353 | 120.5 | 22.1 | 86.8 | 14,950 | .38 | .58 | 5.81 |

SITE 2[c]

| Total age (years) | Number of trees per acre | Basal area per acre | Height of dominant | Average diameter at breast height | Volume per acre | | Periodic annual growth | Mean annual growth | Board-feet per cubic foot |
|---|---|---|---|---|---|---|---|---|---|
| 60 | 417 | 142 | 41.0 | 8.0 | 1.0 | 1,060 | 0.10 | 0.02 | 0.94 |
| 70 | 280 | 165 | 51.0 | 10.4 | 8.0 | 2,660 | .70 | .11 | 3.01 |
| 80 | 222 | 189 | 61.0 | 12.5 | 17.0 | 4,260 | .90 | .21 | 3.99 |
| 90 | 196 | 215 | 71.0 | 14.2 | 27.0 | 6,030 | 1.00 | .30 | 4.48 |
| 100 | 177 | 235 | 81.0 | 15.6 | 38.0 | 7,800 | 1.10 | .38 | 4.87 |
| 110 | 164 | 255 | 91.0 | 16.9 | 48.0 | 9,110 | 1.00 | .44 | 5.27 |
| 120 | 156 | 270 | 97.0 | 17.8 | 56.0 | 10,190 | .80 | .47 | 5.50 |
| 130 | 148 | 283 | 100.0 | 18.7 | 61.0 | 11,050 | .50 | .47 | 5.52 |
| 140 | 148 | 295 | 103.5 | 19.1 | 65.0 | 11,730 | .40 | .46 | 5.54 |
| 150 | 147 | 305 | 107.0 | 19.5 | 68.5 | 12,300 | .35 | .46 | 5.57 |

SITE 3[d]

| Total age (years) | Number of trees per acre | Basal area per acre | Height of dominant | Average diameter at breast height | Volume per acre | | Periodic annual growth | Mean annual growth | Board-feet per cubic foot |
|---|---|---|---|---|---|---|---|---|---|
| 60 | 450 | 124 | 34.0 | 7.1 | ---- | ---- | ---- | ---- | ---- |
| 70 | 331 | 143 | 42.0 | 8.9 | 3.0 | 1,180 | 0.3 | 0.04 | 2.54 |
| 80 | 273 | 164 | 52.0 | 10.5 | 9.0 | 2,600 | .6 | .11 | 3.46 |
| 90 | 229 | 183 | 62.0 | 12.1 | 17.3 | 3,900 | .83 | .19 | 4.44 |
| 100 | 209 | 202 | 71.0 | 13.3 | 25.7 | 5,400 | .84 | .26 | 4.76 |
| 110 | 191 | 219 | 81.0 | 14.5 | 34.0 | 7,000 | .83 | .31 | 4.86 |
| 120 | 178 | 230 | 85.0 | 15.4 | 40.7 | 7,970 | .67 | .34 | 5.11 |
| 130 | 167 | 237 | 88.0 | 16.1 | 45.0 | 8,600 | .43 | .35 | 5.23 |
| 140 | 162 | 243 | 91.0 | 16.6 | 47.7 | 9,100 | .27 | .34 | 5.24 |
| 150 | 158 | 249 | 93.0 | 17.0 | 50.5 | 9,570 | .28 | .34 | 5.28 |

SITE 4[e]

| Total age (years) | Number of trees per acre | Basal area per acre | Height of dominant | Average diameter at breast height | Volume per acre | | Periodic annual growth | Mean annual growth | Board-feet per cubic foot |
|---|---|---|---|---|---|---|---|---|---|
| 60 | 526 | 100 | 28.0 | 5.9 | ---- | ---- | ---- | ---- | ---- |
| 70 | 395 | 118 | 36.0 | 7.4 | 0.5 | 450 | ---- | 0.007 | 1.11 |
| 80 | 335 | 135 | 43.0 | 8.6 | 4.0 | 1,600 | 0.35 | .05 | 2.50 |
| 90 | 296 | 152 | 52.0 | 9.7 | 8.4 | 2,650 | .44 | .09 | 3.17 |
| 100 | 270 | 169 | 60.0 | 10.7 | 13.7 | 3,750 | .53 | .14 | 3.65 |
| 110 | 247 | 182 | 68.0 | 11.6 | 20.2 | 4,800 | .65 | .18 | 4.21 |
| 120 | 221 | 191 | 73.0 | 12.6 | 26.0 | 5,570 | .58 | .22 | 4.67 |
| 130 | 205 | 200 | 76.5 | 13.4 | 30.0 | 6,070 | .40 | .23 | 4.94 |
| 140 | 189 | 205 | 79.0 | 14.1 | 33.0 | 6,500 | .30 | .24 | 5.08 |
| 150 | 177 | 209 | 81.0 | 14.7 | 35.8 | 6,830 | .28 | .24 | 5.24 |

SITE 5[f]

| Total age (years) | Number of trees per acre | Basal area per acre | Height of dominant | Average diameter at breast height | Volume per acre | | Periodic annual growth | Mean annual growth | Board-feet per cubic foot |
|---|---|---|---|---|---|---|---|---|---|
| 60 | 727 | 81 | 21.0 | 4.5 | ---- | ---- | ---- | ---- | ---- |
| 70 | 531 | 94 | 28.0 | 5.7 | ---- | ---- | ---- | ---- | ---- |
| 80 | 429 | 108 | 35.0 | 6.8 | 1.0 | 850 | 0.1 | 0.012 | 1.18 |
| 90 | 375 | 121 | 42.5 | 7.7 | 3.5 | 1,700 | .25 | .04 | 2.06 |
| 100 | 337 | 133 | 50.0 | 8.5 | 6.5 | 2,400 | .30 | .06 | 2.71 |
| 110 | 296 | 143 | 56.5 | 9.4 | 10.2 | 3,050 | .37 | .09 | 3.34 |
| 120 | 273 | 152 | 61.0 | 10.1 | 14.5 | 3,550 | .43 | .12 | 4.08 |
| 130 | 252 | 160 | 63.0 | 10.8 | 18.3 | 3,920 | .38 | .14 | 4.67 |
| 140 | 238 | 166 | 64.5 | 11.3 | 21.5 | 4,280 | .32 | .15 | 5.02 |
| 150 | 229 | 171 | 66.0 | 11.7 | 24.2 | 4,600 | .27 | .16 | 5.26 |

Footnotes on opposite page.

# SHORTLEAF PINE (SECOND GROWTH)

## Table 30. Normal Yields, by Site Index

| Age a (yr.) | Total height, average of dominant and co-dominant trees | Trees 4 in. d.b.h. and larger | | | | | Trees 8 in. d.b.h. and larger | |
|---|---|---|---|---|---|---|---|---|
| | | Stand per acre | Average diameter b | Basal area c per acre | Rough wood d Yield per acre | Rough wood d Growth per acre per year | Yield per acre (Scribner Dec. C Rule) (bd. ft. in tens) | Growth per acre per year (Scribner Dec. C Rule) (bd. ft. in tens) |
| **70-FT. SITE** | | | | | | | | |
| 15 | 26 | 330 | 3.8 | ... | ... | ... | ... | ... |
| 20 | 34 | 780 | 4.6 | 102 | 18 | 0.90 | ... | ... |
| 25 | 42 | 990 | 5.3 | 143 | 31 | 1.24 | 55 | 2 |
| 30 | 49 | 825 | 6.0 | 161 | 41 | 1.37 | 240 | 8 |
| 35 | 55 | 660 | 6.7 | 165 | 49 | 1.40 | 540 | 15 |
| 40 | 61 | 545 | 7.4 | 167 | 56 | 1.40 | 990 | 25 |
| 45 | 66 | 460 | 8.0 | 167 | 61 | 1.36 | 1,430 | 32 |
| 50 | 70 | 405 | 8.6 | 168 | 66 | 1.32 | 1,785 | 36 |
| 55 | 74 | 360 | 9.1 | 168 | 70 | 1.27 | 2,090 | 38 |
| 60 | 77 | 330 | 9.7 | 168 | 73 | 1.22 | 2,345 | 39 |
| **90-FT. SITE** | | | | | | | | |
| 15 | 33 | 610 | 5.0 | ... | 15 | 1.00 | ... | ... |
| 20 | 44 | 800 | 5.8 | 141 | 30 | 1.50 | 110 | 6 |
| 25 | 54 | 660 | 6.9 | 159 | 43 | 1.72 | 450 | 18 |
| 30 | 63 | 525 | 7.9 | 167 | 54 | 1.80 | 1,120 | 37 |
| 35 | 71 | 410 | 8.8 | 171 | 64 | 1.83 | 1,760 | 50 |
| 40 | 78 | 330 | 9.8 | 172 | 73 | 1.82 | 2,340 | 58 |
| 45 | 85 | 280 | 10.6 | 172 | 80 | 1.78 | 2,820 | 63 |
| 50 | 90 | 240 | 11.5 | 173 | 87 | 1.74 | 3,240 | 65 |
| 55 | 95 | 205 | 12.2 | 173 | 93 | 1.69 | 3,580 | 65 |
| 60 | 99 | 180 | 12.9 | 173 | 98 | 1.63 | 3,870 | 64 |

a Average age of dominant trees in stand. If age determinations are made at breast height (4½ ft. from the ground), 3 yr. should be added to get total age. If they are made at a stump height of 1 ft., 2 yr. should be added.

b Diameter at breast height of the tree of average basal area.

c Cross-sectional area in square feet at the point of diameter measurement (4½ ft. from the ground).

d In cords. A cord equals 128 cu. ft. gross volume of stacked cordwood.

Source: This table was assembled from Tables 97, 105, 106, 107, 110, 111, 119, and 120, Volume, yield, and stand tables for second-growth southern pines, U. S. Dept. Agr., *Misc. Publ. No. 50*, 1929. Sites are designated by the height attained on each by the average dominant and codominant trees in a 50-yr.-old stand. This height is called the site index. Thus a site with an index of 70 ft. produces dominant and codominant trees averaging 70 ft. in height at 50 yr.

## SLASH PINE (SECOND GROWTH)
### Table 31. Normal Yields, by Site Index

| Age [a] (yr.) | Total height, average of dominant and co-dominant trees | Trees 4 in. d.b.h. and larger | | | | | Trees 8 in. d.b.h. and larger | |
|---|---|---|---|---|---|---|---|---|
| | | | | | Rough wood [d] | | Yield per acre (Scribner Dec. C Rule) (bd. ft. in tens) | Growth per acre per year (Scribner Dec. C Rule) (bd. ft. in tens) |
| | | Stand per acre | Average diameter [b] | Basal area [c] per acre | Yield per acre | Growth per acre per year | | |
| **70-FT. SITE** | | | | | | | | |
| 15 | 34 | 700 | 4.8 | 85 | 21 | 1.40 | ... | ... |
| 20 | 42 | 840 | 5.1 | 121 | 28 | 1.40 | ... | ... |
| 25 | 49 | 805 | 5.8 | 140 | 34 | 1.36 | 130 | 5 |
| 30 | 56 | 685 | 6.4 | 150 | 40 | 1.33 | 350 | 12 |
| 35 | 61 | 555 | 7.1 | 155 | 46 | 1.31 | 625 | 18 |
| 40 | 64 | 475 | 7.7 | 157 | 49 | 1.22 | 930 | 23 |
| 45 | 67 | 420 | 8.3 | 159 | 53 | 1.18 | 1,210 | 27 |
| 50 | 70 | 375 | 8.8 | 160 | 55 | 1.10 | 1,425 | 28 |
| 55 | 72 | 343 | 9.1 | 161 | 57 | 1.04 | 1,600 | 29 |
| 60 | 74 | 325 | 9.4 | 161 | 59 | .98 | 1,740 | 29 |
| **90-FT. SITE** | | | | | | | | |
| 15 | 43 | 685 | 5.6 | 113 | 32 | 2.13 | 50 | 3 |
| 20 | 54 | 665 | 6.1 | 141 | 41 | 2.05 | 275 | 14 |
| 25 | 63 | 570 | 7.1 | 152 | 48 | 1.92 | 660 | 26 |
| 30 | 71 | 450 | 8.2 | 157 | 54 | 1.80 | 1,230 | 41 |
| 35 | 77 | 350 | 9.2 | 160 | 60 | 1.71 | 1,700 | 49 |
| 40 | 83 | 290 | 10.1 | 162 | 66 | 1.65 | 2,060 | 52 |
| 45 | 87 | 250 | 10.8 | 164 | 70 | 1.56 | 2,345 | 52 |
| 50 | 90 | 220 | 11.4 | 165 | 73 | 1.46 | 2,590 | 52 |
| 55 | 93 | 205 | 12.0 | 165 | 76 | 1.38 | 2,800 | 51 |
| 60 | 95 | 195 | 12.5 | 166 | 78 | 1.30 | 2,960 | 49 |

[a] Average age of dominant trees in stand. If age determinations are made at breast height (4½ ft. from the ground), 3 yr. should be added to get total age. If they are made at a stump height of 1 ft., 2 yr. should be added.

[b] Diameter at breast height of the tree of average basal area.

[c] Cross-sectional area in square feet at the point of diameter measurement (4½ ft. from the ground).

[d] In cords. A cord equals 128 cu. ft. gross volume of stacked cordwood.

Source: This table was assembled from Tables 129, 137, 138, 139, 142, 143, 151, 152, Volume, yield, and stand tables for second-growth southern pines, U. S. Dept. Agr., *Misc. Publ. No. 50*, 1929. Sites are designated by the height attained on each by the average dominant and codominant trees in a 50-year-old stand. This height is called the site index. Thus a site with an index of 70 ft. produces dominant and codominant trees averaging 70 ft. in height at 50 yr.

## EASTERN WHITE PINE
### Table 32.  Yield per Fully Stocked Acre
Massachusetts

| AGE (YEARS). | QUALITY I. | | | QUALITY II. | | | QUALITY III. | | |
|---|---|---|---|---|---|---|---|---|---|
| | 1-Inch Boards. | Cords. | Cubic Feet. | 1-Inch Boards. | Cords. | Cubic Feet. | 1-Inch Boards. | Cords. | Cubic Feet. |
| 25, . . . | 10,825 | 25.1 | 2,080 | 6,750 | 16.4 | 1,300 | 3,975 | 10.8 | 750 |
| 30, . . . | 19,900 | 44.0 | 3,750 | 12,500 | 31.2 | 2,740 | 7,500 | 18.2 | 1,400 |
| 35, . . . | 31,150 | 60 4 | 5,420 | 24,400 | 49.0 | 4,375 | 16,950 | 35.8 | 3,035 |
| 40, . . . | 40,650 | 70.6 | 6,590 | 32,800 | 58.0 | 5,300 | 25,200 | 46.2 | 4,080 |
| 45, . . . | 49,350 | 78.0 | 7,420 | 40,600 | 64.8 | 6,075 | 32,100 | 51.8 | 4,785 |
| 50, . . . | 55,150 | 84.2 | 8,035 | 46,500 | 70.0 | 6,725 | 37,550 | 56.6 | 5,475 |
| 55, . . . | 59,650 | 89.2 | 8,575 | 50,550 | 74 8 | 7,200 | 42,100 | 60.8 | 6,015 |
| 60, . . . | 63,600 | 93.4 | 9,075 | 53,200 | 79.2 | 7,655 | 44,550 | 64.6 | 6,340 |
| 65, . . . | 67,050 | 97.2 | 9,550 | 56,600 | 83.0 | 8,050 | 46,150 | 68.4 | 6,550 |

Source: H. O. Cook, Forest mensuration of the white pine in Massachusetts, State Forester, Boston, Mass., 1911.


## EASTERN WHITE PINE (SECOND GROWTH)
### Table 33.  Yields per Fully Stocked Acre
Wisconsin

SITE INDEX 60 (MEDIUM SITE)

| Age (Yr.) | Height of average dominant tree (Ft.) | Average height of all trees (Ft.) | Average diameter at breast height (In.) | Number of trees 1 in. and over | Total basal area (Sq. ft.) | Yield | | |
|---|---|---|---|---|---|---|---|---|
| | | | | | | Total (cu. ft.) inside bark | Board feet | |
| | | | | | | | International ⅛″ log rule | Scribner Decimal C |
| 30 | 32 | 28 | 3.9 | 2,150 | 179 | 2,250 | | |
| 40 | 47 | 44 | 6.1 | 1,040 | 210 | 4,200 | 10,500 | 4,000 |
| 50 | 60 | 57 | 7.6 | 725 | 230 | 5,800 | 23,000 | 10,700 |
| 60 | 71 | 68 | 9.0 | 546 | 242 | 7,200 | 36,500 | 20,500 |
| 70 | 80 | 77 | 10.1 | 447 | 250 | 8,470 | 49,000 | 31,300 |
| 80 | 88 | 85 | 11.1 | 384 | 257 | 9,500 | 59,000 | 40,900 |
| 90 | 94 | 92 | 11.9 | 337 | 262 | 10,400 | 66,500 | 48,500 |
| 100 | 99 | 97 | 12.6 | 303 | 265 | 11,100 | 72,000 | 55,000 |
| 110 | 103 | 101 | 13.2 | 278 | 267 | 11,700 | 77,000 | 60,500 |
| 120 | 106 | 104 | 13.7 | 263 | 270 | 12,200 | 80,500 | 65,000 |

Source: S. R. Gevorkiantz and Raphael Zon, Second-growth white pine in Wisconsin: its growth, yield, and commercial possibilities, Wisconsin Agr. Exp. Sta. *Res. Bull.* *No. 98*, 1930.

## WESTERN WHITE PINE (SECOND GROWTH)

### Table 34. Yields per Acre, Fully Stocked Stands

Inland Empire

#### POOR SITE—INDEX 40

| Total age (years) | Height of average dominant | All trees 0.6 inch plus | Average d. b. h. of trees 0.6 inch plus | Basal area, trees 0.6 inch plus | Total volume | | | | Average yearly growth | | | |
|---|---|---|---|---|---|---|---|---|---|---|---|---|
| | | | | | Trees 0.6 inch plus | International ⅛-inch rule | | Scribner rule, trees 12.6 inches plus | Cubic-foot, trees 0.6 inch plus | International ⅛-inch rule | | Scribner rule, trees 12.6 inches plus |
| | | | | | | Trees 6.6 inches plus | Trees 12.6 inches plus | | | Trees 6.6 inches plus | Trees 12.6 inches plus | |
| | Feet | No. | Inches | Sq. ft. | Cu. ft. | Bd. ft. | Bd. ft. | Bd. ft. | Cu. ft. | Bd. ft. | Bd. ft. | Bd. ft. |
| 20 | 10 | 11,500 | 0.8 | 45 | 240 | -------- | -------- | -------- | 12 | -------- | -------- | -------- |
| 40 | 30 | 5,600 | 2.2 | 146 | 1,890 | 500 | -------- | -------- | 47 | 12 | -------- | -------- |
| 60 | 49 | 3,020 | 3.6 | 215 | 4,210 | 7,500 | 50 | 50 | 70 | 125 | 1 | 1 |
| 80 | 66 | 1,830 | 5.1 | 257 | 6,500 | 21,600 | 3,200 | 2,300 | 81 | 270 | 40 | 29 |
| 100 | 79 | 1,220 | 6.5 | 286 | 8,420 | 38,000 | 11,000 | 8,300 | 84 | 380 | 110 | 83 |
| 120 | 88 | 980 | 7.6 | 306 | 9,980 | 51,000 | 21,000 | 16,000 | 83 | 425 | 175 | 133 |
| 140 | 94 | 910 | 8.1 | 323 | 11,000 | 59,200 | 28,100 | 21,000 | 79 | 423 | 201 | 150 |
| 160 | 98 | 890 | 8.3 | 338 | 11,650 | 63,600 | 31,700 | 24,300 | 73 | 398 | 198 | 152 |

#### FAIR SITE—INDEX 50

| Total age (years) | Height | All trees | d.b.h. | Basal area | Cu. ft. | 6.6 in. | 12.6 in. | Scribner | Cu. ft. | 6.6 in. | 12.6 in. | Scribner |
|---|---|---|---|---|---|---|---|---|---|---|---|---|
| 20 | 12 | 7,800 | 1.0 | 46 | 320 | -------- | -------- | -------- | 16 | -------- | -------- | -------- |
| 40 | 38 | 3,650 | 2.7 | 148 | 2,270 | 1,900 | -------- | -------- | 57 | 48 | -------- | -------- |
| 60 | 61 | 2,000 | 4.5 | 218 | 5,050 | 13,700 | 1,000 | 700 | 84 | 228 | 17 | 12 |
| 80 | 82 | 1,230 | 6.2 | 260 | 7,750 | 33,300 | 8,400 | 6,500 | 97 | 416 | 105 | 81 |
| 100 | 99 | 820 | 8.0 | 289 | 10,100 | 54,300 | 25,000 | 19,200 | 101 | 543 | 250 | 192 |
| 120 | 110 | 660 | 9.3 | 310 | 12,000 | 70,300 | 44,100 | 32,200 | 100 | 586 | 268 | 368 |
| 140 | 117 | 610 | 10.0 | 327 | 13,250 | 80,400 | 55,600 | 41,000 | 95 | 574 | 397 | 293 |
| 160 | 122 | 590 | 10.3 | 342 | 14,000 | 85,900 | 60,200 | 45,500 | 88 | 537 | 376 | 284 |

#### GOOD SITE—INDEX 60

| Total age (years) | Height | All trees | d.b.h. | Basal area | Cu. ft. | 6.6 in. | 12.6 in. | Scribner | Cu. ft. | 6.6 in. | 12.6 in. | Scribner |
|---|---|---|---|---|---|---|---|---|---|---|---|---|
| 20 | 14 | 4,700 | 1.3 | 46 | 400 | -------- | -------- | -------- | 20 | -------- | -------- | -------- |
| 40 | 45 | 2,210 | 3.5 | 149 | 2,650 | 4,400 | -------- | -------- | 66 | 110 | -------- | -------- |
| 60 | 73 | 1,190 | 5.8 | 221 | 5,880 | 23,300 | 5,000 | 3,700 | 98 | 388 | 83 | 62 |
| 80 | 98 | 720 | 8.2 | 263 | 9,000 | 48,700 | 24,100 | 17,900 | 112 | 609 | 301 | 224 |
| 100 | 118 | 480 | 10.5 | 292 | 11,850 | 73,500 | 54,000 | 40,300 | 118 | 735 | 540 | 403 |
| 120 | 132 | 390 | 12.2 | 314 | 13,950 | 91,200 | 76,300 | 59,000 | 116 | 760 | 636 | 492 |
| 140 | 141 | 355 | 13.1 | 331 | 15,400 | 102,700 | 90,300 | 70,500 | 110 | 734 | 645 | 504 |
| 160 | 146 | 345 | 13.6 | 346 | 16,350 | 109,900 | 98,900 | 76,900 | 102 | 687 | 618 | 481 |

#### EXCELLENT SITE—INDEX 70

| Total age (years) | Height | All trees | d.b.h. | Basal area | Cu. ft. | 6.6 in. | 12.6 in. | Scribner | Cu. ft. | 6.6 in. | 12.6 in. | Scribner |
|---|---|---|---|---|---|---|---|---|---|---|---|---|
| 20 | 16 | 2,800 | 1.7 | 47 | 470 | -------- | -------- | -------- | 24 | -------- | -------- | -------- |
| 40 | 53 | 1,370 | 4.5 | 151 | 3,030 | 8,300 | 600 | 400 | 76 | 208 | 15 | 10 |
| 60 | 86 | 760 | 7.4 | 223 | 6,710 | 33,800 | 13,400 | 10,300 | 112 | 563 | 223 | 172 |
| 80 | 115 | 450 | 10.4 | 266 | 10,350 | 63,500 | 46,000 | 34,600 | 129 | 794 | 575 | 432 |
| 100 | 138 | 300 | 13.5 | 296 | 13,500 | 90,500 | 81,000 | 63,200 | 135 | 905 | 810 | 632 |
| 120 | 154 | 235 | 15.7 | 318 | 15,900 | 109,400 | 103,300 | 81,000 | 132 | 912 | 861 | 675 |
| 140 | 164 | 220 | 16.7 | 335 | 17,500 | 121,300 | 116,100 | 91,600 | 125 | 866 | 829 | 654 |
| 160 | 171 | 215 | 17.2 | 350 | 18,450 | 128,600 | 123,600 | 96,800 | 115 | 804 | 772 | 605 |

Cubic foot volumes are inside bark.

Source: Irvine T. Haig, Second-growth yield, stand, and volume tables for the western white pine type, U. S. Dept. Agr., *Tech. Bull. No. 323,* 1932.

## YELLOW-POPLAR (SECOND GROWTH)
### Table 35. Yields per Fully Stocked Acre, Trees 5 In. D.B.H. and Larger

| Age (yr.) | Site Index | | | | | | |
|---|---|---|---|---|---|---|---|
| | 60 | 70 | 80 | 90 | 100 | 110 | 120 |
| | | | D.b.h. in in. | | | | |
| 10 | | | | | 5.1 | 5.2 | 5.3 |
| 15 | | 5.3 | 5.5 | 5.8 | 6.0 | 6.2 | 6.4 |
| 20 | 5.4 | 5.9 | 6.3 | 6.6 | 6.9 | 7.2 | 7.5 |
| 25 | 5.9 | 6.4 | 6.9 | 7.4 | 7.8 | 8.2 | 8.6 |
| 30 | 6.3 | 7.0 | 7.6 | 8.3 | 8.8 | 9.3 | 9.8 |
| 35 | 6.7 | 7.6 | 8.4 | 9.2 | 9.9 | 10.5 | 11.1 |
| 40 | 7.2 | 8.2 | 9.3 | 10.1 | 10.9 | 11.6 | 12.4 |
| 45 | 7.7 | 8.9 | 10.1 | 11.1 | 12.0 | 12.9 | 13.6 |
| 50 | 8.2 | 9.7 | 11.0 | 12.2 | 13.2 | 14.1 | 14.9 |
| | | | Basal area in sq. ft. per acre [a] | | | | |
| 10 | | | 2 | 8 | 13 | 17 | 21 |
| 15 | 8 | 20 | 30 | 38 | 45 | 50 | 55 |
| 20 | 24 | 39 | 50 | 60 | 68 | 75 | 81 |
| 25 | 39 | 56 | 69 | 80 | 89 | 97 | 103 |
| 30 | 51 | 70 | 85 | 97 | 107 | 116 | 123 |
| 35 | 64 | 84 | 100 | 113 | 125 | 134 | 142 |
| 40 | 75 | 97 | 114 | 128 | 140 | 150 | 159 |
| 45 | 86 | 109 | 128 | 143 | 156 | 167 | 176 |
| 50 | 97 | 122 | 141 | 157 | 172 | 183 | 193 |
| | | | Number of trees per acre | | | | |
| 10 | | | 18 | 66 | 92 | 116 | 135 |
| 15 | 58 | 130 | 173 | 200 | 228 | 238 | 246 |
| 20 | 150 | 206 | 235 | 252 | 264 | 266 | 264 |
| 25 | 206 | 246 | 264 | 268 | 269 | 264 | 256 |
| 30 | 218 | 264 | 268 | 260 | 252 | 244 | 234 |
| 35 | 258 | 268 | 260 | 246 | 236 | 224 | 212 |
| 40 | 265 | 264 | 246 | 230 | 218 | 204 | 190 |
| 45 | 266 | 253 | 230 | 212 | 198 | 184 | 168 |
| 50 | 264 | 240 | 214 | 194 | 176 | 164 | 148 |

[a] At breast height.

## YELLOW-POPLAR (SECOND GROWTH)

### Table 35. Yields per Fully Stocked Acre, Trees 5 In. D.B.H. and Larger
(Continued)

| Age (yr.) | Site Index | | | | | | |
|---|---|---|---|---|---|---|---|
| | 60 | 70 | 80 | 90 | 100 | 110 | 120 |
| Merchantable peeled volume in cu. ft. per acre [b] | | | | | | | |
| 10 | | | | 50 | 135 | 250 | 360 |
| 15 | 80 | 250 | 415 | 600 | 800 | 1,000 | 1,180 |
| 20 | 320 | 600 | 880 | 1,180 | 1,475 | 1,765 | 2,040 |
| 25 | 570 | 955 | 1,340 | 1,745 | 2,145 | 2,550 | 2,900 |
| 30 | 825 | 1,305 | 1,800 | 2,300 | 2,800 | 3,320 | 3,770 |
| 35 | 1,080 | 1,660 | 2,250 | 2,845 | 3,450 | 4,070 | 4,600 |
| 40 | 1,335 | 2,010 | 2,690 | 3,390 | 4,085 | 4,800 | 5,410 |
| 45 | 1,590 | 2,360 | 3,130 | 3,935 | 4,710 | 5,510 | 6,200 |
| 50 | 1,840 | 2,705 | 3,570 | 4,480 | 5,330 | 6,220 | 6,970 |

[b] Peeled volume of merchantable stem, from 1-ft. stump to 3-in. top d.i.b.
Source: E. F. McCarthy, Central States Forest Exp. Sta. (unpublished ms.).

## YELLOW-POPLAR (SECOND GROWTH)

### Table 36. Yields per Fully Stocked Acre, Trees 8 In. D.B.H. and Larger

| Age (yr.) | Site Index | | | | | | |
|---|---|---|---|---|---|---|---|
| | 60 | 70 | 80 | 90 | 100 | 110 | 120 |
| Yield in bd. ft. per acre, International ⅛-In. Rule * | | | | | | | |
| 10 | | | | | | 200 | 400 |
| 15 | 200 | 400 | 530 | 650 | 1,050 | 1,600 | 2,400 |
| 20 | 350 | 650 | 1,200 | 2,000 | 3,400 | 5,180 | 7,000 |
| 25 | 600 | 1,400 | 2,790 | 5,100 | 7,600 | 10,200 | 13,100 |
| 30 | 1,000 | 2,650 | 5,500 | 8,710 | 12,150 | 15,600 | 19,250 |
| 35 | 1,700 | 4,500 | 8,300 | 12,450 | 16,800 | 21,250 | 25,900 |
| 40 | 2,650 | 6,780 | 11,230 | 16,300 | 21,790 | 27,350 | 33,150 |
| 45 | 4,000 | 9,000 | 14,380 | 20,300 | 26,880 | 33,750 | 40,700 |
| 50 | 5,600 | 11,400 | 17,620 | 24,400 | 32,150 | 40,200 | 48,450 |
| Yield in bd. ft. per acre, Scribner Rule * | | | | | | | |
| 10 | | | | 50 | 150 | 220 | 360 |
| 15 | 50 | 100 | 210 | 460 | 870 | 1,390 | 1,960 |
| 20 | 190 | 480 | 1,030 | 1,850 | 2,920 | 4,220 | 5,800 |
| 25 | 450 | 1,180 | 2,370 | 4,120 | 6,180 | 8,450 | 10,810 |
| 30 | 930 | 2,300 | 4,430 | 7,110 | 9,900 | 12,820 | 15,810 |
| 35 | 1,540 | 3,790 | 6.800 | 10,200 | 13,700 | 17,310 | 21,050 |
| 40 | 2,370 | 5,560 | 9,270 | 13,300 | 17,500 | 21,890 | 26,500 |
| 45 | 3,380 | 7,410 | 11,850 | 16,600 | 21,400 | 26,460 | 31,560 |
| 50 | 4,580 | 9,270 | 14,410 | 19,800 | 25,300 | 30,900 | 36,600 |

* From 1-ft. stump to 6-in. top d.i.b.
Source: *Ibid.*

## REDWOOD (SECOND GROWTH)

### Table 37. Yield per Fully Stocked Acre, Site II

Humboldt and Mendocino Counties, California

| Age | Number of Trees per Acre | | Average Height | | Average Diameter Breast High | | Basal Area per Acre | | Volume per Acre (All Trees) | | Logs per M.B.M. for Average Dominant and Codominant | Average Annual Growth (All Trees) | | Board Foot Cubic Foot Ratio | Basis Number of Plots |
|---|---|---|---|---|---|---|---|---|---|---|---|---|---|---|---|
| | All Trees | Dominant and Codominant | All Trees | Dominant and Codominant | All Trees | Dominant and Codominant | All Trees | Dominant and Codominant | Cubic Feet | Board Feet | | Cubic Feet | Board Feet | | |
| Years | | | Feet | Feet | Inches | Inches | Square Feet | Square Feet | | | | | | | |
| 20 | 980 | 500 | 43 | 49 | 7.2 | 9.0 | 278 | 213 | 5100 | 7400 | 53 | 255 | 370 | 1.5 | 3 |
| 25 | 765 | 400 | 53 | 60 | 8.9 | 11.3 | 331 | 270 | 6800 | 22000 | 38 | 272 | 880 | 3.2 | 5 |
| 30 | 628 | 328 | 61 | 71 | 10.4 | 12.9 | 372 | 294 | 8700 | 37500 | 27 | 290 | 1250 | 4.3 | 7 |
| 35 | 543 | 270 | 71 | 80 | 11.6 | 15.1 | 399 | 319 | 10600 | 53000 | 20 | 303 | 1520 | 5.0 | 5 |
| 40 | 489 | 225 | 79 | 90 | 12.5 | 16.9 | 418 | 333 | 12400 | 68000 | 16 | 309 | 1700 | 5.5 | 7 |
| 45 | 447 | 196 | 87 | 100 | 13.3 | 18.4 | 431 | 343 | 13900 | 82200 | 13 | 310 | 1830 | 5.9 | 10 |
| 50 | 406 | 175 | 95 | 109 | 14.1 | 19.8 | 441 | 352 | 15300 | 94900 | 11 | 305 | 1900 | 6.2 | 10 |
| 55 | 374 | 160 | 103 | 118 | 14.7 | 20.8 | 449 | 361 | 16300 | 110000 | 10 | 297 | 1930 | 6.5 | 7 |
| 60 | 348 | 150 | 110 | 126 | 15.4 | 21.7 | 451 | 367 | 17100 | 115000 | 9 | 286 | 1920 | 6.7 | 54 |

Cubic foot volumes are inside bark; board foot volumes are Int. ⅛".

## ENGELMANN SPRUCE

Table 38.  Mean Annual Gross Increment per Acre, in Board Feet by
Scribner Rule, of Selectively Cut Stands *

Colorado

| Reserve volume per acre (bd. ft.) | Number of years after cutting | | | | |
|---|---|---|---|---|---|
| | 20 | 30 | 40 | 50 | 60 |
| | Mean annual growth per acre, bd. ft. | | | | |
| 2,000 | 115 | 104 | 94 | 87 | 81 |
| 3,000 | 148 | 136 | 125 | 116 | 109 |
| 4,000 | 176 | 164 | 152 | 142 | 133 |
| 5,000 | 200 | 190 | 177 | 166 | 156 |
| 6,000 | 221 | 213 | 200 | 188 | 177 |
| 7,000 | 240 | 234 | 221 | 209 | 197 |
| 8,000 | 257 | 254 | 241 | 228 | 216 |
| 9,000 | 272 | 272 | 260 | 247 | 235 |
| 10,000 | 286 | 290 | 278 | 265 | ... |
| 11,000 | 299 | 306 | 296 | ... | ... |
| 12,000 | 311 | 322 | 312 | ... | ... |
| 13,000 | 321 | 336 | ... | ... | ... |
| 14,000 | 331 | 351 | ... | ... | ... |
| 15,000 | 340 | 364 | ... | ... | ... |
| 16,000 | 348 | ... | ... | ... | ... |

* Trees 10 in. d.b.h. and larger, to an 8-in. top.
Source:  E. M. Hornibrook, Yield of cut-over stands of Engelmann spruce, *Jour.
Forestry* 40:778–781, 1942.


## RED SPRUCE (SECOND GROWTH)

Table 39.  Yields per Fully Stocked Acre, Trees 4 In. D.B.H. and Larger
Northeastern United States

| Total age (yr.) | Site index | | | | |
|---|---|---|---|---|---|
| | 70 | 60 | 50 | 40 | 30 |
| | Number of trees | | | | |
| 30 | 404 | 363 | 264 | 143 | |
| 40 | 835 | 790 | 703 | 535 | 175 |
| 50 | 927 | 983 | 1,007 | 903 | 460 |
| 60 | 760 | 868 | 990 | 1,044 | 660 |
| 70 | 569 | 666 | 811 | 973 | 760 |
| 80 | 482 | 566 | 715 | 912 | 815 |
| 90 | 456 | 533 | 665 | 882 | 845 |
| 100 | 439 | 515 | 640 | 855 | 870 |
| 110 | 425 | 497 | 623 | 840 | 881 |

(Continued on page 3·47)

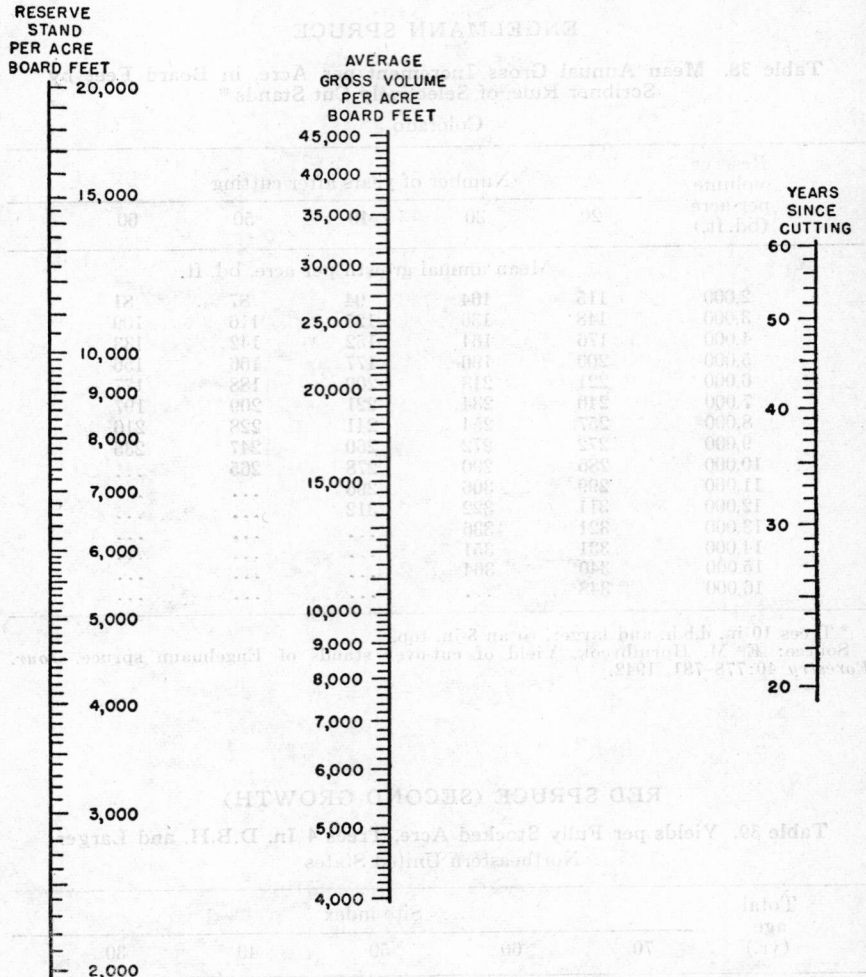

RESERVE
STAND
PER ACRE
BOARD FEET

AVERAGE
GROSS VOLUME
PER ACRE
BOARD FEET

YEARS
SINCE
CUTTING

CORRECTION FACTORS TO IMPROVE ESTIMATES OF YIELD

| Site index | Correction percentages when the percentage of alpine fir in the reserve volume is: | | | | | | | | | |
|---|---|---|---|---|---|---|---|---|---|---|
| | 0 | 5 | 10 | 15 | 20 | 25 | 30 | 35 | 40 | 45 |
| | (Correction in percent) | | | | | | | | | |
| 60 | —16.2 | —12.9 | —9.7 | — 6.4 | — 3.2 | + 0.1 | + 3.3 | + 6.6 | + 9.8 | +13.0 |
| 65 | —13.8 | —10.5 | —7.3 | — 4.1 | — 0.8 | + 2.4 | + 5.7 | + 8.9 | +12.2 | +15.4 |
| 70 | —11.4 | — 8.2 | —4.9 | — 1.7 | + 1.6 | + 4.8 | + 8.1 | +11.3 | +14.5 | +17.8 |
| 75 | — 9.0 | — 5.8 | —2.6 | + 0.7 | + 3.9 | + 7.2 | +10.4 | +13.7 | +16.9 | +20.2 |
| 80 | — 6.7 | — 3.4 | —0.2 | + 3.1 | + 6.3 | + 9.6 | +12.8 | +16.0 | +19.3 | +22.5 |
| 85 | — 4.3 | — 1.0 | +2.2 | + 5.4 | + 8.7 | +11.9 | +15.2 | +18.4 | +21.7 | +24.9 |
| 90 | — 1.9 | + 1.3 | +4.6 | + 7.8 | +11.1 | +14.3 | +17.6 | +20.8 | +24.0 | +27.3 |
| 95 | + 0.5 | + 3.7′ | +6.9 | +10.2 | +13.4 | +16.7 | +19.9 | +23.2 | +26.4 | +29.7 |

Fig. 1.  Yield per acre of selectively cut Engelmann spruce at various intervals after cutting, in board feet, Scribner rule—Colorado.

Trees 10 in. d.b.h. and larger, to an 8-in. top. (E. M. Hornibrook, *Jour. Forestry* 40:778-781, 1942.)

## RED SPRUCE (SECOND GROWTH)

### Table 39. Yield per Fully Stocked Acre, Trees 4 In. D.B.H. and Larger
(Continued)

| Total age (yr.) | Site index | | | | |
|---|---|---|---|---|---|
| | 70 | 60 | 50 | 40 | 30 |
| | | | D.b.h. in inches | | |
| 30 | 4.5 | 4.4 | 4.3 | 4.2 | |
| 40 | 5.3 | 5.1 | 4.8 | 4.5 | 4.2 |
| 50 | 6.4 | 5.9 | 5.5 | 4.9 | 4.3 |
| 60 | 7.7 | 7.0 | 6.3 | 5.4 | 4.6 |
| 70 | 9.2 | 8.2 | 7.2 | 6.0 | 4.9 |
| 80 | 10.1 | 9.1 | 7.8 | 6.4 | 5.0 |
| 90 | 10.5 | 9.5 | 8.2 | 6.6 | 5.1 |
| 100 | 10.8 | 9.7 | 8.4 | 6.8 | 5.1 |
| 110 | 11.0 | 10.0 | 8.6 | 6.9 | 5.2 |
| | | | Basal area in square feet | | |
| 30 | 45 | 38 | 26 | 14 | |
| 40 | 127 | 111 | 88 | 59 | 17 |
| 50 | 206 | 189 | 164 | 120 | 46 |
| 60 | 244 | 231 | 213 | 165 | 77 |
| 70 | 260 | 246 | 228 | 191 | 100 |
| 80 | 269 | 256 | 237 | 203 | 113 |
| 90 | 275 | 261 | 242 | 208 | 119 |
| 100 | 279 | 266 | 246 | 213 | 125 |
| 110 | 282 | 269 | 250 | 216 | 128 |
| | | Merchantable volume in cubic feet inside bark | | | |
| 30 | 500 | 340 | 210 | 88 | |
| 40 | 2,160 | 1,650 | 1,110 | 600 | 138 |
| 50 | 4,780 | 3,770 | 2,760 | 1,670 | 480 |
| 60 | 6,850 | 5,550 | 4,200 | 2,750 | 940 |
| 70 | 8,100 | 6,620 | 5,150 | 3,470 | 1,400 |
| 80 | 8,880 | 7,280 | 5,700 | 3,920 | 1,670 |
| 90 | 9,300 | 7,650 | 6,000 | 4,160 | 1,800 |
| 100 | 9,570 | 7,870 | 6,190 | 4,310 | 1,900 |
| 110 | 9,800 | 8,050 | 6,350 | 4,440 | 1,990 |
| | | | Volume in cords * inside bark | | |
| 30 | 5.3 | 3.6 | 2.2 | 0.9 | |
| 40 | 22.7 | 17.4 | 11.7 | 6.3 | 1.5 |
| 50 | 50.3 | 39.7 | 29.1 | 17.6 | 5.1 |
| 60 | 72.1 | 58.4 | 44.2 | 28.9 | 9.9 |
| 70 | 85.3 | 69.7 | 54.2 | 36.5 | 14.7 |
| 80 | 93.5 | 76.6 | 60.0 | 41.3 | 17.6 |
| 90 | 97.9 | 80.5 | 63.2 | 43.8 | 18.9 |
| 100 | 100.7 | 82.8 | 65.2 | 45.4 | 20.0 |
| 110 | 103.2 | 84.7 | 66.8 | 46.7 | 20.9 |

* At 95 cu. ft. per cord.
Source: W. H. Meyer, Yields of second-growth spruce and fir in the Northeast, U. S. Dept. Agr., *Tech. Bull. No. 142*, 1929.

## RED SPRUCE (SECOND GROWTH)
### Table 40.  Yields per Fully Stocked Acre, Trees 7 In. D.B.H. and Larger
Northeastern United States

| Total age (yr.) | Site index | | | |
|---|---|---|---|---|
| | 70 | 60 | 50 | 40 |
| | Number of trees | | | |
| 40 | 130 | 92 | 49 | . . . |
| 50 | 340 | 276 | 189 | 85 |
| 60 | 485 | 446 | 335 | 192 |
| 70 | 468 | 480 | 441 | 286 |
| 80 | 445 | 463 | 467 | 350 |
| 90 | 426 | 455 | 473 | 376 |
| 100 | 415 | 450 | 474 | 391 |
| 110 | 408 | 443 | 474 | 402 |
| | D.b.h. in inches | | | |
| 40 | 7.6 | 7.5 | 7.5 | . . . |
| 50 | 8.0 | 7.8 | 7.7 | 7.5 |
| 60 | 8.7 | 8.3 | 8.0 | 7.6 |
| 70 | 9.7 | 9.1 | 8.5 | 7.9 |
| 80 | 10.5 | 9.7 | 8.8 | 8.0 |
| 90 | 10.8 | 10.0 | 9.0 | 8.1 |
| 100 | 11.0 | 10.2 | 9.2 | 8.2 |
| 110 | 11.2 | 10.3 | 9.3 | 8.3 |
| | Basal area in square feet | | | |
| 40 | 41 | 28 | 15 | . . . |
| 50 | 119 | 92 | 61 | 26 |
| 60 | 199 | 166 | 117 | 61 |
| 70 | 242 | 215 | 172 | 97 |
| 80 | 260 | 238 | 198 | 122 |
| 90 | 270 | 247 | 211 | 134 |
| 100 | 275 | 254 | 218 | 142 |
| 110 | 279 | 259 | 224 | 150 |
| | Volume in board feet * | | | |
| 40 | 3,300 | 2,200 | 1,200 | . . . |
| 50 | 13,300 | 9,900 | 6,200 | 2,800 |
| 60 | 28,400 | 20,800 | 13,300 | 5,800 |
| 70 | 43,200 | 31,800 | 20,300 | 8,800 |
| 80 | 52,900 | 38,900 | 24,800 | 10,800 |
| 90 | 58,300 | 42,800 | 27,400 | 11,900 |
| 100 | 61,500 | 45,100 | 28,800 | 12,600 |
| 110 | 63,600 | 46,600 | 29,800 | 13,000 |

* Board feet, International ⅛-In. Rule.
Source: *Ibid.*

## SITKA SPRUCE AND WESTERN HEMLOCK

### Table 41. Yields per Fully Stocked Acre, Trees 2.6 In. D.B.H. and Larger *

#### Entire Range

HEIGHT OF DOMINANT AND CODOMINANT TREES OF AVERAGE BREAST-HEIGHT DIAMETER, BY SITE INDEX

| Age (years) | Height by site index— | | | | | | | |
|---|---|---|---|---|---|---|---|---|
| | 60 | 80 | 100 | 120 | 140 | 160 | 180 | 200 |
| | *Feet* | *Feet* | *Feet* | *Feet* | *Feet* | *Feet* | *Feet* | *Feet* |
| 20 | 13 | 17 | 21 | 25 | 30 | 34 | 38 | 43 |
| 30 | 23 | 30 | 37 | 45 | 52 | 60 | 67 | 75 |
| 40 | 31 | 41 | 51 | 62 | 72 | 82 | 92 | 103 |
| 50 | 38 | 51 | 63 | 76 | 88 | 101 | 114 | 126 |
| 60 | 44 | 58 | 73 | 87 | 102 | 117 | 131 | 146 |
| 70 | 49 | 64 | 81 | 97 | 114 | 130 | 146 | 162 |
| 80 | 53 | 70 | 88 | 105 | 123 | 140 | 158 | 176 |
| 90 | 56 | 75 | 94 | 113 | 132 | 151 | 169 | 188 |
| 100 | 60 | 80 | 100 | 120 | 140 | 160 | 180 | 200 |
| 110 | 63 | 84 | 105 | 127 | 147 | 168 | 189 | 211 |
| 120 | 66 | 88 | 110 | 133 | 154 | 176 | 198 | 221 |
| 130 | 69 | 92 | 115 | 138 | 161 | 184 | 207 | 230 |
| 140 | 72 | 96 | 120 | 143 | 167 | 191 | 215 | 239 |
| 150 | 74 | 99 | 124 | 148 | 173 | 198 | 223 | 247 |
| 160 | 77 | 102 | 128 | 153 | 179 | 204 | 230 | 255 |
| 170 | 79 | 105 | 131 | 157 | 184 | 210 | 236 | 262 |
| 180 | 81 | 107 | 134 | 161 | 188 | 215 | 241 | 268 |
| 190 | 82 | 109 | 137 | 164 | 192 | 219 | 246 | 274 |
| 200 | 84 | 111 | 140 | 167 | 195 | 223 | 251 | 279 |

#### NUMBER OF TREES

| Age (years) | Trees per acre by site index— | | | | | | | |
|---|---|---|---|---|---|---|---|---|
| | 60 | 80 | 100 | 120 | 140 | 160 | 180 | 200 |
| | *Number* | *Number* | *Number* | *Number* | *Number* | *Number* | *Number* | *Number* |
| 20 | | 1,200 | 1,600 | 1,800 | 1,900 | 1,800 | 1,700 | 1,550 |
| 30 | 1,500 | 1,800 | 1,900 | 1,700 | 1,390 | 1,130 | 940 | 810 |
| 40 | 1,880 | 1,820 | 1,500 | 1,140 | 870 | 640 | 490 | 395 |
| 50 | 1,820 | 1,450 | 1,075 | 780 | 537 | 382 | 271 | 200 |
| 60 | 1,550 | 1,150 | 840 | 579 | 382 | 276 | 199 | 149 |
| 70 | 1,290 | 957 | 685 | 461 | 305 | 224 | 161 | 121 |
| 80 | 1,085 | 806 | 578 | 390 | 260 | 192 | 139 | 103 |
| 90 | 925 | 685 | 490 | 337 | 228 | 168 | 121 | 90 |
| 100 | 815 | 600 | 434 | 295 | 202 | 148 | 106 | 79 |
| 110 | 718 | 530 | 382 | 264 | 180 | 131 | 95 | 70 |
| 120 | 641 | 475 | 342 | 237 | 162 | 118 | 86 | 63 |
| 130 | 578 | 433 | 308 | 214 | 147 | 106 | 79 | 57 |
| 140 | 527 | 397 | 283 | 195 | 135 | 97 | 73 | 52 |
| 150 | 486 | 364 | 261 | 181 | 124 | 89 | 67 | 48 |
| 160 | 452 | 336 | 242 | 168 | 114 | 83 | 62 | 45 |
| 170 | 420 | 314 | 225 | 157 | 107 | 77 | 58 | 42 |
| 180 | 396 | 295 | 210 | 146 | 101 | 72 | 54 | 39 |
| 190 | 374 | 278 | 198 | 138 | 95 | 68 | 51 | 37 |
| 200 | 352 | 262 | 187 | 129 | 90 | 64 | 49 | 35 |

* Rounded to the nearest 100 cu. ft.

Source for Tables 41 to 44: W. H. Meyer, Yield of even-aged stands of Sitka spruce and western hemlock, U S Dept. Agr., *Tech. Bull. No. 544*, 1937.

## Table 41. Yields per Fully Stocked Acre, Trees 2.6 In. D.B.H. and Larger
### (Continued)

#### BASAL AREA

| Age (years) | Basal area per acre by site index— | | | | | | | |
| --- | --- | --- | --- | --- | --- | --- | --- | --- |
| | 60 | 80 | 100 | 120 | 140 | 160 | 180 | 200 |
| | Sq. ft. | Sq. ft. | Sq. ft. | Sq ft | Sq. ft. | Sq ft. | Sq. ft. | Sq ft. |
| 20 | | 61 | 89 5 | 111 | 130 | 138 | 144 | 149 |
| 30 | 92.5 | 134 | 170 | 188 | 198 | 205 | 211 | 217 |
| 40 | 156 | 184 | 204 | 220 | 234 | 247 | 258 | 271 |
| 50 | 192 | 210 | 228 | 246 | 264 | 281 | 294 | 308 |
| 60 | 211 | 230 | 250 | 270 | 290 | 308 | 324 | 338 |
| 70 | 224 | 245 | 266 | 288 | 308 | 328 | 344 | 359 |
| 80 | 235 | 257 | 278 | 301 | 324 | 343 | 361 | 376 |
| 90 | 244 | 266 | 289 | 313 | 336 | 356 | 375 | 390 |
| 100 | 251 | 274 | 297 | 322 | 345 | 367 | 385 | 402 |
| 110 | 257 | 280 | 304 | 330 | 354 | 375 | 394 | 411 |
| 120 | 261 | 286 | 310 | 336 | 360 | 382 | 401 | 419 |
| 130 | 266 | 291 | 315 | 342 | 366 | 389 | 408 | 426 |
| 140 | 270 | 296 | 320 | 347 | 372 | 395 | 415 | 433 |
| 150 | 274 | 300 | 325 | 352 | 378 | 401 | 421 | 440 |
| 160 | 278 | 304 | 330 | 357 | 383 | 407 | 427 | 446 |
| 170 | 282 | 308 | 334 | 362 | 388 | 412 | 432 | 451 |
| 180 | 285 | 311 | 338 | 366 | 392 | 417 | 437 | 456 |
| 190 | 288 | 314 | 341 | 370 | 396 | 421 | 441 | 461 |
| 200 | 290 | 317 | 344 | 373 | 400 | 425 | 445 | 465 |

#### AVERAGE DIAMETER

| Age (years) | Average breast-height diameter by site index— | | | | | | | |
| --- | --- | --- | --- | --- | --- | --- | --- | --- |
| | 60 | 80 | 100 | 120 | 140 | 160 | 180 | 200 |
| | Inches | Inches | Inches | Inches | Inches | Inches | Inches | Inches |
| 20 | | 3.1 | 3.2 | 3.4 | 3.5 | 3.7 | 3.9 | 4.2 |
| 30 | 3.4 | 3.7 | 4.0 | 4.5 | 5.1 | 5.8 | 6.4 | 7.0 |
| 40 | 3.9 | 4.3 | 5.0 | 5.9 | 7.0 | 8.4 | 9.8 | 11.2 |
| 50 | 4.4 | 5.2 | 6.2 | 7.6 | 9.5 | 11.6 | 14.1 | 16.8 |
| 60 | 5.0 | 6.1 | 7.4 | 9.2 | 11.8 | 14.3 | 17.3 | 20.4 |
| 70 | 5.6 | 6.9 | 8.4 | 10.7 | 13.6 | 16.4 | 19.8 | 23.3 |
| 80 | 6.3 | 7.6 | 9.4 | 11.9 | 15.1 | 18.1 | 21.8 | 25.9 |
| 90 | 7.0 | 8.4 | 10.4 | 13.0 | 16.4 | 19.7 | 23.8 | 28.2 |
| 100 | 7.5 | 9.2 | 11.2 | 14.1 | 17.7 | 21.3 | 25.8 | 30.5 |
| 110 | 8.1 | 9.8 | 12.1 | 15.1 | 19.0 | 22.9 | 27.6 | 32.8 |
| 120 | 8.6 | 10.5 | 12.9 | 16.1 | 20.2 | 24.4 | 29.2 | 34.9 |
| 130 | 9.2 | 11.1 | 13.7 | 17.1 | 21.4 | 25.9 | 30.8 | 37.0 |
| 140 | 9.7 | 11.7 | 14.4 | 18.1 | 22.5 | 27.3 | 32.3 | 39.1 |
| 150 | 10.2 | 12.3 | 15.1 | 18.9 | 23.6 | 28.7 | 33.9 | 41.0 |
| 160 | 10.6 | 12.9 | 15.8 | 19.7 | 24.8 | 30.0 | 35.5 | 42.6 |
| 170 | 11.1 | 13.4 | 16.5 | 20.6 | 25.8 | 31.3 | 37.0 | 44.4 |
| 180 | 11.5 | 13.9 | 17.2 | 21.4 | 26.7 | 32.6 | 38.5 | 46.3 |
| 190 | 11.9 | 14.4 | 17.8 | 22.2 | 27.6 | 33.7 | 39.8 | 47.8 |
| 200 | 12.3 | 14.9 | 18.4 | 23.0 | 28.5 | 34.9 | 40.8 | 49.4 |

### Table 41. Yields per Fully Stocked Acre, Trees 2.6 In. D.B.H. and Larger
(Continued)

CUBIC-FOOT VOLUME PER ACRE, INCLUDING STUMP AND TIP BUT NOT BARK

| Age (years) | Volume per acre by site index— | | | | | | | |
|---|---|---|---|---|---|---|---|---|
| | 60 | 80 | 100 | 120 | 140 | 160 | 180 | 200 |
| | Cubic feet | Cubic feet | Cubic feet | Cubic feet | Cubic feet | Cubic feet | Cubic feet | Cubic feet |
| 20 | | 400 | 800 | 1,200 | 1,600 | 2,000 | 2,200 | 2,600 |
| 30 | 1,100 | 1,600 | 2,300 | 3,200 | 4,200 | 5,000 | 5,700 | 6,400 |
| 40 | 2,100 | 2,900 | 3,900 | 5,300 | 6,800 | 8,100 | 9,200 | 10,200 |
| 50 | 3,100 | 4,200 | 5,500 | 7,400 | 9,400 | 11,200 | 12,600 | 14,000 |
| 60 | 3,900 | 5,300 | 7,100 | 9,300 | 11,800 | 14,200 | 16,000 | 17,700 |
| 70 | 4,600 | 6,200 | 8,400 | 11,000 | 14,000 | 16,800 | 19,000 | 21,000 |
| 80 | 5,200 | 7,100 | 9,500 | 12,400 | 15,800 | 19,000 | 21,500 | 23,800 |
| 90 | 5,800 | 7,800 | 10,400 | 13,700 | 17,500 | 20,900 | 23,700 | 26,200 |
| 100 | 6,300 | 8,400 | 11,300 | 14,800 | 18,900 | 22,600 | 25,600 | 28,300 |
| 110 | 6,700 | 9,000 | 12,100 | 15,800 | 20,200 | 24,100 | 27,400 | 30,200 |
| 120 | 7,100 | 9,500 | 12,700 | 16,700 | 21,300 | 25,500 | 28,900 | 31,900 |
| 130 | 7,400 | 10,000 | 13,300 | 17,500 | 22,300 | 26,700 | 30,200 | 33,400 |
| 140 | 7,700 | 10,400 | 13,900 | 18,200 | 23,200 | 27,800 | 31,500 | 34,800 |
| 150 | 8,000 | 10,800 | 14,400 | 18,900 | 24,100 | 28,800 | 32,700 | 36,100 |
| 160 | 8,300 | 11,200 | 14,900 | 19,600 | 24,900 | 29,800 | 33,800 | 37,300 |
| 170 | 8,500 | 11,500 | 15,400 | 20,200 | 25,700 | 30,700 | 34,800 | 38,500 |
| 180 | 8,700 | 11,800 | 15,800 | 20,800 | 26,400 | 31,600 | 35,800 | 39,600 |
| 190 | 8,900 | 12,100 | 16,200 | 21,300 | 27,100 | 32,400 | 36,800 | 40,700 |
| 200 | 9,100 | 12,400 | 16,600 | 21,800 | 27,800 | 33,200 | 37,700 | 41,700 |

## SITKA SPRUCE AND WESTERN HEMLOCK
### Table 42. Yields per Fully Stocked Acre, Trees 11.6 In. D.B.H. and Larger
Entire Range

NUMBER OF TREES

| Age (years) | Trees per acre by site index— | | | | | | | |
|---|---|---|---|---|---|---|---|---|
| | 60 | 80 | 100 | 120 | 140 | 160 | 180 | 200 |
| | Number | Number | Number | Number | Number | Number | Number | Number |
| 30 | | | | | 8.4 | 21.2 | 36 | 49 |
| 40 | | | 6.6 | 26 | 52 | 83 | 114 | 142 |
| 50 | | 9.8 | 38 | 69 | 112 | 150 | 166 | 159 |
| 60 | 6.8 | 31 | 66 | 110 | 158 | 175 | 162 | 133 |
| 70 | 21.5 | 52 | 93 | 144 | 175 | 174 | 142 | 113 |
| 80 | 38 | 72 | 117 | 163 | 180 | 162 | 127 | 98 |
| 99 | 54 | 92 | 139 | 176 | 176 | 148 | 113 | 86 |
| 100 | 68 | 108 | 155 | 183 | 167 | 134 | 101 | 77 |
| 110 | 82 | 124 | 167 | 184 | 156 | 121 | 91 | 69 |
| 120 | 95 | 138 | 175 | 179 | 144 | 110 | 83 | 62 |
| 130 | 107 | 150 | 179 | 172 | 134 | 101 | 76 | 56 |
| 140 | 119 | 159 | 182 | 164 | 124 | 93 | 70 | 52 |
| 150 | 129 | 166 | 182 | 156 | 115 | 86 | 65 | 48 |
| 160 | 138 | 171 | 179 | 148 | 108 | 79 | 61 | 45 |
| 170 | 146 | 174 | 176 | 141 | 101 | 75 | 57 | 42 |
| 180 | 152 | 177 | 170 | 133 | 96 | 71 | 54 | 39 |
| 190 | 157 | 179 | 164 | 126 | 91 | 67 | 51 | 37 |
| 200 | 161 | 178 | 158 | 119 | 87 | 63 | 49 | 35 |

Source: *Ibid.*

**Table 42. Yields per Fully Stocked Acre, Trees 11.6 In. D.B.H. and Larger**
(Continued)

BASAL AREA

| Age (years) | Basal area per acre by site index— | | | | | | | |
| --- | --- | --- | --- | --- | --- | --- | --- | --- |
| | 60 | 80 | 100 | 120 | 140 | 160 | 180 | 200 |
| | Sq. ft. | Sq. ft. | Sq. ft. | Sq. ft. | Sq. ft. | Sq. ft. | Sq. ft. | Sq. ft. |
| 30 | | | | | 7.7 | 20.3 | 34.8 | 48.4 |
| 40 | | | 6.1 | 25 | 52 | 89 | 132 | 176 |
| 50 | | 9.0 | 36.9 | 69 | 126 | 192 | 249 | 287 |
| 60 | 6.3 | 29.5 | 67 | 122 | 202 | 264 | 306 | 330 |
| 70 | 20 | 51 | 98 | 173 | 253 | 304 | 334 | 356 |
| 80 | 36 | 74 | 130 | 212 | 288 | 328 | 356 | 374 |
| 90 | 53 | 98 | 164 | 246 | 311 | 346 | 372 | 388 |
| 100 | 69 | 120 | 193 | 274 | 328 | 360 | 383 | 400 |
| 110 | 85 | 142 | 219 | 296 | 342 | 370 | 392 | 410 |
| 120 | 101 | 164 | 241 | 309 | 351 | 379 | 400 | 418 |
| 130 | 118 | 186 | 259 | 320 | 359 | 386 | 407 | 426 |
| 140 | 135 | 203 | 277 | 331 | 367 | 393 | 414 | 433 |
| 150 | 150 | 220 | 289 | 340 | 374 | 399 | 420 | 440 |
| 160 | 165 | 236 | 300 | 347 | 380 | 405 | 426 | 446 |
| 170 | 180 | 249 | 310 | 354 | 385 | 410 | 432 | 451 |
| 180 | 192 | 261 | 319 | 359 | 390 | 415 | 437 | 456 |
| 190 | 204 | 272 | 325 | 364 | 394 | 420 | 441 | 461 |
| 200 | 213 | 280 | 330 | 369 | 398 | 424 | 445 | 465 |

AVERAGE DIAMETER

| Age (years) | Average breast-height diameter by site index— | | | | | | | |
| --- | --- | --- | --- | --- | --- | --- | --- | --- |
| | 60 | 80 | 100 | 120 | 140 | 160 | 180 | 200 |
| | Inches | Inches | Inches | Inches | Inches | Inches | Inches | Inches |
| 30 | | | | | 13.0 | 13.2 | 13.3 | 13.5 |
| 40 | | | 13.0 | 13.3 | 13.5 | 14.0 | 14.6 | 15.1 |
| 50 | | 13.0 | 13.3 | 13.7 | 14.4 | 15.3 | 16.6 | 18.2 |
| 60 | 13.0 | 13.2 | 13.6 | 14.3 | 15.3 | 16.6 | 18.6 | 21.3 |
| 70 | 13.1 | 13.4 | 13.9 | 14.8 | 16.2 | 17.9 | 20.8 | 24.0 |
| 80 | 13.2 | 13.7 | 14.3 | 15.4 | 17.1 | 19.3 | 22.7 | 26.5 |
| 90 | 13.4 | 14.0 | 14.7 | 16.0 | 18.0 | 20.7 | 24.6 | 28.8 |
| 100 | 13.6 | 14.3 | 15.1 | 16.6 | 19.0 | 22.2 | 26.4 | 30.9 |
| 110 | 13.8 | 14.5 | 15.5 | 17.2 | 20.1 | 23.7 | 28.1 | 33.0 |
| 120 | 14.0 | 14.8 | 15.9 | 17.8 | 21.1 | 25.1 | 29.7 | 35.2 |
| 130 | 14.2 | 15.1 | 16.3 | 18.5 | 22.2 | 26.5 | 31.3 | 37.3 |
| 140 | 14.4 | 15.3 | 16.7 | 19.2 | 23.3 | 27.8 | 32.9 | 39.1 |
| 150 | 14.6 | 15.6 | 17.1 | 20.0 | 24.4 | 29.2 | 34.4 | 41.0 |
| 160 | 14.8 | 15.9 | 17.5 | 20.7 | 25.4 | 30.5 | 35.8 | 42.6 |
| 170 | 15.0 | 16.2 | 18.0 | 21.5 | 26.4 | 31.7 | 37.3 | 44.4 |
| 180 | 15.2 | 16.4 | 18.5 | 22.2 | 27.3 | 32.7 | 38.5 | 46.3 |
| 190 | 15.4 | 16.7 | 19.1 | 23.0 | 28.2 | 33.9 | 39.8 | 47.8 |
| 200 | 15.6 | 17.0 | 19.6 | 23.8 | 29.0 | 35.1 | 40.8 | 49.4 |

## Table 42. Yields per Fully Stocked Acre, Trees 11.6 In. D.B.H. and Larger
### (Continued)

CUBIC-FOOT VOLUME PER ACRE, INCLUDING STUMP AND TIP BUT NOT BARK [a]

| Age (years) | Volume per acre by site index— | | | | | | | |
|---|---|---|---|---|---|---|---|---|
| | 60 | 80 | 100 | 120 | 140 | 160 | 180 | 200 |
| | Cu. ft. | Cu. ft. | Cu. ft. | Cu. ft. | Cu. ft. | Cu. ft. | Cu. ft. | Cu. ft. |
| 30 | | | | | 200 | 500 | 1,000 | 1,600 |
| 40 | | | 100 | 600 | 1,600 | 3,400 | 5,300 | 7,100 |
| 50 | | 200 | 900 | 2,400 | 5,100 | 8,200 | 11,000 | 13,200 |
| 60 | 100 | 700 | 2,100 | 4,800 | 8,800 | 12,500 | 15,300 | 17,500 |
| 70 | 400 | 1,400 | 3,600 | 7,300 | 11,900 | 15,800 | 18,700 | 20,900 |
| 80 | 800 | 2,300 | 5,100 | 9,400 | 14,400 | 18,300 | 21,300 | 23,700 |
| 90 | 1,400 | 3,300 | 6,500 | 11,300 | 16,500 | 20,400 | 23,500 | 26,200 |
| 100 | 2,000 | 4,200 | 7,900 | 13,000 | 18,300 | 22,300 | 25,400 | 28,300 |
| 110 | 2,600 | 5,100 | 9,200 | 14,400 | 19,700 | 23,900 | 27,300 | 30,200 |
| 120 | 3,200 | 6,000 | 10,300 | 15,600 | 20,900 | 25,400 | 28,800 | 31,900 |
| 130 | 3,800 | 6,900 | 11,300 | 16,700 | 22,000 | 26,600 | 30,200 | 33,400 |
| 140 | 4,400 | 7,700 | 12,300 | 17,700 | 23,000 | 27,700 | 31,500 | 34,800 |
| 150 | 4,900 | 8,400 | 13,100 | 18,500 | 23,900 | 28,800 | 32,700 | 36,100 |
| 160 | 5,400 | 9,000 | 13,800 | 19,200 | 24,800 | 29,800 | 33,800 | 37,300 |
| 170 | 5,900 | 9,600 | 14,500 | 19,900 | 25,600 | 30,700 | 34,800 | 38,500 |
| 180 | 6,300 | 10,200 | 15,100 | 20,500 | 26,300 | 31,600 | 35,800 | 39,600 |
| 190 | 6,700 | 10,700 | 15,600 | 21,100 | 27,000 | 32,400 | 36,800 | 40,700 |
| 200 | 7,000 | 11,200 | 16,100 | 21,600 | 27,700 | 33,200 | 37,700 | 41,700 |

VOLUME IN CORDS [b]

| Age (years) | Volume per acre by site index— | | | | | | | |
|---|---|---|---|---|---|---|---|---|
| | 60 | 80 | 100 | 120 | 140 | 160 | 180 | 200 |
| | Cords | Cords | Cords | Cords | Cords | Cords | Cords | Cords |
| 30 | | | | | 2 | 5 | 10 | 17 |
| 40 | | | 1 | 6 | 17 | 36 | 55 | 74 |
| 50 | | 2 | 9 | 27 | 53 | 85 | 112 | 136 |
| 60 | 1 | 7 | 22 | 49 | 87 | 125 | 157 | 181 |
| 70 | 4 | 15 | 38 | 72 | 117 | 161 | 192 | 217 |
| 80 | 8 | 24 | 53 | 95 | 145 | 189 | 220 | 248 |
| 90 | 15 | 34 | 68 | 117 | 169 | 213 | 246 | 273 |
| 100 | 21 | 44 | 83 | 134 | 187 | 232 | 265 | 295 |
| 110 | 27 | 54 | 96 | 149 | 203 | 249 | 284 | 316 |
| 120 | 33 | 63 | 108 | 163 | 217 | 264 | 301 | 333 |
| 130 | 40 | 72 | 118 | 174 | 229 | 278 | 316 | 349 |
| 140 | 46 | 80 | 128 | 184 | 240 | 290 | 329 | 364 |
| 150 | 51 | 88 | 137 | 192 | 250 | 301 | 342 | 377 |
| 160 | 56 | 94 | 144 | 200 | 259 | 311 | 353 | 390 |
| 170 | 61 | 100 | 151 | 207 | 268 | 321 | 364 | 402 |
| 180 | 66 | 106 | 158 | 214 | 275 | 330 | 374 | 414 |
| 190 | 70 | 112 | 163 | 221 | 282 | 339 | 384 | 425 |
| 200 | 73 | 117 | 168 | 227 | 289 | 347 | 394 | 436 |

[a] Rounded to the nearest 100 cu. ft.
[b] Standard cords (4 × 4 × 8 ft.) of stacked wood, peeled and usually split. Conversion factors based on present utilization practice.

### Table 42. Yields per Fully Stocked Acre, Trees 11.6 In. D.B.H. and Larger
(Continued)

BOARD-FOOT VOLUME [c] SCRIBNER RULE (APPLIED BY 16-FT. LOGS)

| Age (years) | Volume per acre by site index— | | | | | | | |
|---|---|---|---|---|---|---|---|---|
| | 60 | 80 | 100 | 120 | 140 | 160 | 180 | 200 |
| | Board feet | Board feet | Board feet | Board feet | Board feet | Board feet | Board feet | Board feet |
| 30 | | | | | 1,000 | 2,000 | 4,500 | 7,000 |
| 40 | | | | 2,500 | 7,000 | 16,000 | 25,500 | 35,500 |
| 50 | | | 1,000 | 4,000 | 11,000 | 24,500 | 41,000 | 58,500 | 73,500 |
| 60 | | 500 | 3,000 | 9,500 | 23,000 | 44,500 | 66,500 | 86,500 | 104,000 |
| 70 | 1,500 | 6,500 | 16,500 | 36,000 | 62,500 | 87,500 | 110,500 | 129,000 |
| 80 | 3,500 | 10,500 | 24,000 | 47,500 | 78,000 | 105,000 | 129,500 | 149,500 |
| 90 | 6,000 | 15,000 | 31,500 | 59,000 | 91,500 | 120,500 | 146,000 | 167,500 |
| 100 | 9,000 | 20,000 | 39,500 | 69,000 | 104,000 | 134,000 | 161,000 | 184,000 |
| 110 | 12,000 | 25,000 | 46,500 | 78,000 | 115,000 | 146,500 | 174,000 | 198,500 |
| 120 | 15,000 | 29,500 | 53,500 | 86,500 | 124,500 | 157,500 | 186,000 | 211,500 |
| 130 | 18,000 | 34,000 | 59,500 | 94,000 | 133,000 | 167,500 | 197,000 | 223,000 |
| 140 | 21,000 | 38,500 | 65,500 | 101,000 | 141,000 | 177,000 | 207,000 | 234,000 |
| 150 | 24,000 | 43,000 | 71,000 | 107,500 | 148,500 | 185,500 | 216,500 | 244,000 |
| 160 | 26,500 | 46,500 | 76,000 | 113,500 | 155,500 | 193,000 | 225,000 | 253,000 |
| 170 | 29,000 | 50,000 | 80,500 | 118,500 | 161,500 | 200,500 | 233,000 | 262,000 |
| 180 | 31,500 | 53,500 | 85,000 | 123,500 | 167,500 | 207,000 | 240,500 | 270,000 |
| 190 | 34,000 | 57,000 | 89,000 | 128,500 | 173,000 | 213,500 | 248,000 | 278,000 |
| 200 | 36,000 | 60,000 | 93,000 | 133,000 | 178,500 | 220,000 | 255,000 | 285,500 |

[c] To an 8-in. top inside bark, exclusive of a 2-ft. stump. Values rounded off to nearest 500.

## SITKA SPRUCE AND WESTERN HEMLOCK

### Table 43. Deviation from Yields in Table 42 Resulting from Differences in Stand Composition

Entire Range

| Composition | Plots (No.) | Average deviation from normal-yield-table values for— | | | |
|---|---|---|---|---|---|
| | | Basal area (%) | Average breast-height diameter (%) | Cubic-foot volume (%) | Board-foot volume (Scribner Rule) (%) |
| Spruce, 90 percent or more; hemlock, 10 percent or less | 44 | +6.5 | +17.2 | +5.6 | + 9.2 |
| Spruce, 50 to 90 percent; hemlock, 50 percent or less | 138 | + .8 | + 6.5 | + .7 | +16.0 |
| Hemlock, 50 to 90 percent; spruce, 50 percent or less | 245 | + .6 | + 2.0 | + .8 | + 4.3 |
| Hemlock, 90 percent or more; spruce, 10 percent or less | 230 | −3.6 | − .7 | −2.6 | − 5.4 |

Source: *Ibid.*

## SITKA SPRUCE AND WESTERN HEMLOCK

Table 44. Yields per Acre, by Average Diameter, for all Trees 2.6 In. D.B.H. or Larger

### OREGON AND WASHINGTON

| Average breast-height diameter (inches) | Trees | Basal area | Average height | Cubic volume | Board-measure volume | |
|---|---|---|---|---|---|---|
| | | | | | International rule | Scribner rule * |
| | Number | Sq. ft. | Ft. | Cu. ft. | Bd. ft. | Bd. ft. |
| 4 | 1,798 | 157 | 42 | 2,800 | 2,000 | |
| 5 | 1,342 | 183 | 51 | 4,100 | 8,500 | 1,000 |
| 6 | 1,039 | 204 | 59 | 5,300 | 17,000 | 3,000 |
| 7 | 831 | 222 | 66 | 6,400 | 26,000 | 6,500 |
| 8 | 676 | 236 | 73 | 7,500 | 35,500 | 12,000 |
| 9 | 564 | 249 | 80 | 8,600 | 45,000 | 19,000 |
| 10 | 477 | 260 | 86 | 9,600 | 54,500 | 28,000 |
| 11 | 410 | 270 | 92 | 10,600 | 64,000 | 37,000 |
| 12 | 358 | 281 | 99 | 11,600 | 73,500 | 46,000 |
| 13 | 316 | 291 | 105 | 12,600 | 82,500 | 54,500 |
| 14 | 282 | 301 | 111 | 13,500 | 91,500 | 63,000 |
| 15 | 253 | 311 | 116 | 14,400 | 100,000 | 71,500 |
| 16 | 230 | 321 | 121 | 15,300 | 108,000 | 79,500 |
| 17 | 209 | 330 | 126 | 16,100 | 115,500 | 87,000 |
| 18 | 192 | 339 | 131 | 16,900 | 123,000 | 94,500 |
| 19 | 177 | 348 | 136 | 17,800 | 130,500 | 102,000 |
| 20 | 164 | 357 | 141 | 18,600 | 137,500 | 108,500 |
| 21 | 152 | 365 | 145 | 19,400 | 144,500 | 115,000 |
| 22 | 142 | 374 | 150 | 20,200 | 151,500 | 122,000 |
| 23 | 132 | 382 | 155 | 21,000 | 158,500 | 128,500 |
| 24 | 124 | 391 | 159 | 21,800 | 165,000 | 134,500 |
| 25 | 117 | 400 | 164 | 22,600 | 171,500 | 141,000 |
| 26 | 111 | 408 | 168 | 23,300 | 178,000 | 147,000 |
| 27 | 105 | 417 | 172 | 24,100 | 184,000 | 153,000 |
| 28 | 99.4 | 425 | 176 | 24,800 | 190,500 | 159,000 |
| 29 | 94.6 | 434 | 181 | 25,600 | 196,500 | 165,000 |
| 30 | 90.2 | 443 | 185 | 26,400 | 203,000 | 171,000 |
| 31 | 86 | 451 | 189 | 27,100 | 209,000 | 176,500 |
| 32 | 82.4 | 460 | 193 | 27,900 | 215,000 | 182,000 |
| 33 | 79 | 468 | 198 | 28,600 | 221,000 | 187,500 |
| 34 | 75.6 | 477 | 202 | 29,400 | 227,000 | 193,500 |
| 35 | 72.6 | 485 | 206 | 30,200 | 233,000 | 199,500 |
| 36 | 70 | 494 | 210 | 31,000 | 239,000 | 205,000 |
| 37 | 67.2 | 502 | 214 | 31,800 | 245,500 | 211,000 |
| 38 | 65 | 511 | 218 | 32,600 | 252,000 | 217,000 |
| 39 | 62.7 | 520 | 222 | 33,400 | 258,000 | 223,000 |
| 40 | 60.6 | 529 | 226 | 34,000 | 263,000 | 228,000 |

### ALASKA

| | | | | | | |
|---|---|---|---|---|---|---|
| 4 | 1,718 | 150 | 36 | 2,300 | 1,800 | |
| 5 | 1,415 | 193 | 44 | 4,000 | 8,000 | 1,000 |
| 6 | 1,126 | 221 | 52 | 5,400 | 17,500 | 3,000 |
| 7 | 898 | 240 | 59 | 6,600 | 26,500 | 7,000 |
| 8 | 730 | 255 | 65 | 7,700 | 36,000 | 12,000 |
| 9 | 604 | 267 | 72 | 8,800 | 46,000 | 19,500 |
| 10 | 510 | 278 | 78 | 9,800 | 56,000 | 28,500 |
| 11 | 435 | 287 | 85 | 10,800 | 65,500 | 37,500 |
| 12 | 373 | 293 | 92 | 11,700 | 74,500 | 46,000 |
| 13 | 325 | 300 | 98 | 12,600 | 83,000 | 54,500 |
| 14 | 287 | 307 | 104 | 13,500 | 91,500 | 63,000 |
| 15 | 255 | 313 | 110 | 14,300 | 99,000 | 71,000 |
| 16 | 228 | 318 | 116 | 15,100 | 106,500 | 78,500 |
| 17 | 206 | 324 | 123 | 15,900 | 114,000 | 86,000 |
| 18 | 186 | 329 | 129 | 16,700 | 121,000 | 93,000 |
| 19 | 170 | 334 | 134 | 17,400 | 128,000 | 99,500 |
| 20 | 155 | 338 | 140 | 18,200 | 134,500 | 106,000 |
| 21 | 143 | 343 | 146 | 18,900 | 141,000 | 112,000 |
| 22 | 131 | 347 | 152 | 19,600 | 147,000 | 118,000 |

Cubic foot volumes are inside bark.
* Trees 11.6 in d.b.h. and larger; in 16-ft. logs, from 2-ft. stump to an 8-in. top.
Source: *Ibid.*

## WHITE SPRUCE

### Table 45. Yield per Fully Stocked Acre, Trees 7 In. D.B.H. and Larger

Northeastern United States

| Total age (yr.) | Site Index | | | |
|---|---|---|---|---|
| | 70 | 60 | 50 | 40 |
| | Volume in board feet * | | | |
| 40 | 4,200 | 2,950 | 1,720 | 460 |
| 50 | 18,800 | 13,100 | 7,650 | 2,060 |
| 60 | 35,200 | 24,500 | 14,300 | 3,850 |
| 70 | 47,200 | 33,000 | 19,200 | 5,150 |
| 80 | 54,700 | 38,200 | 22,200 | 5,900 |
| 90 | 60,700 | 42,300 | 24,700 | 6,650 |

* Board feet, International ⅛-In. Rule.

Source: W. H. Meyer, Yields of second-growth spruce and fir in the Northeast, U. S. Dept. Agr., *Tech. Bull. No. 142*, 1929.

## SPRUCE-FIR (CUT OVER)

### Table 46. Reference Table for Determining Stand Density for Dominant and Secondary Softwood Sites *

Northeastern United States

| D.b.h. (in.) | D.b.h. tenths of inches | | | | | | | | | |
|---|---|---|---|---|---|---|---|---|---|---|
| | 0.01 | 0.1 | 0.2 | 0.3 | 0.4 | 0.5 | 0.6 | 0.7 | 0.8 | 0.9 |
| | Number of trees per acre | | | | | | | | | |
| 1 | 1,660 | 1,625 | 1,590 | 1,560 | 1,530 | 1,500 | 1,465 | 1,435 | 1,405 | 1,375 |
| 2 | 1,345 | 1,315 | 1,285 | 1,260 | 1,230 | 1,200 | 1,175 | 1,150 | 1,125 | 1,100 |
| 3 | 1,075 | 1,050 | 1,025 | 1,000 | 975 | 950 | 930 | 910 | 890 | 870 |
| 4 | 850 | 830 | 815 | 800 | 782 | 765 | 748 | 732 | 716 | 700 |
| 5 | 685 | 670 | 655 | 640 | 625 | 610 | 595 | 582 | 569 | 555 |
| 6 | 543 | 530 | 518 | 506 | 495 | 485 | 474 | 462 | 452 | 442 |
| 7 | 433 | 424 | 415 | 406 | 398 | 391 | 384 | 376 | 367 | 360 |
| 8 | 352 | 344 | 337 | 330 | 323 | 316 | 309 | 302 | 296 | 290 |
| 9 | 283 | 276 | 269 | 263 | 257 | 251 | 246 | 240 | 235 | 230 |
| 10 | 225 | 220 | 215 | 210 | 205 | 200 | 195 | 191 | 187 | 183 |

* To determine the density of any given spruce stand, from the above table, divide the total number of trees (hardwoods and softwoods) per acre by the tabular number for a stand of the same average diameter.

Source: Marinus Westveld, Yield tables for cut-over spruce-fir stands in the Northeast, Northeastern Forest Exp. Sta., *Occ. Paper No. 12*, 1941.

## SPRUCE-FIR (CUT OVER)

**Table 47. Yield per Acre of Spruce and Fir 6 In. D.B.H. and Larger at Various Intervals After Cutting, by Stand Density and Composition, Dominant Softwood Sites**

Northeastern United States
(20 yr. after cutting)

| Density [a] % | Composition index [b] (Percent) | | | | | | | | | |
|---|---|---|---|---|---|---|---|---|---|---|
| | 10 | 20 | 30 | 40 | 50 | 60 | 70 | 80 | 90 | 100 |
| | Volume in cords | | | | | | | | | |
| 10 | 0.6 | 0.9 | 1.3 | 1.6 | 2.0 | 2.4 | 2.8 | 3.3 | 3.7 | 4.2 |
| 30 | 0.9 | 1.2 | 1.6 | 1.9 | 2.3 | 2.8 | 3.2 | 3.6 | 4.1 | 4.6 |
| 50 | 1.1 | 1.5 | 1.9 | 2.3 | 2.7 | 3.1 | 3.6 | 4.0 | 4.5 | 5.0 |
| 70 | 1.4 | 1.8 | 2.2 | 2.6 | 3.1 | 3.5 | 3.9 | 4.4 | 4.9 | 5.4 |
| 90 | 1.7 | 2.1 | 2.6 | 3.0 | 3.4 | 3.9 | 4.3 | 4.8 | 5.3 | 5.8 |
| 110 | 2.1 | 2.5 | 2.9 | 3.4 | 3.8 | 4.3 | 4.7 | 5.2 | 5.7 | 6.2 |
| 130 | 2.4 | 2.9 | 3.3 | 3.7 | 4.2 | 4.6 | 5.1 | 5.6 | 6.1 | 6.6 |
| 150 | 2.8 | 3.2 | 3.7 | 4.1 | 4.6 | 5.0 | 5.5 | 6.0 | 6.5 | 7.0 |
| 170 | 3.2 | 3.6 | 4.0 | 4.5 | 5.0 | 5.4 | 5.9 | 6.4 | 6.9 | 7.4 |
| 190 | 3.5 | 4.0 | 4.4 | 4.9 | 5.4 | 5.8 | 6.3 | 6.8 | 7.3 | 7.9 |
| 210 | 3.9 | 4.3 | 4.8 | 5.3 | 5.8 | 6.3 | 6.7 | 7.3 | 7.8 | 8.3 |
| 230 | 4.3 | 4.7 | 5.2 | 5.7 | 6.2 | 6.7 | 7.2 | 7.7 | 8.2 | 8.7 |
| 250 | 4.7 | 5.2 | 5.6 | 6.1 | 6.7 | 7.1 | 7.6 | 8.2 | 8.7 | 9.2 |

[a] Obtained from Table 46.
[b] Percent of total number of trees (hardwoods included) which are spruce and fir.
Source: *Ibid.*

## Stocking

**REINEKE'S STAND DENSITY INDEX.** Crown closure and stand density are terms which loosely designate the relative degree of stocking of a forest, that is, the proportion of an area utilized by trees. Reineke's stand density index is a measure of stocking for even-aged stands which is widely used in connection with yield tables. It compares the number of trees in a stand of a certain average diameter with the average number of trees present in fully stocked stands of the same diameter. This average number of trees of fully stocked stands is obtained by plotting the logarithms of number of trees per acre of all measured plots against the average stand diameter of these plots and fitting a straight line to the data. The fitted straight line shows the number of trees per acre in terms of average stand diameter for average stocking. By plotting the data on logarithmic paper, the number of trees themselves can be read directly from the graph. A series of parallel lines as shown in Fig. 2 indicates departures from average stocking at intervals of 10 percent. To determine the density index of a given stand, determine the number of trees per acre and average stand diameter and compare with the corresponding data as given in a yield table.

**Example.**

Average diameter of even-aged stand of upland oak......... 15 in.
Number of trees per acre.................................. 95
Average density (read from Fig. 2)........................ 75 percent

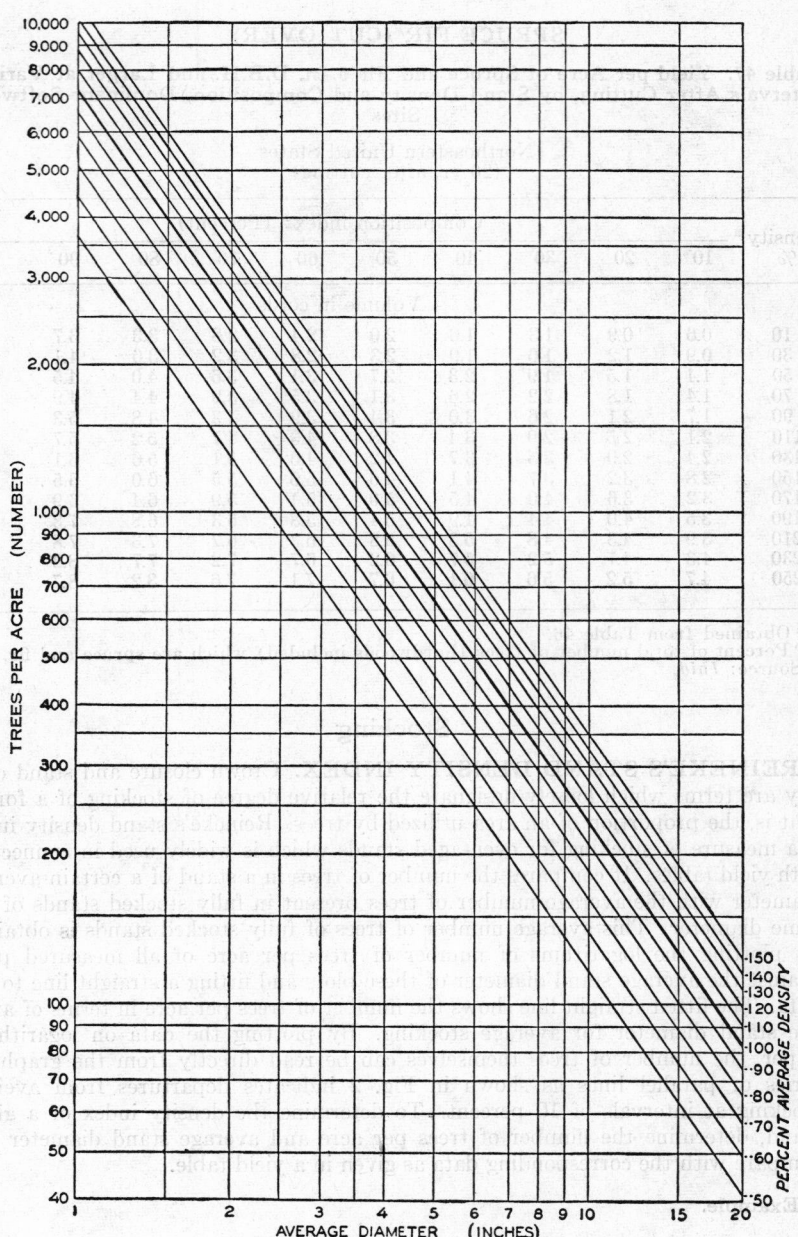

Fig. 2. Stand-density chart for upland oaks.

(U. S. Dept. Agr., *Tech. Bull. No. 560*, 1937.)

Some American yield tables give volume per acre in terms of age and site index by density classes (see Table 19).

Reineke discovered a remarkable uniformity in the rate of decrease of number of trees per acre for 15 species investigated. He expressed the relationship of number of trees per acre $N$ and average stand diameter $D$ by the equation:

$$\text{Log } N = -1.605 \log D + k,$$

and found that the first constant on the right-hand side of the equation was nearly the same for all species, while $k$ varied considerably. Later investigation yielded different values also for the first constant.

The yield table data for even-aged ponderosa pine indicated a definite departure from the straight-line relationship, as shown in Fig. 3. In this case the numerical values of the stand density index represent the number of trees per acre for an average stand diameter of 10 in.

**BASAL AREA AS A MEASURE OF STAND DENSITY.** While basal area increases rapidly with age in young stands, it generally levels off as stand age reaches 40 to 60 yr. or more. Therefore, in older stands basal area may serve as an absolute measure of stand density. It is customary, however, to compare the basal area of a stand of a certain site index and age with the corresponding basal area as listed in a yield table. For example, according to Table 24, the basal area of a 100-yr.-old ponderosa pine stand of site index 80 is equal to 198 sq. ft. If the actual basal area of a stand of the same age and site index is equal to 170 sq. ft., the density of the stand would be:

$$170/198 = 0.86, \text{ or } 86 \text{ percent}$$

**SPACING CRITERIA.** As a field aid in judging stocking of forest stands, Matthews suggests the spacing figure. Matthews' spacing figure $(D/d)$ may be determined from the equation

$$\frac{D}{d} = \frac{185}{\sqrt{BA}}$$

where $D$ = average distance between stems, in feet
$d$ = average d.b.h. of stand in same unit of measurement as $D$
$BA$ = basal area per acre, in square feet

In the absence of more accurate data the spacing figure can be used to determine:

1. An estimate of stocking in terms of basal area per acre, or, knowing the basal area, to estimate stocking in terms of the ratio $D/d$. A well-stocked stand has a high basal area per acre and a low spacing figure. A poorly stocked stand has a low basal area per acre and a high spacing figure. If a suitable normal yield table is available, the normal spacing figure can be computed for several age classes for comparison with actual stands.

2. A guide to spacing of stems in thinning, if average stand diameter and basal area of a well-stocked stand for a given species, site, and age are known.

3. A rough estimate of volume. Solve above equation for basal area, then

$$V = BA(H)(FF)$$

where $V$ = volume per acre, in cubic feet
$BA$ = basal area per acre, in square feet
$H$ = average merchantable height
$FF$ = cylinder form factor or frustum form factor

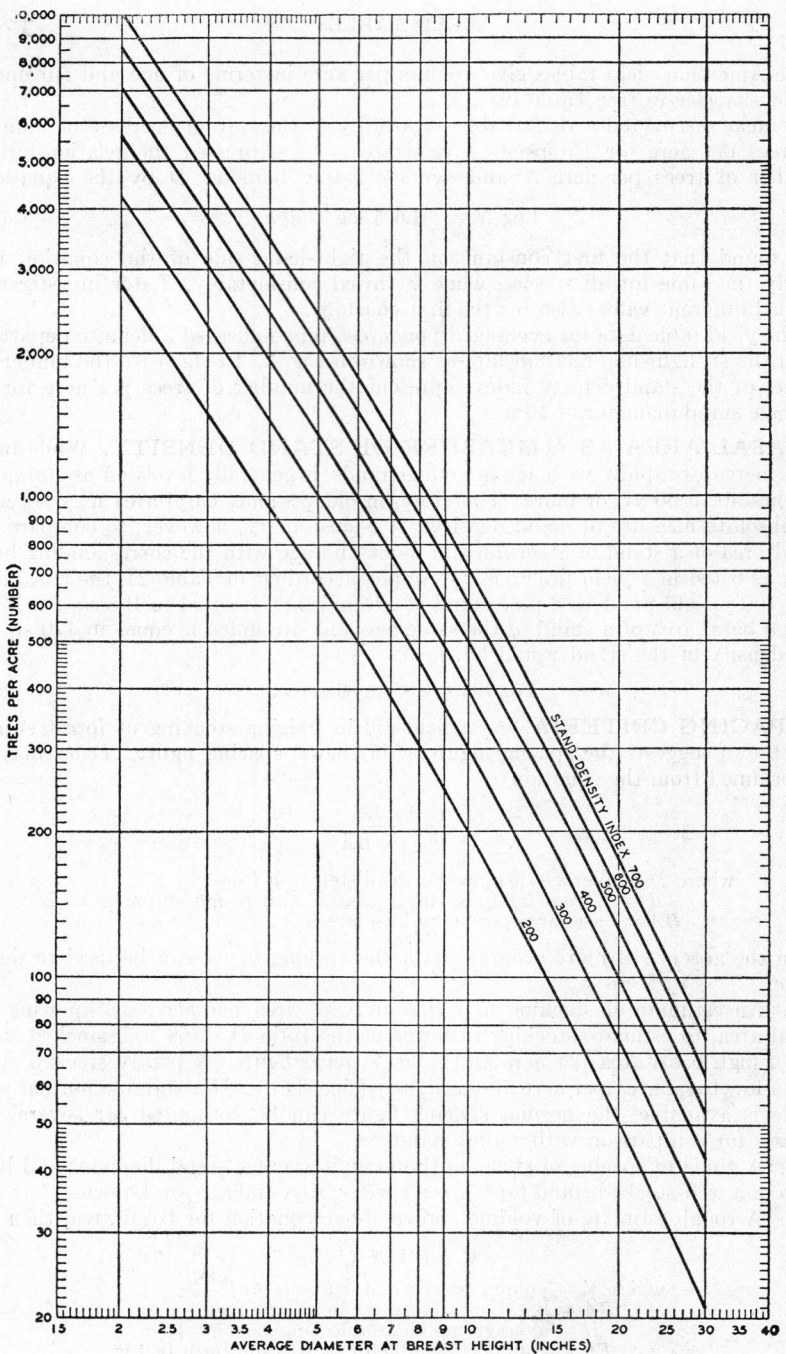

Fig. 3. Stand-density index, even-aged ponderosa pine.

(U. S. Dept. Agr., *Tech. Bull. No. 630*, 1938.)

Volume in cubic feet can be converted to board feet by dividing by 6, to cords by dividing by 80 for hardwoods or 90 for pine, or other factors.

4. Number of trees per acre: $\text{Number} = \dfrac{43{,}560}{D^2}$

Matthews' spacing factor $(D/d)$, as yet unpublished, is a modification of the spacing figure, with $D$ in feet and $d$ in inches:

$$\frac{D}{d} = \frac{15.4}{\sqrt{BA}}$$

For a given stand the spacing factor is ½ of the spacing figure. Use of the spacing factor is recommended because $d$ is in inches, the unit of measure commonly employed.

In thinning, crowded stands should be reduced in basal area to less than the basal area desired. Before thinning again they are allowed to increase in basal area through growth to an amount above the desired basal area. Hence, $D$ as determined by the spacing factor for a normal stand is insufficient space to leave between trees in thinning. To be used as a spacing guide, an allowance must be added to $D$:

$$A = (s)(g)(n)$$

where $A$ = spacing allowance to be added to $D$
  $s$ = spacing factor for a well-stocked stand
  $g$ = periodic annual diameter growth, in inches
  $n$ = estimated number of years between thinnings

For example, an overstocked stand with an average diameter of 10 in. and a spacing between stems of 14 ft. has a periodic annual diameter growth of 0.2 in., and the estimated interval between thinnings is 10 yr.

$$\frac{D}{d} = \frac{14}{10} = 1.4, \text{ and}$$

$$BA = \left(\frac{15.4}{1.4}\right)^2 = 121$$

If the assumed objective is to maintain stands with a basal area of 100 sq. ft. per acre, the correct stem spacing is

$$\frac{D}{10} = \frac{15.4}{100}$$

$$D = \frac{15.4}{10}(10) = 15.4, \text{ and}$$

$$\frac{D}{d} = \frac{15.4}{10} = 1.54$$

The allowance for growing space between thinnings, in feet, is

$A = 1.54(0.2)(10)$

$= 3.08$, and the spacing guide is $15.4 + 3.08 = 18.48$, or 18 to 19 ft.

## BIBLIOGRAPHY

The bibliography for this section is combined with that of the following section because of the integration of the subject matter of the two sections. (See page **4·14**.)

# FOREST MANAGEMENT—CUTTING BUDGET AND ANNUAL CUT

## CONTENTS

# FOREST MANAGEMENT—CUTTING BUDGET AND ANNUAL CUT

## Preparation of a Cutting Budget

Every commercial forestry business, whether supplying raw material for a manufacturing plant or selling stumpage to others, must endeavor to produce a regular flow of wood products in amounts to give, over long periods of time, an approximately equal annual income. The determination of an allowable cut indicates whether a sufficient volume will be available to meet the owner's requirements from a given forest property. But even when the allowable annual cut has been computed for a forest property, it is necessary to determine the specific areas from which the cut is to be harvested and to set up a schedule of cutting, for about 5 yr. in the future. Cutting plans covering long periods in the future probably will have to be revised every few years because of fluctuations in market prices, expansion of road systems, and changes in logging methods.

Wackerman reported a graphic method of presenting timber inventory and growth information in a way that a cutting budget can be prepared with a minimum of computation. A graph presenting a forest inventory, with a cutting budget superimposed on it, is more easily understood by foresters, company management, or public officials, than are lengthy tabular statements.

Wackerman's skyline graph shown in Fig. 1 was prepared for a shortleaf pine–loblolly pine–hardwood forest in Arkansas. The method assumes that the area is generally accessible to logging and that a method of logging is to be used, such as by trucks, in which the order of tracts selected for cutting does not increase logging costs. It assumes that the heaviest stands are to be cut first. Without additional knowledge as to the silvicultural needs of individual stands this is a logical assumption. Even if certain silvicultural work were desirable, cutting the heaviest stands first might be required by economic necessity.

Timber survey data showing volume per acre for each stand, size of stand, and stand description (by number) were arranged in a table in descending rank according to per-acre volume. Old-field stands were not included in the table and they are not shown on the graph because they are to be managed differently from forest-grown stands. However, part of the planned annual cut of 500,000 bd. ft. will be taken from old-field stands, as indicated on the graph.

Fig. 1 is largely self-explanatory. The horizontal scale represents area and the vertical scale represents volume per acre. A unit area on the graph represents a given volume, depending on the scales used. A reserve stand of 3,500 ft. per acre will not be cut. The expected annual growth per acre for a 5-yr. period is indicated by curved dash lines above the line of curved present volume. Although not required, the predicted volume per acre 5 yr. hence for individual stands is also shown. The volume to be cut in any year includes one-half of the current year's growth. The annual cut for each year, approximating 500,000 bd. ft., can be calculated by counting squares or by dividing the total annual cut by the average volume per acre at the time of cutting, less the volume reserved, to obtain the

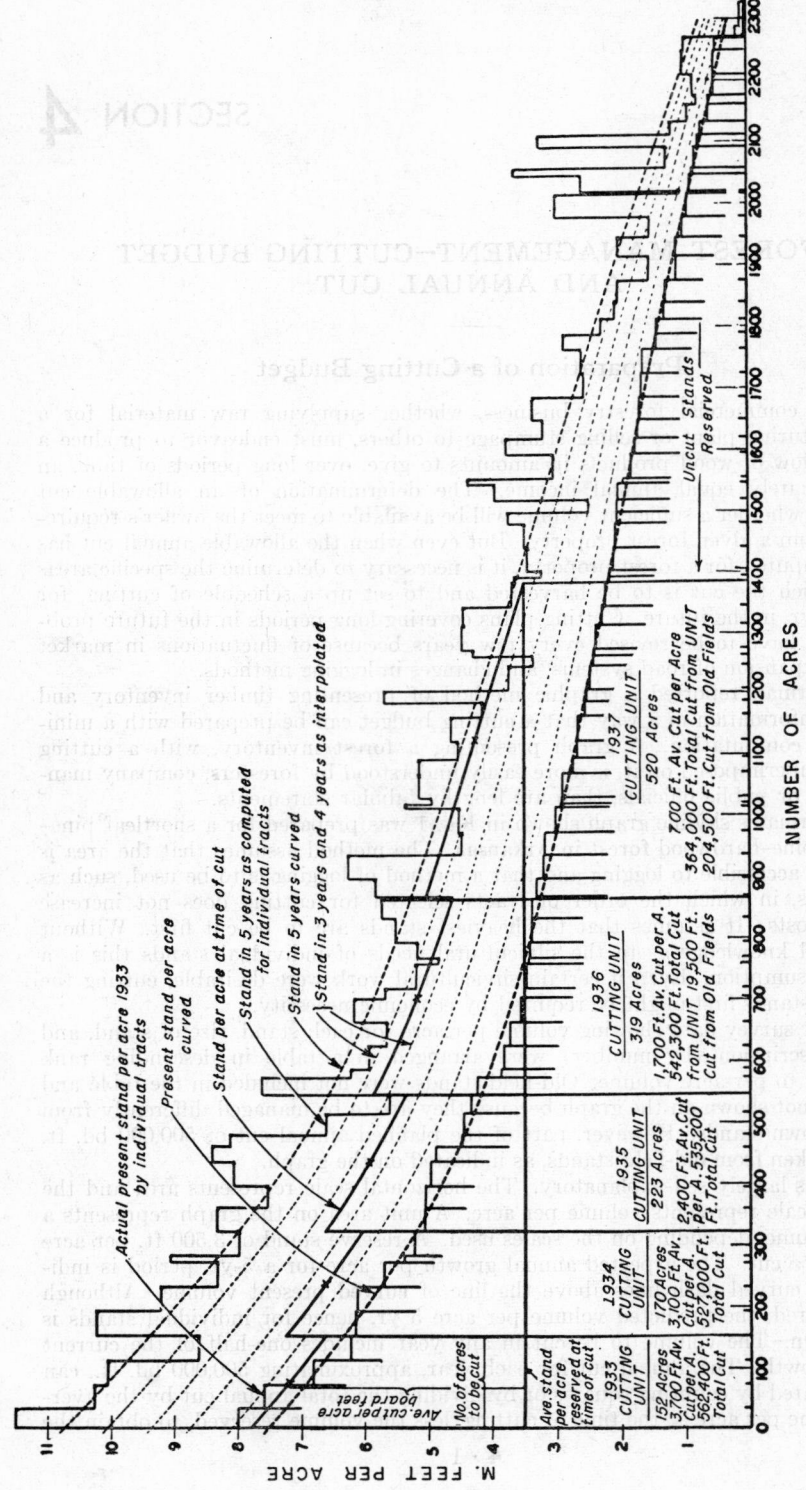

Fig. 1. Forest skyline graph for determining location and amount of cut for next 5 yr.

Individual tracts of forest-grown stands arranged in descending order based on average stand per acre in board feet, with growth for 5-yr. period shown and interpolated for single year. (A. E. Wackerman, Allocating cutting budgets by means of a skyline graph, *Jour. Forestry* 32:4-7, 1934.)

cutting area. Essential information, the year of cut, area to be cut, and total volume to be cut is shown just above the horizontal scale, along with the tract numbers. For a large forest the graph can be plotted to large, easily read scale by using graph paper obtainable in 20- to 50-yard rolls.

An alternative method of showing volume per acre at the time of cutting is to add the growth to individual stands as a rectangular block superimposed on the top of present volume. This alternative is very satisfactory for forests containing homogeneous stands of large area. As Wackerman states, the skyline graph is practical, accurate, and understandable.

## Regulation of the Annual Cut

**FORESTS OF EVEN-AGED STANDS.** Regulation of the annual cut from any forest aims to promote:

1. Regularity of age classes.
2. Optimum growth.

**Area Regulation.** In a forest of species best adapted to even-aged management, growing on a reasonably uniform site, regularity of age classes in the second and subsequent rotations may obviously be achieved by cutting each year an area equal to the total forest area divided by the number of years in the assumed rotation. However, if the present age classes are irregularly distributed, the volume harvested yearly will fluctuate. Strict area regulation is therefore rarely adapted to supplying raw material to a forest industry without supplemental purchase of additional material.

**Volume Regulation.** Several formulas have been used in regulating annual cut by volume. All require an estimate of actual growing stock, either for the entire forest or a representative area. Graphic methods, as used by Matthews and others, are very helpful.

A forest with a regular distribution of age classes and an acreage equal to the rotation $R$ may be shown as the right triangle $AB'C$ in Fig. 2. Graduations on the base $AC$ represent both age of stand and acres of forest. Assume that the forest is of loblolly pine, site index 90, that stands become merchantable at 40 yr., and that a suitable rotation is 80 yr.

At average merchantable age, 60 yr., the stand averages 6,500 cu. ft. per acre. The line $AB'$ extends from the origin of coordinates through this point to the 80-yr. ordinate. Is this forest normally stocked? Superimpose on the figure the curve of normal yield, $AFB$, for this species and site. Its intersection with the 80-yr. ordinate, at $B$, is somewhat below $B'$. Draw $AB$. It is evident from inspection that whereas the area of triangle $ABC$ is considerably less than the normal growing stock represented by $AFBC$, the area of $AB'C$ is nearly equal to $AFBC$. For practical purposes the forest appears normally stocked.

Commercial timber inventories estimate only the merchantable growing stock ($ED'B'C$, Fig. 2). The growing stock below merchantable size is represented by $AD'E$. Unless the allowable annual cut is calculated from the volume of the entire growing stock, $AB'C$, it may be grossly underestimated. In a forest where age-classes are regularly distributed, as represented in Fig. 2, and where merchantability begins halfway through the rotation, 25 percent of the total growing stock is unmerchantable. This will be apparent from Fig. 2. The areas of similar triangles ($AD'E$ and $AB'C$) vary as the square of their bases. Therefore

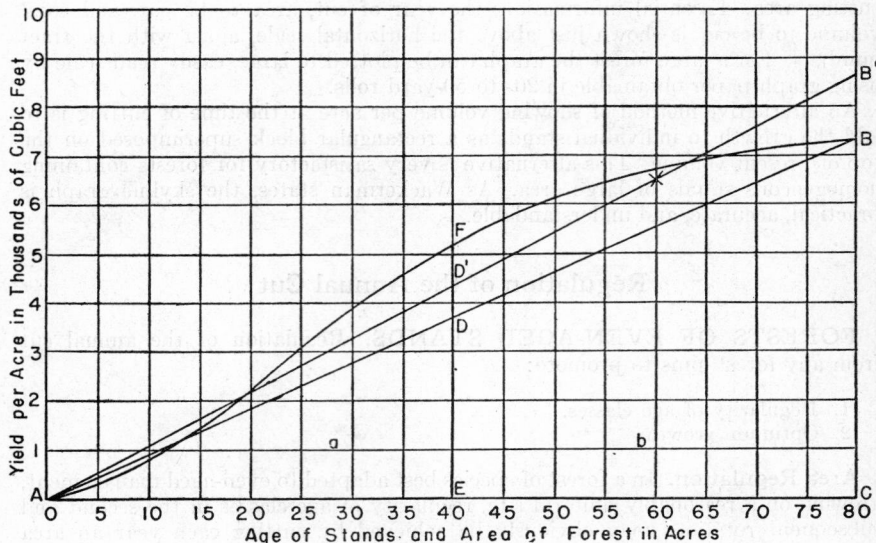

**Fig. 2. Volume regulation, even-aged stands.**

By permission from *Management of American forests*, by D. M. Matthews. Copyright, 1935, by McGraw-Hill Book Co., Inc.

Unmerchantable growing stock: total growing stock :: $AE^2$ : $AC^2$
Unmerchantable growing stock: 100 :: $(40)^2$ : $(80)^2$
Unmerchantable growing stock = 25 percent

To calculate the total growing stock, divide the merchantable volume of the timber survey by 0.75.

Where suitable yield tables are available for the principal species in an even-aged forest, Hundeshagen's formula may be used to determine the annual cut:

$$\text{Annual cut} = \frac{Y_r}{G_n}(G_a)$$

where $G_a$ = actual growing stock in the forest
$Y_r$ = yield (from the yield table) at the rotation age selected
$G_n$ = volume of normal growing stock at the rotation age

$G_n$ is obtained from the yield table by summation as follows:

$$G_n = n\left(V_n + V_{2n} + V_{3n} \ldots + V_{rn} + \frac{V_r}{2}\right)$$

where $n$ = age interval in yield table
$V_n$ = first yield given in yield table
$V_{2n}$ = second yield given in yield table
$V_{3n}$ = third yield given in yield table, etc.
$V_r$ = yield at rotation selected

In the absence of a yield table, the actual growing stock must be assumed to equal the normal growing stock. Von Mantel's formula:

$$\text{Allowable cut} = \frac{\text{Actual growing stock}}{R/2}$$

has long been used as a substitute for Hundeshagen's under such circumstances. Transposing terms, Von Mantel's formula reads:

$$\text{Actual growing stock} = \text{allowable cut} \times R/2$$

Its derivation is then plain from Fig. 2, in which actual growing stock $= AB'C$, cut $= B'C$, and $R/2 = AC/2$; the area of the triangle equals base $\times \frac{1}{2}$ altitude, or altitude $\times \frac{1}{2}$ base. If in using Von Mantel's formula the actual growing stock is taken to be the merchantable stock only, the calculated cut is overly conservative. The formula gives results most nearly satisfactory for short rotations with cubic feet, and for long rotations with board feet.

Heyer's modification of an Austrian formula for calculating the annual cut is:

$$\text{Annual cut} = I + \frac{Ga - Gn}{a}$$

where  $I =$ mean annual increment of the actual forest
  $Ga =$ volume of growing stock on the actual forest
  $Gn =$ volume of growing stock for a normal forest of the same size
  $a =$ period of time during which the forest is to be regulated, commonly one rotation

The Swedish method of calculating the annual cut is based on the volumes present in three broad age groups:

$$\text{Annual cut} = \frac{V_1 + V_2 + \dfrac{V_3}{2}}{R/3}$$

where $V_1 =$ volume of timber $\frac{3}{4}$ of rotation age to rotation age
  $V_2 =$ volume of overmature timber
  $V_3 =$ volume of timber $\frac{1}{4}$ of rotation age to $\frac{3}{4}$ of rotation age

Three broad age groups in the Swedish method (omitting overmature and adding very young timber) offer a means of checking the normality of actual volume distributions:

| Age group (yr.) | Percent of total normal volume |
|---|---|
| 0 to $\frac{1}{4}$ of rotation age | 6 |
| $\frac{1}{4}$ to $\frac{3}{4}$ of rotation age | 50 |
| $\frac{3}{4}$ to rotation age | 44 |

Hanzlik suggested a formula and method for calculating the allowable annual cut for virgin forests or those with a preponderance of mature and overmature growing stock. It attempts to spread the cut in old-growth stands over a sufficient number of years so that second-growth stands will be ready for cutting by the time the last of the old-growth timber is cut:

$$\text{Annual cut} = \frac{V_m}{R} + I$$

where $V_m =$ total volume of mature and overmature timber
  $R =$ rotation in years
  $I =$ total mean annual increment of immature stands

An example of its application, to the Shelton Cooperative Sustained Yield Unit on the Olympic National Forest, Wash., is given by the Department of Agriculture below.

## STEP I

**Volume of available mature timber** on the cooperating lands as of January 1, 1946: 5,329,892 m.b.m., on 270,226 acres.

**Total mean annual increment of immature stands** (preliminary measure derived from the following table): 28,748,672 ft. b.m.

| Forest Survey type No. | Area (acres) | Average present age (yr.) | Total area (acres) | Age at ½ rotation (yr.) | Normal mean increment per acre at ½ rotation (ft. b.m.) | Discounts per acre for Inadequate stocking = 25% (ft. b.m.) | Breakage & defect = 5% (ft. b.m.) | Net mean annual increment per acre at ½ rotation (ft. b.m.) | Total mean annual increment (ft. b.m.) |
|---|---|---|---|---|---|---|---|---|---|
| 8 | 2,885 | 100 | 2,885 | 150 | 590 | 147 | 22 | 421 | 1,214,585 |
| 8 | 3,701 | 70 | 3,701 | 120 | 625 | 156 | 23 | 446 | 1,650,646 |
| 9 | 1,361 | 60 | 1,361 | 110 | 630 | 157 | 24 | 449 | 611,089 |
| 9 | 4,573 | 50 | | | | | | | |
| 15 | 675 | 50 | 5,248 | 100 | 626 | 156 | 23 | 447 | 2,345,856 |
| 9 | 4,946 | 40 | 4,946 | 90 | 609 | 152 | 23 | 434 | 2,146,564 |
| 9 | 10,186 | 30 | 10,186 | 80 | 571 | 143 | 21 | 407 | 4,145,702 |
| 10 | 28,736 | 20 | 28,736 | 70 | 506 | 126 | 19 | 361 | 10,373,696 |
| 10 | 20,367 | 10 | 20,367 | 60 | 396 | 99 | 15 | 282 | 5,743,494 |
| 10 | 2,248 | 5 | 2,248 | 55 | 322 | 80 | 12 | 230 | 517,040 |

## STEP II

From the foregoing, substitutions may be made in the formula

$$C = \frac{V_m}{R} + I$$

in order to ascertain the indicated allowable annual cut:

$$C = \frac{5,329,892M}{100} + 28,749M = 82,048M \text{ b.m.}$$

## STEP III

To determine if cutting at the indicated rate will result in the harvesting of the growing stands on the cooperating lands at ages approximating the culmination of their mean annual growth and will accomplish the cutting of those stands during the current rotation, the following check calculation is required:

$$\frac{\text{Volume of mature timber} = 5,329,892M}{\text{Indicated allowable cut} = 82,030M} = 65 \text{ years required to cut old growth.}$$

| Present age (yr.) | Area (acres) | Range of ages when cut (yr.) | Approximate average age when cut (yr.) | Normal yield per acre* (ft. b.m.) | Discounts per acre for Inadequate stocking = 25% (ft. b.m.) | Breakage and defect = 5% (ft. b.m.) | Net yield per acre (ft. b.m.) | Total anticipated yield (M.b.m.) | Years to cut Periodic (yr.) | Cumulative (yr.) |
|---|---|---|---|---|---|---|---|---|---|---|
| Old growth | 106,715 | | | | | | | 5,329,892 | 65.0 | 65.0 |
| 100 | 2,885 | 165–167 | 166 | 94,680 | 23,670 | 3,550 | 67,460 | 194,622 | 2.4 | 67.4 |
| 70 | 3,701 | 137–140 | 139 | 84,050 | 21,012 | 3,152 | 59,886 | 221,638 | 2.7 | 70.1 |
| 60 | 1,361 | 130–131 | 130 | 80,000 | 20,000 | 3,000 | 57,000 | 77,577 | .9 | 71.0 |
| 50 | 5,248 | 121–123 | 122 | 76,000 | 19,000 | 2,850 | 54,150 | 284,179 | 3.5 | 74.5 |
| 40 | 4,946 | 114–117 | 115 | 72,200 | 18,050 | 2,707 | 51,443 | 254,617 | 3.1 | 77.6 |
| 30 | 10,186 | 108–114 | 111 | 69,960 | 17,490 | 2,623 | 49,847 | 507,741 | 6.2 | 83.8 |
| 20 | 28,736 | 104–123 | 113 | 71,080 | 17,770 | 2,665 | 50,645 | 1,455,335 | 17.8 | 101.6 |
| 10 | 20,367 | 112–125 | 119 | 74,440 | 18,610 | 2,791 | 53,039 | 1,080,245 | 13.2 | 114.7 |
| 5 | 2,248 | 120–122 | 121 | 75,506 | 18,875 | 2,831 | 53,794 | 120,929 | 1.5 | 116.2 |

* Interpolated from U. S. Dept. Agr., *Tech. Bull. No. 201*, Yield of Douglas-fir in the Pacific Northwest, p. 27.

## STEP IV

It is obvious from the above check that the indicated allowable cut is too low since it results in delaying the harvest of the young stands until they have measurably passed the established 100 year rotation age.

An adjusted cut of 90 million feet board measure per year will succeed, as the following calculations show, in bringing about the removal of the growing stands at times more consistent with the established rotation period and with the culmination of their mean annual increment.

The check calculation of 90 million feet board measure adjusted allowable annual cut is given below:

| Present age (yr.) | Area (acres) | Range of ages when cut (yr.) | Approximate average age when cut (yr.) | Normal yield per acre* (ft. b.m.) | Discounts per acre for | | Net yield per acre (ft. b.m.) | Total anticipated yield (M.b.m.) | Years to cut | |
| | | | | | Inadequate stocking = 25% (ft. b.m.) | Breakage and defect = 5% (ft. b.m.) | | | Periodic (yr.) | Cumulative (yr.) |
|---|---|---|---|---|---|---|---|---|---|---|
| Old growth | 106,715 | | | | | | | 5,329,892 | 59.2 | 59.2 |
| 100 | 2,885 | 159–161 | 160 | 92,400 | 23,100 | 3,465 | 65,835 | 189,934 | 2.1 | 61.3 |
| 70 | 3,701 | 131–133 | 132 | 80,900 | 20,225 | 3,034 | 57,641 | 213,329 | 2.4 | 63.7 |
| 60 | 1,361 | 124–125 | 124 | 77,000 | 19,250 | 2,887 | 54,863 | 74,669 | .8 | 64.5 |
| 50 | 5,248 | 114–117 | 115 | 72,200 | 18,050 | 2,707 | 51,443 | 269,973 | 3.0 | 67.5 |
| 40 | 4,946 | 107–110 | 109 | 68,740 | 17,185 | 2,577 | 48,977 | 242,240 | 2.7 | 70.2 |
| 30 | 10,186 | 100–105 | 103 | 64,780 | 16,195 | 2,429 | 46,156 | 470,145 | 5.2 | 75.4 |
| 20 | 28,736 | 95–110 | 102 | 64,120 | 16,030 | 2,404 | 45,686 | 1,312,832 | 14.6 | 90.0 |
| 10 | 20,367 | 100–111 | 105 | 66,100 | 16,525 | 2,479 | 47,096 | 959,204 | 10.7 | 100.7 |
| 5 | 2,248 | 105–107 | 106 | 66,760 | 16,690 | 2,503 | 47,567 | 106,931 | 1.2 | 101.9 |

* Interpolated from U. S. Dept. Agr., *Tech. Bull. No. 201*, Yield of Douglas-fir in the Pacific Northwest, p. 27.

The foregoing adjusted allowable annual cut of 90 million feet board measure per year proves satisfactory because at that rate the second growth stands will be reached for cutting at approximately the rotation age, and the removal of this amount annually can be sustained for slightly over 100 years.

The annual sustained-yield cutting capacity for the period 1947 to 1956, inclusive, is therefore determined to be 90 million feet board measure per year.

Formulas, or any other method of volume regulation, are satisfactory only when applied to forests with an approximately regular distribution of age classes or broad age groups. Although their use builds up understocked stands, it perpetuates age-class irregularities. In a forest predominantly of understocked stands, the calculated cut would have to be concentrated in the relatively small area of good stands; in a forest with excess growing stock, it would come from a relatively large area. In either case the period required to cut over the forest would be altered from the desired rotation, and the second rotation also would be changed.

Matthews suggests the use of growing stock diagrams to determine growth and annual cut for forests with irregular age-class distribution. His Case II, involving a forest with excess area in the younger age classes, probably represents many forest properties in the United States. Timber inventory and growth data are as follows:

(A growing-stock diagram prepared from data given at the top of the following page is shown in Fig. 3.)

| Size classes | Area (acres) | Volume per acre (M ft.) | Range of ages (yr.) | Percent of total area | Area in representative 200-acre sample (acres) |
|---|---|---|---|---|---|
| 14 in. and over.... | 63,505 | 30 | 120–200 | 28.0 | 56 |
| 5 to 14 in. ......... | 42,325 | | 40–120 | 18.5 | 37 |
| 1 to 5 in. ......... | 121,946 | | 0–40 | 53.5 | 107 |
| | 227,776 | | | 100.0 | 200 |

Graduations on the base of the triangle $ABC$ represent both ages of stands and acreages in the 200-acre sample (last column of the table). The hypotenuse was drawn from the origin at $A$ through a point representing the average volume (30M bd. ft.) and the average age (160 yr.) of the timber size class 14 in. and over. The area under it may be referred to as the potential growing stock (it might or might not equal the normal stocking as determined from normal yield tables).

The actual stand is represented by the polygon $AabBC$. Coordinates of point $a$ are 107 (acres) and 7,500 (bd. ft.); the latter point is the intersection of the 40-yr. ordinate with $AB$. Coordinates of $b$ are 144 yr. and 22,500 bd. ft. The polygon $AabB$ represents the deficiency in stocking from the apparent potential.

The total growing stock may be computed from the figure representing the 200 acres and the total acreages (Column 2 of the preceding table), as is shown below:

| Age group | Av. volume per acre, f.b.m. | Area (acres) | Total volume, M f.b.m. |
|---|---|---|---|
| 0–40 | $\dfrac{0 + 7500}{2} = 3{,}750$ | 121,946 | 457,000 |
| 40–120 | $\dfrac{7{,}500 + 22{,}500}{2} = 15{,}000$ | 42,325 | 635,000 |
| 120–200 | 30,000 | 63,505 | 1,905,150 |
| | | 227,776 | 2,997,150 |

Determination of allowable annual cut by formulas will be subject to large error because of the irregular distribution of age groups. It is best accomplished with the help of Fig. 3.

Assume a rotation of 120 yr. The oldest age group has a mean annual increment of 30,000/160 = 187.5 bd. ft.; although its average age is 160 yr., its increment is considered applicable to the period over which the growing stock is being regulated. This period must be long enough to allow stands now younger than they should be to attain rotation age by the time they are cut. A glance at Fig. 3 shows the greatest deficiency to be in the stands now less than 40 yr. old. It will require 107 − 40, or 67 yr., before these stands will have attained a volume in proportion to their acreage—that is, before $a$ has moved to $a'$ on the line of potential stocking. A regulatory period of 67 yr. is therefore selected. During this time all timber 120 yr. or older at the time of cutting will be cut; cutting should obviously begin in the oldest of these stands, and will eventually reach those which attain the rotation age during the regulatory period. Present age of youngest stands to be cut is 120 − 67 = 53 yr., referenced by a vertical line from 53 yr. to $AB$ and a horizontal line to $ab$.

The annual cut during the regulatory period depends on the total present volume of merchantable timber, 120 to 200 yr. of age, the volume of stands at

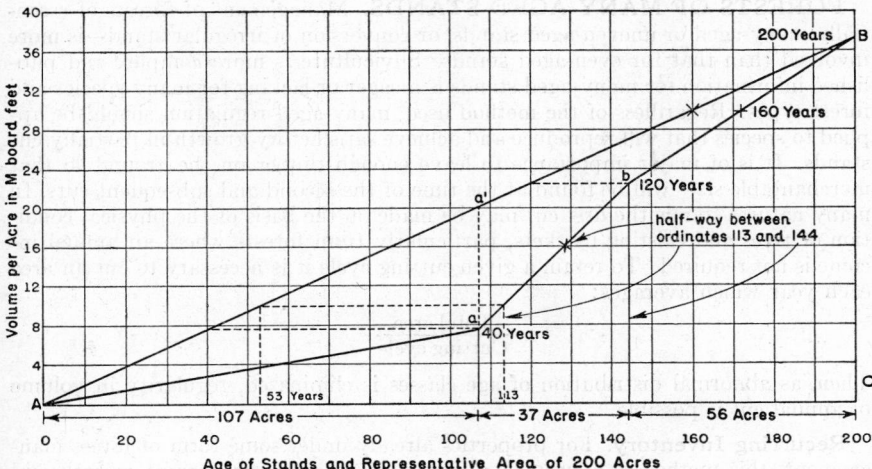

**Fig. 3. Growing stock diagram, forests with irregular age-class distribution.**
By permission from *Management of American forests*, by D. M. Matthews. Copyright, 1935, by McGraw-Hill Book Co., Inc.

present 53 to 120 yr. of age, and the growth that will be put on before the stands are cut. For this forest:

| | M bd. ft. |
|---|---|
| Stands 120–200 yr. | |
| Present merchantable volume | 1,905,150 |
| Stands 53–120 yr. | |
| Area of stands 40–120 yr. of age, 42,325 acres | |
| Area of these stands to be cut, from diagram, | |
| $\dfrac{144-113}{144-107} = 0.838(42,325) = 35,468$ acres | |
| Average volume of stands 53–120 yr., from diagram, 16.0M | |
| Total volume, 16.0M (35,468) = | 567,488 |
| Growth of above stands to be cut | |
| Total area to be cut, 63,505 + 35,468 = 98,973 acres | |
| Mean annual increment, 187.5 ft. | |
| Total growth if no cut occurs, | |
| 187.5(67)98,973 = 1,243,348M | |
| Growth prior to cut, ½(1,243,348M) = | 621,674 |
| Total volume available for cutting during regulatory period | 3,094,312 |

$$\text{Annual cut} = \frac{3,094,312M}{67} = 46,184M \text{ bd. ft.}$$

$$\text{Annual cutting area} = \frac{98,973}{67} = 1,477 \text{ acres}$$

$$\text{Average annual cut per acre} = \frac{46,184M}{1,477} = 31.3M \text{ bd. ft.}$$

A growing stock diagram should then be prepared showing stands as they would exist at the end of the regulatory period. Unsatisfactory deficiencies or excesses in age groups may require adjustment of the length of regulatory period. Deficiencies in age groups, either before or after the regulatory period, may be corrected by buying land supporting stands of the age groups needed.

**FORESTS OF MANY-AGED STANDS.** Management of forests of essentially many-aged or uneven-aged stands, or conversion of irregular stands, is more involved than that for even-aged stands. Silviculture is more complex and published information for many-aged stands is meager or lacking for many species and forest types. Regardless of the method used, many-aged regulation should be applied to species that will reproduce and achieve satisfactory growth in partially cut stands. It is of major importance to leave enough timber on the ground so that merchantable sizes will be found at the time of the second and subsequent cuts. In many natural stands the first cut may be made on the basis of the physical condition of trees and existing markets, particularly from forests where an annual income is not required. To retain a given cutting cycle it is necessary to cut an area each year which averages:

$$\frac{\text{Total area}}{\text{Cutting cycle}}$$

Then, as abnormal distribution of age classes is eliminated, regularity in volume of annual cut is possible.

**Recurring Inventory.** For properties already under some form of forest management, this method is a promising means of determining current growth and regulating the cut. It is intended for forests with stabilized, regular cuts and continuing yields of about the same volume realized in the past. Covering a given period, such as 5 or 10 yr., trees that died are added to a stand table of living trees harvested, and both are added to the stand of living trees inventoried at the close of the period. The difference between this total and the stand at the first inventory is the gross periodic growth. Inventories can be made of large areas, strips, or permanent plots. Because of speed and relative cheapness, it appears best suited to large areas.

**Stand Table Projection.** Both present-day stand tables and the growth data needed to project them into the future are obtained from timber cruises. The procedure for predicting growth is given in Section 1, Forest Measurements. With precautions to minimize errors from sampling in the field and other sources, this method of predicting future growth and volume provides a means for regulating the cut.

**Basal Area Control.** If a decision has been reached concerning the tentative length of the rotation and cutting cycle, a synthetic yield table in terms of basal area by age groups for many-aged conditions is prepared from a yield table for even-aged stands. The range of ages within age groups occurring on an acre in a normal forest is the same as the number of years in the cutting cycle. The number of age groups per acre is the ratio,

$$\frac{\text{Rotation}}{\text{Cutting cycle}};$$

for example, 120/20 = 6. Data for ages below 15 to 20 yr. are not usually given in yield tables; therefore, omit age groups under 20 yr. For the remaining groups, read from the even-aged yield table:

| Age (yr.) | Basal area per acre (sq. ft.) |
|---|---|
| 20 | 102 |
| 25 | 114 |
| 30 | 124 |
| 35 | 133 |
| 40 | 140 |
| | 613 |

When 613 is divided by 5, the result is the basal area of a stand 20–40 yr. of age, 122.6 in this case. Because an acre is shared by six age groups, divide by 6 to obtain 20.4 sq. ft., the basal area allotted to the 20–40 age group. Basal area for other age groups is determined in the same manner. For the 40–60 age group the sum should include the 40-, 45-, 50-, 55-, and 60-yr. age classes.

From yield tables, by site, for several American and European species, Matthews prepared synthetic many-aged basal area tables. For identical age groups, the basal area differed considerably with the species and site, but for a given length of rotation and cutting cycle the **percentage** of basal area in the various age groups was remarkably uniform—within 1 or 2 percent. On this premise, if no yield table is available for the species at hand, one for a species of similar growth characteristics should suffice.

Assume that no satisfactory yield table is available for the hemlock-hardwood forest, of which a representative acre is described in Table 1. A progressive decrease in the volume-basal area ratio for diameters over 19 in. indicates defect and overmaturity; timber 23 in. and larger is known to be overmature, and should be cut along with defective trees from 19 to 22 in. during the first cutting cycle. Hemlocks and associated hardwoods of such diameters average 160 yr. or more. A rotation of 160 yr. is then appropriate, and other conditions suggest a cutting cycle of 20 yr. Matthews' synthetic table most nearly approximating this—"An oak forest, selection arrangement, Site II, rotation 160 years"—gives basal area percentages for the six 20-yr. age groups between 40 and 160 yr.

Table 2 shows the data in Table 1 rearranged by age groups according to these percentages, which are applied to the basal area—95.16 sq. ft.—in trees 22

**Table 1. Stand and Stock Table, Hardwood and Hemlock Forest, Lake States**

Typical acre

| (1) Diam. (in.) | (2) No. of trees | (3) B.A. per diam. class (sq. ft.) | (4) Vol., ft. b.m. | (5) % vol. per diam. class | (6) Vol., ft. b.m. per sq. ft. of B.A. |
|---|---|---|---|---|---|
| 4 | 16 | 1.40 | ... | ... | ... |
| 5 | 16 | 2.20 | ... | ... | ... |
| 6 | 12 | 2.36 | ... | ... | ... |
| 7 | 12 | 3.20 | ... | ... | ... |
| 8 | 9 | 3.14 | ... | ... | ... |
| 9 | 9 | 3.98 | 105 | 0.7 | 26 |
| 10 | 9 | 4.92 | 300 | 2.0 | 56 |
| 11 | 8 | 5.29 | 480 | 3.2 | 90 |
| 12 | 10 | 7.85 | 630 | 4.2 | 80 |
| 13 | 6 | 5.54 | 750 | 5.0 | 135 |
| 14 | 6 | 6.41 | 855 | 5.7 | 133 |
| 15 | 6 | 7.36 | 945 | 6.3 | 128 |
| 16 | 6 | 8.38 | 1,020 | 6.8 | 122 |
| 17 | 6 | 9.45 | 1,065 | 7.1 | 113 |
| 18 | 3 | 5.30 | 1,035 | 6.9 | 195 |
| 19 | 2 | 3.94 | 975 | 6.5 | 248 |
| 20 | 2 | 4.36 | 915 | 6.1 | 210 |
| 21 | 2 | 4.80 | 840 | 5.6 | 175 |
| 22 | 2 | 5.28 | 780 | 5.2 | 148 |
| 23 and up | 12 | 36.98 | 4,305 | 28.7 | 117 |
| Total ...... | 154 | 132.14 | 15,000 | 100 | ... |

in. d.b.h. and smaller, to give the basal areas desired under regulation (Col. 5). These basal areas are then translated into number of trees in diameter groups by the following process, beginning with the 141–160-yr. age group and working backward to the 41–60-yr. group:

**Table 2. Stand and Stock Table Rearranged from Control Table, per Acre; Rotation 160 yr., Cutting Cycle 20 yr.**

| Age group (yr.) | Control table [a] percentage of total basal area | D.b.h. (in.) | No. of trees | Basal area (sq. ft.) | Volume (bd. ft.) |
|---|---|---|---|---|---|
| 1–20[b] | | | | | |
| 21–40[b] | | | | | |
| 41–60 | 12.0 | 4–8 | 62.5 | 11.42 | |
| 61–80 | 14.5 | 8–11 | 26.6 | 13.79 | 770 |
| 81–100 | 16.6 | 11–14 | 19.0 | 15.79 | 1,646 |
| 101–120 | 18.2 | 14–16 | 14.3 | 17.33 | 2,219 |
| 121–140 | 19.1 | 16–18 | 11.4 | 18.18 | 2,497 |
| 141–160 | 19.6 | 18–22 | 8.2 | 18.65 | 3,563 |
| | 100.0 | | 142.0 | 95.16 | 10,695 |
| Overmature timber, 23 in. and larger..... | 12.0 | | | 36.98 | 4,305 |
| | | | 154.0 | 132.14 | 15,000 |

[a] See text.
[b] Small trees not measured.

| | Basal area, sq. ft. | No. of trees | Volume, M bd. ft. |
|---|---|---|---|
| **Age group 141–160 yr.** | | | |
| Percentage of basal area from control table, **19.6** | | | |
| Required basal area, this age group, | | | |
| 0.196 (95.16) = 18.65 sq. ft. | | | |
| 22-in. trees .......................... | 5.28 | 2 | 780 |
| 21-in. trees .......................... | 4.80 | 2 | 840 |
| 20-in. trees .......................... | 4.36 | 2 | 915 |
| 19-in. trees .......................... | 3.94 | 2 | 975 |
| | 18.38 | | |
| Basal area needed from 18-in. trees, 18.65 − 18.38 | | | |
| = 0.27; therefore take 0.27/ 5.30, or 5.1 percent of the number of trees, volume, and basal area, 18-in. trees.......................... | 0.27 | 0.2 | 53 |
| | 18.65 | 8.2 | 3,563 |

The remaining 18-in. trees are included in the 121–140-yr. age group. A regular decrease in diameters and increase in number of trees from oldest to youngest age groups indicates a many-aged condition. Had the diameters and number of trees been concentrated in a few age groups, a tendency toward an even-aged stand would be indicated; if the selection system were applied, volumes available for cutting in future cutting cycles would fluctuate. Table 2 shows that 4,305 bd. ft. in trees 23 in. and larger can be cut immediately; if the stand will not be opened excessively, 3,563 bd. ft. in the 141–160 age class also may be cut. The 121–140-yr. age group will be harvested 20 yr. hence. The difference in number of trees between age groups indicates probable mortality, and these trees might also be removed with the harvest cut if a market exists.

Bourne, among other European foresters, has shown that a managed selection forest contains a much greater volume in large trees than even-aged stands of the same species and age. He therefore rejected the method of basal area control. It appears that basal area control should be restricted to the first phase of converting an unmanaged forest to a managed one.

**Horizontal Cut.** Chapman recommends this method as a substitute for area regulation. It is applicable to many-aged stands with abnormalities in age-class distribution, but the principle may be illustrated by reference to an ideal forest. In changing a forest with a rotation of 100 yr. and a cutting cycle of 1 yr. to a cutting cycle of 20 yr., age classes 80 to 100 yr. are taken during the first year, but by the 20th yr. trees 80 to 120 yrs. will be present and should be cut. Consequently, during each 20-yr. period stand area and volume cut will exceed that intended by 50 percent, and abnormal age class distribution will be perpetuated. To spread the annual cut more evenly, a minimum age to cut is adopted for the cutting cycle: Rotation minus ½ cutting cycle. In the example given it is 90 yr. The first year of the cutting cycle trees 90 to 100 yr. of age are cut, the last year trees 90 to 120 yr. The total number of age classes and area cut are then the same as for a 1-yr. cutting cycle. The annual cut is fixed by calculating the total volume to be cut during the period and dividing by the number of years in the cutting cycle.

Determining the age of individual trees is difficult and the use of broad averages is deceptive. The substitution of tree diameter for age is helpful in marking timber for cutting, but this does not mean cutting to a fixed diameter limit but rather that the minimum diameter of trees is used as a guide in the application of good silviculture.

**Amortization Formula.** Meyer reported a formula for predicting the effect of heaviness of cut on growing stock:

$$V_n = V_o(1 + g_1)^n - \frac{2C(1 + g_1)}{g_1(2 + g_2)}[(1 + g_1)^n - 1]$$

where  $V_n$ = volume at end of $n$ years
  $V_o$ = volume at beginning of period
  $C$ = annual cut
  $g_1$ = rate of growth (including ingrowth), in percent of $V$
  $g_2$ = rate of growth, (excluding ingrowth) in percent of $V$
  $n$ = number of years in period

Growth percents may be computed by the interpolation method (see page 1·91, Forest Measurements), or by other means. The effect of any proposed cut may be determined by substituting it in the equation and noting whether $V_n$ is greater or less than $V_o$. Similarly, if it is desired to build the growing stock up to a specified figure, substitute this in the formula for $V_n$ and solve for $C$.

For example, assume a merchantable stand of 500,000M bd. ft.; that the trees now merchantable will grow during the next 10 yr. at 3 percent, compounded annually; that growth of the entire stand, including trees that will become merchantable during the 10 yr., is 6 percent. Will an annual cut of 20,000M bd. ft. deplete the stand or permit the growing stock to build up?

$$V_{10} = 500,000 \ (1.06)^{10} - \frac{2 \times 20,000 \times 1.06}{0.06 \ (2 + 0.03)}(1.06^{10} - 1).$$

If $1.06^{10} = 1.791$ (see compound interest table, page **15·2**, Economics and Finance, $V = 619,769$M, and growing stock is building up.

## BIBLIOGRAPHY

### (For Sections **2, 3,** and **4.**)

For reference on volume, yield and growth, and stand tables, see footnotes appended to tables.

ALLISON, J. H., and R. M. BROWN. 1946. Management of the Cloquet forest: second ten-year period. Minn. Agr. Exp. Station. *Tech. Bull. No. 171.*

BOURNE, R. A. 1951. A fallacy in the theory of growing stock. *Forestry* (Great Britain) 24:7–18, 159–161.

CHAPMAN, H. H. 1950. *Forest management.* Hildreth Press, Bristol, Conn.

DAVIS, KENNETH P. 1954. *American Forest Management.* McGraw-Hill Book Co., Inc., New York.

HANZLIK, E. J. 1922. Determination of the annual cut on a sustained yield basis for virgin American forests. *Jour. Forestry* 20:611–626.

MATTHEWS, D. M. 1935. *Management of American forests.* 1st ed. McGraw-Hill Book Co. Inc., New York.

MEYER, H. ARTHUR, ARTHUR B. RECKNAGEL, and DONALD D. STEVENSON. 1952. *Forest Management.* The Ronald Press Co., New York.

MEYER, W. H. 1946. Predicting the effect of the heaviness of cut on growing stock. *Jour. Forestry* 44:1092–1094.

U. S. DEPT. AGR. 1941. Methods of forecasting timber growth in irregular stands. *Tech. Bull. No. 796.*

U. S. DEPT. AGR. 1950. Timber management plans on the national forests.

WACKERMAN, A. E. 1934. Allocating cutting budgets by means of a forest skyline graph. *Jour Forestry* 32:4–7.

# GEOLOGY AND SOILS

## CONTENTS

# GEOLOGY AND SOILS

## Soil-Forming Minerals

The earth's crust is composed of more than 90 elements, but only about 15 form the bulk of soil material. These are: oxygen (O), hydrogen (H), carbon (C), phosphorus (P), sulfur (S), chlorine (Cl), silicon (Si), aluminum (Al), iron (Fe), manganese (Mn), calcium (Ca), magnesium (Mg), potassium (K), and sodium (Na). With some exceptions, these elements are combined as minerals, i.e., substances characterized by fixed chemical composition, crystalline form, specific gravity, hardness, and color. A brief discussion of these characteristics follows.

**Color** is a feature which is readily noted but which varies in many minerals because of minute quantities of impurities. The identification of color is best accomplished by means of standard color charts, such as those manufactured by the Munsell Company, Baltimore, Maryland.

**Specific gravity** is the ratio of an equal volume of a substance to the weight of an equal volume of water (in the case of minerals) taken as the standard or unit. It is an important characteristic of minerals. Glauber's salt, the "white alkali" of arid regions, has a specific gravity of 1.5 (that is, it is $1\frac{1}{2}$ times as heavy as water) and is considered a light mineral; magnetite has a specific gravity of 5.2 and is considered a heavy mineral; quartz with its specific gravity of 2.65 exemplifies the medium-weight minerals.

**Hardness** refers to the ease with which the minerals are scratched and is expressed by Mohs' scale as follows: 1 talc, 2 gypsum, 3 calcite, 4 fluorite, 5 apatite, 6 orthoclase, 7 quartz, 8 topaz, 9 corundum, 10 diamond. The fingernail has a hardness of about $2\frac{1}{2}$ and will scratch talc and gypsum. A copper coin will scratch talc, gypsum, and calcite. An ordinary knife blade has a hardness of slightly more than 5 and will scratch calcite, fluorite, and apatite readily, but it will scratch orthoclase only with difficulty. Glass is easily scratched by orthoclase and still harder minerals. These tests can be easily applied in the field and help to distinguish different minerals, e.g., calcite from quartz.

**Crystalline form** occurs in rocks cooled from a molten condition, or where percolating solutions evaporated above or below ground, minerals crystallized into fixed shapes such as cubes, rhombohedrons, prisms terminating in pyramids, etc. The crystals are rarely symmetrical but have definite interfacial angles. The crystal form is constant for a given mineral but, unfortunately, crystals incorporated in rocks commonly appear to the naked eye as irregular grains, aggregates, or masses deformed by metamorphism.

Other characteristics which help to identify minerals are luster, streak, tenacity, cleavage, and fracture.

## DESCRIPTION OF THE MOST IMPORTANT MINERALS.

**Quartz,** $SiO_2$ (silica). A very hard, white to drab mineral of glassy luster. It ordinarily forms prismatic six-sided crystals but has no lines of cleavage and breaks with a conchoidal fracture. Hardness, 7; specific gravity, 2.7. It is resistant to acids, except hydrofluoric, and is slightly soluble in alkalies. It occurs in soils as round or angular grains, often coated with red or yellow iron oxides. Quartz is resistant to weathering and forms the coarse fraction or "skeleton" of the soil. Siliceous sandy soils may have as much as 95 percent of quartz. Chalcedony, chert, and flint are other important natural forms of silica.

**Orthoclase,** KAl-silicate (potassium feldspar). White to red, nearly as hard as quartz, with a well-defined cleavage at angles of about 90° and a specific gravity of 2.5. A rather easily weathered, widely distributed soil-forming mineral; an essential constituent of granitic rocks and a source of potash.

**Plagioclase,** CaNaAl-silicate (sodium-calcium feldspars). White to dark gray, with distinct cleavage, hardness approaching that of quartz, and a specific gravity of 2.7. It is similar to orthoclase but weathers more readily; an essential constituent of granitic and basic rocks.

**Muscovite,** AlKSiO$_4$ (potash mica). White to light-brown folia, known as "isinglass" or "white mica"; very soft and can be scratched with the fingernail. Specific gravity 2.8; widely distributed and is especially abundant in schists; a source of potash, but weathers with difficulty.

**Biotite,** AlFeMgK-silicate (iron-magnesium mica). A black to brown folia, known as "black mica." It is similar to muscovite but less resistant to weathering; source of magnesium, potassium, and iron.

**Hornblende, augite,** and **pyroxene,** FeMg-silicates (ferro-magnesian minerals). Black to green, fairly hard, and rather heavy; specific gravity between 3.0 and 3.7. Common, easily weathered soil-forming minerals; essential constituents of basic rocks and the source of many plant nutrients, particularly calcium, magnesium, potassium, and iron.

**Apatite,** Ca$_5$F(PO$_4$)$_3$ (calcium-fluoro-phosphate). Brown, green or black, of moderate hardness; barely scratches glass. Specific gravity 3.2. A source of phosphorus.

**Calcite,** CaCO$_3$ (calcium carbonate). Colorless, brown, or red; vitreous, with distinctive rhombic cleavage. It effervesces with dilute hydrochloric acid and is scratched by a copper coin, but not by a fingernail; specific gravity 2.7. The essential constituent of limestone soils; causes alkaline reaction, and in excess it is detrimental to forest vegetation.

**Dolomite,** CaMg(CO$_3$)$_2$ (calcium-magnesium carbonate). White to brown, glassy to dull, slightly harder than calcite. It does not readily effervesce in cold dilute hydrochloric acid and has a specific gravity of 2.8. It occurs in many limestone soils, being similar to calcite but more resistant to weathering.

**Gypsum,** CaSO$_4$2H$_2$O (calcium sulfate). Colorless or yellow to brown, crystalline or massive mineral, which can be scratched with a fingernail; specific gravity 2.3; slightly soluble in water and gives off its combined water upon heating to form "plaster of Paris." Accumulates below the zone of carbonates in soils of semiarid regions; it is used as a substitute for lime, often in the form of paper-mill sludge.

**Hematite,** 2Fe$_2$O$_3$ (iron oxide). Red or brown, of an earthy nature, with a cherry-red streak. It is slightly softer than glass and has a specific gravity of 4.5 to 5.3. Commonly formed in forest soils, it imparts a reddish color and indicates oxidizing conditions.

**Limonite,** 2Fe$_2$O$_3$·3H$_2$O (hydrated iron oxide). Yellow to brownish in color, compact or earthy, somewhat softer than hematite, with a specific gravity of 3.6 to 4.0. It occurs as common "iron rust"; causes the yellowish color or yellowish tints of soils and indicates oxidizing conditions.

**Siderite,** FeCO$_3$ (ferrous carbonate). Green or gray to black, somewhat harder than calcite; specific gravity 3.8. It occurs chiefly in waterlogged strata of soils, to which it imparts a greenish color; indicates a deficiency of aeration and a reducing condition.

**Kaolinite,** HAl-silicate (hydrated aluminum silicate). A white or yellow, very soft earthy mineral, having a clay odor; specific gravity 2.5. A widespread constituent of clays.

**Glauconite**, HAlKFe-silicate (hydrated iron-potassium aluminum silicate). Usually occurs in the form of greenish grains, so-called "greensand." A soft mineral having a specific gravity of 2.3. An important source of potassium in many forest soils.

**Zeolites**, $R(SiO_3)^x \cdot nH_2O$ (hydrated silicates). Light-colored, unstable minerals, which swell and lose their combined water upon slight heating. They possess a capacity for cation exchange but because of their instability are rarely found in soils.

**Clay minerals** (aluminum and iron silicates containing bases and hydrogen). These minerals are white, yellow, or brown; soft and have a very high adsorptive or base exchange capacity; found chiefly in soils of heavy texture. Clay minerals were previously classed with zeolites.

## Soil-Forming Rocks

The consolidation of minerals into rocks took place through different geological processes in which heat, pressure, and sedimentation were the most important factors. The rocks thus formed are classified into three groups: (1) igneous rocks, formed by cooling of molten magma; (2) sedimentary rocks, formed by cementation of deposited materials; and (3) metamorphic rocks, formed from the above classes under heat and pressure.

**IGNEOUS ROCKS.** Igneous rocks are classified according to their texture, chemical composition, and minerals; all have a crystalline structure.

**Rocks of Granitoid Texture.** These rocks are formed of interlocking crystals usually large enough to be distinguished by the eye.

1. **Granite.** These are widely distributed rocks having quartz and feldspars as the chief minerals, together with some mica or hornblende. They are usually gray or light colored but may be red or pink due to the feldspar colors. Granites tend to disintegrate into coarse particles, giving sandy loam or loam soils. With intensive weathering the feldspars alter to clays, but the quartz remains as grains of sand.

2. **Syenite.** These rocks are composed of feldspars with little or no quartz but with small amounts of hornblende or mica. They resemble granites but weather more readily and give rise to fine-textured soils.

3. **Diorites.** These are dark-colored, often greenish-black, fine-textured rocks, composed primarily of hornblende and plagioclase feldspars. They weather to heavy clay loam soils.

4. **Gabbro.** These are dark, heavy, coarse-textured rocks high in iron, calcium, and magnesium minerals and low in quartz. Occasionally they contain sufficient magnetite to influence a compass needle.

**Rocks of Felsitic Texture.** The individual crystals are too small to be visible to the naked eye.

1. **Felsites.** These are generally light-colored, fine-textured rocks of volcanic origin, composed chiefly of feldspars. Usually hard and breaking with a conchoidal fracture, they tend to weather slowly and give rise to shallow soils.

2. **Rhyolite.** These include a variety of felsites exhibiting the banding and streakings common to lava flows.

3. **Basalt.** This is a heavy, dark-colored ferro-magnesian "trap" rock, similar to gabbro in composition but fine textured. It often weathers slowly, giving rise to rocky, shallow soils; after sufficient weathering, it gives rise to highly productive soils.

**Rocks of Porphyritic Texture.** This group includes rocks with large crystals or "phenocrysts" embedded in the ground mass.

### Rocks of Glassy Texture.

1. **Obsidian.** This is a general term for rocks of a glassy texture. Such rocks are hard, brittle, and usually dark-colored; they break with conchoidal fracture and weather only slowly, yielding shallow, infertile soils.

2. **Pumice.** This is a spongy vesicular lava, best described as "glass froth."

## SEDIMENTARY ROCKS.

1. **Shales.** These consist of laminated, impermeable rocks formed from silts and clays by consolidation. When exposed, shales are readily fragmented by changes in temperature, but chemical weathering is very slow. Soils from shales are usually silts or clays, but their other properties, particularly the content of lime and silica, vary according to the composition of the sediment. Within the same area siliceous and calcareous shales may give rise to soils of vastly different levels of fertility.

2. **Sandstones.** These are composed of sediments of quartz sand particles, more or less consolidated by pressure and cementing materials. The coherence of the rocks is determined by the nature of the cement, which may be silica, iron oxides, or lime. Soils from sandstones vary in their productivity, depending upon particle size and the amount of "impurities." Pure sandstones can yield only infertile soils. Siliceous cements make durable rocks that weather slowly into infertile shallow and stony soils. Calcareous cements, however, enrich weathered debris with colloids and nutrients and give rise to deep, fertile soils. Sandstones often have considerable pore space and may contain artesian waters.

3. **Conglomerates.** These are cemented gravels formed in the same way as sandstones. Soils from them are usually gravelly, sandy loams.

4. **Limestone rocks.** These include consolidated deposits, rich in carbonates and different impurities such as clay, sand, and chert. Depending upon the composition and structure, four types of calcareous rocks are recognized: limestone, dolomitic limestone, chalk, and calcareous shales. **Limestones** are composed predominantly of calcium carbonate with different amounts of silt and clay. **Dolomitic limestone** is a similar rock containing the double carbonate of calcium and magnesium. **Chalk** is a crumbly limestone composed of microscopic shells. **Calcareous shales** are hardened siliceous deposits rich in lime. Calcareous rocks are usually identified by their ability to effervesce when treated with dilute hydrochloric acid or strong vinegar, a test which is not too reliable with some non-pulverized rocks, particularly dolomitic limestones.

Limestone rocks range from soft and porous to hard and dense. Their nature and degree of weathering greatly modify the potential fertility of the resulting soils. Soils from chalk and pure limestone are often infertile; those from dense calcareous rocks are likely to be shallow or stony, especially in the early stages of development. Considering the requirements of forest vegetation, the most productive soils of calcareous origin are usually derived from limestones or dolomitic limestones possessing a high percentage of clay and an admixture of accessory minerals.

## METAMORPHIC ROCKS.
These are igneous or sedimentary rocks altered by heat and pressure.

1. **Slate.** Slate is formed from shale rocks hardened by the processes of metamorphism. It is characterized by easy splitting and gives rise to shallow unproductive soils.

2. **Quartzite.** This is metamorphosed sandstone, highly silicified and resistant to weathering.

3. **Marble.** This is limestone of a crystalline structure, resistant to weathering.

4. **Gneiss.** This is hard, coarsely banded crystalline rock, similar in composition to granite and other feldspathic rocks.

5. **Schists.** These are finely grained or foliated rocks of widely different composition and structure.

Areas underlain by different rocks or geological deposits of different petrographical origin show considerable variation in the physical and chemical properties of the resulting soils, hydrological features, and forest growth. Rock provinces range from a few acres to hundreds of square miles in extent and are often used as primary divisions for a broad classification of soils, extensive growth studies, or flood control investigations. The nature of soils derived from a particular kind of rock may differ markedly according to climatic conditions and the length of time during which weathering has occurred. In broad classification, however, the geological substrata may be divided into four groups: **feldspathic rocks**, **ferro-magnesian rocks**, **siliceous rocks**, and **calcareous rocks**. The prevailing silvicultural characteristics of soils derived from these groups are briefly outlined below.

**Feldspathic igneous and metamorphic rocks** (light-colored minerals predominant)—granite, granite porphyry, rhyolite porphyry, rhyolite, and other light-colored igneous rocks; many gneisses and schists. Forest soils derived from these rocks tend to have a light loam texture and an acid reaction. They are usually well supplied with potassium and phosphorus, but are low in lime. As a rule, soils derived from acidic igneous and metamorphic rocks are well adapted to all forest trees, with the exception of lime-demanding species.

**Ferro-magnesian igneous and metamorphic rocks** (dark-colored minerals predominant)—gabbros, gabbro porphyries, basalt porphyries, basalt, and other dark-colored igneous rocks; some gneisses and schists. With advanced weathering, basic igneous and metamorphic rocks tend to yield deep, heavy, and fertile soils high in lime, magnesium, iron, and phosphorus; in some instances, however, these soils are low in potassium. Soils derived from basic rocks have a tendency to maintain a neutral or slightly alkaline reaction and are best suited to exacting hardwoods such as sugar maple, oak, beech, tulip-poplar, and ash. On soils overlying rocks of this group, spruce and other conifers in warm climates often suffer from fungus diseases.

**Siliceous sedimentary and metamorphic rocks**—sandstones, conglomerates, and quartzites. The properties of soils derived from siliceous rocks are strongly influenced by the cementing material, especially lime and clay. In general, however, these soils are poor in nutrients, as well as colloids, and support the least exacting forest tree species, particularly pines.

**Calcareous sedimentary and metamorphic rocks**—limestone, dolomite, chalk, calcareous shales, and crystalline limestones. Calcareous rocks commonly produce deep, heavy soils which, especially in regions of moderate and low rainfall, tend to maintain an alkaline reaction and are sometimes deficient in potash and phosphates. These soils are well adapted to hardwoods but are often unfavorable to conifers, with the exception of lime-tolerant species such as white cedar, red cedar, Colorado spruce, Austrian pine, and ponderosa pine. In some instances soft limestones or calcareous deposits favor the occurrence of prairies within forested regions. In humid regions, soils derived from calcareous sedimentary rocks undergo severe leaching and their surface horizons attain a pronounced acid reaction.

**STRUCTURAL FEATURES OF ROCKS.** In many instances soil development and plant growth are strongly influenced by the structural features of rocks, such as joints, cleavage planes, dips, and dikes. **Joints** are crevices more or less perpendicular to the rock surface or sometimes parallel to it. **Cleavage planes** occur in shales, sandstones, and schists and often lead to the development of crevices. **Dip** refers to the angle that the slope of a formation makes with the true horizontal. Steeply dipping shales and schists allow penetration of roots and moisture along the exposed cleavage planes, whereas horizontal beds do not. This factor greatly influences the productivity of overlying shallow soils. Land slippage is likely to occur when the soil surface approximately parallels a steep dip surface, especially over schists and shales.

**Dikes** result when more or less vertical fissures, originally below the surface of the earth, are filled with molten rock; they often remain as ridges or hills when the less resistant overlying rocks have been eroded. **Sills** differ from dikes in that the magma of sills was injected between rather than across the enclosing rock layers or strata. Sills may form the resistant cap rock that gives rise to buttes and mesas.

Sedimentary and metamorphic rocks are often folded, **anticline** and **syncline** being the respective terms for convex and concave folds. Over the convex anticline the rocks are stretched and often shattered, leading to more rapid erosion than in the adjacent syncline. **Faults** are breaks along which rocks have slipped; a **fault scarp** is the steep up-throw side of a major fault.

In rolling or rough topography, the orientation of geological strata leads to pronounced differences in the moisture content of soils. When sloping terrain intersects the declining strata of geological formations, it is called a **dip** or **seepage** slope; such slopes are enriched in water traveling along the fissures of the rock formation. On the other hand, when the terrain intersects the ascending geological strata, it is called a **scarp** or **strike** slope. Such slopes are usually impoverished in moisture content because a considerable part of the precipitation is carried away by the fissures of rocks.

## Surface Geologic Formations and Resultant Soils

Surface geologic formations impart to the soils many important characteristics and constitute a convenient basis for a broad soil classification.

**ROCK OUTCROPS AND MANTLE ROCKS.** Within forest regions, the occurrence of rock outcrops is typical of high mountains, steep slopes, and denuded areas. Root systems of trees clasp the rock surface and penetrate through the fissures, thus changing barren strata into **rock outcrop soils** or **lithosols.** In accordance with mineralogic composition, granitic, sandstone, limestone and other varieties of rock outcrop soils are recognized.

If conditions of climate and gradient permit, weathered material accumulates "in situ" as **mantle rock** or **residuum,** offering forest vegetation a more favorable foothold. Residual soils vary in depth, texture, and chemical composition, depending upon their age and the character of their parent material. Young residual soils consist of slightly weathered, coarse detritus which grades at a shallow depth into **bedrock.** The chemical composition of such soils often resembles that of the underlying substratum. Old residual soils are characterized by a greater depth and more finely divided particles. These soils have been subject to oxidation, hydration, and leaching for a long period and the chemical composition of their surface layers may differ essentially from that of the parent material.

In many instances residual soils are not derived from the bedrock now underlying them but from the residue of rock that has undergone weathering. Because such soils "inherit" certain properties from the weathered material of the pre-existing rock, they are called **inherited** soils.

**TALUS.** Coarse-textured **colluvial deposits,** or **talus slopes,** are formed by fragments of rocks detached from the precipitous outcrops and carried down the slope by gravity. Cliff debris, rock falls, and avalanches are typical examples of rough and droughty talus soils. From the silvicultural standpoint such soils may differ but little from the rock outcrops.

**GLACIAL DEPOSITS.** The invasion of ice sheets during the Pleistocene epoch brought about fundamental changes in the surface geology of the glaciated regions. The glaciers displaced the surface soils, ground the underlying rocks, and deposited **unassorted till,** that is, a mixture of fine and coarse particles up to the size of boulders. Water from the melting ice took up some of the deposited debris and laid it down again as assorted material or **stratified drift.** The hummocky ridges accumulated in front of the invading ice formed **end moraines** or **terminal moraines.** Along the sides of the glacial lobes were deposited **side moraines** or **lateral moraines,** and **interlobate moraines.** Periodic retreats of the ice pro-duced **recessional moraines** similar to end moraines, but often arranged in a series of lobes. The ice movement compressed some material beneath it, and in melting left scattered detritus, thus forming the **ground moraine.** In the regions of ground moraines the action of glaciers sometimes gave rise to **drumlins** or "whalebacks," i.e., smooth, oval-shaped knolls of unassorted material having their long axis parallel to the ice movement.

Soils developed on ground moraines are characterized by a fairly level topog-raphy, often shallow depth, and protruding polished rocks called "sheep backs." The smooth topography and the presence of impervious strata at shallow depths are often responsible for poor drainage of the ground morainic soils. The soils of terminal and recessional moraines are of rough topography, with embedded pebbles and boulders, and have widely variable proportions of sand and clay particles; they rest upon compact unassorted till or "boulder clay." Because of the diversified topography and irregular occurrence of clay till, the drainage of these soils may show great variations within short distances. The soils of drumlins are similar to those of ground moraines.

**FLUVIOGLACIAL DEPOSITS.** Streams and floods from the melting ice sheets carried eroded material, which was gradually deposited in the form of **glacial outwash** or a series of **fans.** The **level outwash** was produced by uniform sedimentation of gravel, sand, and silt over the flat areas, usually at some distance from the terminal moraine. **Pitted outwash,** with its characteristic rolling topog-raphy and "kettle holes," resulted from the melting of ice blocks embedded in the deposit, or from the deposition of material over the rugged surface of the morainic border. Outwash **terraces** are high-bench remnants of fluvioglacial valley fills.

Outwash soils are predominantly of sandy or silt loam texture; other textures occur in rare instances. At a depth of 1 ft. or more the surface layer often grades into stratified coarse sand and gravel. This porous substratum provides very efficient or even excessive drainage. Freedom from stones is an important feature of most outwash soils.

Fluvioglacial deposits of limited distribution include kames and eskers. **Kames** are partly assorted gravelly hills or mounds accumulated by melt waters in ice caves under the glacier. **Eskers** are winding ridges of irregularly stratified sand and gravel deposited by subglacial streams. The soils of both kames and eskers are often coarse and droughty.

**LACUSTRINE DEPOSITS.** Sediments of previous lake bottoms form level beds of sand or clay, with gentle slopes of sandy material marking the original shore line. Lacustrine clays are usually high in organic matter and carbonates but often deficient in both surface and vertical drainage. Most of the lacustrine soils are confined to glacial regions.

**MARINE DEPOSITS.** These represent sea-bottom deposits exposed when the sea receded. The texture of the sediment varies from sand to clay, depending upon the depth of water at the time of deposition and on the force of the current. Skeletons of animals and shells often enrich marine sands and "muds" in calcareous material.

**ALLUVIAL DEPOSITS.** The action of postglacial streams produces three major types of deposits: streambeds, flood plains, and river terraces. **Stream bottom deposits** occur as narrow strips along creeks. A high content of organic matter and a ground water level near the surface are common features of stream-bottom soils. **Flood plain deposits** are a result of the periodic overflow of rivers. The soils of flood plains are often sandy in the proximity of the river but grade into loams or clays farther from the river. This is because the velocity of flood waters decreases from the stream to the limits of the flooded area. The drainage is likely to be adequate near the river, but sluggish at a distance from it. The periodic inundations enrich flood plains with organic matter and soluble salts. **River terraces** are level or nearly level strips of land bordering flood plains. They result from the dissection of previous streambeds and are classified as "second

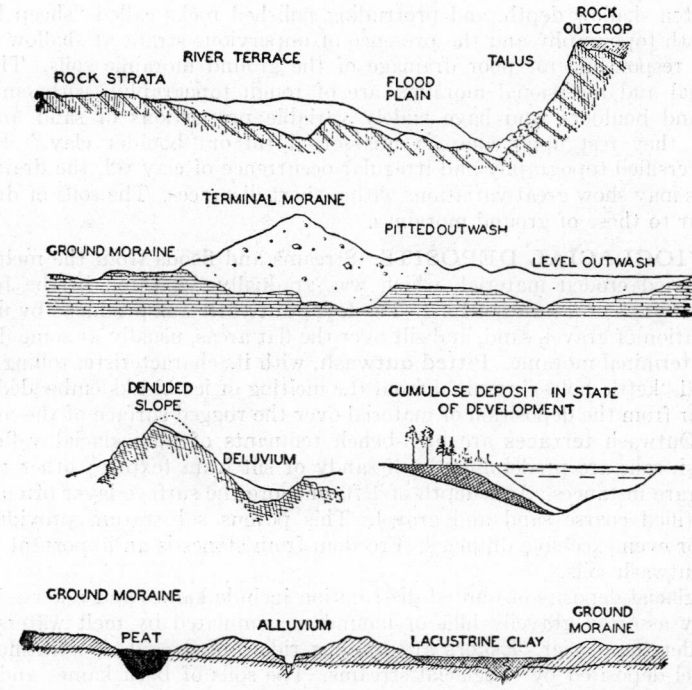

**Fig. 1. Topographical features of some surface geological formations.**

bottom," "third bottom," etc. The soils of river terraces contain less organic matter and soluble salts, and are better drained, than flood plain soils.

**OVERWASH DEPOSITS.** Overwash or "deluvium" is formed on the lower slopes of hills and mountains by the deposition of material eroded from the upper slopes. Soils of overwash, as a rule, have a greater depth, a finer texture, and a higher content of humus and nutrients than the residual soils of the upper denuded areas. In places the deposited material covers "relic" or buried soils; thus overwash soils may have two or more superimposed humus horizons.

**AEOLIAN DEPOSITS.** The action of wind produces two sharply defined types of soil: loess and blow sands. **Loess** is a uniform deposit of comparatively unweathered silt of yellowish buff color, varying in depth from a few inches to nearly a hundred feet. The soils of loessial origin have nearly ideal physical properties and very high potential fertility. Their geographic distribution, however, does not always coincide with climatic conditions favorable to forest growth. **Blow sands** develop where the stabilizing cover of vegetation on sandy soils has been destroyed. In places they form sand dunes which may be over a hundred feet deep, and they may advance over a region at a rate of nearly a hundred feet per year. Wind-blown sands lack colloidal material and are deficient in both moisture and nutrients.

**CUMULOSE DEPOSITS.** Cumulose or "piled up" deposits are formed by the remains of vegetation accumulated in shallow water basins or on uplands of

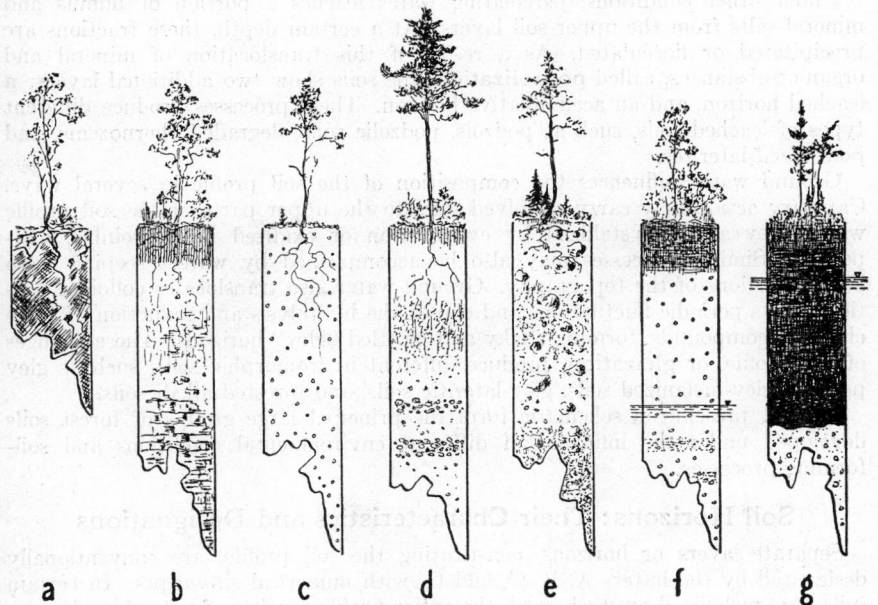

a      b      c      d      e      f      g

**Fig. 2. Schematic presentation of soil profiles of different geologic origin.**

(a) Shallow residual soil of granitic outcrops; (b) deep residual soil derived from dolomitic limestone; (c) wind-blown siliceous sand; (d) outwash silt loam underlain by stratified sand and gravel of glacial drift; (e) morainic loam resting on unassorted glacial till or boulder clay; (f) alluvial sand with a muck-like surface layer deposited in a stream bottom by periodic inundations; (g) peat developed from remains of aquatic vegetation and mosses in the basin of a former glacial lake. (Arrow head indicates ground water level.)

the high mountains and subarctic regions. Deposits of this nature include various types of peat and muck. Lowland prairie or meadow soils may also be considered as cumulose deposits. Forest soils of cumulose deposits are deficient in drainage and often poor in nutrients.

Fig. 1 outlines the topographical features of the surface geological formations. Fig. 2 shows, in a schematic form, soil profiles of different geologic origin.

## Development of Forest Soils and Their Classification on a Genetic Basis

The development of different soils from rocks and deposits proceeds under the influence of climate, topography, ground water, plants, and animals. Young or embryonic forest soils of denuded slopes or recent deposits have only two layers: the upper, an accumulation of plant remains, called litter; the lower, the mineral substratum. After the soil has supported vegetation for a longer period of time, the litter becomes partly decomposed and the humified material is infiltrated by percolating water or incorporated by organisms into the upper portion of the mineral soil, thereby forming a dark, partly mineral and partly organic layer. In some environments, this darkening or **melanization** of the soil surface constitutes the initial as well as the final phase in the morphological development of the soil profile. The resulting varieties of melanized or "black top" soils include brown-earths, rendzinas, weakly podzolized soils, brown podzolic soils, latent podzols, sod soils of the mountains, and other grassland soils invaded by forests.

Under other conditions, percolating water leaches a portion of humus and mineral salts from the upper soil layers. At a certain depth, these fractions are precipitated or flocculated. As a result of this translocation of mineral and organic substances, called **podzolization**, the soils show two additional layers: a leached horizon, and an accumulative horizon. These processes produce different types of leached soils, such as podzols, podzolic soils, degraded chernozems, and podzolized laterites.

Ground water influences the composition of the soil profile in several ways. Capillary action may carry dissolved salts to the upper parts of the soil profile where they are recrystallized by evaporation or oxidized into insoluble compounds. Similar processes may also be accomplished by waters seeping from higher portions of the topography. Ground water also translocates colloidal particles in its periodic fluctuations and causes the hydrolysis and reduction of some chemical compounds, forming sticky and mottled "gley" horizons. These changes of soil profile, or **gleization**, produce different hydromorphic soils, such as gley podzols, gley-melanized soils, gley-lateritic soils, and forested alkali soils.

Table 1 presents in schematic form the principal large groups of forest soils developed under the influence of different environmental conditions and soil-forming processes.

## Soil Horizons: Their Characteristics and Designations

Separate layers or horizons, constituting the soil profile, are conventionally designated by the letters A, B, C, and G, with numerical subscripts. In certain soils, e.g., melanized outwash sand, the entire profile consists of only three layers: forest litter, horizon with incorporated humus, and parent material. In other soils, the profile may include three additional layers, i.e., leached horizon, accumulative horizon, and gley horizon. The outline on page **5 · 12** describes the designation and characteristic composition of the principal horizons encountered in profiles of forest soils.

### Table 1. Genetic Groups of Forest Soils of the United States, Classified on the Basis of Their Relation to Climate, Topography, Geology, Vegetation, and Ground Water

| Macroclimatic soil-forest zones | Degree of leaching and gleization of soil as determined by combined influences of microclimate, topography, parent material, vegetation, and ground water table | | | |
|---|---|---|---|---|
| | Mild leaching | Strong leaching | Partial gleization | Complete gleization |
| | Principal Genetic Types of Soils Formed in Each Zone | | | |
| Mountain skeletal soils Subalpine forest | Mountain sod soils | Mountain podzols | Mountain soils influenced by seepage | Highmoor peat |
| Podzolized soils Boreal forest | Weakly podzolized soils or "mull soils"; rendzinas | Podzols or strongly podzolized soils; calcareous podzols | Podzolized gley soil; swamp podzols | Acid lowmoor peat |
| Prairie-forest soils Oak-hickory forest | Slightly degraded chernozems and prairie soils | Strongly degraded chernozems and prairie soils; podzolic soils | Gley prairie-forest soils | Alkaline peat |
| Melanized soils Mesophytic hardwoods and conifers | Melanized soils rich in bases; brown forest soils | Melanized soils poor in bases; weakly podzolized soils | Melanized gley soils | Neutral or alkaline lowmoor peat |
| Lateritic soils Southern hardwoods and pines | Humus-infiltrated lateritic soils | Podzolized lateritic soils; red and yellow podzolic soils | Gley lateritic soils; ground water podzols | Acid peat, pocosins |

$A_0$: Undecomposed and partly decomposed organic debris, not incorporated with the mineral soil, such as forest litter, raw humus, and peat. In detailed classifications employed by foresters, this layer of ectorganic matter is divided into three subhorizons: L—forest litter, that is, organic debris unaltered by the processes of decomposition; F—fermentation layer, including organic remains whose origin may be detected by ocular examination; and H—humified layer, composed of black amorphous organic matter, the source of which can no longer be recognized because of advanced decomposition.

$A_1$: Melanized horizon, consisting of an intimate mixture of mineral and organic particles produced by incorporation of humus through the activity of soil-inhabiting organisms, by infiltration of organic suspensions, or by decay of root systems. This endorganic horizon is of a dark color and is usually high in nutrients. In most cases its composition reflects the state of soil fertility.

$A_2$: Leached, eluvial, or podzolic horizon, impoverished in soluble salts. It is commonly of a coarser texture than the underlying layer. If leaching is intensive enough to remove iron compounds, the horizon attains a light color; in extreme cases it becomes ashy-gray or white.

B: Enriched, illuvial, or accumulative horizon, containing precipitated soluble salts and coagulated mineral and organic colloids. Depending on the nature of the soil-forming process, it may be structured, compacted, or cemented and may form impervious strata, referred to as "hardpan," "ortstein," or "claypan." The color of the accumulative layer tends to be brownish or reddish. This horizon is sometimes subdivided into $B_1$, $B_2$, etc., depending upon its chemical and morphological composition.

C: Parent material of soil, consisting of either weathered or unweathered geologic strata. This layer may be divided into $C_1$ or $C_2$ to distinguish the strata of

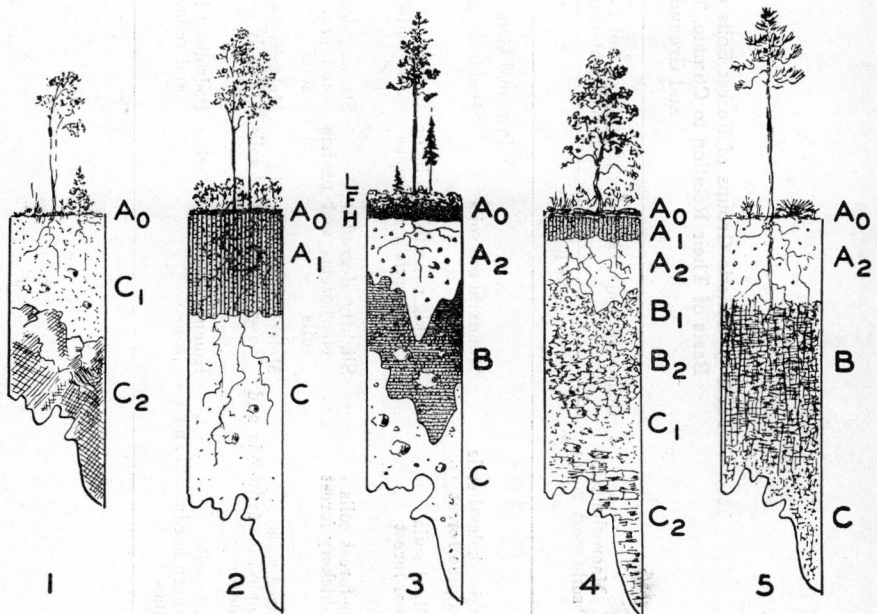

**Fig. 3. Representative genetic profiles of upland forest soils.**

(1) Embryonic soil developing on an eroded substratum; (2) melanized loam; (3) hardpan podzol; (4) nut-structured prairie-forest loam; (5) podzolized lateritic clay.

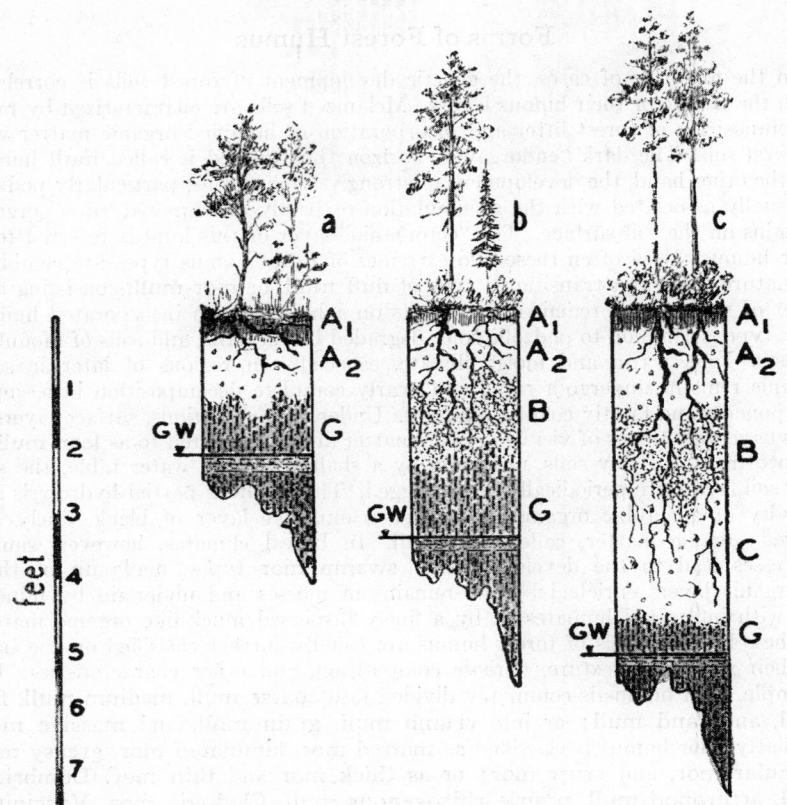

**Fig. 4. Major types of soils influenced by the ground water (GW).**

(a) Shallow-gley soils; (b) mid-gley soils; (c) deep-gley soils. The location of the mottled zone, so-called "gley" horizon, is a feature of far-reaching silvicultural importance, in a large measure determining the extent of root penetration, stabilty of the stand against the wind, and supply of water, air, and nutrients.

different geological origin or to distinguish the weathered part from the solid bedrock.

G : Gley horizon, formed by the influence of ground water and characterized by the presence of ferrous iron and other reduced compounds. Occasionally it has some organic matter and may contain $H_2S$, $CH_4$, and other products of anaerobic decomposition. It is characterized by greenish, bluish, and reddish mottling; in some instances, however, the mottling is masked by infiltrated organic matter. The seasonal fluctuations of ground water may produce distinct eluvial or impoverished gley layers, and illuvial or enriched gley layers, designated as $G_1$ and $G_2$. The accumulation of salts in the surface layers of alkali soils, as well as the formation of ferrallitic crusts of iron and aluminum oxides in laterites, may also be regarded as forms of gleization.

Fig. 3 illustrates the composition of profiles of the more important genetic types of upland forest soils. Fig. 4 outlines the profile morphology of hydromorphic or gley soils influenced by the ground water table.

## Forms of Forest Humus

In the majority of cases, the genetic development of forest soils is correlated with the nature of their humus layers. Melanized soils are characterized by rapid decomposition of forest litter and incorporation of humified organic matter with mineral soil. The dark "endorganic" horizon thus formed is called **mull** humus. On the other hand, the development of strongly leached soils, particularly podzols, is usually associated with the accumulation of partly decomposed "raw" organic remains on the soil surface. The "ectorganic" layer of this kind is referred to as **mor** humus. Very often these two extremes of forest humus types are combined by nature to form a transitional type of **duff mull**, or **mor-mull**, consisting of a layer of raw organic remains which rests on a horizon with incorporated humus. This type is common to podzolic soils, degraded blackearths, and soils of mountain forests. In a warm and moist climate, especially in regions of lateritic soils, organic remains undergo a rapid and nearly complete decomposition into simple components and faintly colored humates. Under such conditions, surface layers of soils have only traces of visible organic matter and are referred to as **lean mull or crypto-mull**. In gley soils, underlain by a shallow ground water table, the surface soil layers are periodically water-logged. The resulting partial hydrolysis and activity of anaerobic organisms produce a mull-like layer of black, finely dispersed organic matter, called **fen mull**. In boreal climates, however, similar processes lead to the development of **swamp mor** types, made up of thick ectorganic layers enriched by the remains of mosses and underlain by mineral soil with infiltrated humates or by a finely dispersed muck-like organic matter.

These broad groups of forest humus are usually further classified on the basis of their structure, texture, floristic composition, and other characteristics. For example, mull humus is commonly divided into **coarse mull, medium mull, fine mull**, and **sand mull**; or into **crumb mull, grain mull**, and **massive mull**. Similarly, mor humus is classified as **matted mor, laminated mor, greasy mor, granular mor**, and **crust mor**; or as **thick mor** and **thin mor**. **Lumbricus mull, arthropod mull, prairie rhizogenous mull, Cladonia mor, Vaccinium mor, Hypnum mor**, and **Sphagnum mor** exemplify further divisions.

The type of humus exerts a far-reaching influence on the silvicultural management of forest stands. Soils with mull humus provide a favorable seedbed for natural reproduction, are resistant against damage by forest fires, and retain their fertility upon clearing and cultivation. Soils with aggregated mull layers readily absorb rain water and undergo moderate erosion. Soils with mor humus often present difficulties in establishing natural reproduction and suffer severe damages by forest fires. Such soils rapidly lose their fertility upon clearing, and on low ground they may undergo swamping if the forest is clearcut. Mor and duff mull types occasionally provide valuable fertilizing material for nurseries and forest plantations. The correlation between the form of humus layers and the rate of forest growth, often implied in the literature, is limited to particular cases.

## Soil Factors Influencing Forest Growth

The distribution and rate of growth of forest stands are influenced by a great many soil characteristics of a physical, chemical, and biological nature. The more important and better known of these are briefly defined in the following discussion. Although by virtue of necessity this discussion treats each soil factor separately, no such division exists in nature, where the growth of trees is influenced by the combined and reciprocal influences of all conditions.

**PHYSICAL PROPERTIES. Depth of Soil.** Soils may be classified on the basis of depth into three categories: (1) shallow—less than 1 ft. deep; (2) medium deep—between 1 and 3 ft. deep; and (3) deep—more than 3 ft. deep. Shallowness of soil may limit the supply of moisture and nutrients available to the forest, as well as reduce its wind-firmness.

**Soil texture** is determined by the relative content of the coarse and fine soil particles. The percentage of fine particles is closely correlated with the water-holding capacity of soil and its aeration. The Soil Survey Manual of the U. S. Department of Agriculture defines soil particles less than 0.002 mm. in diameter as clay, 0.002 to 0.05 mm. as silt, and 0.05 to 2.0 mm. as sand; it defines soils with respect to texture graphically in Fig. 5, and verbally as follows:

**Sands.** Soil material that contains 85 percent or more of sand; percentage of silt, plus 1½ times the percentage of clay, shall not exceed 15.

COARSE SAND: 25 percent or more very coarse and coarse sand, and less than 50 percent any other one grade of sand.

SAND: 25 percent or more very coarse, coarse, and medium sand, and less than 50 percent fine or very fine sand.

FINE SAND: 50 percent or more fine sand (or) less than 25 percent very coarse, coarse, and medium sand and less than 50 percent very fine sand.

VERY FINE SAND: 50 percent or more very fine sand.

**Loamy sands.** Soil material that contains at the upper limit 85 to 90 percent sand, and the percentage of silt plus 1½ times the percentage of clay is not less than 15; at the lower limit it contains not less than 70 to 85 percent sand, and the percentage of silt plus twice the percentage of clay does not exceed 30.

LOAMY COARSE SAND: 25 percent or more very coarse and coarse sand, and less than 50 percent any other one grade of sand.

LOAMY SAND: 25 percent or more very coarse, coarse, and medium sand, and less than 50 percent fine or very fine sand.

LOAMY FINE SAND: 50 percent or more fine sand (or) less than 25 percent very coarse, coarse, and medium sand and less than 50 percent very fine sand.

LOAMY VERY FINE SAND: 50 percent or more very fine sand.

**Sandy loams.** Soil material that contains either 20 percent clay or less, and the percentage of silt plus twice the percentage of clay exceeds 30, and 52 percent or more sand; or less than 7 percent clay, less than 50 percent silt, and between 43 percent and 52 percent sand.

COARSE SANDY LOAM: 25 percent or more very coarse and coarse sand and less than 50 percent any other one grade of sand.

SANDY LOAM: 30 percent or more very coarse, coarse, and medium sand, but less than 25 percent very coarse sand, and less than 30 percent very fine or fine sand.

FINE SANDY LOAM: 30 percent or more fine sand and less than 30 percent very fine sand (or) between 15 and 30 percent very coarse, coarse, and medium sand.

VERY FINE SANDY LOAM: 30 percent or more very fine sand (or) more than 40 percent fine and very fine sand, at least half of which is very fine sand and less than 15 percent very coarse, coarse, and medium sand.

**Loam.** Soil material that contains 7 to 27 percent clay, 28 to 50 percent silt, and less than 52 percent sand.

**Silt loam.** Soil material that contains 50 percent or more silt and 12 to 27 percent clay (or) 50 to 80 percent silt and less than 12 percent clay.

**Silt.** Soil material that contains 80 percent or more silt and less than 12 percent clay.

**Sandy clay loam.** Soil material that contains 20 to 35 percent clay, less than 28 percent silt, and 45 percent or more sand.

**Clay loam.** Soil material that contains 27 to 40 percent clay and 20 to 45 percent sand.

**Silty clay loam.** Soil material that contains 27 to 40 percent clay and less than 20 percent sand.

**Sandy clay.** Soil material that contains 35 percent or more clay and 45 percent or more sand.

**Silty clay.** Soil material that contains 40 percent or more clay and 40 percent or more silt.

**Clay.** Soil material that contains 40 percent or more clay, less than 45 percent sand, and less than 40 percent silt.

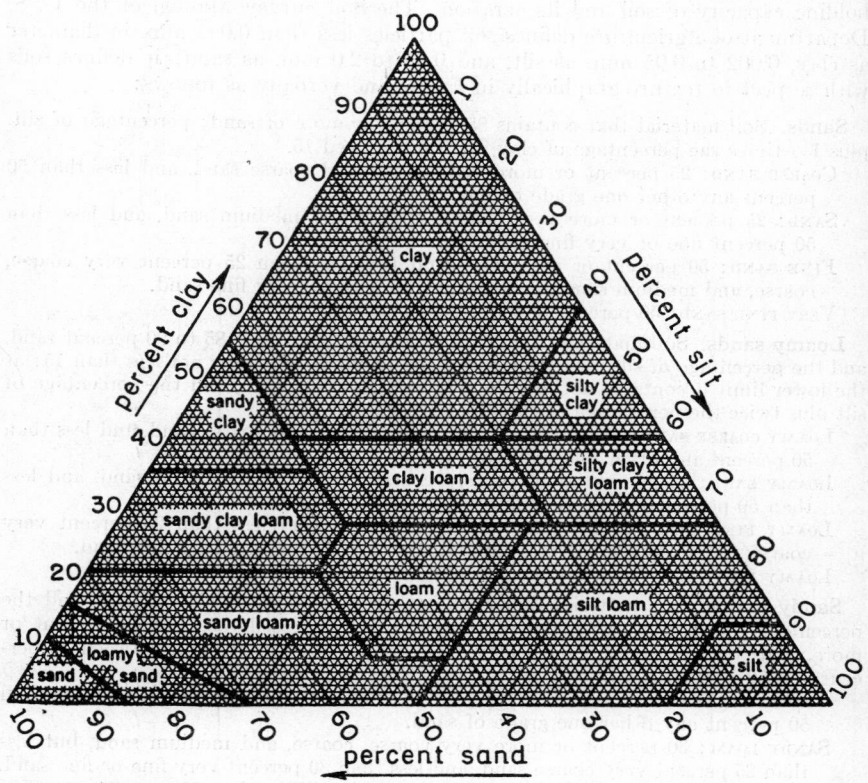

**Fig. 5. Percentages of clay (below 0.002 mm.), silt (0.002 to 0.05 mm.), and sand (0.05 to 2.0 mm.) in the basic soil textural classes.**
(U. S. Dept. of Agriculture, 1951.)

In many instances foresters find it difficult to make use of complicated textural classifications and must be satisfied in their tree-planting work with the following simple scheme based on the content of particles smaller than 0.05 mm. in diameter:

| Soil class | Silt and clay (percent) |
| --- | --- |
| Sand | Less than 7 |
| Loamy sand | 7–15 |
| Sandy loam | 16–25 |
| Light loam | 26–40 |
| Heavy loam | More than 40 |

The simplification of textural classification is justified mainly by the fact that it is impossible for a practicing forester to coordinate his tree planting program with twenty different textural classes of soils based on the proportion of three different separates. Moreover, detailed classification of fine-textured soils has little value in reforestation work because soils carrying more than 40 percent of silt and clay particles satisfy the moisture requirements of the most exacting deciduous and coniferous species, such as black walnut, hard maple, tulip-poplar, different spruces, and firs.

**Organic matter** modifies the effect of soil texture, improves physical properties of the soil, and serves as a source of nutrients, particularly nitrogen. It varies in the surface 6-in. layer of forest soils from a fraction of a percent to more than 30. The percentage required for good tree growth varies with the species and, for a given species, with the region and even the forest type in which it grows. It is known that southern species, particularly pines, grow well in soils containing less than 1 percent of organic matter, and it is probable that black walnut, hard maple, and white spruce, among exacting species, may require as much as 4 percent. An organic-matter content of 2 percent is considered about the minimum for a nursery soil.

**Soil structure.** Aggregated soils are readily infiltrated by rain water, are well aerated, and facilitate penetration of root systems. Soils of massive or puddled structure have the opposite characteristics.

**Soil porosity** is determined by the space in the soil body not occupied by solids. It varies from 30 percent in sands to nearly 70 percent in fine-textured, aggregated soils. Porosity is important in determining the degree of soil aeration at a given moisture content.

**Air content of soils** is determined by the amount of pore space not occupied by water. Soils having a very low air content, perhaps 7 percent by volume, cannot be tolerated for long periods by many tree species, particularly upland hardwoods and certain pines. Some of the lowland species can exist in water-logged soils by utilizing oxygen dissolved in water. Nursery stock requires a minimum air content of 15 percent; lower air content may be tolerated only for short periods.

**Volume weight or bulk density** is the weight of soil per unit volume. It varies from 0.2 in humus layers to 1.8 in coarse sands. The knowledge of this characteristic is essential in analytical determinations of the content of nutrients and other fertility constituents. With the exception of humus layers, volume weight serves as a reasonably accurate expression of soil porosity.

**Permeability of soils.** Soils permeable to air or water have a high infiltration capacity and absorb most of the precipitation water that is not retained by vegetation. Impermeable or puddled soils lose a considerable share of precipitation through runoff or evaporation. Infiltration capacity of 30 ml. per minute and air permeability of 70 mm. of mercury column are the values delineating permeable and difficultly permeable soils.

**Water-holding capacity** is the ability of a saturated soil to retain a certain fraction of water for a definite time. The amount of water retained by a soil during 24 hr. is known as "absolute water-holding capacity," or "field capacity," and is a reasonably definite value. Sandy soils have a low WHC of less than 10 percent by volume; highly colloidal clays have an excessively high WHC of nearly 50 percent. In the majority of cases, the WHC of soils is closely correlated with soil texture.

**Ground water** is subject to wide fluctuations, determined by the depth of the water table, texture of the soil, the gradient of water-bearing strata, and the configuration of surrounding topography. However, the prevailing position of the ground water is marked by the gley horizon, i.e., the discolored or mottled zone. The distance of the gley horizon from the surface determines the accessibility of water, the extent of root penetration, and the depth of well-aerated soil containing available nutrients. This, in turn, influences the composition of forest stands, their rate of growth, the percentage of cull, vigor of competing vegetation, possibilities of natural regeneration, and the stability of the forest against wind.

For the purposes of practical silviculture hydromorphic soils may be classified into three broad groups: (1) shallow gley soils, or semiswamp soils, in which the gley layer occurs at a depth of less than 2 ft.; (2) mid gley soils, or inadequately drained hydromorphic soils, in which the gley layer is located at a depth between 2 and 3 ft.; and (3) deep gley soils, or adequately drained hydromorphic soils, having a gley horizon between 3 and 7 ft. Shallow gley soils are the least productive type of the hydromorphic group and silviculture on these soils encounters many difficulties. Deep gley soils are the most productive type of this group and usually have a much higher silvicultural value than so-called "well-drained" upland soils. Mid gley soils occupy an intermediate position; their unfavorable effects become pronounced in times of prolonged drought or after clearcuttings, which usually lead to the rise of the ground water table and subsequent formation of a temporary swamp.

**Capillary fringe.** This term applies to the moist zone formed by the capillary rise of water above the ground water table. In coarse sandy soils capillary fringe does not exceed a few inches and is of little importance. In fine-textured soils, the fringe attains a height of 7 ft. or more, and thus reduces the possibility of drought injury. Recent studies indicate that the moisture of the capillary fringe may not always be due to the capillary movements of water from below but to the condensation of water from above in the low temperature zone overlying the water table.

**CHEMICAL PROPERTIES.** Soil reaction is expressed either in terms of pH values or as "total acidity" and "total alkalinity." The symbol pH refers to the activity of hydrogen ions in a soil-water suspension as recorded on a potentiometer. The pH scale extends from 0 to 14 and the neutral point is represented by pH 7. Values below 7 indicate an acid reaction; values above 7 indicate an alkaline reaction. The pH scale is logarithmic. Hence, there may be approximately 10 times as many H-ions present at pH 6 as at pH 7, and 100 times as many H-ions at pH 5 as at pH 7. Total acidity and total alkalinity comprise the total amount of hydrogen or hydroxyl ions present in soil in the free and adsorbed state.

**Essential Nutrients.** Ten "major" elements have long been known to be essential to plant growth. Thanks to recent research, the ten original elements have been supplemented by five "minor" elements: B, Mn, Cu, Zn, and Mo. A statement of the principal functions of essential nutrients follows:

1. **Carbon, Hydrogen, Oxygen** (C, H, O). Constituents of plant tissue manufactured by the plants through the process of photosynthesis.
2. **Nitrogen** (N). A constituent of proteins; the "balance wheel" in plant nutrition.
3. **Phosphorus** (P). A component of the nucleus; essential for energy transfers; it is concentrated primarily in seeds and fruits and is important in the development of roots.
4. **Sulfur** (S). A constituent of some proteins and plant oils; stimulates the growth of roots.
5. **Potassium** (K). Functions in the conversion of sugars and starches; important in hardening processes and in maintaining the general vigor of plants.

6. **Calcium** (Ca). Acts as a cementing material in cell walls, and neutralizes toxic metabolic by-products; important in root development.
7. **Magnesium** (Mg). A constituent of the chlorophyll molecule; abundant in seeds.
8. **Iron** (Fe). Essential in the synthesis of chlorophyll; deficiency causes chlorosis.
9. **Manganese** (Mn). Functions in oxidation-reduction reactions and chlorophyll formation.
10. **Boron** (B). Essential in the formation of meristematic tissues and in root development.
11. **Copper** (Cu). Important in plant respiration.
12. **Zinc** (Zn). A constituent of certain plant enzymes.
13. **Molybdenum** (Mo). Apparently functions in nitrate reduction; essential for nitrogen-fixation by legumes.

**Base exchange or cation exchange capacity** refers to the ability of a soil to adsorb positively charged ions, particularly H, Na, K, $NH_4$, Ca, and Mg. This property is due to the presence of aluminum and iron silicate clay minerals and humus, i.e., materials possessing a high specific surface. Under natural conditions the exchange material of soils is saturated largely with hydrogen and calcium.

**Buffering substances** in soils are primarily clay and humus. They prevent the loss of nutrients through leaching, stabilize soil reaction, and moderate fluctuations of soil moisture.

**Toxic Agents.** Soils derived from calcareous rocks may contain carbonates in concentrations detrimental to trees. A toxic concentration of the soil solution is encountered in prairie-forest regions, particularly in depressions receiving runoff water. Hydrogen sulfide, accumulating in poorly drained soils, exerts a harmful effect on the growth of trees. Iron, soluble aluminum, reduced manganese, and other compounds occurring in the gley and ortstein layers may be toxic to root systems.

An injuriously high concentration of salts is often found in the surface layer of nursery soils because of a heavy application of fertilizers or because of the concentration of salts by evaporation. Commercial organic fertilizers, wood ashes, sodium salts, and hard irrigation water are factors that cause chemical injury of germinating seedlings. Soil toxicity may also be due to the application of insecticides, herbicides, and fungicides such as aluminum sulfate, lead arsenate, benzene hexachloride, chlordane, Stoddard solvent, allyl alcohol, and various compounds of mercury and sulfur. Grease from nursery equipment, road oil, creosote, and different waste products are sometimes responsible for the deterioration of nursery stock and forest plantations.

**Chemical Composition of Ground Water.** The two most important chemical properties of ground water are total hardness and the degree of oxygenation. The first characteristic is correlated with the content of bases and other nutrients. Therefore, hard ground water usually acts as a liquid fertilizer. Occasionally, such water contains free carbonates in injuriously high concentrations. Hardness of water is commonly expressed in terms of specific conductance. Very soft ground water analyzes less than 10 mhos $\times 10^5$; hard ground water analyzes at least 25 mhos $\times 10^5$. Oxygenation of water is expressed either in terms of dissolved oxygen or oxidation-reduction potential. Stagnant water has only traces of oxygen and oxidation-reduction potential between $-100$ and $-350$ mv. Oxygenated water carries between 3 and 12 p.p.m. of oxygen or has a redox potential between $-100$ mv. and $+50$ mv.

**ORGANISMS OF FOREST SOILS.** Soil organisms influence the development of the soil and the growth of forest vegetation. They decompose organic remains, promote the formation of soil aggregates, influence the availability of nutrients, hasten the germination of seeds, and, in some cases, injure or destroy living plants. A description of the important soil organisms follows.

**Bacteria** are unicellular miscroscopic organisms of spherical, rodlike, or spiral form. Decomposition of carbohydrates and protein compounds, ammonification, nitrification, fixation of atmospheric nitrogen, and oxidation or reduction of mineral compounds are among the functions which bacteria fulfill in the soil. **Autotrophic bacteria** live wholly or partially without organic matter, utilizing elements or simple compounds for energy and deriving body carbon from carbon dioxide. To this group belong nitrite and nitrate-forming bacteria and bacteria which oxidize sulfur, iron, hydrogen, or carbon monoxide, methane, and similar carbon compounds. **Heterotrophic bacteria** feed chiefly on organic matter. To this group belong free and symbiotic nitrogen-fixing bacteria, bacteria decomposing fats, proteins, cellulose, and other carbohydrates, and some denitrifying bacteria. A considerable portion of the heterotrophic forms live in the absence of oxygen and are called **anaerobic,** in contrast to **aerobic** forms developing in the presence of air.

**Fungi** are multicellular chlorophyll-free thallose plants which derive their energy from the decomposition of living or dead organic material. The fungi in forest soils may be divided into three groups. (1) **Saprophytic fungi** live on dead organic remains. (2) **Parasitic fungi** may utilize living tissues. This group includes the fungi responsible for "damping-off," root-rot, and other diseases of trees. (3) **Mycorrhizal fungi** live in symbiosis with trees and other higher plants. In some tree species the fungus modifies the root structure to form forked, or branched, nodule-like "short roots," which may be detected by ocular examination. In other tree species the fungus is entirely concealed within the root tissues and can be detected only by microscopic examination.

**Actinomycetes** exhibit characteristics of both bacteria and fungi and occur primarily in forest soils. They aid bacteria and fungi in the decomposition of organic remains.

**Algae** are chlorophyll-bearing organisms which occur in filaments or colonies. They hasten the solubility of minerals, increase the organic content of the soil, and possibly facilitate aerobic respiration of roots in poorly drained soils. Some species are capable of fixing atmospheric nitrogen. A symbiosis between algae and fungi produces lichens, organisms which initiate the development of soil from unweathered rocks.

**Protozoa** are unicellular animals, varying in diameter from a few microns to several centimeters. They decompose organic remains and play a definite part in the control of the microbiological population of the soil.

**Nematodes** are transparent, nonsegmented, wormlike organisms which decompose organic matter and improve soil aeration. They consume bacteria, fungi, protozoa, and other nematodes, and sometimes are parasitic on plants.

**Earthworms** are confined chiefly to moist, moderately acid or alkaline soils, high in humus. They pass great quantities of soil through their bodies, thereby promoting humification and the incorporation of organic matter with mineral soils.

**Arachnida** include mites, ticks, and spiders. These organisms are usually confined to the upper few inches of the soil and contribute to humification processes.

**Crustacea** include sow bugs, pill bugs, and crayfish. The first two organisms feed on dead leaves and wood and thus contribute to the processes of humification.

Crayfish are abundant in poorly drained soils of warmer regions and facilitate the drainage of excess water.

**Centipedes** are predatory animals feeding on other members of the soil fauna and favoring the development of mull humus layers.

**Insects.** Some soil-inhabiting forms increase the content of organic matter, aid in humification, and improve soil structure. Other insects feed on the roots and other tissues of trees.

**Mammals.** Most of the larger mammals which inhabit forest soils are moles and rodents. These burrowing animals contribute to the process of humification and cultivation of the soil.

## Forest Nursery Soils

**SELECTION OF FOREST NURSERY SITES.** The establishment of even a small nursery requires, first of all, the careful selection of a site. Accessibility, both to the areas to be planted and to a dependable source of labor, is an economic necessity. Avoid too small a site; allow space for expansion not immediately foreseen.

Climate, topography, and soil are the prime natural factors to be considered:

1. Choose a site where the growing season coincides with that of the average planting site.
2. Avoid sites known or suspected to be subject to climatic extremes, such as early or late frosts, drying winds, etc.
3. Avoid areas subject to overflow. Consider not only the direct evidence of overflow, such as debris lodged on the upstream side of obstacles or silt marks on tree trunks, but also the statements of local residents.
4. Choose a soil of light texture to avoid frost heaving and complications in the control of parasitic organisms and to facilitate weeding and lifting of stock.
5. Avoid stony or gravelly ground, cemented or compacted soils, and poorly drained soils underlain by a mottled or discolored zone (gley horizon); the minimum depth of well-aerated surface soil should be 4 ft.
6. If possible, choose a soil with a favorable reaction—acid for conifers, slightly acid for most hardwoods.
7. Soil should be inhabited by mycorrhizal fungi, and be free from parasitic organisms such as damping-off fungi, white grubs, and cutworms.
8. Choose a site having an abundant source of water suitable for irrigation and domestic purposes.
9. Choose, if possible, a site near suitable deposits of peat, leafmold, clay, and other materials used in soil improvements.

**MAINTENANCE OF NURSERY SOIL FERTILITY. Suitability of Chemical Fertilizers and Lime to Nursery Use.** In all nursery soils available nutrients undergo rapid depletion because of leaching, the activity of microorganisms, and nutrition of seedlings. The fertility of soil may be re-established in a safe and natural manner by applying forest litter or leafmold from productive forest stands. However, the procurement of litter is difficult and costly. Therefore, natural fertilizing materials as a rule must be supplemented by commercial fertilizers.

### Nitrogen Fertilizers.

1. **Sodium nitrate,** or "Chile saltpeter," $NaNO_3$; 16 percent nitrogen. Soluble in water, and easily lost through leaching; tends to produce an alkaline reaction in the soil and is preferable for hardwood stock.

2. **Calcium nitrate,** or "Norwegian saltpeter," $Ca(NO_3)_2$; 16 percent nitrogen. Soluble, and highly deliquescent; occasionally used on acid soils deficient in calcium.

3. **Ammonium nitrate,** $NH_4NO_3$; 35 percent nitrogen. Soluble and acid-forming, suitable for both hardwoods and conifers; tends to cake, unless in the form of coated granules; a possible fire hazard.

4. **Ammonium sulfate,** $(NH_4)_2SO_4$; 20 percent nitrogen. Soluble; continued use increases soil acidity; preferable for coniferous stock.

5. **Calcium cyanamid,** $CaCN_2$; 20 to 25 percent nitrogen. Application involves considerable danger of stock injury because of transitional toxic compounds formed in the soil; must be kept in tightly closed containers.

6. **Uramon,** $(NH_2)_2CO$; 42 percent nitrogen. Soluble; suitable for broadcast application, liquid treatments, and preparation of composts; because of its high analysis, it is as economical to use as the lower cost fertilizers; produces a neutral to slightly acid reaction.

7. **Organic nitrogen fertilizers** include dried blood, tankage, steamed bonemeal, horn shavings and meal, dried ground fish, cottonseed meal, activated sewage sludge, garbage tankage, tobacco stems, castor pomace, linseed meal, and soybean meal. The nitrogen content varies between 2 and 15 percent. Organic fertilizers are rarely used in forest nurseries because of high cost and the danger of root-rot diseases.

## Phosphate Fertilizers.

1. **Rock phosphate,** $Ca_3(PO_4)_2 \cdot CaF_2$ or $Ca_3(PO_4)_2 \cdot CaCl_2$; about 70 percent tricalcium phosphate, or 33 percent $P_2O_5$. Slowly available, especially in slightly acid soils; best results are obtained when finely ground and used with acid organic remains; suitable largely for broadcast applications and preparation of peat composts.

2. **Superphosphate,** $CaH_4(PO_4)_2$; 14 to 25 percent $P_2O_5$. Partially soluble and preferable for calcium-deficient soils.

3. **Double superphosphate,** $CaH_4(PO)_2$; 40 to 50 percent $P_2O_5$. Has a somewhat higher solubility than superphosphate; more economical than other forms of phosphate fertilizers, and is suitable for all soils except those deficient in calcium.

4. **Bone phosphate,** B.P.L., or "bone phosphate of lime"; about 25 percent $P_2O_5$, which is slowly available; expensive if transportation costs are involved, and is rarely used in nurseries.

5. **Basic slag,** $(CaO)_5 \cdot P_2O_5 \cdot SiO_2$; about 12 percent $P_2O_5$. Likely to solidify if stored in a damp place; use is warranted only where local supplies are available.

## Potassium Fertilizers.

1. **Potassium chloride,** or muriate of potash, $KCl$; 50 to 60 percent $K_2O$. Soluble in water; if used in large amounts, the chloride ion may reach a toxic concentration.

2. **Potassium sulfate,** or sulfate of potash, $K_2SO_4$; 48 to 60 percent $K_2O$. Soluble; may be used in somewhat larger quantities than KCl without injury to seedlings.

3. **Manure salts.** Potash salts found in crude or partially refined potash minerals, such as carnallite, kainite, and sylvinite; they contain from 9 to 16 percent $K_2O$; may exert harmful effects on nursery stock owing to toxic impurities.

4. **Wood ashes.** Unleached hardwood ashes contain from 2 to 8 percent $K_2O$, some $P_2O_5$, and a large amount of CaO. Because of the presence of trace elements, they appear to be superior to other sources of potash but are seldom procurable in quantity; should be used with caution if the area is to be seeded to conifers predisposed to damping-off disease.

## Combined Fertilizers.

1. **Potassium nitrate,** $KNO_3$; 13 percent N and 45 percent $K_2O$. Soluble, and less hygroscopic than other nitrate fertilizers; is expensive and used primarily in liquid treatment.
2. **Mono-ammonium phosphate,** "Ammophos," $NH_4H_2PO_4$; 11 percent N and 48 percent $P_2O_5$. Soluble; used chiefly in liquid treatments.
3. **Di-ammonium phosphate,** $(NH_4)_2HPO_4$, 21 percent N and 53 percent $P_2O_5$. Soluble and used chiefly in liquid treatments; is preferable to mono-ammonium phosphate because of the more favorable nitrogen-phosphorus ratio.
4. **Mixed fertilizers,** composed of different mixtures of salts, such as ammonium sulfate, superphosphate, and potassium chloride or potassium sulfate. The composition of these fertilizers is given by their grade or analysis—the percentage of nitrogen, phosphoric acid, and potash, stated in whole numbers. For example, 3–9–18 means 3 percent N, 9 percent $P_2O_5$, and 18 percent $K_2O$. These figures total only 30 percent, or 30 lb. per 100-lb. bag. The remaining 70 lb. are made up by the carriers, such as sulfate, chloride, and other ions. Also, a small amount of filler, e.g., dolomite or sand, may be included. Thus, 100 lb. of 3–9–18 may be comprised of 15 lb. of ammonium sulfate to give 3 lb. of nitrogen, 45 lb. of 20 percent superphosphate to give 9 lb. of $P_2O_5$, and 36 lb. of 50 percent potassium chloride to give 18 lb. of $K_2O$. This totals 96 lb. The remaining 4 lb. is filler. Some common fertilizer mixtures suitable for use in forest nurseries are: 3–9–18, 3–12–12, 6–6–18, 0–10–20, and 0–9–27.
5. **Es-min-el,** or essential minor elements. This type of fertilizer contains varying amounts of manganese, copper, zinc, iron, boron, and traces of other minor elements. It is used in nursery soils where the supply of trace elements has decreased to a critical level.

**Lime.** The term "lime" is used to designate a number of compounds including the oxides, hydroxides, or carbonates of calcium and magnesium; viz., burned lime or quicklime, air-slaked lime, water-slaked or hydrated lime, waste lime or by-product lime, marl, ground shell lime, and ground limestone. With few exceptions, forest nurseries use only ground limestone, obtained by grinding calcitic or dolomitic rock. It is agreed that 75 percent or more of the ground material should pass a 100-mesh sieve and should contain calcium and magnesium carbonate equivalent to not less than 45 percent of calcium oxide.

The use of burned or slaked lime is dangerous because it may lead to the injury or "burning" of roots. Since lime treatment in any form may initiate or encourage damping-off disease, a green manure crop or transplanted stock should intervene between the application of lime and the seeding of conifers.

**ADJUSTMENT OF NURSERY SOIL FERTILITY.** The adjustment of nursery soil fertility factors, such as pH value, exchange capacity, total and available nitrogen, available phosphorus, available potassium, and exchangeable calcium and magnesium, is made on the basis of soil analyses. For carrying out soil analyses and establishing the optimum levels of soil fertility for different tree species, soil specialists in state universities and forestry schools and specific literature should be consulted.

**METHODS OF APPLICATION OF FERTILIZERS.** Broadcast Applications. Chemical fertilizers, compost, peat, or other materials are applied by hand, or with a fertilizer spreader, and are worked into the soil either by plowing, disking and harrowing, plowing and double disking, or more commonly, by rototilling.

**Composted Fertilizers.** Composts are made up of peat, forest litter, mineral fertilizers, topsoil and other available materials. These ingredients are mixed in a pile or a special pit, and the organic matter is allowed to decompose partly and absorb the mineral salts during the storage period.

In mixing the compost, 1 in. of shredded peat is placed on the bottom of the compost pit and a mixture of commercial fertilizers is broadcast on top of it. The fertilizers are covered with about a ¼-in. layer of litter or duff, which is followed by a layer of topsoil, if this is used. The materials are sprinkled with water to moisten them thoroughly. Another 1-in. layer of peat is placed on top of the litter, and the fertilizers and duff are again applied as previously described.

The amount of fertilizer to broadcast over a 1-in. layer of organic material is determined as follows:

$$f = \frac{F \times L \times W}{12 \times 400 \times C}$$

where $F$ is the amount of any fertilizer to be applied per acre; $L$ is the length and $W$ is the width of the pit in feet; and $C$ is the amount of compost in cubic feet to be applied per 100 sq. ft. of seedbed.

In place of stratification, peat, leafmold, mineral fertilizers, and topsoil may be fed in desirable proportions to the shredding machine, directly or by means of a conveyor. The proper amounts of peat, duff, and commercial fertilizers are measured by shovels and scoop cups of known volume.

In general, the concentration of total fertilizer salts should not exceed 60 lb. per cu. yd. of composted organic remains. Composts carrying less than 25 lb. of salts per cu. yd. have been found to be uneconomical, and composts with concentrations of salts exceeding 80 lb. per cu. yd. are likely to cause chemical injury to nursery stock. As a rule, the rate of compost application varies between ½ bu. and 2 bu., or about 2 cu. ft., per 100 sq. ft. Particular care should be exercised to incorporate compost to a depth of at least 8 in. in order to prevent the development of stock with superficial root systems.

**Catch Crops.** The use of catch crops to maintain soil fertility periodically keeps a portion of the nursery out of production. It is, therefore, not the most economical method and is used extensively only where natural organic deposits are scarce.

The method consists of a broadcast application of complete mineral fertilizer and seeding the area to green manure crops, preferably legumes. If legumes are used, nitrogen fertilizers are omitted in favor of inoculation of the seed with nodule bacteria. After the green manure is plowed under, the area should be sown to rye to prevent the loss of nutrients by leaching.

**Fertilizer Solutions.** Ordinarily, the fertilizers described above provide enough nutrients for the growth of seedlings in the nursery. In some cases, however, even fertilized soils may develop nutrient deficiencies because of heavy rains, unexpectedly high germination of seed, or losses of nutrients through biological and chemical fixation. In such cases, the deficiencies of nutrients must be corrected by the application of salts in solution, using readily soluble fertilizers such as ammonium sulfate, ammonium nitrate, potassium nitrate, potassium sulfate, and ammonium phosphate. The proper amount of different fertilizer ingredients to be used in the preparation of fertilizing solutions is conveniently determined by means of the following formula:

$$f = \frac{F \times V}{400 \times S}$$

where $f$ is the amount of fertilizer in pounds to be dissolved, $F$ is the rate of application of this fertilizer on a per-acre basis, $V$ is the volume in gallons of the tank or other container used for preparation of the fertilizer solution, and $S$ is the amount of solution in gallons to be applied per 100 sq. ft.

In general, the amount of total fertilizer salts applied at one time in the form of a solution should not exceed 600 lb. per acre, and the concentration of applied solution should not exceed 20,000 p.p.m., or roughly 15 lb. of total salts per 100 gal. of water. Liquid fertilizer is often prepared in 50-gal. barrels and distributed in 3-gal. watering cans. Larger nurseries, however, use special multisprayers which consist of 200- to 300-gal. tanks mounted on trucks provided with a pressure pump and rotating agitators. The liquid is distributed through horizontal spraying pipes with nozzles adjusted to deliver the solution between rows of seedlings. In some cases fertilizer solution is delivered through the overhead system, but poor distribution of the solution and the danger of pipe corrosion are decided disadvantages of this method.

Liquid fertilizers are applied after the danger of late spring frost is over and 6 or 7 weeks before the early fall frost. The application of liquid fertilizers should be made in the early morning, during the evening, or on a cloudy day. The treated seedlings are washed thoroughly with water immediately after treatment.

Liquid fertilizers are used only in emergency cases, not as a regular means of soil fertility maintenance. Excessive use of liquid fertilizers produces succulent stock with poor root systems and resultant low survival in the field.

**Liquid Humates.** In cases of extreme emergency—when stock has suffered malnutrition or has been injured by chemical, climatic, or biotic agents—recovery of the stock may be attempted by the application of humus suspensions reinforced by high-grade fertilizers, or so-called "liquid humates."

In the preparation of liquid humate, a barrel is half-filled with duff or leafmold. The required amount of mineral fertilizers is added, and the barrel is filled with water. While the water is being added, the mixture is vigorously stirred. After several hours, the mixture is stirred again to bring fine humus particles into suspension. Then the liquid is siphoned into watering cans and applied to the seedbeds like a liquid fertilizer.

The effect of liquid humates varies considerably, depending upon the nature of the organic remains used. Acid debris of friable mor or duff mull types from productive stands of tolerant species appears to provide fertilizers of the best quality. In the preparation of humus suspensions, the choice of chemical fertilizers is largely limited to ammonium sulfate, ammonium phosphate, potassium nitrate, potassium sulfate, and 10–52–17 Victor Take Hold. The amount of different fertilizers is determined by the quantity of nutrients present in the soil and the nature of the nursery stock. A formula suitable for a sandy nursery soil raising pine species may be given as an example: 1½ lb. of 11–48–0 ammonium phosphate, 3 lb. of 13–0–44 potassium nitrate, and 2 lb. of 20 percent ammonium sulfate per 50 gal. of humus suspension. This fertilizer is applied at the rate of 6 gal. per 100 sq. ft.

Careful records of all soil treatments should be made. When subdivided into sections or blocks, the nursery area can be designated by number. A yearly record should be kept for these subdivisions on a map, as well as by written notations. This will be valuable when making the analysis of nursery stock described below.

**ANALYSIS OF NURSERY STOCK.** No matter how careful and presumably scientific the management of nursery soil may be, the actual efficiency of such management can be appraised only by systematic analyses of the nursery stock produced and statistically significant records of stock survival under adverse field conditions. Such an approach, in the long run, will not only be valuable in arriving at a reliable method of nursery stock production but also will help to eliminate differences of opinion between the nursery manager and forestry personnel in charge of reforestation. It should be realized that at the present time production of nursery stock is a highly complicated technical process, involving the use of numerous chemicals—fertilizers, herbicides, insectides, and fungicides. If, under such conditions, the morphological and physiological development of plants is not considered, the production of inferior planting stock is to be expected. Particular attention should be paid to uniformity in the size and color of seedlings, their root-top ratio, probable transpirational losses by crowns, absorbing capacity of roots, specific gravity of stems, and the balance of nutrient elements and other chemical constituents of plant tissues.

**REGULATION OF ARTIFICIAL IRRIGATION. Rate of Watering.** The application of water at unreasonably high rates may produce several detrimental effects: It may (1) leach out certain soluble salts and thus disrupt the proper ratio of nutrients; (2) create an anaerobic condition, thereby decreasing the availability of some nutrients and giving rise to toxic compounds; (3) encourage the development of fungus diseases; and (4) lead to the development of succulent seedlings vulnerable to injury by drought and frost.

For the reliable control of artificial irrigation it is necessary to equip the nursery with a number of rain gauges placed inside and outside the artifically watered area. In conservative watering, the amount of water added to the soil each month by irrigation should not greatly exceed the average monthly rainfall.

A weekly amount of water can be determined, and if the natural rainfall does not supply the determined weekly amount, the insufficiency can be added artificially. The monthly total rainfall may exceed the average monthly rainfall, but there could occur one or more critical periods which would be taken care of only by the weekly schedule.

**Time of Watering.** Watering under a scalding sun decreases the air and soil temperature and in some instances prevents the destruction of stock by heat. On the other hand, the application of water during periods of high temperature may be responsible for the accumulation of soluble fertilizer salts or carbonates near the surface of the soil. Moreover, watering during the heat of the day is not an economical practice because rapid evaporation prevents the penetration of water to any great depth. The most efficient use of water is therefore obtained when it is applied late in the evening or early in the morning; such a practice allows the water to percolate to a depth of several inches, and it is subsequently protected from excessive evaporation by a layer of soil.

**Manner of Watering.** From an economic and physiological standpoint, it is advisable to apply a sufficient amount of water at infrequent intervals. This rule, however, is subject to definite exceptions. On soils of fine texture and those underlain by impervious substrata the application of water should not decrease the aeration of soil below 15 percent by volume for any considerable length of time. On coarse sandy soils, especially those deficient in organic matter, heavy watering may lead to a loss of nutrients through leaching or to the accumulation of soluble salts in toxic concentrations near the soil surface.

**SELECTION OF TREE-PLANTING SITES.** Artificial reforestation usually involves four major steps: (1) selection of tree species to be planted; (2) procurement of reliable seed, and raising stock in the nursery; (3) selection of planting sites; and (4) planting trees in the field.

The selection of tree species for reforestation is a broad regional problem whose solution depends upon conditions of climate and soils, resistance of trees to parasitic insects and diseases, requirements of local industry, the necessity for a rapid financial return, and other economic or recreational motives.

After the planting material is procured, suitable planting sites are selected to conform to the ecological requirements of the trees. In this strictly local problem, the forester first of all must consider topographic and microclimatic conditions such as inundation, danger of soil erosion, exposure to sun and wind, duration of snow cover, possibility of winter killing, frost heaving, or drought injury. Then, attention should be given to biotic factors; namely, competition of herbaceous and woody vegetation, presence of trainers, need for overhead nurse trees to protect shade-tolerant climax species, and danger of plantation injury by insect parasites, diseases, rodents, game, and livestock. In this connection, note should be taken of the occurrence of ground cover vegetation and trees that may attract harmful members of the fauna or serve as alternate hosts for parasites. Finally, investigation should be made of the suitability of soils to the species to be planted, paying particular attention to the depth of soil, position of the ground water table, content of organic matter and mineral colloids, degree of soil acidity or alkalinity, the content of calcium and magnesium carbonates, permeability of surface layers and substrata, and the content of essential nutrients.

# Diagnosis of Adverse Conditions Responsible for Unsatisfactory Growth of Plantations or Forest Stands

Prior to a detailed investigation of adverse soil factors, it is advisable to make sure that the unsatisfactory growth of trees was not caused by critical climatic conditions, previous burning, toxic industrial fumes, or destructive agents, including animals, fungi, and insects (see Section **8**, Protection Against Insects and Diseases). The important soil properties that may cause poor growth and even mortality of natural stands and plantations are listed below:

1. Inadequate content of colloids in soil or substratum and consequent deficiency of moisture.
2. Accumulation of colloids in the lower portion of the soil (B horizon), arresting the vertical movement of water and thus leading to periodic waterlogging or drying out of the soil.
3. A too high content of clay particles inducing frost heaving or cracking of the soil in time of drought.
4. Compaction or sealing of the soil surface by livestock trampling, action of raindrops, or deposition of overwash material leading to increased runoff or puddling and subsequent loss of water by evaporation.
5. Deficiency of moisture due to the competition of grasses and other ground vegetation.
6. High ground water table or excessive water-holding capacity of soil and consequent inadequate aeration.
7. Radical change in the ground water level.
8. Stagnant ground water resulting from impeded surface or subterranean drainage.
9. Unreasonably low temperature of soil due to its insulation by moss cover, especially that made up of Sphagnum species.
10. Unsuitable reaction, deficiency of organic matter, and lack of certain essential nutrients.
11. Presence of toxic substances: free carbonates, highly concentrated soluble salts, hydrogen sulfide, ferrous iron, soluble aluminum and manganese, fresh

## Table 2.  Guide to Remedial Measures for Restoration of Fertility in Depleted Forest

(It is understood that detailed and specific instructions for treating local problems will need to be ob
from other reference works or by consultation with experts.)

| Types of un-productive land | Outstanding adverse conditions of the soil | Analyses which may aid in diagnosis and correction of deficiencies | Possible remedial mea |
|---|---|---|---|
| Burned-over soils | Deficiency of humus, high pH value, and high concentration of soluble salts near soil surface; in time deficiency of nitrogen and mineral nutrients, especially available potash. | Determination of reaction, specific conductance, content of organic matter, total nitrogen, and available nutrients. | Cover crops, especiall umes, with or w application of ferti spreading slash. S plowing or scarificat the ground to enc natural reproduction; ing or planting p species. |
| Grazed soils | Removal of litter, destruction of structural aggregates, and puddling of the surface soil; reduced infiltration capacity and aeration; root injury. | Volume weight, air permeability, and infiltration capacity. Comparison with similar soils supporting ungrazed stands. | Restriction of animals ing compaction. Re ing the soil surface a rototiller, spike-t earthworm, or hand regulation of runoff. ing of legumes, and u planting of soil-cons species, especially rooted shrubs. |
| Eroded loams or clays | Deficiency of organic matter and available nutrients; often unfavorable reaction. Reduced porosity, aeration, and infiltration capacity; absence of root channels and insufficient depth of soil. | Reaction, carbonates, organic matter, available nutrients, volume weight, texture, air permeability, and infiltration capacity. | Cover crops, especially umes, with or w application of ferti spreading slash. Div of water; use of s toothed implements. ing or planting p trees, including black and fruit-bearing sp |
| Eroded sands, especially blow sands | Deficiency of organic matter and available nutrients; low water-holding capacity. | Organic matter and soil texture. | Spreading slash, corn s or hay; establishme stake fences. Plantin xerophytic grasses pioneer species, partic pines. |
| Overwash soils | Deficiency of organic matter and disrupted ratio of available nutrients, unfavorable reaction. Often unsatisfactory physical condition of soil, especially sealing of the soil surface. | Organic matter, reaction, and available nutrients; air permeability or infiltration capacity. Examination of soil profile. | Diversion of runoff. crops with or withou plication of fertilizers of spike-toothed i ments. Seeding and ing pioneer species. |
| Spoil banks | Unfavorable reaction, deficiency of organic matter and certain nutrients; high content of stones and rubble, impermeable substratum and otherwise unsatisfactory physical conditions of soil. | Organic matter, soil texture, reaction, and available nutrients; air and water permeability. | Grading of steep banks, facing. Mulching; sp ing of slash. Cover with or without ap tion of fertilizers; pla of less exacting speci |
| Industrial waste beds | Unfavorable reaction, high concentration of soluble salts or presence of toxic compounds; deficiency of certain nutrients. Presence of cinders and unsatisfactory physical condition of soil. | Reaction, specific conductance, and available nutrients; air and water permeability. | Resurfacing with top Cover crops; plantin halophytic trees and sh after injurious salts been sufficiently ren by rain. |

Table 2. (Continued)

| es of un-active land | Outstanding adverse conditions of the soil | Analyses which may aid in diagnosis and correction of deficiencies | Possible remedial measures |
|---|---|---|---|
| stively ped soils | Deficiency of available nutrients, especially N in heavy soils, and N and K in sandy soils; deficiency of Mg in sludge-treated soils and sometimes deficiency of trace elements. Poor physical condition of soil. | Determination of organic matter and available nutrients in soil; foliar analysis. In heavy soils air and water permeability. | Use of limed and heavily fertilized cover crops, especially clover and other legumes that promise to recover part of cost by sale of seed or hay. Application of fertilizers in closed plantations. Under-planting of soil-improving trees and shrubs. |
| alls and rops | Unfavorable physical conditions of soil. | Ocular examination; determination of reactions and free carbonates. | Filling in crevices with soil and planting pioneer trees and shrubs. |
| an and pan soils, cially zols | Unfavorable physical conditions of soil; deficiency of certain nutrients and possible toxicity of compounds in the B horizon; periodic drought or inadequate aeration; frost heaving. | Reaction of soil. Ocular examination of soil profile to a depth of about 4 ft. Air permeability. | Restricted cuttings; encouragement of natural reproduction by scarification and other means. If practical, exposure of cemented or compacted layer by deep furrowing, with subsequent planting on top of the furrow slice. |
| drained nundated | Excess of water and inadequate aeration; unavailability of certain nutrients and presence of toxic substances, viz.: hydrogen sulfide, ferrous iron, and reduced manganese. | Ocular examination. In some cases, chemical analysis of ground water, especially its hardness and degree of oxygenation. | Removal of water by horizontal or vertical drainage. Acceleration of current in nearby streams. Planting of water-loving species on top of furrow slice or in mounds. |

sawdust (for the proper use of sawdust and wood chips as soil improvers, see the discussion of those products in the section on Utilization), discarded wastes, especially petroleum products, cleaning solutions, etc.; excess of ammonia due to concentration of animals on small areas, such as may be found on mink farms.

12. Lack of mycorrhizal fungi in case of direct seeding on prairie soils, burned-out peat soils, drained beaver flowages, or eroded soils.

In dealing with poor growth of artificially established plantations, it may be desirable to investigate the origin of planting stock, particularly the source of seed, climatic conditions of the region in which the nursery is located, method of stock watering, fertilization, and the control of parasitic organisms, including the use of fungicides, insectides, and herbicides.

Table 2 summarizes common adverse soil conditions and measures for the restoration of fertility in unproductive soils.

## BIBLIOGRAPHY

ASSN. OF OFFICIAL AGRICULTURAL CHEMISTS. 1950. *Official and tentative methods of analysis.* 6th ed. Washington, D. C.

BOWMAN, ISAIAH. 1911. *Forest physiography.* John Wiley & Sons, Inc., New York.

BRAUN, E. L. 1950. *Deciduous forests of eastern North America.* The Blakiston Co., Philadelphia.

BRAUN-BLANQUET, J. 1932. *Plant sociology.* (Trans. rev. and ed. by G. D. Fuller and H. S. Conard.) McGraw-Hill Book Co., Inc., New York.

COILE, T. S. 1952. Soil and the growth of forests. In *Advances in agronomy*. Vol. 4. Academic Press, Inc., New York.

DAUBENMIRE, R. F. 1947. *Plants and environment*. John Wiley & Sons, Inc., New York.

EMERSON, F. V. 1920. *Agricultural geology*. (Rev. ed. by J. E. Smith, 1928.) John Wiley & Sons, Inc., New York.

EMMONS, W. H., G. A. THIEL, C. R. STAUFFER, and I. S. ALLISON. 1939. *Geology, principles and processes*. 2d ed. McGraw-Hill Book Co., Inc., New York.

KITTREDGE, J. 1948. *Forest influences*. McGraw-Hill Book Co., Inc., New York.

KRAMER, P. J. 1949. *Plant and soil water relationships*. McGraw-Hill Book Co., Inc., New York.

LUNDEGÅRDH, H. 1951. *Leaf analysis* (Trans. by R. L. Mitchell). Hilger & Watts, Ltd., London.

LUTZ, H. J., and R. F. CHANDLER. 1946. *Forest soils*. John Wiley & Sons, Inc., New York.

OOSTING, H. J. 1950. *The study of plant communities*. W. H. Freeman & Co., San Francisco.

PIPER, C. S. 1944. *Soil and plant analysis*. Interscience Publishers, Inc., New York.

RUSSELL, E. J. 1950. *Soil conditions and plant growth*. 8th ed. Longmans, Green & Co., Inc., New York.

TAMM, O. 1950. *Northern coniferous forest soils*. Scrivener Press, Oxford, Eng.

THWAITES, F. T. 1946. *Outline of glacial geology*. J. W. Edwards, Ann Arbor, Mich.

TOUMEY, J. W., and C. F. KORSTIAN. 1947. *Foundations of silviculture upon an ecological basis*. 2d ed. John Wiley & Sons, Inc., New York.

TOUMEY, J. W., and C. F. KORSTIAN. 1947. *Seeding and planting in the practice of forestry*. 3d ed. John Wiley & Sons, Inc., New York.

TWENHOFEL, W. H. 1926. *Treatise on sedimentation*. Williams & Wilkins Co., Baltimore.

U. S. DEPT. AGR. 1938. *Soils and men. Yearbook of Agriculture*.

U. S. DEPT. AGR. 1947. Methods of soil analysis for soil fertility investigations, *Cir. 757*.

U. S. FOREST SERV., Southern Forest Exp. Sta. 1951. *Occas. Paper 122*.

WEAVER, J. E., and F. E. CLEMENTS. 1938. *Plant ecology*. 2d ed. McGraw-Hill Book Co., Inc., New York.

WILDE, S. A. 1946. *Forest soils and forest growth*. Chronica Botanica Co., Waltham, Mass.

WILDE, S. A., and G. K. VOIGT. 1955. *Analysis of soils and plants for foresters and horticulturists*. J. W. Edwards, Ann Arbor, Mich.

WILDE, S. A., F. G. WILSON, and D. P. WHITE. 1949. Soils of Wisconsin in relation to silviculture. *Wis. Cons. Dept. Pub. No. 525–49*, Madison.

ZON, R. 1927. *Forests and water in the light of scientific investigation*. Government Printing Office, Washington, D. C.

# SILVICS AND SILVICULTURE

## CONTENTS

# SILVICS AND SILVICULTURE

## Dendrology

The material on dendrology is presented in two tables. Table 1 lists the names and range of the most important forest trees of the United States and Canada, plus various minor species, near-shrubs, and "weed" species. Table 2 sets forth, for as many as possible of the species listed in Table 1, not only the shade tolerance but also soil requirements, rate of growth, longevity, ease or difficulty of natural reproduction under management, and place in the ecological succession. The information in Table 2 was compiled for quick reference by the busy field man. Because of obvious limitations, however, it makes no claim to being complete or final.

### Table 1. Important [a] Tree Species of the United States and Canada

Key to Identification,[b] Common Name,[c] Scientific Name,[d] and Range [e]

---

## EASTERN CONIFERS (GYMNOSPERMS)

Resinous; leaves needle-like or scalelike, "evergreen" (except Nos. 1 and 2); seeds borne on scales of a cone (berry-like in No. 18).

**A.** Leaves shed the first autumn.
  **B.** Leaves needle-like (sometimes scalelike) on slender twigs, mostly shedding with leaves.
    1. BALDCYPRESS (*Taxodium distichum* var. *distichum*); cypress; VII.
      Also PONDCYPRESS (*T. distichum* var. *nutans*).

  **BB.** Leaves needle-like, mostly in clusters on short spur branches.
    2. TAMARACK, LARCH (*Larix laricina*); larch; I–III, V.

**AA.** Leaves persistent 2 yr. or more.
  **C.** Leaves needle-like, more than ½ in. long.
    **D.** Needles in clusters with sheath at base: *Pinus.*
      **E.** Needles 5 in cluster—white (or soft) pines.
    3. EASTERN WHITE PINE (*Pinus strobus*); white pine; I–VI.
      **EE.** Needles 2 or 3 in cluster—yellow (hard, or pitch) pines.
        **F.** Needles 3 in cluster (also 2 in No. 5).
          **G.** Needles more than 8 in. long.

[a] Importance based on one or more of following factors: commercial value of wood or by-products, wide distribution, silvicultural importance (beneficial or detrimental), watershed influence, aesthetic value. Unnumbered species are of minor importance.
[b] Adapted and expanded from key by Elbert L. Little, Jr., *Trees: The Yearbook of Agriculture*, U. S. Dept. Agr., 1949.
[c] U. S. Dept. Agr., Check list of native and naturalized trees of the United States, *Handbook No. 41*. Additional common names are those applied to lumber.
[d] International Code, omitting names of authors.
[e] Information from U. S. Dept. Agr., *Handbook No. 41*, interpreted in terms of the map, "Forest Vegetation of the United States," prepared by U. S. Forest Service, 1948 (Fig. 1).

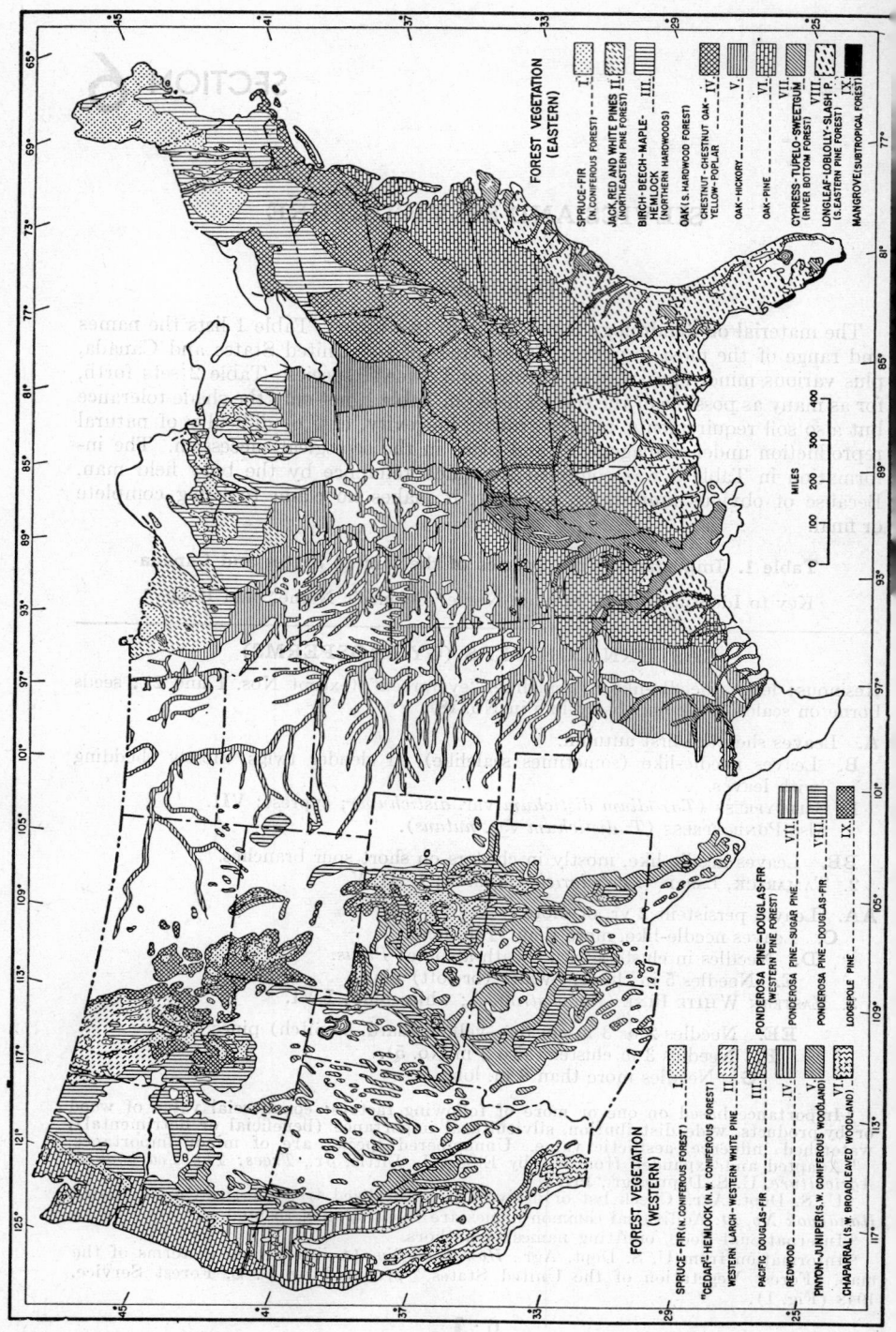

FOREST VEGETATION (EASTERN)

SPRUCE-FIR
(N. CONIFEROUS FOREST) — I.

JACK, RED AND WHITE PINES
(NORTHEASTERN PINE FOREST) — II.

BIRCH-BEECH-MAPLE-
HEMLOCK
(NORTHERN HARDWOODS) — III.

OAK (S. HARDWOOD FOREST) —

CHESTNUT-CHESTNUT OAK-
YELLOW-POPLAR — IV.

OAK-HICKORY — V.

OAK-PINE — VI.

CYPRESS-TUPELO-SWEETGUM
(RIVER BOTTOM FOREST) — VII.

LONGLEAF-LOBLOLLY-SLASH P.
(S. EASTERN PINE FOREST) — VIII.

MANGROVE (SUBTROPICAL FOREST) — IX.

FOREST VEGETATION (WESTERN)

SPRUCE-FIR (N.W. CONIFEROUS FOREST) — I.

"CEDAR"-HEMLOCK (N.W. CONIFEROUS FOREST) —

WESTERN LARCH-WESTERN WHITE PINE — III.

PACIFIC DOUGLAS-FIR —

REDWOOD —

PINON-JUNIPER (S.W. CONIFEROUS WOODLAND) — VI.

CHAPARRAL (S.W. BROADLEAVED WOODLAND) —

PONDEROSA PINE-DOUGLAS-FIR
(WESTERN PINE FOREST) — VII.

PONDEROSA PINE-SUGAR PINE —

PONDEROSA PINE-DOUGLAS-FIR — VIII.

LODGEPOLE PINE — IX.

MILES

0    100   200   300   400

4. LONGLEAF PINE (*P. palustris*); longleaf pine; VIII. Needles 10–15 in. long. Cones prickly, 5–10 in. long.
5. SLASH PINE (*P. elliottii*); longleaf pine; VIII. Needles 8–12 in. long, sometimes 2 in cluster. Cones with minute prickles, 3–6 in. long.

    **GG.** Needles mostly less than 8 in. long.

6. LOBLOLLY PINE (*P. taeda*); shortleaf pine; VI–VIII. Needles 6–9 in. long. Cones 3–5 in. long, persistent only 1 yr., stout prickles.
7. PITCH PINE (*P. rigida*); yellow pine; III, IV, VI. Needles 3–6 in. long. Cones 1½–3 in. long, persistent several years; slender prickles. Also POND PINE (*P. serotina*); VII, VIII; leaves 6–8 in. long.

    **FF.** Needles 2 in cluster (some 3's in No. 8).
      **H.** Needles more than 3 in. long.

8. SHORTLEAF PINE (*P. echinata*); shortleaf pine; IV, V, VII, VIII. Needles 3–5 in. long, some 3 in a cluster. Small resin pockets in bark of older trees.
9. RED PINE (*P. resinosa*); Norway pine; II, III. Needles 5–6 in. long.

      **HH.** Needles less than 3 in. long.

10. JACK PINE (*P. banksiana*); I, II. Needles ¾–1½ in. long. Cones without prickles.
11. VIRGINIA PINE (*P. virginiana*); IV, VI. Cones very prickly. Also TABLE MOUNTAIN PINE (*P. pungens*); IV; SPRUCE PINE (*P. glabra*), VIII; and SAND PINE (*P. clausa*), VIII.

    **DD.** Needles borne singly, not in clusters.
      **I.** Twigs roughened by projecting bases of old needles; cones pendulous, intact when they fall.
        **J.** Needles flat, with short leaf stalks, appearing in 2 rows, white on under surface. Twigs flexible.

12. EASTERN HEMLOCK (*Tsuga canadensis*); hemlock; I–V. Also CAROLINA HEMLOCK (*T. caroliniana*); III, IV (southern Appalachians).

        **JJ.** Needles 4-angled, sharp-pointed, sessile, extending out on all sides of twig. Twig stiff.

13. RED SPRUCE (*Picea rubens*); spruce; I, III (exclusive of Lake States). Twigs hairy. Cones 1½ in. or less, in length. Also BLACK SPRUCE (*P. mariana*); poor sites; I–III.
14. WHITE SPRUCE (*P. glauca*); spruce; I–III. Twigs not hairy. Cones 1½–2 in. long.

      **II.** Twigs smooth; cones upright, falling scale by scale.

15. BALSAM FIR (*Abies balsamea*); eastern fir; I–III. Leaves rounded, often notched, at tip. Also FRASER FIR (*A. fraseri*); III (southern Appalachians).

    **CC.** Leaves scalelike, less than ¼ in. long (on some twigs needle-like, longer).
      **K.** Leafy twigs more or less flattened.
        **L.** Twigs much flattened, about ⅛ in. broad, including leaves.

16. NORTHERN WHITE-CEDAR (*Thuja occidentalis*); white-cedar; I–III.

        **LL.** Twigs slightly flattened, less than 1/16 in. broad, including leaves.

17. ATLANTIC WHITE-CEDAR (*Chamaecyparis thyoides*); white-cedar; IV, VI, VII.

      **KK.** Leafy twigs rounded or 4-angled.

18. EASTERN REDCEDAR (*Juniperus virginiana*); redcedar; III–VI. Fruit a dark blue "berry." Also SOUTHERN REDCEDAR (*J. silicicola*); VII (Ga., Fla.).

## EASTERN HARDWOODS (ANGIOSPERMS)

Nonresinous, with broad leaves. Seeds enclosed in a fruit.

**A.** Monocotyledons. Leaves parallel-veined, evergreen, clustered at top of trunk or large branches. Wood without annual rings.

19. SAW-PALMETTO (*Serenoa repens*); VIII. Leafstalks 1½–2 ft. long, with stout teeth.
20. CABBAGE PALMETTO (*Sabal palmetto*); VII–IX. Leafstalks average 6 to 7 ft. long.

**AA.** Dicotyledons. Leaves net-veined, wood with annual rings.
  **B.** Leaves persistent, leathery at maturity.
    **C.** Leaves opposite.

21. DEVILWOOD (*Osmanthus americanus*); VII–VIII. Leaves 4–5 in. long. Fruit fleshy, oblong, 1 in. long, dark blue.

  **CC.** Leaves alternate.
    **D.** Leaves spiny.

22. AMERICAN HOLLY (*Ilex opaca*); IV, VI–VIII. Fruit a red berry.

    **DD.** Leaves aromatic or sweet to taste; fruit in clusters.

23. SOUTHERN BAYBERRY (*Myrica cerifera*); VI–VIII. Leaves and fruit aromatic. Fruit berry-like, waxy, light green, in short spikes.
24. SWEETLEAF (*Symplocos tinctoria*); IV, VI–VIII. Leaves sweet to taste. Fruit an ovate berry, orange colored or brown, nearly sessile.

    **DDD.** Edges of most leaves serrate or slightly scalloped.

25. LOBLOLLY-BAY (*Gordonia lasianthus*); VII–VIII. Leaves 4–5 in. long. Fruit a woody capsule, on stem 2½–3 in. long.

    **DDDD.** Edges of most leaves smooth (sometimes toothed in Nos. 32, 35, and 36).
      **E.** Twigs with faint ring at base of each leaf. Magnolia.

26. SOUTHERN MAGNOLIA (*Magnolia grandiflora*); VII–VIII. Leaves 5–8 in. long, rusty tomentose below.
27. SWEETBAY (*M. virginiana*); IV, VI–VIII. Leaves 4–6 in. long, nearly white below.

      **EE.** Leaves up to 12 in. long.

28. RHODODENDRON (*R. maximum*); III–IV. Leaves 4–12 in. long, usually clustered at ends of branches.

      **EEE.** Leaves less than 5 in. long.

29. MOUNTAIN-LAUREL (*Kalmia latifolia*); I, III, IV, VI–VIII. Leaves sometimes in pairs or 3's, 3–4 in. long, pointed. Fruit a persistent capsule.
30. RED BAY (*Persea borbonia*); VI–VIII. Leaves 3–4 in. long, midribs orange. Roots yellow.
31. LIVE OAK (*Quercus virginiana*); VII–VIII. Leaves 2–5 in. long, usually rounded at apex, and edges rolled under. Fruit an acorn.
32. CAROLINA LAURELCHERRY (*Prunus caroliniana*); VII–VIII. Leaves 2–4½ in. long, bitter if chewed, leafstalks orange colored. Fruit a cherry.
33. SWAMP CYRILLA (*Cyrilla racemiflora*); VI–VIII. Leaves 2–3 in. long, narrow. Fruit a capsule, less than 1/16 in. long, in racemes.
34. BUCKWHEAT-TREE (*Cliftonia monophylla*); VII–VIII. Leaves 1½–2 in. long. Fruit a winged capsule, ¼ in. long, in racemes.
35. TREE SPARKLEBERRY (*Vaccinium arboreum*); IV–VIII. Leaves ½–2½ in. long. Fruit a shiny black berry.
36. YAUPON (*Ilex vomitoria*); VI–VIII. Leaves 1–2 in. long. Fruit berry-like, scarlet.

  **BB.** Leaves deciduous at end of first growing season.
      **F.** Leaves opposite or in 3's.
        **G.** Leaves palmately compound.

37. BUCKEYE (*Aesculus* spp.); IV–VIII. Twigs stout, with large pith; ill-smelling when bruised. Seeds 1–2 in. broad, 1 or 2 in a thick husk.

    **GG.** Leaves pinnately compound.
      **H.** Leaflets 3 (occasionally 5 in No. 38).

38. BOXELDER (*Acer negundo*); U. S., except New England and Pacific Northwest; Canada: Ont., Man., Sask., Alta. Twigs bright green or purplish green. Leaflets coarsely serrate. Fruit a paired, long-winged "key."
39. BLADDERNUT (*Staphylea trifolia*); III–VI. Twigs pithy, slightly angular, light green striped with white. Fruit a 3-lobed, bladder-like capsule.

      **HH.** Leaflets 5 or more. Pith very large.

40. ELDER (*Sambucus*, E. spp.). Nearly entire eastern U. S. and Canada. Usually a tall shrub. Fruit berry-like, in clusters.

      **HHH.** Leaflets 5 or more. Fruit cylindrical, long-winged, in clusters. Ash.
        a. Leaflets stalked. Bark fissured.

41. WHITE ASH (*Fraxinus americana*); I–VIII. Leaflets and twigs smooth.
42. BLUE ASH (*F. quadrangulata*); IV–V. Twigs 4-angled, sometimes winged.
43. GREEN ASH (*F. pennsylvanica*); I–VIII. Leaflets (underside), leafstalks, and often twigs, velvety pubescent.
44. PUMPKIN ASH (*F. profunda*); VII. Resembles No. 43, but is normally swell-butted. Deep swamps.
        aa. Leaflets sessile. Bark scaly, often corky.
45. BLACK ASH (*F. nigra*); I–V.

    **GGG.** Leaves simple.
      **I.** Leaves deeply 3- or 5-lobed, and edges toothed. Fruit a paired, long-winged "key." Maples.
        b. Teeth of leaves few and blunt. Hard maples.

46. SUGAR MAPLE (*Acer saccharum*); I–VI. Leaf sinuses U-shaped.
Also BLACK MAPLE (*A. nigrum*); III–V.

        bb. Teeth of leaves many and sharp. Soft maples.
47. RED MAPLE (*A. rubrum*); I–VIII. Leaf sinuses V-shaped. Twigs red.
48. SILVER MAPLE (*A. saccharinum*); III–VI. Leaf sinuses U-shaped. Twigs brown.
Also STRIPED MAPLE (*A. pensylvanicum*), MOUNTAIN MAPLE (*A. spicatum*), etc.

      **II.** Leaf edges finely toothed. Fruit fleshy.
49. NANNYBERRY, black haw (*Viburnum* spp.); II–VIII.

      **III.** Leaf edges smooth or slightly scalloped.
50. CATALPA (*Catalpa* spp.); VII–VIII. Leaves 5–12 in. long, heart-shaped, leaf-stalks 4–6 in. long. Fruit a long pod.
51. FRINGE TREE (*Chionanthus virginicus*); IV, VI–VIII. Leaves 4–8 in. long, oblong. Flowers fringelike. Fruit fleshy, dark blue to black.
52. BUTTONBUSH (*Cephalanthus occidentalis*); I–VIII. Leaves 4–7 in. long, narrow. Fruit a dry globular capsule. Leaves sometimes in 3's.
53. FLOWERING DOGWOOD (*Cornus florida*); III–VIII. Leaves 3–6 in. long, elliptical, leafstalks grooved. Flower buds globular, conspicuous. "Flowers" white, showy. Fruit fleshy, bright red.

    **FF.** Leaves alternate.
      **J.** Leaves twice-pinnate (doubly-compound), twigs very stout.
54. KENTUCKY COFFEETREE (*Gymnocladus dioicus*); IV–V. Twigs with very large pink to brown pith. Leaflets entire.
55. DEVILS-WALKING-STICK (*Aralia spinosa*); III–VIII. Twigs very prickly; leaf petioles with scattered prickles. Leaflets serrate.

**JJ.** Leaves once- or twice-pinnate.

56. HONEYLOCUST (*Gleditsia triacanthos*); IV–VII. On young trunks raised, oblong lenticles are very conspicuous; twigs normally bear stout, often 3-forked, spines.

**JJJ.** Leaves once-pinnate (simply compound).
**K.** Twigs spiny.

57. BLACK LOCUST (*Robinia pseudoacacia*); III–VI. Spines in pairs at leaf nodes. Edges of leaflets smooth.
58. PRICKLY-ASH (*Zanthoxylum* spp.); IV–IX. Leaf petioles (as well as twigs) spiny. Leaflets serrate.

**KK.** Leaflets entire, or rachis winged between leaflets.

59. SOAPBERRY (*Sapindus*, E. spp.); V–IX. Leaflets even-numbered (8 to 18).
60. YELLOWWOOD (*Cladrastis lutea*); IV–V. Leaflets odd-numbered, usually alternate on leafstalk. Fruit a pod.
61. POISON-SUMAC (*Toxicodendron vernix*); III–VIII. Poisonous juice turns black on exposure. Leaflets odd-numbered, all but terminal in pairs (opposite). Fruit berry-like, white, very lustrous.
62. SHINING SUMAC (*Rhus copallina*); III–VIII. Rachis winged between leaflets, which may be slightly serrate above middle.

**KKK.** Leaflets serrate, generally 9 or more in number.

63. BLACK WALNUT (*Juglans nigra*); IV–VIII. Stout twigs, with chambered pith. Terminal buds usually less than 1/3-in. long. Mature bark black.
64. BUTTERNUT (*J. cinerea*); III–V. Stout twigs with chambered pith. Terminal buds usually 1/2–3/4 in. long. Mature bark grayish.
65. STAGHORN SUMAC (*Rhus typhina*); I–V. Stout twigs velvety pubescent. Milky juice turns black on exposure.
66. MOUNTAIN-ASH (*Sorbus americana*); I–IV. Slender twigs; winter buds imbricated, sharp-pointed, somewhat gummy. Leaves 6–8 in. long.
67. PECAN (*Carya illinoensis*); V, VIII. Twigs stout, bud scales few, valvate. Leaves 12–20 in. long.
68. WATER HICKORY (*C. aquatica*); VI–VIII. Twigs slender, bud scales few, valvate. Leaves 9–15 in. long.

**KKKK.** Leaflets serrate, generally less than 9 in number; bud scales numerous, imbricated (except in No. 69).

69. BITTERNUT (*C. cordiformis*); III–VII. Twigs slender, bud scales few, valvate, bright yellow. Leaves 6–10 in. long.
70. PIGNUT HICKORY (*C. glabra*); III–VIII. Twigs somewhat stouter than in 69. Leaflets usually 5.
71. MOCKERNUT HICKORY (*C. tomentosa*); III–VIII. Twigs stout. Leaves pubescent, with strong resinous odor; leaflets mostly 7.
72. SHELLBARK HICKORY (*C. laciniosa*); IV–V. Twigs medium stout. Leaves 15–22 in. long, leaflets usually 7. Mature bark shaggy.
73. SHAGBARK HICKORY (*C. ovata*); III–VII. Twigs medium stout. Leaves 8–14 in. long, leaflets usually 5. Mature bark very shaggy.
74. HOPTREE (*Ptelea trifoliata*); IV–VII. Leaflets generally 3. Inner bark bitter, odor disagreeable. Seed is in middle of wafer-like wing, very nearly 1 in. in diameter.

**JJJJ.** Leaves simple.
**L.** Bruised leaves or inner bark of twigs have distinctive odor or taste.

24. SWEETLEAF (*Symplocos tinctoria*); IV–VIII. Mature leaves leathery (persistent southward or at low elevations), sweet to taste.

75. SASSAFRAS (*Sassafras albidum*); III–VIII. Twigs green. Leaves may be entire, 2-lobed, or 3-lobed. Odor and taste peculiar to species.

> **M.** Odor rather pleasant, but taste is bitter of hydrocyanic or prussic acid (characteristic of broken peach pits). Lenticels elongated horizontally, prominent on bark when smooth. Cherries.

76. BLACK CHERRY (*Prunus serotina*); I–VIII. Leaves often have conspicuous pubescence along midrib. Fruit purple, many, in racemes.
77. PIN CHERRY (*P. pensylvanica*); I–V. Fruit red, 5 or fewer, in umbel. Also other cherries, wild plums, sloes (*Prunus* spp.).

> **MM.** Odor and taste of wintergreen. Leaves mostly in pairs on short, spurlike growths.

78. SWEET BIRCH (*Betula lenta*); III–IV. Taste very pronounced. Bark of twigs dark brown; horizontal lenticels conspicuous.
79. YELLOW BIRCH (*B. alleghaniensis*); I–IV. Taste not pronounced. Bark of twigs yellow or silvery white.

> **MMM.** Leaves bitter or "sour" to taste.

122. SOURWOOD (*Oxydendrum arboreum*); IV, VI–VIII. Leaves 5–7 in. long, 2 or 3 times their width.

> **LL.** Juice milky.

80. OSAGE-ORANGE (*Maclura pomifera*); VI. Twigs spiny.
81. RED MULBERRY (*Morus rubra*); IV–VIII. Leaves toothed, sometimes 2-lobed or 3-lobed.

> **LLL.** Winter buds 3 or more in cluster at tip of twig, pith of twigs star-shaped in cross-section; fruit an acorn. Oaks (*Quercus*).
> c. Leaves and their lobes (where present), bristle tipped; acorns maturing in second year. Black oaks.
> d. Leaves broad, more than 2 in. wide, the margins distinctly lobed.
> e. Under surface of leaves green and nearly smooth.

82. NORTHERN RED OAK (*Quercus rubra*); II–VI. Leaves 5–9 in. long, 7- to 11-lobed less than halfway to midrib. Acorns ⅝–1⅛ in. long, cup variable in depth.
83. SCARLET OAK (*Q. coccinea*); III–VI. Leaves 3–6 in. long, deeply 7-lobed nearly to midrib. Acorns ½–¾ in. long, a third to half enclosed by cup. Branches often drooping, persistent.
84. SHUMARD OAK (*Q. shumardii*); IV–VIII. Leaves 3–7 in. long, 5- to 9-lobed more than halfway to midrib. Acorns ⅝–1⅛ in. long, cup variable in depth.
85. PIN OAK (*Q. palustris*); IV–V. Leaves 3–5 in. long, deeply 5- to 7-lobed nearly to midrib. Acorns rounded, about ½ in. in diameter, shallow cup. Branches often drooping, persistent.
86. NUTTALL OAK (*Q. nuttallii*); western VII–VIII. Leaves 4–8 in. long, deeply 5- to 7-lobed. Acorns ¾–1¼ in. long, a third to half enclosed by cup.

> ee. Under surface of leaves with brown or gray tomentum.

87. BLACK OAK (*Q. velutina*); III–VIII. Leaves 4–10 in. long, 7- to 9-lobed about halfway to midrib. Acorns ⅝–¾ in. long, half enclosed by deep cup. Inner bark orange-yellow.
88. SOUTHERN RED OAK (*Q. falcata*); IV, VI–VIII. Leaves 3–8 in. long, of two forms: deeply 3- to 7-lobed nearly to midrib, the terminal lobe often long and narrow; or slightly 3-lobed near broad apex. Acorns rounded, about ½ in. in diameter, with shallow cup.
89. BLACKJACK OAK (*Q. marilandica*); IV–VIII. Leaves 3–7 in. long, broadest and shallowly 3-lobed at the apex. Acorns are ¾ in. long, half enclosed by a deep cup.

dd. Leaves narrow; less than 2 in. wide, with edges smooth or slightly 3-lobed.

90. WATER OAK (*Q. nigra*); VI–VIII. Leaves 1½–5 in. long, extremely variable in shape: willow-like, or "fiddle-shaped" (broadest at shallowly 3-lobed apex), or several-lobed. Acorns rounded, ⅜–⅝ in. in diameter, with shallow cup.

91. LAUREL OAK (*Q. laurifolia*); VI–VIII. Leaves oblong, 2–5½ in. long, smooth or with slightly lobed edges, nearly evergreen. Acorns rounded, ½ in. in diameter, with shallow cup.

92. WILLOW OAK (*Q. phellos*); VI–VIII. Leaves 2–4 in. long and only ⅜–¾ in. broad. Acorns rounded, ⅜ in. in diameter, with shallow cup.

   cc. Leaves and their lobes not bristle-tipped; acorns mature in first year. White oaks.
      f. Leaf edges deeply lobed.

93. BUR OAK (*Q. macrocarpa*); II–V. Leaves 4–10 in. long, broadest above middle, lower part deeply lobed nearly to midrib and the upper half shallowly lobed. Acorns ¾–2 in. long, broad, half enclosed by large cup with fringelike border.

94. OVERCUP OAK (*Q. lyrata*); VI–VII. Leaves 6–8 in. long, deeply lobed nearly to midrib with 7–9 lobes, the widest lobes above the middle. Acorns ½–1 in., nearly enclosed by spherical deep cup.

95. POST OAK (*Q. stellata*); IV–VIII. Leaves 4–8 in. long, deeply 5- to 7-lobed, the lobes broad, and middle lobes the largest. Acorns ½–1 in. long, nearly half enclosed by deep cup.

96. WHITE OAK (*Q. alba*); III–VIII. Leaves 4–9 in. long, deeply or shallowly 5- to 9-lobed. Acorns ¾–1 in. long, with shallow cup.

      ff. Leaf edges wavy, with uniform, rounded teeth.

97. CHINQUAPIN OAK (*Q. muehlenbergii*); IV–VII. Leaves 4–6 in. long, oblong or broadly lance-shaped. Acorns ½–¾ in. long, rounded, half enclosed by a deep cup.

98. CHESTNUT OAK (*Q. prinus*); III–IV. Leaves 5–8 in. long, oblong. Acorns 1–1½ in. long, one-third to one-half enclosed by deep cup. Bark dark brown, generally thick, deeply furrowed.

99. SWAMP CHESTNUT OAK (*Q. michauxii*); IV, VI–VII. Leaves and acorns similar to No. 98. Bark light gray, scaly.

100. SWAMP WHITE OAK (*Q. bicolor*); III–V. Leaves 4–6 in. long, widest above middle. Acorns ¾–1¼ in. long, usually in pairs on stalks 1½–3 in. long. Bark on branches peels off in thin large plates.

   **LLLL.**Winter buds 1 or none at tip of twig.
      **N.** Pith round or nearly so in cross section.
      **O.** Leaves with 3 to 6 lobes.

101. SWEETGUM (*Liquidambar styraciflua*); IV, VI–VIII. Leaves star-shaped, with 5 long, finely serrate, pointed lobes. Twigs somewhat angular, often with corky ridges. Fruit a spiny ball.

102. SYCAMORE (*Platanus occidentalis*); III–VIII. Leaves heart-shaped, coarsely toothed, slightly 3- to 5-lobed. Twigs zig-zag, greenish white; bark on larger branches white, with patches of brown, green, and gray, peeling off in large thin flakes.

103. YELLOW-POPLAR (*Liriodendron tulipifera*); IV–VIII. Leaves square or slightly notched at apex, edges smooth between lobes. Buds valvate, flattened; paired bud scales spoon-shaped, forming a distinct ridge where they meet.

      **OO.** Leaf edges toothed (nearly smooth in No. 111).
      **P.** Leaves with 2 sides unequal (one side larger at base), in 2 rows on twig. See also *Ostrya, Carpinus.*

**Q.** Leaves broad, heart-shaped, stalks 1¼ in. or longer. Stalk of fruit clusters attached to center of strap-shaped bract.

104. BASSWOOD (*Tilia* spp.); III–VII. Bark in cross section has dark funnel-shaped areas alternating with lighter areas.

**QQ.** Leaves elliptical or oblong, with 1 main vein (midrib) and many parallel lateral veins; stalks less than ½ in. long. Fruit flat, bordered by wing. Elm.

105. AMERICAN ELM (*Ulmus americana*); I–VIII. Leaves 3–6 in. long, upper surface at maturity generally rough to touch. Main branches forked, wide-spreading.

106. SLIPPERY ELM (*U. rubra*); III–VII. Leaves 4–8 in. long, very rough to touch on upper surface. Inner bark mucilaginous if chewed.

107. ROCK ELM (*U. thomasii*); IV–V. Leaves 2–4 in. long. Twigs often corky-winged. Fruit ⅝–¾ in. long.

108. WINGED ELM (*U. alata*); IV–VIII. Leaves 1¼–2½ in. long. Twigs usually corky-winged. Fruit ⅜ in. long.

**QQQ.** Leaves resemble elms; at maturity slightly leathery, rough on both sides; winter buds minute; fruit nut-like, with short soft projections.

109. PLANERTREE (*Planera aquatica*); VII.

**QQQQ.** Leaves somewhat pointed, mostly with 3 main veins from base; fruit a nutlet enclosed in thin, dry, sweet flesh. Bark with corky warts or ridges. Hackberry.

110. HACKBERRY (*Celtis occidentalis*); III–VI. Leaf margins sharply toothed except near base. Pith of twigs sometimes chambered.

111. SUGARBERRY (*C. laevigata*); VII–VIII. Leaf margins smooth, or sometimes with a few teeth above middle.

**PP.** Leaves symmetrical, spreading around twig (sometimes unequal at base in Nos. 117 and 118, and in two rows in No. 119).

**R.** Leaves with teeth of two sizes, or irregular.

**S.** Fruit a "cone" (strobile); seeds minute. Birches.

78. SWEET BIRCH (*Betula lenta*); III–IV.

79. YELLOW BIRCH (*B. alleghaniensis*); I–IV.

112. RIVER BIRCH (*B. nigra*); IV–VIII. Bark pink to reddish brown or silvery gray, separating horizontally into papery strips. Fruit erect on twig.

113. PAPER BIRCH (*B. papyrifera*); I–III, V. Bark white, thin, separating horizontally into papery strips. Leaves oval, with stout petioles. Fruit pendulous from twig.

114. GRAY BIRCH (*B. populifolia*); III–IV. Bark white, thin, with dark triangular patches just below junction of most lateral branches with main stem. Leaves triangular, long-pointed, with slender petioles. Fruit pendulous from twig.

**SS.** Most species or individuals spiny. Fruit a fleshy pome (apple-like).

115. HAWTHORN (*Crataegus* spp.); I–VIII. Fruit generally ½ in. or less in diameter. Spines nearly always present, conspicuous.

116. CRAB APPLE (*Malus* spp.); III–VIII. Fruit generally ½ in. or more in diameter. Spines small or lacking.

**SSS.** Bark smooth, gray. Branches and trunk very irregular in cross section.

117. AMERICAN HORNBEAM (*Carpinus caroliniana*); III–VIII. Fruit a nut, borne on prominent 3-lobed bract. Leaves sometimes unequal at base.

**SSSS.** Bark rough, with thin, narrow scales loose at both ends.

118. EASTERN HOPHORNBEAM (*Ostrya virginiana*); II–VIII. Fruit enclosed in bladder-like bract. Leaves sometimes unequal at base.

**RR.** Leaves with regular coarse or fine teeth.

119. BEECH (*Fagus grandifolia*); I–VIII. Bark smooth, gray. Buds pointed, 5 times as long as wide. Leaves in 2 rows, veined like elms, coarsely toothed.
120. BLACK WILLOW (*Salix nigra*); III–VIII. Leaves very finely serrate, several times as long as wide. Seeds minute, hairy.
121. PEACHLEAF WILLOW (*S. amygdaloides*); III–IV. Leaves very finely serrate, 3 or more times as long as wide. Seeds minute, hairy. Transcontinental. Also PUSSY WILLOW (*S. discolor*), SHINING WILLOW (*S. lucida*), etc.
122. SOURWOOD (*Oxydendrum arboreum*); IV, VI. Buds only 1/16 in. long. Leaves finely serrate, 5–7 in. long, 2–3 times as long as wide, bitter or "sour" to taste. Fruit small dry capsules in long clusters.
123. SILVERBELL (*Halesia* spp.); IV, VI–VIII. Leaves oval, very finely serrate. Flowers white, showy, bell-shaped. Fruit 1½–2 in. long, dry, with 2 to 4 broad, thin wings.
124. SERVICEBERRY (*Amelanchier* spp.); III–VIII. Buds ¼ in. long, pointed, elongated. Leaves ovate, often heart-shaped at base. Pith greenish, angular. Fruit berry-like, dark purple at maturity.
125. MOUNTAIN WINTERBERRY (*Ilex montana*); IV. Buds ⅛ in. long, rounded. Inner bark of twigs somewhat bitter. Fruit berry-like, scarlet.

**RRR.** Leaf edges scalloped, or very slightly toothed.

126. WITCH-HAZEL (*Hamamelis virginiana*); III–VIII. Leaves very unequal at base, edges scalloped. Flowers in fall; narrow yellow petals. Fruit a woody pod, ½ in. long.
127. BUCKTHORN (*Rhamnus caroliniana*); IV–VIII. Leaf edges scalloped or slightly toothed, midrib and main veins yellow. Fruit berry-like.

**RRRR.** Leaf edges smooth.
    **T.** Twigs with faint ring at base of each leaf. Magnolia.

128. CUCUMBERTREE (*Magnolia acuminata*); IV. Leaves 5–10 in. long. Twigs relatively slender, with white pith. Fruit conelike, 2–3 in. long; seeds bright red.
27. SWEETBAY (*M. virginiana*); IV, VI–VIII. Leaves 3–5 in. long. Mature twigs bright green. Leaves persistent in southern part of range. Also UMBRELLA MAGNOLIA (*M. tripetala*), etc.

**TT.** Leaves broadest above middle.

129. PAWPAW (*Asimina triloba*); IV–VIII. Leaves 10–12 in. long. Twigs relatively slender, very brittle; pith small, white. Fruit is fleshy, stubby, and from 3 to 5 in. long.
130. BLACKGUM (BLACK TUPELO) (*Nyssa sylvatica*); III–VIII. Leaves 2–5 in. long. Fruit 1 to 3 in cluster, fleshy, less than ⅔ in. long. Branches nearly horizontal. Bark of old trees extremely thick; often forming small, roughly 5-sided "tiles."
131. WATER TUPELO (*N. aquatica*); VII. Leaves 4–6 in. long, edges occasionally toothed. Fruit solitary, fleshy, 1 in. or longer. Butts swollen.
132. GUM BUMELIA (*Bumelia lanuginosa*); V, VII–VIII. Leaves 1–2½ in. long. Fruit fleshy, ½ in. long. Twigs sometimes spiny.
133. EASTERN REDBUD (*Cercis canadensis*); III–VIII. Leaves 3–5 in. long, heart-shaped; stalks 2–5 in. long. Twigs have pith streaked with red; inner bark tastes like dried beans. Fruit a pod.

**TTT.** Leaves broadest below middle, long-pointed.

134. PERSIMMON (*Diospyros virginiana*); III–VIII. Twigs slender, pith or pith cavity relatively large, leaf scars with only 1 bundle-scar apparent. Fruit fleshy, ¾–1¼ in. in diameter, yellow or pale orange.

111. SUGARBERRY (*Celtis laevigata*); IV–VIII. Leaf scars with several bundle-scars. Leaves unequal at base, edges sometimes toothed. Fruit berry-like, ¼ in. in diameter, with thin, dry, sweet flesh. Corky warts on mature bark.

**NN.** Pith irregular, triangular, or star-shaped in cross section.

135. SPECKLED ALDER (*Alnus rugosa*); I–IV. Pith triangular or irregular in cross section, greenish. Leaves very finely and regularly serrate, stalks up to 1 in. long. Fruit a woody "cone."

136. CHESTNUT (*Castanea dentata*); III–IV. Pith star-shaped. Twigs stout, dotted by small, white, raised lenticels. Leaves narrow, 5–9 in. long, coarsely toothed, with many parallel lateral veins, stalks ½ in. long. Fruit a spiny bur.

**U.** Leafstalks at least 1½ in. long, slender. Seeds cottony in long-clustered capsules. Poplars.
Leafstalks round in cross section.

137. BALSAM POPLAR (*Populus balsamifera*); I–III. Winter buds resinous and fragrant. Leaves oval, edges finely serrate, short-pointed, stalks 1½ in. long. Transcontinental.

138. SWAMP COTTONWOOD (*P. heterophylla*); VII. Leaves heart-shaped, short-pointed or rounded at apex, edges finely serrate, stalks 2½–3½ in. long.

Leafstalks compressed laterally.

139. EASTERN COTTONWOOD (*P. deltoides*); IV–VII. Leaves triangular, 3–6 in. long and wide, edges coarsely serrate, stalks yellow tinged with red.

140. BIGTOOTH ASPEN (*P. grandidentata*); I–IV. Leaves ovate, 3–4 in. long and nearly as wide, edges irregularly scalloped.

141. QUAKING ASPEN (*P. tremuloides*); I–IV. Leaves nearly round, 1¼–3 in. long and wide, edges regularly serrate.

## WESTERN CONIFERS (GYMNOSPERMS)

Resinous, with leaves needle-like or scalelike, evergreen (except No. 142) seeds borne on scales of a cone (berry-like in Nos. 171–174, or seeds single in a fleshy scarlet disk in No. 151).

**A.** Leaves shedding in fall, needle-like, many in cluster on short, spur branches. Larch.

142. WESTERN LARCH (*Larix occidentalis*); II, B.C. Cones upright on twigs, 1–1½ in. long, with bracts protruding between scales. Also SUBALPINE LARCH (*L. lyallii*).

**AA.** Leaves persistent for second season or longer, needle-like or scalelike, single or not more than 5 in a cluster.

**B.** Leaves with a sheath at base, in clusters of 2 to 5, needle-like. Pine.
   **C.** Needles 5 in a cluster, 2–4 in. long. White (soft) pines.

143. LIMBER PINE (*Pinus flexilis*); I, VIII, IX. Needles slender. Cones short-stalked, 3–6 in. long, scales thick. Also WHITEBARK PINE (*P. albicaulis*), BRISTLECONE PINE (*P. aristata*), etc.

144. WESTERN WHITE PINE (*P. monticola*); I (Mont., Idaho, B.C., Wash., Ore., Calif.), II. Needles stout. Cones long-stalked, 5–12 in. long, scales thin.

145. SUGAR PINE (*P. lambertiana*); VII. Needles stout. Cones long-stalked, 12–18 in. long, scales thin.

**CC.** Needles 3 or fewer in a cluster. Yellow (hard) pines (Nos. 146–149) and pinyons (No. 150).

    **D.**  Needles more than 4 in. long.
146. PONDEROSA PINE (*P. ponderosa*); VII, VIII. Needles stout, 3, or 2 and 3, in a cluster, 4–7 in. long. Cones short-stalked, 3–6 in. long.
147. JEFFREY PINE (*P. jeffreyi*); VII. Needles stout, 3 in cluster, 5–10 in. long. Cones short-stalked, 5–10 in. long.
148. KNOBCONE PINE (*P. attenuata*); VII. Needles slender, 3 in cluster, 3–7 in. long. Cones clustered, 1-sided, 3–6 in. long, remaining closed on tree indefinitely. Also DIGGER PINE (*P. sabiniana*), MONTEREY PINE (*P. radiata*), etc.

    **DD.**  Needles less than 4 in. long.
10. JACK PINE (*P. banksiana*); Northwest territories, B.C.(N.), Prairie provinces. Needles 2 in cluster, stout, ¾–1½ in. long. Cones without prickles, 1–2 in. long.
149. LODGEPOLE PINE (*P. contorta*); I–III, VII, VIII (not in Ariz., N.M.), IX, B.C., Yukon Ter., Alaska. Needles 2 in cluster, stout, 1–3 in. long. Cones prickly, ¾–2 in. long.
150. PINYON (*P. edulis*); V. Needles 2 (sometimes 3) in cluster, stout, ¾–1½ in. long. Cones ¾–1½ in. long, scales stout, blunt. Seeds ½ in. long, wingless. Also SINGLELEAF PINYON (*P. monophylla*), etc.

  **BB.**  Leaves borne singly, needle-like, without sheath at base, mostly more than ½ in. long.
    **E.**  Twigs roughened by projecting base of old needles.
      **F.**  Needles with stalks, flattened (rounded in No. 153) appearing in 2 rows.
        **G.**  Needles stiff, sharp-pointed, extending down the twig (persistent for many years). Yew.
151. PACIFIC YEW (*Taxus brevifolia*); III, VIII (Mont., Idaho, Wash., Ore.). Needles dark yellow-green above, somewhat paler below. Fruit a fleshy scarlet disk. Bark very thin, purplish-brown, scaly.

        **GG.**  Needles soft, blunt-pointed, not extending down the twig. Hemlock.
152. WESTERN HEMLOCK (*Tsuga heterophylla*); II–III (southern Alaska, B.C.). Needles flat, whitened below by rows of stomata. Cones ¾–1 in. long, brownish.
153. MOUNTAIN HEMLOCK (*T. mertensiana*); I–II (southern Alaska, B.C.). Needles rounded or angled. Cones 1–3 in. long, purplish to brown.

      **FF.**  Needles without stalks, 4-angled (flat in No. 156) sharp-pointed, extending out on all sides of twig. Spruce.
14. WHITE SPRUCE (*Picea glauca*); Alaska, B.C., Prairie provinces, Mont., Black Hills. Needles ½–¾ in. long. Cones 1½–2 in. long, scales rounded.
154. ENGELMANN SPRUCE (*P. engelmannii*); I–II, VIII–IX, B.C., Alta. Needles ⅝–1⅛ in. long. Cones 1½–2½ in. long, scales somewhat pointed.
155. BLUE SPRUCE (*P. pungens*); I, VIII, IX, Central Rockies. Needles ¾–1⅛ in. long, dull blue-green. Cones 2½–4 in. long, scales somewhat pointed.
156. SITKA SPRUCE (*P. sitchensis*); III, California to southern Alaska. Needles flat, ⅝–1 in. long. Cones 2–3½ in. long, scales rounded.

    **EE.**  Twigs smooth or nearly so.
      **H.**  Needles with short stalks. Cones pendulous. Douglas-fir.
157. DOUGLAS-FIR (*Pseudotsuga menziesii*); II–IV, VII–VIII, B.C. Needles flat, ¾–1¼ in. long. Cones 2–4 in. long, with long, 3-toothed bracts protruding between scales.

      **HH.**  Needles without stalks. Cones upright, in top of tree. Fir.
        **I.**  Needles flat.
15. BALSAM FIR (*Abies balsamea*); Manitoba to N.E.Alta. Needles ½–1¼ in. long. Cones purple.
158. WHITE FIR (*A. concolor*); I, II, VII, VIII (not in Canada). Needles 1½–2½ in. long. Cones greenish, purple, or yellow.

159. SUBALPINE FIR (*A. lasiocarpa*); at higher elevations than No. 158, and northward to B.C., Alta., and Yukon Ter. Needles 1–1¾ in. long. Cones purple.
160. PACIFIC SILVER FIR (*A. amabilis*); I, Oregon to southern Alaska. Needles ¾–1¼ in. long, silvery white beneath. Cones purple.
161. GRAND FIR (*A. grandis*); II–IV, VIII, B.C. Needles 1–2 in. long, silvery white beneath. Cones green.

    II.   Needles 4-angled (both 4-angled and flat in No. 162).

162. NOBLE FIR (*A. procera*); VII, Wash. to northern Calif. Needles of lower branches flat, of top branches 4-angled. Cones 4–6 in. long, scales covered by protruding bracts.
163. CALIFORNIA RED FIR (*A. magnifica*); I, Ore., Calif. Cones 6–9 in. long.

  BBB.   Leaves scalelike, less than ¼ in. long, or both scalelike and needle-like (to ¾ in. long).

    J.   Leaves single. Sequoia.

164. REDWOOD (*Sequoia sempervirens*); IV. Leaves both scalelike and needle-like, spreading in 2 rows. Cones ¾–1 in. long.
165. GIANT SEQUOIA (*S. gigantea*); VII, California and extreme southern Oregon. Leaves scalelike, growing all around the twig. Cones 1¾–2¾ in. long.

    JJ.   Leaves in 2's, 3's, or 4's.
      K.   Leafy twigs somewhat flattened.
        L.   Twigs much flattened, more than 1⁄16 in. broad, including leaves.
        M.   Joints of leafy twigs distinctly longer than broad.

166. INCENSE-CEDAR (*Libocedrus decurrens*); VII. Cones ¾–1 in. long.

        MM.   Joints of leafy twigs about as broad as long.

167. WESTERN REDCEDAR (*Thuja plicata*); II, III, VIII, B.C., Alaska. Twigs flattened and branching in one plane. Cones ½ in. long.

        LL.   Twigs slightly flattened, less than 1⁄16 in. broad, including leaves. White-cedar.

168. PORT-ORFORD-CEDAR (*Chamaecyparis lawsoniana*); III, southwestern Ore. and northwestern Calif. Leaves 1⁄16 in. long, bright green, glandular on back. Twigs slender. Bark several inches thick, broad, round ridges.
169. ALASKA-CEDAR (*C. nootkatensis*); III, to southeastern Alaska. Leaves ⅛ in. long, dark green. Twigs stout, 4-angled or slightly flattened. Bark less than 1 in. thick.

      KK.   Leafy twigs rounded or 4-angled.
        N.   Leafy twigs regularly branched almost at right angles. Fruit a hard, nearly spherical cone. Cypress.

170. ARIZONA CYPRESS (*Cupressus arizonica*); V, Tex. to southern Calif. Also GOWEN CYPRESS, MONTEREY CYPRESS, etc. (*Cupressus* spp.).

        NN.   Leafy twigs irregularly branched at small angles. Fruit a fleshy "berry." Juniper.

171. ROCKY MOUNTAIN JUNIPER (*Juniperus scopulorum*); V (except Calif., southern Ore.), B.C., Alta. Leafy twigs about 1⁄32 in. in diameter. Fruit ¼ in. in diameter, usually 2-seeded.
172. ALLIGATOR JUNIPER (*J. deppeana*); V (Tex., N.M., Ariz.). Leafy twigs 1⁄32–1⁄16 in. in diameter. Fruit ½ in. in diameter, 4-seeded.
173. UTAH JUNIPER (*J. osteosperma*); V (Wyo., Ida., Utah, Nev., eastern Calif., Ariz., western N.M.). Leafy twigs 1⁄16 in. or less in diameter. Fruit ¼–½ in. in diameter, 1- or 2-seeded.
174. WESTERN JUNIPER (*J. occidentalis*); V (Mont., Ida., Wash., Ore., Calif.). Leafy twigs 1⁄16 in. or more in diameter. Fruit ¼ in. in diameter, 2- or 3-seeded.

## WESTERN HARDWOODS (ANGIOSPERMS)

Nonresinous, with broad leaves. Seeds enclosed in a fruit.

**A.** Monocotyledons. Leaves parallel-veined, evergreen, clustered at top of trunk or large branches. Wood without annual rings.

175. CALIFORNIA WASHINGTONIA (*Washingtonia filifera*); southwestern Ariz., southeastern Calif. Leaves 5–6 ft. long, nearly as wide, stalks 4–6 ft. long.

176. YUCCA (*Yucca* spp.); Mohave and other southwestern deserts. Leaves 5–48 in. long, very narrow to horny point, clasping base.

**AA.** Dicotyledons. Leaves net-veined, wood with annual rings.
  **B.** Trunk succulent, spiny.

177. SAGUARO (*Cereus giganteus*); deserts, Ariz., Calif. Branches and stems columnar, ribbed, continuous. No leaves.

178. JUMPING CHOLLA (*Opuntia fulgida*); deserts, Ariz. Branches jointed, knobby. Leaves scalelike, ½–1 in. long.

  **BB.** Leaves opposite or in 3's.
  **C.** Leaves simple.

179. DESERT WILLOW (*Chilopsis linearis*); deserts, Utah to Calif., and Tex. Leaves are very narrow (6–12 in. long, ¼–⅓ in. wide). Fruit is a pod of similar dimensions.

180. BIGLEAF MAPLE (*Acer macrophyllum*); III, VII, B.C. Leaves toothed and deeply 3- to 5-lobed. Fruit a paired, long-winged "key."

181. PACIFIC DOGWOOD (*Cornus nuttallii*); III, VII, B.C. Leaves entire. Fruit fleshy, clustered.

52. BUTTONBUSH (*Cephalanthus occidentalis*); V. Leaves sometimes in 3's, entire. Buds minute. Fruit spherical, dry.

  **CC.** Leaves palmately compound.

182. CALIFORNIA BUCKEYE (*Aesculus californica*); VII.

  **CCC.** Leaves pinnately compound.
  **D.** Twigs with conspicuously large pith.

183. ELDER (*Sambucus*, W. spp.); entire western U. S., northward to Alaska.

  **DD.** Twigs not conspicuously pithy; leaflets usually 3.
38. BOXELDER (*Acer negundo*).

  **DDD.** Twigs not conspicuously pithy; leaflets 5 or more.

184. OREGON ASH (*Fraxinus latifolia*); III. Leaves 5–14 in. long; leaflets leathery, mostly without stalks.

185. VELVET ASH (*F. velutina*); V. Leaves 3–6 in. long; the leaflets are narrow and stalked.

43. GREEN ASH (*F. pennsylvanica*); east of Rocky Mts. Leaves 10–12 in. long; leaflets stalked.

  **BBB.** Leaves alternate.
  **E.** Leaves simple.
  **F.** Bruised leaves or inner bark of twigs have distinctive odor or taste.

186. CALIFORNIA LAUREL (*Umbellularia californica*); VII. Leaves aromatic, evergreen, entire.

187. CHERRY (*Prunus* spp.); western U.S., B.C., Prairie provinces. Leaves and inner bark of twigs bitter to taste (see No. 76); leaves deciduous, serrate.

  **FF.** Twigs very stiff, bark red, smooth.

188. MANZANITA (*Arctostaphylos* spp.); S.W., Pacific Coast. Fruit is a berry.

**FFF.** Winter buds 3 or more in cluster at tip of the twig. Fruit is an acorn.
    **G.** Leaves with many parallel lateral veins, evergreen.
189. TANOAK (*Lithocarpus densiflorus*); III. Leaves 3–5 in. long, veins less than ¼ in. apart, margins generally serrate. Acorns ¾–1¼ in. long, scales of cup ⅛–³⁄₁₆ in. long.
190. CANYON LIVE OAK (*Quercus chrysolepsis*); V–VII. Leaves 1–3 in. long, spiny-toothed (young trees) or entire (old trees). Acorns 1–2 in. long, broad, scales inconspicuous.
      **GG.** Leaves lobed halfway or more to midrib.
        **H.** Leaves bristle-tipped.
191. CALIFORNIA BLACK OAK (*Q. kelloggii*); VII. Western Ore., and Calif.
        **HH.** Leaves not bristle-tipped.
192. OREGON WHITE OAK (*Q. garryana*); III–IV, B.C. Leaves 3–6 in. long. Acorns 1–1¼ in. long.
193. CALIFORNIA WHITE OAK (*Q. lobata*); VI, central Calif. Leaves 2½–4 in. long. Acorns 1¼–2¼ in. long, slender and pointed.
194. GAMBEL OAK (*Q. gambelii*); V (not Calif. or northern Nev.). Leaves 4–8 in. long. Acorns ⅝–¾ in. long.
93. BUR OAK (*Q. macrocarpa*); Sask., western Mont. and Wyo., eastward. Leaves 4–10 in. long, widest above middle. Acorns ¾–2 in. long, broad, half enclosed by large cup with fringelike border.
      **GGG.** Leaves not lobed, or only shallowly lobed.
        **I.** Leaves persistent.
195. CALIFORNIA LIVE OAK (*Q. agrifolia*); VI. Leaves bristle-tipped. Acorns ¾–1½ in. long, with deep cup.
Also EMORY OAK (*Q. emoryi*); Ariz., N.M.
        **II.** Leaves deciduous.
196. BLUE OAK (*Q. douglasii*); VI–VII (Calif.). Leaves shallowly 4- or 5-lobed, or coarsely toothed, or entire. Acorns broad.
    **FFFF.** Winter buds 1 or none at tip of twig.
      **J.** Leaves persistent.
197. PACIFIC MADRONE (*Arbutus menziesii*); III, VII. Leaves oval, 3–5 in. long, usually entire, underside pale or whitish. Fruit fleshy, stalks ½–1 in. long.
198. GOLDEN CHINQUAPIN (*Castanopsis chrysophylla*); VII. Leaves oblong to narrow, 2–6 in. long, entire underside coated with golden yellow scales, stalks ¼–⅓ in. long. Fruit a spiny bur.
199. BLUEBLOSSOM (*Ceanothus thyrsiflorus*); III(southern Ore.)–IV. Leaves 1–1½ in. long, serrate. Twigs conspicuously angled. Fruit a dry nutlet.
200. CERCOCARPUS (*Cercocarpus* spp.); VI. Leaves serrate or entire. Twigs rigid. Fruit with long-tailed, persistent style.
      **JJ.** Leaves deciduous.
        **K.** Leaves distinctly lobed.
201. SYCAMORE (*Platanus*, W. spp.); V, Ariz., N.M., Calif. Leaves 3- to 7-lobed, 6–10 in. long, stalks 1–3 in. long.
        **KK.** Leaf edges with uniform, generally small, teeth (coarse teeth in No. 202).
          **L.** Leafstalks more than 1½ in. long. Poplars.
141. QUAKING ASPEN (*Populus tremuloides*); I, IX. Leaves nearly round, short-pointed edges finely serrate, stalks flattened.
202. PLAINS COTTONWOOD (*P. sargentii*); V. Leaves oval, 3–4 in. long, often wider than long, long-pointed, coarsely serrate, stalks round.
203. BLACK COTTONWOOD (*P. trichocarpa*); III, VIII, to southern Alaska. Leaves oval 3–7 in. long, finely serrate, whitish or rusty beneath, stalks round.

137. BALSAM POPLAR (*P. balsamifera*); I to Alaska, B.C., Prairie provinces.

**LL.** Leaves several times longer than wide.
204. PACIFIC WILLOW (*Salix lasiandra*); river banks, western U.S. and Canada to Alaska. Leaves are 4 to 5 in. long, with glandular petioles. Buds have a single scale.
121. PEACHLEAF WILLOW (*S. amygdaloides*); chiefly east of continental divide, southern Canada to Mexico. Leaves 2½–5 in. long, stalks without glands. Buds with single scale.
205. NARROWLEAF COTTONWOOD (*Populus angustifolia*); range as for 121. Leaves 2–3 in. long. Buds with several scales, very resinous.

**LLL.** Leaves elliptical, 2–7 in. long.
206. CASCARA BUCKTHORN (*Rhamnus purshiana*); II–IV, VII. Leaves finely toothed or nearly entire, veins conspicuous. Flowers minute.
207. SERVICEBERRY (*Amelanchier*, W. spp.); III, V, VIII. Leaves coarsely serrate above middle. Flowers conspicuous, white.

**KKK.** Leaf edges doubly-toothed (teeth of 2 sizes), or irregularly toothed.
**M.** Twigs generally spiny. Flowers are showy and the fruit is fleshy.
208. HAWTHORN (*Crataegus*, W. spp.); in most states and provinces.

**MM.** Winter buds without scales. Alder.
209. RED ALDER (*Alnus rubra*); III, to southern Alaska. Leaves 3–5 in. long. Bark red on 1-yr. twigs, eventually pale gray on trunk. "Cones" ½–1 in. long, stalks stout. Also SITKA ALDER (*A. sitchensis*), THINLEAF ALDER (*A. tenuifolia*), etc.

**MMM.** Winter buds covered by scales. Bark separating horizontally into thin papery layers. Birch.
210. WATER BIRCH (*Betula occidentalis*); VIII, B.C. Bark dark orange-brown, very lustrous; inner bark bright orange-yellow. "Cones" 1¼–1½ in. long, stalks stout.
113. PAPER BIRCH (*B. papyrifera*); I–II. Bark orange-brown on twigs, creamy white on older branches. "Cones" 1½ in. long, stalks slender.

**KKKK.** Leaves leathery, generally entire. Fruit fleshy.
211. NETLEAF HACKBERRY (*Celtis reticulata*); VIII. Leaves up to 2½ in. long, netted veins prominent on lower surface.
212. ANAQUA (*Ehretia anacua*); western Texas. Leaves 1–2 in. long. Fruit light yellow, ¼ in. in diameter.

**EE.** Leaves once compound.
213. SOAPBERRY (*Sapindus drummondii*); V, Colo., N.M., Ariz. Leaves without terminal leaflet. Fruit berry-like.
214. NEW-MEXICAN LOCUST (*Robinia neomexicana*); V (not in Calif. or northern Nev.). Spiny. Leaves with terminal leaflet. Fruit a legume.
215. CALIFORNIA WALNUT (*Juglans californica*); VI. Twigs with chambered pith. Leaves with terminal leaflet. Fruit a large nut.

**EEE.** Leaves twice pinnate (doubly compound), without terminal leaflet. Spiny. Fruit a legume.
216. CATCLAW ACACIA (*Acacia greggii*); V. Leaves persistent, 1–3 pairs of pinnae. Ripe legumes curling, contorted.
217. MESQUITE (*Prosopis juliflora*); V (not in northern Utah, northern Nev., or northern Calif.). Leaves mostly deciduous, 1 or rarely 2 pairs of pinnae. Legumes straight or slightly curved.
218. SCREWBEAN MESQUITE (*P. pubescens*); range as for 217. Leaves are mostly deciduous, with 1 or 2 pairs of pinnae. The ripe legumes are usually twisted into a spiral.

# Table 2. Approximate Silvical Characteristics [1] of Tree Species in Specific Regions of the United States and Canada

| Species | Tolerance | Moisture | Growth | Longevity | Reproduction | Place in succession |
|---|---|---|---|---|---|---|
| **I. EASTERN SPECIES** | | | | | | |
| **ALGONQUIN PARK REGION, ONTARIO [2]** | | | | | | |
| (Elevations 1,500–1,800 ft.) [3] | | | | | | |
| SOFTWOODS | | | | | | |
| *Abies balsamea*, balsam fir | VT | m–w | r | S | ve | S |
| (Note: Rots and dies young, never dominates. Never merchantable.) | | | | | | |
| *Larix laricina*, tamarack | I | w–m | a | L? | e | P–S–C |
| (Note: Will tolerate its own shade, grows well on dry sites.) | | | | | | |
| *Picea glauca*, white spruce | VT | m | r | L | e–m | S |
| *P. mariana*, black spruce | T | d&w (not m) | r (slower than *P. glauca*) | L | e (difficult on dry sites) | CSP |
| *P. rubens*, red spruce | VT | m–w | r | L | m–e | C |
| *Pinus banksiana*, jack pine | I | d | r | M–S | d | S |
| *P. strobus*, white pine | Young–M Old–I | d–w | s | L | d | S |
| *Thuja occidentalis*, northern white-cedar | T | d–m–w | ... | ... | e | C |
| (Rots and falls apart at fairly early age.) | | | | | | |
| *Tsuga canadensis*, eastern hemlock. | VT | d | r–a | L | d | S |
| (Poor tree on most sites, rots at early age.) | | | | | | |
| HARDWOODS | | | | | | |
| *Acer rubrum*, red maple | T | w–d (not m) | a | S | e | C |
| *A. saccharum*, sugar maple | T | m–d | r | M (mostly defective trees) | e | C |
| *Betula alleghaniensis*, yellow birch | T | m | r | L (300) | d | S |
| *B. papyrifera*, paper birch | I | d | r | S | e | S |
| *Fagus grandifolia*, beech | T | d–m | a | M | ve | S |
| *Fraxinus nigra*, black ash | VT | w | s–a | M (100) | e | S |
| *Ostrya virginiana*, eastern hophornbeam | T | d | s | S | e | S |
| *Populus balsamifera*, balsam poplar. | I | m–w | a–r | S | e | P |
| *P. tremuloides*, quaking aspen | VI | d | r | S | e | P |
| *Prunus serotina*, black cherry | I | d | a | M (100) | sparse | S |
| *Quercus rubra*, northern red oak | I | d | r | M | vd | S |

[1] Symbols:
Shade tolerance: very intolerant (VI); intolerant (I); medium (M); tolerant (T); very tolerant (VT).
Soil moisture: dry (d); medium (m); wet (w).
Soil reaction: acid (A); neutral (N); basic (B).
Rate of growth: very rapid (vr); rapid (r); medium (m) and average (a), used interchangeably; slow (s); very slow (vs).
Longevity: short (S); medium (M); long (L).
Natural reproduction: very easy (ve); easy (e); medium (m); difficult (d); very difficult (vd).
Place in succession: pioneer (P); subclimax (S); climax (C).
[2] D. H. Burton, Division of Research, Ontario Dept. of Lands and Forests.
[3] Corresponds to Site Region 3b from G. A. Hills, The classification and evaluation of site for forestry, Ontario Dept. of Lands and Forests, *Res. Rept.* 24 (1952).

**Table 2. Approximate Silvical Characteristics [1] of Tree Species in Specific Regions of the United States and Canada** (Continued)

| Species | Toler-ance | Mois-ture | Growth | Lon-gev-ity | Repro-duc-tion | Place in suc-cession |
|---|---|---|---|---|---|---|
| *Tilia americana*, American bass-wood........................ | M | m | r | M | vd | S |
| *Ulmus americana*, American elm... | T–M | m | a | M–L | m | S |

### SOUTHERN ONTARIO [4] [5]

**SOFTWOODS**

| Species | Toler-ance | Mois-ture | Growth | Lon-gev-ity | Repro-duc-tion | Place in suc-cession |
|---|---|---|---|---|---|---|
| *Abies balsamea*, balsam fir......... | VT | m–w | a–r | S | e–me | S |
| *Juniperus virginiana*, redcedar..... | I | d | s | S | m–d | P |
| *Larix laricina*, tamarack......... | I–VI | d–m–w [6] | s–a | M | m–d | P |
| *Picea glauca*, white spruce........ | VT–T | d–m–w | a–r | M–L | Varia-ble m | S–C |
| *P. rubens*, red spruce............. | VT–T | d–m–w | a–r | M–L | Varia-ble m | S–C |
| *P. mariana*, black spruce......... | T–M | d–m–w [6] | a–s | M | m–d | C–S |
| *Pinus banksiana*, jack pine........ | VI | d | r–vr | S | e | P |
| *P. resinosa*, red pine............. | I | d | r | M | d | P–S |
| *P. rigida*, pitch pine............. | I | d–m | r | S | m | P |
| *P. strobus*, white pine............ | I–M | d–m | r | L | m–e | S–P [7] |
| *Thuja occidentalis*, northern white-cedar........................ | VT | d–m–w | a–s | M | m–e | P–C |
| *Tsuga canadensis*, eastern hemlock. | VT | m | a–s | L | m–d | C–S |

**HARDWOODS**

| Species | Toler-ance | Mois-ture | Growth | Lon-gev-ity | Repro-duc-tion | Place in suc-cession |
|---|---|---|---|---|---|---|
| *Acer negundo*, boxelder........... | I | d–m–w | r | S | e | *P* |
| *A. rubrum*, red maple........... | M | m–w | a–r | M–S | m | S |
| *A. saccharinum*, silver maple...... | I | m–w | a–r | M–S | m–e | S–P |
| *A. saccharum*, sugar maple....... | VT | d–m | a–s | L | e | C–S |
| *Alnus rugosa*, speckled alder..... | I–M | w | a–r | S | e | P–S |
| *Amelanchier arborea*, serviceberry. | M–I | d–m | r | S | m | P–S |
| *Asimina triloba*, pawpaw.......... | ... | ... | ... | ... | ... | ... |
| *Betula alleghaniensis*, yellow birch.. | T–VT | m–w | a–s | L | d | C–S |
| *B. papyrifera*, paper birch....... | VI–I | m–d | r–a | S | m–e | P |
| *Carpinus caroliniana*, American hornbeam................... | M | d–m | s | S | d? | S–P |
| *Carya cordiformis*, bitternut hickory | I–M | m–d | a | M | m–d? | P–S |
| *C. tomentosa*, mockernut hickory... | ... | ... | ... | ... | ... | ... |
| *Castanea dentata*, chestnut........ | ... | m–d | ... | ... | ... | ... |
| *Celtis occidentalis*, hackberry....... | ... | ... | ... | ... | ... | ... |
| *Cornus florida*, flowering dogwood.. | ... | ... | ... | ... | ... | ... |
| *Crataegus* spp., hawthorn......... | VI | d–m | ? | S | m | P |
| *Fagus grandifolia*, beech.......... | T–VT | d–m | a–s | M | d–m | S–C |
| *Fraxinus americana*, white ash..... | I–VI | d–m | a–r | M–S | m–e | P–S |
| *F. nigra*, black ash............. | M–T | w | s | S–M | m–d | S |
| *F. pennsylvanica*, green ash........ | Similar to *F. americana*, more moist | | | | | |
| *Hamamelis virginiana*, witch-hazel (shrub) ................... | M–I | d | ? | ? | ? | P–S ? |
| *Juglans cinerea*, butternut......... | I | d–m | m | M–S | d? | P–S |
| *J. nigra*, black walnut............ | I | m | m–r | L–M | d | S |
| *Ostrya virginiana*, eastern hophorn-beam........................ | I | d–m | s | M–S? | e | P? |
| *Populus balsamifera*, balsam poplar. | VI | m–w | a–r | S | e | P |
| | | | Also occurs on dry blowsand areas. | | | |

[1] See page 6·17 for list of symbols used.
[4] J. R. M. Williams, W. R. Grinnell, and C. P. Howard, Division of Reforestation, and G. A. Hills and Dr. David Scott, Division of Research, Ontario Dept. of Lands and Forests.
[5] Corresponds to Site Region 2, *ibid.*
[6] Commonest on wet sites, but has good performance once established on medium to dry sites.
[7] Because of its longevity often occurs in climax.

**6·18**

| Species | Tolerance | Moisture | pH | Growth | Longevity | Reproduction | Place in succession |
|---|---|---|---|---|---|---|---|
| *Populus deltoides*, eastern cottonwood | ... | m? | | ... | ... | ... | P |
| *P. grandidentata*, bigtooth aspen ... | VI | m–d | | vr–r | S | e | P |
| *P. tremuloides*, quaking aspen ...... | VI | m–d | | vr–r | S | e | P |
| *Prunus pensylvanica*, pin cherry.... | VI | d | | r | S | e | P |
| *P. serotina*, black cherry ......... | I | d–m | | a–r | M–S | m–d? | P–S? |
| *P. virginiana*, chokecherry shrub... | VI | d–m | | s | S | e–m | P |
| *Quercus alba*, white oak.......... | M–T | m–d | | s–a | L | d? | S–C |
| *Q. bicolor*, swamp white oak....... | ... | w–m | | ... | ... | ... | |
| *Q. macrocarpa*, bur oak........... | M–T | d–m | | s–a | M–L | d? | P–S–C |
| *Q. rubra*, northern red oak........ | M–I | d–m? | | r–a | M | m–e? | P–S |
| *Q. velutina*, black oak............ | M–I | d | | r–a | M | m–e? | P–S |
| *Rhus typhina*, staghorn sumac shrub | VI | d | | a–r | VS | e (root) | P |
| *Robinia pseudoacacia*, black locust.. | I | m–d | | r | S | e | P |
| *Salix nigra*, black willow......... | I | w | | r | S–M | m? | P |
| *Salix* spp., scrub willow shrub..... | I | w | | ? | VS | e | P |
| *Sambucus canadensis*, elder........ | I | w | | a–r | S | e | P |
| *Sorbus americana*, mountain-ash.... | I | d–m–w | | a? | S | e–m? | P |
| *Tilia americana*, American basswood...................... | I–M | d–m | | r–a | M | d–m (sprouts– e) | P–S–C |
| *Ulmus americana*, American elm.... | T–VT | d–m–w | | a | L–M | m | S–C |
| *U. rubra*, slippery elm............ | T | d–m–w | | a | M–L | m–d | S–C |
| *U. thomasii*, rock elm............. | M | d–m | | a–s | M | d–m | S–P? |

### NEW YORK AND NEW ENGLAND [8]

#### SOFTWOODS

| Species | Tolerance | Moisture | pH | Growth | Longevity | Reproduction | Place in succession |
|---|---|---|---|---|---|---|---|
| *Abies balsamea*, balsam fir....... | VT | w | A | r | S | e | S |
| *Juniperus virginiana*, redcedar... | VI | d | B | s | M | e | P |
| *Larix laricina*, tamarack......... | VI | m | A | s | M | d | S |
| *Picea glauca*, white spruce....... | T | m | N–B | s | L | d | S–C |
| *P. rubens*, red spruce............ | T | m | N–A | s | L | d | S–C |
| *Pinus banksiana*, jack pine....... | VI | d | A | r | S | e | P |
| *P. resinosa*, red pine............ | VI | d | A | m | L | d | P–S |
| *P. rigida*, pitch pine............ | VI | d | A | m | S | e | P |
| *P. strobus*, white pine........... | M | d | N | m | L | e | P–S–C |
| *Thuja occidentalis*, northern white-cedar...................... | I | d–w | B | s | M | e | P–S |
| *Tsuga canadensis*, eastern hemlock | VT | m | N–A | m | L | e | C |

#### HARDWOODS

| Species | Tolerance | Moisture | pH | Growth | Longevity | Reproduction | Place in succession |
|---|---|---|---|---|---|---|---|
| *Acer rubrum*, red maple......... | T | d–w | N–A | a | S | e | P |
| *A. saccharinum*, silver maple...... | I | w | N | r | S | e | P–S |
| *A. saccharum*, sugar maple....... | VT | m | N | a | L | e | C |
| *Amelanchier* spp., serviceberry.... | I | d | N–A | r | S | e | P |
| *Betula alleghaniensis*, yellow birch. | I | m | N–A | a | L | e | C |
| *B. lenta*, sweet birch............ | I | m | N | a | S | d | S |
| *B. papyrifera*, paper birch........ | I | m | N–A | r | M | e | P–S |
| *B. populifolia*, gray birch........ | I | d–w | A | r | S | e | P |
| *Carpinus caroliniana*, American hornbeam .................. | M | m | N | s | S | e | S |
| *Carya cordiformis*, bitternut hickory...................... | M | m–w | N | s | M | m | S |
| *C. glabra*, pignut hickory........ | I | d | N | s | M | m | S |
| *C. ovata*, shagbark hickory........ | I | d | N | s | M | m | S |

[1] See page 6·17 for list of symbols used.
[8] E. W. Littlefield, *Forest management*, N. Y. Conservation Dept.

| Species | Toler-ance | Mois-ture | pH | Growth | Lon-gev-ity | Repro-duc-tion | Place in suc-cession |
|---|---|---|---|---|---|---|---|
| *Cornus florida*, flowering dogwood | T | m | N | s | M | e | S |
| *Fagus grandifolia*, beech | VT | m | N | s | L | d | C |
| *Fraxinus americana*, white ash | I | m | N | r | L | e | S |
| *F. nigra*, black ash | I | w | A | a | M | e | S |
| *Hamamelis virginiana*, witch-hazel | VI | d | N | s | S | e | P |
| *Ilex montana*, mountain winter-berry | I | d | A | a | S | m | P-S |
| *Kalmia latifolia*, mountain-laurel | T | d | A | s | M | e | P-S-C |
| *Liriodendron tulipifera*, yellow-poplar | T | m | N-B | r | L | e | P-S-C |
| *Magnolia acuminata*, cucumbertree | T | m | N | a | L | d | S-C |
| *Nyssa sylvatica*, blackgum (black tupelo) | I | d-w | A | s | M | d | S-C |
| *Ostrya virginiana*, eastern hophorn-beam | VT | m | N-A | s | M | e | S |
| *Platanus occidentalis*, sycamore | I | w | N | a | L | e | S |
| *Populus balsamifera*, balsam pop-lar | I | m | N | r | M | e | S |
| *P. deltoides*, eastern cottonwood | I | w | N | r | M | e | S |
| *P. grandidentata*, bigtooth aspen | I | d | A | r | S | e | P |
| *P. tremuloides*, quaking aspen | I | d | A | r | S | e | P |
| *Prunus pensylvanica*, pin cherry | I | d | A | r | S | e | P |
| *P. serotina*, black cherry | M | m | N | a | M | d | S |
| *P. virginiana*, chokecherry | I | d | N-A | r | S | e | P |
| *Quercus alba*, white oak | I | d-m | N-A | s | L | d | S-C |
| *Q. bicolor*, swamp white oak | I | w | N | s | L | d | C |
| *Q. coccinea*, scarlet oak | I | d | A | s | M | e | P-S |
| *Q. macrocarpa*, bur oak | I | d | N | s | L | d | S-C |
| *Q. palustris*, pin oak | I | w | N | s | L | e | S-C |
| *Q. prinus*, chestnut oak | I | d | N-A | s | M | e | P |
| *Q. rubra*, northern red oak | I | m | N | r | L | e | S |
| *Q. velutina*, black oak | I | d | N-A | a | L | m | S |
| *Rhus typhina*, staghorn sumac | I | d | A-B | r | S | e | P |
| *Robinia pseudoacacia*, black locust | I | d | B | r | M | e | P |
| *Sassafras albidum*, sassafras | I | d | A-B | r | S | e | P |
| *Sorbus americana*, mountain-ash | I | d | A | r | S | e | P |
| *Tilia americana*, American bass-wood | VT | m | N | r | M | e | C |
| *Toxicodendron vernix*, poison-sumac | T | w | B | s | M | e | S |
| *Ulmus americana*, American elm | M | m-w | N | a | L | e | S-C |
| *U. rubra*, slippery elm | M | d-m | N | a | M | e | P-S |
| *U. thomasii*, rock elm | M | m-w | N | a | L | e | C |

## SOUTHEASTERN UNITED STATES [9]

### Softwoods

| Species | Toler-ance | Mois-ture | pH | Growth | Lon-gev-ity | Repro-duc-tion | Place in suc-cession |
|---|---|---|---|---|---|---|---|
| *Juniperus virginiana*, redcedar | I | d-m | B | s | M | m | P |
| *Picea rubens*, red spruce | VT | m-w | A | s | L | e | C |
| *Pinus echinata*, shortleaf pine | I | d | A-N | m | L | m | P |
| *P. elliottii*, slash pine | I | m-w | A-N | vr | M | e | P-S |
| *P. palustris*, longleaf pine | I | d-m | A-N | r | L | d | P-S |
| *P. resinosa*, red pine | I | m | A-N | r | L | m | P-S |
| *P. rigida*, pitch pine | I | d | A-N | m | M | ... | P-S |
| *P. strobus*, white pine | M | m | A-N | r | L | m | P-S |
| *P. taeda*, loblolly pine | I | m-w | A-N | vr | L | m | P-S |
| *P. virginiana*, Virginia pine | I | d-m | A-N | m | S | e | P |
| *Taxodium distichum*, baldcypress | T | w | A | s | L | m | C |
| *Tsuga canadensis*, eastern hemlock | VT | m-w | A-N | s | L | m | C |

[1] See page 6·17 for list of symbols used.
[9] Carl E. Ostrom, James F. Renshaw, and W. G. Wahlenberg, Southeastern Forest Experiment Station, U. S. Forest Service.

| Species | Tolerance | Moisture | pH | Growth | Longevity | Reproduction | Place in succession |
|---|---|---|---|---|---|---|---|
| **HARDWOODS** | | | | | | | |
| *Acer rubrum*, red maple......... | M | m–w | N | r | M | m [10] | P–S |
| *A. saccharum*, sugar maple....... | T | m | N | m | L | e [11] | C |
| *Aesculus octandra*, yellow buckeye. | T | m | A–N | r | M | e | C |
| *Amelanchier* spp., serviceberry.... | T | m | N | s | S | m | S–C |
| *Betula alleghaniensis*, yellow birch. | I | m–w | A–N | r | S–M | m | S–C |
| *B. lenta*, sweet birch............. | I | m | N | m | M | e–m | S–C |
| *B. nigra*, river birch............. | M | w | A | r | S–M | e–m | S–C |
| *Carpinus caroliniana*, american hornbeam................... | M | m–w | N | s | S | m | S |
| *Carya cordiformis*, bitternut hickory...................... | T | d–m | N | s | L | m | C |
| *C. glabra*, pignut hickory......... | T | d–m | N | s | M | m | C |
| *C. ovata*, shagbark hickory........ | T | d–m | N | s | L | m | C |
| *C. tomentosa*, mockernut hickory.. | T | d–m | N | s | L [12] | m | C |
| *Castanea dentata*, chestnut........ | M | d | N | vr | L [12] | m | ? |
| *Cladrastis lutea*, yellowwood..... | ... | m | N | ... | ... | m | S–C |
| *Cornus florida*, flowering dogwood | VT | m | N | vs | S | m | C |
| *Crataegus* spp., hawthorn........ | I | d–m | N | m | S | m | P |
| *Diospyros virginiana*, persimmon... | I | m–w | A | s | S | m | S–C |
| *Fagus grandifolia*, beech......... | T | m | N | s | L | m [13] | C |
| *Fraxinus americana*, white ash.... | M | m | N–B | m–r | M | e | S |
| *F. pennsylvanica*, green ash....... | M | m | N–B | m–r | M | e | S |
| *Gleditsia triacanthos*, honeylocust.. | M | m | N | r | M | ... | P–S |
| *Halesia* spp., silverbell........... | M | m | A | a | M | e | S–C |
| *Hamamelis virginiana*, witch-hazel. | M | m | N | s | S | ... | S |
| *Ilex opaca*, holly................. | VT | m–w | A | vs | M | d | C |
| *Juglans cinerea*, butternut........ | I | m–w | N | r | L | d | P |
| *J. nigra*, black walnut........... | I | m–w | N | r | L | d | P |
| *Kalmia latifolia*, mountain-laurel.. | T | d–w | A | s | S | m | C |
| *Liquidambar styraciflua*, sweetgum | I | m–w | N | r | M | e | P |
| *Liriodendron tulipifera*, yellow-poplar..................... | I | m | N | r | L | m | S |
| *Magnolia acuminata*, cucumber-tree...................... | I | m | N | m–r | M | d | S |
| *M. grandiflora*, southern magnolia. | I | m | N | m–r | M | d | S |
| *Malus* spp., crab apple......... | T | m–w | A | s | S | m | S–C |
| *Nyssa sylvatica*, blackgum (black tupelo)................... | M | m | N | m | M | m | S |
| *Ostrya virginiana*, eastern hophornbeam..................... | I | m | N | m | S | e | P |
| *Oxydendrum arboreum*, sourwood.. | M | m | N | s | S | e [14] | S–C |
| *Platanus occidentalis*, sycamore... | I | w | N | r | M | m | S |
| *Populus deltoides*, eastern cottonwood.................... | I | w | N | vr | M | e | P |
| *P. grandidentata*, bigtooth aspen.. | I | m | N | r | S | e [15] | P |
| *P. tremuloides*, quaking aspen..... | I | m | N | r | S | e [15] | P |
| *Prunus* spp., wild plums......... | I | d–m | N | s | S | e | P |
| *P. pensylvanica*, pin cherry....... | I | m | N | r | S | e | P |
| *P. serotina*, black cherry........ | I | m | N | r | M | e [16] | P–S |
| *P. virginiana*, chokecherry....... | I | m | N | m | S | m | P |
| *Quercus alba*, white oak......... | T | d–m | A–N | s | L | m | C |

[1] See page 6·17 for list of symbols used.
[10] Sprouts vigorously; sprouts often inferior in form and quality.
[11] Sprouts readily.
[12] Pathological rotation very short.
[13] Suckers and sprouts.
[14] Sprouts vigorously.
[15] Suckers easily.
[16] Sprouts vigorously; stump sprouts of poor form.

| Species | Tolerance | Moisture | pH | Growth | Longevity | Reproduction | Place in succession |
|---|---|---|---|---|---|---|---|
| *Quercus coccinea*, scarlet oak..... | M | d | A–N | m | S–M | m | S |
| *Q. falcata*, southern red oak. ..... | M | d–m | A–N | m | M | m | C |
| *Q. marilandica*, blackjack oak..... | T | d | A | s | S | m | S–C |
| *Q. palustris*, pin oak............. | M | m | A–N | m | M | m | S–C |
| *Q. prinus*, chestnut oak.......... | M | d | A–N | m | L | m | C |
| *Q. velutina*, black oak............ | M | d–m | A–N | r | L | m | C |
| *Q. virginiana*, live oak.......... | M | d–m | A–N | r | M | m | C |
| *Rhododendron maximum*, rosebay rhododendron................ | T | d–w | A | s | S | m | C |
| *Rhus typhina*, staghorn sumac.... | I | m | N | m | S | m | P |
| *Robinia pseudoacacia*, black locust. | I | m | N | r | M | e | P |
| *Sabal* spp., palmetto............. | M | m | A–N | m | ... | ... | S |
| *Salix nigra*, black willow........ | I | w | N | r | S | m | P |
| *Sambucus canadensis*, elder....... | I | m | N | s | S | m | P |
| *Sassafras albidum*, sassafras...... | T | d–m | N | s | S | m | P |
| *Serenoa repens*, saw-palmetto.... | T | d | A | s | ? | d | S |
| *Sorbus americana*, mountain-ash.. | I | ... | N | s | S | m | P |
| *Tilia americana*, American basswood.................... | I | m | N | r | M | m | S |
| *T. heterophylla*, white basswood... | I | m | N | r | M | m | S |
| *Toxicodendron vernix*, poison-sumac | M | w | A | a | S | m | S–C |
| *Ulmus americana*, American elm.. | I | m–w | N | m–r | L | e | S |
| *U. rubra*, slippery elm........... | I | m–w | N | m–r | L | e | S |

## II. WESTERN SPECIES

### CANADA [17]

#### SOFTWOODS

| Species | Tolerance | Moisture | pH | Growth | Longevity | Reproduction | Place in succession |
|---|---|---|---|---|---|---|---|
| *Abies amabilis*, Pacific silver fir.... | VT | m | A | a | M | m | C |
| *A. grandis*, grand fir............. | VT | m | A | r | M | m | C |
| *A. lasiocarpa*, subalpine fir....... | T | m | A | a | M | e | C |
| *Chamaecyparis nootkatensis*, Alaska-cedar.................... | M | m | A | s | M | d | S |
| *Juniperus scopulorum*, Rocky Mt. juniper...................... | VI | d | A | s | M | d | S |
| *Larix occidentalis*, western larch... | I | m | A | r | L | e | P |
| *Picea engelmannii*, Engelmann spruce...................... | T | m–w | A | s | M | d | C |
| *P. glauca*, white spruce.......... | T | m–w | A | s | M | d | C |
| *P. sitchensis*, Sitka spruce........ | T | w | A | r | L | m | C |
| *Pinus contorta*, lodgepole pine..... | VI | d–w | A | a | M | e | P |
| *P. flexilis*, limber pine........... | I | d–m | A | s | M | d | C |
| *P. monticola*, western white pine... | M | m | A | r | L | e | S |
| *P. ponderosa*, ponderosa pine..... | I | d | A | a | L | m | C |
| *Pseudotsuga menziesii*, Douglas-fir. | I | m | A | r | L | m | S |
| *P. menziesii* var. *glauca*, Rocky Mt. Douglas-fir............. | M | d–m | A | a | L | e | C |
| *Taxus brevifolia*, yew............ | VT | m–w | A | s | M | m | C |
| *Thuja plicata*, western redcedar... | VT | m | A | r | L | e | C |
| *Tsuga heterophylla*, western hemlock...................... | T | m | A | a | L | e | C |
| *T. mertensiana*, mountain hemlock | M | m | A | s | M | m | C |

#### HARDWOODS

| Species | Tolerance | Moisture | pH | Growth | Longevity | Reproduction | Place in succession |
|---|---|---|---|---|---|---|---|
| *Acer macrophyllum*, bigleaf maple. | M | m | A | r | S | e | P–S |
| *Alnus rubra*, red alder........... | VI | m | A | r | S | e | P |

[1] See page 6·17 for list of symbols used.
[17] B. G. Griffith, George S. Allen, Faculty of Forestry, and T. M. C. Taylor, Department of Biology and Botany, University of British Columbia.

| Species | Tolerance | Moisture | pH | Growth | Longevity | Reproduction | Place in succession |
|---|---|---|---|---|---|---|---|
| *Amelanchier alnifolia*, Saskatoon serviceberry | I | d | A–N | s | S | e | P |
| *Arbutus menziesii*, Pacific madrone | VI | d | A | s | M | m | S |
| *Artemisia tridentata*, big sagebrush | VI | d | A–N | s | S | e | C |
| *Betula occidentalis*, water birch | I | m | A | a | S | e | S |
| *B. papyrifera*, paper birch | I | m | A | a | S | e | P |
| *Ceanothus* spp., ceanothus | M | d | A | s | S | e | S |
| *Cornus nuttallii*, Pacific dogwood | M | m | A | s | S | m | S |
| *Crataegus* spp., hawthorn | I | d–w | A | s | S | m | S |
| *Populus tremuloides*, quaking aspen | I | d–m | A | a | S | e | P |
| *P. trichocarpa*, black cottonwood | I | m–w | A | r | M | m | P–S |
| *Prunus emarginata*, bitter cherry | I | d–w | A | a | S | m | P |
| *P. virginiana*, chokecherry | I | d | A | a | S | m | P |
| *Quercus garryana*, Oregon white oak | VI | d | A | s | M | m | C |
| *Rhamnus purshiana*, cascara buckthorn | M | m–w | A | s | S | m | S |
| *Salix amygdaloides*, peachleaf willow | I | m | A | s | S | e | P |
| *S. lasiandra*, Pacific willow | I | d | A | s | S | e | P |
| *Sambucus* spp., elder | I | d–w | A | m | S | e | S |

## SOUTHWESTERN UNITED STATES [18]

| Species | Tolerance | Moisture | pH | Growth | Longevity | Reproduction | Place in succession |
|---|---|---|---|---|---|---|---|
| **SOFTWOODS** | | | | | | | |
| *Abies concolor*, white fir | M | m | A–N | r | M | e | S–C? |
| *A. lasiocarpa*, subalpine fir | VT | m–w | ... | m | M | e | C |
| *Cupressus arizonica*, Arizona cypress | I | d–m | ... | ... | ... | m | ... |
| *Juniperus scopulorum*, Rocky Mt. juniper | I | m–w | ... | a | L | m | ... |
| *Picea engelmannii*, Engelmann spruce | VT | m–w | ... | s | L | m | C |
| *P. pungens*, blue spruce | M | m–w | ... | r | M | e | S–C? |
| *Pinus edulis*, pinyon | VI | d–m | ... | m | L | d | C? |
| *P. flexilis*, limber pine | M | d–m | ... | s | M | e | S–P[19] |
| *P. ponderosa*, ponderosa pine | VI | m | N | m | L | m | P–C |
| *Pseudotsuga menziesii*, Douglas-fir | M | m | N | a | L | m | S–C[20] |
| **HARDWOODS** | | | | | | | |
| *Acacia* spp., acacia (catclaw) | VI | d | ... | s | L | ... | ... |
| *Arctostaphylos* spp., manzanita | I | d | ... | vs | L | m[21] | ... |
| *Cercocarpus* spp., cercocarpus (mountain mahogany) | I | d | ... | s | L | ... | ... |
| *Opuntia fulgida*, jumping cholla | VI | d | ... | ... | ... | e[22] | ... |
| *Platanus wrightii*, Arizona sycamore | I | w | ... | ... | L | ... | ... |
| *Populus angustifolia*, narrowleaf cottonwood | I | w | ... | ... | M | ... | ... |
| *P. tremuloides*, quaking aspen | VI | m–w | ... | ... | S | e[21] | P |
| *Prosopis juliflora*, mesquite | VI | m | ... | ... | L | e[23] | ... |
| *Quercus gambelii*, Gambel oak | T | m | ... | m | M | m[24] | P |
| *Robinia neomexicana*, New-Mexican locust | M | m | ... | ... | L | m[23] | P |
| *Sambucus* spp., elder | T | m–w | ... | r | S | m | P |

[1] See page 6·17 for list of symbols used.
[18] Herman Krauch, retired, formerly Southwestern Forest and Range Experiment Station, U. S. Forest Service.
[19] On denuded land.
[20] With white fir.
[21] Sprouts.
[22] From dislodged lobes.
[23] Seed and sprouts.
[24] Mostly sprouts.

# Ecology

**IMPORTANT FOREST TYPES OF THE UNITED STATES.** An ability to recognize forest types and the positions of these types in plant succession aids silviculturists in evaluating management and natural regeneration requirements. For example, knowledge that western white pine is a fire type which may occur within several different natural vegetational zones should tell the manager several things. First, the type is not stable. Second, natural succession may follow different courses, depending on the particular habitat. Third, several kinds of trees may compete for the space occupied by the pine. Hence, in order to regenerate and maintain white pine, positive silvicultural measures will be needed. For instance, after clearcutting overmature white pine stands, it may be necessary to destroy unmerchantable trees and advance reproduction of other species in order to make room for a new crop of white pine. Otherwise, the forces of natural succession are likely to cause the disappearance of white pine from the new stand.

The Society of American Foresters defines forest type as follows:

A descriptive term used to group stands of similar character as regards composition and development due to given physical and biological factors, by which they may be differentiated from other groups of stands. The term suggests repetition of the same character under similar conditions . . .

Generally speaking, foresters have classified timber types on a utilitarian basis for convenience in identification, description, and mapping. Classification of forest types is based wholly on tree species in contrast to the plant associations of ecologists, who take all vegetation into consideration. Usually the species or combination of species for which a forest type is named is required to predominate in the dominant stand, but considerable variation exists. For example, in redwood and western white pine types, the named species are required to comprise only 20 percent of the overstory. On the other hand, western hemlock, western redcedar, and Pacific Douglas-fir types must contain 80 percent or more of the named species in the overstory in order to qualify.

Type names in Tables 3, 4, and 5 were taken from publications by the Society of American Foresters. However, only the principal types, generally of major commercial importance, have been listed. Many of the types which have been omitted are regarded as variants rather than as distinct entities. The information on successional stages and climax associations is based chiefly upon the teachings of Weaver and Clements, but with considerable additional interpretation by committee members. Recognition of a Douglas-fir natural vegetational zone, distinct from that of ponderosa pine, follows Daubenmire.

## Table 3. Major Forest Types of the United States
### SOUTH AND APPALACHIANS

| Type name [a] | Region | Principal associate species | Successional stage | Climax association |
|---|---|---|---|---|
| White pine (21) | Appalachian | Yellow-poplar, chestnut, hemlock, red oak, white oak, scarlet oak | Long-lived, temporary on abandoned lands | Northern hardwoods |
| Red spruce–Fraser fir (34) | Appalachian | Hemlock, yellow birch, beech, and maple | Climax | Spruce-fir |
| Scarlet oak (41) | Appalachian | Black oak, chestnut oak, white oak, hickories | Climax on dry soils | Oak-hickory |
| Shortleaf pine (75) | Appalachian & Piedmont | White oak, southern red oak, post oak | Climax on certain areas, old-field type on others | Oak-pine-hickory |
| Shortleaf pine-oak (76) | Appalachian & Piedmont | Black oak, white oak, blackgum, and hickories | Transition | Mixed hardwoods |
| Virginia pine (79) | Appalachian & Piedmont | Shortleaf pine, chestnut oak, white oak, red oak | Temporary, old-field | Oak-pine-hickory |
| White oak–red oak–hickory (52) | Ozarks | Blackgum, red maple, winged elm | Climatic climax | White oak-black oak-hickory |
| Yellow-poplar (57) | Appalachian | Hemlock, basswood, red oak, white oak, red maple, black oak | Temporary | Mixed hardwoods |
| Yellow-poplar–white oak–northern red oak (59) | Appalachian | Chestnut, black oak, chestnut oak, blackgum | Unknown | Unknown |
| Cottonwood (63) | South, river bottoms | Willow, sycamore, river birch, sweetgum | Temporary | Mixed hardwoods |
| Longleaf pine (70) | South | Turkey oak, bluejack oak, slash pine, southern red oak, loblolly pine | Edaphic climax | Pine-hardwoods |

[a] Figures in parentheses refer to the number assigned each type in "Forest Cover Types of North America," Report of the Committee on Forest Types, Society of American Foresters, 1954.

Table 3. **Major Forest Types of the United States** (Continued)

| Type name | Region | Principal associate species | Successional stage | Climax association |
|---|---|---|---|---|
| Longleaf pine–scrub oak (71) | South | Bluejack oak, blackjack oak, post oak, laurel oak, live oak | Near climax | |
| Loblolly pine–short-leaf pine (80) | South | Persimmon, blackgum, post oak, red oak | Subclimax | Pine-hardwoods |
| Loblolly pine (81) | South, Coastal Plain | Sweetgum, southern red oak, blackgum, laurel oak | Subclimax | Pine-hardwoods |
| Loblolly pine–hard-wood (82) | Piedmont & Coastal Plain | Hickories, red maple, scarlet oak, red oak, southern red oak | Transition | Pine-hardwoods |
| Longleaf pine–slash pine (83) | South Coastal Plain | Water oak, laurel oak, post oak, live oak | Subclimax | Pine-hardwoods |
| Slash pine (84) | South Coastal Plain | Pondcypress, swamp tupelo, sweetgum, sweetbay | Subclimax | Pine-hardwoods |
| Cabbage palmetto–slash pine (86) | South Coastal Plain | Pond pine, sweetgum, live oak, myrtle oak | Unknown | Unknown |
| Sweetgum–yellow-poplar (87) | Coastal Plain | Loblolly pine, red maple, ash | Climax | Moist site-hardwoods |
| Sweetgum–nuttall oak–willow oak (92) | South | Water oak, swamp chestnut oak, white oak, ashes | Unknown | Unknown |
| Atlantic white-cedar (97) | Coastal Plain | Pond pine, cypress, blackgum, sweetbay, slash pine | Subclimax | Swamp hardwoods |
| Baldcypress (101) | Coastal Plain | Water tupelo, swamp tupelo, black willow, swamp cotton-wood, red maple | Climax | Cypress-tupelo |
| Water tupelo (103) | Coastal Plain | Baldcypress, blackgum, wet-site hardwoods | Climax | Tupelo-cypress |

| Type name | Region | Principal associate species | Successional stage | Climax association |
|---|---|---|---|---|
| Aspen (217) | Northeast, Lake States, Rocky Mts. and much of Canada | Most local species, but frequently occurs in nearly pure stands | Generally temporary fire type, east of Great Plains; west, often comparatively permanent | Generally northern hardwood or spruce-fir. May be essentially permanent in restricted localities in the West |
| Black cottonwood–willow (222) | Rocky Mts., Prairie States, Mississippi Valley, Canada. East of Cascades in Oregon and Washington | Local broadleaf species, especially American elm, boxelder, green ash, and black ash | First plants to become established on sandbars and flood plains. First stage in flood-plain succession | Eastward: deciduous forest. Grassland region: topographic climax. American elm-ash association follows cottonwood and willow. Westward: (?) |
| Douglas-fir (Pacific, 80%; interior, 50%) (229 and 210) | Pacific Coast and Rocky Mts. into Canada, and south to Mexico | Most western trees native to locality | Generally fire type except in drier habitats where it becomes climax | Climax only on relatively warm, dry habitats. Western redcedar—western hemlock and spruce-fir succeed it on cooler, moister habitats |
| Engelmann spruce–subalpine fir (206) | Rocky Mts. and Cascades into Canada | Most western trees native to locality except "xerophytes" such as ponderosa pine and junipers | Climax, although type may follow directly after logging or fire without intervening stages | Spruce-fir |
| Larch–Douglas-fir (212) | Washington and Oregon east of Cascades, and north Idaho and western Montana, north into Canada | Most local trees | Fire type | Douglas-fir, western hemlock—western redcedar, or spruce-fir |

ᵇ The one or more species for which a type is named generally must exceed 50 percent of the stand or at least exceed the next most important species. A percentage value in parentheses following the type name indicates that the named species must comprise at least the stated percentage of the total stand.

**Table 3. Major Forest Types of the United States** (Continued)

| Type name | Region | Principal associate species | Successional stage | Climax association |
|---|---|---|---|---|
| Lodgepole pine (218) | Rocky Mts. to Pacific Coast and into Canada | Most local trees but frequently occurs in nearly pure stands | Fire type but very stable over large areas in Rocky Mts. | Douglas-fir, western hemlock–western redcedar, or spruce–fir |
| Pinyon-juniper (including Rocky Mountain juniper) (239) | Rocky Mts. to California | Very few tree associates. Limber pine in northern Rockies | Climax | Pinyon-juniper |
| Ponderosa pine (245, 244, 214, 243) | Pacific Coast to Black Hills and Nebraska | Nearly pure stands occur over large areas, but on moister sites, most native trees intermingle. Douglas-fir and white fir are most common associates | Climax on warmest and driest habitats. Temporary on cooler, moister habitats | Ponderosa pine within that vegetational zone. Elsewhere, generally Douglas-fir |
| Port-Orford-cedar (20%)–Douglas-fir (231) | S.W. Oregon and N.W. California | Douglas-fir, western hemlock, western redcedar, tanoak and madrone | May follow fire with Douglas-fir or be climax with western hemlock | Port-Orford-cedar, western hemlock, grand fir, tanoak |
| Red alder (221) | North Pacific Coast | Most local species but frequently occurs in nearly pure stands | Temporary fire or post-logging type | Western redcedar–western hemlock |
| Redwood (20%) (232) | Northern California and southern Oregon | Douglas-fir, western hemlock, western redcedar, and Port-Orford-cedar | Climax, but will also follow fire or cutting | Redwood |
| Sitka spruce (223) | North Pacific Coast to Alaska | Western hemlock, Douglas-fir, Pacific silver fir, and western redcedar | Fire type, but very stable | Western redcedar–western hemlock |
| Western hemlock (80%) (224) | Pacific Coast to Alaska and northern Rocky Mts. | All local species except the "xerophytes" such as ponderosa pine | Climax, but may also directly follow fire or logging | Western redcedar–western hemlock |
| Western redcedar (80%) (228) | Pacific Coast to Canada and northern Rocky Mts. | Most local species | Climax, but may also directly follow fire or logging | Western redcedar–western hemlock |

**Table 4. Northeastern Forest Types Classified into Climax Groups and Objectives of Management ***

| Forest type | S.A.F. type No. | Stage in succession | Ultimate climax group | Species to favor |
|---|---|---|---|---|
| Red spruce .............. | 32 | Climax | | *Primary* |
| Red spruce–Fraser fir...... | 34 | Climax | Spruce-fir | Red spruce |
| Balsam fir ............... | 5 | Climax | | White spruce |
| Black spruce ............. | 12 | Climax | | Black spruce |
| Jack pine ............... | 1 | Subclimax | | Balsam fir |
| Tamarack ................ | 38 | Subclimax | | *Secondary* |
| Aspen .................... | 16 | Subclimax | | Paper birch |
| Pin cherry .............. | 17 | Subclimax | | Aspen |
| Paper birch ............. | 18 | Subclimax | | Cedar |
| | | | | Tamarack |
| | | | | Jack pine |
| Red spruce–yellow birch... | 30 | Climax | Spruce–fir– | *Primary* |
| Red spruce (old field)...... | 32 | Subclimax | hardwoods | Red spruce |
| Paper birch–red spruce– | | | | White spruce |
| balsam fir............... | 35 | Subclimax | | Balsam fir |
| White spruce (old field)... | (36) | Subclimax | | Yellow birch |
| White spruce–balsam fir– | | | | Paper birch |
| paper birch............. | 36 | Climax | | *Secondary* |
| Aspen .................... | 16 | Subclimax | | Aspen |
| Pin cherry .............. | 17 | Subclimax | | Beech |
| Paper birch ............. | 18 | Subclimax | | |
| Yellow birch ............. | (30) | Subclimax | | |
| Red spruce–sugar maple– | | | Hardwoods– | *Primary* |
| beech ................. | 31 | Climax | spruce–fir | Red spruce |
| Red spruce (old field) .... | 32 | Subclimax | | Yellow birch |
| Aspen ................... | 16 | Subclimax | | Sugar maple |
| Pin cherry ............... | 17 | Subclimax | | *Secondary* |
| Paper birch ............. | 18 | Subclimax | | Balsam fir |
| Sugar maple–beech–yellow | | | | Aspen |
| birch .................. | 25 | Subclimax | | Paper birch |
| Yellow birch ............. | (30) | Subclimax | | Beech |

* Marinus Westveld, Ecology and silviculture of spruce-fir in the East, Symposium at Joint Meeting, Canadian Institute of Forestry and Society of American Foresters, 1952.

Table 5. Tentative Forest Type-Site Classification for Spruce-Fir Forest of Eastern North America

| Phyto-geographic zones | Recognized forest types | Major type groups | Ground vegetation equivalents | Ease with which spruce-fir production can be maintained |
|---|---|---|---|---|
| Red spruce | Balsam fir (flat)<br>Red spruce–balsam fir (flat)<br>Red spruce (slope)<br>Red spruce (flat) | Spruce-fir | *Hylocomium-Hypnum*<br>*Cornus*<br>*Oxalis-Hylocomium*<br>(*Hylocomium-Hypnum*)<br>(*Cornus-Maianthemum*) | Easily |
|  | Paper birch–red spruce<br>Balsam fir<br>Red spruce–yellow birch | Spruce-fir-hardwoods | *Cornus-Maianthemum*<br>*Oxalis-Cornus* | Moderately difficult |
|  | Red spruce–sugar maple–beech | Hardwoods-spruce-fir | *Viburnum-Oxalis* | Difficult |
| Black spruce | Black spruce–tamarack<br>Black spruce (swamp)<br>Black spruce–white cedar<br>Black spruce–jack pine<br>Black spruce–balsam fir<br>Balsam fir | Spruce-fir | *Chamaedaphne-Ledum*<br>*Kalmia-Ledum*<br>*Sphagnum-Ledum*<br>*Sphagnum-Carex*<br>*Sphagnum-Cornus*<br>*Sphagnum-Oxalis* | Easily |
|  | Black spruce–paper birch<br>Black spruce–aspen<br>Black spruce–alder | Spruce-fir-hardwoods | *Oxalis-Coptis*<br>*Hylocomium-Mitella* | Moderately difficult |
|  | Aspen–paper birch<br>Black spruce | Hardwoods-spruce-fir | *Galium-Equisetum* | Difficult |
| White spruce | White spruce–black spruce<br>Balsam fir<br>White spruce–balsam fir | Spruce-fir | *Sphagnum*<br>*Sphagnum-Oxalis*<br>*Cornus-Linnea* | Easily |
|  | White spruce–balsam fir–paper birch<br>White spruce–balsam fir–aspen | Spruce-fir | *Rubus parviflorus*<br>*Cornus-Maianthemum* | Moderately difficult |
|  | White spruce–balsam fir–yellow birch<br>Paper birch–white spruce–balsam fir<br>Sugar maple–white spruce–balsam fir<br>Aspen–white spruce | Hardwoods-spruce-fir | *Aralia*<br>*Aster-Corylus*<br>*Smilacina-Polygonatum*<br>*Galium-Equisetum* | Difficult |

Source: Marinus Westveld, Ecology and silviculture of spruce-fir in the East, Symposium at Joint Meeting, Canadian Institute of Forestry and Society of American Foresters, 1952.

# Silvics

**NATURAL REGENERATION OF TREE SPECIES BY SEED.** The following description of the factors involved in natural regeneration of loblolly pine, and some applications to silviculture of the species, typifies the information necessary for the management of almost any species.

**Requirements for Natural Regeneration of Loblolly Pine. 1. Light.** This is not an important factor in the germination of seed, but it is an important factor in subsequent survival and growth.

**2. Moisture.** This is important; seeds must imbibe enough water to start growth processes. Normal rainfall throughout the range of loblolly pine is usually adequate.

**3. Seedbed.** Germination is best on mineral soil, next best where surface debris has been consumed by fire, and poorest on undisturbed litter surfaces.

**4. Temperature.** Loblolly pine seeds do not germinate at temperatures below 40° F. Germination is best at ordinary room temperatures (70–80° F.).

**5. Seed destroyers.** Larvae of cone moths frequently destroy immature cones and may attack the seeds within mature cones. In a good seed year, these losses are not important; in a poor seed year, destruction by insects may be an important factor. Squirrels, mice, and birds also consume seeds, but there is little evidence that they are important factors in the regeneration of loblolly pine.

**6. Competition.** Dense grass and broom sedge may restrict the development of loblolly pine seedlings during the first year or two. However, loblolly pine has long been noted for its ability to reseed abandoned fields.

Competition from hardwood trees and shrubs is another matter. Loblolly pines that get an even start with hardwoods will outgrow their competitors. Overtopped pines gradually become etiolated and in time succumb to drought, defoliation, insects, and disease.

**7. Seed production.** Good seed years occur at intervals of 1 to 5 years. The quantity of seeds produced in an average good year equals that produced in 10 poor years or 4 medium years.

Prevailing winds influence the distribution of seeds. Few sound seeds are carried downwind more than 300 ft., and very few seeds are deposited in the opposite direction at distances greater than 75 to 100 ft.

The viability of seed decreases slightly as distance from seed source increases. The viability varies according to the size of the crop and has been known to be as low as 29 percent in poor years and as high as 78 percent in good years. Viability also varies with time of seed dispersal, the highest percentage coinciding with peak seedfall.

Seed fall begins early in October and peaks early in November. Most of the crop falls before January 1, although in a good seed year some seeds may fall as late as the succeeding June. Warm, dry, windy periods increase the release of seed; cool, moist periods retard it.

During a 13-year period, a mature loblolly pine stand near Duke University, Durham, N. C., produced enough viable seeds in 5 of the 13 years to restock satisfactorily an adjacent cut-over area with 1,000 or more seedlings per acre

Seed production by loblolly pines can be increased by completely releasin[g] selected seed trees. A seven-fold increase in cone production has been obtained o[n] selected trees in a controlled experiment.

Satisfactory seed trees are best selected on the basis of productivity as judge[d] by the abundance of cones borne in previous years. Usually trees less than 11 in in diameter at breast height are too immature to produce large crops.

# Silviculture

## ARTIFICIAL REFORESTATION.

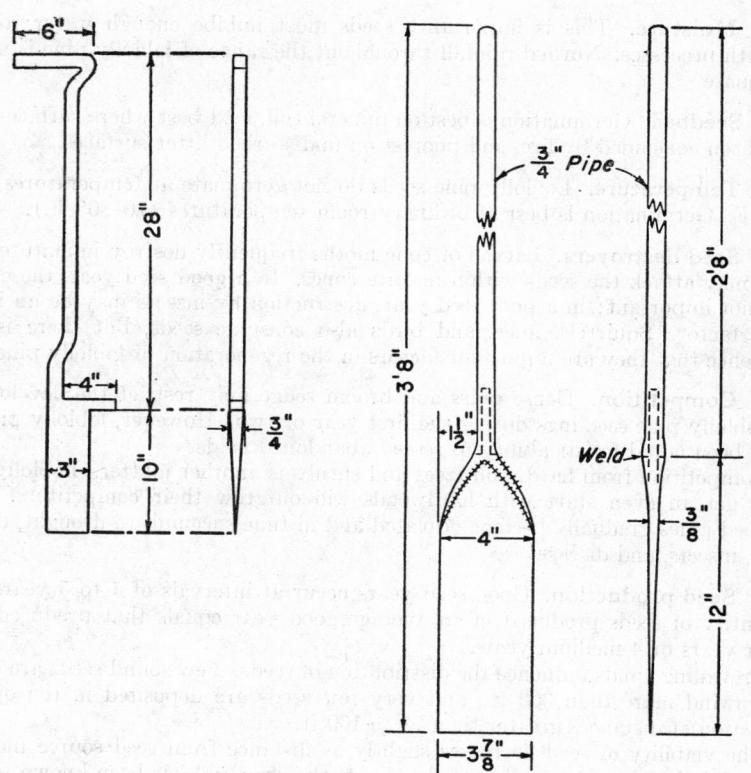

Fig. 2. Two types of planting bar.

**Common Hand Planting Tools.** Grub hoes, mattocks, tile spades, long- and short-handled shovels are universally used. Depending on the type of competing vegetation, the nature of the soil, and the size of stock, good workmen will plant in holes at the rate of 25 to 75 trees per man-hour.

In light, easily worked soils, without heavy ground cover and where the trees can be planted in slits with a planting bar, the rate can be stepped up to 150 trees

**Table 6.  Clean Seed per Pound (Average), Major Timber and Shelterbelt Species**

|  | Seed per lb. | Yield of clean seed from fruit or cones |
|---|---|---|
| **EASTERN CONIFERS** | | |
| Baldcypress | 4,800 | 50 lb. per 100 lb. |
| Fir, balsam | 59,800 | 37–42 oz. per bu. |
| Hemlock, eastern | 187,000 | 3–6 lb. per 100 lb. |
| Pine, eastern white | 20,000 | 5–28 oz. per 100 lb. |
| Pine, jack | 131,000 | 4–11 oz. per bu. |
| Pine, loblolly | 18,400 | 8–24 oz. per bu. |
| Pine, longleaf | 4,200 | 8–19 oz. per bu. |
| Pine, pitch | 62,000 | 12 oz. per bu. |
| Pine, red (Norway) | 52,000 | 9–12 oz. per bu. |
| Pine, Scotch | 78,000 | 7–9 oz. per bu. |
| Pine, shortleaf | 48,000 | 5–24 oz. per bu. |
| Pine, slash | 14,500 | 8–24 oz. per bu. |
| Pine, Virginia | 53,000 | ... |
| Redcedar, eastern | 43,200 | 20–26 lb. per 100 lb. |
| Spruce, black | 404,000 | 2–5 oz. per bu. |
| Spruce, red | 140,000 | 17–24 oz. per bu. |
| Spruce, white | 240,000 | 6–20 oz. per bu. |
| Tamarack | 318,000 | 9 oz. per bu. |
| White-cedar, northern | 346,000 | 11–48 oz. per bu. |
| **WESTERN CONIFERS** | | |
| Douglas-fir | 42,000 | ⅓–1⅓ lb. per bu. |
| Fir, California red | 6,600 | ... |
| Fir, grand | 23,200 | ... |
| Fir, white | 15,100 | 48–82 oz. per bu. |
| Hemlock, western | 297,000 | 3 lb. per 100 lb. |
| Incense-cedar | 15,000 | 2–3 lb. per bu. |
| Larch, western | 143,000 | 8 oz. per bu. |
| Pine, Jeffrey | 4,000 | 33 oz. per bu. |
| Pine, lodgepole | 102,000 | 5–8 oz. per bu. |
| Pine, ponderosa | 12,000 | 9–32 oz. per bu. |
| Pine, sugar | 2,100 | 25–32 oz. per bu. |
| Pine, western white | 27,000 | 12 oz. per bu. |
| Port-Orford-cedar | 210,000 | 20 lb. per 100 lb. |
| Redcedar, western | 414,000 | 12 oz. per bu. |
| Redwood | 122,000 | 11 lb. per 100 lb. |
| Sequoia, giant | 91,000 | ... |
| Spruce, blue | 106,000 | 12–20 oz. per bu. |
| Spruce, Engelmann | 135,000 | 6–16 oz. per bu. |
| Spruce, Sitka | 210,000 | 8–20 oz. per bu. |

(Continued on following page)

per man-hour. This type of planting is quite common in the South and Lake States.

A short-handled grub hoe is employed on steep slopes, such as are encountered in the northern Rocky Mountain region. One man can plant 100 to 125 trees per hour.

Ordinary mouldboard plows, single or double bottom, are satisfactorily used in the Middle West for planting open fields. The first plow furrow makes the trench in which the roots are placed; the second furrow slice is thrown against the first,

### Table 6. Clean Seed per Pound (Average), Major Timber and Shelterbelt Species
(Continued)

| | Seed per lb. | Yield of clean seed from fruit or cones |
|---|---|---|
| **EASTERN HARDWOODS** | | |
| Ash, green | 17,300 | 75 lb. per 100 lb. |
| Ash, white | 10,000 | 12.4 lb. per bu. |
| Basswood, American | 5,000 | 75 lb. per 100 lb. |
| Birch, yellow | 447.000 | 1–3.5 lb. per bu. |
| Boxelder | 11.800 | ... |
| Catalpa, northern | 21.000 | 25–35 lb. per 100 lb. |
| Cherry, black | 4,800 | 20–40 lb. per 100 lb. |
| Cottonwood, eastern | 350,000 | 2 lb. per bushel (var. *virginiana*) |
| Elm, American | 68,000 | 50 lb. per 100 lb. |
| Elm, rock | 7,000 | 7.8 lb. per bu. |
| Hackberry | 4,300 | 40–75 lb. per 100 lb. |
| Hickory, shagbark | 10J | 25–38 lb. per 100 lb. |
| Honeylocust | 2,800 | 20–35 lb. per 100 lb. |
| Locust, black | 24,000 | 15–33 lb. per 100 lb. |
| Maple, silver | 1,400 | ... |
| Maple, sugar | 6,100 | ... |
| Oak, chestnut | 75 | 60–75 lb. per 100 lb. |
| Oak, northern red | 105 | 70–80 lb. per 100 lb. |
| Oak, pin | 410 | 50–70 lb. per 100 lb. |
| Oak, white | 150 | 60–90 lb. per 100 lb. |
| Osage-orange | 14,000 | 2 lb. per bu. |
| Sweetgum | 82,000 | ¾ lb. per bu. |
| Walnut, black | 40 | 30–65 lb. per 100 lb. |
| Yellow-poplar | 14,000 | 7–13 lb. per bu. |

Source: U. S. Dept. Agr., Woody plant seed manual. *Misc. Publ. No. 654,* 1948.

thus covering the roots. The soil around the roots is tamped with the feet. Two hundred to 400 trees can be planted per man-hour with a plow, tractor, and three-man crew.

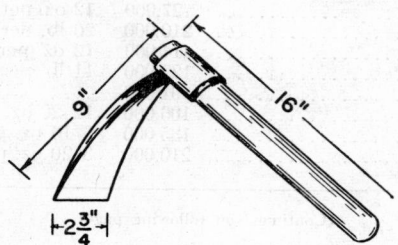

**Fig. 3. Short-handled grub hoe.**

**Planting Machines.** Planting machines (Fig. 4) have replaced hand tools in open, relatively flat terrain. A crew of three men with a tractor and planting machine will set 1,000 to 2,000 trees per hour.

**A Policy for Seed Source.** "Seed source is second in importance only to choice of species in reforestation practice" (U. S. Forest Service, 1948). Therefore, foresters who plant trees have a grave professional responsibility to employ only seed and planting stock which are well adapted to the environment and which have the greatest inherent capacity to produce and survive.

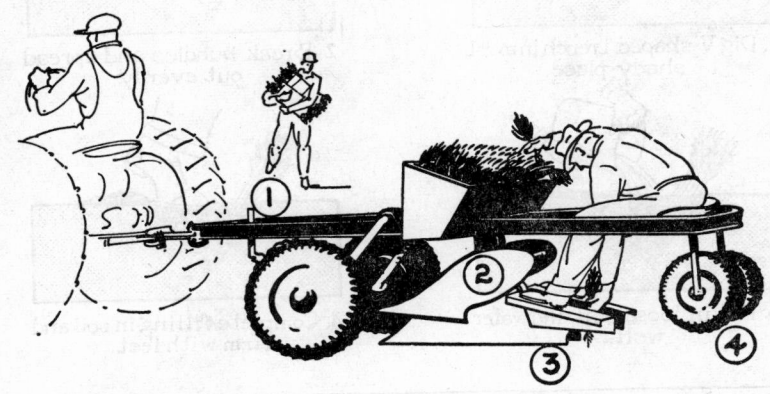

**Fig. 4. Typical tree-planting machine.**

(1) Rolling coulter. (2) Double mouldboard plow or middle buster. Not essential in the absence of heavy ground cover. (3) Planting shoe, which opens the trench. (4) Packing wheels, which close trench and firm the soil.

The following recommendations are adapted largely from the forest seed policy announced by the United States Department of Agriculture in 1939 (U. S. Dept. Agr., Bureau of Plant Industry).

1. Use only seed of known locality of origin and nursery stock grown from such seed.

2. For both seed and nursery stock, require an accurate record of identity, year of seed crop, species, and state, county, locality, and range of elevation where the seed originated.

3. Use local seed from natural stands unless is has been demonstrated that seed from another specific source produces desirable plants for the locality and uses involved. In general terms, local seed means seed from an area subject to similar climatic influences, and may usually be considered as that collected within 100 mi. of the planting site and differing in elevation by less than 1,000 ft. However, where climate differs strikingly, use considerable caution in going as much as 100 mi. from the planting site for seed and place greater weight upon actual climatic factors.

4. When local seed is not available, use seed from a region having as nearly as possible the same length of growing season, the same mean temperature during the growing season, the same pattern and quantities of precipitation, the same latitude, and in other respects, similar environment.

**Direct Seeding as a Means of Artificial Reforestation.** Planting tree seed directly on sites where forests are desired has been practiced or tested widely throughout the world for a great many years. Generally, direct seeding has been less successful than tree planting in the United States and Canada. However, an occasional outstanding success demonstrates that direct seeding is a good method when conditions are right and suitable practices are used. The job ahead is to

# HEELING IN

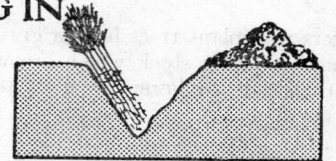

**1.** Dig V-shaped trench in moist shady place.

**2.** Break bundles and spread out evenly.

**3.** Fill in loose soil and water well.

**4.** Complete filling in soil and firm with feet.

# HANDLING SEEDLINGS
## in
# FIELD

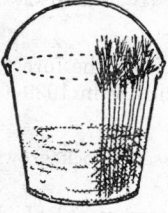

*Correct*
In bucket with sufficient water to cover roots.

*Incorrect*
In hand - roots dry out.

# CORRECT AND INCORRECT DEPTHS

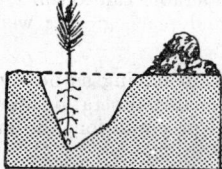
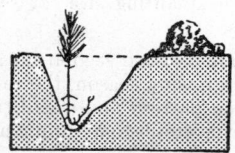
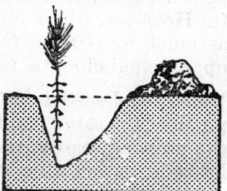

*Correct*
At same depth or ½ deeper than seedling grew in nursery.

*Incorrect*
Too deep and roots bent.

*Incorrect*
Too shallow and roots exposed.

Fig. 5. Planting methods.
(State Forester of Alabama)

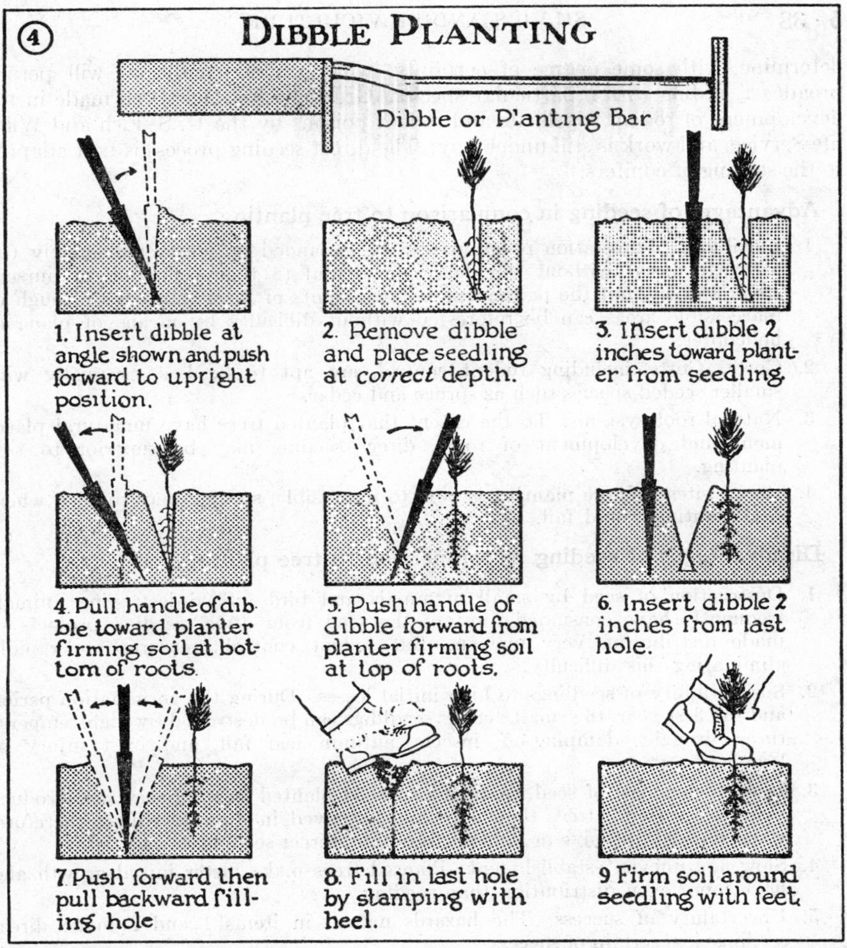

# DIBBLE PLANTING

**(4)**

Dibble or Planting Bar

1. Insert dibble at angle shown and push forward to upright position.

2. Remove dibble and place seedling at *correct* depth.

3. Insert dibble 2 inches toward planter from seedling.

4. Pull handle of dibble toward planter firming soil at bottom of roots.

5. Push handle of dibble forward from planter firming soil at top of roots.

6. Insert dibble 2 inches from last hole.

7. Push forward then pull backward filling hole.

8. Fill in last hole by stamping with heel.

9. Firm soil around seedling with feet.

# MATTOCK PLANTING

**(5)**

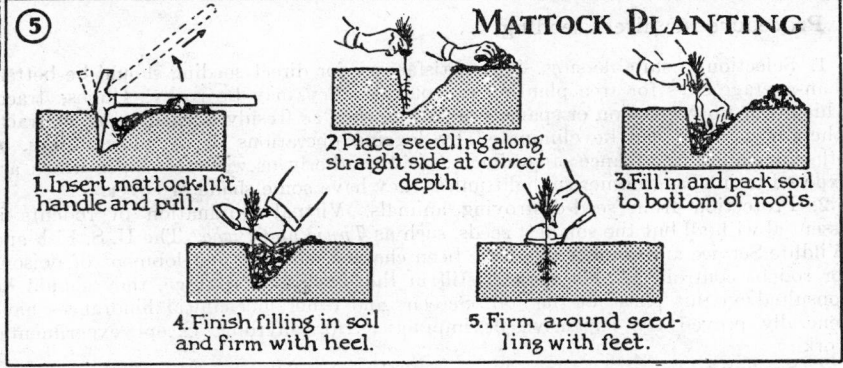

1. Insert mattock-lift handle and pull.

2. Place seedling along straight side at *correct* depth.

3. Fill in and pack soil to bottom of roots.

4. Finish filling in soil and firm with heel.

5. Firm around seedling with feet.

Fig. 5. Planting methods (Continued).

determine, with some degree of certainty, what ground conditions will permit broadcast seeding with a particular species. Great progress has been made in the development of rodent repellents and rodent poisons by the U. S. Fish and Wildlife Service, and work is still under way. The direct seeding process is best adapted to the seeding of conifers.

### Advantages of seeding in comparison to tree planting.

1. Flexibility. Forestation programs can be expanded or contracted quickly (on a yearly basis) without the delays incidental to the production of nursery stock and without the permanent improvements of forest nurseries. Rough or inaccessible areas can be reforested without difficulty by means of plane or helicopter.

2. Costs. Costs, including rodent control, are apt to be less, especially with smaller seeded species such as spruce and cedar.

3. Natural root systems. To the extent that planted trees have unnatural placement and development of roots, direct seeding may be superior to tree planting.

4. Rocky sites. Where planting is next to impossible, seeding may succeed where tree planting would fail.

### Disadvantages of seeding in comparison to tree planting.

1. Destruction of seed by small mammals and birds. Seed-destroying animals frequently have consumed most of the seed from direct seeding projects or made distribution very uneven. But rodent control measures are rapidly eliminating this difficulty.

2. Susceptibility of seedlings to high initial losses. During the germination period and the first year, the small, tender seedlings can be destroyed by high temperatures, drought, damping-off, insects, autumn leaf fall, and frost injury or heaving.

3. Less efficient use of seed. A pound of seed planted in a nursery will produce many times more trees than a pound employed in direct seeding; therefore, when seed is expensive or difficult to obtain, direct seeding is wasteful.

4. Slow and uneven establishment. Planted trees make faster initial growth and have more even distribution than seeding.

5. Uncertainty of success. The hazards named in items 1 and 2 make direct seedings less certain of success.

### Procedure for direct seeding.

1. Selection of suitable sites. Sites satisfactory for direct seeding should be better-than-average sites for tree planting except that they may be rocky. Choose tracts which bear no vegetation or sparse vegetation, such as freshly burned areas, or tracts where vegetation can be eliminated by logging operations or by plows, disks, or other machines in advance of seeding. Avoid southerly or westerly slopes which are exposed to intense summer sunlight unless they have some shade or cover.

2. Protection from seed-destroying animals. Virtual elimination of rodents is essential with all but the smallest seeds, such as *Thuja* and *Picea*. The U. S. Fish and Wildlife Service and some states have been charged with the development of poisons for rodent control. As this work is still in the experimental stage, they should be consulted on this phase of the job. Screens and other mechanical hindrances have generally proved too expensive or impractical for anything except experimental work.

3. Seeding techniques. a. Broadcasting. This operation includes airplane and helicopter seeding, manually operated "cyclone seeders," and hand broadcasting. The

technique of seed and bait distribution from the air has been satisfactorily worked out and commercial flying companies will now contract seeding jobs. Use a minimum of 30,000 viable seeds per acre. Species like hemlock and spruce that have high seedling mortality require several times that number. Sometimes it is desirable to dilute seed with hardwood sawdust or similar substances to insure even distribution from a machine.

b. Drilling. Planting with garden drills in plowed furrows, where terrain and soil permits, is relatively rapid compared with seed spotting and requires less seed than broadcasting. Use 10,000 to 20,000 viable seeds per acre in furrows spaced 8 ft. apart. Production is about 8 to 12 acres per man-day.

c. Seed spotting. Seed spotting is an unsatisfactory method of planting for most species unless definite provision can be made for the removal of surplus trees within 5 to 10 yr. after planting, as is done in Europe. The system is little, if any, faster than planting seedlings. On poor spots, none survive, and on good spots, too many survive; the result is an uneven stand with reduced growth and badly formed trees. The normal procedure is to put in about 1,000 spots per acre with 5 or more seeds per spot. The most unfavorable features of seed spotting can be proportionally reduced by increasing the number of spots per acre and reducing the number of seeds per spot.

A hand planter (the Baker) has been developed at Portland, Oregon (and many others are in the process of development), that will plant a single seed (or two at most) to the spot, either pelleted or bare. This makes possible the planting of a seed or two in every favorable spot very quickly—2,000 or more to the acre. The system is faster than the ordinary seed spot method and offers considerable promise for successful results.

4. Preparation of seed. a. Pregermination treatments. Germination as quickly as possible after sowing is desirable in order to reduce the period when the seeds are in danger of being eaten. Hence, seeds which are subject to delayed germination should be given germination hastening treatments such as soaking, stratification, or seed-coat abrasion. However, treatments which would interfere with the seeding technique should not be employed. For example, stratified white pine seed would be damaged by some mechanical seeders.

b. Seed pelleting. Tree seeds have been pelleted for various purposes, including camouflaging, the addition of repellent substances, addition of nutrients, and change in size and shape. Although the idea unquestionably has merit, to date no remarkable benefits have been demonstrated, except to produce a uniform round pellet that will meter perfectly in a machine.

## Methods for Improvement of Seedbeds and Reduction of Competition.

Experiments have shown that better seedling stands are secured if the seedbed is prepared and competition reduced by prescribed burning or by one of several known mechanical treatments. Regardless of the treatment applied, its effect will be of relatively short duration because the land becomes covered with vegetation again in a few years. Therefore, to obtain the maximum benefit, the treatment should be applied prior to a good seed fall.

**Prescribed burning.** Prescribed burning is commonly used as protection against excessive damage by wildfire and as a tool in silviculture, grazing, and wildlife management. The technique of burning must be varied to meet local conditions and has been described for different localities by various authors. However, in all localities the basic requirement is the same. That requirement is careful planning, with special attention to topography, weather, areas of high hazard, areas to be protected, effect on grazing, period of seedfall, relationship of cost plus damage to probable benefits, and, last but certainly not least, the sequence of firing.

**Disking.** Premature opening of a stand may result in brush encroachment to the exclusion of natural reproduction. Where brush has taken over the ground, artificial means are required to improve the site. The Athens disk, pulled by a 35-hp. crawler-tractor, has been found to be a particularly effective tool for preparing brushy areas for planting (or in advance of a good seedfall). Crossdisking of the brush, the second at right angles to the first, in midsummer turns up the roots of the shrubs and sets back their growth for several years. Disking has been more successful as a means of ground preparation in dense brush than has furrowing with a heavy plow. Thorough disking may require up to 2 tractor hours per acre.

When ground preparation is to be combined with a harvest cut, the cost may be reduced by disking only once prior to logging and at right angles to the direction in which the logs will be skidded. After disking has broken down the undergrowth and cut through the mat of roots, skidding operations have been known to expose mineral soil on 78 percent of the surface. Skidding alone, without preliminary disking, exposed mineral soil on 48 percent of the surface.

**Bulldozing.** Sometimes undesirable species attain a size beyond control by prescribed burning or disking but still of a size and in numbers that make poisoning impractical. (Efforts to poison all trees 1 in. and larger in diameter with ammate have been known to cost more than $30 per acre.) In such cases the forest manager may resort to bulldozing. Usually machines of 60 or more horsepower are required. Trees up to 6 or 8 in. in diameter can be uprooted; larger trees should be girdled or poisoned. Sometimes the debris is pushed into swale holes, ravines, or other areas of low productivity. More often the debris is left where it falls.

Production rates are controlled in large degree by the density of vegetation and nature of the terrain. Accomplishments vary from one-quarter to one acre per tractor hour of operation.

In bulldozing operations, forest managers should make certain they do not encourage erosion. They also must guard against pushing the topsoil into windrows and in so doing lower soil fertility in the intervening strips.

**HARVEST CUTTINGS. Tree Vigor Classifications.** Tree vigor classifications describe characteristics of trees for the purposes of judging vigor, growth rates, and susceptibility to insect attack. They extend the concept of crown classification (dominant, etc.) by including such characteristics as color and texture of the bark, foliage color and retention, crown form, length and density, and occurrence of dead twigs. They have become widely popular among foresters, especially in western United States where orderly harvesting of insect-susceptible, overmature timber is a major silvicultural problem.

Vigor classifications serve especially well both for (1) training new markers, and (2) reducing qualitative descriptions to a uniform basis. However, they should not be regarded as marking rules or silvicultural systems. Although such classifications aid greatly in the application of marking rules, broader ecological, silvicultural, and economic principles should govern the harvesting and regenerating of forests.

Space limitation prevents detailed presentation of the various systems, but several are named and their principal features described in Table 7. An example of one of them is given in detail in Table 8.

**Site Classifications.** See Tables 9 to 32.

## Table 7. Some Tree Vigor Classifications

| Name | Species to which applied | Number of classes | Remarks |
|---|---|---|---|
| Keen [a] | Ponderosa pine and Jeffrey pine | 4 degrees of vigor, 4 age-classes (total 16) | Primarily designed to rate bark-beetle susceptibility but it also is employed widely to estimate growth |
| Risk classification [b] | Ponderosa pine and Jeffrey pine | 4 degrees of risk | Designed to detect short-term decline in vigor and probable bark-beetle mortality, as a guide in sanitation—salvage harvesting in overmature stands |
| Taylor [c] | Lodgepole pine in the Rocky Mountains | 4 degrees of thrift | Designed primarily to estimate relative rates of growth in mature and overmature stands |
| Larch–Douglas-fir [d] | Western larch and Douglas-fir in western Montana | 3 degrees of thrift | Designed primarily to estimate growth of mature and overmature trees |
| Aspen–jack pine–red pine [e] | Aspen, jack pine and second-growth red pine in the Lake States | Relation to surrounding trees —6, Crown density—3, Soundness—5, Form—5, Utility—7 | Designed for improvement cuttings in immature stands. Introduces soundness, form, and utility, which are not factors in vigor |
| Northern & central hardwoods [f] | All northern and central hardwoods | Quality—3 Vigor—3 plus a cull class | For appraisal of value, growth and cull primarily in the management of farm woodlands |
| Western white pine [g] | Western white pine | 4 degrees of thrift | Designed to estimate growth and mortality risk of mature trees |

[a] F. P. Keen, Relative susceptibility of ponderosa pine to bark-beetle attack, *Jour. Forestry* 34:919–927 (1936). (This system is an expansion of Dunning's earlier system, which is still used extensively. See D. Dunning, 1928, A tree classification for the selection forests of the Sierra Nevada, *Jour. Agr. Research* 36:755–771.) For the Black Hills, see E. M. Hornibrook, 1939, A modified tree classification for use in growth studies and timber marking in Black Hills ponderosa pine, *Jour. Forestry* 37:483–488 (1939).

[b] K. A. Salman and J. W. Bongberg, Logging high-risk trees to control insects in the pine stands of northeastern California, *Jour. Forestry* 40:533–539 (1942).

[c] R. F. Taylor, The application of a tree classification in marking lodgepole pine for selection cutting, *Jour. Forestry* 37:777–782 (1939).

[d] Arthur L. Roe, A preliminary classification of tree vigor for western larch and Douglas-fir trees in western Montana, Northern Rocky Mountain Forest & Range Exp. Sta., *Res. Note No. 66* (1948).

[e] S. R. Gevorkiantz, P. O. Rudolf, and P. J. Zehngraff, A tree classification for aspen, jack pine and second-growth red pine, *Jour. Forestry* 41:268–274 (1943).

[f] U. S. Forest Service, Region 9, Suggested hardwood tree class standards for farm foresters, 1943. U. S. Forest Service, Region 9, Comparison of investment and earnings of hardwood trees in the northern Lake States, 1942. U. S. Forest Service, Region 9, Procedures for the analysis of a farm woodlot.

[g] C. A. Wellner, A vigor classification for mature western white pine trees in the Inland Empire, Northern Rocky Mountain Forest & Range Exp. Sta., *Res. Note No. 110* (1952).

### Table 8. Characteristics for Classifying the Vigor of Western Larch and Douglas-Fir Residual Trees in Larch-Fir Type in Western Montana

| Characters | Vigor class | | |
|---|---|---|---|
| | A (Good vigor) | B (Fair vigor) | C (Poor vigor) |
| 1. Position of crown | Usually dominant or co-dominant, occasionally intermediate. | Ordinarily codominant and intermediate, rarely dominant. | Usually intermediate or suppressed, occasionally codominant and rarely dominant. |
| 2. Length of the crown | Crown length 40 percent of the total height or longer. Unusually wide crown may be shorter but not less than 30 percent. | Crown length usually from 20 to 40 percent of total height. In narrow crowns greater length may be allowed. | Crown length usually will not exceed 20 percent of total height. In extremely narrow crowns greater length may be allowed, but not to exceed 50 percent. |
| 3. Width of the crown | Crown width average or wider. | Crown usually average width. May be narrow and long or wide and short. | Crown usually narrow or occasionally of average width. |
| 4. Shape of the crown | Tip usually pointed or round, never flat or spike topped. | Tip usually round, occasionally pointed, and rarely flat topped. | Tip usually flat or spike top, rarely rounded. |
| 5. Branching and foliage | Dead branches in the crown rare, branches and foliage moderately dense or better. Branches in upper half of crown usually strongly up-turned and no drooping branches. | Occasional dead twigs present, usually no dead branches in the crown. Branches and foliage of moderate density. Occasionally large crowns of extremely open density. Usually the upper branches either upturned or horizontal, with drooping branches in the lower half of crown. | Dead twigs and branches showing through the crown. Often branches drooping to the tip. In western larch [a] branches short and stout throughout the length of the crown. |
| 6. Bark | WESTERN LARCH—Bark is usually dark in color and ridged or only slightly scaly with deep fissures between scales. Bark appears rough. **These bark characters apply to western larch only. Do not use on Douglas-fir.** | WESTERN LARCH—Bark is usually dark around base of tree, becoming scaly above. Plates not well defined, but bark appears relatively smooth. **These bark characters apply to western larch only. Do not use on Douglas-fir.** | WESTERN LARCH [b]—Bark usually light in color with well-defined large, smooth bark plates and very shallow fissures between plates. Bark appears very smooth. **These bark characters apply to western larch only. Do not use on Douglas-fir.** |
| | DOUGLAS-FIR—Bark usually has broad, corky ridges at the base, with light brown new bark prominently exposed in the fissures, becoming uniformly and finely ridged and dark above. The upper quarter or more of the bole usually has smooth or slightly checked light gray bark. | DOUGLAS-FIR — Bark has corky ridges at the base of the tree, becoming uniformly and finely ridged above. New light brown bark not as prominent as in A vigor and usually extending only part way up the butt log. Dark, rough bark extends at least three quarters or more up the full length of the bole. | DOUGLAS-FIR — Bark rarely has the light brown new bark exposed in the fissures. Dark bark usually extends to the tip. Frequently the entire bole has dark, finely ridged bark. |
| 7. Disease | No mistletoe infection. | Rarely trees with light mistletoe infection. | Trees with visible indications of moderate to heavy mistletoe infection should be placed in this vigor class. |

[a] Frequently in western larch, short, stout branches near the tip give it the appearance of being pointed. This should not be confused with a pointed growing tip which usually has numerous upper branches and is normally obtusely pointed.

[b] Trees with this type of bark are overmature and usually growing slowly. They should be dropped one class below that in which they would otherwise classify. Thus, if a tree qualifies for A vigor, but possesses the light, smooth bark with well-defined plates and shallow fissures, it should be dropped to the B vigor class.

Source: Arthur L. Roe, U. S. Forest Service, Northern Rocky Mountain Forest & Range Exp. Sta., A preliminary classification of tree vigor for western larch and Douglas-fir trees in western Montana, *Res. Note No. 66* (1948).

**Table 9. Aspen: Height in Feet of Average Dominant Trees, by Site Index ***

| Age (yr.) | Site index | | | | |
|---|---|---|---|---|---|
|  | 40 | 50 | 60 | 70 | 80 |
| 20 | 19 | 23 | 29 | 34 | 36 |
| 30 | 27 | 32 | 40 | 46 | 50 |
| 40 | 33 | 39 | 49 | 57 | 62 |
| 50 | 39 | 47 | 58 | 68 | 74 |
| 60 | ... | 52 | 65 | 76 | 84 |
| 70 | ... | 57 | 70 | 82 | 91 |
| 80 | ... | ... | 74 | 86 | 96 |

* At 50 yr.
Source: Prepared by S. R. Gevorkiantz, Lake States Forest Exp. Sta.

**Table 10. Balsam Fir: Height in Feet of Average Dominant and Codominant Trees, by Site Index ***

| Age (yr.) | Site index | | | | |
|---|---|---|---|---|---|
|  | 30 | 40 | 50 | 60 | 70 |
| 20 | 8 | 9 | 10 | 12 | 13 |
| 30 | 14 | 18 | 22 | 26 | 30 |
| 40 | 21 | 27 | 34 | 40 | 47 |
| 50 | 26 | 34 | 43 | 51 | 60 |
| 60 | 29 | 38 | 48 | 58 | 67 |
| 70 | 31 | 41 | 52 | 62 | 72 |
| 80 | 32 | 43 | 54 | 65 | 76 |
| 90 | 33 | 44 | 56 | 67 | 78 |

* At 65 yr.
Source: Walter H. Meyer, Yields of second-growth spruce and fir in the Northeast, U. S. Dept. Agr., *Tech. Bull. No. 142* (1929).

**Table 11. Douglas-Fir: Height in Feet of Average Dominant and Codominant Trees, by Site Index ***

| Age (yr.) | Site index | | | | | | |
|---|---|---|---|---|---|---|---|
|  | 80 | 100 | 120 | 140 | 160 | 180 | 210 |
| 20 | 21 | 26 | 31 | 37 | 42 | 47 | 54 |
| 30 | 37 | 46 | 55 | 64 | 74 | 83 | 96 |
| 40 | 48 | 60 | 72 | 84 | 96 | 108 | 126 |
| 50 | 56 | 70 | 84 | 98 | 112 | 125 | 146 |
| 60 | 63 | 78 | 93 | 109 | 124 | 140 | 163 |
| 70 | 68 | 85 | 102 | 119 | 135 | 152 | 178 |
| 80 | 73 | 91 | 109 | 127 | 145 | 163 | 190 |
| 90 | 77 | 96 | 115 | 134 | 153 | 172 | 201 |
| 100 | 80 | 100 | 120 | 140 | 160 | 180 | 210 |
| 110 | 83 | 104 | 124 | 145 | 166 | 187 | 218 |
| 120 | 85 | 106 | 128 | 149 | 170 | 192 | 224 |
| 130 | 87 | 109 | 131 | 152 | 174 | 196 | 228 |
| 140 | 88 | 110 | 133 | 154 | 177 | 199 | 232 |
| 150 | 89 | 112 | 134 | 156 | 179 | 201 | 235 |
| 160 | 90 | 113 | 136 | 158 | 181 | 203 | 237 |

* At 100 yr.
Source: U. S. Dept. Agr., *Tech. Bull. No. 201*.

### Table 12. Sweetgum: Height in Feet of Average Dominant Trees, by Site Index *

| Age (yr.) | Site index | | | | | |
|---|---|---|---|---|---|---|
| | 70 | 80 | 90 | 100 | 110 | 120 |
| 10 | ... | 17 | 22 | 30 | 39 | 47 |
| 20 | 31 | 40 | 48 | 57 | 66 | 75 |
| 30 | 47 | 56 | 66 | 75 | 84 | 93 |
| 40 | 60 | 69 | 79 | 89 | 98 | 108 |
| 50 | 70 | 80 | 90 | 100 | 110 | 120 |
| 60 | 77 | 88 | 98 | 108 | 119 | 129 |
| 70 | ... | 94 | 105 | 115 | 126 | 137 |
| 80 | ... | 99 | 110 | 122 | 133 | 144 |
| 90 | ... | 104 | 115 | 127 | 139 | ... |
| 100 | ... | ... | 119 | 131 | 143 | ... |

* At 50 yr.
Source: Robert K. Winters and James G. Osborne, Growth and yield of second-growth red gum in fully stocked stands on alluvial lands in the South, Southern Forest & Range Exp. Sta., *Occ. Paper No. 54* (1935).

### Table 13. Western Hemlock: Height in Feet of Average Dominant and Codominant Trees, by Site Index *

| Age (yr.) | Site index | | | | | |
|---|---|---|---|---|---|---|
| | 60 | 90 | 120 | 150 | 180 | 200 |
| 10 | 4 | 5 | 7 | 9 | 11 | 12 |
| 40 | 31 | 47 | 63 | 78 | 94 | 105 |
| 70 | 49 | 74 | 99 | 123 | 148 | 165 |
| 100 | 60 | 90 | 120 | 150 | 180 | 200 |
| 130 | 66 | 99 | 132 | 165 | 199 | 221 |
| 150 | 69 | 103 | 137 | 171 | 206 | 229 |
| 180 | 71 | 106 | 142 | 177 | 213 | 236 |
| 220 | 72 | 108 | 145 | 181 | 218 | 241 |
| 260 | 73 | 110 | 146 | 182 | 219 | 244 |
| 300 | 74 | 111 | 147 | 184 | 221 | 246 |

* At 100 yr.
Source: George H. Barnes, Site classification for even-aged stands of western hemlock, Pacific Northwest Forest & Range Exp. Sta., *Res. Note No. 50* (1949).

### Table 14. Western Larch: Height in Feet of Average Dominant and Codominant Trees, by Site Class

| Age (yr.) | Site class | | | | |
|---|---|---|---|---|---|
| | V | IV | III | II | I |
| 40 | 29 | 38 | 46 | 54 | 62 |
| 60 | 41 | 54 | 65 | 77 | 89 |
| 80 | 53 | 67 | 82 | 98 | 112 |
| 100 | 61 | 78 | 95 | 112 | 131 |
| 120 | 67 | 85 | 105 | 125 | 143 |
| 140 | 71 | 93 | 112 | 134 | 154 |
| 160 | 74 | 97 | 116 | 139 | 159 |
| 180 | 75 | 98 | 119 | 142 | 163 |
| 200 | 76 | 98 | 121 | 143 | 165 |
| 220 | 77 | 99 | 122 | 144 | 168 |
| 240 | 77 | 100 | 123 | 145 | 168 |

Source: Adapted from curves prepared by Division of Forest Economics, Northern Rocky Mountain Forest & Range Exp. Sta.

### Table 15. Upland Oaks: Height in Feet of Average Dominant and Codominant Trees, by Site Index *

| Age (yr.) | Site index | | | | |
|---|---|---|---|---|---|
| | 40 | 50 | 60 | 70 | 80 |
| 10 | 8 | 13 | 17 | 21 | 26 |
| 15 | 12 | 18 | 24 | 29 | 35 |
| 20 | 17 | 23 | 30 | 36 | 43 |
| 25 | 21 | 28 | 35 | 42 | 50 |
| 30 | 25 | 33 | 41 | 48 | 56 |
| 35 | 29 | 38 | 46 | 54 | 63 |
| 40 | 33 | 42 | 51 | 60 | 69 |
| 45 | 37 | 46 | 56 | 65 | 75 |
| 50 | 40 | 50 | 60 | 70 | 80 |
| 55 | 43 | 53 | 64 | 74 | 85 |
| 60 | 45 | 56 | 67 | 78 | 89 |
| 65 | 46 | 58 | 69 | 81 | 92 |
| 70 | 48 | 60 | 71 | 83 | 95 |
| 75 | 49 | 61 | 73 | 85 | 97 |
| 80 | 50 | 62 | 75 | 87 | 99 |
| 85 | 51 | 63 | 76 | 89 | 101 |
| 90 | 52 | 64 | 77 | 90 | 103 |
| 95 | 52 | 65 | 78 | 91 | 104 |
| 100 | 53 | 65 | 79 | 92 | 105 |

* At 50 yr.
Source: G. L. Schnur, Yield, stand, and volume tables for even-aged upland oak forests, U. S. Dept. Agr., *Tech. Bull. No. 560* (1937).

**Table 16. Yellow-Poplar: Height in Feet of Average Dominant Trees, by Site Index ***

| Age (yr.) | Site index | | | | | |
|---|---|---|---|---|---|---|
| | 70 | 80 | 90 | 100 | 110 | 120 |
| 10 | 28 | 32 | 36 | 40 | 44 | 48 |
| 15 | 39 | 45 | 51 | 57 | 62 | 68 |
| 20 | 47 | 54 | 61 | 68 | 75 | 81 |
| 25 | 53 | 61 | 69 | 76 | 84 | 91 |
| 30 | 58 | 66 | 75 | 83 | 91 | 99 |
| 35 | 62 | 71 | 80 | 88 | 97 | 106 |
| 40 | 65 | 74 | 84 | 93 | 102 | 111 |
| 45 | 68 | 77 | 87 | 97 | 106 | 116 |
| 50 | 70 | 80 | 90 | 100 | 110 | 120 |

* At 50 yr.
Source: Yellow-poplar characteristics, growth and management, U. S. Dept. Agr., *Tech. Bull. No. 356* (1933).

**Table 17. Second-Growth Redwood: Height in Feet of Average Dominant and Codominant Trees, by Site Class**

| Age (yr.) | Site class | | | | |
|---|---|---|---|---|---|
| | V | IV | III | II | I |
| 10 | 9–14 | 15–18 | 19–23 | 24–28 | 29–33 |
| 20 | 18–26 | 27–35 | 36–44 | 45–53 | 54–63 |
| 30 | 26–38 | 39–51 | 52–64 | 65–77 | 78–90 |
| 40 | 33–49 | 50–66 | 67–82 | 83–99 | 100–116 |
| 50 | 41–60 | 61–80 | 81–100 | 101–120 | 121–140 |
| 60 | 46–69 | 70–92 | 93–115 | 116–139 | 140–163 |

Source: Donald Bruce, Preliminary yield tables for second-growth redwood, Univ. of Calif., Agr. Exp. Sta., *Bull. No. 361* (1923).

**Table 18. Black Spruce: Height in Feet of Average Dominant Trees, by Site Class**

| Age (yr.) | Site class | | |
|---|---|---|---|
| | Poor | Medium | Good |
| 20 | 11 | 14 | 17 |
| 30 | 17 | 22 | 26 |
| 40 | 22 | 28 | 33 |
| 50 | 26 | 33 | 39 |
| 60 | 29 | 37 | 44 |
| 70 | 32 | 41 | 49 |
| 80 | 34 | 44 | 52 |
| 100 | 38 | 48 | 58 |
| 120 | 41 | 52 | 62 |
| 140 | 43 | 54 | 65 |
| 160 | 44 | 56 | 67 |
| 180 | 45 | 57 | 69 |

Source: G. D. Fox and G. W. Kruse, A yield table for well-stocked stands of black spruce in northeastern Minnesota, *Jour. Forestry* 37:565–567 (1939).

**Table 19. Red Spruce: Height in Feet of Average Dominant and Codominant Trees, by Site Index ***

| Age (yr.) | Site index | | | | |
|---|---|---|---|---|---|
| | 30 | 40 | 50 | 60 | 70 |
| 20 | 6 | 7 | 8 | 9 | 10 |
| 30 | 12 | 14 | 17 | 20 | 23 |
| 40 | 18 | 23 | 28 | 34 | 39 |
| 50 | 24 | 31 | 39 | 47 | 54 |
| 60 | 28 | 38 | 47 | 57 | 66 |
| 70 | 31 | 42 | 52 | 62 | 73 |
| 80 | 33 | 44 | 55 | 66 | 77 |
| 90 | 34 | 45 | 56 | 68 | 80 |
| 100 | 34 | 46 | 58 | 70 | 82 |
| 110 | 35 | 47 | 59 | 71 | 83 |

* At 65 yr.
Source: Walter H. Meyer, Yields of second-growth spruce and fir in the Northeast, U. S. Dept. Agr., *Tech. Bull. No. 142* (1929).

**Table 20. White Spruce: Height in Feet of Average Dominant and Codominant Trees, by Site Index ***

| Age (yr.) | Site index | | | | |
|---|---|---|---|---|---|
| | 30 | 40 | 50 | 60 | 70 |
| 20 | 8 | 9 | 10 | 11 | 12 |
| 30 | 14 | 18 | 21 | 25 | 28 |
| 40 | 20 | 26 | 32 | 38 | 45 |
| 50 | 26 | 34 | 42 | 50 | 58 |
| 60 | 29 | 38 | 48 | 58 | 67 |
| 70 | 31 | 41 | 52 | 62 | 72 |
| 80 | 32 | 44 | 54 | 66 | 76 |
| 90 | 34 | 45 | 56 | 68 | 80 |

* At 65 yr.
Source: Walter H. Meyer, Yields of second-growth spruce and fir in the Northeast, U. S. Dept. Agr., *Tech Bull. No. 142* (1929).

**Table 21. Jack Pine: Height in Feet of Average Dominant Trees, by Site Class**

| Age (yr.) | Site class | | |
|---|---|---|---|
| | Poor | Average | Good |
| 30 | 27 | 35 | 44 |
| 40 | 34 | 45 | 56 |
| 50 | 40 | 53 | 66 |
| 60 | 45 | 60 | 75 |
| 70 | 49 | 65 | 81 |
| 80 | 52 | 69 | 86 |

Source: S. R. Gevorkiantz and W. A. Duerr, Methods of predicting growth of forest stands, Lake States Forest Exp. Sta., *Economic Notes No. 9* (1938).

**Table 22. Loblolly Pine: Height in Feet of Average Dominant Trees, by Site Index \***

| Age (yr.) | Site index | | | | | | |
|---|---|---|---|---|---|---|---|
| | 60 | 70 | 80 | 90 | 100 | 110 | 120 |
| 15 | 24 | 29 | 33 | 37 | 41 | 45 | 49 |
| 20 | 32 | 38 | 43 | 48 | 54 | 59 | 64 |
| 25 | 39 | 45 | 51 | 58 | 64 | 70 | 77 |
| 30 | 45 | 52 | 59 | 67 | 74 | 81 | 89 |
| 35 | 50 | 58 | 66 | 74 | 83 | 91 | 99 |
| 40 | 54 | 63 | 72 | 81 | 90 | 99 | 108 |
| 45 | 57 | 67 | 76 | 86 | 95 | 105 | 114 |
| 50 | 60 | 70 | 80 | 90 | 100 | 110 | 120 |
| 55 | 62 | 73 | 83 | 93 | 104 | 114 | 125 |
| 60 | 64 | 75 | 85 | 96 | 107 | 118 | 128 |
| 65 | 66 | 76 | 87 | 98 | 109 | 120 | 131 |
| 70 | 67 | 78 | 89 | 100 | 112 | 122 | 133 |
| 75 | 68 | 79 | 90 | 102 | 113 | 124 | 136 |
| 80 | 69 | 80 | 92 | 103 | 115 | 126 | 137 |

\* At 50 yr.
Source: Volume, yield and stand tables for second-growth southern pines, U. S. Dept. Agr., *Misc. Publ. No. 50* (1929).

**Table 23. Lodgepole Pine: Height in Feet of Average Dominant and Codominant Trees, by Site Class**

| Age (yr.) | Site class | | | | |
|---|---|---|---|---|---|
| | V | IV | III | II | I |
| 40 | 18 | 26 | 34 | 42 | 49 |
| 60 | 30 | 41 | 53 | 65 | 76 |
| 80 | 35 | 48 | 62 | 76 | 89 |
| 100 | 39 | 54 | 68 | 82 | 98 |
| 120 | 40 | 57 | 72 | 87 | 104 |
| 140 | 41 | 58 | 75 | 91 | 108 |
| 160 | 43 | 60 | 78 | 94 | 113 |
| 180 | 44 | 61 | 80 | 97 | 116 |
| 200 | 45 | 63 | 81 | 100 | 119 |

Source: Adapted from curves prepared by the Division of Forest Economics, Northern Rocky Mountain Forest & Range Exp. Sta.

## Table 24. Longleaf Pine: Height in Feet of Average Dominant Trees, by Site Index *

| Age (yr.) | Site index | | | | | | |
|---|---|---|---|---|---|---|---|
| | 40 | 50 | 60 | 70 | 80 | 90 | 110 |
| 15 | 14 | 18 | 22 | 26 | 31 | 33 | 41 |
| 20 | 20 | 26 | 31 | 36 | 40 | 46 | 57 |
| 25 | 25 | 32 | 38 | 45 | 51 | 57 | 70 |
| 30 | 30 | 37 | 44 | 52 | 59 | 66 | 81 |
| 35 | 33 | 41 | 49 | 57 | 66 | 74 | 90 |
| 40 | 36 | 45 | 53 | 62 | 71 | 80 | 98 |
| 45 | 38 | 47 | 57 | 66 | 76 | 85 | 104 |
| 50 | 40 | 50 | 60 | 70 | 80 | 90 | 110 |
| 55 | 42 | 53 | 63 | 74 | 84 | 94 | 115 |
| 60 | 44 | 55 | 65 | 77 | 87 | 98 | 120 |
| 70 | 47 | 58 | 70 | 82 | 93 | 105 | 128 |
| 80 | 49 | 61 | 73 | 86 | 98 | 110 | 135 |
| 90 | 51 | 63 | 76 | 89 | 101 | 114 | 139 |
| 100 | 52 | 65 | 77 | 90 | 103 | 116 | 142 |

* At 50 yr.
Source: Volume, yield and stand tables for second-growth southern pines, U. S. Dept. Agr., *Misc. Publ. No. 50* (1929).

## Table 25. Ponderosa Pine: Height in Feet of Average Dominant and Codominant Trees, by Site Index *

| Age (yr.) | Site index | | | | | | | | | | | |
|---|---|---|---|---|---|---|---|---|---|---|---|---|
| | 50 | 60 | 70 | 80 | 90 | 100 | 110 | 120 | 130 | 140 | 150 | 160 |
| 20 | 9 | 12 | 16 | 20 | 25 | 30 | 35 | 40 | 45 | 50 | 55 | 60 |
| 30 | 15 | 20 | 26 | 32 | 38 | 44 | 51 | 57 | 64 | 70 | 77 | 84 |
| 40 | 22 | 28 | 35 | 42 | 49 | 55 | 63 | 70 | 77 | 85 | 93 | 100 |
| 50 | 28 | 35 | 43 | 51 | 58 | 65 | 73 | 80 | 89 | 97 | 105 | 113 |
| 60 | 34 | 42 | 50 | 58 | 66 | 73 | 81 | 90 | 99 | 107 | 115 | 124 |
| 70 | 39 | 47 | 56 | 64 | 73 | 80 | 89 | 98 | 108 | 116 | 125 | 134 |
| 80 | 43 | 52 | 61 | 70 | 79 | 88 | 97 | 106 | 116 | 124 | 133 | 143 |
| 90 | 47 | 57 | 66 | 75 | 85 | 94 | 104 | 113 | 123 | 132 | 142 | 152 |
| 100 | 50 | 60 | 70 | 80 | 90 | 100 | 110 | 120 | 130 | 140 | 150 | 160 |
| 110 | 53 | 63 | 74 | 84 | 95 | 106 | 116 | 127 | 137 | 147 | 158 | 168 |
| 120 | 55 | 66 | 77 | 88 | 100 | 111 | 122 | 133 | 144 | 154 | 165 | 175 |
| 130 | 57 | 69 | 80 | 92 | 104 | 116 | 128 | 139 | 151 | 161 | 172 | 182 |
| 140 | 59 | 71 | 83 | 96 | 108 | 121 | 133 | 145 | 157 | 167 | 179 | 189 |
| 150 | 60 | 73 | 86 | 99 | 112 | 125 | 138 | 151 | 163 | 173 | 185 | 195 |
| 160 | 61 | 75 | 89 | 102 | 116 | 129 | 143 | 156 | 169 | 179 | 191 | 201 |
| 170 | 62 | 77 | 91 | 105 | 119 | 133 | 147 | 161 | 174 | 184 | 196 | 206 |
| 180 | 63 | 78 | 93 | 108 | 122 | 136 | 151 | 165 | 179 | 189 | 201 | 211 |
| 190 | 63 | 79 | 95 | 110 | 125 | 139 | 154 | 169 | 183 | 194 | 205 | 216 |
| 200 | 64 | 80 | 97 | 112 | 128 | 143 | 157 | 172 | 187 | 198 | 209 | 220 |

* At 100 yr.
Source: W. H. Meyer, Yield of even-aged stands of ponderosa pine, U. S. Dept. Agr., *Tech. Bull. No. 630* (1938).

Table 26.  Red Pine: Height in Feet of Average Dominant Trees, by Site Class

| | Site class | | |
| Age (yr.) | Poor | Average | Good |
|---|---|---|---|
| 20 | 15 | 19 | 24 |
| 30 | 24 | 31 | 37 |
| 40 | 33 | 43 | 49 |
| 50 | 40 | 52 | 60 |
| 60 | 46 | 60 | 69 |
| 80 | 55 | 72 | 82 |
| 100 | 62 | 80 | 93 |
| 120 | 65 | 85 | 100 |
| 140 | 67 | 88 | 104 |
| 160 | 68 | 89 | 106 |

Source: F. H. Eyre and Paul Zehngraff, Red pine management in Minnesota, U. S. Dept. Agr., *Circ. No. 778* (1948).

Table 27.  Shortleaf Pine: Height in Feet of Average Dominant Trees, by Site Index *

| | Site index | | | | | | |
| Age (yr.) | 40 | 50 | 60 | 70 | 80 | 90 | 100 |
|---|---|---|---|---|---|---|---|
| 10 | 10 | 13 | 15 | 18 | 20 | 22 | 25 |
| 15 | 15 | 19 | 23 | 26 | 30 | 33 | 37 |
| 20 | 20 | 25 | 30 | 34 | 39 | 44 | 49 |
| 25 | 24 | 30 | 36 | 42 | 48 | 54 | 60 |
| 30 | 28 | 35 | 42 | 49 | 56 | 63 | 70 |
| 35 | 32 | 40 | 47 | 55 | 64 | 71 | 79 |
| 40 | 35 | 44 | 52 | 61 | 70 | 78 | 87 |
| 45 | 38 | 47 | 57 | 66 | 75 | 85 | 94 |
| 50 | 40 | 50 | 60 | 70 | 80 | 90 | 100 |
| 60 | 44 | 55 | 66 | 77 | 88 | 99 | 110 |
| 70 | 47 | 59 | 71 | 82 | 94 | 106 | 117 |
| 80 | 50 | 62 | 74 | 86 | 99 | 111 | 123 |
| 90 | 52 | 64 | 77 | 90 | 103 | 115 | 128 |
| 100 | 53 | 66 | 79 | 93 | 106 | 119 | 133 |

* At 50 yr.
Source: Volume, yield and stand tables for second-growth southern pines, U. S. Dept. Agr., *Misc. Publ. No. 50* (1929).

**Table 28. Slash Pine: Height in Feet of Average Dominant Trees, by Site Index** *

| Age (yr.) | Site index | | | | |
|---|---|---|---|---|---|
| | 60 | 70 | 80 | 90 | 100 |
| 15 | 29 | 34 | 39 | 43 | 48 |
| 20 | 36 | 42 | 48 | 54 | 61 |
| 25 | 42 | 49 | 56 | 63 | 71 |
| 30 | 48 | 56 | 63 | 71 | 79 |
| 35 | 52 | 61 | 69 | 77 | 86 |
| 40 | 55 | 64 | 73 | 83 | 92 |
| 45 | 58 | 67 | 77 | 87 | 96 |
| 50 | 60 | 70 | 80 | 90 | 100 |
| 55 | 62 | 72 | 83 | 93 | 103 |
| 60 | 64 | 74 | 85 | 95 | 106 |

* At 50 yr.
Source: Volume, yield and stand tables for second-growth southern pines, U. S. Dept. Agr., *Misc. Publ. No. 50* (1929).

**Table 29. Second-Growth Eastern White Pine in the Northeast: Height in Feet of Average Dominant Trees, by Site Class**

| Age (yr.) | Site class | | |
|---|---|---|---|
| | III | II | I |
| 10 | 4 | 6 | 7 |
| 20 | 14 | 20 | 24 |
| 30 | 28 | 36 | 44 |
| 40 | 42 | 52 | 61 |
| 50 | 54 | 64 | 74 |
| 60 | 64 | 74 | 86 |
| 70 | 72 | 83 | 94 |
| 80 | 78 | 90 | 102 |
| 90 | 83 | 96 | 108 |
| 100 | 87 | 100 | 113 |

Source: E. H. Frothingham, White pine under forest management, U. S. Dept. Agr., *Bull. No. 13* (1914).

**Table 30. Second-Growth Eastern White Pine in the Lake States: Height in Feet of Average Dominant Trees, by Site Index** *

| Age (yr.) | Site index | | | | |
|---|---|---|---|---|---|
| | 45 | 50 | 60 | 70 | 75 |
| 30 | 24 | 27 | 32 | 38 | 41 |
| 40 | 35 | 39 | 47 | 55 | 59 |
| 50 | 45 | 50 | 60 | 70 | 75 |
| 60 | 53 | 59 | 71 | 82 | 89 |
| 70 | ... | 67 | 80 | 93 | ... |
| 80 | ... | 74 | 88 | 103 | ... |
| 90 | ... | 79 | 94 | 110 | ... |
| 100 | ... | 83 | 99 | 115 | ... |
| 110 | ... | 86 | 103 | 120 | ... |
| 120 | ... | 88 | 106 | 123 | ... |

* At 50 yr.
Source: S. R. Gevorkiantz, Lake States Forest Exp. Sta. (1933).

Table 31. Second-Growth Western White Pine: Height in Feet of Average Dominant Trees, by Site Index *

| Age (yr.) | Site index | | | |
|---|---|---|---|---|
| | 40 | 50 | 60 | 70 |
| 20 | 10 | 12 | 14 | 16 |
| 40 | 30 | 38 | 45 | 53 |
| 60 | 49 | 61 | 73 | 86 |
| 80 | 66 | 82 | 98 | 115 |
| 100 | 79 | 99 | 118 | 138 |
| 120 | 88 | 110 | 132 | 154 |
| 140 | 94 | 117 | 141 | 164 |
| 160 | 98 | 122 | 146 | 171 |

\* At 50 yr.
Source: Irvine T. Haig, Second-growth yield, stand, and volume tables for the western white pine type, U. S. Dept. Agr., *Tech. Bull. No. 323* (1932).

Table 32. Mixed Conifer Old-Growth Forests of California: Height in Feet of Average Dominant and Mature Trees, by Site Index *

| Age (yr.) | Site index | | | | | |
|---|---|---|---|---|---|---|
| | 75 | 100 | 125 | 150 | 175 | 200 |
| 50 | 30 | 41 | 53 | 66 | 80 | 98 |
| 100 | 52 | 67 | 82 | 102 | 122 | 141 |
| 150 | 64 | 84 | 100 | 122 | 144 | 164 |
| 200 | 70 | 92 | 112 | 135 | 158 | 179 |
| 250 | 73 | 97 | 120 | 144 | 168 | 191 |
| 300 | 75 | 100 | 125 | 150 | 175 | 200 |
| 350 | 77 | 103 | 129 | 155 | 181 | 207 |
| 400 | 79 | 105 | 133 | 159 | 185 | 212 |
| 500 | 82 | 110 | 138 | 165 | 192 | 220 |

\* At 300 yr. Measure Dunning Class 3 ponderosa pine, sugar pine, Douglas-fir or white fir.
Source: Duncan Dunning, A site classification for the mixed conifer selection forests of the Sierra Nevada, Calif. Forest & Range Exp. Sta., *Res. Note No. 28* (1942).

**STAND IMPROVEMENT. Rules-of-Thumb for Thinning.** Several rules-of-thumb are useful as guides to desirable stand density. These guides are not intended to serve as marking rules for thinning but as rough checks on the need for or the result of thinning.

1. $D$ plus $x =$ desired spacing in feet, in which $D =$ average d.b.h. in inches, and $x =$ a factor, between 2 and 6. The factor "2" appears to work well for a conservative thinning in young stands of slow-growing, tolerant species like spruce or balsam; "4" is frequently used for northern pines like white or red pine up to 8 in. d.b.h. In pole size, second-growth southern pines, "6" has been advocated as a factor. A single factor for all species and diameters will be unreliable.

2. $D$ times $x =$ desired spacing in feet. This has the advantage of greater consistency, regardless of tree diameters, than the "$D$ plus" rule. For example, the factor "1.75" closely approximates a basal area of 80 sq. ft. Hence, if the desired stocking is about 80 sq. ft., "1.75" is a usable factor. It is recommended in Appalachian and southern regions.

3. Tree height divided by $x$ = desired spacing in feet, in which $x = 6$ or $7$ for tolerants, 5 or 6 for intermediates, 4 or 5 for intolerants. This rule has been used successfully in Lake States conifers.

A thinning method so simple in application as to be considered a rule-of-thumb is "line" or "row" thinning. Every third to sixth row, in closely spaced coniferous plantations, is clear-cut regardless of individual tree dominance or condition. Thus, a thinning intending to remove 20 percent of the basal area would cut every fifth row. Economy of operation and ease of supervision are advantages in favor of this method.

A good principle to employ in thinning is that of planning stand development around selected final crop trees. Other trees which are left in early thinnings should be selected to use space temporarily between the final crop trees and to serve as trainers.

**Tools for Thinning and Cleaning.** For shrubs or trees 1½ in. or less in diameter:

> Pruning shears, two-hand types.
> Machete, 1¾ lb. weight, 20-in. blade.
> Woodman's Pal, 2 lb. weight, 16-in. blade, or equivalent.

For trees 1½ to 4½ in.:

> Axe, s.b. or d.b., wide blade, 2½ lb., 28-in. handle, or 3½ lb., 34–36-in. handle.
> Avoid heavy axes with long handles.

For trees 5 in. and over:

> Frame or bow saw, 36–42-in. blade. Unskilled men have difficulty using as a one-man saw for felling. Excellent for bucking and effective for felling in the hands of skilled men.
> One-man crosscut, 36–48 in.
> One-man power chain saw, 18–24 in.
> Portable circular power saw on sulky, 30-in. blade (not effective on hilly, broken ground).

Efficient use of the sawyer's time in thinning demands a second man with a pike pole. By pushing against the upper bole of the tree being cut, he prevents the saw from being pinched and eliminates the necessity of an undercut by directing the fall.

**Tools and Chemicals for Sanitation and Liberation Cutting.** The conventional tree-felling tools also are used for this type of cutting. However, to overcome subsequent sprouting of hardwoods or to eliminate fire and insect hazards from down or girdled conifers, special methods of killing trees are employed:

**Girdling.** This is done by making a single ring of hacks or chips with an axe or chain saw completely around the trunk. If the cambium is completely severed and the cuts go well into the sapwood, the crown will die, but there is no assurance of eliminating sprouts from any point below the cut.

A more complete but slower kill will result by cutting two rings of hacks 6 in. or more apart and stripping off the intervening bark. By severing the inner bark and cambium only and leaving the sapwood intact, the tree roots are starved, hence lose their capacity to sprout.

**Tree poisons.** Caustic soda, arsenic trioxide, sodium chlorate, and sodium arsenite historically have been used as silvicides. Because they are violently poisonous and dangerous to use, these compounds have been mostly displaced by Ammate (ammonium sulfamate) and the lethal hormones such as 2,4–D and 2,4,5–T.

**Use of Ammate.** For trees up to 4 in., cut off completely, leaving a V-shaped stump. Put a heaping tablespoon of Ammate crystals in the V. Dry crystals are also effective in notches or cups made near the ground by two downward axe-cuts (one is 1 in. above the other and the chip is pried out). Three notches are sufficient for 6-in. trees, and an additional notch for each 2-in. increase in diameter is effective. One tablespoon of Ammate is put in each.

Ammate also is used in solution, 4 lb. per gal. of water, applied in a row of axe-cuts or "frills" made completely around the trunk or in holes spaced at 4- to 8-in. intervals around the trunk. The frills are made by downward, slanting cuts with an axe or sharp spud, well into the sapwood, and the solution is poured into the girdle. The holes are made by an auger or by an (increment) **poisoning axe.** Glass jugs or watering cans with nozzles plugged with perforated corks make good dispensers. To be effective, solutions or crystals of all poisons must be applied to freshly cut wood.

Ammate crystals can be purchased at large seed stores, farm supply stores, drug companies, and through agricultural cooperatives.

**Precautions.** Ammate is very corrosive. The spray gun should be cleaned promptly and thoroughly after each use. Rinse it first with clean water to which lime has been added, then oil the metal parts with lightweight lubricating oil. Other metal equipment should also be rinsed thoroughly. Prolonged handling of Ammate may irritate the skin. Workmen should avoid wearing wet gloves and clothes which have been dipped in Ammate solution or on which Ammate crystals have been spilled.

Ammate is likely to injure or kill any vegetation it touches. Do not spill or spray it on desirable plants.

Before much time or money is spent in applying Ammate to trees other than those where its results have been proved, the dosage and methods of application should be tested on at least 10 trees. If the trees are poisoned in fall or winter, an examination in the middle of the following summer should tell if the poison will work. If the poison is applied in spring or summer, results cannot be judged accurately until midsummer a year later.

**Use of hormone sprays.** The relatively new chemical 2,4–D was developed and used as a killer of broad-leaved succulent weeds. It was later discovered also to be effective on certain woody plants—both shrubs and trees. The resistance of some species to 2,4–D spurred the development of the highly effective but somewhat more expensive, 2,4,5–T. This has been successfully used on many tree species. A solution composed of varying proportions of 2,4–D and 2,4,5–T is also available and is marketed usually as a "brush killer." The carrier for any of these may be water, diesel oil, fuel oil, or kerosene.

The hormone sprays may be used in any one of three ways: as a basal spray, stump spray, or foliage spray. The chemical concentration and method of application will be determined by the factors of species, effectiveness of chemical, cost of chemical and carrier, time of year, and proximity of valuable species which are not to be injured. Basal spraying with oil may be done at any time during the year. The quickest results are obtained during the growing season. This method requires that the plant be thoroughly sprayed from ground line up to 12–15 in., completely around the tree until the solution reaches the point of runoff. Higher **volume** appears to be more important than higher **concentrations.** Foliage spraying in a water solution is most effective on plants not more than 8 ft. tall and when done about mid-growing season. Stump spraying is done immediately after cutting; for best results in the prevention of sprouting, the cut surface and the bark to ground line are wet down to the point of runoff.

On species such as beech, which sprout freely from their roots, a second application, usually an aqueous foliage spray the following summer, will be required after basal or stump spraying to obtain a complete kill.

**Warning.** Residual solutions or deposits in spray equipment will damage susceptible plants. Hence, do not use hormone spray equipment for insecticidal or other plant applications. Neither 2,4–D nor 2,4,5–T is harmful to wildlife or to humans, nor are they corrosive on metal.

**Chemi-peeling.** This is a relatively new technique for getting the bark off standing timber. It involves the application of a solution of sodium arsenite to a freshly peeled girdle around the trunk. During the late spring and early summer, when the cambium is growing rapidly and peeling is easy, a girdle of bark 4 to 6 in. wide is removed from the trunk, as low down as feasible. The freshly exposed wood is then thoroughly painted with a sodium arsenite solution approximating 3 lb. per gal. Care must be taken to protect the skin, especially the hands and arms, from contact with the solution.

During the season of active growth the outer layers of wood cells carry most of the water supply up to the leaves. The arsenite passes into this water column and is quickly translocated upward, killing the cambium; downward movement at this season is small. Some species die quickly, others retain their foliage until autumn. Sometimes the bark can be peeled the same season. If left over winter, the bark loosens and much of it will fall off.

Chemi-peeling permits the treatment of enough trees during a relatively short season to insure a year-round production of peeled wood, once a backlog of treated material has been developed. It is cleaner, faster, and less laborious than sap-peeling. Standing dead, some of the conifers lose a good deal of moisture. The chief handicap is the time lag between treatment and harvest.

**Rules, Methods, and Tools for Pruning.** The following material covers the removal of side branches from standing trees in order to produce knot-free lumber. To improve the shape of Christmas trees by shearing, see page 6·59.

**Rules and methods.** Confine pruning to species and individuals which are capable of producing high-grade products. Timber for pulpwood, railroad ties, etc., or such species as Scotch, jack, Virginia, or lodgepole pines would not be economically pruned.

The wounds on conifers usually are sealed by resin, and there is little danger of infection by wood-decaying organisms as a result of pruning. In hardwoods, however, the exposure of wood over 2 in. in diameter creates a source of infection. Furthermore, hardwoods frequently develop suckers at the point of pruning, which tend to nullify the benefit of the operation.

Because there is a limit to the number of quality trees that can be grown on a given area, no more than 200 to 300 trees per acre should be treated. In dense stands of species with numerous and long-persistent limbs, pruning of a much larger number of trees to a height of about 6 ft. may be a necessary preliminary to further pruning or to other cultural work.

Good pruning practice requires two or three operations: the first when trees are not less than 3 in. nor more than 5 in. d.b.h., at which time branches are removed to a height of 6 or 7 ft., or what can be reached from the ground with short-handled tools. Later operations will remove side branches up to a height of 17 ft. but will take no more than the lower one-third of the live branches. (The so-called "Russian method," known also as bud pruning or finger budding, which annually removes all lateral buds, thus preventing the formation of side branches, still is in the experimental stage.) American experience has demonstrated that growth is depressed following heavy removal of live limbs. If pruning is delayed until trees get above 6 in. d.b.h., costs will increase because of larger branches, and the larger core of knotty wood will reduce the value of the log for lumber.

Pruning becomes a difficult operation at heights above 7 ft. Four methods have been employed, none of which is wholly without fault. Pruning from a ladder is slow, cumbersome, and is done at considerable risk to the operator. When used, the ladder should be a narrow-top, wide-base type, under 16 ft. in length. The "Tarzan" method calls for an agile operator, clothed in stout garments, who climbs to the topmost point of pruning. From that place he works down the stem, sawing off branches en route. On thick-barked species like Douglas-fir and on trees up to 12 in. d.b.h., tree climbers wearing multiple spurs have been used. These spurs do not penetrate the inner bark and permit the operator to climb and remove limbs with relative safety. Pole saws are most frequently used (see below), but the problem of obtaining a pole handle stiff enough to provide pressure to the saw but not so heavy as to be tiresome still remains to be solved. Sawdust which falls in the operator's eyes and heavy branches which pull off bark strips before they are completely severed are other drawbacks. Goggles are recommended to protect workmen's eyes.

**Tools.** 1. Axes. Both single- and double-bit axes have been used successfully to knock off dead lower branches. As a cutting tool for live branches, however, axes are not recommended except in the hands of careful, skilled workmen. They are distinctly hazardous for use off the ground.

2. Clubs. Any club or mace-type tool will break off dead limbs and one in particular, the Hebo pruning club, has been used in the Northwest. Although admittedly faster and safer to use than other tools, most foresters have been reluctant to recommend tools which do not produce clean cuts, flush with the bole.

3. Shears. Most pruning shears do not cut close enough to be satisfactory. Pole models are especially bad because of this reason and because they are tiring to use. The most satisfactory is the type designed to cut close to the main stem—the Porter Pointcut, for example. Although heavy and not efficient for heights above 8 ft., this tool severs live branches under 1½ in. faster than any other tool. Furthermore, it is not subject to gumming, as are saws.

4. Saws. All types of hand saws and some power saws have been tried. Consensus favors the hand saw as the best all-around tool for pruning. It is the easiest and safest to use and does less damage to the tree. The most satisfactory models should have the following specifications: single edge, pull stroke, 5- to 7-point regular teeth, slightly curved blade made of 17-gauge material. For pruning below 7 ft., the length of blade is not important; above 7 ft. and when the saw is used on a pole, the blade should not exceed 16 in. in length. From 8 to 12 ft., use an 8-ft. pole; from 13 to 17 ft., use a 12-ft. pole.

To remove branches up to 17 ft. in well-stocked stands requires less than 5 minutes per man per tree. Vigorous, dominant, or more or less open-grown trees are likely to require a total time of about 12 minutes for pruning in three separate stages to a height of 17 ft. These are the best types of trees to prune because they make rapid diameter growth.

## MANAGING FORESTS FOR CHRISTMAS-TREE PRODUCTION.

**Christmas Trees as a By-Product.** Fully 90 percent of the Christmas trees marketed in the United States come from natural stands and in all probability well over one-half of this as a secondary crop from forests managed for timber. Some forest managers are taking advantage of the Christmas-tree market to thin their stands systematically.

The harvesting of Christmas trees as a by-product is dependent upon the silvicultural practices that are followed in the harvesting of the timber crop. Where the clearcutting and seed tree methods are used, the period of Christmas-tree harvest is usually short lived, depending upon the time it takes the reproduction to outgrow the maximum size of tree that can be marketed, usually 8 ft. When the selection or shelterwood system is used, the cropping of Christmas trees can be continued as new production is established. Since the principal sizes demanded by the Christmas-tree market is for 2 to 6 ft., thinnings are confined to the early stages in the development of the timber stand. The success of this method of making thinnings and release cuttings necessitates that the stump of each Christmas tree that is harvested be killed so as to eliminate the development of witches'-brooms from the live branches left on the stump.

**Christmas Trees as a Continuous Crop.** Landowners who devote their entire time to the production of Christmas trees find that in the neighborhood of 1,000 acres of naturally reproduced stands or from 250 to 500 acres of planted trees represent an economic unit.

**Management practices.** The management practices necessary on naturally reproduced and planted stands vary considerably. On the other hand, both have many common problems which can be handled in essentially the same manner. As in any forest operation, protection from fire comes first and, because of the high value of the crop, protection methods can be applied more intensely. The same applies to the other common enemies of managed forests such as diseases, insects, grazing, and trespass.

Permanent improvements are a must. The short cutting cycle demands a road system that permits access to the entire area. It is a necessity for efficient harvesting and is an essential part for an effective fire protection system since it provides both access and firebreaks. Open areas are necessary for concentration yards. Skid roads are usually cut prior to harvesting. Tight fences are important and in some localities are a means of reducing theft.

**Silvicultural practices.** 1. Weeding. The weeding of undesirable trees, especially hardwoods, from a Christmas-tree farm is an annual cost that must be faced by all operators, even those who plant their original stand. Many of the associated species frequently grow much faster than the tree that is being managed for Christmas-tree production. This is especially true of hardwoods which have a faster growing rate and often originate as sprouts from stumps cleared in the process of preparing the site. Modern weedicides may be used quite successfully in most plantations since the majority of the conifers that are commonly used for Christmas-tree production are immune to these chemicals. The Christmas-tree grower who neglects this operation soon finds himself confronted with a major expenditure that may become prohibitive. Planted Christmas-tree stands that are spaced wide enough to allow mechanical cultivation make this job easier but even then there is a considerable amount of weeding that must be done periodically. When chemicals fail, hand methods are necessary and are costly.

2. Thinning. Thinning is necessary if Christmas-tree farms are to be kept productive. When trees become too thick they quickly lose the quality of a high-grade, marketable product. There is only one remedy, that is to remove some of the trees so as to give additional growing space to those that remain. Thinnings

may be made at two different periods throughout the year: during harvest time and in summer or slack periods when labor is available. Thinnings that are made during harvest must stand the high labor costs that usually exist at this season. In practically all localities at this time of the year those who are engaged in Christmas-tree cutting demand considerably more than the prevailing wage. When thinnings are made at this season it is important to keep the following facts in mind: (1) The tree that should be removed will usually be of poor quality but should be marketable, and in this way accomplish the thinning without additional expense. (2) Save the best trees to increase in size and improve in quality for a later cut. (3) Kill the stump by removing all of the green branches. It is not practical to do this as an off-season job because it is extremely difficult to find these stumps at a later date. If left, the lower branches soon fill in the openings, making it impossible for the trees that remain to take advantage of the additional growing space.

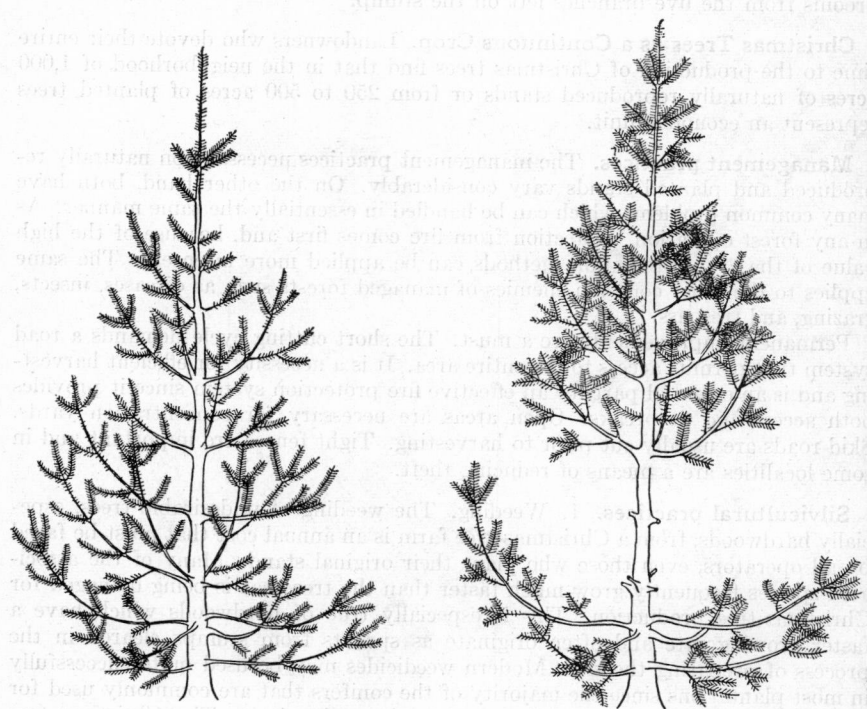

A tree approximately 15 yr. old. Too thin and sparsely foliated to make a marketable Christmas tree.

The same tree after partial pruning to concentrate more growth in the top. Note the whorl of branches near the ground.

**Fig. 6. Christmas trees—pruning.**

Thinnings that are made between harvests, since they represent a direct expense, should be done carefully. The trees that are usually removed are forked and crooked, those that have thin and deformed crowns, trees that are being damaged by disease or parasites, spiked-topped and umbrella or moss-covered trees, and stumps or trees that cannot be improved by pruning. Since it is necessary to keep expenses to a minimum, only those should be cut whose removal will make more room for an adjacent tree of better quality. A study of Christmas-tree operations where thinnings of this nature have been made indicates that the average operator has a tendency to cut too heavily. Frequent light thinnings are best. The operator must keep in mind that both vertical and horizontal dimensions must be considered—horizontal space to permit proper crown development and vertical space to allow smaller trees to reach the light.

3. Pruning. Pruning as it is now applied in the management of Christmas trees, especially in the Northwest, involves the removal of the lower limbs of thin-foliaged trees. Most conifers occasionally produce spiked tops and thin foliage. It usually takes place in those areas where growing conditions are especially good or during a wet cycle. Practice has shown that the removal of part of the lower branches stimulates a heavier growth in the remainder of the top (Fig. 6). This sometimes will cause the crown to thicken enough in two or three years so that the tree can be marketed. The expense of such an operation depends upon the distribution of the trees in the stand. It is more commonly applied in those stands that have originated from natural reproduction. Those who have successfully applied thinning for this purpose confine their operation to the following types of trees: (1) those that are decidedly thin-topped and are not merchantable at the time of thinning; (2) those that will produce a 4- to 6-ft. tree in 2 to 4 yr. after it has been pruned (it is not considered practical to prune smaller trees; they bring low returns and there is a possibility that the crowns will thicken without this operation); (3) trees that will not be overtopped by others before they develop sufficiently to be marketed; (4) trees that are now retarding the development of smaller ones and which after pruning will release these for fuller development; (5) those trees that are forked or have poorly formed crowns; and (6) those which are infested with mistletoe or some type of disease.

Severe pruning may cause the foliage of the trees to become yellow, and it sometimes requires 2 to 3 yr. for them to regain their normal color. In addition to this type of pruning some operators find it desirable to slash the bark on one or two, and sometimes three, sides of the stem. The theory is that this will further retard growth and further assist in the development of a compact crown. This is perhaps the most debatable practice now in use. Some operators can see no beneficial results while others find it necessary to combine both pruning and bark slashing to obtain a satisfactory response.

Forked trees sometimes result from double leaders or when two stump branches develop together (Fig. 7). Two trees about the same size that are growing together can seldom be marketed because both are flat-sided. There are two ways of salvaging trees that develop in this manner. The more common practice is to remove one in the course of the thinning operation, leaving the one remaining to develop in a satisfactory manner. Another method which is practiced successfully by some Christmas-tree operators is to separate the two trees with a short stick. As long as they are not more than 4 ft. in height, both can develop satisfactorily, but one of the trees should be removed as soon as possible; that is, as soon as one is rounded out enough to be marketable. This will make it possible for the remaining tree to develop without interference.

4. Shearing. Shearing is a silvicultural practice that has been applied to a limited extent, and primarily on Christmas-tree farms that originate from planted stock. Growers who have used this practice find that the increased quality of the trees increases the profits considerably. The ideal Christmas tree is one that is about one-half as broad as it is high. These proportions are sometimes impossible

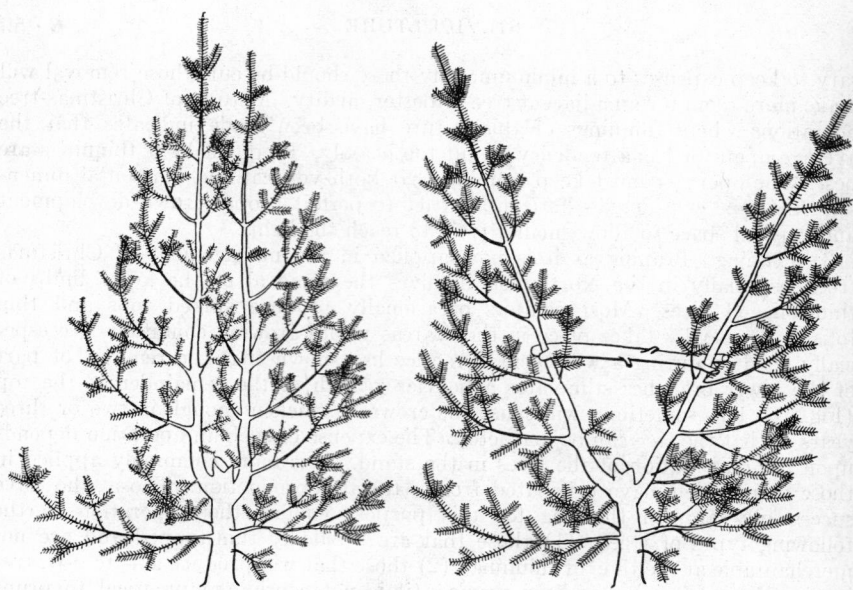

Christmas trees that have not been pruned sometimes develop two branches of equal vigor and height, but become flat-sided and unmerchantable.

This can be corrected by the application of a brace stick to give more growing space.

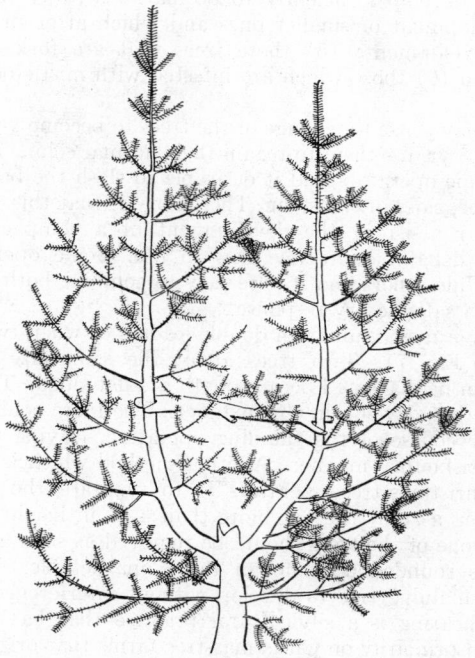

In a comparatively short time, one branch will develop a full crown, permitting it to be harvested.

**Fig. 7. Christmas trees—forked trees.**

to acquire in wide-spaced plantations without some shearing. No written material is available on the shearing of either balsam or Douglas-fir. However, a number of spruce plantations have been successfully sheared with profit. Spruce is perhaps the easiest to handle because shearing can be done almost any season of the year. Ordinary hedge-trimming shears can be used. The only point that must be watched by the operator is to do a complete job so as not to leave individual branches that may develop a lopsided tree. The terminal leader should be trimmed conservatively, usually not shorter than one foot. Side branches should be cut back proportionately, otherwise a flat top will develop.

The shearing of pine is a more exacting procedure. It is now practiced quite extensively in planted Christmas-tree farms in eastern and midwestern states where Scotch and red pine are cultivated. The most successful method is as follows: Shearing commences when the tree is 2 to 3 ft. tall and continues until it is harvested. In fast-growing plantations this sometimes can be accomplished in 3 to 4 yr., but once started it must be continued until the year before the tree is marketed. More specifically, the procedure involves six distinct steps: (1) Prune directly after the new shoots become stiff and the needles show bloom, that is, as soon as they take on the same cast as the older needles. The approximate time for pruning in the northern hemisphere is between June 15 and July 15, depending upon the season. Late pruning may result in adventitious buds or in stag-headed trees. Most operators start as soon as three-fourths of the leaders in the stand show full development. Shoots pruned too soon will continue the elongation until all cells are fully developed and sometimes adventitious buds may send up new shoots. (2) Prune the terminal shoot back far enough to secure the desired spacing for the new whorls, usually not over 12 to 15 in. (3) Cut the laterals in the top whorl to about one-half the length of the terminal. This is necessary to prevent the development of a flat top. (4) If a lateral shoot in a whorl is short, it should have its tip clipped out and the other lateral shoots cut back to match it, otherwise it will grow past all the other shoots after they are pruned. Trees pruned at the right time will develop a short whorl of buds at the severed point. (5) Start pruning when the trees are about knee high and continue each year for 3 or 4 yr. if necessary, but do not prune the year the tree is to be marketed. (6) Prune the side branches so as to give the trees a good symmetrical form.

Most operators use an ordinary pruning knife for taking off the terminal buds of the leader and the top whorls. Side branches may be pruned with ordinary hedge-trimming shears. After the first shearing it will be found that a number of twin leaders frequently develop. When one of the forked leaders is snipped out the following year, choose the one nearest the center. If this practice is not followed a crook will occur in the top which may reduce the quality of the tree. The cost for this type of pruning varies from 5 to 10 cents for the entire operation, which may extend over 4 to 6 yr.

5. Stump Culture. Stump pruning is a practice that is used by all progressive Christmas-tree operators. It is common knowledge among most Christmas-tree farmers that two or more trees may be produced from the same stump. This is made possible by one of the side branches or an adventitious bud gradually developing into a leader and eventually a tree. This process can be hastened considerably by carefully pruning at the time the tree is harvested, and again 2 or 3 yr. later (Fig. 8). A second Christmas tree the same size as the one removed in the first harvest can in many cases be produced in half the time, providing pruning is practiced. Christmas-tree farmers who have taken advantage of this method have increased the production of their farms in a compara-

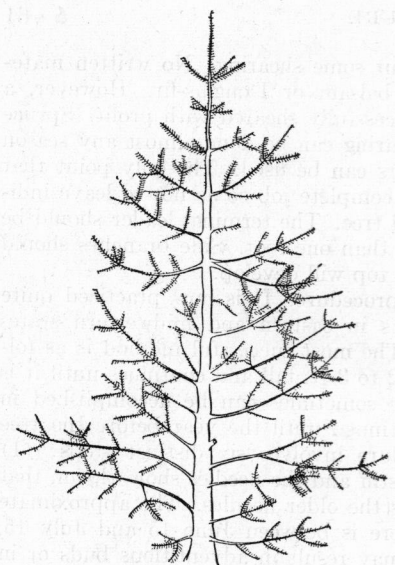

An 8-ft. Douglas-fir tree approximately 15 yr. old from seed, ripe for harvesting.

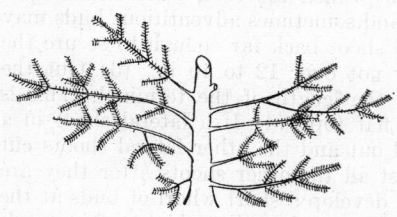

The stump has been pruned. Only those branches were removed that were competing with the main stem.

All but one branch was removed from the top whorl at the time the tree was harvested.

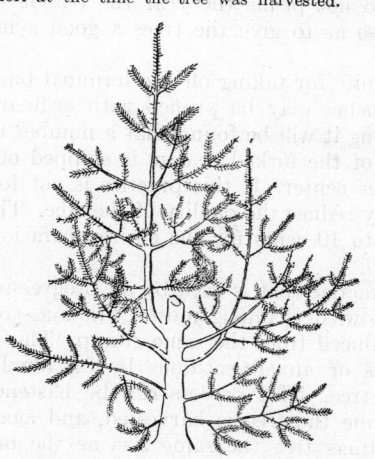

Two years after harvest. The branch from the top whorl has taken the lead. Those that remain have become bushy.

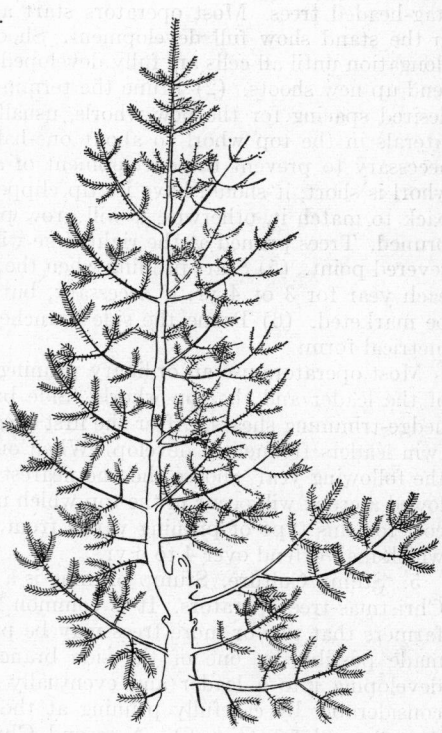

Seven years later another tree has developed from the top branch and will make a marketable Christmas tree the same size that was cut at the first harvest.

## Fig. 8. Christmas trees—stump culture.

tively short time. Stumps with attached side branches that are left in the woods, if not properly treated, soon develop into unprofitable witches'-brooms which take up valuable space and hamper the cutters in the process of harvesting the crop.

The first treatment of the stump can most profitably be carried out at the time the original tree is harvested. If allowed to grow without some preliminary pruning at this time, it sometimes fails to produce an outstanding leader and frequently requires a series of expensive pruning operations before it can be developed into a satisfactory tree (Fig. 8). Or it will develop two leaders which, if allowed to continue, will result in two low-quality, lopsided trees. These disadvantages can be eliminated by removing all but one branch from the top whorl at the time the original tree is harvested. Trained cutters who have used this method at harvest time are able to do the operation without additional expense.

A second pruning should be made 2 to 3 yr. after harvest. At this time two or three, perhaps four, branches should be removed but no more than is necessary to favor the growth of one side branch which in the majority of cases is the one that was left on the top whorl at the time of harvest. It is important that at least two growing seasons have elapsed after the original tree was cut. Were the stump to be severely pruned at the time of harvest it usually dies. It is worth emphasizing that it is necessary to do only enough pruning to release one main branch. As soon as this branch gains the leadership, the remaining branches grow considerably slower. To remove all of the side branches excepting one would be unnecessary, involve extra expense, and in addition will decrease the chance of producing a third or fourth tree from the same stump. Stump culture is best practiced where the trees are growing alone in the open or when adjoining trees are satisfactorily spaced.

6. **Slash Disposal.** The only time that Christmas-tree cutting produces enough slash to create a disposal problem is in the clearing of skid trails, brushing out roads, and in the long butts that are produced when Christmas trees are cut from the top of large trees. When slash resulting from cutting trails and brushing out roads reaches the point that it interferes with skidding and hauling, it should be burned or pulled into open areas and scattered. Long butts, if left untrimmed in the woods, develop a serious fire hazard and in addition hamper the operation of cutters in subsequent years, especially if they are not completely severed from the stumps. All side branches should be trimmed and scattered.

**SHELTERBELTS AND WINDBREAKS. Beneficial Influences.** The beneficial influences of windbreaks and shelterbelts have been well established by land users in the United States and many foreign countries. Such plantings diminish by as much as 20 to 30 percent the amount of fuel that is needed to heat a home. Livestock winter better on less feed and with greater weight gains in the protection of windbreaks and shelterbelts. Properly designed shelterbelts protect cultivated fields from wind erosion and give growing crops considerable protection from wind damage. The saving of one season's crops sometimes compensates for the entire cost of the planting. The average gain in crop yields will more than compensate for the area occupied by shelterbelts. The greatest returns have been realized from plantings established for the protection of orchards. The increase in grade of some fruits frequently runs as much as 25 to 50 percent. The accumulation of water in the form of snow within, and to the leeward of, the shelterbelts is an important factor in building up the ground water supply and providing moisture for growing crops.

The cumulative effect of shelterbelts systematically placed over large acreages has not been thoroughly studied. Such information as we have indicates that the cumulative effect is of considerable importance and should have a place in long-range community planning.

**Establishment.** Modern tree-planting methods, employing mechanical tree planters and specialized cultivating equipment, have stimulated the widespread establishment of both windbreaks and shelterbelts. Community action on the part of country groups and conservation and wildlife organizations has aided in various ways, such as in the acquisition of equipment, custom planting and cultivation, and in the development of community, state, and private nurseries for the production of a wide selection of high-quality nursery stock.

Successful establishment of shelterbelts demands careful attention to details, and adherence to the following well-proven rules:

1. **Planting stock.** The quality of planting stock for shelterbelts and windbreaks should be above that generally used for artificial reforestation.

> **Hardwoods:** Total height above root collar 18 to 30 in. before trimming for shipment; diameter measured at 1 in. above root collar, 7/32 to 3/8 in.
> **Conifers:** Total height 8 to 16 in.; caliper at root collar, 3/16 in. and over. Winter buds well developed, stock dormant, leaf structure showing definite fascicles or individual leaves.

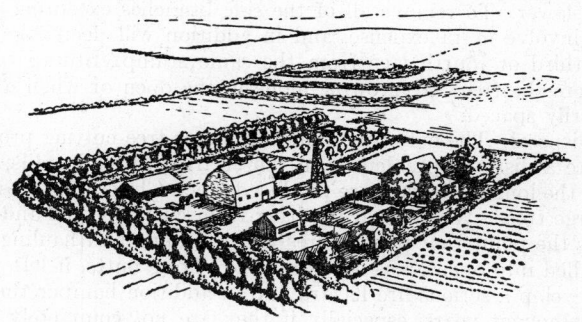

**Fig. 9. Windbreak plantings.**
Windbreaks should protect the entire farmstead and be oriented to intercept the more severe storms.

2. **The layout and location of windbreaks should be considered with care.** In areas where snow will accumulate, they should be placed at least 100 ft. away from buildings, roads, and feed lots. The plantings should be on the windward side and so oriented as to cover the directions from which the more severe winter storms come (Fig. 9). Poor composition, lack of protection and care, and failure to provide an adequate planting to protect the entire farmstead may create a hazard rather than a benefit. Shelterbelts, intended for the protection of cultivated fields, may follow the borders or for full protection be spaced at intervals of 10 rods to ¼ mi., traversing the field at right angles to the prevailing wind. On highly vulnerable areas, principal shelterbelts are sometimes supported by intermediate plantings (referred to occasionally as buffer strips) consisting of one or two rows which provide practically continuous protection. This combination provides the maximum protection with a minimum of planting space (Fig. 10).

3. **Poor composition has caused more inadequate shelterbelts and windbreaks than any other factor.** Shelterbelt plantings must stop ground winds and diffuse

upper air currents. In order to arrest ground surface air currents and retard higher air movement, plantings should contain both close-growing low shrubs and tall trees. Rarely can both high and low air movement be significantly affected by a single row of trees. Multiple-row plantings should follow the pattern indicated in Fig. 11, with a shrub row on the windward side followed by a low branching hardwood tree or a conifer, and in turn, by taller trees whose crowns break the upper air currents into large eddies, thereby extending the effectiveness of the planting to the maximum distance (Fig. 12). Where space permits, it is desirable to use the same combination on the leeward side. If that is not possible, it is especially important that the last row on the lee side be a conifer or a shrub. Too much emphasis cannot be placed upon the necessity for a dense shrub row. Failure of many belts is due to this factor alone. Wind having access under the branches will accelerate in velocity, and may therefore cause increased wind erosion and snow drifting.

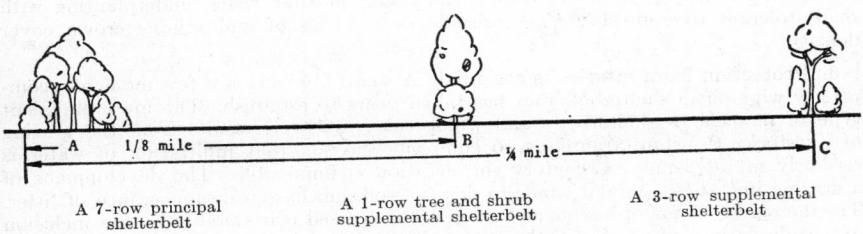

| A | 1/8 mile | B | ¼ mile | C |

A 7-row principal shelterbelt

A 1-row tree and shrub supplemental shelterbelt

A 3-row supplemental shelterbelt

**Fig. 10. Shelterbelts.**

Principal shelterbelts are sometimes supported by intermediate one-, two-, and three-row plantings. Such combinations provide the maxmium protection with a minimum of planting space.

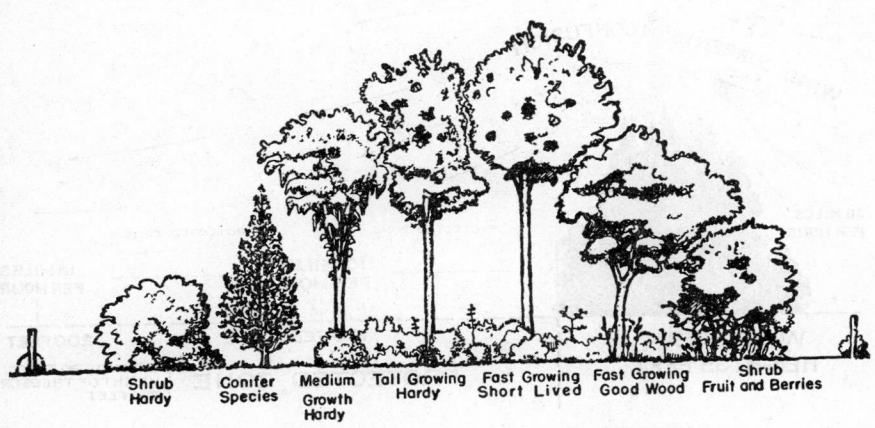

Shrub Hardy    Conifer Species    Medium Growth Hardy    Tall Growing Hardy    Fast Growing Short Lived    Fast Growing Good Wood    Shrub Fruit and Berries

**Fig. 11. Multiple-row planting for shelterbelt.**

Good composition, consisting of hardy conifers, hardwood trees, and close-growing shrubs, is the key to long-lived, effective shelterbelts.

4. **Early realization of the protection afforded by the planting is always desired.** This can be accomplished by careful planting of vigorous stock, thorough cultivation, and protection from grazing, fire, insects, and fungi. The more intensive the cultivation the faster the trees will grow. Cultivation between the trees in the rows by hoeing is very effective. On irrigated land the problem of cultivation is increased considerably because weeds respond to irrigation more quickly than trees and shrubs. Cultivation should continue until the crowns of the trees and shrubs touch sufficiently

to suppress at least 50 percent of the weeds and grass that would otherwise become established in the planting.

5. **Silvicultural problems sometimes become quite complex because shelterbelt and windbreak plantings create unnatural associations of trees and shrubs that are remote from their native habitats.** Careful consideration should be given as to the shade tolerance, root development, and growth requirements of the various kinds of trees and shrubs before they are planted together. Errors may not become evident for many years after planting. When the crowns of trees and shrubs close, silvicultural practices should be initiated that will increase the effectiveness and prolong the life of the planting. After the trees become crowded, trees with short crowns, less than one-third of the tree height, should be removed. Encouragement of healthy crown development without admitting enough light to start weed growth should govern the intensity and frequency of thinning. The production of usable products should be secondary. When crowns become thin in later years, underplanting with shade-tolerant trees or shrubs is desirable as a means of maintaining crown cover density.

6. **Protection from injuries is essential.** A small fire can, in a few moments, completely wipe out a shelterbelt that has taken years to establish. The most prevalent type of damage to shelterbelts and windbreaks, however, results from the grazing of livestock. Constant trampling so compacts the soil that infiltration of water is seriously retarded and satisfactory soil aeration is impossible. The development of a grazing line allows ground winds to dry the soil and hasten disappearance of litter. The damaging effects of insects and fungi are decreased considerably by the inclusion of a wide variety of species in the composition. Special control measures are sometimes necessary.

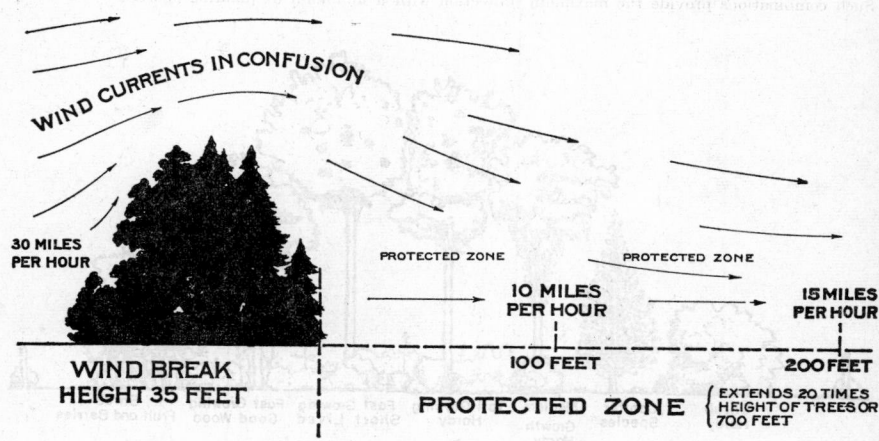

Fig. 12. Effect of windbreaks on wind velocity.
(U. S. Forest Service)

7. **The selection of the right trees and shrubs for each site is important.** A listing of all of the trees that might be used in shelterbelts throughout the United States would require space exceeding that available in this publication. Each locality has numerous well-established varieties of trees and shrubs that are known to be suited for shelterbelts and windbreaks. As a matter of policy a number of authorities in any particular locality should be consulted before undertaking an extensive planting program.

## BIBLIOGRAPHY

BAKER, F. S. 1934. *Theory and practice of silviculture.* McGraw-Hill Book Co., Inc., New York.

COMMONWEALTH FORESTRY BUREAU. *Forestry abstracts.* Oxford, England (quarterly).

DAUBENMIRE, R. F. 1946. The life zone problem in the northern intermountain region. *Northwest Science* 20(2):28–38.

DOMINION FOREST SERVICE. 1949. *Native trees of Canada.* Ottawa.

ISAAC, L. A. 1943. *Reproduction habits of Douglas-fir.* Charles Lathrop Pack Forestry Foundation, Washington, D. C.

MEYER, B. S., and D. B. ANDERSON. 1944. *Plant physiology.* D. Van Nostrand Co., Inc., New York.

OOSTING, HENRY J. 1948. *The study of plant communities.* W. H. Freeman & Co., San Francisco.

PRESTON, RICHARD J., JR. 1948. *Northern American trees.* Iowa State College Press.

SARGENT, CHARLES SPRAGUE. 1933. *Manual of the trees of North America (exclusive of Mexico).* Houghton Mifflin Co., Boston.

SOCIETY OF AMERICAN FORESTERS. 1954. Forest cover types of North America.

TOUMEY, J. W., and C. F. KORSTIAN. 1942. *Seeding and planting in the practice of forestry.* 3d ed. John Wiley & Sons, Inc., New York.

TOUMEY, J. W., and C. F. KORSTIAN. 1947. *Foundations of silviculture.* 2d. ed. John Wiley & Sons, Inc., New York.

U. S. DEPT. AGR.:
  1948. Tree planting in the central, Piedmont and southern Appalachian regions. *Farmers' Bull. 1994.*
  1949. *Trees. The yearbook of agriculture.*
  1950. Forest plantations in the Lake States. *Tech. Bull. No. 1010.*
  1954. Planting the southern pines. *Monograph No. 18.*

U. S. FOREST SERV.:
  1948. Woody plant seed manual. *Misc. Publ. No. 654.*
  1949. Timber stand improvement in the southern Appalachian region. *Misc. Publ. No. 693.*
  1953. *Check list of the native and naturalized trees of the United States (including Alaska).*

WEAVER, JOHN E., and FREDRIC E. CLEMENTS. 1929. *Plant ecology.* McGraw-Hill Book Co., Inc., New York.

# PROTECTION AGAINST FIRES

## CONTENTS

# PROTECTION AGAINST FIRES

## CONTENTS

## PROTECTION AGAINST FIRES

### Fire Prevention

**OBJECTIVE.** The purpose of fire prevention is to reduce the number of man-caused fires to the lowest practicable minimum. In planning and action, prevention efforts should be on a parity with other phases of fire control.

**ANALYSIS OF THE PROBLEM.** An analysis of the problem with which prevention must deal requires that localized risk and hazard surveys be made to determine:

1. Where fires occur—zones of different intensity and the reasons for this.
2. When fires occur—time of year and length of risk season.
3. What causes fires—general and specific causes.
4. Who causes fires—class and source of people responsible.
5. How fires start—specific and contributory conditions and circumstances.
6. Why fires occur—motives and reasons.

**ACTION.** The program of action directed at fire prevention includes:

1. Selection of appropriate prevention measures.
2. Administrative organization and timely application of selected measures.
3. Systematic, recurring evaluation as to relative success.

The following techniques and devices have been used singly or in combination to help control the various causative agents:

1. Debris burners.
   a. Personal contacts with potential or active burners.
   b. Laws and permits restricting burning season, time of day, or conditions.
   c. Encouragement and guidance in burning during safe periods.
   d. Organization of rural suppression crews.
   e. General education.
2. Hunters, fishermen, campers.
   a. Permits to use the woods.
   b. Club programs and committees.
   c. Closures during critical periods.
   d. Habitat improvement projects.
   e. Tours and demonstrations.
   f. General education and reminders.
3. Railroads.
   a. Hazard reduction on right-of-way.
   b. Spark arresters.
   c. Patrols and inspection.
   d. Personal contact with supervisors of maintenance crews.
   e. Organization and training of crews in fire suppression.
4. Logging, lumbering, and other woods operations.
   a. Restrictions on where, when, and how to operate.
   b. Fire tool requirements.
   c. Personal contact with supervisors and crews.
   d. Elimination of fires during critical periods.

**7·1**

    e. Organization and training of suppression crews.
    f. Hazard reduction.
    g. Inspections.
5. Incendiarists.
    a. Personal contacts with suspects.
    b. Law enforcement.
    c. General education.
6. General or "shotgun" methods to reach all groups and to create informed public opinion.
    a. Talks, lectures, motion pictures, and slides.
    b. Exhibits, signs, and newspaper and magazine articles.
    c. Radio—spot announcements, discussions, special programs.
    d. Tours, "show-me" demonstrations.
    e. Printed devices—rulers, blotters, calendars, booklets, etc.
    f. House-to-house canvass in hot spots.
    g. Organization and training of volunteer crews.
    h. "Keep Green" and "More Trees" projects.
    i. Teachers' guides, bibliographies, workshops.
    j. Closure of public areas during critical periods.
    k. Law enforcement, including personal contacts with judges and prosecuting officers.

An intangible but undoubtedly the most valuable preventive influence is an informed and indignant public opinion. Efficiently executed prevention efforts can develop such an attitude.

## SUGGESTIONS FOR IMPROVING FIRE PREVENTION EFFORTS.

1. Analyze and then attack the real reasons for fires.
2. Promote friendly, cooperative relations with the people who live, work, or travel in the area. Solicit their help.
3. Impress upon individuals their personal responsibility for fires. Long experience in the woods and in using fire breeds carelessness.
4. Carry out hazard and risk reduction activities.

## Fire Law Enforcement

Reducing the number of man-caused forest and range fires is a primary objective of protection. When friendly, tactful, and appropriate instructions, reminders, and appeals fail to accomplish results, and for those individuals who maliciously or negligently cause serious fires, law enforcement becomes necessary. Intelligent handling of legal actions is essential if the desired results are to be attained.

In law enforcement work it is necessary that one know thoroughly the locally applicable laws, regulations, and procedures for the jurisdiction in which the offense occurs. A knowledge of the limitations imposed by law on making arrests and searches is also necessary. Wherever possible the cooperation, assistance, and advice of experienced law enforcement officers should be solicited in the actual handling of criminal actions, and if practical such officers should handle the case. It is also very desirable that good cooperative relations be established with court and prosecuting officers, and that they understand the importance of fire prevention action.

**INVESTIGATION OF MAN-CAUSED FIRES.** Crime investigation is a highly technical profession in which experience and scientific equipment are of great value. However, a good field man, by the use of keen observation, common sense, and industry can often solve quite difficult fire cases with little or no assistance from experts. A knowledge of applicable laws, area topography, roads, trails, and the people who work in, live in, or use the area will be of assistance in fire investigations. Particularly valuable are friendly relations with people who know about others in the area and what goes on. The following suggestions may assist an investigator in his work.

**Preparation** in advance is important. Speed in reaching the scene of a fire is necessary to prevent possible obliteration of important information by fire fighters or by the fire itself. Be prepared with a notebook, map, camera, and other equipment.

**Observe** people, tracks, vehicles, and other items en route to and at the scene of the fire. Try to locate the point of origin and protect its vicinity from disturbance by fire fighters. Search systematically in widening circles from the point of origin.

**Clues** are anything which might be connected with the offense or its author. Anything is a potential clue which cannot be accounted for without reference to the offense. A case may hinge on what may seem to be a very unimportant clue.

**Evidence** is a clue which can be directly connected with the offense, its author, or is the result of the offending act. It is the material which can be used in court. It must be identifiable with the offense; its possession continuously from the time of discovery until presented in court must be established; and it must have been legally obtained.

**Record** immediately a description of everything seen, found, and done, with times, location, and details. Record conversations and information received. Prepare a detailed sketch map of the vicinity and locate thereon all pertinent data. All clues should be closely examined and a record made of dimensions, shapes, distinctive and unusual features, and other details.

**Handling** material is to be avoided until its description in place is recorded, and, if possible, photographed. Handle with care anything which may bear fingerprints. If the article is potentially useful as evidence, place an identification mark on it for future reference and guard the article from loss.

**Reconstruct** the offense by developing a working theory of the circumstances and conditions which resulted in the fire. Do not jump to conclusions, and be prepared to revise your theory as more evidence develops. Keep an open mind. Define the problem, reason out developments, and cast about for possible solutions. Test each theory, step by step, by observations.

**A complete case** must satisfactorily answer all of the following questions:

1. What was the offense?
2. Where was it committed?
3. When was it committed?
4. How was it accomplished?
5. Who did it?
6. Why did he do it?

Keep these six key questions constantly in mind, and test every theory and clue to see if it fits into the problem solution by helping to answer one or more of these questions. To be complete enough for presentation in court a case must have an unbroken chain of evidence which is (1) true, (2) complete, and (3) proved by evidence which will stand in court and convince a jury beyond a reasonable doubt.

**Interviewing Witnesses.** A knowledge of people, shrewdness, and tact are very important in interviewing witnesses. Before discussing a fire case with witnesses, including suspects, the investigator should have a knowledge of the circumstances and conditions and, if possible, know something about the habits and character of the witness or suspect.

It is very important that an investigator keep an open mind at all times. Few people like to talk to an investigator unless they have a real or an imagined "axe" to grind. Many witnesses will be evasive, untruthful, or overly positive in their statements. It is a well-known fact that most people do not always see or hear what they think they do because of faulty comprehension, poor observation, or an active imagination. All statements must therefore be carefully analyzed before they can be accepted.

**Take notes** as a witness tells his story, unless the witness is reluctant to talk while notes are being taken. If that is the case, let him tell his story and then promptly write it down and read back to him what has been written. The more complete the notes, the easier to requestion and go back over his story. When the statement appears to be complete, read it to the witness, ask for corrections, change anything he may wish to have changed, then try to have him sign the statement. Also, if possible, have it witnessed. It is desirable to put in writing the circumstances, time, and place of the interview.

**Truthful witnesses** are often reluctant to tell what they know. It is often best to start an interview with talk of things that interest them. Get the witness in a talkative mood, then gradually steer the subject around to the fire. Watch for indications of poor memory, influence of another's statements, strong feeling, temperament, and fear of consequences; requestion the witness on doubtful points.

**Hostile or untruthful witnesses** should be interviewed, if possible, alone and away from friends and familiar grounds. If the witness is a suspect, try to interview him before he realizes that he is suspected. Take detailed notes, be very businesslike, and let the witness tell any story he may wish. Write it down as he talks, then have it signed and witnessed. Then begin to question, starting at a time prior to the offense, and go minutely through the entire story. Contradictions may be revealed which will point up additional leads. Continue to take notes of the revised statement. Make no threats or promises.

**Preparation of a Case for Court Action.** When all possible evidence in a case has been secured, the facts must be recorded in a systematic and workable form. Arrange the material in chronological order, somewhat as follows:

1. The offense—what, where, when, how, by whom, why.
2. Information—(a) rumors, (b) clues.
3. Main evidence—facts (in order) with names of witnesses who will testify to them.
4. Evidence material for rebuttal or to meet possible surprise defense.
5. Appendix—maps, other data.

**Rules of Evidence for Court Presentation.** To be admissible in court, evidence must be:

1. Relevant—directly related to the facts at issue.
2. Competent—the kind of evidence which will prove any relevant fact alleged.
3. Material—having a direct bearing on the facts at issue, and not raising collateral issues.

## Fire Weather

**FIRE WEATHER FORECASTS.** Fire weather forecasts are used in prevention, presuppression, and suppression of forest fires. Pertinent weather forecasts, when combined with the current fire danger rating and tempered by fire causes known to be at work during the season, provide needed information for planning current fire control work (see "Fire Danger Rating," below, for amplification). Fire weather forecasts may be made by supplementing the fire danger rating obtained from fire danger stations with one's own local estimate of to-morrow's weather **or preferably** by supplementing the fire danger rating with special forest fire weather forecasts made by the U. S. Weather Bureau.

The U. S. Weather Bureau issues special fire weather forecasts from stations maintained at the following locations:

| | | | |
|---|---|---|---|
| Alabama | Montgomery | Massachusetts | Boston |
| Arizona | Phoenix | Missouri | Kansas City |
| Arkansas | Little Rock | Montana | Missoula |
| California | Los Angeles | New Mexico | Albuquerque |
| | Mt. Shasta | New York | Albany |
| | San Francisco | North Carolina | Asheville |
| Colorado | Denver | Pennsylvania | Philadelphia |
| Florida | Jacksonville | Oregon | Pendleton |
| | Miami | | Portland |
| | Tallahassee | Utah | Salt Lake City |
| Idaho | Boise | Washington | Olympia |
| Illinois | Chicago | | Seattle |
| Louisiana | Shreveport | | |

**FIRE DANGER RATING.** The term fire danger, or preferably "total" fire danger, refers to the total of both the constant and variable factors which determine whether forest, brush, or grass fires will start, spread, and do damage, and which determine the difficulty of their control. It represents the combined probability of fires starting, spreading, and doing damage **at a given time.** These factors are classified into two groups: constant factors, which are relatively unchanging in an area; and variable factors, which may change from day to day or hour to hour.

| Constant Factors | Variable Factors |
|---|---|
| Quantity, size, arrangement, and continuity of fuels | Moisture content of fuels |
| Age and condition of dead fuels | Seasonal changes in quantity and condition of fuels |
| Climatic characteristics that determine the intensity and duration of the fire season | Humidity of the air |
| | Wind velocity |
| | Wind direction |
| Topography | Temperature of the air and of fuel surfaces |
| Exposure to prevailing winds | |
| Kind of cover | Atmospheric stability |
| Natural fire breaks | Atmospheric visibility |
| Accessibility | Concentration of risk at a given time, and new or abnormal risks |
| Soils and rock | |
| Normal risks | |

The two lists are not entirely exclusive. For example, seasonal changes in hardwood forest fuels in fall and spring which result only from the dropping of leaves or the growth of new ones may be so apparent and of such regularity that their effect can be taken into account satisfactorily in setting up the normal fire season.

In distinguishing between constant and variable risks it is helpful to keep in mind the purpose of these classifications. Constant factors are those which vary **from place to place at any given time.** The objective of presuppression planning is to take them fully into account in permanent plans. The variable factors are those which vary **from time to time at any given place.** The purpose of fire danger ratings is to gauge from their wide fluctuations the potential fire fighting job from day to day.

In practice, the rating of fire danger is restricted to the variable factors. Usually it is further restricted to those variable factors which have a direct effect on the inflammability of fuels and the rate at which fire can be expected to spread in them. When so restricted it is called the "burning index."

**Purposes of Rating.** Fire danger ratings cannot replace experience and good judgment, but they provide a valuable guide to judgment in making administrative decisions. The more important purposes served by these ratings are outlined under "Fire Presuppression Planning," page 7 · 10.

**Methods of Rating.** Fire danger ratings are expressed either in numerical classes (generally 5 to 7), or in whole numbers on a scale of 0 to 100. In both cases the low numbers represent the least danger. Each class or number evaluates the combined effect of the variable fire danger elements. Seven degrees of fire danger are described on page 7 · 10. In all cases the ratings are based on measured data taken several times a day at "fire danger stations" which are maintained at representative locations throughout the protection unit.

The factors commonly measured are air temperature and relative humidity, moisture content of fuels (represented by a standard stick of some moisture absorbent material), wind velocity and direction, amount of current or recent precipitation, and the condition of grass and annual vegetation (from its lush to its cured state). However, few of the fire danger rating systems use all of these data directly.

The most significant factors are fuel moisture and wind. Because it is not commonly feasible to measure the moisture content of composite forest fuels directly, a standard to which the variations in typical fuels can be correlated is often taken instead. The fuel-moisture stick commonly used in the West and the basswood slats used in the East are familiar examples. However, other criteria can be used. In the Lake States the number of days since the last rain is substituted, and in areas where flash fuels are critical, relative humidity and temperature can provide a usable index. Air temperature and humidity, vegetative stage, and precipitation serve chiefly to supplement the data on fuel moisture. Combined data from such sources which reflect existing and prospective inflammability of fuels are then linked with wind velocity to produce a burning index.

**Rating Systems Now in Use.** The systems of rating fire danger now used in various parts of Canada and the United States differ chiefly in the relative weight assigned to fuel moisture as compared with wind velocity. In general, fuel moisture most decisively affects the proportion of all fires which will require action, while wind most decisively affects rate of spread. Therefore, in regions where the machinery of suppression is geared to the number of fires that must be attacked in a given period, it is logical to give most weight to the inflammability of fuels. Where fire hazards are such that each fire which starts has an almost unlimited threat, or "big-fire potential," it is logical to concentrate on the factors—principally wind velocity—which have the most effect on the rate of spread.

Fire danger meters are mechanical devices by which a rating can be determined for a given set of measurements. There is as yet no standard meter, even for one region. Significant variations in design arise from a difference in the purposes to be served; these may be fire prevention and reduction in the number of man-caused fires, or suppression and service to the dispatcher and fire boss.

**Obtaining Relative Humidity by Use of a Sling Psychrometer.** Use clean cotton wicking on the wet-bulb thermometer. Soak the cotton thoroughly in clean water which is at current air temperature. Whirl the instrument for 15 to

| DRY-BULB TEMPERATURE | 22 | 24 | 26 | 28 | 30 | 32 | 34 | 36 | 38 | 40 | 42 | 44 | 46 | 48 | 50 | 52 | 54 | 56 | 58 | 60 | 62 | 64 | 66 | 68 | 70 | 72 | 74 | 76 | 78 | 80 | 82 | 84 | 86 | 88 | 90 | 92 | 94 | 96 | 98 | 100 | 102 | 104 | 106 |
|---|---|---|---|---|---|---|---|---|---|---|---|---|---|---|---|---|---|---|---|---|---|---|---|---|---|---|---|---|---|---|---|---|---|---|---|---|---|---|---|---|---|---|---|
| 32 | 2 | 20 | 39 | 59 | 79 | | | | | | | | | | | | | | | | | | | | | | | | | | | | | | | | | | | | | | |
| 34 | | 8 | 25 | 43 | 62 | 81 | | | | | | | | | | | | | | | | | | | | | | | | | | | | | | | | | | | | | |
| 36 | | | 13 | 29 | 46 | 64 | 82 | | | | | | | | | | | | | | | | | | | | | | | | | | | | | | | | | | | | |
| 38 | | | 2 | 17 | 33 | 50 | 66 | 83 | | | | | | | | | | | | | | | | | | | | | | | | | | | | | | | | | | | |
| 40 | | | | 7 | 22 | 37 | 52 | 68 | 83 | | | | | | | | | | | | | | | | | | | | | | | | | | | | | | | | | | |
| 42 | | | | | 12 | 26 | 40 | 55 | 69 | 85 | | | | | | | | | | | | | | | | | | | | | | | | | | | | | | | | | |
| 44 | | | | | 4 | 16 | 30 | 43 | 56 | 71 | 85 | | | | | | | | | | | | | | | | | | | | | | | | | | | | | | | | |
| 46 | | | | | | 8 | 20 | 32 | 45 | 58 | 72 | 86 | | | | | | | | | | | | | | | | | | | | | | | | | | | | | | | |
| 48 | | | | | | 1 | 12 | 23 | 35 | 47 | 60 | 78 | 86 | | | | | | | | | | | | | | | | | | | | | | | | | | | | | | |
| 50 | | | | | | | 5 | 16 | 27 | 38 | 49 | 61 | 74 | 87 | | | | | | | | | | | | | | | | | | | | | | | | | | | | | |
| 52 | | | | | | | | 9 | 19 | 29 | 40 | 51 | 63 | 75 | 87 | | | | | | | | | | | | | | | | | | | | | | | | | | | | |
| 54 | | | | | | | | 3 | 12 | 22 | 32 | 42 | 53 | 64 | 76 | 88 | | | | | | | | | | | | | | | | | | | | | | | | | | | |
| 56 | | | | | | | | | 7 | 16 | 25 | 34 | 44 | 55 | 65 | 76 | 88 | | | | | | | | | | | | | | | | | | | | | | | | | | |
| 58 | | | | | | | | | 1 | 10 | 18 | 27 | 37 | 46 | 56 | 66 | 77 | 88 | | | | | | | | | | | | | | | | | | | | | | | | | |
| 60 | | | | | | | | | | 5 | 13 | 21 | 30 | 39 | 48 | 58 | 68 | 78 | 89 | | | | | | | | | | | | | | | | | | | | | | | | |
| 62 | | | | | | | | | | 1 | 8 | 16 | 24 | 32 | 41 | 50 | 59 | 69 | 79 | 89 | | | | | | | | | | | | | | | | | | | | | | | |
| 64 | | | | | | | | | | | 4 | 11 | 18 | 26 | 34 | 43 | 51 | 60 | 70 | 79 | 90 | | | | | | | | | | | | | | | | | | | | | | |
| 66 | | | | | | | | | | | | 7 | 14 | 21 | 29 | 36 | 44 | 53 | 61 | 71 | 80 | | | | | | | | | | | | | | | | | | | | | | |
| 68 | | | | | | | | | | | | 3 | 10 | 16 | 23 | 31 | 38 | 46 | 54 | 62 | 71 | 90 | | | | | | | | | | | | | | | | | | | | | |
| 70 | | | | | | | | | | | | | 6 | 12 | 19 | 25 | 33 | 40 | 48 | 55 | 64 | 72 | 81 | 90 | | | | | | | | | | | | | | | | | | | |
| 72 | | | | | | | | | | | | | 3 | 9 | 15 | 21 | 28 | 34 | 42 | 49 | 57 | 65 | 73 | 82 | 91 | | | | | | | | | | | | | | | | | | |
| 74 | | | | | | | | | | | | | | 5 | 11 | 17 | 23 | 29 | 36 | 43 | 50 | 58 | 65 | 74 | 82 | 91 | | | | | | | | | | | | | | | | | |
| 76 | | | | | | | | | | | | | | 3 | 8 | 13 | 19 | 25 | 31 | 38 | 44 | 51 | 59 | 66 | 74 | 82 | 91 | | | | | | | | | | | | | | | | |
| 78 | | | | | | | | | | | | | | | 5 | 10 | 16 | 21 | 27 | 33 | 39 | 46 | 53 | 60 | 67 | 75 | 83 | 91 | | | | | | | | | | | | | | | |
| 80 | | | | | | | | | | | | | | | 3 | 7 | 12 | 18 | 23 | 29 | 35 | 41 | 47 | 54 | 61 | 68 | 75 | 83 | 91 | | | | | | | | | | | | | | |
| 82 | | | | | | | | | | | | | | | | 5 | 10 | 14 | 20 | 25 | 30 | 36 | 42 | 48 | 55 | 61 | 69 | 76 | 84 | 92 | | | | | | | | | | | | | |
| 84 | | | | | | | | | | | | | | | | 3 | 7 | 12 | 16 | 21 | 26 | 32 | 37 | 43 | 49 | 56 | 62 | 69 | 76 | 84 | 92 | | | | | | | | | | | | |
| 86 | | | | | | | | | | | | | | | | 1 | 5 | 9 | 14 | 18 | 23 | 28 | 33 | 39 | 44 | 50 | 57 | 63 | 70 | 77 | 84 | 92 | | | | | | | | | | | |
| 88 | | | | | | | | | | | | | | | | | 3 | 7 | 11 | 15 | 20 | 25 | 30 | 35 | 40 | 46 | 51 | 57 | 64 | 70 | 77 | 85 | 92 | | | | | | | | | | |
| 90 | | | | | | | | | | | | | | | | | 1 | 5 | 9 | 13 | 17 | 22 | 26 | 31 | 36 | 41 | 47 | 52 | 58 | 65 | 71 | 78 | 85 | 92 | | | | | | | | | |
| 92 | | | | | | | | | | | | | | | | | | 3 | 7 | 11 | 15 | 19 | 23 | 28 | 32 | 37 | 42 | 48 | 53 | 59 | 65 | 72 | 78 | 85 | 92 | | | | | | | | |
| 94 | | | | | | | | | | | | | | | | | | 1 | 5 | 9 | 12 | 16 | 20 | 24 | 29 | 33 | 38 | 43 | 49 | 54 | 60 | 66 | 72 | 79 | 85 | 93 | | | | | | | |
| 96 | | | | | | | | | | | | | | | | | | | 3 | 7 | 10 | 14 | 18 | 22 | 26 | 30 | 35 | 39 | 44 | 50 | 55 | 61 | 66 | 73 | 79 | 86 | 93 | | | | | | |
| 98 | | | | | | | | | | | | | | | | | | | 2 | 5 | 8 | 12 | 15 | 19 | 23 | 27 | 32 | 36 | 40 | 45 | 50 | 56 | 61 | 67 | 73 | 79 | 86 | 93 | | | | | |
| 100 | | | | | | | | | | | | | | | | | | | 1 | 4 | 7 | 10 | 13 | 17 | 21 | 24 | 28 | 33 | 37 | 41 | 46 | 51 | 56 | 62 | 68 | 73 | 80 | 86 | 93 | | | | |
| 102 | | | | | | | | | | | | | | | | | | | | 2 | 5 | 8 | 11 | 15 | 18 | 22 | 26 | 30 | 34 | 38 | 43 | 47 | 52 | 57 | 62 | 68 | 74 | 80 | 86 | 93 | | | |
| 104 | | | | | | | | | | | | | | | | | | | | 1 | 4 | 7 | 10 | 13 | 16 | 20 | 23 | 27 | 31 | 35 | 39 | 43 | 48 | 53 | 58 | 63 | 69 | 74 | 80 | 87 | 93 | | |
| 106 | | | | | | | | | | | | | | | | | | | | | 3 | 5 | 8 | 11 | 15 | 17 | 21 | 24 | 28 | 32 | 36 | 40 | 44 | 49 | 53 | 58 | 64 | 69 | 75 | 81 | 87 | 93 | |
| 108 | | | | | | | | | | | | | | | | | | | | | 2 | 4 | 7 | 10 | 12 | 16 | 19 | 22 | 25 | 29 | 33 | 37 | 41 | 45 | 49 | 54 | 59 | 64 | 70 | 75 | 81 | 87 | 93 |
| | 22 | 24 | 26 | 28 | 30 | 32 | 34 | 36 | 38 | 40 | 42 | 44 | 46 | 48 | 50 | 52 | 54 | 56 | 58 | 60 | 62 | 64 | 66 | 68 | 70 | 72 | 74 | 76 | 78 | 80 | 82 | 84 | 86 | 88 | 90 | 92 | 94 | 96 | 98 | 100 | 102 | 104 | 106 |

WET-BULB TEMPERATURE

20 sec. at about 120 rpm, holding it away from the body and other obstructions, in a shaded spot where there is free air circulation. At the end of 15–20 sec., read wet-bulb thermometer. Repeat the process until a lower temperature on the wet-bulb thermometer cannot be obtained. Use the lowest reading obtained. Then read the dry-bulb temperature.

**Use of Table.** Refer to a relative humidity table such as Table 1. Locate on the left side the reading corresponding to the dry-bulb temperature. Locate at the top the reading corresponding to the wet-bulb temperature. The intersection of the two columns gives the relative humidity in percent.

**Correction for Elevation.** The relative humidity at any given temperature rises slightly with increased elevation owing to a reduction in atmospheric pressure. The relative humidity indicated in Table 1 may be corrected by **adding 1** percent when used at elevations between 500 and 1,999 ft. (e.g., for a dry-bulb temperature of 50° and a wet-bulb temperature of 40°, read 38 + 1, or 39 percent); 2 percent between 2,000 ft. and 3,999 ft.; 3 percent between 4,000 ft. and 5,999 ft.; and 5 percent for elevations above 6,000 ft.

## Table 2. Beaufort Scale of Wind Velocity

| Beaufort number | Wind velocity (mph) | Terms used in U.S.W.B. forecast | Description of wind effects |
|---|---|---|---|
| 0 | Less than 1 | Calm | Smoke rises vertically; no movement of leaves, bushes, trees, or grass. |
| 1 | 1–3 | Very light | Direction of wind shown by smoke drift; tall grass and weeds sway slightly; quaking aspen leaves move; small branches move gently; dead leaves on oaks rustle. |
| 2 | 4–7 | Light | Wind felt on face; trees of pole size in open sway gently; small branches of pine move noticeably; dead, dry leaves rustle and move; stands of broom sedge sway. |
| 3 | 8–12 | Gentle | Leaves and small twigs in motion; dry leaves on ground blow about; twigs of hardwood trees move distinctly, and large branches of pine in the open toss; whole trees in dense stands sway; trees of pole size in the open sway noticeably. |
| 4 | 13–18 | Moderate | Small branches move; tops of large hardwood trees sway noticeably; pines of pole size in open sway violently; whole trees in dense stands sway noticeably. |
| 5 | 19–24 | Fresh | Inconvenience is felt in walking against wind; branchlets are broken from trees; small trees in leaf sway; entire hardwood trees sway, their tips whip about violently; twigs broken from pines. |
| 6 | 25–38 | Strong | Progress is impeded when walking against wind; large branches in motion; branches broken from hardwood trees and tops from conifers. |

## Table 3. Normal Peak Fire Seasons *

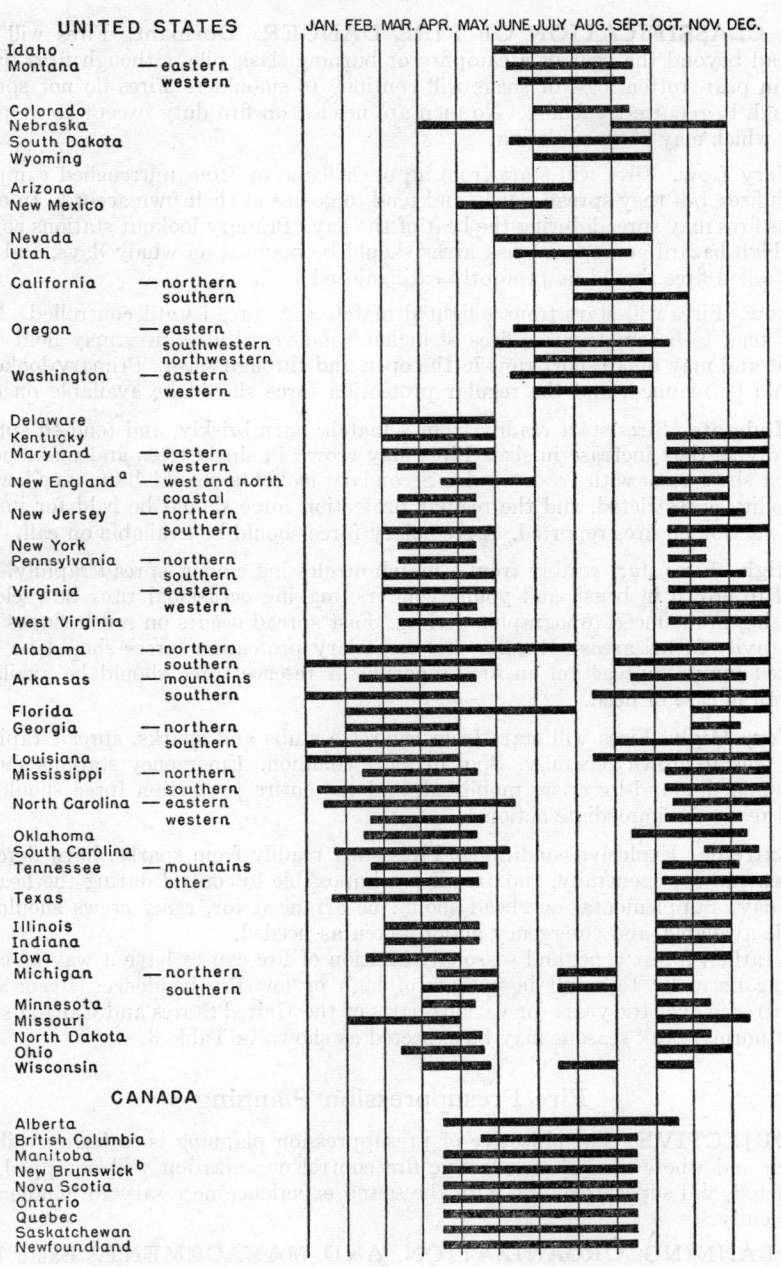

a Includes Maine, New Hampshire, Vermont, Massachusetts, Connecticut, and Rhode Island.
b Includes Prince Edward Island.
* Basic information provided by Washington and Regional Offices of the U. S. Forest Service and H. W. Beall, Forest Research Division, Canadian Department of Resources and Development.

7 · 9

**A CLASSIFICATION OF FIRE DANGER. Dormant.** Fires will not spread beyond the heat of a campfire or burning slash pile, although fires burning in peat, rotten logs, or snags will continue to smoulder. Fires do not spread enough to require trenching. No men are needed on fire duty except to mop up fires which may be smouldering.

**Very Low.** Fires will start from an open flame or from untrenched camp or slash fires, but they spread slowly and tend to go out of their own accord. In open areas fires may spread during the heat of the day. Primary lookout stations covering high hazard and special risk areas should be manned on windy days, and uncontrolled fires should be promptly extinguished.

**Low.** Fires will start from a lighted match and spread until controlled. Peat fires tend to become surface fires at higher wind velocities. Fires may hold over night and may make short runs in the open and through slash. Primary lookouts should be manned, and the regular protection force should be available on call.

**Moderate.** Fires start readily from a match, burn briskly, and tend to spread rapidly as they increase in size. Fires may crown in single trees and make occasional short runs with fresh winds. Secondary lookouts should be manned when visibility is restricted, and the regular protection force should be held for immediate action on fires reported. A secondary force should be available on call.

**High.** Fires start readily from a match or glowing cinder, spread rapidly, and tend to crown in brush and young conifers, making occasional runs but seldom crossing pronounced topographic divides. Fast spread occurs on south slopes and in heavily fueled areas. Regular and secondary protection forces should be mobilized for prompt action on fires reported. A reserve force should be available on call in case of need.

**Very High.** Fires will start from cigarette stubs and sparks, spread rapidly, and tend to crown generally. Spot fires are common. Emergency stations should be manned, stand-by crews mobilized, and the entire protection force should be held ready for immediate action.

**Extreme.** Explosive conditions. Fires start readily from sparks, burn fiercely, crown and spot generally, and are all but impossible to control during the heat of the day. Supplemental overhead should be arranged for, relief crews should be made available, and emergency action taken as needed.

Weather, forest type, and seasonal variation of fire causes have a way of combining normally to result in periods of high or low fire incidence. Records of occurrence over the years for various parts of the United States and Canada show that normal peak seasons may be expected as shown in Table 3.

## Fire Presuppression Planning

**OBJECTIVE.** The objective of presuppression planning is to have available when and where needed an effective fire control organization well equipped, instructed, and supervised, and with the sound experience necessary to handle fires efficiently.

**PLANNING, ORGANIZATION, AND MANAGEMENT. Basic Elements of Presuppression Planning.**

1. Meteorological factors—wind, relative humidity (and fuel moisture), precipitation, seasonal effects, etc.

2. Topographic factors—ridges, slopes, streams, etc., and their relationship to one another, elevation, steepness, barriers, etc.
3. Fuel factors—(a) types of fuel, (b) continuity, density, and arrangement, and (c) resistance to line construction.
4. Incidence of fires—points of origin; occurrence separately for lightning and each man-caused category; times of day and year fires may be expected to start and do damage.
5. Visibility distance as it applies to the distance that class A or small class B fires can be seen by observers, normal daily or seasonal changes in visibility distance, etc.
6. Accessibility—travel time by most appropriate means.
7. Relative values—tangible plus the intangible values at stake.
8. Rate of production of held line per unit of manpower or machines for different conditions, including delineation of areas where machines are usable.
9. Water supplies for suppression—chances for using portable pumper and tanker.
10. Equipment—transportation, pumper, aircraft, tools, etc.
11. Communications for presuppression and suppression—radio and telephone.
12. While not strictly elements of planning, the need must be recognized for planning recruitments to fill suitably each planned fire position, including co-operators and their subsequent training. Recruitment and on-the-job training of able-bodied emergency fire forces must also be planned.

**Development of Master Presuppression Plans. Fire control standards.** A standard is a rule which is established by authority as a measure of quantity, quality, extent, frequency, or completeness. Subunit managers will establish supplementary standards at their level to further unit standards and objectives. A continuing process of inspection, analysis of variations from established standards, commendation for good work, and appropriate disciplinary action for failure will be maintained by the unit manager.

Representative examples of things for which standards are necessary include plans, manning, qualifications and fitness, conduct and appearance, training and drills, preparedness of facilities and men, condition and stock of equipment and supplies, communications, transport system, detection, elapsed time, organization and action on fires, cooperation, safety, and inspection.

**Fire danger rating.** This is an essential tool of fire control management. Each unit should develop a system which will measure and evaluate the variable factors selected to represent changing fire conditions for the area as required. Some of the practices made possible by a knowledge of fire danger ratings are:

1. Shifting presuppression forces to areas of immediate higher danger.
2. General tightening up of fire organization in specific areas.
3. Increased prevention efforts.
4. Alerting cooperators and checking on availability.
5. Holding work crews on stand-by.
6. Varying initial attack and reinforcement strength.
7. Deciding when overtime of fire control forces is required.
8. Temporarily vacating stations because of favorable weather.
9. Adjusting radius of distance from station of work assignments.
10. Granting of leave.
11. Augmenting current presuppression forces.
12. Use for other purposes such as determination of when and where to apply closures, restriction on use of fire in woods, issuing prevention warnings, and informing public.

Fire danger ratings are also useful in aiding officers new to a locality to obtain information about fire danger. They likewise permit comparisons of fire seasons and a determination of the normal length of the fire seasons, and serve as a basis for measuring the efficiency of suppression action.

**Master presuppression plan.** In the development of a presuppression plan for a unit, each of the elements listed under "Basic Elements of Presuppression Planning" above must be studied, the effects evaluated as they apply to the particular area in question, correlated, and the conclusions incorporated in a final master presuppression plan for the area under study. As a minimum, the following plans are usually involved:

1. **Detection** involves visibility distance, zones of past fire occurrence as modified by changes in risk due to changes in use, the area seen from individual points, selection of points by the process of statistical elimination, map showing seen and unseen area from all selected points, dates of occupancy and regulation of occupancy in accordance with measured fire danger, and incorporation of aerial detection—either primary or secondary.

2. **Initial attack** involves mapping of fuels to show combined effects of rates of spread and resistance to control, zones of fire occurrence intensity, accessibility, initial attack strength by zones required for varying degrees of fire danger, location of forces to meet travel time requirements, provision for varying strength of forces by zones of measured fire danger, establishment of dates of employment, rates of pay, etc., and where applicable, a recognition of the need for hard-hitting reinforcement crews.

3. **Equipment** involves the determination of types, quantity, and placement of small tools, transportation equipment, and specialized equipment such as tank trucks, prime movers, plow units, trail builders, portable pumpers, aircraft, etc.

4. **Communication** includes radio and/or telephone for detectors to dispatching base and from dispatching base to initial attack crews (whether cooperators or employed forces), to work crews, and to unit headquarters. A plan must be made to provide communication between parts of a fire line, fire camps and dispatching base, and, if practical, to initial attack crews when away from their stations.

5. **Cooperators.** Determine the extent to which they can be incorporated into presuppression phases of fire control.

6. **Training.** Plan minimum training needs for each presuppression position. Provide for maintaining a current record of each individual's training progress and an analysis of each trainee's prior experience and training to determine, before entrance on duty, his qualifications to handle assigned tasks effectively and safely.

7. **Dispatching.** Prepare annually a dispatching plan providing information on location, strength, and provision for contacting or mobilizing the following: (a) all initial attack stations, both regular and cooperator, (b) all work crews employed by unit, (c) private work crews, (d) initial attack forces of cooperating protection agencies, (e) follow-up forces or facilities of cooperating protection agencies, (f) forces of adjacent units, (g) pick-up fire fighters, (h) overhead, segregated as to skills, (i) cooks, packers, power saw operators, and others having specialized skills, (j) tools and equipment, including transport, line building, tank trucks, etc., (k) food, mess equipment, first-aid, and other supplies and materials, (l) communication equipment, (m) special detectors. Also, the dispatching plan should include ways, means, and authority for varying the disposition of the strength of the presuppression force in accordance with measured fire danger.

8. **Recruitment.** A plan must be prepared and revised annually to provide the best possible (a) presuppression force, (b) force for use in fire emergencies.

9. **Transportation.** Diagram on a map or maps the location and standards of all roads, trails, bridges, airstrips, and helicopter landing spots needed to meet the elapsed time standards for the area.

## COOPERATIVE FIRE CONTROL AGREEMENTS.

All adjoining agencies and ownerships should cooperate actively in the control of fires if efficient action and reduction in costs and losses are to be attained. A plan of cooperation

and coordination should be prepared in order to avoid confusion and misunder-
standing. Such a plan should ordinarily be in the form of a written agreement.
The following outline suggests items which are desirable for inclusion in cooperative fire control agreements:

1. Area to be included, or distance to which aid can be sent.
2. Provision for reporting fires to cooperators.
3. Initial attack—by whom it is to be made.
4. Coordination of fire suppression work by the cooperators.
5. Supervision—provision for designation of the fire boss for the respective areas
   included under the agreement and during the various stages of fire suppression
   operations. (Designate one man as fire boss when the fire involves an area
   under both cooperators' responsibility, or at least provide for liaison between
   supervisors.)
6. Furnishing of fire tools and equipment, food supplies, and transportation.
7. Furnishing of supervision and fire fighters.
8. Release of fire fighters furnished by cooperator after control of fire has been
   accomplished.
9. Distribution of costs (on a prorated acreage basis or otherwise), including
   repair of equipment used or replacement of fire equipment lost.
10. List of fire control personnel available for dispatch under the cooperative
    agreement.
11. A map outlining areas included in the agreement and showing the location of
    fire detection stations, fire suppression personnel, fire equipment, telephone
    lines, radio stations, etc., which contribute to the cooperative agreement.
12. Provision for a cooperative review of large fires on which two or more cooperat-
    ing agencies participate.

## Fire Detection

Early observation, accurate location, and prompt report of every forest and
range fire are objectives of efficient fire control. The more rapid the spread of
fires, the more important prompt action becomes. Fires may be detected by the
following agencies:

1. Planned and established detection organizations such as:
   a. Primary lookout observers.
   b. Combination detection-patrol personnel.
   c. Aerial and/or ground patrol.
   d. Employee and resident cooperative observers.
2. Incidental detection through employee, resident, and transient traveler observations.

For prompt and accurate discoveries and report, the above agencies are listed
in descending order of dependability. But the actual number of fires discovered
by them has often been in the reverse order; this is due to the larger number of
potential discoverers in the latter classes. It is important to take full advantage
of all potential sources of discovery by providing facilities for prompt reporting
to an action agency.

A primary lookout system provides continuity of operation by trained observers,
and a means for prompt reporting and accurate location. The degree to which
a lookout can contribute to economical fire control depends upon (1) the potential
size and difficulty of fire control jobs throughout the territory covered, (2) the
amount of fire danger territory covered, and (3) the probable number of fires
likely to occur there.

Limitations on the effectiveness of fixed lookout observations include (1) maximum practical visibility distance (normally about 15 mi. in the west, 6 mi. in the

east, but further limited by topography and local atmospheric haze), (2) accuracy of equipment, including maps, and (3) dependability, training, and experience of the observer. Even with a relatively complete coverage of the risk areas, supplemental detection may be required during abnormal periods and for observing blind and distant areas.

It may be uneconomical to attempt to provide fixed primary detection in areas of low fire occurrence, slow spread or low values, or for areas with a history of only occasional high intensity of occurrence, such as from lightning or irregular risk sources. For such areas ground or aerial patrol or temporary assignment of secondary lookouts may be an effective and economical substitute. During periods of poor visibility additional detection may be required even in areas having good normal coverage.

## Fire Suppression

**FIRE CAMP LAYOUT.** Figs. 1 and 2 are illustrations of fire camp layouts.

**FIRE CREW RATIONS.** The combination ration table, page 7 · 17, insures a well-balanced ration. Column 1 gives a balanced ration of staple supplies ample for 1 man for 1 day. Column 2 indicates various substitutes of approximately the same food value. In applying the table, first determine the number of daily rations desired by multiplying the total number of men by the number of days, then multiply this figure by the amount of each staple item or one of its substitutes. (Number of men × Number of days × Unit ration.) Advance preparation of lists and arrangements for procurement or storage and transportation to the fire are important.

**ELEMENTS OF INITIAL ACTION ON FIRES.** The statistics in Table 5, for the period 1940 through 1947, are taken from the records of the U. S. Forest Service on upward of 50,000 fires in the western forest regions. About 71 percent of the fires originated from lightning; the balance were man-caused.

**FIRE ORGANIZATION BUILD-UP.** Figs. 3–7, pages 7 · 19 to 7 · 21, show one type of build-up of a fire organization as the size of the suppression crew increases. It is recommended by the Northeastern Forest Fire Protection Commission for conditions in New England and New York. The U. S. Forest Service employs a similar build-up in California and the Lake States. Note that:

1. Elements of the organization are added only **as needed** to maintain control of the suppression force.
2. In the early stages the fire boss and section chiefs handle all of the jobs which they have not assigned to someone else. These jobs are filled as soon as the supervising officer believes the need for men to handle them will arise in a few hours.
3. The size of the fire suppression organization required at any stage of a fire is not necessarily dictated by the acreage of the fire but by the size and distribution of the suppression force and the difficulty of controlling the fire.

**FIRE SAFETY AND ACCIDENT PREVENTION.** Forest fire suppression is dangerous work. First-aid facilities and personnel trained in the treatment of injuries should always be available. Some of the commoner causes of accidents, and suggestions for avoiding them, are as follows:

1. **Rough topography,** steep slopes, loose or slippery rocks, and rolling logs and rocks. Crew leaders must keep close control of their men, watch their movements and

# DIAGRAMMATIC SKETCH OF CAMP LAYOUT

## FOR LARGE CREWS

### (DISTANCES INDICATED ARE DESIRABLE MINIMUM)

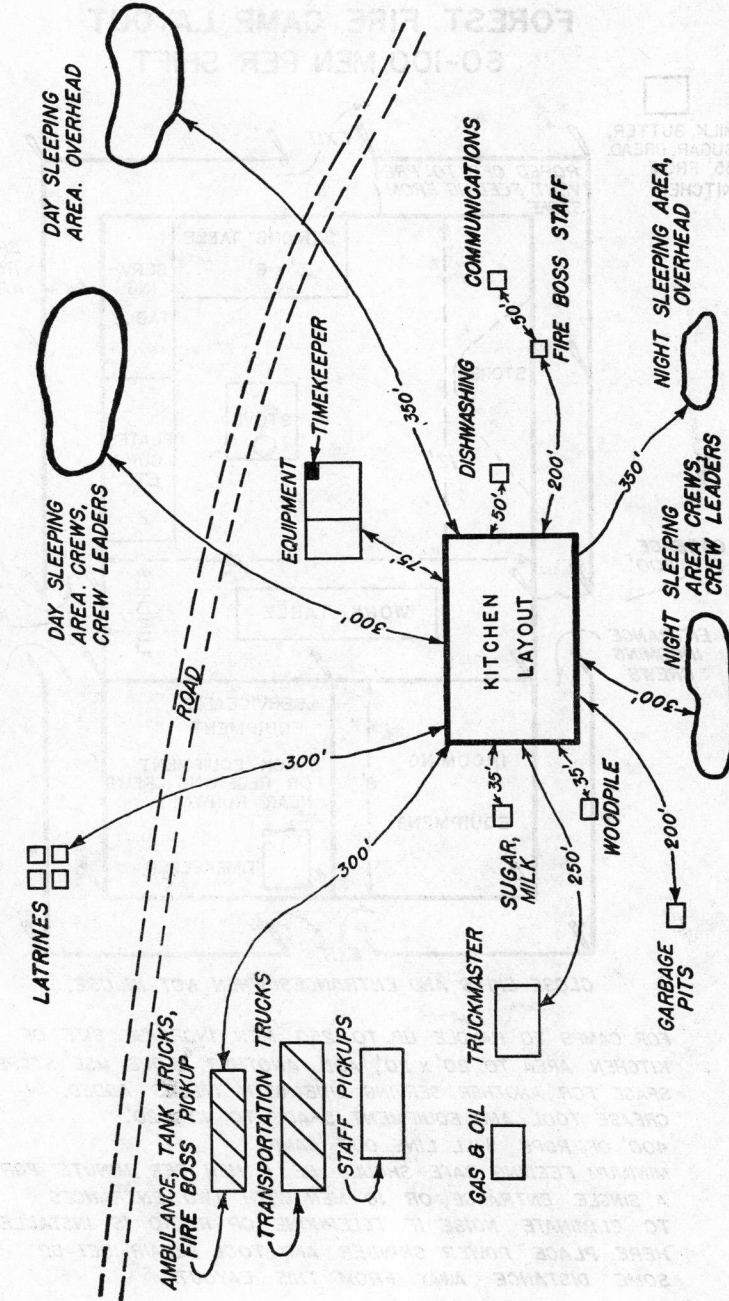

Fig. 1. Diagrammatic sketch of camp layout.

# FOREST FIRE CAMP LAYOUT
## 60-100 MEN PER SHIFT

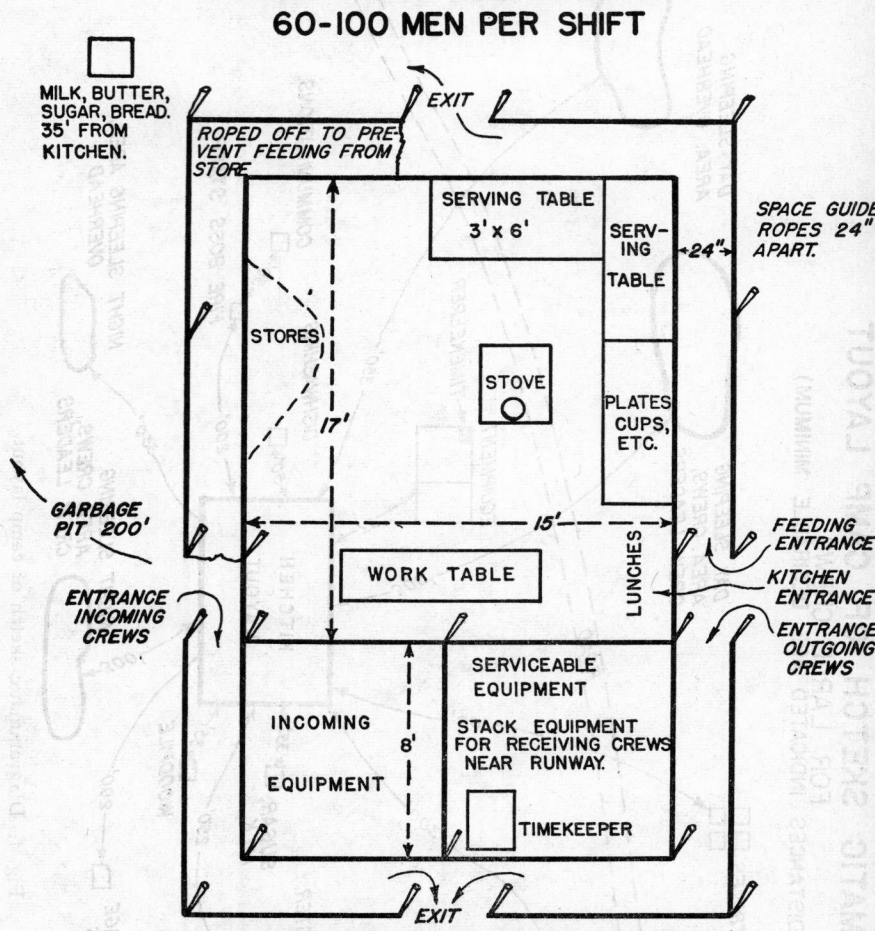

CLOSE EXITS AND ENTRANCES WHEN NOT IN USE.

FOR CAMPS TO HANDLE UP TO 250 MEN, INCREASE SIZE OF
KITCHEN AREA TO 20' X 20', ADD ANOTHER STOVE, USE STORES
SPACE FOR ANOTHER SERVING LINE WITH TABLES ADDED. IN-
CREASE TOOL AND EQUIPMENT SPACE TO 12' X 20'.
400' OF ROPE WILL LINE OUT CAMP.
MINIMUM FEEDING RATE SHOULD BE 5 MEN PER MINUTE FOR
A SINGLE ENTRANCE, OR 10 MEN WITH TWO ENTRANCES.
TO ELIMINATE NOISE IF TELEPHONE OR RADIO IS INSTALLED
HERE, PLACE POWER GRINDER AND TOOL REPAIR SET-UP
SOME DISTANCE AWAY FROM THIS LAYOUT.

Fig. 2. Forest fire camp layout, 60–100 men per shift.

## Table 4. Balanced Ration and Equivalent Substitutes

| (1) Item | Amount a for one man, one day | (2) Equivalent substitutes for staple items in Column 1 |
|---|---|---|
| Fresh meat | 1.50 lb. | Bacon 0.7 lb.; ham 0.9 lb.; canned meat 1.2 lb.; eggs 12; beans 1.0 lb. |
| Cheese | 0.20 lb. | Fresh meat 0.12 lb.; sweet chocolate 0.06 lb.; bologna sausage 0.25 lb. |
| Beans | 0.20 lb. | Rice, hominy 0.20 lb.; baked beans ⅔ can, or 0.5 lb. |
| Bread | 1.00 lb. | Flour 0.8 lb.; crackers 0.7 lb.; cornmeal 0.8 lb.; macaroni 0.7 lb. |
| Baking powder | 0.04 lb. | Yeast (for light bread) ⅕ cake; soda (for sour dough) |
| Oatmeal | 0.15 lb. | Cream of wheat, cornmeal, rice, etc., 0.17 lb. |
| Potatoes | 1.00 lb. | Rice, hominy, beans 0.25 lb.; evap. potatoes 0.15 lb. |
| Fresh vegetables | 0.35 lb. | Peas, corn ⅕ can or 0.25 lb.; tomatoes ½ can or 0.9 lb.; dried vegetables 0.07 lb. |
| Fresh fruit | 0.50 lb. | Dried fruit 0.10 lb.; canned fruit ¼ can or 0.45 lb.; raisins 0.10 lb. |
| Canned fruit | ⅓ can | Jam, jelly, apple butter ¼ can; fruit juices ⅓ can; dried fruit 0.10 lb. |
| Coffee | 0.13 lb. | Tea 0.03 lb.; cocoa 0.08 lb. |
| Sugar | 0.40 lb. | |
| Milk (evaporated) | ⅓ can | Fresh milk ⅔ pt. |
| Butter | 0.12 lb. | Margarine or peanut butter 0.12 lb. |
| Lard | 0.10 lb. | Bacon grease 0.10 lb. |
| Salt | 0.04 lb. | |
| Pepper | 0.06 oz. | |
| Syrup b | 1/12 pt. | |
| Pickles b | 1/15 pt. | |
| Cinnamon b | 0.40 oz. | Ginger, nutmeg, cloves, mustard, or allspice 1/25 oz. |
| Extracts b | 0.03 oz. | |
| Cornstarch b | 0.02 oz. | Tapioca 0.02 oz. |

ACCESSORIES: Candles or lights (including fuel), hand and dish towels, paper or cloth lunch sacks, matches, soap (hand and laundry), toilet paper, waxed paper for lunches, rope, nails (assorted).

NOTE: In ordering initial supplies for a fire crew, special attention should be given to providing suitable lunch material such as fresh bread, butter (or substitute), lunch meat, fruit or jam, sacks, etc.

a All weights are exclusive of cans or other containers.
b Essential only in permanent camps or moderately large temporary camps.

the surrounding terrain, and refrain from traveling or crowding the work too fast for the slower members of the crew. Assign clumsy men to less hazardous jobs and locations.

2. **"Misbehaving" fires,** blow-ups, spot fires, dense smoke, backfires, etc., are potentially dangerous. The crew leader must know at all times what he is doing, where he is going, where every man in his crew is located, and where other adjacent crews are working. Vigilantly observe changes in fire conditions and behavior. Have continually in mind a definite plan of escape under any circumstances. (Inside the burn is often the safest place. Do not run uphill from a fast-burning fire.) Keep the crew alert; if an emergency arises, act decisively.

3. **Fatigue** resulting from too long hours, traveling too fast, or for long distances; heat or smoke; and poor resting conditions—all result in poor coordination of thought and action.

## Table 5. Fire Statistics, U. S. Forest Service, Western Regions

DISCOVERY (Time from estimated origin to discovery)

| | Percent discovered within: | | | | | |
|---|---|---|---|---|---|---|
| | 14 min. | 29 min. | 59 min. | 1 hr. 59 min. | 5 hr. 59 min. | Over 5 hr. 59 min. |
| | | | | (Cumulative) | | |
| Lightning .................. | 13 | 18 | 27 | 38 | 50 | 50 |
| Man-caused ................ | 28 | 42 | 55 | 65 | 79 | 21 |

REPORT (Time from discovery to report of fire to initial action forces)

| | Percent reported within: | | | | | |
|---|---|---|---|---|---|---|
| | 3 min. | 6 min. | 12 min. | 18 min. | 30 min. | Over 30 min. |
| | | | | (Cumulative) | | |
| Lightning .......................... | 28 | 49 | 65 | 71 | 80 | 20 |
| Man-caused ....... ................ | 48 | 69 | 79 | 85 | 92 | 8 |

ATTACK (Time from report to arrival of initial attack forces on fire)

| | Percent attack within: | | | | | | |
|---|---|---|---|---|---|---|---|
| | 18 min. | 30 min. | 48 min. | 59 min. | 1 hr. 59 min. | 6 hr. 59 min. | Over 7 hr. |
| | | | | | (Cumulative) | | |
| Lightning ............. | 9 | 18 | 26 | 35 | 57 | 85 | 15 |
| Man-caused .......... | 55 | 71 | 80 | 85 | 93 | 98 | 2 |

ATTACK STRENGTH (Number of men in initial attack)

| | Percent of fires by number of men in first attack | | | | | | |
|---|---|---|---|---|---|---|---|
| | 1 | 2 | 3 | 4 | 5 | 6–10 | Over 10 |
| Lightning ....................... | 26 | 36 | 17 | 8 | 5 | 6 | 2 |
| Man-caused ..................... | 23 | 24 | 15 | 10 | 8 | 14 | 6 |

CONTROL (Time from arrival of attack forces to time of control)

| | Percent controlled within: | | | | | |
|---|---|---|---|---|---|---|
| | 29 min. | 2 hr. 59 min. | 3 hr. 59 min. | 8 hr. 59 min. | 12 hr. 59 min. | Over 12 hr. 59 min. |
| | | | | (Cumulative) | | |
| Lightning ............. | 26 | 76 | 82 | 92 | 94 | 6 |
| Man-caused ........... | 38 | 77 | 84 | 92 | 94 | 6 |

4. **Lack of proper equipment,** inadequate or unsafe use of what is available. Provide enough good lights for night work and travel. Inspect clothing, especially shoes, to insure reasonable adequacy. Keep unsuitable and poorly maintained fire tools off the line. Leaders should train men in the proper use and handling of tools, and observe their actions. Assign the best qualified men to each type of tool. Keep crew members well spaced.

5. **Snags.** Watch falling snags and spark-throwing snags. Fell dangerous snags, and keep the crew alert and at safe distances from potentially dangerous ones. Especially during mop-up and patrol, inspect surroundings and the location of men.

### Table 6. Travel Speeds by Types of Roads and Mode of Transport

|  | Mph |
|---|---|
| On foot over good trails | 3 |
| On foot across country | 2 |
| On horse over good trails | 3½–4 |
| **Passenger cars or pickup trucks** | |
| 1. Paved highways | 45 |
| 2. Dirt or gravel, below highway standard | 30 |
| 3. Narrow or one-way dirt roads in flat country | 25 |
| 4. Narrow or one-way dirt roads in steep country | 15 |
| **Trucks, 1½-tons** | |
| 1. Paved highways | 35 |
| 2. Dirt or gravel, below highway standard | 25 |
| 3. Narrow or one-way road in flat country | 20 |
| 4. Narrow or one-way road in steep country | 12 |

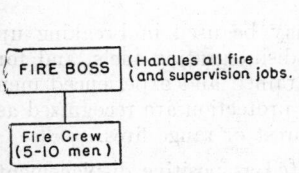

Fig. 3. Fire organization build-up; 5–15 men.

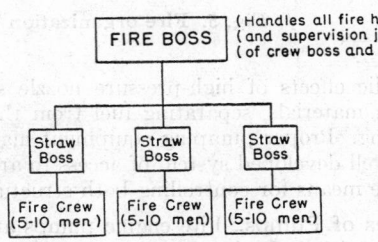

Fig. 4. Fire organization build-up; 20–35 men.

6. **Food, water, and sanitation.** Inspect and supervise to insure proper handling of food; stress cleanliness, prevention of spoilage, proper dishwashing; avoid poor preparation and unsuitable menus. Provide plenty of safe drinking water, but caution men to drink sparingly when hot. Provide accessible and usable sanitary facilities in locations which safeguard water and food.

7. **Poisoning.** Try to avoid unnecessary contact with poison ivy or poison oak, including smoke from burning plants. If contact is unavoidable, wash promptly with strong soapy water. (If the washing is not well done, however, the soap will spread the toxic oil to other parts of the body.)

8. **Physically unfit men.** When recruiting fire fighters, weed out poor risks for the strenuous work to be done.

### MAKE SAFETY A PART OF EVERY JOB

**FIRE FIGHTING WITH WATER.** Water, if properly applied, is the most effective method of controlling or extinguishing fires. Its availability, quantity, and manner of use may determine success or failure in combating fires. The effects of water on a fire include:

1. Retarding effect by reduction of free oxygen in fuels.
2. Reduction of temperature by absorption of heat from fuels.
3. Increase in relative humidity, which also acts as an insulator against spread.
4. Extinguishment through the combined effects of 1, 2, and 3.

Water may be employed as a curtain of fog between the heat or flames and exposed fuels, also as a protection for fire fighters in close approach to a fire. The

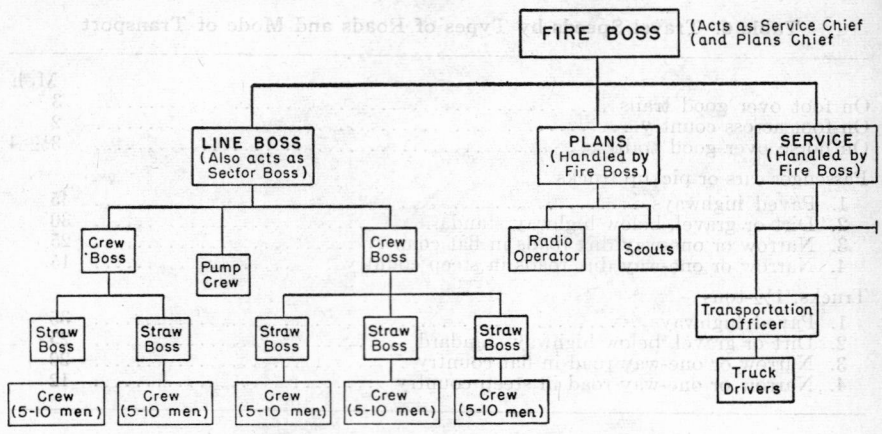

Fig. 5.  Fire organization build-up; 50–75 men.

hydraulic effects of high-pressure nozzle streams may be used in breaking up burning materials, separating fuel from the flames, disintegrating fuels, and for trenching. Proper pumping equipment manned by trained and experienced men and a well developed system of access to areas under protection are recognized as effective means for controlling both structural and forest or range fires.

**Types of Pumps.** Fire engine pumps are designated as positive displacement or nonpositive displacement types. The positive displacement pump is one employing either a piston, gear, rotor, diaphragm, or screw mechanism for impelling the water, the quantity or volume of which is measured and predetermined.

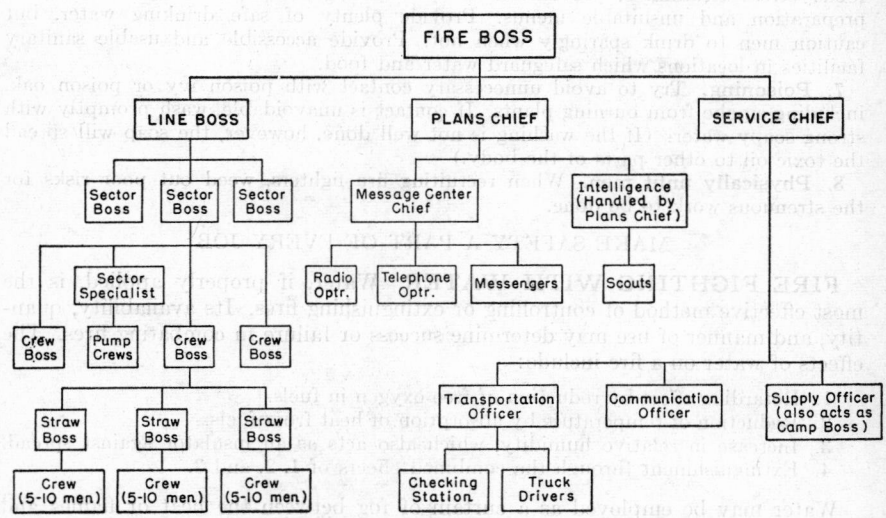

Fig. 6.  Fire organization build-up; 100–200 men.

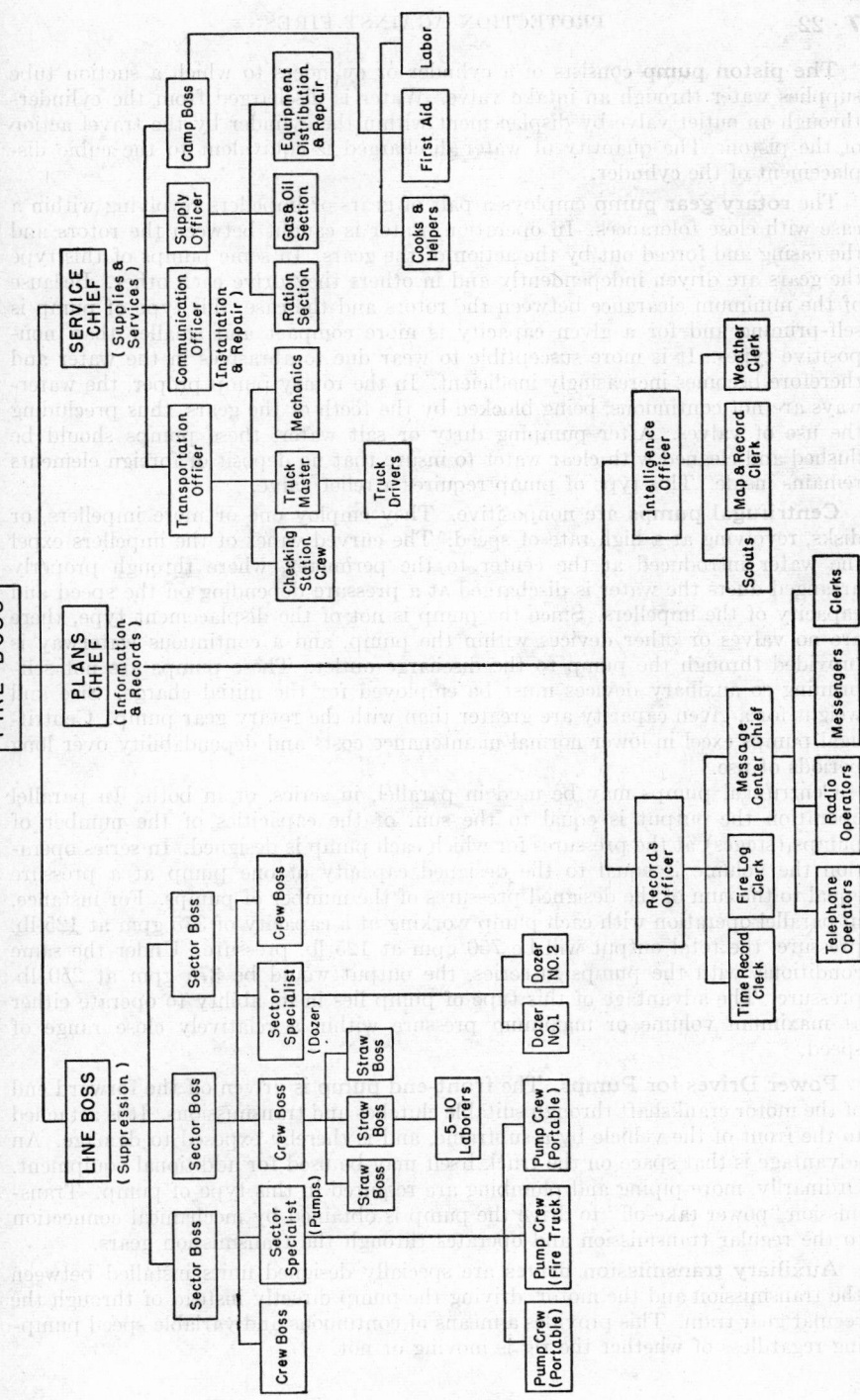

Fig. 7. Fire organization build-up; very large.

**The piston pump** consists of a cylinder or cylinders to which a suction tube supplies water through an intake valve. Water is discharged from the cylinders through an outlet valve by displacement within the cylinder by the travel action of the piston. The quantity of water discharged is equivalent to the cubic displacement of the cylinder.

The **rotary gear pump** employs a pair of gears or impellers revolving within a case with close tolerances. In operation, water is caught between the rotors and the casing and forced out by the action of the gears. In some pumps of this type the gears are driven independently and in others they drive each other. Because of the minimum clearance between the rotors and the case, this type of pump is self-priming and for a given capacity is more compact and smaller than nonpositive types. It is more susceptible to wear due to abrasives in the water and therefore becomes increasingly inefficient. In the rotary pump proper, the waterways are not continuous, being blocked by the teeth of the gears, thus precluding the use of valves. After pumping dirty or salt water, these pumps should be flushed and cleaned with clear water to insure that no deposit of foreign elements remains inside. This type of pump requires a relief valve.

**Centrifugal pumps** are nonpositive. They employ one or more impellers, or disks, revolving at a high rate of speed. The curved vanes of the impellers expel the water introduced at the center to the perimeter, where through properly arranged ducts the water is discharged at a pressure depending on the speed and capacity of the impellers. Since the pump is not of the displacement type, there are no valves or other devices within the pump, and a continuous waterway is provided through the pump to the discharge outlet. These pumps are not self-priming so auxiliary devices must be employed for the initial charge. Size and weight for a given capacity are greater than with the rotary gear pump. Centrifugal pumps excel in lower normal maintenance costs and dependability over long periods of use.

Centrifugal pumps may be used in parallel, in series, or in both. In parallel operation the output is equal to the sum of the capacities of the number of pumps (stages) at the pressures for which each pump is designed. In series operation the volume is equal to the designed capacity of one pump at a pressure equal to the sum of the designed pressures of the number of pumps. For instance, in parallel operation with each pump working at a capacity of 375 gpm at 125 lb. pressure, the total output will be 750 gpm at 125 lb. pressure. Under the same conditions, with the pumps in series, the output would be 375 gpm at 250 lb. pressure. The advantage of this type of pump lies in its ability to operate either at maximum volume or maximum pressure within a relatively close range of speed.

**Power Drives for Pumps.** The **front-end pump** is driven off the forward end of the motor crankshaft through suitable clutches and transmissions. It is attached to the front of the vehicle by a subframe, and is thereby exposed to damage. An advantage is that space on the truck itself may be used for additional equipment. Ordinarily, more piping and plumbing are required in this type of pump. Transmission "power take-off" to drive the pump is obtained by mechanical connection to the regular transmission and operates through the transmission gears.

**Auxiliary transmission drives** are specially designed units installed between the transmission and the motor, driving the pump directly instead of through the regular gear train. This provides a means of continuous and variable speed pumping regardless of whether the rig is moving or not.

**The Pumper Tank-Truck.** Local conditions, budget limitations, and immediate or peculiar needs must dictate selection of this type of equipment, but certain guides and standards apply generally.

1. Horsepower of the engine must be adequate for reasonable highway speeds, to negotiate the steepest grades, and to operate the pump to full capacity without undue stress.
2. The radiator cooling system must be capable of holding the water temperature below 200° F. regardless of the load and atmospheric conditions. An auxiliary cooling system is recommended.
3. Chassis and springs must be of such strength, size, and design as to meet overload conditions, distribute weight properly, and insure stability under adverse conditions. The cab-over type provides better road control and visibility, and reduces wheelbase. Avoid rear overhang. Weight distribution should fall between 40–60 and 30–70 front to rear. The wheelbase should not be over 14 ft., height 7 ft. 9 in., and weight 25,000 lb. fully loaded.
4. Tire size and number (duals) must be adequate for safety at maximum speed fully loaded.
5. Brakes should be of a booster type, with manually operated emergency.
6. The capacity of the tank depends on local requirements and truck load limit. The tank must be rustproofed inside, with adequate longitudinal and lateral baffles (removable), and with a manhole of a size to permit ready access within. A glass water gauge is essential. Outlets should be placed at each end to insure positive discharge on grades. Piping should have flexible connections.
7. The size and amount of hose must be determined by local needs. Usually 1 in. and 1½ in. hose will meet all requirements. The same standard threads should be on all couplings. Adapters to connect to hose of other agencies and other sizes of hose are necessary.
8. Conformity to an adopted standard in the placement of accessory equipment compartments and items contained therein is important.
9. Nozzles and applicators are somewhat controversial, but where conservation of water supply is a factor, the fog nozzle (especially the type with a fan-shaped pattern) is superior to the open tip.
10. Auxiliary equipment must be determined locally. A portable pumper can be used to advantage wherever there are convenient local water supplies and for relaying. Ladders may be required where structural fires are involved. Suction hose of adequate length and size is essential. Fire-fighting tools and miscellaneous equipment such as lights, rope, first-aid kits, etc., are necessary.
11. Avoid overloading.

**The Pump Operator.** To obtain the most effective streams, use the tip or nozzle which will provide the greatest volume at any given pressure. With a knowledge of the length of hose lay, the amount of lift, and the size of tip, the pumper operator can readily determine the pump pressure needed to overcome friction loss and maintain any required nozzle pressure or flow. A convenient table which may be applied to normal requirements and located on the instrument panel for reference is shown in Table 7. It should be noted that smaller nozzles reduce volume but increase pressure. The larger the tip, the greater the effective stream. With increase in lift, smaller tips must be employed to compensate for the loss of pressure due to increased friction loss.

Table 7 covers friction loss and resultant pressures in cotton-jacketed rubber-lined hose. Where unlined hose is used, add 10 percent to pressure.

**The Nozzle Man.** The nozzle man is very important in the effective use and conservation of water. He must distribute properly all of the water supplied. Much experience and training are required. He must have adequate assistance

Table 7. Pump Pressures in Pounds per Square Inch Required for Various Nozzle Pressures and Discharges, with Various Diameters and Length of Hose, on Level Ground [a]

| Length of hose | 50-lb. nozzle pressure per sq. in. | | | | | 100-lb. nozzle pressure per sq. in. | | | | | 150-lb. nozzle pressure per sq. in. | | | |
| --- | --- | --- | --- | --- | --- | --- | --- | --- | --- | --- | --- | --- | --- | --- |
| | 1-in. hose | | 1½-in. hose | | | 1-in. hose | | 1½-in. hose | | | 1-in. hose | 1½-in. hose | | |
| | ¼-in. tip | ⅜-in. tip | ¼-in. tip | ⅜-in. tip | ½-in. tip | ¼-in. tip | ⅜-in. tip | ¼-in. tip | ⅜-in. tip | ½-in. tip | ¼-in. tip | ¼-in. tip | ⅜-in. tip | ½-in. tip |
| 300 | 65 | 111 | 52 | 59 | 76 | 127 | 214 | 104 | 117 | 150 | 189 | 156 | 175 | 224 |
| 400 | 70 | 131 | 53 | 62 | 85 | 136 | 252 | 105 | 123 | 167 | 201 | 158 | 183 | 249 |
| 500 | 75 | 152 | 54 | 65 | 94 | 145 | 290 | 107 | 129 | 184 | 214 | 160 | 192 | 295 |
| 1,000 | 100 | 253 | 57 | 81 | 138 | 191 | | 114 | 157 | 268 | 278 | 169 | 253 | |
| 1,500 | 125 | | 61 | 96 | 181 | 236 | | 121 | 186 | | | 179 | 275 | |
| 2,000 | 149 | | 65 | 111 | 225 | 281 | | 127 | 215 | | | 189 | | |
| 2,500 | 174 | | 69 | 127 | 269 | | | 134 | 243 | | | 198 | | |
| 3,000 | 199 | | 73 | 142 | | | | 141 | 272 | | | 208 | | |
| Discharge [b] | 12.5 | 29.5 | 12.5 | 29.5 | 52 | 18 | 41.5 | 18 | 41.5 | 73.5 | 21.5 | 21.5 | 50.5 | 90 |

[a] For each increase of 10 ft. in elevation between pump and nozzle add 4 lb. to pump pressures in table.

[b] Discharge, in gallons per minute (gpm) $= 29.8\,D^2\sqrt{P}$, where $D$ is diameter of tip, in inches, and $P$ is nozzle pressure, in pounds per square inch.

in moving hose, especially on long lays. In average rough terrain at least one man for each 100 ft. of hose should be assigned to drag a charged line.

In making hose lays, precaution should be taken to provide extra lengths at intervals in case of ruptured lines or to provide longer laterals. Shut-offs along the lay are recommended to conserve water in case of a break and to facilitate replacements.

**Fire Hose.** Hose used in fighting forest fires must meet exacting requirements; hose that fails to do this is expensive, no matter what price was paid for it. For maneuvering over rough terrain or through heavy brush, small hose—¾ to 1½ in. —and small nozzles—⅛ to ½ in.—are the best. To prolong the life of hose, observe the following rules:

1. Protect hose from mechanical injury, such as cutting by sharp rocks or metal on apparatus. Vibration may cause serious damage and is greatest near the pump; protect it there by using chafing boots or socks. In reloading hose, bend it at places different from the previous arrangement.
2. Do not expose the rubber in a hose to vulcanization by hot embers or actual flame.
3. Do not allow grease, oil, gases, or chemicals to come in contact with hose. At least every 60 days run water through each length.
4. Use the best sections of the hose where the pressure is greatest. Shut off at the nozzle slowly to avoid surge pressure, which forms an air hammer of great force.
5. Load hose so it can be removed smoothly and easily, with couplings on the right end. Change the position of hose every 30 days; on live reels change the position every two weeks.
6. After use, wash with cold, clear water, scrub, and dry thoroughly before reloading.
7. Cotton-jacket, rubber-lined (CJRL) hose varies according to grade and type. It should be tested to withstand a hydraulic pressure of 350 lb. without leakage or sweating in hose or couplings. Elongation should not exceed 10 percent. It should withstand a kinking bend at 260 lb. psi.
8. In storage, CJRL hose must have free air circulation, protection from direct sunlight, frequent rerolling to prevent "set." Use spacers between rolls of hose on racks or shelves.
9. All hose couplings should be so fitted as to permit tightening by hand. Avoid the use of spanners and protect the threads. Slotted lug couplings are preferable to pin lugs. Use only powdered graphite on threads. Hose couplings should be "broken" frequently to prevent the setting of washers and threads.
10. Roll the hose by first folding near the center, with the female coupling underneath and the male coupling about 3 ft. shorter, thus enclosing the male coupling within the roll.

## Hose Fittings.

1. A **reducer** is used to reduce the size of hose, or outlets of a hydrant, to a smaller coupling or line. In this case, the female fitting is the larger.
2. An **increaser** performs the opposite function. In this case, the female side is the smaller.
3. An **adapter** is used to convert one type of thread to another. It may be a straight fitting, a reducer, or an increaser.
4. **Siamese** is a term given to a fitting used to bring two or more lines into a single line. It consists of two female threads and one male thread.
5. A **reverse siamese** or "Y" connection converts one hose line into two or more lines. It consists of one male and two female threads.
6. The **double female** connects two lines where they meet together as male to male, or to a hydrant where the male end is present. It is made as a swivel and may be used as an increaser or reducer.

**7. Couplings** are fittings attached to the ends of the hose to provide a means of connection. One is female, the other male.

**Hose Thread Standards.** There is no nationwide standard for hose threads. In some sections of the country, thread standards have been adopted by local public agencies; but enforcement has been impossible. "National Standard" is but a broad designation covering many types of threads. This lack of uniformity imposes upon the forest officer the necessity of carrying adapters sufficient to make such connections as the several threads in use in his locality require. These different threads will generally fall into the following groups:

| | | |
|---|---|---|
| Iron pipe | Chemical hose | National Standard |
| Garden hose | Pacific Coast | U.S.F.S. Standard |

**The Fog Nozzle.** Combustion is made possible by the presence of oxygen. Reducing the size of the water particles to a minimum, increasing their number to a maximum, and subjecting this mass to the heat of a fire result in an expansion, through changing the water to steam, of about 1,700 to 1. The effect of this expansion is to exclude oxygen from the fire. Water converted into a fog mass has a greatly increased capacity to absorb heat because this capacity is in direct proportion to the surface area of the water particles. The more homogeneous the fog vapor, the more effective it is in suffocating fire and reducing temperature.

In actual fire fighting, cold-water fog has the following advantages over a straight stream: (1) It reduces water damage to structures; (2) it protects firemen, often expelling smoke and noxious gases, permitting the men to make a closer approach with equipment, and facilitates rescue work; and (3) it prevents "flashbacks" from explosive gases collected in vapor pockets. It is particularly effective against burning oil or liquefied gases, fires in structures or vehicles, potential dust explosions, and (under certain conditions) low-voltage electrical fires.

Cold-water fog is produced by the impingement of two or more streams or jets at an angle. The pattern of the fog mass depends upon the number, angle, and arrangement of these jets. There are low-velocity or "rolling" fogs, and high-velocity or pressure fogs; each has its special application and use.

### Table 8. Fog Nozzles and Applicators

(Discharge delivery, in gallons per minute)

| Fog nozzle | Approximate diameter of equivalent straight tip * (in.) | Nozzle pressure (psi) | | |
|---|---|---|---|---|
| | | 50 | 75 | 100 |
| 1-in. M.J. tip | 0.273 | 16 | 19 | 22 |
| 1-in. Navy tip | .263 | 15 | 17 | 21 |
| 1-in. 1-pair hole | .125 | 3 | 4 | 5 |
| 1-in. 2-pair hole | .179 | 6 | 8 | 11 |
| 1-in. 3-pair hole | .221 | 10 | 14 | 18 |
| 1½-in. M.J. tip | .403 | 34 | 42 | 48 |
| 1½-in. Navy tip | .444 | 38 | 52 | 62 |
| 2½-in. M.J. tip | .545 | 64 | 78 | 88 |
| 2½-in. Navy tip | .603 | 75 | 95 | 108 |
| Applicators | | | | |
| 1-in. with ½-in. head | .223 | 10 | 13 | 15 |
| 1½-in. with 1-in head | .403 | 30 | 40 | 47 |
| 2½-in. with 1½-in. head | .591 | 70 | 93 | 105 |

* Calculated at nozzle pressures of 50, 75, and 100 psi, and average taken.

Ordinarily a pressure of 100 psi is required to produce maximum results. The most practical nozzle is one which is capable of producing either fog or straight streams by a single movement of the control valve.

**Equivalent Nozzle Discharges.** Should it become necessary to resort to siamese or multiple lays, still maintaining the original volume of delivery as obtained from one large nozzle, the formula $D^2/d^2$ may be used, $D$ being the diameter of the larger nozzle, and $d$ the diameter of the smaller nozzle. Table 9 gives the approximate relative discharge capacities of different size nozzles.

### Table 9. Discharge Capacities of Various Nozzle Sizes

| No. of nozzles | Nozzle size (reduce to decimal equivalent)* | | | | | | |
|---|---|---|---|---|---|---|---|
| (1) | (2) | (3) | (4) | (5) | (6) | (7) | (8) |
| 1 | 1/4 | 3/8 | 1/2 | 5/8 | 3/4 | 7/8 | 1 |
| 2 | 3/8 | 1/2 | 3/4 | 7/8 | 1 1/16 | 1 1/4 | 1 3/8 |
| 3 | 7/16 | 5/8 | 7/8 | 1 1/16 | 1 5/16 | 1 1/2 | 1 3/4 |
| 4 | 1/2 | 3/4 | 1 | 1 1/4 | 1 1/2 | 1 3/4 | 2 |
| 5 | 9/16 | 7/8 | 1 1/8 | 1 3/8 | 1 11/16 | 2 | 2 1/4 |
| 6 | 5/8 | 15/16 | 1 1/4 | 1 1/2 | 1 13/16 | 2 1/8 | 2 7/16 |
| 7 | — | — | 1 3/8 | 1 5/8 | 2 | 2 5/16 | 2 5/8 |
| 8 | — | — | — | 1 3/4 | 2 1/8 | 2 1/2 | |

\* Decimal equivalents:

| | | | |
|---|---|---|---|
| 1/4 = 0.2500 | 7/16 = 0.4375 | 5/8 = 0.6250 | 13/16 = 0.8125 |
| 5/16 = 0.3125 | 1/2 = 0.5000 | 11/16 = 0.6875 | 7/8 = 0.8750 |
| 3/8 = 0.3750 | 9/16 = 0.5625 | 3/4 = 0.7500 | 15/16 = 0.9375 |

**Example.** In Table 9 it is shown that two ½-in. (second line, fourth column) or four ⅜-in. nozzles (fourth line, third column) are required to equal the volume discharge of one ¾-in. nozzle (first line, sixth column).

### Liquid Measures and Equations.

1 foot of water = 0.4335 psi
1 miner's inch = 1.5 cu. ft. water per min.
1 acre-foot = 43,560 cu. ft. water
1 pound water = 0.1198 gal. or 27.68 cu. in.
1 gallon water = 0.1137 cu. ft. or 231 cu. in.
1 cubic foot water = 62.428 lb.
1 cubic foot water = 7.481 gal.
1 gallon water = 8.3454 lb.
Area circle = diameter squared × 0.7854
Volume of cylinder = area × height
Volume of cylindrical container in gallons when dimensions are in inches = $0.0034D^2H$
Volume of cylindrical container in gallons when dimensions are in feet = $5.8756D^2H$
Volume of cylindrical container in gallons when diameter is given in inches and height in feet = $0.0408D^2H$
Volume of rectangular container = length × height × width = $Q$

Volume in gallons of rectangular container when dimensions are in inches = $\dfrac{Q}{231}$

Volume in gallons of rectangular container when dimensions are in feet = $(7.481) Q$
Volume of a sphere = $(0.5236)D^3$
Volume of sphere in gallons when dimensions are in feet = $(3.9171)D^3$
Volume of cylindrical tank with semispherical bottom:

$$\text{Add} \begin{cases} \text{Gallons in bottom} = (1.9585)D^3 \\ \text{Gallons in cylinder} = (5.8756)D^2H \end{cases}$$

**The Back-Pack Pump.** Back-pack fire pumps are useful in fire suppression for knocking down fast-spreading fires in light, flashy fuels and small hot spots, for cooling down smouldering snags out of reach of hand tools, and for mop-up work. The limited capacity, 4 or 5 gal., makes efficient application of the water essential.

1. Use a nozzle tip which provides the most effective means of distribution without waste. A spray can be obtained from a straight tip by holding a finger over the tip.
2. Hold the pump so that the forward hand steadies, guides, and controls direction while the rear hand motivates the pumping action.
3. Work as close as possible to the burning edge and direct the water to the base of the flames.
4. An effective combination is one man equipped with a back-pack pump to knock down the flames on the burning edge and in mop-up work, followed by other men equipped with hand tools to complete the control of the fire.

**Wetting Agents (Penetrants) for Forest Fire Suppression.** In recent years considerable study has been made of the possibilities of increasing the efficiency of plain water for fire suppression. Many soluble chemicals, called wetting agents or preferably "penetrants," have been developed and tested. The solution resulting from the addition of a small amount of the chemical (usually not more than 1 to 5 percent) to water is called "wet water." The effect of the addition of penetrants is to reduce the surface tension of plain water, thereby increasing its spreading, penetrating, and foaming potential.

Tests indicate the following significant differences between water containing penetrants and plain water:

1. Wet water is markedly superior to plain water in its ability to knock down flames quickly, thus permitting access to a fire edge not otherwise accessible. Superiority in reduction of flame intensity by means of wet water is greatest on free burning flames and decreases when only isolated flames remain.
2. Savings up to 23 percent in the volume of water required and 13 percent in time of mop-up have been obtained with wet water applied with reasonable efficiency.
3. Rekindling is reduced by as much as 30 percent on fires mopped up with wet water as compared with plain water.
4. Foaming appears to be a desirable property of wet water in mop-up because it prevents channeling of the water.
5. Dead fuels along the burning edge of a fire remain wet up to 50 percent longer when sprayed with wet water than when sprayed with plain water.
6. Fuels once treated with wet water and allowed to dry may be sprayed later with plain water with results comparable to an original spraying with wet water.
7. Most penetrants increase the corrosive action of water, but this may be wholly corrected by the addition of corrosion inhibitors.

Techniques of application, pattern of spray, foaming, and dermatological effects of wet water are still inadequately determined. Among the manufacturers of penetrants are the Carbide and Carbon Chemicals Corp., New York (UNOX), and Arnold-Hoffman & Co., Providence, R. I. ("Drench").

## Calculation of Burned Area

The degree of accuracy required by the agency charged with forest fire reports and statistics determines the method to be used in the calculation of burned forest area. Generally speaking, a burned area is calculated either by rule of thumb or by a compass survey.

In a rule-of-thumb survey or estimate, the perimeter of the burn is determined by pacing and the area figured by the use of perimeter tables, or the rectangular dimensions are paced as a basis for calculating the extent of the area. When chains are used in rectangular measurements, the area will be in square chains; pointing off one decimal place in the result will give the area in acres. Another commonly used method is to sketch the perimeter of the burn on a topographic or other convenient map of known scale. When the burn approaches a circular

## Table 10. Perimeter of Fire Corresponding with Area Enclosed by It *

| Area | Mini-mum [a] perimeter | Prob-able [b] perimeter | Maxi-mum [c] perimeter | Area | Mini-mum [a] perimeter | Prob-able [b] perimeter | Maxi-mum [c] perimeter |
|---|---|---|---|---|---|---|---|
| 1 | 3.5 | 5.25 | 7.00 | 600 | 86.8 | 130.20 | 173.60 |
| 2 | 5.0 | 7.50 | 10.00 | 700 | 93.7 | 140.55 | 187.40 |
| 3 | 6.1 | 9.15 | 12.20 | 800 | 100.2 | 150.30 | 200.40 |
| 4 | 7.1 | 10.65 | 14.20 | 900 | 106.3 | 159.46 | 212.60 |
| 5 | 8.0 | 12.00 | 16.00 | 1,000 | 112.1 | 168.15 | 224.20 |
| 6 | 8.7 | 13.05 | 17.40 | 1,200 | 122.8 | 184.20 | 245.60 |
| 7 | 9.4 | 14.10 | 18.80 | 1,400 | 132.6 | 198.90 | 265.20 |
| 8 | 10.0 | 15.00 | 20.00 | 1,600 | 141.8 | 212.70 | 283.60 |
| 9 | 10.6 | 15.90 | 21.20 | 1,800 | 150.4 | 225.60 | 300.80 |
| 10 | 11.2 | 16.80 | 22.40 | 2,000 | 158.6 | 237.90 | 317.20 |
| 11 | 11.7 | 17.55 | 23.40 | 4,000 | 222 | 334 | 445 |
| 12 | 12.3 | 18.45 | 24.60 | 6,000 | 270 | 405 | 540 |
| 13 | 12.8 | 19.20 | 25.60 | 8,000 | 317 | 476 | 635 |
| 14 | 13.2 | 19.80 | 26.40 | 10,000 | 355 | 532 | 710 |
| 15 | 13.7 | 20.55 | 27.40 | 12,000 | 388 | 581 | 775 |
| 16 | 14.2 | 21.30 | 28.40 | 14,000 | 417 | 626 | 836 |
| 17 | 14.6 | 21.90 | 29.20 | 16,000 | 447 | 670 | 893 |
| 18 | 15.1 | 22.65 | 30.20 | 18,000 | 475 | 712 | 950 |
| 19 | 15.5 | 23.25 | 31.00 | 20,000 | 500 | 750 | 1,000 |
| 20 | 15.9 | 23.85 | 31.80 | 24,000 | 550 | 825 | 1,100 |
| 25 | 17.7 | 25.55 | 35.40 | 28,000 | 595 | 892 | 1,190 |
| 30 | 19.4 | 29.10 | 38.80 | 32,000 | 635 | 952 | 1,270 |
| 40 | 22.4 | 33.60 | 44.80 | 36,000 | 675 | 1,012 | 1,350 |
| 50 | 25.0 | 37.50 | 50.00 | 40,000 | 710 | 1,065 | 1,420 |
| 60 | 27.5 | 41.25 | 55.00 | 44,000 | 745 | 1,117 | 1,490 |
| 70 | 29.7 | 44.55 | 59.40 | 48,000 | 778 | 1,168 | 1,557 |
| 80 | 31.7 | 47.55 | 63.40 | 50,000 | 794 | 1,191 | 1,588 |
| 90 | 33.6 | 50.40 | 67.20 | 60,000 | 870 | 1,305 | 1,740 |
| 100 | 35.5 | 53.25 | 71.00 | 70,000 | 940 | 1,410 | 1,880 |
| 120 | 38.7 | 58.05 | 77.40 | 80,000 | 1,004 | 1,506 | 2,008 |
| 140 | 41.9 | 62.85 | 83.80 | 90,000 | 1,064 | 1,596 | 2,128 |
| 160 | 44.8 | 67.20 | 89.60 | 100,000 | 1,121 | 1,681 | 2,242 |
| 180 | 47.5 | 71.25 | 95.00 | 120,000 | 1,226 | 1,839 | 2,452 |
| 200 | 50.2 | 75.30 | 100.40 | 130,000 | 1,275 | 1,912 | 2,550 |
| 230 | 53.7 | 80.55 | 107.40 | 140,000 | 1,324 | 1,986 | 2,648 |
| 260 | 57.1 | 85.65 | 114.20 | 150,000 | 1,370 | 2,055 | 2,740 |
| 300 | 61.5 | 92.25 | 123.00 | 160,000 | 1,413 | 2,119 | 2,826 |
| 350 | 66.1 | 99.00 | 130.00 | 170,000 | 1,456 | 2,184 | 2,912 |
| 400 | 70.9 | 106.35 | 141.80 | 180,000 | 1,499 | 2,248 | 2,998 |
| 450 | 75.2 | 112.80 | 150.40 | 190,000 | 1,541 | 2,311 | 3,082 |
| 500 | 79.3 | 118.95 | 158.60 | 200,000 | 1,581 | 2,371 | 3,162 |

* Perimeter is shown in linear units of the same kind as the square units used for area. If area is in square chains, perimeter is in chains.
[a] Perimeter is that of a circle corresponding with the area.
[b] Perimeter is 1.5 times that of a circle corresponding with the area.
[c] Perimeter is 2.0 times that of a circle corresponding with the area.
The smallest perimeter represents a fire which spread uniformly in all directions, while the largest perimeter represents fires which are long and narrow or which finger out. The second figure for perimeter is applicable to the fire of average shape which is neither circular nor extremely elongated.

shape, the accompanying area-perimeter table (Table 10) provides a good estimate of the area burned.

When more accuracy is required in the determination of a burned area, a closed traverse should be made with standard compass and tape. The area can then be determined by plotting the area on cross-section paper, or by the use of a planimeter. If a planimeter is not available, the area can be obtained roughly by counting the number of square inches of area covered by the survey on the cross-section paper and converting to acres according to the scale of the sketch. In most cases this will give an area determination accurate enough for forest fire reports.

## Miscellaneous Fire Control Formulas

**Rate of spread** of a fire may be roughly determined in terms of perimeter increase by multiplying by 3 the rate at which the head of a fire is advancing. The same result may be secured by (1) multiplying the number of feet the head of a fire advances in 10 min. by 0.27, or (2) dividing 180 by the number of minutes required for the head of a fire to advance one chain. These formulas are based on the fact that fires spread primarily in one direction. In the case of very long and narrow fires the ratio tends to approach 2; where a fire spreads equally in all directions, the ratio would approach 6 rather than 3.

**Width of a fire,** by using a fire finder, may be determined from the following formula: Tangent offset in feet equals the number of minutes of angular interval between the ends of the fire times 1½ times the number of miles from the observation point to the point where the offset is taken.

**Manpower requirements** for the control of a fire can be roughly determined from the following formula:

$$N = \frac{R}{2C} + \frac{Rt}{CT}$$

where $N$ represents number of men required to control the fire
$R$ represents the rate of spread in chains per hour
$C$ represents resistance to control in chains per hour
$t$ represents elapsed time, in hours, from origin to arrival
$T$ represents elapsed time, in hours, from arrival to control

**Lightning strike distance** can be measured by counting the number of seconds between observation of the lightning flash and hearing the thunder, and dividing by 5. This is the approximate distance in miles.

**Fire-fighting fatigue** reduces the effectiveness of a crew approximately 10 percent per hour. Line output decreases as time and size of crew increase.

### BIBLIOGRAPHY

DOMINION FOREST SERVICE. 1949. *An outline for forest fire protection standards.* Ottawa, Canada.

HAWLEY, R. C. 1937. *Forest protection.* John Wiley & Sons, Inc., New York.

NATIONAL FIRE PROTECTION ASSN. 1948. *N.F.P.A. handbook of fire protection.* 10th ed. Boston, Mass.

NATIONAL FIRE PROTECTION ASSN. 1951. *Standards for wetting agents.* Boston, Mass.

U. S. DEPT. AGR. 1930. Determination of hour control for adequate fire protection. *Tech. Bull. 209.*

U. S. DEPT. AGR. 1936. Measuring fire weather and forest inflammability. *Cir. 398.*

U. S. DEPT. AGR. 1937. Principles of forest fire detection on the national forests of northern California. *Tech. Bull. 574.*

U. S. DEPT. AGR. 1946. Forest fire danger measurement in the eastern United States. *Agr. Handbook No. 1.*

U. S. DEPT. COMM., WEATHER BUREAU. 1948. *Fire weather forecast terminology.* Washington, D. C.

U. S. DEPT. INTERIOR, BUREAU OF MINES. 1940. *Manual of first aid instructions.* Washington, D. C.

U. S. FOREST SERV. 1939. *Glossary of terms used in forest fire control.*

U. S. FOREST SERV. 1946. *Fire control equipment handbook.*

U. S. FOREST SERV. *Fire control notes.* (Quarterly.)

U. S. FOREST SERV., REGION 1. 1936. *Fire control planning in the Northern Rocky Mountain Region.* Missoula, Mont.

U. S. FOREST SERV., CALIFORNIA FOREST AND RANGE EXP. STA. 1950. *Wet water for forest fire suppression.*

WESTERN FORESTRY AND CONSERVATION ASSN. *Western fire fighters' manual.* Portland, Ore.

# PROTECTION AGAINST INSECTS AND DISEASES

## CONTENTS

# PROTECTION AGAINST INSECTS AND DISEASES

This section of the Handbook aims to enable the average forester, who lacks special training in forest entomology and pathology, to recognize the more common injuries to living trees or wood caused by insects and diseases, and to employ "first-aid" measures for their prevention or control. It is not a key by which to identify an insect, or the sporophore of a fungus, apart from its host.

Separate lists of injuries have been prepared for the more common insects and diseases, although very often both are involved in the killing of a tree or stand, or in the deterioration of wood products. In each case identification is facilitated by presenting separately the organisms attacking germinating seedlings, as in nurseries; those injuring roots, stems, or foliage; those causing eventual death of the entire tree; and finally, those destroying the ultimate product—wood.

For many of these insects and diseases no control is known, or control is at present hopelessly expensive except for specimen trees. For others no human control is recommended because natural factors such as adverse weather, parasites, predators, birds, rodents, and disease may be counted on to correct what temporarily appears as an alarming condition.

For many forest insects and diseases the best control is maintenance of the health of trees and stands. Both in diagnosing injuries and in preventing them, the forester should draw heavily on his knowledge of silvics. Confronted with an ailing tree or stand which does not present outward evidence of the cause of the failure (such as the pitch tubes of bark beetles or the bark lesions of a canker), he should consider whether environmental factors or nonparasitic agencies may not have been at work. Such factors and agencies include:

1. Low-quality site (a, d, and e apply mainly to plantations).
   a. Excessive exposure.
   b. Excessive or imperfect drainage.
   c. Soil thin, or with compacted lower horizons.
   d. Soil depleted from agricultural use (organic and mineral deficiencies).
   e. Extremely high or low pH.
2. Species poorly adapted to site.
   a. As result of seed origin (plantations).
      (1) Environment of parent stock differs too greatly from that of planting site.
      (2) Inferior strain or geographic race.
   b. Occurring near limits of range, or as a transient type in the course of succession.
3. Changes in habitat.
   a. Raising or lowering of water table.
   b. Exposure to increased light or wind movement, as from thinning or from cutting of an adjacent stand.

4. Weather influences.
    a. Prolonged drought, or drought in successive growing seasons.
    b. Excessive spring rains, followed by period of subnormal rainfall and high temperatures.
    c. Unseasonable frost, especially in late spring.
    d. Winter injury.
        (1) Wilting of foliage as a result of drying winds while the ground is frozen.
        (2) Sudden alterations of temperature resulting in foliage wilting, as in (1), or in injury to bark tissues ("sun scald").
    e. Glaze (ice storm) or wet snow.
    f. Lightning.
    g. Hail.
5. Effect of human activities.
    a. Fire.
    b. Grazing by domestic animals.
    c. Leaks from gas mains or fumes from industrial plants.
    d. Leaching of calcium chloride or other salts applied to adjacent roadways.
    e. Careless use of herbicides or insecticides.
    f. Grading (along highways, in real estate developments, etc.).
6. Feeding or mechanical damage by various forms of wildlife.
    a. Browsing.
    b. Girdling, rubbing, or other bark injury.
    c. Feeding on buds.
    d. Roosting (e.g., starlings).
7. Overmaturity of tree or stand.
8. Stagnation as a result of overstocking.

If any of the above factors or agencies have been present, they should be given due weight in the final diagnosis. But it should be recognized that, in many cases, insects and disease may be primary in causing injury or destruction to vast forest areas, without aid from contributing causes or stand conditions.

Obviously, a tree growing under abnormal conditions, as on a lawn or on a city street, will require more intensive protection against insects and disease than forest trees. The controls prescribed in the tables for some organisms are not practicable except for trees of relatively high value.

Prevention of attacks by forest pests should be constantly in the forester's mind. In artificial forestation he can and must employ intensive measures of protection. Seed and transplant beds represent a highly abnormal concentration of trees in their most vulnerable stage; soil treatments, spraying, watering, etc., are generally recognized as imperative if insects and diseases are to be prevented from wiping out the nursery. But in outplanting there is still too little attention paid to (a) mixing of species and (b) choosing species adapted to existing conditions on the site (repeated fires or erosion may have rendered a planting site quite inhospitable to the species of the virgin forest). To plant acres of a favorite species, or to use species just because "they were all the nursery had," is simply to invite attack by insects and disease.

In the natural forest, the better the silvicultural management, the greater the resistance to most native insects and disease. Prevention of severe damage through silvicultural practices is, in many cases, entirely feasible. A few insects and diseases introduced from abroad remain a very serious problem because they have found the environment favorable and lack biological controls, but most of the forest pests of the United States and Canada are native to the forests they inhabit. Because they are an integral part of the forest biotic complex, they may be controlled through adjustment of their environment. The damage of certain species might be reduced to insignificance if forests can be kept in a fast-growing, vigorous condition. Measures to that end include:

1. Protection against uncontrolled fire. This does not exclude burning of logging slash under expert supervision, or "prescribed burning" of woodlands under carefully defined conditions and clearly demonstrated need.
2. Fencing of woodlands (especially hardwoods) against domestic animals, and measures to prevent overpopulation by wildlife.
3. Cleanings and later improvement cuttings to promote mixtures of the greatest possible variety of valuable species. Value should emphatically include silvical as well as commercial value. Illustrations of silvical value are secondary or temporary species serving as nurse trees and the so-called "inferior hardwoods" which may improve soil conditions in coniferous stands. Too heavy intermediate cuttings, especially in species injured by sudden exposure, should be avoided (birch in the Northeast, and hemlock in the Lake States, for example).
4. Thinnings to prevent the excessive reduction in width and depth of live crowns, which results from overcrowding.
5. Harvest cuttings of mature age classes and individuals.
6. Sanitation cuttings—removal of lightning-struck, wind-thrown trees and, of course, those actively attacked by insects or disease or of high susceptibility to such attack.
7. Proper seed source and site selection (nurseries and plantations).

There are a few insects and diseases which successfully attack even fast-growing, thrifty forests, and hence are not controllable by any silvicultural measures known today. Suppression of outbreaks of such species requires direct control action by mechanical or chemical means

It has been demonstrated through research in recent years that some of the newer insecticides, such as DDT, can be effectively and economically applied by means of aircraft. Large forested areas have been treated at costs ranging from $0.70 to $3.00 per acre. The cost depends largely on the size of the area treated, the cost of the insecticide, the type of aircraft and equipment used, and the accessibility of the area to a suitable landing field.

Occasionally damage occurs locally because of an upset in the balance of natural control factors which normally keep the pest within bounds. Such outbreaks may persist for only short periods, so the advisability of applying direct control measures should be carefully considered from an economic standpoint before planning a control program or the expenditure of funds.

It is not possible in a handbook such as this to list all the pests which may be found in the forest, so only those species or groups of species of considerable importance are included. A forester should never fail, however, to report to the proper authorities all cases of severe injury to trees and forests which he knows or suspects are due to insects or disease. The more complete the information furnished, the more effectively may these reports be acted upon. Reports of insect damage, including specimens whenever possible, should be sent to the Division of Forest Insect Investigation, Forest Service, U. S. Department of Agriculture, Washington 25, D. C., or to the nearest forest experiment station. The state entomologist and the entomologist at a local agricultural experiment station, as well as the state foresters, are also proper individuals to contact.

For further information on disease problems, the forester may direct his inquiry to the local district forester of the state forest service, or to the plant pathology department of the state university or experiment station. Inquiries may also be directed to the Division of Forest Disease Investigation, Forest Service, U. S. Department of Agriculture, Washington 25, D. C., or to the nearest forest experiment station.

## Key to Diagnosis and Control of Forest Insect Injuries

| Form of injury, host, range,[a] and insect[b] | Recommended controls | | | |
| --- | --- | --- | --- | --- |
| | Prevention[c] | Direct control[d] | | Stage of insect |
| | | Method | Time of year | |

**SEEDS, CONES, AND FRUIT INJURED.**

**I. Fresh green cones attacked by boring insects.**

| Form of injury, host, range,[a] and insect[b] | Prevention[c] | Method | Time of year | Stage of insect |
| --- | --- | --- | --- | --- |
| **A. Cones wither and die before fully grown.** | | | | |
| 1. Interior of cones mined by small, dark-brown beetles, and small, white, curled larvae. Pines (most regions).......Cone Beetles (Conophthorus spp.). | 10 | ... | Spring[e]<br>Fall & winter | Adults[e]<br>Larvae & pupae |
| 2. Cones deformed, showing exudation of pitch or webbed borings; interior mi ed by active caterpillars. Douglas-fir, firs, pine spruce (most regions).......Cone Moths (Olethreutidae, Phycitidae). | 10 | ...<br>44a | Spring[e] or summer<br>Fall & winter | Adults (before egg-laying)[e]<br>Larvae & pupae |
| **B. Cones reach full growth, but are riddled with insect borings.** | | | | |
| 1. Borings made by active caterpillars which leave pitchy masses of frass within cone and at point of entrance, or larval mines in axis and mature seeds. All conifers (most regions).......Cone Moths (Olethreutidae, Phycitidae, Geometridae). | 10 | ...<br>44a | Spring[e] or summer<br>May & June | Adults (before egg-laying)[e]<br>Larvae & pupae |
| 2. Fresh cones chewed by slugs Incense cedar (PC).......Incense Cedar Sawfly (Augomonoctenus libocedri). | | Consult an entomologist | Spring | Adults |
| 3. Soft cones riddled by small, white, slim maggots which leave fine excrement int unnels, but free from masses of pitch. Fir (PC, RM).......Cone Maggots (Diptera). | | Consult an entomologist | | |

**II. Old, persistent, hard, dry cones mined by slender white round-headed or flat-headed larvae.** Pines (PC). Cone Borers (Cerambycidae, Buprestidae).

| | | | |
|---|---|---|---|
| A. Seeds show no external injury, but are mined by small, white, curled, legless grubs. | | | |
| 1. Conifers (all regions).........SEED CHALCIDS (Chalcidae). | 34a | Fall or winter | Larvae |
| 2. Oaks, chestnuts, hazelnuts (AC, C, S, PC)......... ACORN, CHESTNUT, and NUT WEEVILS (Curculionidae). | 34a | Fall or winter | Larvae |
| 3. Ash (AC, S, PC)......... ASH-SEED WEEVIL (Thysanocnemis fraxini). | 34a | Fall or winter | Larvae |
| 4. Acacia, locust, mesquite, redbud, and other Leguminosae (most regions).........BEAN WEEVILS (Bruchus spp.). | 34a | Fall or winter | Larvae |
| B. Seeds swollen and galled, containing small pink maggots. Conifers (all regions).........SEED MIDGES (Diptera). | | Consult an entomologist | |
| C. Seeds mined by active caterpillars which usually discharge webbed frass through exit hole. | | | |
| 1. Oaks, chestnuts, filberts, hazelnuts (AC, C, S, PC).........FILBERT WORM (Melissopus latiferreanus). | | Consult an entomologist | |
| 2. Pecan (southern AC, S).........PECAN-NUT CASE-BEARER (Acrobasis caryae). | | Consult an entomologist | |
| 3. Hickory, pecan (AC, C, S).........HICKORY SHUCK-WORM (Laspeyresia caryana). | 44a | Winter | Larvae |
| 4. Maple, horsechestnut (AC, C, PC).........MAPLE-SEED CATERPILLAR (Proteoteras aesculana). | 44a | June | Larvae |

## ROOTS OF SEEDLINGS CHEWED, INJURED, OR DYING (Principally in nurseries).

| | | | |
|---|---|---|---|
| I. Rootlets completely bitten off, or the bark badly chewed, by soil-inhabiting insects. | | | |
| A. Curled, white grubs with 3 pairs of prominent legs and brown heads. Various host plants (all regions)......... WHITE GRUBS, or JUNE BEETLES (Scarabaeidae), | 1, 4 | Summer | Larvae (grubs) |
| B. Small, curled, white grubs with small, brown heads, but without legs.........ROOT WEEVILS (Curculionidae). | | | |

[a] Regions of the United States are abbreviated as follows: AC, Atlantic Coast; C, Central; NRM, Northern Rocky Mountain; PC, Pacific Coast; RM, Rocky Mountain; and S, Southern. Canadian ranges are northern extensions of AC, C, PC, and NRM.

[b] For detailed information on these and many other insects attacking trees, see the Bibliography.

[c] For meaning of code numbers see page 8·24, "List of Preventive Measures."

[d] For meaning of code numbers see pages 8·25–26, "List of Methods of Direct Control."

[e] Refers to "Prevention."

## Key to Diagnosis and Control of Forest Insect Injuries (Continued)

| Form of injury, host, range, [a] and insect [b] | Recommended controls | | | |
|---|---|---|---|---|
| | Prevention [c] | Direct control [d] | | |
| | | Method | Time of year | Stage of insect |
| 1. Cedars, hemlock, pine, spruce, yew, and many other plants in the nursery (AC, C, PC).........(Brachyrhinus spp.) | 1, 2 | 20, 26 | Spring | Adults |
| 2. Cedars, junipers (AC).........(Phyllobius intrusus). | ... | 4 | May | Adults |
| C. Long, slender, hard-shelled, yellow or brown "worms" with feebly developed legs. Various host plants (all regions).........Wireworms (Elateridae). | 1 | 20a | Spring & summer | Larvae |
| D. Nearly hairless, soft, sluggish, dark-colored caterpillars working below the surface of the ground. Various host plants (all regions).........Cutworms (Phalaenidae). | 1 | 25 | Spring & summer | Larvae |
| II. Roots infested by soft-bodied sap-sucking insects, often tended by ants. Fir, pines, Douglas-fir (AC, C, PC). .........Root Aphids (Cinara spp.) | 6 | Ants 22 | Spring & summer | All stages |
| **STEMS OF SEEDLINGS OR YOUNG TREES BADLY INJURED** (Partly in nurseries). | | | | |
| I. Stems of young seedlings bitten off or badly chewed. | | | | |
| A. Nearly hairless, sluggish caterpillars working at night (see I-D above). Various host plants (all regions). .........Cutworms (Phalaenidae). | 1 | 25 | Spring & summer | Larvae |
| B. Various host plants (all regions) .........Grasshoppers (Acrididae). | 1, 3 | 24 | Early summer | Nymphs & adults |
| C. Robust weevils feeding on bark at base of seedlings and on twigs of saplings. White pine, red pine, and other conifers (AC, C) ....Pales Weevil (Hylobius pales). | 7 | None | Spring | Adults |
| D. Weevils, similar to above, feeding on bark of twigs; larvae girdling base of saplings. Red, jack, Austrian, Corsican, Scotch pines (AC, C)....Part Root | ... | 27 | Spring or late Sept. | Adults & larvae |

| | | | summer | (workers) |
|---|---|---|---|---|
| **SHOOTS, TERMINALS, OR TWIGS OF SEEDLINGS AND SAPLINGS KILLED** (Some in nurseries). | | | | |
| **I. Shoots tunneled and killed by grubs of weevils ("snout beetles").** | | | | |
| A. Twigs and stems of seedlings and saplings up to 8 ft. in height. | | 12, 44 | | |
|    1. Ponderosa and Jeffrey pines (PC)........(*Cylindrocapurus eatoni*). | | Airplane 1a, 2a | June | Adults |
|    2. Douglas-fir (PC)........(*C. furnissi*). | ...9 | Same as preceding | | |
| B. Terminals of eastern white and jack pines, Norway spruce, and occasionally other conifers (AC,C)........ WHITE PINE WEEVIL (*Pissodes strobi*). | | Knapsack sprayer 11 Helicopter 1a, 2a | Early spring | Adults |
| C. Terminals of Sitka and Engelmann spruces; lodgepole, ponderosa, western white, and sugar pines; Deodar and Atlas cedars, Cedar-of-Lebanon (PC, RM). ........(*Pissodes* spp.). | | No control ever attempted Probably similar to above | | Adults |
| D. Twigs of saplings and larger trees. Pines, firs, spruces, and broad-leaved trees (most regions)........(*Pissodes* and *Magdalis* spp.). | | 43 | Spring | Adults |
| **II. Twigs girdled or tunneled by small beetles (not weevils),** working under bark or in pith of saplings; sometimes in branches and trunks of larger trees, usually those weakened or dying from other causes, or in the vicinity of slash. Conifers and broad-leaved trees (most regions)........ TWIG BEETLES (Scolytidae). | 14 | 43 | Spring | Adults |
| **III. Similar injury by grubs boring or girdling twigs of saplings or larger trees,** particularly those weakened or gradually dying from other causes; sometimes causing galls or swellings on twigs and branches. A few are cone borers. | | | | |
| A. Flat-headed borers; for description see p. 8·19........ (Buprestidae). | | | | |
|    1. Pines, firs, cypress, redwood, oak, willows, etc. (PC, RM, AC, C)........(*Anthaxia* spp.). | 14, 19 | | | |

tions at bases. Various host plants but especially conifers, in the vicinity of nests. (AC, C)........MOUND-BUILDING ANTS (*Formica exsectoides*).

Footnotes on page 8·5.

## Key to Diagnosis and Control of Forest Insect Injuries  (Continued)

| Form of injury, host, range,[a] and insect[b] | Recommended controls | | | |
| --- | --- | --- | --- | --- |
| | Prevention[c] | Direct control[d] | | |
| | | Method | Time of year | Stage of insect |
| 2. Pines, firs, cedars, hemlock (PC, RM)......... (*Chrysophana placida*). | ... | No control ever attempted | | |
| 3. Various broad-leaved trees (most regions). (Species of *Chrysobothris*, *Agrilus*). | 14, 19 | | | |
| B. Round-headed borers; for description see p. 8·20. ..........(Cerambycidae). | | | | |
| 1. Various broad-leaved trees (most regions)....... Twig Girdlers. | 14, 19 | ... | ... | ... |
| 2. Various conifers (PC, RM)........Twig Borers. | 14, 19 | ... | ... | ... |
| 3. Oaks, poplars, willows (AC). Twig borers causing galls or swellings on twigs and branches........ (Species of *Oberea, Saperda, Goes*). | 14, 19 | ... | ... | ... |
| **IV. Shoots, twigs, or terminals of conifers killed or deformed.** Active caterpillars in tunnels; resinous exudations at point of entrance. | | | | |
| A. Ponderosa, jack, red, Scotch, and Austrian pines. (RM, C).......Ponderosa Pitch Moth (*Dioryctria ponderosae*). | 5 | 43, 2b, 4a | Winter, spring | Larvae |
| B. Red, mugho, Scotch, and Austrian pines (AC, C). ......European Pine-Shoot Moth (*Rhyacionia buoliana*). | 5, 8 | 43, 2b, 4a | (Fall-spring) about June 25; repeat in 10 days | Larvae; Young larvae |
| C. Most 2- and 3-needled pines (AC, C, S). Damages tips of leaders and side branches......Nantucket Pine-Tip Moth (*R. frustrana*). | 5 | 2b | Spring, summer | Larvae |
| D. All pines (most regions). Freshly hatched larvae bore into tips, later move to larger branches and trunk of tree. Infested tips turn brown and break off...... | ... | 43 | Summer | Larvae |

| Injury / Insect (key) | Stage to control | Time to control | | |
|---|---|---|---|---|
| **E.** Hard pines (most regions). Larvae bore into twigs or branches below the terminal, and a pitch mass forms over entrance hole.........PITCH-NODULE MOTHS (*Petrova* spp.). | Larvae | Fall to spring | ... | 45 |
| **FOLIAGE DISCOLORED OR DROPPING PREMATURELY; LEAVES AND STEMS NOT CHEWED; SOME OF LEAVES AND TWIGS MAY HAVE SWELLINGS OR GALLS; TREES OF ALL AGES APPEAR SICKLY.** | | | | |
| **I.** Foliage yellowing, rusty, or mottled; covered with fine, nearly invisible webs or a silvery coating. Many host plants (all regions).........SPIDER MITES or RED SPIDER (Acarina). | All stages | Summer | 23 | ... |
| **II.** Leaves, twigs, or bark infested by sucking insects. Hard-bodied, fixed scales; soft-bodied aphids; or actively moving tree hoppers or leaf hoppers. | | | | |
| **A.** Leaves off-color, yellowish, or spotted from feeding punctures of active, jumping insects, which frequently act as carriers of fungus or virus infections. Many host plants (all regions).........LEAFHOPPERS (Cicadellidae), LACE BUGS (Tingidae). | Nymphs | Spring & summer | 17, 2b | ... |
| **B.** Leaves yellowing or dropping prematurely. Trees drip honeydew; sooty mold evident. An abundance of small, soft-bodied bugs with long, conspicuous antennae. Many host plants (all regions).........APHIDS or PLANT LICE (Aphidae, Phylloxeridae). | Eggs & nymphs | Spring & summer | 14, 15, 16, 17, 18, 19 | ... |
| **C.** Leaves, twigs, or branches covered by small circular, oval, or elongated shells or scales, or by small tufts of cottony wax. Various host plants (all regions).........SCALE INSECTS (Superfamily Coccoidea), Certain APHIDS (Cherminae). | Eggs & crawlers | Depends on the species to control | 13, 14, 15, 16, 17 | ... |
| 1. Two- and 3-needled pines (most regions). Foliage of new growth fading or "flagging" in mid- or late summer; white flocculence may be in evidence on twigs and branches.........(*Matsucoccus* spp.). | | | None | ... |
| 2. Firs (AC). White, flocculent masses on trunk and larger branches. Infested twigs swell and appear gouty; foliage turns red.........BALSAM WOOLLY APHID (*Chermes piceae*). | Nymphs | Early spring | 14, 15, 17 | 19 |

Footnotes on page 8·5.

## Key to Diagnosis and Control of Forest Insect Injuries (Continued)

| Form of injury, host, range,[a] and insect[b] | Prevention[c] | Recommended controls | | |
| --- | --- | --- | --- | --- |
| | | Direct control[d] | | |
| | | Method | Time of year | Stage of insect |
| 3. Beech, weakened or dying (AC). White flocculence on trunks and branches........BEECH SCALE (Cryptococcus fagi). | ... | 15, 16 | Early spring | Nymphs |
| 4. White, Scotch, Austrian pines (most regions). Small aphids, covered with flocculent wax, on trunk and branches or in clusters at bases of needles. ......PINE-BARK APHID (Pineus strobi). | ... | 13, 15, 17 | ... | ... |
| 5. Broad-leaved trees (all regions). Brown to grayish oystershell-shaped scales on twigs, branches, and occasionally leaves........OYSTERSHELL SCALE (Lepidosaphes ulmi). | ... | 13, 17 | May-June | Crawlers |
| 6. Pines, all species (all regions). Mature scales pure white, elongated, about ⅛ in. in length, on needles. ......PINE-NEEDLE SCALE (Phenacaspis pinifoliae). | ... | 13, 17 | Early June Early Aug. | Crawlers |
| 7. Jack, Austrian, and Scotch pines (C). Reddish-brown convex scales about ¼ in. long; heavily infested pines covered with sooty mold.......PINE TORTOISE SCALE (Toumeyella numismaticum). | ... | 14a | Early spring | Immature females |
| 8. Pines, Douglas-fir, hemlock (PC, RM). Circular, yellowish-brown to black scales, about 1/16 in. in diameter, on the needles........BLACK PINE-LEAF SCALE (Aspidiotus californicus). | ... | 13, 17 | Spring | Crawlers |
| D. Ends of branches slowly dying; conspicuous frothy masses of spittle surround insects.......SPITTLE BUGS (Cercopidae); | | | | |
| 1. Pines (AC, C, S).......PINE SPITTLE-BUG (Aphrophora parallela). | ... | 19 | June | Nymphs |
| 2. Pines (AC, C). Immature stages at base of sweet fern and other plants. Only the adults feed on pines | ... | 1, 2 | July-Aug. | Adults |

| | | | |
|---|---|---|---|
| **III. Stems, branches, or leaves have swellings or galls, which may cause stunting, or premature shedding, of leaves.** Caused by many species of midges, mites, aphids, or wasps. Various conifers and broad-leaved trees (all regions). | | | |
| A. Pines (PC). Needles blistered within sheaths, causing premature shedding.......PINE-NEEDLE MITE (*Eriophyes pini*). | 23 | Summer | All stages |
| B. Pines, junipers (most regions). Galls on leaves or twigs containing pink or red maggots.......GALL or PITCH MIDGES (Cecidomyiidae, Itonididae). | | Consult an entomologist | |
| C. Spruce (most regions). Conical galls on terminal twigs.......SPRUCE GALL APHIDS (Chermine). | 17 | Early April | Nymphs |
| D. Broad-leaved trees (most regions). Galls inhabited by microscopic 8-legged mites.......GALL MITES (Eriophyidae). | 13, 15, 16 | Consult an entomologist | Adults & eggs |
| E. Broad-leaved trees (most regions). Galls inhabited by white larvae, pink or red maggots, or aphids.......GALL WASPS, MIDGES, APHIDS (Cynipidae, Cecidomyiidae, Aphidae). | | Consult an entomologist | |
| **DEFOLIATION: LEAVES OF TREES OF ALL AGES PARTIALLY OR WHOLLY STRIPPED OR SKELETONIZED.** | | | |
| **I. Defoliation caused by caterpillars with 3 pairs of true legs, and less than 6 pairs of prolegs** (fleshy legs on the abdominal segments). | | | |
| A. Leaves and buds at tips of branches webbed together and fed upon by nearly hairless caterpillars.......BUD MOTHS or BUDWORMS (Tortricidae). | | | |
| 1. Firs, spruces, Douglas-fir, jack, and other pines (AC, C, NRM, RM, PC). Caterpillars dark brown or reddish brown, with conspicuous light-colored, hairy tubercles; heads black.......SPRUCE BUDWORM (*Choristoneura fumiferana*). | 1, 2 | When fir needles have expanded & new twig growth begins to flatten out. | 4th & 5th instar larvae |
| 2. Firs, hemlocks, spruces, Douglas-fir; balsam fir apparently most favored (PC, AC, C, NRM, Canada to Alaska). Caterpillars bright green with black heads.......BLACK-HEADED BUDWORM (*Acleris variana*). | 1, 2 | When fir needles are separating from buds | Larvae |
| B. Leaves eaten by bagworms or casebearers of several families. Various host plants (AC, C, S). | | | |

Footnotes on page 8·5.

## Key to Diagnosis and Control of Forest Insect Injuries (Continued)

| Form of injury, host, range,[a] and insect[b] | Recommended controls | | | |
|---|---|---|---|---|
| | Prevention [c] | Direct control [d] | | |
| | | Method | Time of year | Stage of insect |
| 1. Larch (AC, S)........Larch Casebearer (*Coleophora laricella*). | ... | 15, 16 | Dormant early spring | Larvae |
| 2. Arborvitae and various other evergreens and broad-leaved trees and shrubs (AC, C, S)........Bagworm (*Thyridopteryx ephemeraeformis*). | ... | 2, 2b, 4a, 12 | June & July | Larvae |
| C. Leaves mined. Serpentine, blotch, or tentiform mines. Several families of leaf miners (see also p. 8-15). | | | | |
| 1. Lodgepole pine (PC)........Lodgepole Needle Miner (*Recurvaria milleri*). | ... | 7 | August alternate years | Larvae |
| 2. Pitch, jack, loblolly, red, shortleaf, and Virginia pines (AC)........Pine Needle Miner (*Exoteleia pinifoliella*). | ... | 12 | Mar.-Apr. | Larvae |
| 3. Spruce (AC, C) (*Epinotia nanana*), (AC, C, RM) (*Recurvaria piceaella*), (AC, C, NRM, PC) (*Taniva albolineana*). | ... | 12 | Mar.-Apr. | Larvae |
| D. Leaves injured by skeletonizers (Lyonetiidae), leaf rollers, leaf tiers, and others of several families. Various host plants (all regions)........(Lepidoptera, Coleoptera). | ... | 1, 2, 4, 12 | When larvae are active | Larvae |
| E. Leaves eaten by tentmakers or webmakers. | | | | |
| 1. Broad-leaved forest and fruit trees (all regions). Caterpillars feed outside of tents, but return for resting periods........Tent Caterpillars (*Malacosoma* spp.). | ... | 1, 2, 4 | Spring | Larvae |
| 2. Broad-leaved trees and shrubs (most regions). Hairy caterpillars feeding within webs, enlarging them as necessary........Fall Webworm (*Hyphantria cunea*). | ... | 4, 43 | Summer | Larvae |
| 3. Most pines (AC, C), Yellowish-brown caterpillars with 2 dark-brown longitudinal stripes, feeding within webs filled with frass. ......Pine Web- | ... | 4, 12 | Late summer | Larvae |

| | | | | |
|---|---|---|---|---|
| 4. Oak, cherry, apple, pear, hawthorn, willow, etc. (AC). Small webs, bound with silk on twig tips, contain small, hairy caterpillars from fall to spring, caterpillars then vacate webs and become free feeders. Full-grown caterpillars dark brown to black with broken white line on each side, 2 reddish spots on back near anal end, brown barbed hairs......... BROWN-TAIL MOTH (*Nygmia phaeorrhoea*). | ... | 1, 2, 4, 12 | | Larvae |
| F. Defoliation by free-feeding caterpillars. Some silk may be spun on branches, and some caterpillars may spin down on silken threads, but they do not construct or inhabit tents or webs. Many families, hundreds of species. Numerous host plants (all regions). | | | | |
|   1. Caterpillars hairy or bristly; may have long hair pencils, brushlike tufts, or tussocks. | | | | |
|     a. Sugar maple, oaks, poplars, and other broad-leaved trees (most, regions). Caterpillars spin silken mat, where they congregate while resting or molting. Head and body pale bluish, with a row of keyhole-shaped, white spots along the back......FOREST TENT CATERPILLAR (*Malacosoma disstria*). | ... | 1, 2, 4, 12 | May-June | Larvae |
|     b. (1) Oak types, especially on poor sites, or (2) temporary types, such as gray birch or poplar (AC). Head yellow and black; body dusky, with 5 pairs of blue spots followed by 6 pairs of red spots on back.......GYPSY MOTH (*Porthetria dispar*). | 18a | 1, 2, 4, 12 | May-June | Larvae |
|     c. Douglas-fir, fir (PC, RM, NRM). Head shiny black; body gray or light brown, with 2 long black hair pencils back of head and a similar longer tuft at anal end of body. The back of first four and the last abdominal segments with brown or cream-colored tufts of hairs and numerous red spots.......DOUGLAS-FIR TUSSOCK MOTH (*Hemerocampa pseudotsugata*). | ... | 1 | June-July | Larvae |
|     d. Poplars and willows (AC, PC). Hairy caterpillars; heads black with bluish tinge, body blackish, with a row of white blotches on back and a broken white line on each side......... SATIN MOTH (*Stilpnotia salicis*). | ... | 1, 2, 4, 12 | May to early June | Larvae |

Footnotes on page 8·5.

## Key to Diagnosis and Control of Forest Insect Injuries (Continued)

| Form of injury, host, range,[a] and insect[b] | Recommended controls | | | |
| --- | --- | --- | --- | --- |
| | Prevention[c] | Direct control[d] | | |
| | | Method | Time of year | Stage of insect |
| e. Brown-tail moth (see E-4, above). | | | | |
| f. Douglas-fir, fir, pine, and spruce (RM, PC). Caterpillars clothed with long, dark hairs; gregarious; when partly grown hibernate in dense clusters on twigs........SILVER-SPOTTED HALISIDOTA (*Halisidota argentata*). | ... | 1 | May-June | Larvae |
| 2. Caterpillars nearly naked, or with fine hairs only. | | | | |
| a. Ponderosa and other pines (PC, RM, NRM). Dark-green caterpillars with fine hairs and 2 white stripes on each side........PINE BUTTERFLY (*Neophasia menapia*). | ... | 1 | June, early July | Larvae |
| b. Beech, sugar maple, other broad-leaved trees (AC, S, C). Light-green caterpillars, usually with a saddle-shaped blotch of reddish brown on back. Heads large and banded with red.......... SADDLED PROMINENT. (*Heterocampa guttivitta*). | ... | 1, 2 | June, early July | Larvae |
| c. Oaks (California). Caterpillars dark olive-green, with sparse hairs, and black and yellow longitudinal stripes........CALIFORNIA OAK WORM (*Phryganidia californica*). | ... | 1, 12 | Mar.-Apr., late July & early August | Larvae of two generations |
| 3. Caterpillars with scattered spines or prominent horny or wartlike tubercles on some of the segments. | | | | |
| a. Ponderosa, Jeffrey, and sometimes lodgepole pines (NRM, RM, PC). Leathery, yellowish-green, with numerous stout, branched spines. 2-year life cycle........PANDORA MOTH (*Coloradia pandora*). | ... | 1 | Aug.-Sept. & May; early June | Larvae, early instars, late instars |
| b. Broad-leaved trees, chiefly (most regions). Large caterpillars with sparse, stout tubercles or short, blunt spines........GIANT SILK MOTHS (Sat- | ... | 1, 2, 12 | Summer | Larvae |

| | Stage | Time | | |
|---|---|---|---|---|
| 4. Loopers, spanworms, measuring worms. Naked caterpillars, usually slender; abdominal legs, except those on the 6th and 10th segments, more or less rudimentary or obsolete; when traveling, their bodies form a loop.......(Geometridae). | Larvae | June, July | 1, 2 | ... |
| a. Hemlock, balsam fir, and other trees during outbreaks (northern portions of AC, C). Yellowish-green caterpillars, marked with brown, white, and yellow. Winter passed in egg stage.......HEMLOCK LOOPER (Lambdina fiscellaria fiscellaria). | | | | |
| b. Hemlock, spruce (northwestern portions of PC, NRM). Similar to above. Winter passed in egg stage.......(L. fiscellaria lugubrosa). | Larvae | June, early July | 1, 2 | ... |
| c. Hemlock (southern N. H. to Ohio and south). Similar to above species. Hibernates in pupal stage in duff.......(Lambdina athasaria athasaria). | Larvae | July-August | 1, 2 | ... |
| d. Prefers oak (PC). Similar to hemlock looper. (L. fiscellaria somniaria). | Larvae | June-July | 1, 2 | ... |
| e. Most broad-leaved trees, apple and elm preferred (AC, C; also Colo. and Calif.). Green or nearly black caterpillars, variable, with one or more longitudinal stripes...FALL CANKERWORM (Alsophila pometaria).......SPRING CANKERWORM (Paleacrita vernata). | Larvae | Spring | 1, 2, 4, 12 | ... |
| **II. Defoliation (leaves mined by some species) caused by naked slugs or larvae with 3 pairs of true legs, and 6 or 8 pairs of prolegs.** A few species are coated with slime, and some with a white powder; others bear sparse hairs, bristles, or spines......SAWFLIES (Superfamily Tenthredinoidea). | | | | |
| A. Larvae either solitary or gregarious, but not in nests of webbing and frass. | | | | |
| 1. Pines, spruce, hemlock, larch (all regions)..........(Diprionidae, Tenthredinidae). | Larvae | Consult an entomologist | 1, 2, 4 | ... |
| 2. Broad-leaved trees (all regions)..........(Acorduleceridae, Argidae, Cimbicidae, Tenthredinidae). | Larvae | Consult an entomologist | 1, 2, 4 | ... |
| B. Larvae in nests of webbing and frass. | | | | |
| 1. Conifers and broad-leaved trees (all regions)..........(Pamphiliidae). | Larvae | Consult an entomologist | 1, 2, 4 | ... |

Footnotes on page 8·5.

## Key to Diagnosis and Control of Forest Insect Injuries (Continued)

| Form of injury, host, range,[a] and insect[b] | Recommended controls | | | |
|---|---|---|---|---|
| | Prevention[c] | Direct control[d] | | |
| | | Method | Time of year | Stage of insect |
| C. Leaf miners on broad-leaved trees (all regions). ........(Tenthredinidae, tribe Fenusini). | ... | 6a, 17 | Consult an entomologist | Eggs & newly hatched larvae |
| III. Leaves skeletonized, with midribs and veins still evident, by active grubs with 3 pairs of true legs, or by hard-shelled beetles (see also I-D, p. 8-12); shot-hole effect caused by some adults. Broad-leaved trees (all regions)......... Various leaf beetles (Chrysomelidae). | ... | 1, 2, 4a, 12 | When found causing damage | Adults & larvae |
| 1. Elm (most regions). Dull yellowish to green beetles about ⅕ in. long, with a black stripe along outer sides of wing covers, chewing holes in leaves, or their yellow, black-spotted larvae skeletonizing the foliage......... Elm-leaf Beetle (Galerucella xanthomelaena). | ... | 1a, 2a, 4a, 12 | When found causing damage | Adults & larvae |
| ENTIRE TREE, OR LARGE PART, SICKLY, DYING, OR DEAD; FOLIAGE FADING, TURNING YELLOW OR RED; INNER BARK OF MAIN TRUNK, LARGE BRANCHES, AND SOMETIMES ROOTS, KILLED. | | | | |
| I. Pitch tubes on the bark (conifers) or boring dust in the crevices (conifers and broad-leaved trees). The small beetles (the largest are less than ⅓ in. long) make egg tunnels under the bark, from which the white, legless, curled larvae make diverging tunnels, usually packed with fine borings.........Bark Beetles (Scolytidae and Platypodidae). | Consult an entomologist | ... | All seasons | |
| A. Ponderosa and Coulter pines (PC, NRM). Parent beetles make winding egg galleries in inner phloem; larvae work out into outer bark.........Western Pine Beetle (Dendroctonus brevicomis). | 15, 17, 18 | 5, 36, 42 | All seasons | Larvae & pupae |

| Injury | | | Season | Stage |
|---|---|---|---|---|
| B. Western white, sugar, lodgepole, ponderosa, and other pines within its range (PC, NRM). Parent beetles make long longitudinal egg galleries in phloem. Larvae work in inner phloem.........MOUNTAIN PINE BEETLE (*D. monticolae*). | 15 | Sugar pine 36, 42; lodgepole 31, 38, 39, 40, 41, 42; western white 31, 37, 38, 39, 40, 41, 42 | Fall & spring | Larvae |
| C. Ponderosa, lodgepole, limber, bristlecone, Mexican white, and pinyon pines (C, RM). Parent beetles make long longitudinal egg galleries in phloem. Larvae work in inner bark.......BLACK HILLS BEETLE (*D. ponderosae*). | 15 | 31, 36, 37, 38, 42 | Spring | Larvae & pupae |
| D. Jeffrey pine (California). Egg galleries, long, longitudinal, in phloem. Larvae work in inner bark....... JEFFREY PINE BEETLE (*D. jeffreyi*). | 15, 17 | 36, 42 | Fall, winter, spring | Larvae & pupae |
| E. White, pitch, Virginia, shortleaf, longleaf, loblolly, and spruce pines, and red spruce (southern AC, S). Egg galleries S-shaped. Attacks and kills healthy trees. Larvae bore through phloem then outward into the bark.......SOUTHERN PINE BEETLE (*D. frontalis*). | 15, 16 | 31, 38, 39, 41, 42 | Summer, fall, & spring | Larvae & pupae |
| F. Various pines (AC, C, RM, NRM, PC). Attacks healthy, injured, or dying trees, and freshly cut logs and stumps. Large reddish pitch tubes. Adults largest of genus, 7 to 8 mm. long, reddish. Egg galleries irregular and longitudinal between bark and wood. Lower portion of trunk usually attacked.......RED TURPENTINE BEETLE (*D. valens*). | 16, 19 | 42, 45, 46 | All seasons | Larvae & pupae |
| G. Various pines (New Hampshire south to Florida and Texas). Somewhat similar in appearance and habits to (F) but smaller and darker in color.......BLACK TURPENTINE BEETLE (*D. terebrans*). | 16, 19 | 42, 45, 46 | All seasons | Larvae & pupae |
| H. Red, white, and black spruces (AC, C). Egg galleries unbranched, about 6 in. long, between inner bark and wood. Young larvae feed in common chamber at first, then each forms an individual mine.......EASTERN SPRUCE BEETLE (*D. piceaperda*). | 15, 16, 19, 22 | 36, 38, 39, 42 | Fall & winter | Larvae, pupae & adults |
| I. Engelmann spruce (RM, NRM). Egg galleries short and longitudinal. Larvae fan out in inner bark.......ENGELMANN SPRUCE BEETLE (*D. engelmanni*). | 15, 16 | 31, 40, 42 | Spring & summer | Larvae, pupae & adults |

Footnotes on page 8·5.

## Key to Diagnosis and Control of Forest Insect Injuries (Continued)

| Form of injury, host, range,[a] and insect[b] | Recommended controls | | | |
| --- | --- | --- | --- | --- |
| | Prevention | Direct control[d] | | |
| | | Method | Time of year | Stage of insect |
| J. Eastern larch (AC, C). Dying, felled, or injured trees. Larvae mine inner bark.......EASTERN LARCH BEETLE (*D. simplex*). | 15, 19 | 31, 38, 42 | Spring & summer | Larvae |
| K. Douglas-fir and larch (NRM, RM, PC). Normally attacks injured, weakened, or felled trees. Egg tunnels short, longitudinal. Larvae fan out in inner bark.......DOUGLAS-FIR BEETLE (*D. pseudotsugae*). | 15 | 36, 42 | Fall | All stages |
| L. All pines (all regions). Normally attacks trees that are weakened, dying, or recently felled. Parent beetles make radiating egg galleries in phloem. Larvae work in inner bark.......IPS ENGRAVER BEETLES (various spp. of Ips). | 11, 14, 15 | 5, 31, 38, 42 | All seasons | All stages |
| M. Various conifers (most regions). Kill trees, but do not ordinarily attack vigorous trees.......(Many genera of family Scolytidae). | 11, 14, 15 | 5, 31, 38, 39, 42 | All seasons | All stages |
| N. Ash (AC, C, S, PC). Decadent and felled trees. Egg galleries transverse. Larval mines regularly spaced longitudinally, and do not cross one another.......ASH BARK BEETLES (*Leperisinus* spp.). | 15, 20 | 31, 35, 38 | Late fall & winter | Adults |
| O. Birch, beech, sweetgum, black cherry (AC, C). Decadent or felled trees. The larvae make radiating burrows from a central chamber in the inner bark.......(*Dryocoetes betulae*). | 14, 15, 21, or 23 | 39, 42 | Late fall & winter | Adults |
| P. Elm. Beetles do not kill healthy trees, but breed in inner bark of decadent and felled trees, and spread Dutch elm disease, if present. | | | | |
| 1. (AC, C; introduced from Europe). Egg galleries short, simple, longitudinal. Young beetles injure twigs by feeding in crotches.......SMALLER | 14, 15, 19 | 37, 38, 42 | All seasons | All stages |

| Description | | | | |
|---|---|---|---|---|
| EUROPEAN ELM BARK BEETLE (*Scolytus multistriatus*). 2. (AC, C, S). Egg galleries branched, transverse. Larval burrows in cambium, more or less vertical. ......NATIVE ELM BARK BEETLE (*Hylurgopinus rufipes*). | 14, 15, 19 | 37, 38, 42 | Fall-spring | Adults |
| Q. Hickory (AC, C, S). Beetles kill healthy trees. Larvae make centipede-like engravings on inner bark. Young beetles injure twigs while feeding.......HICKORY BARK BEETLE (*Scolytus quadrispinosus*). | 14, 15, 19, 21 | 42 | Winter | Larvae |
| R. Various broad-leaved trees (all regions). Attacks usually confined to weakened, injured, or recently felled trees.......(Species of family Scolytidae). | 14, 15, 19, 21 | 38, 42 | All seasons | Adults or larvae |
| **II. Bark shows no outward sign of insect attack.** Tunnels under bark, sometimes entering wood, increase in size with the growth of the white, often legless grubs which make them. A. Tunnels or mines flattened, oval in cross-section, usually packed with arclike layers of sawdust-like borings and pellets of wood excrement, made by slender, white, legless grubs shaped like horseshoe nails, having horny plate on both upper and lower side of the enlarged forward segment.......FLAT-HEADED BORERS (Buprestidae). | 15, 19, 23 | 38, 42 | Consult an entomologist | |
| 1. Chestnut, oak, beech, and other hardwoods (AC, C). Attacks living trees, usually those suffering from drought, defoliation, etc. Topmost branches generally first attacked. Emergence holes of adults are D-shaped.......TWO-LINED CHESTNUT BORER (*Agrilus bilineatus*). | 14, 15, 19 | 38, 42 | Fall to spring | Larvae & adults |
| 2. Birches (AC, C, RM, NRM). Weakened or dying trees. Habits similar to No. 1.........BRONZE BIRCH BORER (*A. anxius*). | 14, 15, 19 | 38, 42 | Fall to spring | Larvae & adults |
| 3. Aspens, cottonwood. Habits similar to Nos. 1, and 2. (AC, C, RM, NRM).........(*A. liragus*). | 14, 15, 19 | 38, 42 | Fall to spring | Larvae & adults |
| 4. Most hardwoods (most regions). Attacks particularly trees recently transplanted, injured, or weakened. Larvae make meandering galleries and enter wood to pupate.......FLAT-HEADED APPLE TREE BORER (*Chrysobothris femorata*). | 10, 19 | ... | All year | Adults |

Footnotes on page 8·5.

## Key to Diagnosis and Control of Forest Insect Injuries  (Continued)

| Form of injury, host, range,[a] and insect[b] | Recommended controls | | | |
| --- | --- | --- | --- | --- |
| | Prevention[c] | Direct control[d] | | |
| | | Method | Time of year | Stage of insect |
| 5. Attack weakened or dying trees and green logs. Larvae make oblique galleries between bark and wood. | | | | |
| a. Hemlock (AC, C)........HEMLOCK BORER (*Melanophila fulvoguttata*). | 15, 19, 23 | 42 | Winter & spring | Adults |
| b. Western pine (PC)........(*M. californica*)... | 15, 19, 23 | 42 | Winter & spring | Adults |
| c. Douglas-fir (PC)........(*M. drummondi*).... | 15, 19, 23 | 42 | Winter & spring | Adults |
| 6. Longleaf and possibly other southern pines (S). Beetles feed on foliage in early spring, lay eggs in season checks on turpentine faces, in blazes, or in fire scars. Larvae mine sapwood and heartwood for 3 years. Weakened trees break in wind.........TURPENTINE BORER (*Buprestis apricans*). | 13, 15 | 42 | Spring-fall | Adults |
| B. Galleries broadly oval to nearly circular in cross section made by elongate, fleshy, white, or yellowish grubs, with enlarged thoracic segments, and with a horny plate on top of the first segment near the head, but with none beneath. Galleries may be tightly packed with powdery, flaky, or excelsior-like frass, or kept continually open. Grubs feed beneath the bark then bore into the wood. Many species attack living trees, freshly cut logs, or roots; some attack dry seasoned wood, and a few, decayed wood.........ROUND-HEADED BORERS (Cerambycidae). | 15, 19, 23 | 35, 38, 42 | Consult an entomologist | |
| 1. Beech, elm, hickories, and oaks (AC, C)......... (*Goes, Hammoderus, Romaleum*). | 10, 19 | Not practical in the forest | | |
| 2. Poplars (all regions)........POPLAR BORER (*Saperda calcarata*). | 10, 19 | Not practical in the forest | | |

| | | | | |
|---|---|---|---|---|
| 3. Black locust (most regions)........LOCUST BORER (*Megacyllene robiniae*). | 10, 19 | | Plant only on good sites. Direct control not practical in the forest | |
| 4. Sugar maple (AC)........SUGAR MAPLE BORER (*Glycobius speciosus*). | 10, 19 | | Not practical in the forest | |
| 5. Conifers (all regions)........PINE SAWYER and others (*Monochamus* spp.). | 10, 19 | | Not practical in the forest | |
| C. Tunnels or mines round in cross-section, often lined with shredded wood fibers; ending in pupal cells, partly in the wood. Usually near base, in root collar, or roots of weakened trees........BARK WEEVILS (Curculionidae). | | | Consult an entomologist | |
| 1. Pines, firs, and spruces (most regions). Weakened, suppressed, or decadent trees attacked........ (*Pissodes* spp.). | | | Consult an entomologist | |

**WOOD AND WOOD PRODUCTS TUNNELED OR DESTROYED.**

| | | | | |
|---|---|---|---|---|
| I. Living or dying trees; freshly felled trees and logs; green, unseasoned, and seasoning wood products. | | | | |
| A. Small, circular, open pinholes, often surrounded by dark stains; diameters uniform and less than ⅛ in; made by brown, shining beetles. Conifers and broad-leaved trees (all regions)........AMBROSIA BEETLES (Scolytidae and Platypodidae). | 14, 15, 20, 21, or 22, 24 | 8, 9, 35, 37 | All year | Adults & larvae |
| B. Circular, oval, or irregularly shaped tunnels of varying size but gradually increasing to more than ⅛ in.; usually packed tightly with fine dust or coarse frass, except at ends which are occupied by larvae or pupae. | | | | |
| 1. Flat-headed borers (see II-A of previous section)........(Buprestidae). | 15, 19, 21, or 22 or 23 | 8, 29, 30, 35, 38, 42 | | Consult an entomologist |
| 2. Round-headed borers (see II-B of previous section)........(Cerambycidae). | 15, 19, 21, or 22 or 23 | 8, 29, 30, 35, 38, 42 | | Consult an entomologist |
| 3. Perfectly circular holes in wood (not evident in cambium) made by long, white, cylindrical grubs with small heads, fleshy lobes for thoracic legs, and the body terminating in a sharp, horny prong. Hardwoods and softwoods (all regions)........HORNTAILS (Siricoidea and certain Coleoptera). | 21, 22, or 23 | 35 | All seasons | All stages |

Footnotes on page 8·5.

## Key to Diagnosis and Control of Forest Insect Injuries (Continued)

| Form of injury, host, range,[a] and insect[b] | Recommended controls | | | |
| --- | --- | --- | --- | --- |
| | Prevention[c] | Direct control[d] | | |
| | | Method | Time of year | Stage of insect |
| **II. Sawed lumber, seasoned wood, and utilized wood products.** | | | | |
| **A.** Small wormholes in wood, tightly packed with very fine powder, which is sometimes pushed out through the holes; usually in very dry wood. | | | | |
|   **1.** Tunnels nearly round. Hardwoods mostly (all regions)........POWDER-POST BEETLES (Anobiidae, Bostrichidae, Lyctidae, Ptinidae). | 11, 20, 26, 28, 29, 30 | 29, 30, 35 | All year | All stages |
|   **2.** Irregularly shaped tunnels (see I-B-2) (Cerambycidae). | | | | |
|     **a.** Softwoods (most regions)........OLD HOUSE BORER (Hylotrupes bajulus). | ... | 29, 30, 34 | All year | All stages |
|     **b.** Pine, spruce, hemlock, juniper, cedars (most regions). Attacks logs and lumber with bark left on edges........BLACK-HORNED PINE BORER (Callidium antennatum). | 23, 27 | 34, 35 | All year | Adults |
|     **c.** Juniper. Damages logs, poles, and rails with bark left for rustic work........BLACK-HORNED JUNIPER BORER (C. janthinum). | 23, 27 | 34, 35 | All year | Adults |
|     **d.** Cypress; oak, ash, hickory, chestnut, maple (AC)........(Eburia spp.). | ... | 34, 35 | All year | All stages |
|     **e.** Bamboo (C, S, PC)........BAMBOO BORER (Chlorophorus annularis). | ... | 34, 35 | All year | All stages |
|     **f.** Oak and hickory (AC)........FLAT OAK BORER (Smodicum cucujiforme). | ... | 35 | All year | All stages |
|     **g.** Ash, white oak, mesquite (AC; C, S, RM)........BANDED ASH BORER (Neoclytus caprea). | 20, 23 | 9, 10, 35, 37 | All year | All stages |
|     **h.** Ash, oak, hickory, persimmon, hackberry (AC, C, S, RM)........RED-HEADED ASH BORER (N. acuminatus). | 20, 21, or 23 | 9, 10, 35, 37 | All year | All stages |

## Key to Diagnosis and Control of Forest Insect Injuries (Continued)

| Form of injury, host, range,[a] and insect[b] | Recommended controls | | | |
| --- | --- | --- | --- | --- |
| | Prevention[c] | Direct control[d] | | |
| | | Method | Time of year | Stage of insect |
| B. Large cavities, lightly filled with excrement, pellets, or frass, not tightly packed with dust; in either dry or moist wood. | | | | |
| 1. Injury by big, black ants which leave only a shell to protect workers. Cavities may contain chewed wood fibers or fibers pushed out of the tunnels, leaving them quite clean (most regions)........CARPENTER ANTS (*Camponotus*). | 25 | 22, 29, 30, 33 | All year | All stages |
| 2. Injury by soft, antlike insects with white bodies and brown heads. Large cavities in wood covered with a thin shell to protect workers, usually containing many oblong, impressed excrement pellets. .......TERMITES (*Reticulitermes* spp.) | | | | |
| a. Subterranean (AC, C, S, PC, RM). Ground-living forms, traveling to and from wood through earthlike shelter tubes. Galleries in wood follow the grain (see USDA, *Farmers' Bull. No. 1911*). | 25, 26 | 32 | All year | All stages |
| b. Dry wood (southern AC, S, PC). Galleries are longitudinal chambers cut across the grain of the wood, and the excrement is in small impressed pellets. | ....... | 30, 33, 34 | All year | All stages |

Footnotes on page 8·5.

## LIST OF PREVENTIVE MEASURES

1. Cultivate new ground 1 to 3 years before it is used for a nursery, and practice clean cultivation in the nursery. White grubs, 2-3 years; cutworms, wireworms, and others, 1-2 years.

2. Place a barrier of a sticky substance around seedbeds by encircling them with boards or metal strips on edge in the ground and painted with a sticky tree-banding material such as tanglefoot.

3. Spread poisoned bran mash (see Nos. 24 and 25, "Methods of direct control") in a barrier strip 100 ft. or more wide around the nursery. Several applications at intervals of 4 or 5 days may be necessary.

4. In the nursery, before planting, treat old or new ground with 10 percent chlordane dust, using 100 lb. per acre. Work the material into the ground to a depth of about 8 in.

5. Dip infested stock in a miscible white oil insecticide 50 to 60 sec. (Saybolt viscosity) before transplanting, using 1 gal. of the oil to 99 gal. of water. (There are many brands on the market.)

6. Control ants to prevent them from transporting the aphids to suitable host plants.

7. Do not plant coniferous seedlings on or adjacent to a cut-over pine area until the third year following the cutting operations. Do not pile freshly cut pine logs or lumber near young pine stands or plantations.

8. Restrict planting of red pine to areas where the temperature normally falls to at least −10°F. each winter.

9. Conifers on good sites spaced not more than 5 by 5 ft., or under shade of other trees, suffer the least injury by weevils.

10. Apply 2 to 5 percent DDT as an emulsion or wettable powder in water (emulsifiable concentrates of DDT and wettable DDT powder are carried in stock by insecticide dealers).

11. Apply 5 percent DDT solution in fuel oil to the material (Formula 5, direct control).

12. Clearcut mature and overmature stands (includes all balsam fir stands older than 50-60 years), with adequate reservation of seed sources. Maintain health of immature stands by short cutting cycles. Favor spruce over balsam on suitable sites.

13. Keep coating of gum over turpentined faces at all times to prevent egg-laying by the beetles; in scraping, be careful not to remove any wood. Practice conservative turpentining by shallow chipping with narrow faces.

14. Dispose of slash by burning before bark beetles emerge.

15. Salvage logs, while green, from windfalls, fire-killed, and lightning-killed trees.

16. Early detection of outbreaks and prompt application of control measures. Use special vigilance during droughts.

17. Sanitation-salvage logging in which "high risk" trees are removed and utilized (see chart of degrees of risk in ponderosa pine. *Jour. Forestry*, 40:854-858, 1942).

18. Silvicultural cutting in which susceptible tree classes (including "high risk" trees) are removed and utilized (see chart of Keen's tree classification, *Jour. Forestry*, 41:249-253, 1943).

18a. (1) Develop and maintain conditions in the forest floor which are favorable to the ground fauna. (2) In silvicultural practices, favor northern hardwoods and conifers against oaks.

19. Confine all cuttings to fall and winter, and utilize products before spring. If defoliating insects are in abundance, apply direct control measures.

20. Cut wood in the fall; season during winter months to avoid attacks by bark beetles and ambrosia beetles.

21. Saw logs into lumber within a month after felling or death of trees; square-edge the lumber before piling.

22. Float logs in fresh-water millpond.

23. Peel the logs as they are cut.

24. Pile lumber for rapid drying.

25. Keep wood dry; insulate woodwork from ground and moisture; allow proper ventilation.

26. Wood to be used in contact with the ground should be impregnated by a standard pressure process with a coal-tar creosote solution.

27. Introduce chemicals into sap stream for preservation of material for rustic work. (Cut tree off at base, and with top lodged against or fastened to another tree, lower the base into a container holding a chemical solution such as chromated zinc

## LIST OF PREVENTIVE MEASURES (Continued)

chloride, zinc chloride, and copper sulfate.) Use concentrations of ½ to ¾ lb. per cu. ft. of sapwood to be treated.

28. Dip green wood in a 5 percent hot water solution of borax (180°F. or higher).

29. Dip green wood in a cold 1 or 2 percent water suspension of finely divided sulfur.

30. Dip or spray with linseed oil, other oils, or paraffin to fill pores of wood.

## LIST OF METHODS OF DIRECT CONTROL

1. Solutions of DDT (technical grade): dissolve 1 lb. of DDT in 1 qt. of a high-powered solvent such as xylene, benzene, or methylated naphthalene, and enough carrier oil, such as Diesel or No. 2 fuel oil, to make 1 gal. of spray. (For aircraft at rate of 1 gal. of spray per acre.)

1a. Use above formula at rate of 2 gal. of spray per acre.

2. Emulsions of DDT (technical grade): dissolve 1 lb. of DDT in 1 qt. xylene, 1.5 oz. of an emulsifying agent (such as Triton X 100) and add water to make 1 gal. of spray. A 12½ percent DDT emulsion. (For aircraft at rate of 1 gal. of spray per acre.)

2a. Use above formula at rate of 2 gal. of spray per acre.

2b. DDT (commercial emulsifiable concentrate containing 25 percent DDT): Dilute at the rate of 1 gal. of concentrate in 100 gal. of water. (For hydraulic sprayers.)

3. DDT (50 percent wettable powder): 2 lb. in enough water to make 1 gal. of spray. (Use at rate of 1 gal. of spray per acre in aircraft.)

4. DDT (50 percent wettable powder): 1 lb. in 100 gal. of water. (For use in hydraulic and knapsack sprayers.)

4a. DDT (50 percent wettable powder): 2 lb. in 100 gal. of water. (Hydraulic and knapsack sprayers.)

5. DDT (technical grade): 1 lb. dissolved in 2½ gal. of No. 2 fuel oil. (5 percent solution.) Use as a spray on surface of bark.

5a. DDT (technical grade): 1 lb. dissolved in 6¼ gal. of No. 2 fuel oil (2 percent solution). (Use as a spray.)

6. Benzene hexachloride (10 percent gamma isomer): 1 lb. in enough water to make 1 gal. of spray. As an adhesive, add 3 oz. of oil (1 oz. motor oil and 2 oz. linseed oil). (For use in mist blowers.)

6a. Benzene hexachloride (25 percent Lindane emulsion at rate of 1 pt. to 100 gal. of water). (For use in hydraulic sprayers.)

7. Benzene hexachloride (99 percent gamma isomer): 6 gal., plus enough No. 2 fuel oil (94 gal.) to make 100 gal. of spray. (Apply at rate of 1 gal. of spray per acre.)

8. Benzene hexachloride–fuel oil solution containing 0.4 percent concentration of gamma isomer by weight. (Use as a spray.)

9. Benzene hexachloride aqueous suspension containing 0.2 gamma isomer. (For dipping or spraying lumber.)

10. Benzene hexachloride–oil solution containing 0.5 percent gamma isomer. Spray logs at rate of 1 gal. per 100 sq. ft.

11. Lead arsenate (powdered, finest particle size): 1 part by weight of chemical; water 10 parts; fish oil or linseed oil 0.3 part; spreader (Aresket or Santomerse S) 0.02 to 0.03 part. (For white pine weevil control use a knapsack sprayer with an extension spray rod and a nozzle that will produce a hollow-cone spray. Spray only the terminal shoot or leader.)

12. Lead arsenate (powdered): 4 lb., plus 1 lb. fish oil or linseed oil, and water to make 100 gal. (For use in hydraulic sprayers.)

13. Miscible oil (summer spray): 1 gal. in 99 gal. of water.

14. Miscible oil (dormant spray): 4 gal. in 96 gal. of water. (Apply in spring before buds open.)

14a. Miscible oil (dormant spray for pines): 3 gal. in 97 gal. of water. (Apply with high-pressure sprayer in spring before growth starts.)

15. Lime-sulfur (liquid) 10 gal. to 90 gal. of water. (Spray early in spring just prior to opening of buds.)

16. Lime-sulfur (dry) 12 lb. to 100 gal. of water. (Spray before buds open in spring.)

17. Forty percent nicotine sulfate; 1 pt.; plus 4 lb. of laundry

## LIST OF METHODS OF DIRECT CONTROL (Continued)

soap, and 100 gal. water. (Apply as a contact spray (Hydraulic sprayer).)

18. Derris or cube powder (4 percent rotenone): 1.5 lb., plus 3 lb. of hard soap or 6 lb. of liquid soap in 100 gal. water. (Apply as a contact spray.)

19. Pyrethrum extract: 1 pt. in 50 gal. water. (Apply as a spray.)

20. Chlordane: applied as a dust to the infested ground at the rate of 10 lb. of actual chemical per acre. A diluent can be used to increase the volume. (Cultivate thoroughly to work the insecticide into the soil.)

20a. Chlordane: at rate of 3 to 4 lb. per acre applied as in No. 20.

21. Chlordane (50 percent wettable powder): apply at the rate of 2 oz. per 2 ft. of mound diameter. Add 1 lb. sawdust or ½ lb. dry sand as a carrier. (Scratch the dry mixture an inch or two into the surface of the mound.)

22. Chlordane (50 percent wettable powder): apply as a spray at the rate of 2 teaspoons to 1 gal. water. (The chlordane powder can also be applied by hand duster over the areas frequented by ants.)

23. Miticides. Use a commercial brand and follow directions given by the manufacturer.

24. Bran mash for grasshoppers: bran or shorts 25 lb., sawdust 3½ bu., chlordane (50 percent wettable powder) 1 lb., or toxaphene 2 lb., water 10 to 12 gal. (Mix thoroughly and spread at rate of 10 to 15 lb. per acre.)

25. Bran mash for cutworms: coarse wheat bran 100 lb., sodium fluosilicate 4 lb., water 10 to 12 gal. (Mix thoroughly and scatter at rate of 20 to 40 lb. per acre.)

26. Poisoned bait: powdered calcium arsenate, 5 lb.; ground dried apple pomace, 95 lb. (Mix thoroughly and apply at rate of 50 to 75 lb. per acre.)

27. Ethylene dichloride-dichloroethyl ether emulsion. Commercially prepared stock emulsions containing 50 percent ethylene dichloride (now available on the market) should be diluted with equal parts of water; then add dichloroethyl ether at rate of 5 percent of the dilute emulsion. Mix thoroughly and apply at rate of ½ pt. around the base of each tree 2 to 3 in. in diameter at the base, increasing the amount to 1 pt. for trees up to 6 in.

28. Chlordane, 40 percent emulsifiable concentrate, 1 gal. to 2,000 gal. of water per acre. Apply as a spray, and then turn on the sprinkler system 3 to 4 hours to drive the chlordane into the soil.

29. Pentachlorophenol: 5 percent solution in fuel oil. (Apply as a fine spray or with a brush. Sometimes it is necessary to make 2 or 3 applications.)

30. Orthodichlorobenzene (crude): at full strength, or dissolved in 5 parts fuel oil; or paradichlorobenzene dissolved in light fuel oil or kerosene. (Treat by saturating the wood.)

31. Orthodichlorobenzene: 1 part to 6 parts of fuel oil. Apply to bole as a penetrating oil spray.

32. Poison the soil around foundations at rate of 1-1½ gal. per linear foot with one of the following:

   a. 5 percent DDT (technical) in No. 2 fuel oil at rate of 1 qt. per cu. ft. of soil (or twice as much DDT if the 50 percent wettable powder is used).

   b. 10 percent sodium arsenite (1 lb. of powder in 1 gal. of water).

   c. Coal-tar creosote (1 part in 2 parts light fuel oil).

   d. 5 percent solution of pentachlorophenol in a fuel oil carrier.

   e. Orthodichlorobenzene (1 part in 3 parts light fuel oil).

## LIST OF METHODS OF DIRECT CONTROL (Continued)

33. Dust Paris green, 50 percent DDT powder, or sodium fluoride into holes bored into infested wood with an auger that penetrates insect galleries.

34. Fumigate buildings "packaged" and sealed with building paper, using heavy dosages of toxic gases. (Must be done only by experienced fumigators.)

34a. Fumigate the seeds with any of the common grain fumigants. This should be done only by an experienced operator.

35. Kiln drying or heat treatment. Heat infested stock to a temperature of 125°F. or higher and hold at that temperature for at least one hour.

36. Fell, peel (top half of log) and burn bark.

37. Fell and peel bark.

38. Fell, peel infested logs, and burn bark and tops.

39. Fell and scorch with flame thrower.

40. Spray the bole with fuel oil and burn standing.

41. Fell, sun cure, and roll log.

42. Salvage infested logs, remove to mill, and burn slabs.

43. Prune infested branches or shoots and burn them.

44. Gather and burn infested trees, tops, or limbs.

44a. Gather and burn infested cones, nuts, seeds, and twigs in selected seed-tree areas.

45. Cut out galleries with a chisel and paint wound with pruning paint.

46. Inject carbon disulfide, ethylene dichloride, or fly spray containing naphthalene into egg galleries.

## LIST OF FUNGICIDAL TREATMENTS

(See pages 8·28-39.)

1. Apply aluminum sulfate immediately after sowing at rate of ¼ to 1 oz. dissolved in 1 pt. of water per sq. ft. of bed surface.

2. Apply sulfuric acid (specific gravity 1.82) immediately after sowing at rate of ⅛ to ³⁄₁₆ fl. oz. per pt. of water per sq. ft. of bed.

3. Semesan as per manufacturer's directions.

4. Bordeaux mixture is made by varying the proportions of copper sulfate, hydrated lime, and water. A common formula (A) is 4 lb. of copper sulfate, 4 lb. of lime, and 50 gal. of water —generally referred to as 4-4-50. Other recommended formulas are (B) 2-3-50, (C) 3-4-50, (D) 4-6-50, and (E) 8-8-50. Bordeaux must be freshly prepared for best results, and its effectiveness is increased by adding various stickers and spreaders.

5. Fermate as per manufacturer's directions and (A) with the addition of Santomerse S at rate of 0.5 pt. per 100 gal. of spray.

6. Zerlate as per manufacturer's directions and (A) plus 0.5 pt. Santomerse per 100 gal. of spray.

7. Dormant strength lime-sulfur, (A) 2 percent lime-sulfur.

8. Dusting with commercial sulfur in sufficient amounts to cover foliage to be protected.

9. Special Semesan, 1 lb. per 100 gal. of spray.

10. Ethylene dibromide (40 percent) at 30 to 35 gal. per acre and applied according to manufacturer's direction.

11. Puratized agricultural spray, 1.5 pt. and 3 lb. of Ziram (Zerlate) mixed in 100 gal. water, applied late in February and again just as the buds are swelling.

## Key to Diagnosis and Control of Forest Tree Diseases

| Host | Symptoms | Common name | Cause | Control* |
|---|---|---|---|---|
| **SEEDLING DISEASES** (Forest tree nurseries) | | | | |
| **I. Noninfectious diseases, caused by environmental conditions** | | | | |
| Conifers | Foliage turns pale yellow, then brownish, and finally reddish brown; injury mainly in center of beds and most severe on soils with poor water-holding capacity. | DROUGHT INJURY | Lack of water | Partial shading and adequate watering. |
| Conifers | Root collar and roots of seedlings raised above surface of soil. | FROST HEAVING | Repeated freezing and thawing of soil | Mulch area where damage occurs. |
| Conifers, hardwoods | Yellowing of foliage. | CHLOROSIS | Nitrogen or iron deficiency | For nitrogen deficiency, add ammonium sulfate at rate of 200 lb. or less per acre; for iron deficiency, spray foliage with 1 percent ferrous sulfate, or ¼ to ¾ percent ferric tartrate. |
| Longleaf pine and other conifers | Rotting of bud and other parts above ground. | SAND SPLASH | Mechanical; fungus invasion secondary | Broadcast instead of drill sowing. |
| **II. Diseases caused by fungi** | | | | |
| Conifers | Failure of seeds to germinate or seedlings to emerge. (May be confused with failure of weak seed to germinate fully.) | PRE-EMERGENCE DAMPING OFF | Mainly species of *Pythium, Phytophthora, Fusarium,* and *Rhizoctonia* | Treat beds after seeding with 1 or 2. |
| Conifers | Rotting of seedlings at ground line shortly after emergence; seedlings fall over in bed. | POST-EMERGENCE DAMPING OFF | Mainly species of *Pythium, Phytophthora, Fusarium,* and *Rhizoctonia* | Select low pH site or reduce pH by chemical applications. Avoid excessive watering. Reduce shade in humid periods. Spray affected beds with 3 or 4A for conifers, or 4B for hardwoods. |

| Host | Symptoms | Disease | Causal Agent | Control |
|---|---|---|---|---|
| Conifers, hardwoods | Rotting of roots in seed or transplant beds. Yellowing of young seedlings; dying of seedlings, usually in groups, during late spring and summer. | SEEDLING ROOT ROT | Mainly species of *Pythium, Phytophthora, Fusarium,* and *Rhizoctonia* | Prevention only; select well-drained acid sites for seed and transplant beds; regulate watering. Avoid excessive buildup of organic material, especially buckwheat as cover crop. |
| White pine | Dead or partially killed seedlings with branch and stem swellings. (Note: See Stem Diseases also.) | WHITE PINE BLISTER RUST | *Cronartium ribicola* | Eradicate all currants and gooseberries in a zone 900 ft. wide around nursery and all European black currants in a zone a mile wide. Destroy all infected stock. |
| Slash pine, loblolly pine | Round or spindle-shaped swellings near base of stem, becoming noticeable at end of first growing season. | FUSIFORM RUST | *Cronartium fusiforme* | Spray at weekly intervals from time of seedling emergence until mid-June with 4A, 5A, or 6A; when seedlings are lifted, cull those with basal swellings. |
| Eastern redcedar (Junipers), *Cypress* spp., true cypresses | Browning of foliage caused by stem lesions; presence of minute black fruiting bodies on dead leaves and lesions. | JUNIPER BLIGHT | *Phomopsis juniperovora* | Keep new foliage covered with 9 throughout growing season; avoid overhead irrigation; remove and destroy diseased plants. |
| Conifers | Blighting of new shoot growth. | TOP BLIGHT | *Rhizoctonia* sp. *Diplodia pinea* | Remove shade frames during rainy weather. |
| Conifers | Patches of dead seedlings occurring under deep snow. | SNOW BLIGHT | *Phacidium infestans* | Spray in late fall with 7. Avoid burlap or other heavy covering in winter. |
| Red pine, other pines | Brown spots on needles; death of a part or all of affected needles. | NEEDLE CAST | *Lophodermium pinastri* | Spray with 4E or 7. |
| Longleaf pine (also in natural stands) | Small spots on needles; spots gradually spread and cause dieback of the needles; a large number of dead or partially dead needles; stunting of growth. | BROWN SPOT NEEDLE BLIGHT | *Scirrhia acicola* | Spray with 4A at 2-week intervals from May to October; for natural reproduction, controlled burning under competent supervision. |
| Hardwoods | Small or large, circular or angular, dead areas on leaves; premature shedding of leaves. | LEAF SPOT | Various fungi | Spray to keep new growth covered with 4B or 4C. |

* For meaning of code numbers see "List of Fungicidal Treatments," page 8·27.

## Key to Diagnosis and Control of Forest Tree Diseases  (Continued)

| Host | Symptoms | Common name | Cause | Control* |
|---|---|---|---|---|
| **III. Diseases caused by parasitic flowering plants** | | | | |
| Hardwoods | Yellow or orange threadlike vines which twine around the tops. | DODDER | *Cuscuta* spp. | Plant only clean seed; eradicate dodder from seedbeds. |
| **DISEASES OF FOREST AND SHADE TREES** | | | | |
| **I. Root diseases** | | | | |
| Conifers | Death of affected trees; soft, stringy rot in roots and butt. In ponderosa pine, light-brown striations under bark at root collar; decay confined to single root. | Root Rot | *Fomes annosus* | No control. |
| Conifers and hardwoods, especially after partial cutting | Decline in vigor, loss of branches, and death of trees, usually in groups; in conifers resin flow develops at base of stem; honey-colored mushrooms may occur around base of tree or nearby stumps. Presence of "shoestrings" (rhizomorphs) and white mycelial fans under bark. | SHOESTRING ROOT ROT | *Armillaria mellea* | No practical control. Usually associated with unfavorable environmental conditions. |
| Species of pine, mature stands, also plantations 15-25 years old | Decline in vigor, needles short, becoming yellow then dying; cones appear prematurely; fruiting bodies at base of tree or on ground surface arising from roots. | ROOT AND BUTT ROT | *Polyporus schweinitzii* | Avoid planting white or red pine on poorly drained or high pH soils. |
| Red and white pine (plantations) | Shortening of terminal growth and of needles; progressive dying from top down; sometimes accompanied by copious resin flow on roots and root crown (in white pine), also on base of trunk); red pine tops sometimes bend over and wilt; roots are killed. | ROOT DISEASE, RESINOSIS, RED PINE MALADY | Not fully known; associated with fungus infections but probably a result of planting these species on imperfectly drained soils | None, other than site selection. |

| Host | Symptoms | Disease | Causal organism | Control |
|---|---|---|---|---|
| loblolly pine | growth accompanied by yellowing and reduction in needle length; root systems defective, with many roots dead; affected trees die in 3–10 yr. | | associated with diseased roots on soils with poor internal drainage | needed in affected stands to prevent gradual loss of timber values. |
| Douglas-fir, other western conifers | First symptom is reduction in growth and smaller than normal cones; gradual thinning of foliage; finally all needles turn brown and the tree dies; trees killed in groups. | LAMINATED ROOT ROT | Poria weirii | No control. |

## II. Foliage diseases
### A. HARDWOODS

| Host | Symptoms | Disease | Causal organism | Control |
|---|---|---|---|---|
| Sycamore, oaks | Leaves and tips of twigs turn brown and die in the spring, resembling late frost injury. | LEAF and TWIG BLIGHT; also ANTHRACNOSE | Gnomonia veneta | No control for forest trees. For shade trees spray with 4. |
| Oaks | Blistering, wrinkling, and curling of the leaves. | OAK LEAF BLISTER | Taphrina coerulescens | No control for forest trees. For shade trees spray with 11. |
| Aspen | Foliage blackened; trees often completely defoliated. | LEAF BLIGHT | Marssonia populi | No control for forest trees. |
| Aspen | Black circular to ellipsoidal spots develop on leaves and fall out; leaves die prematurely; successive infections may be fatal. | INK SPOT | Sclerotinia bifrons | No practical control. |
| Willows | Blighting of leaves and tips of young shoots in the spring; repeated annual defoliation often kills the tree. | WILLOW BLIGHT | Fusicladium saliciperdum associated with Physalospora miyabeana | No control. |
| Black locust | Dense or loose erect clusters of branches with leaves and internodes greatly reduced in size. | BROOMING DISEASE | Virus | Eradicate the diseased individuals. |
| Horsechestnut, Ohio buckeye | Small to large dead areas with yellowish margins on leaves; curling of the leaflets common; small black fruiting bodies develop on dead tissue. | LEAF BLOTCH | Guignardia aesculi | No control in forest; shade trees spray with 4. |
| Red maple, silver maple | Light yellowish-green areas which later become shiny black, 1/8 to 1/2 in. diameter; thickened and somewhat raised. | TAR SPOT | Rhytisma acerinum | No control needed. |

* For meaning of code numbers see "List of Fungicidal Treatments," page 8·27.

## Key to Diagnosis and Control of Forest Tree Diseases  (Continued)

| Host | Symptoms | Common name | Cause | Control* |
|---|---|---|---|---|
| **B. CONIFERS** Pines and other conifers | Red or brown discoloration of foliage followed by premature shedding; commonly gives crown a thin, tufted appearance. Elytroderma sometimes causes witches' brooms on ponderosa and pinyon pines. | NEEDLE CAST | Associated with species of *Hypodermella*, *Hypoderma*, *Lophodermium*, and *Elytroderma* | No control known. |
| Two- and three-needle pines | Small, raised, orange-yellow pustules filled with powdery spores on needles; most common on lower crown but may affect practically all needles on small trees; may cause severe defoliation. | PINE NEEDLE RUST | *Coleosporium* spp. | No control usually needed. |
| Ponderosa and Jeffrey pines; also on pinyon, jack, and lodgepole pines | Reddening of foliage in spring, involving all of foliage where severe; witches' brooms formed when infection systemic only in scattered branches. Elongated, dull, dark-colored fruiting bodies on needles. | No common name | *Elytroderma deformans* | Salvage logging of merchantable trees where infection "systemic" over entire crown. Otherwise no control. |
| Douglas-fir | Yellow spots on needles develop in autumn; these turn reddish brown by spring; infected needles drop in June, July; or later all needles killed except youngest when disease is severe; repeated attack retards growth and occasionally kills trees. | NEEDLE CAST | *Rhabdocline pseudotsugae* | No practical control in forest stands. Select resistant trees for crop trees. |
| Douglas-fir (plantations in eastern states) | Needles yellow-green, mottled, or brown, with progressive shedding from older portions of the twig outward. Second-year or older needles have minute black fruiting bodies on under side. | "ADELOPUS" | *Adelopus gaumanni* associated with "brown tip disease" | For small plantations or ornamentals, spray with 4. |

| Host | Symptoms | Disease | Causal organism | Control |
|---|---|---|---|---|
| Eastern redcedar | Globose brown swellings near end of branches; swellings exude orange-colored gelatinous spore horns during moist weather in early summer. | CEDAR-APPLE RUST | *Gymnosporangium juniperi-virginianae* | No control needed on cedar; eradication of cedar sometimes recommended in immediate vicinity of apple orchards. |
| **III. Stem diseases** **A. HARDWOODS** Hardwood species | Depressed lesions which become concentric or target-shaped with age; on birches the bark remains on lesion; on other species the bark is not retained and the exposed wood is rarely decayed. | NECTRIA CANKER | *Nectria* spp. | No direct control; discriminate against cankered trees in thinnings and improvement cuttings. |
| Beech | Small circular lesions, or irregular areas of dead bark, eventually becoming a deeply depressed cavity, followed by wilting of foliage and death of tree. Trunk and branches may be covered with woolly, white down of scales. | BEECH BARK DISEASE (in combination with WOOLLY BEECH SCALE) | *Nectria coccinea var. faginata* associated with *Cryptococcus fagi* | Control measures in experimental stage. |
| Oak species | Diffused depressed bark-covered areas on trunk or lesions with definite concentric ridges and prominent callus folds; the sapwood on canker face often badly decayed. | STRUMELLA CANKER | *Strumella coryneoidea* | No direct control; discriminate against cankered trees in thinnings and improvement cuttings. Kill infected trees by girdling, cutting, or poisoning. |
| Oak species | Elongated sunken lesions on trunk accompanied by irregular swellings and callus folds; soft dark-brown conks of the causal fungus develop on cankers in late summer and fall. | HISPIDUS CANKER | *Polyporus hispidus* | Remove cankered trees in improvement cuttings. |

* For meaning of code numbers see "List of Fungicidal Treatments," page **8·27.**

## Key to Diagnosis and Control of Forest Tree Diseases    (Continued)

| Host | Symptoms | Common name | Cause | Control* |
|---|---|---|---|---|
| American chestnut, Chinquapins | Death of entire crown or individual branches caused by canker. Cankers are slightly sunken or raised, yellow-brown, with a regular or irregular margin. In damp weather twisted, yellowish-brown tendrils of spores ooze from the canker. The bark on old cankers becomes fissured. | CHESTNUT BLIGHT | *Endothia parasitica* | No control; planting of resistant strains of Chinese chestnut and hybrids has shown considerable promise. |
| Sugar maple, red maple | Depressed lesions on trunk with firmly attached bark, usually centering around a branch stub and with slightly raised concentric callus rings; white to buff mycelial fans present. | EUTYPELLA CANKER | *Eutypella parasitica* | Remove cankered trees in improvement cuttings. |
| Aspen | Yellowish to reddish-brown sunken areas centered around a wound, developing into elongated cankers delimited by vertical cracks in the bark; trees commonly break at cankers. | HYPOXYLON CANKER | *Hypoxylon pruinatum* | Remove infected trees in thinnings. |
| Hardwoods | Tumorlike enlargements often of large size and commonly on lower trunk. | GALLS | Bacteria and fungi | No control. |
| B. CONIFERS Ponderosa pine | Progressive killing of twigs and branches, without canker formation. Rust fruits confined to twigs and small branches. | PAINTBRUSH BLISTER RUST | *Cronartium filamentosum* | None. |
| Slash pine, loblolly pine, occasionally longleaf pine | Spindle-shaped swellings on stem and branches, often causing distortion and breakage; orange spores produced in spring on swellings in blister-like pustules. | FUSIFORM RUST | *Cronartium fusiforme* | Encourage early natural pruning by maintaining high density in stands. Prune infected branches, particularly after occasional year of heavy infection. |

| Host | Disease | Symptoms | Causal organism | Control |
|---|---|---|---|---|
| Five-needle pines of eastern and western U.S. | WHITE PINE BLISTER RUST | Yellow to orange lesions develop on bark at base of needle about 2 years after infection; in the third or fourth year these become girdling bark cankers which in spring and summer bear blisters containing orange spores; these infect leaves of currants and gooseberries; cankers grow down branch to stem and kill by girdling. | *Cronartium ribicola* | Eradication of all currants and gooseberries within the stand and in a protective border of variable width up to 900 ft. around the stand; European black currants should be eradicated for a distance of one mile. |
| Lodgepole pine, ponderosa pine, Jeffrey pine | HIP CANKER | Diamond-shaped perennial cankers on stem, causing malformation and breakage. | *Cronartium coleosporioides* | No practical control. |
| Virginia pine, shortleaf pine, pitch pine, Scotch pine (plantations) | EASTERN GALL RUST | Globose swellings on stems and branches; orange spores produced in ridged blisters in spring. | *Cronartium cerebrum* or one of its forms | No control for forest stands, and usually not needed. |
| Ponderosa pine, lodgepole pine, and other pines | WESTERN GALL RUST | Globose, exfoliating galls on branches and stems. | *Cronartium harknessi* | Pruning off of galls. |
| Slash pine, Virginia pine, longleaf pine, shortleaf pine | PITCH CANKER | Stem and branch cankers with heavy resin flow; affected parts killed; no fungus fruiting. | *Fusarium lateritium, F. pini* | None known. |
| Red pine | TYMPANIS CANKER | Shallow, elongated annual cankers centered at branch nodes; the underlying wood becomes resin-soaked and brownish; found only on planted trees. | *Tympanis* spp. | Apply silvicultural practices that will promote stand vigor. Do not plant too far south of climatic range. |
| Two- and three-needled pines | HARD PINE DIE-BACK | Killing back of current season's growth year after year. Trees become stunted, small trees sometimes killed. | *Diplodia pinea* | Pruning of infected twigs and needles; spray with 4 (ornamentals). |
| Douglas-fir | DOUGLAS-FIR GALL | Tumor-like swellings on branches. | *Bacterium pseudostugae* | None. |

---

* For meaning of code numbers see "List of Fungicidal Treatments," page 8·27.

## Key to Diagnosis and Control of Forest Tree Diseases   (Continued)

| Host | Symptoms | Common name | Cause | Control* |
|---|---|---|---|---|
| Spruces | Gummy exudation of resin, especially at branch insertions. | CYTOSPORA CANKER | *Cytospora kunzei* | In forest stands not usually important except on poor sites. For ornamentals, spray with 4 from interior outward early in spring and at 2-week intervals throughout season. |
| **IV. Decays** | | | | |
| Mature trees of all species | Presence of conks of wood-rotting fungi; large open wounds with softened wood; large branch wounds and top injuries; swellings and cankers on trunk. | ROT OR DECAY | Various fungi, especially species of *Fomes* and *Polyporus* | Prevent wounds, such as those caused by fires and logging; avoid pruning wounds over 3 in. in diameter. |
| Young sprout stands of oak species | Large, unhealed stump wounds or dead companion stems. | BUTT ROT | Species of heart-rotting fungi | Remove unwanted companion sprouts before they reach 3 in. in diameter at base and before stands are 20 years of age; in older stands remove companion stems only if they form a low union and leave a wound over 3 in. in diameter. Periodic pruning of dead branches on crop trees. |
| Ponderosa pine | None, except presence of decay and red discoloration in heartwood. | WESTERN RED ROT | *Polyporus anceps* | |
| **V. Systemic diseases—of physiological origin, or infections involving the vascular system** | | | | |
| American elm | Progressive dwarfing and yellowing of leaves, accompanied by various degrees of defoliation; followed by death of branches or entire tree. | DUTCH ELM DISEASE, associated with attacks by SCOLYTID BEETLES | *Ceratostomella ulmi* carried by *Scolytus multistriatus* and *Hylurgopinus rufipes* | Mainly through destruction of infected trees and protection against bark beetles by insecticidal sprays, and maintenance of tree vigor by appropriate pruning and feeding practices. |

| | | | |
|---|---|---|---|
| American elm | Gradual decline of entire crown; rarely a progressive decline, branch by branch; leaves become sparse, yellow, and fall, followed by death of tree; the inner bark is yellowish brown with odor of wintergreen in early stages of disease, later brown. | PHLOEM NECROSIS, associated with attack by a leaf-hopper insect | Virus, carried by *Scaphoideus luteolus* | Immune elms occur frequently in nature, and only tested specimens should be planted. |
| American elm | Similar to those of Dutch Elm Disease. Can be distinguished only by means of cultures. | ELM DIE-BACK | *Dothiorella ulmi* | Removal of affected limbs; spray with 4. |
| Oak species, particularly those of the black oak group | Leaves crinkle and become pale green, later turning brown or bronze; mature leaves shed at any symptom stage; lower branches affected last; trees usually die after the summer symptoms appear. | OAK WILT | *Chalara quercina* | Some promise of control has been obtained by cutting or poisoning healthy oaks for 50-100 ft. around spot infections. |
| Maple | Sudden dying of single branch; followed by others; eventual death of tree. | MAPLE WILT | *Verticillium*, spp. | |
| Sycamore and London plane | Dark-brown or black lens-shaped discoloration of smooth bark in line with grain of wood, followed by development of canker. Bluish-black streaks in the wood. Infected trees do not recover. | CANKER STAIN OF PLANE | *Endoconidiophora* spp. | Avoid bark wounds. All pruning equipment should be disinfected before using on healthy trees. Paint wounds. |
| Persimmon | Sudden wilting of leaves, followed by defoliation and death. | PERSIMMON WILT | *Cephalosporium diospyri* | None. |
| Mimosa | Wilting and yellowing of foliage, followed by death of tree; brown discoloration in outer growth ring. | MIMOSA WILT | *Fusarium oxysporum* f. *perniciosum* | Plant only resistant strains. |

* For meaning of code numbers see "List of Fungicidal Treatments," page **8·27**.

## Key to Diagnosis and Control of Forest Tree Diseases (Continued)

| Host | Symptoms | Common name | Cause | Control* |
|---|---|---|---|---|
| Paper birch, yellow birch | Deterioration and dying of trees. Northeastern U. S. and Maritime Provinces. | BIRCH DIE-BACK, associated with attack by bronze birch borer | Commonly associated with disturbance of natural conditions and with presence of *Agrilus anxius*, but predisposing factors are somewhat obscure | Avoid excessive opening up of stand in partial cuttings. |
| Western white pine | Progressive decrease in terminal growth accompanied by yellowing and reduction of needle length; diameter growth first reduced on one or more sides; lesions accompanied by resin flow develop on flat faces; root systems defective; trees die in one to six years after showing crown symptoms. | POLE BLIGHT | Cause unknown | No control. Salvage feasible in some stands. |
| Eastern white pine | Lack of vigor. Abnormally short needles, often with browning of outer portions; 2d year needles tend to drop prematurely. | EASTERN WHITE PINE BLIGHT | Probably associated with nutritional or water deficiencies, or with root aphids | None, except on individual trees and small areas, by soil amelioration measures. |

## Key to Diagnosis and Control of Forest Tree Diseases (Continued)

| Host | Symptoms | Common name | Cause | Control* |
|---|---|---|---|---|
| **VI. Mistletoe diseases—caused by parasitic flowering plants** | | | | |
| Eastern, western, and southern hardwoods; also conifers in southwest | Tufted clusters of small green leaves or leafless stems on the branches; these bearing some white or pink berries in the fall; degree of infection varies and some trees bear numerous mistletoe clusters. | AMERICAN MISTLETOE | *Phoradendron* spp. | No control usually needed. |
| Conifers | Witches' brooms in the crown, with conspicuous or inconspicuous swelling, these becoming canker-like; trees commonly break at cankers; the mistletoe appears as perennial shoots simple or branched, rarely more than 8 in. long; color varies from yellow through shades of green. | DWARFMISTLETOE | *Arceuthobium* spp. | Leave only healthy seed trees; eliminate affected trees as far as possible in cutting operations. |

* For meaning of code numbers see "List of Fungicidal Treatments," page **8·27**.

## BIBLIOGRAPHY

BAXTER, D. V. 1952. *Pathology in forest practice.* 2d ed. John Wiley & Sons, Inc., New York.

BOYCE, J. S. 1948. *Forest pathology.* 2d ed. McGraw-Hill Book Co., Inc., New York.

CHAMBERLIN, W. J. 1939. *The bark and timber beetles of North America north of Mexico.* O. S. C. Coop. Assn., Corvallis, Ore.

DOANE, R. W., E. C. VANDYKE, W. J. CHAMBERLIN, and H. E. BURKE. 1936. *Forest insects.* McGraw-Hill Book Co., Inc., New York.

ESSIG, E. O. 1929. *Insects of western North America.* The Macmillan Co., New York.

FELT, E. P., and W. H. RANKIN. 1932. *Insects and diseases of ornamental trees and shrubs.* The Macmillan Co., New York.

GRAHAM, S. A. 1939. *Principles of forest entomology.* McGraw-Hill Book Co., Inc., New York.

SOCIETY OF AMERICAN FORESTERS, NEW ENGLAND SECTION. 1952. *Important tree pests of the Northeast.* 2d ed. Evans Printing Co., Concord, N. H.

U. S. DEPT. AGR. 1938. Insect enemies of western forests. *Misc. Publ. No. 273.*

U. S. DEPT. AGR. 1942. Preventing damage to buildings by termites and their control. *Farmers' Bull. No. 1911.*

U. S. DEPT. AGR. 1950. Insect enemies of eastern forests. *Misc. Publ. No. 657.*

# FOREST WILDLIFE MANAGEMENT

## CONTENTS

# FOREST WILDLIFE MANAGEMENT

Because of the tremendous potential capacity of American second-growth woodlands to produce animals, the art of wildlife management is becoming increasingly integrated with forest management, not only in publicly owned lands but in privately owned forests as well. Wildlife management is simply the application of business methods and technical principles to the handling of wildlife and its habitat. Except in limited areas where production of game animals and birds is the primary objective of forest management, wildlife is usually produced in accordance with the concept of multiple use, whereby the forest is made to yield water, wood, wildlife, recreational benefits, and other products and services.

Wildlife species differ considerably in their feeding and breeding habits, travel radius, gregariousness, and other characteristics. Changes in the forest environment may have a profound effect on the habitat, especially food and cover. In order to manage a given area for wildlife as well as for timber, the forester needs to be able to recognize wildlife species to determine the species and numbers present, and to understand their life histories in order to determine what forest practices improve the wildlife environment and what practices disturb it.

An objective of forest-wildlife management, not yet achieved, is to estimate the optimum wildlife production for a given wooded area of known cover type and ecological composition.

Most silvicultural practices have a beneficial effect on wildlife, especially if carried out at the proper season of the year for maximum production of food and cover and for the least disturbance of newly born birds and mammals.

For the optimum production of wildlife the forester needs to know both the beneficial and detrimental effects on birds and animals that may result from pruning, cleaning (weeding), thinning, timber stand improvement, and the various kinds of cutting, as well as the effects resulting from other silvicultural practices. To enable him to understand these relationships, the following tables have been compiled to give in compact form the life histories and other pertinent information for the more important wildlife species.

## Life History Tables

See Tables 1 to 5.

# Table 1. Life History Table: Game Mammals (exclusive of rodents)

| Species | Dental formula* | Description Total length | Description Tail | Description Hind foot | Weight (lb.) | Average young per litter** | Minimum breeding age (yr.) | Gestation period (days) | Mating*** | Approx. home range | General habitat requirements | Habits† | General food requirements |
|---|---|---|---|---|---|---|---|---|---|---|---|---|---|
| **ORDER CARNIVORA** | | | | | | | | | | | | | |
| **FAMILY URSIDAE** | | | | | | | | | | | | | |
| Black Bear.......... *Euarctos americanus* | 3142 3143 | 60 | 5 | 7 | 200–300 | 1–3 | 3 Max. life 20 ± yr. | 210–225 | Probably monogamous | 15 mi. | Forest | Aa‡ | Omnivorous |
| Grizzly Bear.......... *Ursus horribilis* | 3142 3143 | 72–101 | 2 | 10–12 | 500–600 | 2 | 3 Max. life 20 ± yr. | 230 | Monogamous | 10–25 mi. | Mountains and interspersed forest and prairie | Aa‡ | Omnivorous |
| **ORDER ARTIODACTYLA** | | | | | | | | | | | | | |
| **FAMILY CERVIDAE** | | | | | | | | | | | | | |
| American Elk, Wapiti..... *Cervus canadensis* | 0133 3133 | 88–115 | 4.5–8 | 25–26 | 500–800 | 1 | 3 Max. life 15–20 yr. | 255 | Polygamous | Summer-winter migration | Forest and open meadows | Bb | Grass, herbs, browse |
| White-Tailed Deer......... *Odocoileus virginianus* | 0033 3133 | 70–77 | 7–11 | 20 | 100–200 | 1–2 | 1 Max. life 10–15 yr. | 210 | Polygamous | Small | Brushy hardwood and conifer forest | Eb | Herbs, mast, browse |
| MuleDeer, ColumbianBlack-Tailed Deer...... *Odocoileus hemionus, O. columbianus* | 0033 3133 | 68 | 7–8 | 19.5 | 150–250 | 1–2 | 2 Max. life 10–15 yr. | 210 | Polygamous | Summer-winter migration | Conifer forest and brush-grass | Eb | Browse, grass, mast |
| Moose......... *Alces americana* | 0033 3133 | 82–108 | 2.5 | 31 | 600–1000 | 1–2 | 2 | 242–246 | Polygamous | ... | Spruce and aspen thickets near water | Eb | Willows, other browse, aquatic plants |
| Woodland Caribou.......... *Rangifer caribou* | 0133 3133 | 72 | 4 | 22–25 | 150–250 | 1–2 | ... | 210+ | Polygamous | Large | Northern mixed forest | Eb | Grass, sedge, moss, lichen, browse |
| **FAMILY ANTILOCAPRIDAE** | | | | | | | | | | | | | |
| Autelope, Pronghorn...... *Antilocapra americana* | 0033 3133 | 50–54 | 5.5 | 17 | 92–114 | 2 | 1 Max. life 6–8 yr. | 240–250 | Polygamous | May migrate seasonally | Open plains | Bb | Forbs, grasses, browse |

## Table 1. Life History Table: Game Mammals (exclusive of rodents) (Continued)

| Species | Description | | | | | Breeding data | | | | | General characteristics | | |
|---|---|---|---|---|---|---|---|---|---|---|---|---|---|
| | Dental formula* | Measurement (in.) | | | Weight (lb.) | Average young per litter** | Minimum breeding age (yr.) | Gestation period (days) | Mating*** | General habitat requirements | Approx. home range | Habits† | General food requirements |
| | | Total length | Tail | Hind foot | | | | | | | | | |
| **FAMILY BOVIDAE** | | | | | | | | | | | | | |
| American Buffalo, Bison, *Bison bison* | 0033/3133 | 84–132 | 18–24 | 20–24 | 800–1800 | 1 | 3 | 285 | Polygamous | Open prairie | Originally seasonal migration | Bb | Grasses |
| Mountain Sheep, Bighorn, *Ovis canadensis* | 0033/3133 | 54–70 | 5 | 15–16 | 125–300 | 1–2 | 2–3 | 180+ | Polygamous | Barren rocky slopes | Summer-winter migration | Cb | Browse, forbs, grass |
| Mountain Goat, *Oreamnos americanus* | 0033/3133 | 66 | 6.5 | 13.5 | 150–300 | 1–2 | 2 | 147–178 | Probably monogamous | Rough slopes above timberline | Small, usually less than ½ mi. | Db | Herbs, browse, lichens |
| **FAMILY TAYASSUIDAE** | | | | | | | | | | | | | |
| Peccary, Wild Pig, *Pecari angulatus* | 2133/3133 | 34–40 | 0.5 | 8 | 45–40 | 2 | ... | 112–116 | Polygamous | Brushland | ... | Db | Omnivorous |
| **FAMILY SUIDAE** | | | | | | | | | | | | | |
| Wild Boar, *Sus scrofa* | 3413/3413 | 50–55 | 10 | ... | 330–440 | 6 | 1 | 125–140 | Promiscuous | Forest | ... | Db | Mast, roots, grass |

\* Dental formula: incisors, canines, premolars, molars / incisors, canines, premolars, molars = total teeth, given in this order.

\*\* Normally 1 litter per year for all species except bears, which reproduce in alternate years.

\*\*\* Sex ratio 1:1 for all species except all deer, among which ratio varies from 1:1 to 1:4 or 5.

† Aggregation: Solitary, A; large bands, B; bands up to 40–50, C; small bands, D; winter bands, E. Hibernation: Yes, a; no, b.

‡ Habits: winter sleep, maintain high body temperatures.

9·3

## Table 2. Life History Table: Fur Bearers and Predatory Mammals

| Species | Description: Dental formula (1) | Measurement (in.) Total length (2) | Tail (3) | Hind foot (4) | Weight (lb.) (5) | Breeding data: Average young per litter* (6) | Minimum breeding age (yr.) (7) | Gestation period (days) (8) | Mating** (9) | General characteristics: General habitat requirements (10) | Approx. home range (11) | Habitat† (12) | General food requirements (13) |
|---|---|---|---|---|---|---|---|---|---|---|---|---|---|
| **ORDER MARSUPIALIA** | | | | | | | | | | | | | |
| FAMILY DIDELPHIDAE | | | | | | | | | | | | | |
| Opossum........ *Didelphis virginiana* *Didelphis mesamericana* | 5134/4134 | 24-32 | 10-14 | 2-3 | 8-12 | 5-7 | 1 Max. life 8 yr. | 11-12 | Promiscuous | Forest near water | Small (50 acres) | Ab | Omnivorous |
| **ORDER CARNIVORA** | | | | | | | | | | | | | |
| FAMILY PROCYONIDAE | | | | | | | | | | | | | |
| Raccoon........ *Procyon lotor* | 3142/3142 | 30-37 | 10-12 | 4.5-5 | 10-20 | 3-6 | 1 | 63 | Monogamous | Hardwood forest near water | 200 acres | Ba | Omnivorous |
| FAMILY BASSARISCIDAE | | | | | | | | | | | | | |
| Cacomistle, Ring-tailed Cat, Civet Cat........ *Bassariscus astutus* | 3142/3142 | 25-32 | 13-17 | 2-3 | 2.5 | 3-4 | ... | ... | ... | Chaparral or open forest | Small | Ab | Small animals, fruit |
| FAMILY MUSTELIDAE | | | | | | | | | | | | | |
| Marten, Sable, Pine Marten. *Martes americana* | 3141/3142 | 23-27 | 7-9 | 3-3.5 | 1.5-2.5 | 3-4 | 1 | 259-276 | Promiscuous | Dense conifer forest | Large | Ab | Small animals, especially red squirrel |
| Fisher, Pekan........ *Martes pennanti* | 3141/3142 | 36-38 | 15 | 4 | 5-12 | 2-3 | 1 | 327-358 | Monogamous? | Dense conifer forest | Large | Ab | Carnivorous (incl. porcupine) |
| Weasel........ *Mustela spp.*‡ | 3131/3132 | 6-18 | 1-6 | 1-2 | ... | 4-6 | ... | 270± | Polygamous | Each species habitat specific | ... | Ab | Carnivorous |
| Mink........ *Mustela vison* | 3131/3132 | 24-28 | 7-8 | 2.5-3 | 1.5-2 | 5-6 | 1 | 40-76 | Polygamous | Lake and stream shores | 5 mi. | Ab | Carnivorous |
| Wolverine........ *Gulo luscus* | 3141/3142 | 37-41 | 7-8 | 7-8 | 20-25 | 2-3 | ... | 183 | Monogamous | Dense forest and tundra | Very large | Ab | Carnivorous |
| Otter, River Otter........ *Lutra canadensis* | 3141/3132 | 40-50 | 13-19 | 4-6 | 20 | 2-3 | ... | 49-62 | Monogamous | Streams and lakes | Circuit up to 50 mi. | Cb | Carnivorous, especially fish and crayfish |
| Spotted Skunk........ *Spilogale putorius* | 3131/3132 | 16-22 | 5-8 | 1.5-2 | ... | 4-5 | 1 | ... | Polygamous | Open and brushy areas | ... | ... | Chiefly insects, also fruit, rodents |
| Striped Skunk........ *Mephitis mephitis* | 3131/3132 | 23-30 | 7-15 | 2.5-3.5 | 3-7 | 4-7 | 1 | 62-63 | Polygamous | Open and brushy areas | Up to 1 mi. | Da | Chiefly insects, also fruit, rodents |
| Hog-Nosed Skunk........ *Conepatus mesoleucus* | 3121/3132 | 23-27 | 9-12 | 3 | 5-7 | 2-3 | ... | ... | ... | Rocky open brushy areas | Less than ½ mi. | Ab | Insects, rodents |
| Badger........ *Taxidea taxus* | 3131/3132 | 28-31 | 5-6 | 4-5 | 13-14 | 2-5 | 1 Max. life | 210 | Monogamous | Prairies and ... | 1-2 sq. mi. | Aa | Burrowing |

9 · 4

| | (1) | (2) | (3) | (4) | (5) | (6) | (7) | (8) | (9) | (10) | (11) | (12) | (13) |
|---|---|---|---|---|---|---|---|---|---|---|---|---|---|
| **FAMILY CANIDAE** | | | | | | | | | | | | | |
| Red Fox, *Vulpes fulva* / V. regalis | 3142 / 3143 | 36–40 | 14–16 | 7 | 10–11 | 4–10 | 1 / Max. life 12 yr. / 1 | 51 | Monogamous | Forest, brush, or farmland | 2–3 sq. mi. | Cb | Omnivorous |
| Kit Fox, Swift, Desert Fox, *Vulpes macrotis* / V. velox | 3142 / 3143 | 26–33 | 9–12 | 4–5 | 4–5 | 3–5 | | ... | Monogamous | Open prairie | ... | Cb | Small rodents and birds |
| Gray Fox, *Urocyon cinereoargenteus* | 3142 / 3143 | 36–40 | 12 | 5 | 7–11 | 3–5 | Max. life 14–15 yr. / 1 | 50–60 | Monogamous | Prairie, brush, forest | 1–2 sq. mi. | Cb | Omnivorous |
| Coyote, Brush Wolf, *Canis latrans* | 3142 / 3143 | 42–48 | 12–15 | 7 | 22–26 | 5–7 | Max. life 10–15 yr. / 2 | 63 | Monogamous | Brushy or open | 6–10 sq. mi. | Cb | Carnivorous |
| Gray Wolf, Timberwolf, *Canis nubilus* | 3142 / 3143 | 56–64 | 12–16 | 10 | 60–100 | 6–7 | Max. life 15 yr. | 63 | Monogamous | Prairie, brush, forest | Very large | Eb | Carnivorous |
| **FAMILY FELIDAE** | | | | | | | | | | | | | |
| Cougar, Puma, Mountain Lion, *Felis concolor* | 3131 / 3121 | 84–96 | 24–30 | 10 | 150 | 1–4 | 2 | 91 | Monogamous | Forest and chaparral | Very large | Ab | Carnivorous, especially deer |
| Lynx, *Lynx canadensis* | 3121 / 3121 | 36–39 | 4 | 9.5 | 15–20 | 1–4 | 1 | 60 | Monogamous | Dense forest | Large | Ab | Small mammals, especially rabbits |
| Bobcat, *Lynx rufus* | 3121 / 3121 | 32–39 | 7 | 7 | 12–20 | 2–4 | | 50 | Monogamous | Dense brush and forest | 5 mi. | Ab | Small mammals, birds |
| **ORDER RODENTIA** | | | | | | | | | | | | | |
| **FAMILY CASTORIDAE** | | | | | | | | | | | | | |
| Beaver, *Castor canadensis* | 1013 / 1013 | 43 | 16 | 7 | 30–40 | 4 | 2 | 90 | Monogamous | Lake or slow stream near food | Vicinity of ponds | Cb | Poplar, willow, alder bark |
| **FAMILY CRICETIDAE** | | | | | | | | | | | | | |
| Muskrat, *Ondatra zibethica* | 1003 / 1003 | 20–22 | 9–12 | 3 | 1.75–3.5 | 3–6 | 1 | 29 | Monogamous | Lake, stream, or marsh | 200 yd. | Fb | Aquatic plants |
| **FAMILY MYACASTORIDAE** | | | | | | | | | | | | | |
| Nutria, Coypu, *Myacastor coypus* | 1013 / 1013 | 32–40 | 12–16 | 5–6 | 10–15 | 5 (2–11) | 1 | 127–132 | ... | Lake, stream, marsh | Small | Cb | Aquatic plants |

* Normally 1 litter per year, exceptions are: opossum, 1–2; cougar (puma, mountain lion), alternate years; muskrat, 2–5; nutria, 2–3.

** Sex ratio 1:1 with all species.

† Aggregation: Solitary, A; female and young, B; family groups, C; den groups, D; small packs, E; colony, F. Hibernation: Yes, a; no, b

‡ Several species, principally: *M. rixosa, M. faenata, M. erminia.*

## Table 3. Life History Table: Some of the More Important Rodents and Rodent-like Forms of North America

| Species | Dental formula | Description Measurement (in.) Total length | Tail | Hind foot | Weight (lb.) | Breeding data Average young per litter | Average litters per year | Habits* | General habitat requirements | General food requirements |
|---|---|---|---|---|---|---|---|---|---|---|
| | (1) | (2) | (3) | (4) | (5) | (6) | (7) | (8) | (9) | (10) |
| **ORDER RODENTIA** **FAMILY SCIURIDAE** | | | | | | | | | | |
| Woodchuck, Ground Hog........ *Marmota monax* | 1023/1013 | 20-26 | 5-6 | 3-3.5 | 8-10 | 4-5 | 1 | Aa | Meadows and woods borders | Vegetation |
| Marmot, Rockchuck........ *Marmota flaviventris* | 1023/1013 | 22-28 | 6-7 | 3-4 | 10-12 | 5-6 | 1 | Aa | Rock slides, mountain meadows | Vegetation |
| Hoary Marmot, Rockchuck....... *Marmota caligata* | 1023/1013 | 27-30 | 7.5-8.5 | 4 | 10-15 | 4-5 | 1 | Aa | Openings near timber-line | Vegetation |
| Rock Squirrel........ *Otospermophilus grammurus* | 1023/1013 | 17-20 | 7-8 | 2.5 | ... | ... | ... | Ea | Brushland, forest openings | Mast, fruit, vegetation |
| Mantled Ground Squirrel....... *Callospermophilus* spp. | 1023/1013 | 10-12 | 3-4 | 2 | 0.5 | 5-6 | 1 | a | Forested mountain slopes | Fruit, seeds, insects |
| Ground Squirrel........ *Citellus* spp. | 1023/1013 | 7-18 | 1.5-6 | 1-3 | 0.5-2 | 7-9 | 1 | Bb | Many species; variety of habitats in western U.S. | Omnivorous |
| Antelope Ground Squirrel........ *Ammospermophilus* spp. | 1023/1013 | 8-10 | 2-3 | 1.5-2 | ... | 4-12 | 2 | Ae | Arid brushland | Seed, grain, vegetation |
| Western Chipmunk........ *Eutamias* spp. | 1023/1013 | 7-11 | 3-5 | 1-2 | ... | 4-6 | 1+ | Ad | Many species; variety of habitats in western U.S. | Omnivorous |
| Eastern Chipmunk........ *Tamias striatus* | 1013/1013 | 9-11 | 3-4 | 1-2 | ... | 4-5 | 1 | Aa | Forest and brushland | Omnivorous |
| Eastern Gray Squirrel........ *Sciurus carolinensis* | 1023/1013 | 18 | 8.5 | 2.5 | 1.5 | 2-4 | 1-2 | Ac | Hardwood forest | Mast, buds |
| Western Gray Squirrel........ *Sciurus griseus* | 1023/1013 | 22 | 11 | 3 | 1 | 2-3 | 1 | Af | Oak and conifer oak types | Mast, buds |

* Aggregation: Solitary, A; somewhat gregarious, B; gregarious, C; family groups, D; colonies, E. Hibernation: Yes, a; most species, b; partial, c; in north

| Species | | | | | | | | | Habitat | Largely mast |
|---|---|---|---|---|---|---|---|---|---|---|
| Red Squirrel, Chickaree.............. *Sciurus hudsonicus, S. douglasi, S. fremonti* | 1023/1013 | 12-14 | 5-6 | 2 | 0.5 | 4-5 | 1+ | Ac | Conifer forest | Mast, buds |
| Tuft-Eared Squirrel.............. *Sciurus aberti, S. kaibabensis* | 1023/1013 | 19-21 | 8-9 | 2-3 | ... | 3-4 | 2? | Be | Warm, dry conifer forest | Mast, buds |
| Fox Squirrel.............. *Sciurus niger* | 1013/1013 | 20-27 | 10-12 | 3 | 2 | 3 | 1-2 | Ac | Hardwood forest | Mast, buds |
| Flying Squirrel.............. *Glaucomys volans, G. sabrinus* | 1023/1013 | 9-14 | 3.5-7 | 1-2 | 0.2 | 3-6 | 1-2 | Bf | Dense forest | Mast, fruit seeds |
| **FAMILY GEOMYIDAE** | | | | | | | | | | |
| Western Pocket Gopher.............. *Thomomys* spp. | 1013/1013 | 8-12 | 2.5-4 | 1-1.5 | 0.5-1 | 4-8 | 2 | Af | Grassland and brush-land | Roots, tubers, vegetation |
| Eastern Pocket Gopher.............. *Geomys* spp. | 1013/1013 | 8-12 | 2.5-4 | 1-1.5 | 0.5-1 | 4-5 | 1-2 | Af | Grassland and brush-land | Roots, tubers, foliage |
| **FAMILY CASTORIDAE** | | | | | | | | | | |
| Beaver.............. *Castor canadensis* | 1013/1013 | 43 | 16 | 7 | 30-40 | 4 | 1 | Df | Lake or stream near food | Poplar, willow, alder bark |
| **FAMILY CRICETIDAE** | | | | | | | | | | |
| White-Footed Mouse.............. *Peromyscus* spp. | 1003/1003 | 5-9 | 2-5 | 1 | 0.05-0.1 | 4-5 | 3-4 | f | Many species over N. America | Seeds, fruits, mast, vegetation |
| Rice Rat.............. *Oryzomys* spp. | 1003/1003 | 9-12 | 4-6 | 1-1.5 | ... | 4-5 | 1-2+ | f | Wet grassland, brush-land | Seeds, vegetation |
| Cotton Rat.............. *Sigmodon* spp. | 1003/1003 | 9-13 | 4-5 | 1-2 | 0.4 | 6 | 2+ | Cf | Open grasslands | Vegetation |
| Wood Rat, Pack Rat.............. *Neotoma* spp. | 1003/1003 | 11-16 | 5-8 | 1-2 | 0.5 | 3-6 | 1-2 | Df | Open forest to prairies | Fruit, roots, mast, vegetation |
| Lemming Mouse.............. *Synaptomys* spp. | 1003/1003 | 4.5-5.5 | 0.5-1 | 0.5-1 | 0.08 | 2-4 | 1-2+ | Af | Swamps, bogs | Grass, roots |
| Phenacomys.............. *Phenacomys* spp. | 1003/1003 | 5-8 | 1-3 | 0.5-1 | ... | 5-6 | 1+ | Af | Forests | Vegetation |

*(Continued on following page)*

Table 3. Life History Table: Some of the More Important Rodents and Rodent-like Forms of North America (Continued)

| Species | Dental formula | Description Total length | Description Tail | Description Hind foot | Weight (lb.) | Breeding data Average young per litter | Breeding data Average litters per year | Habits* | General habitat requirements | General food requirements |
|---|---|---|---|---|---|---|---|---|---|---|
| | (1) | (2) | (3) | (4) | (5) | (6) | (7) | (8) | (9) | (10) |
| Red-Backed Mouse........ *Clethrionomys* spp. | $\frac{1003}{1003}$ | 5–6.5 | 1–2 | 0.5–1 | 0.07 | 4–8 | 1–3+ | Af | Forests | Vegetation |
| Meadow Mouse......... *Microtus* spp. | $\frac{1003}{1003}$ | 5–8.5 | 1–2.5 | 0.5–1 | 0.1 | 4–8 | 3+ | Ef | Grassy meadows | Vegetation |
| Pine Mouse......... *Pitymys* spp. | $\frac{1003}{1003}$ | 4.5–5.5 | 0.5–1 | 0.5–1 | 0.08 | 1–4 | 1–2+ | Ef | Open forests and brushlands | Roots, tubers |
| Muskrat......... *Ondatra zibethica* | $\frac{1003}{1003}$ | 20–22 | 9–12 | 3 | 1.75–3.5 | 3–6 | 2–5 | Ef | Lakes, streams, marshes | Aquatic plants |
| FAMILY APLODONTIIDAE | | | | | | | | | | |
| Mountain Beaver......... *Aplodontia rufa* | $\frac{1023}{1013}$ | 12.5–17 | 0 | 2–2.5 | 4 | 2–3 | 1 | Ef | Dense forest near streams | Vegetation |
| FAMILY ZAPOPIDAE | | | | | | | | | | |
| Jumping Mouse......... *Zapus* spp. | $\frac{1013}{1003}$ | 8–10 | 4.5–6 | 1–1.5 | 0.06 | 5–6 | 1–2 | Ba | Grassland | Vegetation |
| Jumping Mouse......... *Napeozapus* spp. | $\frac{1003}{1003}$ | 9–10 | 5–6.5 | 1–1.5 | 0.06 | 5–6 | 1–2 | Ba | Brushland, forest | Vegetation |
| FAMILY ERETHIZONTIDAE | | | | | | | | | | |
| Porcupine......... *Erethizon dorsatum, E. Epixanthum* | $\frac{1013}{1013}$ | 32–40 | 6–7 | 3–4 | 15–25 | 1 | 1 | Af | Conifer and conifer-hardwood forest | Bark, herbs |

Table 3. Life History Table: Some of the More Important Rodents and Rodent-like Forms of North America (Continued)

| Species | Description | | | | Breeding data | | | General habitat requirements | General food requirements |
| | Dental formula | Measurement (in.) | | | | | | | |
| | | Total length | Tail | Hind foot | Weight (lb.) | Average young per litter | Average litters per year | Habits* | |
| | (1) | (2) | (3) | (4) | (5) | (6) | (7) | (8) | (9) | (10) |
|---|---|---|---|---|---|---|---|---|---|---|
| **ORDER LAGOMORPHA** | | | | | | | | | | |
| **FAMILY OCHOTONIDAE** | | | | | | | | | | |
| Pika, Coney........ *Ochotona* spp. | 2023 / 1023 | 7–8 | 0 | 1–1.5 | ... | 3–5 | 1–2 | Cf | High rock slides | Vegetation |
| **FAMILY LEPORIDAE** | | | | | | | | | | |
| Varying Hare, Snowshoe Hare...... *Lepus americanus* (largely) | 2033 / 1023 | 18–19 | 1.5 | 5–5.5 | 2.5–4 | 3–4 | 2–4 | Af | Brushy hardwood conifer forest | Buds, bark, herbs |
| White-Tailed Jack Rabbit........ *Lepus townsendii* (largely) | 2033 / 1023 | 23–25 | 3–4.5 | 6 | 6–8 | 3–6 | 1–3 | Af | Prairie | Vegetation |
| Antelope Jack Rabbit........ *Lepus alleni* | 2033 / 1023 | 24 | 2.5 | 5 | 6–7 | 2–4 | 1+ | Af | Arid plains | Vegetation |
| Black-Tailed Jack Rabbit........ *Lepus californicus* (largely) | 2033 / 1023 | 22–24 | 3–4 | 5 | 5–6 | 3–4 | 1–2 | Af | Arid plains | Vegetation |
| Cottontail Rabbit........ *Sylvilagus* spp. | 2033 / 1023 | 12–21 | 1–3 | 3–4 | 2–3.5 | 4–5 | 3–4 | Af | Cropland and brush | Vegetation, browse, fruit |

* Aggregation: Solitary, A; somewhat gregarious, B; gregarious, C; family groups, D; colonies, E. Hibernation: Yes, a; most species, b; partial, c; in north part of range, d; usually not, e; no, f.

## Table 4. Life History Table: Game Birds

| Species | Average size | | | General habitat | General food habits | Migration | Aggregation | Usual nesting site | Breeding data | | |
|---|---|---|---|---|---|---|---|---|---|---|---|
| | Length (in.) | Wing spread (in.) | Weight (oz.) | | | | | | Number of eggs (range) average | Incubation (days) | Mating and broods per year |
| | (1) | (2) | (3) | (4) | (5) | (6) | (7) | (8) | (9) | (10) | (11) |
| **ORDER GALLIFORMES** | | | | | | | | | | | |
| **FAMILY TETRAONIDAE** | | | | | | | | | | | |
| Blue Grouse, Dusky Grouse, Sooty Grouse......... *Dendragapus obscurus* | 17–23 | 27–30 | 29–42 | Conifer forest, brush | Insects, conifer buds and needles, fruit | Slight; vertical | Small winter coveys or solitary | Conifer forest on ground | 7–10 | 21 | Polygamous 1 |
| Spruce Grouse, Fool Hen....... *Canachites canadensis* | 15–17 | 23–24 | 18 | Northern conifer forest | Conifer buds and needles, fruit | No | Family groups | Conifer forest on ground | (8–16) 10–12 | 17 | Monogamous(?) 1 |
| Franklin's Grouse, Fool Hen.... *Canachites franklini* | ... | ... | 16–18 | Conifer forest | Conifer buds and needles, fruit | No | Solitary | Conifer forest on ground | ... | ... | ... |
| Ruffed Grouse............. *Bonasa umbellus* | 15–19 | 23–25 | 16–27 | Hardwood-conifer forest, brush | Browse, fruit | No | Solitary | Forest edges on ground | (5–27) 10–12 | 21–28 | Promiscuous 1 |
| Willow Ptarmigan............ *Lagopus lagopus* | 14–17 | ... | ... | Tundra and brushy valleys | Browse, fruit, insects | Tundra to interior valleys | Large winter flocks | Rocky tundra on ground | (5–17) 7–10 | ... | Monogamous 1 |
| Greater Prairie Chicken. ....... *Tympanuchus cupido* | 17–19 | 28 | 26–32 | Grasslands | Grain, browse | From northern part of range | Winter flocks and on mating grounds | Grassland on ground | (7–17) 12 | 23 | Promiscuous 1 |
| Lesser Prairie Chicken......... *Tympanuchus pallidicinctus* | ... | ... | ... | Grassland | Fruit | Winter largely in central Texas | Winter flocks and on mating grounds | Grassland on ground | 11–13 | 23 | Promiscuous 1 |
| Sharp-Tailed Grouse......... *Pedioecetes phasianellus* | 15–19 | 24–30 | 29–39 | Brushland | Browse, fruit | From northern part of range | Winter flocks and on mating grounds | Grass-brush on ground | (7–17) 12–13 | 21–24 | Promiscuous 1 |

| | (1) | (2) | (3) | (4) | (5) | (6) | (7) | (8) | (9) | (10) | (11) |
|---|---|---|---|---|---|---|---|---|---|---|---|
| Sage Hen, Sage Grouse....... *Centrocercus urophasianus* | 20–30 | ... | 70–120 | Sagebrush, plains and foothills | Largely sagebrush | Vertical in foothills | Winter flocks on mating grounds | Grass-brush on ground | (5–12) 7–8 | 20–22 | Polygamous 1 |
| **FAMILY PERDICIDAE** Hungarian or European Partridge *Perdix perdix* | 12–14 | 18–22 | 12–15 | Farmland with weed-brush patches | Waste grain, seed, grass | No | Winter coveys | Low herbaceous cover | 16–18 | 21–24 | Monogamous 1 |
| Bobwhite, Bobwhite Quail..... *Colinus virginianus* | 9–11 | 14.5–16 | 6 | Open wood-thickets, cultivated land | Seeds, fruit, insects | No | Winter coveys | Herbaceous cover | (7–37) 14 | 23–24 | Monogamous 1 |
| Mountain Quail............ *Oreortyx picta* | ... | ... | 6 | Brushland and conifer | Seeds, fruit, vegetation | Vertical; 20–30 mi. | Small coveys | Low dense cover on ground | (5–15) 10–12 | 21 | Monogamous 1–2 |
| Scaled Quail, Blue Quail..... *Calipepla squamata* | ... | ... | 6 | Arid brushland | Seeds, insects, fruit | No | Small coveys | Under low shrubs on ground | (9–18) 12–14 | 21 | Monogamous 1–2 |
| California Quail, Valley Quail.... *Lophortyx californica* | ... | ... | 6 | Brushland and grassland | Annual seeds, foliage | No | Winter flocks | Variable | (12–17) 15 | 18–23 | Monogamous 1 |
| Gambel's Quail............ *Lophortyx gambeli* | ... | ... | 6 | Arid brushland | Foliage, seeds | No | Winter flocks | Arid brushland | (7–20) 12 | 21–23 | Monogamous 1 |
| Mearn's Quail............ *Cyronyx montezumae* | ... | ... | 6 | Arid brushy rangeland | Roots, mast, fruit | Slight; vertical | Small coveys | Arid brushland | 8–14 | ... | Monogamous 1 |
| **FAMILY PHASIANIDAE** Ring-Necked Pheasant........ *Phasianus colchicus* (largely) | 20–36 | 32 | 40–70 | Thickets, farmland | Grain, seeds, insects | No | Winter flocks | Fencerows, hayfields | (8–13+) 11 | 23–25 | Polygamous 1 |
| **FAMILY MELEAGRIDAE** Wild Turkey............ *Meleagris gallopavo* | 36–48 | ... | 250–650 | Remote forest or brush | Mast, insect, fruit, seed | No | Flocks | Forest near openings | (7–18) 10–12 | 26–28 | Polygamous 1 |

(Continued on following page)

## Table 4. Life History Table: Game Birds (Continued)

| Species | Average size Length (in.) | Wing spread (in.) | Weight (oz.) | General habitat | General food habits | Migration | Aggregation | Usual nesting site | Breeding data Number of eggs (range) average | Incubation (days) | Mating and broods per year |
|---|---|---|---|---|---|---|---|---|---|---|---|
| | (1) | (2) | (3) | (4) | (5) | (6) | (7) | (8) | (9) | (10) | (11) |
| **ORDER CHARADRIIFORMES** | | | | | | | | | | | |
| **FAMILY SCOLOPACIDAE** | | | | | | | | | | | |
| Woodcock.............. *Philohela minor* | 10–12 | 17–19 | 4–9 | Moist woods, brushland | Earthworms, occasionally insects | Yes | Solitary | Thickets | (3–5) 4 | 19–21 | Monogamous 1 |
| Wilson's Snipe, Jack Snipe..... *Capella gallinago* | 10–12 | 17–20 | 4–5 | Moist grassy marshes | Earthworms, insects, seeds | Yes | Small flocks | Grassy meadows | 4 | 20 | Monogamous 1 |
| **ORDER COLUMBIFORMES** | | | | | | | | | | | |
| **FAMILY COLUMBIDAE** | | | | | | | | | | | |
| Band-Tailed Pigeon........... *Columba fasciata* | ... | ... | ... | Open hardwood (especially oak stands) | Acorns, mast, fruit | Yes | Winter flocks | Open hardwoods | (1–2) 1 | 18–20 | Monogamous 1 |
| Mourning Dove............ *Zenaidura macroura* | 11–13 | 17–19 | 4 | Open and brushy areas | Seeds, fruit, mast | Yes | Winter flocks | Trees, brushy thickets | (1–3) 2 | 14 | Monogamous 2+ |
| White-Winged Dove.......... *Melopelia asiatica* | ... | ... | ... | Brushy desert | Fruit, seed | Yes | Winter flocks | Brushy thickets | (1–3) 2 | 15–20 | Monogamous 2 |

| Species * | Present distribution | Spawning season † | Age (years) at sexual maturity | Egg production (range in number per fish) | Development period | | Absorption of yolk sac | |
|---|---|---|---|---|---|---|---|---|
| | | | | | Days | Mean temp. | Days | Mean temp. |
| American Smelt | Northeastern U. S., southeastern Canada; anadromous and freshwater; introduced successfully into Great Lakes Region | Late March to early May | ... | 1,700-60,000 | 36 | 40°-42° | 6+ | ... |
| Atlantic Salmon | Atlantic coast of northern North America and Europe, anadromous | Late Oct. and Nov. | 3-5 | 9,360-20,990 | 120-192 157 | 35°-38° | 40-50 | ... |
| Sebago Salmon | Restricted to cold lakes of New England and Maritime Provinces; introduced unsuccessfully throughout U. S. | Oct. and Nov. | ... | 1,425-3,070 | 169 | 37° | 40 | ... |
| Silver Salmon | Pacific Coast, Japan to Alaska to California; anadromous; introduced to Atlantic Coast with questionable success | Late Sept. to Nov. | 3 | (This species dies after spawning) | | | | |
| King Salmon (Chinook) | Pacific Coast, N. China to Alaska, to California; anadromous; introduced in New England lakes | Late Sept. to Nov. | 3-5 | (This species dies after spawning) | | | | |
| Red Salmon (Sockeye) | Pacific Coast, Japan to Alaska to N. California; anadromous; introduced in New England lakes | Late Sept. to Nov. | 4-5 occasionally 3-8 | (This species dies after spawning) | | | | |
| Kokanee (Landlocked Red Salmon) | Lakes from Idaho, Oregon to Alaska; introduced in New England lakes | Oct. and Nov. | ... | (This species dies after spawning) | | | | |
| Cutthroat Trout | California to British Columbia; anadromous, (also a strictly freshwater form in Columbia River drainage); widely introduced | Feb.-May occasionally Dec.-June | 3-4 | ... | ... | ... | ... | ... |
| Steelhead Trout (Rainbow Trout) | California to Alaska; anadromous (the rainbow trout is a freshwater form of this species) | Feb. to July | 2-3 | 500-3,000 | 42-45 35-38 | 50° 53° | 30 | 55° |

(Continued on following page)

* The common names used are those accepted by the Committee on Common and Scientific Names of Fishes, in a *List of Common and Scientific Names of the Better Known Fishes of the United States and Canada*, Spec. Publ. No. 1, Amer. Fish Soc., 1948.
† The spawning season will vary with altitude and latitude.

## Table 5. Life History Table: Fish (Continued)

| Species | Present distribution | Spawning season | Age (years) at sexual maturity | Egg production (range in number per fish) | Development period | | Absorption of yolk sac | |
|---|---|---|---|---|---|---|---|---|
| | | | | | Days | Mean temp. | Days | Mean temp. |
| Brown Trout.......... | European, now introduced widely in trout waters the world over | Oct. to Jan. | 3–4 | 920–3,000 | 150 112 40 | 33° 39° 70° | 60 35 | 34° 39° |
| Eastern Brook Trout........ | Formerly northern and eastern North America; both freshwater and anadromous; now introduced widely in U. S. and Canada | Sept. to Nov. | 2–3 | 500–1,500 | 125 50 | 37° 50° | 50 40 25 | 33°–35° 37° 50° |
| Lake Trout.............. | Northern North America; south to northern U. S.; freshwater; widely introduced | Oct. and Nov. | 4–5 | 5,000–14,940 | 75–90 | 40°–45° | ... | ... |
| Largemouth Black Bass...... | Originally southern Canada, Great Lakes basin, central U. S.; now widespread | April to June | ... | ... | 7–14 | ... | ... | ... |
| Smallmouth Black Bass...... | Originally southcentral Canada and northcentral U. S.; now widespread over most of U. S. and many foreign countries | April to June | ... | 2,000–10,000 | 21 | 59°–64° | 16 | ... |
| Bluegill................ | Central U. S., now widely introduced in nearly all states | May to June | ... | 17,260–59,500 | ... | ... | ... | ... |
| Muskellunge............. | Great Lakes basin and upper Mississippi Valley | March and April | ... | 100,000–265,000 | 15 | 55° | 15 | 55° |
| Pike.............. | Central U. S. north and east to Alaska and Labrador, also northern Eurasia | March to early May | ... | 60,000–100,000 | 14–15 | ... | ... | ... |
| Yellow Pike Perch (Walleye)............. | Central and eastern Canada to southcentral and eastern U. S. | April and May | ... | 44,850–615,170 | 28 17–20 | 40° 45° | 5–10 | ... |
| Yellow Perch............. | Originally northcentral U. S. and central Canada, now very widely introduced | March to May | ... | 10,000–48,000 | 7 27 | 57° 47° | ... | ... |

# Census Methods

See Tables 6 to 10.

## Table 6. Census Methods for Forest Game: Deer, Elk, Moose, Caribou

| Method | Best season | Manpower and equipment | General technique | Relative cost | Accuracy | Application to management |
|---|---|---|---|---|---|---|
| Drive*............ | Fall, winter | 1 man per 2–4 rods plus counters; 50–100 per mile | Line of drivers advances abreast; animals counted as they run past. | Salary costs prohibitive; other costs low. | Good on level, open range; low elsewhere. Gives actual count. | Practical only where manpower is available; impossible for small groups or agencies; impossible on rough, mountainous range. |
| Strip*............ | Fall, winter, other seasons | 1 man or small crew | Man walks predetermined line or route, records animals by an average distance observed. | Low, if on sample basis. | Uncertain. Results depend on comparable application and conditions. Gives index. | Practical for small force, area, or operation. |
| Pellet count*........ | Fall, winter, spring | 1 man or small crew | Determine density of pellets per unit area on sample basis. Based on 12.5 ± groups per day. | Low, unless area sampled intensively. | Uncertain. Probably widely variable under different conditions. Gives index. | Same as for strip count if results are considered acceptable for management operations. |
| Track count*........ | Fall, spring | Small crew | Count tracks crossing road, stream, etc., daily; usually requires obliteration of tracks after each count. | Moderate; salary costs greatest; travel second. | Fair to excellent, depending on conditions. Gives trend on actual count. | Application conditioned on availability of suitable conditions, such as possibility of intercepting migrating herd. |
| Aerial count†........ | Fall, winter | Pilot and 1 or 2 observers; plane | Systematic count of animals along predetermined route or on sample area; same route or area must be used each year and at same season for comparable results. | Low for census job; per hour cost high. | Good to excellent. Gives trend on year-to-year basis, or actual herd count on given area having suitable terrain for flying and observing. | Very rapid; suitable for large area or operation, or in mountainous range. Not suitable in coniferous timber or before leaf-fall; snow on ground improves observing conditions. Animals or snow trails may be counted. |

\* Possible application for moose and caribou and other vast wilderness species.
† Probably only practicable method for caribou and other vast wilderness species.

### Table 7. Census Methods for Forest Game: Fox and Gray Squirrels

| Method | Best season | Manpower and equipment | General technique | Relative cost | Accuracy | Application to management |
|---|---|---|---|---|---|---|
| Nest count......... | Late summer; fall | 1 man | Count new leaf nests by areas or by ecological types. | Low to moderate | Poor to fair. Number of new leaf nests depends on per cent of young in population, timber, type, age of stand, etc. Results, at best, only poor index. | Too unreliable for general management purposes. |
| Time-area count...... | Fall; other seasons | 1 man | Record number of squirrels observed during definite time period on random plots of known size in each ecological type. | Moderate for area covered | Uncertain; probably gives a fair index if all counts are made under comparable conditions. Populations may be calculated on area basis from data. | Probably too time-consuming for management purposes. |
| Hunting with dog.... | Fall; other seasons | 1 man; dog | Record number of squirrels treed per hour. | Moderate for area covered | Uncertain; index obtained conditioned by factors of weather, time of day, etc. | Probably too time-consuming and variable for management purposes. |
| Live trapping......... | Fall; other seasons | 1 man or small crew; traps; vehicle for hauling | Live-trap and mark squirrels on predetermined area until population is recorded; or trap by some standardized pattern to obtain an index. | High | Absolute for short seasons and small areas; index reliable provided data are obtained under comparable conditions. | Cost and time required prohibitive for management purposes. For research, live-trapping permits broad study of population, including age, composition, sex ratios, and species distribution. |

### Table 8. Census Methods for Forest Game: Ruffed Grouse and Other Grouse

| Method | Best season | Manpower and equipment | General technique | Relative cost | Accuracy | Application to management |
|---|---|---|---|---|---|---|
| Strip*............ | Fall | 1 man or small crew for area of several townships | Man walks predetermined line or route, records birds by distance observed from which average flushing distance is calculated. This factor is used to determine area covered. | Low, unless area is sampled intensively | Uncertain. Results depend on comparable application and conditions. Gives index that may be used to calculate population. | Practical for small force, area, or operation. Regarded as a basic inventory method for grouse. |

* Numerous variations of basic strip census technique are not covered here.

Table 9.  Census Methods for Forest Game: Wild Turkey

| Method | Best season | Manpower and equipment | General technique | Relative cost | Accuracy | Application to management |
|---|---|---|---|---|---|---|
| Flock count or location. | Late summer and fall | 1 man or small crew, or several small crews | Spot and record specific flocks. Knowledge of turkey range requirements key to easy location. | Low to moderate for area covered | Varies with intensity of coverage; may be absolute for number of flocks and fair to good for number of birds. | Probably most practical and satisfactory method for inventorying wild turkeys. Suitable for small force or operation. |
| Gobbler count........ | Spring (breeding season) | 1 man or small crew, or several small crews | Spot and map gobbling range of individual gobblers. Population obtained by multiplying average number of hens per gobbler. | Low to moderate for area covered | Same as above | Specialized technique, useful in spring when specific gobbler ranges are desired or when flock location is not practical. |
| Waterhole count...... | Summer or fall (any dry season in West) | 1 man, vehicle, usually powered truck | Drive predetermined route, usually early morning or late afternoon. Count turkeys (or tracks) around waterholes. | Low for area covered | Probably varies widely with skill of application. Gives index and often sex ratios. | Probably most practical technique in large western regions where turkeys are concentrated around waterholes. |

Table 10.  Census Methods for Forest Game: Woodcock

| Method | Best season | Manpower and equipment | General technique | Relative cost | Accuracy | Application to management |
|---|---|---|---|---|---|---|
| Singing ground count. | Spring (breeding season) | 1 man, vehicle, for general area | Locate singing grounds and count males during characteristic mating flight. | Low to moderate | Good to excellent if all singing grounds are located. Gives index, breeding population, for local areas. | Probably only reliable method for appraising breeding populations. Applicability to large areas is dependent on adequacy of sample. |
| Migration count ..... | Fall | 1 man and dog, or small crew with dogs | Cover predetermined area—alder runs or other feeding-resting grounds—and count birds flushed. | Low to moderate | Good, if counts are made under comparable conditions year to year. Gives index only. | Method comes too late in season to permit best use of data in making regulations. Useful in appraising flight periods and abundance of woodcock year to year. |

**CENSUS METHODS: FISH. Creel Record.** A creel census may be conducted on streams and lakes in one of several ways, depending on the information desired and on the personnel and funds available. Where it is impractical or impossible to contact all fishermen, it is common practice to make a partial census, and compute the results statistically. The census may be carried out on streams and lakes by contacting fishermen as they fish or by having them report at census stations strategically located on roads bordering streams or lakes. An adequate creel census will provide:

1. A record of size, age class, and numbers of fish caught, by species.
2. Weight-length records, through which the condition factor may be determined.
3. A record of fish catch per unit of fishing effort, for comparison with figures for other bodies of water or for other seasons.
4. Survival rates of marked, hatchery-reared fish which have been planted in natural waters.

**POPULATION CENSUS METHODS.** In the management of any body of water it is important to have a knowledge of the size and character of the fish population contained. In both lakes and streams the same basic principle is employed—that of marking and the later recovery of marked and unmarked fish. The population estimate is based on the proportional catch of marked to unmarked fish. It must be assumed that (1) marking and handling will in no way affect the survival rate or the catchability of the fish marked, and (2) there will be no recruitment and no loss to the fish population for the duration of the census, or the amount of such recruitment or loss will be known.

**Stream Census.** Earlier methods of stream population study consisted of seining fish in sample sections of the stream. Snags and other obstructions on the bottom make seining very difficult if not completely unsuccessful. This method has been largely replaced by electric shocking devices which paralyze the fish temporarily and which insure the return of a much higher percentage of the population.

1. **Power unit.** Both alternating and direct current have been used successfully, although many workers now favor the latter since with direct current the fish are attracted to the positive electrode and are more easily recovered. A satisfactory source of power is a light-weight, portable, air-cooled, gasoline-driven generator capable of producing 500 watts with a voltage of 110 to 120, in alternating current of 60 or more cycles. If direct current is used, a unit producing 2,500 watts at 220 to 240 volts is recommended.

2. **Electrodes.** A great variety of electrodes exists, both in shape and size. In general, they will consist of a nonconductive handle, such as a rake handle, to which is mounted a metal frame. On the frame is wound or interlaced a grid of bare copper wire, which carries the electricity to the water.

3. **Procedure.** A section of stream of known length is blocked off with seines to prevent migration in or out of the section. The generator is either located on the bank of the stream or is carried in a small flat-bottom boat behind the operators, who work upstream, pushing the electrodes before them. Immobilized fish are taken with scap nets, marked by removing a fin, and returned to the water. A second run is made through the section, usually at least 24 hr. after the first, and a record kept of marked and unmarked fish recovered. The total population in the section is then estimated by the following formula:

$$P = \frac{AB}{C}$$

where $P$ is the estimate of the total population
   $A$ is the number of marked fish present
   $B$ is the total number of fish recovered, both marked and unmarked
   $C$ is the number of marked fish recovered

**Lake Census.** Electric devices are not generally practical for taking fish in lakes, and netting seems to be the most satisfactory method. The type of net or trap used must take fish consistently and must produce a minimum of mortality. Hoop nets and fyke nets are in common use for this purpose. A hoop net consists of a cylindrical web like a wind-sock and is held open by several hoops. Funnels of mesh project from two or more hoops toward the back of the net. Fyke nets are simply hoop or funnel nets with divergent, vertical wings to guide the fish into the opening.

The method of making estimates in lakes differs from that in streams in that the daily marking and recovery of fish are continued for several days or longer to insure a moderately large proportion of marked fish in the total population of the lake. As the fish are marked and returned to the water each day, they should be scattered to prevent their being retrapped in disproportionate numbers. On all but very small lakes, two or more nets should be used or the single net should be moved to new locations daily to avoid bias in the estimates.

Daily estimates should be continued until such estimates tend to level off and show slight variation. The following formula is used:

$$P = \frac{\Sigma AB}{\Sigma C}$$

where $P$ is the estimated population on any date
   $A$ is the total number of marked fish in the lake on any date
   $B$ is the total number of fish, marked and unmarked, recovered on any date
   $C$ is the number of marked fish recovered on any date
 $\Sigma AB$ is the sum of the product ($AB$) to date
  $\Sigma C$ is the sum of all marked fish recovered to date

# State Game and Fish Commissions and Fish and Wildlife Service Regions and Headquarters

### State Fish and Game Commissions
   State capitals.

**U. S. Fish and Wildlife Service**—U. S. Department of the Interior, Washington, D. C.
   Region 1. California, Idaho, Montana, Nevada, Oregon, and Washington: Swan Island, Portland, Ore.
   Region 2. Arizona, Colorado, New Mexico, Oklahoma, Kansas, Texas, Utah, and Wyoming: Albuquerque, N. M.
   Region 3. Illinois, Indiana, Iowa, Michigan, Minnesota, Missouri, Wisconsin, North Dakota, South Dakota, and Nebraska: Minneapolis, Minn.
   Region 4. Alabama, Arkansas, Florida, Georgia, Kentucky, Louisiana, Mississippi, North and South Carolina, and Tennessee: Atlanta, Ga.
   Region 5. Delaware, Maryland, New England, New Jersey, New York, Ohio, Pennsylvania, Virginia, and West Virginia: Boston, Mass.

Region 6. Alaska: Juneau, Alaska.
Wildlife Research Laboratory: Denver, Colo.
Pocatello Supply Depot: Pocatello, Idaho.
Patuxent Research Refuge, Larvel, Md.

## Methods of Marking Wildlife

**BIRDS.** There are five principal ways of marking birds: leg bands, metal tags, tattooing, mutilation, and conspicuous marking.

Leg bands are supplied by the U. S. Fish and Wildlife Service to bird banders holding federal bird-banding permits for migratory birds. Nonmigratory birds may be marked with leg bands secured from commercial dealers. Colored metal leg bands are the most conspicuous permanent mark that can be fastened to a bird. Metal tags can be inserted through the web of the wing and are fairly permanent. Tattooing may be done in the web of the wing, and mutilation is usually in the form of toe punches. Conspicuous marking by means of a feather or feathers with a bright dye makes possible the recognition of individuals without retrapping. Combinations of added colored tail feathers also make possible identification of the individual. The extra feathers may be glued or tied with thread or fine copper wire.

**MAMMALS.** There are five principal ways of marking mammals: metal tags, rings, branding and tattooing, mutilation, and conspicuous marking.

Metal clips or tags are widely used to mark mammals of all sizes. The most common method is to attach the tag to the ear. Rings have been used on squirrels, the ring being placed around one of the toes between the base of the toe and the large toe pads. Muskrats have been successfully marked with a ring placed around the Achilles tendon between the gastronemious muscle and the ankle. Branding may be done either with a hot iron or by the newer chemical brands. Beaver have been successfully branded on the tail. Tattooing is successful on lighter-skin areas, such as the ears of rabbits. Mutilation by systematically removing toes is frequently used and does little or no harm to the marked individuals. A system may be established so that a maximum number of animals can be marked without removing too many toes. Conspicuous marking of mammals, such as dyeing the hair, is usually temporary and cannot be recognized beyond the next molt.

**FISH.** Fish may be marked either with metal tags in the jaw or operculum, or by removing one or more fins. Fins must be clipped close to the body or they will regenerate.

## Sampling Techniques of Vegetation Use by Big Game

Several of the following methods have been developed for estimating the degree of cropping of range lands by livestock. However, they are likewise applicable to sampling the grazing and browsing of big game animals.

**GENERAL RECONNAISSANCE METHOD.** Estimates of the intensity of plant use are based on general observations of the total plant height or volume removed from extensive areas. A refinement of this method is first to estimate the percent of plants actually grazed, and then the percentage of cropping of these grazed plants. The intensity of plant use is commonly divided into light, medium, and heavy, as shown by the following indicators:

1. Abundance of key plant species.
2. Grazing or browsing of inferior species.
3. Uniformity of grazing or browsing.
4. Presence of browse lines.
5. Accessibility of palatable species.
6. Condition of timber reproduction.
7. Presence of dead or dying plants.
8. Condition of the animals.

**ACTUAL WEIGHT METHOD.** This is based on comparisons of sets of random plots or transects on used and unused areas. On one set the browse or stubble remaining after the season of use is clipped and weighed; and on the other set the full crop of ungrazed forage is clipped and weighed. The comparison indicates the degree of use.

**OCULAR ESTIMATE, BY-PLOT METHOD.** This method is based on volume-weight relationships. Visual estimates of the degree of cropping are made on small plots, and the degree of vegetation use is expressed as a percent of the total weight of all the plants of each species removed as shown by the total volume removed. Volume-weight relationships can be determined by clipping and weighing samples. Observations are made on small plots; this makes possible more accurate decisions, and errors in personal judgment tend to be compensating. The ocular estimate by-plot method is rapid, adaptable to all classes of forage, and has given reliable estimates of use.

**TWIG MEASUREMENT METHOD.** This offers a simple, mechanical technique for determining the annual percentage utilization of each browse species in winter deer yards. One or more lateral branches of a shrub or tree are tagged and the twig growth beyond the tag is measured before the animals enter the yard or range, and again after they leave.

**ALDOUS DEER BROWSE SURVEY METHOD.** This is designed primarily for evaluating winter browsing of deer, but it can be used with variations for sampling summer browsing of twigs and tips and for checking vegetation use by game animals other than deer. It has found considerable use in various parts of the United States and Canada.

SAMPLE FIELD TALLY FORM USED WITH ALDOUS METHOD
Showing hypothetical entries for a survey of 10 plots in a deeryard

| Plot No. | 1 Dens. | 1 Brwg. | 2 Dens. | 2 Brwg. | 3 Dens. | 3 Brwg. | 4 Dens. | 4 Brwg. | 5 Dens. | 5 Brwg. | 6 Dens. | 6 Brwg. | 7 Dens. | 7 Brwg. | 8 Dens. | 8 Brwg. | 9 Dens. | 9 Brwg. | 10 Dens. | 10 Brwg. | Total No. of plots 10 — Degree of density | Degree of browsing |
|---|---|---|---|---|---|---|---|---|---|---|---|---|---|---|---|---|---|---|---|---|---|---|
| White Cedar | 5 | 0 | 5 | 0 | 5 | 70 | | | 5 | 30 | 30 | 30 | | | 30 | 70 | 5 | 70 | 30 | 30 | 115 | 300 |
| Balsam | | | 30 | 0 | 5 | 30 | | | | | 5 | 0 | | | 5 | 0 | | | 5 | 0 | 50 | 30 |
| Mountain Maple | | | | | 5 | 5 | 5 | 0 | | | | | | | | | | | | | 10 | 5 |
| Red Osier Dogwood | | | | | | | | | 5 | 70 | | | | | | | | | | | 5 | 70 |
| Black Spruce | 5 | 0 | 5 | 0 | | | 30 | 0 | | | 5 | 0 | 5 | 0 | 5 | 0 | | | 5 | 0 | 60 | 0 |
| Total | | | | | | | | | | | | | | | | | | | | | 240 | 405 |

The method consists of making a percentage sample survey of the occurrence of browse and its degree of utilization in a given area. The percentage of sampling may vary with the degree of intensity desired, and plant species may be all-inclusive or restricted to key species only. Circular plots of 1/100 acre (11.7-ft. radius) are commonly used, located mechanically.

The occurrence or availability of individual plant species is rated as **dominant** (50 percent of stand), **moderate** (10 to 50 percent), or **sparse** (trace to 10 percent). Browsing is rated as **heavy** (50 percent or more), **moderate** (10 to 50 percent), **light** (trace to 10 percent), or **none.** For recording data on tally sheets, single numerical values can be assigned to these percentage ranges to represent the average between the two extremes in each class. Dominant or heavy, with a percentage range of 50 to 100, has an average of 75; however, since few plots ever have 100 percent density or browsing, 70 percent is used for this class. Moderate, with a percentage range of 10 to 50, is represented by 30; and sparse or light, with a percentage range up to 10, is represented by 5.

## Steps in Calculating Percent of Browse Used and Available by Aldous Method.

1.  Average density $= \dfrac{\text{Total densities}}{\text{Total No. of plots}}$ (numerators)

    Example: White Cedar $= \dfrac{115}{10} = 11.5$

2.  Average degree of browsing $= \dfrac{\text{Total browsing figures}}{\text{No. of plots where species was found}}$ (denominators)

    Example: White Cedar $= \dfrac{300}{8} = 37.5$

3.  Utilization factor = Average density × Average degree of browsing

    Example: White Cedar $= 11.5 \times 37.5 = 431.2$

4.  Percent of food eaten $= \dfrac{\text{Utilization factor for each species}}{\text{Total of utilization factors}}$

    Example: White Cedar $= \dfrac{431.2}{498.7} = 86.5\%$

5.  Percent of browse available $= \dfrac{\text{Average density of each species}}{\text{Total of density figures}}$

    Example: White Cedar $= \dfrac{11.5}{24.0} = 48\%$

The following sample summary shows in tabular form the results of the computations for all species in the above deeryard. While the percentages in the last two columns were computed in different manners, a comparison of these figures for each species indicates an overbrowsed, underbrowsed, or balanced condition.

SAMPLE SUMMARY OF DATA BY ALDOUS METHOD

| Browse species | Percent of plots where present | Average density | Average degree of browsing | Utilization factor | Percent of food eaten | Percent of browse available |
|---|---|---|---|---|---|---|
| White Cedar ........ | 80 | 11.5 | 37.5 | 431.2 | 86.5 | 48.0 |
| Balsam ............. | 50 | 5.0 | 6.0 | 30.0 | 6.0 | 21.0 |
| Mountain Maple .... | 20 | 1.0 | 2.5 | 2.5 | 0.5 | 4.0 |
| Red Osier Dogwood... | 10 | 0.5 | 70.0 | 35.0 | 7.0 | 2.0 |
| Black Spruce ....... | 70 | 6.0 | 0.0 | 0.0 | 0.0 | 25.0 |
| Total ............ | | 24.0 | | 498.7 | 100.0 | 100.0 |

**RANGE INVENTORIES.** Range inventories must be taken to determine the condition of vegetation and soil. The line-point and line-interception methods have been employed with satisfactory results. These methods give an analysis of ground cover, shrub, tree form, and age classes, and a determination of the intensity of utilization. These methods not only determine present conditions but are useful in appraising future trends.

Tables 11A and 11B will assist in determining the identity of wildlife species feeding upon or damaging vegetation.

**Line-Point Method.** An adaptation of the line-point method as outlined by Dasmann (1951) is given in detail and is here condensed to give the essentials of the method. Portions are directly quoted from Dasmann's article.

Permanent plots 100 ft. long are marked by iron stakes. A tape is stretched between stakes and the dominant class of cover occurring directly over or under each of the foot marks on the tape is recorded on a field form. Because there are 100 marks on the tape, the number of hits made on each class of cover is read directly as a percentage. In scattered vegetation, plots 200 to 300 ft. long are advisable. Frequency of cover classes is recorded rather than the area of ground surface of each class of cover. The assumption is made that frequency of cover is directly proportional to percentage coverage of the ground surface.

Each cover class is defined. Bare ground and rock are easily defined. Litter is any vegetable matter on the ground surface.

Some forbs may be considered as hit when their leaves dominate the area directly under the line-point, but hits on grasses may be limited to those points that are directly over the basal area of the grass plants. With shrubs, bushy trees, and some forbs, a hit may be recorded when the point falls within the circumference of the perennial crown, even though the point is directly over or under an interspace. Were such interspaces recorded as misses, the growth or loss of a few leaves or twigs might result in data indicating changes in coverage not warranted by actual stand conditions. The same standard may be applied to dead shrubs which are still in place.

Form and age classes are recorded on the field sheet.

Shrubs not browsed or lightly browsed will assume their natural shapes, but as utilization becomes greater, departure from the normal shape becomes quite evident. Hedging or high-lining, or partly dead plants, are indicative of a poor range condition and a declining yield of browse.

**Line-Interception Method.** In this method, the linear amount of cover along a stretched tape is measured. The bare soil, rock, litter, live and dead shrubs which the transect line intercepts are measured to the nearest inch. As with the line-point method, these data are expressed in percentages. The method assumes that linear spread of cover along a line is in direct proportion to the area covered by each type of ground cover. Form and age classes of plants and the degree of utilization are recorded as with the line-point method.

Usually a minimum of 20 plots is needed per sampling unit, and a statistical analysis should be made to determine whether or not the sample is adequate for the purpose at hand.

Forage utilization surveys should be made annually. They indicate the intensity of use and may assist in recommending the kind and extent of the harvest. The data on ground cover constitute an index of present range conditions and, repeated at 5-yr. intervals, it determines range trends. The form classes of browse plants indicate the degree of past use and the availability of forage, while the age classes are indicative of the condition of the stand.

### Table 11A.  Identification of Wildlife Damaging Woody Plants

| Animal | Plant parts affected | How damaged | Identified by * |
|---|---|---|---|
| Bear | Branches | Broken down | Broken at crotches; claw marks |
| | Bark | Clawed or eaten | Claw marks; height |
| | Wood | Excavations clawed out | Irregular splintery holes at bee or ant nests |
| Beaver | Sprouts | Eaten | Location and slanting cut |
| | Bark | Gnawed off | Tooth marks; † height |
| | Entire tree | Felled or flooded | Tooth marks or dams |
| Mountain beaver | Twigs | Clipped off | Smooth slanting cut |
| | Leaves | Eaten | Tooth marks, saplings |
| | Bark | Eaten | Trimmed and topped |
| Deer | Twigs | Eaten | Rough broken ends, ⅛″–¼″ diam. commonly to 5′–7′ above ground |
| | Bark | Stripped | Long narrow strips eaten |
| | | Rubbed | Scored and shredded by antlers |
| Elk and Moose | Twigs and branches | Eaten | Rough broken ends, up to 1″–1½″ diam. commonly to 8′–10′ above ground |
| | Bark | Stripped | Tooth marks wide, if present |
| | | Rubbed | Scored and shredded by antlers |
| Mouse ‡ | Bark of trunk, branches, or roots | Gnawed | Tooth mark size;† from ground line or slightly below, up to snow line of previous winter |
| | Branches and small stems | Gnawed | Appear like miniature beaver cuttings |
| Porcupine | Foliage | Eaten | Ragged appearance |
| | Twigs | Gnawed | Slanting cut, tooth size† |
| | Bark | Gnawed | Location, tooth marks |
| Rabbit and Hare | Twigs | Clipped off | Smooth slanting cut |
| | Bark | Gnawed | Tooth marks;† up to 1½′ above ground or snow line |
| Squirrel | Buds | Clipped off | Entire bud removed, leaving no marks |
| | Twigs | Gnawed | Tooth marks;† location |
| Wildcat | Bark | Clawed | Claw marks |
| Wood rat | Twigs | Clipped | Nest location |
| | Bark | Chewed | Tooth marks |
| Pocket gopher | Roots | Bark gnawed | Location; tunnels and mounds |
| Crossbill, Finch, and Grosbeak | Buds | Eaten | Inner bud, scales only removed |
| Grouse | Buds | Eaten | No toothlike marks; usually high location; twigs usually very ragged |
| | Small twigs | Eaten | |
| Sapsucker | Bark | Holes drilled | Regular rows of ¼″ holes |

* Where extensive feeding occurs, droppings will usually permit identification of the animal involved.
† See following table.
‡ Damage severe only at peak of cyclic abundance (generally every 4 years).

### Table 11B.  Average Widths of Incisor Teeth and Tooth Marks

| | Average width in inches | |
|---|---|---|
| | Incisors | Tooth marks |
| Beaver | 0.24 | 0.20 |
| Porcupine | .14 | .10 |
| Rabbit | .10 | .08 |
| Mouse | .06 | .04 |
| Squirrel | .03 | .01 |

**Permanent Plots.** With many of the foregoing browse sampling methods, permanent sample plots can be established to be rechecked periodically. This method of using the same locations for observations or measurements will reveal changing or static conditions over a period of years. The degree of accuracy will depend upon the method of sampling originally chosen and followed.

**Photographs.** The use of comparative photographs is extremely valuable in supplementing and substantiating plot observations and figures. Wherever permanent plots are established, permanent camera points should be marked. Records of photographs taken should show plot number or location, date, time of day, weather, direction of shot, exposure, and name of photographer.

**Exclosures and Inclosures.** These are not sampling techniques in themselves but are devices for controlling food supply and use for analysis by one of the sampling methods above, or for other purposes such as animal nutrition and weighing experiments. Exclosures are generally used to determine the response of vegetation to the absence of grazing or browsing, and for purposes of comparing used and unused areas. Inclosures can be used to determine species and quantities of various foods used by a given number of animals, as well as their response to various diets. Areas of one acre are commonly fenced for such experiments.

## Repellents and Poison Baits

**REPELLENTS. Deer.** Goodrite Z.I.P. has been tested widely and found effective under many conditions. One gallon of paste diluted with 5 gal. of water can be sprayed on trees or cultivated crops (except those for human consumption such as lettuce or greens). A single application will protect trees through a dormant season. Repeat applications are necessary for growing crops. Other effective repellents are Diamond "L" Brand Deer Repellent, naphthalene flakes tied in small bags and hung from trees, and commercial lime-sulfur spray.

**Rabbits.** Repellent 96a (Fish and Wildlife Service) may be applied with brush or hand spray to all parts within reach of rabbits. It has minimized damage from black-tailed and white-tailed jack rabbits, cottontail rabbits, and snowshoe hares. Apply to deciduous trees during dormant season only; it may damage tender foliage. One gallon will treat about four hundred 2- to 3-year-old deciduous trees or 1,500 to 2,000 coniferous seedlings in nursery beds.

Goodrite Z.I.P. has also been found effective as a rabbit repellent.

Another repellent consists of 2 parts ordinary rosin dissolved in 1 part ethyl alcohol. Pulverize the rosin and add to alcohol in a container with a cover tight enough to permit shaking at intervals. Do not heat; the alcohol is inflammable. When dissolved, which may take from 1 to 2 days, apply with paint brush to tree trunks. One treatment lasts throughout the dormant season.

**Mice.** Damage by mice to trees may be minimized by applying any of the repellents listed for rabbits. The base of the tree, which is vulnerable, must be coated. Repellent 96a, because of its high resistance to weathering, is the most useful.

**Porcupines.** Damage to wooden buildings may be minimized by painting with a preparation of 1 lb. copper naphthenate to 2½ qt. of mineral spirits. This will impart a green color to the wood. Goodrite Z.I.P. has prevented porcupine damage to fruit trees and may be effective in reducing damage to other things.

**POISON BAITS.** Because one important phase of forest management is the recreational dividend from picnicking, camping, hunting, and fishing, in which wildlife plays no small part, it is incumbent upon the forester to conduct any necessary control of a destructive species in such a way that the public will find no fault. The proper selection and use of poisons requires a fundamental knowledge of animal behaviorisms that few individuals possess. Wherever possible, therefore, the forester should seek professional advice. Where this is not possible, select and use control formulas from the following list:

### Porcupine Poison.

| | |
|---|---|
| Powdered alkaloid strychnine | 1 oz. |
| Finely crystallized table salt | 1 lb. |

In dry climates add to the above ½ oz. of magnesium carbonate, or mix salt and strychnine with a little lard or soft fat. Place poison on flat rocks in dens, or drill holes in blocks of wood for cups, and nail in "rest trees" out of reach of beneficial animals.

### Prairie Dog, Ground Squirrel, and Chipmunk Poison.

| | |
|---|---|
| Strychnine | 25 oz. |
| Saccharin | 2 oz. |
| Soda | 1¼ lb. |
| Borax | 2½ lb. |
| Salt | 2½ lb. |
| Starch | 1 lb. |
| Syrup | 3 qt. |
| Water | 9 qt. |
| Glycerine | 1 qt. |
| Rolled oats | 500 lb. |

Dissolve starch in about 1 qt. of cold water. Place salt, borax, and saccharin in 8 qt. of water and bring to a boil. Add syrup and glycerine and, while boiling, add starch. Stir to prevent scorching and lumping, and cook until a clear paste is formed. Mix soda and strychnine dry, and then stir in a little of the starch paste until a thick creamy paste is formed. Add the remainder of the starch paste and mix well. Pour this mixture over the grain and mix until it is thoroughly coated.

More effective formulas for poisoning rodents and predators, using thallium or Compound 1080, may be used under cooperative programs with the U. S. Fish and Wildlife Service.

### Pocket Gopher Poison. Root baits.

| | |
|---|---|
| Vegetables (cut 1½" long and ½" square) | 2 qt. |
| Strychnine alkaloid (powdered) | ⅛ oz. |

Sift strychnine over the moist vegetables (sweet potatoes or carrots) and mix thoroughly. Put two or three pieces in a runway and cover the hole with sod or a lump of dirt.

### Leaf baits.

| | |
|---|---|
| Fresh green clover or alfalfa leaves | 1¼ lb. |
| Strychnine alkaloid (powdered) | ⅛ oz. |

Sift strychnine over leaves while stirring thoroughly. Place a small handful in a runway and cover the runway as above.

**Grain baits.** Use bait prepared as for prairie dogs, placing a level tablespoonful in a runway, and cover as above.

### Rat Poison.

    Warfarin (Compound 42, 0.5% powder)
    Cereal (cornmeal, dry bread crumbs, or oatmeal) ....... 90%
    Powdered sugar .................................... 5%
    Any vegetable oil .................................. 5%

Mix the above ingredients in the ratio of 1 lb. Warfarin to 19 lb. bait. Rats and mice must feed on this preparation for 5 to 10 consecutive days to effect control.

    Red squill (powdered, fortified—toxicity mg. or less per
      kg.) .................................................. 1½ oz.
    Ground fresh meat or canned fish .................... 1 lb.

Mix red squill with a little water to form a thin paste and then mix thoroughly with meat or fish.

### Rabbit Poison. Twig baits.

    Sulfate of strychnine ............................. 1 part
    Borax ............................................. ⅓ part
    White syrup ....................................... 1 part
    Water ............................................. 10 parts

Mix well and apply with a brush to twigs of native species. **Warning:** This is toxic to livestock and deer.

### Leaf baits.

    Strychnine sulfate .................................. 1 oz.
    Saccharin .......................................... ⅕ oz.
    Alfalfa hay ........................................ 15 lb.
    Water ............................................. 1 gal.

Dissolve strychnine and saccharin in water and sprinkle over alfalfa hay until saturated. Tie in small bundles to brush 8–10 in. above ground or snow level. **Warning:** This is toxic to livestock and deer.

**Grain baits.** Use bait as prepared for prairie dogs, placing a cupful for a bait.

### Magpie Poison.

    Suet (ground fine) ................................. 1 lb.
    Strychnine alkaloid (powdered) ..................... ¼ oz.
    Glycerine ......................................... 1 tablespoon

Stir strychnine into glycerine and stir both into the cold suet. Bore holes in 2 × 4 blocks for the poison and nail to the top of a tall pole or tree limb. Poison while birds are concentrated during winter months.

## Conservation Practices

See Tables 12 to 14C.

## Table 12. Woody Plants of Value for Game Food and Cover

KEY
Region:
E—East of Rocky Mts.
W—Rocky Mts. and West.
Note: Species shown out of their natural ranges are being planted successfully where indicated.

Site:
D—Dry.
M—Medium, well-drained.
W—Wet.

Form:
Ss—Small shrub.
Sl—Large shrub.
Ssp—Spreading shrub.
Ts—Small Tree.
Tl—Large Tree.
V—Vine.

Game use:
F—Food.
C—Cover.

Fruit available:
Numbers indicate months covering period when fruit ripens and is available to game or for collection.

See page 9·31 for footnotes.

| Botanical name | Common name | Region | Form | Site | Game use | Month fruit available | Average no. clean seeds per pound | Average germination (%) |
|---|---|---|---|---|---|---|---|---|
| **Conifers** | | | | | | | | |
| Abies balsamea | Balsam fir | E | Tl | M,W | F,C | 9 | 59,800 | 22 |
| Chamaecyparis thyoides | Atlantic white-cedar | E | Tl | W | C | 9-10 | 460,000 | 84 |
| Juniperus communis | Common juniper | E-W | Ssp | D,M | F,C | 8-9 | 46,800 | 5 |
| Juniperus scopulorum | Rocky Mountain juniper | W | Tl | D | F,C | 11-5 | 28,600 | 22 |
| Juniperus virginiana | Eastern redcedar | E | Tl | D,M | F,C | 9-4 | 24,000 | 32 |
| Picea abies | Norway spruce | E | Tl | M | C | 9 | 64,000 | 70 |
| Picea glauca | White spruce | E | Tl | M | C | 9 | 240,000 | 49 |
| Pinus banksiana | Jack pine | E | Tl | D,M | C | 9 | 131,000 | 68 |
| Pinus echinata | Shortleaf pine | E | Tl | D,M | C | 9 | 48,000 | 68 |
| Pinus resinosa | Red pine | E | Tl | D,M | C | 9 | 52,000 | 75 |
| Pinus rigida | Pitch pine | E | Tl | D,M | F,C | 9-10 | 62,000 | 77 |
| Pinus strobus | Eastern white pine | E | Tl | M | C | 7 | 27,000 | 64 |
| Pinus sylvestris | Scotch pine | E | Tl | M | C | 9-10 | 78,000 | 72 |
| Pinus virginiana | Virginia pine | E | Tl | D,M | F,C | 8 | 53,000 | 65 |
| Pseudotsuga menziesii | Douglas-fir | E | Tl | M | C | 9-10 | 42,000 | 85 |
| Thuja occidentalis | Northern white-cedar | E | Tl | M,W | F,C | 8-9 | 346,000 | 46 |
| Tsuga canadensis | Eastern hemlock | E | Tl | M | F,C | 9-10 | 187,000 | 38 |
| **Broadleaf Species** | | | | | | | | |
| Acer negundo | Boxelder | E | Tl | D,M | F,C | 9-4 | 11,800 | 33 |
| Acer saccharinum | Silver maple | E | Tl | M | C | 4-6 | 1,400 | 76 |
| Acer saccharum | Sugar maple | E | Tl | M | C | 9-10 | 6,100 | 39 |
| Alnus incana | Speckled alder | E | Ts | M | F | 9-10 | 666,000 | 32 |
| Amelanchier alnifolia | Juneberry | W | Sl | M | F,C | 6-9 | 82,000 | 74 |
| Amelanchier canadensis° | Juneberry | E | Sl | M | F | 6-8 | 82,000 | 74 |
| Amorpha fruticosa° | Indigobush | E | Sl | M | F | 8 | 77,000 | 67 |

| | | | | | | | | |
|---|---|---|---|---|---|---|---|---|
| *Arctostaphylos uva-ursi* | Bear berry | E–W | Ssp | D | F | 8–3 | 256,000 | 24 |
| *Aronia arbutifolia* | Red chokeberry | E | Ss–S1 | D,M,W | F | 8–6 | 276,000 | 94 |
| *Aronia melanocarpa* [c] | Black chokeberry | E | Ss | D,M,W | F,C | 8–6 | | 22 |
| *Artemisia tridentata* | Big sagebrush | W | Ss–S1 | D | F | 9 | | |
| *Asimina triloba* | Pawpaw | E | Ts | M | F | 8–10 | 697 | 62 |
| *Atriplex canescens* | Fourwing salt bush | W | S1 | D | C,F | 10 | 22,500 | 18 |
| *Baccharis viminea* | Mulefat | W | S1 | D | F,C | | 50,000 | 79 |
| *Benzoin aestivale* | Spicebush | E | S1 | M,W | F | | 4,500 | 85 |
| *Berberis aquifolium* | Oregon grape | W | Ss | D,M | F | 9–10 | 100,000 | |
| *Berberis thunbergi* [c] | Japanese barberry | E | Ss | M | F | 9–10 | 27,000 | 96 |
| *Caragana arborescens* [c] | Siberian pea | E–W | Ss | D,M,W | F,C | 8 | 17,000 | 76 |
| *Carpinus caroliniana* | American hornbeam | E | Ts | M | F | 6 | 30,000 | 5 |
| *Carya ovata* | Shagbark hickory | E | T1 | M | F | 8–10 | 100 | 80 |
| *Castanea sativa* | European chestnut | E | T1 | M | F | 9–10 | | |
| *Celastrus scandens* [b] | Bittersweet | E | V | M | F,C | 9–10 | 26,000 | 9 |
| *Celtis occidentalis* | Hackberry | E | T1 | D | F,C | 9–12 | 4,300 | 41 |
| *Cercis canadensis* | Eastern redbud | E | Ts | M | F | 6–11 | 18,000 | 80 |
| *Cercocarpus ledifolius* | Curlleaf cercocarpus | W | S1–Ts | D | C,F | 7–4 | 44,000 | 29 |
| *Cornus amomum* [a] | Silky dogwood | E | Ss | M | F,C | | 10,200 | 10 |
| *Cornus asperifolia* | Rough-leaf dogwood | E | S1 | M | F | 8–9 | 15,700 | 25 |
| *Cornus florida* [e] | Flowering dogwood | E | Ts | M,W | F | 8–10 | 4,500 | 35 |
| *Cornus occidentalis* | Western dogwood | W | S1 | M,W | F | 9–2 | 15,500 | |
| *Cornus paniculata* | Gray dogwood | E | Ss | D,M,W | F,C | 7–10 | | 47 |
| *Cornus stolonifera* [b] | Red-osier dogwood | E | S1 | M,W | F | 8–5 | 18,700 | 39 |
| *Corylus americana* [b] | Hazelnut | E | Ss | D,M | F | 8–5 | 476 | 15 |
| *Cowania stansburiana* | Cliff rose | W | Ss–S1 | D | F | 7–2 | 92,000 | 40 |
| *Crataegus* spp. | Hawthorn | E–W | Ss–Ts | M,W | F,C | 10 | 6,000–40,000 | |
| *Diervilla lonicera* [c] | Bush honeysuckle | E | Ss | D,M | F,C | 8–9 | | 61 |
| *Diospyros virginiana* [e] | Common persimmon | E | Ts | D,M,W | F | 8–9 | 1,185 | 34 |
| *Elaeagnus angustifolia* [c] | Russian olive | W | S1–Ts | D,M | F,C | 8–10 | 5,200 | 90 |
| *Elaeagnus argentea* | Silverberry | W | Ss–Ts | D,M,W | F,C | 8–10 | 2,000 | 30 |
| *Eriogonum fasciculatum* | Bush buckwheat | W | Ss | D | F,C | 8–10 | 365,000 | 58 |
| *Eurotia lanata* | Winterfat | W | Ss | D | F | 6–8 | 90,000 | 85 |
| *Fagus grandifolia* | American beech | E | T1 | M | F,C | 8–10 | 1,600 | 40 |
| *Fraxinus americana* | White ash | E | T1 | M | C | 9–10 | 10,000 | 52 |
| *Fraxinus pennsylvanica* | Green ash | E | T1 | M | C | 10–11 | 17,300 | 20 |
| *Gaylussacia baccata* | Black huckleberry | E | Ss | D,M | F | 7–9 | 380,000 | 90 |
| *Hamamelis virginiana* | Witch-hazel | E | S1–Ts | D,M,W | F,C | 8–12 | 9,800 | 60 |
| *Ilex opaca* [e] | American holly | E | T1 | D,M,W | F,C | 8–6 | 26,500 | 65 |
| *Juglans cinerea* | Butternut | E | T1 | M | F | 9–11 | 30 | |

(Continued on following page)

## Table 12. Woody Plants of Value for Game Food and Cover (Continued)

| Botanical name | Common name | Region | Form | Site | Game use | Month fruit available | Average no. clean seeds per pound | Average germination (%) |
|---|---|---|---|---|---|---|---|---|
| Juglans nigra | Black walnut | E | Tl | M | F | 9-10 | 40 | 75 |
| Kalmia latifolia | Mountain-laurel | E | Sl | D,M,W | F | 9 | | |
| Lespedeza bicolor[a] | Bicolor lespedeza | E | Sl | M | F,C | | | |
| Lespedeza sericea | Silky lespedeza | E | Ss | M | F,C | | | |
| Liquidambar styraciflua | Sweetgum | E | Tl | D,M,W | F | 9-11 | 82,000 | 70 |
| Liriodendron tulipifera | Yellow-poplar | E | Tl | D,M | F | 9-11 | 14,000 | 5 |
| Maclura pomifera | Osage-orange | E,W | Ts | D,M,W | C | 9-10 | 14,000 | 58 |
| Magnolia acuminata | Cucumbertree | E | Tl | M,W | F | 8-10 | 4,600 | 55 |
| Malus floribunda | Japanese flowering crab | E | | | F | | | |
| Morus rubra[c] | Red mulberry | E | Ts | D,M,W | F | 5-8 | 360,000 | 33 |
| Myrica carolinensis[a] | Bayberry | E,W | Ss | D,M,W | F | 6-4 | 55,000 | 70 |
| Opuntia spp | Cactus | W | | D | F,C | | | |
| Ostrya virginiana | Eastern hophornbeam | E | Ts | D,M,W | F | 8-10 | 30,000 | 85 |
| Parthenocissus quinquefolia[c] | Woodbine | E | V | M,W | F | 8-2 | 12,000 | 69 |
| Photinia arbutifolia | Christmas berry | W | Sl-Ts | D,M | F,C | 10-2 | 24,000 | 73 |
| Populus tremuloides | Quaking aspen | E,W | Ts-Tl | D,M | F,C | 5-6 | 3,600,000 | 89 |
| Prosopis juliflora var glandulosa | Honey mesquite | W | Sl | D,M,W | F,C | 9-10 | 14,000 | |
| Prosopis pubescens | Screwbean mesquite | W | Sl | D,M,W | F,C | 7-10 | | |
| Prunus americana[c] | American plum | E,W | Ts | D,M,W | F | 7-10 | 840 | 60 |
| Prunus ilicifolia | Hollyleaf cherry | W | Sl-Ts | D,M,W | F | 10-12 | 240 | |
| Prunus serotina | Black cherry | E | Tl | D,M,W | F | 6-11 | 4,800 | 63 |
| Prunus virginiana | Common chokecherry | W | Sl | | F,C | 7-10 | | |
| Purshia tridentata | Bitter brush | W | Ss-Sl | D,M | F | 8 | 20,000 | |
| Quercus agrifolia | California live oak | E | Tl | D,M | F,C | 9-10 | 200 | 69 |
| Quercus alba | White oak | W | Tl | D | F | 9-10 | 150 | 73 |
| Quercus arizonica | Arizona white oak | W | Sl-Ts | D,M | F | 9-11 | | 78 |
| Quercus dumosa | California scrub oak | W | Ts | D,M | F | 9-11 | 100 | |
| Quercus gambelii | Gambel oak | W | Sl-Ts | D,M | F,C | 8-10 | | |
| Quercus macrocarpa | Burr oak | E | Tl | M | F,C | 8-10 | 650 | 46 |
| Quercus palustris | Pin Oak | E | Tl | M,W | F | 9-11 | 140 | 95 |
| Quercus rubra | Northern red oak | E | Tl | M | F | 10-11 | 400 | 58 |
| Quercus stellata | Post oak | E | Tl | D,M | F,C | 9-11 | 250 | 41 |
| Quercus velutina | Black oak | E | Tl | D,M | F | 10-11 | 12,000 | 26 |
| Rhamnus purshiana | Cascara buckthorn | W | Ss-Sl | D,M | F | 8-9 | | |

| | | | | | | | | |
|---|---|---|---|---|---|---|---|---|
| *Rhus integrifolia* | Lemonade sumac | W | Sl–Ts | D | C | 8–9 | 7,400 | 84 |
| *Rhus ovata* | Sugar sumac | W | Sl | D,M | C | 8 | 21,700 | 35 |
| *Rhus trilobata* | Skunkbush | E,W | Sl | D,M | F,C | 7 | | 30 |
| *Rhus typhina* | Staghorn sumac | E | Sl | D,M | F | 9 | 53,300 | 40 |
| *Robinia pseudoacacia* | Black locust | E,W | Ts–Tl | D,M,W | F,C | 9–4 | 24,000 | 68 |
| *Rosa acicularis* | Wild rose | E,W | Ss | M | F,C | 9 | | |
| *Rosa blanda* | Wild rose | E | Ss | M | F,C | 9 | 45,000 | 36 |
| *Rosa californica* | Wild rose | W | Sl | M | F,C | 9 | | |
| *Rosa multiflora* [a] | Multiflora or Japanese rose | E,W | Ssp | M | F,C | | 70,000 | |
| *Rosa setigera* | Prairie rose | E | Ssp | D,M | F,C | 9 | | |
| *Rubus laciniatus* | Cut-leaved or evergreen blackberry | E | Ss | D,M | F,C | 8 | | 64 |
| *Rubus occidentalis* | Blackcap or black raspberry | W | Ss–Sl | M,W | F,C | 7–9 | 334,000 | |
| *Salix* spp. [a] | Willow | E,W | Ss–Tl | M,W | F | | 232,000 | 63 |
| *Sambucus canadensis* [c] | American elder | E | Ss | D | F,C | 8–10 | 120,000 | 17 |
| *Sambucus glauca* | Blue elderberry | W | Sl–Ts | D,M | F | 8–9 | 3,000 | |
| *Sassafras albidum* | Sassafras | E,W | Ts | D | F | 9–10 | 41,000 | 57 |
| *Shepherdia argentea* | Silver buffaloberry | E,W | Sl | D,M,W | F | 7–8 | 350,000 | 60 |
| *Solanum dulcamara* | Bitter nightshade | E | V | D,M,W | F | 8–5 | 160,000 | 15 |
| *Sorbus americana* [c] | American mountain-ash | E | Ts | D,M,W | F | 8–3 | 73,000 | 1 |
| *Symphoricarpos occidentalis* | Snowberry | E,W | Ss | D,M,W | F,C | 9–1 | 144,000 | 81 |
| *Symphoricarpos orbiculatus* [b] | Coralberry, Indian currant | E | Ss | D,M | F,C | 9–6 | | |
| *Tamarix articulata* | Evergreen tamarisk | W | Sl–Ts | D,M,W | C | 8–10 | 5,000 | 29 |
| *Tilia americana* | American basswood | E | Tl | D,M | F | 7–9 | | |
| *Vaccinium angustifolium* | Lowbush blueberry | E | Ss | M,W | F | 10–12 | 28,000 | 98 |
| *Viburnum dentatum* [b] | Arrowwood | E | Sl | D,M | F | 8–9 | 5,700 | 51 |
| *Viburnum lentago* [b] | Nannyberry | E | Sl | D,M,W | F | 9–5 | 13,200 | 33 |
| *Viburnum trilobum* | Highbush cranberry | E | Sl | M,W | F | 7–8 | 15,200 | 82 |
| *Vitis californica* | California grape | W | V | M,W | F,C | 8–9 | 14,500 | |
| *Vitis labrusca* | Fox grape | E | V | D,M,W | F,C | 8–9 | | |
| *Vitis vulpina* [c] | Riverbank grape | E | V | M | F,C | 6–11 | | |

[a] Region 1 of the Soil Conservation Service has made extensive planting tests of over 100 species of shrubs and vines in the Northeast. It recommends ("Shrub Plantings for Soil Conservation and Wildlife Cover in the Northeast," by F. C. Edminster and R. M. May, Soil Conservation Service, Upper Darby, Pa., June, 1950, mimeographed) only seven species for general use in this region: *Cornus amomum* (silky dogwood), *Elaeagnus umbellata* (autumn olive), *Lespedeza bicolor* (bicolor lespedeza), *Lonicera tatarica* (Tatarian honeysuckle), *Myrica carolinensis* (bayberry), *Rosa multiflora* (multiflora rose), and *Salix purpurea* (purple-osier willow). Five of these species are included in the above table, and are indicated by a.

[b] Species tested for planting in the Northeast by the Soil Conservation Service (see footnote a) and recommended for limited or special use.

[c] Shrubs, tested but not recommended for planting in the Northeast by the Soil Conservation Service (see footnote a).

# Table 13. Some Forest Management Practices for Improving Game Habitat

| Desirable marking practices | Desirable logging practices | Stand improvement | Desirable habitat improvement practices | Miscellaneous practices |
|---|---|---|---|---|
| **DOUGLAS-FIR FORESTS** | | | | |
| Clearcut old growth Douglas-fir and cedar-hemlock types with staggered settings seldom over 40 acres each. This is good silviculture and serves wildlife with "edge" of food and cover. Under sustained yield, provides uniform wildlife production with new areas developing as tree growth reduces values in old cuttings.<br><br>Leave buffer strips along major streams for watershed protection, maintenance of desirable water temperatures, and important recreation values. | With cable logging, skid uphill or away from live streams. In so far as possible keep tractors off steep ground. Exercise firm control of skidding. No skidding down draws or watercourses. Keep landings out of watercourses. | Timber stand improvement affords little benefit to game. | Preserve berry vines, thickets, and orchards for wildlife cover and food. Maintain openings by any suitable method, including prescribed burning in small spots. | Prescribed burning of slash, a standard silvicultural method, particularly where it is an abnormal hazard or so heavy it impedes planting or natural reforestation and where no real damage to soil will result.<br>Note: In virgin forests low in wildlife production, natural and man-made openings constitute the key to wildlife production. |
| **WESTERN PINE FORESTS** | | | | |
| Heavy cutting of white and ponderosa pine is desirable for elk. For deer, insect risk marking where used is insufficient. It is generally desirable to mark at least 35% of the ponderosa pine volume selectively. Clearcutting at least temporarily eliminates the needed cover for deer. Cut in units and keep well spaced in order to create a varied pattern of age classes. On important winter ranges in timber zones, release oaks or other producers of forage needed for critical periods. Cut heavily in browse areas on important winter ranges to promote forage growth.<br><br>Clearcutting in lodgepole pine should be in strips or blocks with small pattern to develop varied age classes on small units.<br><br>Preserve canopy over live streams, thus maintaining desirable water temperatures and shelter conditions. | Logging practices satisfactory from a silvicultural standpoint are satisfactory for wildlife. Log away from water courses. Where this is not possible, cross at right angles. There should be no skidding down water courses, dry or wet. Exercise firm control of tractors on areas with or without adequate cover. Strictly enforce good watershed management practices aimed at soil and water conservation. Do not cut or destroy such important browse species as service berry, redstem ceanothus, maple, willow, dogwood, and bitterbrush.<br><br>Use low grades on logging roads and drain adequately. Place waterbreaks on steep skid trails and reseed as desirable.<br><br>Spruce and other stream-bottom conifers provide an important moose cover in the north. Skid away from spruce-lined water courses.<br><br>If possible, there should be no skidding across meadows, parks, or grasslands. Roads that must cross | Preserve or release mast-producing oaks and other important food species on winter ranges and elsewhere as desirable.<br><br>On white pine plantations in the North, reserve 10% of area in openings, 1-4 acres in size. This would include not only unplantable areas but parts of better sites in large burns on important big game winter range. Plant only to provide escape cover or for avenues for travel in deep snow. | Preserve berry vines and other thickets and old apple trees on old homesteads for wildlife cover and food. Develop springs and seeps for wildlife but in a manner that will not attract livestock. Plant road shoulders and landings with browse if stock is available or to grasses for elk or for indirect benefit to other wildlife where resulting forage will absorb livestock use.<br><br>Avoid this practice where livestock use is not controlled and excessive livestock concentration may develop. Such planting is primarily an erosion control expedient.<br><br>Plant small permanent openings to perennial grasses. If necessary, fence against livestock.<br><br>Plant or encourage growth of low conifers in vicinity for escape cover.<br><br>In extensive browse types on wintering areas, plant conifer islands for cover and travel ways in deep snow. | No prescribed burning in commercial timber stands except spots or brush piles on cut-over areas. This practice needs additional research and testing in western pine type.<br><br>Treat browse stands that have grown out of reach to promote new growth from root crown.<br>Note: Many problems require control of deer and livestock herds to make forest management measures effective.<br><br>Do not use machine brush piling equipment on big game ranges supporting such important browse plants as bitterbrush. |

## SOUTHERN FORESTS

Even-aged shelterwood management with frequent thinning (actually thinning) is desirable from both game and timber production standpoints. Favor tupelo, live oak, turkey oak, pines as needed for mast, and water oak.

The degree of cutting desirable for timber production is desirable for wildlife. Too heavy intermediate cutting may release species noxious to both.

Protect food species such as dogwood, youpon, etc., where scarce. Logging and skidding under good forestry practices stimulates food production. Erosion is rarely a problem. Fire lanes and old fire lines contribute edge and interspersion to otherwise uniform types.

Avoid logging turkey nesting areas during nesting season.

Leave fruit-bearing trees in pine stands. Leave designated den trees.

Fertilize fire lanes and seed both lanes and old fire lines (used in fire suppression) to lespedeza and other food plants. No hand treatment of food plots or openings is needed.

Establish ¼-acre to 5-acre food plots of bicolor lespedeza, hegira cane, chufas, rice, and other food plants for turkey.

Prescribed burning for brown-spot control and for other purposes is most valuable in maintenance of wildlife habitats. However, it must be competently handled. Green growth following is valuable for deer and turkey.

## NORTHERN AND NORTHEASTERN FORESTS

Mark for heaviest selective or shelterwood cut consistent with good silviculture.

Remove at least 40% of overstory to stimulate food production. Cut in small units at regular intervals to provide varied patterns of age classes and densities.

Favor conifers in deciduous stands for needed winter cover (hemlock, spruce, white-cedar are best).

Retain some beech (in northern part only) birch, oaks, cherry, black gum, basswood, white ash, red maple, and hickory; also yellow-poplar, persimmon, sassafras in southern part.

Clearcut selected areas of approximately 1 acre each maintaining 1% of forest in openings. Preserve food and cover species on 50 ft. strip around field edges. Preserve trees along streams to maintain desirable water temperatures and stabilize stream banks.

Avoid downhill skidding on steep slopes.

Keep logging roads out of creek beds.

Use animals for logging steep slopes subject to erosion. If tractors must be used, choose smallest machines practical.

Use low grades on logging roads, provide adequate drainage.

In Lake States avoid summer logging in key wintering areas. Make browse in tops and on limbs available in winter.

Protect stream-bottom food and cover types as required. Protect old apple orchards, wild grape, hawthorns, dogwood, and viburnums for grouse and turkey.

Skid trails should cross creeks at right angles, if at all.

Save some brush piles and unlopped tops for birds and small game as needed.

Favor species noted in Col. 1. Generally reserve 6 oak mast trees per acre. Remove up to 50% of total volume of second-growth hardwoods in chemical pulp operations. Leave blocks of pine and other conifers unpruned where small game cover is needed.

Maintain old fields and openings to provide increased forest edge and needed food production. Reduce shrub and tree invasion by hand or other suitable methods. Reseed openings, abandoned logging roads, road shoulders, etc., to orchard grass, fescue, ladino clover, or other desirable species for food (and soil holding) purposes. In Lake States use white clover. Also plant buckwheat food patches for turkey, and possibly control burn to maintain openings in grass and low brush cover.

In connection with logging operations and otherwise, break down tall shrubbery where overly abundant and not available to game. Plant conifers or other tree species for cover and forest value. Develop springs and seeps which result in bare ground for scratch and early green feed.

Maintain woods roads in usable condition to distribute hunting effort. Release and prune old orchards. Under intensive management, plow, disc, and fertilize openings and plant as desirable.

(Continued on following page)

# Table 13. Some Forest Management Practices for Improving Game Habitat (Continued)

## CENTRAL HARDWOOD FORESTS

| Desirable marking practices | Desirable logging practices | Stand improvement | Desirable habitat improvement practices | Miscellaneous practices |
|---|---|---|---|---|
| Mark for heavy selective or shelterwood cut consistent with good silviculture. Remove at least 40% of overstory to stimulate food production.<br><br>Cut in small units at regular intervals to provide varied patterns of age classes and densities.<br><br>In the north, favor conifers for winter cover where needed (hemlock, spruce, white-cedar in the East, eastern redcedar and shortleaf pine in the Lake States).<br><br>Retain some beech (except in the South), birch, oaks, cherry, black gum, yellow-poplar, persimmon, sassafras, basswood, white ash, red maple, dogwood, black locust, and hickory where scarce. Retain some hemlock and white pine. Clearcut selected areas (leaving seed trees) of approximately 1 to 10 acres each, maintaining 1% of forest in openings. Preserve food and cover species on 50 ft. strips on field edges.<br><br>Preserve canopy over streams for shade, thus maintaining desirable water temperatures. Because of less mobility of small game, further breaking up of uniform types is desirable. | Avoid downhill skidding on steep slopes.<br><br>Keep logging roads out of creek beds and as far from them as feasible.<br><br>Use animals (or small tractors) for logging steep slopes subject to erosion.<br><br>Use low grades on logging roads; provide adequate drainage.<br><br>Protect stream-bottom food and cover types as required. Protect old apple orchards, wild grape, hawthorns, laurel, rhododendrons, dogwood, and viburnums in the North for grouse and turkey. Skid trails and roads should cross creeks at right angles, if at all. | Favor species noted in Col. 1. Generally leave 6 oak mast trees per acre. Release white pine and other conifers in unbroken hardwood stands for birds. Leave fruit-bearing trees in pine areas and in hardwoods as required. Leave den trees for squirrels and raccoons. Where feasible, treat key game areas on a rotation basis, not more than one-fifth each year. | Maintain old fields and openings to provide increased forest edge and needed food production. Reduce shrub and tree invasion by hand or other suitable method.<br><br>Reseed openings, abandoned logging roads, road shoulders, etc., to orchard grass in pine areas, and other desirable species for food (and soil holding) purposes. Use white clover in the Lake States.<br><br>In connection with logging operations and otherwise, break down tall shrubbery not available to game, making additional food available and creating openings.<br><br>Plant conifers or other tree species for cover or to break up heavy laurel cover or for forest value.<br><br>Develop springs and seeps which result in bare ground for scratch feed and early green feed. | Maintain woods roads in usable condition to distribute hunting efforts. Establish camping places in less accessible places for the same purpose.<br><br>Release and prune old orchards. Under intensive management, plow, disc, and fertilize openings and plant as desirable. |

9 · 34

Table 14A. Management Practices for Forest and Range Small Game: Food

| Practice | Species affected* | Manpower and equipment | General technique | Relative cost | Effectiveness and application to management |
|---|---|---|---|---|---|
| Food patches........... (grain or other annuals) | Squirrels Rabbits Raccoons Turkeys Grouse Quails Pheasants | Labor crew and tractor- or horse-drawn disc, harrow, and other equipment; seed | Patches preferably located parallel to permanent woody or herbaceous cover; may extend into forest openings. Culture generally broadcast for small grains; row for corn and head grains (kaffir, etc.), or strips of regular grain crops left unharvested. | Annual operation; moderate to high for area developed | Most useful for farm game. Effective in producing food but too expensive for general application on large area except under subsidized conditions. Practical for individual landowner in conjunction with farming operation. A declining practice, present concept being that food is generally dependent on cover availability. |
| Feeding stations......... | Same as above | Labor and feed (corn or other grain; hay) | Food (grain, etc.) placed on definite sites, or scattered, during severe weather. Distribution by truck, horse, plane, or by men on foot. Hoppers or other containers may be used; corn shocks or ear corn may be placed along woods borders. | High for volume of food distributed, because both labor and feed are required | An emergency practice to be used with discretion. May aid game during food shortage, but more often serves to concentrate birds and mammals, thus increasing predation and other losses occurring from deficient cover. Present concept is that adequate cover prevents most food emergencies. |
| Permanent plantings...... (food trees, shrubs, vines, canes, etc.) | Same as above | Labor crew, stock, and planting tools | Spot-planting in stands along fencerows, etc. Species planted varies widely by region and game to be benefited. Old apple orchards revitalized for grouse, etc. | First-year and replant operation; generally low | Excellent for improving stand composition from game-food, and often cover, standpoints. Other values accruing from plantings may include fuel wood, posts, props, nuts, berries, etc. |

* Listing includes several species making only limited use of forest land or cover.

Table 14B. Management Practices for Small Forest and Range Game: Cover

| Practice | Species affected* | Manpower and equipment | General technique | Relative cost | Effectiveness and application to management |
|---|---|---|---|---|---|
| Planting, general......... | All, in varying ways and degrees | Labor crew, stock, and planting tools | Spot or plantation planting on a wide variety of sites and under many different conditions. Food-producing or timber species may be used. | Low to high, depending on intensity and conditions affecting planting; in general, moderate | Probably the best means of improving cover composition and interspersion, or of developing new cover areas. Permits cover improvement for game in conjunction with forest planting, erosion control, range improvement, etc. Improvement of game-food conditions may result from cover planting. |
| Grazing, exclusion of...... Grazing, controlled | All, in varying ways and degrees | Labor and materials to construct excluding fences, or to move fences as required; personnel required to negotiate agreements | Fencing of cover areas. | Low to moderate, according to size and location of area fenced | Probably the cheapest and quickest means of developing herbaceous, and later woody, cover. Other values include more rapid growth of timber, improvement of site, prevention of erosion, and improvement of game food conditions. Controlled grazing may be employed to reduce density of cover where desirable. |
| Burning, prevention of.... Burning, controlled | All, in varying ways and degrees | Labor and tools ordinarily used in fire suppression; personnel required to negotiate agreements | Personnel trained to suppress forest, range, and grass fires, or to effect controlled burning. | Widely variable, depending on hazards, nature of cover, etc.; usually low for area protected | Essential to the preservation of cover capable of being destroyed by burning. Fire protection permits natural succession of vegetational complex and usually insures good interspersion of grasses, forbs, shrubs, and trees prior to climax development. Controlled burning permits development of "edge" in pure forest stands, and variation in vegetational complex. |

* Squirrels, rabbits, raccoons, turkeys, grouse, quails, pheasants.

| Practice | Species affected | Manpower and equipment | General technique | Relative cost | Effectiveness and application to management |
|---|---|---|---|---|---|
| Cutting (including thinning) | Grouse Turkeys Squirrels Raccoons Rabbits | None if handled through sales; otherwise, regular lumbering equipment | Varies from light thinning to clearcut. Most desirable from game standpoint is selection cutting giving control of species and volume removed. | Covered by terms of sale; otherwise low to high according to operation | Most effective practice for breaking up large and/or pure stands, thus providing "edge" in habitat; amount of "edge" is dependent on kind and degree of cut. Game may be favored by leaving large food and den trees. |
| Border planting | All, in varying ways and degrees | Labor, planting stock, and farm machinery. | Establishment of herbaceous-shrub borders around woods edges, lowest-growing species next to fields or openings. | Low to moderate | Excellent "edge"-producing practice, resulting in great improvement in cover and often food on otherwise nearly barren strip around woods. Reduces wind velocity, and thus drying effect, in stand. |
| Hedge and fencerow development. | All, in varying ways and degrees | Labor, planting stock, and planting tools | Establishment of shrub or hedge species around woods borders. | Low to moderate | Approximately same as above. |
| Artificial dens. | All cavity-denning species, squirrels and raccoons especially | Labor, lumber, and hardware for den construction | Provision of dens in stands deficient in this respect, as in young timber. | Moderate to high | Recommended only where intensive management is practical. All-age stands usually contain ample den cavities. |

## Table 14C. Management Practices for Small Forest and Range Game: Water

| Practice | Species affected | Manpower and equipment | General technique | Relative cost | Effectiveness and application to management |
|---|---|---|---|---|---|
| Waterhole development | Western quails* Turkeys* Doves* Bobwhite quail* | Labor and earthmoving equipment (bulldozer, tractor, etc.); cement and building materials for dam construction | Development of impoundment area, by excavation or dam or both, on sites with suitable runoff or seepage, properly protected from erosion. Location should be near permanent cover to insure availability to game. | High to moderate on acre basis, but long life (10-15 years up) offers long amortization period | Provides one of the basic habitat factors in arid regions. |
| "Guzzler" construction. | Western quails | Labor and building materials, including cement and form lumber or equivalent; fencing materials where needed | Construction of underground water storage tanks, with slanting approach on sites with suitable runoff and basic food and cover conditions. | High to moderate per unit, but long life insures long amortization period | Same as above. |

* Western and southwestern states only.

## The Forester's Job in Inland Fisheries Management

Most fresh-water fishery biologists agree that habitat management, or producing and protecting good environmental conditions for fishes, is priority number one in inland fisheries management. Since most spiny-rayed fish are very tolerant, and trout are very intolerant, of a wide range of environmental conditions, the discussion to follow emphasizes trout management. This is a forester's or land manager's job. We will be concerned here but very little with artificial propagation of trout, since the major task is that of environmental protection and improvement.

However, we should not spend all of our time, and all of our funds, in the production or biological fields of this job. After all, the ultimate purpose of fisheries management is recreation. All wildlands and waters have high recreational values, and foresters as land managers should consider the job to be done on lakes and streams also as a means of producing good sport. Fishing is a lot of fun; many million anglers enjoy this sport. If streams are so crowded that poor sport is had, the recreational values are lowered or lost. Regulation of angler take is something that must come through the state fish and game commissions, but foresters should be interested in the true recreational values of the sport and in working toward improving the quality of the sport so that the lands and waters for which they are responsible meet the ultimate objectives and purposes of lake and stream management. Isolation is the key to good sport fishing.

**THE FOREST-WATERSHED BACKGROUND OF FISHERIES MANAGEMENT.** Watersheds aid in controlling water flows and in preventing serious soil erosion. Floods and silt are the two worst enemies of trout. Serious soil erosion and trout do not get along together.

Forest cover aids in supplying continuous water supplies and in maintaining suitable temperatures for trout. Certain trace elements are probably gradually leached from the watersheds of trout streams. These supply the elements necessary for both trout food and trout growth in the stream.

Fertilized trout eggs are buried in the gravels of the stream bed. The suitability of spawning gravels depends upon the character of the watershed geological formation. If spawning gravels are unclean or have silt deposited upon them, or if spawning beds are worked out and undermined by floods, millions of young trout are lost.

Through countless generations the native fishes and their natural food supplies have, through evolution, adapted themselves to growth and reproduction in the local stream habitat. Largely this is an adaptation to the character of the watershed. In fisheries management foresters should consider the effect of various watershed uses on the natural character of the stream environment.

**WHAT A TROUT STREAM SHOULD BE.**

1. A good trout stream should be a deep, moving body of clean, clear water averaging around 58° F. during summer periods.
2. It must include adequate spawning areas of coarse gravel in moderately fast water.
3. It should be about 50 percent pools and 50 percent riffles, well spaced. The riffles are mainly food-producing areas.
4. Streamside cover is almost as important for trout as food and stream temperatures. In streams 5 to 20 ft. in width, a cover of 50 to 75 percent of tall-growing shrubs along each side is an absolute requirement. Some sunlit areas, too, are

necessary. Cover along wide streams is not so important a factor, since water depth itself is cover.

5. It should not be subject to abnormal floods which cause changes in stream courses each year, and lateral erosion of stream bank and stream bank vegetation; these are very destructive to trout populations. Normal floods may be expected in spring and these floods, if they do not cause heavy silting, destruction of natural spawning beds, and channel changes, are not very serious.

## COORDINATION OF MULTIPLE USES OF WATERSHEDS. Logging.

Depending upon the temperature of the stream, forests of conifer or hardwoods may or may not be necessary to provide shade. If a trout stream in summer exceeds temperatures of 65° to 75° F., it is too warm. The high incidence of disease organisms occurs with higher stream temperatures. Trout are intolerant of high temperatures, and shade and channeling deeper flow of the stream itself may be necessary. However, streamside cover, i.e., the shrubs bordering streams, are most important. These are a necessary part of the trout environment. In logging practices, trout streams should not be crosshauled, and all but a minimum of logging debris must be kept out of the streamside areas to prevent damming the stream and warming the water above the tolerance of trout. The question of leaving forest trees along streams will depend upon local ecology and, too, the aesthetic values associated with recreational sport fishing.

Logging roads and skidways should have such postlogging care as to drain properly and to stabilize all disturbed soil areas within a period of several growing seasons.

Where forests are removed in large blocks, snowpacks increase and may be expected to increase water yields. Depending upon local situations, this may or may not be detrimental to trout streams. If heavy spring runoffs followed by very low summer water deliveries are a result of forest cutting, then foresters must learn how to harvest forest crops of watersheds on the basis of area and intervals which will not cause flooding damage or water shortages. On the other hand, if larger permanent waterflows are needed and would benefit trout waters, forest harvesting might bring about an improvement in the trout environment both as to water depths and water temperatures. Usually such local forest influences are not known by foresters, therefore the services of state and federal fishery authorities should be used in planning large-scale forest cuttings in relation to this effect on stream conditions.

**Grazing Uses.** Domestic cattle and big game, including deer, elk, and moose, tend to concentrate their use along stream bottoms. Total destruction of streamside cover by browsing animals can be seen along stretches of many streams. Destruction of streamside cover contributes to the breaking up and erosion of stream banks. Stable streamside cover and banks are necessary to channelize water flows.

Probably one of the best methods to use in coordinating cattle grazing uses and trout streams is a pole or 3-wire fence constructed a short distance from the stream, with water gaps at intervals to permit stock watering. The distance from the water will depend on the amount and size of streamside trees and shrubs. Such fences would tend to reduce, but would not eliminate, big game and domestic sheep use.

**Mining Uses.** Coordination of mining and trout stream uses is apt to be a very difficult task. Placer mining in the West has ruined stream fishing along many miles of good trout water. Where chemical or silt pollution is occurring, state and federal authorities should be consulted as to the application of mining laws on the stream concerned. Considerable progress is being made in this field. Often, action is best taken through legislative prevention, since the cost of new installations to control pollutants may be equal to the original investment in the mining equipment. Many states are now working on such legislation in an effort to control this problem.

**Beaver.** Depending again upon local ecology, beaver may or may not be desirable in the trout environment. Often in logged-over areas beaver tend to construct dams at points where logging debris has partially dammed the stream, forming many small dams which tend to silt up the streambeds and to slow down water flows. Where summer stream temperatures are high, beaver are very apt to be seriously detrimental to trout. However, in some areas beaver may develop rather large ponds of two to ten acres in extent, which tend to warm the waters in very cold streams at high elevations and to increase noticeably the food supply and growth of trout. These ponds often afford excellent fishing.

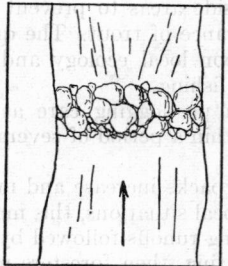

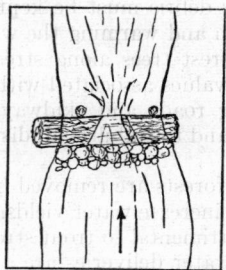

**Fig. 1. Boulder dam causes digging action downstream, creating a pool.**

**Fig. 2. Log dam with notch creates a pool but at the same time concentrates the water flow to facilitate fish migration. Ends of digging log are buried in the bank.**

**Stream Improvement.** Habitat improvement work in streams is very expensive and, generally, the beneficial effects produced are short-lived unless the factor or factors that bring about the need for improvement are first removed. It is logical, then, that to achieve satisfactory lasting results the silt-producing, barren headwater slopes should be reforested, overgrazing should be prevented, and any other factor or practice causing damage to the stream should be corrected. Then improvement devices may be installed in the stream itself with more assurance of successful results.

Although such devices may change most of the undesirable features in many streams, little can be accomplished in deep, slow-moving sections with only a slight gradient. Existing devices and practices may be expected to accomplish the following:

1. Water temperature can be made to approach the desired level by controlling the amount of streamside vegetation, trees, and shrubs, and by increasing or decreasing the extent of wide, shallow stretches of stream. In streams approaching the upper limit of temperature tolerated by trout, the bank vegetation may be increased and the wide, shallow sections may be channeled. Where water temperature is too low, some of the streamside trees and shrubs may be

removed to let more sunlight strike the stream, and low dams may be installed to create shallows. (Trees and shrubs may be necessary, especially on curves, to prevent bank erosion.)

2. The food supply of trout is often improved when shallows are created, but the danger of excess warming of the water should not be overlooked.

3. Most of the streams in need of improvement have a scarcity of suitable pools absolutely necessary for large trout. These can usually be created by one of the several devices illustrated. Deflectors are generally preferred since they do not block the streams to boats and prevent migration of trout, as dams often do.

4. Where suitable spawning gravel is scarce or lacking, it may be provided by bulldozing gravel banks into the stream or by installing deflectors that will wash silt from the underlying gravel.

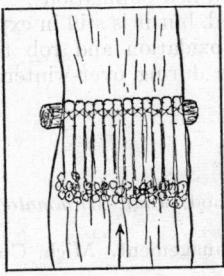

Fig. 3. "Hewitt dam" consists of parallel poles spiked and wired to digging log and with upstream ends buried in the streambed.

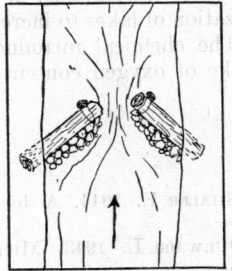

Fig. 4. V-type deflector of logs.

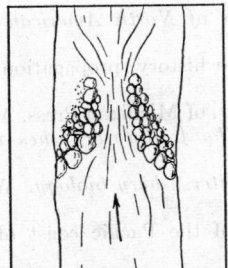

Fig. 5. Y-type deflector of boulders.

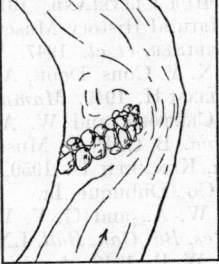

Fig. 6. Straight deflector installed on curve to create a pool.

Most trout waters are fairly productive, except where pollution has caused deterioration of trout stocks. It is believed that many of our trout streams which do not suffer silt and industrial pollution are now as productive as they ever were and are producing as many pounds of trout as they ever did. The difference is that this poundage of trout is being taken by many more anglers each year, and the catch or yield is, therefore, distributed among many more people. Artificial propagation seldom increases the total production of trout poundage in streams. Even the planting of legal-sized fish results in a very small increase in the poundage of trout in streams. Habitat improvement of pool conditions and spacing, and the creation of spawning areas, however, may increase the trout poundage production. As stated before, this is very expensive work and should have the benefit of trial methods before large-scale operations are attempted.

**Lake Improvement.** Possibly one of the most effective fishing management improvement devices is creating new waters. Often in forest areas small lakes may be created through the construction of small dams. Usually it is necessary to seek areas where considerable water can be stored at low cost. Dams 10 ft. high and 30 ft. wide often may create good lakes from 10 to 40 acres in extent.

Such dams should be provided with extra large spillways, and with a culvert and gate for future drainage at the base of the dam. Often exotic fishes used for bait are accidentally introduced into such waters, and drainage is far less costly and a far more efficient way of eliminating unwanted fish populations.

Fertilization of lakes to increase fish has been tried, but it is still in experimental stages. The chemical introduced may speed up oxidation and rob the waters of the lake of oxygen content, especially desirable during over-wintering conditions.

## BIBLIOGRAPHY

ALDOUS, SHALER E. 1944. A deer browse survey method. *Jour. Mammalogy* 25:130–136.

ALLEN, DURWARD L. 1943. Michigan fox squirrel management. Mich. Cons. Dept., Lansing.

ALLEN, DURWARD L. 1954. *Our wildlife legacy.* Funk & Wagnalls Co., New York.

ANTHONY, H. E. 1928. *Field book of North American mammals.* G. P. Putnam's Sons, New York.

BACHRACH, MAX. 1930. *Fur—a practical treatise.* Prentice-Hall, Inc., New York.

BARICK, F. B. 1945. Environmental analysis of forest edges in relation to wildlife. *Trans. Tenth North Amer. Wildlife Conf.*

BENT, ARTHUR CLEVELAND. 1919–1946. *Life histories of North American birds.* 16 vols. Natural History Museum, Washington, D. C.

BUMP, GARDINER, et al. 1947. The ruffed grouse: life history, propagation, management. N. Y. Cons. Dept., Albany.

BURT, WILLIAM H. 1949. *Mammals of Michigan.* Univ. of Michigan Press, Ann Arbor.

CARL, G. CLIFFORD, and W. A. CLEMENS. 1948. *The freshwater fishes of British Columbia.* B. C. Prov. Museum, Victoria, B. C.

CARLANDER, KENNETH D. 1950. *Handbook of freshwater fishery biology.* William C. Brown Co., Dubuque, Ia.

CLEMENS, W. A., and G. V. WILBY. 1946. Fishes of the Pacific coast of Canada. *Fish. Res. Bd. Can. Bull.* LXVIII, Ottawa.

DASMANN, W. P. 1948. A critical review of range survey methods and their application to deer range management. *Calif. Fish & Game* 34:189–207.

DASMANN, W. P. 1951. Some deer range survey methods. *Calif. Fish & Game* 37:43–52.

EINARSEN, ARTHUR S. 1948. *The pronghorn antelope and its management.* Wildlife Mgt. Inst., Washington, D. C.

FORBES, E. STANLEY, and JOHN E. HARNEY, JR. 1952. The bulldozer; a tool of wildlife management. Penn. Game Comm., Harrisburg.

FORBUSH, E. H., and JOHN B. MAY. 1939. *Natural history of the birds of eastern and central North America.* Houghton Mifflin Co., New York.

GRAHAM, S. A. 1945. Ecological classification of cover types. *Jour. Wildlife Mgt.* 9:182–190.

HAMILTON, W. J., JR. 1939. *American mammals: their lives, habits and economic relations.* McGraw-Hill Book Co., Inc., New York.

HOFFMAN, RALPH. 1927. *Birds of the Pacific states.* Houghton Mifflin Co., New York.

HUBBS, CARL L., and KARL F. LAGLER. 1949. *Fishes of the Great Lakes region.* Cranbrook Inst. Sci., Bloomfield Hills, Mich.

KENDALL, WILLIAM C. 1935. The fishes of New England: the salmon family. Part 2, the salmons. *Mem. Boston Soc. Nat. Hist.* 9(1), Boston, Mass.

LAGLER, KARL F. 1952. *Freshwater fishery biology.* William C. Brown Co., Dubuque, Ia.

LEOPOLD, ALDO. 1933. *Game management.* Charles Scribner's Sons, New York.

MOSBY, HENRY, and CHARLES O. HANDLEY. 1943. The wild turkey in Virginia: its status, life history and management. Comm. of Game & Inland Fisheries, Richmond.

MURIE, O. J. 1951. *The elk of North America.* The Stackpole Co., Harrisburg, Penn.

NEEDHAM, PAUL R. 1938. *Trout streams.* Comstock Publ. Co., Ithaca, N. Y.

PALMER, E. LAURENCE. 1949. *Field book of natural history.* McGraw-Hill Book Co., Inc., New York.

PECHANEC, J. F., and G. D. PICKFORD. 1937. A weight estimate method for the determination of range or pasture production. *Jour. Amer. Soc. of Agron.* 29(11) : 894–904.

PETERSON, ROGER TORY. 1941. *A field guide to western birds.* Houghton Mifflin Co., New York.

PETERSON, ROGER TORY. 1947. *A field guide to the birds.* Houghton Mifflin Co., New York.

RAND, R. W. 1950. Branding in field work on seals. *Jour. Wildlife Mgt.* 14:128–132.

RICKER, WILLIAM E. 1948. Methods of estimating vital statistics of fish populations. Ind. Univ. Publ., *Sci. Ser. No. 15.*

ROUNSEFELL, GEORGE A., and W. HARRY EVERHART. 1953. *Fishery science, its methods and applications.* John Wiley & Sons, Inc., New York.

SCHMIDT, KARL P., and D. DWIGHT DAVIS. 1941. *Field book of snakes.* G. P. Putnam's Sons, New York.

SCHRENKEISEN, RAY. 1938. *Field book of fresh-water fishes of North America north of Mexico.* G. P. Putnam's Sons, New York.

SETON, E. T. 1929. *The lives of game animals.* 4 vols. Doubleday & Co., Inc., New York.

STODDARD, HERBERT L. 1931. *The bobwhite quail; its habits, preservation, and increase* Charles Scribner's Sons, New York.

TRIPPENSEE, R. E. 1948. *Wildlife management.* McGraw-Hill Book Co., Inc., New York.

WADKINS, L. A. 1948. Dyeing birds for identification. *Jour. Wildlife Mgt.* 7:388–391.

WANDELL, W. N. 1943. A multi-marking system for ring-necked pheasants. *Jour. Wildlife Mgt.* 7:378–382.

WEBB, SAMUEL, et al. 1952. *Records of North American big game.* Charles Scribner's Sons, New York.

WIGHT, H. M. 1938. *Field and laboratory technique in wildlife management.* Univ. of Michigan Press, Ann Arbor.

WING, LEONARD E. 1951. *Practice of wildlife conservation.* John Wiley & Sons, Inc., New York.

WRIGHT, ANNA A., and ALBERT H. WRIGHT. 1942. *Handbook of frogs and toads.* Comstock Publ. Co., Ithaca, N. Y.

U. S. COMM. FISH & FISHERIES. 1898. A manual of fish-culture, based on the methods of the United States Commission of Fish and Fisheries. App. *Report U. S. Comm. Fish & Fisheries* (1897). Government Printing Office, Washington, D. C.

U. S. COMM. FISH & FISHERIES. 1939. Artificial propagation of brook trout and rainbow trout, with notes on three other species. App. *Report U. S. Comm. Fish & Fisheries for 1923* (rev. 1939). Government Printing Office, Washington, D. C.

U. S. CONGRESS, SENATE. 1945. Fisheries resources of the United States. *Senate Doc. No. 51.* Government Printing Office, Washington, D. C.

U. S. Dept. Agr., Bureau Biol. Surv. 1936. Marking wild animals for identification.
U. S. Fish & Wildlife Service. 1947. Identifying injury by wildlife to trees and
shrubs in Northeastern forests. *Res. Report No. 13.*
U. S. Forest Serv., Region 9. 1940 Wildlife handbook. Rev. ed. Milwaukee, Wis.
U. S. Forest Serv., Region 5. 1947. Wildlife management handbook for forest officers.
San Francisco, Calif.

# WATERSHED MANAGEMENT

## CONTENTS

# WATERSHED MANAGEMENT

## CONTENTS

# WATERSHED MANAGEMENT

Because much of the water for irrigation, power, industry, navigation, domestic use, and recreation has its source on forest and range lands (especially the former), watershed management has become increasingly important to the practicing forester. The greatly increased demand for water for these purposes requires that he have an understanding of the hydrologic cycle and the relative importance of the various factors involved. Seldom will the forester be expected to make a detailed analysis of runoff and streamflow, but it behooves him to understand the principles upon which such a study is based and to know how the factors under his control (interception, transpiration, evaporation, infiltration, percolation, and soil erosion) may be altered to give the greatest returns in water yield, in flood control, and in erosion and sediment control.

## The Hydrologic Cycle

The distribution and transport of water (solid, liquid, or vapor) obey a fundamental law of equilibrium—the hydrologic cycle:

$$RO = P - (T + E) \pm S$$

where $RO$ is runoff, $P$ is precipitation, $T$ is transpiration, $E$ is evaporation, and $S$ is soil moisture and ground water storage. It is shown diagrammatically in Fig. 1. In the temperate zones, in general, about 30 percent of the total annual precipitation falling on land surfaces appears as runoff. Transpiration and evaporation, and on some watersheds deep seepage, account for the remainder.

At any given time, some water is in storage in the soil mass and underlying aquifers (water-bearing rocks). Partly because of variations in the amount of this stored water, the runoff resulting from a single storm varies greatly, even on small areas. To predict the amount of runoff from a given quantity of precipitation, it is necessary to determine the deficit in soil moisture which must be satisfied before runoff can occur, to know how rapidly water can enter (infiltrate) the soil surface, and how rapidly it can percolate downward after it enters the surface pores. Where surface conditions produce low infiltration rates, or where subsurface conditions result in percolation rates less than the rates of infiltration, runoff may occur before the deficit is satisfied.

## Precipitation

**FORMS AND CAUSES.** Rain, snow, hail, fog, dew, and sleet are the principal sources of water on the earth's surface. All are derived from the atmosphere, where moisture exists as:

1. An invisible gas: water vapor.
2. A liquid: minute particles of water held in a suspended cloud mass, and as fully developed raindrops.
3. A solid: snow or hail.

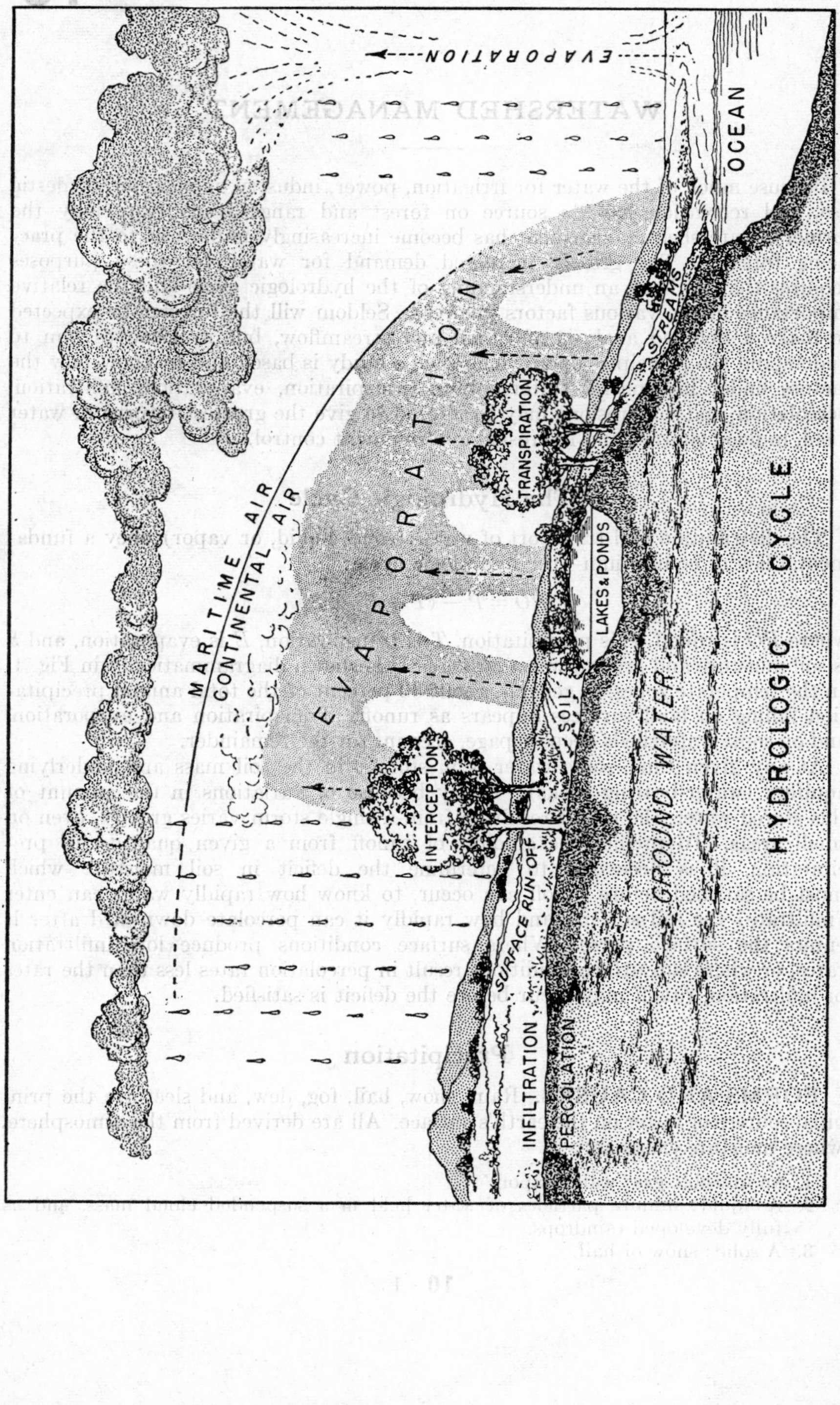

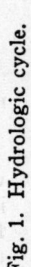

Fig. 1. Hydrologic cycle.

Precipitation is a process of condensation of water vapor caused by reduction of atmospheric temperature or volume, or both, with resultant reduction in vapor capacity. The chief causes of precipitation are:

1. Contact or radiational cooling, causing dew (hoar frost when frozen).
2. Mixture of air masses of unequal temperature, causing mist or fog.
3. Expansional or dynamic cooling due to vertical convection, the major source of precipitation. Three main cases are recognized: (a) **convection,** resulting from temperature gradients caused by heating of the ground surface; (b) **cyclonic,** caused by converging winds of unequal temperature; (c) **orographic,** caused by the forced rise of air masses by underrunning cool winds, or the flow of air over barriers of cold air or land elevations.

**METHODS OF MEASURING.** Precipitation varies with the type of storm, with topography, elevation, the season of the year, and with climatic cycles. The only practical way of determining amounts of precipitation is by obtaining an estimate from one or more samples. Catchment gauges are the most common devices used for measuring precipitation in all forms. For snow, a second method is the sampling tube.

**Standard Gauge.** (Fig. 2a.) U. S. Weather Bureau specifications call for a cylindrical can topped by an interceptor ring, 8 in. inside diameter, with a funnel conveying the catch into an inner tube of such diameter that the depth of catch is increased tenfold.

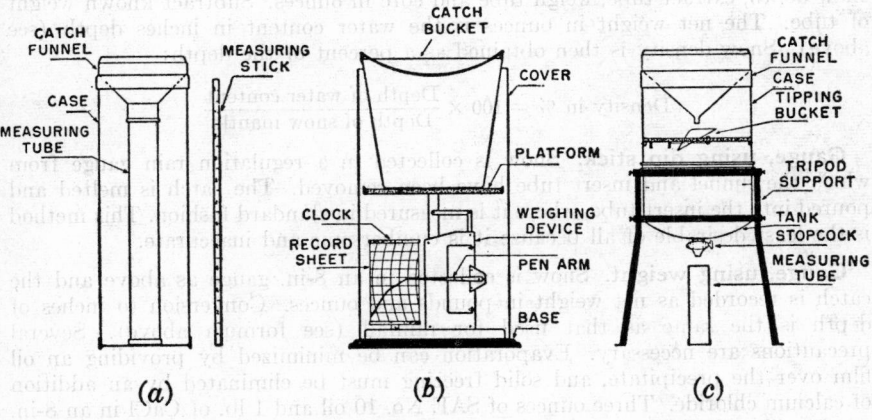

*(a)*                     *(b)*                     *(c)*

**Fig. 2. Rain gauge types.**
(American Society of Civil Engineers.)

**Automatic Recording.** This gives data on amount of precipitation, time of occurrence, intensity of fall, and rate of evaporation between successive catches.

**Tipping bucket** (Fig. 2c). This device registers increments of fall in a small bucket which fills, tips, and by so doing closes an electrical contact. This in turn activates a pen, producing a mark on a chart revolved by a clock. The number of marks represents quantity; spacing indicates intensity.

**Float type.** The catch is collected in a container and the rise in level is transmitted by means of a float to a recording chart.

**Weighing type** (Fig. 2b). The catch is collected in a pail from which the increment is transmitted to a recording chart by a linkage responding to successive increases in the weight of the pail. This is the most common type of gauge in use. The recent development of radio transmitters connected to automatic recording gauges permits collection of data from isolated locations with a minimum of maintenance and provides up-to-the-minute records of precipitation.

**Snow Tube.** The most commonly used type is the Utah snow tube. Its chief feature is a duralumin tube assembled in 2½-ft. sections to lengths needed. The steel cutter head has an inside diameter of 1.485 in., so designed because 1 in. of water in a cylinder of this diameter weighs 1 oz. Comparing the weight of an equal quantity of snow gives the density of the snow and permits conversion of total inches of snow to inches of water. Graduations in inches on the outside of the tube give depth of snow mantle.

**Measurement of Rainfall. Gauge, using dip stick.** Use a graduated stick inserted into the collector tube which magnifies depth by 10. Sticks manufactured for the purpose are designed to give a direct reading (see Fig. 2a).

**Gauge, using weight.** Weigh the gauge with its collected precipitation, subtract weight of gauge, and convert weight in pounds and ounces to inches of depth by use of the following conversion factor: 1 lb. water in 8-in. gauge = 0.55 in. depth.

**Measurement of Snowfall. Snow tube.** Insert tube into snow mantle, read snow depth, extract tube, weigh tube and core in ounces. Subtract known weight of tube. The net weight in ounces is the water content in inches depth (see above). Snow density is then obtained as a percent of the depth:

$$\text{Density in } \% = 100 \times \frac{\text{Depth of water content}}{\text{Depth of snow mantle}}$$

**Gauge, using dip stick.** Snow is collected in a regulation rain gauge from which the funnel and insert tube have been removed. The catch is melted and poured into the insert tube, where it is measured in standard fashion. This method is the least desirable of all because it is cumbersome and inaccurate.

**Gauge, using weight.** Snow is collected in an 8-in. gauge as above and the catch is recorded as net weight in pounds and ounces. Conversion to inches of depth is the same as that used for rainfall (see formula above). Several precautions are necessary. Evaporation can be minimized by providing an oil film over the precipitate, and solid freezing must be eliminated by an addition of calcium chloride. Three ounces of SAE No. 10 oil and 1 lb. of CaCl in an 8-in. gauge will ordinarily suffice for one winter season. They are retained in the gauge, and precipitation increment is determined by subtracting the weight of the preceding reading from the weight at the current reading. For best results, such gauges should be equipped with a snow shield (Alter or Nipher) to deflect wind and allow wind-borne snow to enter the gauge, thereby increasing the accuracy of the catch. Even with a shield, however, a catchment gauge exposed to strong wind movements is likely to give inaccurate measurements because of air turbulence. Recording gauges are used in this same manner but have the added feature of recording the rate of evaporation, if any, of the precipitation.

**DISTRIBUTION.** Total precipitation over a watershed is a function of the area and the average depth of precipitation. On small watersheds, and where the number of gauges is necessarily limited, the arithmetical mean—the sum of

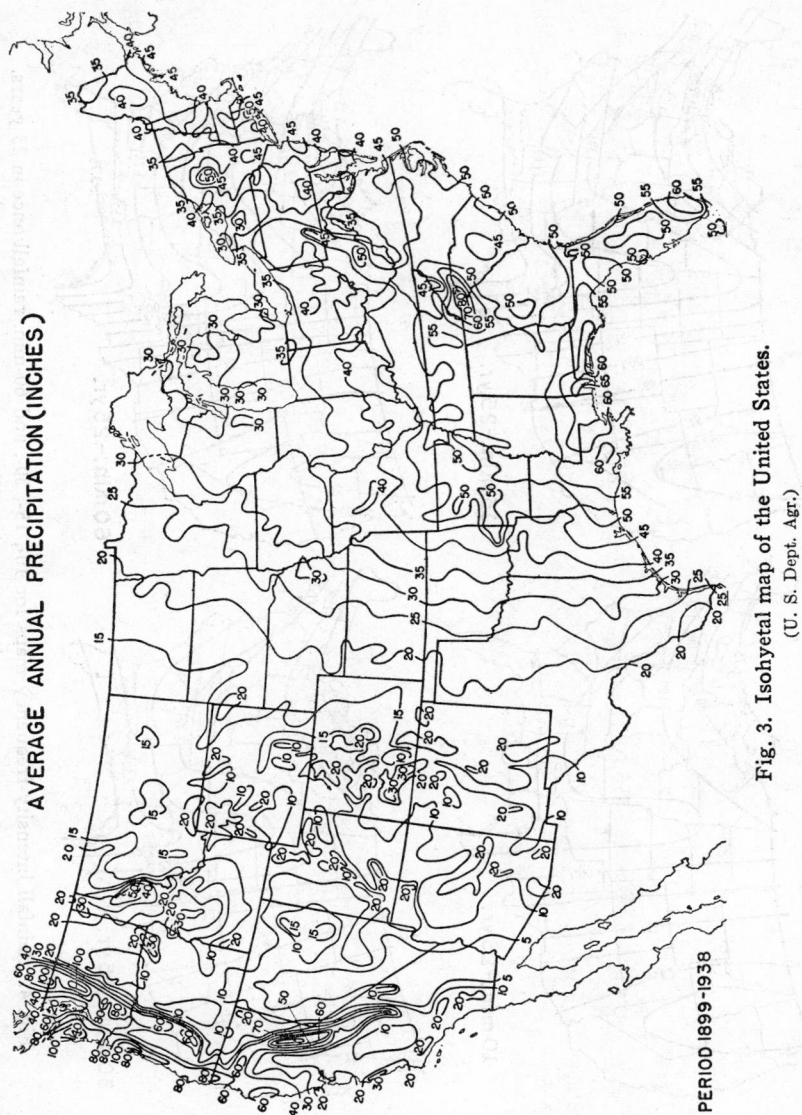

AVERAGE ANNUAL PRECIPITATION (INCHES)

PERIOD 1899-1938

Fig. 3. Isohyetal map of the United States.
(U. S. Dept. Agr.)

individual gauge readings divided by the number of gauges—is the simplest measure of precipitation.

Several methods of weighting precipitation are used, the most accurate of which is an isohyetal map (Fig. 3) prepared from gauge readings in the same way that a contour map is prepared from scattered readings of elevation. In general, isohyets will roughly follow contour lines. The area between isohyets can be determined by planimeter or a grid and multiplied by the median precipitation to give total precipitation within zones.

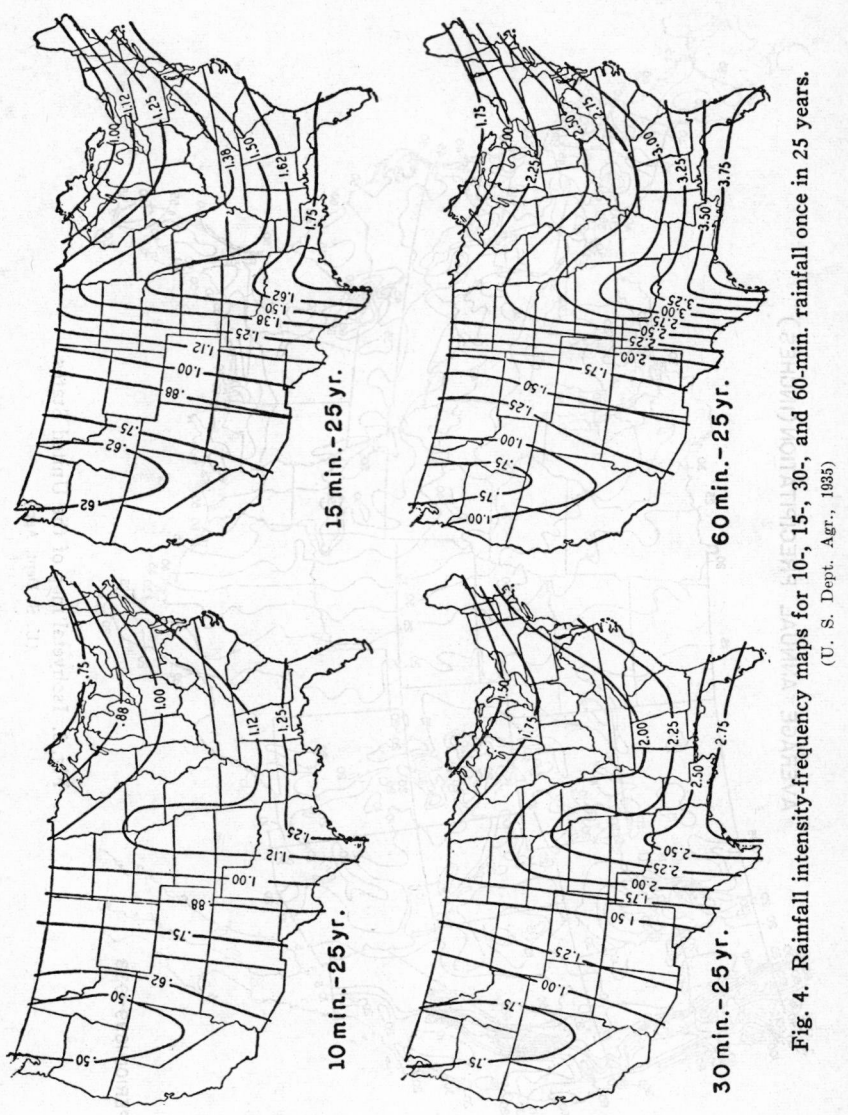

Fig. 4. Rainfall intensity-frequency maps for 10-, 15-, 30-, and 60-min. rainfall once in 25 years.

(U. S. Dept. Agr., 1935)

**INTENSITY.** Rainfall intensity, expressed in inches per hour, is obtained from recording rain gauges. High intensities of precipitation, such as those exceeding infiltration capacities of the soil, are significant because of their effects on run-off and erosion. Data sufficient for predicting with reasonable accuracy the period of recurrence of intense precipitations in any part of the United States have been developed. Tables and charts have been prepared showing the maximum precipitation in periods of 5 min. to 24 hr. that may be expected to occur with average frequencies of 2 to 100 yr. Fig. 4 is an example.

**INTERCEPTION AND STEMFLOW.** Interception is the process by which precipitation is caught and held by foliage, twigs, branches of trees, and lesser vegetation, or by surface debris, and evaporated from these exposed surfaces. The result is a reduction in the precipitation reaching the ground. The amount of intercepted precipitation over a given area is influenced by these factors:

1. Season of year. In a deciduous forest it is greater during the growing season than during the dormant season.
2. Size of storm. More interception results from a series of small storms than from an equal quantity of precipitation coming in one large storm.
3. Density and distribution of tree crowns and other foliage.
4. Climatic conditions. High rates of evaporation increase losses due to interception. Wind may reduce such losses by shaking intercepted moisture to the ground.
5. Stemflow rates. Some intercepted precipitation reaches the ground by flowing down the trunk and stems of trees and other vegetation. The amount is negligible in the case of rough-barked species, but it can be considerable in the case of smooth-barked species with erect branches. High rates (10 percent of total percipitation) are found for beech, for example, while less than 0.1 percent has been measured in mature lodgepole pine and Engelmann spruce.

The combined effect of these factors is unpredictable from present information. Kittredge compiled instances of intercepted precipitation in many forest types—for example, mature eastern hemlock, 13 to 48 percent of total precipitation; eastern deciduous species, 6 to 43 percent; ponderosa pine, 22 to 40 percent; brushy species in southern California, 3 to 31 percent.

## Transpiration

Transpiration is the process whereby free water in a plant structure is released as vapor to the atmosphere through the leaves or bark. The rate varies throughout the day, from one day to another, and from season to season. Temperature, relative humidity, wind velocity, and perhaps barometric pressure appear to affect transpiration in much the same fashion as they affect evaporation from the soil. Transpiration is to a considerable extent influenced by the moisture (including ground water) available, duration of sunlight, and stage of plant development.

Experimental evidence is still not generally available as to transpiration rates of various plant species, expressed in inches of water. A reasonable estimate of transpiration, in climates where moisture is generally available for a continuous vegetative cover, is obtainable from the equations:

$$\text{March to July:} \qquad T = 0.084t - 3.38$$
$$\text{August to November:} \quad T = 0.087t - 3.72$$

where $T$ is transpiration in inches per month, and $t$ is the average monthly temperature in degrees F.

Experimental cutting of all vegetation on a 33-acre watershed in the mountains of North Carolina almost completely eliminated transpiration and increased runoff the first year by 17 in. Ceanothus brush on the West Coast is estimated to use about 24 in. of water annually. In general, transpiration from brush and forest-covered watersheds is probably 5 to 25 in., with a possible maximum, in dense stands, of 35 in.

Where plant roots reach to the water table, and an unlimited supply of water is available, the foregoing formulas do not hold. Thus, in arid regions, riparian vegetation has been found to use a large proportion of the water flowing in streams. Along the Gila River in Arizona a partial cover of bottomland vegetation was found to be using the equivalent of 20 to 43 in. of annual rainfall, or two to three times the actual precipitation.

## Evaporation

Evaporation is the process by which a liquid is changed to vapor. The term is sometimes used to include losses from interception and transpiration. Evaporation of available moisture is affected directly or indirectly by (1) atmospheric pressure, (2) wind velocity, (3) atmospheric humidity, (4) temperature, and (5) solar radiation. Losses through evaporation occur from water, land, and snow surfaces.

**WATER SURFACES.** Over bodies of free water, a continuous supply of moisture is available, and evaporation depends upon climatic and meteorologic factors. The standard circular pan used by the U. S. Weather Bureau to measure such evaporation has a diameter of 48 in. and a depth of 10 in.; it is set with the bottom 6 in. above ground, and the water level is maintained within 2 and 3 in. from the top. To reduce observed losses in such a pan to the approximate loss from large bodies of water, multiply by 0.70. Records of evaporation from free water surfaces in the United States range from 1 to 14 in. per month.

**Horton's Formula.** Horton's empirical formula for computing anticipated evaporation, from meteorologic data alone, is:

$$E = C\frac{Bo}{B}(e_w - e_a) + C(1 - 2.718^{-KV})e_w$$

where  $E$ = evaporation in inches per 24 hr.
$Bo$ = barometric pressure of 29.9 in. mercury at sea level
$B$ = barometric pressure at the actual elevation
$e_w$ = vapor pressure of saturated air at the temperature of the water surface in inches of mercury
$e_a$ = actual vapor pressure at temperature of the dew point
2.718 = base of natural logarithms
$V$ = wind velocity in miles per hour
$K$ = constant with a value approximately 0.2
$C$ = a constant; for standard U. S. Weather Bureau pans it is 0.4

Table 1 presents examples of evaporation computed by Horton's formula. The influence of different conditions of weather and surface cover indicates that:

1. On a hot day, evaporation under forests may be one-half or less than that in the open.
2. When rain is warmer than the air into which it is falling, some evaporation of the drops occurs.
3. Snow falling into warm air acquires additional moisture by condensation.
4. Evaporation may occur from a snow cover in the open while condensation occurs in the forest, primarily because of decreased wind velocity in the forest.

In Horton's equation, the term for vapor pressure difference $(e_w - e_a)$ represents the rate of diffusion of water vapor molecules between a water surface and the adjacent atmosphere. Relative humidity is the ratio of the actual vapor pressure to the saturated vapor pressure at the same temperature. If the actual vapor pressure of the atmosphere is less than the saturated vapor pressure at the

Table 1. Evaporation or Condensation at Sea Level Computed by Horton's Formula for Different Combinations of Physical Conditions

| | Hot, dry day | | Rain | Snow | Snow cover | |
|---|---|---|---|---|---|---|
| | Open | Forest | | | Open | Forest |
| Temperature of the water surface, °F. | 75 | 70 | 70 | 32 | 32 | 32 |
| Temperature of the air, °F. ........ | 90 | 85 | 60 | 60 | 41 | 42 |
| Relative humidity, % ............... | 20 | 30 | 100 | 100 | 70 | 69 |
| Wind velocity, mph ................ | 20 | 3 | 2 | 2 | 2 | 0 |
| Evaporation, in. per 24 hr. ......... | 0.574 | 0.281 | 0.183 | −0.110 | 0.025 | −0.002 |

water temperature, evaporation occurs. Because saturation vapor pressure increases with temperature, if the temperature of the water surface is greater than the temperature of the adjacent air, the vapor pressure difference is positive and evaporation is indicated. On the other hand, if the temperature of the surface is less than the temperature of the air, the vapor pressure difference becomes negative; and if the numerical value exceeds that of the wind term, condensation occurs. Thus on still nights condensation occurs in the form of dew or frost if the earth surface cools sufficiently.

LAND SURFACES. Measurement of evaporation over land surfaces is very difficult because a continuous supply of moisture is not always available. In order for evaporation to occur from soil, the soil particles must be enveloped by a film of water in excess of hygroscopic moisture. When hygroscopic moisture conditions are reached, soil moisture is in equilibrium with atmospheric moisture and evaporation stops. Evaporation from soil is therefore intermittent unless the rate of capillary flow from the water table is continuous.

It has been shown that evaporation from land surfaces covered with vegetation is less than that from bare soil. The main reasons for this are reduction of solar radiation, of maximum temperatures, of vapor pressure differences, and of wind velocities. Windbreaks influence evaporation on their leeward side as much as five times their height. Table 2 compares evaporation in several forest types with that in the open.

SNOW SURFACES. The same principles apply over snow as over free water surfaces. However, the fact that snow temperatures are often below 32° F. leads to frequent periods of condensation which balance losses by evaporation (Table 1). When the snow surface has a temperature of 32° F., as is the case during most of the melting period, the following equation expresses the relation between relative humidity (or vapor pressure) and temperature, when evaporation (or condensation) is zero:

$$\log H_r = 2.52 - 0.017t$$

where $H_r$ = percent relative humidity

$t$ = temperature in degrees F.

Any combination of relative humidity and temperature that results in an intersection above the line plotted from this equation indicates condensation, and any intersection below the line indicates evaporation, provided, of course, that $t$ is above 32° F.

**Table 2. Evaporation in Different Forests Relative to That in the Open as 100, from Atmometer and Evaporimeter Data**

| Forest type | Density and age | Location | Relative evaporation |
|---|---|---|---|
| Chamise | | 6,000 ft., S. Calif. | 94 |
| Jeffrey pine | Open | 6,000 ft., S. Calif. | 91 |
| Jeffrey pine | Group | 6,000 ft., S. Calif. | 86 |
| Jeffrey pine | Heavy shade | 6,000 ft., S. Calif. | 79 |
| Jeffrey pine | Reproduction | 6,000 ft., S. Calif. | 72 |
| Manzanita-ceanothus | | 6,000 ft., S. Calif. | 71 |
| Ponderosa pine | | 7,250 ft., Ariz. | 70 |
| California scrub oak | | 6,000 ft., S. Calif. | 68 |
| Jeffrey pine | 30 ft. high | 6,000 ft., S. Calif. | 68 |
| Mixed chaparral | | 6.000 ft., S. Calif. | 67 |
| Maple-birch | Partially cut | N. Y. | 68 |
| Aspen | | Mich. | 57 |
| Oak-chestnut | Open | N. Y. | 50 |
| Aspen | 0.8 density | Minn. | 48 |
| Ceanothus velutinus | | Idaho | 45 |
| Jack pine | 0.5 density, 25 ft. high | Minn. | 67 |
| Pitch pine | Open | N. Y. | 60 |
| White and red pine | Young growth | Mich. | 54 |
| Eastern hemlock | | N. Y. | 52 |
| Western white pine | Half cut | Idaho | 47 |
| Ponderosa pine | | E. Wash. | 43 |
| Red pine | 0.8 density | Minn. | 40 |
| Western larch–Douglas-fir | | E. Wash. | 32 |
| Hemlock-hardwood | | N. Y. | 39 |
| Maple-beech | | N. Y. | 38 |
| Oak-chestnut | Dense | N. Y. | 33 |
| Western redcedar | | E. Wash. | 29 |
| Western white pine | Uncut | Idaho | 25 |
| Chestnut-ash-basswood | Dense | N. Y. | 14 |
| Gum–ash–yellow poplar | Swamp | N. Y. | 10 |

Source: Kittredge.

Actual determinations of evaporation from snow are meager. Some typical values are:

Utah (7,000 ft. elevation) ...................... 0.017 in. per day
Utah (8,700 ft. elevation) ...................... .04  in. per day
Ohio ........................................... .023 in. per day
California (5–6,000 ft. elevation)............. .007 in. per day
Colorado (9,200 ft. elevation) ................A total of about 2.0 in. during a 60-day melting season (April and May)

# Infiltration

Infiltration is the movement of water from the surface of the ground into the soil mantle. In a rainstorm, infiltration normally begins at a high rate. As rainfall continues, this decreases to a constant rate, $fc$, which continues until the soil is saturated. After this the rate of water movement into the soil is governed by its percolation capacity.

Factors affecting infiltration are:

1. Soil texture, or size of soil particles.
2. Soil structure, or arrangement of soil particles, and the resultant porosity or voids between particles.
3. Moisture content of soil through the influence of swelling or shrinking of colloids and the degree of filling of pores by water.
4. Turbidity of water due to suspended fine particles and resultant clogging and sealing of pores.
5. Depth and character of freezing of surface.
6. Amount and kind of soil cover, including plants and their remains as litter.

The occurrence of large pore spaces in the soil has a major influence on infiltration. The soils of undisturbed forest and grassland, high in incorporated organic matter, penetrated by root systems, and channeled by decayed roots and burrowing animals, usually show high infiltration rates.

## MEASUREMENT OF INFILTRATION.

1. Surface runoff from a small plot subjected to simulated rainfall of calibrated intensity. Infiltration is indicated as the difference between the runoff and the "rainfall" applied.
2. Runoff or streamflow (by weir or stream gauge) following natural rainfall (gauged) on a watershed of known area.
3. Water absorbed by the soil from a volume of water applied in a tube or ring to a small area of ground surface.
4. Intake of water by soil from irrigation flooding of the surface with a known volume of water.

**INFLUENCE OF VEGETATION.** Numerous tests under a variety of conditions show the influence of vegetation on infiltration rates. Gaiser, in one study made in the Central states, found more than 4,000 root channels per acre under a stand of hardwoods. Such channels, plus numerous smaller ones left by decaying roots and channels made by the burrowing activity of natural fauna found under vegetative cover, greatly increase the rate at which water enters and percolates through the soil.

Transpiration by vegetation decreases the quantity of water stored in the soil, which in turn increases the rate of infiltration. An example of a high infiltration rate when a soil is dry, as compared with that when soil moisture increases, is cited by Kittredge:

| Wetness of soil, in percent of field capacity | Infiltration, in inches of water per hour | Wetness of soil, in percent of field capacity | Infiltration, in inches of water per hour |
|---|---|---|---|
| 20 | 0.91 | 80 | 0.17 |
| 40 | .43 | 100 | .11 |
| 60 | .26 | 120 | .08 |

In midsummer, when transpiration is at its peak, even heavy rains rarely produce surface runoff from well-forested watersheds.

Using the third method of measurement listed above, Auten (see Table 3) found that undisturbed oak woods in Arkansas and Illinois had a much higher absorption rate than burned woods or open pasture. (Because water introduced into the soil by this technique is not muddied, as raindrops are when they fall on exposed soil, absorption rather than infiltration is here being measured.)

The beneficial effect of good vegetative cover was found by Auten not only on sandy and cherty soils (Arkansas examples), which naturally have a high infiltration rate, but also on the Illinois loam soils with a generally lower infiltration rate. Decreased absorption with each successive application of water was marked, except in the undisturbed oak woods on loam soil, but in general it appears that saturation was not reached even with the application of 4 liters of water per sq. ft.

**Table 3. Rate of Water Absorption[a] Under Various Vegetative Covers**

| Soil type | Site conditions | First liter | Second liter | Third liter | Fourth liter |
|---|---|---|---|---|---|
| Yellow silt loam, Illinois | Undisturbed oak woods | 21.83 | 23.36 | 22.78 | 21.23 |
| | Burned oak woods | 7.60 | 4.63 | 3.40 | 2.64 |
| | Open pasture | 2.52 | 1.34 | 1.01 | 0.86 |
| Cherty silt loam, Arkansas | Undisturbed oak woods | 55.87 [d] | 44.87 [d] | 38.76 | 32.05 |
| | Burned oak woods | 14.25 | 9.78 | 6.12 [b] | 5.10 [c] |
| | Open pasture | 17.73 [d] | 10.47 [d] | 6.16 | 4.74 |
| | Old-field pine woods | 53.19 | 35.21 | 21.10 [b] | 14.71 [c] |
| | Open pasture | 12.32 | 7.66 | 8.04 [b] | 6.37 [c] |
| Sandy soil, Arkansas | Undisturbed oak woods | 64.10 | 46.08 | 40.00 | 30.50 |
| | Open pasture | 24.33 | 16.84 | 14.35 | 12.92 |

[a] In cubic centimeters per second per square foot of soil.
[b] Each figure represents the average of 100 tests unless otherwise indicated. All items over three times standard deviation are eliminated.
[c] Less than 100 tests.
[d] 200 tests.
Source: Central States Forest Exp. Sta., The effect of forest burning in the Ozarks on the water absorption of forest soils, *Sta. Note No. 16, 1934.*

Erosion, by removing the more porous A horizon of a soil, and by sealing the large surface pores with fine material carried in turbid water, effectively reduces infiltration, as shown in another experiment (Table 4).

**Table 4. Reduction of Infiltration by Erosion**

| Soil type | Depth of A horizon (In.) | Infiltration (In. per hr.) | Erosion |
|---|---|---|---|
| Cecil sandy loam ...................... | 11 | 0.55 | Little |
| Cecil sandy clay loam .................. | 3 | .42 | Considerable |
| Cecil clay loam ........................ | 1 | .09 | Excessive |
| Ruston sandy loam (clear water).......... | 8 | 2.06 | ... |
| Ruston sandy loam (turbid water for 2 hr.) ............................... | 8 | 0.82 | ... |

## Soil Moisture

**CLASSIFICATION. Gravitational Water.** Water which drains freely through the soil under the influence of gravity is called gravitational water. Its rapid draining away makes it unimportant to plants, but it is of hydrologic significance as temporary storage until it reaches the water table or stream channels by subsurface flow.

**Capillary Water.** Water which moves under the influence of surface tension through small pores between soil particles, after gravitational water has drained out, is called capillary water. It supplies most of the requirements of growing plants for water but does not contribute directly to streamflow. However, the capillary moisture-holding capacity of soils is hydrologically significant because of its marked variation with texture, structure, and organic content. The influence of texture is shown in Table 5.

**Hygroscopic Water.** Water which is retained—after removal of capillary water—as a thin film around the soil particle by forces of adsorption so great that it is not available to plants is called hygroscopic water. In fine clays, hygroscopic water may amount to as much as 20 percent of the dry weight of soil; in sands it may be less than 1 percent.

### Table 5. Capillary Moisture-Holding Capacity of Soils

| Character of soil | Depth of water in inches, per foot of soil depth |
|---|---|
| Fine sand | 0.5 |
| Sandy loam | 1.7 |
| Silt loam | 2.5 |
| Loam | 3.3 |
| Clay | 4.5 |

**CONSTANTS.** The amount of moisture present in a soil may be expressed by four constants, defined below:

**Moisture Equivalent.** The moisture equivalent is the moisture content which the soil retains when it has been subjected to a centrifugal force of 1,000 times gravity to reach a state of capillary equilibrium.

**Field Capacity.** The field capacity represents the moisture content that a soil retains after excess gravitational water has drained away, usually 2 to 5 days following a thorough wetting of the soil. It represents a dividing line between capillary water and gravitational water.

**Wilting Point.** The wilting point represents the moisture content of a soil at the time when the leaves of a plant growing therein first undergo a permanent drying out due to soil moisture deficiency.

**Hygroscopic Coefficient.** The hygroscopic coefficient is approximately the moisture content of a thin layer of dry soil that has reached equilibrium with a near-saturated atmosphere. Soils at this point are at the upper limit of the hygroscopic moisture content and can supply no water for plant growth.

**METHODS OF MEASUREMENT. Direct Measurement.** Weigh a sample of soil; dry it for 24 hr. at 105–110° C.; reweigh; the difference, divided by the dry weight, is the percentage of moisture, $M$. To express soil moisture as inches of depth of water, $d$, use this formula:

$$d = \frac{M \times VW \times D}{100}$$

where $VW$ = volume weight and $D$ = depth of soil in inches. Volume weight (or bulk density) is the ratio between the oven-dry weight of a given volume of undisturbed soil and the weight of an equal volume of water. It varies greatly with soil type and horizon. For the $A_0$ horizon it is usually about 0.2; for the $A_1$ horizon it is commonly less than 1.0 (because of the pore space); for deeper horizons it may be 1.5 or more.

**Indirect Measurement.** The most promising method of measuring soil moisture in place is electrical. Electrical resistance varies with the moisture content of a soil. Two electrodes, separated at a constant distance by a porous medium, such as plaster of Paris, nylon, or Fiberglas, are buried, after calibration, in the soil at the desired depth. After an interval sufficient for the porous medium to absorb moisture to the same degree as the surrounding soil, an electric current is passed through lead wires attached to the electrodes, and the resistance is measured by an ohmmeter. The plaster of Paris–nylon type of unit soil moisture blocks and ohmmeter were developed by G. J. Bouyoucos and A. H. Mick, Agricultural Experiment Station, Michigan State College. The Fiberglas soil moisture units and an ohmmeter were developed by E. A. Colman of the California Forest and Range Experiment Station.

**Effect of Vegetation on Soil Moisture.** The influence of the type and density of vegetation on soil moisture is in great part governed by the extent to which roots penetrate the soil mantle. In general, deep-rooted species, such as most trees, many shrubs, legumes, and grasses, during the growing season will remove soil water from a greater depth than the shallower rooted perennials or annuals; they therefore create more capacity for storage of fall and winter precipitation in the soil. In most parts of the United States soil moisture within the root zone will be reduced to near the wilting point during the growing season.

On the other hand, the rates of infiltration and percolation of most soils increase with increasing density of cover. Consequently, a larger percentage of the precipitation enters the soil, satisfying any moisture deficiency below field capacity to the depth it penetrates, and, when in sufficient amount, adding to the gravitational water, which in turn contributes to the ground water supply.

## Runoff and Streamflow

**UNITS OF FLOW RATES.** The most commonly used units are (1) gallons per minute, used for springs and wells, and (2) cubic feet per second (cfs), used for streams. For domestic, industrial, and irrigation uses of water, flow may be expressed as acre-feet per day, area inches per hour, cubic feet per second (or second-feet) per square mile (csm), millions of gallons per day, etc. For equivalents, see Tables 14 and 16.

**COMPONENTS.** The amount of water flowing in a stream channel $(Q)$ is equal to the cross-sectional area of the flowing water $(a)$ multiplied by its mean velocity $(v)$; thus $Q = av$. A stream 10 ft. wide, 1 ft. deep, and having a mean velocity of 2 ft. per sec., flows 20 cfs. Because a constant flow of 1 cfs is equal to 646,317 gal. per day, the watershed produces 12,926,340 gal. per day. A convenient rule of thumb is: 1 cfs = 2 acre-ft. per day.

Runoff in stream channels comes from several sources. The **base flow** of perennial streams is continuous even during nonstorm periods. Its source is ground water discharge from sustaining aquifers that are intermittently recharged during periods of rainfall or snow melt. Base flow is also called ground water flow, and in the North Temperate Zone generally has the highest rate per unit area in the spring. The rate grows less throughout the summer, the rate of decrease following a regular pattern.

During storm periods water may also enter the stream channel directly as (1) **channel precipitation,** (2) **surface storm runoff** over the surface of the ground, or (3) **subsurface storm runoff** through the very porous upper layers of the soil. In (3), storm water actually enters the soil but moves laterally, through porous soil layers, rapidly enough to reach the stream channel in time to contribute to the stormflow. When streams rise rapidly, some water may also pass temporarily into porous stream banks. This bank-stored water returns to the channel and contributes to streamflow on falling stages of the stream.

It is not always possible to differentiate between types of water reaching the stream channel because they merge imperceptibly and because different portions of a watershed may be contributing different types at the same time. It is much easier to differentiate the components of runoff for small watersheds of uniform vegetation and topography than for large drainage basins. To interpret the effects on streamflow of different types of vegetation and land-use practices, fundamental processes of land-use hydrology must be studied on small experimental watersheds. With a working knowledge of these processes established, it is then possible to proceed in interpreting the effect of land use on larger streams.

**ESTIMATION OF MAXIMUM STORM RUNOFF.** For estimating the maximum storm runoff to be expected from small watersheds of several acres up to 100 acres, relatively simple formulas are used. Those most commonly used for the design of storm sewers and culverts are based on the maximum expected rainfall for the locality, expressed as inches per hour, for a period equal to the time required for the maximum concentration of storm water at the outlet of the drainage area. These formulas take the form of a so-called "rational formula":

$$Q = CI_tA$$

in which $Q$ = rate of discharge, in cubic feet per second.

$C$ = a coefficient, the watershed factor, representing the percentage of the rainfall appearing as surface runoff.

$I_t$ = average rainfall intensity, in inches per hour, during the time of concentration; that is, during the period required for all parts of the specific drainage basin to contribute their quotas of streamflow.

$A$ = drainage area in acres.

In applying the above formula, the values of $C$ have been variously estimated and in some cases determined by actual watershed experiments. The highest value, 1.00, would indicate that all of the rainfall becomes storm runoff and concentrates in the channel. This may be used as a safety factor where snow melt is important, but it is not reached under field conditions except approximately, following previous periods of rain when the ground surface and the soil mass have become saturated. Ramser suggests the following values of $C$ for small watersheds:

| Kind of watershed | Values of $C$ |
|---|---|
| Cultivated rolling, 5 to 10 percent slope | 0.60 |
| Cultivated hilly, 10 to 30 percent slope | .72 |
| Pasture rolling, 5 to 10 percent slope | .36 |
| Pasture hilly, 10 to 30 percent slope | .42 |
| Timber rolling, 5 to 10 percent slope | .18 |
| Timber hilly, 10 to 30 percent slope | .21 |

$C$ also varies with area of the drainage. For watersheds of 2 to 5 sq. mi., values between 0.20 and 0.30 should be used; from areas of 5 to 50 sq. mi., from 0.10 to 0.20; and from watersheds 50 to 200 sq. mi., from 0.05 to 0.10.

The intensity of rainfall ($I$) in the formula is the maximum rate of fall to be expected in an interval equal to the time ($t$) of concentration. Where $t$ is not known, approximate values are assigned; for example, 20 min. for a 10-acre watershed, and progressively increasing to about 110 min. for 500 acres. If experience figures are not available, the rate ($I$) that may be expected for the time of concentration ($t$) may be obtained from rainfall-intensity maps. Fig. 4 indicates that for a period of 15 min. the maximum 25-yr. rainfall intensity in northern Tennessee can be expected to be 1.38 in. Multiplying this by 4 (to obtain inches per hour) gives a value of 5.52 for $I_t$. Assuming a value of 0.30 for $C$, and a watershed of 10 acres,

$$Q = 0.30 \times 5.52 \times 10 = 16.56 \text{ cfs.}$$

## ESTIMATION OF TOTAL RUNOFF AND PEAK RUNOFF. Small Watersheds. Total runoff.
If 1 in. of rain falls in 1 hr. on a watershed, and if none of this precipitation is able to infiltrate into the soil, the total storm runoff per acre is 43,560/12, or 3,630 cu. ft.; divided by 3,600, this approximates 1 cfs. This assumes that the rates of precipitation and runoff are both uniform.

**Peak runoff.** Actually, storm water does not leave a small watershed at a uniform rate because it is first concentrated into a single channel. At first only those portions of the watershed nearest the outlet contribute to the flow in the channel; eventually, all do so simultaneously. The storm hydrograph (runoff plotted over time) for a specific watershed tends to follow a fairly definite pattern for similar patterns of rainfall, regardless of the total runoff. Thus the hydrograph of a particular 10-acre watershed may establish that after brief but heavy rains the peak discharge is reached during the 5 min. after the rain stops, and that during these 5 min. 35 percent of the total storm discharge takes place. Assume that 1 in. of rain falls in 20 min. on this watershed, at a uniform rate. If the ground is already saturated, so that 100 percent of the rain becomes storm runoff,

$$\text{Peak discharge} = \frac{3,630 \text{ cu. ft.}}{5 \text{ min.} \times 60 \text{ sec.}} \times 10 \text{ acres} \times 35\% \times 100\%$$

$$= 42.35$$

This is cubic feet per second (cfs); if expressed as cubic feet per second per square mile of watershed (csm), it must be multiplied by 640/10, and is 2,710. If only 50 percent of the rain becomes storm runoff, the peak discharge is obviously only one-half as great, or 1,355 csm. If in the foregoing example 1.84 in. of rain (instead of 1.0 in.) fell in 20 min., of which 30 percent became surface runoff, the computation is as follows:

$$\frac{3,630}{300} \times 10 \times 0.35 \times (0.30 \times 1.84) = 23.38 \text{ cfs.}$$

Highest instantaneous peaks will be 10 to 20 percent above the mean for the maximum 5 min. of discharge.

Considering that peak discharge, like total storm runoff, is a function of the precipitation which fails to infiltrate into the soil of the watershed (the $C$ of the formula on page 10 · 15), the importance of the watershed conditions which affect $C$ becomes very obvious.

**Large Watersheds.** Relatively large watersheds are more complex than small ones with regard to slope, topography, soil, and vegetative cover; also, larger watersheds may have a continuous flow, which must be subtracted from the total storm runoff; and channel storage and valley storage may become more complex with larger watersheds. These factors make it difficult to establish a formula generally valid for all watersheds.

**ESTIMATION OF WATER YIELDS.** Since rainfall is usually expressed as inches depth on a drainage basin, it is convenient to express runoff on the same basis. Runoff can best be considered as a residual remaining after various other demands are supplied. For this reason the amounts of rainfall lost by evaporation, transpiration, and deep seepage are more constant than is runoff. For basins having a rainfall of 50 in. or more, runoff will be equal to about 50 percent of the rainfall. The percent of runoff will always be less in warm regions than in cool regions. However, there exists no simple relation by which runoff can be calculated with accuracy from known precipitation. Records of water yields for different parts of the country are reported by the U. S. Geological Survey Water Supply papers, and those must be referred to for individual localities. When long-term records are available for both runoff and rainfall, it is possible to establish a fairly good relation between the two.

In the Gulf States the average annual water loss that must be subtracted from the total precipitation to account for runoff is about 38 in., while in the northern states to the Canadian line the annual loss is only 18 in. Sections between these localities show a rather uniform increase in annual water loss from north to south. For the dry sections of the West as a whole, evaporation and transpiration combined are always at least equal to the annual precipitation, and runoff originates chiefly from the higher mountainous localities.

When transpiration or evaporation losses are significantly reduced, there may be a corresponding increase in the amount of water for runoff. The amount of increase depends on the extent to which a reduction in one of these factors is offset by an increase in the other. Cutting forest trees, for example, reduces interception and transpiration, but exposure of the ground to sun and wind may increase evaporation to such an extent as to partially offset the reduction in transpiration.

## Erosion

Erosion by water only is considered here. Wind erosion also is extremely important in parts of the United States and Canada.

**CLASSES OF EROSION. Geologic Erosion.** Geologic erosion is a natural process over which man has little or no control. It is usually slow, except in arid regions supporting sparse vegetation and subject to occasional torrential rains, wind action, or both.

**Accelerated Erosion.** An increased rate of movement and destruction of soil resulting from man's activities is called accelerated erosion. Two types are commonly recognized:

**Sheet erosion.** Where natural vegetation has been removed and bare soil is exposed to the impact of heavy rainfall or to rapid snow melt, particles of the surface soil are loosened and moved down the slope by surface flow. Also, fine soil particles are washed into the large surface pores, reducing the capacity of the soil to infiltrate the rain. The finer particles (silt, and especially clay) may flow off with the surface water into water courses or settle into depressions. Sheet erosion is not conspicuous but is serious because it breaks down the soil structure and removes the top soil. It is recognizable as "galled spots" in fields and by a gradual exposure of lighter colored subsurface soils.

**Gully erosion.** When water begins to concentrate in depressions associated with sheet erosion, small "finger" or "shoestring" gullies are formed. Such gullies are easily obliterated by cultivation. They do not seriously handicap machine farming nor do they by themselves prevent re-establishment of vegetative cover. However, unless they are halted by natural or artificial reduction or diversion of runoff, gullies usually increase in width and depth until bedrock or stable channel gradients have been reached.

**HYDRAULICS OF EROSION.** Soil erosion results from two independent processes: (1) detachment of soil particles, and (2) transportation of soil particles. During rainstorms the principal agents which detach soil are raindrops and water flowing over the surface. The splash of raindrops detaches most of the soil removed by sheet erosion; a beating rain on a bare acre of highly erodible soil may splash 100 tons of soil several inches into the air. Surface flow detaches most of the soil removed by rill and gully erosion. In general, clays are of low detachability and high transportability, while the reverse is usually true of sands.

Water derives its power to erode soil from the velocity imparted by gravity. In general:

1. Increasing the gradient four times doubles the velocity of water running over it.
2. Doubling the velocity of water increases its erosive power four-fold.
3. The quantity of material of a given size that can be transported by water varies with the fifth power of its velocity; i.e., if the velocity is doubled, the amount that can be carried is increased 32 times.
4. The size of particles which may be rolled or pushed by the action of water varies with the sixth power of its velocity; i.e., if the velocity is doubled, the size of the particles which may be moved is increased 64 times.

The average water velocity required to carry, sweep, or roll various-sized particles is given in Table 6.

**Table 6. Average Water Velocity Required to Carry Various-Sized Particles**

| Average velocity in ft. per sec. | Material |
|---|---|
| 0.25 | Fine clay |
| .5 | Fine sand |
| .67 | Coarse sand |
| 1.0 | Fine gravel |
| 2.0 | Pebbles up to 1 in. in diameter |
| 3.0 | Slippery, angular, egg-size stones |

**CONTROL OF EROSION.** The best control of erosion is, of course, prevention. Prevention is accomplished by proper land use—the maintenance of adequate vegetative cover, either natural or established by artificial means on a watershed. Such protective cover will increase the rates of infiltration and percolation, decrease the amount and velocity of surface runoff, and stabilize the soil in place.

To control erosion, once started:

1. Stop the cultivation, overgrazing, or burning practice that is aggravating erosion. Where climate is favorable and erosion has not reached the stage of severe gullying, this step alone often permits natural revegetation of an eroded area.

2. Where necessary, supplement natural revegetation by artificial seeding or planting.
3. Retard excessive surface runoff and further development of gullies by such measures as diversion channels, terraces, check dams, contour furrows, or contour plowing followed by protective mulching.

**Permanent Structures.** Where permanent structures are needed, one of the following types may be used:

**Soil-saving dams.** These are permanent structures to collect and hold soil and facilitate natural revegetation as well as to prevent further erosion by downward and headward cutting.

**Concrete and masonry check dams.** These are permanent check dams for control of large volume or high velocity discharge where watershed or soil conditions do not permit quick re-establishment of effective vegetation.

**Concrete and masonry checks.** These low check dams, in broad shallow ditches or gullies used for permanent drainage channels, are so spaced that the top of each is slightly higher than the bottom of the one above.

**Loose-rock check dams.** Semipermanent structures can be used in conjunction with vegetative control measures.

**Crib dams.** These are semipermanent structures constructed of a combination of logs and field stone. They are useful in large gullies carrying a comparatively heavy runoff.

**Concrete or rock paving.** Paving is used for carrying runoff at high velocities. It is usually employed where the volume of runoff water is not large.

**Temporary Structures.** Temporary structures are used primarily to aid in the establishment of vegetation by checking runoff and erosion. Their expected life must be consistent with the expected time required to obtain a permanent protective cover of vegetation. They should be employed with caution wherever their failure is likely to cause substantial damage or loss of life. The severity of some floods in southern California, for example, has been attributed in part to the failure of a series of temporary check dams in mountain channels.

**Log or plank check dams.** These are low structures not exceeding 3 ft. in height. They are used where the volume of water is large and considerable time is required to obtain a heavy growth of vegetation.

**Brush and wire check dams.** Such structures have a wide range of adaptability. The effective height is 12 in. They are used to collect and hold silt and moisture in gully bottoms to provide favorable growing conditions for vegetation. Examples of common types of brush and wire check dams are:

1. Brush checks, Fig. 5.
2. Single-post brush dam, Fig. 6.
3. Wire dam, Fig. 7.

**Brush paving.** This consists of stabilizing gully channels with brush bundles to permit growth of vegetation.

**Diversion ditches.** These result in reduction and control of runoff and aid vegetative control.

**Contour furrows.** Furrows plowed on the contour create a series of basins which catch and hold precipitation. Their effectiveness may be destroyed in a short time if the vegetation between furrows is not sufficient to prevent heavy sheet erosion and consequent filling of trenches.

**Plowing and mulching.** The most effective means for obtaining quick results in gully control is by plowing in and filling. The loose material, when covered with straw, hay, or brush, creates an excellent planting site. The method is not practical, however, where gullies are deep or numerous. Bulldozers have been used on badly eroded areas to level the land prior to seeding and mulching. Where

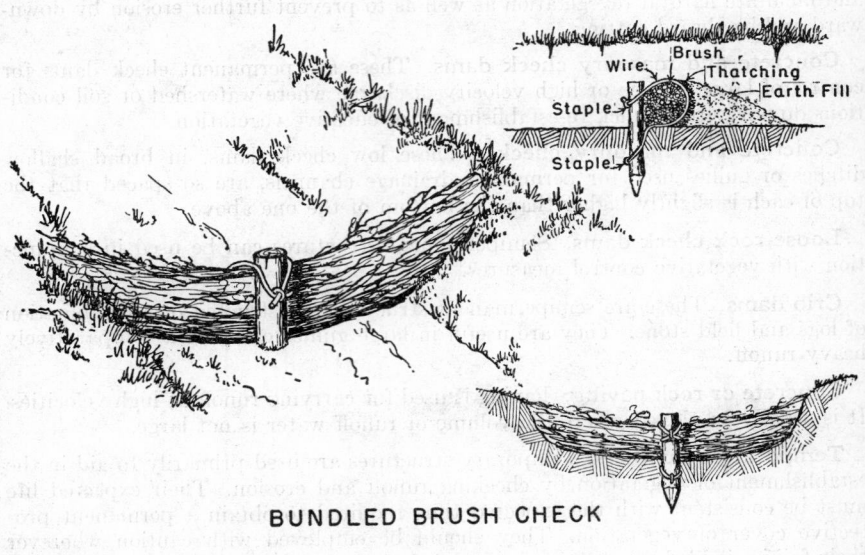

**BUNDLED BRUSH CHECK**

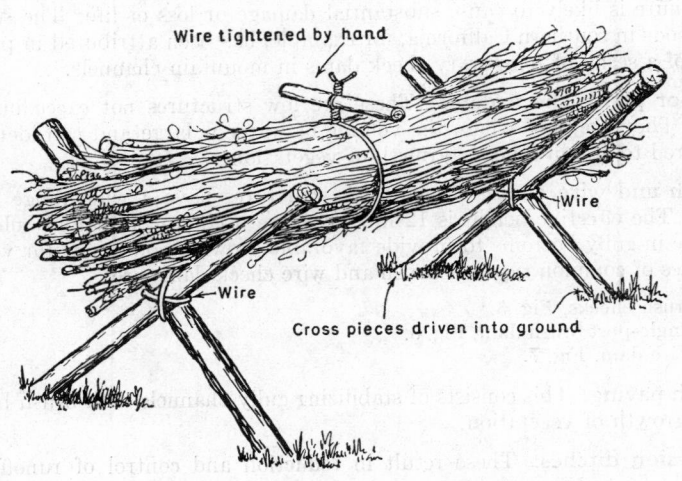

**BRUSH BUNDLER**

Fig. 5. Brush check dams.

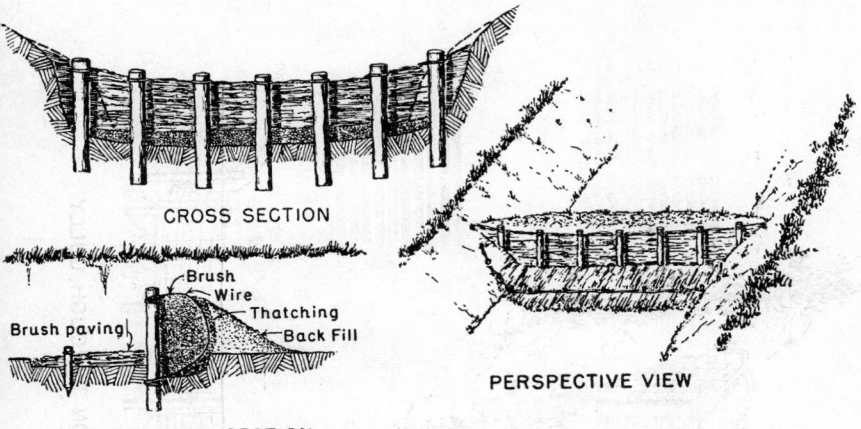

CROSS SECTION

Brush paving

Brush
Wire
Thatching
Back Fill

LONGITUDINAL SECTION

PERSPECTIVE VIEW

Fig. 6. Single-post brush dam.

rapid correction is necessary, this often proves to be the best method of permanent control.

Most of the engineering structures mentioned above are designed to so stabilize soil conditions that an adequate vegetative cover can become established. On the more severe sites, better results can often be obtained by using mulches of brush, litter, straw, etc. Frequently it is necessary to slope the edges or heads of gullies and road banks to aid further in establishing vegetation. For most conditions a slope of 1½ to 1 is satisfactory.

**Seeding and Planting.** A large variety of species have been and are being tested for erosion control. The choice of species to be used in establishing permanent vegetation on treated areas should be based on the experience of local agencies conversant with erosion-control planting.

**EROSION AND SEDIMENTATION.** Accelerated erosion can lead to serious sedimentation damage to valleys and streams. Many formerly productive bottomland areas have become waterlogged because the silting of stream channels has raised the water table. Other bottomlands have been rendered infertile by deposits of gravel and other erosion debris.

The siltation of lakes, reservoirs, channels, and harbors represents the costly damage resulting from accelerated erosion. The rates of sedimentation are extremely variable. Reported losses of storage capacity in the United States have ranged from less than 0.05 to more than 6.0 percent, annually. In 1936, it was estimated that 21 percent of American water supply reservoirs would have a useful life of less than 50 yr., and another 25 percent, a life of only 50–100 yr. Similar reduction in the life and operating efficiency of flood-control, irrigation, and multiple-purpose reservoirs results from accelerated erosion and ensuing sedimentation.

Among other damaging effects, sedimentation increases the cost of filtering and treating a water supply. In the Piedmont section of North Carolina it has been estimated that a 30 percent reduction in suspended load would result in a direct saving of $1.50 per million gallons in the cost of treatment, and as much as $7 per million gallons when the cost of maintaining silting basins and filtering and purification works is included.

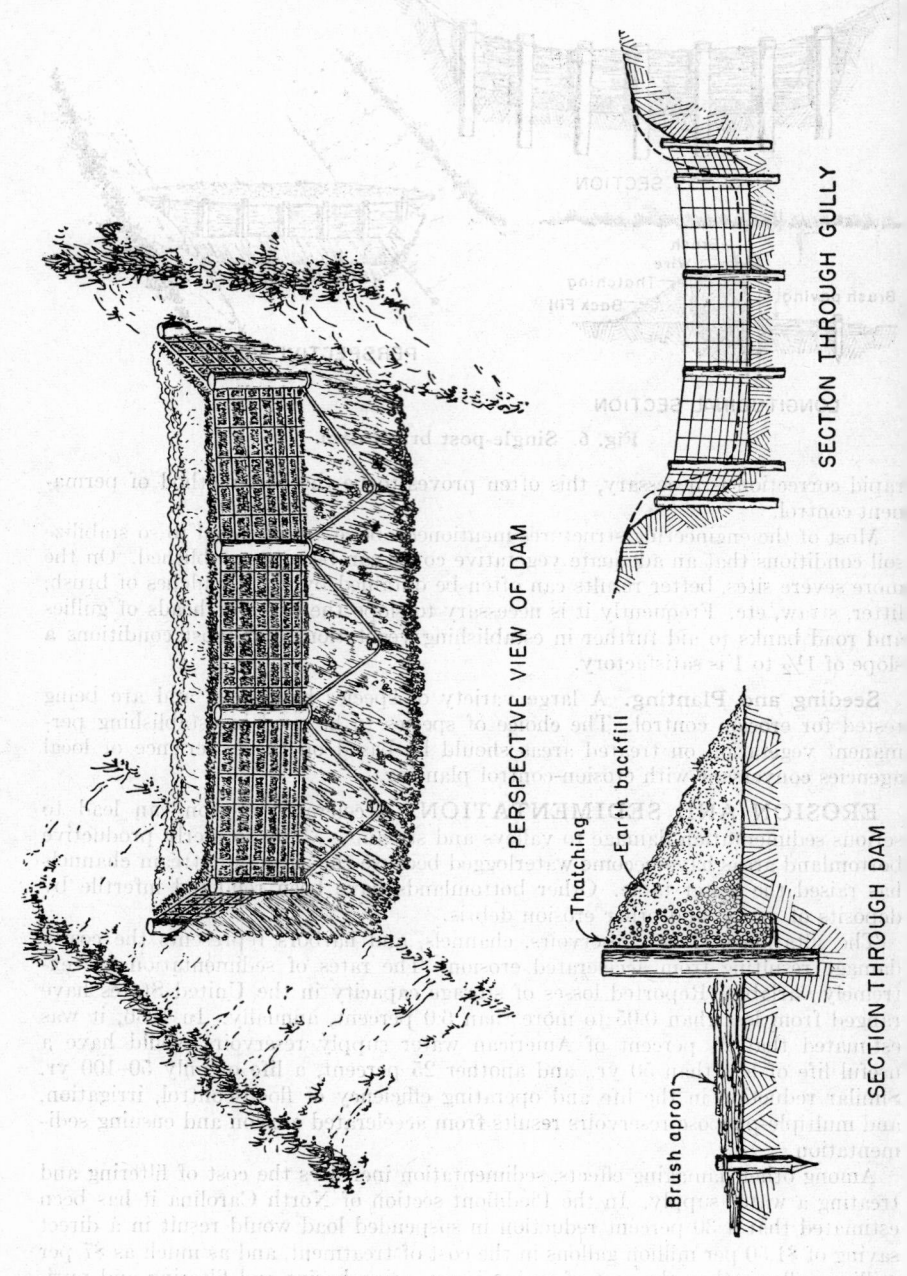

PERSPECTIVE VIEW OF DAM

SECTION THROUGH GULLY

SECTION THROUGH DAM

Thatching

Earth backfill

Brush apron

# Use of Water

## Table 7. Domestic and Industrial Requirements for Water

| DOMESTIC | AVG. USE gpd |
|---|---|
| h member of the family for all purposes, ing drinking, cooking, laundry, house ng, toilet flushing, bathing, and lawn and n watering | 50 |
| lavatory | 1½ |
| bathtub | 36 |
| bath | 25 |
| g toilet | 7 |
| h hose with sprinkling | 275-300 gal per hour |
| prinkler | 120-150 gal per hour |

### INDUSTRIAL

uantities reported below are clearly those of water that is, the amount which is piped into an estab-t—rather than consumptive use—the amount dis-to the atmosphere or incorporated into the prod-a process. Thus, the wide ranges sometimes given ot only differences in processes or products, but ces in the use of water. In arid areas, where even t rigorous conservation methods are economically "intake" is only a fraction of what it may be in here water is abundant, although "consumptive irtually the same.

| als | UNIT | WATER REQUIRED gal |
|---|---|---|
| industrial, proof) | gal | 120 |
| a (Bayer ss) | ton | 6,300 |
| ium sulfate | ton | 200,000 |
| ne | ton | 20,000-660,000* |
| carbide | ton | 30,000 |
| dioxide flue gas) | ton | 20,000 |
| eed oil | gal | 20 |
| der or ives | ton | 200,000 |
| en | ton | 660,000 |
| liquid | 1,000 cu ft | 2,000 |
| aundry) | ton | 500 |
| h (ammonia process) 58% | ton | 18,000 |
| chlorate | ton | 60,000 |
| acid (contact ss) 100% | ton | 650-4,875* |
| | ton | 500-1,000† |
| | 100 cases #2 cans | 750-25,000† |
| vet-milling) | bu corn | 140-240† |
| rup | bu corn | 30-40† |
| (edible) | ton | 13,200-20,000† |
| ing | ton live animals | 4,130 |
| ng house eration | 100 hog units | 55,000 |

rom no reuse to maximum recycling.
overs various products or processes involved.

| | UNIT | WATER REQUIRED gal |
|---|---|---|
| **Milk and milk products:** | | |
| Butter | ton | 5,000 |
| Cheese | ton | 4,000 |
| Receiving & bottling | ton | 9,000 |
| **Sugar:** | | |
| Beet sugar | ton | 2,160 |
| Cane sugar | ton | 1,000 |
| **Paper & Pulp** | | |
| Ground wood pulp | ton dry | 4,000-50,000* |
| Kraft pulp | ton dry | 93,000 |
| Soda pulp | ton dry | 85,000 |
| Sulfate pulp | ton dry | 70,000 |
| Sulfite pulp | ton dry | 70,000-133,000* |
| Paper | ton | 39,000 |
| Paperboard | ton | 15,000-90,000* |
| Strawboard | ton | 26,000 |
| **Petroleum** | | |
| Gasoline natural | gal | 20 |
| Oil refining | 100 bbl | 77,000 |
| Refined products | 100 bbl | 15,000-1,500,000* |
| **Synthetic fuel** | | |
| By coal hydrogenation | 100 bbl | 728,600 |
| From coal | 100 bbl | 1,115,000 |
| From natural gas | 100 bbl | 373,600 |
| From shale | 100 bbl | 87,300 |
| **Textiles** | | |
| Cotton. | | |
| Bleaching | ton produced | 60,000-80,000 |
| Dyeing | ton produced | 8,000-16,000 |
| Rayon: | | |
| Cuprammonium (11% moisture) | ton yarn | 90,000-160,000† |
| Viscose | ton yarn | 200,000 |
| Weave, dye & finish | 1,000 yard | 15,000 |
| Woolens | ton produced | 140,000 |
| **Miscellaneous** | | |
| Cement, portland | ton | 750 |
| Coal & coke: | | |
| By product coke | ton | 1,500-3,600† |
| Washing | ton | 200 |
| Electric power, steam-generated | kwhr | 80-170* |
| Hospitals | bed per day | 135-150 |
| Iron ore (brown) | ton | 1,000 |
| Laundries: | | |
| Commercial | ton work | 8,600-11,400† |
| Institutional | ton work | 6,000 |
| Leather tanning: | | |
| Vegetable | 100 bbl raw hide | 800 |
| Chrome | 100 bbl raw hide | 800 |
| Rock wool | ton | 5,000 |
| Rubber, synthetic: | | |
| Buna S | ton | 631,450 |
| GR-S | ton | 28,000-670,000* |
| Steel (rolled) | net ton | 15,000-110,000* |
| Sulfur mining | ton | 3,000 |

—Compiled by the American Water Works Assn., New York (Nov. 1953).

## Table 8. Estimated Daily Use of Water in the United States

|  | Billion gallon |
|---|---|
| Municipal supplies | 12–14 [a] |
| Rural domestic use | 3 |
| Irrigation | 75–100 |
| Converted to steam in generation of electricity | 35 |
| Other industrial use | 35–45 |
| Total | 160–197 [b] |

[a] Average per capita use for towns of less than 500 population, 60 gal.; up to 140 ga in cities of more than 10,000 population. Includes normal public and commercial use i addition to purely domestic consumption.
[b] Equivalent to about 15 percent of total average daily flow of all streams into ocea waters.

## Water Units and Measurements

An estimation of the volume of flowing water is obtained from the formula:

$$Q = av \qquad \text{(see page 10·14)}$$

where $Q$ = quantity of flow in cubic feet per second
$\quad a$ = cross-sectional area of flowing stream (depth in feet times width in feet
$\quad v$ = velocity of flow in feet per second

Measurements of the quantity of flow over weirs and dams and through pipes and culverts are special determinations which are derived from the basic formula given above.

**FLOW IN OPEN CHANNELS.** Manning's velocity equation can be writ ten:

$$v = \frac{1.486}{n} \sqrt[3]{(a/p)^2} \sqrt{s}$$

where $v$ = velocity in feet per second
$\quad n$ = coefficient of roughness
$\quad a$ = cross-sectional area of the channel
$\quad p$ = perimeter of the wetted channel (excluding the water surface)
$\quad s$ = slope in feet, per foot of channel reach

The coefficient of roughness, $n$, varies with the material of which the channel is made, or the character of the natural channel, as shown in Table 9.

**WEIRS.** A weir is a water-measuring device consisting of a dam placed across the stream with a notch through which water pours. The most common types are rectangular weirs with a notch less than the width of the channel, and 90° tri-angular notch weirs. A weir with a sharpened blade on the upstream edge, so that the water springs clear, is called a sharp-crested weir. A weir approximately rectangular in cross section, such as a concrete wall, is termed a broad-crested weir.

Water measurements made by means of a weir are accurate only when the weir is properly set and the head is read at a point some distance (at least twice the depth of the notch) upstream so that the reading will not be affected by the downward curve of the water. The bottom of the notch must be set above the bottom of the channel at a height equal to at least twice the maximum head, preferably more.

### Table 9. Value of *n* in Manning's Velocity Equation

| Description of channel | Range of *n* |
|---|---|
| Glazed brick | 0.011–0.015 |
| Brick in mortar | .012– .017 |
| Neat cement | .010– .013 |
| Concrete pipe | .012– .016 |
| Plank flumes | .010– .016 |
| Concrete-lined channels | .012– .018 |
| Cement rubble | .017– .030 |
| Dry rubble | .025– .035 |
| Dressed stonework | .013– .017 |
| Smooth metal flumes | .011– .015 |
| Corrugated metal flumes | .022– .030 |
| Earth canal, straight and uniform | .017– .025 |
| Rock canal, trimmed smooth and uniform | .025– .035 |
| Rock canal, rough | .035– .045 |
| Sluggish, winding channels | .022– .030 |
| Canals, stony bed, weeds along bank | .025– .040 |
| Earth bottom, rubble sides | .028– .035 |
| Natural channels | |
| (1) Clean, straight, full stage, no pools | .025– .033 |
| (2) As above with weeds and stones | .030– .040 |
| (3) Winding; pools, shallows, but clean | .033– .045 |
| (4) As above at low stages | .040– .055 |
| (5) As (3), with weeds and stones | .035– .050 |
| (6) As (4), with large stones | .045– .060 |
| (7) Sluggish, weedy, or with deep pools | .050– .080 |
| (8) Very weedy and sluggish | .075– .150 |

The mean velocity in the channel above the weir is called the velocity of approach. If it is high, the discharge as determined must be corrected by adding to the observed heads the velocity head ($V^2/g$) when $V$ = velocity of approach and $g$ = acceleration due to gravity, taken as 32.16.

Table 10. Discharge Capacity of Broad-Crested Weirs; for Use with Embankment Spillways, Masonry Dams, and Side-Spillway Earth Dams*

| Depth or head on crest | Length of notch or width of spillway in feet | | | | | | | | | | | | |
|---|---|---|---|---|---|---|---|---|---|---|---|---|---|
| | 2 | 4 | 6 | 8 | 10 | 12 | 14 | 16 | 18 | 20 | 22 | 26 | 30 |
| (ft.) | (cfs) | (cfs) | (cfs) | (cfs) | (cfs) | (cfs) | (cfs) | (cfs) | (cfs) | (cfs) | (cfs) | (cfs) | (cfs) |
| 0.5 | 2.3 | 4.5 | 6.8 | 9.1 | 11.3 | 13.6 | 15.8 | 18.1 | 20.4 | 22.6 | 24.9 | 29.4 | 33.9 |
| 1.0 | 6.4 | 12.8 | 19.2 | 25.6 | 32.0 | 38.4 | 44.8 | 51.2 | 57.6 | 64.0 | 70.4 | 83.2 | 96.0 |
| 1.5 | 11.8 | 23.5 | 35.2 | 47.0 | 58.8 | 70.5 | 82.3 | 94.1 | 105.8 | 117.6 | 129.3 | 152.8 | 176.4 |
| 2.0 | 18.1 | 36.2 | 54.3 | 72.4 | 90.5 | 108.6 | 126.7 | 144.8 | 162.9 | 181.0 | 199.1 | 235.3 | 271.5 |
| 2.5 | 25.3 | 50.6 | 75.9 | 101.2 | 126.5 | 151.8 | 177.1 | 202.4 | 227.7 | 253.0 | 278.3 | 328.9 | 379.5 |
| 3.0 | 33.3 | 66.5 | 99.8 | 133.0 | 166.3 | 199.5 | 232.8 | 266.0 | 299.3 | 332.5 | 365.8 | 432.3 | 498.8 |
| 3.5 | 41.9 | 83.8 | 125.7 | 167.6 | 209.5 | 251.4 | 293.4 | 335.3 | 377.2 | 419.1 | 461.0 | 544.8 | 628.6 |
| 4.0 | 51.2 | 102.4 | 153.6 | 204.8 | 256.0 | 307.2 | 358.4 | 409.6 | 460.8 | 512.0 | 563.2 | 665.6 | 768.0 |
| 4.5 | 61.1 | 122.2 | 183.3 | 244.4 | 305.5 | 366.6 | 427.7 | 488.8 | 549.8 | 610.9 | 672.0 | 794.2 | 916.4 |
| 5.0 | 71.6 | 143.1 | 214.7 | 286.2 | 357.8 | 429.3 | 500.9 | 572.4 | 644.0 | 715.5 | 787.1 | 930.2 | 1,073.3 |
| 5.5 | 82.6 | 165.1 | 247.7 | 330.2 | 412.8 | 495.4 | 577.9 | 660.5 | 743.0 | 825.6 | 908.2 | 1,073.3 | 1,238.4 |
| 6.0 | 94.1 | 188.2 | 282.2 | 376.3 | 470.4 | 564.5 | 658.6 | 752.6 | 846.7 | 940.8 | 1,034.9 | 1,223.0 | 1,411.2 |
| 6.5 | 106.0 | 212.1 | 318.1 | 424.2 | 530.2 | 636.3 | 742.3 | 848.4 | 954.4 | 1,060.5 | 1,166.5 | 1,378.6 | 1,590.7 |
| 7.0 | 118.5 | 237.1 | 355.6 | 474.1 | 592.6 | 711.2 | 829.7 | 948.2 | 1,066.8 | 1,185.3 | 1,303.8 | 1,540.9 | 1,777.9 |
| 7.5 | 131.5 | 262.9 | 394.4 | 525.8 | 657.3 | 788.7 | 920.2 | 1,051.6 | 1,183.1 | 1,314.6 | 1,446.0 | 1,708.9 | 1,971.8 |
| 8.0 | 144.8 | 289.7 | 434.5 | 579.3 | 724.2 | 869.0 | 1,013.8 | 1,158.7 | 1,303.5 | 1,448.3 | 1,593.2 | 1,882.8 | 2,172.5 |

* Computed by formula: $Q = 3.2LH^{3/2}$; where $Q$ = discharge in cubic feet per second; $L$ = length of spillway in feet; $H$ = head of water on crest of spillway in feet.
Source: Iowa Eng. Exp. Sta. Bull. 121.

Table 11. Sharp-Crested Weirs: Flow over Rectangular and Right-Angled V-Notch Weirs

| Head in feet | V-notch [a] discharge (cfs) | Rectangular [b] discharge (cfs per foot of length) | Head in feet | V-notch [a] discharge (cfs) | Rectangular [b] discharge (cfs per foot of length) |
|---|---|---|---|---|---|
| 0.05 |       | 0.041 |      |       |       |
| .10  | 0.008 | .113  | 1.05 | 2.843 | 3.558 |
| .15  | .023  | .205  | 1.10 | 3.189 | 3.842 |
| .20  | .047  | .314  | 1.15 | 3.559 | 4.102 |
| .25  | .082  | .435  | 1.20 | 3.954 | 4.367 |
| .30  | .129  | .569  | 1.25 | 4.373 | 4.637 |
| .35  | .189  | .714  | 1.30 | 4.818 | 4.912 |
| .40  | .262  | .868  | 1.35 | 5.288 | 5.192 |
| .45  | .351  | 1.033 | 1.40 | 5.785 | 5.477 |
| .50  | .455  | 1.206 | 1.45 | 6.309 | 5.767 |
| .55  | .576  | 1.387 | 1.50 | 6.860 | 6.062 |
| .60  | .714  | 1.576 | 1.55 | 7.439 | 6.361 |
| .65  | .870  | 1.773 | 1.60 | 8.05  | 6.665 |
| .70  | 1.044 | 1.977 | 1.65 | 8.68  | 6.973 |
| .75  | 1.238 | 2.188 | 1.70 | 9.35  | 7.286 |
| .80  | 1.452 | 2.406 | 1.75 | 10.04 | 7.604 |
| .85  | 1.687 | 2.630 | 1.80 | 10.76 | 7.925 |
| .90  | 1.943 | 2.861 | 1.85 | 11.52 | 8.251 |
| .95  | 2.220 | 3.097 | 1.90 | 12.30 | 8.580 |
| 1.00 | 2.520 | 3.340 | 2.00 | 13.96 | 9.252 |

[a] Discharge in cubic feet per second over right-angled V-notch weirs by the formula $Q = 2.52H^{2.47}$.

[b] Discharge in cubic feet per second per foot of length over sharp-crested weirs without velocity of approach correction, by the formula $Q = 3.34H^{1.47}$.

Source: Selected values by permission from *Handbook of hydraulics,* by H. W. King. Copyright, 1939, 3d ed., McGraw-Hill Book Co., Inc.

## PIPES.

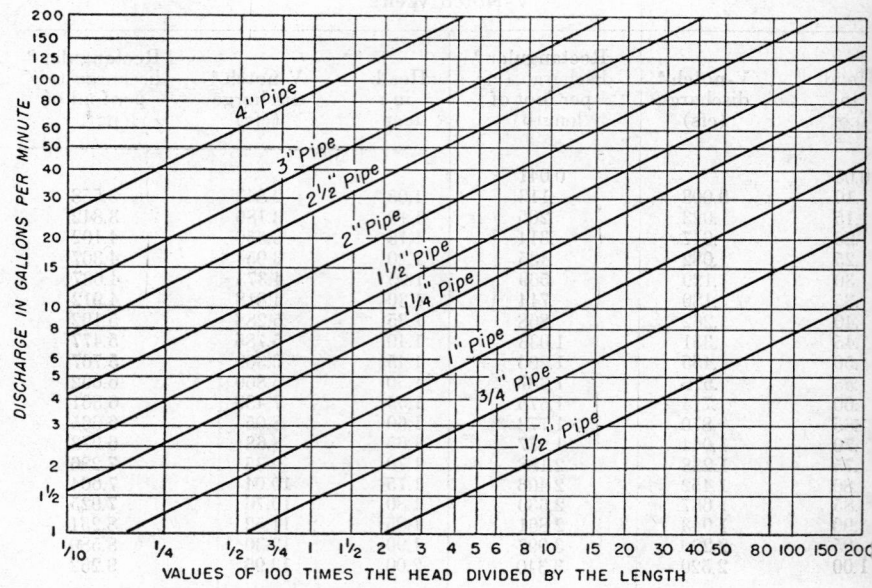

Fig. 8. Discharge capacity of straight water pipes.

Directions: Measure the vertical distance in feet from the delivery end of the pipe to the surface of the water in the spring or tank; multiply this distance by 100 and divide the product by the length of the pipe in feet; find this value on the lower horizontal line of the diagram and follow vertically upward to the inclined line or lines showing pipe sizes; from such intersection follow horizontally to the left to find the discharge in gallons per minute.

Example. How much water will be discharged by 128 ft. of 1-in. pipe under a head of 32 ft.?
Solution: Thirty-two multiplied by 100 equals 3,200; 3,200 divided by 128 equals 25; enter the diagram at 25, follow upward to the line marked 1-in. pipe, and then follow to the left where the discharge is seen to be 15 gal. per min.
Minimum grade for water pipe is 4/10 of 1%. (U. S. Forest Service, Region 4.)

## CULVERTS.

### Table 12.  Capacity of Culverts *

| Slope in percent | Diameter of pipe in inches | | | | | | | | | | |
|---|---|---|---|---|---|---|---|---|---|---|---|
| | 8 | 10 | 12 | 15 | 18 | 24 | 30 | 36 | 48 | 60 | 72 |
| | (cfs) | (cfs) | (cfs) | (cfs) | (cfs) | (cfs) | (cfs) | (cfs) | (cfs) | (cfs) | (cfs) |
| 0.1 | 0.2 | 0.4 | 0.6 | 1.3 | 2.1 | 4.7 | 8 | 12 | 25 | 47 | 85 |
| .2 | .3 | 0.6 | 1.0 | 2.0 | 3.1 | 6.8 | 12 | 19 | 42 | 77 | 130 |
| .3 | .4 | 0.8 | 1.3 | 2.4 | 3.9 | 8.3 | 15 | 25 | 53 | 97 | 150 |
| .4 | .5 | 0.9 | 1.5 | 2.8 | 4.4 | 9.5 | 17 | 28 | 62 | 110 | 180 |
| .5 | .6 | 1.0 | 1.7 | 3.0 | 4.9 | 10.0 | 19 | 31 | 68 | 120 | 190 |
| .6 | .6 | 1.1 | 1.9 | 3.3 | 5.4 | 11.0 | 21 | 33 | 72 | 130 | 210 |
| .8 | .8 | 1.2 | 2.1 | 3.7 | 6.1 | 13.0 | 23 | 37 | 77 | 140 | 220 |
| 1.0 | .8 | 1.4 | 2.3 | 4.0 | 6.5 | 14.0 | 24 | 39 | 80 | 140 | 230 |
| 1.2 | .8 | 1.5 | 2.4 | 4.3 | 6.8 | 14.0 | 25 | 40 | 82 | 150 | 230 |
| 1.4 | .9 | 1.6 | 2.5 | 4.4 | 7.0 | 15.0 | 25 | 40 | 83 | 150 | 230 |
| 1.6 | .9 | 1.6 | 2.6 | 4.5 | 7.1 | 15.0 | 26 | 40 | 83 | 150 | 230 |
| 1.8 | .9 | 1.6 | 2.6 | 4.6 | 7.1 | 15.0 | 26 | 40 | 83 | 150 | 230 |

* With water surface at inlet same elevation as top of pipe, and outlet unsubmerged.
NOTE: The values underlined indicate discharge at the approximate "critical slope," when $n = 0.021$ (Manning's equation, page 10·24). Slopes steeper than critical do not result in increased discharge.

### Table 13.  Acres Drained by Culverts *

| Diameter of culvert in inches | Mountainous country $C = 1$ | Rolling country $C = \frac{1}{3}$ | Level country $C = \frac{1}{5}$ |
|---|---|---|---|
| 12 | ¾ | 3 | 6 |
| 15 | 1 | 6 | 11 |
| 18 | 2 | 9 | 18 |
| 21 | 3 | 14 | 28 |
| 24 | 5 | 20 | 39 |
| 30 | 8 | 36 | 71 |
| 36 | 14 | 59 | 116 |
| 42 | 20 | 89 | 175 |
| 48 | 29 | 126 | 250 |
| 54 | 40 | 174 | 345 |
| 60 | 53 | 229 | 453 |
| 66 | 68 | 295 | 584 |
| 72 | 86 | 373 | 737 |
| 78 | 107 | 461 | 912 |
| 84 | 130 | 562 | 1,111 |

* Based on Talbot Formula: $A = C \sqrt[4]{M^3}$; where $A$ = waterway necessary in square feet; $M$ = area drained in acres; $C$ = coefficient, $\frac{1}{5}$, $\frac{1}{3}$, and 1 used for flat, rolling, and mountainous areas, respectively. This formula is based on a large number of observations, with maximum rainfall of approximately 4 in. per hr., and a velocity of flow of less than 10 ft. per sec.

## Table 14. Discharge Equivalents [a]

| Unit | Gpd | Ft.³/day | M.³/day | Gpm | L./sec | Gps | Acre-ft./day | Cfs | M.³/sec. |
|---|---|---|---|---|---|---|---|---|---|
| Gallon per day......... | 1 | 0.134 | 0.00379 | $6.94 \times 10^{-4}$ | $4.38 \times 10^{-5}$ | $1.16 \times 10^{-5}$ | $3.07 \times 10^{-6}$ | $1.55 \times 10^{-6}$ | $4.38 \times 10^{-8}$ |
| Cubic foot per day........ | 7.48 | 1 | 0.0283 | $5.19 \times 10^{-3}$ | $3.28 \times 10^{-4}$ | $8.66 \times 10^{-5}$ | $2.30 \times 10^{-5}$ | $1.16 \times 10^{-5}$ | $3.28 \times 10^{-7}$ |
| Cubic meter per day...... | 264 | 35.3 | 1 | 0.183 | 0.0116 | $3.06 \times 10^{-3}$ | $8.11 \times 10^{-4}$ | $4.09 \times 10^{-4}$ | $1.16 \times 10^{-5}$ |
| Gallon per minute........ | 1,440 | 193 | 5.45 | 1 | 0.0631 | 0.0167 | $4.42 \times 10^{-3}$ | $2.23 \times 10^{-3}$ | $6.31 \times 10^{-5}$ |
| Liter per second......... | 22,800 | 3,050 | 86.4 | 15.8 | 1 | 0.264 | 0.0700 | 0.0353 | 0.001 |
| Gallon per second........ | 86,400 | 11,600 | 327 | 60 | 3.79 | 1 | 0.265 | 0.134 | $3.79 \times 10^{-3}$ |
| Acre-foot per day........ | $3.26 \times 10^{5}$ | 43,560 | 1,230 | 226 | 14.3 | 3.77 | 1 | 0.504 | 0.0143 |
| Cubic foot per second..... | $6.46 \times 10^{5}$ | 86,400 | 2,450 | 449 | 28.3 | 7.48 | 1.98 | 1 [b] | 0.0283 |
| Cubic meter per second.... | $2.28 \times 10^{7}$ | $3.05 \times 10^{6}$ | 86,400 | 15,800 | 1,000 | 264 | 70.0 | 35.3 | 1 |

[a] Exponential powers of 10 indicate the number of places to the right or to the left that the decimal point should be moved; e.g., $2.45 \times 10^{9} = 2,450,000,000$, or $4.09 \times 10^{-10} = 0.000000000409$.

Note: The value 1 cfs (cubic foot per second per square mile (csm) is equivalent to 0.03719 in. depth of runoff from one square mile over a period of one day.

[b] A flow of one cubic foot per second per square mile (csm) is equivalent to 0.03719 in. depth of runoff from one square mile over a period of one day.

Table 15. Volume Equivalents

| Unit | Cm.³ | In.³ | L. | Gal. | Ft.³ | Yd.³ | M.³ | Acre-ft. | Sfd |
|---|---|---|---|---|---|---|---|---|---|
| Cubic centimeter | 1 | 0.0610 | 0.001 | $2.64\times10^{-4}$ | $3.53\times10^{-5}$ | $1.31\times10^{-6}$ | $10^{-6}$ | $8.11\times10^{-10}$ | $4.09\times10^{-10}$ |
| Cubic inch | 16.4 | 1 | 0.0164 | 0.00433 | $5.79\times10^{-4}$ | $2.14\times10^{-5}$ | $1.64\times10^{-5}$ | $1.33\times10^{-8}$ | $6.70\times10^{-9}$ |
| Liter | 1,000 | 61.0 | 1 | 0.264 | 0.0353 | 0.00131 | 0.001 | $8.11\times10^{-7}$ | $4.09\times10^{-7}$ |
| Gallon | 3,790 | 231 | 3.78 | 1 | 0.134 | 0.00495 | 0.00379 | $3.07\times10^{-6}$ | $1.55\times10^{-6}$ |
| Cubic foot | 28,300 | 1,728 | 28.3 | 7.48 | 1 | 0.0370 | 0.0283 | $2.30\times10^{-5}$ | $1.16\times10^{-5}$ |
| Cubic yard | $7.65\times10^{5}$ | 46,656 | 765 | 202 | 27 | 1 | 0.765 | $6.20\times10^{-4}$ | $3.12\times10^{-4}$ |
| Cubic meter | $10^{6}$ | 61,000 | 1,000 | 264 | 35.3 | 1.31 | 1 | $8.11\times10^{-4}$ | $4.09\times10^{-4}$ |
| Acre-foot | $1.23\times10^{9}$ | $7.53\times10^{7}$ | $1.23\times10^{6}$ | $3.26\times10^{5}$ | 43,560 | 1,610 | 1,230 | 1 | 0.504 |
| Second-foot-day | $2.45\times10^{9}$ | $1.49\times10^{8}$ | $2.45\times10^{6}$ | $6.46\times10^{5}$ | 86,400 | 3,200 | 2,450 | 1.98 | 1 |

Note: Exponential powers of 10 indicate the number of places to the right or to the left that the decimal point should be moved; e.g., $2.45\times10^{9} = 2,450,000,000$, or $4.09\times10^{-10} = 0.000000000409$.

### Table 16.  Equivalents in Making Drainage Computations

| | |
|---|---|
| 1 acre | 43,560 sq. ft. |
| Water 1 in. deep on 1 acre | 3,630 cu. ft. |
| Water 1 in. deep on 1 sq. mi. | 2,323,200 cu. ft. |
| 1 cu. ft. of water weighs | 62.4 lb. |
| 1 cu. ft. of water | 7.48 gal. |
| 1 in. of water on 1 acre | 101.3 tons |
| Velocity of 1.467 ft. per sec. | 1 mph |
| Velocity of 1 ft. per sec. | 0.682 mi. |
| 1 cfs | 448.8 gal. per min. |

### Table 17.  Weight of Units of Volume of Water *

| Unit of volume | Weight of various units of volume | | | | |
|---|---|---|---|---|---|
| | Grains | Oz. | Lb. | Grams | Kilograms |
| 1 cubic centimeter.. | 15.4324 | 0.035274 | 0.002205 | 1 | 0.001 |
| 1 cubic inch........ | 252.893 | 0.578040 | 0.036128 | 16.3872 | 0.016387 |
| 1 pint (liquid)...... | — | 16.6909 | 1.04318 | 473,179 | 0.473179 |
| 1 quart (liquid)..... | — | 33.3818 | 2.08636 | 946,359 | 0.946359 |
| 1 liter ............ | — | 35.2749 | 2.20468 | 1.000 | 1 |
| 1 gallon ........... | — | 133.527 | 8.34545 | 3,785.43 | 3.78543 |

* A liter is equivalent to the volume occupied by the mass of a kilogram of pure water at its maximum density (4° C.), and under a pressure of 760 mm. It is actually equivalent in volume to 1.000027 cubic decimeters. In forestry measurements, however 1 liter is considered as weighing 1 kilogram and having a volume of 1 cubic decimeter

### Table 18.  Rainfall per Unit Area

| Rainfall | In cubic inches | In gallons | In cubic feet | In liters |
|---|---|---|---|---|
| 1 inch per acre........ | 6,272,640 | 27,154 | 3,630 | 102,788.0 |
| 1 millimeter per acre.. | 246,954 | 1,069 | 143 | 4,076.7 |

## Table 19. Hydroelectric Units

| | |
|---|---|
| 1 second-foot* falling  8.8 feet | = 1 horsepower (100% efficiency) |
| 1 second-foot* falling 11.8 feet | = 1 kilowatt    (100% efficiency) |
| 1 horsepower | = 550 foot-pounds per second |
| | = 0.707 British thermal unit (Btu.) per second |
| | = 76 kilogram-meters per second |
| | = 746 watts (0.746 kilowatt) |
| 1 kilowatt | = 1.341 horsepower |
| | = 737 foot-pounds per second |
| | = 102 kilogram-meters per second |
| | = 0.95 Btu. per second |
| | = 1,000 watts |
| 1,000 British thermal units | = 0.393 horsepower-hour |
| | = 0.293 kilowatt-hour |
| | = 252 kilogram-calories |
| 1 British thermal unit | = 777.5 foot-pounds |
| | = 107.5 kilogram-meters |
| 1 acre-foot* lifted (or falling) 1 foot | = 2,720,000 foot-pounds |
| | = 1.372 horsepower-hours |
| | = 1.025 kilowatt-hours |
| | = 3,496 British thermal units |
| 1 million gallons* lifted (or falling) 1 foot | = 8,350,000 foot-pounds |
| | = 4.22 horsepower-hours |
| | = 3.15 kilowatt-hours |
| | = 10,720 British thermal units |

* Of water.

# BIBLIOGRAPHY

AMERICAN SOCIETY OF CIVIL ENGINEERS. 1949. *Hydrology handbook.* Manual of engineering practice 28. Washington, D. C.

ARMCO DRAINAGE & METAL PRODUCTS CO. 1948. *Handbook of culverts and drainage practice.* Middletown, Ohio.

AYRES, Q. C. 1936. *Soil erosion and its control.* McGraw-Hill Book Co., Inc., New York.

BENNETT, H. H. 1939. *Soil conservation.* McGraw-Hill Book Co., Inc., New York.

COPELAND, E. B. 1932. Transpiration by chaparral and its effect upon the temperature of leaves. *Univ. of Calif. Press Publications in Botany* 17 (1). Berkeley.

ELLISON, W. D. 1948. Soil detachment by water in erosion processes. *Trans. Amer. Geophy. Union.*

FLINN, ALFRED D., *et al.* 1918. *Waterworks handbook.* McGraw-Hill Book Co., Inc., New York.

FOSTER, EDGAR E. 1948. *Rainfall and runoff.* The Macmillan Co., New York.

GAISER, RICHARD N. 1952. Root channels and roots in forest soils. *Soil Sci. Proc.* 16:62–65.

GATEWOOD, J. S., *et al.* 1950. Use of water by bottomland vegetation in lower Safford Valley, Arizona. *Geol. Survey Water Supply Paper 1103.* Government Printing Office, Washington, D. C.

HOOVER, M. D. 1945. Effect of removal of forest vegetation upon water yields. *Trans. Amer. Geophy. Union.*

HOOVER, M. D. 1949. Report of committee on evaporation and transpiration. *Trans. Amer. Geophy. Union.*

HUMPHREYS, C. E. 1929. *Physics of the air.* 2d ed. McGraw-Hill Book Co., Inc., New York.

IOWA ENGINEERING EXP. STA. 1935. Recommendations for the control and reclamation of gullies. *Bull. 121.*

KING, H. W. 1939. *Handbook of hydraulics.* 3d ed. McGraw-Hill Book Co., Inc., New York.

KITTREDGE, JOSEPH. 1948. *Forest influences.* McGraw-Hill Book Co., Inc., New York.

KRAMER, PAUL J. 1949. *Plant and soil water relationships.* McGraw-Hill Book Co., Inc., New York.

LINSLEY, RAY K., JR., et al. 1949. *Applied hydrology.* McGraw-Hill Book Co., Inc., New York.

LUTZ, H. J., and R. F. CHANDLER. 1946. *Forest soils.* John Wiley & Sons, Inc., New York.

MEINSER, OSCAR E. (ed.). 1942. *Physics of the earth—IX hydrology.* McGraw-Hill Book Co., Inc., New York.

NATURAL RESOURCES COMMITTEE. 1938. *Low dams.* Government Printing Office, Washington, D. C.

NORCROSS, T. W. 1936. *Handbook of erosion control engineering on the national forests.* Government Printing Office, Washington, D. C.

STEEL, ERNEST W. 1938. *Water supply and sewage.* McGraw-Hill Book Co., Inc., New York.

TVA, DIV. FORESTRY RELATIONS. 1939. *Manual for soil erosion control in the Tennessee Valley.* Norris, Tenn.

U. S. DEPT. AGR. 1935. Rainfall intensity—frequency data. *Misc. Pub. 204.*

U. S. DEPT. AGR. 1941. *Climate and man: Yearbook of agriculture.*

U. S. FOREST SERV. 1949. *Converting factors and tables of equivalents used in forestry.*

U. S. FOREST SERV. 1951. *Some fundamentals of plant-soil-water relations in watershed management.*

U. S. FOREST SERV., Region 4. 1935. *Recreation handbook.* Ogden, Utah.

U. S. FOREST SERV., Southeastern Forest Exp. Sta. 1947. *Water resource management in the southeastern states.*

WOLMAN, ABEL (ed.). 1925. *Water works practice; a manual.* American Water Works Assn., New York.

# FOREST RANGE MANAGEMENT

## CONTENTS

## CONTENTS—*Continued*

### Prescribed Burning in Southern Pine and Hardwood Forests in Relation to Grazing

# FOREST RANGE MANAGEMENT

## Forest Rangelands and Range Management

Since this section discusses care and management of rangelands, it is important, at the outset, to understand what constitutes "range," what is meant by "range management," and the meaning of a few other terms.

RANGELANDS. "Rangelands" are large, naturally vegetated, mostly unfenced areas located in regions of low rainfall. They are grazed by domestic livestock and game mammals.

There are 800 million acres of range lying between the eastern border of the Great Plains and the Pacific. Approximately 90 percent of this area is grazed by livestock. A large part of this land lies at relatively low elevations and is grazed for long seasons, sometimes all year. The high mountain range is of great importance to livestock growers for its summer grazing. Much of the latter is national forest land.

Problems of production on the western range differ markedly from those in the East and South. The main reasons are low and often poorly distributed precipitation, associated with shallow, readily erosive soils. The resultant sparse vegetation gives rise to many intricate problems of land use.

Some natural grazing lands in the Southern States are likewise referred to as range, but more commonly as "pasture." On all these wild lands livestock and game animals consume practically all the accessible palatable vegetation.

PASTURE. Areas spoken of as "pasture" in the West are usually fenced and have often been improved by reseeding, fertilizing, or irrigation. In the Midwest and East, pastures receive abundant rainfall. They may be permanent or temporary. Permanent pastures are seeded to perennial grasses; temporary pastures are planted to annual forage plants and are re-established each year. The term "pasture" is strictly applied to small, fenced grazing lands but is often used for any area where domestic livestock are grazed.

PASTURAGE. "Pasturage" and "forage" are synonymous terms. Pasturage embraces all vegetation consumed by grazing animals, including fruits and twigs of trees and shrubs. Palatable woody vegetation is called "browse," and feed consisting of berries, acorns, and the like is termed "mast."

RANGE MANAGEMENT. The improvement and maintenance of the vast and diversified rangelands is the function of range management. It is difficult to give a completely satisfactory definition of range management because it is based upon many unrelated fields and must be regarded both as a science and an art. In the following definition the overlapping disciplines have been kept in mind:

**Range management is the science and the art of planning and directing range use so as to obtain maximum livestock production consistent with conservation of the range resources.**

This definition, among other things, presupposes familiarity of the operator or manager with his range resource. It implies a sustained yield of livestock over a long period of time and suggests selection of the most suitable kind of livestock, recognition of proper seasons of grazing, and degree of range use. Sustained production can be obtained only by conservative use of the forage crop.

**GRAZING MANAGEMENT.** Grazing management has to do with such things as the proper distribution of animals over the range; with water development in the interest of the animals; and with their protection on the range from injury or death losses. Good grazing management is important, if not essential, to the application of good range management practices, but the term refers to the handling and care of the livestock on the range and should not be confused with range management, which is directly concerned with the welfare of the plant cover and the soil.

## Rangeland Soils

When we think of rangeland we usually picture it in terms of vegetation type and carrying capacity. However, the type of vegetation and its annual forage yield are the resultants of many ecological forces, the most important of which are climate, soil, and the landscape setting. The soil is a reservoir of both mineral nutrients and water. It is from this reservoir that the developing plant draws most of the elements essential for its vital processes. The soil therefore plays a profound even if not a fully appreciated role in the utilization or value of rangelands.

Soils, to soil scientists, have properties which readily permit the recognition of many different types. The vegetation is often even more discriminating than the soil scientists, and rather subtle changes in the soil sometimes have profound effects upon the plants. The soil has an important selective influence upon vegetation.

Soils are the product of the interaction of climate, parent rock, relief and aspect (landscape setting), and biotic influences, and their historical sequences. Because soils can be so variable in age, and because there are so many possible combinations of climate, parent rock, landscape, and other factors, there are almost unlimited numbers of types in nature.

The parent material on which a soil is formed may have a direct effect upon vegetation, aside from the indirect influences exerted through the nature of the soil profile. For example, grassland soils derived from serpentine rock are notably unproductive. Their sparse, stunted cover cannot reasonably be improved by seeding or other intensive practices. Other rock formations may yield selenium or molybdenum which are toxic to certain range plants and to livestock grazing upon them. On the other hand, deficiencies in certain regions of mineral nutrients, such as cobalt and phosphorus, necessitate special feeding of such nutrients and emphasize another important effect of the soil parent materials.

**CHARACTERISTICS OF GRASSLAND SOILS.** By studying the characteristics of grassland soils, which are most productive from the range standpoint, certain broad conclusions can be drawn. They generally have a dark color, ranging from brown to reddish brown to dark gray. The surface reaction may vary from slightly acid to calcareous, but the profile becomes more basic with depth and may be strongly calcareous in the subsoil. Textures may range from medium to heavy (e.g., loams, clay loam, clay), structure is normally granular, and the organic content and nutritive level are fairly high. The physical profiles may vary considerably, but normally more than 1½ ft. of soil material is present above the bedrock or pan, which may inhibit root penetration. Such soils are found in all temperate climates, under semiarid or humid moisture conditions.

Those characteristics of soils which favor a natural cover of mixed and tall grass also favor the production of cultivated crops. Consequently, today much of the more productive original native grassland is cropped, and the steeper, drier, rockier sites remain as forage-producing areas.

The less productive browse and browse-grass ranges are found mostly on the light-colored desert soils, which in general are calcareous, light in texture, lower in organic matter, and occur under arid conditions. Lithosols, which are characteristically shallow and stony and occur under a wide variety of climatic conditions, also provide limited amounts of forage in the form of browse and grass. An important group of rangeland soils with a high potential for improvement are those associated with chaparral in California.

## SOME SOIL CHARACTERISTICS RELATED TO RANGE MANAGEMENT.
The variability of soils in nature and the different uses to which they are subjected make generalizations about management difficult. It is generally advisable to consult a local soil expert about management problems. A few points can, however, be emphasized.

Depth of soil must be considered in management. Areas having less than a foot of effective root-feeding zone are prone to be droughty and incapable of furnishing much forage. Because of their limited water-holding capacity and the tendency to excessive runoff, shallow soils may also be subject to severe erosion, hence must be grazed conservatively at all times. Some good rangeland soils may be 3 or 4 ft. deep, or even deeper, but it does not follow that all deep soils will produce abundant forage. Timberland soils cleared for conversion to grass will sometimes be found to be too acid and too infertile to produce well without fertilization.

Different soils have different capacities for absorbing and retaining water, this depending primarily upon their texture and structure. Texture and structure also affect the erodibility of soils and the amount of stock trampling they can withstand when wet. Sandy or light-textured soils erode readily if on slopes, especially if the surface is underlain by a dense clay subsoil. Sandy soils, however, are not inclined to puddle when trampled while wet. The heavier-textured, more clayey soils are less subject to erosion but can be badly puddled if trampled while wet. Puddling results in loss of permeability to water and air, increasing erosion, and decreasing vigor of the vegetative cover.

Rangeland soils on steep slopes often withstand less grazing pressure than those on gentle slopes. Surface runoff and erosion increase greatly as slope increases. Productivity on steep slopes can be maintained only by conservative grazing use, thereby maintaining an adequate ground cover to prevent erosion and to encourage percolation of precipitation into the soil.

Some rangeland alluvial soils have alkali accumulations which greatly affect the nature of the plant cover. If treated with chemicals and flooded to leach out the alkali, such soils may be reclaimed to produce cultivated crops or forage. Some alkali land is subject to improvement merely by flooding. Grasses or legumes seeded on alkali soils must be selected with consideration for their capacity to tolerate the alkali concentrations in the soil to be seeded.

The above brief and generalized discussion of rangeland soils cannot be used as a guide for detailed treatment or management of specific soil units. However, it should serve to point out the basic fact that rangeland soils can differ greatly in their physical and chemical characteristics. Land managers must study and classify the soils they work with, as well as the overlying vegetation, if they are to achieve maximum production of usable forage.

## Range Vegetation of the Broad Forest Regions, by Types

The range region of the West lies essentially between elevations of 2,000 feet in the plains country and 10,000 feet or more in the mountains. The vast contrast in topography largely accounts for the wide differences in climate, soil, and vegetation. Most of this region is classified as semiarid to arid, but the mountains are more humid. The cover ranges from sparsely vegetated deserts in the Southwest to alpine glades, subalpine meadows, and coniferous forest in the Rockies and the West Coast mountains.

Most of the range region supports perennial drought-enduring bunchgrasses which differ in species and in height largely according to the amount of precipitation received. The difference in stature has led to the terms "tall grasses," such as big bluestem stands in the Midwest, "midgrasses," such as a cover dominated by wheatgrasses and prairie Junegrass where rainfall is somewhat less abundant, and "short grasses," such as areas of blue grama and buffalograss in the semiarid plains. Few woody plants are found in the tall grass and midgrass associations, but the drier regions, notably the Southwest desert, commonly support stands of brush, some species of which provide superior browse for livestock and game. Most grasslands are characterized by frequent summer rains. Regions having mild temperatures and abundant rainfall in winter, as on the Pacific Coast, support "winter annuals" composed of grasses and forbs which mature at the inception of the long hot, dry summer weather.

In the South grazing of forested and other lands is likewise important, particularly in the Coastal Plain which extends through the lower Southern States near the coast of the Carolinas to Texas. Although these lands are most valuable for timber production, grazing may furnish most of the income from clearcut areas for a few years while the timber crop is developing.

To make best use of the native range one should know what the principal forage plants are. Associated with the distinctive forest types (regions) are certain pasture and other plants common to each. Since these types are of special interest to this work, the more typical species are listed by types in Table 1, according to Forest Service administration regions.

## Range Ecological Techniques for Study of Vegetation

There are four basic quantitative measurements of range vegetation: **area, height, weight,** and **number.** All other measurements are either combinations of these, indices derived from them, or interpretations made from them.

**AREA.** Area measurement is used for basal area, foliar density, or crown cover of vegetation. The values are usually expressed in percent but may also be stated in absolute terms, e.g., square inches of leaf surface. Devices used to measure or estimate area fall into three geometric categories: the point, the line, and the quadrat, or combinations of these.

**The Point.** Theoretically, a point has no dimension and a unit of vegetation of that "size" is completely homogeneous. When a sharply pointed pin is let down through vegetation it either hits a plant or it does not and a record of an infinite number of such hits and misses gives the horizontal pattern of vegetation. The number of pins hitting vegetation divided by the total number of pins used gives the density of the vegetation or area covered by it in percent.

Instead of a single point, an apparatus consisting of a frame of 10 points is used for grassland vegetation surveys. Several values can be determined with it. **Foliar density** is obtained by summing the first hits of each of the pins and dividing by the total number of pins. **Overlapping density,** also called cover repetition, is obtained by summing all hits the points make as they pass downward through the foliage and dividing by the total number of pins that hit vegetation. **Basal area** is the sum of all final (ground level) hits on vegetation divided by total pins. Percentage of bare ground is the complement of foliar density; it can also be computed directly. Area covered by litter can be measured either as overlapping density or basal area. Species composition can be calculated if total hits are recorded by species. The total number of hits on one species divided by total hits on vegetation then gives the percentage composition by species.

**The Line.** The objectivity secured in recording the vegetation traversed by a line, as with the point, is highly reliable. The intercept of the base or the crown of plants (or the crown projected vertically to the line) is measured on the line in any standard unit of length. The sum of all the units of intercept divided by total length of line gives density or crown cover in percent.

The line intercept method can be adapted to most range vegetation types. It was originally used in desert grassland where perennial grasses dominate in low densities. A wire tautly stretched just above the soil surface crosses over and through the bases of grasses and forbs. The distance of intercept is tabulated by species. This gives basal area. For browse plants, the intercept by the canopy is measured.

Another device used is a pointed steel rod, 1 m. long, and graduated in 1 cm. intervals. The pointed end facilitates pushing the rod forward through dense vegetation without disturbing it. The plants touching on one side of the rod can be measured directly in millimeters.

The line-intercept method is especially useful for perennial bunchgrasses and for shrub types. Other methods are better for annuals, single-stemmed species, and sod-formers.

**The Quadrat.** A quadrat or plot is, in a sense, a blunt point. The vegetation within it is heterogeneous and the measurement of it therefore is subject to bias. Quadrats have various shapes and sizes and are used in many ways. The shape is generally a matter of convenience. Circular plots are easy to establish and mark. Two pins connected with a chain the length of the plot's radius is the only equipment needed; a single center stake marks the plot for relocation. Square plots are ideal where subdivision into quadrants is used for estimations or where uniformity within plots is desired. At least two stakes are needed for marking. As with the circle, all portions of the plot are equally visible. Rectangular plots are advantageous where there is a noticeable or suspected change of value, or gradient, in one or more factors. The longer dimension of the plot is oriented parallel to this gradient. Line and belt transects are in this category. Measurements are read in consecutive subdivisions as it is usually impossible to encompass the entire plot in one observation.

The size of the plot depends on the growth form of the vegetation to be studied and its homogeneity. Grasses are best sampled with small plots, say 1 square

Table 1. Range Vegetation of Forest

| TYPE | REGION 1<br>Montana and N. Idaho | REGION 2<br>Colorado and Wyoming | REGION 3<br>Arizona and New Mexico |
|---|---|---|---|
| Alpine and subalpine, including mountain meadows | Alders, bentgrasses, blueberries, bluebells, bluegrasses, bromes, groundsels, ledums,[b] menziesias,[b] mountain timothy, reedgrasses, sedges, trisetums, willows | Bluegrasses, cinquefoils,[b] mountain timothy, rushes, sedges, spike bentgrass, Thurber fescue, trisetums, tufted hairgrass, yarrow, willows | Cinquefoils,[b] bentgrasses, bluegrasses, fescues, hairgrasses, lupines, rushes, sedges, trisetums, tufted hairgrass, willows |
| Aspen | | Kentucky bluegrass, fescues, mountain brome, peavines, penstemons, roses, snowberry, vetches, wheatgrasses | Bluebells, bluegrasses, bromes, geraniums, needlegrasses, peavines, sedges, snowberry, vetches, willows |
| Dense timber, including lodgepole; grazed chiefly by game; forage inferior, limited | Arnica,[b] asters, bluegrasses, bromes, ceanothi, fescues, maples, lupines, reedgrasses, roses, sedges, serviceberry, snowberry, sweetroot, willows | Barberry,[b] cinquefoils,[b] groundsels, ligusticum, needlegrasses, sedges, timber danthonia | Bluegrasses, bromes, dogwood,[b] geraniums, lupines, peavines, reedgrasses, sedges, snowberry, vetches |
| Open conifer, mostly ponderosa pine | Elk sedge, fescues, Koeleria, needlegrasses, sagebrushes, Sandberg bluegrass, serviceberry, wheatgrasses, wild cherries | Bluegrasses, fescues, mountain muhly, needlegrasses, sedges, true mountain-mahogany, wheatgrasses | Bluegrasses, deer vetches, Fendler ceanothus, fescues, gramas, mountain-mahoganies, muhlys, pine dropseed, snowberry |
| Pinyon-juniper | | Arizona fescue, bitterbrush, blue grama, curly-mesquites, mountain-mahoganies, ricegrasses, sagebrushes, serviceberry | Bitterbrush, bluegrasses, bluestems, cliffrose, gramas, hilarias, mountain-mahoganies, needlegrasses, ricegrasses, sumacs, wheatgrasses |
| Chaparral and mountain brush | | Big sagebrush, blue grama, bluestem wheatgrass, fringed sagebrush, needle-and-thread, wild cherries, wheatgrasses | Barberry,[b] buckthorn, cliffrose, dropseeds, gramas, fourwing saltbush, hilarias, mountain-mahoganies, mutton bluegrass, silvertassel |
| Oak woodland | | Big sagebrush, bitterbrush, blue grama, bluestem wheatgrass, geraniums, Letterman needlegrass, mountain-mahoganies, wildryes | Arizona fescue, bluestems, cliffrose, gramas, lovegrasses, mountain-mahoganies, needlegrasses, penstemons |

[a] The names here used conform with those of *Standardized plant names* (Kelsey and Dayton).
[b] Of little or no forage value.
[c] Bluestems of the South furnish no less than half of the native forage in the pine and upland

## Regions Where Grazing Is Important[a]

| REGION 4<br>Utah, S. Idaho, West Wyoming, and Nevada | REGION 5<br>California | REGION 6<br>Oregon and Washington east of Cascades | REGION 8<br>The South; Coastal plain |
|---|---|---|---|
| Asters, bluebells, bluegrasses, currants, dandelion, fescues, fleabanes, geraniums, hairgrasses, mountain timothy, needlegrasses, penstemons, sedges, trisetums, wheatgrasses, willows, yarrow | Barleys, bentgrasses, bluegrasses, clovers, elders, hairgrasses, hawksbeards, hairgrasses, lupines, mannagrasses, melics, mountain timothy, peavines, sedges, trisetum, waterleafs, wheatgrasses, willows | Asters, bluegrasses, cinquefoils,[b] dandelions, erigerons,[b] green fescue, groundsels, hairgrasses, lupines, mountain timothy, needlegrasses, rushes, sedges, spike bentgrass, trisetums, tufted hairgrass, willows, yarrow | (Embracing most of longleaf-slash pine, shortleaf-loblolly-hardwood, and bottomland-hardwood forest types.)<br><br>Bluestems: little, pine hills, slender, yellow, others[c] |
| Bluebells, bluegrasses, bromes, cherry, coneflower, cowparsnip, currants, geraniums, paintedcups,[b] penstemons, sedges, snowberry, wheatgrasses, willows |  |  | Carpetgrass, common chokeberry, common lespedeza, cut-over muhly[d] |
|  |  |  | Dropseeds: blue, Curtiss[d] |
| Arnica,[b] barberry,[b] blueberry, bromes, currant, dogwood,[b] elderberry, lupines, ninebark, pachistima, reedgrasses, sedges, wheatgrasses, willows | Alder, bentgrasses, bluegrasses, asters, azaleas,[b] currant, dogwood,[b] hairgrasses, peavines, willows | Bentgrasses, elk sedge, hawksbeard, lupines, pinemat, manzanita, reedgrasses, snowberry, spirea | Gallberry,[b] greenbrier,[b] green sedge, hardwood sprouts, palmetto,[b] panicums, paspalums, pineland three-awn,[d] switch cane, wiregrasses[d] |
| Arnica,[b] balsamroot, bitterbrush, bluegrasses, bromes, fescues, Gambel oak, larkspurs, needlegrasses, monkshood,[b] penstemons, reedgrasses, snowberry, wheatgrasses | Bluegrasses, bitterbrush, deerbrush, dogwood,[b] fescues, larkspurs, fleabanes, lupines, manzanitas, needlegrasses, sedges, squirrel-tails | Arnica,[b] bentgrasses, bluegrasses, bitterbrush, elk sedge, fleabanes, Idaho fescue, Koeleria, lupines, reedgrasses, snowberry, wheatgrasses, yarrow |  |
| Balsamroot, big sagebrush, bitterbrush, bluegrasses, cliffrose, fescues, needlegrasses, paintedcups,[b] rabbit brushes, ricegrasses, squirrel-tails, wheatgrasses | Blue wildrye, bitterbrush, buckthorn, ceanothi, eriogonum,[b] fescues, hairgrasses, manzanitas, needlegrasses, rushes, sagebrushes, sedges, squirrel-tails | Balsam root, bearded bluebunch wheatgrass, big sagebrush, bitterbrush, cheatgrass, bromes, Idaho fescue, Sandberg bluegrass |  |
| Balsamroot, bluegrasses, bitterbrush, bromes, geraniums, maples, mountain-mahoganies, oaks, paintedcups,[b] sagebrushes, serviceberry, snowberry, wheatgrasses, wild cherries | Alfilaria, bromes, buckthorn, bur-clover, California scruboak, ceanothi, chamise, deathcamas,[b] deer vetch, foxtail fescue, fleabane, interior liveoak, manzanita, needlegrasses, nitgrass, Pacific poisonoak, yerbasanta,[b] many annual herbs<br>Alfilaria, blueoak, bromes, buckthorn, bur-clover, ceanothi, danthonias, deer vetches, digger pine,[b] foxtail fescue, interior liveoak, manzanitas, Pacific poisonoak, wildryes |  |  |

hardwood forest regions of Mississippi, Lousiana, eastern Texas, eastern Oklahoma, and Arkansas.
  [d] Wiregrass is a collective term for such fire-tolerant grasses as pineland three-awn, Curtiss dropseed, and cut-over muhly.

meter in size or less, whereas shrubs and trees are sampled with larger plots, 100 sq. ft. or more. If two growth forms are associated, e.g., grasses and shrubs, and it is desired to sample both together, it is considered more efficient to use two different quadrat sizes, so as not to oversample one group or undersample the other, but if only one is used, the larger growth form should determine the quadrat size.

The purpose of the study should decide what type of quadrat to use. For example, nonpermanent plots in which foliar density is estimated are useful where grasses are being evaluated for maximum cover for erosion control. On the other hand, foliar density is of little value in succession and trend studies where grazing is variable. Here, basal area is the most stable measure, fluctuating but little from a year of good rainfall to one of poor, from spring to autumn, or from grazed to ungrazed areas. Again, basal area is meaningless in annual grassland, as in California.

Table 2 presents various kinds of quadrats with comments on their usefulness. The table is helpful in selecting appropriate kinds of plots to fulfill particular objectives. However, it should be emphasized that the use of quadrats may not necessarily be better than points or lines in any one case; in the last analysis, selection of the kind of quadrat will depend in part upon the purpose of the study.

**Combination of Point and Quadrat.** The most effective compromise between a point and a plot has been found to be a circle ¾-in. in diameter. Recording of vegetation or of a species within a loop of this size combines the objectivity of the point method and the easy relocation of quadrats. Skillful placement of a number of such loops to satisfy sampling theory as well as practicability constitutes the first step of the "3-Step Method" for measuring trend and range condition.

**Combination of Line and Quadrat.** A belt or strip transect combines some of the properties of the line and the quadrat. The wider the transect, the more it assumes the characteristics and the drawbacks of the quadrat. The line-transect with a width of 1 cm. loses little in objectiveness from the line intercept method, while the addition of the second dimension permits recording attributes other than percentage density.

**HEIGHT.** Height or length measurements indicate growth, utilization, availability, and, in combination with area, the volume of vegetation. Depending upon the purpose of the study, either maximum, minimum, or average heights can be taken. Of the three, the latter is the most difficult to obtain without bias. A good way to obtain average height would be to record the height of the first hit of a number of randomly placed pins of a point frame. Maximum heights are obtained by measuring the tallest leaders, culms, or leaf blades of a random sample of plants. Variations of this system may be devised, such as averaging the four tallest of each plant. In shrubby vegetation where a browse line exists, knowledge of mean minimum heights may be of value. For utilization studies, the difference between average heights before and after grazing is a better value than is the difference between maximum heights.

Volume is an index derived from area and height measurements. As such, it can be no more accurately obtained than either area or height. This three-dimensional expression of abundance is rarely used in range work. However, peripheral surface—a function of volume—is a valuable datum, especially in surveys dealing with the availability of browse. Here, hedging or form classes modify the area × height values.

Table 2. Advantages and Limitations of Plots Commonly Used in the Study of Range Vegetation

| Type or purpose of study | Kind of quadrat | Advantages and limitations |
| --- | --- | --- |
| Succession and trend | Permanent quadrats | The detail and amount of time spent on each plot often justify selection rather than randomization. Fundamental principles, such as what happens to certain species under a particular set of environmental conditions, may be the primary objective. Permanent plots are valuable in research work, less so for general surveys. |
| Detail for individual plants | Chart quadrats | Useful in bunchgrass and sod grass vegetation. Charting can be done with pantograph or free-hand on coordinate paper. |
| Aggregation and competition | Basal area plots | Basal area of all plants on plots measured with listing ruler; with less accuracy, basal area is estimated by subdivisions and then averaged for the whole plot. |
| Invasion and establishment | Denuded quadrats | Measurements can be made by any of above methods. |
| Condition (status quo) | Randomized plots | For vegetation surveys, sampling with randomized (or sometimes systematically placed) plots, in ample number, gives the best picture of the range as a whole. The results can be used for description or for comparison. Thus, such plots can also be used for succession and trend studies if the range is resampled with an adequate number of plots. |
| Basal area Foliar density Species composition | Small plots from 1 sq. ft. to 1 square meter in size | Measurements are actually ocular estimates with varying degrees of accuracy. In general, smaller plots can be estimated most accurately, but then a larger number of plots is needed. Such plots have been used for type mapping, range condition surveys, assessing factors correlated with density but not directly measurable, and for measuring response to experimental treatments. |
| Vegetation survey | Point-observation-plot | Circular plots of 100 sq. ft. are laid out at predetermined intervals. The technician figuratively places all vegetation together compactly in a segment of the circle and estimates the total area. This is directly a percentage figure. Errors in estimating may be considerable and these are more apt to be cumulative than compensatory. |
| Reconnaissance survey | Entire vegetation type is a single plot | A single estimate gives no measure of variance, therefore no measure of reliability. Although this method has been little used in recent years, a quick appraisal by an experienced estimator may sometimes be justified. A single good estimate is better than a large number of biased estimates based on smaller plots. |

**WEIGHT.** One of the best measures of forage production is obtained by clipping and weighing samples of vegetation. The advantages are: (1) weight combines all the other measurements into one value which can be measured as accurately as the reading of an analytical balance; (2) it can represent the exact portion taken by a grazing animal without the need of questionable conversion factors to estimate the same thing from area and height data; and (3) it gives reasonably accurate information on species composition if careful hand separations are made.

Disadvantages are: (1) time and equipment necessary are excessive compared to other measurements; (2) clipping affects the physiology of the plants so that the plot cannot be reclipped in the sense of a repeated reading; (3) hand separations into species or groups are laborious, and when green-weight/dry-weight ratios are to be determined, the interval of time needed to segregate the clipped plants introduces errors of considerable magnitude. Generally, only small subsamples of the clipped material are separated by hand and the proportions are applied to the whole sample.

The various sizes and shapes of clip plots used in sampling for weight have about the same advantages and disadvantages as those mentioned for density plots. Determinations of forage yield are frequently made by estimating the green or dry weight of the plant cover, in total or by species, on a number of plots. A few of the plots are actually clipped and weighed at periodic intervals to serve as a check on the estimates.

**NUMBER.** Plots used to obtain data on plant numbers are called census plots. No consideration is given to the difference in size of individual plants. With some species, such as crown-sprouting shrubs, sod grasses, or stoloniferous plants, a single plant or plant unit must be arbitrarily defined. There are three kinds of census plots, each used for a specific purpose: the list quadrat, the stocked quadrat, and the frequency-index quadrat.

The list quadrat method consists of counting the number of stems or plants of each species. It is useful in evaluating seedling stands and in annual grassland or vegetation where size classes and forms have little variability. Mortality rates can be determined with list quadrats.

The stocked quadrat is an adaptation of the list method, but instead of actual enumeration, the plant species are expressed in qualitative terms. For example, in evaluating success of seedling establishment, 10 or more seedlings per square yard may be called good stocking, 5–10 fair, and less than 5 poor. Other variations of this method exist.

The frequency-index quadrat records the presence of species on plots. Data from such quadrats can be used to describe the effects of grazing on native plant populations. The method is no longer popular, however, especially since the results are influenced by the size of plot and because the data obtained are semi-qualitative.

A number of different characteristics of range vegetation can be derived from these basic measurements. Vigor, preference, utilization, proper use factor, plant succession and degeneration, and range indicators are a few examples. A method for determining vigor is to measure the maximum leaf length of each of 50 random plants of a species within a plot. Utilization studies depend upon the measurements of changes in weight or height of forage before and after grazing. Preference is based on differential utilization by species while use factor is an index derived from measuring total annual yield and yearly consumption. Evidence of plant succession or degeneration is obtained when the basal area of certain species increases or decreases or when the frequency-index of certain species changes. Information on indicator plants is also taken from frequency data.

**CONCEPTS OF SAMPLING.** The man who samples range vegetation must not only be equipped with the various kinds of apparatus needed to delineate plots but he must know the fundamentals of sampling procedure. The concept of randomness, the meaning of bias, the difference between an estimate and a measurement and between accuracy and precision are as basic to sampling as the physical material that is being sampled. Several books discuss this level of the vast subject of statistics. Briefly, good sampling procedure is based on the following concepts:

If every square meter (or other plot size) of a plant association has an equal chance of being drawn into the sample, randomness has been achieved. Non-randomness is bias. Selection other than by chance need not necessarily be in one direction to introduce bias into a sample.

Ocular estimates are "measurements" made without the aid of an instrument. On the other hand, measurements, such as might be made with a planimeter, calipers, or balance, are "estimates" with great accuracy. Accuracy means how close to the true value a given estimate or measurement comes. Precision means the frequency in which a given measured value is obtained, whether it is accurate or not. Accuracy is obtained through reading a plot objectively; precision is obtained by reading a large number of plots. Both qualities are requisite of a good sample.

Adequacy of plot numbers can be obtained by formulas especially constructed for each situation. The procedure is too long and intricate to develop here but is presented in an easily comprehensible manner in most standard texts.

## Range Surveys

The main purpose of a range survey is to assemble all important facts needed for preparing range management plans for the area surveyed. Range surveys are the systematic inventory and analysis of all factors relating to the use of a range that includes drafting a plan to manage the forage resource. Range surveys inventory the amount and the forage value of vegetation present on the range and furnish the basis to determine how to obtain best use of the forage. They obtain data needed to correlate use of the range forage with the management of other related resources, plan improved practices that can be effected with a definite action program, and properly emphasize problem areas. Range survey data shown in place on maps are guides to the number of livestock that should be permitted to graze, to periods of time that should be spent in range units, to pounds of salt that should be distributed at specific locations, to needs for water development, and to many other essentials for sound range management. Range survey maps, together with range management plans, aid in correcting specific problems and in keeping account of the progress made in their solution.

Range surveys generally consist of an assembly of three kinds of data:

1. Dependable maps of the range types and subtypes and such culture as might influence their grazing values or its management.
2. Reliable estimates of the kind, condition, and distribution of the range vegetation and soil stability.
3. Detailed descriptions of the problems in range livestock management on the area supplemental with proposals for corrective measures.

Weakness in any one of these phases lessens the usefulness of the survey as an aid in accomplishing the objective of range management.

All three kinds of data generally are obtained on a single trip through the range, the field examiner drawing the field map, making the forage estimates, and evaluating management problems as he progresses. These are usually supplemented from existing records and knowledge of the history of the range and its use.

**MAPPING.** Range survey maps show in place such features as vegetation types and subtypes; acreage and relative grazing capacity of subtypes; problem areas such as location and extent of accelerated erosion, rodent infestations, areas in need of reseeding, and concentrations of poisonous plants; important topographic features, especially those that will affect movement of livestock; watering places, dependability of water supply and opportunities for water development; existing culture influencing management such as roads, trails, fences, corrals, buildings, telephone lines, etc.; and land ownership, if important to range management. Such maps usually are on a scale of 2 in. to the mi. but may be of any scale. Map legends are somewhat standardized, but vary with agencies. A sample legend is shown in Fig. 1.

## RANGE INVENTORY LEGEND

| | EXISTING | PROPOSED |
|---|---|---|
| ALLOTMENT BOUNDARY | | |
| MANAGEMENT UNIT BOUNDARY | | |
| TRAIL | | |
| LAND SURVEY CORNER FOUND | | |
| SPRING | | |
| DITCH | | |
| WATER DEVELOPMENT | | |
| RESERVOIR, or STOCK TANK | | |
| DAM | | |
| WELL | | |
| FENCE | | |
| FENCE (Abandoned) | | |
| CORRAL | | |
| SALT GROUND | | |
| PROBLEM AREA; RESEEDING, ETC. | | |
| STOCK DRIVEWAY | BROWN | BROWN |
| SHEEP CAMP | | |
| RANGE HEADQUARTERS | | |
| HOUSE | | |
| WINDMILL | | |
| NATURAL BARRIER | | |
| LAMBING GROUNDS | | |

VEGETATION TYPE & SYMBOL — E-5 / 6 — EXAMINER'S INITIAL - WRITEUP NO. / TYPE NO. OR DESIGNATION / DENSITY - FORAGE ACRE FACTOR

RANGE INVENTORY DATA — SURFACE ACRES — ANIMAL MONTHS / FORAGE ACRES MEADOW - FORAGE ACRES OTHER

Fig. 1. Sample legend for range survey maps.

**Table 3. Standard Forage Types and the Standardized System of Coloring for Range Maps**

| No. | Type [a] | Color [b] | Brief description |
|---|---|---|---|
| 1 | Grassland<br>(S) Short grass<br>(T) Tall grass | Light Yellow<br>(Mongol 817)<br>Dark Yellow<br>(Mongol 867) | Perennial grasses predominate and determine the aspect; weeds and browse may be present. Examples: grama-buffalo-grass, bunchgrass, and bluestem. |
| 2 | Meadow | Cadmium Orange<br>(Mongol 862) | Sedges, rushes, and mesic grasses predominate; areas usually remain moist. |
| 3 | Perennial forb | Lake Red<br>(Mongol 866) | Untimbered areas where perennial weeds predominate; more or less temporary. |
| 4 | Sagebrush | Stone Brown<br>(Mongol 893) | Untimbered lands where sagebrush and similar appearing shrubs predominate. |
| 5 | Browse-shrub | Olive Green<br>(Mongol 888) | Browse, except sagebrush, predominate; usually a transition zone like chaparral. |
| 6 | Conifer | Dark Green<br>(Mongol 858) | Coniferous timber dominates, but grasses, forbs, and browse may be present. |
| 7 | Waste | Blue Green<br>(Mongol 898) | Includes areas uneconomical for grazing such as dense timber, sparse forage, and inaccessibility. |
| 8 | Barren | Blank | Includes areas lacking natural vegetation. |
| 9 | Pinyon-juniper | Light Green<br>(Mongol 848) | Includes pinyon-juniper, juniper, and digger pine. |
| 10 | Broadleaf trees | Pink<br>(Mongol 846) | Includes all ranges in deciduous timber. |
| 11 | Creosote | Bottle Green<br>(Mongol 855) | Includes all areas where creosote bush (*Covillea*) predominates. |
| 12 | Mesquite | Yellow Earth<br>(Mongol 853) | Includes areas where mesquite (*Prosopis*) constitutes the predominant vegetation. |
| 13 | Saltbush | Slate<br>(Mongol 819) | Saltbush (*Atriplex*) family dominates and/or gives the characteristic aspect. |
| 14 | Greasewood | Royal Purple<br>(Mongol 864) | Greasewood (*Sarcobatus*) predominates or gives the characteristic aspect. |
| 15 | Winterfat | Light Tan<br>(Mongol 813) | Winterfat (*Eurotia*) predominates or gives the characteristic aspect. |
| 16 | Desert shrub | Dark Tan<br>(Mongol 863) | Areas where desert shrubs, except for the above types, predominate to give the characteristic aspect. Example: Acacia. |
| 17 | Half shrub | Wistaria<br>(Mongol 844) | Areas of semiwoody perennials of low stature such as *Aplopappus* and *Gutierrezia* dominate. |
| 18 | Annuals (weeds or grasses) | Red Terra Cotta<br>(Mongol 876) | Includes areas in which annual weeds or grasses dominate. Examples: Downy chess, and Russian thistle. |
|  | Abandoned lands |  | Abandoned lands should be classified according to aspect. |

[a] Grazing types, designated according to aspect, have no ecological basis, but are determined rather by the dominating species, or what appears to be dominating.
[b] As formulated by the Inter-Agency Range Survey Committee and adopted by the Western Range Survey Conference, April 24, 1937.

The most commonly used methods of mapping are the aerial photographic method, the gridiron method, and the topographic method. Of the three methods, the aerial photographic method is preferred because it facilitates field examination and results in the most reliable maps. Their use is recommended whenever aerial photographs and planimetric base maps are available. (See pages 19·1–2 for information concerning existing photography.)

Reasonably accurate planimetric base maps on which to present the location and extent of forage types, improvements, and management features are pre-requisite to any range survey. Ordinarily such maps are available from various agencies dealing with land management problems.

Standard forage or range types adopted for use by the Forest Service, Soil Conservation Service, Bureau of Land Management, and Bureau of Indian Affairs in 1937 are in general use (instructions for range surveys as formulated by the Inter-Agency Range Survey Committee and adopted by the Western Range Survey Conference, April 24, 1937). These types are usually shown by standard colors on range survey maps. The standard types and colors used to identify them are shown in Table 3.

Types are divided into subtypes on the basis of major differences in plant composition, plant density, and range condition. Types and subtypes are ordinarily drawn to a minimum size of 10 acres unless they are desired for identification features on the final map. High grazing capacity meadows are ordinarily drawn to 5 acres.

The three methods of mapping are described below, listing equipment and some of the field techniques.

**Aerial Photographic Method.** (For general information on the use of aerial photographs refer to Section 19, Aerial Photography.) When mapping with aerial photographs the examiner usually uses aerial photographs as the field work map and draws most of the needed information directly on each photograph in the field (Fig. 2). The vegetation types and subtype boundaries, General Land Office corners, streams, springs, roads, and all other natural and cultural features needed from the survey are shown. These are all transferred to a planimetric base map when preparing the final map.

Equipment and materials needed for using the aerial photographic method of survey are as follows:

1. Aerial photographs of the area to be surveyed. (Photographs to the scale of 1:24,000 or 3.16 in. to the mile are most widely used.)
2. Planimetric base maps showing cultural, drainage, topography, General Land Office lines, and other features.
3. Acetate base overlays to fit aerial photographs and frosted on one side (optional if it is desired to conserve photographs).
4. Field stereoscope for studying aerial photographs.
5. Compass and protractor, Abney level, rule and straight edge, and other surveying equipment and materials needed in compass and pacing surveying, determining slopes, etc.
6. Field notebook or clip board for carrying field sheets.
7. Colored pencils, inks, and other mapping materials.

The following techniques have proved helpful in conducting field work when using aerial photographs.

1. Before initiating field work, draw in as much as possible the type boundaries on the field photographs, using a stereoscope. These should be revised in the field.
2. Map on the central portion of each photograph, avoiding the distorted margins.

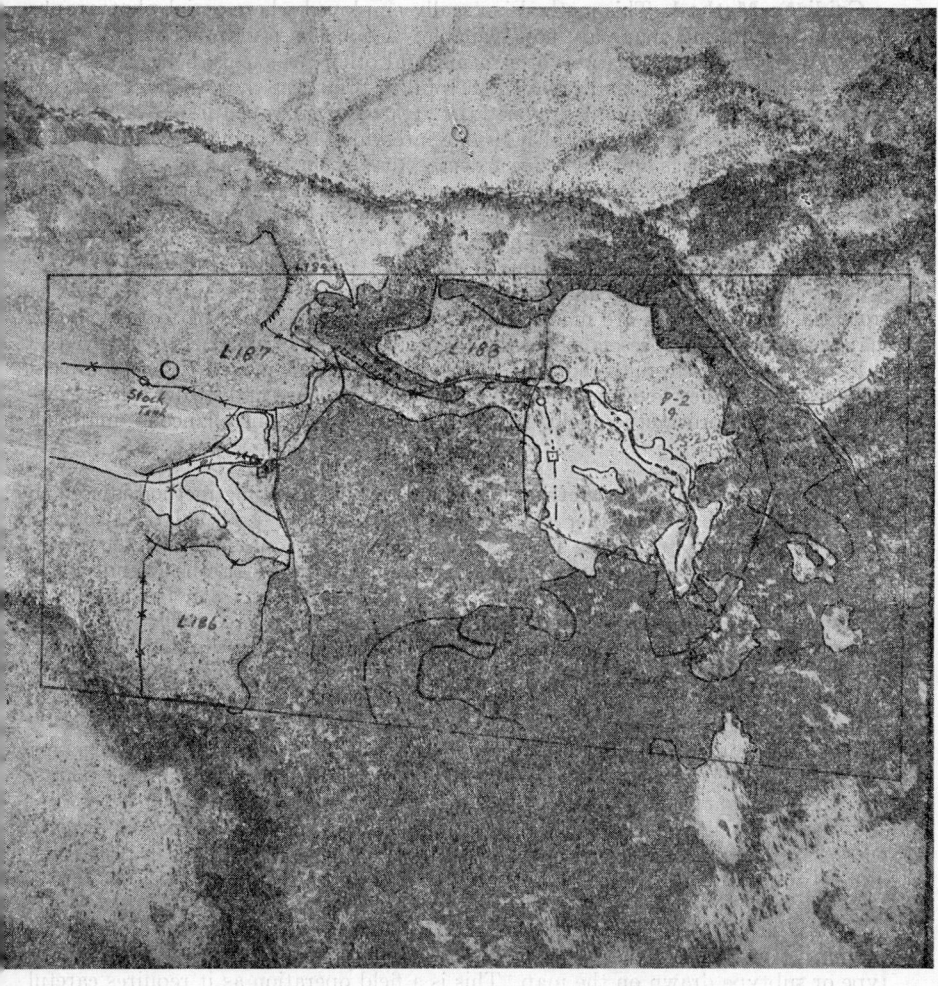

**Fig. 2. Aerial photograph as a field work map for range surveys.**

3. If possible, map consecutively on contiguous photographs and be sure all mapping is completed on the photograph before leaving an area. Be sure type and subtype lines, etc. on adjacent photographs are "jibed."

4. Location of stock watering places, section corners, study plots, etc. can be recorded on the photographs by pricking a small hole in the photograph with a needle or pin and noting on the back of the photograph. This procedure gives a permanent mark yet does not obscure adjacent features.

The intensity of survey usually desired by this method requires that the examiner go into each type or subtype sufficiently to obtain a good look at all grazing areas.

**Gridiron Method.** This method is usually employed where aerial photographs or good topographic maps are not available. A good base map showing General Land Office land lines, locations of streams, and other principal physical features, while not absolutely necessary, is very helpful in preparing more reliable maps.

The general procedure is to traverse the area being surveyed in a grid manner, the traverse lines being spaced at half-mile intervals (1-mi. intervals for extensive surveys). Mapping is done by using features already on the base map and by use of mapping control carried forward by compass and pacing. Section corners and quarter-section corners or any other previously established land markers are used as control points for mapping. The examiner draws boundaries between types and subtypes and maps the locations of all essential natural and cultural features for a distance of one-fourth mile on both sides of the traverse line. Sufficient offsets from the traverse lines are made as needed to check locations of features being mapped and to see representative samples of all the range area being surveyed.

Equipment and supplies required for using this mapping method are compass, tally register, Abney level, aneroid barometer, reliable base maps, rule for measuring distances, protractor, field notebook, maps, and miscellaneous mapping supplies.

**Topographic Mapping Method.** The topographic mapping method is used to a lesser extent than the other two procedures described. It is adapted for use where good topographic base maps are available, the topography is too rough for easy use of the gridiron procedure, and where aerial photographs are not available. The method is best adapted to terrain where mapping can be done from vantage points of good visibility and is not adapted to relatively level, flat topography. It is most widely used where range types are limited in extent, isolated, or of low value. Materials and equipment required for this method are the same as for the gridiron method, except that in addition a reliable topographic base map is required.

To use this procedure the field examiner works his way over the range, checking locations either by use of the map, by rough triangulation on prominent points, compass and pacing, or by other means. Boundaries of vegetation types and subtypes and cultural and natural features of importance are recorded directly on the topographic base map in relation to the topography. The usual survey intensity required is at least one visit to each vegetative subtype.

**FORAGE INVENTORY METHODS.** The forage inventory consists of estimating in the field the forage value of the vegetation within each vegetation type or subtype drawn on the map. This is a field operation as it requires careful examination of each separate area. Two groups of methods are in common use: (1) methods based on forage acre estimates and (2) methods based on range condition classification.

**Forage Acre Methods.** In forage acre methods the forage estimate is based upon field estimates of average density and composition of the vegetation in each subtype. These estimates are used as a basis for computing forage acres which in turn are an index to grazing capacity. There are two common methods of estimating plant density and composition in use in range surveys—the reconnaissance and the square-foot density methods.

**The Reconnaissance Method.** The procedure in estimating average density and composition of vegetation within a subtype with the reconnaissance method is accomplished by the examiner going far enough into the subtype until he is satisfied that he is acquainted with the vegetation on it. He then selects a small, definitely bounded area which he considers to be typical of the subtype. On this area he estimates the average density (percentage of ground covered by vegetation) and checks this by estimating the percentage of bare ground apparent. The two estimates should equal 100 percent. Such estimates are usually to the nearest 5 or 10 percent and are recorded as decimals. Having determined the total density of all vegetation, he then obtains values for species by estimating the percentage each comprises of the density. These species estimates, known as percentage composition, should total 100 percent. He then proceeds through the type, mentally evaluating density and composition values as he travels. If important changes in density or percentage composition occur, the examiner checks them against his original write-up and revises it accordingly. If changes in density and composition are major, he usually selects another typical area and makes a new estimate, which may be substituted for the first or averaged with it. Seldom are more than two complete write-ups of typical areas made to obtain an average for a subtype with this method. More frequently the first write-up is revised in the light of floristic changes which are encountered later within the subtype as the work proceeds.

The usual practice is to include all plant species which are important because of abundance, palatability, poisonous or noxious properties, or because of their value as indicators of range condition and trend. Plant species that are of less than 1 percent composition and that are not significant to range management often are not considered.

Detail records taken as well as computations made from them are shown on Form 764a (Fig. 3). In the example, the average density and average percent of weeds, of grasses and grasslike plants, and of shrubs for the subtype were obtained by averaging four separate estimates made on the subtype as recorded in the lower left of the form. The percent composition by individual species of each group was then obtained by dividing the total percent composition of each group among the species proportional to their occurrence.

**The Square-Foot Density Method.** When estimating plant densities of a subtype by the square-foot density method, the examiner establishes a number of small plots at specified intervals and limits his estimates to these plots. The plots are usually circular in shape and 100 sq. ft. in area. When the examiner is mapping subtypes with the aid of aerial photographs or an accurate topographic map on an intensive survey, three to six plots are generally established in subtypes smaller than 20 acres, five to ten plots in subtypes larger than 20 but smaller than 80 acres, and ten to twenty plots in subtypes ranging from 80 to 640 acres. If the examiner is using the "strip survey" method, 20 plots per sq. mi. are usually taken, spaced at intervals of 8 chains (528 ft.) on two parallel lines that are ½ mi. apart.

In estimating density the examiner counts the square feet of ground covered by foliage within the plot, using a square frame of 1-ft. dimensions as a guide to his estimate. Since the plot area is 100 sq. ft., 1 sq. ft. of vegetation is equivalent to a density of 1 percent. Density estimates are made for each species which exhibits a foliage cover of 0.5 sq. ft. (0.5 percent density) or more. The density of all vegetation on the plot is obtained by adding these figures. Averaging values obtained from all plots taken within a subtype gives the density of vegetation and of each species in that subtype.

Vegetation records taken are shown in Fig. 4.

## RANGE INVENTORY WRITE-UP SHEET
### Reconnaissance Method

National forest ___Modoc - Surprise Valley R.D.___　　　Write-up No. ___S-151___

Examiner ___Harry E. Shaw___　　　Date ___9-15-___　　　Photo No. ___DEM 31-2___

Section ___35___　　　Township ___38N___　　　Range ___16E___　−　___M.D.M.___
(Use above 3 items when legal subdivision desired)

Type designation ___4 Atr-Fid-Asp___　　Density ___.40___

Range condition:　　　　　　　　　　　　　　　Type forage value factor ___32.6___

___High Fair (Good 50%, Fair 30%, Poor 20%)___ Gross F. A. factor for C & H ___.1304___
(Very poor, poor, fair, good, excellent; percent of type in each class)

　　　　　　　　　　　　　　　　　　　　　for S & G _____

Range trend ___Up___
(Up, down, stationary)

Utilization Adjustments: Slope, ___-___%; Unstable soils, ___10___%; Erosion, ___-___%; Timber, ___5___

Lack of water ___-___%; ___-___, ___-___%; _____, ___-___%; Total adjustment, ___15___

Current utilization ___30___%　　　Net F. A. factor ___.1108___

Site productiveness ___Average___　　　F. A. requirement ___.6___
(Low, average, high)

　　　　　　　　　　　　　Surface acres per ⎰ C. M. ___5.4___
　　　　　　　　　　　　　　　　　　　　　⎱ S. M. ___-___

Plant vigor ___Fair___
(Poor, fair, good)

### PRINCIPAL PLANT SPECIES

| WEEDS<br>___15___ percent | Percent composition by species | Plant use factor | Forage value factor | GRASSES AND GRASSLIKE PLANTS<br>___40___ percent | Percent composition by species | Plant use factor | Forage value factor | SHRUBS<br>___45___ percent | Percent composition by species | Plant use factor | Forage value factor |
|---|---|---|---|---|---|---|---|---|---|---|---|
| Wmo | 6 | 10 | .6 | Fid | 23 | 80 | 18.4 | Atr | 35 | 0 | |
| Lca | 5 | 40 | 2.0 | Asp | 7 | 70 | 4.9 | Sal | 5 | 20 | |
| Ala | 2 | 20 | .4 | Shy | 5 | 50 | 2.5 | Cle | 3 | 10 | |
| SEN | 2 | 30 | .6 | Pse | 3 | 30 | .9 | Cna | 2 | 0 | |
| | | | ——<br>3.6 | Scl | 2 | 50 | 1.0 | | | | |
| | | | | | | | ——<br>27.7 | | | | |

| | D | W | G | S | | | | | | | |
|---|---|---|---|---|---|---|---|---|---|---|---|
| | 45 | 10 | 45 | 45 | | | | 3.6 | .326 × 40 = .130 | | |
| | 40 | 13 | 40 | 47 | | | | 27.7 | = F.A. | | |
| | 35 | 20 | 45 | 35 | | | | 1.3 | | | |
| | 40 | 17 | 30 | 53 | | | | 32.6 = F.V. | | | |
| T= | 160 | 60 | 160 | 180 | | | | | | | |
| Av.= | .40 | 15 | 40 | 45 | | | | | | | |
| TOTAL | | x x x | | | | | x x x | | | x x x | |

Form 764a
(Rev. June 1949)　　　　　　　　(OVER)　　　　　　　16—12890

Fig. 3A. Detailed record and computations form for reconnaissance method of range forage inventory (front).

## TYPE COMMENTS

graphy *Gradual slopes with occasional rock outcrops and*
(Rock outcrops, rugged, rolling, etc.)
*"islands" of White Fir.*

ge improvements needed ... *None*

er *Scattered White Fir - Non-commercial* ............
(Species) (Age) (Size class) (Condition) (Reproduction)

ering places *Springs on North and West edges of type.*
(Kind—Stream, lake, spring, tank, etc.) (Distance of type from water)
*Permanent* — *Adequate*
(Permanent—temporary) (Adequacy)

nous plants ..... *None* — —
(Kinds) (Recommendations)

ous range plants ....... *None.* — —
(Species) (Abundance—Sparse, colonies, widely distributed)

nts ...... *Scarce* — —
(Species and abundance) (Evidence of damage) (Control recommended)

## SOIL AND SOIL EROSION

(Check one item in each column. Check two items under "Gully" if gullies are present.)

| RENT MATERIAL | CLASS | TOP SOIL DEPTH | TEXTURE | LITTER AND MULCH | SLOPE | EROSION | | |
|---|---|---|---|---|---|---|---|---|
| | | | | | | WIND | WATER | |
| | | | | | | | Sheet | Gully |
| | | (Inches) | | (Percent) | (Percent) | | | |
| nitic | | 0–⑥ ✓ | Light | 0–10 | 0–5 | None | None | None ✓ |
| as ✓ | Residual | | | 11–20 ✓ | 6–10 | Class I ✓ | 10% of area Class I | Occasion-al |
| dstones | | 7–13 | Medium ✓ | 21–40 | 11–20 ✓ | | | Frequent |
| les | Trans-ported | 14–24 | Heavy | 41–60 | 21–40 | Class II | Class II | Shallow |
| estones | | | ✓ | | 41–60 | | | |
| cial deposits | | Over 24 | Stony | Over 60 | Over 60 | Class III | Class III | Deep |

**Explanation of soil and erosion terms.**—Residual soils are found on the rock masses from which they e derived; transported soils have been moved to new sites by water, gravity, wind, etc. Texture: Light soils ade sands and sandy loams; medium soils include loams and silt loams; heavy soils include the clay loams, clays, and the clays. Degree of erosion: Class I—Soil movement and loss of soil noticeable; slight shoe-g gullying; plant roots occasionally exposed; Class II—Very evident sheet erosion; plant roots definitely sed; erosion scars present; erosion pavement forming in gravelly soil; gullies rapidly forming; Class III—id land destruction; topsoil all removed or nearly so; conspicuous erosion scars; frequent and deep gullies; ies: "Deep" is where gully has cut into subsoil. Gullies are "occasional" when 50% or less of the drain-ways are gullied.

ies originating ...... *None.* — —
(Outside type—where)

se of erosion *erosion - in shallow - soil upland.* Active or healing ... *Static*
*Slight wind and* (In type) *sheet* *+ flats.*

itional type comments *Allotment temporarily being managed as a sheep unit -*
*grasses are underutilized and on the increase.*

NOTE.—The information contained on this sheet is primarily a forage inventory. When and if further data are secured on timber, r, soils, erosion, wildlife, etc., by specialists along these lines, such information should be further correlated to best serve range agement needs.

U. S. GOVERNMENT PRINTING OFFICE 16—12890-1

Fig. 3B. Detailed record and computations form for reconnaissance method of range forage inventory (back).

FORM 764B
Revised March 1, 1939

## RANGE SURVEY WRITE-UP SHEET
### SQUARE FOOT DENSITY METHOD

Project _Range Inventory - Modoc N.F._     Type No. _S-151_

Examiner _Harry Shaw_     Transect No. _1_

Type _4 Atr - Fid - Asp_     Date _9-15- —_

Surface Acres _-_     Location _S35, T 38N, R16E - DEM 31-_
       S., T. & R. -- Aerial Photo No.

Forage Acres _-_     _Surprise Valley Ranger Dist._
       _Hot Mt. allotment._

F. A. Requirement _.6_ For _C&H_     Grazing Capacity — Months _____ For _____
      C&H or S&G                                    C&H or S

Utilization Cuts:— Slope _-_ % Timber _5_ % Rocks _-_ % Lack of Water _-_ % Erosion _-_ %

          Unstable Soils _10_ % Total Cut _15_ % Net Forage Factor _-_

                                                    Net Forage Factor _.1122_

### SPECIES DENSITY BY PLOTS

| SPECIES | 1 | 2 | 3 | 4 | 5 | 6 | 7 | 8 | 9 | 10 | TRANSECT DENSITY | AVERAGE DENSITY | P.U.† | F.F |
|---|---|---|---|---|---|---|---|---|---|---|---|---|---|---|
| TOTAL | | | | | | | | | | | - | % | | |
| Grasses   Fid | 10 | 6 | 7 | 5 | 9 | 8 | 12 | 11 | 10 | 12 | 90 | 9 | 80 | .072 |
| Asp | 4 | 2 | 2 | 1 | 3 | 2 | 4 | 4 | 3 | 5 | 30 | 3 | 70 | .021 |
| Shy | 2 | 1 | 0 | 0 | 3 | 1 | 4 | 2 | 3 | 4 | 20 | 2 | 50 | .010 |
| Pse | 0 | 1 | 1 | 2 | 1 | 1 | 0 | 0 | 2 | 1 | 9 | 1 | 30 | .003 |
| Scl | 1 | 0 | 0 | 0 | 2 | 1 | 2 | 1 | 1 | 2 | 10 | 1 | 50 | .005 |
| Weeds   Wmo | 4 | 3 | 3 | 5 | 2 | 4 | 3 | 2 | 3 | 2 | 31 | 3 | 10 | .003 |
| Lca | 3 | 2 | 3 | 3 | 2 | 2 | 2 | 0 | 2 | 1 | 20 | 2 | 40 | .008 |
| Ala | 1 | 0 | 1 | 0 | 2 | 2 | 1 | 1 | 1 | 1 | 10 | 1 | 20 | .002 |
| SEN | 2 | 1 | 0 | 1 | 1 | 2 | 0 | 1 | 1 | 0 | 9 | 1 | 30 | .003 |
| Shrubs   Atr | 13 | 18 | 16 | 17 | 12 | 13 | 10 | 13 | 11 | 8 | 131 | 13 | 0 | .000 |
| Sal | 2 | 0 | 1 | 0 | 3 | 2 | 3 | 2 | 2 | 5 | 20 | 2 | 20 | .004 |
| Cle | 1 | 1 | 2 | 1 | 1 | 1 | 0 | 0 | 1 | 1 | 10 | 1 | 10 | .001 |
| Cna | 1 | 1 | 1 | 2 | 1 | 0 | 1 | 0 | 1 | 0 | 10 | 1 | 0 | .000 |
| | | | | | | | | | | | 400 | 40 | | .132 |
| | | | | | | | | (100% minus Util. Cuts) = | | | | | | X |
| | | | | | | | | | | | | | | .66 |
| | | | | | | | | | | | | | | .1056 |
| | | | | | | | | | | | | | | .1122 |

†Proper use factor

Fig. 4A. Record and computations form for the square-foot density method of range forage inventory (front).

## TYPE COMMENTS

ent forage utilization: **Over - Proper - Under** ✓
(Check one)

Forage plant vigor: **Poor - Fair - Good** ✓
(Check one)

ge condition: **Poor - Fair - Good** ✓
(Check one)

Relative productiveness of site: **Low - Average - High** ✓
(Check one)

ering places ..... _Springs_ ✓
(Kind - lake, spring, etc.)

_N. & W. edges of type_ ✓ _adequate_ ✓ _--- perm._
(Distance) (Adequacy) (Perm. - Temp.)

nous plants ..... _None_
(Kinds)

(Recommendations)

. of stock best suited to range: **Cattle - Horses - Sheep - Goats** ✓
(Check one or more)

er grazing period; **Spring - Summer - Fall - Winter - Yearlong** ✓
(Check one or more)

life ..... 
(Game, Predators, Rodents - Species and abundance)

er _Scattered White Fir - non-commercial_
(Comp.)

(Cond.)

(Reprod.) (Dens.)

(Injury) (Cause)

## SOIL AND SOIL EROSION•

(Under "Gully" check two. Check one in other columns. Under "Texture" check "Stony" **also** if applicable.)

| PARENT MATERIAL | CLASS | TOP SOIL DEPTH INCHES | TEXTURE | SLOPE % | EROSION | | |
|---|---|---|---|---|---|---|---|
| | | | | | WIND | WATER | |
| | | | | | | SHEET | GULLY |
| anitic | | 0-6 ✓ | Light | 0-5 | | 10% of Area | Occasional |
| vas ✓ | Residual ✓ | | | 6-10 | Class I ✓ | Class I ✓ | None ✓ |
| ndstones | | 6-12 | Medium ✓ | 11-20 ✓ | | | Frequent |
| ales | | 12-24 | Heavy | 21-40 | Class II | Class II | Shallow |
| nestones | Transported | | | 41-60 | | | |
| acial Dep. | | Over 24 | Stony ✓ | Over 60 | Class III | Class III | Deep |

planation of soil and erosion terms: **Residual** soils are found on the sites of the rock masses from which they were derived; **transported** soils
been moved to new sites by water, gravity, wind, etc. **Texture.** Light soils include sands and sandy loams; medium soils include loams
ilt loams; heavy soils include the clay loams, silty clays, and the clays. **Degree of erosion.** Class 1 - Definite recognizable soil loss; slight
ng; plant roots occasionally exposed. Class 2 - Very evident sheet erosion; plant roots definitely exposed; erosion scars present; vegetation
ted; gullies rapidly forming. Class 3 - Rapid land destruction; topsoil all removed or nearly so; conspicuous erosion scars; frequent and
gullies. **Gullies .** "Shallow" is less than two feet deep. Gullies are "occasional" when they are more than 100 feet apart.

se of erosion _Water and wind action on Shallow-soil upland flats._ Active or healing _Static_

itional type comments _This allotment is temporarily being managed as a sheep allotment. The very light use made of the grasses shows up in an increasing vigor and abundance of these species._

niner should note anything of importance in the type, such as condition of forage, grazing use, degree of utilization by domestic livestock
wildlife, or inaccessibility of area to livestock.

(OAKLAND-5-2-39-50,000)

**Fig. 4B.** Record and computations form for the square-foot density method of range forage inventory (back).

A study of the relative reliability of forage estimate by the reconnaissance and square-foot density method showed that about 36 plots per square mile are required by the square-foot density method to obtain forage estimates of similar reliability to those obtained by the reconnaissance method when traversing the range at one-half mile intervals.

**Basis for Density Estimates.** Both the reconnaissance and square-foot density methods are based on ocular estimates, the density being the percent of ground which appears to be covered by foliage when vegetation is viewed from directly above. Figs. 5 and 6 for the reconnaissance method illustrate principles used. Special considerations are as follows:

1. Include only the current year's growth of vegetation which is in reach of livestock.
2. Spreading plants usually are estimated on the basis of the foliage raised to form an angle of 30 degrees with the central stem or axis.
3. Density of two-story vegetation is estimated as for one-story vegetation: by using a downward projection of the whole without allowance for overlap.
4. With shrubs, density also includes twig growth of the current year.

With both the reconnaissance and square-foot density methods the optimum time for estimating density is during the period when important range plants are at or near their maximum development. It is impractical, however, to restrict range surveys to such a limited season. Densities, therefore, must be estimated previous to and subsequent to the maximum growth stage of forage plants, and also in years of above and below normal rainfall. In order to normalize the density estimates somewhat, attempts are made to visualize plants as they would appear at maximum growth. Differences in density estimates resulting from differences between climate in different years are largely compensated for by determining a separate forage acre factor for each survey.

**Estimating Grazing Capacity.** Grazing capacity estimates are determined from the general formula:

$$\text{Grazing capacity (animal months)} = \frac{\text{Forage factor} \times \text{Surface acres}}{\text{Forage acre requirement}}$$

$$= \frac{\text{Forage acres}}{\text{Forage acre requirement}}$$

The **forage factor** (forage acre factor) is the expression of relative forage value of a subtype. It is a decimal fraction obtained from multiplying plant density by its plant use factor. A **plant use factor** (also variously called **proper use factor** and **palatability ratings**) for a range forage species is obtained from research or at least careful observation of actual range forage utilization. They are the percentages of current herbage production of the various species which it is estimated would be utilized when the range is properly grazed under the best practical range management. The plant use factor for a species does not exceed the use it can withstand each year and still maintain its density and vigor.

To compute the forage factor of a subtype from data obtained by the reconnaissance method, the percentage compositions of plant species are each multiplied by the plant use factor for that species. These products are added to obtain a weighted plant use factor or **forage value factor** for the subtype. The forage value factor is multiplied by the density of vegetation to obtain the forage factor.

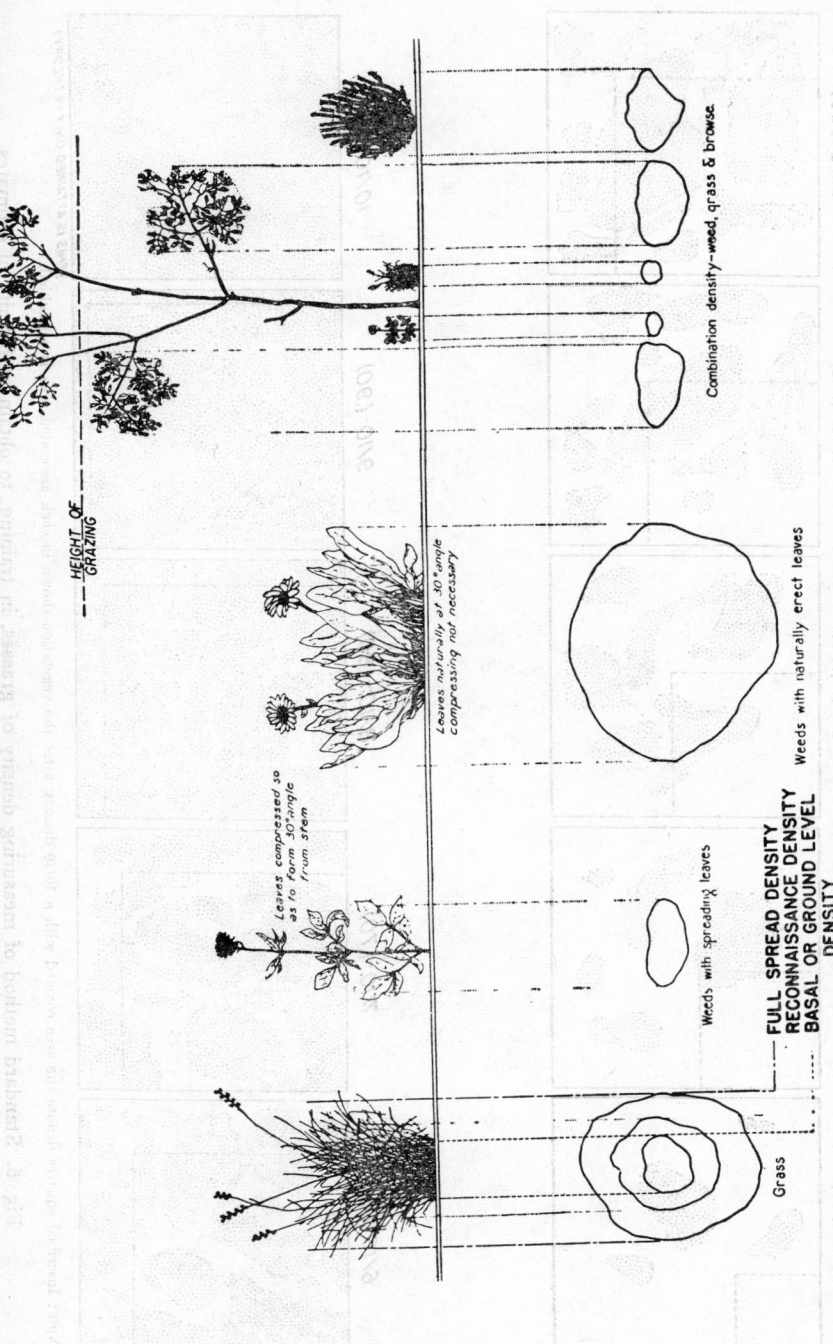

Fig. 5. Methods of judging reconnaissance densities for grasses, weeds, and browse.

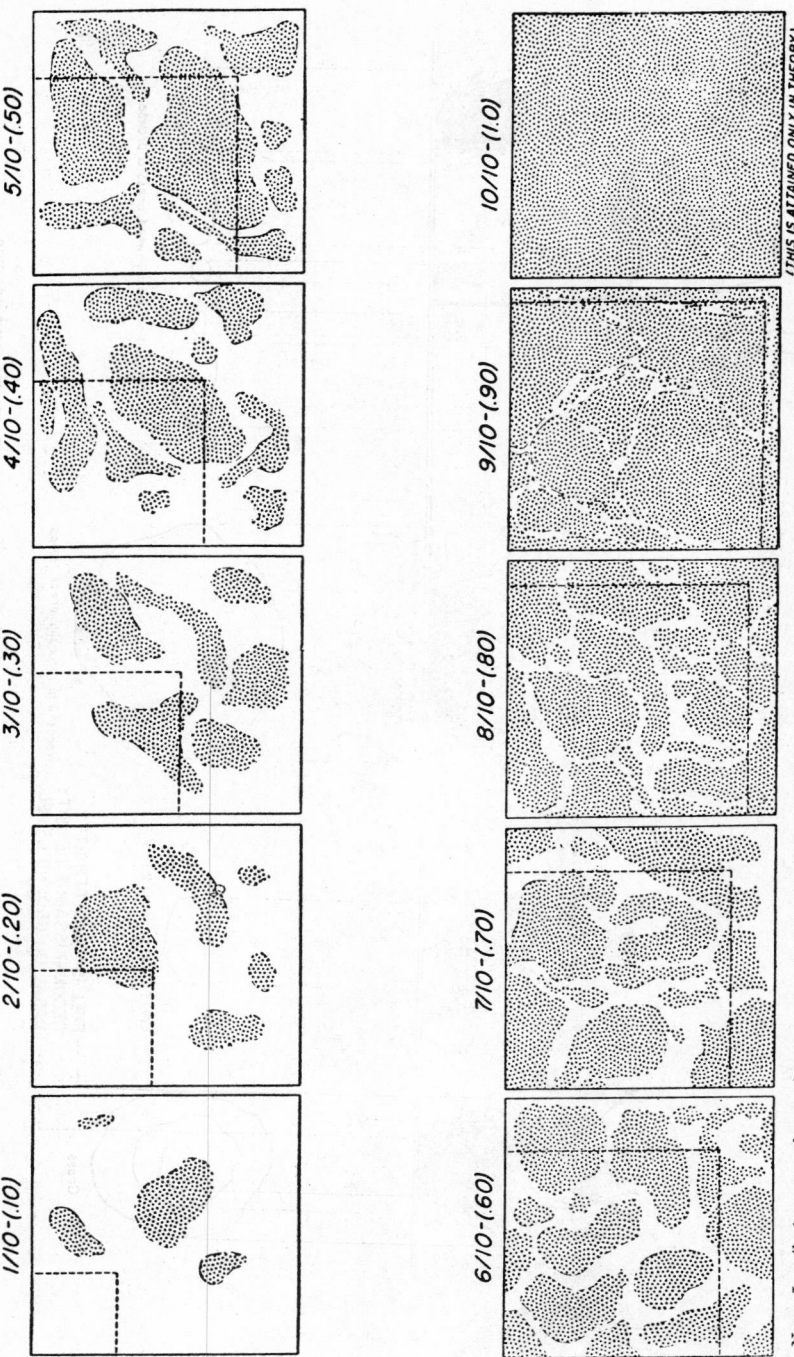

NOTE: Inscribed squares denote the area covered with a 10/10 density after the vegetation shown in each associated area is assembled.

Fig. 6. Standard method of measuring density of grasses, in training, to obtain uniformity of estimates.

To compute the forage factor of a subtype from data obtained by the square-foot density method the average density of each plant species is multiplied by its plant use factor and the resulting products added.

Other ways of expressing grazing capacity ratings used are:

$$\text{Surface acres per animal month} = \frac{\text{Forage acre requirement}}{\text{Forage factor}}$$

$$\text{Animal months per surface acre} = \frac{\text{Forage factor}}{\text{Forage acre requirement}}$$

The **net forage factor** is the forage factor after it is adjusted by utilization adjustments or cuts. **Utilization adjustments** are reductions applied to the forage estimate to take care of conditions which make it impossible or undesirable to make full use of the herbage on a subtype for forage. Dense standing and down timber, excessive rockiness, steep slopes, lack of water, and unstable soils are examples of such factors. They must be determined for each subtype and are applied by making a percentage reduction on the forage factor.

The **forage acreage** of a subtype is computed by multiplying the forage factor and surface acreage. Forage acreage is a quantitative measure of the subtype's forage value. A forage acre, theoretically, is an acre of range completely covered with foliage which properly can be utilized completely by livestock. This situation does not exist in nature, for in the case of dry meadows which may have a complete or 100 percent density, the foliage can seldom be used more than 70 or 80 percent and maintain the plant cover successfully. Forage acreage, therefore, is always less than surface acreage.

The **forage acre requirement** is a factor to convert forage acreage to an estimate of grazing capacity. The true grazing capacity of a range area is the amount of grazing it can support over a long period of years under the proper range management system without injury to the forage or soil resource. The proper level at which to establish grazing capacity, therefore, is not higher than the level of forage production in the average climatic year. In regions where drought recurs, grazing capacity must be based on forage production somewhat below the long-time average as a precaution during dry periods against livestock starvation and serious injury to the range.

Range surveys may have to be made regardless of climatic conditions, and consequently plant densities above or below average may have to be measured. This fluctuation in density value results in a determination of forage acreage which may be higher or lower than normal, depending on the climatic condition prevailing. In order that the calculation of current forage acreage on a range area be reduced to an estimate of its true grazing capacity, forage-acre requirements for each range survey project in each year should be developed by careful study. Forage acre requirements known to be adequate on comparable areas and results from longtime grazing capacity research are aids to studies of this nature.

The general procedure in developing a forage acre requirement is to select a pasture or well-controlled range unit within the surveyed area on which numbers of livestock grazed have been accurately recorded for several years, preferably ten or more, and which exhibits vegetation and soil in good condition. The average number of livestock grazed and the average grazing period are determined and are usually reduced to an expression of average grazing use in terms of cow months or sheep months.

The forage acreage of the pasture or unit as obtained by the range survey is divided by this use figure to obtain the forage acreage required to support a cow or a sheep for one month. If the forage acre requirement can be determined from several such pastures or range units, it will provide a better basis than a single area.

**Methods Based Upon Range Condition Classification.** When using methods based upon range condition classifications, stocking and management are based upon results of range condition estimates made of each range subtype mapped. Observations of density and composition made by either the reconnaissance, square-foot density, line transect, point observation, or other method, together with plant vigor observations and other factors, are recorded on "score cards" or write-up forms and used as a basis for estimating range condition and trend in range condition. These estimates are compared with standards developed by range specialists for each vegetation type to give the estimate of grazing capacity. Often it is possible to obtain substantiating information from test pastures or surveys of similar range using the forage acre method.

**Range Condition Standards.** Range condition is generally defined as "range health." It is the relative position of a range with respect to its potential as determined by climate and soil under long-time proper grazing use. In other words, it is the state of present productivity of both forage and soil as classified in terms of what the range can and will support under the prevailing climate and soil and as related to and modified by range management objectives. Condition classes are commonly designated as excellent, good, fair, poor, and very poor. Excellent is ideal, with good satisfactory, and the remaining classes unsatisfactory. Criteria for describing each of these condition classes are generally based on the amount of plant cover, floristic composition, vigor, litter, and soil characteristics, especially with respect to erosion. In general the better condition classes have higher infiltration rates and lower erosion indices than the poor condition classes. In this respect objectives are similar to those of watershed management. Forage production is greatest generally in the higher condition classes because desirable forage species are abundant, they are in top vigor, and soil moisture conditions are more favorable for growth. Change in either direction is influenced most by grazing treatment. The management objective is thus either upward from the bottom of the scale or, if at the top, the objective is to maintain this condition.

The basic classification of range condition in adjective terms and the general approach of establishing the standards are relatively uniform. However, the standards are arbitrary and the relative percents of potential production, densities, composition, and other basic measurements may vary between localities according to the different characteristics and conditions encountered and also because of changes in techniques and concepts.

In primary plant succession soil and vegetation develop concurrently, but successional changes in plant cover induced by grazing use are usually more rapid than soil changes. Thus a deteriorating plant cover may not be accompanied by marked soil losses. This is especially noticeable on many mountain meadows and parks where the terrain is level. It may also be observed, for example, on steep slopes where the spaces between the original bunchgrasses may have become covered with moss, but the original soil mantle is largely intact. Conversely an improving plant cover may not be immediately accompanied by reductions in soil losses, for there often is a lag between betterment of vegetation and soil condition. It is suggested that in order to be more specific about the meaning of "range condition" and to secure greater uniformity in its appraisal, two expressions be employed—forage or vegetation condition, and soil condition or soil stability.

UNITED STATES DEPARTMENT OF AGRICULTURE
SOIL CONSERVATION SERVICE

## RANGE CONDITION CLASS DESCRIPTION

(3-1-48)

ch __Campbell__

ner __Harry Shaw__

rict __Surprise Valley__   Work Unit __Hat Mtn.__

ge Type __4 - Atr - Fid__

Sheet No. __S-151__

Aerial Photo No. _____

Date __9/15/__

Location: T. __38N__ R. __16E__ Sec. __35__

| PRINCIPAL FORAGE SPECIES | | | | | | |
|---|---|---|---|---|---|---|
| VEGETATION GROUPS | DESIRABLE | PERCENT | LESS DESIRABLE | PERCENT | UNDESIRABLE | PERCENT |
| sses ss-like **40 %** | Fid | 23 | Shy | 5 | | |
| | Asp | 7 | Scl | 2 | | |
| | Pse | 3 | | | | |
| | | | | | | |
| | | | | | | |
| os eds) **15 %** | | | Lca | 5 | Wma | 6 |
| | | | | | Ala | 2 |
| | | | | | SEN | 2 |
| | | | | | | |
| ubs **45 %** | Sal | 5 | | | Atr | 35 |
| | | | | | Cha | 2 |
| | | | | | Cle | 3 |
| **%** | Total | 38 | Total | 12 | Total | 50 |

OSION: None ____ Slight __✓__ Moderate ____ Severe ____

TER: Abundant ____ Moderate __✓__ Slight ____ Scarce ____

AGE VIGOR: Strong ____ Moderate __✓__ Rather Weak ____ Weak ____

NGE CONDITION: Excellent ____ Good ____ Fair __✓__ Poor ____ Very Poor ____

DUCTIVENESS OF SITE: High ____ Average __✓__ Low ____

CK USING RANGE: Cattle __✓__ Horses ____ Sheep ____

PER GRAZING SEASON: Spring ____ Summer __✓__ Fall ____ Winter ____

CKING REDUCTIONS    ( See Par. 52414.1)

Slope ____ % Rocks ____ % Brush __5__ % Lack of Water ____

Unstable soils __10__ % Erosion ____ % Total __15 %__

RFACE ACRES REQUIRED PER COW MONTH __6.0__

ditional Comments: __Allotment temporarily managed as sheep range. Very light use of grasses shows up in increasing vigor and abundance of these species.__

Fig. 7A. Example of a range condition score card (front).

## SOILS AND EROSION

Slope _____ _15_%_ _____

Alkali:   Evident _____      Not evident___✓_____

Active Gully Erosion: *                          Soil Texture** ( to 6 inches deep )

| GULLIES | SHALLOW | DEEP |
|---------|---------|------|
| Occasional | | |
| Frequent | | |
| Stabilized | | |

| | NO STONE OR GRAVEL | GRAVELLY | STONY |
|---|---|---|---|
| Light | | | |
| Medium | | ✓ | |
| Heavy | | | |

Wind Erosion:
   Deposition evident _____
   Removal evident ____✓_____

* Explanation of Gully Terms -- Occasional gullies are gullies more than 100 feet apart. Frequent gullies are gullies less than 100 feet apart. Shallow gullies are those easily crossable by stock. Deep gullies are those deep enough to interfere with stock movement.

** Light soils are sandy, medium soils are loam, heavy soils are clay.

**Fig. 7B.  Example of a range condition score card (back).**

The method of survey based on range condition classification is in its early stages of development. The usual procedure is to designate natural vegetation types by standard range survey symbols and to color in or otherwise designate the forage condition situations within these types. Many agencies and technicians are working to develop better procedures. As a consequence there are numerous variations in methods of measurement, evaluations of basic factors, and ways of expressing conditions and grazing capacity. Figs. 7 and 8 illustrate two examples of condition score cards used and the criteria relied upon in their development.

**Influence of Specific Factors as Measurements in Determining the Degree of Forage Production. Forage density** is generally greatest on ranges that are in the best condition; i.e., good to excellent. The maximum densities vary according to vegetation type, character of the site (wet or dry, etc.), and the relative producing potential. A decrease in density of a vegetation type normally indicates too heavy grazing use and a lowered stage of range condition. Density may be maintained by the invasion or increase of inferior species which replace the more desirable forage plants. It is therefore important to differentiate between total density and the density of desirable forage plants.

**Composition of plant cover.** A predominance and variety of the most desirable forage plants (generally the climax, perennial grasses) is characteristic of ranges in the better condition classes. A decrease in abundance and variety of these species indicates a lowered range condition and a downward trend. Occasionally a decrease in desirable forage plants is accompanied by an increase in annual weeds and grasses and such undesirable species as sagebrush, which indicates deterioration.

## RANGE CONDITION SCORE SHEET

Forage type: (18) Annual grasses & forbs
District: San Diego County
Date:

| Factors evaluated | Excellent | Good | Fair | Poor | Very poor |
|---|---|---|---|---|---|
| | % | % | % | % | % |
| I. Relative potential forage yield . . . . . . . . . . . . . . . . . | 90-100 | 75-90 | 50-75 | 20-50 | 0-20 |
| II. IMPORTANT DESIRABLE forage plants . . . . . . . . . . . . 1. Bur-clover . . . . . . (Mhi) 2. Cutleaf filaree . . . . (Ecl) | 85-100 | 65-85 | 45-65 | 30-45 | 0-30 |
| III. LESS DESIRABLE forage plants . . . . . . . . . . . . . . . 1. Broadleaf filaree . (Ebo) 2. Foxtail fescue . . . (Fme) | 1-10 | 10-20 | 20-45 | 30-70 | 20-90 |
| IV. UNDESIRABLE forage plants. 1. Tarweed . . . . . . (HEM) 2. Gumweed . . . . . . (GRI) | 0-5 | 5-10 | 10-35 | 25-60 | 25-85 |
| V. Plant residue or litter per acre . . . . . . . . . . . . . . . . | 900 to 1500 lb. | 700 to 900 lb. | 500 to 700 lb. | 200 to 500 lb. | 50 to 200 lb. |
| VI. Erosion . . . . . . . . . . . . . . . | none | slight | moderate sheet & rill | sheet & gully erosion active | severe and active |
| VII. Acres per A.U.M . . . . . . . . | .5-1 | 1½-2½ | 3-5 | 5-7 | 7 + |

. . . . . . . . . . . . . . . . . . . . . . . . . . . . . . . . . . . . . .
(Signature)

**Fig. 8. Example of a range condition score card.**

**Plant vigor** denotes the thriftiness, rate of growth, and volume production of the plant. Continuous seasonal grazing and heavy utilization result in decreased volume of growth, delayed seasonal development, and the eventual killing out of the preferred or key forage plants. Indicators of decreased vigor are:

1. Sickly color or etiolation of foliage.
2. Delayed seasonal development.
3. Retarded growth rate and stunted plants.
4. Low volume production.
5. Decreased root growth—killing or stunting of the root system.
6. Reduced production of seed.
7. Dead and dying plants.

Plant vigor is based upon the key forage plants for the livestock using the range and can be judged by comparing the forage growth on inaccessible, unused, or lightly used areas of similar character in the close vicinity. Care must be taken to differentiate the effects of weather variations and drought from those of grazing pressure. The effects of grazing are first reflected in the appearance and seasonal development of the plant. Vigor of the key species is one of the most important factors to observe first and to judge correctly. To be reliable, observations must consider the plants preferred by the kind of livestock grazing the range.

**Volume production** is the weight or volume of forage produced by the forage plant and is closely correlated with plant vigor. It may be judged by the height growth and basal density of the plant or vegetation cover. A decrease in volume of growth by heavy grazing or drought is accompanied by a reduction in the plant's root system. Such a change results in lower range condition and grazing capacity.

**Compaction** affects the structure, infiltration capacity, and aeration of the top layers of soil. Compaction of the first few inches of the topsoil decreases the possibility for air and water to enter. Compaction reduces the chance for a good seedbed and is a contributory cause of reduced productivity, increased runoff and erosion, and general range deterioration. Heavy livestock trampling and grazing use (as well as other soil abuses) during a period when the soil is moist are major causes of soil compaction.

**Exposed soil** is normally expected to be dependent on soil fertility, the amount of soil moisture and the period of time it is available for plant growth and development of a litter layer. The extent of exposed soil is indicative of the severity of past use and management. Abnormal degrees of exposed soil result in increased susceptibility to compaction, pulverization, and loss of soil by wind and water, leading to range deterioration.

**Organic matter** is the decomposed and partially decomposed plant and animal material in the soil. It is an essential ingredient contributing to soil fertility, structure, and water-holding capacity. The lack of organic material indicates a lower production potential or range deterioration, or both.

**Slope, texture, and stability of soils.** Slope influences the stability of soils owing to the increasing effect of runoff and erosion with slope increase. Light-textured soils have less water-holding capacity and are more susceptible to erosion than are those of heavy texture.

**Setting the Standard.** 1. Select areas that are producing at or near the site potential as judged by the most favorable aspects of the above criteria that can be found. These should be ranges where little or no grazing use has occurred, or where there has been good management of grazing and other land uses over a long period of time. Measurements of the basic factors of condition on such an area will set the values for each, which, when considered together, will indicate the reasonable forage-producing potential for comparable types of range. This set of measurements is the Range Condition Standard for the given type of range and top condition class.

2. Similar measurements must then be made for each comparable range type in varying stages of deterioration. This set of measurements will then provide a complete series of data from which standards may be established for all range condition classes in terms of relative forage production.

3. The grazing capacity for each condition class should then be made by actual

grazing tests on adequately controlled pastures or range in each stage of condition, basing the amount of actual use on established utilization standards.

**OTHER DATA COLLECTED.** Regardless of the method of mapping or making the forage inventory, complete data should be obtained for the area surveyed on the following:

1. Range condition and trend.
2. Areas needing reseeding.
3. Noxious plant areas needing treatment.
4. Rodent problems.
5. Poison plant areas.
6. Soil erosion problems.
7. Stock water development.
8. Stock water problems and plans for their solution.
9. Special topographic or other features that will affect the use of the range.
10. Big game populations and use of the forage by them.
11. Relation of use of forage to other uses of the land.
12. Relation of grazing use of area surveyed to use of commensurate properties.
13. Current and past history of range use.
14. Data on any other factors that will affect use of the area.

**APPLICATION OF RANGE SURVEYS.** To meet their objectives, range surveys should provide the basis for managing the range. To be most effective, prompt preparation of the management plan and vigorous field application of the plan is required. A management plan based on painstaking range surveys may become worthless through lack of prompt, effectual action, for if processes of range deterioration are allowed to continue unduly after the inventory is finished, the value of the inventory is diminished.

Most questions regarding results of range surveys arise from the grazing capacity estimate. This is because the grazing capacity figures are regarded as being the final figure while in reality they are only estimates subject to errors of sampling, personal error of estimating plant density, seasonal and yearly variations in composition and forage values, and variations in range use by livestock. Grazing capacity estimates have been very useful when properly applied. However, in every case the survey should be followed by intensive, objective range inspections in years following the survey to check on results. If careful study indicates the grazing capacity estimate for the area to be low or high, the survey is in no sense invalidated, for the relative capacity values between different parts of the area are still usable and the entire estimate may be raised or lowered as found to be necessary.

## Range Utilization

The maintenance, improvement, and production of the range are governed by the way the area is grazed. Too heavy forage use ultimately leads to reduced forage yield and loss of soil fertility. Too light use is wasteful of vegetation that might well be converted into livestock and wildlife. The important question then is: How closely can the range be grazed and still have range values maintained or increased?

In recent years considerable attention has been given to developing utilization standards for different—but far from all—range types and species.

**UTILIZATION STANDARDS AND THEIR USES.** These standards define the limit of grazing use that a given range or forage species can endure without deterioration. Utilization standards are also commonly called **proper use factors.** They usually differ for different range types and forage species. Some of the standards that have been developed for species and types on forest ranges are shown in Table 4.

Utilization on the range is estimated or measured in the same terms as the standard. A comparison is then made between the utilization value obtained for the range and for the standard. If the range value exceeds the standard value, the range is overutilized. If the range value equals or is less than the standard value, the range is properly grazed or is undergrazed.

**Table 4.  Utilization Standards for Different Species and Types of Forest Ranges**

| | | | Utilization standards | |
| | | | Stubble height (in.) | Utilization of current yield (percent) |
| Vegetation | Scientific name | Occurrence: Forest Service Region | | |
| --- | --- | --- | --- | --- |
| **Grasses and grasslike plants:** | | | | |
| Arizona fescue | *Festuca arizonica* | Southwestern | 5 | |
| Black grama | *Bouteloua eriopoda* | Southwestern | | 80–85 |
| Blue grama | *Bouteloua gracilis* | Northern | 1.6 | 29 |
| Blue grama | *Bouteloua gracilis* | Rocky Mountain | 1¼–1¾ | |
| Blue grama | *Bouteloua gracilis* | Southwestern | 2 | 55 |
| Bluebunch wheatgrass | *Agropyron spicatum* | Pacific Northwest | 3 | |
| Bluestem wheatgrass | *Agropyron smithii* | Northern | 6.5 | 20 |
| Buffalograss | *Buchloë dactyloides* | Rocky Mountain | 1¼–1¾ | |
| Curly mesquite | *Hilaria belangeri* | Southwestern | 3 | |
| Galleta | *Hilaria jamesii* | Intermountain | 1–1½ | |
| Green fescue | *Festuca viridula* | Pacific Northwest | 3 | 50 |
| Indian ricegrass | *Oryzopsis hymenoides* | Intermountain | 2–3 | 75 |
| Sandberg bluegrass | *Poa secunda* | Pacific Northwest | 3 | |
| Sideoats grama | *Bouteloua curtipendula* | Southwestern | 4 | |
| Threadleaf sedge | *Carex filifolia* | Northern | 2.2 | 19 |
| Tobosa grass | *Hilaria mutica* | Southwestern | 4 | |
| **Shrubs:** | | | | |
| Bitterbrush | *Purshia tridentata* | California | | 60 |
| Black sagebrush | *Artemisia nova* | Intermountain | | 60 |
| Common winterfat | *Eurotia lanata* | Intermountain | | 55 |
| Redstem ceanothus | *Ceanothus sanguineus* | Northern | | 60 |
| **Range types:** | | | | |
| Annual grassland | | California | | 60 (Photo rating) |
| Ponderosa pine– bunchgrass | | Rocky Mountain | | 35–40 |
| Sagebrush–wheatgrass | | Intermountain | | 60–65 |
| Subalpine grassland | | Pacific Northwest | 3 | 50 |
| Salt desert-shrub | | Intermountain | | 75 |

**HOW STANDARDS ARE EXPRESSED.** Range utilization can be viewed in many ways; hence utilization standards are expressed in different ways, as for example:

1. Percent of current year's forage production grazed.
2. Percent of current year's plant height or twig growth grazed.
3. Percent of total number of plants or flower stems grazed.
4. Height of forage stubble remaining on the ground after grazing.
5. Weight of plant residue remaining on the ground after grazing.
6. Photographs at end of grazing season.

Some of the quantities expressed in these standards can be determined by indirect measurements. For example, the relationship between plant height, stubble height, and yield has been worked out for a number of species. By using suitable tables or scales the percentage utilization of the current year's forage production can be determined from measurements of grazed and ungrazed plant height. These tables and scales have been used almost entirely in technical investigations so far and are not generally available for administration. They are found mainly in offices of experiment stations and land managing agencies.

**APPRAISAL OF RANGE UTILIZATION.** The information needed to arrive at a utilization rating for the range or a species can be obtained by estimation, by measurement, or by a combination of these. Some measurement procedures, such as those involving clipping of the forage, setting up cages or exclosures, or similar devices, are too time-consuming in most cases for practical appraisal of utilization. The most usable procedures are those employing ocular estimation and simple measurements. Determination of a satisfactory utilization value is dependent on getting an adequate sample of the range as well as on the accuracy of the estimates or measurements. In most cases the decision on the type of estimates or measurements to be employed is arrived at by balancing accuracy of measurement against range coverage.

Determination of utilization in the field can be approached by two general methods: (1) the reconnaissance method, or (2) the plot method (see "Range Surveys").

In the reconnaissance method the examiner walks or rides over the range and estimates, ocularly, the condition and utilization rating for the range area or for one or more species. He may check his estimation of some of the factors involved in a utilization rating, such as plant height, stubble height, or plant weight with actual measurements. The reconnaissance procedure is general and sacrifices accuracy in unit values for coverage. However, it permits viewing a comparatively large portion of the range and therefore gives a broader picture of utilization over the entire range than is possible in using a plot method.

In the plot method, information is obtained on specific locations or plants are marked temporarily for a particular examination, or permanently for repeat examinations. The limited area involved in a plot permits greater accuracy in estimates and allows for greater use of specific measurements. Usually, however, many plots are required to obtain a reasonable if not an adequate sample of the range. Therefore, what may be gained in accuracy on the one hand may be sacrificed by lack of coverage. A combination of plot estimates or measurements and more general estimates over a larger area around the plots has merit in maintaining a reasonable balance between accuracy and coverage.

The number of plots needed to sample a given range area or species ranges from a minimum of about 20 to over 100, depending on the variability of utilization. Usually fewer plots are needed in comparison between seasons than between different areas, especially where permanent plots are established. The plots commonly used range in size from 1 sq. ft. to 100 sq. ft. and vary in shape from square, oblong, to circular. Or the plot may consist of a line. The plots are distributed over the range at random or in some systematic way so as to sample the area or species.

A photographic method of arriving at a utilization rating was developed for annual-type ranges in California. In this method the appearance of the utilized range is checked against a series of photographs showing different degrees of use on similar range. One photograph depicts proper use. The photographs are assigned numbers from 0 to 100 covering the range from no use to complete use. Utilization is rated according to those numbers.

**WHERE TO LOOK FOR UTILIZATION.** Characteristically, range utilization is uneven, especially on forest ranges which are generally rugged and diverse. Different species and different areas are usually grazed in various degrees because of the grazing habits of the animals and their preferences for different species and areas, distribution and interrelation of vegetative types, topography, location of water, salt grounds, fences, the season and intensity of grazing, and other factors.

The use pattern differs with different kinds of livestock because of their preference for different kinds of plants. The pattern of use can be modified to some extent by changing the kind of stock, the stocking rate, season of grazing, and livestock distribution, but the uneven use arising from the grazing habits of the animals cannot be eliminated. Knowledge of this fact is helpful in determining range utilization.

**KEY AREAS.** Because of the magnitude of the job, it is not practicable to appraise utilization on every acre of the range, whether by ocular estimation, photographs, or measurement methods. Of necessity, therefore, utilization appraisal has to be limited to a portion of the range. This portion lies between the normally heavily and lightly grazed areas.

Areas around water, salt grounds, and certain favored grazing grounds are invariably heavily grazed, whereas areas bordering the limits of normal livestock distribution are lightly grazed. Appraisal of utilization in these two situations would give essentially the same picture of use under light or heavy stocking. The intermediate areas, however, respond most sensitively to difference in grazing pressure and are the best units on which to judge utilization. These areas are often called key areas. The location of key areas varies from one range to the next because of difference in the character of the range and the management. The locations are determined primarily by the utilization pattern on a particular range.

**KEY SPECIES.** Within the key areas some forage species are usually cropped consistently more closely than others because the livestock prefer these species to others. The utilization on any one of the most abundant of these preferred species can be used to indicate the grazing use on the key area. For example, 60 percent use of the key species may be indicative of 40 percent use on the key area as a whole. Once the relation between the use on the key area and key species is established, utilization on the key area can be judged by the use of the key species. Such a guide is most useful in comparing the degree of grazing on a given area from one time to another.

**WHEN TO JUDGE UTILIZATION.** The best time to judge utilization is at the end of the grazing season. On most forest ranges the division between one grazing season and the next is in the fall and coincides roughly with the start of the next seasonal precipitation cycle. At this time the vegetal cover is usually dry and reduced to its minimum density and yield. Utilization should be judged at about the same time each year even though grazing is terminated earlier.

## Range Livestock Breeds

Successful livestock ranching implies that the breed of animal reared is suited to harvesting the forage crops locally produced. When feed is abundant yearlong any of several breeds will do well, although some will do better than others.

**BREEDS OF RANGE CATTLE.** On ranges of the far West and in the South the grower raises cattle for beef. All the better beef breeds are now found in the range country to some extent. The major breeds are Hereford, Shorthorn, and Aberdeen-Angus (Hultz). In the warmer areas the Brahman is finding a place of importance, whereas in a few tropical or semitropical areas the Santa Gertrudis is being tried out limitedly.

The Hereford, second largest of the European breeds, outnumbers all other beef breeds in the United States. The Hereford is noted for its hardiness, strong constitution, and superior rustling qualities and is particularly popular on the western range. It has the capacity for getting through a severe winter even where forage is sparse.

The Shorthorn, the largest of our cattle, is second numerically among beef breeds in the United States. Where forage is abundant yearlong, Shorthorns are superior for beef production. They are not as good rustlers as the Hereford and are therefore not likely to replace the "white faces" on the western range.

The Aberdeen-Angus, although somewhat smaller than the Hereford and Shorthorn, are excellent beef animals. These polled black cattle are not especially popular on the open range because of their nervous disposition, which complicates handling them. However, they are good rustlers and produce a superior carcass.

The Brahman, recognized by the large hump on the withers, loose folds of skin forming the dewlap and navel, and long drooping ears, is not as good a beef type as the breeds previously discussed. Brahmans endure heat well, are hardy, excellent rustlers, and are resistant to external parasites such as the fever tick. Bulls carrying one-fourth to one-half Brahman blood are being crossed to advantage with temperate-zone beef breeds in the hotter and more humid areas of the United States, such as the Gulf region, and in various tropical regions of the world.

The Santa Gertrudis, a strictly American breed of beef cattle, was developed on the King ranch in Texas by crossing Shorthorn and Brahman. This large, dark-red breed is known to be resistant to subtropical climatic conditions but has not yet been distributed for wide use.

**BREEDS OF RANGE SHEEP.** Most of the breeds of sheep raised in the United States were developed in England, although Spain and France made valuable breed contributions. While there are many breeds of sheep, most of them can be classified into four general groups. Instead of discussing each individual breed in detail, the principal use, advantages, and disadvantages of each group are presented in Table 5.

**Table 5. Grouping of Breeds of Sheep**

| Fine wools | Long wools | Medium wool dual purpose | Medium wool mutton breeds |
|---|---|---|---|
| Rambouillet | Romney | Columbia | Hampshire |
| Merino | Lincoln | Corriedale | Suffolk |
| | Cotswold | Romeldale | Shropshire |
| | Leicester | Targhee | Southdown |
| | Border | Panama | Dorset |
| | Leicester | | Cheviot |
| | | | Oxford |

The fine wools (Table 5) were selected from the original Spanish Merino and have been the basic breed for range sheep production.

Advantages:

1. Rugged. Withstand extremes of heat and cold and can exist under unfavorable feed conditions.
2. Produce a desirable clip of wool. Fine wool normally sells for the highest price per pound on a clean basis.
3. Possess herding instinct. Will band together under range herding conditions.
4. Breed early. Will breed in April, May, June, and July to lamb in the fall. Important where winter lambs are produced, as in California and the Southern States.
5. Long-lived. Many ewes will live to be 10 to 12 years of age.

Disadvantages:

1. Lack the mutton conformation characteristic of the mutton breeds. With more and more emphasis on the income from lamb, the importance of mutton conformation increases.
2. Ewes are not as good milk producers as those of the other groups and consequently do not produce as rapidly growing or high-grading lambs.
3. Fine-wool sheep are more subject to fly-strike because of the wrinkles and wool close to the anus and vulva.
4. Some of the wool is too short in staple to bring the best price.
5. Shrinkage is relatively high.

The long-wool breeds of sheep (Table 5) were developed in England under cool, moist conditions where feed supplies are favorable. They are not well adapted to a wide variety of range conditions.

Advantages:

1. Largest sheep belong to long-wool breeds.
2. Rapid-growing but late-maturing sheep.
3. Some long-wool breeds, particularly the Lincoln, cross well with fine-wool breeds to produce intermediate or dual-purpose sheep.
4. Ewes are good milk producers.
5. Can endure wet weather, and the claim is made that the Romney is more resistant to foot-rot than other breeds.
6. Produce heavy clip of wool, low shrinking, and coarse in texture.

Disadvantages:

1. Not adapted to hot, dry climate. This limits their usefulness on the range.
2. Must have an adequate feed supply. Are not as rugged as fine-wool sheep.
3. Do not produce as desirable a carcass as mutton breeds.
4. Wool sells for lower price because coarse wool is not in as large demand as fine wool, but the increased yield may compensate for the lower selling price.
5. Lack herding instinct.

The medium-wool dual-purpose breeds (Table 5) have been developed by crossing the long-wool breeds with the fine-wool breeds in an attempt to combine as many of the desirable characters of both groups as possible and to eliminate many of the undesirable qualities. All of these breeds, except the Targhee, are essentially ½ long-wool and ½ fine-wool breeding. The Targhee is approximately ¾ fine-wool and ¼ long-wool. A goodly proportion of the commercial range ewes have some mixture of the fine-, medium-, and long-wool whiteface breeds.

Advantages:

1. Mutton conformation and milk production are improved over the fine-wool breeds and, as a result, lambs produced by these medium-wool ewes reach market weight at a younger age and are more desirable from a conformation and carcass standpoint.
2. Length of staple and weight of the wool clip is increased over the fine-wool breeds, but the wool is still fine enough to receive a good price per pound.
3. Wool produced is free of black fibers and has desirable quality.
4. Maintain herding instinct of fine-wool sheep.

Disadvantages:

1. Are not as rugged as fine-wool sheep.
2. Are generally not as large as long-wool sheep.
3. Generally will not breed as early as fine-wool breeds.

The mutton breeds (Table 5) were developed primarily for their lamb-producing capacity. Their principal use under most range conditions is to furnish sires for the production of market lambs.

Tests have shown that Hampshire and Suffolk rams sired lambs that weighed more at marketing time and returned the greatest income per ewe bred. Southdown rams produced lambs of the highest carcass quality but the lambs were small. The Shropshire-sired lambs were intermediate in size and quality. Romney-sired and Rambouillet-sired lambs were inferior in carcass quality to lambs sired by the mutton-type rams. Because of the increased size of the lambs produced, Hampshire or Suffolk rams are often selected to sire market lambs.

The mutton breeds as commercial sheep have the following characteristics:

Advantages:

1. Lambs of excellent quality and grade can be produced.
2. Ewes are prolific, good milkers, and good mothers.

Disadvantages:

1. Ewes breed late; very few lambs are born in the fall.
2. Ewes are short-lived.
3. Wool clip is light in weight and may be contaminated with black fiber.
4. Mutton breeds will not herd; do not have banding instinct.

For the above reasons, it is **not** recommended that mutton-breed ewes or mutton-breed crossbred ewes be used as commercial breeding ewes on the range.

**BREEDS OF RANGE GOATS.** Goats raised on the range are confined mostly to the West and are of the Angora breed rather than of the milk breeds. Angoras are raised for two products—mohair, and meat (called chevon). Ranchers may also keep a few goats to suppress or destroy brush.

As a rule goats are kept on areas where the browse will be utilized more efficiently by these animals than by other stock. No goats are now permitted to be grazed on national forest range because of their tendency to destroy timber reproduction by close browsing.

## Range Nutrition and Supplemental Feeding on the Range

Supplemental range feeding aims to provide livestock foods to balance nutrient deficiencies in the forage. Such feeding may mean the difference between profit and loss in some seasons or localities. Before entering into range feeding practices it is important to consider a few background facts and some terms commonly employed in animal nutrition.

**BACKGROUND CONSIDERATIONS.** Stocker (breeding or growing) animals are usually kept on a maintenance ration during the time of year when forage nutrition is low. The practice is to have the animals make their major weight increases on green spring feed, as that provides the cheapest gains.

A **maintenance ration** is a ration which consists of the minimum amount of food required to sustain the essential body processes without gain or loss in body weight or change in body composition. When forage values are low the natural forage must be supplemented.

**Supplemental feeding** is usually associated with the stage of forage growth. Forage nutrients decrease with advancement in growth stage, and the lowest levels occur in standing mature forage that has been leached and bleached. Nutrients such as protein, phosphorus, and carotene are commonly deficient in mature range forage, hence these are the ones usually supplemented.

On perennial grass ranges late fall, winter, and early spring are nutritionally the most critical seasons. On annual grass ranges forage values drop rapidly after ripening. On such ranges supplemental feeding should begin a month or two after ripening and continue until green feed is again plentiful.

Proper ratios of nutrients are important. A diet containing suitable relative amounts of nutritive elements is more efficiently utilized by the animal than one in which there is an unbalance. Proper proportions are expressed as **ratios**; two ratios in common use are the nutritive ratio, and the calcium-phosphorus ratio.

**The nutritive ratio** is the ratio of the digestible protein to the sum of digestible carbohydrates and fats. As the nutritive ratio becomes wider, i.e., where there is a smaller proportion of digestible protein in the diet, the digestibility of all nutrients tends to be lower.

**The calcium-phosphorus ratio** is the ratio of calcium to phosphorus. If the ratio is heavily in favor of calcium, as is often the case late in the growing season, the assimilation of phosphorus is interferred with, hence phosphorus may be inadequate even though amounts of phosphorus appear to be sufficient.

In addition to deficiencies caused by seasonal weather conditions, such as leaching and bleaching, there are deficiencies caused by mineral lacks in the soil. Elements that are deficient over wide areas include phosphorus and iodine. Elements that may be deficient locally include calcium, cobalt, copper, and iron. In addition, sodium and chlorine must almost always be supplied in the form of common salt.

The following four tables summarize various phases of nutritional range problems. Table 6 lists some of the more common deficiencies in range forage and typical symptoms arising therefrom; Table 7 presents nutrient analyses of several common hays and concentrates; Table 8 gives the daily nutrient requirements of a pregnant cow, and the poundage and digestible nutrients of dry range forage, alfalfa, hay, and cottonseed cake; and Table 9 presents recommended nutrient allowances for livestock according to daily digestible nutrient requirements and needed intake of certain minerals and carotene.

**Table 6. Common Deficiencies in Range Forage, Typical Symptoms, Basis for Physiological Disturbances, and Corrective Measures**

| Deficiency | Symptoms | Basis | Correction |
|---|---|---|---|
| Energy intake.. | Weight loss, slow growth, reproduction failure, increased mortality. | Underfeeding, overstocking, or low digestibility of forage. | Feed concentrates or good quality hay; increase pasturage or reduce herd. |
| Protein........ | Failure of oestrus and milk secretion; poor appetite and low gain. | Weathering of forage. | Supplementary feeding: Concentrates (cottonseed cake, etc.) 1–2 lb./day for cattle; ¼–⅓ lb./day for sheep. Roughages (alfalfa hay, etc.) of good quality are also high in protein. |
| Phosphorus.... | Irregularity or cessation of oestrus; decrease in appetite and rate of gain; bone, stone, dirt, or wood chewing; lameness, stiffness, bone fracture; rickets; weak offspring. | Deficiency in soil; weathering of forage. | Feed seed-derived concentrates or bone meal; dissolve disodium phosphate in drinking water—6.5 gm. per 6 gal. |
| Carotene, from which Vitamin A is formed. | Staggering, spasms, loss of appetite, night blindness, eye lesions, abortion or birth of weak calves, diarrhea in young calves. | Lack of green feed for several months. | Feed green, leafy hay, yellow corn, dehydrated alfalfa, leaf meal, or pellets. |
| Iodine........ | Goiter; dead or weak calves; stunted growth. | Deficiency in soil —found especially in the Northern States. | Feed iodized block salt containing 0.02% potassium iodide; or mix 1 oz. powdered potassium iodide w/300 lb. fine ground salt. |

## Table 7. Nutrient Analyses of Feeds *

| Feed | Crude protein (%) | Total digestible nutrients (%) | Calcium (%) | Phosphorus (%) | Carotene (mg. per lb.) | Nutritive ratio | Calcium-phosphorus ratio |
|---|---|---|---|---|---|---|---|
| Alfalfa hay....... | 14.8 | 50.3 | 1.47 | 0.24 | 11.4 | 1:3.8 | 6.1:1 |
| Prairie hay, good quality........ | 5.7 | 49.6 | 0.36 | 0.18 | 9.3 | 1:22.6 | 2:1 |
| Native western mountain hay, good quality.... | 8.1 | 52.0 | 0.39 | 0.12 | 9–14 | 1:9.6 | 3.2:1 |
| Native western mountain hay, weathered...... | 3.9 | 36.6 | ... | ... | 4–8 | 1:21.9 | ... |
| Cottonseed cake... | 34.6 | 77.2 | 0.39 | 0.87 | 0.14 | 1:1.5 | 0.3:1 |

* Hay varies widely in nutrient content according to the species, growth stage when cut, care in curing, and subsequent weathering. Concentrates also vary according to the processes by which they were derived. The values above should be taken only as general indications of nutrient values.

## Table 8. Nutrient Requirements of a 1,000-Lb. Pregnant Cow and the Digestible Nutrients in Dry Range Forage, Cottonseed Cake, and Alfalfa Hay *

| | Total feed (lb.) | Total digestible nutrients (lb.) | Protein (lb.) | Calcium (gm.) | Phosphorus (gm.) | Carotene (mg.) |
|---|---|---|---|---|---|---|
| Requirements........ | 18 | 9.0 | 0.9 | 16 | 15 | 55 |
| Dry mixed range forage . | 18 | 7.2 | 0.2 | 86 | 13 | 0 |
| Cottonseed cake (43% protein)........... | 2.5 | 1.88 | 0.88 | 2.5 | 12.5 | 0 |
| Range forage plus cake (A)................ | 20.5 | 9.08 | 1.08 | 88.5 | 25.5 | 0 |
| Dry mixed range forage . | 9 | 3.6 | 0.1 | 43 | 6.5 | 0 |
| Alfalfa hay........... | 11 | 5.5 | 1.2 | 75 | 10.4 | 213.4 |
| Range forage plus alfalfa (B)........... | 20 | 9.1 | 1.3 | 118 | 16.9 | 213.4 |

* Examples of common winter nutrient shortages and how they may be supplemented with alfalfa hay and cottonseed cake. In Table 8 these two supplements are fed separately, except in examples "A" and "B," which illustrates the differences in their composition.

It should be noted that dry mixed range forage, cottonseed cake, and mixture A (range forage plus cake) are deficient in carotene, whereas mixture B (range forage plus alfalfa) contains a poor calcium-phosphorus ratio. A mixture of cake and hay is a more satisfactory supplement in this case than either alone.

**DETERMINING THE AMOUNT OF HAY IN STACKS.** Frequently stockmen wish to inventory the amount of hay on hand, or to purchase additional supplies. Formulas for determining tonnage are convenient to use where weighing is impracticable. The volume of hay can be determined by measurement. The tonnage of hay stacks may be approximated as follows: (1) determine the volume of hay by measurement; (2) divide the volume by cubic feet of hay in a ton (Table 10).

Table 9. Recommended Nutrient Allowances for Livestock on Basis of Daily Digestible Nutrient Requirements and Needed Intake of Calcium, Phosphorus, and Carotene [a]

| Treatment | Age class | Body weight (lb.) | Daily feed per animal (lb.) | Digestible nutrients (% in ration) | Digestible protein (% in ration) | Calcium (% in ration) | Phosphorus (% in ration) | Daily carotene per animal (mg.) |
|---|---|---|---|---|---|---|---|---|
| BEEF CATTLE [b] | | | | | | | | |
| Wintering | Weanling calves | 400–600 | 11–15 | 55–53 | 6.4–5.3 | 0.32–0.24 | 0.24–0.18 | 25–35 |
| Wintering | Yearlings | 600–900 | 16–18 | 50 | 5.0–4.5 | 0.22–0.20 | 0.17–0.15 | 35–50 |
| Wintering | Pregnant cows and heifers | 700–1,200 | 18–22 | 50 | 4.5 | 0.20 | 0.18 | 55–65 |
| | Cows nursing calves | 900–1,100 | 28 | 50 | 5.0 | 0.24 | 0.18 | 300 |
| Normal growth | Heifers and steers | 400–1,000 | 12–21 | 58–50 | 7.5–4.3 | 0.37–0.16 | 0.28–0.16 | 25–55 |
| Growth and maintenance | Bulls | 600–1,800 | 16–26 | 63–54 | 8.1–5.4 | 0.33–0.15 | 0.25–0.15 | 35–100 |
| RANGE SHEEP [c] | | | | | | | | |
| Wintering | Bred ewes | 100–130 | 3.5–3.8 | 50 | 5.0 | 0.20 | 0.16 | 6–8 |
| Wintering | Bred ewes [d] | 100–150 | 4.0–4.4 | 53–55 | 5.0 | 0.24 | 0.18 | 6–9 |
| Growth and maintenance | Ewes nursing lambs | 100–150 | 4.5–5.0 | 58 | 6.0–6.2 | 0.30 | 0.22 | 6–10 |
| Growth and maintenance | Ewes, lambs, yearlings | 70–130 | 3.0–3.8 | 58–54 | 7.3–5.3 | 0.22–0.18 | 0.20–0.16 | 4–7 |
| | Rams, lambs, yearlings | 75–175 | 3.5–4.5 | 58–60 | 6.8–5.1 | 0.24–0.18 | 0.20–0.16 | 4–9 |

a All feeds or rations are calculated on the basis of 90 percent dry matter.   b Guilbert.   c Pearson.   d Last 6 weeks before lambing.

Formulas for obtaining volume in stacks of different types are:

1. Oblong stacks:
   a. Low, round-topped stacks (Great Plains type)

$$V = (0.52 \times O) - (0.44 \times W) \times W \times L$$

   b. High, round-topped stacks (Intermountain type)

$$V = (0.52 \times O) - (0.46 \times W) \times W \times L$$

   c. Square, flat-topped stacks (Pacific type)

$$V = (0.56 \times O) - (0.55 \times W) \times W \times L$$

where $V$ = volume; $O$ = over-measurement; $W$ = width; $L$ = length (in feet)

2. Round stacks:

$$V = (0.04 \times O) - (0.012 \times C) \times C^2$$

$C$ = circumference in feet; "over" should be an average of two measurements at right angles to each other ("over-measurement" is taken from the base on one side of the stack, over the stack, to the base on the other side)

Volume, expressed in cubic feet per ton of hay, varies with the kind of hay and length of time it has been stacked. Standard volume measures of common hays are shown in Table 10.

### Table 10. Standard Volume Measures per Ton for Different Hays

| Kind of hay | Cubic feet in a ton after stacking | |
|---|---|---|
| | 30 to 90 days | Over 90 days |
| Alfalfa | 485 | 470 |
| Timothy and timothy mixed | 640 | 625 |
| Wild | 600 | 450 |

## SALT AND WATER REQUIREMENTS OF RANGE LIVESTOCK.

The importance of adequate salt and water for the welfare of range livestock has been discussed elsewhere. It is helpful to know what the daily livestock requirements of salt and water are, in order to supply these essentials adequately. Table 11 presents the salt requirements and Table 12 the water requirements.

### Table 11. Salt Requirements for Range Livestock

| Kind of stock | Kind of salt | Recommended salt allowance with: | | Pounds per year |
|---|---|---|---|---|
| | | Green forage (lb. per mo.) | Dry, cured forage (lb. per mo.) | |
| Cattle | Soft block | 2.0–2.5 | 1.0–1.5 | 20 |
| Sheep | Granulated, placed in containers | 0.5–1.0 | 0.3–0.5 | 6–9 |

**Table 12. Water Requirements for Range Livestock**

| Kind of stock | Quantity (gal. per day) | Watering interval |
|---|---|---|
| Cattle ............ | 10 | Daily during warm weather, oftener with dry feed during hot summer periods; at 2-day or less frequent intervals during cool weather and when dew, rain, or snow is on forage. |
| Sheep ........... | 1 | Daily during warmest weather, with dry forage; at 2- or 3-day intervals with average forage and weather conditions; at weekly or less frequent intervals with cool weather and especially with considerable moisture (dew, rain, snow) on forage. Can do without water for an entire summer season on succulent high altitude weed range. |

# Management Highlights

This section summarizes the more important principles and practices of range management. Even though some repetition with preceding discussions may occur, re-emphasis of certain tested management procedures should serve the better to keep them in mind.

**PROPER KINDS OF LIVESTOCK.** It is well known that some kinds of livestock are better suited to utilize a given range than others. The factors most instrumental in determining the best kind of livestock to graze are: topography and the forage types, presence of timber reproduction, poisonous plants, insects and diseases, and distribution of water.

**Topography and Types of Forage.** Horses prefer both open and rolling lands with grass as the primary forage. Coarse grasses are utilized when finer ones are not plentiful.

Cattle are also well adapted to lands suitable for horses, and do fairly well in mountain areas with slopes that are not too steep and on ridge tops. Grass forage is preferred but cattle will eat some forbs and browse.

Sheep are adapted to variable range topography and will graze rougher and steeper areas than cattle. A variety of forage plants is utilized by sheep. They do well on prairie grasslands with grasses predominating, as well as on ranges producing mainly browse and weeds.

Goats are "at home" on lands of a wider range of topography than other kinds of livestock. Browse is preferred, but goats will thrive on grass and forbs.

**Timber Reproduction.** In general livestock will not damage coniferous reproduction on timber lands if they are managed on a sustained yield basis in keeping with good conservation practices. With heavy utilization, sheep and goats will damage coniferous reproduction by trampling and to some extent by browsing upon the seedlings, especially after the herbaceous vegetation has matured. Cattle, sheep, and goats will damage hardwood reproduction unless the stocking rates are properly balanced with the amount of forage present. In the past the damage to hardwood reproduction could have been avoided if grazing had been on the basis of sustained yield and if the right kind of livestock had been grazed. In the longleaf pine area of the South hogs have done considerable damage by rooting up young trees and eating the roots.

**Poisonous Plants.** Poisonous plants may determine the kind of livestock to graze on a given range. Ranges heavily infested with larkspur may be safely grazed by sheep but not by cattle. Sheep are readily poisoned on ranges supporting a considerable quantity of deathcamas, greasewood, horse brush, lupine, rubberweed, sneezeweed, and bitterweed, but cattle are reasonably safe on such areas because they seldom eat these plants. Ranges which support large amounts of the following plants are poisonous to both cattle and sheep: arrowgrass, loco, milkweed, chokecherry, halogeton, and selenium-bearing plants.

**Insects and Diseases.** On forest ranges in the West cattle may suffer loss of flesh from blood-sucking insects, hence management facilities should be provided, where possible, to cope with such situations. Sheep are not disturbed by blood-sucking insects and may, under certain types of management, replace cattle for a part of the season. During periods of warm weather, as in the forests of the South, ticks, heel flies, and some other insects annoy cattle greatly and cause them to lose flesh. Brahman cattle are resistant to some of these insects. Sheep have not proved successful to date in a rotation with cattle in the South, hence other means of combating the tick problem must be a part of future planning in that area.

**Water Requirements and Water Distribution.** In general, the water requirements of livestock are based upon the kind of stock, climate, and the nature of the forage. Sheep and goats require little water on mountain ranges where snow, rain, or heavy dew is prevalent. Under such conditions sheep need not be watered oftener than every 3 to 7 days, depending upon the succulence of the forage. Watering every day or two is necessary under ordinary circumstances, especially when the weather is hot and dry.

Cattle and horses require water frequently. Generally during the summer cattle should have water every day; however, if feed is succulent and the weather is not too hot, they may receive water only every other day and still be maintained in good flesh.

Horses may drink every day but are known to go 3 to 4 days without water with no apparent physical discomfort or ill effects. Since few horses are grazed on forest ranges, their management is of little importance.

The kind of animal that should be selected to graze upon a given range may sometimes be determined more by the distribution of the water than by the character of the forage or other factors. If watering places are too far apart, the zone around the drinking places will become seriously overgrazed. Since sheep require water less frequently than cattle, they are more suitable to utilize poorly watered range. Without satisfactory distribution of water over the range, it is impossible to obtain satisfactory utilization of the forage. Properly distributed water, like rationally spaced salt grounds, is an effective tool in luring cattle to graze upon all parts of the range. The amount of water consumed by livestock and methods of water development are discussed elsewhere.

**BASIS FOR PROPER STOCKING.** One highly practical and important question the range manager must decide is the basis for stocking a range. Forage production fluctuates widely from year to year because of changes in such growth factors as precipitation and temperature. Some years the volume of growth is several times greater than in other years. It is impossible to predict far ahead what the seasonal growth will be. Expansion or contraction of livestock numbers to any appreciable extent is not always immediately practicable.

The safest and best stocking rate should be based on production between the average and the poorest seasons. In large portions of the Rocky Mountain area this would result in use in excess of the Proper Use Factors on an average of about 1 yr. in 4; in the Southwest the intervals might be closer. This practice of stocking a bit below average production is usually the wisest plan for most situations, but the question must be settled for each area after carefully considering all local factors that are applicable.

A helpful procedure has been developed and used by some cattlemen who normally carry young animals through the second year on the range. Then, by marketing the surplus stock at a younger age, a heavy reduction in breeding herd can be avoided in years of stress.

**Establishing Grazing Periods.** One of the fundamental jobs of range managers is to determine and apply proper seasons of use. To do this, several factors must be known. A grazing opening date should be set, having in mind the average time the range is ready to graze. The growth should be far enough advanced to afford the livestock a "good bite." Generally the leaf blades of bunchgrasses should be from 3 to 5 in. in length, depending, however, on the species and their habit of growth.

If the need to get the stock onto the range in the spring is not urgent, the opening date should be late enough so the range will not be grazed too early even in the occasional late years. But if it is urgent to get stock on the range as soon as possible in the spring, the average time of vegetational readiness may be used as the opening date. Stock should be held off on late years and may be admitted to the range sooner when the seasons are early. Ranch operations should be planned so the animals can be carried on feed lots or winter ranges until the spring or summer ranges are ready to graze.

There is a close relationship between seasons of use and numbers of stock grazed. Obviously the longer the livestock are on the range the fewer can be grazed, and vice versa. The carrying capacity is determined in terms of total annual months' use.

Usually ranges should be grazed on a seasonal zone basis. The earliest range should be grazed first for a few weeks, followed by use of the next higher elevational zone. Stock may be held down on the zone to be grazed by several means, such as the use of zone fences, fences across canyons and other places ordinarily traveled by stock from the lower to higher range areas, and the use of herders to keep the stock from drifting to the higher areas. Although control by herders is some help it is less dependable than the other two methods.

**Natural Regeneration.** Range plants live from one or two to several years, depending upon whether they are annuals, biennials, or perennials. In any case, sooner or later they must be replaced by new plants. On depleted ranges the main job is to get a crop of new plants started to increase the density. Sometimes this is accomplished through artificial reseeding, but so far as possible it should be provided for naturally by good range management. Some plants reproduce vegetatively by rootstalks, but most species rely wholly or in part on the production of seeds. This fact makes it highly important to insure that seeds are produced and that the resulting seedlings have a chance to become established.

**Deferred and rotation grazing.** Deferred grazing usually means that livestock are kept off a portion of the range until after seed maturity, although any delay in the commencement of grazing can be considered deferred grazing. Rotation grazing refers to a division of the range area into units, usually 3 to 5, with an average of 4, so that the grazing can be rotated among the different units. The relative grazing capacity of each unit is so determined that each will receive its proportionate number of animal months' use. Under the deferred and rotation system of grazing, one unit is grazed first, another second, and so on, leaving one area ungrazed until the seed crop of the main forage species has ripened. The area is then grazed, and the movement of the animals helps to scatter and trample the seed into the ground. Grazing does not begin on the same area first each year but alternates among the units.

**Seedling protection.** It is important to give the young seedlings a chance to get a good start the year following grazing deferment until seed maturity. This can be accomplished either by deferring a unit 2 yr. in succession, or at least grazing it next to last the second year so the seedlings will not be grazed or trampled before mid-season. After one area has been deferred a year or two until seed maturity, another area is so deferred in rotation until all portions of the range have a chance to produce ripe seed over a period of years.

Some form of rotation grazing is essential for ranges predominantly bunchgrass, especially mountain lands with a short growing season, to maintain the plant cover in a high state of vigor. The advantages appear less pronounced on sod grass range, especially at lower elevations where moderate season-long cropping appears not to weaken the plants so much.

**JUDGING RANGE CONDITION AND TREND.** Determining the present condition of rangelands and whether or not they are on the upgrade or downgrade are basic techniques of range management. The range manager must be able to detect the earliest indications of retrogression resulting from misuse so that corrective measures can be applied at once. He must be able to determine when a range is in poorer condition than it should be so that steps can be taken for its restoration. Not only must the range be kept in good condition from a range use standpoint, but also because damage to the watershed, timber, wildlife, and recreation resources usually goes hand in hand with abuse of the forage resource. Usually the turn of range condition for the better or for worse is not readily apparent, and unless the range manager can detect it he will not realize what is happening to the area.

Range condition and trend are determined by observations of the plant cover, the soil, water runoff, and sometimes condition of the livestock. The latter is not a reliable guide, as the animals sometimes may be in good flesh and make good gains at the expense of the range. Experienced range managers can make deductions on range history and trends from the signs they may observe. For example, overgrazed browse species assume a hedged appearance when closely cropped. If grazing use is lightened, regrowth usually soon becomes apparent. By cutting off a number of representative twigs above and below the point where hedging occurred and counting the annual rings, it can be determined how long stagnation lasted. Sometimes willows or other brush reclaim sides of gullies or grow on a gully outwash or on a "sore spot" on the range, and the ages of the plants, determined by annual ring counts, give a good indication when recovery began.

A method for measuring trend in range condition on National Forest Ranges has been fairly well standardized. Permanently marked transects are established. Data are taken to give: (1) density of desirable, intermediate, and undesirable forage species; (2) a classification of current soil stability; and (3) an estimation of current trend in range condition and in vegetation. Photographs are taken to form a visual record. The transects are marked for future measurement and study of trend in condition of the range.

Many signs can be read from soil and plant conditions. Commonly the density of plant cover is reduced by overgrazing; deep-rooted perennials are replaced by shallow-rooted plants, including many annuals; the soil is eroding through the agencies of wind and water. The finer soil is washed or blown away, leaving an accumulation of the coarser pebbles on the surface, called "erosion pavement." Clumps of deep-rooted plants bind the soil and hold it in place while it is being removed from around them, leaving the clumps atop pedestals with their roots exposed around the edges. As soil moves down the slope, it piles up on the upper side of plant clumps and is moved away from the lower side. This action, in addition to hillside trails by foraging animals, creates a terraced effect. The forage on the more accessible areas is depleted first, causing sore spots to expand outward. Stock trails become more frequent and show evidence of much use.

As leaves fall from browse and trees they normally form a layer on the ground. In succeeding years fresh layers are piled on top. With passage of the years, the older layers disintegrate and eventually merge with the topsoil, which becomes rich in organic matter. Usually the layers from several years' leaf deposits can be discerned. When a range is overgrazed, the scant leafage and other accumulation of organic matter, such as grass stems, is washed away. On the typical overgrazed range, leaf layering is largely absent, little organic matter accumulates, and it is typical to see debris accumulate on the upper sides of obstructions such as rocks or logs as it moves down the slopes. When ranges begin to improve and the plant cover is partly restored, the soil and surface litter are again left in place. Lack of litter, and evidence of its movement, is an indication of deterioration, whereas its accumulation is usually evidence of recovery.

The above discussion points out only a few range indicators. Table 13 gives some of the more common indicators of both decline and improvement in an abbreviated form.

**ECONOMIC PRINCIPLES OF RANGE MANAGEMENT.** Economics deals with the human relationships growing out of man's efforts to make a living. Emphasis is on human relationships in using resources and in producing and exchanging things to satisfy wants. Thus the economics of range management deals with man's activities in satisfying wants through the use of rangeland. Land (natural resources), labor, capital, and management are the raw materials for production. The primary problem in economics is to combine and manage these factors so as to create the most satisfaction with the least expenditure of effort and resources.

A basic concept in economics is the "principle of diminishing returns." It holds that successive units of any factor added to the production process will at first increase output per unit of input, additional units will decrease output per unit of input, and still more will decrease output in absolute terms. For example, one bull with a hundred cows on a given range is not enough; two bulls may get a lot more calves; four may get even more, but not more per bull; whereas ten bulls may be too many and actually decrease the total output of the herd. A point is reached where additional factors in production do not "pay."

But factors in production can be combined in different ways. Thus the "principle of variable proportions" holds that land, labor, capital, and management be combined to attain a "most profitable" combination. Generally the cheaper factors will be used in relatively greater amounts than the more costly ones. For

Table 13. Reliable Indicators of Both Range Decline and Recovery

| Indicator | Misuse and decline of range | Proper use and recovery of range |
|---|---|---|
| Current utilization | Exceeds proper use factor of key species at close of season. Disproportionately excessive compared to length of time stock have been on the range prior to close of season. Use of less palatable species in excess of their proper use factor. | Not in excess of proper use factor of key species at close of season. Moderate use of key species in relation to length of time stock have been on the range prior to close of season. Use of less palatable species proportionate to their proper use factors. |
| Utilization previous year—shown by use of last year's twig growth on browse, amount of residue of last year's clumps of grass and stems of forbs. | Exceeded proper use factors of key species and other species. | Not in excess of proper use factors. |
| Condition of palatable shrubs. | Closely hedged, with dead or dying limbs or twigs and some whole plants dead or dying. "High line" evident at height of grazing owing to excessive removal of leaves and twigs currently and in the past. On some species, reduced size of leaves on portions of plants heavily grazed. | Palatable shrubs improving. "High line" becoming less evident owing to new shoots and leafage "getting away" below the height of grazing. Healthy new growth on previously weakened plants. |
| Plant vigor | Key species lacking in vigor as shown by sickly color, spring growth retarded, delay in producing flowers and seeds, growth reduced, fewer seed stalks, etc. | Good forage species vigorous as shown by healthy color, good volume, normal spring growth and development of vegetative parts, production of vigorous shoots, etc. |
| Grass clumps | Dead spots at sides or within clumps causing separation of larger clumps into several smaller individual clumps, or complete killing of the larger clumps. General lack of vigor. | Clumps enlarging vegetatively. Dead places healing. New clumps starting and expanding in size. |
| Plant succession | Key species diminishing and being replaced by less palatable species. Annuals increasing. Palatable species more prevalent in protected places out of reach of stock, such as within or under shrubs. | Good forage species increasing in places within reach of stock, and invading bare places or areas with light cover or covered with annuals. Annuals decreasing. Plants of different "succession stages" growing together often shows a dynamic situation. |

| | | |
|---|---|---|
| Regeneration | Scarcity or total absence of seedlings and young plants of key species except in places protected from grazing. New plants of species, such as aspen, that grow from underground stems, grazed too near the ground each year and unable to establish height growth. | Seedlings and young plants of key species becoming established in places within reach of stock. |
| Poisonous plants. Some poisonous plants, such as tall larkspur, grow naturally with key species in certain sites, and some are palatable. Presence of poisonous plants or losses from them are not always an indication of range decline. | Most poisonous plants are less palatable than the key species and their increase shows deterioration of the better forage plants. Increase of losses from poison plants usually indicates more use of them owing to a decrease of better forage species. | Decreasing losses from poisonous plants. |
| Bare spots caused by "yarding" or excessive use. | Much in evidence. Expanding in number, size, and degree of denudation. | Healing over by invasion of new plants. Expansion halted. Invasion of bare spots usually evident both by plants growing inward from the sides and by new plants getting established within the areas. First invaders are usually secondary species followed by better forage species. |
| Stock trails | Much in evidence and well worn. | Becoming less evident. Plant growth "catching hold" on tread. Plants growing in from the sides on the ground and browse twigs growing in from the sides above, tending to close the openings made by the trails. |

**Table 13. Reliable Indicators of Both Range Decline and Recovery** (Continued)

| Indicator | Misuse and decline of range | Proper use and recovery of range |
| --- | --- | --- |
| Erosion | Active in various forms. Presence of gullies with vertical sides. Raw, exposed soil on sides. Plants tipping over into gullies as they become undermined, sometimes re-establishing themselves temporarily on gully sides. Gullies expanding outward and headward, evidenced by overhanging banks, "cave-ins," etc. Sheet erosion manifested by plants on pedestals or hummocks, exposed crowns or roots of plants, terraced effect on hillsides, piling of debris behind obstructions, and cutting away of soil on the lower side of obstructions, lack of litter on surface, erosion pavement, top horizon gone, lack of organic matter, no accumulated layers of old leaves, soil washed away below lichen line on rocks, dust storms. | Erosion arrested or healing. Gullies rounding out. Outward and headward extension halted. Plants becoming established on sides and bottom of gullies. Leaf litter and other movable material accumulating on ground surface. Leaf litter adding organic matter to top soil, terracing arrested and becoming less evident. New plant clumps forming with crowns at ground level. Movement of soil by wind and water diminishing. |
| Runoff | High water frequent and concurrent with storms; water silt-laden. | Occurrence of high water and muddy streams diminishing. |
| Timber reproduction | Hedged appearance. Terminal buds and new shoots cropped. Hardwood seedlings and new shoots grazed close to the ground. | Hedging diminishing. Terminal buds unharmed. If terminal bud gone, a lateral bud sometimes becomes dominant and makes an upward growth. Hardwood seedlings and new shoots not excessively grazed, and height growth accumulating each year. |
| Condition of livestock | May or may not be in poor condition. Sometimes are in good condition at expense of the range and watershed, such as use of key and other species in excess of proper use factors. Stock in poor flesh, except during abnormal droughts or when they reach the range in poor flesh, is usually an indication of a poor range condition. In extreme cases, deaths occur from malnutrition, or the animals lose flesh and the calf crop is reduced. | Stock in good flesh, or gaining if arrived on range in poor flesh. Substantial gains being made. |

example, in the days of the open range, large acreages of land were used relative to the labor, capital, and management. Now with land becoming more dear, it pays to use it more intensively, i.e., more labor, capital, and management per acre. Ranchers strive to produce the most meat or wool for each dollar of costs. Some costs are fixed, or relatively so, while others can be varied in response to physical productivity and relative prices of inputs and product. Forest rangers also strive to "produce" the most forage, timber, clear water, scenery, or other products for each unit of costs. As a rule, the most human satisfaction is achieved when the factors of production are combined in such a way that the last unit of each factor added just pays for itself.

The most "economical" rate of stocking is a common problem in the economics of range management. The answer must take into account the class of livestock, gains in weight or healthy maintenance, calf or lamb crops, death loss, and effects of different rates of use on the range. An illustration is found in the gains on growing animals. Twenty 700-lb. steers on a given section of range may gain 200 lb. apiece during a 6-month grazing season, or a total gain of 4,000 lb. Thirty steers on the same land may gain only 150 lb. apiece but total gain has been increased to 4,500 lb. Add another 10 steers and gains on each may drop to 90 lb., thus decreasing the total gain to 3,600 lb. The choice obviously lies between using 20 or 30 head.

Now consider relative prices of inputs and product. The inputs are land (in terms of rent, taxes and interest, or grazing fees), capital—primarily the cost of the steers and interest on that amount—labor costs, and management costs. In this example probably land costs are fixed and labor and management costs are fairly small items. The output is beef which may vary in selling price per pound as well as total pounds available for sale.

A gain of 200 lb. on each animal may make him grade "Good," which will bring perhaps 20 cents a pound on the market. A gain of 150 lb. may make him grade "Commercial," which will bring only 16 cents. Twenty 900-lb. "Good" steers will sell for $3,600 while thirty 850-lb. "Commercial" steers will sell for $4,080. Is the extra $480 gross income worth the added expense, risk, and drain on the range feed supply?

An additional alternative might be to stock at the rate of 30 steers and feed a supplement, in which case each steer may gain 225 lb. and grade "Choice" on reaching the market. This action requires greater costs for animals, feed, facilities, and labor. The decision of what kind and how much supplement to feed also is involved. Without working out this example in further detail, it is apparent that recognition of the concepts of diminishing returns and variable proportions will lead to a most profitable combination of land, labor, management, and capital in the form of steers, feed, and facilities.

Consider now an additional factor in this example. Grazing this section of range with 20 steers under proper management may permit some improvement in the forage cover, 30 steers may only maintain present range conditions, and 40 steers may do damage. So in addition to the most profitable input-output ratio for a single grazing season, thought must be given to the most profitable combination for as far into the future as the "management" wishes to plan—termed the "economic horizon" by some. Needless to say, the distance to this horizon from the present varies with the individual. A public manager of rangeland may have a much farther horizon than a rancher; a rancher who is well financed and established may have a much farther horizon than one pressed by debt. Security of tenure, financial position, business outlook, and many other factors affect the distance one sees into the future and the values he finds there.

A dollar income this year is worth more now than the prospect of a dollar income next year. The amount of the additional value of present over future income depends upon what each individual sees on his economic horizon and how far away it is. In the aggregate, the premium paid for present over future income is the going rate of interest on money. If the rancher, in the example given, decides this year to forego the income from the 30 steers and take only the income from 20 so as to increase the future production of his land resources, he figures that the added future production will be great enough in physical terms and valuable enough in economic terms to more than pay him for waiting for that income.

The business of producing from rangeland is much like any other productive enterprise, but with some unique features arising from the nature of the resources and the social institutions. Rangeland productivity per acre is relatively low and, in general, it has no alternative uses other than to provide forage for grazing animals (multiple use will be considered briefly later). The rancher's practical alternatives are to use his land for grazing cattle or sheep, or combinations of them, or not use it at all. He can choose between a steer operation and a cow-calf operation, or other combinations of livestock, but he cannot choose between beef cattle and cotton or between sheep and soybeans. So the fortunes of the livestock industry inescapably determine the management of rangeland. This means, for one thing, that development of a livestock industry in the South will not put the West out of business as has been averred by some. It may mean, however, that such a development will reduce the capital structure now supported by the western range and livestock industry.

Since rangeland generally is of low productivity, its value also is low. This often leads to costly mistakes in evaluation, both with respect to purchase price and to appraisal for taxation. One frequently sees rangeland selling for $7.50 an acre when it may be worth only $5.00. One seldom sees tilled land sell for $750 an acre when its worth is only $500; yet the relative difference is the same. Difficulty of appraisal is one reason for this. Another is that a few cents an acre difference in price does not sound very big, but in the aggregate these few cents may determine the financial success of the ranch. On the other hand, little land is so poor that it cannot be used profitably if it can be had at the right price. "Submarginal land" exists only when land is misused or burdened with a false capital structure.

This leads to a consideration of another of the common questions about the economics of range management, namely, what is the most economical rate of investment in range improvements? In general, the capacity of rangeland to respond to added inputs of labor and capital is fairly low, so considerable care must be exercised in making investments in improvements. This means only that the "point of diminishing returns" may be reached rather quickly. One dollar an acre added investment may give high returns, even $5 may give satisfactory returns, but $10 may be far too much for profitable operation. The price of land before improvement in relation to the cost of improvement is of no consequence, but the value of the land after the improvement in relation to the cost of it is of considerable significance.

Again, since rangeland productivity generally is low per acre, large acreages are required for economic units. Space alone makes the economics of range management unique. For one thing, it means relatively loose control over the resources employed. For another, it has perhaps contributed to the establishment of many operating units too small to be economical. None of the homestead laws, for example, lets a man get fee simple control of enough rangeland to be economically operated.

Owing to the nature and location of most of the land generally considered as the "range," the concept of multiple use has assumed greater importance than with other resources used in agriculture. Rangeland is the basic resource for the rancher's business, but it is also the habitat for game, the watershed for irrigation districts and cities, scenery, and a dozen other things of varying importance. This often results in two or more management plans being superimposed on the same land by as many different entrepreneurs, each with differing concepts of costs, incomes, and economic horizons. Each plan may be put into effect to a greater or lesser degree, depending on the nature of the land tenure in a legal sense and the ability of the tenant to enforce control. Obviously these different interests and resources complicate the economics of range management.

Another unique feature of rangeland is the nature of the land tenure and the tenure pattern. Much of the range is in public ownership and even more is used in conjunction with public land, so the public is more intimately involved than is the case with other types of agricultural land. Here is not the place to explore in detail the institutional and administrative climate of public control of the range. Suffice it to say that this climate controls man's action in pursuit of economic activity as surely as the cold winds and frosty nights of autumn impel a range cow to seek the meadows of the homeland.

Nevertheless, the economics of range management is much like the economics of any production process. Each industry has its unique characteristics imposed by the physical relationships between inputs and product, and by the institutional environment within which it operates. The characteristics of rangeland are unique, the major ones being briefly sketched above. Other considerations are ranch organization and management, range appraisal, range and ranch financing, taxation, livestock marketing, and many other topics which also are part of the subject matter of the economics of range management but cannot be discussed here.

## Range Improvements

Physical range improvements, principally fences and water developments, are necessary for the control and welfare of livestock and especially to obtain equitable distribution and proper utilization of the range. Before undertaking an improvement project a critical appraisal should be made of the cost and the probable benefits to be expected in terms of improved forage conditions and benefits to the livestock. The availability of native material on the construction site should also be explored.

**FENCES.** Fences are commonly used for the following purposes:

1. Boundary. To prevent trespass.
2. Drift. To prevent livestock from getting off the range allotted to it; to confine herds to proper elevational and seasonal zones in line with forage development; and to avoid drift onto main roads or into recreational areas.
3. Division. To divide ranges into management units for obtaining equitable and proper utilization of each portion of the range, and to facilitate rotation management.
4. Pasture. To provide facilities better to handle livestock on the range, such as enclosures for saddle and pack animals; to hold livestock temporarily during roundups or at any other time; or to reserve feed for special uses, such as for game animals.
5. Protection. To prevent use of areas that are particularly susceptible to damage from livestock, such as those being treated in erosion control, or to keep livestock away from heavy stands of poisonous plants.

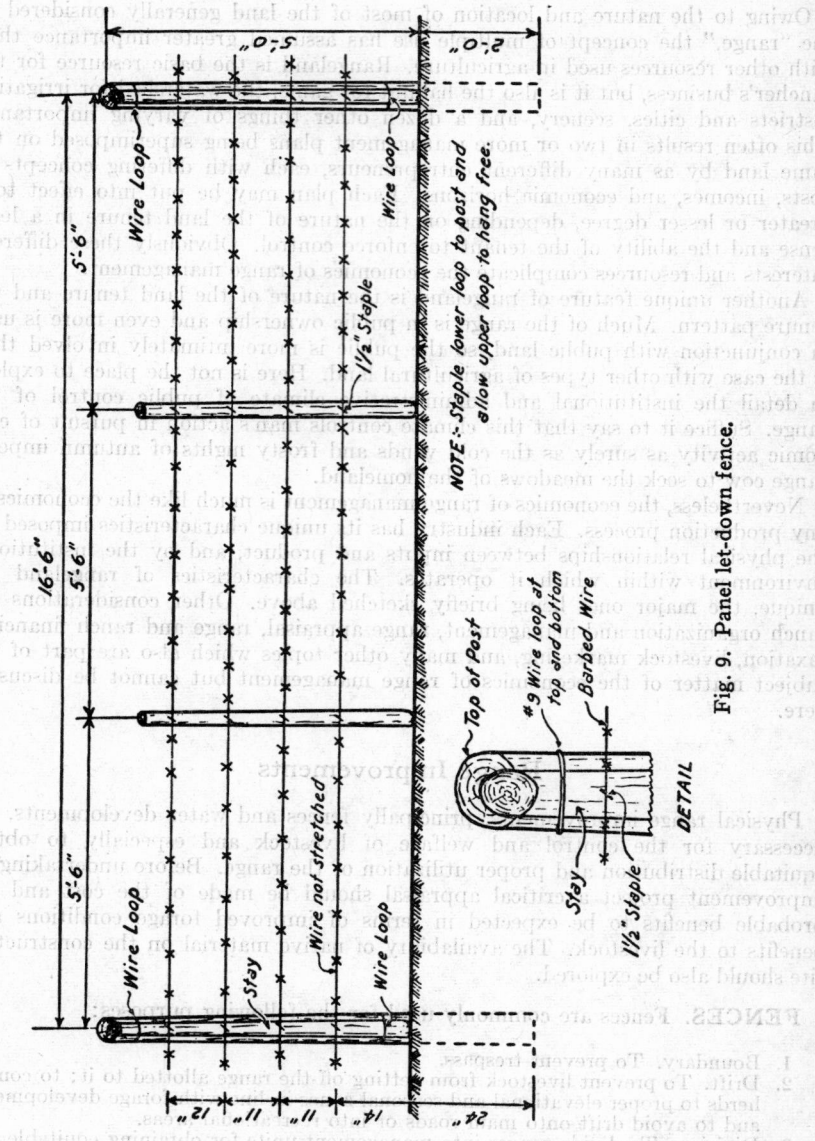

Fig. 9. Panel let-down fence.

**Types of Fences.** For areas of abundant snow where wires are subject to heavy strain during winter and spring, the let-down or panel type fence is used. The wire should be stapled to stays. There should be two stays between each post and another opposite each post. The fence is constructed in ⅛- to ¼-mi. sections. A wide loop is stapled to the top and bottom of each post to hold panels upright (Fig. 9).

Buck and pole fences use poles of native material. The panels should be 12 ft.

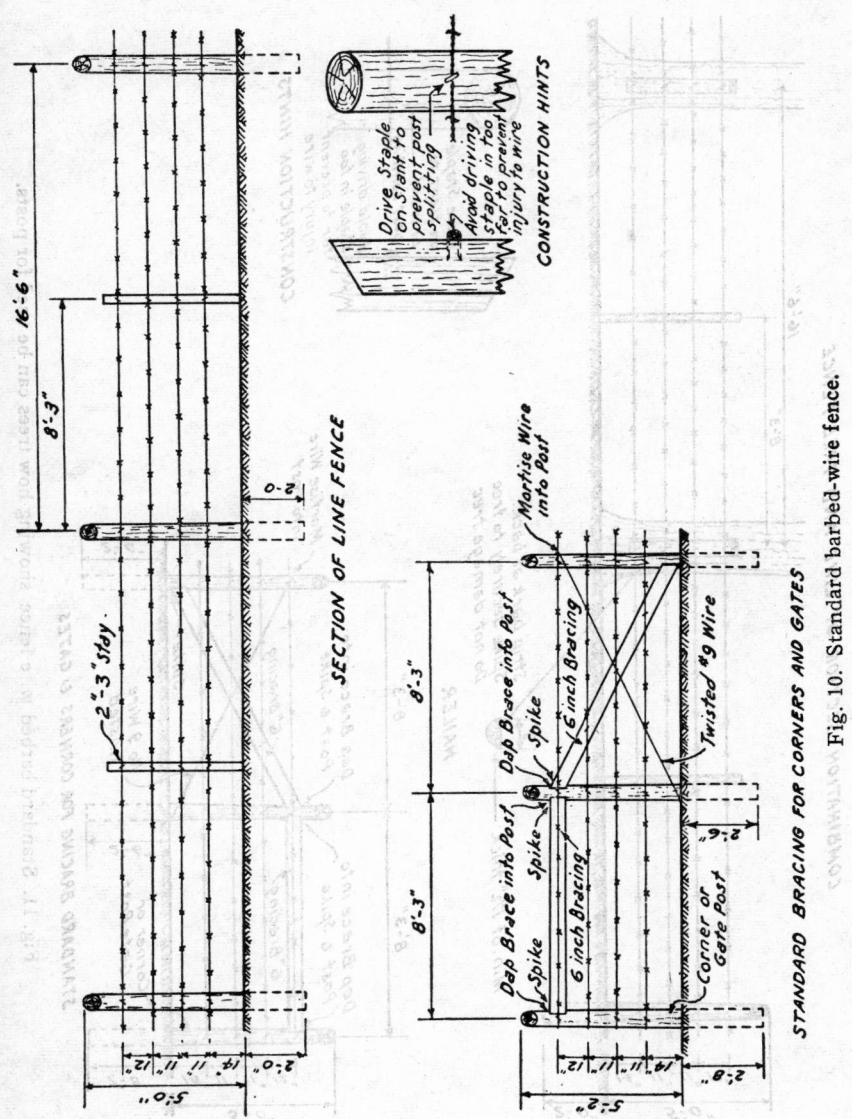

Fig. 10. Standard barbed-wire fence.

or shorter to lessen the possibility of sag. Poles are spiked to cross bucks with 50d or 60d spikes.

Special fence construction is needed in rocky country where digging post holes is difficult. "Rock Jack" and "Figure Four" wire fence is effective where native wood and rock are readily available. The Rock Jack is built as a tripod with a pole floor. The floor is weighted with from 100 to 200 lb. of rock and the Jacks are used at intervals for anchors, and for corners. The Figure Four uses three lengths of material, put together in the form of a triangle. The upright side of the

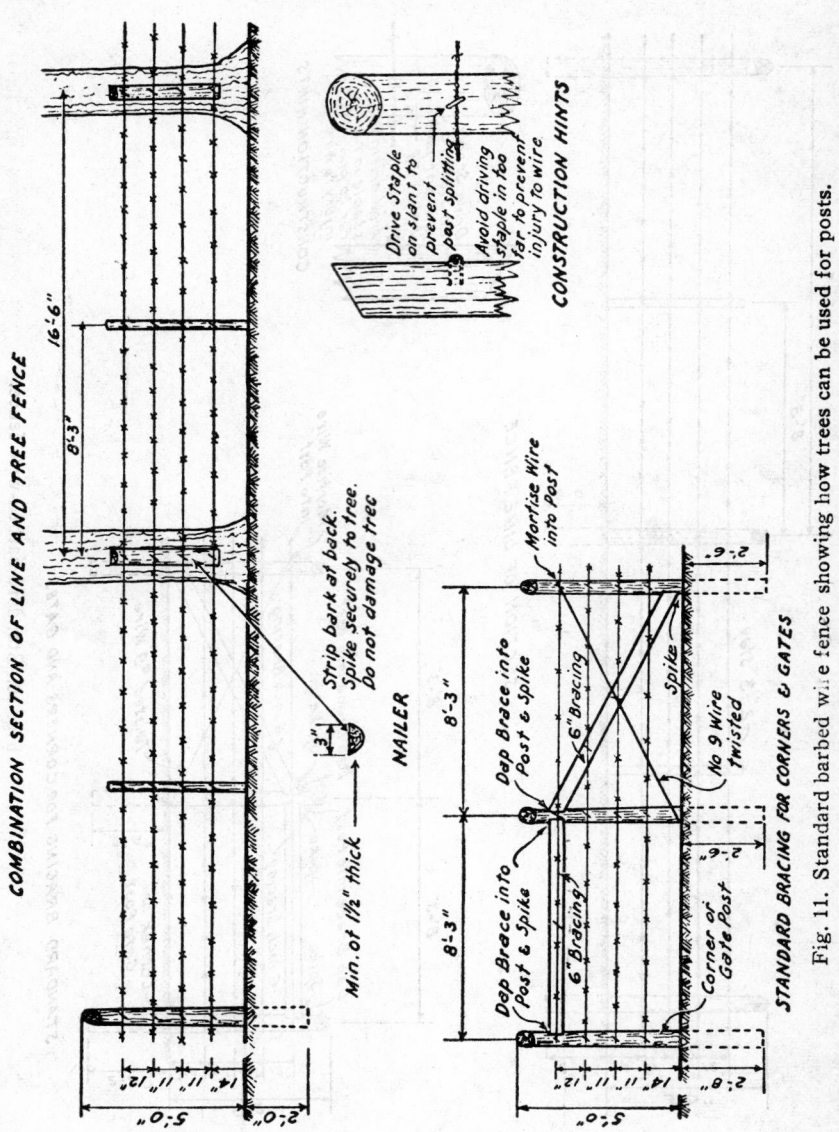

Fig. 11. Standard barbed wire fence showing how trees can be used for posts.

triangle is used to hold the fence wire. The Figure Fours are spaced between the Jacks.

Wire fences with steel posts are in common use. Even in rocky areas, where the country is not too steep to navigate with tractor and compressor, steel posts may be used. Holes for the posts may be drilled with a jack hammer.

The so-called standard barbed-wire fence is used either with durable wood posts or steel posts, in situations where post holes can be dug or posts driven at a relatively low cost (Figs. 10 and 11).

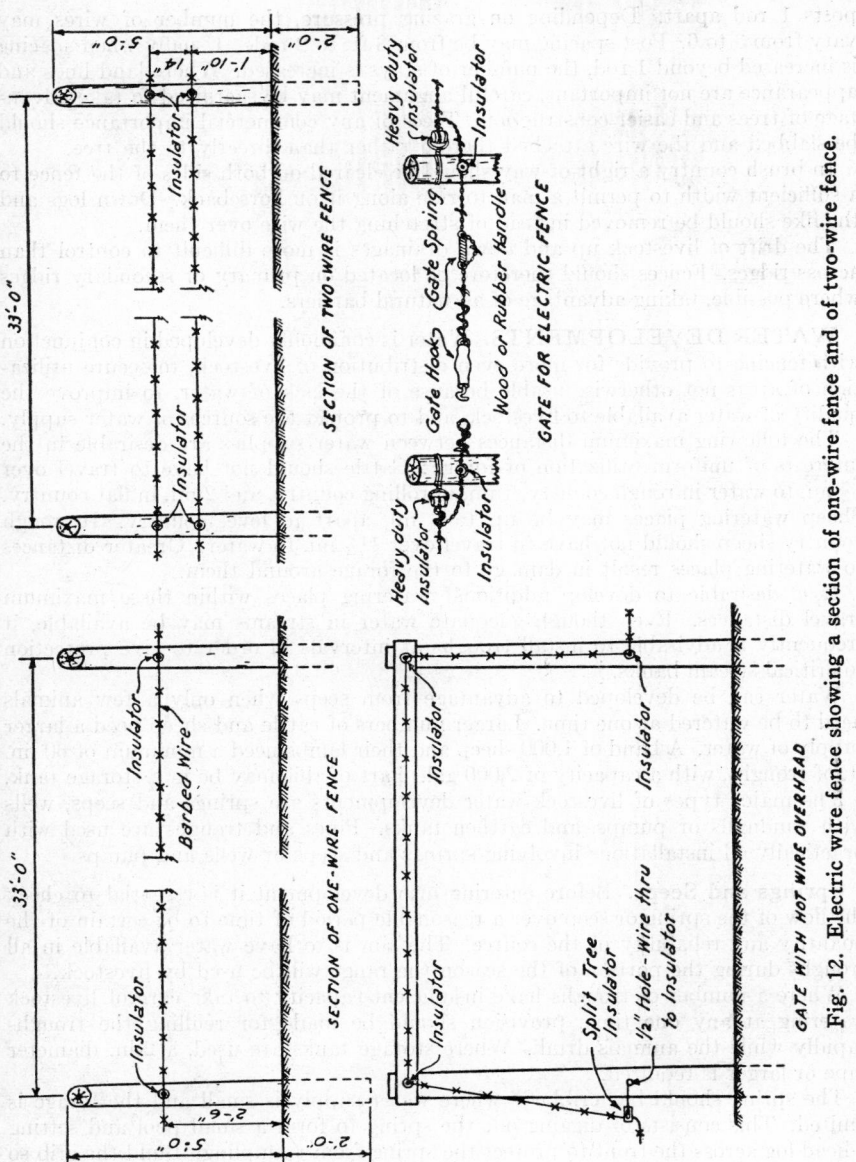

Fig. 12. Electric wire fence showing a section of one-wire fence and of two-wire fence.

Temporary fence installations are built with two electrified wires. One wire is strung on solid knob insulators; the other may be fastened directly to the posts. It is important that all brush and weeds clear wires, to avoid grounding (Fig. 12).

**Standards of Fence Construction.** Construction standards should be varied to fit the exact situation on the ground. The standard fence uses four wires with posts 1 rod apart. Depending on grazing pressure, the number of wires may vary from 3 to 6. Post spacing may be from 8 ft. to 2 rods. Usually when spacing is increased beyond 1 rod, the number of stays is increased. Where land lines and appearance are not important, careful alignment may be sacrificed to take advantage of trees and easier construction. Trees of any commercial importance should be slabbed and the wire attached thereto rather than directly to the tree.

In brush country a right-of-way should be cleared on both sides of the fence to a sufficient width to permit a man to ride along it on horseback. Down logs and the like should be removed instead of stretching the wire over them.

The drift of livestock up and down drainages is more difficult to control than across ridges. Fences should therefore be located on primary or secondary ridges where possible, taking advantage of all natural barriers.

**WATER DEVELOPMENTS.** Water is commonly developed in conjunction with fencing to provide for more even distribution of livestock, to secure utilization of areas not otherwise usable because of the lack of water, to improve the quality of water available to livestock, and to protect the sources of water supply.

The following maximum distances between water supplies are desirable in the interests of uniform utilization of forage: Cattle should not have to travel over ½ mi. to water in rough country, 1 mi. in rolling country, and 2 mi. in flat country. Sheep watering places may be up to 3 mi. apart in level country. In rough country sheep should not have to travel over 1½ mi. to water. Greater distances to watering places result in damage to the forage around them.

It is desirable to develop additional watering places within these maximum travel distances. Even though adequate water in streams may be available, it frequently is advisable to install troughs at intervals in order to give protection to critical stream banks.

Water can be developed to advantage from seeps when only a few animals need to be watered at one time. Larger numbers of cattle and sheep need a larger supply of water. A band of 1,000 sheep and their lambs need a minimum of 60 lin. ft. of troughs, with a capacity of 2,000 gal. Part of this may be in a storage tank.

The major types of livestock water developments are springs and seeps, wells with windmills or pumps, and earthen tanks. Pipes and troughs are used with practically all installations involving springs and seeps or wells and pumps.

**Springs and Seeps.** Before entering into development it is essential to check the flow of the spring or seep over a reasonable period of time to be certain of the quantity and reliability of the source. The aim is to have water available in all troughs during the portion of the season the range will be used by livestock.

Where a number of troughs have insufficient capacity to take care of livestock watering at any one time, provision should be made for refilling the troughs rapidly while the animals drink. Where storage tanks are used, a 2-in. diameter pipe or larger is required.

The spring should be "cribbed" where water supply is small and the forage is limited. This consists of digging out the spring to form a small pool and setting a head log across the front to protect the spring from trampling. Build the crib so that animals will not step into the pool (Fig. 13).

Standard spring development is as follows: Dig out the spring head at the source of water supply; use rock, concrete, plank, or a corrugated iron culvert to make a permanent collection basin in which to install an outlet pipe to the tank or trough; cover the spring head, and fence if necessary for protection; install a trough at a suitable site below and as close to the spring as is feasible, to minimize the amount of pipe required (Figs. 14 and 15).

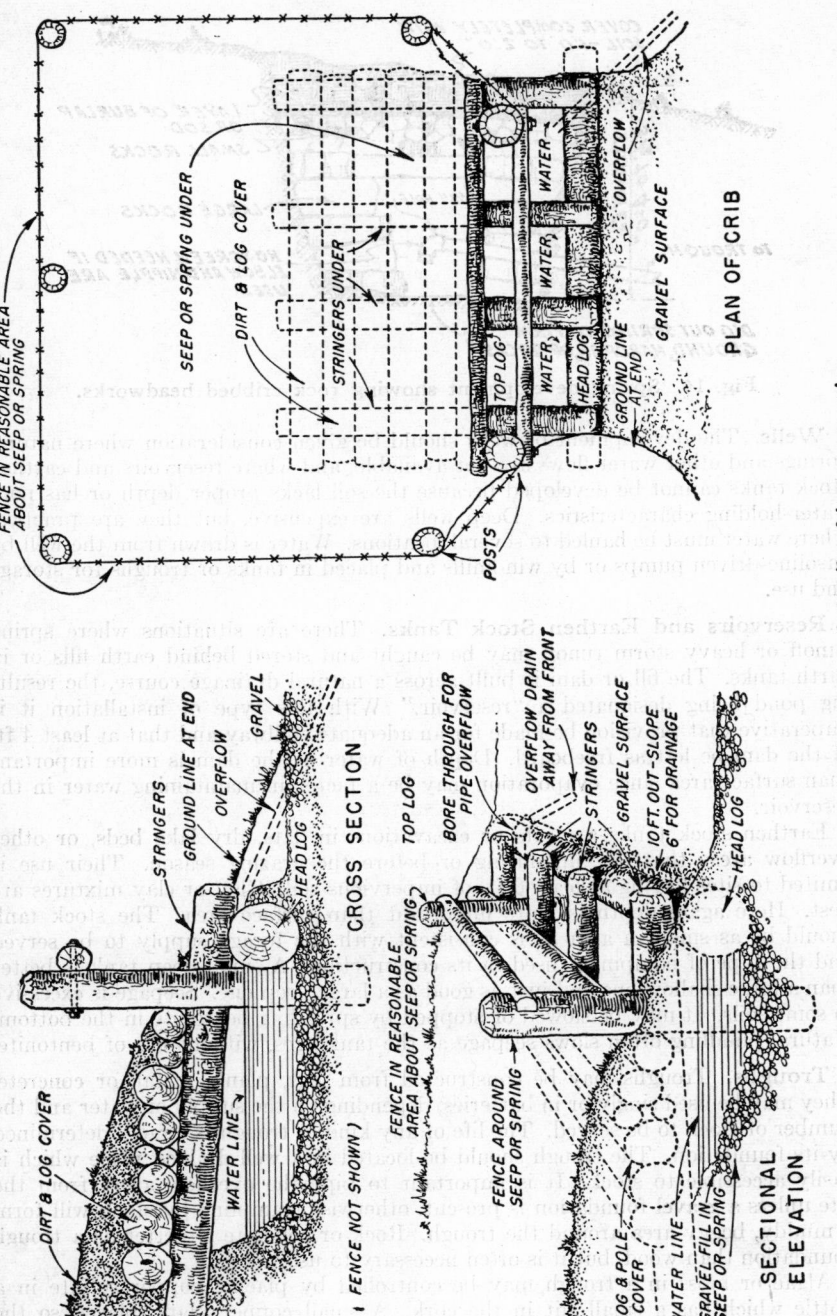

Fig. 13. Crib water development and details of its construction.

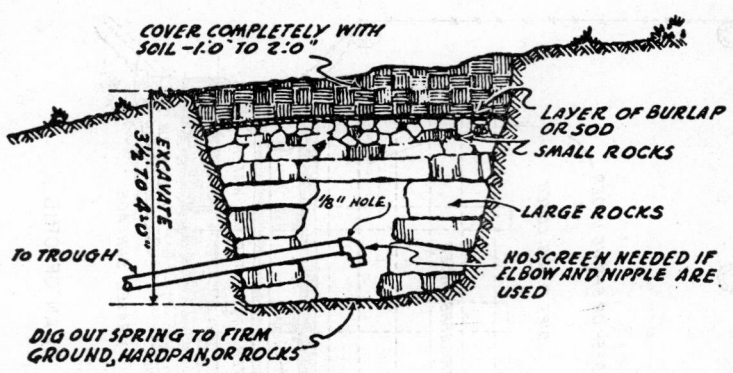

**Fig. 14. Spring development showing rock cribbed headworks.**

**Wells.** The development of wells should be given consideration where natural springs and other water flows are not available, and where reservoirs and earthen stock tanks cannot be developed because the soil lacks proper depth or has poor water-holding characteristics. Deep wells are expensive, but they are practical where water must be hauled to several locations. Water is drawn from the well by gasoline-driven pumps or by windmills and placed in tanks or troughs for storage and use.

**Reservoirs and Earthen Stock Tanks.** There are situations where spring runoff or heavy storm runoff may be caught and stored behind earth fills or in earth tanks. The fill or dam is built across a natural drainage course, the resulting pond being designated a "reservoir." With this type of installation it is imperative that provision be made for an adequate spillway and that at least 4 ft. of the dam be left as freeboard. Depth of water at the dam is more important than surface area since evaporation may be a factor in maintaining water in the reservoir.

Earthen stock tanks are pits or excavations in flats, dry lake beds, or other overflow areas that dry up during or before the grazing season. Their use is limited to sites having at least 6 ft. of impervious soil. Clay or clay mixtures are best. Here again depth is more important than surface area. The stock tank should be as small in area as is consistent with the forage supply to be served and the type of equipment used in its construction. A small deep tank is better than a large shallow one and just as good as a large deep one. Seepage is excessive in some soils. It may be slowed or stopped by spreading bentonite in the bottom. Natural puddling often slows seepage as the tank ages, without use of bentonite.

**Troughs.** Troughs may be constructed from logs, plank, metal, or concrete. They may be used singly or in batteries, depending on the supply of water and the number of stock to be served. The life of any kind of trough is largely determined by its foundation. The trough should be located in a well-drained place which is easily accessible to stock. It is important to pipe the overflow away from the site unless a gravel foundation is present, otherwise trampling by stock will form a muddy, boggy area around the trough. Rock or concrete is better as a trough foundation than wood, but it is often necessary to use wood.

Algae or moss in a trough may be controlled by placing copper sulfate in a bottle which has a small slit in the cork. A small copper plate, placed so the intake water runs over it, will also control algae.

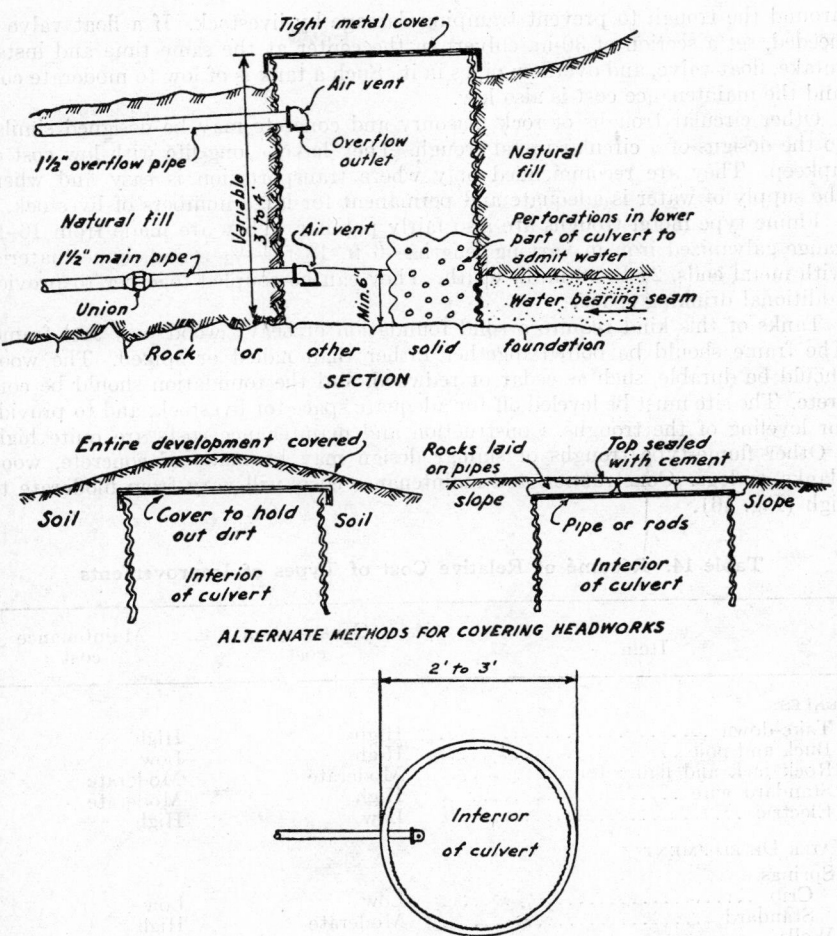

around the trough to prevent trampling and mudholes. If a float valve is needed, set in simultaneously with the trough to save time and install trouble float valves, outlets, and inlets below frost line are to promote cost and the maintenance cost is less...

[text partially visible] ...other, eminent frost, or rock, frost, [illegible]... to the occasional silting up of the pool, should... upkeep. They are located in places commonly... the supply of water is abundant, permanent...

Some types of... some culverts...

Tanks of the...

The frame should be... should be durable... crete. The... for leveling...

**Fig. 15. Spring development culvert headworks.**

**Kinds of Troughs for Cattle.** Circular corrugated iron troughs are available in the following sizes.

| Diameter (ft.) | Capacity (gals.) |
|---|---|
| 5 | 250 |
| 6 | 300 |
| 7 | 350 |
| 8 | 400 |

Install by pouring a concrete slab with 1-2-4 mix. Reinforce with light steel, telephone wire, or wire mesh. Set trough in concrete while wet and level accurately, tamp well, add concrete inside to provide a slight slope to drain, and finish with neat cement. Inlet and overflow pipes should be brought through the concrete floor at the low point of the drain near the center. Leave a concrete apron around the trough to prevent tramping damage by livestock. If a float valve is needed, set a section of 30-in. culvert in the center at the same time and install intake, float valve, and overflow pipes in it. Such a tank is of low to moderate cost and the maintenance cost is also low.

Other circular troughs of rock masonry and concrete may be designed similar to the designs of a circular metal trough. They have a long life with low cost of upkeep. They are recommended only where transportation is easy and where the supply of water is adequate and permanent for large numbers of livestock.

Flume type metal troughs are also fairly popular. They are made from 16–18 gauge galvanized iron in varying lengths—6 to 18 ft.—½ round flume material with metal ends, 24 to 36 in. in width. They can be coupled together to provide additional drinking space.

Tanks of this kind require a solid foundation of heavy wood post and frame. The frame should be bolted together rather than nailed or spiked. The wood should be durable, such as cedar or redwood, and the foundation should be concrete. The site must be leveled off for adequate space for livestock, and to provide for leveling of the troughs. Construction and maintenance costs are quite high.

Other flume-type troughs of similar design may be made of concrete, wood planks, or logs. Construction and maintenance costs will vary from moderate to high (Fig. 16).

### Table 14. Résumé of Relative Cost of Types of Improvements

| Item | Construction cost | Maintenance cost |
|------|-------------------|------------------|
| **FENCES** | | |
| Take-down .......................... | High | High |
| Buck and pole ....................... | High | Low |
| Rock jack and figure four........... | Moderate | Moderate |
| Standard wire ....................... | High | Moderate |
| Electric ............................ | Low | High |
| **WATER DEVELOPMENT** | | |
| Springs | | |
| Crib ............................ | Low | Low |
| Standard ........................ | Moderate | High |
| Wells | | |
| Shallow ......................... | Moderate | Moderate |
| Deep ............................ | High | High |
| Reservoirs .......................... | Moderate to high | Moderate |
| Earthen stock tanks ................. | Low to moderate | Moderate |
| **TROUGHS—CATTLE** | | |
| Circular metal ...................... | Low to moderate | Low |
| Circular concrete or masonry ........ | High | Low |
| Metal flume type .................... | High | Moderate to high |
| Concrete ............................ | High | Low |
| Wood planks ......................... | Moderate | Moderate |
| Logs ................................ | High | Low |
| **TROUGHS—SHEEP** | | |
| Metal flume type .................... | High | Moderate to high |
| Battery type | | |
| Metal ........................... | Moderate | Low |
| Wood plank ...................... | Moderate | Moderate |

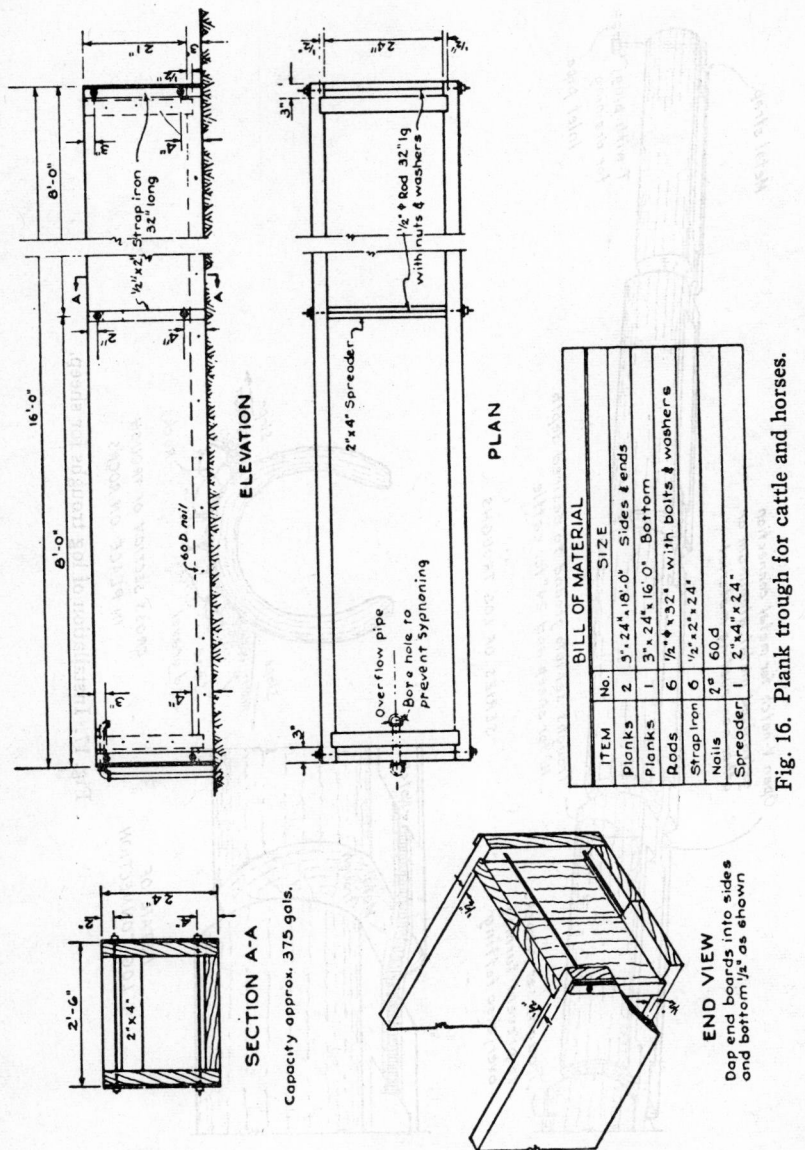

**BILL OF MATERIAL**

| ITEM | No. | SIZE |
|------|-----|------|
| Planks | 2 | 5"x 24"x 18'-0"  Sides & ends |
| Planks | 1 | 3"x 24"x 16'-0"  Bottom |
| Rods | 6 | ½"∅ x 32"  with bolts & washers |
| Strap Iron | 6 | ½"x 2"x 24" |
| Nails | 2⁸ | 60d |
| Spreader | 1 | 2"x 4"x 24" |

ELEVATION

PLAN

SECTION A-A

Capacity approx. 375 gals.

END VIEW
Dap end boards into sides
and bottom ⅛" as shown

Fig. 16. Plank trough for cattle and horses.

**Kinds of Troughs for Sheep.** Metal flume-type troughs, Lennon type, are popular. They are made from 16 to 18 gauge metal, ½ round flume material, 30 in. wide, and 10 ft. sections. Lengths should be 60 to 90 ft. The number of batteries, lengths, and width will be determined by the number of sheep and the daily supply of water. This type of tank requires a substantial bolted wood frame or concrete foundation and a level site to avoid excessive excavation. Construction and maintenance costs are moderate to high.

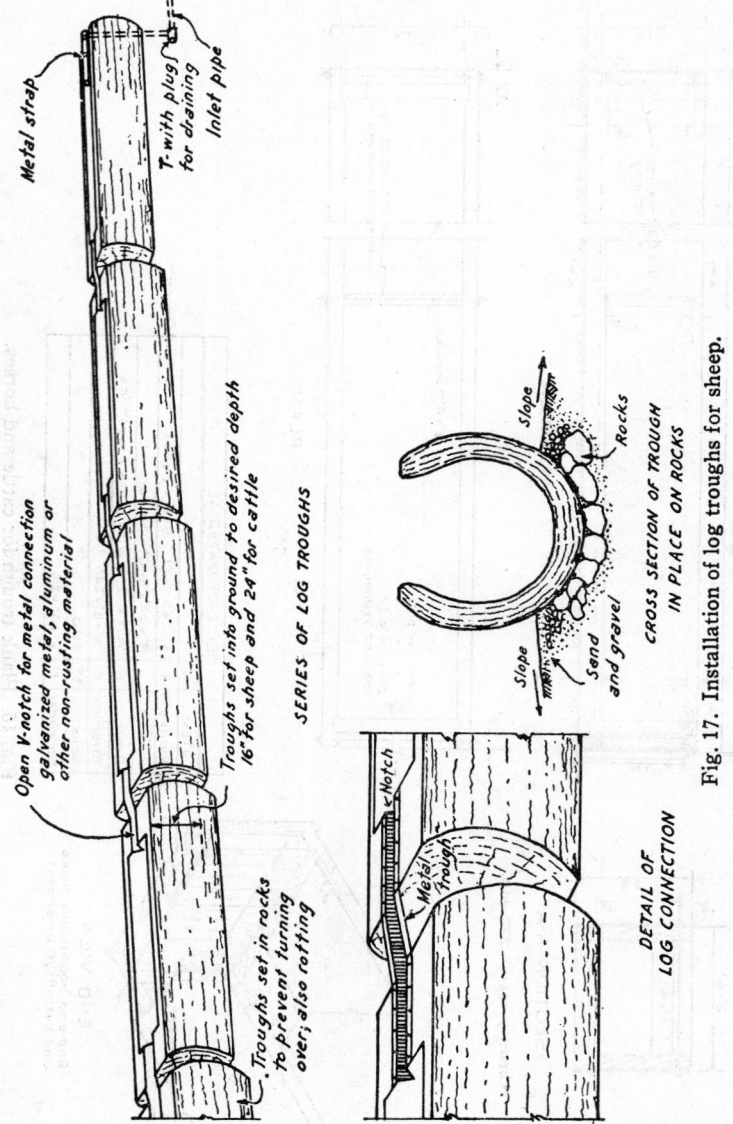

Metal strap

T with plug for draining

Inlet pipe

Open V-notch for metal connection galvanized metal, aluminum or other non-rusting material

Troughs set into ground to desired depth 16" for sheep and 24" for cattle

SERIES OF LOG TROUGHS

Troughs set in rocks to prevent turning over; also rotting

Slope

Rocks

Slope

Sand and gravel

CROSS SECTION OF TROUGH IN PLACE ON ROCKS

V-Notch

Metal Trough

DETAIL OF LOG CONNECTION

Fig. 17. Installation of log troughs for sheep.

"Step-Down" or "Battery" type metal or log troughs are suitable to sloping or steep areas and can be laid on the curvature of the slope. They consist of a series of metal, plank, or hewn log troughs placed end to end and connected together by pipe or metal overflow from one to another on progressively lower levels. If made of metal, the trough should be of heavy corrugated galvanized iron with a flat heavy bottom. It has a long life and the maintenance cost is low to negligible (Fig. 17).

## Prescribed Burning in Southern Pine and Hardwood Forests in Relation to Grazing

When considering grazing in southern forests, two points should be recognized at the outset: (1) Grazing and timber production are not completely compatible on the same land—management for maximum returns from one will necessarily reduce returns from the other. (2) Most southern forest lands are more valuable for timber production than for native forage. Consequently, timber production should usually receive first priority in management, although grazing may provide considerable supplemental income.

**OBJECTIVES OF PRESCRIBED BURNING.** Fire is recognized in the South as a valuable tool in the management of pine but not of hardwoods. It is widely used by managers of pine lands for such purposes as hazard reduction, hardwood control, disease control, and seedbed preparation. It is also a valuable tool for improving wildlife habitat and cattle range. Burning generally favors grazing in this region in two ways: It encourages the growth of grasses and other herbaceous species and retards woody species, and it improves the palatability and nutritive value of the herbage. As a rule, benefits are greatest in the types where burning is also applied most frequently for protection or silvicultural purposes. All references to fire or burning in this section refer to **prescribed burning,** briefly defined as the plan-wise application of fire under prescribed conditions for specific purposes.

Several accepted benefits of prescribed burning to the longleaf–slash forest, and more limitedly of other forest types, as well as to forage covers, are listed in Table 15.

**Table 15. Some Beneficial as Well as Harmful Effects of Prescribed Burning to Forest Types and Grazing Covers**

| Timber and forage type | Accepted status of fire use in forest management, and relative need or benefit for grazing |
|---|---|
| Longleaf–slash pine ............... | Widely used for protection and several aspects of silviculture. |
| a. Wiregrass ................... | Essential for adequate cattle gain in spring and summer; greatly increases forage quality. |
| b. Bluestem ................... | Beneficial but not essential; improves forage quality in spring. |
| Shortleaf–loblolly pine–hardwoods . | In limited use now; advocated for hardwood control and seedbed preparation where erosion hazard is low. |
| a. Bluestem ................... | Beneficial; improves quality and availability; helps control shrubs and to maintain grass. |
| b. Miscellaneous grasses ........ | Little benefit except for maintaining grass. |
| Pond pine–hardwoods.............. | In limited use now; essential for pine regeneration but difficult to apply. |
| a. Switch cane ................ | Not needed for quality; infrequent burning desirable for maintaining forage stands and controlling shrubs. |
| Bottomland hardwoods ........... | No burning is recommended. |
| a. Switch cane ................ | Not warranted in association with hardwoods. |
| b. Miscellaneous species ........ | Not warranted in association with hardwoods. |
| Upland hardwoods ................ | No burning; grazing not recommended in Appalachian region; limited grazing in Ozarks. |

Three conditions are of particular importance in the successful use of fire, namely, to recognize the best time to burn, to be familiar with the techniques of burning, and know how best to manage grazing on burned areas.

**WHEN TO BURN.** The time of burning in relation to age or condition of the forest stand as well as time of year should be dictated by forest management aspects treated elsewhere in this handbook. Under prescribed conditions, fire can often be applied successfully in pine stands at any stage after crop trees are 8 to 15 ft. tall (longleaf tolerates burning in the grass stage). As a rule, prescribed burning is done in late fall and winter, which fits in well with grazing management. However, most of the forage species tolerate burning at any season.

**HOW TO BURN.** Prescribed burning is a distinctly technical measure. To give maximum benefits it involves an analysis of forest and fuel conditions; and, based on this analysis and the objectives desired, a detailed burning plan or prescription specifying the type of fire (backfire, flankfire, etc.), time of day, weather conditions, crew size and duties, etc., should be prepared. Successful burning is difficult even for experienced men. Guides and instructions are available locally and should be thoroughly studied by inexperienced men before burning is attempted, for misguided efforts to burn are almost certain to produce disastrous results.

A few generalizations can be mentioned. Backfires are recommended where trees are small (less than 3 in. d.b.h.); flankfires can be used under larger trees and are cheaper because they spread faster. With very light fuels, headfires are feasible. The best wind condition is a constant, northerly breeze of from 3 to 10 mi. an hour. Burning should not be attempted unless such wind conditions are forecast to continue at least 12 hr. These conditions usually occur during the clear weather following winter rains. Day burning is easiest, but night burning is necessary when minimum fire intensity is required.

**Table 16. Guides to Grazing Capacity of Major Southern Forest Types**

| Type | Acres per animal unit per month | Notes and precautions in relation to burned range |
|---|---|---|
| Wiregrass (longleaf–slash pine) ... | 2–7 | Allow a minimum of 8 acres of burn per animal. Keep cattle off burns until grass is 4 to 6 in. tall. |
| Bluestem (longleaf pine) .......... | 1–3 | If burning is practiced, provide enough for 4 months grazing. |
| Bluestem (shortleaf–loblolly pine) | 2–8 | Avoid overgrazing on erosive sites. |
| Switch cane (pond pine) ......... | ½–2 | Very sensitive to grazing damage after burning. Defer grazing until July or later; stock lightly to utilize 40 percent of the foliage or less. |
| Bottomland types .............. | ½–7 | Desirable hardwood seedlings are palatable, winter grazing preferable. |

**GRAZING CAPACITY OF MAJOR TYPES, AND MANAGEMENT PRECAUTIONS.** Forage production is inversely related to timber stand density. The guides indicated in Table 16 refer to relatively open to moderately stocked timber stands.

Cattle are so strongly attracted to burned range in the spring and early summer that often they will not graze adjacent unburned areas except under the compulsion of acute hunger. Consequently, weight losses are increased or gains reduced when burned range is provided too early in the season or in too limited amounts. In addition, excessively close utilization on burns may result in range deterioration. It is therefore important that grazing capacity be based entirely on the burned acreage during spring and early summer and that cattle be held off burned range until sufficient new growth has developed to support the herd. A good criterion is to aim at less than 50 percent utilization on burns at the end of the season. However, range deterioration from temporary overuse is not usually serious if a recovery period is provided.

Burning different areas each year essentially accomplishes rotational grazing and allows forage plants to recover from the close grazing that is likely to occur on fresh burns. In most cases this procedure is also most appropriate from the forest management viewpoint.

## Control of Brush on Rangelands

Brush invasions on rangelands in various parts of the United States have caused serious decline in grazing capacity during the past 50 yr. or so. Each major range region has brush species that are well adapted to grow and reproduce vigorously under the prevailing conditions.

**CHARACTERISTIC BRUSH SPECIES.** Four extensive brush associations occur on the western range. In the Great Basin region and adjacent lands big sagebrush now occupies a large acreage that formerly supported perennial forage grasses.

In the Southwest—Arizona, New Mexico, and Texas—thousands of square miles of former grassland are now occupied by brush. Mesquite is the most widespread and troublesome species, but oaks, acacias, juniper, cacti, chollas, lotewood, and privet lippia are serious pests locally. In Texas alone, 60 million acres of former grassland are now occupied by brush.

In the southern Great Plains sand sagebrush is the most widespread and aggressive shrub on grasslands, but oaks, plums, and cacti are also to be contended with. These plants sometimes grow so densely as largely to replace the grass.

In California the brush (or chaparral) consists of three associations: the true chaparral, characterized by sprouters such as chamise, manzanitas, oaks, ceanothi, toyon, and chaparral pea; the woodland-grass-chaparral, most commonly composed of nonsprouting species of ceanothus, oaks, and manzanita; and the timberland-chaparral, of which ceanothi and manzanitas are characteristic. Much of the timberland-chaparral association is suitable for timber production.

**CAUSES OF BRUSH INVASIONS.** It is not to be assumed that all the factors favoring invasions of brush on grasslands are well understood. However, the aggressive nature of the brush species mentioned, the capacity of sprouts and seedlings to survive droughts, and their relatively low site quality requirements for growth and reproduction appear to account, in part, for their conquest of the range. The tendency to expand their foothold is greatly favored by destructive grazing which weakens, thins out, and eventually may destroy the grass cover. Frequent fires may hold some forms of brush in check, but it may also destroy many of the better forage plants and at the same time induce loss of soil by erosion. On the other hand, fires followed by many years of protection may favor the establishment of numerous sprouts and brush seedlings. Rodents may also play an important role by storing seed of brush species in their shallow food caches, thereby creating ideal conditions for germination.

**SELECTION OF BRUSH AREAS FOR REHABILITATION.** Since productivity of brushlands varies from extremely low to fairly high in most localities, the sites selected for conversion must be carefully chosen so that returns will be commensurate with the cost of rehabilitation. The most suitable areas are generally those found on flats and gentle slopes where the soil is fairly deep and relatively free from gullies and exposed rocks. Luxuriant stands of invading brush, alternating with heavy remnants of grass, usually indicate soils suitable for forage growth. On the other hand, areas dominated by brush in primary successions commonly occupy thin soils and inferior sites, and in many instances are not worthy of improvement effort. For good grass growth the soil should average not less than 12 in. in depth and should be free from hardpan below this depth.

**METHODS OF BRUSH REMOVAL.** Burning, mechanical brush removal, browsing with goats or sheep, and spraying with herbicides are the methods most commonly employed. In California and some other localities controlled burning is the most common and cheapest method of disposing of the top growth. Reburning every few years, although objectionable because of adverse effects on the site, is sometimes necessary in order to destroy the reinvading brush. In localities where fire cannot be used safely, or where it is desired to uproot and immediately destroy the brush, the bulldozer is commonly employed. The uprooted brush, which is pushed into windrows by the bulldozer, is burned in the winter. Close and continued browsing by goats or sheep is sometimes employed to suppress, and eventually kill, brush sprouts and seedlings. Stocking newly burned palatable brush areas at the rate of about 1½ goats or sheep per acre for the first 2 yr., and at lighter rates thereafter, usually results in destroying most of the brush stand in 3 to 5 yr. Another means of brush control is the use of hormone or other chemical sprays. Although control by spraying is presently receiving much attention, it is still in the experimental stage.

Successful use of hormone type sprays requires careful attention to particular details of procedure. Special attention must be given, among other things, to the stage of plant development when the spray is applied, concentration of the spray, and the carrier to be used. For example, with big sagebrush successful results have been obtained by spraying with 1 lb. 2, 4, 5-T ester per acre, or 2 lb. 2, 4-D ester per acre when applied in 3 to 5 gal. of diesel oil carrier at the time the sagebrush leaves are about half grown in the spring. At an earlier or later growth stage, results are much poorer. Also, different esters give different results. New materials and methods of chemical control are being developed so rapidly that no recommendation of formulas to follow or prediction as to the practicability of their use is yet possible. Accordingly, the fieldman should consult with local technicians for latest information on the subject. If this is done, costly or disappointing results may be avoided.

**REVEGETATION AND MANAGEMENT OF CLEARED AREAS.** Before clearing a brush area, plans should be decided upon for its speedy revegetation. A good grass cover is needed at the outset primarily to protect the soil and suppress the brush seedlings, and secondarily to provide forage for livestock. In some instances the entire area should be seeded artificially, but in other cases only the more exposed or steeper portions need be planted. Since the cost of brush removal, seeding, and essential management is relatively high, the question should be asked at the outset: Will this particular area pay its way? The results of today's treatment of the land had best be considered ten years or so ahead.

In order to take full advantage of the gains made of a clearing program, a grazing season should be adopted which will result in maintaining a satisfactory cover and at the same time crop the forage when it is most nutritious.

## Stock-Poisoning Range Plants

From 3 to 5 percent of all livestock grazed on the western range die annually from consuming poisonous plants. Still larger numbers lose in condition and market value. Losses are also heavy on ranges in the South. The percentage loss is much the same among cattle, horses, sheep, and goats.

Information on the chemical nature of plant poisons and their physiological effects on the animal has proved helpful in diagnosing doubtful cases. Plant poisons occur both as organic products, such as glucosides, saponins, tremetol, essential oils, resins, and fluorescent pigments, and as metallic salts, of which selenium and molybdenum are common. The organic products are the more troublesome.

**CONTROLLING LOSSES.** Heavy livestock losses from poisoning seldom occur where adequate suitable forage is available. Accordingly, good range management must be relied upon primarily for controlling poisonous plant losses.

The following points should be given consideration in localities where plant poisoning may occur:

1. Avoid overgrazing the range; remove the animals when the forage has been properly utilized.
2. Do not graze the range too early or too late in the season. To do so may force the hungry animals to consume unwholesome plants.
3. Do not hurry the animals while moving them from one part of a range to another. Animals tend to select wholesome feed when moved leisurely.
4. Graze the kind of stock that is least likely to be poisoned by the plants present. Lupines and deathcamas cause heavy losses among sheep but few among cattle; larkspur accounts for heavy losses among cattle but none among sheep.
5. Provide ample salt and essential minerals that are known to be deficient in the local feed. Salt seems to prevent animals from eating plants that they do not ordinarily graze.
6. Where practicable, destroy patches of poisonous plants by disking, grubbing, frequent cutting, or by spraying with herbicides, followed by reseeding. If hormone formulas (2,4-D or 2,4,5-T) are to be used, consult the range specialist who knows about the suitability of the different sprays and their effect on the vegetation as a whole.
7. Where the cost of eradication is excessive, fence well-defined patches of poisonous plants to exclude livestock.
8. Do not rely on treating poisoned animals as a solution to the poison-plant problem. However, where poisoning is critical, a veterinarian should be called. Pending his arrival, remove the animals to an area free from poisonous plants.

Table 17 lists the principal poisonous plants and the more essential information concerning them.

## Table 17. Essential Facts About the Principal Poisonous Plants

| Common and scientific names of plant | Location | Animals most commonly poisoned | Parts of plant that usually cause poisoning | Conditions under which poisoning usually occurs, and minimum quantity required | Characteristic effects |
|---|---|---|---|---|---|
| Arrowgrass (*Triglochin maritima* L.). | Salt or alkaline marshes and wet places throughout the United States. | Cattle and sheep. | Leaves and stems. | Eating about 1 percent of animal's weight of green plants in a few minutes. | Difficult breathing, spasms, coma, illness of short duration. |
| Aster, Parry (*Aster parryi* A. Gray). | Dry flats of Wyoming. | Sheep. | Leaves and stems. | Eating 1.25 lb. of green plants in a day when animals are hungry. | Weakness, prostration, rapid weak pulse, increased urination, and cyanosis. |
| Azalea, western (*Rhododendron occidentale* (Torr. and Gray) Gray). | Moist places in Coast Range and Sierra Nevada Mountains of California. | Sheep. | Leaves. | Eating a few ounces of leaves. | Salivation, vomiting, and weakness. |
| Baccharis (*Baccharis ramulosa* (DC.) A. Gray). | Hillsides of western Texas and southern New Mexico and Arizona. | Cattle. | Leaves. | Scarcity of feed in fall and early winter. | Extreme prostration, severe inflammation of stomach. |
| Black laurel (*Leucothoë davisiae* Torr.). | Springy ground in Sierra Nevada Mountains of Calif. | Sheep. | Leaves. | Eating 0.2 lb. in a day's feeding. | Salivation, vomiting, weakness. |
| Bracken (*Pteridium* sp.). | Thickets, hills, and rich woods throughout the United States. | Horses and cattle. | Fronds. | Eating 5 lb. daily for about a month. | Horses: lack of control of legs, weakness. Cattle: hemorrhages in various parts of body. |
| Cherry, wild (*Prunus* sp.). | Hillsides, along streams, in woods throughout the United States. | Sheep and cattle. | Leaves. | Eating 1 percent of animal's weight of green plants in a few minutes. | Difficult breathing, spasms, coma, illness of short duration. |
| Cocklebur (*Xanthium* sp.). | In fields and waste land of the eastern half and low wet places of the western half of the United States. | Pigs and cattle. | First or primary leaves of seedlings. | Eating 0.75 percent of animal's weight of green plants in a few minutes. | Prostration, inflamed stomach. |
| Copperweed (*Oxytenia acerosa* Nutt.). | Colorado Basin in Colorado, Utah, and New Mexico to southern California. | Cattle and sheep. | Leaves. | Eating the plant in the fall when other feed is scarce. | Loss of appetite, depression, weakness, and coma. |
| Deathcamas (*Zigadenus* sp.). | Gravelly hills, depressions, and meadows in western half of the United States. | Sheep and cattle. | Leaves and stems. | Eating 0.5 percent of animal's weight of green plants in a day. | Vomiting, frothing, and weakness. |
| Drymary, thickleaf (*Drymaria holosteoides* Benth. *D. pachyphylla* Wooten and Standley). | Denuded areas in western Texas and southern New Mexico. | Cattle. | Leaves and stems. | Eating 0.5 percent of animal's weight of green plants in a day. | Depression, weakness, inflamed stomach and intestines. |
| Dutchmans-breeches (*Dicentra cucullaria* (L.) Bernh.). | In woods, eastern half of United States north of Georgia. | Cattle. | Leaves. | Feeding on plant, particularly in spring and early summer. | Trembling, frothing at the mouth, and convulsions. |
| Greasewood (*Sarcobatus vermiculatus* (Hook.) Torr.). | Somewhat alkaline fields in western part of the United States. | Sheep. | Leaves. | Eating 1.5 lb. in a few minutes. | Depression, kidney lesions. |
| Halogeton (*Halogeton glomeratus* (Bieb) Mey). | Principally in Nevada, west Utah, S. Idaho, and Montana. Spreading throughout lower elevations of the West. Alkali soils, disturbed or depleted areas. | Sheep, cattle occasionally. | Dry leaves, stems, seeds. | Late fall and winter. Scarce feed or trailing animals. Sheep eating 1.5 lb. in short time. | Difficult breathing, rapid death. |
| Horsebrush (*Tetradymia glabrata* Gray; *T. canascens* DC.) | Principally in Utah, Nevada, and eastern California. | Sheep. | Leaves and small stems. | Usually eaten by hungry animals while being trailed. | May cause bighead as the result of sensitization to light. |

| Plant | Where found | Part eaten | Animals affected | Conditions of poisoning | Symptoms |
|---|---|---|---|---|---|
| Horsetail (*Equisetum* sp.). | Wet meadows throughout United States. | Tops. | Horses. | Eating the plant in hay. | Weakness, craving for the plant, diarrhea, loss of flesh, lack of control of legs. |
| Larkspur (*Delphinium* spp.). | Mountains and plains throughout United States. | Leaves of young plants. | Cattle. | Eating 0.5 percent of animal's weight, especially of young plants, within a few minutes. | Weakness, trembling, constipation. |
| Laurel, sheep (*Kalmia angustifolia* L.). | Moist soil, hillsides, and swamps, Maine and New York to Georgia. | Leaves. | Cattle, sheep, and goats. | Eating 0.2 percent of animal's weight of green plants in a day. | Salivation, vomiting, and weakness. |
| Locoweed (*Astragalus* sp.,* *Oxytropis* sp.). | Plains and some mountain valleys, western half of United States. | Leaves and stems. | Cattle, horses, sheep and goats. | Feeding for several days or weeks on the plants. | Constipation, craving for the plants, rough coat, incoordination, and peculiar actions. |
| Lupine (*Lupinus* sp.). | Throughout United States. | Leaves of young plants, and fruit. | Sheep and cattle. | Eating 0.5 percent of animal's weight of green plants or fruit in a day. | Sheep: nervousness from some species, depression from others. Cattle: weakness and trembling. |
| Milkweed (*Asclepias labriformis* M. E. Jones). | Southeastern Utah. | Leaves. | Sheep and cattle. | Eaten by hungry animals, often during the fall and winter. | Weakness, shallow respiration, spasms, violent struggling. |
| Milkweed, broadleaf (*A. eriocarpa* Benth.; *A. latifolia* (Torr.) Raf.) | *A. eriocarpa*: dry valleys in southern half of California. *A. latifolia*: dry plains of Southwest; along ditches, in abandoned fields and dry places, Colorado to Mexico and California. | Leaves. | Sheep. | Eating 0.1 percent of animal's weight of green plants in a day. | Depression, weakness, inflamed stomach and intestines. |
| Milkweed, whorled (*A. galioides* H. B. K.; *A. mexicana* Cav.). | Dry plains and foothills—*A. galioides*: Kansas to Utah and south to Texas, Arizona, and Mexico; *A. mexicana*: Southern Mexico northward to Washington, Idaho, Utah, and Arizona. | Leaves and stems. | Cattle and sheep. | Eating 0.2 percent of animal's weight of green plants in a day. | Incoordination followed by severe spasms. |
| Mountain-laurel (*Kalmia latifolia* L.). | Woods and hillsides. | Leaves. | Cattle, sheep, and goats. | Eating 0.4 percent of animal's weight of green plants in a day. | Salivation, vomiting, and weakness. |
| Nightshade, black (*Solanum nigrum* L.). | Waste ground from Maine to California. | Green fruit and leaves. | Cattle, sheep, goats, chickens, ducks, and geese. | Feeding on green plant. | Thirst, diarrhea, loss of appetite, weakness, lack of coordination. |
| Oaks, shin and Gambel (*Quercus* spp.). | Sand hills and lower mountains of Colorado, Utah, and Southwest. | Leaves and leaf buds. | Cattle. | Feeding largely on oak for 2 weeks or more, especially in spring. | Emaciation, scabby nose, constipation, followed by diarrhea and weakness. |
| Oleander, common (*Nerium oleander* L.). | Fields, roadsides, edge of woods in southern part of United States. | Leaves. | All animals. | Eating small quantities. | Stupor, trembling, convulsions, paralysis, vomiting, and diarrhea. |
| Paperflower, greenstem (*Psilostrophe sparsiflora* (A. Gray) A. Nels.). | Northern Arizona and southern Utah. | Leaves and flowers. | Sheep. | Eaten during the early spring or late fall when other feed is scarce. | Depression, weakness, emaciation. |
| Peganum, Harmal (*Peganum harmala* L.). | Texas and New Mexico. | Fruits, leaves, and stems. | Sheep and cattle. | Scarcity of desirable feed. | Nervousness, incoordination, and paralysis. |
| Poisonbean (*Daubentonia drummondii* Rydb.). | Coastal plains of Florida and Texas. | Seeds. | Cattle, sheep, and goats. | Eating small quantities of seeds. | Depression, diarrhea, and rapid pulse. |

(Continued on following page)

* Some poisonous species of *Astragalus* are not locoweeds.

## Table 17. Essential Facts About the Principal Poisonous Plants (Continued)

| Common and scientific names of plant | Location | Parts of plant that usually cause poisoning | Animals most commonly poisoned | Conditions under which poisoning usually occurs, and minimum quantity required | Characteristic effects |
|---|---|---|---|---|---|
| Poisonhemlock (*Conium maculatum* L.). | Widely distributed. | Fruits and leaves. | Sheep and cattle. | Seldom eaten when other feed is available. | Nervous tremors, weakness, and respiratory paralysis. |
| Poisonvetch (*Astragalus* spp.). | Mountains, foothills, and valleys of Intermountain States. | Leaves and stems. | Cattle and sheep. | Eating considerable quantities during a day's feeding. | Difficult breathing, nausea, and weakness. |
| Ragwort, or groundsel (*Senecio* spp.). | Throughout United States. | Leaves and stems. | Cattle and horses. | Feeding for several days on one of the poisonous species. | Jaundice, scabby nose, discomfort, loss of appetite, uneasiness, and loss of flesh. |
| Rayless goldenrod (*Aplopappus heterophyllus* (A. Gray) Blake). | Fields along ditches in western Texas, New Mexico, and Arizona. | Leaves and stems. | Cattle, sheep, and horses. | Feeding on the plant frequently for several days. | Marked weakness and trembling, especially after exercise. |
| Rubberweed, bitter (*Actinea odorata* (DC.) Kuntze). | Western Texas to southeastern California. | Leaves, stems, and flowers. | Sheep. | Eating small quantities daily for several days. | Vomiting, weakness. |
| Rubberweed, Colorado (*A. richardsonii* (Hook.) Kuntze.) | Gravelly hills and flats in mountains of Colorado, New Mexico, Utah, and Arizona. | Leaves and stems. | Sheep. | Eating small quantities daily for several days. | Vomiting, weakness. |
| St. Johnswort (*Hypericum perforatum* L.). | Fields, waste places, and hills across northern half of the United States. | Leaves. | Animals with areas of white skin and hair. | Feeding on the plant and being in bright sunlight. | Sore, scabby areas on white skin, itching, rapid respiration. |
| Snakeroot, white (*Eupatorium rugosum* Houtt.). | Rich woods and ravines in eastern half of the United States. | Leaves and stems. | Cattle and sheep. | Feeding on the plant for several days. | Marked trembling and weakness, especially after exercise. |
| Sneezeweed (*Helenium hoopesii* Gray). | Mountains, meadows, and valleys from Montana to Arizona. | Leaves. | Sheep and cattle. | Feeding on the plant for 2 weeks or more. | Profuse vomiting and weakness. |
| Tarweed (*Amsinckia intermedia* F. and M.). | Northwest, principally in eastern Washington, eastern Oregon, and northern Idaho. | Seeds. | Horses, cattle, and swine. | Eaten when mixed with wheat chaff or screenings. | Loss of appetite, jaundice, emaciation, and, in horses, a tendency to walk continuously. |
| Waterhemlock (*Cicuta* sp.). | Wet places throughout the United States. | Roots and rootstocks. | Sheep and cattle. | Eating very small quantities. | Violent spasms. |

Source: Reproduced from *Yearbook of Agriculture 1942*, except for information regarding halogeton.

# Range Reseeding

The primary purpose of range reseeding is quickly to improve depleted ranges that cannot be improved by good range management alone within a reasonable period. Natural plant recovery through improved management is usually a much cheaper method than range reseeding and should be encouraged wherever practicable. However, where natural recovery is likely to be too slow, artificial seeding should be used to improve the range wherever possible and practical. Research and large-scale plantings have demonstrated that seedings can restore the forage on vast areas of deteriorated range and watershed lands. Not only is additional forage produced but, by use of early growing or late maturing species, forage can be made available in early spring or during other seasons when forage is badly needed. Additional planted forage at key areas may also permit natural improvement on large areas of surrounding range.

Range seedings should be carefully planned. If properly planned and carried out, they are a sound investment; if poorly planned, they are usually a waste of time and money. Some of the major factors to be considered in planning a range seeding operation are as follows:

1. Can the land be improved in a reasonable period and at less expense by the natural increase of native plants? Often a good forage cover is weakened by overuse and requires only a relatively short period of light grazing or change in season of use to bring about substantial improvement.

2. Is the seeding financially sound? Unless the value of the expected returns in total or seasonal forage equals or exceeds the cost of getting a stand of grass, reseeding for forage production alone should not be undertaken.

Some depleted rangelands need seeding to control erosion. This often requires expensive seeding which can be justified for the watershed protection. Where water runs off eroding slopes too fast, terraces or other structures are often necessary to hold the soil and water in place until reseeded plants become established.

Another purpose of range seeding is that of improving the forage and at the same time reducing fire hazard under southern pines. Louisiana white clover, Dallisgrass, and carpet grass have proved to be suitable under light tree canopies. Productive clover stands are maintained by heavy fertilization with lime, phosphate, and potash. These grasses and clover, with fertilization, withstand close grazing and give fire protection during the period when badly needed.

3. The use of fertilizers to meet soil deficiencies to give higher production of forage from seeded ranges is attracting considerable attention throughout the United States. Phosphorus and sulfur have been found to increase legume growth on some rangelands and incidentally to build up soil fertility. Grasses, associated with the legumes, then become more productive. Nitrogenous fertilizer has stimulated grass growth on a large variety of rangeland but has been found most practicable on humid and subhumid areas, and on moist meadows. An extensive program of range fertilization test plots must be instituted to determine the specific requirements of the soils of localized areas before a broad application of fertilizers can rationally be recommended. Wise use of fertilizer can often give increased forage production at seasons when growth is otherwise scarce, raise the nutritive level of forage, and aid in obtaining better distribution of livestock over the range.

4. Reseed the better lands first. Reseeding on favorable planting sites with deep soil, good organic matter, ample moisture, and relatively level topography is likely to be most successful and yield the biggest returns. Steep slopes, rocky areas, and lands with scanty, low-growing stands of vegetation, which indicate poor growing conditions, should be avoided.

Thick, vigorous stands of native vegetation usually indicate productive sites. Many poor and eroded soils, if not extremely poor or too alkaline, are also often suitable seeding sites. In some cases it may be necessary to use lime and commercial fertilizer on range soils to get a good stand of forage species.

5. Seed only where there is enough precipitation to insure successful stands. Seeding in the West is generally best with 12 in. or more of annual precipitation, a considerable part of which must come during the early growing season. Seeding where precipitation is less than 10 in. is hazardous and should be done only on the better sites and with drought resistant species such as crested, desert, Siberian, and bluebunch wheatgrasses.

6. Use methods of seedbed preparation and seeding which will eliminate plant competition and get the seed in the ground to give seedlings the best possible chance of developing into vigorous, mature plants, consistent with costs. Information on different methods of removing competition, preparing a seedbed, and seeding, should be obtained from experienced range technicians as some methods are more efficient and less expensive than others.

Some plants of low value for domestic livestock but necessary for food or shelter for game birds or animals should be left in preparing to reseed rangelands. These plants may be left on rocky or steeply sloping areas or in strips across the field on contour if feasible.

7. Use only species and strains of species which are adapted to the soil and climatic condition and which will produce forage at a season when it is most needed. (For example, early growing grasses such as crested and desert wheatgrasses are good for early spring grazing.) Although introduced species have generally given best results, adapted native species should not be overlooked. Wherever legumes are adapted they should be seeded with the grasses. Legume seed should be inoculated before seeding. Some of the most used species are listed in Table 18. Before seeding in any area, it is best to consult with the county agent or federal agencies doing seeding work in the area.

Good, viable seed increases the chances for success. Tests made by state seed laboratories are the best way to get reliable data on seed quality before purchase. Enough seed is needed for a good stand, but using too much seed is wasteful. Recommended seeding rates for some of the more commonly used species are shown in Table 18.

See *Grass: Yearbook of Agriculture 1948,* beginning on page 743, for species which are adapted to generalized areas, with average purity, germination, seed longevity, seeds per pound, and suggested seeding rates per acre.

8. Whether to use mixtures or single species on rangelands will depend upon the site and upon the purpose of the seeding. Single species can be planted by using techniques specifically adapted to their seed requirements. Species can be used which will produce forage when needed. Early and late growing species should be seeded in separate areas to prolong the season of green forage. Single species are easier to manage under grazing, as all plants are of similar palatability.

Mixtures are more suitable to sites where soil or other conditions vary considerably within short distances and a single species is not uniformly adapted. Mixtures provide a more varied forage. Legumes in a mixture often improve the nutritive value of the forage and help build up soil fertility. Mixtures are often difficult to drill. Because of the varied palatability of the species in the mixture, the maintenance of certain species under grazing may be a problem. While complete information on mixtures is not available, sample mixtures which can be used are shown in Table 18.

9. Seed at a season when there will be enough moisture for seed germination and seedling growth for 1 to 2 months of growing weather. This varies with total precipitation and the season when it falls as related to growing temperatures and moisture holding capacity of the soil.

10. Protect the seedling stands from grazing until the first seed crop is produced and then manage properly. Usually 1 to 2 yr. are required for the first seed crop to be produced; then grazing can be started. Moderate grazing of a good stand will maintain the increased forage supply almost indefinitely. Good stands of crested wheatgrass have been maintained for over 20 yr. under proper grazing use.

## Range Rodents and Livestock Predators

**RANGE RODENTS.** The impact that jack rabbits and such rodents as ground squirrels, prairie dogs, pocket gophers, kangaroo rats, and field and meadow mice have on rangelands is of great economic importance. It is the change in plant cover incident to man's use of the land, probably more than all other factors combined, that affects the rodent population and the volume of forage these animals consume.

Grazing use that results in thinning out of the more desirable grasses and otherwise altering the habitat tends to favor increased numbers of rodents to a point where they become pests. Rodent pests, by definition, do not occur on virgin areas; but soon after man places his animals on the land, certain kinds of rodents begin to compete for forage and may soon become "pests."

The kinds of food plants present largely determine the species of rodents that will predominate in the area. Wherever domestic livestock graze wild lands, even when cropped only lightly or moderately, the composition of the cover is altered to some extent. This change often lowers the suitability of the site for some kinds of rodents but improves it for others, particularly for ground squirrels and jack rabbits.

The question often arises as to how effective the natural predators are in regulating the population densities of rodents and rabbits. When man cannot economically control a pest species by artificial means, then the natural predators must be relied on to curb the rodent population. In general the predators, consisting chiefly of coyotes, bobcats, hawks, and snakes, are only partially successful in holding rodent numbers in check. In recent years artificial control has been used extensively and with good results on the range.

A factor concerning range rodents and rabbits that must not be overlooked is the public health hazard. These animals not only are known to carry diseases such as plague, tularemia, Rocky Mountain spotted fever, and relapsing fever that may be transmitted to man, but they may serve as a reservoir for other diseases of both man and domestic animals. Much is yet to be learned on this subject.

**LIVESTOCK PREDATORS.** Few people question the wisdom of predator control when livestock are currently being killed by them. It is well known that two predators—coyote and mountain lion (cougar or puma)—are particularly costly to the livestock producer. Most of the other predators are not especially troublesome, except locally at times. Of these, bears and bobcats are the most common intruders.

There can be no doubt that the restriction of the population density of coyotes and cougars by artificial control has been of appreciable benefit to the livestock

Table 18. Some of the More Important Species with Sample Mixtures, Seeds per Pound, and Rate per Acre for Seeding Selected Sites Within Seven Broad Range Types[a]

| Species | Approximate seeds per pound (thousands) | Amount of seed if seeded alone (lb. per acre) | Broad range types, with variation in annual precipitation | | | | | | |
|---|---|---|---|---|---|---|---|---|---|
| | | | Southwestern pinyon-juniper 14–18 in. (lb. per acre) | Palouse prairie and Pacific bunchgrass 8–16[b] in. (lb. per acre) | Mountain brush, Palouse prairie, and upper sagebrush-grass 15–19 in. (lb. per acre) | Western open pine, mountain brush and Palouse prairie 20–24 in. (lb. per acre) | Western mountain parks and aspen 22 or more in. (lb. per acre) | Southern open pine forests 40–60 in. (lb. per acre) | Pacific bunchgrass 10–60 in. (lb. per acre) |
| **SPECIES SHOWING SAMPLE MIXTURES**[c] | | | | | | | | | |
| Weeping lovegrass (*Eragrostis curvula*) | 1,463 | 1–2 | ½ | | | | | | x |
| Desert wheatgrass (known commercially as standard crested wheatgrass) (*Agropyron desertorum*) | 175 | 4–8 | 6 | 4 | 3 | 2 | | | |
| Intermediate wheatgrass (*Agropyron intermedium*) | 88 | 5–10 | | | 2 | 3 | 2 | | |
| Tall oatgrass (*Arrhenatherum elatius*) | 150 | 7–10 | | | 2 | 3 | 3 | | |
| Smooth brome (*Bromus inermis*) | 136 | 8–15 | | 2 | 2 | | 4 | | |
| Orchardgrass (*Dactylis glomerata*) | 654 | 3–7 | | | | 2[d] | 2 | | x |
| Timothy (*Phleum pratense*) | 1,230 | 2–6 | | | | | 1 | | |
| Carpetgrass (*Axonopus affinis*) | 1,222 | 3–10 | | | | | | 3 | x |
| Dallisgrass (*Paspalum dilatatum*) | 220 | 5–15 | | | | | | 4 | |
| Common lespedeza (*Lespedeza striata*) | 190 | 6–12 | | | | | | 5 | |
| Big trefoil (*Lotus uliginosus*) | 1,000 | 1–5 | | | | | | 2 | x |
| **Total for mixtures** | | | 6½ | 6 | 9 | 10 | 12 | 14 | x |
| **ADDITIONAL USEFUL SPECIES** | | | | | | | | | |
| Sand dropseed (*Sporobolus cryptandrus*) | 5,298 | 1–3 | x | | | | | | |
| Fourwing saltbush (*Atriplex canescens*) | 22 | 10–15 | x | | | | | | |
| Blue grama (*Bouteloua gracilis*) | 825 | 4–10 | x | | | | | | |
| Side-oats grama (*B. curtipendula*) | 191 | 8–15 | x | | x | | | | |
| Indian ricegrass (*Oryzopsis hymenoides*) | 141 | 6–10 | x | | x | | | | |
| Bluebunch wheatgrass (*Agropyron spicatum*) | 95 | 6–10 | | | x | x | | | |
| Beardless wheatgrass (*A. inerme*) | 150 | 6–10 | | | x | x | | | |
| Crested wheatgrass (*A. cristatum*) | 200 | 3–7 | | | x | x | x | | |
| Siberian wheatgrass (*A. sibiricum*) | 170 | 4–8 | | | x | x | | | |
| Russian wild-rye (*Elymus junceus*) | 175 | 4–8 | | | x | x | x | | |
| Bluestem wheatgrass (*Agropyron smithii*) | 110 | 8–15 | | | x | x | | | |
| Pubescent wheatgrass (*A. trichophorum*) | 100 | 5–10 | | | x | x | x | | x |

| Species | Seeds per lb (thousands) | Rate (lb per acre) |
|---|---|---|
| Tall wheatgrass (A. elongatum) | 79 | 5-10 |
| Antelope bitterbrush (Purshia tridentata) | 18 | 12-20 |
| Big bluegrass (Poa ampla) | 882 | 4-8 |
| Sheep fescue (Festuca ovina)—several forms | 680 | 4-8 |
| Red fescue (F. rubra)—several forms | 615 | 4-8 |
| Meadow brome (Bromus erectus) | 71 | 8-15 |
| Alfalfa (Medicago sativa)—several forms | 200 | 5-12 |
| White sweetclover (Melilotus alba) | 260 | 5-12 |
| Yellow sweetclover (M. officinalis) | 260 | 5-12 |
| Slender wheatgrass (Agropyron trachycaulum) | 159 | 6-12 |
| Bearded wheatgrass (A. subsecundum) | 117 | 6-12 |
| Mountain brome (Bromus carinatus) | 71 | 8-15 |
| Tomentose brome (B. tomentellus) | 100 | 8-15 |
| Kentucky bluegrass (Poa pratensis) | 2,177 | 4-10 |
| Tall fescue (Festuca elatior arundinacea) | 227 | 6-12 |
| Reed canarygrass (Phalaris arundinacea) | 533 | 5-10 |
| Meadow foxtail (Alopecurus pratensis) | 576 | 6-15 |
| Redtop (Agrostis alba) | 4,990 | 4-10 |
| White clover (Trifolium repens) | 800 | 1-4 |
| Ladino clover (T. repens ladino) | 800 | 1-4 |
| Crimson clover (T. incarnatum) | 140 | 10-20 |
| Bermuda-grass (Cynodon dactylon)—improved strains | 1,787 | 4-8 |
| Bahia grass (Paspalum notatum)—improved strains | 166 | 8-15 |
| Pangolagrass (Digitaria decumbens) | ... | Vegetative |
| St. Augustinegrass (Stenotaphrum secundatum) | | Vegetative |
| Hairy indigo (Indigofera hirsuta) | 200 | 8-10 |
| Sericea lespedeza (Lespedeza cuneata) | 350 | 10-15 |
| Hardinggrass (Phalaris tuberosa var. stenoptera) | 355 | 4-6 |
| Smilograss (Oryzopsis miliacea) | 884 | 4-5 |
| Rose clover (Trifolium hirtum) | 140 | 4-6 |
| Burnet (Sanguisorba minor) | 90 | 8-12 |
| Sub clover (Trifolium subterraneum) | 72 | 4-6 |
| Purple stipa (Stipa pulchra) | 108 | 6-8 |
| California bur-clover (Medicago hispida) | 140 | 6-8 |

a Adapted from Grass: Yearbook of Agriculture 1948, and other sources.
b 8 to 14 in. in the north, 10 to 16 in. in the south.
c These adapted species are listed to show sample mixtures. These species can also be seeded alone.
d x indicates that the species is adapted and can either be seeded alone at the indicated rate or in a mixture at a reduced rate.

industry. These predators and domestic livestock cannot live harmoniously in the same areas, particularly when lambs, calves, and colts are involved. Arguments concerning predator control have arisen primarily as to just how much control is needed and what are the best methods to use.

**CONTROL MEASURES.** Since the procedure for controlling rodents, rabbits, and livestock predators varies with species, from place to place, and with the seasons, it is urged that anyone contemplating control measures consult their local U. S. Fish and Wildlife Service, state, or county agency that is responsible for this kind of work. In this way costly mistakes may be avoided. Space is not available, nor is it desirable here, to describe the various methods of bait preparations for the different poisons or traps that are employed for the many situations that arise.

## Grazing Fees on Federal and State Lands, and Their Disposition

Two approaches are used in establishing grazing fees on public lands. One approach is that of recognizing commensurable values, which aims to relate the grazing fees to prices paid for comparable privately owned land. The other approach is that of meeting minimum administration cost fees. This is adequate only for paying the direct costs of administration.

**FOREST SERVICE.** Grazing fees on the national forests are designed to approximate the value of the forage and are subject to change with changes in economic factors. Since 1933, grazing fee charges have been adjusted annually so as to relate them to annual fluctuations in the average market prices received for beef cattle and lambs.

In applying this system the fees in effect on the various national forests in 1931 and which were related to (but were substantially less than) prices paid for comparable privately owned land were used as base fees. These base fees varied widely by forests and subdivisions of forests. Base prices were the average prices received during a selected period prior to 1933, and average $6.62 per cwt. for beef cattle and $9.15 per cwt. for sheep.

**Example.** In 1952 the average market price of $24.50 per cwt. received for beef cattle was 370 percent of the $6.62 per cwt. base price for cattle. Therefore the 1953 fee to be charged on a range with a 1931 base fee of 12 cents per head per month would be 370 percent of the 12-cent base fee, or 44 cents per head per month.

**BUREAU OF LAND MANAGEMENT.** Since this Bureau has adopted the minimum-cost-of-administration approach, the grazing fees are low—8 cents per animal unit month for cattle and 1.6 for sheep and goats.

"Section 15" lands—those lands presently not included in the grazing districts—are let by lease for grazing rather than by issuance of grazing permits. The fee is not less than $1.00 for cattle per annum, and varies from 1 cent to 5 cents per acre depending on the quality of the land.

During 1950 the Forest Service issued 19,900 pay permits to livestock men authorizing them to graze 1,191,680 cattle and 3,006,185 sheep for a part of the season. During the same year the Bureau of Land Management issued 20,887 licenses authorizing the grazing of 2,237,477 cattle and 6,229,189 sheep. The early spring and winter ranges of the low-lying areas of the Bureau of Land Management, and the cool summer grazing on the more elevated lands of the national forests, provide an ideal range combination.

**INDIAN LANDS.** Permits to nontribal stockmen to graze their animals upon Indian lands is granted only after local tribal grazing privileges have been met.

The lands are administered on a permit system by which a charge is made on a per-head basis. Since leases are secured through competitive bidding, the fees are currently comparable to those of similar private lands.

**STATE LANDS.** Several western states own and administer some grazing land, most of which consists of scattered tracts. State grazing fees vary widely from one state to another, but many states charge a more or less fixed rental for a parcel of land. The charge is computed similarly to that of the Forest Service, the rental scale being based on the market price for livestock and their products. In most instances the charge is several cents more per acre, or per animal unit, than for lands administered by the Bureau of Land Management. Several of the states have disposed of their land grants, but Arizona, New Mexico, Montana, Washington, and South Dakota have retained a large part of theirs.

**DISPOSAL OF FEES.** The Forest Service returns from the U. S. Treasury to the counties containing national forest lands an amount equal to 25 percent of the grazing fees and other cash returns for expenditures on local roads and schools. An additional 10 percent of the receipts is expended for roads on the national forests in the states of origin.

The Bureau of Land Management returns from the U. S. Treasury to the states 2 cents per head of the cattle grazing fee and ⅖ cent per head of the sheep and goats fees for use in range improvement in the counties in which the lands are located.

The Bureau of Indian Affairs distributes its surplus grazing fees and other cash returns proportionately among the tribal Indians after first expending such funds as agreed upon locally for range and other improvements.

Revenue from state lands is generally expended for the construction and maintenance of schools, roads, and benevolent institutions, but in some states the fund goes into the treasury for use as needed.

## BIBLIOGRAPHY

ANONYMOUS. 1950. 1950 forest grazing fees. *The National Wool Grower.* 60 (2): 7, Salt Lake City.

ARCHER, S. G., and C. E. BUNCH. 1953. *The American grass book.* Univ. of Oklahoma Press, Norman.

BENNETT, H. H. 1939. *Soil conservation.* McGraw-Hill Book Co., Inc., New York.

BISWELL, H. H., and M. D. HOOVER. 1945. Appalachian hardwood trees browsed by cattle. *Jour. Forestry* 43:675–676.

CALIF. AGR. EXP. STA.:
1935. Crossbreeding investigation in the production of California spring lambs *Bull. No. 598.*
1939. Composition of common California foothill plants as a factor in range management. *Bull. No. 627.*
1947. Improving California brush ranges. *Circ. No. 37.*
1947. Control of field rodents in California. *Circ. No. 138.*

CALIF. STATE DIV. FORESTRY:
1947. The use of fire as a tool in the management of brush ranges in California.
1954. Cost and returns of controlled brush burning for range improvement in northern California. *Range Improvement Studies No. 1.*

CANFIELD, R. H. 1941. Application of the line interception method in sampling range vegetation. *Jour. Forestry* 39:388–394.

CANFIELD, R. H. 1944. A short-cut method for checking degree of forage utilization. *Jour. Forestry* 42:294–295.

CHAPLINE, W. R., and R. S. CAMPBELL. 1938. Managing our range resources. *Jour. Forestry* 36:849–852.

CLAWSON, M. 1950. *The western range livestock industry.* McGraw-Hill Book Co., Inc., New York.

COCHRAN, W. G. 1953. *Sampling technique.* John Wiley & Sons, Inc., New York.

CRAFTS, E. C. 1938. Height-weight distribution of range grasses. *Jour. Forestry* 36:1182–1185.

FISHER, C. E. 1950. The mesquite problem in the southwest. *Jour. Range Management* 3 (1): 60–70.

GUILBERT, H. R., P. GERLAUGH, and L. L. MADSEN. 1945. Recommended nutrient allowances for beef cattle. *A report of the Committee on Animal Nutrition of the National Research Council.* Washington, D. C.

HALL, L. K. 1953. Improved cattle forage under southern pines. *Southern Lumberman* (Dec. 15 issue).

HANSON, H. C., and W. S. BALL. 1928. An application of Raunkiaer's law of frequency to grazing studies. *Ecology* 9:467–473.

HULTZ, F. S. 1930. *Range beef production.* John Wiley & Sons, Inc., New York.

HYDER, D. N. 1954. Controlling big sagebrush with growth regulators. *Jour. Range Management* 6 (2):109–116.

KELSEY, H. R., and W. A. DAYTON. 1942. *Standardized plant names.* 2d ed. J. Horace McFarland Co., Harrisburg, Pa.

LEVY, E. B., and E. A. MADDEN. 1933. The point method of pasture analysis. *New Zealand Jour. Agric.* 46:267–279.

LOMMASON, T., and C. JENSEN. 1938. Grass volume tables for determining range utilization. *Science* 87(2263):444.

LOUISIANA STATE UNIV. AGR. EXP. STA. 1951. Grazing values for cattle on pine forest ranges in Louisiana. *Bull. 452.*

MAYNARD, L. A. 1947. *Animal nutrition.* McGraw-Hill Book Co., Inc., New York.

MONTANA STATE COLLEGE AGR. EXP. STA. 1952. Range plants poisonous to livestock in Montana. *Circ. 197.*

MORRISON, F. B. 1948. *Feeds and feeding.* 23d ed. The Morrison Publishing Co., Ithaca, New York.

OREGON AGR. EXP. STA. 1944. Reseeding eastern Oregon summer ranges. *Circ. 159.*

PEARSON, P. B., H. M. BRIGGS, W. G. KAMMLADE, J. I. MILLER, and R. F. MILLER. 1949. Recommended nutrient allowances for sheep. *A report of the Committee on Animal Nutrition of the National Research Council.* Rev. Washington, D. C.

PECHANEC, J. R., and G. D. PICKFORD. 1937. A comparison of some methods used in determining percentage utilization of range grasses. *Jour. Agr. Research* 54:753–765.

PECHANEC, J. R., and G. D. PICKFORD. 1937. A weight estimate method for the determination of range or pasture production. *Agron. Jour.* 20 (11):894–904.

SAMPSON, A. W. 1951. *Range management, principles and practice.* John Wiley & Sons, Inc., New York.

SAMPSON, A. W., and ASSOCIATES. 1951. A symposium on rotation grazing in North America. *Jour. Range Management* 4 (1):19–55.

SAUNDERSON, M. H. 1950. *Western livestock ranching.* Univ. of Minnesota Press, Minneapolis.

SHEPHERD, W. O., M. KAUFMAN, and H. H. BISWELL. 1946. Forest grazing in North Carolina. *Southern Lumberman* 173 (2177):228–238.

SNEDECOR, G. W. 1946. *Statistical methods.* The Iowa State College Press, Ames.

STEWART, G., and S. S. HUTCHINGS. 1936. The point-observation-plot (square-foot density) method of vegetation survey. *Agron. Jour.* 28:714–722.

STODDARD, L. A., and A. D. SMITH. 1943. *Range management.* McGraw-Hill Book Co., Inc., New York.

TAYLOR, W. P. 1930. Methods of determining rodent pressure on the range. *Ecology* 11 (3):523–542.

TEXAS A & M EXP. STA. 1951. Recent developments in the chemical control of brush on Texas ranges. *Bull. 721.*

U. S. DEPT. AGR.:
    1916. Prevention of losses of livestock from poisonous plants. *Farmers' Bull. 720.*

1919. Production of goats on far western ranges. *Bull. 749.*
1926. Grazing periods and forage production on the national forests. *Bull. 1405.*
1926. The use of salt in range management. *Circ. 379.*
1932. Rodent-control studies develop specific methods for different species. *Year-book of Agriculture.*
1934. The influence of precipitation and grazing upon black grama grass range. *Tech. Bull. 409.*
1938. The influence of climate and grazing on spring-fall sheep range in southern Idaho. *Tech. Bull. 100.*
1939. Weather and plant development data as determinants of grazing periods on mountain range. *Tech. Bull. 686.*
1939. Factors affecting maintenance nutrition, feed utilization, and health of farm animals. *Yearbook of Agriculture.*
1939. The effect of intensity and frequency of clipping on density and yield of black grama and tobasa grass. *Tech. Bull. 681.*
1940. The line-transect method, an improved method of studying range vegetation. Mimeo.
1941. Climate and livestock production. *Yearbook of Agriculture.*
1941. Climate and grazing. *Yearbook of Agriculture.*
1941. Artificial reseeding on western mountain range lands. *Circ. 178.*
1942. Growth and carbohydrates content of important mountain forage plants in central Utah as affected by clipping and grazing. *Tech. Bull. 818.*
1942. Basis for judging subalpine grassland ranges of Oregon and Washington. *Circ. 655.*
1942. How to graze blue grama on southwestern ranges. *Leaflet 215.*
1943. Reseeding to increase the yield of Montana range lands. *Farmers' Bull. 1924.*
1944. Judging condition and utilization of short-grass ranges on the Central Great Plains. *Farmers' Bull. 1949.*
1944. Sagebrush burning—good and bad. *Farmers' Bull. 1948.*
1947. Regrassing the range. *Yearbook of Agriculture.*
1948. Grass and the soil. *Yearbook of Agriculture.*
1948. Poisonous plants. *Yearbook of Agriculture.*
1949. Reseeding range lands of the Intermountain Region. *Farmers' Bull. 1823.*
1949. Grazing spring-fall sheep ranges of southern Idaho. *Circ. 808.*
1949. Stocking northern Great Plains sheep range for sustained high production. *Circ. 804.*
1949. Grazing on forested lands. *Yearbook of Agriculture.*
1952. The mesquite problem on southern Arizona ranges. *Circ. 908.*
1953. Effect of grazing intensity upon vegetation and cattle gains on ponderosa pine-bunch grass ranges on the front range of Colorado. *Circ. 929.*
1953. Increasing forage yields and sheep production on Intermountain winter range. *Circ. 925.*
U. S. DEPT. OF THE INTERIOR. 1939. A field method of judging range utilization. Div. Grazing. Mimeo.
U. S. FOREST SERV.:
1937. *Range plant handbook.*
1951. A method of measuring trend in range condition on national forest ranges. Administrative Studies (processed).
California Region. 1940. Handbook for range managers.
Calif. Forest & Range Exp. Sta. 1942. Standards for judging the degree of forage utilization on California annual-type ranges. *Tech. Note 21* (processed).
Calif. Forest & Range Exp. Sta. 1943. A method of estimating grazing use of bitter-brush. *Res. Note 35* (processed).
Southwestern Forest & Range Exp. Sta. 1938. Tentative range utilization standards of black grama (*Bouteloua eripoda*). *Res. Note 26.* Mimeo.
Southwest Region. 1952. *Range management handbook.* Mimeo.
Pacific Northwest Region. 1951. *Range management field handbook.* Mimeo.

U. S. SENATE. 74th CONG., 2d SESS. 1936. Climatic fluctuations. In: U. S. Dept. Agr. Forest Service. The Western Range. *Document 199*:135–150.

UPCHURCH, M. L. 1953. Economic factors in western range management. *Jour. Farm Economics* 35:728–741.

UTAH STATE AGR. EXP. STA. 1953. The halogeton problem in Utah. *Bull. 364.*

WEAVER, J. E., and F. E. CLEMENTS. 1938. *Plant ecology.* 2d ed. McGraw-Hill Book Co., Inc., New York.

YOUNG, S. P., and E. A. GOLDMAN. 1944. *The wolves of North America.* American Wildlife Inst.

YOUNG, S. P., and E. A. GOLDMAN. 1946. *The puma.* American Wildlife Inst.

YOUNG, V. A., and G. F. PAYNE. 1948. Utilization of "key" browse species in relation to proper grazing practices in cutover white pine lands in northern Idaho. *Jour. Forestry* 46:35–40.

# FOREST RECREATION

## CONTENTS

SECTION 12

# FOREST RECREATION

## CONTENTS

# FOREST RECREATION

## Cultural Treatments

**COMPOST PREPARATION AND USE ON RECREATIONAL SITES.** Compost is any mixture of vegetable matter and soil, with or without animal matter, adaptable to use as a fertilizer. It is made up of a variety of fermented or decomposed materials, or refuse matter such as lawn clippings, leaves, straw, vegetable refuse, and manure. It should **not** include any materials infected with fungus diseases or infested by insect pests. The objectives in preparing or keeping a compost pile are to dispose of all refuse, and to have on hand a source of organic fertilizer and soil conditioner. Compost may be used to fertilize flower beds, trees, and shrubs and is invaluable as a top-dressing for lawns.

Directions for composting fertilizers for nursery use are given in Section **5**.

### Preparation of the Compost Pile.

1. Select a location which is dry and with sufficient space available so that one can get around the pile with a wheelbarrow, or whatever is used, to transport refuse to the pile and to remove the compost.
2. The pile should be 6 to 8 ft. wide, the length depending upon the amount of compost to be made.
3. If a concrete base is constructed on which to build the compost pile, the fluids which drain from the pile can be collected and poured back over the pile at intervals.
4. Spread the refuse, vegetable matter, etc., in a layer 4 in. thick, followed by a layer of soil 3 in. thick, continuing to spread alternate layers in this proportion until the pile reaches a height of about 5 ft.
5. The pile should be mixed or stirred occasionally (about once a month) to aid decomposition and to mellow the mixture. In mixing it thoroughly, the new pile should be kept compact and sufficiently moist to exclude oxygen and prevent the loss of nitrogen. Sufficient water should be added occasionally to prevent the pile from becoming too dry for fermentation and decomposition.
6. A small amount of a complete commercial fertilizer should be spread over each layer of soil to improve the quality and hasten decomposition. There are several brands of compost chemicals sold commercially which will aid and hasten decomposition.

Where compost chemicals are used, sufficient decomposition will have taken place in 6 months to provide usable compost. One year will produce completely decomposed compost.

### Compost Uses.

1. Lawns. Apply a comparatively heavy dressing before winter (100 lb. per 500 sq. ft.), a medium heavy dressing in spring (75 lb. per 500 sq. ft.), and a very light dressing several times during the summer (25 lb. per 500 sq. ft.)
2. Shrubbery borders and flower beds. Apply as a mulch 2 in. thick in the fall.
3. Nurseries. Compost is commonly applied at the rate of 2 to 5 tons an acre every 2 to 3 yr.

**PRINCIPAL LAWN GRASSES.** Tables 1A to 1C list the principal lawn grasses for cool humid, warm humid, and arid regions with recommendations for their use and care and moisture and shade requirements.

**Table 1A. Principal Lawn Grasses for the Cool Humid Region ***

| Species | Region | Use | Soil | Tolerance (shade) | Moisture | Seed | Growth | Mowing | General |
|---|---|---|---|---|---|---|---|---|---|
| Alta fescue | Entire | 1,2,3 | 11,14,18 | 32 | 41 | 51 | 63,64,69 | 80 | 92 |
| Bent grasses | Entire | 1,5,6 | 11,12,13,18 | 30 | 40,41 | 53 | 64,70 | 82 | 94 |
| Canada bluegrass | Entire | 4 | 14,16 | 33 | 41 | … | 65 | … | … |
| Chewings fescue | Best in North | 1,2 | 10,14 | 33 | 41 | … | 68 | 80 | … |
| Creeping red fescue | Best in North | 1,2,3,5,6 | 10,14,20 | 32 | 40 | 51 | 64,68,69,70 | 80 | … |
| Kentucky bluegrass | Tenn. north | 1,2,3,5,6 | 10,12,13,20 | 30 | 41 | 51 | 64,70 | 80 | 93 |
| Manila grass | Southern half | 1,2,3,5,6 | 11,14,15 | 31 | 41 | 53 | 62,64,66 | 81 | 62 |
| Red top | Entire | 1,4,5,6 | 11,18 | 31 | 41 | 51 | 65,70 | 80 | 63,95 |
| Rough-stalked blue-grass | Entire | 1,6 | 11,13 | 32,33 | 42 | … | 68 | … | … |

**Table 1B. Principal Lawn Grasses for the Warm Humid Region ***

| Species | Region | Use | Soil | Tolerance (shade) | Moisture | Seed | Growth | Mowing | General |
|---|---|---|---|---|---|---|---|---|---|
| Bermuda grass | Entire | 1,2,3,5,6 | 10,13,15 | 30 | 40 | 51 | 60,67,69 | 81 | 90,93 |
| Domestic ryegrass | Entire | 1,6 | 10,13,15 | 32,33 | | 52 | 63 | 81 | 91,94 |
| Red top | Entire | 1,4,5,6 | 11,14,18 | | 41 | 51 | 60,65 | 80 | 91,92,95 |
| Kentucky bluegrass | Tenn. north | 1,2,3,5,6 | 10,12,13,20 | 30 | 40 | 51 | 64,70 | 80 | 93 |
| Manila grass | Lat. 40° south | 1,2,3,6 | 10,13,15 | 32,33 | 41 | 53,54 | 62 | 81 | 90,94 |
| Centipede-grass | Tenn. south | 1,6 | 10,12,14,17 | 31 | 42 | 53 | | 81 | 90,92 |
| Carpet-grass | Deep South | 1,3,6 | 10,14,16 | 30,31 | 42 | 51 | 61,64,70 | 81 | 90,92 |
| St. Augustine grass | Deep South | 1,2,6 | 11,13,16 | 32,33 | 42 | 53 | 64,65,70 | 81 | 90,94 |

* For meaning of code numbers see the opposite page.

## Table 1C. Principal Lawn Grasses for the Arid Region

| Species | Region | Use | Soil | Tolerance | Moisture | Seed | Growth | Mowing | General |
|---|---|---|---|---|---|---|---|---|---|
| Blue grama | Great Plains west | 1, 6 | 10, 14, 19 | 30 | 41 | 50 | 83 | 80 | 96 |
| Buffalo-grass | Great Plains west | 1, 2, 6 | 10, 14, 16 | 30 | 41 | 50 | 64, 69, 70 | 80 | 96 |
| Crested wheat grass (fairway strain) | Great Plains west | 1, 2, 6 | 10, 14 | 30 | 41 | 51 | 64 | 80 | 97 |
| Kikuyu grass | Calif. Coast | 2, 6 | | | 41 | | 65 | | 97 |
| Love grass | Southern Great Plains | 5, 6 | 14, 16, 19 | | 40, 41 | 51, 53 | 64, 67 | 80 | |

### Code Numbers, Table 1A–1C

1. Lawns.
2. Playfields.
3. Roadsides.
4. Nonuse roadsides.
5. Airfields.
6. Areas of rough grass.

10. Prefers well-drained soil.
11. Satisfactory in poorly drained soil.
12. Good on wet soils.
13. Prefers high-fertility soil.
14. Satisfactory in low-fertility soil.
15. Satisfactory in heavy soil.
16. Prefers light sand to sandy loam soil.
17. Grows in a variety of soils.
18. Satisfactory in entire range of acidity.
19. Can stand high alkalinity.
20. Can stand slight acidity.

30. Requires full sunlight.
31. Requires a medium amount of sunlight.
32. Requires little sunlight.
33. Will grow in the shade.

40. Can stand a moderate amount of drought.
41. Quite drought-resistant.
42. Needs a lot of moisture.

50. Sow 1 lb. per 1,000 sq. ft.
51. Sow 2 lb. per 1,000 sq. ft.
52. Sow 4 lb. per 1,000 sq. ft.
53. Sprigs used to establish.
54. Slow to establish good turf.

60. Spreading habit of growth.
61. Spreads by underground stems.
62. Slow to germinate and start.
63. Fast grower, but a temporary cover.
64. Develops a dense turf.

65. Loose, coarse growth.
66. Green in the heat of summer.
67. Can stand heat.
68. Cannot stand as high a temperature as Kentucky bluegrass.
69. Wears well.
70. Aggressive creeper.

80. Mow to 1½–2 in. when well fertilized.
81. Mow to ½–1 in. when well fertilized.
82. Mow to 3/16 in. when well fertilized.
83. Little top growth during drought.

90. Not green in winter.
91. Green in winter.
92. Needs little care.
93. Needs a medium amount of care.
94. Needs much care.
95. Can stand some salt spray.
96. Scars heal rapidly.
97. Crowds out Bermuda grass.

## FOREST CLEANUP FOR PUBLIC USE AND AESTHETIC PURPOSES.

**Definition:** Forest cleanup relates to the removal, or disposal by other means, of dead wood in selected locations within a forest area to improve conditions with respect to use, appearance, and protection of the forest. Forest cleanup does not extend to the cutting or removal of living forest vegetation (see "Special Cuttings in Recreational Areas"). Forest protection aspects of the subject are not given primary consideration under this heading.

### Primary Purposes of Forest Cleanup in Recreational Forests.

1. Removal of obstructions to access and use.
2. Removal of hazards to human safety.
3. Improvement of aesthetic appearances.

### Possible Additional Benefits of Forest Cleanup in Recreational Forests.

1. Reduction of fire hazards.
2. Forest sanitation with respect to destructive insects and diseases.
3. Improvement of conditions for forest regeneration.
4. Soil erosion control.
5. Salvage of usable or marketable forest products.

### Locations and Conditions in Which Forest Cleanup May Be Justified.

1. Camp and picnic grounds, other public-use sites, roadsides, and trailsides in forest areas containing abnormally heavy accumulations of dead standing or fallen trees or parts of trees, such as commonly occur following logging, fire, severe wind or sleet storms, insect or disease attacks.
2. Selected areas beyond the above locations, and with similar forest conditions, where unsightly appearances are objectionable to view from public-use sites or along roads or trails.

### Methods of Disposing of Wood Material. Salvage for use, sale, or donation.

Salvage possibilities deserve consideration in all cleanup operations and should be applied when part of the material to be disposed of is usable, needed, and economically accessible for removal, for (1) use by the administering agency, (2) sale, or (3) donation to needy and deserving individuals or agencies, possibly in exchange for its removal subject to specified conditions.

**Removal for disposal elsewhere.** When unusable or unmarketable material cannot suitably or safely be disposed of, removal to another area must be considered. The volume of material to be removed and the hauling distance are important practical and economic considerations.

**Piling and burning within the cleanup area.** This method may be used in locations and under conditions in which it is safe to burn without danger of the fire escaping or damaging nearby vegetation, where the volume of material requiring treatment is too great to be disposed of economically or suitably by other methods, or where the method is advisable as a fire hazard reduction measure. Application of this method requires that all rules and practices for safe burning be observed. Broadcast burning should not be permitted in any area where living vegetation is to be retained.

**Lopping and flattening or chipping.** Lopping and flattening to the ground within the cleanup area, or chipping by use of a portable chipper and spreading chips on the ground, may be applied where use and aesthetic requirements do not necessitate immediate elimination of the material (removal or burning) and where it is desirable to retain the material for its beneficial effects on soil erosion control and regeneration. On slopes susceptible to erosion, logs and larger limbs should be placed parallel to the contours and blocked to prevent them from rolling. In that position they will help check erosion.

**Combinations.** A combination of two or more of the preceding methods should be applied where the volume of material is so great or where conditions are such that disposal by two or more methods will accomplish the desired results more effectively and economically than a single method. Examples are: (1) Where the lopping and flattening method is applied and an excess of material remains which it would not be suitable or safe to leave, the excess must be disposed of by another method; (2) where part of the material is salvaged and additional unsalvageable material remains to be disposed of by other means; (3) where conditions are suitable for safe piling and burning in some parts of the cleanup area but not in others, a change in method within the same area may be advisable; and (4) where cleanup by removal or burning is called for, such as in a roadside strip, and a gradual shift to lopping and flattening in the zone beyond would be appropriate.

**Some Principles and Practices Involved in Performing Forest Cleanup Work.** 1. Treatment should be confined to selected areas of designated extent and applied therein in a manner and to a degree that is suited to the conditions and to the specific useful purposes that are to be served. Even within a given cleanup area the type and intensity of treatment may often need to be varied in accordance with conditions and needs. Cleanup treatment should not be indiscriminate as to location, extent, type, or intensity.

2. The human tendency to "tidy up" the woods needs restraint wherever natural or near-natural appearances are desired. Some dead standing and fallen trees are a normal component of the forest. Within public-use areas it is usually unsafe to leave dead standing trees, but it is often advisable to leave, properly placed, some of the fallen or cut material in such areas where it will serve (a) as barriers to keep vehicles within bounds; (b) to aid in confining foot travel within desired limits or routes; (c) to reduce the rate, intensity, and extent of wear, trampling, compaction, and erosion of the soil; and (d) on decaying to help restore or maintain the organic layer over the mineral soil, with consequent benefit to living vegetation in the area.

3. Cleanup of the twig-picking and leaf-raking variety has no place or justification in forest areas except in narrow zones or firebreaks (a) around sources of ignition such as fireplaces to prevent escape of fire to the woods, (b) around buildings to prevent possible forest fires from spreading to the buildings, and (c) to remove sources of dampness from building foundations.

4. Many dead standing and fallen trees provide homes and nesting places for wildlife. Except where it is unsafe or otherwise objectionable to leave them, not all such trees should be removed in cleanup operations. If some of the dead trees are left in areas surrounding public-use sites, or beyond roadside strips, wildlife will be encouraged to stay where the greatest number of people can see them.

5. Care should be exercised in cleanup operations to prevent damage to living vegetation and to avoid starting soil erosion.

6. Stumps should be cut as close to the ground as practicable.

7. The volume and kinds of wood material in an area have an important bearing on the degree of fire hazard. Arrangement of the individual logs and limbwood is often the principal factor determining the severity of a fire hazard. Other conditions being equal or unchanged, fire hazard is considerably less where the pieces are placed in close contact with the ground than where they are massed or lodged in elevated positions off the ground. Dead wood lying close to the ground maintains a higher moisture content, decays faster, and therefore disappears more

rapidly as potential fuel for forest fires than similar material otherwise arranged. It is inadvisable to leave piles of cleanup material in or near public-use areas, except as safeguarded for use as fuelwood. It is likewise inadvisable to leave windrows of material along roads or utility lines where they may be readily ignited and quickly produce intense fires which are likely to spread rapidly.

8. Conditions for germination, survival, and development of forest regeneration are generally more favorable in treated than in untreated areas. Accumulations of dead material physically obstruct and suppress seedlings, and young trees are damaged when dead trees fall. Seedbed conditions are improved for most species in cleanup areas where the material has been flattened to the ground.

9. Maintenance treatment will be required at varying intervals to retain the conditions and results accomplished by the initial cleanup work.

**SPECIAL CUTTINGS IN RECREATIONAL AREAS. Types of Cuttings Involved.** Clearcuttings and selective thinnings are made in the forests of recreational areas to accomplish one or more of the following purposes, as applicable:

1. To clear sites for the construction of buildings, roads, parking areas, etc.
2. To meet requirements for access, use, safety, aesthetic appearance, sunlight, and air circulation in public use, utility, and administration areas.
3. To "daylight" road curves as a safety measure.
4. To open vistas for scenic views and to facilitate display and interpretation of special features of interest to visitors.
5. To restore or maintain historic conditions or to preserve the typical character of a landscape as of a certain period.
6. To control destructive insect or disease epidemics.
7. To salvage forest products from stands killed by fire, insects, disease, wind storm, sleet storm, flood, etc.

See "Forest Cleanup for Public Use and Aesthetic Purposes" with respect to items 6 and 7, and in regard to slash disposal and cleanup measures following cutting for any of the above purposes.

**Cuttings for Construction and To Meet Use Requirements.** As a general rule, dense forest stands are not suitable for residence or camp sites, picnic, play, utility, administration, or most other types of use areas. Wherever possible, such stands should be avoided in selecting locations for use areas. Moreover, with respect to road locations particularly, opening up shallow-rooted stands in situations which are exposed to strong winds is likely to result in extensive windthrow, beginning at the vulnerable edge thus created and extending beyond into the stand.

The proper selection of forested sites for use areas and their development to accommodate an intended specific type of use require consideration of the following factors in regard to removal and retention of trees.

1. The advisability of reserving the area or stand from development, or of restricting development within it. Locations within the finest or most unusual forest stands in a recreational area are too often selected as development sites, with resulting destruction, reduction in extent, or impairment of such stands.
2. Requirements for space, access, safety (including dangerous overhanging limbs as well as hazardous trees), aesthetic effect, sunlight and shade, air circulation, and reduction of dampness and humidity.
3. The probable windfirmness and life expectancy of selected residual trees, if any, to be left within or bordering the site, considering the likely effects of opening up the stand, of excavating or filling, if planned, and possible damage due to construction. It often takes considerable time for trees that have

developed in the forest, particularly older trees and trees in dense stands, to become adjusted to the life of a shade tree and to develop that appearance.

4. Interference or effect of proposed residual trees and their roots on the completed structure or area, or on the use thereof.

5. The value and possible need of retaining trees and shrubs in some locations for screen purposes, as barriers to keep vehicles and foot travel within intended bounds or routes, or to confine the extent of soil compaction and erosion. Unless completely cleared conditions or unobstructed access is called for, the removal of trees and undergrowth should be done with restraint, particularly where heavy use is anticipated. The trampling, wear and tear of human use, and changes in site factors due to cutting and construction tend to kill, damage, or devitalize remaining vegetation to the extent that it is likely to be thinned out within a few years beyond what is planned or desired. More satisfactory results will usually be accomplished by opening up gradually, in two or more partial selective thinnings, than by attempting to do it all at once.

6. The possible need for and means of preventing or controlling any undesired sprout or seedling growth that may come in following opening up of the stand.

7. Stump removal, if necessary, and whether by cutting flush with the ground or by pulling or digging out.

**Cuttings to "Daylight" Road Curves.** The governing purpose in cuttings of this type is to provide sufficient sight distance at curves to make the road safe for motorists and pedestrians, keeping it in proportion to the standards of construction and regulations for use of the road. That purpose must be the dominant factor in determining where and to what extent cutting will be done. Historic or other trees of unusual interest may occur within the cutting area. Where they would obstruct vision to a hazardous extent if allowed to remain, road relocation is likely to be the only alternative to their removal if safety requirements are to be met.

Where the available road plans show roadside vegetation conditions, cuttings for sight distance can first be laid out on paper and then executed accordingly on the ground. In the absence of such plans, or to check cuttings that have been done in accordance with a plan, the cutting lines can be sighted in as the driver would see them and checked by measurement for conformance with sight distance standards applicable to the type of road. Subsequent sprout or seedling growth within the cleared areas will need to be kept down as a roadside maintenance operation.

**Vista Cutting.** The location, length, width, and openness of vistas will be determined by the purposes to be served and the physical conditions involved. The opening up of vistas is usually a matter of clearcutting, but not all vistas need to be completely open. Moreover, leaving some well-selected trees in suitable locations where they can be allowed to develop as specimens or groups without obstructing the view or line of vision to a focal point generally improves the aesthetic appearance of a vista. Some of these trees may also be appreciated for their shade and individual ornamental value. Vulnerability of the vista edges to windthrow requires consideration of the windfirmness of the tree species involved in relation to exposure of the location to strong winds. Irregular or naturalistic vista edges are usually more pleasing to the eye than those cut to a straight line.

A major consideration with respect to vistas is their maintenance. In highly developed areas, and where power mowing equipment is available, it is often most practical to clear and seed vistas to grass. Elsewhere, the periodic removal of sprout or seedling growth by manual or chemical means will usually be necessary to keep vistas open. In cases where erosion becomes a problem and grass is inappropriate, the establishment of a ground cover or planting of low-growing shrubs may be called for.

**Cuttings for Historic or Landscape Effect.** The location, extent, and type of cutting for purposes of this kind are dictated by the conditions to be restored or maintained. A knowledge of such conditions, therefore, is prerequisite to undertaking the work. Removal of forest growth for the purpose of restoring fields or openings where they existed before will normally necessitate clearcutting.

Selective cuttings designed to change the density or composition of stands so as to recreate a historic or characteristic forest condition of a certain period or location should not be attempted without first obtaining the advice of a competent ecologist or silviculturist for the forest types involved. In connection with such cuttings it is important to bear in mind that vegetation is not static and that it is difficult or impossible to establish and hold indefinitely, as though fixed, a desired forest condition in a given area. The principles and considerations mentioned above concerning the maintenance of vistas are essentially applicable to cuttings under this heading also.

**Cuttings for Insect or Disease Control or Timber Salvage.** Cuttings for forest protection and utilization purposes are discussed in other sections of this handbook. The same general principles and methods are applicable to such cuttings in recreational forests as in other forests. Special care and precautionary measures to prevent or reduce damage to residual vegetation from felling and removal operations are often justifiable in recreational forests.

## Development Policies and Standards

### TYPES OF RECREATIONAL AREAS.

1. Superlative areas. Areas with unique scenic values, so stupendous as to affect almost everyone.
2. Primeval or natural areas. Areas that exhibit primitive conditions of forest growth in which human activities have never upset the normal processes of nature.
3. Wilderness areas. Wild or primitive forest areas where wilderness enthusiasts and recreationists may enjoy unmodified nature. To qualify, there must be no roads, no commercial timber cutting, and no special use permits for commercialized recreation.
4. Roadside and streamside areas. Timber strips adjoining roads and streams for the enjoyment of the traveler.
5. Camp-site areas. Land reserved for camping.
6. Picnic areas. Land reserved for picnicking.
7. Residency areas. Land reserved for summer homes, hotels, resorts, group camps, and service areas.
8. Outing areas. Tracts of land which have not been severely injured scenically and on which one can get away from man-made sounds.

### TYPICAL USES OF RECREATIONAL AREAS IN THE EASTERN UNITED STATES.

During the ECW program, prior to 1940, Region One (comprising Ohio, Kentucky, Tennessee, Mississippi, Louisiana, and all states east of these) of the National Park Service, by a series of sample checks and surveys at existing recreational areas over a number of states, obtained data on weekly summer attendance from various zones of travel, the ratio of children to adults, attendance as to the time of day and day of the week, and the type of recreation participated in. While the ratios obtained from these data are necessarily averages and may not apply equally to all areas, they are a useful starting point in calculating probable attendance at a specific area.

Thus, in Table 2, the population (Column 2) within each zone of travel (Column 1) is multiplied by the percentage (Column 3) of the population in attendance during an average week in summer at this or other recreational areas. Column 4 gives the total number of such recreationists. Attendance at the specific area is, however, reduced by the competition of similar areas at various travel distances, and with various facilities and attractions. Residual percentages (Column 5) are applied to the number of persons in Column 4 to obtain the attendance at the specific area (Column 6).

**Table 2.** Example of Weekly Summer Attendance at a Specific Recreational Area as Determined by Distance and Size of Surrounding Populations

| Zone: Distance in miles from recreational area (1) | Population of zone (2) | Weekly attendance at this and other recreational areas | | Weekly attendance at specific area | |
|---|---|---|---|---|---|
| | | Percent of population of zone (3) | Number (4) | Percent of those attending any recreational area (5) | Number (6) |
| 0–5 | 8,500 | 0.0970 | 824 | 100.0 | 824 |
| 6–10 | 8,500 | .0630 | 536 | 100.0 | 536 |
| 11–15 | 32,000 | .0409 | 1,309 | 100.0 | 1,309 |
| 16–20 | 32,000 | .0266 | 851 | 70.0 | 596 |
| 21–25 | 59,500 | .0172 | 1,023 | 40.0 | 409 |
| 26–30 | 59,500 | .0112 | 666 | 25.0 | 166 |
| 31–40 | 130,000 | .0059 | 762 | 20.0 | 152 |
| 41–50 | 430,000 | .0025 | 1,062 | 10.0 | 106 |
| Totals | 760,000 | | 7,033 | | 4,098* |

\* Children 943, or 22.9 percent; adults, 3,155, or 77.1 percent.

**Table 3.** Example of Weekly Summer Attendance,\* as Determined by Day of Week and Time of Day

| Day or days and time of day | Number of persons | Percent of total number |
|---|---|---|
| 5 weekdays | | |
| Morning | 369 | 9.0 |
| Afternoon | 902 | 22.0 |
| Evening | 389 | 9.5 |
| Total 5 weekdays | 1,660 | 40.5 |
| Saturday | | |
| Morning | 114 | 2.8 |
| Afternoon | 287 | 7.0 |
| Evening | 119 | 2.9 |
| Total Saturday | 520 | 12.7 |
| Sunday | | |
| Morning | 426 | 10.4 |
| Afternoon | 1,049 | 25.6 |
| Evening | 443 | 10.8 |
| Total Sunday | 1,918 | 46.8 |
| Total entire week | 4,098 | 100.0 |

\* At the same recreational area as that given in Table 2.

**Table 4. Example of Types of Recreation During the Summer on Sunday** [a]

| | Participants [b] | |
|---|---|---|
| Types of recreation | Percent | Number of persons |
| Scenic use ..................... | 46.9 | 899 |
| Picnicking ..................... | 32.0 | 614 |
| Swimming ..................... | 26.3 | 504 |
| Hiking ......................... | 13.9 | 267 |
| Boating ....................... | 8.5 | 163 |
| Camping ....................... | 5.4 | 104 |
| Horseback riding ............... | 4.1 | 79 |
| Fishing ....................... | 3.6 | 69 |
| Nature study .................. | 2.8 | 55 |

[a] At the same recreational area as that given in Tables 2 and 3.
[b] Because many persons indulged in more than one form of recreation, the total percentage exceeds 100.0 and the total number of persons exceeds 1,918 (Sunday total of Table 3).

## REQUIREMENTS OF RECREATION PLANNING IN PUBLIC FORESTS.

(Based on statements and material prepared by the National Park Service, U. S. Dept. Interior, and the Forest Service, U. S. Dept. Agr.) The preparation of a sound recreational system plan must be based upon a determination of the following major factors as exactly as possible:

1. The recreational requirements of the population to be served, by kind and quantity.
2. The kind and quantity of land needed to meet those requirements.
3. The lands available and suitable for the kinds of recreation to be supplied and not more valuable for uses other than recreation.

**Objectives.** The objectives of recreational planning and management in public forests are definitely to recognize, preserve, develop, and administer all natural resources which through public health and enjoyment make their highest economic and social contribution to the national welfare.

**Place.** The place for outdoor recreation in public forest management may be as follows:

1. Dominant. Within areas of exceptional scenic quality and of natural or historic interest, or areas subject to heavy present or prospective recreational use because they are the best or only areas available for such use by considerable numbers of people.
2. Coordinate. Within areas which afford material opportunity for various forms of recreation and are, or probably will be, in public demand for that purpose, and where use for that purpose will not conflict to an unjustifiable degree with other major functions or services of the forests, or entail unwarranted sacrifices of other economic or public interests.
3 Subordinate. Within areas where present or prospective recreational use is, or probably will be, small, or where the scenic or recreational qualities are unimportant, or where extensive recreational use would conflict to an unjustifiable degree with other more important functions or services of the forests or result in unwarranted sacrifices of other important economic or public interests.

**Priority of Recreational Uses.** The principle of "the greatest good to the greatest number in the long run" should be followed. Preference should invariably be given to the form of occupancy representing the highest utilization of the area on the basis of broad public service and interest. The order of priority of the various types of use is generally as follows:

1. Superlative natural and primitive areas set aside for scenic, inspirational, scientific, and educational purposes.
2. Scenic roads, trails, and waterways for public use—touring, hiking, boating.
3. Public picnic and campgrounds and winter sports areas for general public use.
4. Recreation, health, and education camps maintained by or for nonprofit public or semipublic organizations for public use.
5. Hotels, resorts, camps, and public services operated on a commercial basis for the accommodation of the general public.
6. Private camps, resorts, clubs, and campgrounds maintained by private organizations for the exclusive use of their membership.
7. Recreation cabins for the exclusive use of permittees and their families.

## Inventories and Classifications of Recreational Resources.

1. Inventory of existing public and private recreational developments inside or within the sphere of influence of the forest to show the pattern of types and distribution.
2. Determination of areas most valuable for scenic, inspirational, scientific, and educational purposes which are unique and cannot be duplicated.
3. Classification of roads, trails, and waterways in the order of their priority in recreational value and use, present and potential, and the establishment of standards for each.
4. Determination of areas most valuable for general public use.
   a. Under intensive development along modern lines of landscape design— parks, playgrounds, winter sports areas, bathhouses and beaches, intensive camp and picnic areas.
   b. Under normal conditions of forest development and utilization, with as little disturbance of natural forest conditions as possible to satisfy the sanitary, fire prevention, and service needs.
   c. As primitive areas, with absolute minimum development.
5. Determination of areas most valuable for exclusive special use.
   a. As general community developments.
   b. As hotel, resort, school, sanatoria, camp, and clubhouse sites for public and semipublic use.
   c. As sites for commercial services and utilities.
   d. As private camps, clubs for the exclusive use of their membership and not available to the general public.
   e. As exclusive recreation cabin sites for family use.

## Coordination with Other Public Forest Purposes and Uses.

1. Timber production.
2. Grazing.
3. Wildlife and fish management.
4. Watershed protection, water power, and municipal water supply.
5. Mineral production.
6. Road and trail location and construction.
7. Research reserves, experimental forests, etc.
8. Other economic requirements of local communities.
9. Fire control management.
10. Administrative and protective sites.

## Coordination with Other Public and Private Agencies.

1. National, state, county, and municipal parks, present and potential.
2. Semipublic recreational land programs.
3. Public and private commercial land programs for the public.
4. Exclusive private land programs.

### Planning of an Intensively Used Area.

1. Landscape design.
   a. General topographic survey.
   b. General broad scale area planning.
   c. General layout of structures, facilities, and utilities.
   d. Detail locations and design of roads and trails, grading, etc.
   e. Retention thinning of present forest cover.
   f. Planting design of trees, shrubs, etc.
2. Architectural and structural quality standards, types, and designs.
3. Planning of public service utilities—water supply, sanitation, garbage disposal, fuelwood supply, etc.
4. Operation standards.
   a. Full-time personnel; custodian, concessionaire, maintenance person, etc.
   b. Part-time personnel.
   c. Scheduled periodic personnel.
   d. Periodic personnel as demand warrants.
   e. No planned personnel.
5. Minimum maintenance standards.
   a. Of general community areas.
   b. Of public service areas.
   c. Of individual camp or picnic sites, lots, or tracts.
   d. Of structures.
   e. Of road and scenic strips.
6. Job analysis for recreational area forest guard.
   a. Cleanup of recreation area.
   b. General maintenance work.
   c. Relations with the public.
   d. Enforcement of regulations.
   e. Improvement work.
   f. Keeping a daily record.
   g. Protecting and accounting for tools and supplies.
   h. Personal appearance and conduct.
   i. Supervision of helpers.
   j. Duties of life guards and other special helpers.

## FACTORS INVOLVED IN LOCATING, DEVELOPING, AND OPERATING AN ORGANIZED CAMP. Site Factors To Consider in Locating a Camp.

A. Climatic.
   1. Temperature and humidity.
   2. Prevailing winds.
   3. Average rainfall.
   4. Snow conditions.

B. Topographic.
   1. Soil.          4. Open area.
   2. Slope.         5. Forest cover.
   3. Level space.

C. Water.
   1. Lakes and ponds.
   2. Streams and rivers.
   3. Lake site.
   4. Springs.
   5. Underground water.
   6 Bottom of swim area.

D. General.
   1. Accessibility.
   2. Size of area.
   3. Privacy.
   4. Character of adjoining developments.
   5. General elevation.
   6. Ventilation.
   7. Fire hazards
   8. Building materials.

E. Richness of environment.
   1. Plants.
   2. Animals.
   3. Geologic.
   4. Varied topography.
   5. Ethnologic.
   6. Historic.

F. Undesirable factors.
  1. Fogs and dampness.
  2. Swamps.
  3. Floods.
  4. Excessive dust.
  5. Dangerous cliffs.
  6. Dangerous rapids.
  7. Poisonous plants.
  8. Poisonous reptiles.
  9. Insect pests.

## Factors To Be Considered in Developing a Camp.

A. Roads and trails.
  1. Entrance road.
  2. Parking area.
  3. Service roads.
  4. Storage areas.
  5. Foot trails and paths.

B. Camp Layout.
  1. Number and size of buildings.
    a. Type of construction.
    b. Appearance and exterior treatment.
  2. Arrangement, distances, spacing.
  3. Camp units.
    a. Sleeping cabins or tents.
    b. Unit wash house and latrine.
    c. Unit lodge.
  4. Administration and basic services.
    a. Office.
    b. Infirmary.
    c. Central wash house and latrine.
    d. Water supply.
    e. Electric wiring and plant.
    f. Telephone.
    g. Central hot showers.
    h. Laundry.
    i. Trading post.
    j. Garage or workshop.
  5. Recreational and cultural activities.
    a. Central lodge.
    b. Recreation building.
    c. Play areas.
    d. Swimming areas.
    e. Boating facilities.
    f. Forest improvements and planting.
    g. Wildlife.
    h. Museum—nature lore.
    i. Craft shop.
    j. Campfire ring.
    k. Chapel.
  6. Dining facilities.
    a. Dining lodge.
    b. Kitchen.
    c. Outdoor kitchen shelter.
    d. Fireplaces, tables, cupboards.
    e. Refrigeration.
    f. Waste disposal, incinerator.

C. Drainage, erosion control, or eradication.

## Personnel To Be Considered in Operating a Camp.

A. Camp director.
  1. Program director.
    a. Swimming.
    b. Campcraft.
    c. Nature lore.
    d. Handicraft.
    e. Boating.
    f. Games.
    g. Dramatics.
    h. Music, etc.
  2. Secretary.
     All records, correspondence, etc.
  3. Doctor.
     Sanitation and health.
  4. Dietician.
     Kitchen and dining room staff.
  5. Tent or cabin counselors.
  6. Maintenance technician.

## Activities To Be Considered in Operating a Camp.

A. Daily routines.
  1. Orderliness of cabins.
  2. Upkeep of grounds.
  3. Personal cleanliness.
  4. Care of personal belongings.
  5. Share in preparation and serving of food.
  6. Balance between activity and rest.

B. Water sports.
  1. Swimming.
  2. Life saving.
  3. Rowing.
  4. Canoeing.
  5. Sailing.
  6. Fishing.

C. Campcraft.
   1. Use of wood tools—knife, axe, compass.
   2. Fire building and outdoor cooking.
   3. Map reading and exploring trips.
   4. Overnight or longer trips.
   5. Building bivouacs—temporary shelters.

D. Nature lore.
   1. Nature trails.
   2. Nature games.
   3. Bird and game sanctuaries.
   4. Aquaria and terraria.
   5. Museum and workshop.
   6. Nature crafts.
   7. Nurseries, gardens.

E. Handicrafts.
   1. Wood carving.
   2. Leather craft.
   3. Making camp equipment.
   4. Developing camp improvements.

F. Games.
   1. Indoor types.
   2. Water games.
   3. Swim meets.
   4. Stunt races.
   5. High degree of organization—baseball, etc.
   6. Low degree of organization—circle type.

G. Special activities.
   1. Plays and pageants.
   2. Music.
   3. Campfire ceremonials.
   4. Storytelling.

## Facilities

For designs of structures suitable to recreational areas, see Section 13, Materials, Structures, and Facilities.

## SPACE REQUIREMENTS FOR RECREATIONAL FACILITIES.

| Facility | Unit | Minimum space requirement |
|---|---|---|
| Parking ....... | 1 car | 10 × 20 ft. plus 20 ft. for turning in and backing out. |
| | Multiple car-parking area | Compute on basis of 300 sq. ft. per car, assuming that a 20-ft. turning width is located between and serves two parallel rows of parking spaces. Add space needed for entrance and exit roads; lawn, shrub, or tree islands; buildings; walks or paths. |
| Picnicking .... | 1 picnic unit, 8 people, maximum. (Includes 1 combination table and bench, 1 fireplace, 1 trash receptacle.) | 15 × 15 ft. over-all, or 225 sq. ft. per unit. Add space needed for parking and a buffer zone for privacy. Maximum distance to nearest drinking water and latrine, 250 ft. |
| Camping ...... | 1 tent camp site. (Includes 1 fireplace, parking space for car and utility trailer, and space for tent or tent fly.) | 25 × 30 ft. over-all, or 750 sq. ft. per unit. Add a buffer zone between units for privacy. Maximum distance to nearest drinking water and latrine, 250 ft. |
| | 1 trailer camp site. (Includes 1 fireplace, parking spurs for car and house trailer, and space for tent or tent fly.) | 30 × 40 ft. over-all, or 1,200 sq. ft. per unit. Add a buffer zone between units for privacy. Maximum distance to nearest drinking water and latrine, 250 ft. |

## CAMPGROUND AND PICNIC AREA LAYOUT STANDARDS.

Generally speaking, there are three types of forest camps, classified by use for the following purposes: picnicking only, overnight camping only, and the dual use of picnicking and camping on the same tract. The segregation of the activities in the tract plan in accordance with existing or contemplated use would be as follows: (1) group picnic area, (2) individual camp or picnic units, (3) sports and children's play areas, (4) assembly area, (5) administration area, (6) maintenance area, and (7) reservoir area.

The area layout plan normally will determine the type and extent of forest camp development for the tract. The planner then is concerned with the proper layout of the improvements in relation to topography, cover, and existing improvements. The following principles and practices are suggested.

**Entrance and Interior Roads.** Entrance to the tract should be well identified by an entrance sign with a sight distance consistent with the normal speed of traffic on the forest road or highway. An average sight distance for high speed highway locations is 300 ft., for forest roads 150 ft. On fast-traveled highways a deceleration and acceleration lane approximately 300 ft. long (150 ft. on both sides of the entranceway) on both sides of the highway at the entrance should be planned. The centerline turning radius for the entrance and interior roads should not be less than 50 ft. A turning radius of 100 to 200 ft. from the highway will often be desired. The width of road, grade, clearing, grading, drainage, surfacing, etc., should conform to minimum specifications for forest roads. The entrance road, as well as all connecting interior roads where two-way traffic is planned, should conform to the one and one-half lane standard for medium logging traffic. The interior roads should be planned in a loop design, topography permitting, for one-way traffic and should conform to the minimum standards for one-lane road for low-service general use. The interior road should be designed not closer than 100 ft. from a lake or stream, and should not be located within the 200-ft. roadside zone unless absolutely necessary. The interior road loop should be at least 200 ft. in diameter to allow for the spacing of camp and picnic units. Interior roads terminating in a turn-around should be of the one and one-half lane standard with the turn-around of one-lane standard.

**Group Picnic Area.** The group picnic area should usually be the center of activity in the tract layout. The entrance road should terminate at this point, and the loop road system to the individual camp and picnic units should radiate from it. The site should be level or moderately sloping and in an open or semiopen park-like timber stand, or in a type capable of being thinned to allow freedom of movement for groups of people. Direct accessibility to the dominant feature of the area such as a lake or stream should be planned. The layout design of the facilities within the group picnic area should be guided by the topographic conditions, cover, and view. Picnic tables generally are 10 ft. in length, arranged individually and in groups. In some forest areas and on areas where rains occur during the normal picnicking season, a stove shelter will often be desirable in the group picnic area. Community kitchens are to be discouraged, other than in very heavily used forest camps, because of their limited use compared to the cost of construction, difficulties of administration, etc. Water should be piped to the area, unless a nearby well or spring will fulfill this requirement. Garbage cans or garbage pits should be provided within the immediate area, and an ample parking area should be laid out. Small camp stoves will often be desirable in the table groups to augment the large picnic stove, where a quick warm-up of coffee or other smaller quantities of food or drink is desired.

**Individual Camp and Picnic Units (Including Trailer Camp Unit).** The individual camp and picnic unit is usually designed to accommodate up to eight persons. The planned layout of the camp and picnic unit should provide for combined use in order to allow for a flexible use of the area. For reasons of privacy and to prevent deterioration of the area, individual units should be planned not closer than 100 ft. from each other. The separation of camp sites by more than 100 ft. will have to be decided by the planner as the local conditions of each site dictate and the economy of road, water pipe, toilet facilities, etc., demand. Each site should have provisions for a stove, table, and tent space. Parking facilities should be designed to accommodate one car singly, and at varying intervals space for a combination car and trailer should be provided. Toilet facilities should be planned not farther than 300 ft. from any camp or picnic unit. Water should be piped to serve an average of four or more units from each hydrant; garbage pits or cans should be placed to serve two or more units. The camp table generally should be not more than 6 ft. in length. The camp stove should be a low, unobtrusive type which may or may not be convertible to warming fire use. Where use justifies, a rustic type bench may be included in plans for the camp and picnic unit. The layout should provide for reasonably close access between the parking area and the center of the unit. The stove should be so oriented with the prevailing winds that smoke will cause as little annoyance as possible to persons using the site. The table should be located for ease of access to the stove and to take advantage of scenic views. Care should be taken to see that the unit does not infringe upon the location of recreation trails planned along the lake shore or streamside.

**Sports and Children's Play Area.** Facilities for a children's play area should include swings, teeters, sand boxes, wading pond, sand beach, etc., planned in a location central to the group picnic area in order to make parental supervision easier. The site location should take into account such hazards as roads, deep or swift water, drop-offs, etc. Children usually run for the playground area upon first arriving at the picnic area, as well as after they have eaten. While the parents are preoccupied in arranging the picnic and in cleaning up afterward, they will want to be able to see that the youngsters are playing in safety.

Sports facilities often include horseshoe pitching courts, softball grounds, and a swimming pond in the form of a dammed-up stream, together with a bathhouse, diving board, swimming float, bathing beach, etc. The horseshoe pitching court is often located in the group picnic area and off to one side for safety reasons. As an addition to the horseshoe court, a shoe storage rack and benches may be provided. The location of the larger sports facilities is dictated by local conditions. Reasonably close accessibility to the entire camp area is desired. The site location should be studied to avoid undue construction costs and disfiguration of the landscape. Often the grading required for softball grounds or the borrow required to make an earth-fill dam defeats the purpose for which the development was intended. For artificial swimming ponds, the planner should consider the maximum depth to be at 5 ft., both for reasons of safety and for warmer water. The planner should further explore the possibilities for the development of a series of shallow settling ponds to allow the sun to warm the water before it enters the swimming pond.

**Assembly Area.** The campfire circle, amphitheater, and community buildings, such as winter sports shelters, etc., have been developed in the past as assembly areas. The campfire circle is generally accepted as the most popular assembly area development because of its low cost and its effect of informality. The seating capacity is governed by anticipated or actual use. Large campfire circles and amphitheaters are planned only at large forest camps and picnic areas where picnicking by organized groups is popular and the need for an assembly area is evident. The best location is an area where there is no conflict with other activities in the camp and where the scenic setting is attractive and noises are subdued. It should be reasonably close to the group picnic area; otherwise little use will be made of the campfire circle.

**Administration Area.** The administration area is usually in the form of a guard station which is manned by a forest guard whose duties are entirely or partially recreation administration. Generally there are two locations for the administrator's or attendant's station—at the entrance to the forest camp facing the highway or entrance road, or at a central location within the forest camp. Either location depends upon local conditions and administrative requirements. Facilities should include adequate signs, public parking, and service road or court space as needed. Often a large rustic-type information sign near the entrance to the station will be a silent dispenser of information when the guard is engaged elsewhere. The design of the station should include facilities for public contact under cover and separate from the living quarters of the building.

**Maintenance Area.** Most of the larger forest camps need a maintenance area of one form or another to take care of the many maintenance items that are a perennial problem to the administrative officer. One of the most important facilities to be included in the maintenance area plan is the wood storage shelter, or outside wood storage. Additional facilities may or may not include an incinerator for burning the camp garbage and refuse, a concrete washing platform for cleaning out garbage cans, and a storage and equipment repair building where equipment can be stored through the winter and facilities made available for repairs. The maintenance area should be located off the beaten track of the camp visitor and in a location reasonably close to the guard station. The size of the area will depend on the volume of work to be done. This area will often be the central work area for fabricating parts, storage, and assembling materials and equipment in the construction of the camp or picnic area.

**Reservoir Area.** The source of the water supply should be determined early in the development of the camp plan in order that all proposed improvements can be planned with a view to maintaining purity of the water supply. Often the source of supply will be a stream or spring at a higher elevation than the camp, where chances of human contamination are remote. Other sources of supply may be at points lower in elevation than the camp, requiring a pump or ram to force the water to a tank reservoir at a higher level. Drilling a well or direct take from a spring on the site may be the only method of securing water.

**Miscellaneous Improvements: Trails, Steps, and Benches.** The camp and picnic area plan should include a well laid out trail system which provides direct access to toilets, garbage pits, etc., and which parallels the lake or stream shore or other scenic attraction. Width, grade, and location depend on the site requirements and public use and no hard and fast rule can be set up. Popular trails in large camps often may be planned at 6-ft. width, with steps designed for grades exceeding 15 percent. Steps, built of cedar or rock, will often solve a difficult trail location and grading problem, and provide interest in the layout. Benches along trails at vantage points or on steep climbs are desired.

**Bridges (Auto, Foot, and Horse).** The various types of bridges needed in a camp and picnic area should be a part of the tract plan. Auto and foot bridges are direct results of the road and trail layout design. Horse bridges may be needed in the camp when a bridle trail is projected through the area.

**Toilets.** A maximum distance of 300 ft. to the nearest toilet should be planned from any picnic or camping unit. Toilets of the single pit type are generally designed for use by one occupant and those of the multiple flush type for occupancy by six or more persons. Flush type toilets should be planned only at large camps where supervision and maintenance is constant, otherwise the pit type should be selected. Both the pit type and the disposal field for the flush type should be planned not closer than 150 ft. from any stream or lake. While it is desirable to locate the toilet in a setting of timber and lesser vegetation, it is by no means desirable to hide it completely or to place it too far from the heavily used part of the area. Past experience seems to bear out the fact that the toilet should be readily seen, be easily accessible from the main trail or roads, and have enough vegetative material around it so as not to be too bare or obvious.

**Barriers, Walls, and Fences.** Barriers are designed principally to define roadways and parking areas. The camp plan should provide for barriers only at places where unregulated driving will result in harm to the vegetative cover. Existing natural barriers such as rocks and trees which can become a part of the barrier system should be allowed to remain in place. Barriers frequently will be low, continuous rock curbing, individually placed partially buried rocks, or a combination of low rock or concrete posts with a log rail. Walls frequently will be needed, such as a riprap wall to protect a bank face from erosion, or a retaining wall to hold a graded area. Fences in a forest camp may be planned to form a decorative feature in the administrative area, a boundary fence to keep out livestock, or to serve as a guard rail at hazardous places. The guard rail fence must be built for stability and permanence. In this respect, combinations of concrete, rock, pipe, cable, or wire mesh should be considered. Log posts placed in the ground are not desirable as they rot out rather rapidly, cause undue maintenance work, and create possible safety hazards.

**Water Hydrants and Pump Stands.** Water hydrants should be planned to serve an average of four individual camp and picnic units. Hydrants will be needed at stove shelter sites and at the individual picnic table groups. The combination of drinking fountain and hydrant will often be desirable for both picnic and camp areas. Drinking fountains should be included at such strategic points as junctions of trails, at the top of a steep climb, overlook areas, in children's playgrounds and adult sports areas, at swimming ponds, etc. Where piped water is not feasible, the drilling of a well will be necessary. Pump stands to cover the wells should be used. The wells should be located in, or immediately adjacent to, the group picnic area and be designed to serve six or more camp sites.

**Garbage Disposal.** Garbage and other refuse disposal will ordinarily be taken care of by garbage cans or pits. An adequate distribution of the cans or pits in the forest camp will go a long way toward keeping the area clean. Plans should include one garbage can to serve two individual camp or picnic units, or one garbage pit to serve four camp and picnic units. One garbage can should serve each picnic table group, and a can should be placed at the stove shelter, bathhouse, fire circle, etc. One or two garbage pits usually will serve the group picnic area, depending on its size. Plans will include a stand for each garbage can. The garbage can and stand should be located as near the camp road as possible to facilitate loading the full cans onto a trailer or truck. Both garbage cans and pits should be readily visible to the camper or picnicker so that he will not be inclined to throw garbage elsewhere. Garbage cans should be planned only for those camps where pick-up can be accomplished at least once every week during the season of use.

**Signs.** Forest camp signs generally can be classified as approach, entrance, directional, informational, regulatory, and cautionary. The camp plan should include a complete layout of all signs needed for the area.

**Registers.** The inclusion of a registration box or shelter in a forest camp plan will depend upon the local requirements as determined by the administrative officer in charge. It is not general practice to include facilities for registration at every forest camp. The register box or shelter can be located at the start of an important recreation trail near the group picnic area or parking area or at some other point of public concentration. Often an information sign or bulletin board will be all that is necessary and will take the place of a register.

**Planting.** Plans should include the type and amount of planting to take place. Planting often will be necessary about buildings, signs, cut banks and fill slopes, at entranceways, along road edges and parking areas, and as screening between camping and picnicking units. Use of native materials existing in the area should be the rule.

## FUELWOOD REQUIREMENTS FOR RECREATIONAL AREAS.

Climate, seasonal use, local custom, and other factors influence the quantity of fuel used in recreational areas, making generalizations concerning requirements impossible. At a Pennsylvania picnic ground remote from large cities 2 cords of fuelwood annually are supplied to each open fireplace; the season of use is 7 to 8 months. The New Jersey Department of Conservation and Economic Development operates twelve state parks and six state forests. The state is heavily populated, and these areas are adjacent to New York and Philadelphia. Charcoal is the only fuel permitted in all but one park. The department estimates that the following quantities of wood, **per person per day,** are used by visitors for camp or cook fires where its use is permitted.

| | |
|---|---:|
| Picnickers | 0.0016 cord |
| Campers | .019 cord |
| Cabins | .037 cord |
| Organized camps | .030 cord |

The season of outdoor recreation is about 8 months. The department reports that only 42 percent of the picnickers use fires, and that one-fourth of these bring their fuel with them.

## DEVELOPMENT OF WATER SUPPLY IN RECREATIONAL

**AREAS.** The water essential to recreation areas may be obtained from either surface or subsurface sources. **Any** water source can be contaminated, and should be tested frequently. Water is not necessarily safe because it is cold, clear, and tasteless. In limestone country the catchment basin for a spring may be a sinkhole miles away from where the water comes to the surface; if the sinkhole is contaminated, the spring may be.

The area around a source of water should contain no pollution. Springs should be fenced, and they should be protected from surface wash. Water should be piped from a spring, so that vessels cannot be dipped into it. The spring itself should be walled up with rock and cement, and covered with a tight cover removable only by the caretaker. It should be cleaned at least once a year to remove sand, silt, or other materials.

The daily water requirement of campers for cooking, dish washing, and personal use (other than in showerbaths or flush toilets) will vary considerably, but will hardly exceed 5 gal. per person. A horse will require 10 gal. a day. The New Jersey Department of Conservation and Economic Development estimates the quantity of water used by its recreationists, **per person per day,** as follows:

    Picnickers  .................................... 3.1 gal.
    Campers  ...................................... 5.5 gal.
    Cabins  ....................................... 18.4 gal.
    Organized  camps  ............................ 15.0 gal.

**Flow of Water in Pipes.** When water is to be piped from a spring or other source to a point of use below it, there is a constant relation between the quantity which can be delivered, the size and length of the pipe, and the head (or difference in elevation) between the water source and the point of delivery. Fig. 1 expresses this relationship. Scale 1 is the volume delivered (discharge), and Scale 2 is the diameter of the pipe. The greater the head, the faster water can discharge through a pipe of a given diameter. But due to friction, the longer the pipe, the slower the rate of discharge. Scale 3 of the chart is therefore a quotient, obtained by dividing 1,000 times the head, in feet, by the length of the pipe, also in feet.

**Example 1.** How much water will be discharged by 128 ft. of 1-in. pipe under a head of 32 ft.? Multiply 32 by 1,000, and divide by 128; the quotient is 250. A straight line connecting 250 on Scale 3 with 1 on Scale 2 crosses Scale 1 at 15. The discharge is therefore 15 gpm.

**Example 2.** How large a pipe is necessary to deliver 20 gal. of water a minute through 2,000 ft. of pipe under a head of 100 ft.? Multiply 100 ft. by the constant, 1,000, and divide by 2,000 ft.; the quotient is 50. Connect 50 on Scale 3 with 20 on Scale 1; the line intersects Scale 2 at 1½. A 1½-in. pipe is therefore needed.

**Hydraulic Rams.** Where the best source of water is a spring, flowing well, or stream **below** the point of use, a hydraulic ram may often be used to raise the water to the desired elevation. The first cost of a ram is low, and there is no cost of operation beyond occasional replacement of a valve or valve seat. As Table 5 shows, a ram is wasteful of water and therefore not adapted for use with a limited

**Table 5. Gallons of Water Lifted per Gallon Received by Hydraulic Rams**

| Fall in feet | Height delivered in feet | | | | | | | |
|---|---|---|---|---|---|---|---|---|
|  | 12 | 18 | 24 | 30 | 36 | 48 | 60 | 72 |
| 2 | 0.1 | | | | | | | |
| 4 | .18 | 0.15 | 0.1 | | | | | |
| 6 | .33 | .2 | .17 | 0.13 | 0.1 | | | |
| 8 | .42 | .28 | .2 | .17 | .15 | 0.1 | | |
| 10 | .54 | .36 | .27 | .22 | .18 | .14 | 0.1 | |
| 12 | .67 | .44 | .33 | .26 | .22 | .16 | .13 | 0.1 |

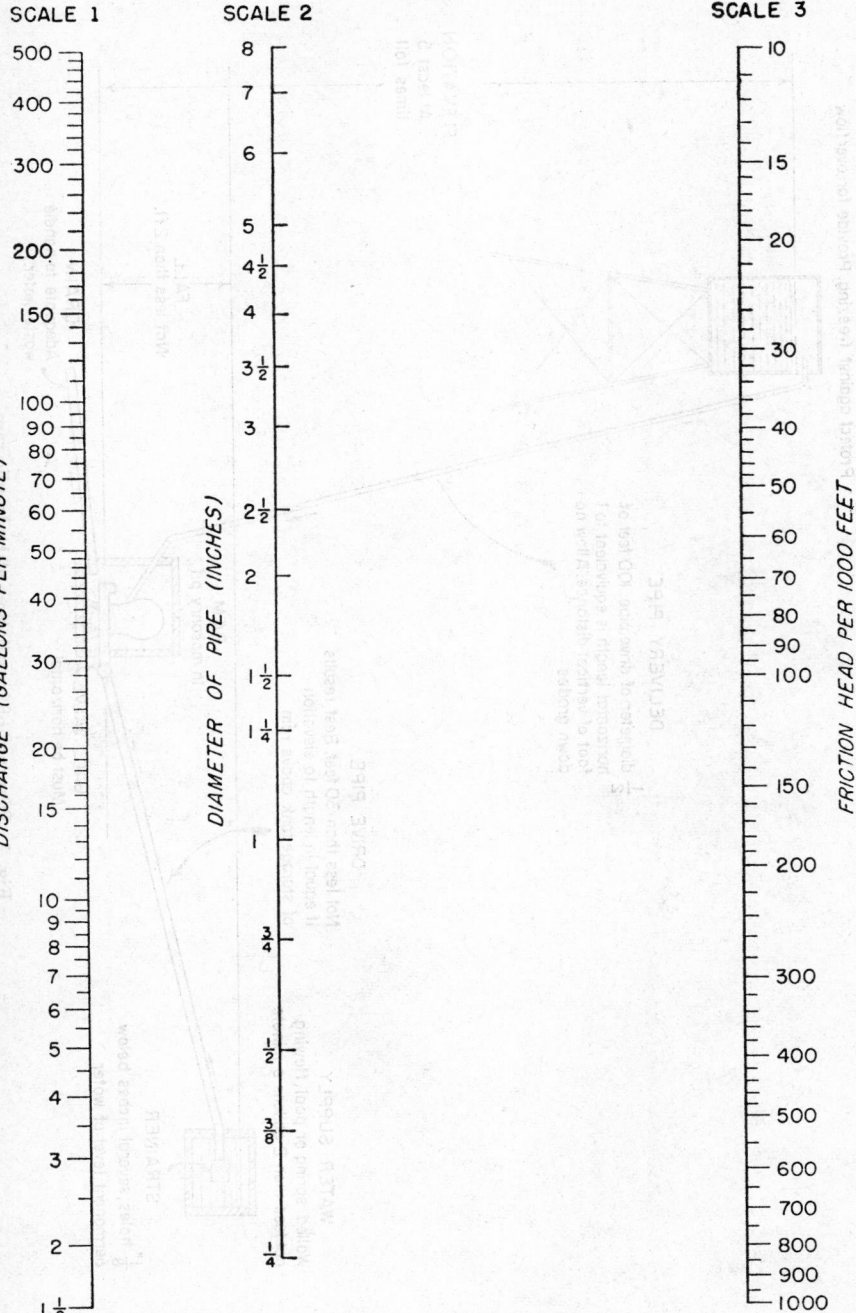

Fig. 1. Flow of water in pipes.

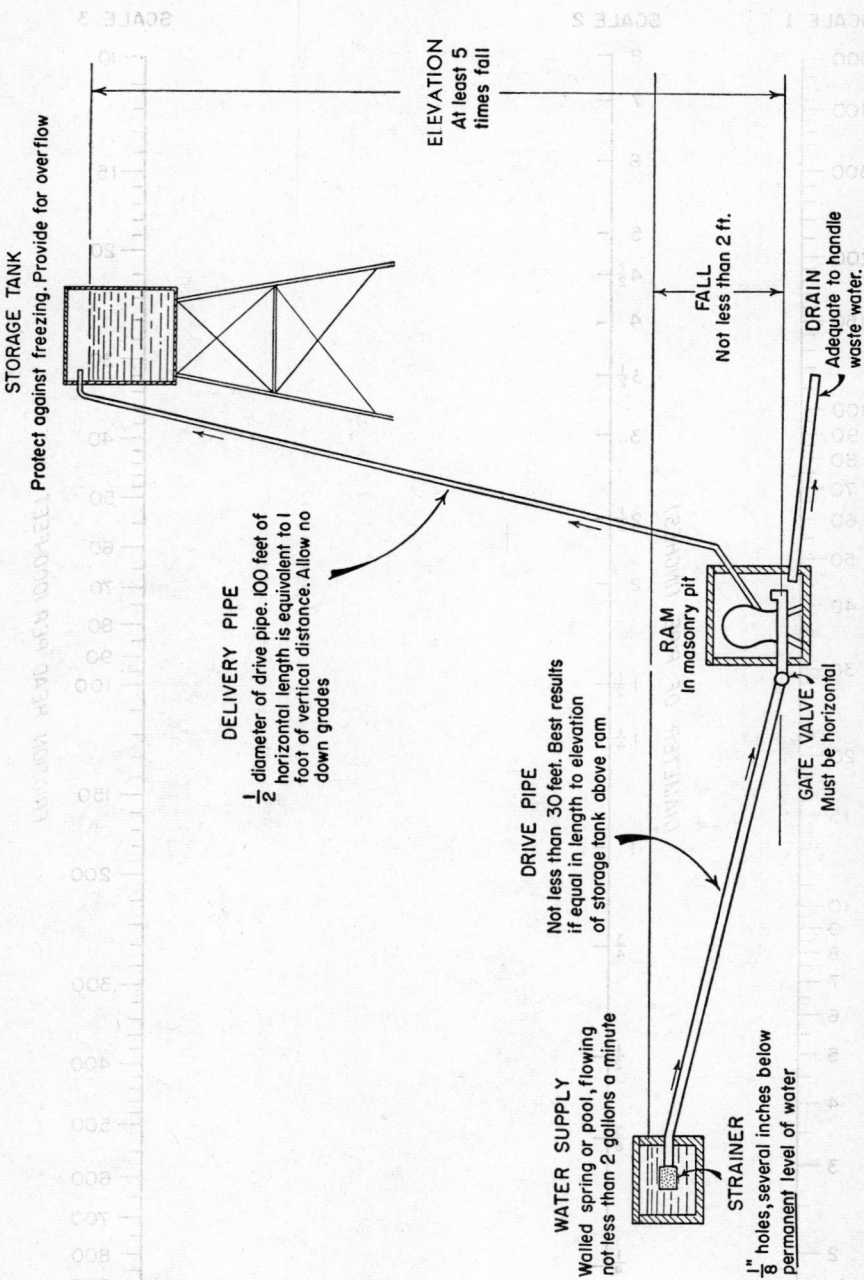

Fig. 2. Diagram of installation of hydraulic ram.

supply; however, it operates 24 hr. a day, and adequate storage facilities largely offset this waste. All makes of rams built for a given size of drive pipe use about the same amount of water. The ram designed for a 1-in. drive pipe uses 2 to 4 gpm; 1¼-in., 3 to 6 gal.; 1½-in. 5 to 10 gal.; 2-in., 7 to 15 gal.; 2½-in. 10 to 25 gal.

The manufacturer will supply a diagram illustrating the design and operation of his ram and adequate directions for installing it. However, certain minima of available flow, fall, elevation, etc., must be met before a ram can be efficiently employed; these are indicated in Fig. 2. To provide a ram fitted to local conditions, the manufacturer must know (1) gallons of water available at the source of supply, per minute; (2) vertical fall in feet from supply to ram; (3) vertical height, in feet, to which water must be raised above ram; (4) gallons of water required at storage point, per day; (5) distance in feet from source of supply to the ram; (6) distance in feet from ram to storage point.

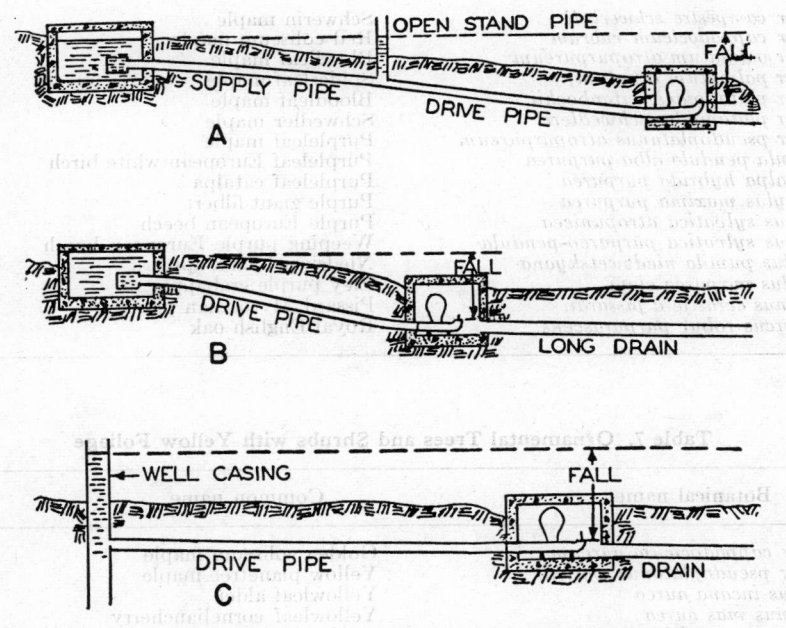

Fig. 3. Installation of ram under various conditions.

Where ground conditions prevent so locating the ram with reference to the water supply that the drive pipe is equal in length to the elevation against which the ram delivers water, a supply pipe (at least one size larger than the drive pipe) is used to convey the water to a tank or an open standpipe (Fig. 3A). Installations to meet other conditions are illustrated in Figs. 3B and 3C. Note that if the drive pipe to a ram is connected to the casing of a flowing well (Fig. 3C), **the casing must be left open.**

**Double-acting rams.** When the flow of a spring is too small to operate a single-acting ram, the flow of a nearby stream, even though contaminated, may be employed by a double-acting ram to deliver approximately two-thirds of the spring water, uncontaminated, to a desired elevation. Details are obtainable from manufacturers.

## Maintenance, Characteristics, and Uses of Vegetation

**ORNAMENTAL TREES WITH COLORED FOLIAGE.** Tables 6 and 7 list the botanical and common names of trees with colored foliage.

**Table 6. Ornamental Trees with Red or Purple Foliage**

| Botanical name | Common name |
| --- | --- |
| *Acer campestre schwerinii* | Schwerin maple |
| *Acer cappadocicum rubrum* | Red coliseum maple |
| *Acer palmatum atropurpureum* | Bloodleaf maple |
| *Acer palmatum ornatum* | Spiderleaf maple |
| *Acer platanoides reitenbachii* | Bloodleaf maple |
| *Acer platanoides schwedleri* | Schwedler maple |
| *Acer pseudoplatanus atropurpureum* | Purpleleaf maple |
| *Betula pendula alba purpurea* | Purpleleaf European white birch |
| *Catalpa hybrida purpurea* | Purpleleaf catalpa |
| *Corylus maxima purpurea* | Purple giant filbert |
| *Fagus sylvatica atropunicea* | Purple European beech |
| *Fagus sylvatica purpureo-pendula* | Weeping purple European beech |
| *Malus pumila niedzwetskyana* | Niedzwetskyana apple |
| *Malus purpurea eleyi* | Eley purple crabapple |
| *Prunus cerasifera pissardii* | Pissard Myrobalan plum |
| *Quercus robur purpurascens* | Royal English oak |

**Table 7. Ornamental Trees and Shrubs with Yellow Foliage**

| Botanical name | Common name |
| --- | --- |
| *Acer cappadocicum aureum* | Golden coliseum maple |
| *Acer pseudoplatanus worleii* | Yellow planetree maple |
| *Alnus incana aurea* | Yellowleaf alder |
| *Cornus mas aurea* | Yellowleaf corneliancherry |
| *Fraxinus excelsior aurea* | Golden European ash |
| *Populus canadensis aurea* | Golden Carolina poplar |
| *Quercus robur concordia* | Golden English oak |
| *Tilia platyphyllos aurea* | Goldtwig bigleaf linden |
| *Ulmus glabra lutescens* | Yellowleaf Scotch elm |
| *Ulmus procera aurea* | Yellowleaf English elm |

## NATIVE AND EXOTIC SHRUBS, TREES, AND VINES FOR SPECIAL CONDITIONS AND USE.

The map "Climatic Zones of the United States and Canada" (Fig. 4), which accompanies the following tables of native and exotic shrubs, trees, and vines for special conditions and use (Tables 8–10), appeared in an article by Harlan P. Kelsey in *American forests.* The source is probably Rehder's *Manual of cultivated trees and shrubs,* and closely similar maps appear in publications by Donald Wyman. In his *Trees for American gardens* Wyman states: "Many local variations in the small map submitted are to be expected.—In the lists a plant is usually listed in the coldest zone where it will grow normally, while at the same time it can be expected to grow in many of the warmer zones. Maximum temperatures and drought conditions would prove to be the major limiting factors." Wyman's practice in designating zones is followed in the tables on pages **12 · 26–36**.

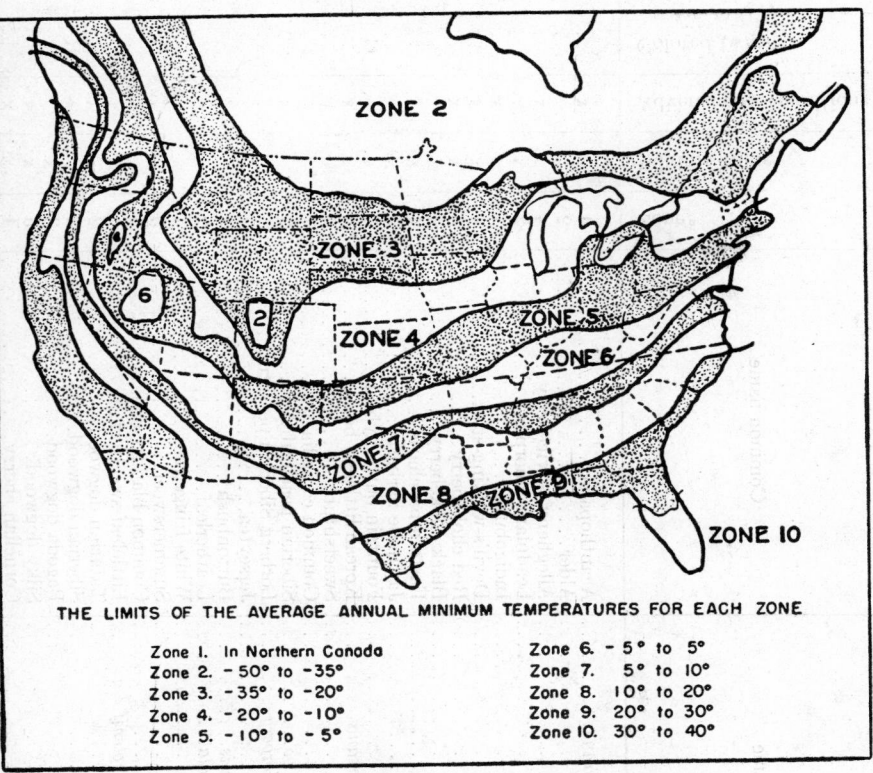

THE LIMITS OF THE AVERAGE ANNUAL MINIMUM TEMPERATURES FOR EACH ZONE

| | |
|---|---|
| Zone 1. In Northern Canada | Zone 6. − 5° to 5° |
| Zone 2. − 50° to −35° | Zone 7. 5° to 10° |
| Zone 3. − 35° to −20° | Zone 8. 10° to 20° |
| Zone 4. − 20° to −10° | Zone 9. 20° to 30° |
| Zone 5. − 10° to − 5° | Zone 10. 30° to 40° |

**Fig. 4. Climatic zones of the United States and Canada.**
(After Rehder.)

Table 8. Shrubs for Special Conditions and Use

| Latin name | Common name | Zone[a] | Wildlife value | Adverse city conditions | Colored twigs[b] | Dry, sandy soils | Low growing (under 3 ft.) | Shady locations | Steep banks | Tall (over 15 ft.) | Wet soils |
|---|---|---|---|---|---|---|---|---|---|---|---|
| Acanthopanax sieboldianus | Acanthopanax | 4 | | x | | x | | x | x | | |
| Alnus spp. | Alder | 2 | x | x | | | | x | | x | x |
| Amelanchier laevis | Allegheny serviceberry | 4 | x | x | | x | | x | | x | |
| Amorpha canescens | Leadplant amorpha | 2 | x | | | x | x | | | | |
| Amorpha fruticosa | Indigobush | 4 | x | x | | x | | x | | x | |
| Aralia spinosa | Devil's-walking-stick | 4 | x | x | | | | x | | x | |
| Aronia arbutifolia | Red chokeberry | 5 | x | | | | | x | | | x |
| Aronia melanocarpa | Black chokeberry | 4 | x | | | x | x | x | | | x |
| Baccharis halimifolia | Eastern baccharis | 4 | | x | | x | | | | x | x |
| Berberis thunbergii | Japanese barberry | 5 | x | x | G | x | | x | | | |
| Buddleia alternifolia | Fountain butterflybush | 5 | | | | x | | | | x | |
| Buxus microphylla koreana | Korean littleleaf box | 4 | | | | | x | x | | | |
| Calycanthus floridus | Sweetshrub | 4 | | x | | | | x | | | |
| Camellia japonica | Common camellia | 7 | | | | | | x | | x | |
| Caragana arborescens | Siberian peashrub | 2 | x | x | | x | | | | x | |
| Caragana arborescens lorberg | Lorberg Siberian peashrub | 2 | | x | | x | | | | x | |
| Ceanothus americanus | Jerseytea | 4 | x | | | x | x | | | | |
| Cephalanthus occidentalis | Buttonbush | 4 | x | x | | | | x | | | x |
| Chamaedaphne calyculata | Leatherleaf | 2 | | | | | x | | | | x |
| Chionanthus virginicus | White fringetree | 4 | x | | | | | x | | x | |
| Clethra alnifolia | Summersweet | 3 | | x | | | | x | | | x |
| Colutea arborescens | Common bladdersenna | 5 | | x | | x | | | | x | |
| Comptonia peregrina asplenifolia | Littleleaf sweetfern | 2 | | | | x | x | | | | |
| Cornus alba | Tatarian dogwood | 2 | x | x | R | | | | | x | |
| Cornus alba sibirica | Siberian dogwood | 2 | | x | R | | | | | | |
| Cornus alternifolia | Pagoda dogwood | 3 | x | | G | | | x | | x | |
| Cornus amomum | Silky dogwood | 5 | x | x | | | | x | | | x |
| Cornus mas | Cornelian cherry | 4 | x | x | | x | | | | x | |

| Latin name | Common name | Zone [a] | Wildlife value | Adverse city condit. | Colored twigs [b] | Dry, sandy soils | Low growing (under) | Shady locations | Steep banks | Tall (over 15 ft.) | Wet soils |
|---|---|---|---|---|---|---|---|---|---|---|---|
| *Cornus stolonifera* | Redosier dogwood | 2 | x | x | R | | | x | x | | x |
| *Cornus stolonifera coloradensis* | Colorado Redosier dogwood | | | | R | | | x | | | |
| *Cornus stolonifera flaviramea* | Yellowtwig redosier dogwood | 4 | x | x | Y | | | x | x | x | |
| *Corylus americana* | American hazel (filbert) | 5 | x | x | | | | x | x | x | |
| *Cotinus coggygria* | Common smoketree | 4 | | x | | | x | | | | |
| *Cotoneaster adpressa* | Creeping cotoneaster | 4 | | | | | x | x | | | |
| *Cotoneaster apiculata* | Cranberry | 4 | | | | | x | x | | | |
| *Cotoneaster horizontalis* | Rock | 4 | x | x | | | x | x | | | |
| *Crataegus phaenopyrum* | Washington hawthorn | | | x | | | | | x | | |
| *Crataegus spp.* | Hawthorn | | x | x | | x | | x | | x | x |
| *Cytisus praecox* | Warminster broom | 5 | | x | Gr | x | | | | x | |
| *Cytisus scoparius* | Scotch broom | 5 | | | Gr | x | | | x | | |
| *Cytisus supinus* | Bigflower broom | 5 | | | Gr | x | | | | | |
| *Deutzia scabra* | Fuzzy deutzia | 5 | | | | x | | | | | |
| *Dirca palustris* | Atlantic leatherwood | 4 | | x | | | | x | | | x |
| *Elaeagnus angustifolia* | Russianolive | 2 | x | x | G | x | | x | | x | |
| *Elaeagnus umbellata* | Autumn elaeagnus | 3 | | x | | x | | x | | x | |
| *Euonymus europaeus* | European euonymus | 3 | | x | | x | | x | | x | |
| *Euonymus fortunei vegeta* | Bigleaf wintercreeper | | | | | | x | x | | | |
| *Exochorda giraldii wilsonii* | Wilson redbud pearlbush | 5 | x | x | | x | | x | x | x | x |
| *Forsythia spp.* | Forsythia | | x | x | | x | | x | | | |
| *Gaultheria shallon* | Salal | 5 | x | x | R | x | | x | | | x |
| *Gaylussacia baccata* | Black huckleberry | 5 | x | x | | x | | x | | | |
| *Genista tinctoria* | Common woodwaxen | 2 | | x | | x | | | x | | |
| *Hamamelis virginiana* | Witch hazel | 2 | x | | R | x | | x | x | x | |
| *Hamelia erecta* | Scarlet hamelia | 4 | | | | x | | | | x | |
| *Hibiscus syriacus* | Shrubalthea | | x | x | | | | x | x | x | |
| *Hydrangea arborescens grandiflora* | Snowhill hydrangea | 5 | | x | | | x | x | | | |
| *Hypericum densiflorum* | Dense hypericum | 4 | x | x | R | | x | x | x | x | |
| *Hypericum frondosum* | Golden St. Johnswort | 5 | | x | | x | x | x | | | x |

[a] See Fig. 4.  [b] G, gray; Gr, green; R, red; Y, yellow.

Table 8. Shrubs for Special Conditions and Use (Continued)

| Latin name | Common name | Zone [a] | Wildlife value | Adverse city conditions | Colored twigs [b] | Dry, sandy soils | Low growing (under 3 ft.) | Shady locations | Steep banks | Tall (over 15 ft.) | Wet soils |
|---|---|---|---|---|---|---|---|---|---|---|---|
| Hypericum kalmianum | Kalm St. Johnswort | 4 | | | | × | × | | | | |
| Ilex decidua | Possumhaw | 5 | × | | G | | | × | | | × |
| Ilex glabra | Inkberry | 3 | × | | | | | × | | | × |
| Ilex verticillata | Winterberry | 3 | × | | | | | × | | | × |
| Ilex vomitoria | Yaupon | 7 | × | | | | | × | | × | × |
| Itea virginica | Virginia sweetspire | 5 | | | | | | × | | | |
| Juniperus communis | Common juniper | 2 | | × | | × | | | × | | |
| Juniperus horizontalis | Creeping juniper | 2 | | | | × | × | | × | | |
| Kalmia angustifolia | Lambkill kalmia | 2 | × | | | | | × | | | × |
| Kalmia latifolia | Mountain-laurel | 4 | | | | | | × | | × | × |
| Kalmia polifolia | Bog kalmia | 2 | | | | | × | × | | | × |
| Kerria japonica | Japanese kerria | 4 | | × | Gr | | | × | × | | |
| Kerria japonica aureovittata | Striped Japanese kerria | | | × | Y | | | × | × | | |
| Lespedeza bicolor | Shrub lespedeza | 4 | | × | | × | | × | | | |
| Leucothoe catesbaei | Drooping leucothoe | 4 | | × | | | | × | × | | × |
| Ligustrum spp. | Privet | 2 | × | × | | | | × | | | |
| Lindera benzoin | Spicebush | 4 | × | × | | | | × | | | × |
| Lonicera alpigena nana | Dwarf alps honeysuckle | 5 | | × | | | × | × | | | |
| Lonicera deflexicalyx | Moronel honeysuckle | 5 | | × | | | | × | × | | |
| Lonicera fragrantissima | Winter honeysuckle | 5 | | × | | | | × | × | × | |
| Lonicera japonica halliana | Halls Japanese honeysuckle | 4 | | × | | × | | × | × | | |
| Lonicera morrowi | Morrow honeysuckle | 4 | × | × | G | | | × | × | | |
| Lonicera prostrata | Creeping honeysuckle | 4 | | × | | | × | × | | | |
| Lonicera syringantha | Lilac honeysuckle | 3 | | × | | | | × | × | | |
| Lonicera tatarica | Tatarian honeysuckle | 4 | × | × | G | | | × | × | | |
| Lycium halimifolium | Matrimonyvine | 5 | × | × | | × | | × | × | | |
| Mahonia aquifolium | Oregongrape | 5 | | × | | × | × | × | | | |
| Mahonia nervosa | Cascades mahonia | 5 | × | × | | × | × | × | × | | × |

| Latin name | Common name | Zone[a] | Wildlife value | Adverse city condition | Colored twigs[b] | Dry, sandy soils | Low growing (under 3 ft) | Shady locations | Steep banks | Tall (over 15 ft.) | Wet soils |
|---|---|---|---|---|---|---|---|---|---|---|---|
| *Myrica gale* | Sweetgale | 1 | x | | | x | | x | x | | x |
| *Osmanthus fragrans* | Sweet osmanthus | 4 | | x | | | | x | | | |
| *Philadelphus lewisii* | Lewis mockorange | 2 | x | x | | x | | x | x | | |
| *Physocarpus opulifolius* | Common ninebark | 5–6 | | | | | | | | x | |
| *Physocarpus opulifolius nanus* | Dwarf ninebark | 2 | x | x | | x | x | | | | |
| *Poncirus trifoliata* | Trifoliate-orange | 6–7 | | | Gr | | | | | x | |
| *Potentilla fruticosa* | Bush cinquefoil | 2 | x | | | x | x | | | | |
| *Prunus laurocerasus* | Laurelcherry | 2 | | | | | | x | | | |
| *Prunus pumila* | Sandcherry | 2 | | x | | x | x | x | | | x |
| *Rhamnus cathartica* | Common buckthorn | 2 | | x | | x | | x | x | | |
| *Rhamnus frangula* | Glossy buckthorn | 7 | x | | | | | x | x | x | x |
| *Rhododendron austrinum* | Florida azalea | 3 | | | | | | x | x | | |
| *Rhododendron maximum* | Rosebay rhododendron | 3 | x | | | | | x | x | | x |
| *Rhododendron nudiflorum* | Pinxterbloom azalea | 3 | | | | | | x | x | | |
| *Rhododendron viscosum* | Swamp azalea | | | x | | | | x | x | | x |
| *Rhodotypos kerrioides* | Jetbead | 2 | | x | | x | | x | x | | |
| *Rhus spp.* | Sumac | 2 | x | | R | x | | | x | | |
| *Ribes alpinum* | Alpine currant | 4 | | | R | | | x | x | | |
| *Rosa acicularis* | Prickly rose | | | | R | x | | x | x | | |
| *Rosa canina* | Dog rose | 4 | | | R | x | | | x | | |
| *Rosa coriifolia* | Leatherleaf rose | 4 | x | x | | x | | | x | | |
| *Rosa kochiana* | Koch rose | 5 | | x | | x | | | x | | |
| *Rosa palustris* | Swamp rose | 3 | | | | | | | x | | x |
| *Rosa setigera* | Prairie rose | 5 | | | | x | | | x | | |
| *Rosa virginiana* | Virginia rose | 3 | | x | R | x | x | | x | | |
| *Rosa wichuraiana* | Wichura rose | 2 | | x | R | x | x | x | x | | |
| *Rubus odoratus* | Fragrant thimbleberry | 3 | x | | Gr | | x | x | x | | |
| *Salix tristis* | Dwarf pussy willow | | x | | | | x | | | | x |
| *Sambucus canadensis* | American elder | 3 | x | x | | x | | | | | x |

[a] See Fig. 4.  [b] G, gray; Gr, green; R, red; Y, yellow.

**Table 8. Shrubs for Special Conditions and Use** (Continued)

| Latin name | Common name | Zone [a] | Wildlife value | Adverse city conditions | Colored twigs [b] | Dry, sandy soil | Low growing (under 3 ft.) | Shady locations | Steep banks | Tall (over 15 ft.) | Wet soils |
|---|---|---|---|---|---|---|---|---|---|---|---|
| Severinia buxifolia | Chinese boxorange | 8 | | | | | | x | | | |
| Shepherdia canadensis | Russet buffaloberry | 2 | x | x | | x | | | x | x | |
| Sorbaria arborea glabrata | Smooth tree falsespirea | | | x | | | | | x | x | x |
| Sorbaria sorbifolia | Ural falsespirea | 5 | | | | | x | | | | |
| Spiraea bullata | Crispleaf spiraea | 4 | | | | | x | | | | |
| Spiraea bumalda anthony waterer | Anthony Waterer spiraea | 4 | | | | | x | | | | |
| Spiraea salicifolia | Willowleaf spiraea | 4 | | | | | | | | | x |
| Spiraea tomentosa | Hardhack spiraea | 4 | x | | | | | | | | x |
| Spiraea vanhouttei | Vanhoutte spiraea | 3 | | x | | | | x | x | | |
| Symphoricarpos albus | Snowberry | 2 | x | x | | | | x | x | | |
| Symphoricarpos orbiculatus | Coralberry | 4 | x | x | | x | x | x | x | | |
| Syringa amurensis japonica | Japanese tree lilac | 3 | | x | | | | x | x | x | |
| Syringa vulgaris | Common lilac | 2 | | x | | | | x | x | | |
| Tamarix pentandra | Fivestamen tamarix | 4 | | x | | x | | x | x | | |
| Taxus baccata | English yew | 6 | x | x | R | | | x | x | x | x |
| Vaccinium corymbosum | Highbush blueberry | 3 | x | x | | | | x | x | | x |
| Vaccinium virgatum | Rabbiteye blueberry | 7 | x | x | | | | x | x | x | |
| Viburnum acerifolium | Mapleleaf viburnum | 3 | x | x | | | | x | | | |
| Viburnum cassinoides | Witherod viburnum | 3 | x | x | | | | x | x | | x |
| Viburnum lentago | Nannyberry | 2 | x | x | | | | x | x | x | x |
| Viburnum opulus nanum | Dwarf cranberrybush | | | x | R | | x | x | | | x |
| Viburnum prunifolium | Blackhaw viburnum | 3 | x | x | | x | | x | x | | |
| Viburnum sieboldii | Siebold viburnum | 4 | | x | | | | x | x | x | x |
| Vitex agnuscastus | Lilac chastetree | 6–7 | x | x | | x | | | x | x | |
| Xanthorhiza simplicissima | Yellowroot | 4 | | | | | x | | | | x |
| Yucca spp. | Yucca | | | | | x | | | x | | |
| Zanthoxylum americanum | Common prickly ash | 3 | x | | Y | | | x | x | | |
| Zenobia pulverulenta | Dusty zenobia | 5 | | | | | | x | x | | x |

| Latin name | Common name | Zone [a] | Ornamental fruits | Autumn coloring [b] | Dry, sandy soil | Insect and disease resistant | Seashore | For shade | Smoke resistant | Wet places | Weeping |
|---|---|---|---|---|---|---|---|---|---|---|---|
| Abies balsamea | Balsam fir | 3 | | | | | | x | | x | |
| Abies concolor | White fir | 4 | | | | | | x | x | | |
| Abies fraseri | Fraser fir | 4 | | | | | | x | | | |
| Abies lasiocarpa | Subalpine fir | 4 | | | | | | x | | | |
| Acacia spp. | Acacia | 8,9 | | | | | | | | | |
| Acer negundo | Boxelder | 2 | | Y | x | | | | | | |
| Acer pensylvanicum | Striped maple | 3 | | Y | x | | | | | | |
| Acer platanoides | Norway maple | 3 | | Y | | | | x | | | |
| Acer rubrum | Red maple | 3 | x | R | | | | x | x | x | |
| Acer saccharinum | Silver maple | 3 | | Y | | | | | | x | |
| Acer saccharinum wieri | Wier maple | 3 | | | | | | | | | x |
| Acer saccharum | Sugar maple | 3 | | O-Y | | | | x | x | | |
| Acer tataricum | Tatarian maple | 4 | | S | x | | | | | | |
| Aesculus hippocastanum | Common horsechestnut | 3 | | | | | | x | x | | |
| Ailanthus altissima | Ailanthus (tree of heaven) | 4 | | | x | x | | | x | | |
| Alnus spp. | Alder | 2 | | | | | | | | x | |
| Amelanchier canadensis | Shadblow serviceberry | 4 | x | R | | | | | | | |
| Betula alba pendula gracilis | Weeping cutleaf birch | 2 | | | | | | | | | x |
| Betula alba pendula youngi | Young's weeping birch | 2 | | | | | | | | | x |
| Betula papyrifera | Paper birch | 2 | | Y | | | | x | | x | |
| Betula populifolia | Gray birch | 4 | | Y | x | | x | x | x | x | |
| Carpinus caroliniana | American hornbeam | 2 | | R | | | | | | x | |
| Carya floridana | Shrub hickory | 9,10 | | | x | | | | | | |
| Carya laciniosa | Shellbark hickory | 5 | | | x | | | | | x | |
| Casuarina equisetifolia | Horsetail casuarina (beefwood) | 9,10 | | | x | | x | | | x | |
| Catalpa speciosa | Northern catalpa | 4 | | Y | | | | x | x | | |
| Cedrus deodara | Deodar cedar | 7 | | | x | | | | x | | |

[a] See Fig. 4. [b] O-Y, orange-yellow; R, red; S, scarlet; Y, yellow.

(Continued)

**Table 9. Trees for Special Conditions and Use** (Continued)

| Latin name | Common name | Zone[a] | Ornamental fruits | Autumn coloring[b] | Dry, sandy soil | Insect and disease resistant[c] | Seashore | For shade | Smoke resistant | Wet places | Weeping |
|---|---|---|---|---|---|---|---|---|---|---|---|
| Celtis occidentalis | Common hackberry | 2 | | | | | | | x | x | |
| Ceratonia siliqua | Carob | 9,10 | | | x | x | | | | | |
| Cercidiphyllum japonicum | Katsuratree | 4 | | Y | | | | | | | |
| Chamaecyparis lawsoniana pendula | Weeping Lawson falsecypress | 5 | | | | | | | | | x |
| Chamaecyparis obtusa pendula | Weeping Hinoki falsecypress | 3 | | | | | | | | | x |
| Chamaecyparis thyoides | Atlantic white-cedar | 3 | | | | | | | | x | |
| Chionanthus virginicus | Fringetree | 4 | | Y | | | | | | x | |
| Coccoloba uvifera | Seagrape | 10 | | | x | | x | | | | |
| Cornus florida | Flowering dogwood | 4 | x | S | x | | | | | | |
| Cornus florida pendula | Weeping flowering dogwood | 4 | x | | | | | | | | x |
| Crataegus spp. | Hawthorn | 2 | x | | x | | | | x | | |
| Cupressus arizonica | Arizona cypress | 7 | | | x | | | | | | |
| Eucalyptus citriodora | Lemon eucalyptus | 9 | | | | | | | | | |
| Eucalyptus rudis | Moitch eucalyptus | 3 | | | | | | | | | |
| Fagus grandifolia | American beech | 4 | | O–Y | | | x | x | | | |
| Fagus sylvatica pendula | Weeping European beech | 4 | | | | | | x | | | x |
| Fagus sylvatica purpurea pendula | European weeping purple beech | 4 | | | | | | | | | x |
| Ficus aurea | Florida strangler fig | 10 | | | | | | | | | |
| Fraxinus americana | White ash | 3 | | Y | | | | | | | |
| Fraxinus excelsior pendula | Weeping European ash | 3 | | | | | | | | | x |
| Fraxinus nigra | Black ash | 2 | | | | | | | | x | |
| Ginkgo biloba | Maidenhair ginkgo | 4 | | Y | | x | x | x | x | | |
| Gleditsia triacanthos | Honeylocust | 4 | | Y | | x | | | x | | |
| Gymnocladus dioicus | Kentucky coffeetree | 4 | | Y | | x | | | | | |
| Halesia carolina | Mountain silverbell | 4 | | Y | | x | | | | | |
| Ilex cassine | Dahoon (holly) | 7 | x | | | | | | | | |
| Ilex opaca | American holly | 5 | x | | | | x | x | x | x | |

| Latin name | Common name | Zone[a] | Ornamental fruits | Autumn coloring[b] | Dry, sandy soil | Insect and disease resistant | Seashore | For shade | Smoke resistant | Wet places | Weeping |
|---|---|---|---|---|---|---|---|---|---|---|---|
| Juniperus virginiana | Eastern redcedar | 2 | | | | | x | x | | | |
| Juniperus virginiana pendula | Weeping eastern redcedar | 2 | | | | x | x | | | | x |
| Koelreuteria paniculata | Panicled goldenraintree | 5 | | Y | | | | | x | | |
| Laguncularia racemosa | White-mangrove | 10 | | | | | x | | | x | |
| Larix decidua pendula | Weeping European larch | 2 | | | | | | | | | x |
| Larix laricina | Tamarack | 1 | | | | | | | | x | |
| Larix leptolepis | Japanese larch | 4 | | | | | | | | | |
| Libocedrus decurrens | Incense-cedar | 5 | | | | x | x | x | | | |
| Liquidambar styraciflua | Sweetgum | 4 | | R | | x | x | x | x | | |
| Liriodendron tulipifera | Yellow-poplar (tuliptree) | 4 | | Y | | | | x | x | | |
| Magnolia grandiflora | Southern magnolia | 7 | | | | x | x | x | x | | |
| Magnolia virginiana | Sweetbay | 5 | | | | x | | | | x | |
| Malus baccata | Siberian crabapple | 2 | x | | | x | | | | | |
| Melaleuca leucadendron | Cajeput-tree | 4,5 | | | | | x | | | x | |
| Morus alba pendula | Weeping white mulberry | 7 | | | | | | | | | x |
| Nyssa aquatica | Water tupelo | 4 | | R | | | | x | | x | |
| Nyssa sylvatica | Black tupelo (blackgum) | 4 | | Y | | x | x | x | x | x | |
| Ostrya virginiana | Eastern hophornbeam | 4 | | | | x | | x | | | |
| Oxydendrum arboreum | Sourwood | 4 | | S | | | | x | | | |
| ———— | Palm | 9,10 | | | | | x | | | | |
| Persea littoralis | Shorebay | 3 | | | | | x | | | | |
| Phellodendron amurense | Amur corktree | 2 | x | Y | | x | | x | x | | |
| Picea abies pendula | Weeping Norway spruce | 2 | | | | | | | | | x |
| Picea engelmanii | Engelmann spruce | 2 | | | | | x | x | | | |
| Picea glauca | White spruce | 2 | | | | x | x | x | | | |
| Picea mariana | Black spruce | 2 | | | | | x | x | | x | |
| Picea pungens | Blue spruce | 2 | | | x | x | x | x | | | |

[a] See Fig. 4.  [b] O-Y, orange-yellow; R, red; S, scarlet; Y, yellow.

Table 9. Trees for Special Conditions and Use (Continued)

| Latin name | Common name | Zone[a] | Ornamental fruits | Autumn coloring[b] | Dry, sandy soil | Insect and disease resistant | Seashore | For shade | Smoke resistant | Wet places | Weeping |
|---|---|---|---|---|---|---|---|---|---|---|---|
| Picea pungens glauca | Colorado blue spruce | 2 | | | | | x | x | | x | |
| Picea rubens | Red spruce | 2 | | | | | | x | | | |
| Picea sitchensis | Sitka spruce | 6 | | | | | | x | | | |
| Pinus banksiana | Jack pine | 2 | | | x | | x | | | x | |
| Pinus clausa | Sand pine | 9 | | | x | | | | | | |
| Pinus mugo | Swiss mountain pine | 2 | | | | | | x | x | | |
| Pinus nigra | Austrian pine | 4 | | | x | | | | x | | |
| Pinus resinosa | Red pine | 2 | | | x | | | | x | | |
| Pinus rigida | Pitch pine | 4 | | | x | | x | | | | |
| Pinus strobus | Eastern white pine | 3 | | | x | | | | x | | |
| Pinus sylvestris | Scotch pine | 2 | | | x | | | x | | | |
| Pithecellobium dulce | Blackbead (apes-earring) | 10 | | | | | | | | x | |
| Platanus occidentalis | American sycamore (planetree) | 4 | | | x | | | x | x | | |
| Plumeria spp. | Frangipani | 10 | | Y | | | | | | x | |
| Populus alba | White poplar | 3 | | Y | x | | x | | | | |
| Populus balsamifera | Balsam poplar | 2 | | Y | | | x | | | x | |
| Populus tremuloides | Quaking aspen | 1 | | | x | | x | | | | |
| Prunus maritima | Beach plum | 3 | | | x | | x | | | | |
| Prunus padus commutata | Harbinger European bird cherry | 3 | x | | | | x | | | x | |
| Prunus pensylvanica | Pin cherry | 2 | | | x | | x | | | | |
| Prunus serotina | Black cherry | 3 | | | x | | x | | | | |
| Prunus serrulata | Oriental cherry | 4,5 | | | x | | | | | | x |
| Prunus subhirtella pendula | Weeping Higan cherry | 5 | | | | | x | | | | x |
| Pseudotsuga menziesii | Douglas-fir | 6 | | | x | | x | x | | | |
| Quercus coccinea | Scarlet oak | 4 | S | | | x | | | | | |
| Quercus laurifolia | Laurel oak | 7 | | | x | | x | | | | |
| Quercus myrtifolia | Myrtle oak | 9 | | | x | | x | x | | | |

| Latin name | Common name | Zone[a] | Ornamental fruits | Autumn coloring[b] | Dry, sandy soil | Insect and disease resistant | Seashore | For shade | Smoke resistant | Wet places | Weeping |
|---|---|---|---|---|---|---|---|---|---|---|---|
| Quercus nigra | Water oak | 6 | | | | | | x | | | |
| Quercus palustris | Pin oak | 4 | S | | x | | | | x | | |
| Quercus rubra | Northern red oak | 7 | | | | | x | | x | | |
| Quercus virginiana | Live oak | 7 | Y | | x | | x | | x | | |
| Robinia pseudoacacia | Black locust | 3 | | | | | | | | x | |
| Sabal palmetto | Cabbage palmetto | 9,10 | | | | | x | | | x | |
| Salix alba | White willow | 2 | | | | | | | | | |
| Salix alba vitellina pendula | Weepinggold yellowstem white willow | 2 | | | | | | | | | x |
| Salix babylonica | (Babylon) Weeping willow | 5,6 | Y | | | | | | | x | x |
| Salix blanda | Wisconsin weeping willow | 4 | | | | | | | | | x |
| Salix caprea pendula | Kilmarnock goat willow | 4 | | | | | | | | | x |
| Salix elegantissima | Thurlow weeping willow | 4 | | | | | | | | | x |
| Salix sepulcralis | Solomon weeping willow | 4 | | | | | | | | | x |
| Sassafras albidum | Sassafras | 4 | | | x | x | | | | | |
| Schinus molle | (California) Peppertree | 5 | | | x | | | | | | |
| Sciadopitys verticillata | Umbrella pine | 5 | | | | | | | | | |
| Sophora japonica | Japanese pagodatree | 4 | x | | x | | | | | | |
| Sophora japonica pendula | Weeping Japanese pagodatree | 4 | | | | | | | | | x |
| Sorbus americana | American mountain-ash | 2 | | | | | | | | | |
| Sorbus aucuparia pendula | Weeping European mountain-ash | 2 | | | | | | | | | x |
| Taxodium distichum | Baldcypress | 4 | | | | | | | | x | |
| Taxodium distichum pendens | Weeping baldcypress | 4 | | | | | | | | | x |
| Taxus baccata pendula | Weeping English yew | 6 | | | | | | x | | | x |
| Taxus brevifolia | Pacific yew | 6 | | | | | | | | | |
| Taxus cuspidata | Japanese yew | 4 | | | | x | | x | x | | |
| Thuja occidentalis | Northern white-cedar | 2 | | | | | | x | x | x | |
| Thuja plicata | Western redcedar | 5 | | | | | | x | x | | |

[a] See Fig. 4.  [b] O-Y, orange-yellow; R, red; S, scarlet; Y, yellow.

## Table 9. Trees for Special Conditions and Use (Continued)

| Latin name | Common name | Zone[a] | Ornamental fruits | Autumn coloring[b] | Dry, sandy soil | Insect and disease resistant | Seashore | For shade | Smoke resistant | Wet places | Weeping |
|---|---|---|---|---|---|---|---|---|---|---|---|
| *Tilia americana* | American basswood | 2 | | Y | | | | | | x | |
| *Tilia petiolaris* | Silverpendent linden | 5 | | | | | | x | | | x |
| *Tsuga canadensis* | Eastern hemlock | 4 | | | | x | | x | | x | |
| *Tsuga canadensis pendula* | Weeping Canada hemlock | 4 | | | | | | | | | x |
| *Tsuga heterophylla* | Western hemlock | 6 | | | | x | | x | | | |
| *Tsuga mertensiana* | Mountain hemlock | 5 | | | | | | | | | |
| *Ulmus americana* | American elm | 2 | | Y | | x | | | x | x | |
| *Ulmus glabra camperdownii* | Camperdown Scotch elm | 4 | | | | | | | | | x |
| *Ulmus procera* | English elm | 5 | | | | | | | x | | |
| *Ulmus rubra* | Slippery elm | 3 | | Y | | | | | x | x | |

[a] See Fig. 4. [b] O-Y, orange-yellow; R, red; S, scarlet; Y, yellow.

## Table 10. Vines for Special Conditions and Use

| Method of climbing [a] | Species | | Use [b] | Zone [c] |
|---|---|---|---|---|
| Tw | *Actinidia arguta* | Bower actinidia | 1,2,4 | 4 |
| Tw | *Actinidia chinensis* | Yangtao actinidia | 2,4 | 7 |
| Tw | *Actinidia polygama* | Silvervine actinidia | 1,4 | 4 |
| Tw | *Akebia quinata* | Fiveleaf akebia | 3,4 | 4 |
| Te | *Ampelopsis arborea* | Peppervine | 3 | 7 |
| Tw | *Aristolochia durior* | Common dutchman's-pipe | 1,4 | 4 |
| Te | *Bignonia capreolata* | Crossvine | 2 | 6 |
| Te | *Boussingaultia ramosa* | Mignonette madeiravine | 2 | 10 |
| C | *Campsis radicans* | Common trumpetcreeper | 1,2 | 4 |
| Tw | *Celastrus angulata* | Anglestem bittersweet | 1,3 | 7 |
| Tw | *Celastrus orbiculata* | Oriental bittersweet | 1,3 | 4 |
| Tw | *Celastrus scandens* | American bittersweet | 1,3 | 2 |
| Te | *Clematis jackmanii* | Jackman clematis | 2,4 | 5 |
| Te | *Clematis paniculata* | Sweetautumn clematis | 1,2,4 | 5 |
| Te | *Clematis vitalba* | Travelersjoy | 1,4 | 4 |
| Te | *Cobaea* | Cobaea | 2 | 9 |
| Te | *Distictis* | Distictis | 2 | 9 |
| C | *Euonymus fortunei coloratus* | Purpleleaf wintercreeper | 4 | 5 |
| — | *Euonymus obovatus* | Running euonymus | 3 | 3 |
| C | *Hedera helix* | English ivy | 3 | 5 |
| C | *Hedera helix baltica* | Baltic ivy | 4 | 5 |
| C | *Hydrangea petiolaris* | Climbing hydrangea | 1,2,4 | 4 |
| Tw | *Lonicera henryi* | Henry honeysuckle | 3 | 4 |
| Tw | *Lonicera japonica halliana* | Halls Japanese honeysuckle | 1,2,3,4 | 4 |
| Tw | *Mandevilla suaveolens* | Chilejasmine | 2 | 9 |
| Tw | *Menispermum canadense* | Common moonseed | 3,4 | 4 |
| Tw | *Muehlenbeckia complexa* | Common wirevine | 3 | 5 |
| Te | *Parthenocissus henryana* | Silvervein creeper | 3,4 | 8 |
| Te | *Parthenocissus quinquefolia* | Virginia creeper | 1,3,4 | 3 |
| Te | *Parthenocissus tricuspidata* | Japanese creeper | 1,4 | 4 |
| Te | *Passiflora caerulea* | Bluecrown passionflower | 2 | 7,8 |
| C | *Phaedranthus buccinatorius* | Mexican bloodtrumpet | 2 | 9 |
| C | *Pileostegia viburnoides* | Tanglehead | 2,4 | 7 |
| C | *Plumbago capensis* | Cape plumbago | 2 | 9 |
| Te | *Polygonium aubertii* | Silvervine fleeceflower | 2 | 4 |
| Te | *Pueraria thunbergiana* | Thunberg kudzubean | 3 | 6 |
| — | *Rosa* | Ramblers | 2 | 5 |
| — | *Rosa wichuraiana* | Wichura rose | 3 | 5 |
| Tw | *Smilax* | Greenbrier | 4 | 4,7 |
| Tw | *Trachelospermum asiaticum* | Japanese starjasmine | 2,4 | 7,8 |
| — | *Tripterygium regelii* | Regelis threewingnut | 2 | 4 |
| — | *Vinca minor* | Common periwinkle | 4 | 5 |
| Te | *Vitis vulpina* | Frost grape | 1,4 | 5 |
| Tw | *Wistaria floribunda* | Japanese wistaria | 1 | 4 |
| Tw | *Wistaria sinensis* | Chinese wistaria | 1,2 | 5 |

[a] Method of climbing—Tw, twining; Te, tendrils; C, clinging by rootlets, rootlike holdfasts, or tendrils with discs.
[b] Use—1, vigorous climbers; 2, good flowering vines; 3, vines making a good ground cover; 4, shade-enduring.
[c] See Fig. 4.

## BIBLIOGRAPHY

AMERICAN PLANNING AND CIVIC ASSN. *American planning and civic annuals.* Washington, D. C.

ARNOLD ARBORETUM. *Arnoldia.* Harvard University, Cambridge, Mass.

BURKHARDT, HARRY. 1943. *Turf for wear and tear.* Ohio State Highway Dept., Columbus.

CONNECTICUT COLLEGE. 1940. *A plant handbook. Bull. No. 3.* Connecticut College, New London.

FENSKA, RICHARD R. 1954. 2d ed. *Tree experts manual.* A. T. De La Mare Co., Inc., New York.

GRAHAM, S. A., and E. C. O'ROKE. *On your own.* University of Minnesota Press, Minneapolis.

GRANT, JOHN A., and L. CAROL. 1943. *Trees and shrubs for northwest gardens.* F. Caffrey, Seattle, Wash.

HARLOW, WILLIAM, and ELLWOOD HARRAR. 1941. *Dendrology.* 2d ed. McGraw-Hill Book Co., Inc., New York.

HARRISON, CARTER. 1944. Rough grass for highways and recreation areas. *Greenskeepers Reporter* 12(3), St. Charles, Ill.

HOTTES, A. C. 1946. *The book of trees.* A. T. De La Mare Co., Inc., New York.

HOTTES, A. C. 1948. *The book of shrubs.* A. T. De La Mare Co., Inc., New York.

KELSEY, HARLAND P. 1949. Arborways for America. *American Forests* (Dec.).

MICHIGAN STATE COLLEGE. 1933. *Regular Bull. 281,* East Lansing.

MICHIGAN STATE COLLEGE. 1943. The hydraulic ram. *Extension Bull. 171,* East Lansing.

MONTEITH, JOHN. 1941. Better turf for playgrounds. *Recreation Magazine* 52(2).

PIRONE, P. P. 1948. *Maintenance of shade and ornamental trees.* Oxford University Press, New York.

REHDER, ALFRED. 1940. *Manual of cultivated trees and shrubs,* hardy in North America exclusive of the subtropic and warmer temperature zones. The Macmillan Co., New York.

ROBINS, FREDERICK. 1946. *The story of water supply.* Oxford University Press, New York.

SARGENT, C. S. 1933. *Manual of trees of North America.* Houghton Mifflin Co., Boston.

SPRAGUE, HOWARD. 1940. *Better lawns.* McGraw-Hill Book Co., Inc., New York.

STURKIE, D. C. 1941. Lawn grass for the South. *American Nurseryman* (Sept.).

TAYLOR, A. D. 1935. *The complete garden.* Garden City Publishing Co., Inc., New York.

TAYLOR, NORMAN. 1942. *The garden dictionary.* Houghton Mifflin Co., Boston.

*Trees Magazine.* 1941. Grass for hard traffic. (July.)

U. S. DEPT. AGR. 1946. Safe water for the farm. *Farmers Bull. 1978.*

U. S. DEPT. AGR. 1948. *Grass: Yearbook of agriculture.*

U. S. DEPT. AGR. 1949. *Trees: Yearbook of agriculture.*

U. S. FOREST SERV., Regions 3, 4, 5, 6, 7, 8, 9. 1935. *Handbook of administration: recreation plans, policy, procedure.*

U. S. FOREST SERV. 1937. *Camp stoves and fireplaces.*

U. S. FOREST SERV. 1950. *National forest vacations.*

U. S. PARK SERV. 1938. *Park and recreation structures.* Parts I, II, and III.

U. S. PARK SERV. 1941. *Yearbook, park and recreation progress.*

WYMAN, DONALD. 1949. *Shrubs and vines for American gardens.* The Macmillan Co., New York.

WYMAN, DONALD. 1951. *Trees for American gardens.* The Macmillan Co., New York.

# MATERIALS, STRUCTURES, AND FACILITIES

## CONTENTS

# MATERIALS, STRUCTURES, AND FACILITIES

## CONTENTS

# MATERIALS, STRUCTURES, AND FACILITIES

The primary purpose of any construction is to provide a structure that satisfies
the need. A second consideration is to make a structure that is pleasing to the
eye of the public. A third consideration, and one that has been sorely neglected in
the development of many recreation areas, is ease and economy of maintenance.
Many foresters and recreation area supervisors are today reaping the whirlwind
from the seed of rustic appeal. The "Natural Look" is a necessary item in planning a forest recreation area, but it should be attained without sacrificing length
of service. For example, stone is just as natural to many areas as is wood, and it
could be used to advantage over wood in many places, such as comfort stations,
trail markers, barriers, etc. It is true that stone construction requires a greater
initial outlay than wood, but it does not have to be replaced because of rot or
hatchet work. In planning new structures or facilities, or in replacing unservice-
able ones, maintenance should be carefully considered.

## Materials

**CONCRETE. Selection of Materials.** Choosing suitable materials is the first
step in making concrete which will be strong, durable, and watertight. The
qualities of Portland cement, mixing water, and aggregates which make them
suitable for use in a concrete mixture are listed below.

**Portland Cement.** Portland cement shall conform to the Standard Specifications for Portland Cement (ASTM Designation C150–46). These specifications
cover five types of Portland cement, as follows:

**Type I.** For use in general concrete construction when the special properties
specified for Types II, III, IV, and V are not required.
**Type II.** For use in general concrete construction exposed to moderate sulfate
action, or where moderate heat of hydration is required.
**Type III.** For use when high early strength is required.
**Type IV.** For use when a low heat of hydration is required.
**Type V.** For use when high sulfate resistance is required.

Cement should be kept dry at all times prior to use. Cement which contains
lumps that cannot readily be pulverized by striking lightly with a trowel should
not be used. Cement that is caked due to the weight of cement piled on it can be
reconditioned by rolling the sack. Attention is called to the fact that cements
conforming to the requirements for Type IV and Type V are not usually carried
in stock. In advance of specifying their use, purchasers should determine whether
these types of cement are available.

**Water.** In general, water that is suitable for drinking is satisfactory for mixing
with cement. Water that is clean and free from oil, alkali, or acid is most
suitable.

**13 · 1**

**Aggregates.** Aggregates usually are divided into fine and coarse—sand being the most common form of fine aggregate; and pebbles, crushed stone, or crushed slag, the most common form of coarse aggregate. Sand or other fine aggregate, such as stone screenings, includes all particles from very fine (exclusive of dust) up to those which will just pass through a screen having meshes $\frac{1}{4}$-in. square. Coarse aggregate includes pebbles, crushed stone, or crushed slag ranging from $\frac{1}{4}$ to $1\frac{1}{2}$ in. or larger.

**Strength of Concrete.** The quality of the Portland cement paste used determines how strong, how watertight, and how durable the hardened concrete will be. The quality of the paste is determined by the quantity of water mixed with the cement.

A cement paste made in a proportion of not more than 5 gal. of water to one sack of cement will produce satisfactory concrete for work subjected to severe wear, weather, or weak acid and alkali solutions. Jobs that require this kind of concrete include colored topping for sidewalks, tennis courts, and floors and plain topping for all two-course work.

A 6-gal. paste produces concrete which is watertight and satisfactory when subjected to moderate wear and weather. Watertight floors, foundation walls, driveways, sidewalks, and swimming pools are the types of work which require concrete of this quality.

A 7-gal. paste will produce concrete which is suitable for use where it will not be subjected to wear, weather, or water pressure. This quality is satisfactory for use in footings and other mass concrete.

**Effect of Moisture in Sand.** After selecting the total amount of water to be used with each sack of cement to make a paste of the quality desired, it is necessary to consider the amount of water carried by the fine aggregate. Water added at the mixer may be reduced by $\frac{1}{4}$ to 2 gal., depending on the wetness of the sand and the desired consistency of the paste. The amount carried by coarse aggregate is generally so small that it can be overlooked.

**Mixing of Concrete.** Although machine mixing is preferred, first-class concrete can be mixed by hand. Whichever method is used, mixing should continue until every pebble is completely coated with a thoroughly mixed mortar of Portland cement and sand.

If a tight floor is not available for mixing concrete, a watertight mixing platform should be made. It should be large enough for two men using shovels to work upon at one time. A good size is 7 ft. wide by 12 ft. long. This platform is preferably made of matched lumber so that the joints will be tight. Strips are nailed along three sides to prevent materials from being pushed off in mixing.

The measured quantity of sand is spread out evenly on the platform and on this the required amount of Portland cement is evenly distributed. The cement and sand are turned with square-pointed shovels to produce a mass of uniform color, free from streaks of brown and gray. Such streaks indicate that the cement and sand are not thoroughly mixed. The required amount of coarse aggregate is then measured and spread in a layer on top of the Portland cement and sand mixture. Mixing is continued until the cement and pebbles have been thoroughly and uniformly combined.

The concrete should be placed in the forms within 30 minutes after mixing. It should be well tamped or spaded as it goes into the forms. This operation

## Table 1. Volume Factors for Concrete Mixes

| Kind of concrete work | Mix by volume job damp materials | | | Workability or consistency | Water added at mixer, per bag (gal.) | A 1-bag batch makes this volume of concrete (cu. ft.) | Total water per bag (gal.) | Materials for 1 cu. yd. of concrete | | | | Materials for 100 sq. ft. 1 in. in thickness | | |
|---|---|---|---|---|---|---|---|---|---|---|---|---|---|---|
| | Cement (bags) | Sand (cu. ft.) | Stone, gravel (cu. ft.) | | | | | Cement (bags) | Sand (cu. ft.) | Stone, gravel (cu. ft.) | Water added at mixer (gal.) | Cement (bags) | Sand (cu. ft.) | Stone, gravel (cu. ft.) |
| Footings, heavy foundations... | 1 | 3.75 | 5 | Stiff | 6.4 | 6.2 | 8.00 | 4.3 | 16.3 | 21.7 | 27.6 | 1.34 | 5.02 | 6.71 |
| Watertight concrete for cellar walls and walls above ground... | 1 | 2.5 | 3.5 | Medium | 4.9 | 4.5 | 6.00 | 6.0 | 15.0 | 21.0 | 29.5 | 1.85 | 4.63 | 6.48 |
| Driveways Floors Walks } one course... | 1 | 2.5 | 3 | Stiff | 4.4 | 4.1 | 5.50 | 6.5 | 16.3 | 19.5 | 28.7 | 2.03 | 5.09 | 6.08 |
| Driveways Floors Walks } two course... | 1 | Top 2 | 0 | Stiff | 3.6 | 2.14 | ... | 12.6 | 25.2 | ... | 45.3 | 3.89 | 7.78 | ... |
| | 1 | Base 2.5 | 4 | Stiff | 4.9 | 4.8 | 6.00 | 5.7 | 14.2 | 22.8 | 27.8 | 1.75 | 4.38 | 7.01 |
| Pavements... | 1 | 2.2 | 3.5 | Stiff | 4.3 | 4.2 | 5.25 | 6.4 | 14.1 | 22.4 | 27.5 | 1.98 | 4.35 | 6.91 |
| Watertight concrete for tanks, cisterns, and precast units (piles, posts, thin reinforced slabs, etc.)... | 1 | 2 | 3 | Medium | 4.1 | 3.8 | 5.00 | 7.1 | 14.2 | 21.3 | 29.3 | 2.18 | 4.35 | 6.54 |
| | 1 | 2 | 3 | Wet | 4.9 | 3.9 | 5.75 | 6.9 | 13.8 | 20.7 | 33.7 | 2.13 | 4.26 | 6.39 |
| Heavy duty floors... | 1 | 1.25 | 2 | Stiff | 3.4 | 2.8 | ... | 9.8 | 12.3 | 19.6 | 33.9 | 3.03 | 3.79 | 6.06 |

Source: *Practical builder.*

forces the coarse aggregate back from the face, making a dense concrete with smooth surfaces.

**Curing.** Do not permit the newly placed concrete to dry out. Protect it from the sun or drying winds for a week or 10 days, otherwise the water necessary for proper hardening will evaporate, resulting in loss of strength. Floors, walks, and similar surfaces can be protected by covering with earth or straw kept moist by occasional sprinkling as soon as the concrete has hardened sufficiently so that it will not be injured.

Walls and other sections which cannot be conveniently covered by this method can be protected by hanging moist canvas or burlap over them and wetting down the work frequently for 7 days or so after placing. In cold weather, work should be protected but need not be kept moist.

## Table 2. Safe Loads for Concrete Slabs

SAFE LOADS, UNIFORMLY DISTRIBUTED IN POUNDS PER SQUARE FOOT, SLAB SUPPORTED ON TWO SIDES

| Thickness of slab (in.) | Span—in feet | | | | | | | Round reinforcing bars,[a] transverse between supports |
|---|---|---|---|---|---|---|---|---|
| | 4 | 5 | 6 | 7 | 8 | 10 | 12 | |
| 4 | 433 | 259 | 164 | 107 | 71 | 27 | | ½ in.—spaced 8½ in. |
| 4½ | | 360 | 233 | 156 | 106 | 48 | | ½ in.—spaced 7¼ in. |
| 5 | | 468 | 319 | 218 | 152 | 75 | 33 | ½ in.—spaced 6¼ in. |
| 5½ | | | 414 | 286 | 203 | 105 | 52 | ⅝ in.—spaced 8¾ in. |
| 6 | | | 520 | 362 | 260 | 139 | 74 | ⅝ in.—spaced 7¾ in. |

SQUARE SLABS (SUPPORTED ALONG FOUR SIDES) SAFE LOAD, UNIFORMLY DISTRIBUTED IN POUNDS PER SQUARE FOOT

| Thickness of slab (in.) | Size of slab—in feet | | | | | | | 2-way round reinforcing bars [b] |
|---|---|---|---|---|---|---|---|---|
| | 6x6 | 7x7 | 8x8 | 9x9 | 10x10 | 12x12 | 14x14 | |
| 3 | 150 | 100 | 67 | 45 | 28 | | | ⅜ in.—spaced 7 ″ each way |
| 3½ | 253 | 174 | 123 | 88 | 63 | 30 | | ⅜ in.—spaced 5¾″ each way |
| 4 | 378 | 264 | 192 | 140 | 104 | 58 | 28 | ½ in.—spaced 8½″ each way |
| 4½ | | 368 | 268 | 200 | 152 | 98 | 50 | ½ in.—spaced 7¼″ each way |
| 5 | | 498 | 366 | 278 | 212 | 128 | 78 | ½ in.—spaced 6¼″ each way |

[a] The amount of longitudinal or temperature reinforcing—parallel to supports—depends on area of slab. For small- and medium-sized slabs ⅜-in. round bars spaced 12 in. apart will be sufficient.

[b] Square slabs are reinforced in two directions, bars lying at right angles to each other; in other words, in a 3-in. thick square slab the reinforcing will consist of 2 systems of bars at right angles to each other and *each* system consisting of ⅜-in. round bars spaced 7 in. on centers.

Source: *Practical builder.*

**Reinforcement.** A reinforcement of steel rods or mesh may be placed in the concrete to increase its strength where it is subjected to forces tending to bend or pull it apart. Care should be taken to place the reinforcement in the correct position in the part of the concrete mass where it will be most effective from a structural point of view.

## Table 3. Safe Loads in Pounds Uniformly Distributed for Simple Beams

| Depth of beam in inches | Span—in feet | | | | | | Depth to center line of steel | Depth below center line of steel | Steel area |
|---|---|---|---|---|---|---|---|---|---|
| | 5 | 6 | 7 | 8 | 9 | 10 | | | |
| For beams 6 in. wide | | | | | | | | | |
| 8 | 2,760 | 2,160 | 1,764 | 1,440 | 1,188 | 960 | 7.00 | 1.00 | 0.258 |
| 9 | 3,390 | 2,736 | 2,226 | 1,824 | 1,512 | 1,260 | 7.75 | 1.25 | .282 |
| 10 | 4,380 | 3,528 | 2,900 | 2,400 | 2,000 | 1,680 | 8.75 | 1.25 | .318 |
| 11 | 5,490 | 4,428 | 3,654 | 3.072 | 2,592 | 2,220 | 9.75 | 1.25 | .354 |
| 12 | 6,720 | 5,472 | 4,536 | 3,840 | 3,240 | 2,760 | 10.75 | 1.25 | .396 |
| For beams 8 in. wide | | | | | | | | | |
| 8 | 3,680 | 2,880 | 2,352 | 1,920 | 1,584 | 1,280 | 7.00 | 1.00 | .344 |
| 9 | 4,520 | 3,648 | 2,968 | 2,432 | 2,016 | 1,680 | 7.75 | 1.25 | .376 |
| 10 | 5,840 | 4,704 | 3,867 | 3,200 | 2,667 | 2,240 | 8.75 | 1.25 | .424 |
| 11 | 7,320 | 5,904 | 4,872 | 4,096 | 3,456 | 2,960 | 9.75 | 1.25 | .472 |
| 12 | 8,960 | 7,296 | 6,048 | 5,120 | 4,320 | 3,680 | 10.75 | 1.25 | .528 |
| For beams 10 in. wide | | | | | | | | | |
| 10 | 7,300 | 5,880 | 4,760 | 4,000 | 3,330 | 2,800 | 8.75 | 1.25 | .530 |
| 11 | 9,150 | 7,380 | 6.090 | 5,120 | 4,320 | 3,700 | 9.75 | 1.25 | .590 |
| 12 | 11,200 | 9,120 | 7,560 | 6,400 | 5,400 | 4,600 | 10.75 | 1.25 | .660 |
| 13 | 13,000 | 10,440 | 8,680 | 7,360 | 6,300 | 5,400 | 11.50 | 1.50 | .700 |
| 14 | 15,300 | 12,480 | 10,430 | 8,800 | 7,560 | 6,500 | 12.50 | 1.50 | .760 |

Unit stress for concrete considered as 500 psi in compression; for steel as 14,000 psi in tension. Extra conservative design.

Source: *Practical builder*. Based on information contained in *Concrete, plain and reinforced,* by Taylor and Thompson.

## Table 4. Colors To Be Used in Concrete Floor Finish

| Color desired | Pounds of color required per sack of cement to secure | | Commercial names of colors for use in cement |
|---|---|---|---|
| | Light shade | Medium shade | |
| Grays, blue-black, and black..... | ½ | 1 | Germantown lampblack * or |
| | ½ | 1 | Carbon black * or |
| | 1 | 2 | Black oxide of manganese* or |
| | 1 | 2 | Mineral black * |
| Blue shade ................... | 5 | 9 | Ultramarine blue |
| Brownish-red to dull brick red... | 5 | 9 | Red oxide of iron |
| Bright red to vermillion ........ | 5 | 9 | Mineral turkey red |
| Red sandstone to purplish-red... | 5 | 9 | Indian red |
| Brown to reddish-brown ........ | 5 | 9 | Metallic brown (oxide) |
| Buff, colonial tint, and yellow.... | 5 | 9 | Yellow ochre or |
| | 2 | 4 | Yellow oxide |
| Green shade .................. | 5 | 9 | Chromium oxide or |
| | 6 | | Greenish-blue ultramarine |

* Only first-quality lampblack should be used. Carbon black is light and requires very thorough mixing. Black oxide or mineral black is probably most advantageous for general use. For black, use 11 pounds oxide per sack of cement.

Source: *Practical builder*.

**Lightweight Aggregates.** (Adapted from *Practical builder*.) While not a new material, lightweight aggregates have been getting greater attention recently because of the insulating properties of the materials and the economies made possible by weight-saving benefits. Precast slabs, cast-in-place sections, and fireproof concrete for structural steel have accelerated the study of the variety of aggregates now available. Principal benefits resulting from the use of such materials are:

1. Reduction of dead load conserves structural steel and consequently saves on bearing foundations.
2. The multitude of dead air spaces in aggregate material gives high insulating properties.
3. The rough surface of the products also contributes to soundproofing advantages.

Many lightweight aggregate units are waterproof, allowing plaster to be applied directly to masonry walls. Interior trim can be nailed directly to the units with finishing nails. Speed in cutting and channeling permits easy installation of plumbing and electrical equipment.

**Cinder concrete.** Uses: Cinders do not make a light concrete; however, a floor fill can be made weighing 80 lb. per cu. ft. In installations requiring structural strength, concrete weighing 120 lb. per cu. ft. compares favorably with stone concrete.

How to mix and use: Cinders used in concrete should average pea size, and be free from fine ash and large clinkers. Mixing is easier and the batches are more uniform if the cinders are dampened before use. Cinder concrete must be placed wet to insure best results. A dry mixture will be weak and crumble after it is set. A mix of 1 part cement, 2 parts sand, and 5 parts cinders will make a concrete weighing 108 lb. per cu. ft., having the strength of normal gravel concrete. The weight can be reduced by adding more cinders and lessening the amount of sand.

**Haydite.** Uses: Haydite can be used wherever dead load reduction is desired, or where sound and thermal insulation is needed, without loss of structural strength. It is made into a large variety of precast concrete products. Of particular interest are haydite masonry units, weighing only 27 lb. per block as compared to 55 lb. when made from ordinary concrete.

How to mix and use: When mixed with approximately the same volume of cement as ordinary aggregates, haydite equals the strength of regular concrete. It will fully protect reinforcing bars and steel members, and manufacturing control insures uniform strength and size of aggregate.

**Perlite.** Uses: Used as a pour-in insulation, perlite will level off and will not settle or pack. It can be cast in blocks, panels, and other precast building products. Beams cast of perlite will not crack when loaded and return almost to their former position when the load is removed. Used as an insulating fill, perlite is superior for refrigerators and cold rooms.

How to mix and use: Perlite is used as an aggregate and also mixes with Keen cement or plaster of Paris to make a superior wall plaster that is 1 ton lighter per 100 sq. yd. of surface than sand plaster in standard 3-coat work. This makes possible a saving of 12 man-hours in application time per 100 sq. yd.

**Vermiculite.** Uses: Vermiculite is used as an aggregate for concrete and plaster and as insulating fill for roof construction. It can be made to form cant and saddles and is also used for precast structural roof slabs.

How to mix and use: Vermiculite concrete is mixed in a plaster-type mixer with positive paddle agitation. The proper amount of water for the batch is first put into the mixer, then the correct amount of cement is added and thoroughly mixed with the water (all lumps must be broken up). Add the entire quantity of vermiculite quickly. If the aggregate is added slowly, part of the batch will be overmixed, resulting in loss of volume. The mass should remain in the mixer only long enough to distribute the moisture evenly through the batch. After it is properly mixed, vermiculite must be poured immediately.

**Waylite.** Uses: Waylite concrete can be used for insulating floor and roof fill, precast structural units, and building blocks. Because of the sound absorption qualities, this material is ideal for buildings needing reflective sound control. Plaster can be applied directly to waylite masonry walls without danger of condensation. Finishing time is saved because interior trim can be nailed directly to the masonry. Waterproof finish for exterior of walls can be had with two coats of a Portland base cement.

How to mix and use: When mixing waylite concrete, about 50 percent greater cement volume is needed than in regular concrete to gain the same plasticity and compressive strength. It also requires a higher proportion of fine aggregate than ordinary concrete, due to the larger size and general coarseness of waylite aggregate. To obtain maximum workability with minimum weight, the aggregate and water must be mixed before cement is added, and then mixed for several additional minutes. A harsh-appearing mix will improve in plasticity by continued mixing without additional water.

### Table 5. Weight of Aggregate and Concrete, by Type of Aggregate

| Type of aggregate | Aggregate weight per cubic foot (lb.) | Weight per cubic foot of concrete using aggregate (lb.) |
|---|---|---|
| Gravel | 120 | 150 |
| Sand | 90–100 | 150 |
| Crushed stone | 100 | 145 |
| Crushed bank slag | 80 | 110–130 |
| Haydite (expanded clay, shale) | 40– 60 | 100–120 |
| Foamed slag | 40– 60 | 90–100 |
| Cinders | 40– 50 (plus sand) | 110–115 |
| Pumice | 30– 60 | 60– 90 |
| Diatomite | 28– 40 | 55– 70 |
| Perlite | 6– 16 | 40– 65 |
| Vermiculite | 6– 10 | 25– 50 |

**BRICK.** (See Tables 6 to 10.)

### Table 6. Number of Brick per 1,000 Sq. Ft. of Wall

| Width of joint (in.) | Thickness of wall (in.) | | | |
|---|---|---|---|---|
| | 4 | 8 | 12 | 16 |
| ¼ | 6,980 | 14,000 | 20,900 | 27,000 |
| ⅜ | 6,550 | 13,100 | 19,600 | 26,200 |
| ½ | 6,160 | 12,300 | 18,500 | 24,600 |
| ⅝ | 5,810 | 11,600 | 17,400 | 23,200 |
| ¾ | 5,490 | 11,000 | 16,500 | 21,900 |

### Table 7. Square Feet of Wall per 1,000 Brick

| Width of joint (in.) | Thickness of wall (in.) | | | |
|---|---|---|---|---|
| | 4 | 8 | 12 | 16 |
| ¼ | 143 | 71.6 | 47.7 | 35.8 |
| ⅜ | 153 | 76.4 | 50.9 | 38.2 |
| ½ | 162 | 81.2 | 54.1 | 40.6 |
| ⅝ | 172 | 86.1 | 57.4 | 43.1 |
| ¾ | 182 | 91.2 | 60.8 | 45.6 |

### Table 8. Mortar Quantities per 1,000 Brick

| Width of joint (in.) | Thickness of wall (in.) | | | |
|---|---|---|---|---|
| | 4 | | 8, 12, 16, and larger | |
| | Cu. ft. | Cu. yd. | Cu. ft. | Cu. yd. |
| ¼ | 5.7 | 0.21 | 8.7 | 0.32 |
| ⅜ | 8.7 | 0.32 | 11.8 | 0.44 |
| ½ | 11.7 | 0.43 | 15.0 | 0.56 |
| ⅝ | 14.8 | 0.55 | 18.3 | 0.68 |
| ¾ | 17.9 | 0.66 | 21.7 | 0.80 |

### Table 9. Mortar Color Quantities per 1,000 Brick
Laid with ½-in. joints, running or common bond

| | Lb. | Qts. |
|---|---|---|
| Black, standard (dark gray mortar)................ | 125 | 80 |
| Black, double strength (dense black)............... | 100 | 70 |
| Buff ............................................... | 100 | 75 |
| Chocolate, double strength ........................ | 100 | 55 |
| Green ............................................. | 100 | 50 |
| Red ............................................... | 125 | 60 |

### Table 10. Fire Brick Estimating
Following data based on use of standard 2½ x 4½ x 9-in size of firebrick. From 400 to 600 lb. of high-temperature cement or fireclay are sufficient to lay 1,000 straight brick.

1 sq. ft. 2½″ thick wall requires 3.58 brick
1 sq. ft. 4½″ wall requires 6.31 brick
1 sq. ft. 9″ wall requires approx. 14 brick
1 sq. ft. 13½″ wall requires approx. 21 brick
1 cu. ft. of fire-brickwork requires 17 brick
1 cu. ft. of fire-brickwork weighs 125–140 lb.

Source of Tables 6 to 10: *Practical builder.*

**PAINT.** (See Tables 11 and 12.)

**Table 11. Painting Materials for 1,000 Sq. Ft. of Surface**

REPAINTING (Figures are totals for two coats)

| Kind of surface | Gallons paint | White lead | Linseed oil | Lead mixing or reducing oil | Turpentine | Liquid drier |
|---|---|---|---|---|---|---|
| Exterior wood ......... | 3 | 45 lb. | 1⅛ gal. | ... | 3 pt. | ¾ pt. |
| Wood shingles .......... | 3¾ | 55 lb. | 1⅜ gal. | ... | ½ gal. | 1 pt. |
| Interior wood, plaster, and wallboard ........ | 2½ | 40 lb. | ... | 1¼ gal. | ... | ... |
| Exterior stucco, concrete, stone, and brick..... | 5 | 70 lb. | 3 qt. | 2 gal. | ... | ... |

NEW WORK (Figures are totals for three coats)

| Kind of surface | Gallons paint | White lead | Linseed oil | Lead mixing or reducing oil | Turpentine | Liquid drier |
|---|---|---|---|---|---|---|
| Exterior wood ......... | 4¾ | 62 lb. | 1⅞ gal. | ... | 3 qt. | 1¼ pt. |
| Wood shingles .......... | 8⅝ | 105 lb. | 3⅝ gal. | ... | 1⅝ gal. | 2¼ pt. |
| Interior wood .......... | 4 | 56 lb. | 2 qt. | 1¼ gal. | 3 pt. | ¼ pt. |
| Interior plaster and wallboard ....... | 3¾ | 57 lb. | ... | 2 gal. | ... | ... |
| Exterior stucco, concrete, and stone .......... | 10 | 135 lb. | 2¼ gal. | 3½ gal. | ... | ... |
| Exterior brick .......... | 10 | 120 lb. | 3½ gal. | 2 gal. | ⅝ gal. | 1¼ pt. |

Source: *Practical builder.*

**Table 12. Covering Capacities per Gallon***

| Material | Sq. ft. per gal. |
|---|---|
| Bleaching solutions .................. | 250–300 |
| Lacquer .............................. | 200–300 |
| Lacquer sealer ....................... | 250–300 |
| Paste wood filler .................... | 40–50 (per lb.) |
| Liquid filler ........................ | 250–400 |
| Water stain .......................... | 350–400 |
| Oil stain ............................ | 300–350 |
| Pigment oil stain .................... | 350–400 |
| Nongrain raising stain ............... | 275–325 |
| Paint ................................ | 650–750 |
| Spirit stain ......................... | 250–300 |
| Shellac .............................. | 300–350 |
| Rubbing varnish ...................... | 450–500 |
| Flat varnish ......................... | 300–350 |
| Paste wax ............................ | 125–175 |
| Liquid wax ........................... | 600–700 |

* General average—will vary considerably, depending on thickness of coat, application to porous or nonporous surface, etc.
Source: *Practical builder.*

**PORTLAND CEMENT PAINT.** Surfaces: Apply only to surfaces such as concrete, Portland cement stucco, building tile, brick, stone, concrete blocks, Portland cement plaster, or concrete ceilings. Do not use on any glazed or vitrified surface. Do not use on concrete floors.

Coverage: Surface covering capacity ranges from 20 to 35 sq. ft. per lb. of paint for 1 coat. This coverage does not apply to exceptionally rough or extremely porous surfaces such as cinder and other lightweight aggregate blocks or units. Ten pounds of paint mixed with water will make approximately 1½ gal.

Previous coatings: All previous coatings, including oil paints, lime-bound cement paint, dust efflorescence, dirt, or grease, must be removed. It is not necessary to remove previous applications of Portland cement paint, but it must be cleaned. On new work, form oil must be removed.

Dense surfaces: In the case of very dense surfaces caused by the use of pressed wood forms or rubbing stone, omit wetting of the surface, but spray several times while hardening. Smoothly finished cast stone trim and also old swimming pools should be treated in the same manner.

**Mixing Proportions.** First coat—Use 5 qt. of water with 10 lb. of paint. Second coat—Use 4 qt. of water with 10 lb. of paint. Be sure to wet first coat before applying the second.

For "scrubbed in" applications on open-textured, porous surfaces the procedure is as follows: First coat—Use from 3 to 4 qt. of water to 10 lb. of paint. Scrub-brush method should be used. Second coat—Use 4 qt. of water with 10 lb. of paint. Be sure to wet first coat before applying the second.

For swimming pools: First coat—Use 4 qt. of water with 10 lb. of paint. Second coat—Use 3½ qt. of water to 10 lb. of paint.

**Preparation of Surface.** It is recommended that all surfaces be brushed with a wire brush, with special attention to cracks, to remove any accumulated dirt or loose particles on the surface or in the cracks. Hairline cracks are easily filled by brushing the paint thoroughly into the crack with the first coat.

Thoroughly clean out all loose, crumbling particles from large cracks before painting and fill with a heavy paste made by mixing the dry paint and a little water. Cut out large cracks as shown in the diagram so that the paste keys itself in. The large cracks should be sprinkled before filling with paste. The filled crack and adjoining wall should be sprayed frequently until the paste filling the crack is dry.

In applying the first coat, work paint into all cracks with a short-bristle brush.

The surface to be painted should be wet down thoroughly with a fine spray of water from a garden hose. Be sure that the wall is thoroughly wet, but allow time for the surface film of water to disappear before applying the paint. This does not apply to very dense surfaces, as described above.

After mixing, it may be found that there will be some lumps in the paint. For this reason, it should be poured through window screen wire several times to remove any lumps or foreign matter. **Apply within 2 hr. after mixing. Portland cement paint, under ordinary conditions, will attain its initial set in from 1 to 2 hr.** While painting, stir the paint each time the brush is dipped. This prevents the paint from settling to the bottom. It is advisable to brush the bottom of the container each time the brush is dipped into the paint.

**Application.** First coat, smooth surfaces: Use a bristle, whitewash, calcimine, Dutch, or wall brush in applying the paint. In brushing, use a horizontal sweeping motion, keeping the brush full of paint. Flow the paint on; do not "brush out" the paint.

First coat, for rough surfaces and rain penetration resistance: Use a scrub brush, dipping it into the paint, then scrub the paint very thoroughly into the surface with a circular motion in order to get all the little cracks and pores filled with paint. For even color, the paint should be kept thoroughly stirred during this operation. Three to 4 qt. of water are used with 10 lb. of cement paint. Keep the first coat damp by spraying lightly until hard.

Second coat, any surface: The second coat can be applied the day following the first coat. Wet the first coat before applying. Use the same brush as in applying the first coat on smooth surfaces and be sure the paint is stirred from the bottom each time the brush is dipped. Paint is applied with a long, even horizontal stroke.

# CHIMNEYS. (See Tables 13 and 14.)

## Table 13. Minimum Vent, Flue, and Chimney Sizes, With and Without Flue Linings

### Gas Appliances, Stoves and Ranges

| Use | Types of flues (minimum) | | |
| --- | --- | --- | --- |
| | Round lining, inside dimensions | Rectangular lining, outside dimensions | Unlined flue, inside dimensions |
| Gas vents, small capacity | 6" | 4½" x 8½" | 4" x 8" |
| Gas vents, multiple | 8" | 7½" x 7½" | 8" x 12" |
| Gas vents, large capacity | 8" | 4½" x 13" | 8" x 12" |
| Small stoves, special | 6" | 7½" x 7½" | 8" x 8" |
| Stoves and ranges | 8" | 8½" x 8½" | 8" x 12" |
| Fireplaces | 8" | 8½" x 13" | 8" x 12" |

Source: *Practical builder.*

## Table 14. Chimney Flue Sizes *

| Fireplace dimensions | | For chimneys over 20 ft. high | | | For chimneys under 20 ft. high | | |
| --- | --- | --- | --- | --- | --- | --- | --- |
| Finished width | Opening height | Standard flue | Modular flue | Round flue | Standard flue | Modular flue | Round flue |
| 28" | 24" | 8½" x 13" | 12" x 12" | 10" | 8½" x 13" | 12" x 12" | 10" |
| 32" | 26" | 8½" x 13" | 12" x 12" | 10" | 13" x 13" | 12" x 16" | 12" |
| 36" | 28" | 13" x 13" | 12" x 16" | 12" | 13" x 18" | 12" x 16" | 12" |
| 40" | 30" | 13" x 13" | 12" x 16" | 12" | 13" x 18" | 16" x 16" | 15" |
| 48" | 32" | 13" x 18" | 16" x 16" | 15" | 13" x 18" | 16" x 20" | 15" |
| 60" | 36" | 13" x 18" | 16" x 20" | 15" | 18" x 18" | 20" x 20" | 18" |

* Outside dimensions shown for standard and modular flues—inside dimensions for round flues. Chimney height is measured from hearth.
Source: Heatilator, Inc.

## DEPRECIATION OF STRUCTURES.

**Table 15. Depreciation of Structures**

| Frame | | | | The constituent parts of buildings | Brick, shingle roofs | | | |
|---|---|---|---|---|---|---|---|---|
| Stores | | Dwellings | | | Dwellings | | Stores | |
| Average duration (yr.) | Depreciation per year (%) | Average duration (yr.) | Depreciation per year (%) | | Average duration (yr.) | Depreciation per year (%) | Average duration (yr.) | Depreciation per year (%) |
| 30 | 3⅓ | 40 | 2½ | Base | 40 | 2½ | 30 | 3⅓ |
| ... | ... | ... | ... | Brick | 75 | 1⅛ | 66 | 1½ |
| 30 | 3⅓ | 40 | 2½ | Cornice | 40 | 2½ | 40 | 2½ |
| 40 | 2½ | 50 | 2 | Dimension lumber | 75 | 1⅓ | 66 | 1⅓ |
| 25 | 4 | 30 | 3⅓ | Doors and trim | 30 | 3⅓ | 30 | 3⅓ |
| 13 | 8 | 20 | 5 | Floors | 20 | 5 | 13 | 8 |
| 13 | 8 | 20 | 5 | Hardware | 13 | 8 | 20 | 5 |
| 30 | 3⅓ | 30 | 3⅓ | Inside blinds | 30 | 3⅓ | 30 | 3⅓ |
| 16 | 6 | 16 | 6 | Outside blinds | 16 | 6 | 16 | 6 |
| 5 | 20 | 7 | 14 | Paint, inside | 7 | 14 | 6 | 16 |
| 5 | 20 | 5 | 20 | Paint, outside | 7 | 14 | 6 | 16 |
| 16 | 6 | 20 | 5 | Plaster | 30 | 3⅓ | 30 | 3⅓ |
| 20 | 5 | 20 | 5 | Porches | 20 | 5 | 20 | 5 |
| 16 | 6 | 16 | 6 | Shingles of wood | 16 | 6 | 16 | 6 |
| 40 | 2½ | 50 | 2 | Sheathing | 50 | 2 | 50 | 2 |
| 30 | 3⅓ | 30 | 3⅓ | Siding | ... | ... | ... | ... |
| 25 | 4 | 25 | 4 | Sills and first floor joists | 40 | 2½ | 30 | 3⅓ |
| 20 | 5 | 30 | 3⅓ | Stairs | 30 | 3⅓ | 20 | 5 |
| 25 | 4 | 30 | 3⅓ | Windows | 30 | 3⅓ | 30 | 3⅓ |

Source: Fire Underwriters' Assn.

# SOIL FOUNDATIONS AND HAND EXCAVATIONS. (See Tables 16 and 17.)

### Table 16. Safe Loads for Soil Foundations

| Material | Lb. per sq. ft. |
|---|---|
| Soft, wet clay or soft clay and wet sand mixed ........................ | 2,000 |
| Sand and clay—firm clay or wet sand ............................... | 4,000 |
| Dry, solid clay or firm, dry sand ................................... | 5,000 |
| Hard clay—firm, coarse sand—gravel .............................. | 8,000 |
| Firm, coarse sand and gravel mixed ................................ | 12,000 |
| Hardpan ......................................................... | 20,000 |

Source: *Practical builder.*

### Table 17. Hand Excavation: Time Estimates

The table gives the approximate number of man-hours required per cubic yard of pick-loosened and shoveled excavation. A selection of three depths (3′0″, 6′0″, and 8′0″) is provided under each of the three types of soil.

| Item of work, includes trimming banks, cutting out corners, level grading bottoms | Type of soil excavated | | | | | | | | |
|---|---|---|---|---|---|---|---|---|---|
| | Loose, dry | | | Wet, heavy | | | Compact, hard | | |
| | 3′0″ | 6′0″ | 8′0″ | 3′0″ | 6′0″ | 8′0″ | 3′0″ | 6′0″ | 8′0″ |
| Trench work, piping ....... | 1.00 | 1.25 | 1.75 | 2.00 | 2.25 | 3.25 | 2.25 | 3.0 | 3.75 |
| Rectangular footings, pits .. | 1.25 | 1.5 | 2.0 | 2.0 | 2.75 | 3.5 | 2.5 | 3.5 | 4.0 |
| Small cellars, throw out .... | | 1.25 | 1.5 | | 2.5 | 3.0 | | 2.75 | 3.25 |
| Wheelbarrow, 100-ft. haul.... | 2.00 | 2.5 | 3.0 | 3.5 | 4.0 | 4.25 | 3.0 | 3.75 | 4.5 |
| Wheelbarrow, 50-ft. haul..... | 1.75 | 2.25 | 2.75 | 3.0 | 3.5 | 3.75 | 2.75 | 3.5 | 4.0 |
| Loading in carts or trucks... | 0.5 | 0.5 | 0.5 | 0.75 | 0.75 | 0.75 | 0.6 | 0.6 | 0.6 |
| Back-fill and tamp ......... | 0.7 | 0.8 | 0.9 | 1.0 | 1.2 | 1.4 | 0.75 | 0.85 | 0.95 |

Source: *Practical builder.*

### Table 18. Nail Sizes

| Common wire size, pennyweight | Length (in.) | Approximate number per lb. | Finishing nails, approximate number per lb. | Staples, length (in.) | Approximate number per lb. |
|---|---|---|---|---|---|
| 2 | 1 | 875 | 1,350 | 1 | 120 |
| 3 | 1¼ | 570 | 807 | 1¼ | 98 |
| 4 | 1½ | 315 | 585 | 1½ | 80 |
| 5 | 1¾ | 270 | 500 | 2 | 55 |
| 6 | 2 | 180 | 310 | | |
| 7 | 2¼ | 160 | 239 | | |
| 8 | 2½ | 105 | 190 | | |
| 9 | 2¾ | 95 | 172 | | |
| 10 | 3 | 69 | 120 | | |
| 12 | 3¼ | 63 | 113 | | |
| 16 | 3½ | 50 | 90 | | |
| 20 | 4 | 30 | 62 | | |
| 30 | 4½ | 24 | | | |
| 40 | 5 | 18 | | | |
| 50 | 5½ | 14 | | | |
| 60 | 6 | 11 | | | |

Source: Sechrist.

**NAILS.** (See Table 18.) Nail sizes are designated by pennyweight. The more commonly used nails and their uses can be classified, according to Sechrist, as follows:

> Common wire nails, for rough work such as outside construction, building repair, etc.
> Finishing nails, for interior trim, ceiling, and bevel siding.
> Casing nails, nearly the same as finishing nails, but slightly smaller in diameter, for drop siding, casings, fine work, or repairing.
> Spikes, from 10d to 12d, larger in diameter than common wire nails, for heavy construction.
> Shingle nails, larger in diameter than common wire nails, used for nailing wood shingles.
> Roofing nails, designated by length in inches instead of by pennyweight, for composition roofing.
> Blued wire nails, for lath.

Using average spacing for nails, the approximate quantities of nails which should be used for several kinds of work are:

> 1,000 shingles—4 to 5 lb. of 4d or 3 to 4 lb. of 3d.
> 1,000 bd. ft. of lath, 1 by 4 in.; 2 nailings, 16 to 20 in. on center—38 to 48 lb. of 8d nails.
> 1,000 bd. ft. of covering boards; boards 6 to 12 in. wide, nails spaced 16 to 30 in. on centers; 2 nailings—18 to 22 lb. of 8d or 24 to 26 lb. of 10d.
> 1,000 bd. ft. of flooring, 1 by 4 in.—26 to 32 lb. of 8d flooring nails.
> 1,000 bd. ft. of finish; nails 12 to 16 in. on centers—12 to 25 lb. of 8d finishing nails.

**MANILA ROPE.** Ropes used on construction work are usually made of manila hemp. They are of either three or four strands. A four-strand rope is more pliable, but is also more liable to kink. Manila rope should always be coiled clockwise to prevent kinking. When it is to be uncoiled, the end first laid down should be pulled up through the eye of the coil. Table 19 gives the strengths of manila rope based on a safety factor of 4. The table is for new rope and is based on strengths adopted by rope manufacturers and other authorities. Allowance should be made in the use of the strength table for deterioration of the rope due to weather, age, abuse, and other causes. A quick computation of the safe load in tons which a manila rope will carry may be found by squaring the diameter in inches. Thus the safe load on a ¾-in. rope is $¾ \times ¾ = \frac{9}{16}$ ton = 1,125 lb.

### Table 19. Manila Rope Strength, Based on Safety Factor of 4

| Circumference (in.) | Diameter (in.) | Breaking load (lb.) | Safe load (lb.) |
|---|---|---|---|
| 1½ | ½ | 2,000 | 500 |
| 2¼ | ¾ | 4,000 | 1,000 |
| 2¾ | ⅞ | 6,000 | 1,500 |
| 3 | 1 | 8,000 | 2,000 |
| 3½ | 1⅛ | 10,000 | 2,500 |
| 4 | 1¼ | 12,000 | 3,000 |
| 4¼ | 1⅜ | 14,000 | 3,500 |
| 4¾ | 1½ | 16,000 | 4,000 |
| 5½ | 1¾ | 24,000 | 6,000 |
| 6 | 2 | 30,000 | 7,500 |

Knots, slings, fasteners, hitches, and anchors are illustrated in Figs. 1 and 2.

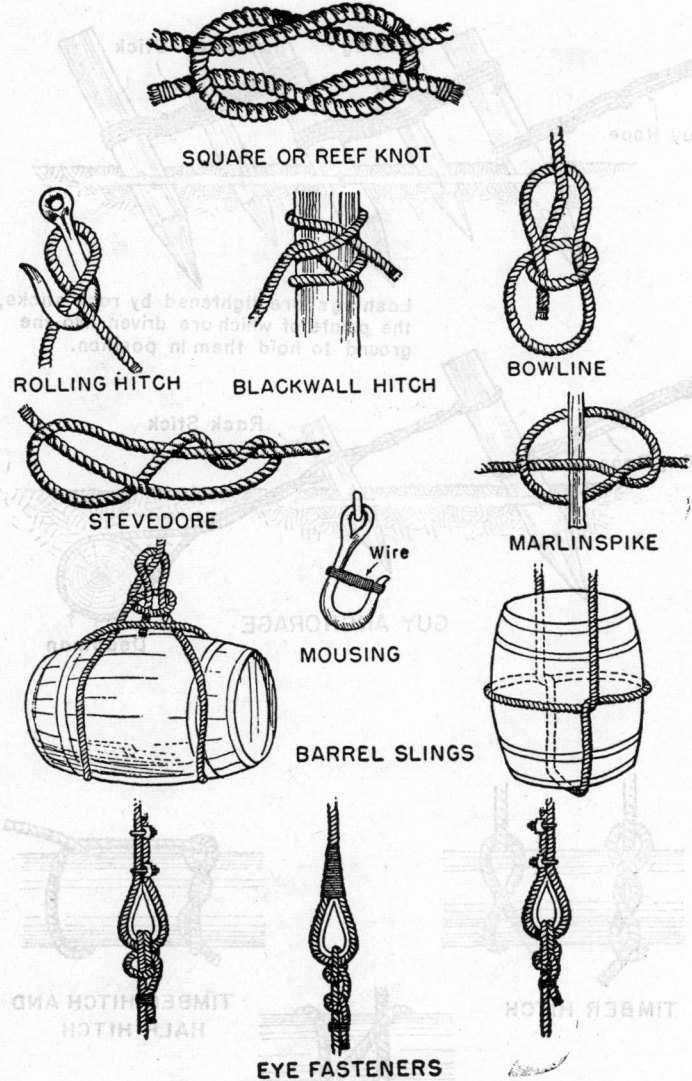

Fig. 1. Knots, slings, and fasteners.
(U. S. Forest Service, *Improvement handbook*.)

**Lashings** are often necessary for making the connections illustrated in Fig. 3. The most commonly used lashing is that for a pair of shears. The two timbers for

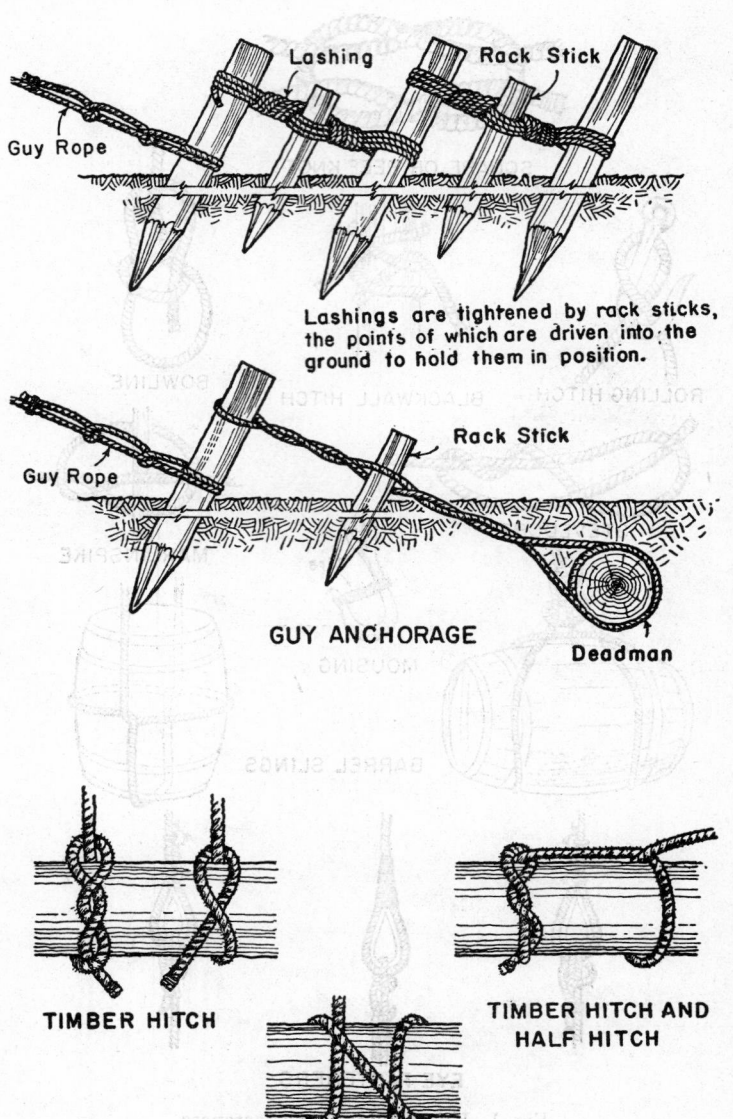

Lashings are tightened by rack sticks, the points of which are driven into the ground to hold them in position.

**GUY ANCHORAGE**

**TIMBER HITCH**

**TIMBER HITCH AND HALF HITCH**

**CLOVE HITCH**

Fig. 2.  Hitches and anchors.
(U. S. Forest Service, *Improvement handbook.*)

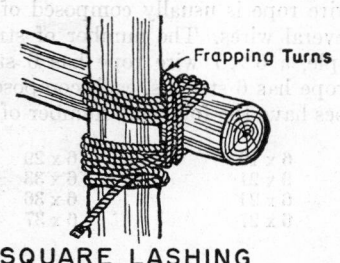

## SQUARE LASHING

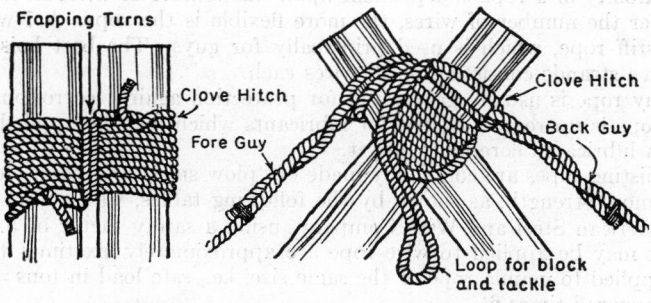

## LASHING FOR A PAIR OF SHEARS

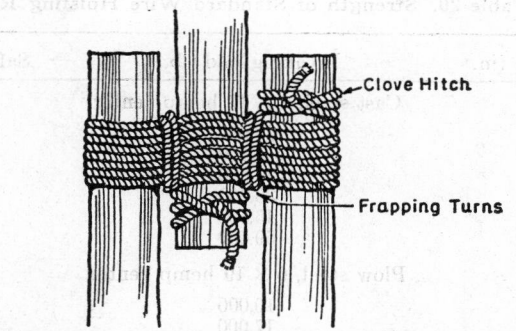

## LASHING FOR A TRIPOD OR GIN

**Fig. 3. Lashings.**

(U. S. Forest Service, *Improvement handbook.*)

the shears are laid alongside each other with their butts on the ground, and with the points below where the lashing is to be made resting on a skid. A clove hitch is made around one timber and the lashing is taken loosely eight or nine times about the two timbers above the hitch without riding. Two frapping turns are then taken between the spars, and the lashing is finished off with a clove hitch above the turns on one side of the timbers. The butts of the timbers are then opened out and a sling is passed over the fork, to which the block is hooked or lashed. The fore and back guys are made fast with clove hitches to the bottom and top timbers respectively, just above the fork.

**WIRE ROPE.** A wire rope is usually composed of 6 or 8 strands and each strand is made up of several wires. The number of strands of wire is indicated by numbers. For example, a 6 × 7 wire rope has 6 strands, each composed of 7 wires; a 6 × 19 wire rope has 6 strands, each composed of 19 wires. The more commonly used wire ropes have the following number of strands and wires:

| | | | |
|---|---|---|---|
| 5 x 19 | 6 x 19 | 6 x 29 | 6 x 41 |
| 6 x 7 | 6 x 21 | 6 x 33 | 6 x 42 |
| 6 x 8 | 6 x 24 | 6 x 36 | 7 x 18 |
| 6 x 12 | 6 x 27 | 6 x 37 | 8 x 19 |
| 6 x 17 | | | |

The flexibility of a rope is dependent upon the number of wires in each strand. The greater the number of wires, the more flexible is the rope. A 7-wire strand makes a stiff rope, which is used principally for guys. The best hoisting ropes should have strands consisting of 19 wires each.

Steel guy rope is usually galvanized for protection against corrosion, but steel hoisting rope is untreated, except for lubricants which may be applied. All wire rope has a lubricated core built into it.

Wire hoisting ropes are commonly made of "plow steel" and "cast steel." Plow steel has more strength, as shown by the following tables, which were developed by the American Steel and Wire Company, using a safety factor of 5. The safe loads that may be applied to wire rope are approximately six times that which may be applied to manila rope of the same size, i.e., safe load in tons = diameter in inches squared times 6.

**Table 20.  Strength of Standard Wire Hoisting Rope**

| Diameter (in.) | Breaking load (lb.) | Safe load (lb.) |
|:---:|:---:|:---:|
| Cast steel, 6 × 19 hemp center | | |
| ⅜ | 9,000 | 1,800 |
| ½ | 15,400 | 3,080 |
| ⅝ | 23,600 | 4,720 |
| ¾ | 33,600 | 6,720 |
| ⅞ | 45,600 | 9,120 |
| 1 | 59,000 | 11,800 |
| Plow steel, 6 × 19 hemp center | | |
| ⅜ | 10,000 | 2,000 |
| ½ | 17,000 | 3,400 |
| ⅝ | 26,200 | 5,240 |
| ¾ | 37,400 | 7,480 |
| ⅞ | 50,800 | 10,160 |
| 1 | 66,000 | 13,200 |

Source: American Steel & Wire Co.

The weights of wire of gauges 1 to 20 are given in Fig. 4.

**CHAINS.** Chains are widely used as slings for hoisting heavy construction materials. Chains smaller than ½ in. are usually made of mild open-hearth steel and are electrically welded. Chains larger than ½ in. are usually made by hand-welding wrought-iron bars. Bending and welding reduces the strength of a chain so that it is not twice but only about 1.5 to 1.7 times as strong as the original bar. Safe loads which may be placed on chains are shown in Table 21. Chains which

| Steel Wire Gauge No. | Sizes of Wire Common Fractions | Sizes of Wire Decimally | Weight one mile pounds | Pounds per foot | Feet to pound |
|---|---|---|---|---|---|
| 1 | | .2830 | 1,128.0 | .2136 | 4.681 |
| | ⁹⁄₃₂ | .28125 | 1,114.0 | .211 | |
| 2 | | .2625 | 970.4 | .1838 | 5.441 |
| | ¼ | .250 | 880.2 | .1667 | |
| 3 | | .2437 | 836.4 | .1584 | 6.313 |
| 4 | | .2253 | 714.8 | .1354 | 7.386 |
| | ⁷⁄₃₂ | .21875 | 673.9 | .1276 | |
| 5 | | .2070 | 603.4 | .1143 | 8.750 |
| 6 | | .1920 | 519.2 | .0983 | 10.17 |
| | ³⁄₁₆ | .1875 | 495.1 | .0937 | |
| 7 | | .1770 | 441.2 | .0835 | 11.97 |
| 8 | | .1620 | 369.6 | .070 | 14.29 |
| | ⁵⁄₃₂ | .15625 | 343.8 | .0651 | |
| 9 | | .1483 | 309.7 | .0586 | 17.05 |
| 10 | | .1350 | 256.7 | .0486 | 20.57 |
| | ⅛ | .1250 | 220.0 | .0416 | |
| 11 | | .1205 | 204.5 | .0387 | 25.82 |
| 12 | | .1055 | 156.7 | .0296 | 33.69 |
| | ³⁄₃₂ | .09375 | 123.8 | .0234 | |
| 13 | | .0915 | 117.9 | .0223 | 44.78 |
| 14 | | .0800 | 90.13 | .0170 | 58.58 |
| 15 | | .0720 | 73.01 | .0138 | 72.32 |
| 16 | ¹⁄₁₆ | .0625 | 55.0 | .0104 | 95.98 |
| 17 | | .0540 | 41.07 | .0077 | 128.6 |
| 18 | | .0475 | 31.77 | .006 | 166.2 |
| 19 | | .0410 | 23.67 | .0044 | 223.0 |
| 20 | | .0348 | 17.05 | .0032 | 309.6 |

**Fig. 4. Steel wire sizes and weights.**
(American Steel & Wire Co.)

are in constant use require lubrication and frequent annealing. Hoisting chains and sling chains should be annealed at least once each year to prevent hardening and unexpected failure.

### Table 21. Safe Loads for Chains

| Diameter of metal (in.) | Safe load (lb.) | Diameter of metal (in.) | Safe load (lb.) |
|---|---|---|---|
| ¼ | 1,330 | ¾ | 12.000 |
| ⅜ | 2,660 | ⅞ | 16,330 |
| ½ | 5,330 | 1 | 20,830 |
| ⅝ | 8,330 | | |

**TACKLES AND LEVERS. Rope Tackle.** The arrangement of the tackle is the same for both manila and wire rope. The term includes the ropes, blocks, and hooks which are used for hoisting. Hoisting tackle and slings are illustrated in Fig. 5.

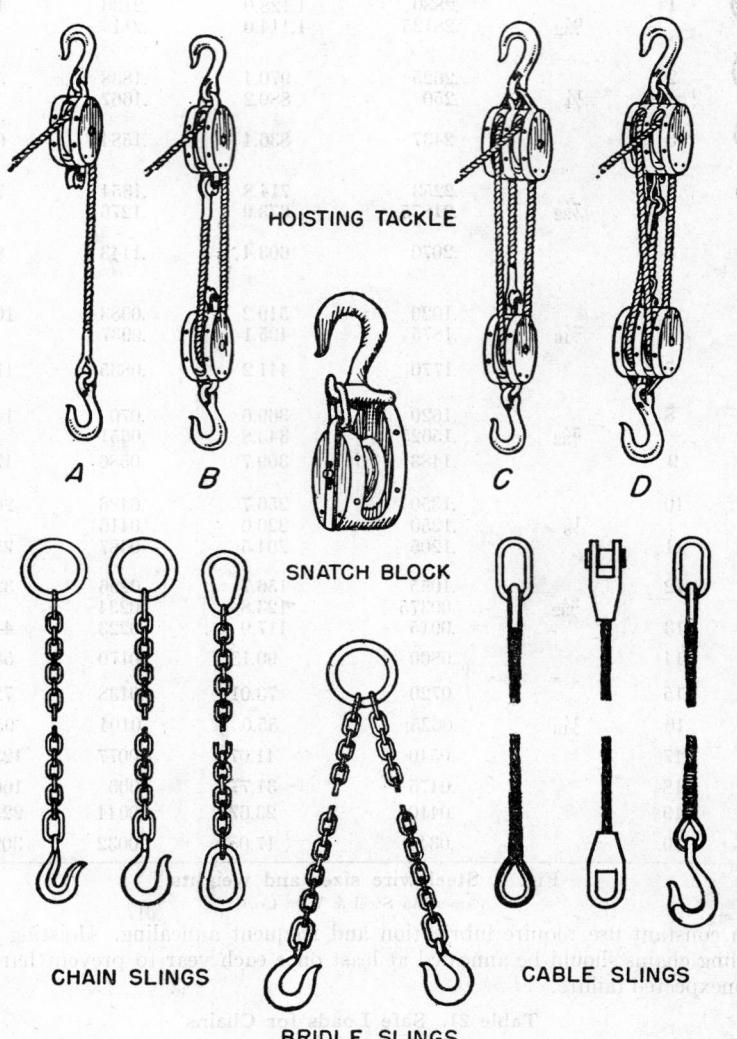

HOISTING TACKLE

SNATCH BLOCK

CHAIN SLINGS     CABLE SLINGS

BRIDLE SLINGS

**Fig. 5. Tackle.**
(U. S. Forest Service.)

The parts of a block are the shell or frame, the sheave or wheel upon which the rope runs, and the pin on which the wheel turns in the shell. A strap of iron passes around the shell to form attachments for a hook at one end and an eye at the other. The strap is replaced by bolts for metal blocks. Wooden blocks are usually used with manila rope while metal blocks are usually used with wire rope.

A snatch block is a single block with the shell and strap open on one side to admit a rope.

The strength of the body of a tackle block is usually greater than that of the rope which is used with it. The hook is generally the weakest part of the block because it has a tendency to open out when subjected to a heavy load. Blocks intended for heavy work should be fitted with shackles. Shackles are much stronger than hooks of the same size, as shown by Tables 22 and 23, which are based on a safety factor of 5.

### Table 22. Safe Load on Hooks

| Diameter of metal (in.) | Breaking load (lb.) | Safe load (lb.) |
|---|---|---|
| ¾ | 3,500 | 700 |
| ⅞ | 5,000 | 1,000 |
| 1 | 7,500 | 1,500 |
| 1¹⁄₁₆ | 10,000 | 2,000 |
| 1⅜ | 15,000 | 3,000 |
| 1⁷⁄₁₆ | 20,000 | 4,000 |
| 1⅝ | 25,000 | 5,000 |
| 1⅞ | 30,000 | 6,000 |
| 2 | 37,500 | 7,500 |

### Table 23. Safe Load on Shackles or Sockets

| Diameter of metal (in.) | Breaking load (lb.) | Safe load (lb.) | Diameter of metal (in.) | Breaking load (lb.) | Safe load (lb.) |
|---|---|---|---|---|---|
| ¾ | 37,500 | 7,500 | 1½ | 110,000 | 22,000 |
| ⅞ | 50,000 | 10,000 | 1⅝ | 137,500 | 27,500 |
| 1 | 70,000 | 14,000 | 1¾ | 150,000 | 30,000 |
| 1⅛ | 82,500 | 16,500 | 1⅞ | 170,000 | 34,000 |
| 1¼ | 87,500 | 17,500 | 2 | 210,000 | 42,000 |
| 1⅜ | 90,000 | 18,000 | | | |

During the hoisting operation, each part of the rope, progressing from the bucket toward the fall end or lead line, has to overcome an increasing amount of friction. Each block through which the rope passes adds a certain amount to the friction which must be overcome. Snatch blocks and additional sheaves outside of the hoisting tackle over which the fall end passes cause still further loss of power. The net lifting capacity of the tackle then depends on the strength of the lead line which remains after deducting the pull necessary to overcome friction.

This assumption is based upon the other parts of the tackle being sufficiently strong. Table 24, giving the safe lifting capacity of tackle, takes the friction losses into account.

The internal friction in a rope and the possibility of breaking the wires will be less with each increase in size of the sheave. The capacity of any block can be determined by computing the strength of the pin and the straps that support the sheaves. Table 25 gives the recommended sheave and drum diameter for use with wire rope.

The maximum sheave diameters for use with manila rope should be 6 times the diameter of the rope.

In Fig. 5 the mechanical advantages are 1, 2, 3, and 4, respectively, for the hoisting tackles A, B, C, and D. The mechanical advantage of the hoisting tackle

### Table 24. Safe Lifting Capacity of Tackle Without Snatch Blocks

| New manila rope | | | | Wire rope | | | |
|---|---|---|---|---|---|---|---|
| Size rope (in.) | Diameter sheaves (in.) | Total No. of sheaves | Safe lifting capacity (lb.) | Size rope (in.) | Diameter sheaves (in.) | Total No. of sheaves | Safe lifting capacity (lb.) |
| ¾ | 7 | 2 | 1,500 | ½ | 10 | 2 | 8,000 |
| ¾ | | 3 | 2,000 | ½ | | 3 | 10,000 |
| ¾ | | 4 | 2,800 | ½ | | 4 | 14,000 |
| ¾ | | 5 | 3,500 | ½ | | 5 | 18,000 |
| ¾ | | 6 | 4,000 | ½ | | 6 | 20,000 |
| | | | | ½ | | 7 | 22,000 |
| 1 | 10 | 2 | 2,000 | | | | |
| 1 | | 3 | 4,000 | ⅝ | 12 | 2 | 12,000 |
| 1 | | 4 | 6,000 | ⅝ | | 3 | 16,000 |
| 1 | | 5 | 8,000 | ⅝ | | 4 | 22,000 |
| 1 | | 6 | 10,000 | ⅝ | | 5 | 26,000 |
| | | | | ⅝ | | 6 | 30,000 |
| 1¼ | 12 | 2 | 4,000 | ⅝ | | 7 | 34,000 |
| 1¼ | | 3 | 7,000 | | | | |
| 1¼ | | 4 | 10,000 | ¾ | 14 | 2 | 16,000 |
| 1¼ | | 5 | 12,000 | ¾ | | 3 | 24,000 |
| 1¼ | | 6 | 14,000 | ¾ | | 4 | 32,000 |
| 1¼ | | 7 | 16,000 | ¾ | | 5 | 38,000 |
| | | | | ¾ | | 6 | 44,000 |
| 1½ | 14 | 2 | 8,000 | ¾ | | 7 | 50,000 |
| 1½ | | 3 | 10,000 | | | | |
| 1½ | | 4 | 13,000 | | | | |
| 1½ | | 5 | 17,000 | | | | |
| 1½ | | 6 | 20,000 | | | | |
| 1½ | | 7 | 23,000 | | | | |

is, therefore, the number of ropes that support the weight or load. The true or actual mechanical advantage is this value less the frictional and other losses incurred in operation.

### Table 25. Drum Diameters for Use with Wire Rope

| Wire rope size | Average sheave or drum size | Minimum sheave or drum size |
|---|---|---|
| 6 × 7 | 72 times rope diameter | 42 times rope diameter |
| 6 × 19 | 45 times rope diameter | 30 times rope diameter |
| 6 × 37 | 27 times rope diameter | 18 times rope diameter |
| 8 × 19 | 31 times rope diameter | 21 times rope diameter |

Where snatch blocks are used, in the lead line, deduct 10 percent to 15 percent from the capacity for each block so used.

**Levers.** The following formula can be applied to the two classes of levers shown in Fig. 6.

$$P = \frac{A}{B} \times W$$

where $P$ = the effort required, $W$ = the weight, and $A$, $B$ = the distances.

**RIGGING EQUIPMENT. Winches.** Winches are designed for use with either manila or wire rope. Drums used with manila rope are usually smaller in diameter and longer than those used with wire rope. Manila rope drums average

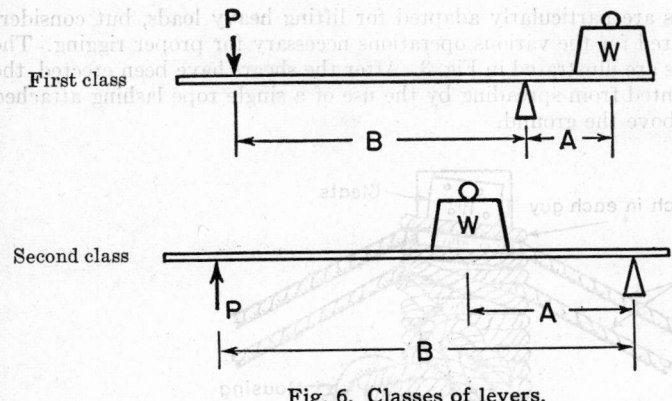

First class

Second class

Fig. 6. Classes of levers.

between 4 and 6 in. in diameter and are usually not less than 24 in. long. Wire rope drums average between 8 and 10 in. in diameter and have a maximum length of 20 in.

**Gin Poles.** A gin pole is the most common type of rigging equipment used for lifting loads vertically. It consists of an upright pole, equipped with hoisting tackle, which is properly guyed at the top so that it will maintain its upright position. Gin poles should not be longer than 60 times their diameter because of their tendency to buckle under compression strain. Gin pole timbers should be straight and free from any serious defects. Table 26 gives the safe lifting capacity of spruce poles.

A gin pole should be rigged as shown in Figs. 7 and 8. All work should be done with the pole lying flat on the ground. After the top-tackle lashings, the lower snatch-block lashings, and the upper guy attachments have been made, the pole should be raised on its footing blocks to the proper operating position.

**Table 26. Safe Capacity of Spruce * Gin Poles**

| Cross-section dimensions (in.) | Length (ft.) | Safe lifting capacity (lb.) |
|---|---|---|
| 6 × 6 | 20 | 12,000 |
| 6 × 6 | 25 | 8,000 |
| 6 × 6 | 30 | 4,000 |
| 8 × 8 | 25 | 30,000 |
| 8 × 8 | 30 | 22,000 |
| 8 × 8 | 35 | 16,000 |
| 8 × 8 | 40 | 10,000 |
| 8 × 8 | 45 | 4,000 |
| 10 × 10 | 25 | 56,000 |
| 10 × 10 | 30 | 48,000 |
| 10 × 10 | 35 | 36,000 |
| 10 × 10 | 40 | 30,000 |
| 10 × 10 | 45 | 22,000 |
| 10 × 10 | 50 | 14,000 |
| 12 × 12 | 30 | 76,000 |
| 12 × 12 | 40 | 56,000 |
| 12 × 12 | 50 | 36,000 |
| 12 × 12 | 60 | 16,000 |

* For longleaf pine or Douglas-fir, increase these capacities by ⅓; for oak and ash, ¼.

**Shears.** Shears are particularly adapted for lifting heavy loads, but considerable time is required for the various operations necessary for proper rigging. The lashing operations are illustrated in Fig. 3. After the shears have been erected, the legs can be prevented from spreading by the use of a single rope lashing attached to the legs just above the ground.

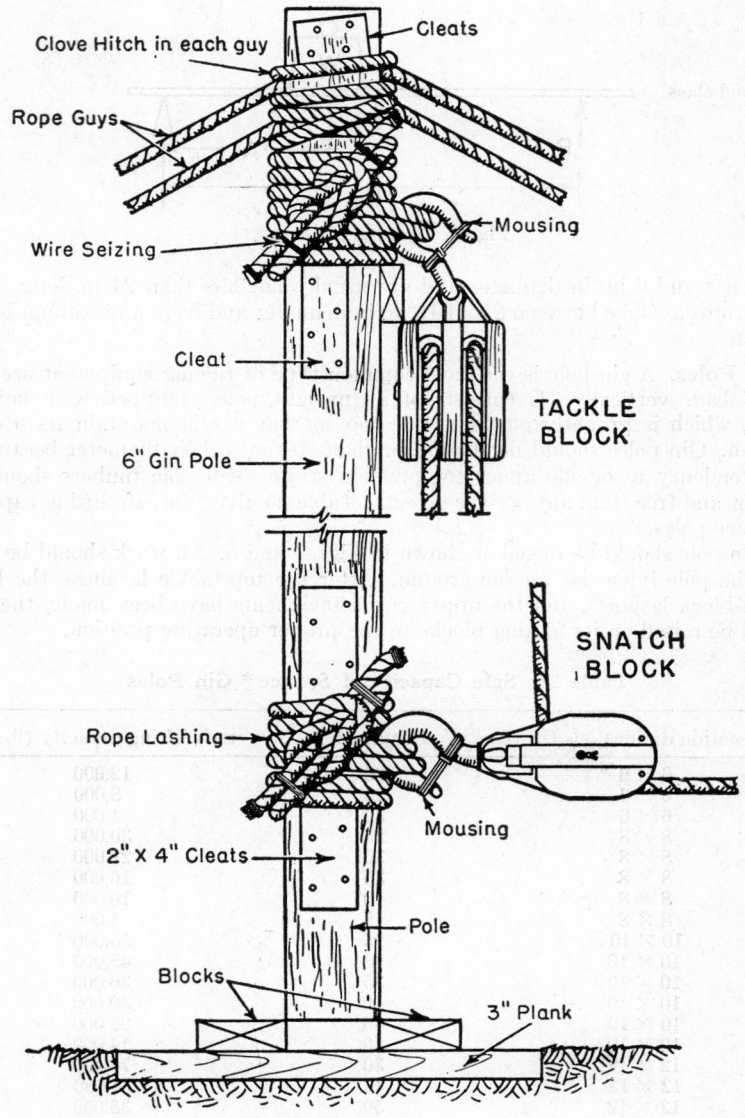

**Fig. 7. Gin pole.**

(U. S. Forest Service, *Improvement handbook*.)

**Derricks. Guy derricks.** A pole or guy derrick is essentially a gin pole constructed with a sill and having knee braces at the bottom. It is frequently equipped with a sheave inserted in the upper portion of the mast. The sill and braces give the derrick stability in two directions so that usually only one front guy and one rear guy are necessary, but additional guys may be used if required. A simple guy derrick is illustrated in Fig. 8.

**Stiff-leg derrick.** The stiff-leg derrick differs from the guy derrick in the method which is used to hold the mast in a vertical position. The method of

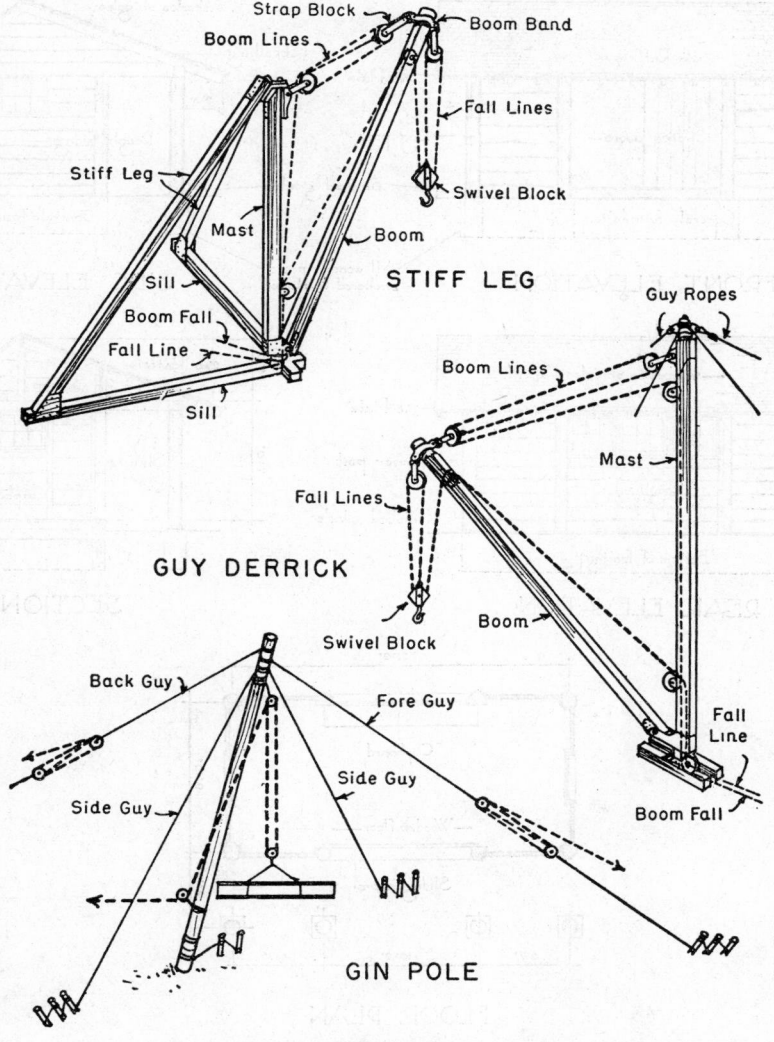

Fig. 8. Rigging equipment.
(U. S. Forest Service, *Improvement handbook*.)

rigging is the same for both types, as is shown by the illustration in Fig. 8. The stiff-leg derrick may be operated either by hand or by mechanical power. The sills should be weighted or anchored so that the derrick will not be overturned when too heavy a load is placed on the boom.

## Plans for Structures and Facilities

See Figs. 9 to 18.

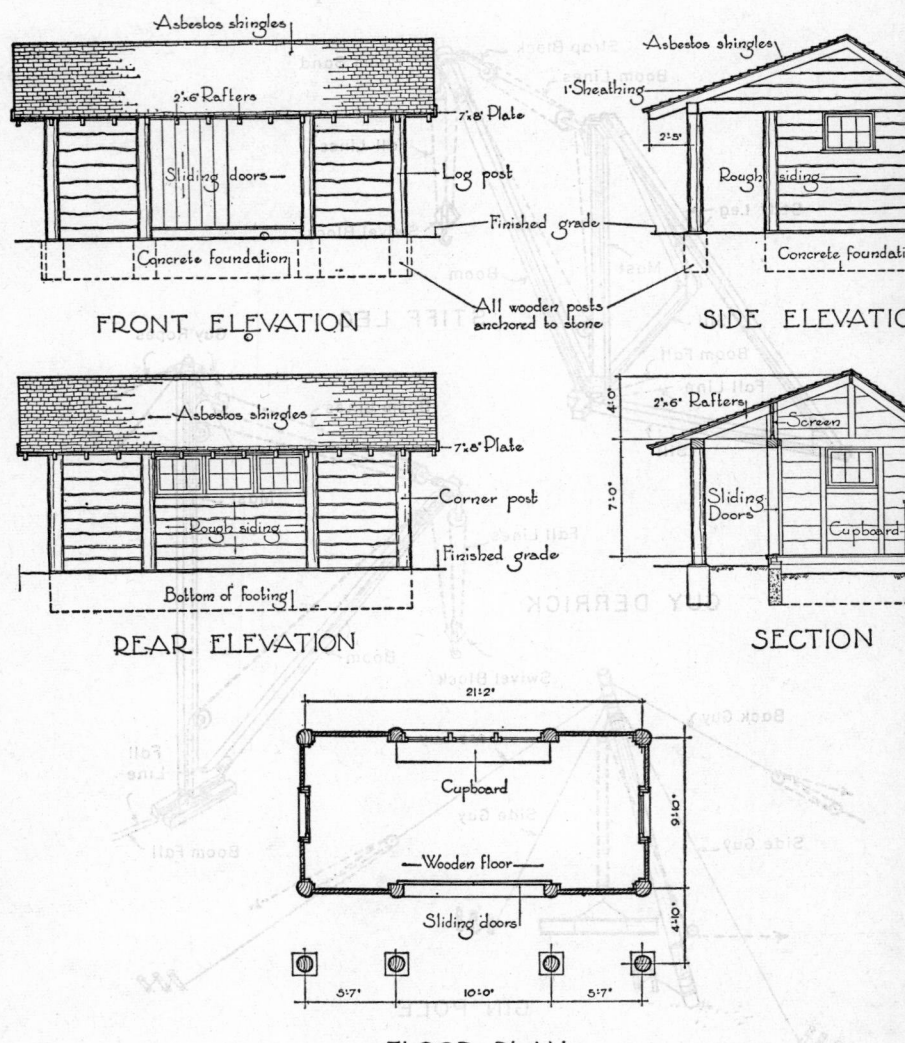

FRONT ELEVATION

SIDE ELEVATION

REAR ELEVATION

SECTION

FLOOR PLAN

**Fig. 9. One-room cabin constructed of logs and rough siding.**
Swinging rather than sliding doors may be used if preferred. (U. S. Park Service.)

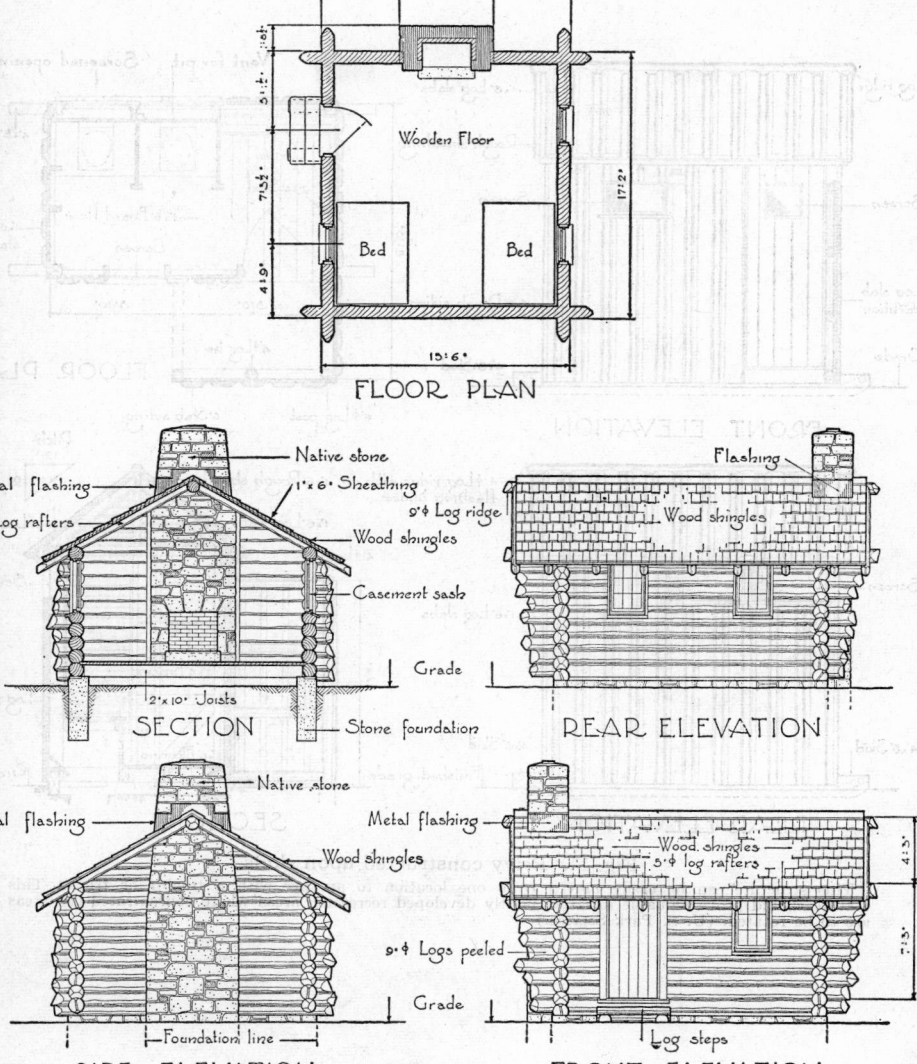

**Fig. 10. One-room cabin of log construction.**

Note the fitting cup on the bottom of each log. Cabins and other buildings may be economically stained a rich brown color by painting with well-thinned creosote. This treatment will also help prevent infestation by wood-boring insects and wood-rotting fungi. The bottom of footer logs and the cup fittings should receive a coating of creosote as the building is constructed. (U. S. Park Service.)

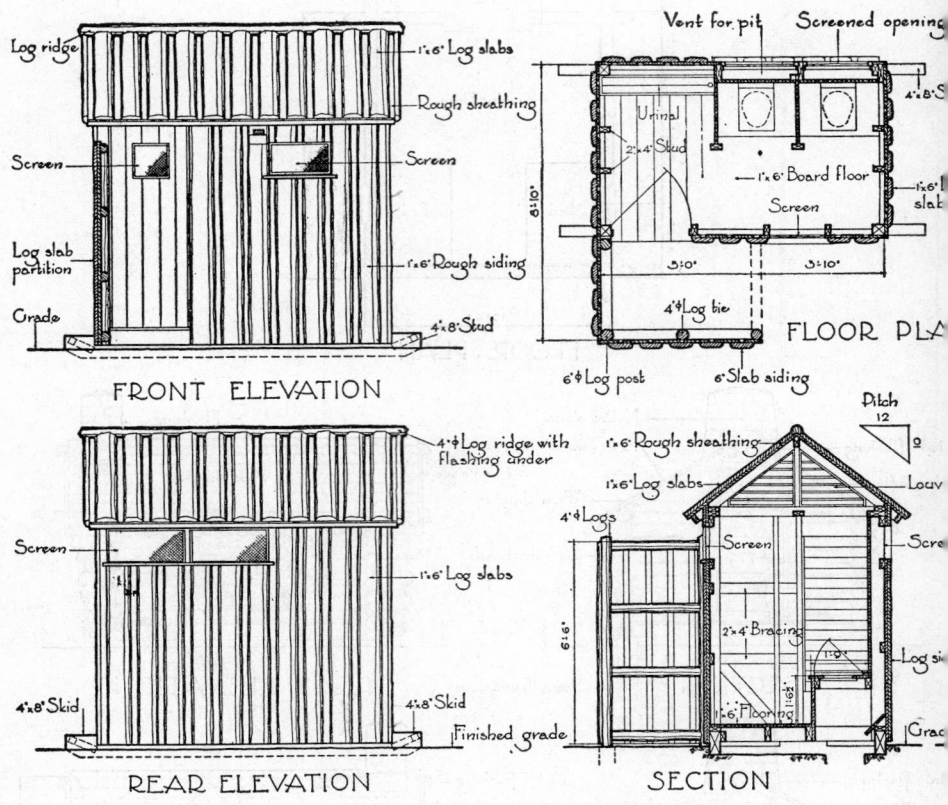

**Fig. 11. Privy constructed upon skids.**

This structure can be easily moved from one location to another with a tractor or truck. This feature should prove valuable in large, lightly developed recreation areas where concentrated use areas are to be rotated. (U. S. Park Service.)

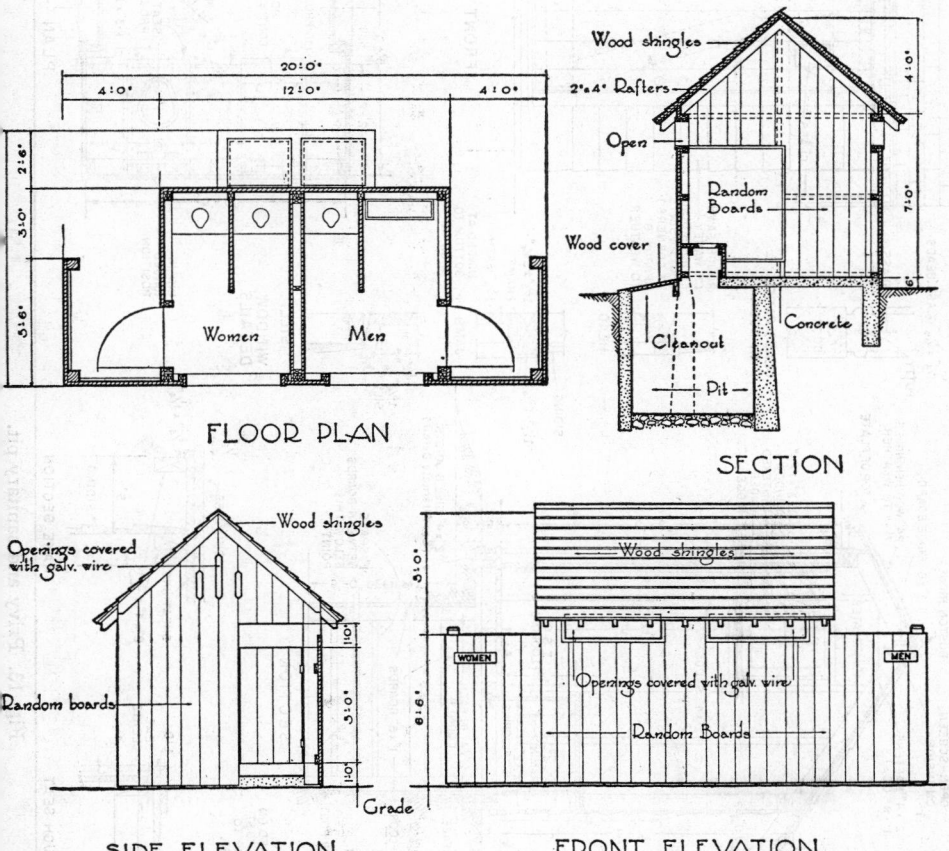

**Fig. 12. Privy built to accommodate both men and women.**

In porcupine country it is well to place salt blocks near comfort stations during the warm months to prevent porcupines from chewing the structure in search of salt. (U. S. Park Service.)

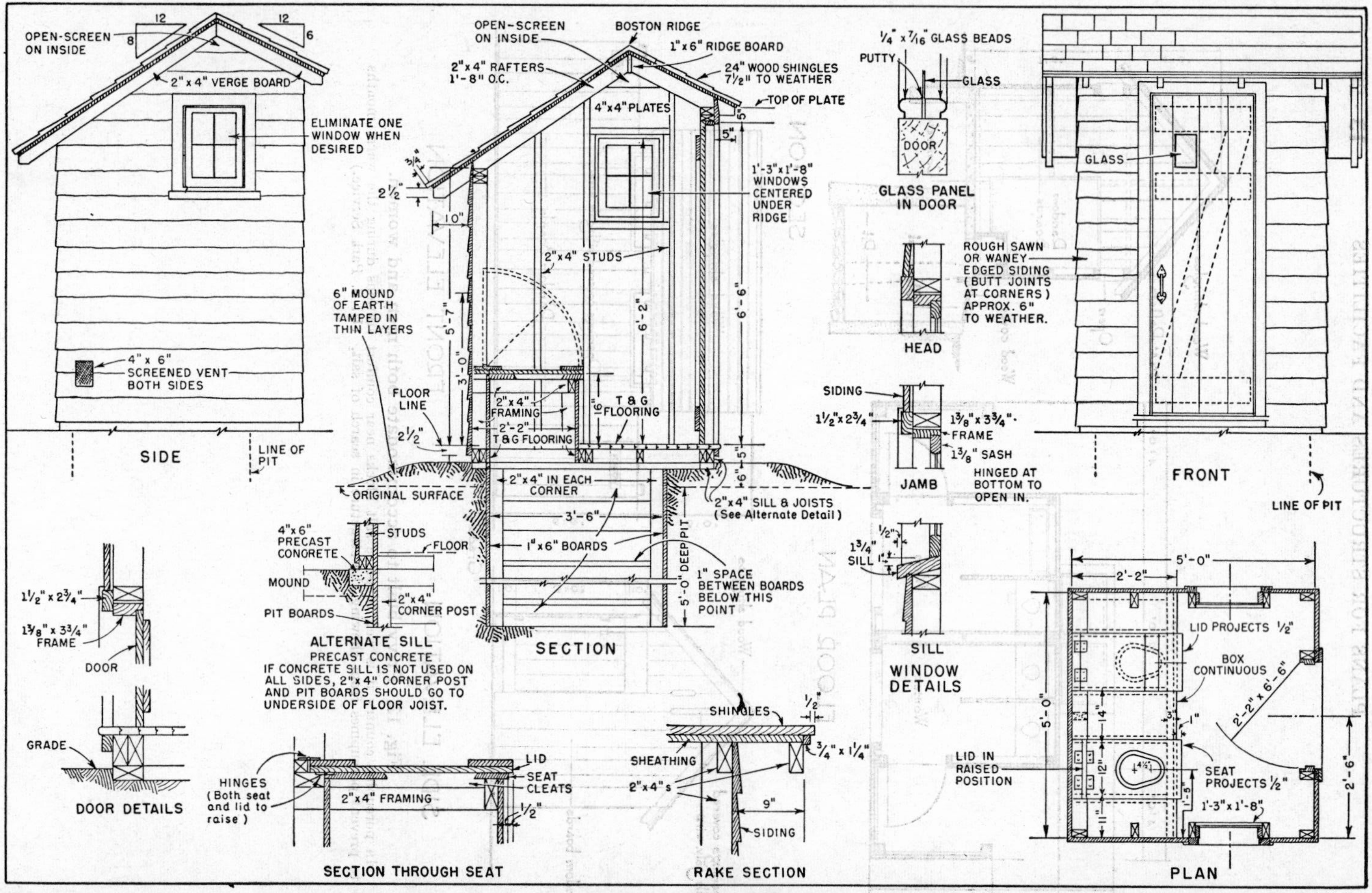

Fig. 13. Privy and sanitary pit.

## Bill of Materials and Specifications for Privy Shown in Fig. 13.

### LUMBER:

| No. of pieces or quantity | Dimensions or description | Purpose |
|---|---|---|
| 4 | 2 × 4— 6 [a] | Pit posts |
| 2 | 2 × 4—10 | Sill |
| 5 | 2 × 4—10 | Floor framing |
| 7 | 2 × 4— 6 | Seat framing |
| 12 | 2 × 4— 8 | Studs |
| 4 | 2 × 4— 6 | Studs |
| 2 | 2 × 4—10 | Plate |
| 9 | 2 × 4— 6 | Rafters |
| 1 | 1 × 6— 8 | Ridge board |
| 110 bd. ft. | 1 × 6 sheathing | Pit walls |
| 63 bd. ft. | 1 × 6 sheathing | Roof |
| 140 bd. ft. | 1 × 8 siding [b] | Siding |
| 49 sq. ft. | 24-in. shingles [c] | Roof |
| 65 bd. ft. | 1 × 4 T & G flooring | Floor, seat top and lining, and lid |
| 22 lin. ft. | 1 × 6 cleats | Door and seat lids |
| 40 lin. ft. | ¾ × 2 cant strip | Bottom siding and shingle courses |
| 18 lin. ft. | ¾ × 1¼ cover strip | At rake |
| 28 lin. ft. | 1⅜ × 3¾ frame (rabbeted) | Door and windows |
| 4 lin. ft. | 1¾ × 5¾ sill (rabbeted) | Windows |
| 33 lin. ft. | 1½ × 2¾ trim | Door and windows |
| 17 bd. ft. | 1 × 8 V'd board, T & G | Door |
| 2 casement windows | 1'3" × 1'8" × 1⅜" | 4-light, glazed |
| 2 full screens for windows | 16-mesh copper wire (also screen for gable vents) | |

[a] 2 in. by 4 in., 6 ft. long, etc.
[b] Waney edge (or rough sawn), laid 6 in. to weather. (If siding is used which is not beveled, increase thickness of door and window casings to 2½" or use double casings.)
[c] Random width, laid 7½ in. to weather.

### PAINT:

1 gal. of stain mixed as follows:
  10 parts boiled linseed oil.
  2 parts turpentine.
  1 part burnt umber in oil.

### HARDWARE:

1 Latch handle set (dead black finish).
1 ½ pair T-hinges, 4-in. Door.
1 spring, 10 in. long (coppered steel springs). Door.
6 pairs 3-in. × 3-in. butts (fast pin). Windows, seat, seat lids.
2 catches (rim type). Windows.
2 chains, 12 in. Windows.
8 lb. 4d zinc-coated shingle nails.

4 lb. 6d finishing nails.
4 lb. 8d finishing nails.
5 lb. 8d common nails.
5 lb. 20d common nails.
3 lb. 8d flooring nails.
2 coat hooks.
4 sets hooks and eyes, 2-in. Window screens.
1 toilet-paper holder.

### ALTERNATE FOR CONCRETE SILLS:

2 pieces 4" × 6"—5 ft.
2 pieces 4" × 6"—52 in.
Precast slabs of A 1:2¼:4 mix

## SPECIFICATIONS:

Pit mound. A mound shall be constructed around the top of the pit curbing and level with the curbing for a distance of not less than 18 in., thence outward to meet the surrounding ground surface with a slope not greater than 1 in 3, by tamping the excavated earth in thin layers.

Lumber. Shall conform to Federal Spec. #MM–L–751. All lumber to be S4S and of the following grades:

Framing. No. 1 Dimension—Douglas-fir, western larch, southern yellow pine.

Sheathing and cleats. No. 2, same species.

Siding (beveled, waney edge, or rough sawn). No. 1 common coast type red cypress, hemlock, pine, or chestnut.

Exterior finish. "C" finish. Edge-grain Douglas-fir, western redcedar, white pine.

Door and window frames, and door. No. 1 edge-grain Douglas-fir, western redcedar, white pine.

Sash (standard sash grade). Clear stock white pine, ponderosa pine, edge-grain Douglas-fir, southern yellow pine.

Flooring. No. 1 Common, flat-grain southern yellow pine, Douglas-fir, larch, oak.

Shingles. No. 1 24-in. edge-grain redcedar, coast-type red cypress.

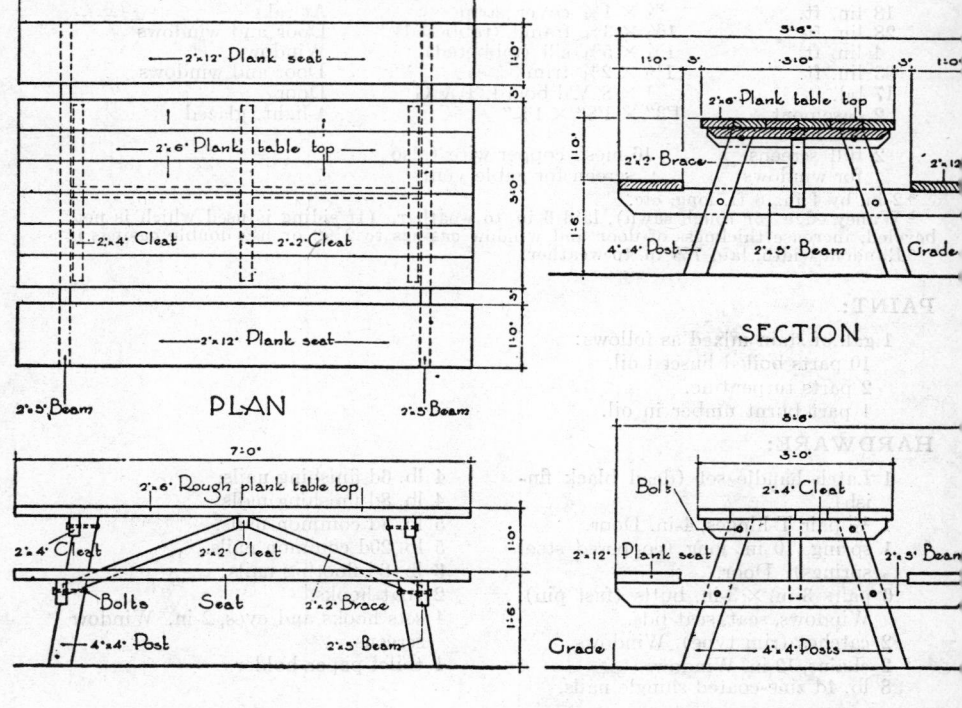

**Fig. 14. Picnic unit with plank table top and seats.**

This table has the advantage of being very simple to construct and is adaptable to areas where it is desirable or permissible to move the picnic units occasionally. (U. S. Park Service.)

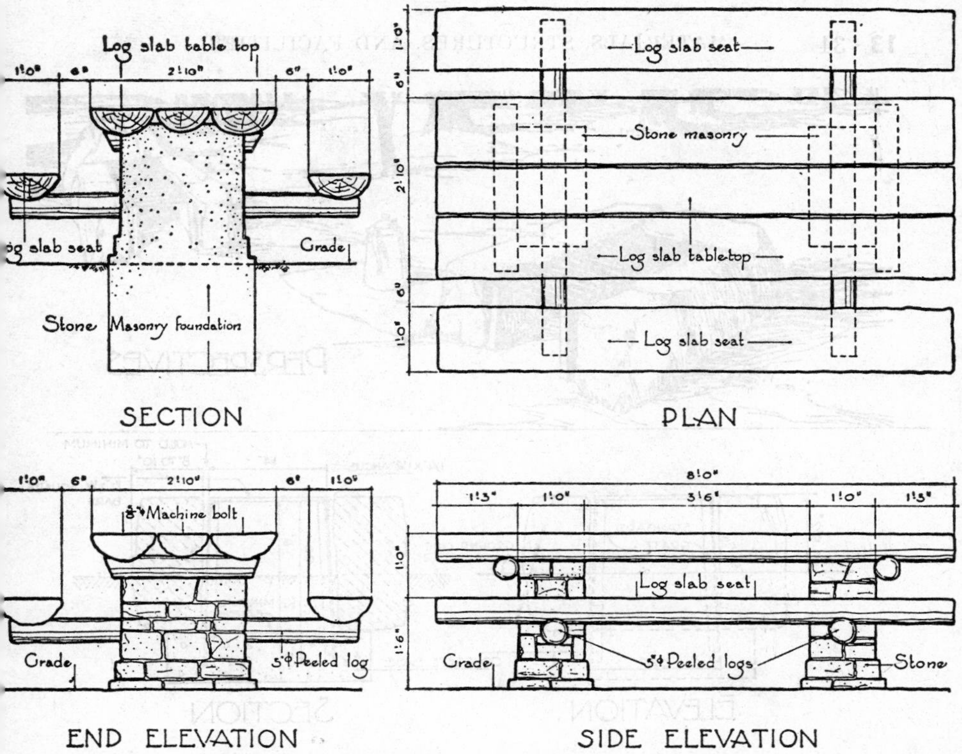

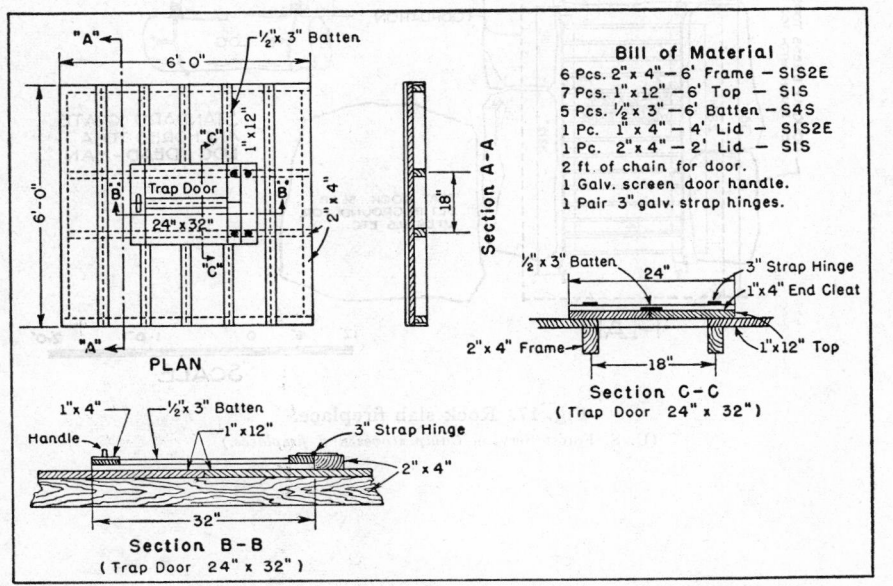

**SECTION**

**PLAN**

**END ELEVATION**

**SIDE ELEVATION**

**Fig. 15. Picnic table of masonry and split logs.**

This table will remain where it is intended to be. This plan should be modified to allow the seat support logs to pass through holes in the masonry large enough to permit replacement. The support log may be held stationary with large bolts passing through the masonry and the log. (U. S. Park Service.)

**Bill of Material**

6 Pcs. 2"x 4" — 6' Frame — S1S2E
7 Pcs. 1"x12" — 6' Top — S1S
5 Pcs. ½"x 3" — 6' Batten — S4S
1 Pc. 1"x 4" — 4' Lid — S1S2E
1 Pc. 2"x 4" — 2' Lid — S1S
2 ft. of chain for door.
1 Galv. screen door handle.
1 Pair 3" galv. strap hinges.

**PLAN**

**Section A-A**

**Section C-C**
( Trap Door 24" x 32" )

**Section B-B**
( Trap Door 24" x 32" )

**Fig. 16. Garbage pit cover and bill of material.**
(U. S. Forest Service, *Handbook of administration.*)

**13 · 33**

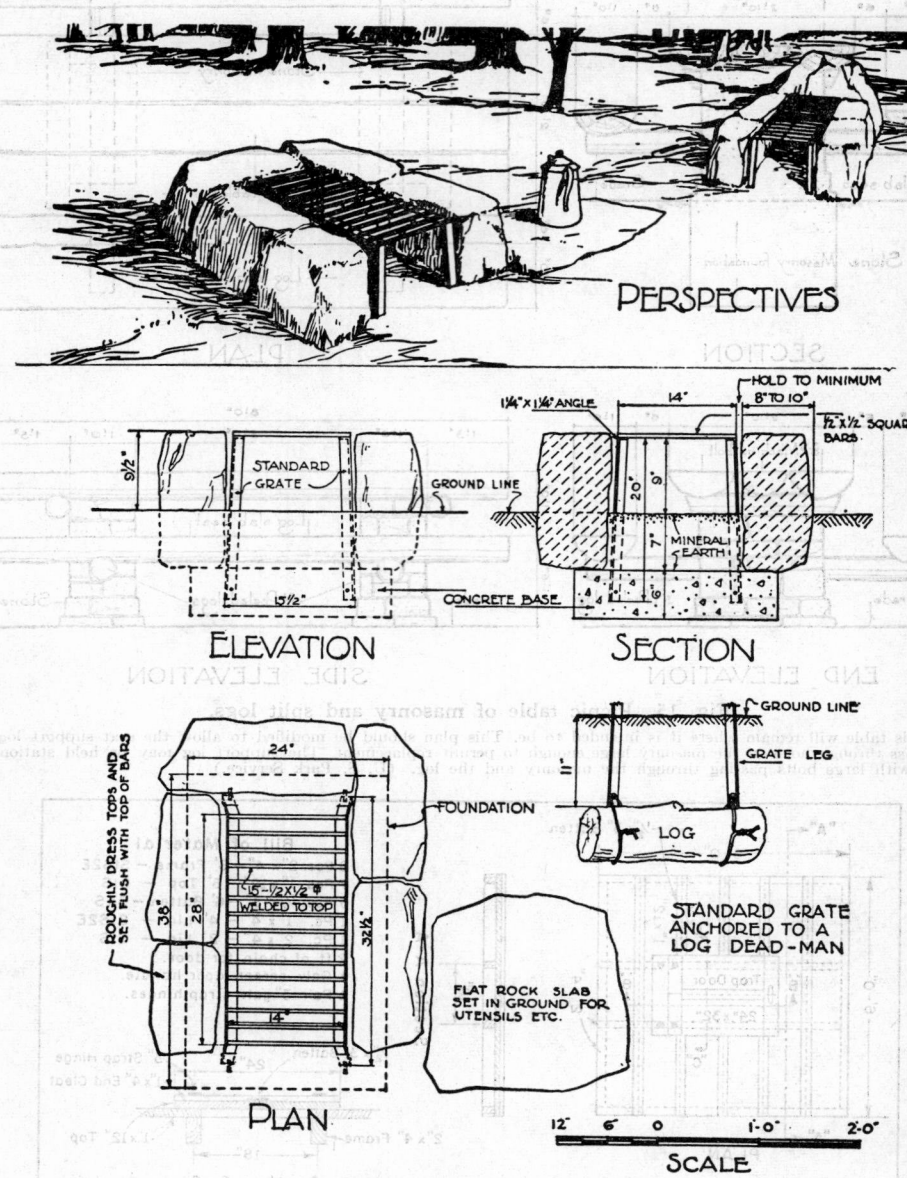

**PERSPECTIVES**

**ELEVATION**

**SECTION**

**PLAN**

**SCALE**

**Fig. 17. Rock slab fireplace.**

(U. S. Forest Service, *Camp stoves and fireplaces.*)

FIREPLACE CUT IN ROCK LEDGE

ARTIFICIAL LEDGE EFFECT

OPEN END SINGLE STONE TYPE

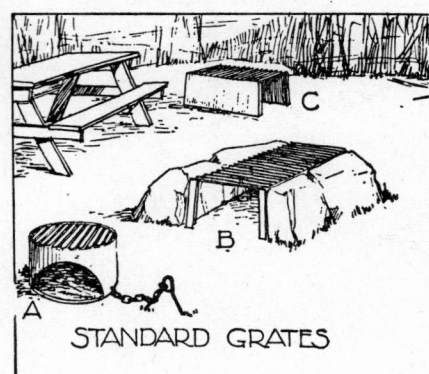

STANDARD GRATES

Fig. 18. Types of fireplaces.
(U. S. Forest Service, *Camp stoves and fireplaces*.)

## BIBLIOGRAPHY

*Practical builder*. 1949. Data and Specifications Issue: May. Chicago.
SECHRIST, W. D. 1939. *Foresters field manual*. The Craft Press, Inc., Fayetteville, **Pa.**
U. S. DEPT. AGR. 1945. Building with logs. *Misc. Publ. No. 579*.
U. S. FOREST SERV. 1937. *Camp stoves and fireplaces*.
U. S. FOREST SERV. 1937. *Improvement handbook*.
U. S. FOREST SERV., Region 7. 1938. *Handbook of administration: recreation plans, policy, procedure*. Philadelphia, Pa.
U. S. PARK SERV. 1935. *Park structures and facilities*.
U. S. PARK SERV. 1938. *Park and recreation structures*.

ARTIFICIAL LEDGE EFFECT

FIREPLACE CUT IN ROCK LEDGE

STANDARD CRATES

OPEN END SINGLE STONE TYPE

Fig. 16. Types of fireplaces.

## BIBLIOGRAPHY

Portland Cement Co., 1929. Data and Specifications Leaflet. May. Chicago.

Saunders, W. H., 1929. Adventures in Architecture. The Good Press, Inc., Somerville, Pa.

U. S. Dept. Agr., 1918. Building with logs. *Misc. Pub. No. 579.*

U. S. Forest Serv., 1937. Camp stoves and fireplaces.

U. S. Forest Serv., 1935. Improvement handbook.

U. S. Forest Serv., Region 7, 1938. Monogram of administrative recreation plans, regions, area survice, Philadelphia, Pa.

U. S. Park Serv., 1934. Park structures and facilities.

U. S. Park Serv., 1938. Park and recreation structures.

# UTILIZATION AND WOOD TECHNOLOGY

## CONTENTS

## CONTENTS (*Continued*)

# UTILIZATION AND WOOD TECHNOLOGY

## Lumber Manufacture

**HEAD SAWS AND AUXILIARY EQUIPMENT.** Logs are converted into lumber by three distinct types of head saws—circular, gang, and band. These same types may be used in resawing. Variations occur in all types, particularly in circular head saws.

Primary objectives in lumber manufacture may be (1) maximum production, (2) minimum cost of machines and labor, (3) maximum recovery of lumber from the logs, (4) accurate lumber dimensions, or (5) highest lumber grade and value. Not all of these objectives are by any means equally attainable with any one type of sawmill.

Circular head saws are low in initial cost and upkeep. They are adapted to sawing small to medium logs into lumber of the highest grades and any required thickness, but with maximum waste in sawdust and only medium uniformity of dimensions, and are often used to edge or resaw. Top saws are recommended for logs over 36 in.

Variations include (1) the log splitter, with the essential resaw equipment; (2) twin-circular head saws for slabbing cants or making crossties; (3) short log or bolter sawmills with a carriage travel of 4 to 8 ft.; and (4) highly portable wheel-mounted mills capable of moving from woodland to woodland with only 2 or 3 hours of sawing time lost between settings. The twin-circular, short log saw or bolter, and usually the log splitter, use very small logs of poorer quality than can justifiably be handled at regular sawmills; such logs could be even more economically sawed on gang mills.

Gang head saws require medium initial cost and upkeep. Sash-gang saws are adapted to the rapid sawing of small, knotty, and low-grade logs into lumber of uniform thickness with a minimum of sawdust. They are not adapted to sawing for grade, or variety of thicknesses. They require considerable power, and must be accompanied by edger or resaws. Sorting of logs by size increases output. Circular-gang head saws are also available but the wide kerf is wasteful.

Band head saws are adapted to sawing logs of all sizes into products of uniform dimensions, with small waste in sawdust, highest grade, and any required thickness. They are generally accompanied by edger or resaws. Portable band mills are also available.

**LABOR REQUIREMENTS FOR SMALL SAWMILLS.** The number of man-hours required per M bd. ft. of lumber production, in general, increases with mill capacity for any species. Table 2, based on Forest Products Laboratory mill studies, shows a lower number of man-hours per M bd. ft. in the West due to larger log sizes and greater mill power.

## Table 1. A Tabular Summary of Head Saw Ratings

| | Type of head saw | | | | | |
| | Gang | | | Circular | | |
| Requirements and conditions | Sash gang | Circular gang | Band[a] | Wheel-mounted | Semiportable or stationary | Short log mills |
|---|---|---|---|---|---|---|
| Yield from logs: | | | | | | |
| Volume | High | Low-med. | Med. to high | Low | Low | Med. to high |
| Grade | Low-med. | Low-med. | High | High | High | High |
| Thickness uniformity | High | High | Med.-high | Low [b] | Low [b] | Low-med. |
| Kerf width (in.) | 7/64-3/16 | 5/32-1/4 | 3/32-7/32 | 3/16-5/16 | 3/16-3/8 | 5/32-1/4 |
| Production rate per hr. bd. ft. [c] | 6-10 M | High | 2-8 M | 1/2-1 M | 1/2-4 M | 3/8-1 M |
| Horsepower requirements | 80-400 | 80-400 | 50-400 | 35-100 | 60-400 | 30-100 |
| Machine cost | Med. | Med. | High | Low | Low-med. | Low |
| Maintenance cost | Low | Low | High | Low | Low-med. | Low |
| Initial investment | Med. | Med. | High | Low | Low-med. | Low |
| Labor cost per M bd. ft. | Low | Low | High | Low | High | Low-med. |
| Flexibility: | | | | | | |
| Thickness | Low | Low | High | High | High | High |
| Log size | Med. | Med. | High | Med. | Med. | Low |
| Timber requirements per set. | 5-15 yr. | 5-15 yr. | 15-50 yr. | 5 M bd. ft. min. | 40 M bd. ft. min. | 10 M bd. ft. min. |

[a] Data listed are for stationary band head saw. Operation and investment costs for portable band mills are similar to stationary circular mills. Yield and uniformity of lumber rank very high.

[b] Ratings are averages; individual mills may rate high to medium.

[c] Production rates per hour vary also with the size of head saw, amount of resawing, and species of timber sawed. For example, a large circular headrig with top saw and resaws could even exceed the upper production rate of 4 M bd. ft. per hr.

Source: U. S. Dept. Agr., Small sawmill operator's manual, *Handbook No. 27*; N. C. Brown, *Lumber*, and several miscellaneous sources.

## Table 2. Mill Labor Required to Produce M Bd. Ft. of Lumber

| Species | Labor per M bd. ft. | | Number of mill employees * |
| --- | --- | --- | --- |
| | Range (man-hours) | Average (man-hours) | |
| Ponderosa pine, redwood, Douglas-fir.. | 2.4 to 5.2 | 3.9 | 6 to 26 |
| Eastern white pine .................. | 3.5 to 5.5 | 4.5 | 2 to 8 |
| Eastern hardwoods .................. | 3.3 to 11.7 | 6.8 | 4 to 10 |
| Southern pine ....................... | 5.2 to 10.3 | 7.5 | 6 to 10 |

\* Includes pond men and stackers.
Source: U. S. Dept. Agr., Small sawmill operator's manual, *Handbook No. 27.*

**POWER REQUIREMENTS.** Power requirements on the head saw are affected by (1) width of saw kerf, (2) width of cutting face or width of board being sawed, (3) thickness of chip or feed rate, and (4) wood density or species. Saws such as band saws with narrow kerf require less power than inserted-tooth circular saws. Even when he has ample power, an inefficient sawyer can, by fast feed in a high density log with a wide cutting face, build up power loads beyond the capacity of the saw to cut accurately. Power requirements for auxiliary mill equipment, when driven from the main power unit, frequently are the prime cause for insufficient head-saw power.

## Table 3. Power Requirements for Equipment Other Than the Head Saw of a Small Mill

| Equipment item | Type | Horsepower required |
| --- | --- | --- |
| Log haul ................... | Car and inclined trackway, friction drive | 6 |
| | Gear drive | 15 |
| | Chain lift from sluice opposite deck | 10 |
| Log conveyor chains on deck.. | | 5 |
| Log turners ................. | Double-bar friction kickers | 3 |
| | Overhead shaft and chain, friction drive | 6 |
| | Single-bar type, friction drive | 6 |
| | Rocker-arm shaft type | 15 |
| Carriage drive .............. | Heavy type | 10 |
| | Light- or medium-weight type | 5 |
| Carriage setworks ........... | | 3 |
| Carriage dogs .............. | | 1 |
| Carriage log unloader ........ | | 5 |
| Sawdust chain .............. | | 1 |
| Sawdust blower ............. | | 5 |
| Refuse chain ................. | Heavy type | 20 |
| Live rolls ................. | | 5 |
| Transfer and conveyor chains.. | | 15 |
| Sorter chains ............... | | 5 |
| Edger ..................... | Single-saw, manual type | 5 |
| | 2- to 3-saw, 27-in. | 15 |
| | 2- to 3-saw, 33-in. | 20 |
| | 4-saw, heavy-duty | 100 |
| Two-saw trimmer ............ | | 15 |
| Cut-off saw ................. | | 8 |
| Slab cut-off saw ............. | | 5 |

Source: U. S. Dept. Agr., Small sawmill operator's manual, *Handbook No. 27.*

### Table 4. Power Requirements of Large Sawmills

| Machine | Minimum horsepower | Maximum horsepower |
|---|---|---|
| Jackladder | 15.0 | 125 |
| Cut-off saws on deck | 25.0 | 100 |
| Log kicker | 15.0 | 50 |
| Steam nigger | 15.0 | 50 |
| Carriage, steam feed | 25.0 | 100 |
| Head saws, band | 50.0 | 300 |
| Head saws, circular | 60.0 | 400 |
| Live rolls, each | 0.3 | 1 |
| Edger | 25.0 | 300 |
| Trimmer | 25.0 | 75 |
| Slasher | 25.0 | 75 |
| Band resaw, vertical | 75.0 | 200 |
| Band resaw, horizontal | 75.0 | 200 |
| Gang resaw | 50.0 | 400 |
| Hog | 25.0 | 200 |
| Conveyors and transfer chains | 3.0 | 30 |

Source: N. C. Brown, *Lumber*, John Wiley & Sons, New York, 1947.

### Table 5. Circular Head Saws

| Horsepower and source | Saw diameter 2-in. classes | Gauge | Number of teeth | Style of tooth |
|---|---|---|---|---|
| 17–32—gas | 40–48 | 9–10 | 32–40 | B or 3 |
| 32–42—gas | 44–48 | 9–10<br>8– 9 | 30–40 | B or 3 |
| 20—electric<br>15–20—steam | 46–50 | 8– 9<br>7– 8 | 36–44 | B or 3 |
| 50—diesel or gas<br>30—electric<br>20–25—steam | 48–50 | 8– 9<br>7– 8 | 40–48 | B or F |
| 60–70—diesel or gas<br>40—electric<br>25–30—steam | 48–52 | 8– 9<br>7– 8 | 46–50 | F |
| 80—diesel or gas<br>50—electric<br>35–40—steam | 48–54 | 7– 8 | 46–60 | F or 2½ |
| 100 or over—diesel<br>60 or over—electric<br>40 or over—steam | 50–60 | 7– 8 | 48–66 | F or 2½ |

As power is increased, saws may carry more teeth, more speed, and more feed. Saws operated in frozen timber should always be 7–8 gauge. Saws cutting small knotty logs should carry more teeth than average.

Source: Simonds Saw and Steel Co., Simonds manual of wood cutting tools.

## Table 6. Saw Gauge Equivalents

| Gauge (Birmingham) | Fraction (in.) | Thousandths (in.) | Millimeters |
|---|---|---|---|
| | 1 | 1.000 | 25.40 |
| | ⅞ | 0.875 | 22.225 |
| | ¾ | .750 | 19.05 |
| | ⅝ | .625 | 15.875 |
| | ½ | .500 | 12.70 |
| | 15/32 | .468 | 11.905 |
| 0000 | 29/64 | .454 | 11.53 |
| 000 | 27/64 full | .425 | 10.79 |
| 00 | ⅜ full | .380 | 9.65 |
| 0 | 11/32 scant | .340 | 8.64 |
| 1 | 5/16 scant | .300 | 7.62 |
| 2 | 9/32 | .284 | 7.21 |
| 3 | ¼ full | .259 | 6.57 |
| 4 | 15/64 | .238 | 6.04 |
| 5 | 7/32 | .220 | 5.59 |
| 6 | 13/64 | .203 | 5.18 |
| 7 | 3/16 scant | .180 | 4.57 |
| 8 | 5/32 full | .165 | 4.19 |
| 9 | 5/32 scant | .148 | 3.76 |
| 10 | ⅛ full | .134 | 3.40 |
| 11 | ⅛ scant | .120 | 3.05 |
| 12 | 7/64 | .109 | 2.77 |
| 13 | 3/32 | .095 | 2.41 |
| 14 | 5/64 full | .083 | 2.10 |
| 15 | 5/64 scant | .072 | 1.82 |
| 16 | 1/16 full | .065 | 1.65 |
| 17 | 1/16 scant | .058 | 1.47 |
| 18 | 3/64 | .049 | 1.24 |
| 19 | ... | .042 | 1.06 |
| 20 | ... | .035 | 0.89 |
| 21 | 1/32 | .032 | .81 |
| 22 | ... | .028 | .71 |
| 23 | ... | .025 | .64 |
| 24 | ... | .022 | .56 |
| 25 | ... | .020 | .51 |
| 26 | ... | .018 | .46 |
| 27 | 1/64 | .016 | .41 |
| 28 | ... | .014 | .36 |
| 29 | ... | .013 | .33 |
| 30 | ... | .012 | .30 |

Source: R. Hoe & Co., Inc., *Useful facts—sawmills and saws.*

**SAWING METHODS.** Due to cheapness of manufacture, most lumber is plain-sawed (flat-grain), i.e., sawed so that the growth rings form an angle of less than 45° with the widest surface of the piece. A considerable amount, however, is quarter-sawed (edge-grain), i.e., sawed so that the growth rings form an angle of 45° to 90°. The advantages of quarter-sawed lumber as compared to flat-sawed are (1) less shrinking or swelling across the width, (2) less tendency to warp or splinter, (3) specialized grain or figure effects, (4) greater resistance (usually) to abrasion and wear, and (5) a tendency to take a finish more uniformly. The principal disadvantages of quarter-sawed lumber are the higher manufacturing cost due to frequent log turning, and added waste in sawing.

General rules for sawing quality lumber include:

1. Preferably, saw no thicker than 1-in. until the cant is square or rectangular. Gradual opening up of log will disclose defects such as knots, checks, shakes, and pitch streaks. The best lumber is generally found immediately inside the bark; therefore, cut slabs thin and make following cuts ¼ (1 in.), or those thicknesses, such as cants, which may bring the most favorable prices.
2. Do not cut any log "alive" (without turning) if there is any opportunity for clear lumber.
3. Make two cuts when slabbing.
4. Make cants as large as possible, and always follow the grade around the log. In Douglas-fir, thin cants are frequently taken from the outside to produce vertical-grain lumber. These cants are generally 4 to 6 in. thick.
5. Do not leave any steam-nigger or dog marks on the lumber if possible.
6. Place crooked logs with the "belly" into the saw or away from it, never with the "belly" up or down. Saw crooked logs into 1-in. lumber rather than 2-in. and thicker lumber.
7. Saw a log with a large check parallel to the crack. It is obvious that if boards are sawed across the check, narrower boards will be produced or the defect will appear in many of them.
8. Use the taper lever on logs that taper rapidly. By this method, the loss that comes from sawing a tapered log is taken from that part of the log where financial loss is least, namely, the center of the log.

**STANDARD LUMBER ABBREVIATIONS.** The following standard lumber abbreviations are customarily used in contracts and other documents related to purchase and sale of lumber.

| | |
|---|---|
| AD | Air dried. |
| ADF | After deducting freight. |
| ALS | American lumber standard. |
| AST | Antistain treated. |
| B1S | Beaded one side. |
| B2S | Beaded two sides. |
| BBS | Box bark strips. |
| bd. ft. or b.f. | Board foot; that is, an area of 1 sq. ft., 1 in. thick. |
| bdl. | Bundled. |
| B/L | Bill of lading. |
| b.m. | Board (foot) measure. |
| Btr. | Better. |
| c.i.f. | (Named port.) Cost, insurance, and freight to a named port. |
| c.i.f.e. | (Named port.) Cost, insurance, freight, and exchange to a named port. This is the same as c.i.f., with the additional provision that the seller guarantees the buyer against loss due to a decline in the rate of exchange. |
| Clg. | Ceiling. |
| Clr. | Clear. |
| CM | Center matched; that is, the tongue and groove joints are worked along the center of the edges of the piece. |
| Com. | Common. |
| D&CM | Dressed (one or two sides) and center matched. |
| D&M | Dressed and matched; that is, dressed, one or two sides, and tongued and grooved on the edges. The match may be center or standard. |
| D&SM | Dressed (one or two sides) and standard matched. |
| D2S&CM | Dressed two sides and center matched. |
| D2S&SM | Dressed two sides and standard matched. |

| | |
|---|---|
| DET | Double-end-trimmed. |
| Dim. | Dimension. |
| DS | Drop siding. |
| E | Edge. |
| E&CB1S | Edge and center bead one side; surfaced one or two sides and with a longitudinal edge and center bead on a surfaced face. |
| E&CB2S | Edge and center bead two sides. |
| ECM | Ends center matched. |
| E&CV1S | Edge and center V one side. |
| E&CV2S | Edge and center V two sides. |
| EG | Edge grain (also rift or comb grain). |
| EM | End matched—either center or standard. |
| FAS | Firsts and seconds (combined in one grade). |
| F.a.s. vessel | (Named port.) Free alongside vessel at a named port. |
| FG | Flat grain (also plain or bastard sawed). |
| Flg. | Flooring. |
| f.o.b. | Free on board at a named shipping point. |
| f.o.k. | Free of knots. |
| f.o.w. | First open water. |
| GM | Grade marked. |
| H&M | Hit and miss. |
| H.bk. | Hollow back. |
| HorM | Hit or miss. |
| Hrt. | Heart. |
| Hrtwd. | Heartwood. |
| KD | Kiln-dried. |
| l.c.l. | Less than carload lots. |
| lin.ft. | Linear foot; that is, 12 in. |
| LR | Log run. |
| LR, MCO | Log run, mill culls out. |
| M | Thousand. |
| M.b.m. | Thousand (feet) board measure. |
| MCO | Mill culls out. |
| MR | Mill run. |
| m.w. | Mixed widths. |
| P | Planed. |
| Pat. | Pattern. |
| Pky. | Pecky. |
| Qtd. | Quartered (or quarter-sawed)—when referring to hardwoods. |
| RES | Resawed. |
| Rfrs. | Roofers. |
| Rgh. | Rough. |
| r.l. | Random lengths. |
| r.w. | Random widths. |
| S1E | Surfaced one edge. |
| S2E | Surfaced two edges. |
| S1S | Surfaced one side. |
| S2S | Surfaced two sides. |
| S1S1E | Surfaced one side and one edge. |
| S4S | Surface 4 sides. |
| S4SCS | Surfaced four sides with a calking seam on each edge. |
| S&CM | Surfaced one or two sides and center matched. |
| Sdg. | Siding. |
| S&E | Surfaced one side and one edge. |
| SE | Square edge. |
| Sel. | Select. |
| S/Lap | Shiplap. |
| S&M | Surfaced and matched. |

| | |
|---|---|
| s.n.d. | Sap no defect. |
| Sq.E.&S. | Square edge and sound. |
| SSND | Sap stain no defect. |
| Std. | Standard. |
| STR | Structural. |
| SW | Sound wormy. |
| Symbols | $"$ = inch or inches, as 12$"$. |
| | $'$ = foot or feet, as 12$'$. |
| | $\times$ = by, as 6$"$ $\times$ 8$"$ timber. |
| | ⁴⁄₄, ⁵⁄₄, ⁶⁄₄, ⁸⁄₄, etc. = 1 in., 1¼ in., 1½ in., 2 in., etc., when referring to the thickness of lumber. |
| T&G | Tongued and grooved. |
| V1S | V one side; that is, a longitudinal V-shaped groove on one face of a piece of lumber as in ceiling. |
| VG | Vertical grain; same as EG |
| WHAD | Worm holes a defect. |
| WHND | Worm holes no defect. |
| 1s&2s | Ones and twos combined in one grade—same as FAS. |

## Lumber Specifications and Grades

Lumber is classified into (1) yard lumber, (2) shop or factory grades, and (3) structural grades.

**HARDWOOD LUMBER GRADING.** The rules considered standard in grading hardwood lumber in the United States and Canada are those adopted by the National Hardwood Lumber Association, Chicago, Ill. Hardwood grades, broadly classified as factory or shop grades, are generally based upon the percentage, number, and size of cuttings that can be obtained from the usable portions of the board. Grades are determined from the poorer side—the face with the lowest grade—unless otherwise specified. The grading rules define the minimum or poorest piece of lumber in any given grade, but the grade contains all pieces up to the next higher grade.

The standard grades for hardwood lumber are shown in Table 7. First and Seconds are usually combined as one grade, FAS. Sound Wormy shall grade not below No. 1 Common except that wormholes, bird pecks, stain, sound knots not exceeding ¾ in. in diameter, and other sound defects not exceeding these are admitted in the cuttings.

Hardwood dimension lumber, i.e., lumber processed to a point where maximum waste is left at the dimension mill, has (1) clear two faces, (2) clear one face, (3) paint, (4) core, and (5) sound grades. Grading follows Department of Commerce Commercial Standard CS 60–48 (2d ed.), as approved January 1, 1951.

**Example** of how a board is graded: A board 12 in. wide and 16 ft. long contains the following clear-face cuttings measured in units according to width in inches and length in feet, as follows:

$$
\begin{array}{rl}
5¼" \times 8' & = 42 \text{ units} \\
6¼" \times 3½' & = 21¾ \text{ units} \\
3¼" \times 3' & = 9¾ \text{ units} \\
7" \times 3' & = 21 \text{ units} \\
12" \times 3' & = \underline{36 \text{ units}} \\
\text{Total} & \overline{130½ \text{ units}}
\end{array}
$$

**Table 7. Chart of Cutting Requirements for Standard Grades of Hardwoods** (for exceptions and other requirements, see the National Hardwood Lumber Assn.'s rules book)

| | FIRSTS | SECONDS | SELECTS | NO. 1 COMMON | NO. 2 COMMON |
|---|---|---|---|---|---|
| Widths | 6" and wider | 6" and wider | 4" and wider | 3" and wider | 3" and wider |
| Lengths | 8 to 16 feet | 8 to 16 feet | 6 to 16 feet | 4 to 16 feet | 4 to 16 feet |
| *S.M. % Cl.Face Cuts | 4 to 9' 91-2/3 — 1; 10 to 14' " — 2; 15' & up " — 3 | 4' & 5' 83-1/3 — 1; 6' & 7' " — 2; 8' to 11' " — 3; 12' to 15' " — 4; 16' & up " — ... | 2' & 3' 91-2/3 — 1 | 1' Clear; 2' 75; 3' & 4' 66-2/3 — 1; 5' to 7' " — 2; 8' to 10' " — 3; 11' to 13' " — 4; 14' & up " — 5 | 1' 66-2/3 — 1; 2' & 3' 50 — 1; 4' & 5' — 2; 6' & 7' — 3; 8' & 9' — 4; 10' & 11' — 5; 12' & 13' — 6; 14' & up — 7 |
| | | 6' to 15' S.M. will admit 1 additional cut to yield 91-2/3% Cl. Face. ** | Reverse side cutting sound. 4' and over shall grade on one face as required in Seconds with reverse side of board not below No. 1 Common or reverse side of cuttings sound. See Rule (Par. 69) defining edges of boards 4" and 5" wide. | 3' to 7' S.M. will admit 1 additional cut to yield 75% Cl. Face. | 2' to 7' S.M. will admit 1 additional cut to yield 66-2/3% Cl. Face. |
| Minimum cutting | 4" x 5' or 3" x 7' | 4" x 5' or 3" x 7' | | 4" x 2' or 3" x 3' | 3" x 2' |

*Surface measure.

**Admits also, pieces 6" to 7" wide of 6' to 10' surface measure and pieces 8" to 9" wide of 8' to 12' surface measure that will yield 97% in two clear-face cuttings of any length, full width of the board.

Source: National Hardwood Lumber Association, *Rules for the measurement and inspection of hardwood lumber,* 1952.

The surface footage of the board is 16.

To obtain a grade of FAS, the total of clear-face cuttings would have to be 83⅓ percent of the surface measure, or 10/12. To determine the correct number of units needed, multiply the surface measure 16 by 10 to equal 160 units. This board does not contain enough units, 160, to make an FAS board. The number of units required for 66⅔ percent clear-face cuttings is 8 times the surface measure 16, or 128 units.

This board has more than enough units for this percent clear cuttings, therefore it is graded as a No. 1 common board.

**SOFTWOOD LUMBER GRADING.** Softwood lumber is graded under a number of different association rules. The following classification of softwood lumber gives the grade names used by lumber manufacturers' associations for the various classes of material under the American Lumber Standards.

### Table 8.  General Classification of Softwood Lumber

| | | | Grades |
|---|---|---|---|
| Softwood lumber (this classification applies to rough or dressed lumber; sizes given are nominal) | Yard lumber (lumber less than 5 in. thick, intended for general building purposes; grading based on use of the entire piece) | Finish (less than 3 in. thick and 12 in. and under in width) | A select<br>B select<br>C select<br>D select |
| | | Boards (less than 2 in. thick and 8 in or over in width).  Strips (under 8 in. in width) | No. 1 boards<br>No. 2 boards<br>No. 3 boards<br>No. 4 boards<br>No. 5 boards |
| | Structural material (lumber 5 in. or over in thickness and width, except joist and plank; grading based on strength and on use of entire piece) | Dimension (2 in. and under 5 in. thick and of any width) | Planks (2 in and under 4 in. thick and 8 in. and over wide) — No. 1 dimension / No. 2 dimension / No. 3 dimension |
| | | | Scantling (2 in. and under 5 in. thick and under 8 in. wide) — No. 1 dimension / No. 2 dimension / No. 3 dimension |
| | | | Heavy joists (4 in. thick and 8 in. or over wide) — No. 1 dimension / No. 2 dimension / No. 3 dimension |
| | | Joist and plank (2 in. to 4 in. thick and 4 in. and over wide)<br>Beams and stringers (5 in. and over thick and 8 in. and over wide)<br>Posts and timbers (6 by 6 in. and larger) | |
| | Factory and shop (grading based on area of piece suitable for cuttings of certain size and quality) | Factory plank graded for door, sash, and other cuttings 1 in. to 4 in. thick and 5 in. and over wide | Factory clears upper grades — Nos. 1 and 2 clear factory / No. 3 clear factory<br>Shop lower grades — No. 1 shop / No. 2 shop / No. 3 shop |
| | | Shop lumber graded for general cut up purposes | 1 in. thick (northern and western pine, and Pacific coast woods) — Select Shop<br>All thicknesses (cypress, redwood, and North Carolina pine) — Tank and boat stock, firsts and seconds, selects, No. 1 shop, No. 2 shop, box |

Source: U. S. Dept. Agr., *Wood handbook*, 1940.

Footnotes for Table 9:

ᵃ The thicknesses apply to all widths and the widths to all thicknesses, with the following exceptions: In tongue-and-groove flooring and in tongue-and-groove and shiplapped ceiling ⁵⁄₁₆, ⁷⁄₁₆, and ⁹⁄₁₆-in. thick, board measure, the tongue or lap shall be ³⁄₁₆ in. wide, with over-all widths ³⁄₁₆-in. wider than the face widths shown above. In all other patterned material, ¹¹⁄₁₆, ³⁄₄, 1, 1¼, and 1½ in. thick, board measure the tongue shall be ¼ in. wide in tongue-and-groove lumber and the lap ³⁄₈ in. wide in shiplapped lumber with the over-all widths ¼ and ³⁄₈ in. wider, respectively, than the face widths shown above. In patterned material 2 in. and thicker, board measure, the tongue shall be ³⁄₈ in. wide in tongued and grooved (D & M) lumber and the lap ½ in. wide in shiplapped lumber, with the over-all width ³⁄₈ in. and ½ in. wider, respectively, than the face widths shown above.

ᵇ 20 percent may be ¹⁄₃₂-in. scant.

ᶜ Based on kiln-dried lumber.

ᵈ 10 percent may be ¹⁄₃₂-in. scant.

ᵉ Minimum.

ᶠ Face width when shiplapped; when dressed and matched the face width is ⅛-in. greater; when grooved for splines the face width is ½-in. greater.

Source: U. S. Dept. Agr. *Wood handbook*, 1940.

## Table 9. Summary of American Standard Thicknesses and Widths[a] for Softwood Yard Lumber

Includes finish, boards, dimension, and heavy joist, siding, flooring, ceiling, partition, shiplap, and dressed and matched lumber

| Product | Rough green or nominal sizes (board measure): Thickness (in.) | Rough green or nominal sizes (board measure): Width (in.) | Minimum rough-dry dimensions: Thickness: Standard yard[b] (in.) | Minimum rough-dry dimensions: Thickness: Standard industrial (in.) | Minimum rough-dry dimensions: Width (in.) | Dressed dimensions: Thickness: Standard yard (in.) | Dressed dimensions: Thickness: Standard industrial (in.) | Dressed dimensions: Width (face when worked) (in.) |
|---|---|---|---|---|---|---|---|---|
| Finish | ... | 3 | ... | ... | 2 3/4 | 5/16 | ... | 2 5/8 |
| | ... | 4 | ... | ... | 3 5/8 | 7/16 | ... | 5 1/2 [c] |
| | ... | 5 | ... | ... | 4 5/8 | 9/16 | ... | 4 1/2 [c] |
| | ... | 6 | ... | ... | 5 5/8 | 11/16 | ... | 5 1/2 [c] |
| | 1 | 7 | 29/32 | 30/32 [d] | 6 5/8 | 25/32 | 28/32 | 6 1/2 |
| | 1 1/4 | 8 | 1 3/16 | ... | 7 3/8 | 1 1/16 | ... | 7 1/4 [c] |
| | 1 1/2 | 9 | 1 7/16 | ... | 8 3/8 | 1 5/16 | ... | 8 1/4 [c] |
| | 1 3/4 | 10 | 1 9/16 | ... | 9 3/8 | 1 7/16 | ... | 9 1/4 [c] |
| | 2 | 11 | 1 6/8 | 1 7/8 [b] | 10 3/8 | 1 5/8 | 1 6/8 | 10 1/4 [c] |
| | 2 1/2 | 12 | 2 1/4 | ... | 11 3/8 | 2 1/8 | ... | 11 1/4 [c] |
| | 3 | ... | 2 6/8 | ... | ... | 2 5/8 | ... | ... |
| Common boards and strips | 1 | 3 | 29/32 | 30/32 [d] | 2 3/4 | 25/32 | 25/32 | 2 5/8 |
| | 1 1/4 | 4 | 1 3/16 | ... | 3 3/4 | 1 1/16 | ... | 3 5/8 |
| | 1 1/2 | 5 | 1 7/16 | ... | 4 3/4 | 1 5/16 | ... | 4 5/8 |
| | ... | 6 | ... | ... | 5 3/4 | ... | ... | 5 5/8 |
| | ... | 7 | ... | ... | 6 3/4 | ... | ... | 6 5/8 |
| | ... | 8 | ... | ... | 7 5/8 | ... | ... | 7 1/2 |
| | ... | 9 | ... | ... | 8 5/8 | ... | ... | 8 1/2 |
| | ... | 10 | ... | ... | 9 5/8 | ... | ... | 9 1/2 |
| | ... | 11 | ... | ... | 10 5/8 | ... | ... | 10 1/2 |
| | ... | 12 | ... | ... | 11 5/8 | ... | ... | 11 1/2 |
| Bevel siding | ... | 4 | ... | ... | ... | 7/16 by 3/16 [e] | ... | 3 1/2 |
| | ... | 5 | ... | ... | ... | 10/16 by 3/16 | ... | 4 1/2 |
| | ... | 6 | ... | ... | ... | ... | ... | 5 1/2 |
| Wide bevel siding | ... | 8 | ... | ... | ... | 7/16 by 3/16 [e] | ... | 7 1/4 |
| | ... | 10 | ... | ... | ... | 9/16 by 3/16 | ... | 9 1/4 |
| | ... | 12 | ... | ... | ... | 11/16 by 3/16 | ... | 11 1/4 |
| Rustic and drop siding (shiplapped) | ... | 4 | ... | ... | ... | 9/16 | ... | 3 1/8 |
| | ... | 5 | ... | ... | ... | 3/4 | ... | 4 1/8 |
| | ... | 6 | ... | ... | ... | ... | ... | 5 1/16 |
| | ... | 8 | ... | ... | ... | ... | ... | 6 7/8 |
| Rustic and drop siding (D. & M.) | ... | 4 | ... | ... | ... | 9/16 | ... | 3 1/4 |
| | ... | 5 | ... | ... | ... | 3/4 | ... | 4 1/4 |
| | ... | 6 | ... | ... | ... | ... | ... | 5 3/16 |
| | ... | 8 | ... | ... | ... | ... | ... | 7 |
| Flooring | ... | 2 | ... | ... | ... | 5/16 | ... | 1 1/2 |
| | ... | 3 | ... | ... | ... | 7/16 | ... | 2 3/8 |
| | ... | 4 | ... | ... | ... | 9/16 | ... | 3 1/4 |
| | 1 | 5 | ... | ... | ... | 25/32 | ... | 4 1/4 |
| | 1 1/4 | 6 | ... | ... | ... | 1 1/16 | ... | 5 3/16 |
| | 1 1/2 | ... | ... | ... | ... | 1 5/16 | ... | ... |
| Ceiling | ... | 3 | ... | ... | ... | 5/16 | ... | 2 3/8 |
| | ... | 4 | ... | ... | ... | 7/16 | ... | 3 1/4 |
| | ... | 5 | ... | ... | ... | 9/16 | ... | 4 1/4 |
| | ... | 6 | ... | ... | ... | 1 1/16 | ... | 5 3/16 |
| Partition | ... | 3 | ... | ... | ... | 3/4 | ... | 2 3/8 |
| | ... | 4 | ... | ... | ... | ... | ... | 3 1/4 |
| | ... | 5 | ... | ... | ... | ... | ... | 4 1/4 |
| | ... | 6 | ... | ... | ... | ... | ... | 5 3/16 |
| Shiplap | 1 | 4 | ... | ... | ... | 25/32 | ... | 3 1/8 |
| | ... | 6 | ... | ... | ... | ... | ... | 5 1/8 |
| | ... | 8 | ... | ... | ... | ... | ... | 7 1/8 |
| | ... | 10 | ... | ... | ... | ... | ... | 9 1/8 |
| | ... | 12 | ... | ... | ... | ... | ... | 11 1/8 |
| Dressed and matched | 1 | 4 | ... | ... | ... | 25/32 | ... | 3 1/4 |
| | 1 1/4 | 6 | ... | ... | ... | 1 1/16 | ... | 5 1/4 |
| | 1 1/2 | 8 | ... | ... | ... | 1 5/16 | ... | 7 1/4 |
| | ... | 10 | ... | ... | ... | ... | ... | 9 1/4 |
| | ... | 12 | ... | ... | ... | ... | ... | 11 1/4 |
| Dimension and heavy joist | 2 | 2 | 1 3/4 | 1 7/8 [b] | 1 3/4 | 1 5/8 | 1 3/4 | 1 5/8 |
| | 2 1/2 | 4 | 2 1/4 | ... | 3 3/4 | 2 1/8 | ... | 3 5/8 |
| | 3 | 6 | 2 3/4 | ... | 5 3/4 | 2 5/8 | ... | 5 5/8 |
| | 4 | 8 | 3 3/4 | ... | 7 5/8 | 3 5/8 | ... | 7 1/2 |
| | ... | 10 | ... | ... | 9 5/8 | ... | ... | 9 1/2 |
| | ... | 12 | ... | ... | 11 5/8 | ... | ... | 11 1/2 |
| Factory flooring, heavy roofing, heavy decking, and sheet piling | 2 | 4 | 1 3/4 | ... | ... | 1 5/8 | ... | 3 [f] |
| | 2 1/2 | 6 | 2 1/4 | ... | ... | 2 1/8 | ... | 5 [f] |
| | 3 | 8 | 2 3/4 | ... | ... | 2 5/8 | ... | 7 [f] |
| | 4 | 10 | 3 3/4 | ... | ... | 3 5/8 | ... | 9 [f] |
| | ... | 12 | ... | ... | ... | ... | ... | 11 [f] |

Footnotes on opposite page.

**Table 10. Allowable Unit Stresses for Stress-Grade Lumber**

| (1) Species and commercial grade [a] | (2) Rules under which graded | Allowable unit stresses (psi) | | | | |
|---|---|---|---|---|---|---|
| | | (3) Extreme fiber in bending "f" and tension parallel to grain "t" | (4) Horizontal shear "H" | (5) Compression perpendicular to grain "c⊥" | (6) Compression parallel to grain "c" | (7) Modulus of elasticity "E" [h] |
| **DOUGLAS-FIR, COAST REGION:** | | | | | | |
| Dense Select Structural[d] | J.&P.[b]–B.&S.[b] | 2,150 | 145 | 455 | 1,550 | 1,760,000 |
| Select Structural | J.&P.[b]–B.&S.[b] | 1,900 | 120 | 415 | 1,450 | |
| 1700 f.—Dense No. 1[d] | J.&P.[b]–B.&S.[b] | 1,700 | 145 | 455 | 1,325 | |
| 1450 f.—No. 1 | J.&P.[b]–B.&S.[b] | 1,450 | 120 | 390 | 1,200 | |
| 1100 f.—No. 2 | J.&P.[b] | 1,100 | 110 | 390 | 1,075 | |
| Dense Select Structural[d] | P.&T. | … | … | 455 | 1,550 | |
| Select Structural | P.&T. | … | … | 415 | 1,450 | |
| Dense No. 1[d] | P.&T. | … | … | 455 | 1,400 | |
| No. 1 | P.&T. | … | … | 390 | 1,200 | |
| **PINE, SOUTHERN:[c]** | | | | | | |
| Dense Select Structural[d] | J.&P.–B.&S. | 2,400 | 120[e] | 455 | 1,750 | 1,760,000 |
| Dense Structural[d] | J.&P.–B.&S. | 2,000 | 120[e] | 455 | 1,400 | |
| Dense Structural S.E.&S.[d] | J.&P.–B.&S. | 1,800 | 120[e] | 455 | 1,300 | |
| Dense No. 1 Structural[d] | J.&P.–B.&S. | 1,600 | 120[e] | 455 | 1,150 | |
| No. 1 Dense 1400 f[d, g] | J.&P.–B.&S. | 1,400 | 140 | 455 | 1,400 | |
| No. 1 1200 f[g] | J.&P.–B.&S. | 1,200 | 120 | 390 | 1,200 | |
| No. 1 Dense[d] | J.&P.[f] | 1,700 | 150 | 455 | 1,400 | |
| No. 1 | J.&P.[f] | 1,450 | 125 | 390 | 1,200 | |
| No. 2 Dense[d] | J.&P.[f] | 1,250 | 100 | 455 | 1,025 | |
| No. 2 Dense 1200 f[g] | J.&P.,B.&S., P.&T. | 1,200 | 100 | 455 | 1,025 | |
| No. 2 | J.&P.[f] | 1,100 | 85 | 390 | 875 | |
| No. 2 1050 f[g] | J.&P.,B.&S., P.&T. | 1,050 | 85 | 390 | 875 | |
| Dense Select Structural[d] | P.&T. | … | … | 455 | 1,750 | |

Table 10. Allowable Unit Stresses for Stress-Grade Lumber (Continued)

| (1) Species and commercial grade [a] | (2) Rules under which graded | (3) Extreme fiber in bending "f" and tension parallel to grain "t" | (4) Horizontal shear "H" | (5) Compression perpendicular to grain "$c_\perp$" | (6) Compression parallel to grain "c" | (7) Modulus of elasticity "E" [h] |
|---|---|---|---|---|---|---|
| Dense Structural [d] | P.&T. | | | 455 | 1,400 | 1,650,000 |
| Dense Structural S.E.&S. [d] | P.&T. | | | 455 | 1,300 | |
| Dense No. 1 Structural [d] | P.&T. | | | 455 | 1,150 | |
| No. 1 Dense 1400 f [d, g] | P.&T. | 1,400 | 140 | 455 | 1,400 | |
| No. 1 1200 f [g] | P.&T. | 1,200 | 120 | 390 | 1,200 | |
| OAK, RED AND WHITE: | National Hardwood Lumber Association. | | | | | |
| 2150 f Grade | J.&P. | 2,150 | | | 1,550 | |
| 1900 f Grade | J.&P.–B.&S. | 1,900 | 145 | | 1,375 | |
| 1700 f Grade | J.&P.–B.&S. | 1,700 | 145 | | 1,200 | |
| 1450 f Grade | J.&P.–B.&S. | 1,450 | 145 | | 1,050 | |
| 1300 f Grade | B.&S. | 1,300 | 120 | | 950 | |
| 1325 c Grade | P.&T. | | | | 1,325 | |
| 1200 c Grade | P.&T. | | | 600 [h] | 1,200 | |
| 1075 c Grade | P.&T. | | | | 1,075 | |

[a] Abbreviations: J.&P., Joists and Planks; B.&S., Beams and Stringers; P.&T., Posts and Timbers; S.E.&S., Square Edge and Sound.

[b] The allowable unit stresses for tension parallel to grain "t" for compression parallel to grain "c" given for these Joist and Plank and Beam and Stringer grades are applicable when the following additional provisions are applied to the grades:

The sum of the sizes of all knots in any 6 in. of the length of the piece shall not exceed twice the maximum permissible size of knot. Two knots of maximum permissible size shall not be within the same 6 in. of length of any face.

[c] According to 1948 Standard Grading Rules, including Supplement No. 1.

[d] These grades meet the requirements for density.

[e] The grading rules provide a basis for obtaining higher shearing stresses of 140, 160 and 180 psi when specified.

[f] These grades are applicable to 2-in. thickness only.

[g] These grades are applicable only in sizes 3 in. and thicker.

[h] In columns 5 and 7, the single values opposite the species apply to all grades of the species.

Source: National Lumber Mfrs. Assn., *National design specifications for stress-grade lumber and its fastenings*, revised 1954. Values are illustrative only; check source for limitations.

**STRUCTURAL LUMBER GRADES.** Stress-grade lumber (graded for strength) is used for structural load-supporting members. The purpose of structural grading is to provide material of uniform strength to which appropriate working stresses may be assigned for a particular use in construction (Table 10).

Checks, knots, slope of grain, and shakes are defects which are limited in structural grades. Density and decay are also considered. Dense grades of southern pine and Douglas-fir must average 6 rings per in. and must be at least ⅓ summerwood. Most stress-graded lumber is either southern pine or Douglas-fir.

Laminated structural members are also stress-graded. Structural glued laminated lumber, technically speaking, refers only to those glued laminated structural members in which the grain of all laminations of a member is approximately parallel. Allowable unit stresses are available for dry and for wet conditions for Douglas-fir (Coast region) and southern pine.

**GRADE MARKING.** Softwood lumber, including structural grades, is commonly marked for grade. Such marking is usually done under the supervision of an inspection service. Grade marks are a combination of letters and symbols indicating (1) the grade, (2) identity of mill or inspector, and (3) the association whose grading rules are applicable.

Hardwoods are typically certified for grade rather than grade-marked, since their use is primarily industrial; also, the hardwood grade can change with surfacing and seasoning.

**ORGANIZATIONS ISSUING GRADING RULES.** The principal lumber associations issuing grading rules are listed below:

| Name and Address | Woods Covered by Rules |
|---|---|
| Southern Pine Association, New Orleans, La. | Southern yellow pine |
| Hardwood Dimension Manufacturers Association, Louisville, Ky. | Hardwood dimension or cut stock |
| National Hardwood Lumber Associations, Chicago, Ill. | Hardwoods, cypress, eastern redcedar |
| Northeastern Lumberman's Association, New York, N. Y. | Eastern white pine, balsam fir, eastern hemlock, red pine, eastern spruce |
| Northern Hemlock and Hardwood Manufacturers Association, Oshkosh, Wis. | Eastern hemlock, tamarack, northern white-cedar |
| Maple Flooring Manufacturers Association, Chicago, Ill. | Maple, beech, birch (flooring) |
| National Oak Flooring Manufacturers Association, Memphis, Tenn. | Oak, pecan, ash, and miscellaneous southern hardwoods |
| West Coast Lumbermen's Association, Portland, Ore. | Douglas-fir, Sitka spruce, western redcedar, Port-Orford-cedar, western hemlock |
| Western Pine Association, Portland, Ore. | Western pines, larch, Douglas-fir, true firs, western spruce, and western redcedar |
| Redwood Association, San Francisco, Calif. | Redwood |
| American Walnut Manufacturers Association, Chicago, Ill. | Walnut |

**LUMBER GRADES AND PRICES.** The effect of grade on the price of lumber may be illustrated by prices received for shortleaf pine lumber, 1915–49.

An analysis of these for a substantial volume of such lumber, by grades, was made by the U. S. Forest Service committee on southern pine log and tree grades. It shows the existence, except during World War II, of a fundamentally constant price structure. Table 11 gives proposed quality indices for shortleaf pine based on this grade-price analysis.

**Table 11.** Proposed Grade-Width-Thickness Quality Indices for Shortleaf Yellow Pine Lumber

| Nominal thickness (in.) | Grade | Nominal width (in.) | | | | |
| --- | --- | --- | --- | --- | --- | --- |
| | | 4 | 6 | 8 | 5 & 10 | 12 |
| 1 | B & B | 220 | 220 | 220 | 235 | 310 |
| | C | 180 | 180 | 180 | 200 | 245 |
| | No. 1 | 155 | 155 | 155 | 165 | 200 |
| | No. 2 | 85 | 100 | 100 | 100 | 115 |
| | No. 3 | 60 | 80 | 85 | 85 | 85 |
| | No. 4 | 45 | 45 | 45 | 45 | 45 |
| 5/4, 6/4, 7/4 | B & B | 240 | 240 | 240 | 280 | 340 |
| | Other | Indices same as for corresponding width and grade of 1-in. material. | | | | |
| 2 | B & B | 265 | 260 | 260 | 280 | 340 |
| | No. 1D | 110 | 100 | 105 | 115 | 130 |
| | No. 2D | 100 | 90 | 95 | 100 | 110 |
| | No. 3D | 65 | 65 | 65 | 65 | 65 |
| 3 or more | No. 1 Tbr. | 105 | 105 | 105 | 125 | 135 |
| | No. 2 Tbr. | 90 | 90 | 90 | 100 | 120 |

Basis: 8–20-ft. lengths for timbers, 16-ft. length for dimension, standard lengths for others. RG for timbers, KD and S4S for other No. 2 or better material, AD and S4S for other material. All indices are expressed as percentages of current price per MBM of No. 2 common 1 x 8-in. board in standard lengths.
Source: U. S. Forest Service, Report of southern pine log and tree grade committee of Nov. 1, 1950 (unpublished).

# Key for the Identification of Woods without the Aid of a Hand Lens or Microscope *

## HARDWOODS

I. Pores visible as minute rounded openings on smoothly cut end grain and as fine grooves on planed side-grain surfaces.

A. Ring-porous; that is, the pores at the beginning for each annual ring (springwood) are comparatively large, forming a distinct porous ring, and decrease

* Key prepared by Arthur Koehler, former chief of the Division of Silvicultural Relations, Forest Products Laboratory, Forest Service, U. S. Dept. Agr., Madison, Wis. It is reproduced here from *Trees: Yearbook of Agriculture 1949*.
  Unless otherwise directed, all observations as to structure should be made on the end surface of rings of average width, cut smoothly with a very sharp knife; and all observations as to color should be made on a freshly cut longitudinal surface of the heartwood. A reading glass will help to see some of the structural features more distinctly but should not be used in judging visibility with the unaided eye. Odor can best be determined on freshly cut surfaces of the heartwood.

in size more or less abruptly in the outer part of each annual ring (summerwood) where they are not visible without magnification.

1. Summerwood figured with light and dark irregular V-shaped radial patches.

(a) Many of the rays broad and conspicuous. Wood is heavy to very heavy.

The OAKS

(a₁) Many usually without reddish tinge. The large pores of the heartwood mostly closed (wood of the chestnut oak is an exception).

The WHITE OAK GROUP:
WHITE OAK
SWAMP WHITE OAK
BUR OAK
POST OAK
CHINQUAPIN OAK
SWAMP CHESTNUT OAK
OVERCUP OAK
CHESTNUT OAK
OREGON WHITE OAK
CALIFORNIA WHITE OAK

(b₁) Wood with reddish tinge, especially near knots. The large pores of the heartwood mostly open (wood of the blackjack oak is an exception).

The RED OAK GROUP:
NORTHERN RED OAK
EASTERN RED OAK
SOUTHERN RED OAK
SWAMP RED OAK
BLACK OAK
SCARLET OAK
PIN OAK
WATER OAK
WILLOW OAK
LAUREL OAK
BLACKJACK OAK
CALIFORNIA BLACK OAK

(b) Rays not noticeable. Color grayish brown. Wood moderately light.
AMERICAN CHESTNUT

2. Summerwood figured with short or long wavy tangential lines or brands, in some woods (elms, hackberry, sugarberry, and mulberry) throughout the summerwood, in others more pronounced toward the outer part of the summerwood.

(a) Heartwood bright cherry red. Pores in springwood mostly open and very distinct.

(a₁) Rays plainly visible. Tangential bands in summerwood usually distinct except in narrow rings. Pith small, commonly size of lead in ordinary pencil. Sapwood usually more than three-fourths inch wide. Wood very heavy.

HONEYLOCUST

(b₁) Rays not plainly visible. Tangential bands in summerwood obscure. Pith large, 0.2 to 0.3 inch in diameter. Sapwood usually less than three-fourths inch wide. Wood heavy.

KENTUCKY COFFEETREE

(b) Heartwood brown with reddish tinge.

(a₁) Tangential bands long and very conspicuous throughout the summerwood.

($a_2$) The porous ring of the springwood from 2 to 4 pores wide. Sapwood mostly less than 1 inch wide. Heartwood with characteristic odor of slippery elm bark. Wood moderately heavy.

SLIPPERY ELM

($b_2$) The porous ring of the springwood only one pore wide, except in very wide rings. Sapwood mostly more than 1 inch in width.

($a_3$) Pores in springwood fairly conspicuous, open, and close together. Wood moderately heavy.

AMERICAN ELM

($b_3$) Pores in springwood inconspicuous because comparatively small, closed, and not close together. Wood heavy.

ROCK ELM
CEDAR ELM
WINGED ELM

($b_1$) Tangential bands short, inconspicuous, and limited to outer summerwood. Springwood zone several pores wide. Sapwood more than 1 inch, usually several inches wide. Wood heavy.

WHITE ASH
GREEN ASH
OREGON ASH

(c) Heartwood yellowish or golden brown becoming dark brown on exposure. Pores in heartwood completely closed. Sapwood less than three-fourths inch wide.

($a_1$) Wood heavy. Tangential bands uniformly distributed throughout the summerwood. Rays distinct.

RED MULBERRY

($b_1$) Wood very heavy to very, very heavy. Tangential bands confined to, or more pronounced in, the outer portion of the summerwood. Rays not distinct.

OSAGE-ORANGE

Osage-orange sometimes is difficult to distinguish from black locust wood, but when put on a wet cloth or blotter, Osage-orange heartwood gives off a distinct yellow color in a few minutes, whereas black locust does so only faintly or not at all. Dry black locust heartwood fluoresces brilliant yellow in ultra-violet light; Osage-orange does not fluoresce when dry.

(d) Heartwood greenish brown. Pores in heartwood completely closed. Rays not distinct. Sapwood less than three-fourths inch wide. Woods very heavy to very, very heavy.

BLACK LOCUST

(e) Heartwood silvery brown, with spicy odor and taste. Rays not distinct. Sapwood less than three-fourths inch wide. Wood moderately heavy.                                                   SASSAFRAS

(f) Heartwood grayish brown with lavender tinge; after prolonged exposure resembling butternut or black walnut in color. Sapwood narrow, rarely more than three-fourths inch wide. Wood moderately light.                                        NORTHERN CATALPA

(g) Heartwood yellowish or light greenish gray, not distinct from the sapwood. Tangential bands long and very conspicuous throughout the summerwood (resembling slippery elm except for color). Rays fairly distinct. Wood moderately heavy.

HACKBERRY
SUGARBERRY

3. Summerwood not figured with radial or tangential patterns visible without a lens.
(a) Heartwood reddish brown. Sapwood more than 1 inch wide.

($a_1$) Pores decreasing in size abruptly from springwood to summerwood. Wood heavy to very heavy.

TRUE HICKORIES:
SHAGBARK HICKORY
SHELLBARK HICKORY
MOCKERNUT HICKORY
PIGNUT HICKORY

($b_1$) Pores decreasing in size more or less gradually from springwood to summerwood. Wood heavy.  PECAN
WATER HICKORY

(b) Heartwood light cherry red. Sapwood usually less than three-fourths inch wide. Wood heavy.  KENTUCKY COFFEETREE

(c) Heartwood grayish brown. Sapwood usually less than three-fourths inch wide. Wood moderately heavy.  BLACK ASH

B. Diffuse-porous; that is, no ring of large pores is formed at the beginning of each annual ring, the pores being uniform in size or gradually decreasing in size from the inner to the outer part of each annual ring.

  1. Individual pores plainly visible on end grain and side grain, gradually decreasing in size from inner to outer part of each annual ring.

   (a) Some rays broad and conspicuous, fully as wide as the largest pores. Pores arranged in radial groups extending across the annual rings.
   ($a_1$) Southern species. Wood exceedingly heavy.  LIVE OAK
   ($b_1$) Western species. Wood very heavy.  CANYON LIVE OAK

   (b) All rays smaller than the largest pores. The pores not arranged in radial groups extending across the rings.
   ($a_1$) Tangential surface marked with very fine bands which run across the grain and are due to the storied arrangement of the rays. Heartwood black, or brownish black (usually very small). Sapwood wide, white or pale gray. Wood very, very heavy.
   COMMON PERSIMMON
   ($b_1$) Tangential surface not marked with fine cross bands.
   ($a_2$) Heartwood reddish brown. Sapwood wide. Wood heavy.
   WATER HICKORY
   ($b_2$) Heartwood chocolate or purplish brown. Sapwood narrow to moderate in width. Wood heavy.  BLACK WALNUT
   ($c_2$) Heartwood light chestnut brown, frequently with dark springwood and pinkish-brown summerwood. Sapwood narrow. Wood moderately light.  BUTTERNUT

  2. Individual pores barely visible under conditions of good light and a very smoothly cut surface, fairly uniform in size throughout each annual ring.

   (a) Pores not crowded on end surface. Heartwood reddish brown.
   ($a_1$) Wood heavy to very heavy. Pith flecks very rare.  YELLOW BIRCH
   SWEET BIRCH
   ($b_1$) Wood moderately heavy. Pith flecks common.  PAPER BIRCH
   RIVER BIRCH

   (b) Pores crowded on end surface. Wood light.
   ($a_1$) Heartwood grayish.  COTTONWOOD
   ($b_1$) Heartwood dark reddish brown.  BLACK WILLOW
   ($c_1$) Heartwood light reddish brown.  WHITE WILLOW

II. Pores not visible.

  A. Rays comparatively broad and conspicuous. Color of heartwood in various shades of light reddish brown.

   1. The rays crowded on end grain; up to three-sixteenths inch high on radial and tangential surfaces, producing pronounced, crowded "flakes" when quarter-sawed. No denser and darker bank of summerwood noticeable. Wood usually has interlocked grain; moderately heavy.
   SYCAMORE

   2. The broad rays not crowded; up to one-eight inch high on radial and tangential surfaces, producing scattered "flakes" when quarter-sawed. A

distinct, denser, and darker band of summerwood present. Wood usually fairly straight-grained; heavy.     BEECH

B. Rays not conspicuous but distinctly visible.

   1. Heartwood deep, rich, reddish brown. Sapwood narrow, usually less than 1 inch wide. Annual rings clearly defined. Rays very distinct. Wood moderately heavy.     BLACK CHERRY

   2. Heartwood dingy, reddish brown, often with darker streaks. Sapwood moderately wide, usually more than 1 inch. Annual rings not clearly defined. Rays relatively not very distinct. Wood moderately heavy.     SWEETGUM

   3. Heartwood light grayish brown with reddish tinge. Sapwood more than 1 inch wide. Annual rings clearly defined by a thin, darker reddish-brown layer. Rays very distinct.

    (a) Wood heavy; difficult to cut across the grain. Pith flecks very rare.     SUGAR MAPLE
    BLACK MAPLE

    (b) Wood moderately heavy; rather easy to cut across the grain. Pith flecks often abundant.     SILVER MAPLE
    RED MAPLE
    BIGLEAF MAPLE

   4. Heartwood light yellowish brown with greenish tinge, occasionally purplish. Sapwood usually more than 1 inch wide. Annual rings clearly defined. Rays fairly distinct. Wood moderately light to moderately heavy.     YELLOW-POPLAR
    CUCUMBERTREE
    SOUTHERN MAGNOLIA

   5. Heartwood creamy brown. Sapwood wide and not sharply defined from the heartwood. Rays fairly distinct. Wood light.     BASSWOOD

C. Rays not distinctly visible.

   1. Annual rings not clearly divided into a band of soft springwood and denser and darker band of summerwood and, therefore, not conspicuous.

    (a) The heartwood distinctly darker than the sapwood.

     (a$_1$) Heartwood reddish brown. Wood not cross-grained.
      (a$_2$) Wood heavy to very heavy. Pith flecks very rare.     YELLOW BIRCH
      SWEET BIRCH

      (b$_2$) Wood moderately heavy. Pith flecks common.     PAPER BIRCH
      RIVER BIRCH

      (c$_2$) Wood light.
       (a$_3$) Heartwood dark reddish brown.     BLACK WILLOW
       (b$_3$) Heartwood light reddish brown.     WHITE WILLOW

     (b$_1$) Heartwood grayish brown.
      (a$_2$) Wood cross-grained; moderately light to moderately heavy.     BLACK TUPELO (BLACKGUM)
      WATER TUPELO

      (b$_2$) Wood fairly straight-grained; light.     COTTONWOOD

    (b) The heartwood light-colored and not distinctly darker than the sapwood.

     (a$_1$) Wood light in weight; odorless and tasteless.
      (a$_2$) Color yellowish white.     YELLOW BUCKEYE
      OHIO BUCKEYE

      (b$_2$) Color plain white, sometimes partly discolored to pale salmon brown near center of tree or around knots.     QUAKING ASPEN
      BIGTOOTH ASPEN

## SOFTWOODS

(b₁) Wood moderately light. Odor of heartwood spicy; color pale brown.                                    PORT-ORFORD-CEDAR

(c₁) Wood moderately heavy. Odor of heartwood pungently disagreeable, not spicy; color light canary yellow.    ALASKA-CEDAR

2. Annual rings clearly divided into a band of soft springwood and a denser and darker band of summerwood. Although the summerwood may not be pronounced, yet the annual rings are always clearly defined by it.

(a) Wood resinous, as indicated by exudations of resin, or pitch, especially when heated, the presence of occasional pitch pockets or pitch streaks, or the presence of longitudinal surfaces of brownish lines (resin ducts) from a fraction of an inch to several inches long.

(a₁) Heartwood darker than the sapwood.

(a₂) Heartwood reddish brown or orange brown. Resin ducts abundant. Heartwood with "piney" odor.

(a₃) The summerwood inconspicuous and not much darker or harder than the springwood. Wood light to moderately light.

The SOFT PINES:

(a₄) Eastern species.     EASTERN WHITE PINE
(b₄) Western species.     WESTERN WHITE PINE
                                    SUGAR PINE

(b₃) The summerwood conspicuously darker and harder than the springwood.

The HARD PINES:

(a₄) Wood moderately light.
(a₅) Western species.

(a₆) Heartwood not much darker than sapwood. Tangential surface slightly dimpled, as if hit lightly with coarse shot. Sapwood usually less than 2 inches wide.

LODGEPOLE PINE

(b₆) Heartwood distinctly darker than sapwood after exposure to air and light. Tangential surface not dimpled, or only in narrow-ringed wood. Sapwood usually more than 2 inches wide.

PONDEROSA PINE

(b₅) Northeastern species.

JACK PINE
RED PINE

(b₄) Wood moderately heavy to very heavy. Eastern and southern species.

VIRGINIA PINE
PITCH PINE
SHORTLEAF PINE
LOBLOLLY PINE
POND PINE
LONGLEAF PINE
SLASH PINE

(b₂) Heartwood light orange red to cherry red. Resin ducts scarce. Tangential surface not dimpled. Heartwood with characteristic, but not "piney", odor.

DOUGLAS-FIR

(c₂) Heartwood pinkish to pale reddish brown. Resin ducts scarce. Tangential surface slightly dimpled, as if lightly hit with coarse shot, except in wide-ringed wood. Wood without distinct odor.

SITKA SPRUCE

(b₁) Heartwood not appreciably darker than the sapwood. Resin ducts present but scarce and inconspicuous. Wood without distinct odor.

WHITE SPRUCE
RED SPRUCE
ENGELMANN SPRUCE

(b) Wood not resinous.

(a₁) Heartwood decidedly darker than the sapwood.

(a₂) Heartwood medium to dark reddish brown.

(a₃) Heartwood without odor or taste. Wood moderately light.　REDWOOD

(b₃) Heartwood with spicy odor and taste (like cedar shingles). Wood light.

WESTERN REDCEDAR

(c₃) Heartwood with aromatic odor and taste. Wood moderately heavy.

EASTERN REDCEDAR

(b₂) Heartwood light brown, with juicy odor and taste. Wood light.

NORTHERN WHITE-CEDAR

(c₂) Heartwood light pinkish brown, with aromatic odor. Wood light.

ATLANTIC WHITE-CEDAR

(d₂) Heartwood variable from pale brown to dark brown, with rancid odor but without taste. Wood variable from moderately light to moderately heavy.

BALDCYPRESS

(b₁) Heartwood only slightly darker than sapwood.

(a₂) Heartwood light canary yellow, odor not spicy or aromatic, somewhat disagreeable. Wood moderately heavy.

ALASKA-CEDAR

(b₂) Heartwood pale brown, odor pungently spicy. Wood moderately light.　PORT-ORFORD-CEDAR

(c₁) Heartwood not appreciably darker than sapwood when dry.

(a₂) Springwood white, summerwood light brown with lavender tinge.　WHITE FIR
GRAND FIR

(b₂) Springwood and summerwood pale reddish brown.

(a₃) Heartwood with disagreeable odor, especially when moist.　NOBLE FIR
CALIFORNIA RED FIR

(b₃) Heartwood without disagreeable odor.

EASTERN HEMLOCK
WESTERN HEMLOCK

# Physical and Mechanical Properties of Wood

Physical properties such as coefficient of thermal expansion, specific heat of wood, and others of like nature may be found in Section 21, Chemistry and Physics of Wood.

**SELECTED DEFINITIONS. 1. Static bending.** Load on a beam is increased at a slow rate, typically resulting in deflections of a fraction of an inch per minute.

**2. Proportional limit (elastic limit).** This is the limit of proportionality between load (stress) and deformation (strain). With an increase in load beyond the proportional limit, deformation increases by a greater percentage than the load. Stressing beyond the proportional limit results in permanent deflections, thus proportional limit values are upper limits to stresses used in designing permanent structures.

3. **Stress at proportional limit.** In static bending this is the stress that exists in the top and bottom fibers of a beam at the proportional limit load. It expresses the maximum stress to which a beam can be subjected without permanent deformation.

4. **Modulus of rupture.** This is the breaking strength of a beam expressed in terms of stress per unit area. It is computed by determining the fiber stress in the top and bottom fibers of a beam at maximum load. It serves as a practical strength comparison for the different species of timber.

5. **Modulus of elasticity.** This is a measure of the stiffness or rigidity of a beam or column. It is the ratio of stress per unit area to deformation per unit of length and applies only within proportional limits.

**NATURAL DEFECTS IN WOOD. 1. Decay.** Decay is caused by organisms known as fungi. Fungi requirements are food, air, suitable temperature, and suitable moisture content. Wood with moisture content less than approximately

**Table 12. Average Percentage Deficiency in Strength Properties of Cross-Grained Material of Various Slopes with Respect to Straight-Grained Material**

| Species of wood and slope of grain | Static bending | | | Impact bending maximum drop | Compression parallel to grain, maximum crushing strength |
|---|---|---|---|---|---|
| | Modulus of rupture | Modulus of elasticity | Work to maximum load | | |
| White ash: | | | | | |
| 1:25 ............... | 4 | 2 | 9 | 6 | 0 |
| 1:20 ............... | 6 | 3 | 17 | 12 | 0 |
| 1:15 ............... | 11 | 4 | 27 | 22 | 0 |
| 1:10 ............... | 18 | 7 | 43 | 37 | 1 |
| 1:5 ............... | 36 | 22 | 61 | 59 | 7 |
| Douglas-fir: | | | | | |
| 1:25 ............... | 7 | 4 | 17 | 1 | ... |
| 1:20 ............... | 10 | 6 | 24 | 4 | ... |
| 1:15 ............... | 15 | 8 | 34 | 13 | ... |
| 1:10 ............... | 25 | 14 | 46 | 31 | ... |
| 1:5 ............... | 54 | 40 | 68 | 65 | ... |
| Sitka spruce: | | | | | |
| 1:25 ............... | 2 | 2 | 14 | 8 | ... |
| 1:20 ............... | 4 | 4 | 21 | 13 | ... |
| 1:15 ............... | 8 | 7 | 33 | 22 | ... |
| 1:10 ............... | 17 | 13 | 55 | 45 | ... |
| 1:5 ............... | 44 | 36 | 76 | 69 | ... |
| Average: | | | | | |
| 1:25 .......... | 4 | 3 | 13 | 5 | ... |
| 1:20 .......... | 7 | 4 | 21 | 10 | ... |
| 1:15 .......... | 11 | 6 | 31 | 19 | ... |
| 1:10 .......... | 19 | 11 | 48 | 38 | ... |
| 1:5 .......... | 45 | 33 | 68 | 64 | ... |

Source: U. S. Dept. Agr., Strength and related properties of woods grown in the United States, *Tech. Bull.* 479, 1935.

20 percent will not decay owing to the lack of sufficient moisture for fungi development. Wood under water will not decay because the air supply of fungi is lacking. Decay affects shock resistance at a very early incipient stage (see "Wood Preservation," page **14·46**, for additional information).

2. **Cross grain.** This term denotes the deviation of wood fibers from a direction parallel to the longitudinal axis of a piece of wood. It is expressed as a slope, such as 1 in 15, meaning that the grain deviates 1 in. from the axis in a distance of 15 in. Subtypes include diagonal, spiral, and irregular grain. Grain may slope on both flat-sawed and quarter-sawed faces.

$$\text{Resultant slope} = \frac{\sqrt{a^2 + b^2}}{ab}$$

where $a$ = slope on flat-sawed face

$b$ = slope on quarter-sawed face

**Example.** Slopes = 1 in 5 and 1 in 12

$$\frac{\sqrt{5^2 + 12^2}}{5 \times 12} = \frac{13}{60} = 1 \text{ in } 4.6$$

3. **Knots.** Cut at right angles, a knot is round; cut diagonally, it is oval; and cut lengthwise, it is a spike knot. An intergrown knot has continuous growth at limb and trunk junction; encased knots occur after the limb dies, when the fibers of knot and trunk are not continuous. The effect on bending strength of intergrown and encased knots is about equal. They seriously affect bending strength on the tension face, less seriously on the compression side. They are of little importance in stiffness or shear. Knots are unimportant in long columns, but they reduce intermediate and short-column strength in approximate proportion to their size.

4. **Compression wood** (red wood, *rotholz*). This is abnormal growth frequently occurring on the under side of leaning trees and limbs of softwoods. It is denser and harder than other wood, is characterized by wide, eccentric annual rings, lack of contrast between spring and summerwood, and is more or less darkreddish to brown in color. Generally compression wood has high longitudinal shrinkage, low stiffness, and for its weight, a general deficiency in most other properties.

5. **Insect holes.** Occasional wormholes do not seriously weaken wood. Numerous holes have a somewhat similar effect as knots, except that no grain distortion is involved. Such holes are classified as pin holes, grub holes, and powder post. Strength can be seriously impaired with little surface evidence showing.

6. **Molds and stains.** These ordinarily do not significantly affect strength in themselves but cause degrade of lumber. They feed on cell contents rather than on the cell itself and are forerunners of decay fungi.

7. **Pitch pocket.** This is a well-defined opening extending parallel to the annual rings; it contains free resin and is confined to pines, spruces, Douglas-fir, tamarack, and western larch. A large number may affect strength and can indicate shake.

8. **Shake.** This is separation of wood along the grain, primarily between or within annual rings. In beams, shakes encourage horizontal shear failures and seriously affect strength.

## Table 13. Approximate Comparison of Seven Properties[a] Important in the Processing and Use of Wood

| Common names of species | Ease of kiln drying[b] | Ability to stay in place | Work-ability[c] | Nail-holding ability | Ease of gluing[d] | Resistance to decay (heart-wood) | Ability to hold paint (outside use)[e] |
|---|---|---|---|---|---|---|---|
| | 1 | 2 | 3 | 4 | 5 | 6 | 7 |
| **HARDWOODS** | | | | | | | |
| Alder, red | 2 | 3 | 2 | ... | 1 | ... | 3 |
| Ash, black | 3 | 4 | 3 | ... | 2' | 4 | 5 |
| Ash, white | 2 | 3 | 3 | 1 | 3 | 4 | 5 |
| Aspen | 2 | 3 | 2 | 4 | 2 | 5 | 3 |
| Baldcypress | 3 | 2 | 2 | 3 | 2 | 1 | 1 |
| Basswood | 2 | 3 | 1 | 4 | 2 | 5 | 3 |
| Beech | 4 | 4 | 3 | 1 | 3 | 4 | 4 |
| Birch, paper | 2 | 4 | 2 | ... | 2' | 4 | 4 |
| Birch, sweet and yellow.. | 2 | 4 | 3 | 1 | 3 | 4 | 4 |
| Buckeye, yellow | 2 | 3 | 1 | 4 | 2' | ... | 3 |
| Butternut | 2 | 2 | 2 | ... | 2 | 3 | 5 |
| Cherry, black | 4 | 3 | 3 | 2 | 3 | ... | 4 |
| Chestnut | 2 | 2 | 2 | 3 | 1 | 1 | 4 |
| Cottonwood, black | 3 | 4 | 2 | 4 | 2 | 5 | 3 |
| Cottonwood, eastern | 2 | 4 | 2 | 4 | 2 | 5 | 3 |
| Cucumbertree | 2 | 4 | 2 | 3 | 3 | ... | 4 |
| Dogwood, flowering | 2 | 5 | 5 | 1 | 3' | ... | |
| Elm, American | 3 | 5 | 3 | 2 | 3 | ... | 5 |
| Elm, rock | 3 | 5 | 3 | 1 | 3 | ... | 5 |
| Hackberry | 2 | 4 | 3 | 2 | 1 | ... | 5 |
| Hickory, shagbark | 4 | 5 | 3 | 1 | 3 | 4 | 4 |
| Maple, red | 3 | 3 | 3 | 2 | 3' | 4 | 4 |
| Maple, sugar | 3 | 4 | 3 | 1 | 3 | 4 | 4 |
| Oak, red | 4, 5[f] | 4 | 3 | 1 | 3 | 4 | |
| Oak, white | 4, 5[f] | 4 | 3 | 1 | 3 | 2 | 4 |
| Persimmon, common | 4 | 4 | 3 | 1 | 3 | ... | |
| Sweetgum | 2, 4[g] | 4 | 2 | 2 | 3 | 3 | 4 |
| Sycamore, American | 4 | 4 | 3 | 2 | 3 | ... | 4 |
| Tupelo, black | 2 | 5 | 3 | 2 | 3 | 5 | 4 |
| Walnut, black | 4 | 2 | 2 | 2 | 3 | 1 | 5 |
| Willow, black | 2 | 3 | 1 | 4 | 1 | 5 | 5 |
| Yellow-poplar | 2 | 2 | 1 | 3 | 2 | 4 | 3 |

[a] Species which are rated relatively high in the property listed are assigned the lowest numbers; species rated low in the property are assigned the highest numbers. For some properties the woods are divided into five groups; for other properties into three or four groups.

[b] Softwoods are in general easier to dry than hardwoods. A softwood given the same numerical rating as a hardwood is, therefore, regarded as slightly easier to dry. These ratings are based on ease of removal of moisture without visible degrade but do not take into account susceptibility to reduction in strength when dried under high temperatures.

[c] Workability is based on a combination of the hardness, texture, and character of the surfaces obtained. Thus woods assigned a "1" rating have a soft, uniform texture and finish to a smooth surface.

[d] Class 1 woods are those which glue easily with different glues under a wide range of gluing conditions. Class 2 woods glue satisfactorily with moderate care in the gluing operation. Class 3 woods require carefully controlled gluing conditions, or special treatment before gluing. The prime mark following the number indicates that inadequate data are available and that the classification is based on the similarity of the wood to species of known gluing properties.

[e] The classification of woods on the basis of paint-holding ability applies to outdoor use only, e.g., painted house or barn siding. The classification does not hold for hardwoods if special applications, such as wood filler, are made prior to painting, and it does not necessarily hold for any woods for interior painting, particularly natural finishes.

[f] 4 refers to the upland type of oak and 5 to the lowland type of oak.

[g] 2 refers to sapwood and 4 to heartwood, known commercially as sap gum and red gum, respectively.

Table 13. Approximate Comparison of Seven Properties [a] Important in the Processing and Use of Wood (Continued)

| Common names of species | Ease of kiln drying [b] | Ability to stay in place | Work- ability [c] | Nail- holding ability | Ease of gluing [d] | Resist- ance to decay (heart- wood) | Ability to hold paint (outside use) [e] |
|---|---|---|---|---|---|---|---|
| | 1 | 2 | 3 | 4 | 5 | 6 | 7 |
| **SOFTWOODS** | | | | | | | |
| Cedar, Alaska | 1 | 1 | 2 | 3 | 2 | 1 | 1 |
| Cedar, incense- | 1 | 1 | 1 | 4 | 2' | 1 | 1 |
| Cedar, northern white- | 2 | 1 | 1 | ... | 2' | 1 | 1 |
| Cedar, Port-Orford- | 2 | 2 | 2 | 3 | 2' | 1 | 1 |
| Cedar, western redcedar | 2, 3 [h] | 1 | 1 | 4 | 1 | 1 | 1 |
| Douglas-fir | 1 | 3 | 3 | 2, 3 [i] | 2 | 3 | 4 |
| Fir, grand, noble and white | 1 | 3 | 2 | 4 | 1 | 5 | 3 |
| Fir, subalpine and balsam | 1 | ... | 2 | 4 | 1' | 5 | 3 |
| Hemlock, eastern | 2 | 3 | 2 | 4 | 2' | 4 | 3 |
| Hemlock, western | 2 | 3 | 2 | 3 | 1 | 4 | 3 |
| Larch, western | 3 | 3 | 3 | 2 | 2 | 3 | 4 |
| Pine, eastern white | 2 | 1 | 1 | 4 | 1 | 3 | 2 |
| Pine, jack | 1 | 3 | 2 | ... | 2' | ... | 3 |
| Pine, lodgepole | 1 | 2 | 2 | 4 | 2' | ... | 3 |
| Pine, ponderosa | 1 | 2 | 1 | 4 | 2 | ... | 3 |
| Pine, red | 1 | 3 | 2 | 3 | 2' | ... | 4 |
| Pine, southern yellow | 1 | 3 | 3 | 2 | 2 | 3 | 4 |
| Pine, sugar | 2 | 1 | 1 | 4 | 1 | ... | 2 |
| Pine, western white | 3 | 2 | 1 | 4 | 1 | ... | 2 |
| Redwood | 3, 4 [j] | 2 | 2 | 3 | 1 | 1 | 1 |
| Spruce, Engelmann | 2 | 2 | 2 | 4 | 2' | 4 | 3 |
| Spruce, red and white | 1 | 2 | 2 | 3 | 1 | 4 | 3 |
| Spruce, Sitka | 1 | 2 | 2 | 3 | 1 | 4 | 3 |
| Tamarack | 2 | 3 | 3 | ... | 2' | 3 | 4 |

[h] 2 refers to material from upper logs and 3 to material from butt logs, which are generally susceptible to collapse.

[i] 2 refers to coast-type Douglas-fir and 3 to Rocky Mountain type.

[j] 3 refers to material from upper logs and 4 to sinker stock from butt logs.

Source: Revised from Table 7, U. S. Dept. Agr., Strength and related properties of woods grown in the United States, *Tech. Bull. 479*, 1935.

9. **Checks.** These are separations along the grain, the greater part occurring across the annual rings, and generally occur in seasoning. They reduce beam strength, which is due to lowering of resistance to horizontal shear, and cause serious weakening in tension perpendicular to the grain.

10. **Mineral streaks.** These are traceable to bird pecks or holes. Discolored streaks are caused by oxidation or other chemical changes in the wood; they may impair its appearance, but they have little effect on the strength of the wood.

**COMPARISON OF SPECIES WITH RESPECT TO IMPORTANT PROPERTIES.** Tables 13, 14, and 15 summarize data concerning properties of various species of trees in the processing and use of wood, including ease of kiln drying, workability, resistance to decay, strength properties, and weight per cubic foot. The common and botanical names used in these tables conform to the official nomenclature used in the wood handbook of the U. S. Forest Service, source of the tables.

## Table 14·26. Strength Properties of Some Commercially Important Woods Grown in the United States

(Results of tests on small,[a] clear specimens in the green and air-dry condition [b])

| Commercial and botanical name of species | Moisture content (%) | Specific gravity [c] | Static bending — Fiber stress at proportional limit (psi.) | Static bending — Modulus of Rupture (psi.) | Static bending — Modulus of Elasticity (1,000 psi.) | Impact bending, height of drop causing complete failure (50-pound hammer) (in.) | Compression parallel to grain, maximum crushing strength (psi.) | Compression perpendicular to grain, fiber stress at proportional limit (psi.) | Shear parallel to grain maximum shearing strength (psi.) | Hardness — Load required to embed a 0.444-inch ball to ½ its diameter: End (lb.) | Hardness — Side (lb.) |
|---|---|---|---|---|---|---|---|---|---|---|---|
| Alder, red (Alnus rubra) | 98 | 0.37 | 3,800 | 6,500 | 1,170 | 22 | 2,960 | 310 | 770 | 550 | 440 |
|  | 12 | .41 | 6,900 | 9,800 | 1,380 | 20 | 5,820 | 540 | 1,080 | 980 | 590 |
| Ash, black (Fraxinus nigra) | 85 | .45 | 2,600 | 6,000 | 1,040 | 33 | 2,300 | 430 | 860 | 590 | · · · |
|  | 12 | .49 | 7,200 | 12,600 | 1,600 | 35 | 5,970 | 940 | 1,570 | 1,150 | · · · |
| Ash, commercial white [d] (Fraxinus sp.) | 43 | .54 | 5,300 | 9,500 | 1,400 | 37 | 4,060 | 860 | 1,350 | 1,010 | 940 |
|  | 12 | .58 | 8,900 | 14,600 | 1,680 | 40 | 7,280 | 1,510 | 1,920 | 1,680 | 1,260 |
| Ash, Oregon (Fraxinus latifolia) | 48 | .50 | 4,200 | 7,600 | 1,130 | 39 | 3,510 | 650 | 1,190 | 850 | 790 |
|  | 12 | .55 | 7,000 | 12,700 | 1,360 | 33 | 6,040 | 1,540 | 1,790 | 1,430 | 1,160 |
| Aspen (Populus tremuloides) | 94 | .35 | 3,200 | 5,100 | 860 | 22 | 2,140 | 220 | 660 | 280 | 300 |
|  | 12 | .38 | 5,600 | 8,400 | 1,180 | 21 | 4,250 | 460 | 850 | 510 | 350 |
| Baldcypress (Taxodium distichum) | 91 | .42 | 4,200 | 6,600 | 1,180 | 25 | 3,580 | 500 | 810 | 440 | 390 |
|  | 12 | .46 | 7,200 | 10,600 | 1,440 | 24 | 6,360 | 900 | 1,000 | 660 | 510 |
| Basswood (Tilia americana) | 105 | .32 | 2,700 | 5,000 | 1,040 | 16 | 2,220 | 210 | 600 | 290 | 250 |
|  | 12 | .37 | 5,900 | 8,700 | 1,460 |  | 4,730 | 450 | 990 | 520 | 410 |
| Beech (Fagus grandifolia) | 54 | .56 | 4,300 | 8,600 | 1,380 | 43 | 3,550 | 670 | 1,290 | 970 | 850 |
|  | 12 | .64 | 8,700 | 14,900 | 1,720 | 41 | 7,300 | 1,250 | 2,010 | 1,590 | 1,300 |
| Birch [c] (Betula sp.) | 62 | .57 | 4,400 | 8,700 | 1,560 | 48 | 3,510 | 1,250 | 1,160 | 910 | 850 |
|  | 12 | .63 | 10,100 | 16,700 | 2,070 | 52 | 8,310 | 1,550 | 2,020 | 1,660 | 1,340 |
| Birch, paper (Betula papyrifera) | 65 | .48 | 3,000 | 6,400 | 1,170 | 49 | 2,360 | 340 | 840 | 470 | 560 |
|  | 12 | .55 | 6,900 | 12,300 | 1,590 | 34 | 5,690 | 740 | 1,210 | 890 | 910 |
| Butternut (Juglans cinerea) | 104 | .36 | 2,900 | 5,400 | 970 | 24 | 2,420 | 270 | 760 | 410 | 390 |
|  | 12 | .38 | 5,700 | 8,100 | 1,180 | 24 | 5,110 | 570 | 1,170 | 570 | 490 |
| Cedar, Alaska- (Chamaecyparis nootkatensis) | 38 | .42 | 3,800 | 6,310 | 1,140 | 27 | 3,050 | 430 | 840 | 540 | 440 |
|  | 12 | .44 | 7,100 | 11,100 | 1,420 | 29 | 6,310 | 770 | 1,130 | 790 | 580 |
| Cedar, Atlantic white- (Chamaecyparis thyoides) | 35 | .31 | 2,500 | 4,700 | 750 | 18 | 2,390 | 300 | 690 | 400 | 290 |
|  | 12 | .32 | 4,800 | 6,800 | 930 | 13 | 4,700 | 500 | 800 | 520 | 350 |

(Continued)

| Species | No. of tests | Sp. gr. | | | | | | | | | |
|---|---|---|---|---|---|---|---|---|---|---|---|
| Cedar, eastern redcedar (*Juniperus virginiana*) | 35 | .44 | 3,400 | 7,000 | 650 | 35 | 3,570 | 860 | 1,010 | 760 | 650 |
| | 12 | .47 | 3,800 | 8,800 | 880 | 22 | 6,020 | 1,140 | 830 | 900 | |
| Cedar, incense- (*Libocedrus decurrens*) | 108 | .35 | 3,900 | 6,200 | 840 | 17 | 3,150 | 460 | 880 | 570 | 390 |
| | 12 | | 5,900 | 8,000 | 1,040 | 17 | 5,200 | 730 | 620 | 830 | 470 |
| Cedar, northern white- (*Thuja occidentalis*) | 55 | .29 | 2,600 | 4,200 | 640 | 15 | 1,990 | 290 | 850 | 320 | 230 |
| | 12 | .31 | 4,900 | 6,500 | 800 | 12 | 3,960 | 380 | 830 | 450 | 320 |
| Cedar, Port-Orford- (*Chamaecyparis lawsoniana*) | 43 | .40 | 4,000 | 6,200 | 1,420 | 22 | 3,130 | 350 | 1,080 | 460 | 400 |
| | 12 | .42 | 7,700 | 11,300 | 1,730 | 28 | 6,470 | 760 | 710 | 730 | 560 |
| Cedar, western redcedar (*Thuja plicata*) | 37 | .31 | 3,200 | 5,100 | 920 | 17 | 2,750 | 340 | 860 | 430 | 270 |
| | 12 | .33 | 5,300 | 7,700 | 1,120 | 17 | 5,020 | 610 | 1,130 | 660 | 350 |
| Cherry, black (*Prunus serotina*) | 55 | .47 | 4,200 | 8,000 | 1,310 | 33 | 3,540 | 440 | 1,700 | 750 | 660 |
| | 12 | .50 | 9,000 | 12,300 | 1,490 | 29 | 7,110 | 850 | 800 | 1,470 | 950 |
| Chestnut (*Castanea dentata*) | 122 | .40 | 3,100 | 5,600 | 930 | 24 | 2,470 | 380 | 1,080 | 530 | 420 |
| | 12 | .43 | 6,100 | 8,600 | 1,230 | 19 | 5,320 | 760 | 930 | 720 | 540 |
| Cottonwood, eastern (*Populus deltoides*) | 111 | .37 | 2,900 | 5,300 | 1,010 | 21 | 2,280 | 240 | 600 | 380 | 340 |
| | 12 | .40 | 5,700 | 8,500 | 1,370 | 20 | 4,910 | 470 | 1,020 | 580 | 430 |
| Cottonwood, black (*Populus trichocarpa*) | 132 | .32 | 2,900 | 4,800 | 1,070 | 20 | 2,160 | 200 | 990 | 280 | 250 |
| | 12 | .35 | 5,300 | 8,300 | 1,260 | 22 | 4,420 | 370 | 1,340 | 540 | 350 |
| Cucumbertree (*Magnolia acuminata*) | 80 | .44 | 4,200 | 7,400 | 1,560 | 30 | 3,140 | 410 | 930 | 600 | 520 |
| | 12 | .48 | 8,000 | 12,300 | 1,820 | 35 | 6,310 | 710 | 1,140 | 950 | 700 |
| Douglas-fir (coast region) (*Pseudotsuga menziesii*) | 36 | .45 | 4,800 | 7,600 | 1,550 | 24 | 3,890 | 510 | 870 | 510 | 480 |
| | 12 | .48 | 8,100 | 11,700 | 1,920 | 30 | 7,420 | 910 | 1,190 | 760 | 670 |
| Douglas-fir ("Inland Empire" region) (*Pseudotsuga menziesii*) | 42 | .41 | 3,600 | 6,800 | 1,340 | 22 | 3,240 | 500 | 880 | 530 | 470 |
| | 12 | .44 | 7,400 | 11,300 | 1,610 | 27 | 6,700 | 950 | 1,070 | 720 | 630 |
| Douglas-fir (Rocky Mountain region) (*Pseudotsuga menziesii*) | 38 | .40 | 3,600 | 6,400 | 1,180 | 20 | 3,000 | 450 | 1,000 | 450 | 400 |
| | 12 | .43 | 6,300 | 9,600 | 1,400 | 26 | 6,060 | 820 | 1,510 | 740 | 630 |
| Elm, American (*Ulmus americana*) | 89 | .46 | 3,900 | 7,200 | 1,110 | 38 | 2,910 | 440 | 1,270 | 680 | 680 |
| | 12 | .50 | 7,600 | 11,800 | 1,340 | 39 | 5,520 | 850 | 1,920 | 1,110 | 1,110 |
| Elm, rock (*Ulmus racemosa*) | 48 | .57 | 4,600 | 9,500 | 1,190 | 54 | 3,780 | 750 | 1,110 | 980 | 980 |
| | 12 | .63 | 8,000 | 14,800 | 1,540 | 56 | 7,050 | 1,520 | 1,630 | 1,510 | 1,510 |
| Elm, slippery (*Ulmus fulva*) | 85 | .48 | 4,000 | 8,000 | 1,230 | 47 | 3,320 | 510 | 610 | 750 | 660 |
| | 12 | .53 | 7,700 | 13,000 | 1,490 | 45 | 6,360 | 1,010 | 710 | 1,120 | 860 |
| Fir, balsam (*Abies balsamea*) | 117 | .34 | 3,000 | 4,900 | 960 | 16 | 2,400 | 210 | 750 | 290 | 290 |
| | 12 | .36 | 5,200 | 7,600 | 1,230 | 20 | 4,530 | 380 | 930 | 510 | 400 |
| Fir, commercial white [f] (*Abies* sp.) | 108 | .36 | 3,800 | 5,800 | 1,120 | 22 | 2,810 | 360 | 1,070 | 390 | 340 |
| | 12 | .38 | 6,300 | 9,300 | 1,470 | 20 | 5,380 | 610 | 1,590 | 710 | 700 |
| Hackberry (*Celtis occidentalis*) | 65 | .49 | 2,900 | 6,500 | 950 | 48 | 2,650 | 490 | 850 | 760 | 500 |
| | 12 | .53 | 5,900 | 11,000 | 1,190 | 43 | 5,440 | 1,100 | 1,060 | 1,110 | 400 |
| Hemlock, eastern (*Tsuga canadensis*) | 111 | .38 | 3,800 | 6,400 | 1,070 | 21 | 3,080 | 440 | 810 | 500 | 500 |
| | 12 | .40 | 6,100 | 8,900 | 1,200 | 21 | 5,410 | 800 | 1,170 | 810 | 430 |
| Hemlock, western (*Tsuga heterophylla*) | 74 | .38 | 3,400 | 6,100 | 1,220 | 22 | 2,990 | 390 | | 520 | 500 |
| | 12 | .42 | 6,800 | 10,100 | 1,490 | 26 | 6,210 | 680 | | 940 | 580 |

a Test specimens 2 by 2 in. in section.  Bending specimens 30 in. long; others shorter depending on kind of test.
b The values in the first line for each species are from tests of green material; those in the second line are from tests of seasoned material adjusted to an average air-dry condition of 12 percent moisture.
c Based on weight when oven dry and volume when green or at 12-percent moisture content.
d Average of blue ash (*Fraxinus quadrangulata*), green ash (*F. pennsylvanica*), and white ash (*F. americana*).
e Average of sweet birch (*Betula lenta*) and yellow birch (*B. alleghaniensis*).
f Average of lowland white fir (*Abies grandis*) and white fir (*A. concolor*).

**Table 14. Strength Properties of Some Commercially Important Woods Grown in the United States (Continued)**

| Commercial and botanical name of species | Moisture content (%) | Specific gravity | Static bending — Fiber stress at proportional limit (psi.) | Static bending — Modulus of Rupture (psi.) | Static bending — Modulus of Elasticity (1,000 psi.) | Impact bending, height of drop causing complete failure (50-pound hammer) (in.) | Compression parallel to grain, maximum crushing strength (psi.) | Compression perpendicular to grain, fiber stress at proportional limit (psi.) | Shear parallel to grain, maximum shearing strength (psi.) | Hardness — Load required to embed a 0.444-inch ball to ½ its diameter — End (lb.) | Hardness — Side (lb.) |
|---|---|---|---|---|---|---|---|---|---|---|---|
| Hickory, pecan [g] (Carya sp.) | 68 | .59 | 5,300 | 9,900 | 1,380 | 60 | 4,320 | 980 | 1,260 | 1,274 | 1,308 |
|  | 12 | .65 | 9,100 | 16,300 | 1,780 | 57 | 8,280 | 2,040 | 1,770 | 1,930 | 1,820 |
| Hickory, true [h] (Carya sp.) | 57 | .65 | 6,100 | 11,300 | 1,570 | 88 | 4,570 | 1,080 | 1,360 | 1,440 | 1,390 |
|  | 12 | .73 | 10,900 | 19,700 | 2,180 | 75 | 8,970 | 2,310 | 2,140 | 1,860 | 1,580 |
| Honeylocust (Gleditsia triacanthos) | 63 | .60 | 5,600 | 10,200 | 1,290 | 47 | 4,420 | 1,420 | 1,660 | … | … |
|  | 12 | … | 8,800 | 14,700 | 1,630 | 47 | 7,500 | 2,280 | 2,250 | … | … |
| Larch, western (Larix occidentalis) | 58 | .48 | 4,600 | 7,500 | 1,350 | 24 | 3,800 | 560 | 920 | 470 | 450 |
|  | 12 | .52 | 7,900 | 11,900 | 1,710 | 32 | 7,490 | 1,080 | 1,360 | 1,110 | 760 |
| Locust, black (Robinia pseudoacacia) | 40 | .66 | 8,800 | 13,800 | 1,850 | 44 | 6,800 | 1,430 | 1,760 | 1,640 | 1,570 |
|  | 12 | .69 | 12,800 | 19,400 | 2,050 | 57 | 10,180 | 2,260 | 2,480 | 1,580 | 1,700 |
| Magnolia, southern (Magnolia grandiflora) | 105 | .46 | 3,600 | 6,800 | 1,110 | 54 | 2,700 | 570 | 1,040 | 780 | 740 |
|  | 12 | .50 | 6,800 | 11,200 | 1,400 | 29 | 5,460 | 1,060 | 1,530 | 1,280 | 1,020 |
| Maple, bigleaf (Acer macrophyllum) | 72 | .44 | 4,400 | 7,400 | 1,100 | 23 | 3,240 | 550 | 1,110 | 760 | 620 |
|  | 12 | .48 | 6,600 | 10,700 | 1,450 | 28 | 5,950 | 930 | 1,730 | 1,330 | 850 |
| Maple, black (Acer nigrum) | 65 | .52 | 4,100 | 7,900 | 1,330 | 48 | 3,270 | 740 | 1,130 | 940 | 840 |
|  | 12 | .57 | 8,300 | 13,300 | 1,620 | 40 | 6,680 | 1,250 | 1,820 | 1,700 | 1,180 |
| Maple, red (Acer rubrum) | 63 | .49 | 3,800 | 7,700 | 1,390 | 32 | 3,280 | 500 | 1,150 | 780 | … |
|  | 12 | .54 | 8,700 | 13,400 | 1,640 | 32 | 6,540 | 1,240 | 1,850 | 1,430 | … |
| Maple, silver (Acer saccharinum) | 66 | .44 | 3,100 | 5,800 | 940 | 29 | 2,490 | 460 | 1,050 | 670 | 590 |
|  | 12 | .47 | 6,200 | 8,900 | 1,140 | 25 | 5,220 | 910 | 1,460 | 1,140 | 700 |
| Maple, sugar (Acer saccharum) | 58 | .56 | 5,100 | 9,400 | 1,550 | 40 | 4,020 | 800 | 1,460 | 1,070 | 970 |
|  | 12 | .63 | 9,500 | 15,800 | 1,830 | 39 | 7,830 | 1,810 | 2,330 | 1,840 | 1,450 |
| Oak, red [i] (Quercus sp.) | 80 | .57 | 4,400 | 8,500 | 1,360 | 43 | 3,520 | 800 | 1,220 | 1,050 | 1,030 |
|  | 12 | .63 | 8,400 | 14,400 | 1,810 | 43 | 6,920 | 1,260 | 1,830 | 1,490 | 1,300 |
| Oak, white [j] (Quercus sp.) | 70 | .59 | 4,700 | 8,100 | 1,200 | 42 | 3,520 | 850 | 1,270 | 1,110 | 1,070 |
|  | 12 | .67 | 7,900 | 13,900 | 1,620 | 39 | 7,040 | 1,410 | 1,890 | 1,420 | 1,330 |
| Pine, lodgepole (Pinus contorta) | 65 | .38 | 3,000 | 5,500 | 1,080 | 20 | 2,610 | 310 | 680 | 320 | 330 |
|  | 12 | .41 | 6,700 | 9,400 | 1,340 | 20 | 5,370 | 750 | 880 | 530 | 480 |

| Species | n / M.C. | Sp. gr. | | | | | | | | | |
|---|---|---|---|---|---|---|---|---|---|---|---|
| [name cut off] …white | 12 | .36 | 6,000 | 8,800 | — | 19 | 4,840 | 550 | 860 | 500 | 400 |
| Pine, Norway (*Pinus resinosa*) | 54 | .44 | 3,700 | 6,400 | 1,280 | 28 | 3,080 | 360 | 780 | 360 | 340 |
|  | 12 | .48 | 9,400 | 12,500 | 1,380 | 25 | 7,340 | 830 | 1,230 | 670 | 580 |
| Pine, ponderosa (*Pinus ponderosa*) | 91 | .38 | 3,100 | 5,000 | 970 | 20 | 2,400 | 360 | 680 | 300 | 310 |
|  | 12 | .40 | 6,300 | 9,200 | 1,260 | 17 | 5,270 | 740 | 1,160 | 550 | 450 |
| **Pines, southern yellow:** | | | | | | | | | | | |
| Loblolly (*Pinus taeda*) | 81 | .47 | 4,100 | 7,300 | 1,410 | 30 | 3,490 | 480 | 850 | 420 | 450 |
|  | 12 | .51 | 7,800 | 12,800 | 1,800 | 30 | 7,080 | 980 | 1,370 | 750 | 690 |
| Longleaf (*Pinus palustris*) | 63 | .54 | 5,200 | 8,700 | 1,600 | 35 | 4,300 | 590 | 1,040 | 550 | 590 |
|  | 12 | .58 | 9,400 | 14,700 | 1,990 | 34 | 8,440 | 1,190 | 1,500 | 920 | 870 |
| Shortleaf (*Pinus echinata*) | 81 | .46 | 3,900 | 7,300 | 1,390 | 30 | 3,430 | 440 | 850 | 410 | 440 |
|  | 12 | .51 | 7,700 | 12,800 | 1,760 | 33 | 7,070 | 1,000 | 1,310 | 750 | 690 |
| Pine, sugar (*Pinus lambertiana*) | 137 | .35 | 3,400 | 5,100 | 940 | 17 | 2,530 | 350 | 680 | 320 | 310 |
|  | 12 | .36 | 5,700 | 8,000 | 1,200 | 18 | 4,770 | 590 | 1,050 | 530 | 380 |
| Pine, western white (*Pinus monticola*) | 54 | .36 | 3,400 | 5,200 | 1,170 | 19 | 2,650 | 290 | 640 | 310 | 310 |
|  | 12 | .38 | 6,200 | 9,500 | 1,510 | 23 | 5,620 | 540 | … | 440 | 370 |
| Redwood (virgin) (*Sequoia sempervirens*) | 112 | .38 | 4,800 | 7,500 | 1,180 | 21 | 4,200 | 520 | 800 | 570 | 410 |
|  | 12 | .40 | 6,900 | 10,000 | 1,340 | 19 | 6,150 | 860 | 940 | 860 | 480 |
| Spruce, eastern ᵏ (*Picea sp.*) | 46 | .38 | 3,300 | 5,600 | 1,110 | 21 | 2,600 | 290 | 710 | 390 | 340 |
|  | 12 | .40 | 6,500 | 10,100 | 1,440 | 22 | 5,590 | 590 | 1,070 | 630 | 490 |
| Spruce, Engelmann (*Picea engelmannii*) | 100 | .31 | 2,500 | 4,200 | 830 | 14 | 1,980 | 290 | 590 | 250 | 240 |
|  | 12 | .33 | 6,000 | 8,500 | 1,160 | 15 | 4,580 | 640 | 1,010 | 450 | 310 |
| Spruce, Sitka (*Picea sitchensis*) | 42 | .37 | 3,300 | 5,700 | 1,230 | 24 | 2,670 | 340 | 760 | 430 | 350 |
|  | 12 | .40 | 6,700 | 10,200 | 1,570 | 25 | 5,610 | 710 | 1,150 | 840 | 510 |
| Sugarberry (*Celtis laevigata*) | 62 | .47 | 3,200 | 6,600 | 810 | 33 | 2,800 | 580 | 1,050 | … | 740 |
|  | 12 | .51 | 6,200 | 9,900 | 1,140 | 36 | 5,620 | 1,240 | 1,280 | 1,280 | 960 |
| Sweetgum (*Liquidambar styraciflua*) | 81 | .44 | 3,700 | 6,800 | 1,150 | 33 | 2,840 | 460 | 1,070 | 630 | 520 |
|  | 12 | .49 | 8,100 | 11,900 | 1,490 | 32 | 5,800 | 860 | 1,610 | 950 | 690 |
| Sycamore (*Platanus occidentalis*) | 83 | .46 | 3,300 | 6,500 | 1,060 | 26 | 2,920 | 450 | 1,000 | 700 | 610 |
|  | 12 | .49 | 6,400 | 10,000 | 1,420 | 28 | 5,380 | 860 | 1,470 | 920 | 770 |
| Tamarack (*Larix laricina*) | 52 | .49 | 4,200 | 7,200 | 1,240 | 23 | 3,480 | 480 | 860 | 400 | 380 |
|  | 12 | .53 | 8,000 | 11,600 | 1,640 | 30 | 7,160 | 990 | 1,280 | 670 | 590 |
| Tupelo, black (*Nyssa sylvatica*) | 55 | .46 | 4,200 | 7,000 | 1,030 | 30 | 3,040 | 600 | 1,100 | 790 | 640 |
|  | 12 | .50 | 7,300 | 9,600 | 1,200 | 22 | 5,520 | 1,150 | 1,340 | 1,240 | 810 |
| Tupelo, water (*Nyssa aquatica*) | 97 | .46 | 4,200 | 7,300 | 1,050 | 30 | 3,370 | 590 | 1,190 | 800 | 710 |
|  | 12 | .50 | 7,200 | 9,600 | 1,260 | 23 | 5,920 | 1,070 | 1,590 | 1,200 | 880 |
| Walnut, black (*Juglans nigra*) | 81 | .51 | 5,200 | 9,500 | 1,420 | 37 | 4,300 | 600 | 1,220 | 960 | 900 |
|  | 12 | .55 | 10,500 | 14,600 | 1,680 | 34 | 7,580 | 1,250 | 1,370 | 1,050 | 1,010 |
| Yellow-poplar (*Liriodendron tulipifera*) | 64 | .38 | 3,400 | 9,200 | 1,090 | 18 | 2,420 | 330 | 740 | 390 | 340 |
|  | 12 | .40 | 6,100 | … | 1,500 | 20 | 5,290 | 580 | 1,100 | 560 | 450 |

ᵍ Average of bitternut hickory (*Carya cordiformis*), nutmeg hickory (*Carya myristicaeformis*), water hickory (*C. aquatica*), and pecan (*C. illinoensis*).
ʰ Average of shellbark hickory (*Carya laciniosa*), mockernut hickory (*C. tomentosa*), pignut hickory (*C. glabra*), and shagbark hickory (*C. ovata*).
ⁱ Average of black oak (*Quercus velutina*), laurel oak (*Q. laurifolia*), pin oak (*Q. palustris*), red oak (*Q. rubra*), scarlet oak (*Q. coccinea*), southern red oak (*Q. falcata*), cherrybark oak (*Q. falcata var. pagodaefolia*), water oak (*Q. nigra*), and willow oak (*Q. phellos*).
ʲ Average of bur oak (*Quercus macrocarpa*), chestnut oak (*Q. prinus*), post oak (*Q. stellata*), swamp chestnut oak (*Q. michauxii*), swamp white oak (*Q. bicolor*), and white oak (*Q. alba*).
ᵏ Average of black spruce (*Picea mariana*), red spruce (*P. rubens*), and white spruce (*P. glauca*).
Source: U. S. Dept. Agr. *Wood handbook*, revised 1940.

### Table 15. Weights of Commercially Important Woods Grown in the United States

| Species | Weight per cubic foot Green (lb.) | Air-dry (12-percent moisture content) (lb.) | Weight per 1,000 board feet (nominal size) air-dry (12-percent moisture content) (lb.) | Species | Weight per cubic foot Green (lb.) | Air-dry (12-percent moisture content) (lb.) | Weight per 1,000 board feet (nominal size) air-dry (12-percent moisture content) (lb.) |
|---|---|---|---|---|---|---|---|
| Alder, red | 46 | 28 | 2,330 | Hickory, pecan d | 62 | 45 | 3,750 |
| Ash, black | 52 | 34 | 2,830 | Hickory, true e | 63 | 51 | 4,250 |
| Ash, commercial white a | 48 | 41 | 3,420 | Honeylocust | 61 | ... | ... |
| Ash, Oregon | 46 | 38 | 3,160 | Larch, western | 48 | 36 | 3,000 |
| Aspen | 43 | 26 | 2,170 | Locust, black | 58 | 48 | 4,000 |
| Baldcypress | 51 | 32 | 2,670 | Magnolia, cucumber | 49 | 33 | 2,750 |
| Basswood | 42 | 26 | 2,170 | Magnolia, evergreen | 59 | 35 | 2,920 |
| Beech | 54 | 45 | 3,750 | Maple, bigleaf | 47 | 34 | 2,830 |
| Birch b | 57 | 44 | 3,670 | Maple, black | 54 | 40 | 3,330 |
| Birch, paper | 50 | 38 | 3,160 | Maple, red | 50 | 38 | 3,170 |
| Butternut | 46 | 27 | 2,250 | Maple, silver | 45 | 33 | 2,750 |
| Cedar, Alaska | 36 | 31 | 2,580 | Maple, sugar | 56 | 44 | 3,670 |
| Cedar, Atlantic white- | 26 | 23 | 1,920 | Oak, red f | 64 | 44 | 3,670 |
| Cedar, eastern redcedar | 37 | 33 | 2,750 | Oak, white g | 63 | 47 | 3,920 |
| Cedar, incense- | 45 | ... | ... | Pine, lodgepole | 39 | 29 | 2,420 |
| Cedar, northern white- | 28 | 22 | 1,830 | Pine, northern white | 36 | 25 | 2,080 |
| Cedar, Port-Orford- | 56 | 29 | 2,420 | Pine, Norway | 42 | 34 | 2,830 |
| Cedar, western redcedar | 27 | 23 | 1,920 | Pine, ponderosa | 45 | 28 | 2,330 |
| Cherry, black | 45 | 35 | 2,930 | Pines, southern yellow: | | | |
| Chestnut | 55 | 30 | 2,500 | Pine, loblolly | 53 | 36 | 3,000 |
| Cottonwood, eastern | 49 | 28 | 2,330 | Pine, longleaf | 55 | 41 | 3,420 |
| Cottonwood, northern black | 46 | 24 | 2,000 | Pine, shortleaf | 52 | 36 | 3,000 |
| Douglas-fir (coast region) | 38 | 34 | 2,830 | Pine, sugar | 52 | 25 | 2,080 |
| Douglas-fir ("Inland Empire" region) | 36 | 31 | 2,580 | Pine, western white | 35 | 27 | 2,250 |
| Douglas-fir (Rocky Mountain region) | 35 | 30 | 2,500 | Redwood | 50 | 28 | 2,330 |
| Elm, American | 54 | 35 | 2,920 | Spruce, eastern h | 34 | 28 | 2,330 |
| Elm, rock | 53 | 44 | 3,670 | Spruce, Engelmann | 39 | 23 | 1,920 |
| Elm, slippery | 56 | 37 | 3,080 | Spruce, Sitka | 33 | 28 | 2,330 |
| Fir, balsam | 45 | 25 | 2,080 | Sugarberry | 48 | 36 | 3,000 |
| Fir, commercial white c | 46 | 27 | 2,250 | Sweetgum | 50 | 34 | 2,830 |
| Hackberry | 50 | 37 | 3,080 | Sycamore | 52 | 34 | 2,830 |
| Hemlock, eastern | 50 | 28 | 2,330 | Tamarack | 47 | 37 | 3,080 |
| Hemlock, western | 41 | 29 | 2,420 | Tupelo, black | 45 | 35 | 2,920 |
| | | | | Tupelo, water | 56 | 35 | 2,920 |
| | | | | Walnut, black | 58 | 38 | 3,170 |
| | | | | Yellow-poplar | 38 | 28 | 2,330 |

a Average of blue ash, green ash, and white ash.
b Average of sweet birch and yellow birch.
c Average of lowland white fir and white fir.
d Average of bitternut hickory, nutmeg hickory, water hickory, and pecan.
e Average of bigleaf shagbark hickory, mockernut hickory, pignut hickory, and shagbark hickory.
f Average of black oak, laurel oak, pin oak, red oak, scarlet oak, southern red oak, swamp red oak, water oak, and willow oak.
g Average of bur oak, chestnut oak, post oak, swamp chestnut oak, swamp white oak, and white oak.
h Average of black spruce, red spruce, and white spruce.

Source: U. S. Dept. Agr., *Wood handbook*, rev., 1940.

## ALLOWABLE LOADS ON WOODEN BEAMS AND COLUMNS.

**Formulas and Examples of Their Use.** Material for this section was taken essentially from *Modern timber engineering* by W. F. Schofield and W. H. O'Brien.

**Beams.** 1. Extreme fiber stress in bending. The following formula can be used for calculating ultimate bending strength or safe load:

$$f = \frac{Mn}{I} = \frac{M}{S}$$

where $f =$ unit stress in extreme fiber in bending, psi ($f =$ modulus of rupture if the ultimate strength is desired; if a safe load is desired, $f$ is the safe extreme fiber stress for the kind and grade of material used).

$M =$ maximum bending or resisting moment, inch-pounds.

$M = PL/4$ (for a concentrated load on a simply supported beam at the center of span)

$M = WL/8$ (simply supported beam, uniformly distributed load)

$W =$ total load, uniformly distributed over span $L$, in pounds

$P =$ concentrated load at center of span, in pounds

$L =$ span, in inches

$n =$ distance from neutral axis to extreme fiber, in inches

$I =$ moment of inertia of section, in.$^4$ ($bd^3/12$ for rectangular beams)

$S =$ section modulus, in.$^3$ ($bd^2/6$ for rectangular beams)

**Example.** Find the unit fiber stress in a nominal 2" x 10" beam, 10' span with a concentrated load of 800 lb. at midspan.

$$M = \frac{WL}{4} = \frac{800 \times 10 \times 12}{4} = 24,000 \text{ in.-lb.}$$

$$f = \frac{M}{S} = \frac{24,000}{24.44} = 982 \text{ psi}$$

2. Horizontal shear.

$$H = \frac{VQ}{Ib} = \frac{3V}{2bd} \text{ for a rectangular beam}$$

where $H =$ unit horizontal shear stress, psi

$V =$ total vertical shear or reaction, in pounds

$Q =$ statical moment of the area above or below the neutral axis

$b =$ beam width, in.

$d =$ beam depth, in.

In calculating $V$ in this formula (1) neglect all loads within a distance equal to the height of the beam from both ends; (2) place the heavy concentrated moving load at a distance three times the height of the beam from the support, but not more than ¼ the span length from support; (3) treat all other loads in the usual manner.

**Example.** Check the horizontal shearing stress in a 6" x 12" beam with a clear span of 10', carrying a uniform load of 1,000 lb. per ft. Actual depth of 12" beam is 11½" and neglecting loads within distance of height of beam from each end, the value for $V$ is based on a load for a beam length of 10' minus 2 times 11½" = 8.0833'.

$$V = \frac{1,000 \times 8.0833}{2} = 4,042 \text{ lb. (neglecting beam weight)}$$

$$H = \frac{3V}{2bd} = \frac{3 \times 4,042}{2 \times 64.69} = 94 \text{ psi}$$

3. Compression perpendicular to the grain. For bearing of any length at the ends of a beam and for bearings 6 in. or more in length at any other place along the beam, the unit stress in compression perpendicular to the grain for the grade and species apply. However for shorter bearings not closer than 3 in. from the end, the allowable load per square inch may be increased by:

$$\frac{l + \frac{3}{8}}{l}$$

(l is the length of bearing in inches measured along the grain)

**Example.** Check the unit compression perpendicular to grain stress on a 4″ x 12″ beam supporting a 4″ x 4″ post with a load of 5,250 lb. The allowable unit compression stress for the grade is 380 psi.

Area of 4″ x 4″ = 13.14 sq. in. (actual std. dimensions) 5,250/13.14 = 400 psi.

Increasing the allowable unit stress (assuming short bearing not closer than 3 in. from the end) by the formula:

$$\frac{4 + \frac{3}{8}}{4} = 1.1 \times 380 = 418 \text{ psi}$$

Thus the beam will be adequate in compression perpendicular to grain.

4. Deflection. When deflection is a factor in design, usual formulas are:

a. Uniformly loaded beams, supported at both ends

$$D = \frac{5Wl^3}{384\,EI}$$

b. Concentrated load at center, supported both ends

$$D = \frac{Pl^3}{48\,EI}$$

where  $D$ = deflection, in inches
$W$ = total distributed load, in pounds
$l$ = span, in inches
$E$ = modulus of elasticity, in inches
$I$ = moment of inertia, in.$^4$
$P$ = concentrated load, in pounds

Deflection is usually limited to 1/360 of the span. Limitation for highway bridges is usually 1/200; stringers in railway bridges are usually from 1/200 to 1/300 of the span.

Seasoned timber takes a permanent set under a long-time load which is about equal to the short-time deflection which is calculated for the species used. Unseasoned timber will deflect much more.

5. Lateral deflection. Beams that are narrow in relation to their depth should be supported laterally. In floor joists this is accomplished by diagonal bridging placed at intervals not exceeding 8 ft. between bridging or between bridging and bearing.

Following are approximate rules for providing lateral restraint for rectangular beams and joists.

a. If the ratio of depth to breadth is 2 to 1, no support is needed.
b. If the ratio is 3 to 1, the ends should be held in position.
c. If the ratio is 4 to 1, the piece should be held in line, as in a well-bolted chord member in a truss

d. If the ratio is 5 to 1, one edge should be held in line.

e. If the ratio is 6 to 1, diagonal bridging as described above for floor joists should be used.

f. If the ratio is 7 to 1, both edges should be held in line.

6. Form factor. When the height of a timber beam of rectangular cross-section is increased, the modulus of rupture decreases slightly. The form factor is the ratio of the unit strength value of a beam of structural size to the corresponding unit value for a beam 2 x 2 in. in cross-section. The form factor $F$, is inserted in the usual beam formula as follows:

$$M = \frac{FfI}{n}$$

The value $F$ is calculated by means of the formula:

$$F = 1 - 0.07 \left( \sqrt{\frac{d}{2}} - 1 \right)$$

In the allowable unit fiber stresses assigned to structural grades of lumber, this factor is already applied and therefore does not have to be applied in calculations for ordinary rectangular beams.

In beams of circular section and of square section with a diagonal vertical, the form factor of a circular section is 1.18; that of a square section is 1.414.

**Columns.** In general, the allowable unit design stress in compression parallel to grain $c$, for the species and grade of lumber used, is the maximum stress in pounds per square inch of cross-sectional area which should be induced in a column or similar member. It applies when the $l/d$ of the column is equal to or less than $\sqrt{0.30E/c}$.

For columns with $l/d$ greater than $\sqrt{0.30E/c}$ the maximum unit load in pounds per square inch is determined by the formula:

$$P/A = \frac{0.30\,E}{(l/d)^2}$$

where $l$ = length, in.
$c$ = compression parallel to grain, psi
$P$ = total load, pounds
$E$ = modulus of elasticity, psi
$d$ = depth, in. (least cross-sectional dimension)
$A$ = area, sq. in.

The $l/d$ ratio for solid columns should not exceed 50.

Relative strength values for "built-up" columns (planks, etc., spiked or bolted together) as compared to solid columns are shown in Table 16.

**Table 16. Strength of Built-up Columns as Compared to Solid Columns of Similar Grade**

| $l/d$ ratio | Percentage of solid column strength | $l/d$ ratio | Percentage of solid column strength |
|:---:|:---:|:---:|:---:|
| 6 | 82 | 18 | 65 |
| 10 | 77 | 22 | 74 |
| 14 | 71 | 26 | 82 |

Source: W. F. Schofield and W. H. O'Brien, *Modern timber engineering*, Southern Pine Assn., 1954.

Component planks should not be wider than five times their thickness. Spikes should penetrate two planks and extend well into a third plank and should not be placed farther apart longitudinally than six times the plank thickness. Edges should be tied together with cover plates.

**Table 17.  Representative Allowable Unit Compressive Stress $P/A$ for Wood Columns**

From $P/A = \dfrac{0.30E}{(l/d)^2}$; but must not exceed $c$ for species and grade modified according to the load provisions of standard design procedures.

| * | | | | | $P/A$ | | | |
|---|---|---|---|---|---|---|---|---|
| $(l/d)$ | $(l/d)^2$ | $E = 1{,}000{,}000$ | $E = 1{,}100{,}000$ | $E = 1{,}200{,}000$ | $E = 1{,}300{,}000$ | $E = 1{,}400{,}000$ | $E = 1{,}500{,}000$ | $E = 1{,}600{,}000$ |
| 10 | 100 | 3,000 | 3,300 | 3,600 | 3,900 | 4,200 | 4,500 | 4,800 |
| 11 | 121 | 2,479 | 2,727 | 2,975 | 3,223 | 3,471 | 3,719 | 3,967 |
| 12 | 144 | 2,083 | 2,292 | 2,500 | 2,708 | 2,917 | 3,125 | 3,333 |
| 13 | 169 | 1,775 | 1,953 | 2,130 | 2,308 | 2,485 | 2,663 | 2,840 |
| 14 | 196 | 1,531 | 1,684 | 1,837 | 1,990 | 2,143 | 2,296 | 2,449 |
| 15 | 225 | 1,333 | 1,467 | 1,600 | 1,733 | 1,867 | 2,000 | 2,133 |
| 16 | 256 | 1,172 | 1,289 | 1,406 | 1,523 | 1,641 | 1,758 | 1,875 |
| 17 | 289 | 1,038 | 1,142 | 1,246 | 1,349 | 1,453 | 1,557 | 1,661 |
| 18 | 324 | 926 | 1,019 | 1,111 | 1,204 | 1,296 | 1,389 | 1,481 |
| 19 | 361 | 831 | 914 | 997 | 1,080 | 1,163 | 1,247 | 1,330 |
| 20 | 400 | 750 | 825 | 900 | 975 | 1,050 | 1,125 | 1,200 |
| 21 | 441 | 680 | 748 | 816 | 884 | 952 | 1,020 | 1,088 |
| 22 | 484 | 620 | 682 | 744 | 806 | 868 | 930 | 992 |
| 23 | 529 | 567 | 624 | 682 | 737 | 794 | 851 | 907 |
| 24 | 576 | 520 | 573 | 625 | 677 | 729 | 781 | 833 |
| 25 | 625 | 480 | 528 | 576 | 624 | 672 | 720 | 768 |
| 26 | 676 | 444 | 488 | 533 | 577 | 621 | 666 | 710 |
| 27 | 729 | 412 | 453 | 494 | 535 | 576 | 617 | 658 |
| 28 | 784 | 383 | 421 | 459 | 497 | 536 | 574 | 612 |
| 29 | 841 | 357 | 392 | 428 | 464 | 499 | 535 | 571 |
| 30 | 900 | 333 | 367 | 400 | 433 | 467 | 500 | 533 |
| 31 | 901 | 312 | 343 | 375 | 406 | 437 | 468 | 499 |
| 32 | 1,024 | 293 | 322 | 352 | 381 | 410 | 439 | 469 |
| 33 | 1,089 | 275 | 303 | 331 | 358 | 386 | 413 | 441 |
| 34 | 1,156 | 260 | 285 | 311 | 337 | 363 | 389 | 415 |
| 35 | 1,225 | 245 | 269 | 294 | 318 | 343 | 367 | 392 |
| 36 | 1,296 | 231 | 255 | 278 | 301 | 324 | 347 | 370 |
| 37 | 1,369 | 219 | 241 | 263 | 285 | 307 | 329 | 351 |
| 38 | 1,444 | 208 | 229 | 249 | 270 | 291 | 312 | 332 |
| 39 | 1,521 | 197 | 217 | 237 | 256 | 276 | 296 | 316 |
| 40 | 1,600 | 188 | 206 | 225 | 244 | 262 | 281 | 300 |
| 41 | 1,681 | 178 | 196 | 214 | 232 | 250 | 268 | 286 |
| 42 | 1,764 | 170 | 187 | 204 | 221 | 238 | 255 | 272 |
| 43 | 1,849 | 162 | 178 | 195 | 211 | 227 | 243 | 260 |
| 44 | 1,936 | 155 | 170 | 186 | 201 | 217 | 232 | 248 |

* Note: $l/d$ of a simple solid column shall not exceed 50.

Source: W. F. Schofield and W. H. O'Brien, *Modern timber engineering*, Southern Pine Assn., 1954.

# Wood Fastenings

**NAILS AND SPIKES.** Nail point types include (1) long and sharp, (2) common, (3) blunt, and (4) blunt tapered. Generally, long sharp-pointed nails have greater holding power but encourage splitting; blunt points reduce splitting but have reduced holding power.

Nail shank types include common round, barbed, longitudinally grooved, square, triangular, helically grooved, and annularly grooved shanks. The plain round shank generally has the lowest resistance to withdrawal. Cement-coated nails have 85 to 100 percent greater withdrawal resistance when freshly driven in light woods; within approximately one month, about ½ the increase will remain. Helically and annularly grooved nails may have several times the withdrawal resistance and lateral load-carrying capacity of plain shank nails.

Common wire spikes are simply large nails. Lengths vary from 3 to 12 in.; diamond or chisel points are common.

When nails or spikes are driven in unseasoned wood which will subsequently season under load, allowable withdrawal loads should be taken as one-fourth of the values for seasoned lumber. Nails driven into end grain have 50 to 75 percent of side grain withdrawal resistance; the effect is more pronounced in softer woods.

For further information on the use of nails and wood screws, and full information on **lag screws,** see *National design specifications for stress grade lumber and its fastenings,* National Lumber Manufacturers Assn.

### Table 18.  Nail Dimensions; Screw Gauges and Diameters

NAIL DIMENSIONS

| Pennyweight .... | 6 | 8 | 10 | 12 | 16 | 20 | 30 | 40 | 50 | 60 |
|---|---|---|---|---|---|---|---|---|---|---|
| Length   (in.).... | 2 | 2½ | 3 | 3¼ | 3½ | 4 | 4½ | 5 | 5½ | 6 |
| Diameter   (in.).. | 0.113 | 0.131 | 0.148 | 0.148 | 0.162 | 0.192 | 0.207 | 0.225 | 0.244 | 0.263 |

SCREW GAUGES AND DIAMETERS

| Gauge ............... | 0 | 1 | 2 | 3 | 4 | 5 | 6 | 7 | 8 |
|---|---|---|---|---|---|---|---|---|---|
| Diameter   (in.) ....... | 0.060 | 0.073 | 0.086 | 0.099 | 0.112 | 0.125 | 0.138 | 0.151 | 0.164 |

SCREW GAUGES AND DIAMETERS (Continued)

| Gauge ............... | 9 | 10 | 11 | 12 | 14 | 16 | 18 | 20 | 24 |
|---|---|---|---|---|---|---|---|---|---|
| Diameter   (in.) ....... | 0.177 | 0.190 | 0.203 | 0.216 | 0.242 | 0.268 | 0.294 | 0.320 | 0.372 |

**TIMBER CONNECTORS. Split Ring.** This is a device for transmitting loads between two pieces of wood. Split rings are placed in precut grooves made with standard grooving tools. The tongue and groove split in the ring permits simultaneous bearing of the inner surface of the ring against the core left in grooving and the outer face of the ring against the outer wall of the groove. Beveled TECO split rings afford easy assembly, but they are not recommended for use unless power tools are available.

(Timber Engineering Co.)

Sizes: 2½ in.—for trussed rafters or lumber construction involving 2-in. nominal dimension lumber; 4 in.—for truss spans from 30 to 150 ft.

**Toothed Ring.** This is used to transfer stress between two timber members in light, simple structures. No grooves are required; toothed rings are embedded in the faces of members by pressure. Special installation tools are available from the Timber Engineering Company, Washington, D. C. The load-carrying capacity of toothed rings is less than for split rings; they are often used where grooving is undesirable or impossible.

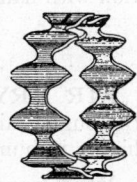
(Timber Engineering Co.)

Sizes: 2 in. and 2⅝ in.—usually used in 4-in. widths of lumber; 3⅜ in. and 4 in. —usually used in 6-in. widths of lumber.

**Shear Plate.** Shear plates are intended primarily for wood-to-steel connections or demountable wood-to-wood connections. They are placed in precut daps and are completely embedded in the timber when in position, being flush with the surface of the timber, and are used to attach columns to footings through steel straps, in connection with steel gusset plates, and for other steel-to-wood connections.

Sizes: 2⅝-in. shear plates compare with 2½-in. split rings; 4-in. shear plates compare with the 4-in. split rings.

**Spike Grid.** This is specially designed for use with piles and poles in trestle construction, piers and wharves, and transmission lines. The single curved grid joins a curved pole or pile surface to a flat-sawed timber; the flat grid joins two flat timbers. The grids are installed by pressure in the manner of toothed rings.

(Timber Engineering Co.)

(Timber Engineering Co.)

**Framing Anchors.** These are devices formed from 18-gauge, zinc-coated, sheet steel. They are available in three basic types in lefts and rights, nails furnished. Toe-nailing is eliminated in framing operations. Typical uses are as joist hangers, rafter spacers (increased anchorage against wind uplift), and as spacers for roof joists.

Detailed information, literature, and typical design data for the use of timber connectors are available from the Timber Engineering Company, Washington, D. C.

(Timber Engineering Co.)          (Metal Industries Inc.)

**Toothed-Ring Burrlock Fastener.** This is similar to a toothed ring except that it is smaller. These fasteners are available in ½-, 1-, and 1½-in. diameters. They are pressed into lumber and may be used in framing members in combination with nails driven through the core of the wood inside the toothed ring.

## Lumber Seasoning

**AIR DRYING.** In most parts of the country, the moisture content of thoroughly air-dried lumber is 12 to 15 percent; it is lower in arid regions and higher in humid regions.

**Yard Layout.**

1. The site should preferably be on high ground that is level, well-drained, and not adjacent to water bodies or wind-obstructing objects.
2. Main alleys should run north and south for maximum sunshine to melt snow and dry up alleys.

3. The ground surface should be free of debris and vegetation. Vegetation can be controlled by crude oil, salt, or weed killers. Cinders, gravel, shells, crushed stone, blacktop, or concrete may be used for alleys and other areas. Hand-stacking yards require only main and cross alleys to be paved. Fork lifts require additional paving areas; paving should be maintained in good condition for safe, efficient operation.

4. Hand-stacking yards. Main alleys should be 16 to 20 ft., cross alleys (transportation and fire protection) 60 ft. or wider, rear alleys 8 ft., side distance pile to pile 2 to 6 ft.

5. Unit packages piled by fork lift. Main alleys should be 24 to 30 ft.; there are usually no rear alleys; piles are placed in rows of 2 to more than 20 running from one main alley to the next; cross alleys are 60 ft. or wider, with 2 to 6 ft. side distance between piles.

**Foundations.** Foundation piers are made of concrete, masonry, preservative-treated blocks or posts of any species, or untreated heartwood of decay-resistant species. Wood posts are usually about 6 by 6 in., spaced about 4 to 5 ft. apart lengthwise and not over 6 ft. laterally. Concrete or masonry piers should extend below frost line. Wood piers may be set in the ground or on sills or sleepers. Pier tops should be in a common plane, horizontal or sloped; the slope should be about 1 in. per ft. of length from front to rear, with rear piers high enough to provide 18-in. clearance from the ground to the first course of boards.

Stringers, running lengthwise of the pile, are steel I-beams, railroad rails, or timbers; timbers should be about 6 by 8 in., preservative treated. Cross beams are placed across stringers and so spaced as to support sticker tiers, 4 by 4 in. to 4 by 6 in. If no stringers are used and cross beams are directly on posts or piers, they should be preservative treated. Stringers and cross beams of foundations for hand-stacked piles are usually arranged so that pile length is perpendicular to the alley.

Unit-package piles are placed parallel to main alleys; foundations may be level or sloped (newer fork lifts will tilt 5°). Pile foundations must be spaced to permit entrance and exit of fork lift; thus stringers cannot be used if rows consist of more than two piles. Where stringers are used, the bolsters are placed across them like cross beams for hand-stacked piles. Unit packages are commonly placed on 4 by 4 in. bolsters on the ground, resulting in poor ground clearance.

Good pile foundations for unit packages consist of 4 to 6 fixed cross beams (concrete, timbers, railroad rails) 2 to 4 ft. apart at both ends, with a central space of 8 ft. or more. Cross beams may be directly on the ground or supported by posts or framework; a removable cross beam is provided for the central 8 ft. or more space. There should be cross beams every 4 ft. and a few at 2-ft. intervals for short stack. Bolsters are typically 4 by 4 in., 2 by 4 in. on edge, or two 2 by 4 in. members placed flatwise; they are usually several inches longer than the package width and provide space for insertion of the forks.

**Piling.** Lumber is typically sorted on the basis of species, grade, and thickness; in addition, sorting is done by width and lengths, and to separate heartwood from sapwood. For example, 1-in. sap gum requires rapid drying to prevent blue stain unless it is antistain dipped, while 1-in. southern lowland red and white oak are susceptible to checking and thus should be dried more slowly.

Box piling is widely used and recommended. A box pile has a square appearance at both ends, has all outer board ends and most inner board ends supported by stickers, and has the outer ends of stickers supported by boards. Box-piled random-length lumber should have the longest boards in the outer tiers; tiers of shorter boards are placed between the tiers of long boards. Ends of shorter boards may be flush with the front, or they may alternate between front and rear in adjacent tiers; boards within a tier should be directly above one another. Unit packages follow the same pattern.

Pile widths for hardwoods vary from 6 to 16 ft. for hand-stacked lumber, the narrower widths predominating. Softwoods are often self-stickered, with piles being equal in length and width. Unit packages are typically 3 to 4½ ft. wide, 4 ft. being common.

Hand-stacked piles range in height from 9 to 16 ft.; mechanical stackers may stack up to 20 to 30 ft. in height. Unit-package piles range from 4 to 30 ft. in height.

For board spacing for flue (under 6 in.) and chimney (over 6 in.) space, a rough rule is 20 percent of the pile width. Chimneys may be straight or tapered so as to be narrower at the top. Unit packages to be kiln-dried later in cross circulation kilns often have boards placed edge to edge; natural-circulation kilns require edge spacing.

**Stickers.** Stock stickers are boards of the same species as the lumber but are usually in narrow widths. Special stickers are made from any species but should preferably be of heartwood. Special stickers for hand-piled softwoods are often nominal 1 in. thick by 4 in. wide; hardwoods 1 in. by 1¼ in. Alignment of stickers with cross beams should be good and should follow pile pitch. Softwoods commonly have 3 to 5 tiers of stickers for 16-foot lumber; hardwoods commonly have 16 in. to 24 in. spacing.

Unit package stickers are usually dressed to ¾ in., are 1½ to 2 in. wide, and the number of stickers used is about the same as for hand-stacked lumber. Stickers flush with board ends, or overhanging, help prevent end-checking and splitting.

**Pile Roofs.** For a hand-stacked, sloped pile, the roof should project about 1 ft. at the front, 2½ ft. at the rear, and 6 in. at the sides. Level unit packages should have a 2-ft. roof projection front and rear, and 6 in. at the sides (except that on the machine side, projections interfere with verticals on the forks). Roof construction varies, but in general it should be tight, with 6 in. of clearance provided.

**KILN DRYING. Current Kiln Schedules Recommended by the Forest Products Laboratory.** These are given in Tables 19A and B.

**General Composition of Schedules.** As temperature and relative humidity do not bear the same relationship to the moisture content of the wood with respect to their effect in causing seasoning defects, temperature and humidity schedules have been made up separately and are shown independent of each other in Table 20.

There are 14 temperature schedules, ranging from the mildest (T1) to the most severe (T14). For instance, T1 has been found suitable for hickory handle stock to prevent pinking, and T14 is commonly used to accelerate the drying of such species as southern pine lumber. The initial temperature is maintained until the moisture content of the stock drops to 30 percent. The final temperature is reached in five steps during the time the moisture content changes from 30 to 15 percent.

The humidity schedules are given in terms of the wet-bulb depression and consist of eight sets of values, identified by numbers from 1 to 8. Each schedule, or set, has a different initial value, but the same final value of 50° F. In each, the final value is reached in six steps, at progressively greater rates that have been found safe and desirable. Another phase of the humidity schedules is the moisture

## Table 19A. Index of Schedules for Kiln Drying Hardwoods

| Species | For lumber | | | | For special items | | | |
|---|---|---|---|---|---|---|---|---|
| | 4/4, 5/4, 6/4 | | 8/4 | | Name | | Temperature | Humidity |
| | Temperature | Humidity | Temperature | Humidity | | | | |
| Alder, red.............. | T10 | D4 | T8 | D3 | | | | |
| Apple................. | T6 | C3 | T3 | C2 | | | | |
| Ash, white............ | T8 | B4 | T5 | B3 | | | | |
| Aspen................ | T12 | E7 | T10 | E6 | | | | |
| Basswood............. | T12 | E7 | T10 | E6 | | | | |
| Beech ............... | T8 | C2 | T5 | C1 | 1-in. squares.......... | | T8 | C3 |
| | | | | | 2-in. squares.......... | | T5 | C2 |
| Birch, paper.......... | T10 | C4 | T8 | C3 | 1-in. squares.......... | | T10 | C6 |
| | | | | | 2-in. squares.......... | | T8 | C4 |
| Birch, yellow.......... | T8 | C4 | T5 | C3 | 1-in. squares.......... | | T8 | C5 |
| | | | | | 2-in. squares.......... | | T5 | C4 |
| Buckeye, yellow........ | T10 | F4 | T8 | F3 | | | | |
| Butternut............. | T10 | E4 | T8 | E3 | | | | |
| Cherry, black......... | T8 | B4 | T5 | B3 | | | | |
| Chestnut............. | T10 | E4 | T8 | E3 | | | | |
| Chinquapin........... | T4 | F1 | T2 | E1 | | | | |
| Cottonwood, black..... | T10 | F5 | T8 | F4 | | | | |
| Dogwood............. | T6 | C3 | T3 | C2 | Shuttles.............. | | T3 | B2 |
| Elm, American........ | T8 | D4 | T6 | D3 | | | | |
| Hackberry............ | T8 | C4 | T6 | C3 | | | | |
| Hickory.............. | T8 | D3 | T6 | D1 | White handles {Small | | T1 | D2 |
| | | | | | {Large | | T1 | C2 |
| | | | | | Pink or red handles {Small | | T8 | D1 |
| | | | | | {Large | | T8 | C1 |
| Holly................ | T6 | D4 | T4 | C3 | | | | |
| Hop-hornbeam (ironwood).............. | T6 | B3 | T3 | B1 | | | | |
| Laurel (California laurel, Oregon myrtle)...... | T8 | C4 | T5 | C3 | | | | |
| Locust, black......... | T6 | A3 | T3 | A1 | | | | |
| Madrone.............. | T6 | D2 | T3 | D1 | | | | |
| Magnolia............. | T10 | D4 | T8 | D3 | | | | |
| Mahogany............ | T6 | C4 | T4 | C3 | | | | |
| Maple, silver......... | T8 | C4 | T6 | C3 | | | | |
| Maple, sugar.......... | T8 | C3 | T5 | C2 | Bowling pins (end coated)............. | | T3 | A3 |
| | | | | | 1-in. squares.......... | | T8 | C4 |
| | | | | | 2-in. squares.......... | | T5 | C3 |
| Oak, California black.... | T4 | E2 | T3 | E1 | | | | |
| Oak, red.............. | T4 | D2 | T3 | D1 | | | | |
| Oak, white............ | T4 | C2 | T3 | C1 | | | | |
| Oak, southern lowland.. | T2 | C1 | ... | ... | | | | |
| Oak, tan............. | T4 | E1 | T3 | D1 | | | | |
| Osage-orange.......... | T6 | A2 | T3 | A1 | | | | |
| Persimmon........... | T6 | C3 | T3 | C2 | Shuttles.............. | | T3 | B2 |
| Sweetgum (sap gum).... | T12 | F5 | T11 | D4 | | | | |
| Sweetgum (red gum).... | T8 | C4 | T5 | C3 | | | | |
| Sycamore............. | T6 | D2 | T3 | D1 | | | | |
| Tupelo, black......... | T12 | E5 | T11 | D3 | | | | |
| Tupelo, water......... | T12 | E5 | T11 | D3 | | | | |
| Walnut, black......... | T6 | D4 | T3 | D3 | Gunstock blanks...... | | T3 | D4 |
| Willow, black......... | T10 | F4 | T8 | F3 | | | | |
| Yellow-poplar ........ | T11 | D4 | T10 | D3 | | | | |

Source: U. S. Forest Service, Forest Products Laboratory, Schedules for the kiln drying of wood, 1951.

content at which the various wet-bulb depressions are used. It has been found that the first change in humidity can be made at a moisture content that bears

### Table 19B. Index of Schedules for Kiln Drying Softwood *

| Species | For lumber | | | | For special purposes | | |
| --- | --- | --- | --- | --- | --- | --- | --- |
| | 4/4, 5/4, 6/4 | | 8/4 | | | | |
| | Temperature | Humidity | Temperature | Humidity | | Temperature | Humidity |
| Baldcypress............ | T12 | E4 | T11 | E3 | | | |
| Cedar, Alaska......... | T12 | A4 | T11 | A3 | | | |
| eastern red......... | T10 | A4 | T8 | A3 | To preserve {4/4, 5/4, oil for    6/4 chests    8/4 | T7 T5 | A4 A3 |
| incense............. | T12 | E5 | T11 | E4 | | | |
| northern white...... | T12 | B5 | T11 | B4 | | | |
| Port-Orford......... | T12 | B4 | T11 | B3 | | | |
| southern white....... | T12 | A5 | T11 | A4 | | | |
| western red (light)... | T12 | B5 | T11 | B4 | | | |
| (sinker).. | T8 | F5 | T6 | F4 | | | |
| Douglas-fir............ | T13 | A4 | T12 | A3 | Commons *.......... Strips .............. | T7 T14 | A4 A6 |
| Fir, alpine............ | T14 | B5 | T12 | B4 | | | |
| balsam.............. | T14 | E5 | T12 | E4 | | | |
| grand.............. | T14 | E5 | T12 | E4 | | | |
| noble ............. | T14 | A5 | T12 | A4 | | | |
| Pacific silver........ | T14 | B5 | T12 | B3 | | | |
| red (California)...... | T14 | E5 | T12 | E4 | | | |
| white............... | T14 | E5 | T12 | E4 | | | |
| Hemlock, eastern...... | T13 | E5 | T12 | E4 | | | |
| western............ | T13 | C5 | T12 | C4 | | | |
| Larch, eastern (tamarack)............. | T12 | B4 | T11 | B3 | | | |
| western............. | T12 | B4 | T11 | B3 | | | |
| Pine, eastern white..... | T11 | C5 | T10 | C4 | | | |
| lodgepole........... | T12 | C5 | T11 | C4 | | | |
| ponderosa........... | T10 | C6 | T8 | C5 | To reduce brown stain 4/4, 5/4, 6/4                8/4 | T7 T7 | E6 E5 |
| red................ | T12 | B5 | T11 | B4 | | | |
| southern yellow...... | T14 | B5 | T12 | B4 | | | |
| sugar.............. | T10 | E6 | T8 | E5 | To reduce brown stain 4/4, 5/4, 6/4                8/4 | T7 T7 | F6 F5 |
| western white (Idaho) | T10 | B5 | T8 | B4 | | | |
| Redwood (light)........ | T6 | D5 | T6 | D4 | | | |
| (sinker)............ | T6 | F5 | T6 | F4 | | | |
| Spruce, eastern (black, red, white)........ | T14 | B5 | T12 | B4 | | | |
| Engelmann.......... | T14 | B5 | T12 | B4 | | | |
| Sitka.............. | T14 | B5 | T12 | B4 | | | |

\* The schedules given are based mainly on the moisture content of the heartwood and are intended for average stock and for all grades and items that do not have special drying requirements. One modification would be in the drying of commons to prevent the development of loose knots. In this case, the temperature schedule should be T7 and the conditions given in step 3 of both temperature and humidity schedules should be maintained as final conditions until the desired moisture content is reached. As trouble of this kind becomes somewhat less with increases in thickness, step 4 instead of step 3 in the humidity schedule can be used for final conditions, if desired, to accelerate the drying of 8/4 stock.

Source: U. S. Forest Service, Forest Products Laboratory, Schedules for the kiln drying of wood, 1951.

some relationship to the original green moisture content of the wood. For that reason, six classes of moisture content steps have been made, identified by the letters A to F, any one of which can be used with any one of the eight wet-bulb depression sets to make up a humidity schedule that is best suited to the wood being dried. A total of 48 combinations is possible.

Suggested schedules for hardwoods are listed in Table 19A. Using ¼ red oak as an example, the complete schedule is given as T4–D2, which means that temperature schedule T4 must be used in combination with humidity schedule D2. Although the same schedule is recommended for ¼, 5/4, and 6/4 material it does not mean that they should be dried in the same kiln charge. Thick lumber dries slower and tends to check more than ¼ material. For that reason a milder schedule is recommended for 8/4 lumber.

## Table 20. Forest Products Laboratory Schedules for the Kiln Drying of Wood (1951)

### TEMPERATURE SCHEDULES (dry bulb temperatures)*

| Step No. | Moisture content | | Temperature schedule number | | | | | | | | | | | | | |
|---|---|---|---|---|---|---|---|---|---|---|---|---|---|---|---|---|
| | From | To | T1 | T2 | T3 | T4 | T5 | T6 | T7 | T8 | T9 | T10 | T11 | T12 | T13 | T14 |
| | % | % | °F. | °F. | °F. | °F. | °F. | °F. | °F. | °F. | °F. | °F. | °F. | °F. | °F. | °F. |
| 1 | Initial | 30 | 100 | 100 | 110 | 110 | 120 | 120 | 130 | 130 | 140 | 140 | 150 | 160 | 170 | 180 |
| 2 | 30 | 25 | 105 | 110 | 120 | 120 | 130 | 130 | 140 | 140 | 150 | 150 | 160 | 170 | 180 | 190 |
| 3 | 25 | 20 | 105 | 120 | 130 | 130 | 140 | 140 | 150 | 150 | 160 | 160 | 160 | 170 | 180 | 190 |
| 4 | 20 | 15 | 115 | 130 | 140 | 140 | 150 | 150 | 160 | 160 | 160 | 170 | 180 | 180 | 190 | 200 |
| 5 | 15 | Final | 120 | 150 | 160 | 180 | 160 | 180 | 160 | 180 | 160 | 180 | 180 | 180 | 190 | 200 |

### HUMIDITY SCHEDULES (wet bulb depression)*

#### "A" Schedules

| Step No. | Moisture content | | Humidity schedule number | | | | | | | |
|---|---|---|---|---|---|---|---|---|---|---|
| | From | To | A1 | A2 | A3 | A4 | A5 | A6 | A7 | A8 |
| | % | % | °F. | °F. | °F. | °F. | °F. | °F. | °F. | °F. |
| 1 | Initial | 30 | 3 | 4 | 5 | 7 | 10 | 15 | 20 | 25 |
| 2 | 30 | 25 | 4 | 5 | 7 | 10 | 14 | 20 | 30 | 35 |
| 3 | 25 | 20 | 6 | 8 | 11 | 15 | 20 | 30 | 40 | 50 |
| 4 | 20 | 15 | 10 | 14 | 19 | 25 | 35 | 50 | 50 | 50 |
| 5 | 15 | 10 | 25 | 30 | 35 | 40 | 50 | 50 | 50 | 50 |
| 6 | 10 | Final | 50 | 50 | 50 | 50 | 50 | 50 | 50 | 50 |

#### "B" Schedules

| Step No. | Moisture content | | Humidity schedule number | | | | | | | |
|---|---|---|---|---|---|---|---|---|---|---|
| | From | To | B1 | B2 | B3 | B4 | B5 | B6 | B7 | B8 |
| | % | % | °F. | °F. | °F. | °F. | °F. | °F. | °F. | °F. |
| 1 | Initial | 35 | 3 | 4 | 5 | 7 | 10 | 15 | 20 | 25 |
| 2 | 35 | 30 | 4 | 5 | 7 | 10 | 14 | 20 | 30 | 35 |
| 3 | 30 | 25 | 6 | 8 | 11 | 15 | 20 | 30 | 40 | 50 |
| 4 | 25 | 20 | 10 | 14 | 19 | 25 | 35 | 50 | 50 | 50 |
| 5 | 20 | 15 | 25 | 30 | 35 | 40 | 50 | 50 | 50 | 50 |
| 6 | 15 | Final | 50 | 50 | 50 | 50 | 50 | 50 | 50 | 50 |

* See Table 21.

Source: U. S. Forest Service, Forest Products Laboratory, Schedules for the kiln drying of wood, 1951.

## Table 20. Forest Products Laboratory Schedules for the Kiln Drying of Wood (1951) (Continued)

### "C" Schedules

| Step No. | Moisture content From | Moisture content To | Humidity schedule number C1 | C2 | C3 | C4 | C5 | C6 | C7 | C8 |
|---|---|---|---|---|---|---|---|---|---|---|
| | % | % | °F. | °F. | °F. | °F. | °F. | °F. | °F. | °F. |
| 1 | Initial | 40 | 3 | 4 | 5 | 7 | 10 | 15 | 20 | 25 |
| 2 | 40 | 35 | 4 | 5 | 7 | 10 | 14 | 20 | 30 | 35 |
| 3 | 35 | 30 | 6 | 8 | 11 | 15 | 20 | 30 | 40 | 50 |
| 4 | 30 | 25 | 10 | 14 | 19 | 25 | 35 | 50 | 50 | 50 |
| 5 | 25 | 20 | 25 | 30 | 35 | 40 | 50 | 50 | 50 | 50 |
| 6 | 20 | Final | 50 | 50 | 50 | 50 | 50 | 50 | 50 | 50 |

### "D" Schedules

| Step No. | Moisture content From | Moisture content To | Humidity schedule number D1 | D2 | D3 | D4 | D5 | D6 | D7 | D8 |
|---|---|---|---|---|---|---|---|---|---|---|
| | % | % | °F. | °F. | °F. | °F. | °F. | °F. | °F. | °F. |
| 1 | Initial | 50 | 3 | 4 | 5 | 7 | 10 | 15 | 20 | 25 |
| 2 | 50 | 40 | 4 | 5 | 7 | 10 | 14 | 20 | 30 | 35 |
| 3 | 40 | 35 | 6 | 8 | 11 | 15 | 20 | 30 | 40 | 50 |
| 4 | 35 | 30 | 10 | 14 | 19 | 25 | 35 | 50 | 50 | 50 |
| 5 | 30 | 25 | 25 | 30 | 35 | 40 | 50 | 50 | 50 | 50 |
| 6 | 25 | Final | 50 | 50 | 50 | 50 | 50 | 50 | 50 | 50 |

### "E" Schedules

| Step No. | Moisture content From | Moisture content To | Humidity schedule number E1 | E2 | E3 | E4 | E5 | E6 | E7 | E8 |
|---|---|---|---|---|---|---|---|---|---|---|
| | % | % | °F. | °F. | °F. | °F. | °F. | °F. | °F. | °F. |
| 1 | Initial | 60 | 3 | 4 | 5 | 7 | 10 | 15 | 20 | 25 |
| 2 | 60 | 50 | 4 | 5 | 7 | 10 | 14 | 20 | 30 | 35 |
| 3 | 50 | 40 | 6 | 8 | 11 | 15 | 20 | 30 | 40 | 50 |
| 4 | 40 | 35 | 10 | 14 | 19 | 25 | 35 | 50 | 50 | 50 |
| 5 | 35 | 30 | 25 | 30 | 35 | 40 | 50 | 50 | 50 | 50 |
| 6 | 30 | Final | 50 | 50 | 50 | 50 | 50 | 50 | 50 | 50 |

### "F" Schedules

| Step No. | Moisture content From | Moisture content To | Humidity schedule number F1 | F2 | F3 | F4 | F5 | F6 | F7 | F8 |
|---|---|---|---|---|---|---|---|---|---|---|
| | % | % | °F. | °F. | °F. | °F. | °F. | °F. | °F. | °F. |
| 1 | Initial | 70 | 3 | 4 | 5 | 7 | 10 | 15 | 20 | 25 |
| 2 | 70 | 60 | 4 | 5 | 7 | 10 | 14 | 20 | 30 | 35 |
| 3 | 60 | 50 | 6 | 8 | 11 | 15 | 20 | 30 | 40 | 50 |
| 4 | 50 | 40 | 10 | 14 | 19 | 25 | 35 | 50 | 50 | 50 |
| 5 | 40 | 35 | 25 | 30 | 35 | 40 | 50 | 50 | 50 | 50 |
| 6 | 35 | Final | 50 | 50 | 50 | 50 | 50 | 50 | 50 | 50 |

**Table 21. Relative Humidity and Equilibrium Moisture Content Table for Use with Dry-Bulb Temperatures and Wet-Bulb Depressions**

| Temperature Dry Bulb (°F.) | Wet-Bulb Depression (°F.) 1 | 2 | 3 | 4 | 5 | 6 | 7 | 8 | 9 | 10 | 11 | 12 | 13 | 14 | 15 | 16 | 17 | 18 | 19 | 20 | 21 | 22 | 23 | 24 | 25 | 26 | 27 | 28 | 29 | 30 | 32 | 34 | 36 | 38 | 40 | 45 | 50 | Temperature Dry Bulb (°F.) |
|---|---|---|---|---|---|---|---|---|---|---|---|---|---|---|---|---|---|---|---|---|---|---|---|---|---|---|---|---|---|---|---|---|---|---|---|---|---|---|
| 30 | 89 | 78/15.9 | 67/12.9 | 57/10.8 | 46/9.0 | 36/7.4 | 27/5.7 | 17/3.9 | 6/1.6 | | | | | | | | | | | | | | | | | | | | | | | | | | | | | 30 |
| 35 | 90 | 81/16.8 | 72/13.9 | 63/11.9 | 54/10.3 | 45/8.8 | 37/7.4 | 28/6.0 | 19/4.5 | 11/2.9 | 3/0.8 | | | | | | | | | | | | | | | | | | | | | | | | | | | 35 |
| 40 | 92 | 83/17.6 | 75/14.8 | 68/12.9 | 60/11.2 | 52/9.9 | 45/8.6 | 37/7.4 | 29/6.2 | 22/5.0 | 15/3.5 | 8/1.9 | | | | | | | | | | | | | | | | | | | | | | | | | | 40 |
| 45 | 93 | 85/18.3 | 78/15.6 | 72/13.7 | 64/12.0 | 58/10.7 | 51/9.5 | 44/8.5 | 37/7.5 | 31/6.5 | 25/5.3 | 19/4.2 | 12/2.9 | 6/1.5 | | | | | | | | | | | | | | | | | | | | | | | | 45 |
| 50 | 93 | 86/19.0 | 80/16.3 | 74/14.4 | 68/12.7 | 62/11.5 | 56/10.3 | 50/9.4 | 44/8.5 | 38/7.6 | 32/6.7 | 27/5.7 | 21/4.8 | 16/3.9 | 10/2.8 | 5/1.5 | | | | | | | | | | | | | | | | | | | | | | 50 |
| 55 | 94 | 88/19.5 | 82/16.9 | 76/15.1 | 70/13.4 | 65/12.2 | 60/11.0 | 54/10.1 | 49/9.3 | 44/8.4 | 39/7.6 | 34/6.8 | 28/6.0 | 24/5.3 | 19/4.5 | 14/3.6 | 9/2.5 | 5/1.3 | | | | | | | | | | | | | | | | | | | | 55 |
| 60 | 94 | 89/19.9 | 83/17.4 | 78/15.6 | 73/13.9 | 68/12.7 | 63/11.6 | 58/10.7 | 53/9.9 | 48/9.1 | 43/8.3 | 39/7.6 | 34/6.9 | 30/6.3 | 26/5.6 | 21/4.9 | 17/4.1 | 13/3.2 | 9/2.3 | 5/1.3 | 1/0.2 | | | | | | | | | | | | | | | | | 60 |
| 65 | 95 | 90/20.3 | 84/17.8 | 80/16.1 | 75/14.4 | 70/13.3 | 66/12.1 | 61/11.2 | 56/10.4 | 52/9.7 | 48/8.9 | 44/8.3 | 39/7.7 | 36/7.1 | 32/6.5 | 27/5.8 | 24/5.2 | 20/4.5 | 16/3.8 | 13/3.0 | 8/2.3 | 6/1.4 | 2/0.4 | | | | | | | | | | | | | | | 65 |
| 70 | 95 | 90/20.6 | 86/18.2 | 81/16.5 | 77/14.9 | 72/13.7 | 68/12.5 | 64/11.6 | 59/10.9 | 55/10.1 | 51/9.4 | 48/8.8 | 44/8.3 | 40/7.7 | 36/7.2 | 33/6.6 | 29/6.0 | 25/5.5 | 22/4.9 | 19/4.3 | 15/3.7 | 12/2.9 | 9/2.3 | 6/1.5 | 3/0.7 | | | | | | | | | | | | | 70 |
| 75 | 95 | 91/20.9 | 86/18.5 | 82/16.8 | 78/15.2 | 74/14.0 | 70/12.9 | 66/12.0 | 62/11.2 | 58/10.5 | 54/9.8 | 51/9.3 | 47/8.7 | 44/8.2 | 41/7.7 | 37/7.2 | 34/6.7 | 31/6.2 | 28/5.6 | 24/5.1 | 21/4.7 | 18/4.1 | 15/3.5 | 12/2.9 | 10/2.3 | 7/1.7 | 4/0.9 | 1/0.2 | | | | | | | | | | 75 |
| 80 | 96 | 91/21.0 | 87/18.7 | 83/17.0 | 79/15.5 | 75/14.3 | 72/13.2 | 68/12.3 | 64/11.5 | 61/10.9 | 57/10.1 | 54/9.7 | 50/9.1 | 47/8.6 | 44/8.1 | 41/7.7 | 38/7.2 | 35/6.8 | 32/6.3 | 29/5.8 | 26/5.4 | 23/5.0 | 20/4.5 | 18/4.0 | 15/3.5 | 12/3.0 | 10/2.4 | 7/1.8 | 5/1.1 | 3/0.3 | | | | | | | | 80 |
| 85 | 96 | 92/21.2 | 88/18.8 | 84/17.2 | 80/15.7 | 76/14.5 | 73/13.5 | 70/12.5 | 66/11.8 | 63/11.2 | 59/10.5 | 56/10.0 | 53/9.5 | 50/9.0 | 47/8.5 | 44/8.1 | 41/7.6 | 38/7.2 | 36/6.7 | 33/6.3 | 30/6.0 | 28/5.6 | 25/5.2 | 23/4.8 | 20/4.3 | 18/3.9 | 15/3.4 | 13/3.0 | 11/2.4 | 9/1.7 | 4/0.9 | | | | | | | 85 |
| 90 | 96 | 92/21.3 | 89/18.9 | 85/17.3 | 81/15.9 | 78/14.7 | 74/13.7 | 71/12.8 | 68/12.0 | 65/11.4 | 61/10.7 | 58/10.2 | 55/9.7 | 52/9.3 | 49/8.8 | 47/8.4 | 44/8.0 | 41/7.6 | 39/7.2 | 36/6.8 | 34/6.5 | 31/6.1 | 29/5.7 | 26/5.3 | 24/4.9 | 22/4.6 | 19/4.2 | 17/3.8 | 15/3.3 | 13/2.8 | 9/2.1 | 5/1.3 | 1/0.4 | | | | | 90 |
| 95 | 96 | 92/21.3 | 89/19.0 | 85/17.4 | 82/16.1 | 79/14.9 | 75/13.9 | 72/12.9 | 69/12.2 | 66/11.6 | 63/11.0 | 60/10.5 | 57/10.0 | 55/9.5 | 52/9.1 | 49/8.7 | 46/8.2 | 44/7.9 | 42/7.5 | 39/7.1 | 37/6.8 | 34/6.4 | 32/6.1 | 30/5.7 | 28/5.3 | 26/5.1 | 23/4.8 | 22/4.4 | 20/4.0 | 17/3.6 | 14/3.0 | 10/2.3 | 6/1.5 | 2/0.6 | | | | 95 |
| 100 | 96 | 93/21.3 | 89/19.0 | 86/17.5 | 83/16.1 | 80/15.0 | 77/13.9 | 73/13.1 | 70/12.4 | 68/11.8 | 65/11.2 | 62/10.6 | 59/10.1 | 56/9.6 | 54/9.2 | 51/8.9 | 49/8.5 | 46/8.1 | 44/7.8 | 41/7.4 | 39/7.0 | 37/6.7 | 35/6.4 | 33/6.1 | 30/5.7 | 28/5.4 | 26/5.2 | 24/4.9 | 22/4.6 | 21/4.2 | 17/3.6 | 13/3.1 | 10/2.4 | 7/1.6 | 4/0.7 | | | 100 |
| 105 | 96 | 93/21.4 | 90/19.0 | 87/17.5 | 83/16.2 | 80/15.1 | 77/14.0 | 74/13.2 | 71/12.6 | 69/11.9 | 66/11.3 | 63/10.8 | 60/10.3 | 58/9.8 | 55/9.4 | 53/9.0 | 50/8.7 | 48/8.3 | 46/7.9 | 44/7.6 | 42/7.3 | 40/6.9 | 37/6.7 | 35/6.4 | 34/6.1 | 31/5.7 | 29/5.4 | 28/5.2 | 26/4.8 | 24/4.6 | 20/4.2 | 17/3.6 | 14/3.1 | 11/2.4 | 8/1.8 | | | 105 |
| 110 | 97 | 93/21.4 | 90/19.0 | 87/17.5 | 84/16.2 | 81/15.1 | 78/14.1 | 75/13.3 | 73/12.6 | 70/12.0 | 67/11.4 | 65/10.8 | 62/10.4 | 60/9.9 | 57/9.5 | 55/9.2 | 52/8.8 | 50/8.4 | 48/8.1 | 46/7.7 | 44/7.5 | 42/7.2 | 40/6.8 | 38/6.6 | 36/6.3 | 34/6.0 | 32/5.7 | 30/5.4 | 28/5.2 | 26/4.8 | 23/4.5 | 20/4.0 | 17/3.5 | 14/3.0 | 11/2.5 | 4/1.1 | | 110 |
| 115 | 97 | 93/21.4 | 90/19.0 | 88/17.5 | 85/16.2 | 82/15.1 | 79/14.1 | 76/13.4 | 74/12.7 | 71/12.1 | 68/11.5 | 66/10.9 | 63/10.4 | 61/10.0 | 58/9.6 | 56/9.3 | 54/8.9 | 52/8.6 | 50/8.2 | 48/7.8 | 45/7.6 | 43/7.3 | 41/7.0 | 40/6.7 | 38/6.5 | 36/6.2 | 34/5.9 | 32/5.6 | 31/5.4 | 29/5.2 | 26/4.7 | 23/4.3 | 20/3.9 | 17/3.4 | 14/2.9 | 8/1.7 | 2/0.4 | 115 |
| 120 | 97 | 94/21.3 | 91/19.0 | 88/17.4 | 85/16.2 | 82/15.1 | 80/14.1 | 77/13.4 | 74/12.7 | 72/12.1 | 69/11.5 | 67/11.0 | 65/10.5 | 62/10.0 | 60/9.7 | 58/9.4 | 55/9.0 | 53/8.7 | 51/8.3 | 49/7.9 | 47/7.7 | 45/7.4 | 43/7.2 | 41/6.8 | 40/6.6 | 38/6.3 | 36/6.1 | 34/5.8 | 33/5.6 | 31/5.4 | 28/5.0 | 25/4.6 | 22/4.2 | 19/3.7 | 17/3.3 | 10/2.3 | 5/1.1 | 120 |
| 125 | 97 | 94/21.2 | 91/18.9 | 88/17.3 | 86/16.1 | 83/15.0 | 80/14.0 | 77/13.4 | 75/12.7 | 73/12.1 | 70/11.5 | 68/11.0 | 65/10.5 | 63/10.0 | 61/9.7 | 59/9.4 | 57/9.0 | 55/8.7 | 53/8.3 | 51/8.0 | 48/7.7 | 47/7.5 | 45/7.2 | 43/7.0 | 41/6.7 | 39/6.5 | 38/6.2 | 36/6.0 | 35/5.8 | 33/5.5 | 30/5.2 | 27/4.8 | 24/4.4 | 22/4.0 | 19/3.6 | 13/2.7 | 8/1.6 | 125 |
| 130 | 97 | 94/21.0 | 91/18.8 | 89/17.2 | 86/16.0 | 83/14.9 | 81/14.0 | 78/13.4 | 76/12.7 | 73/12.1 | 71/11.5 | 69/11.0 | 67/10.5 | 64/10.0 | 62/9.7 | 60/9.4 | 58/9.0 | 56/8.7 | 54/8.3 | 52/8.0 | 50/7.8 | 48/7.6 | 47/7.3 | 45/7.0 | 43/6.8 | 41/6.6 | 40/6.4 | 38/6.1 | 37/5.9 | 35/5.6 | 32/5.3 | 29/4.9 | 26/4.6 | 24/4.2 | 21/3.8 | 15/3.0 | 10/2.0 | 130 |
| 140 | 97 | 95/20.7 | 92/18.6 | 89/16.9 | 87/15.8 | 84/14.8 | 82/13.8 | 79/13.2 | 77/12.5 | 75/11.9 | 73/11.4 | 70/10.9 | 68/10.4 | 66/10.0 | 64/9.6 | 62/9.4 | 60/9.0 | 58/8.7 | 56/8.4 | 54/8.0 | 53/7.8 | 51/7.6 | 49/7.3 | 47/7.1 | 46/6.9 | 44/6.6 | 43/6.4 | 41/6.2 | 40/6.0 | 38/5.8 | 35/5.5 | 32/5.1 | 30/4.8 | 27/4.4 | 25/4.1 | 19/3.4 | 14/2.6 | 140 |
| 150 | 98 | 95/20.2 | 92/18.4 | 90/16.6 | 87/15.5 | 85/14.5 | 82/13.7 | 80/13.0 | 78/12.4 | 76/11.8 | 74/11.2 | 72/10.8 | 70/10.3 | 68/9.9 | 66/9.5 | 64/9.2 | 62/8.9 | 60/8.6 | 58/8.3 | 57/8.0 | 55/7.8 | 53/7.5 | 51/7.3 | 49/7.1 | 48/6.9 | 46/6.7 | 45/6.4 | 43/6.2 | 42/6.0 | 41/5.8 | 38/5.5 | 36/5.2 | 33/4.9 | 30/4.5 | 28/4.2 | 23/3.6 | 18/2.9 | 150 |
| 160 | 98 | 95/19.8 | 93/18.1 | 90/16.2 | 88/15.2 | 86/14.2 | 83/13.4 | 81/12.7 | 79/12.1 | 77/11.5 | 75/11.0 | 73/10.6 | 71/10.1 | 69/9.7 | 67/9.4 | 65/9.1 | 64/8.8 | 62/8.5 | 60/8.2 | 58/7.9 | 57/7.7 | 55/7.4 | 53/7.2 | 52/7.0 | 50/6.8 | 49/6.7 | 47/6.4 | 46/6.2 | 44/6.0 | 43/5.8 | 41/5.5 | 38/5.2 | 35/4.9 | 33/4.6 | 31/4.3 | 25/3.7 | 21/3.2 | 160 |
| 170 | 98 | 95/19.4 | 93/17.7 | 91/15.8 | 89/14.8 | 86/13.9 | 84/13.2 | 82/12.4 | 80/11.8 | 78/11.3 | 76/10.8 | 74/10.4 | 72/9.9 | 70/9.6 | 69/9.2 | 67/9.0 | 65/8.6 | 63/8.4 | 62/8.0 | 60/7.8 | 59/7.6 | 57/7.3 | 55/7.2 | 53/6.9 | 52/6.7 | 51/6.6 | 49/6.4 | 48/6.2 | 47/6.0 | 45/5.7 | 43/5.5 | 40/5.2 | 38/4.9 | 35/4.6 | 33/4.4 | 28/3.7 | 24/3.2 | 170 |
| 180 | 98 | 96/18.9 | 94/17.3 | 91/15.5 | 89/14.5 | 87/13.7 | 85/12.9 | 83/12.2 | 81/11.6 | 79/11.1 | 77/10.6 | 75/10.1 | 73/9.7 | 72/9.4 | 70/9.0 | 68/8.8 | 67/8.4 | 65/8.1 | 63/7.8 | 62/7.6 | 60/7.4 | 58/7.2 | 57/7.0 | 55/6.8 | 54/6.5 | 52/6.4 | 51/6.2 | 50/6.0 | 48/5.8 | 47/5.7 | 45/5.4 | 42/5.2 | 40/4.8 | 38/4.6 | 35/4.4 | 30/3.8 | 26/3.3 | 180 |
| 190 | 98 | 96/18.5 | 94/16.9 | 92/15.2 | 90/14.2 | 88/13.4 | 85/12.7 | 84/12.0 | 82/11.4 | 80/10.9 | 78/10.5 | 76/10.0 | 75/9.6 | 73/9.2 | 71/8.9 | 69/8.6 | 68/8.2 | 66/7.9 | 65/7.7 | 63/7.4 | 62/7.2 | 60/7.0 | 58/6.8 | 57/6.6 | 56/6.4 | 54/6.2 | 53/6.0 | 51/5.9 | 50/5.7 | 49/5.5 | 46/5.3 | 44/5.0 | 42/4.8 | 39/4.5 | 37/4.4 | 32/3.8 | 28/3.3 | 190 |
| 200 | 98 | 96/18.1 | 94/16.4 | 92/14.9 | 90/14.0 | 88/13.2 | 86/12.4 | 84/11.8 | 82/11.2 | 80/10.8 | 79/10.3 | 77/9.8 | 75/9.4 | 74/9.1 | 72/8.8 | 70/8.4 | 69/8.1 | 67/7.7 | 66/7.5 | 64/7.2 | 63/7.0 | 61/6.9 | 60/6.6 | 58/6.4 | 57/6.2 | 55/6.0 | 54/5.9 | 53/5.7 | 52/5.6 | 51/5.4 | 48/5.2 | 46/4.9 | 43/4.7 | 41/4.5 | 39/4.3 | 34/3.8 | 30/3.3 | 200 |
| 210 | 98 | 96/17.7 | 94/16.0 | 92/14.6 | 90/13.8 | 88/13.0 | 86/12.2 | 85/11.7 | 83/11.1 | 81/10.6 | 79/10.0 | 78/9.7 | 76/9.2 | 75/9.0 | 73/8.7 | 71/8.3 | 70/8.0 | 68/7.6 | 67/7.4 | 65/7.1 | 64/6.9 | 63/6.8 | 61/6.5 | 60/6.3 | 59/6.1 | 57/5.9 | 56/5.8 | 54/5.5 | 53/5.4 | 52/5.3 | 50/5.1 | 47/4.8 | 45/4.6 | 43/4.4 | 41/4.2 | 36/3.7 | 32/3.2 | 210 |

Schedules for softwoods are listed in Table 19B. As the drying periods for softwoods are relatively short, the schedules as given may have more steps than are practical to use. For instance, if, after one day of drying, the moisture content is below the minimum value given in the succeeding step, the latter step can be omitted and drying conditions called for by the moisture content of the stock as given in the schedule can be established immediately.

**Drying Previously Air-Dried Lumber.** During the kiln drying of lumber green from the saw, a moisture gradient is established within the wood that permits the use of the intermediate and final temperatures and relative humidities that are shown in the schedules. In air-dried lumber at the same moisture content, however, the moisture gradient may be relatively flat, and it is desirable to start with higher relative humidities until a definite moisture gradient has been established before using the scheduled conditions. This procedure is more important for air-dried stock taken from the yard during or immediately following a rainy or high-humidity period than for stock taken in during hot, fast-drying weather.

**Equalizing and Conditioning Treatments.** If precise drying is required, the stock should be given an equalizing and conditioning treatment in the final stages of the drying process. The equalizing treatment precedes the conditioning treatment. Its purpose is to reduce the variation in moisture content between individual boards or items in the charge. The conditioning treatment serves two purposes; it establishes a more uniform moisture content throughout the thickness of each board or item, and it relieves casehardening. Table 22 is a general guide for equalizing and conditioning lumber to any desired final average moisture content.

Allow the charge to condition until the stock is free of casehardening (see Fig. 1 for method of sampling). The time required for relieving casehardening in lumber will depend upon the species, thickness, moisture content, and degree of stress present. It may vary from 4 hr. for some ¼ softwoods to 48 hr. or more for some ¾ hardwoods.

**Table 22. Recommendations for Equalizing and Conditioning a Charge of Lumber**

| Final desired average moisture content (%) | Moisture content to which driest sample should be dried before equalizing (%) | Equilibrium moisture content at which charge should be equalized (%) | Desired moisture: content of wettest sample at end of equalizing (%) | Equilibrium moisture content values for conditioning treatment | |
|---|---|---|---|---|---|
| | | | | For softwoods (%) | For hardwoods (%) |
| 5 | 3 | 3 | 5 | 7–8 | 8–9 |
| 6 | 4 | 4 | 6 | 8–9 | 9–10 |
| 7 | 5 | 5 | 7 | 9–10 | 10–11 |
| 8 | 6 | 6 | 8 | 10–11 | 11–12 |
| 9 | 7 | 7 | 9 | 11–12 | 12–13 |
| 10 | 8 | 8 | 10 | 12–13 | 13–14 |
| 11 | 9 | 9 | 11 | 13–14 | 14–15 |

The higher the temperatures that can be used during the conditioning treatment, the faster and better will be the relief of casehardening. It is sometimes impossible, however, to obtain the equilibrium moisture content required for this treatment at very high temperatures. Generally, in most commercial kilns, the

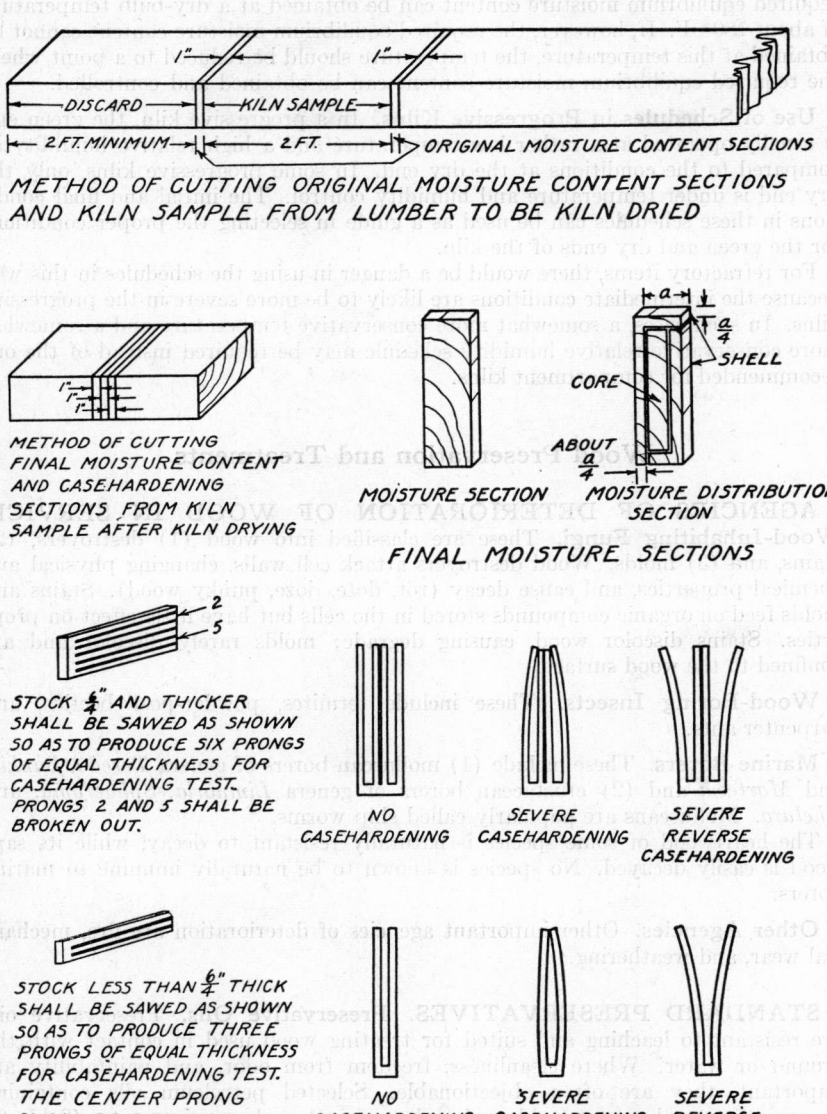

METHOD OF CUTTING ORIGINAL MOISTURE CONTENT SECTIONS
AND KILN SAMPLE FROM LUMBER TO BE KILN DRIED

METHOD OF CUTTING
FINAL MOISTURE CONTENT
AND CASEHARDENING
SECTIONS FROM KILN
SAMPLE AFTER KILN DRYING

SHELL

CORE

ABOUT
$\frac{a}{4}$

MOISTURE SECTION

MOISTURE DISTRIBUTION
SECTION

FINAL MOISTURE SECTIONS

STOCK $\frac{6}{4}$" AND THICKER
SHALL BE SAWED AS SHOWN
SO AS TO PRODUCE SIX PRONGS
OF EQUAL THICKNESS FOR
CASEHARDENING TEST.
PRONGS 2 AND 5 SHALL BE
BROKEN OUT.

NO
CASEHARDENING

SEVERE
CASEHARDENING

SEVERE
REVERSE
CASEHARDENING

STOCK LESS THAN $\frac{6}{4}$" THICK
SHALL BE SAWED AS SHOWN
SO AS TO PRODUCE THREE
PRONGS OF EQUAL THICKNESS
FOR CASEHARDENING TEST.
THE CENTER PRONG
SHALL BE BROKEN OUT.

NO
CASEHARDENING

SEVERE
CASEHARDENING

SEVERE
REVERSE
CASEHARDENING

CASEHARDENING SECTION: SECTION TO BE ROOM DRIED
BEFORE CONCLUSION IS MADE AS TO CASEHARDENING

Fig. 1. Kiln sample and test sections used for determining final condition of
lumber.

required equilibrium moisture content can be obtained at a dry-bulb temperature of about 180° F. If, however, the required equilibrium moisture content cannot be obtained at this temperature, the temperature should be reduced to a point where the required equilibrium moisture content can be obtained and controlled.

**Use of Schedules in Progressive Kilns.** In a progressive kiln, the green end is usually operated at a rather low temperature and a high relative humidity as compared to the conditions at the dry end. In some progressive kilns, only the dry end is under temperature and humidity control. The initial and final conditions in these schedules can be used as a guide in selecting the proper conditions for the green and dry ends of the kiln.

For refractory items, there would be a danger in using the schedules in this way because the intermediate conditions are likely to be more severe in the progressive kilns. In such cases, a somewhat more conservative temperature and a somewhat more conservative relative humidity schedule may be required instead of the one recommended for compartment kilns.

# Wood Preservation and Treatments

**AGENCIES OF DETERIORATION OF WOOD IN SERVICE.**
**Wood-Inhabiting Fungi.** These are classified into wood (1) destroyers, (2) stains, and (3) molds. Wood destroyers attack cell walls, changing physical and chemical properties, and cause decay (rot, dote, doze, punky wood). Stains and molds feed on organic compounds stored in the cells but have little effect on properties. Stains discolor wood, causing degrade; molds rarely discolor and are confined to the wood surface.

**Wood-Boring Insects.** These include termites, powder-post beetles, and carpenter ants.

**Marine Borers.** These include (1) molluscan borers of genera *Teredo, Bankia,* and *Martesia* and (2) crustacean borers of genera *Limnoria, Sphaeroma,* and *Chelura.* Molluscans are popularly called ship worms.

The heartwood of some species is naturally resistant to decay, while its sapwood is easily decayed. No species is known to be naturally immune to marine borers.

**Other Agencies.** Other important agencies of deterioration are fire, mechanical wear, and weathering.

**STANDARD PRESERVATIVES. Preservative Oils.** Preservative oils are resistant to leaching and suited for treating wood used in contact with the ground or water. Where cleanliness, freedom from odor, and paintability are important, they are often objectionable. Selected petroleum oils containing preservatives such as pentachlorophenol can meet such requirements. Table 24 lists preservative oils in common use.

**Water-Borne Preservatives.** These preservatives are employed principally where wood is not to be used in contact with the ground or water, and where an oily surface is objectionable, i.e., where wood requires painting. They are applied principally by pressure-treating methods and occasionally by nonpressure methods.

**Table 23. Relative Durability of Heartwood of Common Woods of the United States and Canada**

| Softwoods (conifers) | Hardwoods |
|---|---|
| CLASS 1. Very Durable | |
| Baldcypress | Catalpas |
| Cedars (practically all) | Chestnut |
| Junipers | Locust, black |
| Redwood | Mulberry, red |
| Yew, Pacific | Osage-orange |
| | Sassafras |
| | Walnut, black |
| CLASS 2. Intermediate | |
| Douglas-fir | Honeylocust |
| Larch, western | Oak, chestnut |
| Pine, eastern white | Oak, white |
| Pine, lodgepole | Sassafras |
| Pine, southern yellow * | Sweetgum |
| Tamarack | |
| CLASS 3. Nondurable | |
| Firs, true | Ashes |
| Hemlocks | Aspen |
| Spruces | Basswood |
| | Beech |
| | Birches |
| | Cottonwood |
| | Hickories |
| | Maple, sugar |
| | Oaks, red |
| | Sycamore |
| | Tupelo |
| | Willows |
| | Yellow-poplar |

* Including shortleaf, loblolly, and nondense longleaf pines.
Note: The species in each class are listed alphabetically and not in order of relative durability.
Source: G. M. Hunt and G. A. Garratt, *Wood preservation*, 1953.

**Table 24. Common Preservative Oils**

| | Specifications covered by | |
|---|---|---|
| Preservative | Federal | A.W.P.A.[a] |
| Coal-tar creosote ................................. | TT–W–556a | P1–51 |
| Coal-tar creosote for nonpressure treatments: | | |
| Anthracene oil ................................ | TT–W–531 ⎱ | P7–51 |
| Crystal free oil ................................ | TT–W–560 ⎰ | |
| Creosote-petroleum solution ...................... | TT–W–568 | P3–51 |
| Creosote-coal tar solution ....................... | TT–W–566a | P2–51 |
| Pentachlorophenol solutions ..................... | TT–W–570 | P8–51 [b] |
| Copper naphthenate solutions .................... | | P8–51 |

[a] American Wood Preservers' Assn.
[b] These specifications cover preservative chemicals only. A.W.P.A. Standard P9–51 covers petroleum used in pentachlorophenol and copper naphthenate solutions.

#### Table 25. Preservatives Recognized in Wood-Preserving Standards

| Preservative | Composition | Percent | Federal | A.W.P.A. |
|---|---|---|---|---|
| Boliden salts... | Arsenic acid<br>Sodium arsenate<br>Sodium dichromate<br>Zinc sulfate | 20<br>21<br>16<br>43 | | Tentative<br>standard |
| Celcure ....... | Copper sulfate<br>Sodium dichromate<br>Sufficient acetic acid to<br>maintain solution | 50<br>50 | TT–W–546 | Tentative<br>standard |
| Chemonite .... | Copper hydroxide<br>Arsenic trioxide<br>Acetic acid<br>Ammonia<br>(in water as solvent for<br>above chemicals) | 57.7<br>40.7<br>1.6<br>2.8 | TT–W–549 | Tentative<br>standard |
| Greensalt .....<br>(Ascu,<br>Erdalith) | Potassium dichromate<br>Copper sulfate<br>Arsenic pentoxide | 56<br>33<br>11 | | Tentative<br>standard |
| Tanalith ...... | Sodium fluoride<br>Disodium hydrogen<br>arsenate<br>Sodium chromate<br>Dinitrophenol | 25<br><br>25<br>37.5<br>12.5 | TT–W–573 | P5–51 |
| Zinc chloride... | Zinc chloride, not less<br>than | 94 | TT–W–576a | P5–51 |
| Zinc chloride...<br>(chromated) | Zinc chloride, not less<br>than<br>Sodium dichromate, not<br>less than | 77.5<br><br>17.5 | TT–W–557 | P5–51 |
| Zinc chloride...<br>(copperized<br>chromated) | Zinc chloride<br>Sodium dichromate<br>Cupric chloride | 73<br>20<br>7 | | Tentative<br>standard |
| Zinc meta<br>arsenite ..... | Arsenious acid<br>Zinc oxide<br>Sufficient acetic<br>acid to maintain solu-<br>tion | 60<br>40 | TT–W–581 | P5–51 |

**Water-Repellent Preservatives.** These preservatives are used principally in applications for the treatment of millwork products such as sash and exterior doors. Water repellents give combined decay and weathering resistance. They retard moisture changes in wood but do not prevent them. These preservatives help to control blue stain and, to varying degrees (depending on the thoroughness of treatment), decay and termite attack. When applied by widely used brush or dip methods, they do not provide a high degree of protection to wood used in contact with the ground or continuously exposed to moisture. Water-repellent preservatives are sold under many trade names.

**Table 26. Specifications Covering Water-Repellent Preservatives**

| Specification | Preservative * |
|---|---|
| Federal Specification TT–W–572 | a. Pentachlorophenol, 5 percent<br>b. Copper naphthenate (2 percent copper equivalent) |
| Military Specification MIL–W–906 (Ships) | a. Copper naphthenate, 0.15 lb. copper per gal.<br>b. Chlorinated phenols, 0.35 lb. per gal.<br>c. Phenyl mercury oleate, 0.035 lb. per gal. |
| National Woodwork Mfrs. Assn. | Pentachlorophenol, 5 percent or equivalent |

* Dissolved in a suitable petroleum solvent with the required quantity of water-repellent materials.

**WOOD PRESERVING METHODS. Preparation for Treatment. Bark removal.** Some processes, such as end-diffusion methods, must or may be applied to round timbers without removing bark. In most processes removal of outer and inner bark is essential. Bark removal is accomplished by hand peeling or by machine peeling. Specifications covering the treatment of poles, piling, and posts generally require complete removal of the outer bark and restrict inner bark to patches not exceeding 1 in. by 6 in. at the ground-line zone and in other areas where good penetration is important for protection.

**Seasoning and conditioning.** With the exception of diffusion methods, wood should be seasoned or conditioned before treatment. Procedures are air-seasoning, kiln-drying, conditioning by steaming and vacuum, boiling in preservative oil under vacuum (Boultonizing), and vapor-drying (wood surrounded by hot vapors).

**Machining.** Cutting to final dimensions, adzing, framing, and boring of holes should be completed before treatment. When the material must be cut or bored after treatment, thoroughly treated material should be specified and exposed surfaces should be liberally coated with preservative.

**Incising.** Woods, such as heartwood Douglas-fir, that are resistant to treatment are often incised to improve preservative penetration and distribution.

**Principal Processes. Surface treatments.** Superficial applications of preservative, usually oils, by brushing, spraying, or dipping (30 sec. to 3 min. usually) result in shallow penetration and low retention; such treatments provide limited protection to the wood.

**Cold soaking, steeping, and diffusion.** Cold soaking involves prolonged immersion (several hours or days) in an unheated preservative oil of low viscosity. Soaking periods of 24 to 48 hr. furnish good penetration and fair retention in seasoned sapwood of most pines. The treatment of heartwood and sapwood of most other woods is less satisfactory.

Steeping involves prolonged soaking of wood in solutions of water-borne preservatives. In steeping green wood, the preservative penetrates mainly through diffusion. In dry wood, penetration is mainly by capillary absorption. Steeping in a mercuric chloride solution is called Kyanizing.

In other diffusion treatments, a water-soluble preservative is applied in the form of a water solution, paste, or powder to green wood. In the Osmose process, the preservative is applied to the surface of green wood in a creamy or pasty consistency which then penetrates by diffusion.

**Hot-and-cold bath treatment and adaptations.** These are used for the treatment of poles with thin sapwood (western species, such as western redcedar and lodgepole pine) with preservative oils; also for treatment of lumber, timbers, and posts with oils or water-borne preservatives.

The usual hot-and-cold bath treatment consists of two operations: (1) a heating bath in preservative oil, and (2) a cold or cooling bath. A typical schedule for butt treatment of air-seasoned western redcedar poles using coal-tar creosote is a hot bath for 5½ hr. after reaching 235° F. (total time in hot bath 9 hr.) and a cold bath for 10 hr. at 125° to 145° F. A shorter schedule would be used for seasoned lodgepole pine poles, and a lower temperature in the hot bath could be used with oil solutions of lower viscosity and flash point than creosote.

To provide the cold bath, hot preservative may be (1) removed from the treating tank and replaced by preservative at a substantially lower temperature, (2) wood may be removed from the preservative and immersed in a tank of cold preservative, or (3) hot preservative and the wood may be cooled together.

**Pressure treatments.** Pressure treatments are made in pressure-tight steel cylinders in which preservative is forced into wood at 100 to 200 pounds per square inch. The two main types of pressure processes are full-cell and empty-cell. In the full-cell process, vacuum is applied to wood in a treating cylinder before preservative is admitted. In the empty-cell process, no preliminary vacuum is drawn. Wood is first subjected to atmospheric air pressure (Lowry process) or to pressure higher than atmospheric pressure (Reuping process). The preservative is forced into the wood against the back pressure of the air which the wood contains. Release of pressure and the application of final vacuum then permits imprisoned air to force some of the preservative out of the wood.

The full-cell process is used for maximum injection, particularly in impregnating with water-borne preservatives and for products requiring the highest possible retentions. Empty-cell processes are used to obtain good penetration with limited quantities of preservative.

Specifications covering pressure treatment indicate maximum pressures and temperatures permitted for conditioning and treating various wood products and species; they also indicate minimum requirements for preservative penetrations and retentions, and recommended procedures for handling material after treatment.

**Specialized Wood Treatments. Fire retardants.** Lumber and plywood may be pressure impregnated with chemical solutions to resist fire. Retentions of up to 6 lb. of chemical (dry basis) per cubic foot of wood are necessary to secure adequate resistance to fire—up to 12 times as much as required for decay resistance. Fire-proofing chemicals also give a high degree of decay resistance. Treated doors have been tested and rated by Underwriters' Laboratories, Inc., and are commercially available bearing the Underwriters' label. Drawbacks to more extensive use include (1) insufficient recognition of value, (2) lack of generally accepted standards and specifications, and (3) the fact that treating cost is not offset by lowered insurance and amortization rates.

Coatings are also available. They have received less recognition than impregnants owing to a lack of performance standards. No such coatings have proved effective for exterior performance—they are typically for interior use.

Good effects can be obtained with either coatings or impregnants. Coatings are more temporary but are easily renewed. Due to water solubility of chemicals, coated or impregnated material is typically for interior use.

Table 27. Minimum Retentions, in Pounds of Preservative per Cubic Foot of Product, as Stipulated for Various Preservatives and Products by Federal Stock Catalog Specifications TT-W-571c, June 7, 1950

| Preservative | Ties[a] | Lumber and structural timbers | | | | Piles | | | Poles | Posts |
|---|---|---|---|---|---|---|---|---|---|---|
| | | In coastal waters | | In fresh water, or ground contact[c] | No water or ground contact | In coastal waters | | In fresh water, or ground contact[c] | | |
| | | Douglas-fir[b] | Southern yellow pine | | | Douglas-fir[b] | Southern yellow pine | | | |
| Coal-tar creosote | 8 | 14 | 20 | 10 | 6 | 14 | 20 | 12 | 8 | 6 |
| Creosote coal-tar solution | 8 | 14 | 20 | 10 | 6 | 14 | 20 | 12 | 8 | 6 |
| Creosote petroleum solution | 9 | ... | ... | 12 | 7 | ... | ... | 14 | ... | 7 |
| Pentachlorophenol, 5% in petroleum | ... | ... | ... | 10[d] | 6 | ... | ... | ... | 8 | 6 |
| Copper naphthenate (0.5% copper metal) in petroleum | ... | ... | ... | 10[d] | 6 | ... | ... | ... | 8 | 6 |
| Celcure (acid cupric chromate) | ... | ... | ... | ... | 0.50[e] | ... | ... | ... | ... | 0.75 |
| Chemonite (ammoniacal copper arsenite) | ... | ... | ... | ... | 0.30[e] | ... | ... | ... | ... | 0.45 |
| Chromated zinc chloride | ... | ... | ... | ... | 0.75[e] | ... | ... | ... | ... | 1.15 |
| Tanalith | ... | ... | ... | ... | 0.35[e] | ... | ... | ... | ... | 0.55 |
| Zinc chloride | ... | ... | ... | ... | 1.00[e] | ... | ... | ... | ... | 1.50 |
| Zinc meta-arsenite | ... | ... | ... | ... | 0.35[e] | ... | ... | ... | ... | 0.55 |

a Includes crossties, switch ties, and bridge ties.
b Coast variety.
c For use in contact with the ground; fresh water use not indicated.
d Also for important structural members not in contact with water or the ground.
e Minima should be increased 50 percent for use under moderate leaching conditions.

**Resin impregnations.** Impregnation of wood with urea-formaldehyde and phenol-formaldehyde resins results in an increase in compressive strength, shear strength, and hardness; it reduces tensile, toughness, and impact strength. Both resins cut down shrinking and swelling of thoroughly impregnated wood, but phenol resins do so to a greater extent. Such impregnations (impreg) are not, in general, economical and their use is very limited.

Compreg is formed when veneers impregnated with phenol-formaldehyde resin are laminated and densified under heat and pressure to specific gravities of 1.3 to 1.4. Compressive and shear strengths are high. Cost is high. Uses include airplane propellers, tooling jigs, knife handles, picker sticks, silent gears, and other highly specialized uses.

**Stain control.** See Tables 28 and 29.

**Table 28. Solutions for Prevention of Stain, Mold, and Decay in Lumber**

| Product | Suggested number of pounds per 100 gal. of water * | Limitations or advantages |
|---|---|---|
| Borax ................... | 32 | Usually effective on hardwoods only. |
| Dowicide G.............. | 7 | Not recommended for hand dipping unless special precautions are taken to protect workmen's hands. |
| Dowicide H.............. | 6 | In the South recommended only for hardwoods. |
| IN–4400A ............... | 4 | A new product not yet extensively tested. |
| Lignasan ................ | 2 | In bulked pine and in situations where drying is particularly slow this may allow some molding. |
| Noxtane ................ | 10 | Test results indicate that control may be somewhat inconsistent where drying is particularly slow. |
| Permatox 10s ........... | 10 | |
| Santobrite ............. | 7 | Not recommended for hand dipping unless special precautions are taken to protect workmen's hands. |
| Mixture 1<br>Lignasan plus.......... | 1 | Particularly effective under severe conditions. |
| Dowicide G or Santobrite ............... | 4 | |
| Mixture 2<br>Lignasan plus ........ | ½ | Particularly effective under severe conditions. |
| Dowicide G or Santobrite plus .......... | 2 | |
| Borax ................. | 6 | |

* For severe seasoning conditions the proprietary products may be used profitably at a higher concentration. For timber spraying and for use on lumber that must be bulked for more than a few days, increase the concentration of all chemicals by at least one-half.

Source: A. F. Verrall and T. C. Scheffer, Control of stain, mold, and decay in green lumber and other wood products, *Proc. For. Prod. Res. Soc.*, 1949.

**Table 29. Fungicidal Solutions for Chemical Treatment of Logs**

| Chemical* | Suggested amount per 100 gals. of water |
|---|---|
| Dowicide G (sodium pentachlorophenate).............................. | 21 lb. |
| Dowicide H (sodium tetrachlorophenate)†.......................... | 21 lb. |
| IN–5499 (phenyl mercuric oleate)................................... | 8.5 qt. |
| Lignasan (ethyl mercuric phosphate)............................... | 6 lb. |
| Permatox 10s (sodium pentachlorophenate plus borax)................. | 30 lb. |
| Santobrite (sodium pentachlorophenate)............................. | 21 lb. |

* Materials are listed in alphabetical order and not in order of effectiveness.
† In the Southern States recommended only for hardwoods.
    Source: A. F. Verrall and T. C. Scheffer, Control of stain, mold, and decay in green lumber and other wood products, *Proc. For. Prod. Res. Soc.*, 1949.

# Round Timbers

**POSTS.** There are no generally accepted specifications for posts. Dimensions and defects depend upon needs of users and are largely determined by local custom. Some railroads and most state highway departments have reasonably well-established post specifications but these differ considerably. Fence posts are commonly 4 to 6 in. in diameter; corner and gate posts 8 to 12 in. In some cases, 2½-in. posts are considered suitable for highway guard fences. Split posts are seldom less than 5 in. in least dimension. Fence posts are customarily set 2½ ft. in the ground, and extend about 6 in. above the top rail or wire. The common post is 7 to 8 ft. long; however, highway posts are shorter.

The principal post requirement other than dimension, is straightness. Knots are rarely considered defects. Decay and large splits cause rejection.

Species selection depends upon whether or not preservative treating is feasible. Untreated posts should be predominantly heartwood of the durable woods such as cedars, cypress, redwood, Osage-orange, black locust, catalpa, and white oak. Treated posts should be of species that have a high proportion of sapwood in post sizes in order to insure thorough treatment. Posts are commonly sold by the piece.

**POLES.** The American Standards Association combined wood pole specifications for the commonly used species under one specification in 1948. Normally the purchaser specifies the species, length, and class of poles, type of treatment, and complete details for roofing, gaining, boring, and branding.

Pole species are broken down into six groups based on bending strength:

Group I: Fiber stress 3,600 psi
    Northern white-cedar (*Thuja occidentalis*)

Group II: Fiber stress 5,600 psi
    Western redcedar (*Thuja plicata*)

Group III: Fiber stress 6,000 psi
    Ponderosa pine (*Pinus ponderosa*)

Group IV: Fiber stress 6,600 psi
    Western firs (true firs)
        Red fir (*Abies magnifica*)

Grand fir (*Abies grandis*)
Noble fir (*Abies procera*)
Pacific silver fir (*Abies amabilis*)
White fir (*Abies concolor*)
Lodgepole pine (*Pinus contorta*)
Northern pines
   Jack pine (*Pinus banksiana*)
   Red (Norway) pine (*Pinus resinosa*)

Group V: Fiber stress 7,400 psi
Douglas-fir—all types (*Pseudotsuga menziesii*)
Western hemlock (*Tsuga heterophylla*)
Southern pines
   Longleaf pine (*Pinus palustris*)
   Shortleaf pine (*Pinus echinata*)
   Loblolly pine (*Pinus taeda*)
   Slash pine (*Pinus elliottii*)
   Pond pine (*Pinus serotina*)

Group VI: Fiber stress 8,400 psi
Western larch (western tamarack) (*Larix occidentalis*)

Prohibited defects include cross-breaks, bird holes, plugged holes (except increment borer holes), hollow butts or tops, marine borer damage, splits or through-checks in the top, decay, and nails, spikes, and other metal not specifically authorized by purchaser.

Permitted defects include sap stain, firm red heart, and limited spiral grain. In 30-ft. and shorter poles one complete twist of grain is permitted in any 10 ft.; 35-ft. to 40-ft. poles permit one complete twist in any 16 ft.; poles 50 ft. and longer permit one complete twist in any 20 ft. Hollow pith centers are also permitted in tops, butts, or knots where the pole is to be treated full length.

Limited defects include butt checks and splits, shakes, insect damage, knots, scars (turpentine), dead streaks, compression wood, defective butts (decay in cedar butts, splintering), and shape.

Poles less than 50 ft. in length cannot be more than 3 in. shorter or 6 in. longer than nominal length. Poles 50 ft. or longer cannot be more than 6 in. shorter or 12 in. longer than nominal length.

Poles are classified by measuring the circumference at 6 ft. from the butt. This dimension determines the pole class, provided the top dimension is large enough; otherwise the top circumference will determine the true class, provided the 6-ft.-from-butt circumference does not exceed the specified minimum by more than 7 in.

The outer bark must be removed from poles. Inner bark is limited, usually, to patches 1 in. wide by 6 in. long. Poles must be neatly sawed and trimmed. Framing must be done before preservative treatment in the case of full-length treatments.

Most poles are preservative treated with creosote, creosote-coal-tar, or creosote-petroleum solutions to retentions of 8 to 10 lb. per cu. ft. of wood. Penetrations are specified and sapwood must be virtually completely penetrated. Copper naphthenate, pentachlorophenol, and salt solutions (water-borne) may also be used.

**PILES.** Timber piles are classified by the American Standards Assn. as:

Class A: Piles suitable for use in heavy railway bridges and trestles.
Class B: Piles suitable for use in docks, wharves, highway work, and general construction.

Class C: Piles suitable for use in foundations which will always be completely submerged, for cofferdams, falsework, and sundry temporary work.

The general quality of Class A and Class B piles includes freedom from decay, excessive splits, shake, twisted grain, or unsound knots. They shall be cut from sound live trees, except that fire-killed, blight-killed, or wind-felled timber is permissible if free from decay or insects. Knots and limbs shall be trimmed smoothly. Butt and tip are normally cut square with the pile axis. Piles for untreated use shall have a minimum of sapwood; piles to be treated shall contain a maximum of sapwood. Piles shall be peeled, including the inner bark, soon after cutting. They shall be free from short or reverse bends, and crooks greater than one-half the pile diameter at the middle of the bend. A line from the center of the butt to the center of the tip shall lie within the body of the pile.

Class C piles are of lower quality but shall be of sound, live timber that will stand driving. They need not be peeled if used untreated. They shall be free from bad knots, decay, and shakes affecting strength. Other specifications are similar to those for Class A and Class B piles.

## Mine Timbers

The term "mine timbers" is a collective designation denoting a variety of forms of wooden supports used in the construction of tunnels, shafts, and other mine openings or chambers. Mine timbers represent the seventh most important use of wood. Hardwoods, principally oak, supply about one-half the timber used; southern pine and other softwoods supply the remainder.

Slightly over half the timbers used are round, the remainder being sawed. Some split and hewn material is used. Round timbers are used for most temporary timbering and sawed timbers for more permanent installations. The species used must be high in bending and column strength, have a high strength-to-weight ratio, and must be free from brashness. Most mine timbers come from farm woodlots and timber properties adjacent to the mines. Material is usually taken down to 4-in. diameters, thus providing an outlet for small sizes and lengths.

Durability importance varies with the length of service required. Naturally durable or preservative treated timbers are used for long service operations. Creosote, penthachlorophenol, and water-borne preservatives are used. Nondurable woods may have a service life of one year and heartwoods of durable species may last no longer than 3 to 4 years owing to optimum growth conditions for fungi. Properly treated timbers will last 10 to 20 or more years.

No standard specifications are available. Timbers are usually cut to a purchase order and may be purchased by the lineal foot, per ton, or per M bd. ft.

## Railroad Ties

Railroad ties are generally classified as crossties and switch ties. Switch ties are used in sets, increasing by uniform increments of length (usually 6 in.) from single tie length to double length.

Bridge ties, used on open-deck bridges and trestles, are more in the nature of structural timbers and are not generally included in railroad tie specifications. Bridge engineers have made efforts to standardize the cross-sectional dimensions of bridge ties at 7 by 9 in. Lengths vary in accordance with the requirements of the design. Ordinary crossties are used on ballasted deck bridges.

Most ties are manufactured by sawing; some are hewn.

There are a number of standard specifications for ties (for dimensions see Table 30). All specifications for ties stipulate that ties must be well manufactured (of uniform dimensions) and straight; straightness is defined. Limitations are placed on decay and numerous or large holes and knots, particularly in the neighborhood of the tie-plate area. Shakes and splits are also limited, although they may be somewhat controlled by the use of antisplitting devices.

Standard railways almost universally require that ties be preservative treated. For such ties there is no limitation on sapwood and almost none on species, but they must commonly be peeled of all outer and inner bark before treating in order to insure good penetration of the preservative. Untreated ties, if accepted, must generally be of reasonably durable species such as black locust, white oak, black walnut, Douglas-fir, hard pine, larch, cedar, cypress, redwood, catalpa, chestnut, sassafras, red mulberry and occasionally others. It is common to stipulate the maximum sapwood that will be accepted on untreated ties. Some railroads prefer hardwood to softwood ties because of their increased resistance to mechanical wear.

Crossties are priced by the piece according to size. Switch ties may be sold in sets but generally the lengths desired are specified; prices are per M bd. ft.

**Table 30. Dimensions Specified by the American Railway Engineering Association for Crossties and Switch Ties (Reapproved 1948)**

| Commercial designation | Length (ft.) | Thickness (in.) | Top width (in.) | Portions of tie where thickness and top width are measured |
|---|---|---|---|---|
| **CROSSTIES** | | | | |
| Size 0 * | 5, 5½, 6, 6½, 7 | 5 | 5 | Throughout the two portions between 15 and 25 in. from middle of tie |
| Size 1 * | " | 6 | 6 | |
| Size 2 | 8, 8½, 9 | 6 | 7 | Throughout the two portions between 20 and 40 in. from middle of tie |
| Size 3 † | " | 6 | 8 | |
| Size 4 | " | 7 | 8 | |
| Size 5 | " | 7 | 9 | |
| Size 6 | " | 7 | 10 | |
| **SWITCH TIES** | | | | |
| None | 9, 9½, 10, 10½, etc. | 6 | 6 | Throughout length between points 12 in. from each end of tie |
| | " | 6 | 7 | |
| | " | 6 | 8 | |
| | " | 6 | 9 | |
| | " | 7 | 7 | |
| | " | 7 | 8 | |
| | " | 7 | 9 | |

*Narrow gauge. None accepted as standard-gauge railway ties.
† Railways which specify both 6″ by 8″ and 7″ by 7″ ties, sawed or hewn on top and bottom only, and which desire to separate the two sizes designate the 7″ by 7″ ties as 3A.

## Veneer and Plywood

**VENEER.** A veneer is a thin sheet of wood of uniform thickness produced by peeling, slicing, or sawing logs, bolts, and flitches (see Fig. 2).

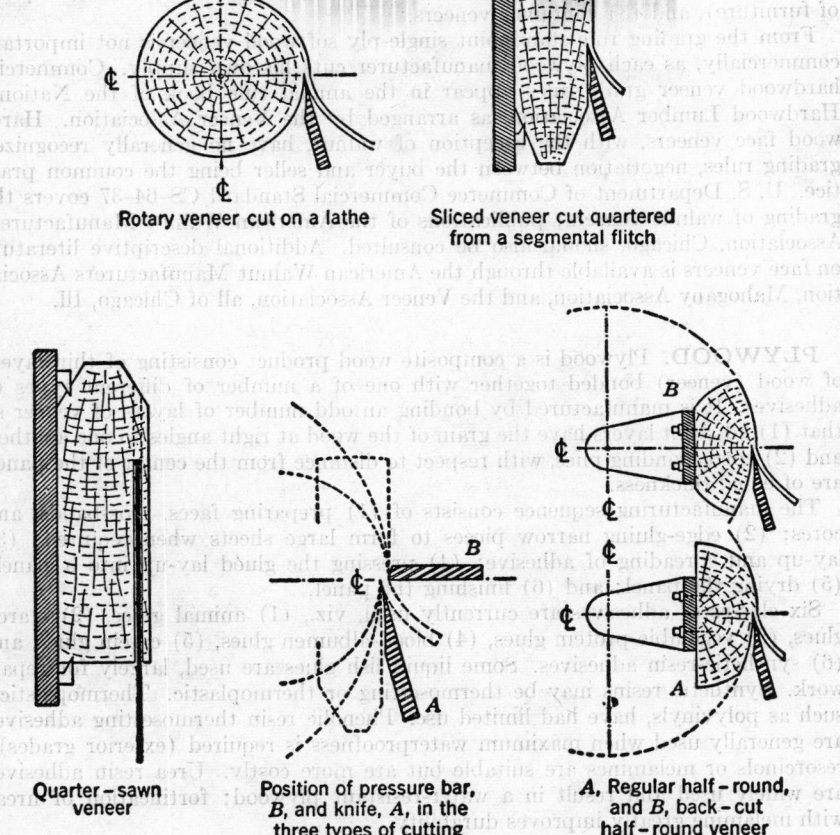

**Rotary veneer cut on a lathe**

**Sliced veneer cut quartered from a segmental flitch**

**Quarter – sawn veneer**

**Position of pressure bar, B, and knife, A, in the three types of cutting**

**A, Regular half – round, and B, back – cut half – round veneer**

**Fig. 2. Methods of making veneers by the rotary, slicing, and sawing processes.**
(N. C. Brown, *Forest Products*.)

Veneer may be air-dried, kiln-dried, or dried in veneer driers. Veneer driers may be conveyorized or hot-plate driers. Conveyor driers having rollers, racks, or wire mesh belts are common; hot-plate driers have a smaller capacity. Roller and plate driers produce flat veneers.

Logs, bolts, or sections of species having moderate density are usually steamed or cooked in vats before cutting. Some species such as basswood, Douglas-fir, spruce, and cottonwood are cut cold to prevent fuzzy, fibrous veneer. Times and temperatures of cooking or steaming vary with species, size, log age, and character of veneer to be cut. In general the denser the species and the more difficult to cut, the longer the preparation period and the lower the temperature. Stumps and crotches (for slicing) require very low temperature (100 degrees F.) for several days.

More than half the total annual American veneer output is from red gum (sweetgum) and Douglas-fir. There are distinctly separate hardwood and softwood veneer industries. The hardwood veneer industry is broken down to (1) face veneers, (2) commercial veneers (crossbands, cores, backs, concealed parts of furniture), and (3) container veneers.

From the grading rule standpoint single-ply softwood veneer is not important commercially, as each plywood manufacturer cuts his own supply. Commercial hardwood veneer grade rules appear in the annual rule book of the National Hardwood Lumber Association, as arranged by the Veneer Association. Hardwood face veneers, with the exception of walnut, have no generally recognized grading rules, negotiation between the buyer and seller being the common practice. U. S. Department of Commerce Commercial Standard CS–64–37 covers the grading of walnut veneers; publications of the American Walnut Manufacturers Association, Chicago, should also be consulted. Additional descriptive literature on face veneers is available through the American Walnut Manufacturers Association, Mahogany Association, and the Veneer Association, all of Chicago, Ill.

**PLYWOOD.** Plywood is a composite wood product consisting of thin layers of wood (veneer) bonded together with one of a number of different types of adhesives. It is manufactured by bonding an odd number of layers of veneer so that (1) adjacent layers have the grain of the wood at right angles to one another, and (2) corresponding plies, with respect to distance from the center of the panel, are of equal thickness.

The manufacturing sequence consists of (1) preparing faces, crossbands, and cores; (2) edge-gluing narrow pieces to form large sheets when required; (3) lay-up and spreading of adhesive; (4) pressing the glued lay-up into a panel; (5) drying the panel; and (6) finishing the panel.

Six classes of adhesives are currently used, viz., (1) animal glues, (2) starch glues, (3) vegetable-protein glues, (4) blood-albumen glues, (5) casein glues, and (6) synthetic-resin adhesives. Some liquid fish glues are used, largely for repair work. Synthetic resins may be thermosetting or thermoplastic. Thermoplastics, such as polyvinyls, have had limited use. Phenolic resin thermosetting adhesives are generally used when maximum waterproofness is required (exterior grades); resorcinols or melamines are suitable but are more costly. Urea resin adhesives are widely used and result in a water-resistant plywood; fortification of ureas with melamine greatly improves durability.

Types of plywood construction include (1) all-veneer construction—the typical fundamental type being made of an aggregate of veneers; (2) lumber-core construction—usually 5-ply with face, back, and lumber core having parallel grain, plus face and back crossbands; and (3) two-ply construction—limited use, not balanced.

Plywood may be made in flat sheets (typical) or molded-to-curvature (boat hulls, aircraft fuselages, etc.).

More detailed information is available for softwood plywood than for hardwood plywood. Much of the comment and information presented under Softwood Plywood would apply in a general way for hardwood plywood. Plywood is available having hardwood faces and softwood cores.

**Softwood Plywood.** Softwood plywood is estimated to account for two-thirds of the total volume of plywood produced in the nation. Production is concentrated in the area west of the Cascade Mountains in Washington, Oregon, and northern California. Of the softwood plywood production, about 95 percent is of Douglas-fir; the remaining output is of other native softwoods such as hemlock, redwood, the true firs, and the western pines. The industry trade association is the Douglas Fir Plywood Association, Tacoma, Wash., made up of Douglas-fir plywood producers.

**Physical properties.** In plywood, longitudinal grain is provided both lengthwise and crosswise of the panel. Consequently, plywood functions as a structural diaphragm or as a bracing, and also where plate action, with all edges supported, is involved. The cross-lamination in plywood tends to equalize the properties in each direction and to minimize certain weaknesses. Shrinkage, for example, is reduced in plywood so as to be negligible in many services.

Tests in the Douglas Fir Plywood Association laboratory on fir plywood showed the following expansion from an oven-dried condition to a saturated one, after 7 days' soaking:

Percent expansion based on oven-dry dimensions

| Thickness | Length | Width |
|---|---|---|
| ¼"—3 ply | 0.15–0.20 | 0.18–0.19 |
| ⅜"—3 ply | .18– .20 | .18– .26 |
| ¾"—5 ply | .18– .22 | .22– .26 |

Under normal service conditions, the variation in moisture content for plywood might range from 6 percent to 15 percent, or only about ⅓ of the range that caused maximum swelling in the tests. In practice this means an expansion of ± 0.06 percent, or about 0.06 in., for an 8-ft. long panel and ± 0.08 percent, or 0.04 in., for a 4-ft. width.

Plywood possesses great resistance to splitting and puncture because of the alternate grain direction of adjacent veneers.

Except in mild climates, wherever plywood is used for outer wall sheathing or siding, the inside wall covering should provide vapor-resistance at least equivalent to that of the sheathing, etc. An interior plywood wall lining, painted or finished, constitutes a good vapor barrier.

**Mechanical properties.** When plywood is subject to a tensile or compressive force lengthwise, only those plies having their grain running lengthwise are considered as carrying the load. The cross plies, stressed across the grain, do not contribute any significant amount to strength in tension or compression.

Similarly, in bending or flexure, only the plies running parallel with the span are considered in most cases in computing the moment of inertia, $I$, of the cross-section.

When plywood is used in flexure with its face grain perpendicular to the span, however, the face plies will contribute considerably to the stiffness, and also to the strength of 3-ply panels, provided in the latter case that the face plies consist of single sheets of veneer or of strips edge-glued to form wide faces.

Shearing stresses in plywood are of two distinctly different types, either one of which may be the critical factor in design. One kind of shear is that perpendicular to the plane of the panel, as horizontal (or vertical) shear in a built-up beam with a plywood web. This shear is computed over the full cross-sectional area of the panel. A common example of this type of shear is in plywood used as wall sheathing.

The second type of shear is that in the plane of the panel. In plywood, the wood fibers in the ply at right angles to the principal shearing force tend to roll, and a so-called "rolling shear" is induced.

Plywood, when attached securely to a lumber frame, imparts extraordinary rigidity in the plane of the panel. Fig. 3 shows some comparable values, as determined by tests at the U. S. Forest Products Laboratory.

| Sheathing Material | Relative Rigidity | Relative Strength |
|---|---|---|
| **1x8˝ DIAGONAL SHEATHING** | 1.0 | 1.3 |
| **29/32˝ FIBERBOARD** (8d nails, spaced 3˝ at all vertical edges, 5½˝ to 6˝ elsewhere.) | 1.6 | 2.1 |
| **HORIZONTAL SHEATHING** (1x8 sheathing; 1x4 let in braces; 8d nails, 2 per stud crossing.) | 1.5 | 2.2 |
| **1/4˝ PLYWOOD NAILED** (6d nails spaced 5˝ at edges, 10˝ elsewhere.) | 2.0 | 2.8 |
| **1/4˝ PLYWOOD GLUED TO FRAME** | 3.7 | 4.0 |

Fig. 3. Strength and rigidity of frame walls.

**Peeler log grades.** Logs for plywood are graded under log scaling and grading rules for the geographical district involved. A typical grading rule for Douglas-fir peeler logs requires:

**No. 1 peelers**—suitable for manufacture of not less than 50 percent of net scaled content, suitable for rotary cutting, at least 90 percent surface clear. Minimum net diameter (small end) of 30 in. Net length (plus trim) of 16 ft. shall contain at least 8 rings to the inch in the outer portion equal to at least 50 percent of the volume. Slope of grain is limited to 1 in. per ft. in logs of 30 to 35 in., up to 2½ in. per ft. on logs 5 ft. and more in diameter. Limits are placed also on other defects.

### Table 31. Nail-Bearing Loads

(Maximum ultimate loads for plywood nailed to 1⅝˝ Douglas-fir lumber Plywood panels butted at the center lines of studs. Any change in edge-distance will decrease load.)

| Plywood thicknesses (in.) | Nail size | | | | | | | |
|---|---|---|---|---|---|---|---|---|
| | 6d com. | | 8d com. | | 10d com. | | 16d com. | |
| | Load (lb.) | Plywood edge-distance (in.) | Load (lb.) | Plywood edge-distance (in.) | Load (lb.) | Plywood edge-distance (in.) | Load (lb.) | Plywood edge-distance (in.) |
| ⁵⁄₁₆ | 275 | ⅜ | 305 | ⅜ | | | | |
| ⅜ | 275 | ⅜ | 340 | ⅜ | | | | |
| ½ | | | 350 | ⅜ | 425 | ⅜ | | |
| ⅝ | | | 350 | ⅜ | 425 | ⅜ | 445 | ⅜ |
| ¾ | | | | | 410 | ⅜ | 445 | ⅜ |

**No. 2 peelers**—in general must produce 35 percent of "clear, uniform-colored veneer," be suitable for rotary cutting, and be at least 75 percent surface clear.

**No. 3 peelers**—must be suitable for peeling and produce veneer for centers, cores, and backs, and be at least 50 percent surface clear. Other defects are also somewhat limited.

In Bending, Tension and Compression (except bearing and 45° stresses) consider only those plies with their grain direction $\parallel$ to the principal stress.

| Type of stress | EXT·DFPA·A-A | EXT·DFPA·A-B, EXT·DFPA·Plyshield·(A-C) | EXT·DFPA·Utility·(B-C), EXT·DFPA·Sheathing·(C-C), EXT·DFPA·Concrete Form·(B-B), Plyform·(B-B), Plyscord·(C-D) | Interior·A-A, A-B; Plypanel·(A-D); Plybase·(B-D) (Note: Apply the following percentages to the stresses for the corresponding Exterior grade. See example below.) |
|---|---|---|---|---|
| | WET OR DAMP LOCATION | DRY LOCATION | DRY LOCATION | |
| **Extreme Fiber in bending** | | | | |
| Face grain $\parallel$ to span | 2,188 | 2,000 | 1,875 | 100% |
| Face grain $\perp$ to span | 1,875 | 1,875 | 1,875 | 80% |
| **Tension** | | | | |
| $\parallel$ to face grain (3-ply only)[a] | 2,188 | 2,000 | 1,875 | 100%[c] |
| $\perp$ to face grain | 1,875 | 1,875 | 1,875 | 80% |
| $\pm$ 45° to face grain | 337 | 320 | 310 | 85% |
| **Compression** | | | | |
| $\parallel$ to face grain (3-ply only)[a] | 1,605 | 1,460 | 1,375 | 100%[c] |
| $\perp$ to face grain | 1,375 | 1,375 | 1,375 | 70% |
| $\pm$ 45° to face grain | 496 | 472 | 460 | 80% |
| Bearing (on face) | 405 | 405 | 405 | 100% |
| **Shear, rolling, in plane of plies[b]** | | | | |
| $\parallel$ or $\perp$ to face grain | 79 | 72 | 68 | 75% |
| $\pm$ 45° | 105 | 96 | 90 | 75% |
| **Shear, in plane $\perp$ to plies[b]** | | | | |
| $\parallel$ or $\perp$ to face grain | 210 | 192 | 180 | 85% |
| $\pm$ 45° | 420 | 384 | 360 | 85% |
| **Modulus of Elasticity in bending** | | | | |
| Face grain $\parallel$ to span | 1,600,000 | 1,600,000 | 1,600,000 | 100% |
| Face grain $\perp$ to span | 1,600,000 | 1,600,000 | 1,600,000 | 70% |

[a] For tension or compression, $\parallel$ to grain, in 5-ply or thicker, use values for 3-ply, but in next lower grade.
[b] For certain conditions where stress concentrations exist these working stresses for rolling shear should be reduced by 50%. See Table 1, F.P.L. Bulletin, Approximate Methods of Calculating the Strength of Plywood. [c] For 5 or more plies use 90%.

Where moisture content exceeds 16%, decrease by 20% values shown for Dry Location for these properties: Extreme fiber in bending, tension and compression both $\parallel$ and $\perp$ to the grain and at 45°, and bearing. (No change in values for shear or modulus of elasticity.)

Example: The working stress in compression $\parallel$ for Plypanel 5-ply (1,238 psi) is found by multiplying the value for EXT·DFPA·Plyshield 5-ply, 1,375 psi, by 90%, the reduction factor shown in the last column and footnotes [a] and [c].

Source: Douglas Fir Plywood Assn, Technical data on plywood (rev.), 1948.

**Specifications and standards.** Types and grades of Douglas-fir plywood are based on Department of Commerce Commercial Standard CS45–48, Table 33. Types are Exterior and Interior, with several grades available, depending on the quality of veneers. Exterior is suitable for permanent outdoor exposure; Interior is water-resistant and intended for use where the moisture content in service will not exceed 20 percent.

**Table 33. Types and Grades of Douglas-Fir Plywood Based on Department of Commerce Standard CS45-48**

INTERIOR TYPE GRADES—MINIMUM QUALITY OF VENEERS

| Grade | Industry Grade-Trademarks | Face | Back | Inner plies * | Additional limitation |
|-------|---------------------------|------|------|---------------|------------------------|
| A–A, Int.....Interior·A–A·DFPA | | A | A | D | Sanded two sides |
| A–B, Int.....Interior·A–B·DFPA | | A | B | D | Sanded two sides |
| A–D, Int.....PlyPanel | | A | D | D | Sanded two sides |
| B–D, Int.....PlyBase | | B | D | D | Sanded two sides |
| C–D, Int.....PlyScord | | C | D | D | Unsanded grade. No belt sanding permissible. |
| B–B, Int.....Plyform | | B | B | C | Edge-sealed and, unless otherwise specified, mill-oiled. Sanded two sides. |

EXTERIOR TYPE GRADES—MINIMUM QUALITY OF VENEERS

| Grade | Industry Grade-Trademarks | Face | Back | Inner plies | Additional limitation |
|-------|---------------------------|------|------|-------------|------------------------|
| A–A, Ext.....EXT–DFPA·A–A | | A | A | C | Sanded two sides |
| A–B, Ext.....EXT–DFPA·A–B | | A | B | C | Sanded two sides |
| A–C, Ext.....EXT–DFPA·PlyShield·A–C | | A | C | C | Sanded two sides |
| B–C, Ext.....EXT–DFPA·Utility·B–C | | B | C | C | Sanded two sides |
| C–C, Ext.....EXT–DFPA·Sheathing·C–C | | C | C | C | Unsanded grade. No belt sanding permissible. |
| B–B, Ext.....EXT–DFPA·Concrete Form·B–B | | B | B | C | Edge-sealed and, unless otherwise specified, mill-oiled. Sanded two sides. |

* Except center ply of panels with 5 or more plies.

Ponderosa pine and sugar pine plywood meet the requirements specified in the Department of Commerce Commercial Standard CS–157–49 and are satisfactory for interior use since the bonds are classified as moisture resistant.

**Hardwood Plywood.** This industry consists of several hundred manufacturers, ranging from large corporations to small shops. Trade associations include the Hardwood Plywood Institute, Chicago, Ill., and the Southern Plywood Manufacturers Association, Atlanta, Ga. Manufacturers as a group follow the inspection, test, and approved methods for fabrication set forth in U. S. Department of Commerce, Hardwood Commercial Standard CS35–49. Veneers commonly used include both foreign and domestic species, classified as to density (Table 34).

**Table 34. Hardwood Plywood Density Classification**

| High density | Medium density | Low density |
|---|---|---|
| Ash, commercial white | Ash, black | Basswood, American |
| Beech, American | Cherry, black | Chestnut, American |
| Birch, yellow, sweet | Elm, American (white or gray) | Cottonwood, eastern, black |
| Elm, rock | Hackberry | |
| Maple, black (hard) | Magnolia | Willow, black |
| Maple, sugar (hard) | Mahogany, African | Yellow-poplar |
| Oak, commercial red | Mahogany, American | |
| Oak, commercial white | Maple, red (soft) | |
| Pecan, commercial | Maple, silver (soft) | |
| | New Guinea wood | |
| | Oriental wood | |
| | Paldoa | |
| | Primavera | |
| | Sweetgum | |
| | Sycamore | |
| | Tupelo, water, black | |
| | Walnut, American | |

Types of hardwood plywood include:

Technical—fully waterproof bond. The construction of this type is designed to satisfy requirements where plywood may be subjected to highly stressed conditions. The bond shall withstand full weather and marine exposure and shall be unaffected by microorganisms. The bond shall be of such quality that specimens will withstand the cyclic wet and dry test.

Type I—fully waterproof bond. The bond shall withstand full weather exposure and shall be unaffected by microorganisms. The bond shall be of such quality that specimens will withstand the cyclic wet and dry test, and cyclic boil.

Type II—water-resistant bond. The bond shall retain practically all of its strength when occasionally subjected to a thorough wetting and drying. The bond shall be of such quality that specimens will withstand the cold soak test.

Type III—dry bond. The bond is suitable for use where it will not be subjected to water, dampness, or high humidities.

The standard sizes and thicknesses of finished hardwood plywood are:

1. Widths: 24, 30, 36, 42, and 48 in. Tolerance ± 1/32.
2. Lengths: 48, 60, 72, 84, and 96 in. Tolerance ± 1/32.
3. Thicknesses: 1/8, 3/16, 1/4, 5/16, 3/8, 1/2, 5/8, 3/4, 13/16, 7/8, and 1 in. Tolerance: unsanded panels ± 1/32, sanded panels + 0 in., − 1/32.

Commercial standard hardwood plywood panels shall be square within 1/16 in., measured on the short dimension.

**Allied Panel Products.** In addition to standardized plywood materials, manufacturers produce allied products having special properties as follows:

1. Specialty products. In general, these are Douglas-fir plywood with special appearance properties. One or both surfaces may be striated, embossed,

brushed, sand-blasted or otherwise prepared to achieve appearance properties for varying decorative treatments.

2. Plastic surfaced plywood. This is an advanced type of panel material incorporating all the inherent properties of plywood plus surfaces of special characteristics—smoothness or hardness, or both.

3. Hardboard surfaced plywood. Initial production of hardboard surfaced plywood was recently undertaken by several fir plywood manufacturers. The composite is manufactured in the same manner as plywood except that hardboard sheets are substituted for face veneers of the panels. The properties of smoothness and hardness of hardboards are thereby combined with the strength, lightness, and workability of plywood.

## Hardboard

Hardboard is variously defined. It was originally a screen-backed, wet-felted board with a specific gravity of 0.9 to 1.1. A more comprehensive definition is a fiberboard composed of vegetable fiber and natural and added binders, formed in a mat, and pressed and heated so that the resulting product is an essentially homogeneous sheet. The minimum specific gravity is subject to debate. Realistically, 0.6 is about the minimum for particle-type hardboards now being produced as corestock for furniture panels; the specific gravity of super hardboards may range from 1.35 to 1.45.

Board types are essentially in two broad categories:

1. Fibrous—made by fiberizing wood substance by essentially pulping procedures and forming boards either by conventional wet-felting or by air-felting of dry or partially dry fiber. Maximum thickness usually $5/16''$.

2. Particle—resin-bonded boards made from shavings, sawdust, or wood chips. The volume of such boards is now small but is expanding rapidly. Thickness range is about $1/8$ to 1 in.

**MANUFACTURING PROCESSES. 1. Wet-felting.** Chips are reduced to high-yield pulp by defiberizing. A slurry is formed, deposited, and felted on a screen. Water is removed by drainage, suction, or squeezing. The mat is then compressed and dried in a hot press; boards are screen-backed to allow excess moisture to escape. A variation of this process dries the mat before hot-pressing, thus producing a hardboard with two smooth faces.

2. **Air-felting.** This is used in the Pacific Northwest. Fiberboard mats are formed from air suspensions rather than water. Fibers, after resin additions, are conveyed mechanically or by air (instead of a slurry), deposited, and felted. The dry mat is then compressed into hardboard; boards may be either smooth on one face or smooth on both faces, depending on moisture content of the fibers when pressed.

3. **Dry mix.** Particle boards from slivers or granules of wood are mechanically mixed with a liquid or a powder adhesive (such as urea or phenolic resins) and pressed into a board of the desired thickness in a hot press. Particles may be from millwork waste, veneer clippings, slabs, edgings, etc. Particle size and shape and resin distribution are critical. These mixtures are also being molded into such items as croquet balls, chair backs, and toilet seats. The molded wood-particle field is expanding rapidly.

4. **Tempered boards.** The boards are subjected to a final treatment with drying oils to improve water-resistance and strength; they are dipped in oil and baked.

**USES.** Many uses of hardboard duplicate those of plywood. It is used in the furniture industry as mirror backs, drawer bottoms, corestock for panels, crossbanding in panels, and backs for chests of drawers and wardrobes. It is also used in templets and jigs, backs for radios and television sets, facings for flush doors, cabinet paneling, and counter tops. In buildings hardboard is used for paneling, concrete forms, subflooring, and exterior wall covering. Other uses are as facings for plywood and as a base for plastic overlays.

**Table 35. Wood Adhesives: Mixing, Application, and Requirements for Best Use of Glues in Common Use**

| Glue | Mixing and application | Temperature requirements | Water resistance | Common uses | Available from |
|---|---|---|---|---|---|
| Animal | Soaked in water and melted; applied warm by hand or mechanical spreaders. | Control of temperature of glue, of room, and of wood important. | Low. | Furniture, cabinet, and millwork. | Retail sources; specific grades usually obtained only from manufacturers. |
| Starch | Mixed with water and alkali, usually with heat; applied cold by mechanical spreaders; too thick for hand spreading. | Used at ordinary room temperatures. | Very low. | Plywood and veneered panels for furniture; not well suited to home use. | Manufacturers. |
| Casein | Mixed with water at room temperatures; applied cold by hand or mechanical spreader. | Used at ordinary room temperatures. | Medium. | Used in gluing lumber, millwork, and plywood. | Retail sources. |
| Urea-resin: a. Room-temperature setting; b. Heat-setting. | a. Powder form mixed with water at room temperatures; liquid form mixed with hardener at room temperatures. | a. Not recommended for use below 70° F. b. Requires heat for curing; hot presses commonly used. | High. ... | a. Furniture, cabinet, and millwork. b. Plywood | a. Retail sources. b. Manufacturers. |
| Phenol-resin | Powder form mixed at room temperatures with water or water-alcohol mixtures; liquid form may require addition of hardeners; film form used as received. | Requires heat for curing; hot presses commonly used, but kilns have been employed. | Very high. | Plywood and laminated wood products for severe service; not well suited for home use. | Manufacturers. |
| Resorcinol-resin | Resin usually supplied in liquid form with which a powdered or liquid hardener is mixed at room temperatures. | Not recommended for use below 70° F. | Very high. | Millwork and laminated wood products for severe service. | Retail sources. |
| Melamine-resins | Resin powder mixed with water at room temperature. | Requires heat for curing; hot presses commonly used. | Very high. | Plywood; not well suited for home use. | Manufacturers. |
| Polyvinyl-resin | Ready-to-use; applied by hand or mechanical spreaders. | Used at ordinary room temperatures. | Low. | Furniture, cabinet, and millwork. | Manufacturers. |

Source: In part, U. S. Dept. Agr., *Trees: Yearbook of Agriculture 1949.*

# Wood Containers

**CONTAINER WOODS.** The woods commonly used in box and crate construction have been classified according to nail-holding ability, resistance to splitting by nails, and other characteristics, into four groups. All of the species within each group can be used interchangeably as far as thickness of material and the size and spacing of nails are concerned.

The groupings (as shown below) have been universally adopted and form a part of practically all specifications for containers involving the use of wood.

**Grouping of Woods According to Nail-Holding Qualities and Other Important Properties. Group 1** embraces the softer woods of both the coniferous and the broad-leaved species. These woods are relatively free from splitting in nailing, have moderate nail-holding power, moderate strength as a beam, and moderate shock-resisting capacity. They are soft, light in weight, easy to work, hold their shape well after manufacture, and, as a rule, are easy to dry.

| | | |
|---|---|---|
| Aspen (popple) | Cucumbertree | Red pine (Norway pine) |
| Baldcypress | Eastern white pine | Redwood |
| Balsam fir | Grand fir | Spruce |
| Basswood | Jack pine | Subalpine fir |
| Buckeye | Lodgepole pine | Sugar pine |
| Butternut | Magnolia | Western white pine |
| California red fir | Noble fir | White fir |
| Cedar | Pacific silver fir | Willow |
| Chestnut | Ponderosa pine | Yellow-poplar |
| Cottonwood | | |

**Group 2** consists of the heavier coniferous woods and includes no hardwood species. These woods usually have a pronounced contrast in the hardness of the springwood and the summerwood. They have greater nail-holding power than the Group 1 woods, but are more inclined to split; the hard summerwood bands often deflect the nails and cause them to run out at the side of the piece.

| | |
|---|---|
| Douglas-fir | Larch (tamarack) |
| Hemlock | Southern yellow pine |

**Group 3** consists of hardwoods of medium density. No coniferous species are included. These woods have about the same nail-holding power and strength as a beam as the Group 2 woods, but are less inclined to split and shatter under impact. Group 3 species are the most useful woods for box ends and cleats. They also furnish most of the rotary-cut lumber for wire-bound and plywood boxes.

| | |
|---|---|
| American elm (white elm) | Pumpkin ash |
| Black ash | Sweetgum (red gum) |
| Black tupelo (blackgum) | Sycamore |
| Maple, soft | Water tupelo |

**Group 4** woods are hardwood species. They have both the greatest shock-resisting capacity and the greatest nail-holding power, but because of their extreme hardness they present difficulties with respect to the driving of nails and also have the greatest tendency to split. They are the heaviest and hardest domestic woods and are difficult to work. They are especially useful where high nail-holding power is required, and many of them make excellent rotary-cut lumber for wire-bound and plywood boxes.

| Beech | Hickory |
|-------|---------|
| Birch | Maple, hard |
| Elm, rock | Oak |
| Hackberry | White ash |

A partial list of specifications for shipping containers in which these groupings are used is given in Table 36.

### Table 36. Partial List of Specifications for Shipping Containers

JOINT ARMY-NAVY SPECIFICATIONS * FOR PACKAGING AND PACKING FOR OVERSEAS SHIPMENT

| Designation | Name of specification |
|-------------|----------------------|
| JAN-P-103 | Boxes, wood-cleated, solid fiberboard |
| JAN-P-105A | Boxes, wood-cleated, plywood |
| JAN-P-106 | Boxes, wood, nailed |
| JAN-P-107 | Boxes, wood, wirebound |
| JAN-P-138 | Boxes, wood, fiberboard-lined (for weight of contents not exceeding 500 lb.) |
| JAN-P-104 | Crates, sheathed, wood, nailed |
| JAN-P-132 | Crates, unsheathed, wood, nailed (for maximum net load of 2,500 lb.) |

FEDERAL SPECIFICATIONS FOR CONTAINERS USED IN DOMESTIC SHIPMENTS

| NN-B-591 | Boxes, wood-cleated, fiberboard |
|----------|--------------------------------|
| NN-B-601a | Boxes, wood-cleated, plywood |
| NN-B-621a | Boxes, wood, nailed and lock corner |
| NN-B-631b | Boxes, wood, wire-bound |

* Copies of Joint Army-Navy Specifications may be obtained as indicated in the Index of United States Army, Joint Army-Navy and Federal Specifications Used by the War Department. Copies of this index and of the federal specifications may be obtained from the Superintendent of Documents, Government Printing Office, Washington, D. C.

There are three general classes of wood boxes:

1. Nailed wood. Available in many sizes and capacities, have maximum resistance to puncturing, crushing, and corner mashing but are heavier than other classes.
2. Cleated plywood. Sides, ends, top and bottom are one-piece plywood panels reinforced with cleats; package, when shipped, is bound with stapled steel straps. They are light in weight, resist mashing, diagonal distortion, and puncturing; essentially dustproof, easy to handle, difficult to open in transit; can carry up to 1,000 lb. but are generally used for much lighter loads.
3. Wire-bound. Light in weight, made of veneer or thin boards with reinforcing cleats, and bound together with wire. Usually carries loads not exceeding 500 lb.

**COOPERAGE.** Cooperage is a collective term descriptive of a variety of wood containers consisting of assemblies of staves and heads held together with hoops. Barrels, casks, and kegs designed to hold liquids, or products processed in liquids, are classified as tight cooperage. Similar containers for packaging dry commodities are called slack cooperage. Large tanks and vats made of staves and heads bound together with metal rods or straps are heavy cooperage.

**Tight Cooperage.** Staves for tight cooperage are made principally from white oak, red oak, white ash, Douglas-fir, yellow birch, sugar maple, and sweetgum.

Staves should be quarter-grained and not over 6 in. wide. Headings are made from the same species. Wood must be kiln-dried to prevent subsequent opening in storage. Standard barrels recognized by the industry trade association, Associated Cooperage Industries of America, Inc., St. Louis, Mo., are:

1. Bourbon barrel. Whiskey barrel, straight-grained, sap-free, quarter-sawed, charred.
2. White oak barrel, sap clear. Straight-grained, quarter-sawed, sap-free, not charred. Usually used unlined for acids, alcoholic liquids, extracts, vinegar, and similar products.
3. White oak barrel, tight sap. Narrow, tight-grained, quarter-sawed, free from open pores. Used unlined for fruit juices and meats; used lined for products similar to those shipped in sap-clear barrels.
4. White oak barrel, sound sap. Free from rotten or discolored sap; usually lined.
5. Red oak barrel. Free from discolored and rotten sap. Used lined or unlined for various products.
6. Gum barrel. Free from discolored and rotten sap. Used lined or unlined.
7. Ash barrel (no pumpkin ash permitted). Used lined or unlined.
8. Douglas-fir barrel. From live timber, edge-grain staves and headings. Used largely on West Coast. Lined when used to package foodstuffs.

Linings for tight cooperage include animal glue, paraffin, silicate of soda, rubber latex, and vinyl-base materials. The capacity of barrels ranges from 5 to 57 gal.

**Slack Cooperage.** Slack cooperage is used for a great variety of items for domestic and export shipment. For packaging foodstuffs, the taste impartation qualities of wood must be considered. Staves and heads are cut from sweetgum, beech, birch, maple, elms, hackberry, ash, sycamore, cottonwoods, spruces, Douglas-fir, western hemlock, oaks, black tupelo, and pines.

Nine standard slack barrels are recognized by the Associated Cooperage Industries of America, Inc. They are:

1. No. 1 barrel. Made of No. 1 staves and headings. Staves may be either tongued and grooved or plain jointed. Heading may be either tongued and grooved and glued, butt jointed and glued, or plain jointed. Bag liner may be used. Powdered milk, dried eggs, chemicals, sugar, salt, spices, etc., are shipped in No. 1 barrels.
2. No. 2 barrel. Made of No. 2 grade staves. Staves may be either tongued and grooved or plain jointed, heading is usually plain jointed. Used largely for hardware, valves, fittings, low grade chemicals, and for products where package sturdiness is important.
3. Meat and poultry barrel. Made of No. 2 staves and headings; for packing turkeys, ducks, chickens, pork, beef, etc. Generally made with single head, top open.
4. Glass and pottery barrel. Similar to meat and poultry barrel but is double-headed.
5. Potato barrel. Made of pine or hardwood plain jointed staves and headings.
6. Apple barrel. Made of pine or hardwood plain jointed staves and headings.
7. Fish barrel. A No. 2 barrel with one or two heads.
8. Vegetable barrel. Made with No. 2 staves and headings.
9. Nail and spike kegs. Pine staves and headings.

Slack barrels are made in a number of sizes. Large tobacco **hogsheads** have straight walls and are now generally made from Douglas-fir plywood.

**Tanks and Vats.** Tanks and vats fabricated with staves and headings are designated as **heavy cooperage.** Assembly is usually in the field. Staves and heads are made from lumber, tongue-and-grooved jointed. White oak, Douglas-fir, baldcypress, and redwood are the principal species used. Typical uses are for (1) storage of sour petroleum oil crudes, sulfite cooking liquors in the pulp and paper industry, brine processing of onions, olives, pickles, etc., fermentation and aging of malt beverages, raw whiskeys, ciders, and fruit juices, (2) water storage, (3) extractor tanks and vats for tanning hides, and (4) fabric dyeing in the textile industry.

**Veneer Baskets.** Rotary-cut veneer is typically used for veneer baskets. The principal species used include beech, elm, hard and soft maples, black and yellow birches, sweetgum, black and water tupelo, basswood, northern black cottonwood, yellow-poplar, some ash, spruce and white pine. Classes of veneer baskets include (1) berry boxes, (2) till baskets (square or rectangular shaped like an inverted frustum of a pyramid), (3) hampers (flat-bottomed baskets shaped like an inverted frustum of a cone), (4) round-stave baskets, (5) splint or market baskets, and (6) grape baskets (rounded ends, continuous walls, solid-wood bottoms).

## Shingles

Nearly all shingles manufactured in the United States conform to the following American Standards Sizes: 16 in. long by 5/2 thick, 18 in. long by 5/2¼ thick, and 24 in. long by 4/2 thick. (Shingles are measured at the butt ends, and their thickness designated as the number required to constitute a specified unit. Hence 5/2, 5/2¼, and 4/2 mean, respectively, 5 shingles to 2 in., 5 shingles to 2¼ in., and 4 shingles to 2 in.) Shingles are normally random-width; standard widths for dimension shingles 16 and 18 in. long are 5 and 6 in., and for 24-in. shingles, 6 in.

Shingles are universally packed so that 4 bundles, when laid on a roof with the prescribed exposure to weather, will cover 100 sq. ft. of roof surface. The unit of measurement is the "square." If shingles are used on side walls, 3 bundles will cover a side wall square.

#### Table 37. Shingle Exposure to Weather

| Shingle size (in.) (random width) | Number of courses per bundle * | Number of bundles | Exposure to weather (in.) | Number of bundles | Exposure to weather (in.) |
|---|---|---|---|---|---|
| 24 | 13/14 | 4 | 7½ | 3 | 10 |
| 18 | 18/18 | 4 | 5½ | 3 | 7½ |
| 16 | 20/20 | 4 | 5 | 3 | 6¾ |

* 13⁄14 means 13 courses on one end, 14 courses on the other; a total of 27.

Nearly all shingles are made from western redcedar (principally), California redwood, and southern cypress. A very small quantity of shingles is made from the eastern cedars, white pine, and perhaps other species. Shingles made for local consumption do not necessarily conform to national size or quality standards.

The first grades of the three principal shingle woods conform to U. S. Department of Commerce Commercial Standard CS–31: 100 percent heartwood, well-manufactured, neatly packed, with strictly vertical grain and no defects such as knots, wormholes, decay, sapwood, etc. Lower grades of shingles will admit the above-mentioned defects to a greater or less extent as defined by appropriate grading rules.

Commercial Standard vertical grain shingles are the only kind permitted for use in municipalities where fire laws permit the use of wood shingles.

Shakes (shingles which are split or rived to an equal thickness at both ends) are made in limited quantities but are gradually disappearing.

## Excelsior Manufacture

Excelsior consists of thin, narrow, ribbon-like strands of wood. The name "wood wool" is reserved for a small proportion of the output consisting of certain special grades of extra thin and narrow stock.

The property of greatest importance in excelsior is resilience. Wood used for excelsior is usually light in weight and color, soft, tough, straight-grained, absorbent, and free from odor. For certain uses, a slight odor is not objectionable, and excelsior having some resin is readily accepted. The bulk of commercial excelsior has always been produced from cottonwood, aspen, southern yellow pine, and basswood.

Much excelsior is consumed by the furniture and allied industries as loose excelsior and excelsior pads. Large amounts are also used to pack glassware, glass food containers, earthenware, and similar fragile articles.

Excelsior is used in low-priced upholstery and mattresses. To a certain extent it is used for insulation in cooling systems, as filtering material, animal bedding, and toy stuffing. Low-grade excelsior is sometimes used as a filler in cement and magnesite building boards. An important use for excelsior in the West is in the packing of fruit.

Bolts are usually cut 37 to 56 in. long, and must be free from gross defects and reasonably straight-grained. Well-seasoned bolts are trimmed and cut to the proper lengths for excelsior making. The following are specifications of an excelsior plant that buys 60-in. bolts:

Wood to be sawed 5 ft. long, peeled clean of bark; sticks to be straight, sound, free from large knots, and not less than 4 in. at the small end. Pieces 4 in. to 7 in. not to be split; bolts 7 in. to 11 in. to be split once; from 11 in. to 14 in. quartered; and over 14 in. split in proportion. All wood to be closely corded 4 ft. 8 in. high, 8 ft. long, and 5 ft. wide.

Excelsior machines are of two types: horizontal and upright. In the upright type the scoring knives move up and down; in the horizontal machines the knives move back and forth. The average excelsior machine of either type will cut from 800 to 1,200 lb. of excelsior in an 8-hour day. A cord of dry wood will yield 1,800 to 2,000 lb. of excelsior, varying with the dimensions and quality of the bolts, the grade of the product, and the kind of wood. The waste in manufacture is approximately one-fourth of the original wood volume.

Excelsior is graded according to the thickness and width of the strands, and the kind and color of the wood. Standard excelsior is 18 in. long or the length of the stick, 0.01 in. thick, and is divided into width classes as follows: fine, $\frac{1}{26}$ in. wide; medium, $\frac{1}{8}$ in. wide; and coarse, $\frac{7}{32}$ in. wide. Certain special grades of excelsior, classified as "wood wool," vary in dimensions according to particular specifications, but are usually 0.005 in. thick and $\frac{1}{32}$ in. wide. Wood wool is made as thin as 0.002 in. and as narrow as $\frac{1}{64}$ in. Material of this type is manufactured only for special purposes. Coarse excelsior runs from 0.012 to 0.02 in. in thickness and from $\frac{1}{32}$ to $\frac{1}{4}$ in. wide. Probably 80 to 90 percent of the output of excelsior is of the standard and coarse grades.

Excelsior is sold by the ton. It is packed in bales of ordinary size weighing about 100 lb. and in large bales of 200 lb. or more.

# Wood Chips

**MACHINES.** Wood-chipping machines are typically portable, mounted on tractors, jeeps, trucks, or trailers and will operate while in motion. The head is a disk or a cylinder mounting 3 to 6 knives. Knives may be straight or toothed Particle size can be varied from shavings to coarse chips in some types; round or slabbed material can be chipped. Machine prices range from approximately $700 to $6,000; production ranges from about 1 to 4 roundwood cords per hour. All species can be handled, wet or dry—green wood chips more easily, dry wood more uniformly. The approximate horsepower range of the machine is 30 to 60. Chips are forcibly discharged; they may be blown into trucks, containers, or on the ground. The cylinder-type chipper was originally developed to dispose of brush; the disk type is said to produce chips more acceptable for pulping.

**COST OF CHIPS.** Costs of chipping per roundwood cord (weight about 2 tons) including machine (fixed and operational charges) and labor (crew, supervision, taxes, insurance) vary from about $2 to $5 per roundwood cord. Cost varies greatly with machine type, feed rate, material, weather and ground conditions, chip size, etc. The cost of chipping per bushel (fuel) varies from about 1 to 6 cents. Machines are available in New England at $5 per hr. for machine and one man, the material to be ready and labor furnished for feeding. Pulpwood chips could probably be delivered anywhere in New England at $5 per ton.

**WEIGHT OF CHIPS.** The weight of green chips per cubic foot will vary from about 13 to 20 lb. Examples are red maple, 14.9 lb.; oaks, 19.0 lb.; white pine, 13 lb. (17 lb. settled). Roughly speaking, a chipped roundwood cord results in about twice the original volume in chips. A test on southern pine resulted in a cord (128 cu. ft.) of roundwood making 232 cu. ft. of chips piled into a freight car.

**USES.** 1. **Soil improver.** Wood chips increase organic content, reduce runoff, prevent soil baking and excessive evaporation, and help prevent water and wind erosion. Soil tilth is improved and tillage labor is lessened. Structure is improved. Soils are not made sour or acid; continued use of wood will raise pH values. About ⅓ of 1 percent nitrogen is a rule-of-thumb for adding nitrogen with chips to prevent soil denitrification (approximately 50 lb. of ammonium sulfate per ton of chips). Chips can be applied at the rate of 10 to 20 tons per acre; usually about 10 tons per acre to build up worn-out soils.

2. **Mulch.** Chips control weeds, keep soil surface loose and friable, absorb energy of raindrop impact, reduce soil temperatures, or insulate soil against early and quick freezes. They are used for orchards (5 to 7 in. depth), berries (3 to 7 in.), vegetables and flowers (2 to 3 in.). Extra nitrogen is added in some cases.

3. **Bedding and litter.** Ten lb. of bedding per animal-day is a general recommendation (chips are absorbent, resilient, and easy to handle). A cord of pole wood provides enough chips for 1 animal-year. Uniformly small wood chips (⅛ to ¼ in.) make excellent poultry litter.

4. **Pulping.** Mills have been reluctant to buy chips, even free from bark, because of species and moisture content variation, and need for new handling and transportation equipment. Economic separation of bark from wood must be worked out; bark content varies from 15 to 40 percent.

5. **Fuel.** Material should be screened to get rid of fines and oversize; uniform ¼ in. chips work well in sawdust burners. Coarse chips are adapted to large boilers with interchangeable stokers for wood or coal. Chips from low-grade wood

from logging waste or improvement cuttings can be delivered in New England for $4 to $5 per ton; they have 50 percent of the fuel value of steam coal, which costs two to four times as much.

6. **Compost.** Compost from this material turns easily, but takes two to three times as long as herbaceous material to decompose. A cord of wood should yield about 3 tons of compost.

7. **Pavements.** Chips make excellent pavement around barns and sheds or over muddy areas trampled by stock; they have been used on parade grounds and on recreational areas.

## Sawdust and Shavings

**SAWDUST.** Between 10 and 13 percent of the total content of the log is reduced to sawdust. Classifications are softwood, hardwood, mixed softwood, and mixed softwood and hardwood; it may be sold green, air-dry, or kiln-dry. Green softwood sawdust is used mostly as a fuel near the production point; most sawdust sold for industrial use is air- or kiln-dry.

The demand has become exacting, thus sawdust is often graded for size and in some cases for species. Hardwood sawdust is often sifted into 8- to 40-mesh sizes. Softwood sawdust is seldom sifted.

Utilization is limited by handling charges, transportation costs, lack of uniformity, quantity available, and the physical state of the sawdust.

**Uses.**

1. Bedding. For stables and kennels; coarse sawdust is about as absorbent as hay, fine sawdust about twice as absorbent. Also compares favorably with straw. Six pounds of coarse dry sawdust furnishes clean bedding for 1 cow-day.
2. Absorbent. Butcher shops, markets, shops, etc.
3. Leather manufacture. Moistening hides for stretching; must be free of dirt, grease, and splinters.
4. Fur conditioner. Moistening skins, cleaning, fluffing, and restoring luster. Hard maple preferred.
5. Cleaning, drying, and polishing metals. Removing oil and grease from metal and metal products.
6. Packing. In shipment of grapes and other fruit, fragile articles, etc.
7. Insulation.
8. Curing of freshly poured concrete.
9. Soil improver. Improves soil structure, increases organic content, reduces runoff, prevents baking, lessens tillage labor. Up to 20 tons per acre have been used with excellent results. Soils are not made sour or acid; continued use will raise pH values. To prevent soil denitrification (indicated by yellowing leaves and slow growth of crop), a rule of thumb is to add 1 percent of nitrogen per ton of sawdust; for example, 150 lb. of ammonium sulfate, or 100 lb. of ammonium nitrate.
10. Mulch. A 10-in. mulch has been used on mature apple trees, with 6 to 7 lb. of ammonium sulfate added per tree. Mulch is usually 4 to 6 in. for many plants, and remains effective for 3 to 5 yr. without maintenance.
11. Meat and salt smoking. Green hickory preferred; maple, oak, walnut, and mahogany also used.
12. Filler. Used as raw material for wood flour, in composition flooring, stucco, gypsum compositions, abrasives, floor-sweeping compounds, plastics, hardboards, wallboards.
13. Fuel (see Wood Fuel below).

**SHAVINGS.** Uses duplicate those listed under sawdust in many cases. Major uses are as fuel, packing, bedding, mulch, wood flour, and wallboards. Shavings are often baled in 80- to 240-lb. units.

# Wood Flour

Wood flour is finely ground wood, resembling wheat flour in texture and appearance. It must be light in color and weight, fluffy, and highly absorptive. The wood used must be light-colored and of low resin content. About 75 percent of the wood flour made in the United States is from the white pines (eastern, western, and sugar). Other species used are spruce, poplar, maple, birch, hemlock, Douglas-fir, and cedar. Uses of wood flour are expanding, mostly due to the expansion of plastics industries. Principal uses are in dynamite, linoleum, plastics, glue, fine wallboard, face powder, and leather cleaning, the largest amount being used in plastics, linoleum, and dynamite.

The grade of wood flour is usually designated by size of mesh. Sizes most commonly used are 60-, 80-, 100-, and 120-mesh; some 400-mesh has been marketed. Canadian and European wood flour offer competition to United States firms.

Three principal types are:

1. Technical wood flour. Made typically from white pine shavings and sawdust; must be 60-mesh or finer, light-colored, free from staining ingredients. If other than white pine is used, flour from each species must be kept separate. Largely used as a plastic filler.
2. Nontechnical wood flour. Made to less rigid specifications. May be a mixture of hardwoods and softwoods.
3. Granulated wood flour. A special grade of technical wood flour. Particles must conform to a specific weight.

Manufacturing mills are of the attrition, impact, or crushing types. Sawdust, shavings, and in some cases slabs, edgings, and trimmings, are raw material sources. Raw material is usually seasoned to 8 to 10 percent moisture content.

# Wood Fuel

Both domestic and industrial uses of wood for fuel are declining. Some areas (such as Washington and Oregon), however, have increased the use of wood by improving burning equipment.

Advantages of wood as a fuel include cleanliness (little smoke or soot), easy starting, quick heating, and low ash content. Disadvantages include bulkiness, difficulty of maintaining a low fire, more man-hours to produce (per fuel unit) than coal or oil, necessity of seasoning, and nonuniformity as to moisture content.

One lb. of oven-dried wood substance of any species has a calorific value of about 8,600 Btu. The presence of oils, resins, and extractives will increase this value.

Wood fuel should be as dry as possible. A pound of oven-dried red oak wood, with a calorific value of 8,600 Btu, yields about 7,100 Btu of usable heat with 50 percent excess air, and a flue gas temperature of 450° F.; air-dried wood yields about 5,700 Btu; and green wood, about 3,400 Btu. Green wood of most native species has about 60 percent of the heat value of well air-dried wood. Wood is being increasingly sold for fuel on a weight basis. On a cord basis, green wood yields about 80 percent of the available heat as compared with the heat produced by the burning of well air-dried wood. The evaporation of moisture absorbs about 1,000 Btu per lb. of moisture. At temperatures below 500° F., the distillation of volatile matter also absorbs heat. Unburned volatiles cause a large loss in efficiency; they also cause trouble in stoves and furnaces due to creosote, tarry substances, and acetic acid which they contain. Creosoting is avoided by burning dry wood in a small hot fire rather than in a large smoldering one; refueling at frequent intervals helps; and short stovepipes and inside chimneys help to prevent creosote condensation.

Improved furnaces and stoves for wood fuel have been developed. Essentially they provide sufficient secondary air for more complete combustion, and flame travel is such that gases are burned before contacting heat-absorbing surfaces.

Wood fuel may be in the form of cordwood, hogged wood, wood chips, sawdust, shavings, mill residues, or brickettes. Sawdust is used extensively for domestic heating in the Northwest; it is sold in units (200 cu. ft.), as it comes from the saw, containing about 80 cu. ft. of solid wood; about 1½ to 2 units heats a room during a normal winter.

Brickettes are wood residues, such as sawdust and shavings, which are compressed in a press; in some cases binders such as coal-tar pitch, petroleum refuse, and waste sulfite liquor are added. "Pres-to-log" is a common brickette made without the use of added binder; each log is a cylinder 4⅛ in. in diameter by 12¾ in. in length. "Burnets" are small cylinders, 1⅛ in. in diameter, broken into short lengths. Charcoal is also used for fuel and in many cases is marketed in the form of brickettes.

**Table 38. Approximate Weight and Heating Value per Cord (80 cu. ft.) of Different Woods, Green and Air-Dry (20 Percent Moisture) ***

| Woods | Weight (lb.) | | Available heat (million Btu) | | Equivalent in coal tons | |
|---|---|---|---|---|---|---|
| | Green | Air-dry | Green | Air-dry | Green | Air-dry |
| Ash ..................... | 3,840 | 3,440 | 16.5 | 20.0 | 0.75 | 0.91 |
| Aspen ................. | 3,440 | 2,160 | 10.3 | 12.5 | .47 | 0.57 |
| Beech, American ....... | 4,320 | 3,760 | 17.3 | 21.8 | .79 | 0.99 |
| Birch, yellow ........... | 4,560 | 3,680 | 17.3 | 21.3 | .79 | 0.97 |
| Douglas-fir ............. | 3,200 | 2,400 | 13.0 | 18.0 | .59 | 0.82 |
| Elm, American ......... | 4,320 | 2,900 | 14.3 | 17.2 | .65 | 0.78 |
| Hickory, shagbark ...... | 5,040 | 4,240 | 20.7 | 24.6 | .94 | 1.12 |
| Maple, red ............. | 4,000 | 3,200 | 15.0 | 18.6 | .68 | 0.85 |
| Maple, sugar ........... | 4,480 | 3,680 | 18.4 | 21.3 | .84 | 0.97 |
| Oak, red .............. | 5,120 | 3,680 | 17.9 | 21.3 | .81 | 0.97 |
| Oak, white ............ | 5,040 | 3,920 | 19.2 | 22.7 | .87 | 1.04 |
| Pine, eastern white ..... | 2,880 | 2,080 | 12.1 | 13.3 | .55 | 0.60 |
| Pine, southern yellow ... | 4,000 | 2,600 | 14.2 | 20.5 | .64 | 0.93 |

* Data from the U. S. Forest Products Laboratory, except for Douglas-fir and southern pine. Heat value of coal, under similar conditions of combustion, is considered to be 11,000 Btu.

Source: A. J. Panshin *et al., Forest products,* 1950.

## Pulpwood

The pulpwood market provides an outlet for a large volume of wood not usable as logs and for species in small demand. Tolerance in size and quality of wood used for pulp permits salvaging the wood fiber in thinnings, tops left in logging, and sawmill leftovers. The usual minimum diameter at the small end of pulpwood sticks at eastern mills is 4 in., inside bark. On the West Coast most of the wood is in logs. Lengths run from 4 ft. at most groundwood and sulfite mills, to 5 ft. at most Appalachian mills and west of the Mississippi River in the South; 5 ft., 3 in. in the Southeast; 100 in. in the Lake States; log size in the Northwest is often 40 ft.

In the Northwest pulpwood logs are often sorted out from higher grade logs, in water dumps. There they are scaled by board foot or special pulpwood scale. Sanitation cutting removes trees liable to insect attack, i.e., the less vigorous mature trees. "Farmer wood" is less developed than in the East.

Increasing use is made of sawmill and veneer plant leftovers, which are shipped by truck, rail, or barge to the pulpmill. Hydraulic barking of logs before the head saw permits economical handling. Some western mills get a large part of their supply in chips from veneer and sawmills. A number of large sawmills in the South have installed log barkers and slab chippers to increase the use of mill leftovers in pulping.

## WOOD REQUIRED BY VARIOUS PAPERMAKING PROCESSES.

Each mill has somewhat different methods, products, and usable species. Some mills buy peeled wood only; others want it unpeeled. Every mill has economic limits beyond which it cannot go for supplies. Some mills make paper from pulp produced elsewhere. "Integrated" plants make pulp that is pumped to paper mills in the same establishment. Many mills buy one kind or group of species for certain digesters, another kind or group for other equipment. A single plant may house several processes under one roof.

The business is highly competitive. Anyone planning to sell pulpwood should get definite, up-to-date information on specifications and markets before commencing to cut.

Pulp from more than one process may be blended, as groundwood and sulfite in newsprint. Processes tend to evolve and sometimes merge. "Neutral sulfite" is a modification that gives bright pulp from conifers and hardwoods. The semichemical processes with high yields, are expanding. Chemi-groundwood is among the variations.

The long fibers of coniferous species give greater strength than the shorter fibers of deciduous woods, but great strength is not needed in some kinds of paper.

## SPECIFICATIONS AND AGREEMENTS.

Each mill lists the kinds of wood desired, with species groupings and specifications. These vary somewhat from mill to mill because of the different kinds of paper they make. Wood going into white paper may need different preparation from that used for coarse paper. In general, specifications call for sound straight wood from living trees, with knots and limbs trimmed close to the surface of the stick, sawed into standard lengths, and not less than the stated minimum diameter. Wood must be free of charred portions, nails, wire, and other metal. Unsplit crotches and very rough wood are usually unacceptable. Peeling and splitting (large sticks only) are required by some mills. Others will not accept split wood. Settlement on mill measurement or weighing is usually specified. Inspection bureau scaling is customary in the Pacific Northwest.

Quotations may be for wood delivered by truck at mill, rail sidings, or barge landing, or f.o.b. cars at named sidings, or on barge at landings, or in booms at named points, or ranked alongside highway.

## Table 39. Pulping Processes, by Regions, Generalized

| Process | Regions [a] | Preferred species [b] | Principal products | Cords of wood per ton of pulp [c] |
|---|---|---|---|---|
| Groundwood .. | All | SPRUCE, BALSAM FIR (NE, L, NW), ASPEN (L), birch (NE, L), PINE (S), HEMLOCK, SPRUCE, FIR (NW). | Newsprint, catalog, book, building board. | 0.93 |
| Exploded wood | S, NW | PINE, gum (S), REDWOOD, Douglas-fir (NW). | Hardboard, building board. | 0.93 |
| Sulfite........ | All | SPRUCE, BALSAM FIR, hemlock (NE, A, L), HEMLOCK, SPRUCE, FIR (NW), ASPEN (NE, L), birch, maple (NE, L), PINE (S). | Newsprint, dissolving pulp, writing, tissue, book. | 1.94 |
| Sulfate........ | All | PINE (NE, L, S), DOUGLAS-FIR, pine, cedar (NW); practically all species including hardwoods (NE, A) also gum (S). | Strong wrapping, bag, boxboard. When bleached, book, magazine, writing, bond, specialty. | 1.64 |
| Soda......... | NE, A, NW | ASPEN and other Populus species, LINN or BASSWOOD, gum, birch, maple, beech (NE, A), cottonwood (NW). | Bulky printing papers, blotter, litho. | 1.79 |
| Semichemical.. | NE, A, L, S | HARDWOODS (NE, L), chestnut (A), ASPEN, birch (L), GUM, bay, magnolia (S). | Corrugating, insulating board, roofing felt, wrapping, book, magazine. | 1.20 |

[a] Regions are Northeast (NE), Appalachian (A), South (S), Lake States (L), Northwest (NW).

[b] Major wood species in capitals; minor in small letters.

[c] Unpeeled wood. To convert rough wood to peeled, a factor of 15 percent is generally acceptable. Consider species variations.

The essential points of a pulpwood contract are:

1. How many cords (or other units as specified).
2. What species or kinds.
3. The specifications (dimensions, how prepared).
4. Where delivered.
5. The price per cord or other unit.
6. Time limitation (varies from a few weeks to a year or more).

## Naval Stores

The gum naval stores industry is concentrated in the slash and longleaf pine belts of Georgia, Florida, and Alabama. High labor costs, competition from stumpwood distillation products, and increased production of synthetic materials have resulted in a sharp decline in the gum crop. Recently central steam stills, gum cleaning, and acid stimulation of trees have brought about better products, higher yields, and lowered costs. Gum farming handled by timber owners, and separation of production and distilling, are present industry features. Integrated with the production of saw logs, pulpwood, and ties, the naval stores industry can be an important part of forest management, bringing in early returns from short-boled, poorly formed trees, while still permitting their later use for other types of products.

## GOOD NAVAL STORES PRACTICE.

Species: Work only slash and longleaf pines.
Form of trees: Large-crowned trees are high yielders.
Size: Work only trees 9 in. and over in diameter.
Selection: Reserve unchipped trees that are good prospective pole or saw-log trees.
Number of faces: Use one on trees under 14 in. in diameter, two on larger trees.
Width of face: One-third of the bark circumference.
Depth of streak: Shallow bark streaks, if acid treated; ½ in., if untreated.
Height of streak: ½ in. or less.
Chipping interval: Weekly, if untreated; biweekly, if acid treated.
Facing and cup hanging: During January and February.
Chipping season: Usually March 15 to November 1.
Chipping height: Acid, 12 in. annually; untreated, 20–24 in. annually.
Years of chipping per tree: 5 or 6.
Dipping interval: Average 4 weeks.
Raising cups and tins: Good practice at the end of the first, second, and third year's work; tins should be nailed on.
Cup material: Use rust-free aluminum, zinc, lead-coated, or clay material; galvanized iron cups should be replaced when rusty.
Cup covers: Canvas or wooden cup covers keep gum free of trash and increase yield and quality.
Marketing: Crude gum is bought at numerous central stills and gum buying markets. It is bought on grade and is graded on color and cleanliness.

### Table 40.  Yields per Crop [a] by Tree Diameter and Species

| | Gum yields | | | | | | Average site turpentine yields | |
| | Slash pine | | | Longleaf pine | | | | |
| Diam. (in.) | Poor site (bbl.) [b] | Good site (bbl.) | Aver. site (bbl.) | Poor site (bbl.) | Good site (bbl.) | Aver. site (bbl.) | Slash pine (units) [c] | Longleaf pine (units) |
|---|---|---|---|---|---|---|---|---|
| 6 | 73 | 108 | 91 | 78 | 108 | 93 | 21 | 20 |
| 7 | 101 | 140 | 121 | 101 | 135 | 118 | 28 | 26 |
| 8 | 129 | 172 | 151 | 124 | 163 | 144 | 35 | 32 |
| 9 | 154 | 207 | 181 | 147 | 191 | 169 | 42 | 37 |
| 10 | 181 | 239 | 210 | 170 | 218 | 194 | 49 | 43 |
| 11 | 210 | 271 | 240 | 193 | 246 | 220 | 56 | 49 |
| 12 | 234 | 306 | 270 | 216 | 274 | 245 | 63 | 54 |

[a] A crop is 10,000 faces.
[b] A 50-gal. barrel of gum weighs 435 lb. net.
[c] A unit is one 50-gal. barrel of turpentine and 1,400 lb. of rosin.
Source: U. S. Dept. Agr., *A naval stores handbook*, Misc. Publ. No. 209.

**Table 41.  Gum Yields for Two Years of Turpentining with Different Frequencies of Chipping and Treatment**

| Chipping frequency and treatment * | Relative percentages of gum yields | | | |
| | Slash pine | | Longleaf pine | |
| | 1945 | 1946 | 1945 | 1946 |
|---|---|---|---|---|
| Weekly | | | | |
| Untreated ............... | 100 | 100 | 100 | 100 |
| Acid ..................... | 154 | 144 | 197 | 174 |
| Acid-arsenic ............. | 135 | ... | 195 | ... |
| Biweekly | | | | |
| Acid-arsenic ............. | 106 | ... | 101 | ... |
| Triweekly | | | | |
| Acid-arsenic ............. | 75 | ... | 99 | ... |

* Forty percent sulfuric acid used on slash pine and 60 percent on longleaf. Acid-arsenic solution used, 11.5 grams of arsenic pentoxide per liter of acid.
Source: Southeastern Forest Exp. Sta., *Tech. Note No. 68.*

**LABOR RETURNS AND OUTPUT.** Returns per man-hour from turpentining 400 acid-treated faces on the 53-acre Olustee Woodlot are given in the tabulation below, based on a 4-yr. average, 1944–47. This area is part of a U. S. Forest Service experimental forest.

The lot contained 37 acres in pine, which was chipped weekly in 1944, biweekly thereafter.

| | |
|---|---|
| Aver. annual gum yield ................................. | $209.00 |
| Cost equipment and supplies ........................... | 17.65 |
| Net value produced by labor ........................... | 191.35 |
| Aver. time worked, man-hours .......................... | 173.30 |
| Net returns per man-hour .............................. | 1.10 |

The labor output per 7-hr. man-day resulted in:

| | |
|---|---|
| Chipping ................. | 1,050 faces |
| Dipping .................. | 2 bbl. gum |
| Installing virgin cups ..... | 1,300 cups for 6-man crew |
| Raising cups and tins ..... | 1,270 cups and tins, including pulling and chipping first streak per six-man crew |

**DISTILLATION: Old and New Processes.** With old-style fire stills, now obsolescent, a batch of 10 or 12 bbl. of gum is put in a copper kettle connected to a condenser worm in a water-cooling vat. Water is continually added as the charge cooks. With temperatures rising gradually over a period of an hour and a half from 205° F. to 310° F., turpentine vapors and steam condense into spirits of turpentine and water. They are separated by gravity and the turpentine is dehydrated by passing it through rock salt.

When nearly all of the turpentine has been distilled, the water is cut and boiled off, and the residual rosin is drawn off and passed through three strainers, the bottom one lined with cotton batting, to remove all trash and dirt. It is then collected into drums or bags for shipment.

## Table 42. Woods Equipment Needed in Naval Stores Operation
### (Based on 1,000 faces)

| Equipment | Item | Size | Quantity |
|---|---|---|---|
| For facing ...................... | Cups | 2 qt. | 1,000 |
| | Flat strips | 1½ in. wide | 200 lb. |
| | Crimp gutters | 2½ in. wide | 490 lb. |
| | Nails | 20-penny | 50 lb. |
| For tin setting ................. | Maul | 8–10 lb. | 1 |
| | Cupping axe | 10 or 12 in. | 1 |
| For cup raising ................. | Tin puller | | 1 |
| | Tacks, rustless | | |
| | Coated hide | No. 18 | 5½ lb. |
| For chipping low faces | | | |
| A. Untreated faces ........... | Hack | No. 00 or 0 | 2 |
| | Hack weight | 5 to 6 lb. | 1 |
| | Hack stock | | 1 |
| | Hack cutters | | 3 |
| | Stone whetter | | 4 |
| | Cup cover | | 2 |
| B. Treated faces ............. | Stone whetter | | 4 |
| | Cup cover | | 2 |
| | Bark hack | | 2 |
| | Plastic acid spray bottles | | 2 |
| For pulling high faces ........... | Puller | No. 0 or 1 | 2 |
| | Puller handle | | 2 |
| For collecting gum and scrape.... | Gum barrel | Large | 3 |
| | Dip barrel head | Standard | 2 |
| | Dip bucket | Standard | 2 |
| | Dip paddle | Standard | 2 |
| | Scrape irons: | | |
| | Shove down | Standard | 1 |
| | Double edge | Standard | 1 |
| | Wing scrape box | Standard | 2 |
| For fire control ................. | Hoes | Heavy | 2 |
| | Back-type fire pump | 5 gal. | 2 |
| | Fire rakes | Standard | 2 |
| | Fire flaps | Standard | 2 |

Source: Modified from Georgia Agr. Ext. *Bull. No. 532*, rev. June, 1950.

The new steam stills mix all gum received, filter and wash the gum, and then still it by using steam instead of direct fire. This Olustee process involves pressure filtration of turpentine-diluted gum with oxalic acid added to remove any iron that may be present in the gum. This is followed by washing with hot water and settling to remove soluble impurities. The washed and filtered gum is then run to the steam still where the turpentine is condensed with the steam in improved condensers and dehydrated, as with the other types of distillation, by being run through coarse salt. This improved turpentine can be sold in metal containers. The rosin made by the Olustee process is brilliant, clean, and free of iron.

The continuous still, capable of processing 7,500 lb. of cleaned gum per hour, has been tested and is offered to the industry. It is saving in time and is most economical. The purity of the products can be controlled. Other possibilities are yet to be explored.

#### Table 43. Average Turpentine and Rosin Yields from Gum and Scrape

| Per 100 lb. gum | | | | | | Per 100 lb. scrape | | |
| Longleaf | | | Slash | | | | | |
| Turp. (gal.)* | Rosin (lb.) | Waste (lb.) | Turp. (gal.) | Rosin (lb.) | Waste (lb.) | Turp. (gal.) | Rosin (lb.) | Waste (lb.) |
|---|---|---|---|---|---|---|---|---|
| 2.53 | 69.1 | 12.7 | 2.57 | 69.2 | 12.3 | 1.85 | 68.3 | 18.4 |

* One gal. of turpentine weighs 7.2 lb. at 70°F.
Source: Mimeograph data, Naval Stores Station, Georgia Bur. Agr. Chem. and Eng.

### PRINCIPAL USES OF TURPENTINE AND ROSIN.

TURPENTINE                                            ROSIN
(In decreasing order of importance)

| TURPENTINE | ROSIN |
|---|---|
| Chemicals and pharmaceuticals | Paper and paper size |
| Ester gums and synthetic resins | Chemicals and pharmaceuticals |
| Paint, varnish and lacquer | Ester gums and synthetic resins |
| Railroads and shipyards | Paint, varnish and lacquer |
| Shoe polish and materials | Soap |
| Foundries and supplies | Linoleum and floor coverings |
| Rubber | Adhesives and plastics |
| Printing ink | Oils and greases |
| Adhesives and plastics | Rubber |
| Asphaltic products | Railroads and shipyards |
| Furniture | Printing ink |
| Insecticides and disinfectants | Shoe polish and materials |

An unreported, but by far the largest, use for turpentine is as a paint thinner.

**ROSIN GRADES.** Twelve rosin grades are recognized; they are based on color, which ranges from pale yellow to dark red. These grades are: X, WW, WG, N, M, K, I, H, G, F, E, and D.

**SECONDARY GUM NAVAL STORES PRODUCTS.** Chemical products derived from gum, turpentine, or gum rosin include:

| | |
|---|---|
| Alpha pinene | Terpene alcohols |
| Beta pinene | Terpineol |
| Camphene | Borneol |
| Dipentene | Geraniol |
| Maleopimaric acid | Linalool |
| Maleic and phenolic resins | Modified rosins (by treating with heat, or catalysts or |
| Metallic resinates | both, with or without added chemicals) |
| Gloss oil | |

Competing with, but not in the field of, gum naval stores are wood naval stores from pine stumps, and sulfate naval stores products derived from pulping southern pines. There are also some allied products obtained from fir, larch, and other trees.

## BIBLIOGRAPHY

AMERICAN WOOD PRESERVERS' ASSN. *Manual of recommended practice.* Revised annually. Washington, D. C.

ASSOCIATED COOPERAGE INDUSTRIES OF AMERICA, INC. 1951. *The wooden barrel manual.* St. Louis, Mo.

BROWN, N. C. 1947. *Lumber.* John Wiley & Sons, Inc., New York.

BROWN, N. C. 1950. *Forest products.* John Wiley & Sons, Inc., New York.

DOUGLAS FIR PLYWOOD ASSN. 1948. Technical data on plywood. Tacoma, Wash.

GEORGIA AGR. EXT. SERV. 1950. Naval stores industry. *Bull. No. 532.*

GRONDAL, BROR L., and W. W. WOODBRIDGE. 1942. *Centigrade handbook of red cedar shingles.* Red Cedar Shingle Bureau, Seattle, Wash.

HANSEN, H. J. 1948. *Timber engineer's handbook.* John Wiley & Sons, Inc., New York.

HUNT, G. M., and G. A. GARRATT. 1953. *Wood preservation.* McGraw-Hill Book Co., Inc., New York.

JONES, R. E. 1952. Uses and manufacture of wood flour. *Jour. Forest Prod. Res. Soc.* (2) 2.

McINTYRE, A. C. 1952. Wood chips, wood chippers, and conservation farming. *Jour. Forest Prod. Res. Soc.* (2) 2.

MILLER, R. H. P. 1951. Characteristics of wood as fuel. *Proc. Forest Prod. Res. Soc. 5.*

NATIONAL LUMBER MANUFACTURERS ASSN. 1954. National design specifications for stress-grade lumber and its fastenings. Washington, D. C.

PANSHIN, A. J., *et al.* 1950. *Forest products.* McGraw-Hill Book Co., Inc., New York.

PERRY, T. D. 1948. *Modern plywood.* 2d ed. Pitman Publ. Corp., New York.

SCHOFIELD, W. F., and W. H. O'BRIEN. 1954. *Modern timber engineering.* 4th ed. Southern Pine Assn., New Orleans, La.

SOUTHERN PINE ASSN. 1951. *Structural glued laminated southern pine.* New Orleans, La.

TIMBER ENGINEERING Co. 1952. *Design manual for Teco timber connector construction.* Washington, D. C.

U. S. DEPT. AGR.:
 1935. Strength and related properties of wood grown in the United States. *Tech. Bull. No. 479.*
 1940. *Wood handbook.*
 1952. *Small sawmill operators' manual.* Agr. Handbook No. 27.

U. S. DEPT. COMMERCE:
 1939. *American lumber standards for softwood lumber.*
 1948. *Commercial standards for Douglas-fir plywood.*
 1949. *Commercial standards for hardwood plywood.*
 1949. *Commercial standards for ponderosa pine and sugar pine plywood.*

U. S. FOREST SERV., FOREST PRODUCTS LAB.:
 1940. The detection and relief of case-hardening, *Tech. Note. No. 213.*
 1942. Wood tanks, *Bull. No. R1285.*
 1948. Excelsior manufacture, *Report No. R1711.*
 1949. Bark-peeling machines and methods, *Report No. D1730.*
 1949. Resin-treated, laminated compression wood (compreg), *Mimeo. 1381.*
 1950. Air drying of lumber. *Bull. No. R1657.*
 1950. Making wood fire retardant. *Mimeo. D1760.*
 1951. Schedules for the kiln drying of wood. *Bull. No. D1791.*

VERRALL, A. F., and T. C. SCHEFFER. 1949. Control of stain, mold, and decay in green lumber and other wood products. *Proc. Forest Prod. Res. Soc.*

WANGAARD, F. 1951. *The mechanical properties of wood.* John Wiley & Sons, Inc., New York.

WEST COAST LUMBERMEN'S ASSN. 1951. Structural glued laminated lumber. Portland, Ore.

# ECONOMICS AND FINANCE

## CONTENTS

# ECONOMICS AND FINANCE

### Compound Interest Tables

**NATURE AND USE OF THE TABLES.** The following symbols will be used to explain the tables:

$V_0$ = value (or value equivalent) of a sum, at the beginning of the interest-bearing period

$V_n$ = value (or value equivalent) of a sum, at the end of the interest-bearing period

$i$ = the rate of interest, expressed as a decimal

$n$ = the number of unit time periods (generally years) in the interest-bearing period

$r$ = the value of one of a series of equal payments, to be made annually

Table 1A gives the value of the factor $(1 + i)^n$ in the formula:

$$V_n = V_0 (1 + i)^n$$

It is useful in solving problems such as the following:

A tract of timber was purchased for $1,000 in 1940. What equivalent value must be recovered in 1955 to repay this investment and 4 percent interest on it, if there are no intermediate incomes or expenses? Here:

$$V_0 = \$1,000; \qquad i = 0.04; \qquad n = 1,955 - 1,940 = 15$$

From Table 1A, $(1 + i)^n = 1.801$; then $V_n = \$1,000 \,(1.801) = \$1,801$.

Table 1A is basic in the sense that all the others may be derived from it arithmetically. Because of the frequent occurrence of certain types of problems, Tables 1B, 1C, and 1D are presented for convenience in making valuation calculations.

**Table 1A. Value of $1 (Compounded Annually) at the End of an Interest-Bearing Period of *n* Years**

| Years | Rate of interest (percent per year) | | | | | | |
|---|---|---|---|---|---|---|---|
| | 0.5 | 1.0 | 1.5 | 2.0 | 2.5 | 3.0 | 3.5 |
| | Dollars | | | | | | |
| 1 | 1.005 | 1.010 | 1.015 | 1.020 | 1.025 | 1.030 | 1.035 |
| 2 | 1.010 | 1.020 | 1.030 | 1.040 | 1.051 | 1.061 | 1.071 |
| 3 | 1.015 | 1.030 | 1.046 | 1.061 | 1.077 | 1.093 | 1.109 |
| 4 | 1.020 | 1.041 | 1.061 | 1.082 | 1.104 | 1.126 | 1.148 |
| 5 | 1.025 | 1.051 | 1.077 | 1.104 | 1.131 | 1.159 | 1.188 |
| 6 | 1.030 | 1.062 | 1.093 | 1.126 | 1.160 | 1.194 | 1.229 |
| 7 | 1.036 | 1.072 | 1.110 | 1.149 | 1.189 | 1.230 | 1.272 |
| 8 | 1.041 | 1.083 | 1.126 | 1.172 | 1.218 | 1.267 | 1.317 |
| 9 | 1.046 | 1.094 | 1.143 | 1.195 | 1.249 | 1.305 | 1.363 |
| 10 | 1.051 | 1.105 | 1.161 | 1.219 | 1.280 | 1.344 | 1.411 |
| 11 | 1.056 | 1.116 | 1.178 | 1.243 | 1.312 | 1.384 | 1.460 |
| 12 | 1.062 | 1.127 | 1.196 | 1.268 | 1.345 | 1.426 | 1.511 |
| 13 | 1.067 | 1.138 | 1.214 | 1.294 | 1.379 | 1.468 | 1.564 |
| 14 | 1.072 | 1.149 | 1.232 | 1.319 | 1.413 | 1.513 | 1.619 |
| 15 | 1.078 | 1.161 | 1.250 | 1.346 | 1.448 | 1.558 | 1.675 |
| 16 | 1.083 | 1.173 | 1.269 | 1.373 | 1.485 | 1.605 | 1.734 |
| 17 | 1.088 | 1.184 | 1.288 | 1.400 | 1.522 | 1.653 | 1.795 |
| 18 | 1.094 | 1.196 | 1.307 | 1.428 | 1.560 | 1.702 | 1.857 |
| 19 | 1.099 | 1.208 | 1.327 | 1.457 | 1.599 | 1.753 | 1.923 |
| 20 | 1.105 | 1.220 | 1.347 | 1.486 | 1.639 | 1.806 | 1.990 |
| 21 | 1.110 | 1.232 | 1.367 | 1.516 | 1.680 | 1.860 | 2.059 |
| 22 | 1.116 | 1.245 | 1.388 | 1.546 | 1.722 | 1.916 | 2.132 |
| 23 | 1.122 | 1.257 | 1.408 | 1.577 | 1.765 | 1.974 | 2.206 |
| 24 | 1.127 | 1.270 | 1.429 | 1.608 | 1.809 | 2.033 | 2.283 |
| 25 | 1.133 | 1.282 | 1.451 | 1.641 | 1.854 | 2.094 | 2.363 |
| 26 | 1.138 | 1.295 | 1.473 | 1.673 | 1.900 | 2.157 | 2.446 |
| 27 | 1.144 | 1.308 | 1.495 | 1.707 | 1.948 | 2.221 | 2.532 |
| 28 | 1.150 | 1.321 | 1.517 | 1.741 | 1.997 | 2.288 | 2.620 |
| 29 | 1.156 | 1.334 | 1.540 | 1.776 | 2.046 | 2.357 | 2.712 |
| 30 | 1.161 | 1.348 | 1.563 | 1.811 | 2.098 | 2.427 | 2.807 |
| 35 | 1.191 | 1.417 | 1.684 | 2.000 | 2.373 | 2.814 | 3.334 |
| 40 | 1.221 | 1.489 | 1.814 | 2.208 | 2.685 | 3.262 | 3.959 |
| 45 | 1.252 | 1.565 | 1.954 | 2.438 | 3.038 | 3.782 | 4.702 |
| 50 | 1.283 | 1.645 | 2.105 | 2.692 | 3.437 | 4.384 | 5.585 |
| 55 | 1.316 | 1.729 | 2.268 | 2.972 | 3.889 | 5.082 | 6.633 |
| 60 | 1.349 | 1.817 | 2.443 | 3.281 | 4.400 | 5.892 | 7.878 |
| 65 | 1.383 | 1.909 | 2.632 | 3.623 | 4.978 | 6.830 | 9.357 |
| 70 | 1.418 | 2.007 | 2.835 | 4.000 | 5.632 | 7.918 | 11.11 |
| 75 | 1.454 | 2.109 | 3.055 | 4.416 | 6.372 | 9.179 | 13.20 |
| 80 | 1.490 | 2.217 | 3.291 | 4.875 | 7.210 | 10.64 | 15.68 |
| 85 | 1.528 | 2.330 | 3.545 | 5.383 | 8.157 | 12.34 | 18.62 |
| 90 | 1.567 | 2.449 | 3.819 | 5.943 | 9.229 | 14.30 | 22.11 |
| 95 | 1.606 | 2.574 | 4.114 | 6.562 | 10.44 | 16.58 | 26.26 |
| 100 | 1.647 | 2.705 | 4.432 | 7.245 | 11.81 | 19.22 | 31.19 |

**Table 1A. Value of $1 (Compounded Annually) at the End of an Interest-Bearing Period of $n$ Years (Continued)**

| Years | Rate of interest (percent per year) | | | | | | |
|---|---|---|---|---|---|---|---|
| | 4.0 | 4.5 | 5.0 | 5.5 | 6.0 | 6.5 | 7.0 |
| | Dollars | | | | | | |
| 1 | 1.040 | 1.045 | 1.050 | 1.055 | 1.060 | 1.065 | 1.070 |
| 2 | 1.082 | 1.092 | 1.103 | 1.113 | 1.124 | 1.134 | 1.145 |
| 3 | 1.125 | 1.141 | 1.158 | 1.174 | 1.191 | 1.208 | 1.225 |
| 4 | 1.170 | 1.193 | 1.216 | 1.239 | 1.262 | 1.286 | 1.311 |
| 5 | 1.217 | 1.246 | 1.276 | 1.307 | 1.338 | 1.370 | 1.403 |
| 6 | 1.265 | 1.302 | 1.340 | 1.379 | 1.419 | 1.459 | 1.501 |
| 7 | 1.316 | 1.361 | 1.407 | 1.455 | 1.504 | 1.554 | 1.606 |
| 8 | 1.369 | 1.422 | 1.478 | 1.535 | 1.594 | 1.655 | 1.718 |
| 9 | 1.423 | 1.486 | 1.551 | 1.619 | 1.689 | 1.763 | 1.839 |
| 10 | 1.480 | 1.553 | 1.629 | 1.708 | 1.791 | 1.877 | 1.967 |
| 11 | 1.539 | 1.623 | 1.710 | 1.802 | 1.898 | 1.999 | 2.105 |
| 12 | 1.601 | 1.696 | 1.796 | 1.901 | 2.012 | 2.129 | 2.252 |
| 13 | 1.665 | 1.772 | 1.886 | 2.006 | 2.133 | 2.267 | 2.409 |
| 14 | 1.732 | 1.852 | 1.980 | 2.116 | 2.261 | 2.415 | 2.579 |
| 15 | 1.801 | 1.935 | 2.079 | 2.233 | 2.397 | 2.572 | 2.759 |
| 16 | 1.873 | 2.022 | 2.183 | 2.355 | 2.540 | 2.739 | 2.952 |
| 17 | 1.948 | 2.113 | 2.292 | 2.485 | 2.693 | 2.917 | 3.159 |
| 18 | 2.026 | 2.208 | 2.407 | 2.621 | 2.854 | 3.107 | 3.380 |
| 19 | 2.107 | 2.308 | 2.527 | 2.766 | 3.026 | 3.309 | 3.617 |
| 20 | 2.191 | 2.412 | 2.653 | 2.918 | 3.207 | 3.524 | 3.870 |
| 21 | 2.279 | 2.520 | 2.786 | 3.078 | 3.400 | 3.753 | 4.141 |
| 22 | 2.370 | 2.634 | 2.925 | 3.248 | 3.604 | 3.997 | 4.431 |
| 23 | 2.465 | 2.752 | 3.072 | 3.426 | 3.820 | 4.256 | 4.741 |
| 24 | 2.563 | 2.876 | 3.225 | 3.615 | 4.049 | 4.533 | 5.072 |
| 25 | 2.666 | 3.005 | 3.386 | 3.813 | 4.292 | 4.828 | 5.428 |
| 26 | 2.772 | 3.141 | 3.556 | 4.023 | 4.550 | 5.141 | 5.807 |
| 27 | 2.883 | 3.282 | 3.733 | 4.245 | 4.822 | 5.476 | 6.214 |
| 28 | 2.999 | 3.430 | 3.920 | 4.478 | 5.112 | 5.832 | 6.649 |
| 29 | 3.119 | 3.584 | 4.116 | 4.724 | 5.418 | 6.211 | 7.114 |
| 30 | 3.243 | 3.745 | 4.322 | 4.984 | 5.744 | 6.614 | 7.612 |
| 35 | 3.946 | 4.667 | 5.516 | 6.514 | 7.686 | 9.062 | 10.68 |
| 40 | 4.801 | 5.816 | 7.040 | 8.513 | 10.29 | 12.42 | 14.98 |
| 45 | 5.841 | 7.248 | 8.985 | 11.13 | 13.77 | 17.01 | 21.00 |
| 50 | 7.107 | 9.033 | 11.47 | 14.54 | 18.42 | 23.31 | 29.46 |
| 55 | 8.646 | 11.26 | 14.64 | 19.01 | 24.65 | 31.93 | 41.32 |
| 60 | 10.52 | 14.03 | 18.68 | 24.84 | 32.99 | 43.75 | 57.95 |
| 65 | 12.80 | 17.48 | 23.84 | 32.46 | 44.14 | 59.94 | 81.27 |
| 70 | 15.57 | 21.78 | 30.43 | 42.43 | 59.08 | 82.12 | 114.0 |
| 75 | 18.95 | 27.15 | 38.83 | 55.46 | 79.06 | 112.5 | 159.9 |
| 80 | 23.05 | 33.83 | 49.56 | 72.48 | 105.8 | 154.2 | 224.2 |
| 85 | 28.04 | 42.16 | 63.25 | 94.73 | 141.6 | 211.2 | 314.5 |
| 90 | 34.12 | 52.54 | 80.73 | 123.8 | 189.5 | 289.4 | 441.1 |
| 95 | 41.51 | 65.47 | 103.0 | 161.8 | 253.5 | 396.5 | 618.7 |
| 100 | 50.50 | 81.59 | 131.5 | 211.5 | 339.3 | 543.2 | 867.7 |

**Table 1A. Value of $1 (Compounded Annually) at the End of an Interest-Bearing Period of *n* Years** (Continued)

| Years | Rate of interest (percent per year) | | | | | |
|---|---|---|---|---|---|---|
| | 7.5 | 8.0 | 8.5 | 9.0 | 9.5 | 10.0 |
| | Dollars | | | | | |
| 1 | 1.075 | 1.080 | 1.085 | 1.090 | 1.095 | 1.100 |
| 2 | 1.156 | 1.166 | 1.177 | 1.188 | 1.199 | 1.210 |
| 3 | 1.242 | 1.260 | 1.277 | 1.295 | 1.313 | 1.331 |
| 4 | 1.335 | 1.361 | 1.386 | 1.412 | 1.438 | 1.464 |
| 5 | 1.436 | 1.469 | 1.504 | 1.539 | 1.574 | 1.611 |
| 6 | 1.543 | 1.587 | 1.631 | 1.677 | 1.724 | 1.772 |
| 7 | 1.659 | 1.714 | 1.770 | 1.828 | 1.888 | 1.949 |
| 8 | 1.783 | 1.851 | 1.921 | 1.993 | 2.067 | 2.144 |
| 9 | 1.917 | 1.999 | 2.084 | 2.172 | 2.263 | 2.358 |
| 10 | 2.061 | 2.159 | 2.261 | 2.367 | 2.478 | 2.594 |
| 11 | 2.216 | 2.331 | 2.453 | 2.580 | 2.714 | 2.853 |
| 12 | 2.382 | 2.518 | 2.662 | 2.813 | 2.971 | 3.318 |
| 13 | 2.560 | 2.720 | 2.888 | 3.066 | 3.254 | 3.452 |
| 14 | 2.752 | 2.938 | 3.133 | 3.342 | 3.563 | 3.797 |
| 15 | 2.959 | 3.172 | 3.400 | 3.642 | 3.901 | 4.177 |
| 16 | 3.181 | 3.426 | 3.689 | 3.970 | 4.272 | 4.595 |
| 17 | 3.419 | 3.700 | 4.002 | 4.327 | 4.678 | 5.054 |
| 18 | 3.676 | 3.996 | 4.342 | 4.717 | 5.122 | 5.560 |
| 19 | 3.951 | 4.316 | 4.712 | 5.142 | 5.609 | 6.116 |
| 20 | 4.248 | 4.661 | 5.112 | 5.604 | 6.142 | 6.728 |
| 21 | 4.566 | 5.034 | 5.547 | 6.109 | 6.725 | 7.400 |
| 22 | 4.909 | 5.437 | 6.018 | 6.658 | 7.364 | 8.140 |
| 23 | 5.277 | 5.871 | 6.530 | 7.258 | 8.064 | 8.954 |
| 24 | 5.673 | 6.341 | 7.085 | 7.911 | 8.830 | 9.850 |
| 25 | 6.098 | 6.849 | 7.687 | 8.623 | 9.668 | 10.83 |
| 26 | 6.556 | 7.396 | 8.340 | 9.399 | 10.59 | 11.92 |
| 27 | 7.047 | 7.988 | 9.049 | 10.24 | 11.59 | 13.11 |
| 28 | 7.576 | 8.627 | 9.818 | 11.17 | 12.69 | 14.42 |
| 29 | 8.144 | 9.317 | 10.65 | 12.17 | 13.90 | 15.86 |
| 30 | 8.755 | 10.06 | 11.56 | 13.27 | 15.22 | 17.45 |
| 35 | 12.57 | 14.79 | 17.38 | 20.41 | 23.96 | 28.10 |
| 40 | 18.04 | 21.73 | 26.13 | 31.41 | 37.72 | 45.26 |
| 45 | 25.90 | 31.92 | 39.30 | 48.33 | 59.38 | 72.89 |
| 50 | 37.19 | 46.90 | 59.09 | 74.35 | 93.48 | 117.4 |
| 55 | 53.39 | 68.92 | 88.85 | 114.4 | 147.2 | 189.1 |
| 60 | 76.65 | 101.3 | 133.6 | 176.0 | 231.7 | 304.5 |
| 65 | 110.0 | 148.8 | 200.9 | 270.8 | 364.7 | 490.4 |
| 70 | 158.0 | 218.6 | 302.1 | 416.7 | 574.1 | 789.7 |
| 75 | 226.8 | 321.2 | 454.2 | 641.1 | 903.8 | 1,272 |

**Table 1B. Value, at the Beginning of the Period, of $1 Received after an Interest-Bearing Period of _n_ Years**

| Years | Rate of interest (percent per year) | | | | | | |
|---|---|---|---|---|---|---|---|
| | 0.5 | 1.0 | 1.5 | 2.0 | 2.5 | 3.0 | 3.5 |
| | | | | Dollars | | | |
| 1 | 0.9950 | 0.9901 | 0.9852 | 0.9804 | 0.9756 | 0.9709 | 0.9662 |
| 2 | .9901 | .9803 | .9707 | .9612 | .9518 | .9426 | .9335 |
| 3 | .9851 | .9706 | .9563 | .9423 | .9286 | .9151 | .9019 |
| 4 | .9802 | .9610 | .9422 | .9238 | .9060 | .8885 | .8714 |
| 5 | .9754 | .9515 | .9283 | .9057 | .8839 | .8625 | .8420 |
| 6 | .9705 | .9420 | .9145 | .8880 | .8623 | .8375 | .8135 |
| 7 | .9657 | .9327 | .9010 | .8706 | .8413 | .8131 | .7860 |
| 8 | .9609 | .9235 | .8877 | .8535 | .8207 | .7894 | .7594 |
| 9 | .9561 | .9143 | .8746 | .8368 | .8007 | .7664 | .7337 |
| 10 | .9513 | .9053 | .8617 | .8204 | .7812 | .7441 | .7089 |
| 11 | .9466 | .8963 | .8489 | .8043 | .7621 | .7224 | .6849 |
| 12 | .9419 | .8874 | .8364 | .7885 | .7436 | .7014 | .6618 |
| 13 | .9372 | .8787 | .8240 | .7730 | .7254 | .6810 | .6394 |
| 14 | .9326 | .8700 | .8118 | .7579 | .7077 | .6611 | .6178 |
| 15 | .9279 | .8613 | .7999 | .7430 | .6905 | .6419 | .5969 |
| 16 | .9233 | .8528 | .7880 | .7284 | .6736 | .6232 | .5767 |
| 17 | .9187 | .8444 | .7764 | .7142 | .6572 | .6050 | .5572 |
| 18 | .9141 | .8360 | .7649 | .7002 | .6412 | .5874 | .5384 |
| 19 | .9096 | .8277 | .7536 | .6864 | .6255 | .5703 | .5202 |
| 20 | .9050 | .8195 | .7425 | .6730 | .6103 | .5537 | .5026 |
| 21 | .9005 | .8114 | .7315 | .6598 | .5954 | .5375 | .4856 |
| 22 | .8961 | .8034 | .7207 | .6468 | .5809 | .5219 | .4692 |
| 23 | .8916 | .7954 | .7100 | .6342 | .5667 | .5067 | .4533 |
| 24 | .8872 | .7876 | .6995 | .6217 | .5529 | .4919 | .4380 |
| 25 | .8828 | .7798 | .6892 | .6095 | .5394 | .4776 | .4231 |
| 26 | .8784 | .7720 | .6790 | .5976 | .5262 | .4637 | .4088 |
| 27 | .8740 | .7644 | .6690 | .5859 | .5134 | .4502 | .3950 |
| 28 | .8697 | .7568 | .6591 | .5744 | .5009 | .4371 | .3817 |
| 29 | .8653 | .7493 | .6494 | .5631 | .4887 | .4243 | .3687 |
| 30 | .8610 | .7419 | .6398 | .5521 | .4767 | .4120 | .3563 |
| 35 | .8398 | .7059 | .5939 | .5000 | .4214 | .3554 | .3000 |
| 40 | .8191 | .6717 | .5513 | .4529 | .3724 | .3066 | .2526 |
| 45 | .7990 | .6391 | .5117 | .4102 | .3292 | .2644 | .2127 |
| 50 | .7793 | .6080 | .4750 | .3715 | .2909 | .2281 | .1791 |
| 55 | .7601 | .5785 | .4409 | .3365 | .2572 | .1968 | .1508 |
| 60 | .7414 | .5504 | .4093 | .3048 | .2273 | .1697 | .1269 |
| 65 | .7231 | .5237 | .3799 | .2761 | .2009 | .1464 | .1069 |
| 70 | .7053 | .4983 | .3527 | .2500 | .1776 | .1263 | .0900 |
| 75 | .6879 | .4741 | .3274 | .2265 | .1569 | .1089 | .0758 |
| 80 | .6710 | .4511 | .3039 | .2051 | .1387 | .0940 | .0638 |
| 85 | .6545 | .4292 | .2821 | .1858 | .1226 | .0811 | .0537 |
| 90 | .6383 | .4084 | .2619 | .1683 | .1084 | .0699 | .0452 |
| 95 | .6226 | .3886 | .2431 | .1524 | .0958 | .0603 | .0381 |
| 100 | .6073 | .3697 | .2256 | .1380 | .0846 | .0520 | .0321 |

**Table 1B.  Value, at the Beginning of the Period, of $1 Received after an Interest-Bearing Period of *n* Years** (Continued)

| Years | Rate of interest (percent per year) | | | | | | |
|---|---|---|---|---|---|---|---|
| | 4.0 | 4.5 | 5.0 | 5.5 | 6.0 | 6.5 | 7.0 |
| | Dollars | | | | | | |
| 1 | 0.9615 | 0.9569 | 0.9524 | 0.9479 | 0.9434 | 0.9390 | 0.9346 |
| 2 | .9246 | .9157 | .9070 | .8985 | .8900 | .8818 | .8734 |
| 3 | .8890 | .8763 | .8638 | .8516 | .8396 | .8278 | .8163 |
| 4 | .8548 | .8386 | .8227 | .8071 | .7921 | .7773 | .7629 |
| 5 | .8219 | .8025 | .7835 | .7651 | .7473 | .7299 | .7130 |
| 6 | .7903 | .7679 | .7462 | .7252 | .7050 | .6854 | .6663 |
| 7 | .7599 | .7348 | .7107 | .6873 | .6651 | .6435 | .6227 |
| 8 | .7307 | .7032 | .6768 | .6515 | .6274 | .6042 | .5820 |
| 9 | .7026 | .6729 | .6446 | .6177 | .5919 | .5674 | .5439 |
| 10 | .6756 | .6439 | .6139 | .5855 | .5584 | .5328 | .5083 |
| 11 | .6496 | .6162 | .5847 | .5549 | .5268 | .5003 | .4751 |
| 12 | .6246 | .5897 | .5568 | .5260 | .4970 | .4697 | .4440 |
| 13 | .6006 | .5643 | .5303 | .4985 | .4688 | .4411 | .4150 |
| 14 | .5775 | .5400 | .5051 | .4726 | .4423 | .4141 | .3878 |
| 15 | .5553 | .5167 | .4810 | .4478 | .4173 | .3888 | .3624 |
| 16 | .5339 | .4945 | .4581 | .4246 | .3936 | .3651 | .3387 |
| 17 | .5134 | .4732 | .4363 | .4024 | .3714 | .3428 | .3166 |
| 18 | .4936 | .4528 | .4155 | .3815 | .3504 | .3219 | .2959 |
| 19 | .4746 | .4333 | .3957 | .3615 | .3305 | .3022 | .2765 |
| 20 | .4564 | .4146 | .3769 | .3427 | .3118 | .2838 | .2584 |
| 21 | .4388 | .3968 | .3589 | .3249 | .2942 | .2665 | .2415 |
| 22 | .4220 | .3797 | .3418 | .3079 | .2775 | .2502 | .2257 |
| 23 | .4057 | .3634 | .3256 | .2919 | .2618 | .2350 | .2109 |
| 24 | .3901 | .3477 | .3101 | .2766 | .2470 | .2206 | .1971 |
| 25 | .3751 | .3327 | .2953 | .2623 | .2330 | .2071 | .1842 |
| 26 | .3607 | .3184 | .2812 | .2486 | .2198 | .1945 | .1722 |
| 27 | .3468 | .3047 | .2678 | .2356 | .2074 | .1826 | .1609 |
| 28 | .3335 | .2916 | .2551 | .2233 | .1956 | .1715 | .1504 |
| 29 | .3207 | .2790 | .2429 | .2117 | .1846 | .1610 | .1406 |
| 30 | .3083 | .2670 | .2314 | .2006 | .1741 | .1512 | .1314 |
| 35 | .2534 | .2142 | .1813 | .1535 | .1301 | .1104 | .0937 |
| 40 | .2083 | .1719 | .1420 | .1175 | .0972 | .0805 | .0668 |
| 45 | .1712 | .1380 | .1113 | .0898 | .0726 | .0588 | .0476 |
| 50 | .1407 | .1107 | .0872 | .0688 | .0543 | .0429 | .0340 |
| 55 | .1157 | .0888 | .0683 | .0526 | .0406 | .0313 | .0242 |
| 60 | .0951 | .0713 | .0535 | .0403 | .0303 | .0229 | .0173 |
| 65 | .0781 | .0572 | .0420 | .0308 | .0226 | .0167 | .0123 |
| 70 | .0642 | .0459 | .0329 | .0236 | .0169 | .0122 | .0088 |
| 75 | .0528 | .0368 | .0258 | .0180 | .0126 | .0089 | .0062 |
| 80 | .0434 | .0296 | .0202 | .0138 | .0094 | .0065 | .0045 |
| 85 | .0357 | .0237 | .0158 | .0106 | .0071 | .0047 | .0032 |
| 90 | .0293 | .0190 | .0124 | .0081 | .0053 | .0035 | .0023 |
| 95 | .0241 | .0153 | .0097 | .0062 | .0039 | .0025 | .0016 |
| 100 | .0198 | .0123 | .0076 | .0047 | .0030 | .0018 | .0012 |

**Table 1B.  Value, at the Beginning of the Period, of \$1 Received after an Interest-Bearing Period of *n* Years**  (Continued)

| Years | Rate of interest (percent per year) | | | | | |
|---|---|---|---|---|---|---|
| | 7.5 | 8.0 | 8.5 | 9.0 | 9.5 | 10.0 |
| | Dollars | | | | | |
| 1 | 0.9302 | 0.9259 | 0.9217 | 0.9174 | 0.9132 | 0.9091 |
| 2 | .8653 | .8573 | .8496 | .8418 | .8340 | .8264 |
| 3 | .8050 | .7938 | .7829 | .7722 | .7616 | .7513 |
| 4 | .7488 | .7350 | .7215 | .7084 | .6954 | .6831 |
| 5 | .6966 | .6806 | .6649 | .6498 | .6353 | .6209 |
| 6 | .6481 | .6302 | .6129 | .5963 | .5800 | .5645 |
| 7 | .6028 | .5835 | .5650 | .5470 | .5297 | .5131 |
| 8 | .5607 | .5403 | .5206 | .5018 | .4838 | .4664 |
| 9 | .5216 | .5002 | .4798 | .4604 | .4419 | .4241 |
| 10 | .4852 | .4632 | .4423 | .4225 | .4036 | .3855 |
| 11 | .4513 | .4289 | .4077 | .3874 | .3685 | .3505 |
| 12 | .4198 | .3971 | .3757 | .3555 | .3366 | .3186 |
| 13 | .3906 | .3677 | .3463 | .3262 | .3073 | .2897 |
| 14 | .3634 | .3405 | .3192 | .2997 | .2807 | .2633 |
| 15 | .3380 | .3152 | .2941 | .2745 | .2563 | .2394 |
| 16 | .3144 | .2919 | .2711 | .2519 | .2341 | .2176 |
| 17 | .2925 | .2703 | .2499 | .2311 | .2138 | .1978 |
| 18 | .2720 | .2502 | .2302 | .2120 | .1952 | .1799 |
| 19 | .2531 | .2317 | .2122 | .1945 | .1783 | .1635 |
| 20 | .2354 | .2145 | .1956 | .1784 | .1628 | .1486 |
| 21 | .2190 | .1987 | .1803 | .1637 | .1487 | .1351 |
| 22 | .2037 | .1839 | .1662 | .1502 | .1358 | .1228 |
| 23 | .1895 | .1703 | .1531 | .1378 | .1240 | .1117 |
| 24 | .1763 | .1577 | .1411 | .1264 | .1132 | .1015 |
| 25 | .1640 | .1460 | .1301 | .1160 | .1034 | .0922 |
| 26 | .1525 | .1352 | .1199 | .1064 | .0944 | .0839 |
| 27 | .1419 | .1252 | .1105 | .0977 | .0863 | .0763 |
| 28 | .1320 | .1159 | .1019 | .0895 | .0788 | .0694 |
| 29 | .1228 | .1073 | .0939 | .0822 | .0719 | .0630 |
| 30 | .1142 | .0993 | .0865 | .0754 | .0657 | .0573 |
| 35 | .0796 | .0676 | .0575 | .0490 | .0417 | .0356 |
| 40 | .0554 | .0460 | .0383 | .0318 | .0265 | .0221 |
| 45 | .0386 | .0313 | .0254 | .0207 | .0168 | .0137 |
| 50 | .0269 | .0213 | .0169 | .0134 | .0107 | .0085 |
| 55 | .0187 | .0145 | .0112 | .0087 | .0068 | .0053 |
| 60 | .0130 | .0099 | .0075 | .0057 | .0043 | .0033 |
| 65 | .0091 | .0067 | .0050 | .0037 | .0027 | .0020 |
| 70 | .0063 | .0046 | .0033 | .0024 | .0017 | .0012 |
| 75 | .0044 | .0031 | .0022 | .0016 | .0011 | .0008 |

Table 1B gives the value of the factor $\dfrac{1}{(1+i)^n}$ in the formula:

$$V_0 = V_n\left[\frac{1}{(1+i)^n}\right]$$

An illustration of its use is as follows:

If an investment earns 3 percent per year, what sum must be placed in the investment this year if proceeds of \$2,500 are desired 10 years hence? Here:

$$V_n = \$2,500; \quad i = 0.03; \quad n = 10$$

From Table 1B,

$$\frac{1}{(1+i)^n} = 0.7441;$$

then $V_0 = \$2,500\ (0.7441) = \$1,860.25.$

Table 1C gives the value of the factor $\dfrac{(1+i)^n - 1}{i}$ in the formula:

$$V_n = r\frac{(1+i)^n - 1}{i}$$

An illustration of its use is as follows:

Taxes of \$100 are paid on a timber property at the end of each year for 10 years. What is the value equivalent of all taxes paid at the end of the period, if interest is compounded annually at 5 percent? Here:

$$r = \$100; \quad i = 0.05; \quad n = 10$$

From Table 1C,

$$\frac{(1+i)^n - 1}{i} = 12.58$$

then $V_n = \$100\ (12.58) = \$1,258.$

Table 1D gives the value of the factor $\dfrac{(1+i)^n - 1}{i\,(1+i)^n}$ in the formula:

$$V_0 = \frac{V_n}{(1+i)^n} = r\,\frac{(1+i)^n - 1}{i\,(1+i)^n}$$

An illustration of its use is as follows:

If invested funds earn 2½ percent, what sum must be invested now to cover annual property tax payments of \$100 per year for the next 15 years? (Assume taxes are paid by withdrawal of invested funds at the end of each year.)

$$r = \$100; \quad i = 0.025; \quad n = 15$$

From Table 1D,

$$\frac{(1+i)^n - 1}{i\,(1+i)^n} = 12.38$$

then $V_0 = \$100\ (12.38) = \$1,238.$

**Table 1C.  Value of a (Finite) Series of *n* Annual Payments of $1 (Compounded Annually) at the Date of the Last Payment**

| Years | Rate of interest (percent per year) | | | | | | |
| | 0.5 | 1.0 | 1.5 | 2.0 | 2.5 | 3.0 | 3.5 |
|---|---|---|---|---|---|---|---|
| | | | | Dollars | | | |
| 1 | 1.000 | 1.000 | 1.000 | 1.000 | 1.000 | 1.000 | 1.000 |
| 2 | 2.005 | 2.010 | 2.015 | 2.020 | 2.025 | 2.030 | 2.035 |
| 3 | 3.015 | 3.030 | 3.045 | 3.060 | 3.076 | 3.091 | 3.106 |
| 4 | 4.030 | 4.060 | 4.091 | 4.122 | 4.153 | 4.184 | 4.215 |
| 5 | 5.050 | 5.101 | 5.152 | 5.204 | 5.256 | 5.309 | 5.362 |
| 6 | 6.076 | 6.152 | 6.230 | 6.308 | 6.388 | 6.468 | 6.550 |
| 7 | 7.106 | 7.214 | 7.323 | 7.434 | 7.547 | 7.662 | 7.779 |
| 8 | 8.141 | 8.286 | 8.433 | 8.583 | 8.736 | 8.892 | 9.052 |
| 9 | 9.182 | 9.369 | 9.559 | 9.755 | 9.955 | 10.16 | 10.37 |
| 10 | 10.23 | 10.46 | 10.70 | 10.95 | 11.20 | 11.46 | 11.73 |
| 11 | 11.28 | 11.57 | 11.86 | 12.17 | 12.48 | 12.81 | 13.14 |
| 12 | 12.34 | 12.68 | 13.04 | 13.41 | 13.80 | 14.19 | 14.60 |
| 13 | 13.40 | 13.81 | 14.24 | 14.68 | 15.14 | 15.62 | 16.11 |
| 14 | 14.46 | 14.95 | 15.45 | 15.97 | 16.52 | 17.09 | 17.68 |
| 15 | 15.54 | 16.10 | 16.68 | 17.29 | 17.93 | 18.60 | 19.30 |
| 16 | 16.61 | 17.26 | 17.93 | 18.64 | 19.38 | 20.16 | 20.97 |
| 17 | 17.70 | 18.43 | 19.20 | 20.01 | 20.86 | 21.76 | 22.71 |
| 18 | 18.79 | 19.61 | 20.49 | 21.41 | 22.39 | 23.41 | 24.50 |
| 19 | 19.88 | 20.81 | 21.80 | 22.84 | 23.95 | 25.12 | 26.36 |
| 20 | 20.98 | 22.02 | 23.12 | 24.30 | 25.54 | 26.87 | 28.28 |
| 21 | 22.08 | 23.24 | 24.47 | 25.78 | 27.18 | 28.68 | 30.27 |
| 22 | 23.19 | 24.47 | 25.84 | 27.30 | 28.86 | 30.54 | 32.33 |
| 23 | 24.31 | 25.72 | 27.23 | 28.84 | 30.58 | 32.45 | 34.46 |
| 24 | 25.43 | 26.97 | 28.63 | 30.42 | 32.35 | 34.43 | 36.67 |
| 25 | 26.56 | 28.24 | 30.06 | 32.03 | 34.16 | 36.46 | 38.95 |
| 26 | 27.69 | 29.53 | 31.51 | 33.67 | 36.01 | 38.55 | 41.31 |
| 27 | 28.83 | 30.82 | 32.99 | 35.34 | 37.91 | 40.71 | 43.76 |
| 28 | 29.97 | 32.13 | 34.48 | 37.05 | 39.86 | 42.93 | 46.29 |
| 29 | 31.12 | 33.45 | 36.00 | 38.79 | 41.86 | 45.22 | 48.91 |
| 30 | 32.28 | 34.78 | 37.54 | 40.57 | 43.90 | 47.58 | 51.62 |
| 35 | 38.15 | 41.66 | 45.59 | 49.99 | 54.93 | 60.46 | 66.67 |
| 40 | 44.16 | 48.89 | 54.27 | 60.40 | 67.40 | 75.40 | 84.55 |
| 45 | 50.32 | 56.48 | 63.61 | 71.89 | 81.52 | 92.72 | 105.8 |
| 50 | 56.65 | 64.46 | 73.68 | 84.58 | 97.48 | 112.8 | 131.0 |
| 55 | 63.13 | 72.85 | 84.53 | 98.59 | 115.6 | 136.1 | 160.9 |
| 60 | 69.77 | 81.67 | 96.21 | 114.1 | 136.0 | 163.1 | 196.5 |
| 65 | 76.58 | 90.94 | 108.8 | 131.1 | 159.1 | 194.3 | 238.8 |
| 70 | 83.57 | 100.7 | 122.4 | 150.0 | 185.3 | 230.6 | 288.9 |
| 75 | 90.73 | 110.9 | 137.0 | 170.8 | 214.9 | 272.6 | 348.5 |
| 80 | 98.07 | 121.7 | 152.7 | 193.8 | 248.4 | 321.4 | 419.3 |
| 85 | 105.6 | 133.0 | 169.7 | 219.1 | 286.3 | 377.9 | 503.4 |
| 90 | 113.3 | 144.9 | 187.9 | 247.2 | 329.2 | 443.3 | 603.2 |
| 95 | 121.2 | 157.4 | 207.6 | 278.1 | 377.7 | 519.3 | 721.8 |
| 100 | 129.3 | 170.5 | 228.8 | 312.2 | 432.5 | 607.3 | 862.6 |

**Table 1C. Value of a (Finite) Series of $n$ Annual Payments of $1 (Compounded Annually) at the Date of the Last Payment** (Continued)

| Years | Rate of interest (percent per year) | | | | | | |
|---|---|---|---|---|---|---|---|
| | 4.0 | 4.5 | 5.0 | 5.5 | 6.0 | 6.5 | 7.0 |
| | | | | Dollars | | | |
| 1 | 1.000 | 1.000 | 1.000 | 1.000 | 1.000 | 1.000 | 1.000 |
| 2 | 2.040 | 2.045 | 2.050 | 2.055 | 2.060 | 2.065 | 2.070 |
| 3 | 3.122 | 3.137 | 3.152 | 3.168 | 3.184 | 3.199 | 3.215 |
| 4 | 4.246 | 4.278 | 4.310 | 4.342 | 4.375 | 4.407 | 4.440 |
| 5 | 5.416 | 5.471 | 5.526 | 5.581 | 5.637 | 5.694 | 5.751 |
| 6 | 6.633 | 6.717 | 6.802 | 6.888 | 6.975 | 7.064 | 7.153 |
| 7 | 7.898 | 8.019 | 8.142 | 8.267 | 8.394 | 8.523 | 8.654 |
| 8 | 9.214 | 9.380 | 9.549 | 9.722 | 9.897 | 10.08 | 10.26 |
| 9 | 10.58 | 10.80 | 11.03 | 11.26 | 11.49 | 11.73 | 11.98 |
| 10 | 12.01 | 12.29 | 12.58 | 12.88 | 13.18 | 13.49 | 13.82 |
| 11 | 13.49 | 13.84 | 14.21 | 14.58 | 14.97 | 15.37 | 15.78 |
| 12 | 15.03 | 15.46 | 15.92 | 16.39 | 16.87 | 17.37 | 17.89 |
| 13 | 16.63 | 17.16 | 17.71 | 18.29 | 18.88 | 19.50 | 20.14 |
| 14 | 18.29 | 18.93 | 19.60 | 20.29 | 21.02 | 21.77 | 22.55 |
| 15 | 20.02 | 20.78 | 21.58 | 22.41 | 23.28 | 24.18 | 25.13 |
| 16 | 21.82 | 22.72 | 23.66 | 24.64 | 25.67 | 26.75 | 27.89 |
| 17 | 23.70 | 24.74 | 25.84 | 27.00 | 28.21 | 29.49 | 30.84 |
| 18 | 25.65 | 26.86 | 28.13 | 29.48 | 30.91 | 32.41 | 34.00 |
| 19 | 27.67 | 29.06 | 30.54 | 32.10 | 33.76 | 35.52 | 37.38 |
| 20 | 29.78 | 31.37 | 33.07 | 34.87 | 36.79 | 38.83 | 41.00 |
| 21 | 31.97 | 33.78 | 35.72 | 37.79 | 39.99 | 42.35 | 44.87 |
| 22 | 34.25 | 36.30 | 38.51 | 40.86 | 43.39 | 46.10 | 49.01 |
| 23 | 36.62 | 38.94 | 41.43 | 44.11 | 47.00 | 50.10 | 53.44 |
| 24 | 39.08 | 41.69 | 44.50 | 47.54 | 50.82 | 54.35 | 58.18 |
| 25 | 41.65 | 44.57 | 47.73 | 51.15 | 54.86 | 58.89 | 63.25 |
| 26 | 44.31 | 47.57 | 51.11 | 54.97 | 59.16 | 63.72 | 68.68 |
| 27 | 47.08 | 50.71 | 54.67 | 58.99 | 63.71 | 68.86 | 74.48 |
| 28 | 49.97 | 53.99 | 58.40 | 63.23 | 68.53 | 74.33 | 80.70 |
| 29 | 52.97 | 57.42 | 62.32 | 67.71 | 73.64 | 80.16 | 87.35 |
| 30 | 56.08 | 61.01 | 66.44 | 72.44 | 79.06 | 86.37 | 94.46 |
| 35 | 73.65 | 81.50 | 90.32 | 100.3 | 111.4 | 124.0 | 138.2 |
| 40 | 95.03 | 107.0 | 120.8 | 136.6 | 154.8 | 175.6 | 199.6 |
| 45 | 121.0 | 138.8 | 159.7 | 184.1 | 212.7 | 246.3 | 285.7 |
| 50 | 152.7 | 178.5 | 209.3 | 246.2 | 290.3 | 343.2 | 406.5 |
| 55 | 191.2 | 227.9 | 272.7 | 327.4 | 394.2 | 475.9 | 575.9 |
| 60 | 238.0 | 289.5 | 353.6 | 433.5 | 533.1 | 657.7 | 813.5 |
| 65 | 295.0 | 366.2 | 456.8 | 572.1 | 719.1 | 906.8 | 1,147 |
| 70 | 364.3 | 461.9 | 588.5 | 753.3 | 967.9 | 1,248 | 1,614 |
| 75 | 448.6 | 581.0 | 756.7 | 990.1 | 1,301 | 1,716 | 2,270 |
| 80 | 551.2 | 729.6 | 971.2 | 1,300 | 1,747 | 2,356 | 3,189 |
| 85 | 676.1 | 914.6 | 1,245 | 1,704 | 2,343 | 3,234 | 4,479 |
| 90 | 828.0 | 1,145 | 1,595 | 2,233 | 3,141 | 4,437 | 6,287 |
| 95 | 1,013 | 1,433 | 2,041 | 2,924 | 4,209 | 6,084 | 8,824 |
| 100 | 1,238 | 1,791 | 2,610 | 3,827 | 5,638 | 8,342 | 12,382 |

**Table 1C.  Value of a (Finite) Series of *n* Annual Payments of $1 (Compounded Annually) at the Date of the Last Payment** (Continued)

| Years | Rate of interest (percent per year) | | | | | |
| --- | --- | --- | --- | --- | --- | --- |
| | 7.5 | 8.0 | 8.5 | 9.0 | 9.5 | 10.0 |
| | Dollars | | | | | |
| 1 | 1.000 | 1.000 | 1.000 | 1.000 | 1.000 | 1.000 |
| 2 | 2.075 | 2.080 | 2.085 | 2.090 | 2.095 | 2.100 |
| 3 | 3.231 | 3.246 | 3.262 | 3.278 | 3.294 | 3.310 |
| 4 | 4.473 | 4.506 | 4.540 | 4.573 | 4.607 | 4.641 |
| 5 | 5.808 | 5.867 | 5.925 | 5.985 | 6.045 | 6.105 |
| 6 | 7.244 | 7.336 | 7.429 | 7.523 | 7.619 | 7.716 |
| 7 | 8.787 | 8.923 | 9.060 | 9.200 | 9.343 | 9.487 |
| 8 | 10.45 | 10.64 | 10.83 | 11.03 | 11.23 | 11.44 |
| 9 | 12.23 | 12.49 | 12.75 | 13.02 | 13.30 | 13.58 |
| 10 | 14.15 | 14.49 | 14.84 | 15.19 | 15.56 | 15.94 |
| 11 | 16.21 | 16.65 | 17.10 | 17.56 | 18.04 | 18.53 |
| 12 | 18.42 | 18.98 | 19.55 | 20.14 | 20.75 | 21.38 |
| 13 | 20.81 | 21.50 | 22.21 | 22.95 | 23.72 | 24.52 |
| 14 | 23.37 | 24.21 | 25.10 | 26.02 | 26.98 | 27.97 |
| 15 | 26.12 | 27.15 | 28.23 | 29.36 | 30.54 | 31.77 |
| 16 | 29.08 | 30.32 | 31.63 | 33.00 | 34.44 | 35.95 |
| 17 | 32.26 | 33.75 | 35.32 | 36.97 | 38.71 | 40.54 |
| 18 | 35.68 | 37.45 | 39.32 | 41.30 | 43.39 | 45.60 |
| 19 | 39.35 | 41.45 | 43.67 | 46.02 | 48.51 | 51.16 |
| 20 | 43.30 | 45.76 | 48.38 | 51.16 | 54.12 | 57.27 |
| 21 | 47.55 | 50.42 | 53.49 | 56.76 | 60.26 | 64.00 |
| 22 | 52.12 | 55.46 | 59.04 | 62.87 | 66.99 | 71.40 |
| 23 | 57.03 | 60.89 | 65.05 | 69.53 | 74.35 | 79.54 |
| 24 | 62.30 | 66.76 | 71.58 | 76.79 | 82.42 | 88.50 |
| 25 | 67.98 | 73.11 | 78.67 | 84.70 | 91.25 | 98.35 |
| 26 | 74.08 | 79.95 | 86.35 | 93.32 | 100.9 | 109.2 |
| 27 | 80.63 | 87.35 | 94.69 | 102.7 | 111.5 | 121.1 |
| 28 | 87.68 | 95.34 | 103.7 | 113.0 | 123.1 | 134.2 |
| 29 | 95.26 | 104.0 | 113.6 | 124.1 | 135.8 | 148.6 |
| 30 | 103.4 | 113.3 | 124.2 | 136.3 | 149.7 | 164.5 |
| 35 | 154.3 | 172.3 | 192.7 | 215.7 | 241.7 | 271.0 |
| 40 | 227.3 | 259.1 | 295.7 | 337.9 | 386.5 | 442.6 |
| 45 | 332.1 | 386.5 | 450.5 | 525.9 | 614.5 | 718.9 |
| 50 | 482.5 | 573.8 | 683.4 | 815.1 | 973.4 | 1,164 |
| 55 | 698.5 | 848.9 | 1,033 | 1,260 | 1,538 | 1,881 |
| 60 | 1,009 | 1,253 | 1,560 | 1,945 | 2,428 | 3,035 |
| 65 | 1,454 | 1,847 | 2,352 | 2,998 | 3,828 | 4,894 |
| 70 | 2,093 | 2,720 | 3,542 | 4,619 | 6,033 | 7,887 |
| 75 | 3,011 | 4,003 | 5,332 | 7,113 | 9,503 | 12,709 |

## Table 1D. Value at the Beginning of the Period of a (Finite) Series of Annual Payments of $1 Paid over a Period of *n* Years

| Years | Rate of interest (percent per year) | | | | | | |
|---|---|---|---|---|---|---|---|
| | 0.5 | 1.0 | 1.5 | 2.0 | 2.5 | 3.0 | 3.5 |
| | Dollars | | | | | | |
| 1 | 0.9950 | 0.9901 | 0.9852 | 0.9804 | 0.9756 | 0.9709 | 0.9662 |
| 2 | 1.985 | 1.970 | 1.956 | 1.942 | 1.927 | 1.913 | 1.900 |
| 3 | 2.970 | 2.941 | 2.912 | 2.884 | 2.856 | 2.829 | 2.802 |
| 4 | 3.950 | 3.902 | 3.854 | 3.808 | 3.762 | 3.717 | 3.673 |
| 5 | 4.926 | 4.853 | 4.783 | 4.713 | 4.646 | 4.580 | 4.515 |
| 6 | 5.896 | 5.795 | 5.697 | 5.601 | 5.508 | 5.417 | 5.329 |
| 7 | 6.862 | 6.728 | 6.598 | 6.472 | 6.349 | 6.230 | 6.115 |
| 8 | 7.823 | 7.652 | 7.486 | 7.325 | 7.170 | 7.020 | 6.874 |
| 9 | 8.779 | 8.566 | 8.361 | 8.162 | 7.971 | 7.786 | 7.608 |
| 10 | 9.730 | 9.471 | 9.222 | 8.983 | 8.752 | 8.530 | 8.317 |
| 11 | 10.68 | 10.37 | 10.07 | 9.787 | 9.514 | 9.253 | 9.002 |
| 12 | 11.62 | 11.26 | 10.91 | 10.58 | 10.26 | 9.954 | 9.663 |
| 13 | 12.56 | 12.13 | 11.73 | 11.35 | 10.98 | 10.63 | 10.30 |
| 14 | 13.49 | 13.00 | 12.54 | 12.11 | 11.69 | 11.30 | 10.92 |
| 15 | 14.42 | 13.87 | 13.34 | 12.85 | 12.38 | 11.94 | 11.52 |
| 16 | 15.34 | 14.72 | 14.13 | 13.58 | 13.06 | 12.56 | 12.09 |
| 17 | 16.26 | 15.56 | 14.91 | 14.29 | 13.71 | 13.17 | 12.65 |
| 18 | 17.17 | 16.40 | 15.67 | 14.99 | 14.35 | 13.75 | 13.19 |
| 19 | 18.08 | 17.23 | 16.43 | 15.68 | 14.98 | 14.32 | 13.71 |
| 20 | 18.99 | 18.05 | 17.17 | 16.35 | 15.59 | 14.88 | 14.21 |
| 21 | 19.89 | 18.86 | 17.90 | 17.01 | 16.18 | 15.42 | 14.70 |
| 22 | 20.78 | 19.66 | 18.62 | 17.66 | 16.77 | 15.94 | 15.17 |
| 23 | 21.68 | 20.46 | 19.33 | 18.29 | 17.33 | 16.44 | 15.62 |
| 24 | 22.56 | 21.24 | 20.03 | 18.91 | 17.88 | 16.94 | 16.06 |
| 25 | 23.45 | 22.02 | 20.72 | 19.52 | 18.42 | 17.41 | 16.48 |
| 26 | 24.32 | 22.80 | 21.40 | 20.12 | 18.95 | 17.88 | 16.89 |
| 27 | 25.20 | 23.56 | 22.07 | 20.71 | 19.46 | 18.33 | 17.29 |
| 28 | 26.07 | 24.32 | 22.73 | 21.28 | 19.96 | 18.76 | 17.67 |
| 29 | 26.93 | 25.07 | 23.38 | 21.84 | 20.45 | 19.19 | 18.04 |
| 30 | 27.79 | 25.81 | 24.02 | 22.40 | 20.93 | 19.60 | 18.39 |
| 35 | 32.04 | 29.41 | 27.08 | 25.00 | 23.15 | 21.49 | 20.00 |
| 40 | 36.17 | 32.83 | 29.92 | 27.36 | 25.10 | 23.11 | 21.36 |
| 45 | 40.21 | 36.09 | 32.55 | 29.49 | 26.83 | 24.52 | 22.50 |
| 50 | 44.14 | 39.20 | 35.00 | 31.42 | 28.36 | 25.73 | 23.46 |
| 55 | 47.98 | 42.15 | 37.27 | 33.17 | 29.71 | 26.77 | 24.26 |
| 60 | 51.73 | 44.96 | 39.38 | 34.76 | 30.91 | 27.68 | 24.94 |
| 65 | 55.38 | 47.63 | 41.34 | 36.20 | 31.96 | 28.45 | 25.52 |
| 70 | 58.94 | 50.17 | 43.15 | 37.50 | 32.90 | 29.12 | 26.00 |
| 75 | 62.41 | 52.59 | 44.84 | 38.68 | 33.72 | 29.70 | 26.41 |
| 80 | 65.80 | 54.89 | 46.41 | 39.74 | 34.45 | 30.20 | 26.75 |
| 85 | 69.11 | 57.08 | 47.86 | 40.71 | 35.10 | 30.63 | 27.04 |
| 90 | 72.33 | 59.16 | 49.21 | 41.59 | 35.67 | 31.00 | 27.28 |
| 95 | 75.48 | 61.14 | 50.46 | 42.38 | 36.17 | 31.32 | 27.48 |
| 100 | 78.54 | 63.03 | 51.62 | 43.10 | 36.61 | 31.60 | 27.66 |

**Table 1D. Value at the Beginning of the Period of a (Finite) Series of Annual Payments of $1 Paid over a Period of *n* Years** (Continued)

| Years | Rate of interest (percent per year) | | | | | | |
|---|---|---|---|---|---|---|---|
| | 4.0 | 4.5 | 5.0 | 5.5 | 6.0 | 6.5 | 7.0 |
| | Dollars | | | | | | |
| 1 | 0.9615 | 0.9569 | 0.9524 | 0.9479 | 0.9434 | 0.9390 | 0.9346 |
| 2 | 1.886 | 1.873 | 1.859 | 1.846 | 1.833 | 1.821 | 1.808 |
| 3 | 2.775 | 2.749 | 2.723 | 2.698 | 2.673 | 2.648 | 2.624 |
| 4 | 3.630 | 3.588 | 3.546 | 3.505 | 3.465 | 3.426 | 3.387 |
| 5 | 4.452 | 4.390 | 4.329 | 4.270 | 4.212 | 4.156 | 4.100 |
| 6 | 5.242 | 5.158 | 5.076 | 4.996 | 4.917 | 4.841 | 4.767 |
| 7 | 6.002 | 5.893 | 5.786 | 5.683 | 5.582 | 5.485 | 5.389 |
| 8 | 6.733 | 6.596 | 6.463 | 6.335 | 6.210 | 6.089 | 5.971 |
| 9 | 7.435 | 7.269 | 7.108 | 6.952 | 6.802 | 6.656 | 6.515 |
| 10 | 8.111 | 7.913 | 7.722 | 7.538 | 7.360 | 7.189 | 7.024 |
| 11 | 8.760 | 8.529 | 8.306 | 8.093 | 7.887 | 7.689 | 7.499 |
| 12 | 9.385 | 9.119 | 8.863 | 8.619 | 8.384 | 8.159 | 7.943 |
| 13 | 9.986 | 9.683 | 9.394 | 9.117 | 8.853 | 8.600 | 8.358 |
| 14 | 10.56 | 10.22 | 9.899 | 9.590 | 9.295 | 9.014 | 8.745 |
| 15 | 11.12 | 10.74 | 10.38 | 10.04 | 9.712 | 9.403 | 9.108 |
| 16 | 11.65 | 11.23 | 10.84 | 10.46 | 10.11 | 9.768 | 9.447 |
| 17 | 12.17 | 11.71 | 11.27 | 10.86 | 10.48 | 10.11 | 9.763 |
| 18 | 12.66 | 12.16 | 11.69 | 11.25 | 10.83 | 10.43 | 10.06 |
| 19 | 13.13 | 12.59 | 12.09 | 11.61 | 11.16 | 10.73 | 10.34 |
| 20 | 13.59 | 13.01 | 12.46 | 11.95 | 11.47 | 11.02 | 10.59 |
| 21 | 14.03 | 13.40 | 12.82 | 12.28 | 11.76 | 11.28 | 10.84 |
| 22 | 14.45 | 13.78 | 13.16 | 12.58 | 12.04 | 11.54 | 11.06 |
| 23 | 14.86 | 14.15 | 13.49 | 12.88 | 12.30 | 11.77 | 11.27 |
| 24 | 15.25 | 14.50 | 13.80 | 13.15 | 12.55 | 11.99 | 11.47 |
| 25 | 15.62 | 14.83 | 14.09 | 13.41 | 12.78 | 12.20 | 11.65 |
| 26 | 15.98 | 15.15 | 14.38 | 13.66 | 13.00 | 12.39 | 11.83 |
| 27 | 16.33 | 15.45 | 14.64 | 13.90 | 13.21 | 12.57 | 11.99 |
| 28 | 16.66 | 15.74 | 14.90 | 14.12 | 13.41 | 12.75 | 12.14 |
| 29 | 16.98 | 16.02 | 15.14 | 14.33 | 13.59 | 12.91 | 12.28 |
| 30 | 17.29 | 16.29 | 15.37 | 14.53 | 13.76 | 13.06 | 12.41 |
| 35 | 18.66 | 17.46 | 16.37 | 15.39 | 14.50 | 13.69 | 12.95 |
| 40 | 19.79 | 18.40 | 17.16 | 16.05 | 15.05 | 14.15 | 13.33 |
| 45 | 20.72 | 19.16 | 17.77 | 16.55 | 15.46 | 14.48 | 13.61 |
| 50 | 21.48 | 19.76 | 18.26 | 16.93 | 15.76 | 14.72 | 13.80 |
| 55 | 22.11 | 20.25 | 18.63 | 17.23 | 15.99 | 14.90 | 13.94 |
| 60 | 22.62 | 20.64 | 18.93 | 17.45 | 16.16 | 15.03 | 14.04 |
| 65 | 23.05 | 20.95 | 19.16 | 17.62 | 16.29 | 15.13 | 14.11 |
| 70 | 23.39 | 21.20 | 19.34 | 17.75 | 16.38 | 15.20 | 14.16 |
| 75 | 23.68 | 21.40 | 19.48 | 17.85 | 16.46 | 15.25 | 14.20 |
| 80 | 23.92 | 21.57 | 19.60 | 17.93 | 16.51 | 15.28 | 14.22 |
| 85 | 24.11 | 21.70 | 19.68 | 17.99 | 16.55 | 15.31 | 14.24 |
| 90 | 24.27 | 21.80 | 19.75 | 18.03 | 16.58 | 15.33 | 14.25 |
| 95 | 24.40 | 21.88 | 19.81 | 18.07 | 16.60 | 15.35 | 14.26 |
| 100 | 24.50 | 21.95 | 19.85 | 18.10 | 16.62 | 15.36 | 14.27 |

**Table 1D. Value at the Beginning of the Period of a (Finite) Series of Annual Payments of $1 Paid over a Period of _n_ Years** (Continued)

| Years | Rate of interest (percent per year) | | | | | |
|---|---|---|---|---|---|---|
| | 7.5 | 8.0 | 8.5 | 9.0 | 9.5 | 10.0 |
| | | | Dollars | | | |
| 1 | 0.9302 | 0.9259 | 0.9217 | 0.9174 | 0.9132 | 0.9091 |
| 2 | 1.796 | 1.783 | 1.771 | 1.759 | 1.747 | 1.736 |
| 3 | 2.601 | 2.577 | 2.554 | 2.531 | 2.509 | 2.487 |
| 4 | 3.349 | 3.312 | 3.276 | 3.240 | 3.204 | 3.170 |
| 5 | 4.046 | 3.993 | 3.941 | 3.890 | 3.840 | 3.791 |
| 6 | 4.694 | 4.623 | 4.554 | 4.486 | 4.420 | 4.355 |
| 7 | 5.297 | 5.206 | 5.119 | 5.033 | 4.950 | 4.868 |
| 8 | 5.857 | 5.747 | 5.639 | 5.535 | 5.433 | 5.335 |
| 9 | 6.379 | 6.247 | 6.119 | 5.995 | 5.875 | 5.759 |
| 10 | 6.864 | 6.710 | 6.561 | 6.418 | 6.279 | 6.145 |
| 11 | 7.315 | 7.139 | 6.969 | 6.805 | 6.647 | 6.495 |
| 12 | 7.735 | 7.536 | 7.345 | 7.161 | 6.984 | 6.814 |
| 13 | 8.126 | 7.904 | 7.691 | 7.487 | 7.291 | 7.103 |
| 14 | 8.489 | 8.244 | 8.010 | 7.786 | 7.572 | 7.367 |
| 15 | 8.827 | 8.559 | 8.304 | 8.061 | 7.828 | 7.606 |
| 16 | 9.142 | 8.851 | 8.575 | 8.313 | 8.062 | 7.824 |
| 17 | 9.434 | 9.122 | 8.825 | 8.544 | 8.276 | 8.022 |
| 18 | 9.706 | 9.372 | 9.055 | 8.756 | 8.471 | 8.201 |
| 19 | 9.959 | 9.604 | 9.268 | 8.950 | 8.650 | 8.365 |
| 20 | 10.19 | 9.818 | 9.463 | 9.129 | 8.812 | 8.514 |
| 21 | 10.41 | 10.02 | 9.644 | 9.292 | 8.961 | 8.649 |
| 22 | 10.62 | 10.20 | 9.810 | 9.442 | 9.097 | 8.772 |
| 23 | 10.81 | 10.37 | 9.963 | 9.580 | 9.221 | 8.883 |
| 24 | 10.98 | 10.53 | 10.10 | 9.707 | 9.334 | 8.985 |
| 25 | 11.15 | 10.67 | 10.23 | 9.823 | 9.438 | 9.077 |
| 26 | 11.30 | 10.81 | 10.35 | 9.929 | 9.532 | 9.161 |
| 27 | 11.44 | 10.94 | 10.46 | 10.03 | 9.618 | 9.237 |
| 28 | 11.57 | 11.05 | 10.57 | 10.12 | 9.697 | 9.307 |
| 29 | 11.70 | 11.16 | 10.66 | 10.20 | 9.769 | 9.370 |
| 30 | 11.81 | 11.26 | 10.75 | 10.27 | 9.835 | 9.427 |
| 35 | 12.27 | 11.65 | 11.09 | 10.57 | 10.09 | 9.644 |
| 40 | 12.59 | 11.92 | 11.31 | 10.76 | 10.25 | 9.779 |
| 45 | 12.82 | 12.11 | 11.47 | 10.88 | 10.35 | 9.863 |
| 50 | 12.97 | 12.23 | 11.57 | 10.96 | 10.41 | 9.915 |
| 55 | 13.08 | 12.32 | 11.63 | 11.01 | 10.45 | 9.947 |
| 60 | 13.16 | 12.38 | 11.68 | 11.05 | 10.48 | 9.967 |
| 65 | 13.21 | 12.42 | 11.71 | 11.07 | 10.50 | 9.980 |
| 70 | 13.25 | 12.44 | 11.73 | 11.08 | 10.51 | 9.987 |
| 75 | 13.27 | 12.46 | 11.74 | 11.09 | 10.51 | 9.992 |

**Untabulated Years.** In Tables 1A and 1B values for untabulated years may be both interpolated and extrapolated by simple multiplication. The value for a specified period is equal to the product of the values for any two periods which add up to the specified period.

**Example.** What is the value of one dollar placed at 3 percent interest for 68 years? Two periods which add to 68 are 50 and 18, which have tabulated values (Table 1A) of 4.384 and 1.702 respectively. The factor for 68 years is (4.384) × (1.702) = 7.462.

The procedure just outlined must not be used with Tables 1C and 1D. To interpolate in Table 1C, substitute the appropriate valuation factor from Table 1A in the expression $\dfrac{(1+i)^n - 1}{i}$. In Table 1D, substitute the appropriate valuation factor from Table 1A in the expression $\dfrac{(1+i)^n - 1}{i\,(1+i)^n}$.

**INTEREST COMPOUNDED OTHER THAN ANNUALLY.** The tables are presented in terms of a unit interest-bearing period of one year and annual rates of interest; that is, the tables read directly for interest compounded annually. Tables 1A and 1B may also be used to obtain valuation factors in cases where the unit interest-bearing period is other than one year. To do this, convert the interest rate from an annual basis to a rate per unit interest-bearing period and read the actual number of unit interest-bearing periods in the "years" column.

**Example.** What valuation factor should be used to find the value equivalent 10 years hence of $1 invested now at 4 percent interest, compounded semiannually? If interest is thus compounded every 6 months, the rate per unit interest-bearing period is one-half of 4 percent, or 2 percent, and the number of unit interest-bearing periods is twice 10. Using the 2 percent column of Table 1A and 20 "years" we obtain a valuation factor of $1.486, which is the value equivalent of $1 at 4 percent for 10 years, compounded semiannually.

The annuity tables, 1C and 1D, may be treated similarly, provided that payments are made at the same time that the interest is compounded (e.g., semiannual payments and semiannual compounding). Where the timing of payments is different from the period of compounding, the formula for periodic series of equal payments must be used (see page 15 · 16).

**ANNUITIES PAID AT THE BEGINNING OF A YEAR.** Note that Tables 1C and 1D assume that each payment is made at the end of the year. If valuation factors are desired for a series of payments similar to those of Tables 1C and 1D, except that payments are made at the beginning of each year, multiply the tabulated valuation factor by $(1 + i)$.

## Commonly Used Compound Interest Formulas

Valuation problems which cannot be solved by direct application of the preceding tables may be handled by use of one or more of the formulas described below. The following symbols will be used:

$V_o$ = value of a series of payments, at the beginning of the series
$V_n$ = value of a series of payments, at the end of the series
$r$ = a single payment in a series of equal payments
$n$ = number of payments in a series
$t$ = interval between payments in a series, in years
$i$ = annual rate of interest, expressed as a decimal

**Note.** In the illustrations which follow, assume $i = 0.05$.

## VALUE OF A PERPETUAL SERIES OF EQUAL ANNUAL PAYMENTS.

$$V_0 = \frac{r}{i}$$

**Example.** What is the present value of a normal forest which will yield equal annual net incomes of $10,000 in perpetuity?

$$V_0 = \frac{\$10,000}{0.05} = \$200,000$$

## VALUE OF A PERPETUAL SERIES OF EQUAL PERIODIC PAYMENTS.

$$V_0 = \frac{r}{(1+i)^t - 1}$$

(Assumes first payment $t$ years hence. Note that where $t = 1$, this formula reduces to the preceding formula.)

**Example.** What is the present worth of $100 net income, received 5 years hence, plus an additional $100 every 5 years thereafter?

Using Table 1A to evaluate the expression $(1 + i)^t$, where $t = 5$,

$$V_0 = \frac{\$100}{(1.05)^5 - 1} = \frac{\$100}{1.276 - 1} = \$362.32$$

## VALUE, AT THE END OF THE SERIES, OF $n$ PAYMENTS MADE ONCE EVERY $t$ YEARS.

$$V_n = \frac{r[(1+i)^{nt} - 1]}{(1+i)^t - 1}$$

**Example.** What is the accumulated cost at the end of 1980 of fire insurance which requires a premium of $1,000 in 1953 and renewal premiums of the same amount every third year thereafter? With $n = 10$ and $t = 3$, use Table 1A to write

$$V_n = \frac{\$1,000 [(1.05)^{30} - 1]}{(1.05)^3 - 1} = \frac{\$1,000 [4.322 - 1]}{1.158 - 1}$$

$$= \$21,025$$

## VALUE, AT THE BEGINNING OF THE SERIES, OF $n$ PAYMENTS MADE ONCE EVERY $t$ YEARS.

$$V_0 = \frac{r[(1+i)^{nt} - 1]}{[(1+i)^t - 1](1+i)^{t(n-1)}}$$

**Example.** What is the present worth of the cost of four successive thinnings, each costing $100, if the first thinning is made this year and the others at subsequent 10-year intervals? With $n = 4$ and $t = 10$, use Table 1A to write

$$V_0 = \frac{\$100 [(1.05)^{40} - 1]}{[(1.05)^{10} - 1](1.05)^{30}} = \frac{\$100 [7.040 - 1]}{[1.629 - 1] 4.322}$$

$$= \$222.18$$

## COMPUTATION OF SINKING FUND PAYMENTS.
If $r =$ the amount of the payment to be made annually into a sinking fund, such that at the end of $n$ years the fund will contain a predetermined amount $V_n$,

$$r = \frac{V_n (i)}{(1+i)^n - 1}$$

**Example.** A sinking fund is set up in 1951 in order to accumulate reserves to redeem a $1,000,000 bond issue at the end of 1965. What sum must be placed in the sinking fund each year in order to provide the $1,000,000 at the end of 1965, if earnings on the sinking fund are 5 percent per year?

With $n = 15$ and $V_n = $1,000,000$, use Table 1A to write

$$r = \frac{$1,000,000\ (.05)}{(1.05)^{15} - 1} = \frac{$50,000}{2.079 - 1} = $46,339$$

## VALUE OF A SERIES OF ANNUAL PAYMENTS WHICH DE-CREASE BY EQUAL ANNUAL AMOUNTS.

Let $p = $ amount of initial payment, and $n = $ number of payments. Then,

$$V_n = \frac{p}{n}\left[\frac{(1 + i)^n\ (ni - 1) + 1}{i^2}\right]$$

**Example.** General property taxes on a stand of old-growth timber amount to $10,000 this year. The area is to be cut at a uniform rate over the next 10 years. Each year new cut-over lands will be classified under a yield tax law which exempts standing timber from general property taxes. Hence, general property taxes will decrease each year by one-tenth of the initial amount. At the end of the 10-year period, what will be the cumulative total of expenditures for general property taxes on the timber?

$$V_n = \frac{$10,000}{10}\left[\frac{(1.05)^{10}\ (10 \times 0.05 - 1) + 1}{0.05^2}\right]$$

$$V_n = $1,000\left[\frac{1.629\ (0.5 - 1.0) + 1}{0.0025}\right] = $1,000\left[\frac{-0.8145 + 1.000}{0.0025}\right]$$

$$= $74,200$$

## VALUE, AT THE BEGINNING OF THE SERIES, OF A SERIES OF ANNUAL PAYMENTS WHICH DECREASE BY EQUAL ANNUAL AMOUNTS.

The value of a decreasing series at the beginning of the series may be calculated by first determining the value at the end of the series by the preceding formula and then reducing this single value to its equivalent at the beginning of the series by applying Table 1B.

## VALUE OF A SERIES OF ANNUAL PAYMENTS WHICH IN-CREASE BY EQUAL ANNUAL AMOUNTS.

The value of a series which increases by equal annual amounts may be computed by (1) calculating the value of a series of equal annual payments, each of which is the same as the final payment in the increasing series (by means of Table 1C), and (2) deducting from this the value of a decreasing series whose initial payment is equal to the final payment of the increasing series (value of a series of annual payments which decreases by equal annual amounts).

# Stumpage Appraisal

**OBJECTIVES AND METHODS.** The primary objective of stumpage appraisal is to determine as accurately as possible the monetary value of standing timber to be converted into commercial products such as lumber or pulpwood. The intangible values of timber, such as those for watershed protection or recreation, cannot be established by the methods which are outlined in this section.

In making an appraisal, gross income and costs of production are first summarized, related to log production, and expressed in terms of the scaled unit of product. When the total costs per unit of product are subtracted from the average gross income per unit, the margin remaining is termed "conversion return." The appraiser must then apportion this margin fairly between stumpage value (which is the timber owner's share) and the margin allowed for profit and risk (the share of the operator who converts the timber into usable products).

Of the many methods of arriving at stumpage value, the following are most commonly used: (1) overturn methods, (2) investment methods.

The overturn methods of calculating the margins allowed for stumpage and for profit and risk are most useful on small timber sales where (a) heavy expenditures are not required, (b) a single simple product such as saw logs is produced, (c) output is sold promptly on a stable market, say on a contractual basis, and (d) most of the investment, and hence operating risk, involves working capital. But where a long-term stumpage supply, costly improvements, and complex conversion operations are involved, it is best to use the investment method of appraisal.

**OVERTURN METHODS.** Overturn methods first develop the conversion return from the product by subtracting its cost of production from its sale value. If joint products can be produced and marketed, the appraisal should develop separate conversion returns for each product. Otherwise, the appraisal may give erroneous results.

**Example.** In the following case of a small timber sale it is assumed that the trees 6 to 12 in. d.b.h. will be sold to a pulpwood cutter and that the trees larger than 12 in. will be sold to a saw-log operator. Calculation of the conversion returns is as follows:

For Pulpwood:
Sale value of product:
    10 cords per acre at $15 per cord ........................................ $150
Variable cost:
    10 cords per acre at $10 per cord ........................................ 100

| | | |
|---|---|---|
| Felling and bucking | at $1.75 per cord | |
| Skidding and loading | at 4.50 per cord | |
| Hauling | at 2.75 per cord | |
| Logging overhead, etc. | at 1.00 per cord | |
| Total cost | $10.00 per cord | |

Surplus per acre ................................................... $ 50

For Saw Logs:
Sale value of product:
    2 M bd. ft. per acre at $55 per M ....................................... $110
Variable cost:
    2 M bd. ft. per acre at $20 per M ....................................... 40

| | | |
|---|---|---|
| Felling and bucking | at $4.60 per M bd. ft. | |
| Skidding and loading | at 5.85 per M bd. ft. | |
| Hauling, etc. | at 6.55 per M bd. ft. | |
| Logging overhead, etc. | at 3.00 per M bd. ft. | |
| Total cost | $20.00 per M bd. ft. | |

Surplus per acre ................................................... $ 70

Fixed improvement costs estimated at $20 per acre must now be allocated in proportion to the surplus per acre. Thus:

| | | |
|---|---|---|
| Pulpwood surplus per acre .......... | $ 50 | 41.7% |
| Saw-log surplus per acre ............. | 70 | 58.3 |
| | $120 | 100.0% |

| | Pulpwood | Saw logs |
|---|---|---|
| Surplus per acre ......................................... | $50.00 | $70.00 |
| Fixed improvement costs: | | |
| Pulpwood, $20 per acre × 41.7% ......................... | 8.34 | |
| Saw logs, $20 per acre × 58.3% .......................... | | 11.66 |
| Conversion returns per acre ............................. | $41.66 | $58.34 |
| Conversion returns per unit of product .................. | 4.17/cord | 29.17/M |
| Total cost per unit of product ......................... | 10.83/cord | 25.83/M |
| Sale value per unit of product .......................... | $15.00/cord | $55.00/M |

The final step in the appraisal is to split conversion return between stumpage and the operator's margin for profit and risk. A 50–50 split is often used. In the above instance, stumpage values at $2.08 per cord for pulpwood and $14.58 per M for saw logs would then result.

**Operating and Profit Ratios.** The 50–50 split between operator and stumpage owner is a purely arbitrary one. A better basis for determining the operator's share is found in the operating and profit ratios commonly used by business analysts. These are defined as follows:

$$\text{Operating Ratio} = \frac{\text{Cost of operation plus stumpage}}{\text{Income from sales}}$$

$$\text{Profit ratio} = \frac{\text{Margin for profit and risk}}{\text{Cost of operation plus stumpage}}$$

Let $V$ = sale value per unit of product
$C$ = cost per unit
$S$ = stumpage per unit
$M$ = margin for profit and risk per unit
$OR$ = operating ratio
$PR$ = profit ratio

$$\text{Then } OR = \frac{C + S}{V}, \quad \text{and} \quad PR = \frac{M}{C + S}$$

If, in the foregoing example, $S$ and $M$ are assumed to be equal (the 50–50 split), the following operating ratios would obtain:

$$\text{Pulpwood operation } OR = \frac{\$10.83 + \$2.08}{\$15} = 0.861$$

$$\text{Saw-log operation } OR = \frac{\$25.83 + \$14.58}{\$55} = 0.735$$

The corresponding profit ratios would be:

$$\text{Pulpwood operation } PR = \frac{\$2.09}{\$10.83 + \$2.08} = 0.162$$

$$\text{Saw-log operation } PR = \frac{\$14.59}{\$25.83 + \$14.58} = 0.362$$

Note that if we split the conversion return 50–50 between margin and stumpage, 86.1 cents out of every income dollar of the pulpwood operation goes to cover the operator's cost, but only 73.5 cents out of the saw-log operator's dollar is needed to cover his costs. The pulpwood operator gets a margin of only 13.9 cents per dollar of income while the saw-log man gets 26.5 cents on the dollar. Similarly, the pulpwood operator is allowed only 16.2 percent of his total costs as margin for profit and risk, whereas the saw-log operator is allowed 36.2 percent. Conceivably, a greater risk might be experienced in the saw-log portion of the operation than in the pulpwood portion, but it is quite possible that the reverse might be the case. In any event, it is within the province of the appraiser to evaluate relative risk. The operating ratios or profit ratios common to local businesses or stumpage transactions of comparable risk should be used by him as a guide. This means that he should be informed as to selling values and costs in relation to stumpage prices for tracts of timber comparable, from the risk standpoint, to the one he is appraising. In the absence of such specific information on timber sales transactions, the profit or operating ratios of other business in the region which attracts venture capital may be used as a guide, although such ratios will not be as reliable as data applicable to units of the timber industry.

The equations for the operating ratios, $OR = \dfrac{C + S}{V}$ and $PR = \dfrac{M}{C + S}$, may both be solved for stumpage value $(S)$, with the following results:

$$S = V\,(OR) - C \qquad \text{and} \qquad S = \frac{V}{PR + 1.0} - C$$

With these equations in mind, we may illustrate the use of the ratios.

**Example.** Assume the appraiser has obtained the following data from an actual sale of pulpwood stumpage which appears to have been satisfactory to both parties.

1. Selling price of pulpwood $(V)$ ............................ $20.00 per cord
2. Total cost $(C)$ .......................................... 14.50 per cord

3. Conversion return $(CR)$ ................................. $ 5.50 per cord
4. Stumpage $(S)$ .......................................... 3.00 per cord

He then calculates:

5. Operating ratio ......................................... 0.875 per cord
6. Margin ................................................. 2.50 per cord
7. Profit ratio ........................................... 0.143 per cord

He decides that the operating ratio 0.875 is fair for pulpwood and, because no greater risk apparently attaches to saw-log operations, he accepts it for saw logs as well. Applying it to the combined pulpwood–saw-log operation previously described, stumpage would be appraised as follows:

$$S = V\,(OR) - C$$

Pulpwood stumpage: $S = \$15\,(0.875) - \$10.83$
$= \$2.30$ per cord

Saw-log stumpage: $S = \$55\,(0.875) - \$25.83$
$= \$22.30$ per M bd. ft.

But suppose the appraiser does not have such detailed data on actual sales but does know that the margin allowed on costs (including stumpage) in another transaction was 0.143. He considers this adequate for pulpwood operations but believes that saw-log operations should be appraised on the basis of a profit ratio of 0.200. The appraisal would then be as follows:

$$S = \frac{V}{PR + 1.0} - C$$

Pulpwood stumpage: $S = \dfrac{\$15}{0.143 + 1.000} - \$10.83$

$= \$2.29$ per cord

Saw-log stumpage: $S = \dfrac{\$55}{0.200 + 1.000} - \$25.83$

$= \$20.00$ per M. bd. ft.

**Operating and Profit Ratios in Relation to Unit Cost and Values.** Operating ratio and profit ratio are mathematically related to each other, and to operating costs, gross income, and conversion returns. Table 2 shows the way in which the percentage of conversion return which may equitably be apportioned to stumpage varies with changes in the ratios, and with changes in the relation of operating costs to income.

**Table 2. Stumpage Value as a Percent of Conversion Return**

| Operating ratio | Profit ratio | Costs (without stumpage) in percent of income | | | | | | | | | | |
|---|---|---|---|---|---|---|---|---|---|---|---|---|
| | | 40 | 45 | 50 | 55 | 60 | 65 | 70 | 75 | 80 | 85 | 90 |
| 0.95 | 0.0526 | 91.6 | 91.0 | 90 | 88.9 | 87.5 | 85.7 | 83.3 | 80 | 75.0 | 66.6 | 50.0 |
| .94 | .0638 | 90.0 | 89.1 | 88 | 86.7 | 85.0 | 82.9 | 80.0 | 76 | 70.0 | 60.0 | 40.0 |
| .93 | .0753 | 88.3 | 87.3 | 86 | 84.4 | 82.5 | 80.0 | 76.7 | 72 | 65.0 | 53.4 | 30.0 |
| .92 | .0870 | 86.6 | 85.5 | 84 | 82.2 | 80.0 | 77.1 | 73.3 | 68 | 60.0 | 46.7 | 20.0 |
| .91 | .0990 | 85.0 | 83.6 | 82 | 80.0 | 77.5 | 74.3 | 70.0 | 64 | 55.0 | 40.0 | 10.0 |
| .90 | .1111 | 83.3 | 81.9 | 80 | 77.8 | 75.0 | 71.4 | 66.7 | 60 | 50.0 | 33.3 | 0.0 |
| .89 | .1235 | 81.6 | 80.0 | 78 | 75.5 | 72.5 | 68.6 | 63.3 | 56 | 45.0 | 26.7 | |
| .88 | .1363 | 80.0 | 78.2 | 76 | 73.3 | 70.0 | 65.7 | 60.0 | 52 | 40.0 | 20.0 | |
| .87 | .1495 | 78.3 | 76.4 | 74 | 71.1 | 67.5 | 62.8 | 56.7 | 48 | 35.0 | 13.3 | |
| .86 | .1626 | 76.6 | 74.6 | 72 | 68.8 | 65.0 | 60.0 | 53.3 | 44 | 30.0 | 0.7 | |
| .85 | .1765 | 75.0 | 72.7 | 70 | 66.6 | 62.5 | 57.1 | 50.0 | 40 | 25.0 | 0.0 | |
| .84 | .1905 | 73.3 | 70.9 | 68 | 64.4 | 60.0 | 54.3 | 46.7 | 36 | 20.0 | | |
| .83 | .2048 | 71.6 | 69.0 | 66 | 62.2 | 57.5 | 51.4 | 43.3 | 32 | 15.0 | | |
| .82 | .2195 | 70.0 | 67.2 | 64 | 60.0 | 55.0 | 48.5 | 40.0 | 28 | 10.0 | | |
| .81 | .2345 | 68.3 | 65.4 | 62 | 57.8 | 52.5 | 45.7 | 36.7 | 24 | 5.0 | | |
| .80 | .2500 | 66.6 | 63.6 | 60 | 55.5 | 50.0 | 42.8 | 33.3 | 20 | 0.0 | | |

**Stumpage Value as a Percent of Conversion Return.** Table 2 serves as a useful appraisal tool, particularly in small stumpage sales where detailed cost studies are not required.

**Example.** Assume that an operating ratio 0.87 (corresponding to a profit ratio of about 0.15) is being used as a general guide for appraisals in a certain district. The stumpage on two similar tracts of timber is to be appraised. Logs from both will be delivered to the same mill. Log values and logging costs are:

| | |
|---|---|
| Delivered log value .................... | $40.00 per M bd. ft. |
| Average cost F.O.B. trucks ........... | 20.00 per M bd. ft. |
| Hauling cost—Tract A ............... | 2.00 per M bd. ft. |
| Hauling cost—Tract B ............... | 8.00 per M bd. ft. |

Then, operating cost as a percentage of log value is

$$\frac{\$22}{\$40} = 55\% \text{ for Tract A, and } \frac{\$28}{\$40} = 70\% \text{ for Tract B}$$

And, conversion return = $40 − $22 = $18 per M bd. ft. for Tract A and $40 − $28 = $12 per M bd. ft. for Tract B. From Table 2, stumpage value can be calculated as follows:

$$\text{Tract A: } S = \$18.00 \ (0.711) = \$12.80 \text{ per M bd. ft.}$$
$$\text{Tract B: } S = \$12.00 \ (0.567) = \$ \ 6.80 \text{ per M bd. ft.}$$

In this illustration the stumpage difference between the two tracts is exactly the same as the difference between conversion returns as a value per M bd. ft. It does not follow, however, that if conversion returns differ by certain amounts, stumpage values will differ by identical amounts. Assume that the unit value of logs produced on Tract A was only $34 per M bd. ft. because of size or species. Conversion returns for both tracts would now be $12 per M bd. ft. However, cost as a percent of log value on Tract A would be approximately 65 percent. Using the table, stumpage on Tract A is 62.8 percent of $12, or $7.53 per M bd. ft., whereas on Tract B it remains at $6.80 per M bd. ft.

Under these circumstances, stumpage can be considered more valuable on Tract A than on Tract B because of the fact that a conversion return of $12 per M bd. ft. can be obtained by the expenditure of $22 per M on Tract A, whereas on Tract B an expenditure of $28 per M is required to obtain the same return.

**Check on Adequacy of Margin by Calculating Return to Operator.** In the use of overturn ratios, it is always well for the appraiser to check the adequacy of the appraised margins for stumpage and profit to the operator by computing the earnings of the operator over the period of a month, say, on the basis of the total production in that period. If, in spite of reasonable costs of operation and a reasonable volume of production, his net income will not be comparable to that of efficient operators in the locality, the margin allowed for profit and risk is too low.

**INVESTMENT METHOD.** In the investment method, the margin for profit and risk is related to the investment in plant, equipment, and working capital required to operate the business during the estimated life of the timber sale. It is used where large investments are required to develop and log a large timber tract. No operator will risk large amounts of capital in a timber-converting enterprise unless the price paid for standing timber will allow a proper interest return on the invested capital, plus repayment of it, and an allowance for the risk taken in the venture. The margin, then, is here related to the money invested.

Investment is required for plant, equipment, and working capital. The amount of each type of capital needed in the operation should be estimated separately.

By the following formula the profit-bearing investment in each physical asset is estimated as an average for the period during which the timber is to be cut:

$$AI = \left(\frac{I + R}{2}\right)\frac{n}{y} + \frac{D}{2}$$

where $AI$ = average profit-bearing investment
$I$ = original cost or value of item at time of purchase or beginning of operating period
$R$ = residual value of the item at end of use or end of operating period
$n$ = years used during operating period
$y$ = duration of operating period
$D$ = average annual depreciation of item during operating period

The investment in working capital is made up of an estimate of capital constantly tied up during the operating period in the following categories:

1. Logs in transit or in the woods.
2. Logs in pond or log dump at mill.
3. Yard piles of lumber.
4. Accounts receivable.

**Example.** The following demonstrates appraisal, by the investment method, of the stumpage value of a 60,000 M bd. ft. tract of mixed timber to be logged during an operating period of 4 yr. The rate of production is 15,000 M bd. ft. per year (Doyle rule). The appropriate operating ratio is considered to be 0.87, with a consequent profit ratio of 0.15.

### TIMBER ESTIMATE

| Species | Volume M bd. ft (Doyle rule) | Estimated overrun % | Selling price M bd. ft. mill tally | Price per M bd. ft. log scale |
|---|---|---|---|---|
| Birch ......... | 30,000 | 40 | $90.00 | $126.00 |
| Maple ........ | 20,000 | 40 | 70.00 | 98.00 |
| Hemlock ...... | 10,000 | 20 | 50.00 | 60.00 |
| Total ......... | 60,000 | | | |

**Variable Operating Costs.** The first step in the appraisal is to estimate direct operating costs, such as labor and material items, which will vary in total amount with the total volume logged. In this example these items are estimated as follows:

| | Hardwoods per M bd. ft. | Hemlock per M bd. ft. |
|---|---|---|
| Variable logging costs (log scale basis)....................... | $35.00 | $30.00 |
| Variable milling costs (mill tally basis)....................... | $20.00 | $15.00 |

The milling cost items are next converted to a log scale basis by multiplying by unity plus the overrun percentage. Thus, milling costs of $20 per M mill tally become $20 (1.00 + .40), or $28 per M log scale.

**Operating Surplus.** These variable costs are next deducted from the selling price of the lumber produced by the operation to determine the surplus over and above variable costs.

| | Birch | Maple | Hemlock |
|---|---|---|---|
| Lumber selling price, per M bd. ft. log scale........... | $126 | $98 | $60 |
| Less: | | | |
| Variable logging costs, per M bd. ft. log scale........ | 35 | 35 | 30 |
| Variable milling costs, per M bd. ft. log scale........ | 28 | 28 | 18 |
| Operating surplus ..................................... | $ 63 | $35 | $12 |

This operating surplus represents the sum available to cover the fixed costs of the operator, to pay for the stumpage, and to provide a margin for profit and risk for the operator.

**Investment and Fixed Costs.** The next step is to estimate the average profit-bearing investment in the plant and equipment, and the depreciation applying to it, as shown in the following schedule. The average profit-bearing investment is here computed by the formula given on page **15** · **22**.

PROFIT-BEARING INVESTMENT AND DEPRECIATION SCHEDULE

| Item | Invest-ment | Life yrs. | Years used in oper. period | Annual deprec. | Resi-dual value | Average p.b.i. |
|---|---|---|---|---|---|---|
| Manufacturing plant .. | $600,000 | 20 | 4 | $30,000 | $480,000 | $555,000 |
| Main access logging roads .............. | 50,000 | 4 | 4 | 12,500 | nil | 31,250 |
| Main interior logging roads .............. | 20,000 | 4 | 4 | 5,000 | nil | 12,500 |
| Spur roads built an-nually ............. | 20,000 | 1 | 1 | 5,000 | nil | 5,000 |
| Tractors ............... | 40,000 | 4 | 4 | 10,000 | nil | 25,000 |
| One set of camps...... | 15,000 | 4 | 4 | 3,750 | nil | 9,375 |
| Trucks ............... | 20,000 | 2 | 2 | 5,000 | nil | 7,500 |
| Trucks ............... | 30,000 | 4 | 4 | 7,500 | nil | 18,750 |
| Small tools, 4 sets 1 year .............. | 5,000 | 1 | 1 | 1,250 | nil | 1,250 |
| | $800,000 | | | $80,000 | | $665,625 |

WORKING CAPITAL SCHEDULE

| | |
|---|---|
| Logs in woods and in transit, 1,000M at $20..................... | $ 20,000 |
| Logs in pond, 2,000M at $30................................... | 60,000 |
| Yard lumber, 5,000M at $70................................... | 350,000 |
| Accounts receivable ......................................... | 70,000 |
| Total average working capital................................ | $ 500,000 |

Then:

| | |
|---|---|
| Total average working capital ............................... | $ 500.000 |
| Average fixed interest-bearing investment..................... | 665,625 |
| Total average profit-bearing investment....................... | $1,165,625 |

**Margin for Profit and Risk.** It is usual to allow from 10 to 20 percent as a margin for profit and risk, depending on the estimated degree of risk. In an area where risk is fairly well known a rate of 10 percent could be safely used, but in new areas where there is no guiding precedent, a rate as high as 20 percent might be advisable. The rate allowed must depend on the appraiser's judgment after he has investigated the property concerned. In the present case a rate of 15 percent per year seems appropriate. The margin thus becomes 0.15($1,165,625), or $174,843. In further calculations this should be rounded to $175,000 per year.

**Determination of Stumpage Values.** This margin for profit and risk, along with the annual depreciation charge and costs of general overhead, must now be deducted from the operating surplus. The overhead items in question are estimated at $75,000 per year for supervision and general expense, and $30,000 per year for income taxes on the operation.

The first step is to calculate the total annual surplus available to meet these charges. Using the operating surplus for each species, as determined above, the estimated gross annual surplus becomes:

Birch:  7,500 M per year × $63/M = $472,500
Maple:  5,000 M per year ×  35/M =  175,000
Hemlock: 2,500 M per year × 12/M =   30,000

Total surplus                    = $677,500 per year

From this total the following items must be met:

| | |
|---|---|
| Overhead costs: Supervision | $75,000 |
| Income tax | 30,000 |
| | $105,000 |
| Depreciation, per schedule........... | 80,000 |
| Margin for profit and risk........... | 175,000 |
| Total .............................. | $360,000 |

These deductions may now be expressed as a proportion of the total surplus, thus:
Deductions per dollar of surplus

$$\frac{\$180,000 \text{ (Overhead costs and depreciation)}}{\$677,500 \text{ (Surplus)}} = \$0.273$$

$$\frac{\$175,000 \text{ (Margin for risk)}}{\$677,500 \text{ (Surplus)}} = \$0.259$$

$$\text{Total deductions per dollar} = \$0.532$$

Finally, this deduction per dollar may be applied to the operating surplus previously calculated for each species, giving the cost applied to that species to cover overhead, depreciation, and margin for profit and risk. The remainder of the surplus becomes the appraised stumpage value.

| | Birch | Maple | Hemlock |
|---|---|---|---|
| Surplus ........................... | $63.00 per M | $35.00 per M | $12.00 per M |
| Deduction for margin, depreciation, and overhead costs................. | $0.532 per dollar of surplus | | |
| Deduction per M..................... | 33.52 per M | 18.62 per M | 6.38 per M |
| Balance = stumpage value........... | 29.48 per M | 16.38 per M | 5.62 per M |

These values should now be rounded to the nearest ten cents, giving the following final appraisal results: birch, $29.50 per M; maple, $16.40 per M; hemlock, $5.60 per M.

If 6 percent is considered to be a safe rate of business interest, it will be noted that the risk allowance is 9 percent of $1,165,000, or $105,000 annually. This amounts to about $7 per M on the estimated annual cut of 15,000 M bd. ft. A decline of $7 in the estimated selling price or an equivalent increase in direct costs would wipe out this annual risk allowance. But if no fluctuations in unit costs or values of more than $7 per M bd. ft. are expected, and if the capital required for the business is correctly estimated, then the margin of 15 percent is justified.

Under this method of appraisal, negative stumpage values could develop if the total of overhead costs, depreciation, and margin exceeded the estimated gross annual surplus. If this should be the case, the timber tract should not be put up for sale until economic conditions are more favorable or better logging methods produce lower operating costs.

## Damage Appraisal

**LEGAL ASPECTS.** Because all damage cases are potential court cases, the forester who makes a damage appraisal has a more exacting job than that of the ordinary timber or forest land appraiser. Moreover, damage cases inevitably require as much attention to legal technicalities as they do to those of valuation. From the beginning, the damage appraiser must be governed by the thought that he may be called upon to appear in court as an expert witness, testifying for a contending party. He must be ready to answer the questions of opposing attorneys, giving his honest opinion. He is supposedly unbiased, but because of the sequence of questions put to him on the witness stand, or because of the inferences and interpretations drawn from them, his testimony may lead to other than an unbiased opinion.

The appraiser must expect legal arguments to be raised against the validity of his work in an attempt to discredit it. He must be prepared to justify his appraisal before a jury under vigorous cross-examination and in the face of contradicting appraisals and be able to convince the court and jury of the accuracy of his own work. With this in mind, the forester builds his case in the light of the following fundamentals:

1. Does he represent plaintiff or defendant?
2. Was the damage done innocently, or with intent to commit wrong or injury?
3. Was it a natural damage or incidence, such as in the case of a dam breaking and causing damage downstream?
4. What factors are to be considered in determining damage?
5. What rules of evidence will govern the case?
6. How do these rules and the type of case (e.g., tort, trespass, or conversion) affect the type of data which should be collected and the extent to which damages are allowable?
7. What specific damages are involved? What factors may be recognized as affecting them? What methods of determining values are permissible?

Before beginning work it is of the utmost importance that the damage appraiser discuss the case with his client's attorney. He must know in advance the legal fundamentals that will govern the presentation of his findings and conclusions. These aspects of the case may strongly influence the nature of the field data to be collected, the design of data sheets, questionnaires, and other guides to the investigation, the methods of appraisal to be used, and the way in which field data are analyzed and weighed in the preparation of court evidence and testimony.

Some of the more important legal principles which must be recognized in damage appraisals are discussed below, but unless the forester has a thorough background on all legal aspects before he goes to the field, he will be working under a severe handicap.

**Damage.** The term "damage" indicates the loss caused by one person to another, or to his property, either with the design of injuring him, or by negligence and carelessness, or by inevitable accident.

**Damages.** The indemnity recoverable by a person who has sustained an injury through the act or default of another is termed "damages." **Exemplary damages** are those allowed for torts committed with fraud, malice, or the like, as a punishment to the defendant and as a warning to other wrongdoers.

The purpose of damage appraisal is to indemnify the plaintiff by awarding him a sum of money equal to the difference between the value of the whole property before damage and the value of the whole property after damage. The value of the part destroyed does not ordinarily equal the loss to the property as a whole. For example, the destruction of part of a stand lowers the stumpage value of the residual undamaged timber, and this loss must be added to the value of the timber destroyed to arrive at damages to the property as a whole.

The intent in the appraisal is to "make the owner whole" by awarding that amount of damages which will make the claimant as well off with the money, but without the property which was destroyed, as he would have been with his proprty but without the money. The real controversy in evaluating property lies in he definition of the word "value," rather than in the technique of determining it. The appraiser's conclusions must be based on personal knowledge and judgment, ot on theoretical rules.

The appraisal of damages should attempt to measure the value of the property o the owner. This **value to the owner** must be distinguished from **fair market value**, the concept of value ordinarily used in appraising for acquisition or sale. Fair market value uses exchangeability as the test of value. Value to the owner differs from this by considering the particular situation of the owner, not exchangeability, as the basis of value. Value is determined by reference to the conditions of ownership which apply to the case in question.

**Example.** In an area of keen competition for wood between a number of pulp mills, a carelessly started fire has destroyed a block of timber owned by one of the mills. The block had been reserved for cutting 23 years hence and would have supplied the mill with wood for two years. The fire converted the type from pine to ow-grade hardwoods not usable in the mill; it upset the working plan for the area n which the tract lies; it will result either in reduced output from the mill at some uture date or in higher costs for the wood supply necessary to maintain production. The loss in **value to the owner** includes the loss on account of these adverse effects nd may thus far exceed the **fair market value** of the timber destroyed. On the other and, if competition for timberland were not keen and if the tract could readily be eplaced by buying property similar to that destroyed, fair market value might be losely equivalent to value to the owner.

**FUNDAMENTALS OF VALUATION.** The following general fundamentals of valuation apply, but they should be verified locally because laws may differ with the jurisdiction or recent court decisions, or reversals may modify them.

1. Where it is certain that damage has resulted, mere uncertainty as to the amount of the damage does not preclude the right to recovery.
2. Where property can be procured in the market, the measure of damages is the value of the property in the market.
3. Appraisal must be with reference to the most remunerative use for which the property is adapted.
4. Damage must be reasonably certain to occur.
5. Damage must be traceable to the cause in question. Indirect damages are thus allowable.
6. The value of the property is not necessarily the sum of the values of its several component parts.
7. Appraisal of damage may be based on loss of income, provided this is converted to terms of present capital value by discounting.
8. Deferred income is a recognizable basis for value. provided such income is reasonably certain to occur. Such incomes must not include speculative elements which depend on uncertain future factors (e.g., an increase in prices).
9. Allowable damages do not include losses which, although resulting from the cause in question, could have been checked or minimized by the owner.
10. Exemplary damages do not survive; when the wrongdoer dies before an action is brought to trial, only compensatory damages can be recovered.

Two appraisals are needed, one giving the value of the property before damage and the other the value afterward. For either of these, several alternative pproaches may be used. These include market value, replacement cost, reproduction cost less depreciation, present worth of future income, and comparative value. All may be used as sources of evidence to support a given appraisal.

Each approach is applicable to particular classes of property under certain con ditions. The preferable technique is the one which most closely anticipates the reasoning that a potential buyer would use in deciding whether or not to buy Choice of methods may be based on the nature of the plaintiff's claim, the marke available for the property, its location, and other relevant factors. Proper prepa ration of the case requires that appraisal be made by all adaptable methods (even though the appraiser is certain that only one method is sound). Otherwise the appraiser's testimony may not be effective under cross-examination or in rebuttal

**Market Value.** Market value is based on evidence of transactions, similar in time and place, in which similar property was exchanged. The current marke value of property is the amount which a seller, who is willing and able but no compelled to sell, will accept for the property from a purchaser who is willing and able but not compelled to buy.

Where markets exist for property of the kind being appraised, evidence of market value is most useful because of the relative ease of obtaining it and because where active markets exist, market value may closely approximate value to the owner.

Evidence of market value should be provided in the form of statements of the actual prices at which properties have changed hands, along with detailed descriptions of the quantity, quality, location, and other economic characteristics of each of the properties (or kinds of property) involved. The latter type of information is essential to demonstrate comparability of these properties to the one being appraised. If damage occurs on or near a national forest (or other public forest) with similar stands and economic conditions, use of stumpage rates employed on the national forest under similar circumstances may eliminate or reduce controversy as to timber values. Where national forest stumpage values are used, note that they should include the full value of the stumpage. Thus, on sales where separate charges for road construction, stand improvement, planting, slash disposal, or other work have been deducted from the amount paid by the buyer for the timber, the effect of these charges should be recognized in determining the actual stumpage value.

Market value may be applicable to any kind of property for which an actual market exists; hence it may be used in appraising damages to standing timber, land, harvested forest products, structures, equipment, etc. In applying it, however, the distinction between fair market value and value to the owner should be kept in mind.

A concept related to market value and often used where salvage values are involved is that of **immediate cash sale value.** It differs from market value as defined above in that the seller is under pressure to sell within a limited period of time. It may be applicable, for example, to timber which must be sold at once to prevent loss of value due to stain, decay, or insect attack.

**Reproduction Costs.** Reproduction cost may be made the basis of appraisal where market values are inapplicable or do not exist. Such appraisals may have particular weight where good cost records are available, because these remove the element of uncertainty present in other valuation methods. However, it is the present cost of producing property like that destroyed which is relevant, not the historical cost of the destroyed items. This is particularly important during periods of inflation. Thus, a structure which cost $10,000 in 1940 might be appraised for $15,000 in 1950. As the structure has been deteriorating ever since its completion, the apparent increase in value reflects the decline in the value of money relative to the value of labor and materials. In addition, the costs used hould be those of an average operator. Otherwise the efficient operator is penalized and the inefficient one is favored. In the case of buildings or similar structures, depreciation must be deducted from the cost of reproduction. Annual depreciation should be allowed for the expired life of the damaged property. However, as long as a building can be used, its worth will ordinarily be not less than 20 percent of its original cost, and it should not be depreciated below that figure.

The most reliable method of determining reproduction cost is to prepare a bill of materials contained in the structure, estimate the cost of putting them in place, and add these items along with appropriate allowances for the architect's fee, contractor's profit, and interest on investment during the construction period. Other methods involve determining the size and type of construction of the building and multiplying the size by unit-cost factors for that particular type of structure. Such unit-cost factors may relate to costs per lineal foot of outside wall, square feet of building area, cubic content from foundations to eaves or to half the roof height, or to other logical and convenient measures of size. Unit-cost factors can usually be obtained from contractors, mill shops, or architects. They may relate to different types of wall construction, different types of interior or exterior finish, number of stories, etc. Adjustments may be applied to them to allow for electric wiring and fixtures, plumbing, heating, or other special facilities.

Reproduction cost is used most often to appraise damage to plants, buildings, or other structures, and for specialized equipment. Under certain circumstances it may be applicable to immature forest plantations.

**Replacement Cost.** Replacement cost is distinguished from reproduction cost and is the cost that would be incurred by the owner in acquiring an acceptable substitute for the property damaged or destroyed. If replacement is made by buying a substantially identical property, replacement cost becomes indistinguishable from the market value of such property. If replacement is by constructing a new property just like the old one, replacement cost becomes identical with reproduction cost. More often, replacement would involve the substitution of the most advantageous new and modern similar property; for instance, the replacement of an old machine by a new one of equal efficiency. Such a replacement might well have a different cost from that of an identical replacement. Given the acceptability of the substitute, the courts are likely to favor whichever type of replacement is most economical.

The method may be generally applicable to all classes of property, provided the damaged item is replaceable in the market. It is often used in the case of damaged equipment, and might even apply to standing timber if an active market exists for such property.

**Capitalized Prospective Net Income.** Capitalized prospective net income is an applicable basis of valuation in the case of long-lived realty with a stable outlook for costs and returns. It must take account of incomes receivable from the highest and best use of the property, must assume that it is managed with customary ability, and must provide, in the determination of net income, for depreciation allowances sufficient to replace improvements at the end of their useful life. Care must be used to exclude any income not derived from the property itself, such as income derived from a business located on the property or by the owner or occupant as a result of his own industry.

A crucial step in this method is the determination of the rate of capitalization or discount to be used. The current rate of return in the locality, on investments involving comparable risks, is usually applicable.

**The Comparative Method.** The comparative method values the damage by considering previous sales of the same property in the light of contemporaneous sales of similar property. It is likely to be particularly useful in connection with condemnation actions. Sales of the same property are considered only when they are sufficiently near in point of time and made under such circumstances as to have a bearing on present value. Forced sales, sales remote in time and sales prior to substantial physical changes in the property may not be considered. The weight to be given to sales of other property in making the comparison is determined by application of the tests of proximity in time, proximity in location, and similarity of property.

**Straight-line Appreciation.** Straight-line appreciation applies the ordinary business concept of straight-line depreciation to the problem of appraisal. The method is based on the market value of the asset at some future date of maturity, on the total length of time required for the asset to appreciate from zero value to mature value, and on the assumption that this appreciation takes place at an equal annual rate.

**Example:** A stand of jack pine is completely destroyed by fire at age 40. At age 50 it would have reached maturity for pulpwood use and would then have had a volume of 15 cords per acre worth $4 per cord. The value at maturity is thus $60 per acre. This value is assumed to accrue at an equal annual rate over the 50-year period of growth. Hence, with straight-line appreciation, the present value would be

$$\$60 - \frac{10}{50} (\$60) = \$48 \text{ per acre}$$

Because the straight-line pattern of appreciation is approximately valid for only short periods of time, the applicability of this method is limited to stands within a few years of maturity.

**FIELD WORK. Land Survey.** Prerequisite to all other field work is the establishment of the relationship between property boundaries and the damaged area. Unless this is done accurately, the rest of the field work may be worthless. Retrace as much of the land survey as is necessary to establish correct property boundaries. Subdivision may be required.

**Mapping.** Prepare a map showing the damaged area and its location with respect to established corners or landmarks. This is one of the most important parts of the work, as it fixes the location of the damage and the area and extent of the loss which landowners suffered. Use aerial photographs wherever possible, as damage is often confined to certain forest types, diameter classes, densities of stocking, to topography, or to other features which can be readily recognized and mapped by photo interpretation. Photographs taken before the fire or other damage help to determine stand conditions then. Postdamage photographs will show the outline of the damaged area and indicate the extent of damage. Such photographs should be taken after foliage has become discolored but before it has fallen off, even though all of the damage may not have become apparent.

Where mapping is by ground methods, errors of closure should be clearly recorded on field sheets. Adjustment of these errors should be made only on the final map. This map should show detailed forest types for the land in question and for adjacent land, all pertinent culture (including roads, trails, portages, highways and railroads both active and abandoned, buildings, power lines, etc.), natural features (including lakes, streams, rock outcrops, etc.), and any other information which will aid in demonstrating the damage done or which will con-

ribute to a correct understanding of the case (for instance, point of origin of a
ire, wind direction at the time, or topography of mountain country).

**Determining Physical Damages.** Wherever possible, use sample plots with
measured dimensions and take actual measurements of trees or stumps on each
plot. This will minimize personal errors and will be more impressive in court than
mere estimates. Show the location of each sample plot on the map and mark it
in the field. Record data separately for each plot. If measurements or borings
are taken from sample trees, a record should be made of their location. Should
he court decide to visit the area to view contradictory evidence, these records
vill help in giving all possible aid to the court in its attempt to render a just
decision. Make notations on soil, humus, duff, and litter during the progress of
field work, and on the probability of surviving seeds of desirable tree or forage
species. In some cases it may be necessary to examine adjoining stands thoroughly
in order to visualize the original state of the stand, ground cover, and soil condi-
ions in the damaged area.

Damage done to the forest may involve any or all of the following: harvested
forest products; mature timber; immature timber and reproduction; land or soil;
orest floor; wildlife, aesthetic, or recreational features; buildings, bridges, or
other improvements.

Field work must be designed to gather all available information on the following points:

**Harvested forest products.** Volume of logs (or other products) on the damaged area immediately prior to the damage; volume of such products which was
salvaged; volume remaining on the area which is still salvageable; volume destroyed. Each of these volume estimates should be segregated by type of product,
species, size, and quality. In the case of salvaged material, data should be collected
on the names of buyers of salvaged material, the prices paid for it, when and
where the material was bought and received, and the names of witnesses to salvage
transactions.

**Mature timber.** Volume of trees cut or destroyed, classified as to species,
quality, products into which they were made, and their highest potential use. For
stands under management, the rotation, contemplated type of utilization, and related information relevant to valuation must also be noted. In the case of timber
trespass or theft where volume estimates are obtained from a stump cruise, remaining standing timber in the vicinity should be measured to establish correlation between stump diameter and d.b.h., height, form, and extent of defect of the
damaged trees. Stump diameters show the maximum diameter of the utilizable
bole. Utilized length may often be determined from the mark on the ground made
by the butt of the tree as it fell and from the location of the unutilized top. The
latter also shows the top diameter utilized. The number of logs bucked may be
inferred from residual sawdust. (Because falling trees, particularly on steep
slopes, may "jump" from the stump, the distance from the stump itself to the unutilized top is not a reliable measure. Again, tops may be dragged out of their
original position in the course of log removal.)

**Immature timber and reproduction.** Acreage of immature stands and reproduction by type, size class, predamage stand density; percentage of each of these
classes which was destroyed or removed, and the percentages killed, damaged, and
likely to die because of injuries. (Seed trees or large trees scattered through reproduction should be disregarded or appraised separately as merchantable timber.)

**Soil and forest floor.** These are concerned with productive values of the land surface and ignore speculative or mineral values. Soil analyses and studies of profiles must be made for the damaged soil and for a soil which represents undamaged conditions. If applicable yield tables are available, they may be used to measure the effect of soil depreciation on timber productivity. If they are not available, a study must be made of similar forest types on soils similar to the damaged and undamaged conditions. (This phase of the appraisal requires the services of someone fully competent in soil science.)

**Buildings and other improvements.** A complete inventory of mills, shops, camps, warehouses, bridges, culverts, residences, fences, and other improvements is needed, along with an estimate of the damage to each structure. A similar inventory should be prepared covering any tractors, yarders, loaders, trucks, and other items of damaged or destroyed equipment.

**Other values destroyed.** Where aesthetic, wildlife, or other values are destroyed, as complete a description as possible should be obtained of the "before" and "after" conditions of the property in question.

**ECONOMIC DATA.** A complete tabulation of the physical damages, as described above, will indicate the specific items of economic information, such as market price, cost, or other value, which will be required. In connection with market prices, note that actual transactions, not mere offers to buy or sell, have evidential value. All market transactions must be documented with the date, name of buyer and seller, place of delivery, complete description of property sold, and the names of witnesses to the transaction. In the case of sale of standing timber, logs, or other forest products, price data should be segregated by species, type of product sold, and grade or quality. Total volumes involved and terms of sale should also be noted. The search is for data on bona fide sales. Prices which are far out of line from those of similar transactions, or prices which suggest collusion, family relationship, or other biasing influence, should not be used as evidence.

Where cost bases of valuation are involved, cost records should be gathered with similarly detailed breakdown. Remember that it is usually the costs of an operator of average efficiency, not those of the particular property owner, which are relevant. In periods of rapid price change or where costs extend over a long period of time, adjustments for trends in cost may be required. Wherever possible, such adjustments should be based on applicable published price indices, such as those on wage rates, stumpage prices, or building costs. Where valuation is based on present worth of future net incomes, costs and prices are ordinarily projected at present levels. This is justified on the basis that it is a middle ground between increasing and decreasing trends, either one of which may presumably eventuate.

**WITNESSES AND EVIDENCE.** In choosing witnesses the forester should consider:

1. The witness's reputation and record in his home community.
2. His background, experience, and means of livelihood.
3. His apparent knowledge of the factors and values involved in the case at hand.
4. The credibility of his testimony and his ability to express himself.
5. Likelihood that he will omit relevant material or include extraneous matter.
6. Logic of his reasoning in arriving at conclusions.
7. His ability to stand firmly under cross-examination.
8. His interests and motives for testifying.

n the light of these things the forester chooses his witnesses with consideration or the impression that they will make upon the court and the jury.

Obtain the full name of each witness, his address and place of residence, and a lear synopsis of the relevant facts within his knowledge. Whenever possible, btain an affidavit which relates these latter facts. If a potential witness refuses o make a statement, submit a brief summary of the facts of which this person las probable personal knowledge.

The search for evidence must be broad in its scope and may include details vhich may at first seem irrelevant to ascertaining damages, but which, because of heir relation to the cause of the damage, may be very important as aggravating or mitigating factors. Every effort should be made to collect **all** the evidence. The orester cannot know in advance what arguments the opposition will use, what evidence it will present, and hence what evidence will be useful in his own case.

In interviewing potential witnesses and in studying adverse witnesses, points to teep in mind are:

1. All facts which are relevant to the action are admissible in evidence, unless some specific rule forbids.
2. Is there evidence showing motive, or absence of motive, for the commission of the wrong?
3. Have any threats been made against either litigant or against their property?
4. Is there evidence indicating preparation for committing the wrong?
5. Has the defendant made any statement from which, in connection with other facts, his guilt might be inferred?
6. Is there any evidence that evidence has been suppressed or concealed?
7. Has the opposing party or witness made any admission as to a relevant matter that would contradict his testimony and tend to discredit him?
8. Can it be shown that the witness has a pecuniary motive for testifying?

**REPORT.** The final report on the appraisal should include all detailed data and information which has been collected, written up in such a manner as to be intelligible to the client and his attorney. It should include a complete analysis of the data, state clearly all assumptions made, and indicate the methods used in determining values. It should state the appraiser's valuation of the property and his conclusion as to damages, supported by the particular logical argument which was used to arrive at the estimate.

Specifically, the report should include:

1. Description of the tract or property appraised.
2. Date on which the appraisal was made.
3. The **effective** date of appraisal.
4. Map.
5. Area and volume of salable timber damaged, by extent of damage (e.g., killed, partially killed, probably killed, etc.), and by types, diameter classes, original stand densities, species, and kinds of products.
6. Value of each class of damaged material.
7. Prevailing local stumpage values.
8. Physical and valuation data for each of the other types of property damaged, similarly classified.
9. Appraiser's affidavit and signature.
10. Acknowledgment before a notary.

Original field sheets should be filed in a safe place and preserved from mutilation. As the original record of the appraisal, they should not be changed in any way or made the subject of office adjustments. They may be called for in court, or they may be needed for further reference if the client requests a revised report.

## Land and Timber Valuation

**METHOD OF VALUATION.** The method of valuation of an acre of land and timber depends broadly on whether the acre is a part of an all-aged forest in which cuttings are made annually, or whether the forest of which it is a part is operated as an even-aged stand, clearcut periodically at rotation age.

In the case of the all-aged acre, the present capital value is determined by dividing the annual net revenue by a selected interest rate. The formula can be written:

$$V_0 = \frac{AR - AE}{0.0p}$$

where $V_0$ = present capital value
$AR$ = annual revenue
$AE$ = annual expense
$p$ = selected interest rate

This is a forest value (i.e., value of land and timber), rather than a soil value alone. The calculations can be simply and quickly completed without the aid of tables.

In the second case, the value in question is that of bare land on which trees are to be established and carried to maturity before the final crop is harvested. Intermediate net income from thinnings, if any, should be considered in practice, but this item is neglected for simplicity in the following tables, which are designed to give only a first approximation to the present value of the land under the selected conditions. The formula can be written:

$$V_0 = \frac{I_r - PC_2}{(1.0p^r - 1)} - \left( PC_1 + \frac{AC}{0.0p} \right)$$

where $V_0$ = present capital value
$I_r$ = income at end of rotation
$PC$ = planting costs; $PC_1$, first rotation; $PC_2$, succeeding rotations
$p$ = selected interest rate
$r$ = rotation in years
$AC$ = annual carrying charges

For convenience in estimating $V_0$ on this basis, Tables 3 and 4 are presented for the term $(I_r - PC)/(1.0p^r - 1)$ at interest rates of 3, 4, and 5 percent respectively, and for the term $AC/0.0p$ (which represents the capital sum required to support the annual carrying charges) at the same rates of interest. Use of these tables is illustrated in the following:

**Example.** Assume planting costs of $10 per acre, carrying charges of 50 cents per year, timber to be sold at the end of a 60-year rotation for $410. Using 4 percent interest, what is the present value of one acre? From Table 3 we find the value at 4 percent $I_r - PC = $400 and rotation 60 years to be $42.02. From Table 4 we find that $12.50 is required at 4 percent to provide for annual carrying charges of 50 cents. This $12.50 plus the planting costs of $10.00, or $22.50, is deducted from the $42.02 to give the present value per acre, $19.52. Table data may be interpolated for intermediate incomes, carrying charges, and interest rates.

**FOREST LAND VALUE SCHEDULES.** The valuation of forest land for sale or acquisition is based on the appraiser's analysis and judgment of the fair market value of the property. (See the previous discussion of fair market value.) Where property values are high, detailed and careful appraisal of each individual tract is in order. However, where the value of each property is small and where the number of properties to be valued is large, the effort of making a

**Table 3.** Value of $(I_r - PC)/(1.0p^r - 1)$ for Selected Rotation Periods, Interest Rates, and Final Incomes Minus Succeeding Planting Costs

| Rotation (Years) | Final income minus succeeding planting costs (dollars) | | | | | | | | |
|---|---|---|---|---|---|---|---|---|---|
| | 100 | 200 | 300 | 400 | 500 | 600 | 700 | 800 | 900 |
| A. Present value (dollars)—Interest rate 3 percent | | | | | | | | | |
| 20 | 124.05 | 248.11 | 372.16 | 496.22 | 620.27 | 744.32 | 868.38 | 992.43 | 1,116.49 |
| 30 | 70.06 | 140.12 | 210.19 | 280.25 | 350.31 | 420.37 | 490.44 | 560.50 | 630.56 |
| 40 | 44.21 | 88.42 | 132.63 | 176.83 | 221.04 | 265.25 | 309.46 | 353.67 | 397.88 |
| 50 | 29.55 | 59.10 | 88.66 | 118.21 | 147.76 | 177.31 | 206.86 | 236.41 | 265.97 |
| 60 | 20.44 | 40.89 | 61.33 | 81.77 | 102.22 | 122.66 | 143.10 | 163.55 | 183.99 |
| 70 | 14.46 | 28.91 | 43.37 | 57.82 | 72.28 | 86.73 | 101.19 | 115.64 | 130.10 |
| 80 | 10.37 | 20.74 | 31.12 | 41.49 | 51.86 | 62.23 | 72.61 | 82.98 | 93.35 |
| 90 | 7.52 | 15.04 | 22.56 | 30.07 | 37.59 | 45.11 | 52.63 | 60.15 | 67.67 |
| 100 | 5.49 | 10.98 | 16.47 | 21.96 | 27.44 | 32.93 | 38.42 | 43.91 | 49.40 |
| B. Present value (dollars)—Interest rate 4 percent | | | | | | | | | |
| 20 | 83.96 | 167.91 | 251.87 | 335.82 | 419.78 | 503.74 | 587.69 | 671.65 | 755.60 |
| 30 | 44.58 | 89.15 | 133.73 | 178.30 | 222.88 | 267.45 | 312.03 | 356.60 | 401.18 |
| 40 | 26.31 | 52.62 | 78.93 | 105.24 | 131.54 | 157.85 | 184.16 | 210.47 | 236.78 |
| 50 | 16.38 | 32.75 | 49.13 | 65.50 | 81.88 | 98.25 | 114.63 | 131.00 | 147.38 |
| 60 | 10.50 | 21.01 | 31.51 | 42.02 | 52.52 | 63.03 | 73.53 | 84.04 | 94.54 |
| 70 | 6.86 | 13.73 | 20.59 | 27.45 | 34.31 | 41.18 | 48.04 | 54.90 | 61.76 |
| 80 | 4.54 | 9.07 | 13.61 | 18.14 | 22.68 | 27.21 | 31.75 | 36.28 | 40.82 |
| 90 | 3.02 | 6.04 | 9.06 | 12.08 | 15.10 | 18.12 | 21.14 | 24.16 | 27.17 |
| 100 | 2.02 | 4.04 | 6.06 | 8.08 | 10.10 | 12.12 | 14.14 | 16.16 | 18.18 |
| C. Present value (dollars)—Interest rate 5 percent | | | | | | | | | |
| 20 | 60.49 | 120.97 | 181.46 | 241.94 | 302.43 | 362.91 | 423.40 | 483.88 | 544.37 |
| 30 | 30.10 | 60.21 | 90.31 | 120.41 | 150.52 | 180.62 | 210.72 | 240.83 | 270.93 |
| 40 | 16.56 | 33.11 | 49.67 | 66.23 | 82.78 | 99.34 | 115.89 | 132.45 | 149.01 |
| 50 | 9.55 | 19.11 | 28.66 | 38.21 | 47.77 | 57.32 | 66.87 | 76.43 | 85.98 |
| 60 | 5.66 | 11.31 | 16.97 | 22.63 | 28.28 | 33.94 | 39.59 | 45.25 | 50.91 |
| 70 | 3.40 | 6.80 | 10.19 | 13.59 | 16.99 | 20.39 | 23.79 | 27.19 | 30.58 |
| 80 | 2.06 | 4.12 | 6.18 | 8.24 | 10.30 | 12.36 | 14.41 | 16.47 | 18.53 |
| 90 | 1.25 | 2.51 | 3.76 | 5.02 | 6.27 | 7.53 | 8.78 | 10.03 | 11.29 |
| 100 | .77 | 1.53 | 2.30 | 3.07 | 3.83 | 4.60 | 5.36 | 6.13 | 6.90 |

**Table 4.** Value of $AC/0.0p$, or Capital Sum Required to Support Selected Annual Carrying Charges at Selected Rates of Interest

| Rate of interest | Annual carrying charges (dollars) | | | | | | | | |
|---|---|---|---|---|---|---|---|---|---|
| | 0.10 | 0.20 | 0.30 | 0.40 | 0.50 | 0.60 | 0.70 | 0.80 | 0.90 |
| Capital sum required (dollars) | | | | | | | | | |
| 3% | 3.33 | 6.67 | 10.00 | 13.33 | 16.67 | 20.00 | 23.33 | 26.67 | 30.00 |
| 4% | 2.50 | 5.00 | 7.50 | 10.00 | 12.50 | 15.00 | 17.50 | 20.00 | 22.50 |
| 5% | 2.00 | 4.00 | 6.00 | 8.00 | 10.00 | 12.00 | 14.00 | 16.00 | 18.00 |

detailed appraisal of each tract may not be justified. In such cases forest land value schedules may be developed as guides to judgment.

To be useful, such schedules must reflect closely the particular conditions of the forest land market in the local area at the particular time at which they are used. As forest land values vary widely from region to region and have changed markedly from time to time during recent years, it is not possible to present usable standard schedules. But the forester who has a considerable volume of land appraisal business may find it worth while to prepare such schedules for his own use, using the following model as a guide.

Land value schedules should be constructed from a background of experience in the sale or purchase of similar lands, or on the basis of examination of a substantial number of actual transactions. Where this is not possible, as in the case of an area where the market for forest land has been dormant for a long time, preliminary schedules may be constructed by careful analysis of the factors affecting land value. Such schedules must then be carefully tested against a selected array of cases. If such case properties actually sell at or near the schedule values, the schedules may be applied with confidence.

The schedules should recognize all factors which will, in fact, influence buyers or sellers of forest land in pricing property. Depending on local conditions, these factors might include (1) site quality; (2) species of timber present; (3) size, age, and density of stocking of the stand; (4) slope, roughness, or other ground characteristics; (5) accessibility to market; (6) size and shape of tract; (7) extent of commercial values other than timber; (8) ease of obtaining additional stocking; and other factors. The following hypothetical forest land value schedule illustrates how a variety of such factors may be recognized.

### HYPOTHETICAL FOREST LAND VALUE SCHEDULE

(Both factors included and values assigned must be adapted, in the light of experience, to the area to which the schedule is to apply.)

A. Forest Soil and Young Growth Values per Acre.

| Site * | Stocking † | Trees 10″–up d.b.h. | Poles 4″–10″ d.b.h. | Saplings 10′ hgt. to 4″ d.b.h. | Seedlings 0–10′ hgt. | Unstocked | | |
|---|---|---|---|---|---|---|---|---|
| | | | | | | Natural regeneration expected | Easy to plant | Hard to plant |
| A | Well stocked | $7.00 | $5.00 | $3.00 | $2.00 | ... | ... | ... |
| | Poorly stocked | 5.00 | 3.20 | 2.50 | 1.70 | $1.50 | $1.00 | $.70 |
| B | Well stocked | 6.00 | 4.20 | 2.50 | 1.70 | ... | ... | ... |
| | Poorly stocked | 4.00 | 2.50 | 2.00 | 1.50 | 1.30 | .90 | .60 |
| C | Well stocked | 5.00 | 3.50 | 2.00 | 1.50 | ... | ... | ... |
| | Poorly stocked | 3.00 | 2.00 | 1.50 | 1.20 | 1.10 | .80 | .50 |
| D | Well stocked | 4.00 | 2.50 | 1.50 | 1.20 | ... | ... | ... |
| | Poorly stocked | 2.00 | 1.50 | 1.20 | 1.00 | .90 | .70 | .40 |

* Site is classified for the purpose of this schedule as follows:

| | Site A | Site B | Site C | Site D |
|---|---|---|---|---|
| Total height of dominants at age 50 .................... | 80+ | 65+ | 50+ | 40+ |
| Surface .................... | Not over 20% rock | Not over 35% rock | Not over 60% rock | |
| Slope .................... | Not over 25% | Not over 45% | Not over 75% | |
| Brush .................... | Not more than 20% of the area | Not over 40% | Not over 60% | |

† "Well stocked" is 70 percent of complete crown coverage or better and "Poorly stocked" at least 30 percent. (Stocking might well be specified as a minimum number of stems per acre.)

B. Supplementary Valuation Data

Unproductive types, barren and water: $0.25 per acre

Provide for relative accessibility by deduction from the average per acre value found from the schedule. Compute the accessibility deduction by multiplying the number of miles of road by the appropriate percentage figure from the table below, and by one of the following factors:

| | |
|---|---|
| Paved road ................... | $1.00 |
| Graded earth road............ | 1.50 |
| Poor earth road ............. | 2.00 |

| Miles from market ............. | 0–3 | 3–6 | 6–10 | 10–15 | 15–20 | 20 up |
|---|---|---|---|---|---|---|
| Deduction (percent per mile)..... | 0 | 2% | 4% | 6% | 9% | 12% |

**Example.** A tract of 100 acres of cut-over land on Site A consists of the following:

> 20% well stocked with trees 10″ and up
> 25% poorly stocked with poles
> 30% well stocked with seedlings
> 25% unstocked but easy to plant
> 
> 100%

A market for the timber is reached over 11 mi. of graded earth road plus 5 mi. of paved highway.

Using the valuation schedule above and ignoring accessibility for the moment, we have:

$$0.20(\$7.00) + 0.25(\$3.20) + 0.30(\$2.00) + 0.25(\$1.00) \qquad = \$3.05/\text{acre}$$

To adjust for accessibility, we deduct:

| | | |
|---|---|---|
| For 5 mi. of paved road, $1.00 × 5 × 2% | = | $0.10 |
| For 11 mi. of graded dirt road, $1.50 × 11 × 6% = | | .99 |
| Total deduction for accessibility | | 1.09 |
| Average land value per acre = $3.05 − $1.09 | | = $1.96/acre |

# Basic Cost and Return Records for Use in Timber-Growing Operations

**RECORDS.** Records which are sufficient for income, payroll, and other tax purposes must be maintained by all enterprises to which such tax laws apply. In addition to meeting legal requirements, records of timber-growing operations developed according to sound forestry and accounting principles are often invaluable to inform and guide forest managers and owners. Be sure, on the other hand, that every record justifies the time consumed in keeping it; if experience shows that it is not filling a real need, drop it.

**GENERAL PRINCIPLES AND DEFINITIONS.** The following concepts and principles governing the treatment of the several kinds of cost must be clearly understood and applied in developing the record system.

**Original Cost of Timberlands.** Expenditures which must be capitalized as part of the original cost of the forest property include the consideration to the seller, unpaid taxes or assessments assumed by the buyer, commissions, attorney fees for examining the title, preparing abstracts and handling the purchase, costs of surveying and marking boundary lines, and the costs of an initial timber estimate to determine the amount of timber purchased. Where the consideration covered purchase of both timberland and other forms of property, the total original cost must be apportioned on some reasonable basis to land, timber, and plant and equipment.

**Subsequent Improvements.** Expenditures for subsequent improvements to timberland properties such as roads, drainage systems, clearing the land, and reforestation must be capitalized.

**Carrying Charges.** Expenditures for taxes, fire protection, property maintenance, and similar recurring expenses are carrying charges. They should be capitalized while the property is being developed to income-producing status. Capitalization is permitted for income tax purposes if the taxpayer so elects. However, during its development period, he may elect instead to deduct carrying charges on timberland property from income derived from other sources. His election, once made, is binding for future years on the same property until income-producing status is reached. After the timberlands reach income-producing status, carrying charges are treated as operating expenses.

**Depletion.** The cost of timber cut is recovered through a charge called depletion. For each separate timber account, the annual depletion charge is determined by multiplying the number of units of timber felled during the year by the appropriate depletion rate. Depletion occurs at the moment the timber is cut, but if it is not practicable to measure the volume of timber at that time, the depletion charge may be figured on the basis of the earliest possible subsequent volume determination, such as a log scale report at the loading point or mill. Depletion may be recorded on a monthly basis instead of annually.

The depletion rate per unit of timber is determined as follows: Divide (1) the cost (or other allowable basis of valuation) of the timber at the beginning of the year, plus the cost of additional timber acquired, plus other proper additions to capital (original cost and subsequent improvements), by (2) the number of units of merchantable timber on hand at the beginning of the year, plus the number of units acquired, plus (or minus) the adjustment required to correct the number of units of merchantable timber shown as remaining in the account to the best estimate of the volume of timber actually available. Such adjustments should be applied periodically to reflect growth, loss through insect, fire, or other damage, and changing standards of merchantability. The depletion rate obtained from this computation is such that the total depletion obtained by applying the calculated rate to all of the then remaining merchantable timber would equal the remaining cost (or other allowable basis of the valuation) of timber, as shown in the account.

**Depreciation.** The cost of plant and equipment is recovered through a charge called depreciation. Total cost less expected net salvage value may be divided by (1) expected useful life of the item or (2) by economic life of the timber stand, whichever is shorter, or (3) by units of timber in the stand. Methods (1) and (2) give total depreciation for the period; method (3) gives a rate which is multiplied by the number of units of timber cut to determine the periodic depreciation.

**BASIC RECORDS.** A suitably designed system of double-entry bookkeeping showing individual earnings, the financial results of the business, and related records will be sufficient to meet the various tax requirements. A certain amount of information (such as time worked by hourly employees) must be obtained from operating personnel in order to keep these minimum records. From the operating personnel additional information may be obtained in basic reports which, when analyzed according to cost-accounting principles, will not only make possible prompter and better informed control over current operations but will also provide data essential to the long-term financial planning which timber growing involves. All of the basic records described below (except possibly "activity reports") should be kept as part of a minimum system. The amount of detailed information kept in each record will depend on the use to be made of it. In the descriptions which follow, minimum requirements for each basic record are first outlined; then additional data are suggested which should prove useful if further accounting analysis is contemplated.

**Labor Records.** Timber growers employing labor must generally withhold federal income taxes from wages paid. Depending upon the circumstances, they may be subject also to taxes based on payrolls under various social security and unemployment compensation insurance laws.

A **time record** must be kept of the hours worked by each employee each day. This is approved by the supervisor, then used in preparing payroll summary sheets. The employee may be asked to sign the time record when receiving his pay.

The **payroll summary sheet** shows for each employee the hours worked, rate of pay, gross pay, deductions, and net pay. When properly approved, it becomes the authority for preparing individual checks or pay envelopes and for posting details of earnings and deductions to each employee's individual earnings record.

An **individual earnings record** is kept for each employee to show the hours worked, rates of pay, gross pay, deductions, and net pay. From this information, quarterly tax returns are made for federal social security and state unemployment compensation insurance tax purposes; annual returns are made for federal unemployment compensation insurance and income tax withholding purposes; and annual statements of wages paid and income tax withheld are prepared for individual employees.

For cost analysis purposes, an **individual weekly labor report** or **time record** might be prepared for each employee. This shows the type of work performed and the place of work, in addition to the number of hours. Payroll summary sheets might then be expanded to analyze labor costs by operations and locations, or the individual weekly time records might be analyzed statistically for this purpose.

**Equipment Records.** A separate account in an **equipment subsidiary ledger** should be maintained for each item of equipment capitalized. This should show original cost and accumulated depreciation. It is used to support annual tax returns and to determine capital gain or loss at the time of disposition of the asset.

Where individual operating costs are desired, **weekly cost and use records** might be kept for each item of equipment. Each such sheet will show miles or hours run, nature and location of work performed, and operating costs in detail. **Delivery tickets** or other memoranda supporting costs should be attached. With this information, actual costs per mile or hour of equipment use can be determined for each period and used in allocating costs to operations and locations, in the accounts or statistically. **Standard costs** per mile or hour might be developed and compared with actual costs for control purposes.

**Records of Other Expenses.** Appropriate ledger accounts should be set up to classify other expenses (e.g., rent, general property taxes, etc.) in sufficient detail for financial statement (and income tax) purposes. Persons approving invoices for payment should indicate the accounts to be charged. This information, coded on a copy of the check paying the invoice, is posted to the indicated ledger account, usually after entry in a **cash disbursement journal.**

If cost analyses are recorded in the accounts, **working unit accounts** and other cost center accounts are provided (see "Cost Accounting," below, for a detailed description of these accounts). Invoices are coded to these detailed accounts. Postings to the cost center accounts may be made from recapitulations of cash disbursements journal columns or from individual check copies, with control over totals established through the cash disbursements journal.

**Inventory Records.** Materials and supplies purchased in quantity and stored until used should be charged to **inventory accounts.** Physical inventories must be taken periodically in order to determine the amounts which have been used.

For better control over inventories, **perpetual inventory records** might be maintained in the accounts. **Weekly inventory reports** might be prepared by the custodians of the inventories, showing opening balance, amounts received and issued, and closing balance. If detailed cost records are maintained, the weekly inventory report would indicate in detail the use made of all the items which have been issued.

**Timber Tract Records.** The cost of timberland properties may be carried in only three accounts, **Land, Timber,** and **Plant and Equipment,** with capitalized expenditures charged to the appropriate account as incurred. It has been suggested above that each item of equipment be carried in a separate account in a subsidiary ledger, controlled by one account in the general ledger. The same procedure is recommended for the individual timber tracts, with the cost of each apportioned reasonably between land and timber. Other possibilities include carrying each individual purchase in a separate account (properly subdivided), combining several purchases in the same area into one block, or carrying timber cost by species or according to forest products, such as pulpwood, poles, and saw timber.

**Cutting Records.** Detailed records should be maintained to show for each timber account the volume of timber cut and the income from or use made of the timber. The volume of timber cut must be known in order to determine the depletion charge, while the detailed income records help keep management informed on the profitability of the timber-growing operations.

**Timber Estimates.** An accurate timber estimate as of the time of acquisition should be prepared for each timber tract. This estimate should be used as a guide in apportioning total cost to land, timber, and plant and equipment, for setting the initial depletion rate, and for various timber-management purposes. Subsequent estimates should be made periodically and used, in part, as a basis for revising depletion rates.

**Activity Reports.** For management information and control purposes, each supervisor should submit a weekly activity report setting forth the work accomplished by the labor and equipment under his direction, measured in terms of acres, miles, volume of timber, or other appropriate work unit.

For cost analysis purposes, these reports might show the location of the work performed. Total costs are then divided by units of work accomplished to determine actual cost per unit of work. Actual costs may be compared with engineered standard costs or with past performance, and variations called to the attention of management for investigation.

**USE OF BASIC RECORDS. Records to Suit Needs of Owners.** Even the smallest timber-growing operation must have basic records for tax purposes.

From properly kept simple records, financial statements may be prepared to show the financial position and operating results of the business. They may also be used for management information, in obtaining credit, and in many other ways.

Refinements, some of which have already been suggested, can make these basic records extremely valuable for management purposes through control features which may help to insure efficient operations according to plans and through cost analyses which may help to guide forestry programs along the most profitable lines. Only a few broad suggestions can be added here. Competent foresters and accountants cooperating with one another can develop and interpret such records to any extent desired by progressive timber growers.

**Budgetary Control.** Modern principles of budgetary control over sales, expenses, and operations may be applied to timber-growing enterprises. This involves a cutting program designed by competent foresters to assure good forest management, and a protection, maintenance, and development program designed to fit the needs of the timberlands within the limits of available resources. Actual results, shown by the basic records, are compared with budgeted standards to inform management of variances requiring attention.

**Cost Accounting.** The principles of cost accounting, including standard costs, may be applied to timber-growing operations. Timberlands are divided into working units of convenient size, with natural or other well-defined boundaries. Timber estimates, cutting records, and management planning are based on these working units, which in the accounting records are set up as the cost centers to which all expenditures are charged or ultimately distributed. Additional cost centers used in assembling the data include administrative offices, field headquarters, repair shops, company houses, and railroads, among others. Labor, equipment operation costs, material and supplies, taxes, and other expenditures are charged currently to the appropriate cost centers. At the end of the year (or oftener) all of the costs charged to the other cost centers are distributed on suitable bases to the working units, to which all costs are thus ultimately charged. This may be done in the regular accounting records. On the other hand, part or all of this cost analysis may be handled statistically, apart from but controlled by the regular accounting records.

**Comparative Valuation Analysis.** This method of economic analysis and planning can be readily developed from the records already suggested. For each working unit, estimates are made of the present timber stand and of rates of growth and volumes of possible cuts under various programs of forest management. Corresponding estimates are prepared of the costs of carrying out each prospective management program. Future incomes and projected costs are reduced by compound interest and discount calculations to their present value. Through such studies, expected financial results of the various silviculturally possible forest management programs may be considered by the timber grower at the start of operations, as one important factor governing his choice among these programs.

Long-term forecasting of income and expenses cannot be expected to yield accurate absolute dollar results. But, assuming that timber prices and costs of growing timber will change in the same direction and in somewhat similar proportions, comparative valuations of various management programs may prove reasonably reliable. These possibilities are open to the timber grower who has adequate records competently interpreted.

## SAMPLE TIMBER SALE AGREEMENT.

.................. ...................., of ...................., ...............,
    (I or we)        (Name of purchaser)        (Post office)        (State)
hereinafter called the purchaser, agree to purchase from .............. of ..........,
                                                        (Seller's name)    (Post office)
........, hereinafter called the seller, the designated trees from the area described
  (State)
below.

I. Description of Sale Area:

(Describe by legal subdivisions, if surveyed, and approximate, if not)

..........................................................................

..........................................................................

II. Trees designated for cutting: (Cross out A or B—use only one clause)

A. All .......... trees marked by the seller, or his agent, with paint spots
         (Species)
below stump height; also dead trees of the same species which are merchantable for
.......................
  (Kind of forest products)

B. All .......... trees merchantable for ...................... which
         (Species)                              (Kind of forest products)
measure ......... inches or more outside the bark at this point not less than 6 inches
above the ground; also other .......... trees marked with paint spots below stump
                               (Species)
height by the seller or his agent.

III. Conditions of Sale:

A. The purchaser agrees to the following:

1. To pay the seller the sum of $...... for the above-described trees and
to make payments in advance of cutting in amounts of at least $...... each.

2. To waive all claim to the above-described trees unless they are cut and
removed on or before .................
                         (Date)

3. To do all in his power to prevent and suppress forest fires on or
threatening the Sale Area.

4. To protect from unnecessary injury young growth and other trees not
designated for cutting.

5. To pay the seller for undesignated trees cut or injured through carelessness at the rate of $...... each for trees measuring 10 to ...... inches in diameter
at stump height and $...... each for trees...... inches or over in diameter.

6. To repair damage caused by logging to ditches, fences, bridges, roads,
trails or other improvements damaged beyond ordinary wear and tear.

7. To carry Public Liability Insurance with minimum limits of $......
and $......; Property Damage Insurance with minimum limits of $......; and
Workmen's Compensation Insurance. These insurance policies are to remain in effect
at all times until the completion of the logging, and the seller may require proper
evidence covering the force of these insurance policies.

8. Not to assign this agreement in whole or in part without the written
consent of the seller.

B. The seller agrees to the following:

1. To guarantee title to the forest products covered by this agreement
and to defend it against all claims at his expense.

2. To allow the purchaser to use unmerchantable material from tops of trees cut or from trees of ............ species for necessary logging improvement free of charge, provided such improvements are left in place by the purchaser.

3. To grant the freedom of entry and right-of-way to the purchaser and his employees on and across the area covered by this agreement and also other privileges usually extended to purchasers of stumpage which are not specifically covered, provided they do not conflict with specific provisions of this agreement.

C. The Seller will not be responsible, and the Purchaser hereby releases and quit-claims to said Seller of and from all liability in the case of theft of timber, either standing or cut, in the Sale Area during the operation of this agreement.

D. In case of dispute over the terms of this agreement we agree to accept the decision of an arbitration board of three selected persons as final. Each of the contracting parties will select one person and the two selected will select a third to form this board.

Signed in duplicate this ............ day of .................... 19....

.......................................  .....................................................
    (Witness)             (Purchaser)

.......................................
    (Witness)

         .........................................................
                (Seller)

.......................................
    (Witness)

.......................................
    (Witness)

## Forest Taxation

**FOREST TAX LAWS IN THE UNITED STATES.** In an effort to provide equitable forms of taxation for forest land a variety of forest tax laws have been adopted by the several states as substitutes for the general property tax on standing timber. The types now in use include:

**Yield Tax.** In lieu of the general property tax on timber, a yield tax is paid at the time timber is cut. The amount of the tax is established as a fixed percentage of the stumpage value of the timber cut.

**Deferred Timber Tax.** Beginning with the first year following classification, the tax currently payable is the amount levied under the general property tax, diminished by $7\frac{1}{2}$ percent the first year and by an additional $7\frac{1}{2}$ percent each successive year through the tenth. Thereafter the tax currently payable remains at 25 percent of the levy. The accumulated deferred tax levies are payable when the timber is cut. Interest at 3 percent is payable annually on the amount of the accumulated deferred tax.

**Differential Tax.** Timber is assessed in the same way as other forms of property but is taxed at a fraction of the current general property tax rate. The differential rate is prescribed by law.

**Fixed Assessment.** Annual taxes are computed by applying the current general property tax rate to a fixed assessed value of timber which is prescribed by law.

**Tax Exemption.** Classified timber is exempt from taxation.

### Table 5. Forest Tax Laws in the United States [a]

| State | Type of tax | Year of enactment | Acreage classified exempt or receiving bounty payments in 1945 [b] | Percentage of forest area classified | Rate of tax on timber |
|---|---|---|---|---|---|
| Alabama | Yield | 1923 | 45,069 | 0.25 | 8% |
| California | Exemption | 1926 | ... | ... | ... |
| Colorado | Exemption | 1911 | ... | ... | ... |
| Connecticut | Yield | 1913 | 3,665 | .21 | 2–10% |
| Connecticut | Exemption | 1929 | 16,918 | .97 | ... |
| Delaware | Exemption | 1931 | 5 | ... | ... |
| Idaho | Yield | 1929 | 253,000 | 9.07 | 12½% |
| Idaho | Exemption | 1937 | ... | ... | ... |
| Indiana | Fixed assessment | 1921 | 121,446 | 3.82 | c |
| Iowa | Fixed assessment | 1906 | 59,406 | 2.71 | d |
| Kansas | Exemption | 1941 | ... | ... | ... |
| Louisiana | Yield | 1910 | 713,155 | 4.71 | 6% |
| Maine | Exemption | 1872 | ... | ... | ... |
| Massachusetts | Yield | 1914 | ... | ... | 1–6% |
| Michigan | Yield (woodlot) | 1911 | 2,337 | .02 | 5% |
| Michigan | Yield (commercial) | 1925 | 99,036 | .89 | 2–10% |
| Minnesota | Yield | 1927 | 42,223 | .61 | 10% |
| Mississippi | Yield (nonoptional) | 1940 | ... | ... | Variable |
| Missouri | Yield | 1946 | ... | ... | 4–6% |
| New Hampshire | Yield | 1949 | ... | ... | 10–7% |
| New Jersey | Exemption | 1943 | ... | ... | ... |
| New York | Yield | 1912 | 13,563 | .13 | 6% |
| North Carolina | Exemption | 1939 | ... | ... | ... |
| Ohio | Differential rate | 1925 | 57,660 | 1.25 | ½ local rate |
| Oregon | Yield | 1929 | 826,043 [e] | 8.28 | 12½% |
| Rhode Island | Exemption | 1878 | 200 | .05 | ... |
| Washington | Yield | 1931 | 400,136 | 4.09 | 1–12½% |
| Washington | Deferred timber | 1941 | ... | ... | 50–25% |
| Wisconsin | Yield | 1927 | 153,192 | 1.39 | 10% |
| Wisconsin | Exemption | 1935 | 46,981 | .43 | ... |

[a] Source: U. S. Forest Service. Does not include severance taxes, which are privilege taxes imposed in addition to regular property or yield taxes, in the states of Alabama, Arkansas, Louisiana, New Mexico, Oregon, and Virginia.
[b] Compiled from data supplied by state foresters and state tax commissions.
[c] The general property tax rate applies to a fixed assessment of $1 per acre on land and trees.
[d] The general property tax rate applies to a fixed assessment of $4 per acre on land and trees.
[e] Total area classified 1,001,043 acres, of which 175,000 is estimated to be in county ownership.

## INCOME TAX REPORTING BY NONINDUSTRIAL OWNERS.

Because taxation of income is a complex subject, this discussion must be limited to some of the most significant provisions of the federal Internal Revenue Code and Regulations. Records which are complete enough for federal income tax purposes will generally contain the data needed for the various state income tax returns.

Assistance in preparing federal returns may be obtained without charge from employees of the Bureau of Internal Revenue. State employees often furnish similar aid for state returns. However, if income from timber or timberlands is material in amount, the taxpayer should consult some competent accountant or attorney to determine the minimum amount of tax due and to present the required data in the proper form for the tax collector.

**Income Taxes on Receipts from Timber Cutting.** Income from timber cutting may be taxed as ordinary income at full rates, or at reduced rates as a capital gain under the special provisions outlined below. In either case, to determine the amount of taxable income, the gross income from timber cutting is reduced by the amount of allowable **depletion,** depreciation, and trade and business deductions, which in general include all expenses necessary to carry on the operation. (By depletion is meant the cost or value claimed for the timber at the time of acquisition.) Records to develop the income and cost data required by Form T— Timber of the U. S. Bureau of Internal Revenue are described, and principles governing their design and use are discussed, under "Basic Cost and Return Records for Use in Timber-Growing Operations," page **15 · 37**.

**Timber as a capital asset.** Standing timber sold by one not in the lumber or timber business has long been considered a capital asset. The federal Internal Revenue Code of 1954 [Sec. 631] also permits an owner to elect to treat as a capital asset timber cut by him and sold as logs, or cut and used by him in further manufacturing, provided he owned the timber, or had held a contract right to cut it, for more than 6 months prior to his taxable year.

The federal Internal Revenue Code provides for special tax treatment of gains and losses from sales or exchanges of capital assets. Long-term capital gains or losses (assets held more than 6 months) are divided in half before being taxed, and the tax is further limited to a maximum of 25 percent of a long-term capital gain.

Certain capital assets are given even more favored tax treatment in that a net long-term loss is deductible in full without limitation.

The capital gain or loss under Sec. 631 is determined by deducting the allowable depletion from the fair market value of the timber at the beginning of the taxable year. The fair market value must be established by the taxpayer to the satisfaction of the Commissioner of Internal Revenue. (Where stumpage is sold outright at a fixed price per M bd. ft. or other unit, this value is identical with the stumpage price.) This fair market value is also considered as the cost of the timber in determining gain or loss on logs sold, or on further manufacturing operations. Such gains are taxable as ordinary income rather than as capital gains.

**Example.** An owner who qualifies under Sec. 631 sold and delivered to the buyer's mill 5 M bd. ft. of saw logs for $250. The owner establishes the fair market value of the standing timber at $25 per M and the allowable depletion at $7 per M. The actual costs of felling, bucking, and delivering the logs total $75. Then:

Fair market value of timber = 5 ($25/M)  = $125
Allowable depletion = 5 ($7/M)  = 35
___
Income taxable as capital gain at rates of Sec. 631  = $ 90

and:

Gross revenue  = $250
Less: Fair market value of timber  = $125
Costs of felling, bucking, and delivery  = 75
___
200
Income taxable at full rates  = $ 50

In contrast, if the owner did not qualify under Sec. 631, the following determination would apply:

| Gross revenue | | = | **$250** |
| Less: Allowable depletion | = | $ 35 | |
| Costs of felling, bucking, and delivery | = | 75 | |
| | | | 110 |
| Income taxable at full rates | | = | **$140** |

Determination of stumpage values at the time a property was acquired is easiest in localities where comparable timber is commonly sold, and current prices per M bd. ft. or other unit are of record. Local lumber companies or timber operators are often willing to furnish this information. If the property was inherited, stumpage values established at the time for inheritance tax purposes must of course be used.

**Income Taxes on Receipts from Sale of Stumpage.** A farmer or other landowner who makes an outright sale of stumpage which he has owned for more than 6 months may report the net income as capital gain, and pay only half as much federal income tax as on ordinary income. Assuming that the standing timber is part of a property consisting of woodland, farmland, improvements, etc., and was not separately valued at the time of acquisition, tax procedure is usually as follows:

1. Appraise the improvements and land other than woodland on the basis of actual sales of comparable units, of record at the time of the acquisition and in the same general locality. **Do not use** current replacement value of improvements.
2. Subtract the totals of Par. 1 from the over-all price or appraised value of the property. The remainder is the value of the woodland—land and timber.
3. Assign a nominal value to the land under the timber—as little as $5 or $10 an acre, even when cleared land is selling at $200–$300 an acre. (The cost of clearing, stump removal, drainage, etc., necessary to convert this to farmland is very high.) Subtract from the value of the woodland, Par. 2. The remainder is the value of the standing timber.
4. Assume that the volume of the timber—in whatever units, such as board feet or cords, it is now salable—was the same at the time of acquisition as it was just before the current sale.
5. Divide this volume into the sum arrived at in Par. 3 to obtain a stumpage value per unit at the time of acquisition. This is the "depletion rate" of the standard tax instructions.
6. If possible, check the value arrived at in Par. 5 against actual sales of neighboring timber at the time the property was acquired.
7. From the stumpage price per unit actually received during the tax year for timber sold from the woodland, subtract the depletion value, Par. 5. The difference is capital gain per unit.
8. Multiply the volume of timber removed during the tax year by the unit figure, Par. 7. The result is total capital gain. (A loss on timber is of course possible; it is deductible in full, without the limitation imposed on loss of many other kinds of capital.)
9. Where cutting is not clear, but is spread over a number of years, continue to claim depletion at the rate set in Par. 5 until the total volume at the time of acquisition (Par. 4) has been cut. Subsequently, no depletion may be claimed by the present owner for timber volume materializing through growth or as a result of improved standards of utilization.

"The Treatment of Income from Farm Woodlands Under the Revenue Act of 1943," which applies in part to other types of ownership, is obtainable from the U. S. Forest Service. It clarifies many aspects of a complicated law.

## Calculation of Optimum Growing Stock

This material is a digest of concepts and data, and an approximation of a method, developed by Duerr and Bond.

**METHOD.** In planning the management of a selection forest, the forester must decide how heavily the forest area should be stocked. The degree of stocking which is optimum from the financial standpoint provides an important guide in answering such questions.

Using financial criteria, the optimum level of stocking is that at which the value of the marginal value growth, expressed as a percent return on the value of the marginal unit of growing stock (forest capital), equals the rate of earnings on alternative capital investments (after taxes, and with due allowance for differential risks). In other words, stocking should be increased to the point where the additions to earnings resulting from a given increase in stocking equal the earnings which could be obtained by putting into the best alternative investment the additional capital needed to obtain that increased growing stock.

The concept and the method of calculating the optimum growing stock are illustrated by Table 6, which applies to a selection stand of loblolly–shortleaf pine on a good site.

**Table 6.  Determination of Optimum Stocking of a Loblolly–Shortleaf Pine Stand on One Acre of Good Site**

| Volume * | | Value | | Current value growth (5) | Average marginal investment required (6) | Marginal value growth per year (7) | Marginal rate of return, percent per year (8) |
|---|---|---|---|---|---|---|---|
| Now (1) | After 5 yr. (2) | Now (3) | After 5 yr. (4) | | | | |
| 5,000 | 7,340 | $210.00 | $317.30 | $107.30 | | | |
| | | | | | $56.15 | $3.54 | 6.3 |
| 6,000 | 8,670 | 257.30 | 382.30 | 125.00 | | | |
| | | | | | 57.20 | 3.20 | 5.6 |
| 7,000 | 9,960 | 306.50 | 447.50 | 141.00 | | | |
| | | | | | 58.05 | 2.86 | 4.9 |
| 8,000 | 11,190 | 357.40 | 512.70 | 155.30 | | | |
| | | | | | 58.90 | 2.48 | 4.2 |
| 9,000 | 12,300 | 410.10 | 577.80 | 167.70 | | | |
| | | | | | 59.80 | 2.08 | 3.5 |
| 10,000 | 13,520 | 464.70 | 642.80 | 178.10 | | | |
| | | | | | 60.40 | 1.64 | 2.7 |
| 11,000 | 14,610 | 521.00 | 707.30 | 186.30 | | | |

* In bd. ft., International ¼-in. Rule.

In Table 6, Columns 1 and 2 are based on growth estimates for the forest tract in question. Assume a 5-yr. cutting cycle. A stand now stocked with 5,000 bd. ft. per acre will contain 7,340 bd. ft. 5 yr. hence, etc. Stumpage values are appraised for the tract and applied to these volume data. This gives the total values of growing stock shown in Columns 3 and 4. Column 5 shows the current growth in value of growing stock during the 5-yr. period, and is the difference between Columns 3 and 4. The average marginal investment required (Column 6) measures the additional capital investment needed to increase initial stocking from, say, 5,000 bd. ft. to 6,000 bd. ft. At the beginning of the 5-yr. period the increased investment is $257.30 − $210.00, or $47.30 per acre. At the end of the period the increased investment is $382.30 − $317.30, or $65.00 per acre. Thus, the average increase in investment over the 5-yr. period is $56.15. (Other entries in Column 6 are calculated in similar fashion, from Columns 3 and 4.) The marginal value growth (Column 7) is simply the average annual increase in current value growth (Column 5) obtained as a result of each successive increase in stocking. Column 8 then expresses this marginal value growth (Column 7) as a percentage of the increased capital required to obtain it (Column 6).

Thus, the marginal rate of return of Column 8 shows the rate of earnings on the additional capital required to expand initial stocking from a given level to the next succeeding level of Column 1. Suppose, now, that it is known that capital invested in nonforest businesses of comparable risk can be expected to earn 4 percent per year. Column 8 indicates that investment in increased forest growing stock will yield earnings greater than 4 percent up to the point where initial stocking is 9,000 bd. ft. per acre. But if growing stock is increased to 10,000 bd. ft., the capital required to build up this last thousand feet of growing stock will earn only 3.5 percent. Hence, it would be more profitable to put this marginal capital into the alternative 4 percent investment rather than into increasing growing stock beyond the 9,000 bd. ft. level. Thus, under these conditions, 9,000 bd. ft. per acre would closely approximate the optimum growing stock.

Similarly, inspection of the table shows that, where alternative investments are earning 5 percent per year, optimum stocking would be obtained at a level slightly below 7,500 bd. ft. per acre. At 3 percent the optimum is about 10,000 bd. ft.

This method of determining optimum stocking can be applied to any stand for which data on periodic growth and stumpage values at alternative levels of stocking are available. Such data are used to complete the first four columns of a table like Table 6. The remaining columns and the optimum stocking solution follow by calculation, as described above.

## BIBLIOGRAPHY

AMERICAN PULP AND PAPER ASSOC. 1949. *The statistics of paper.* 2d ed. New York.

BUTTRICK, P. L. 1943. *Forest economics and finance.* John Wiley & Sons, Inc., New York.

CANADIAN BUREAU OF STATISTICS, PRICES BRANCH. *Prices and price indexes, 1913–1943,* and current supplements. Ottawa.

CHAPMAN, H. H., and W. H. MEYER. 1947. *Forest valuation.* McGraw-Hill Book Co., Inc., New York.

DUERR, W. A., and W. E. BOND. 1952. Optimum stocking of a selection forest. *Jour. Forestry* 50:12–16.

MATTHEWS, D. M. 1935. *Management of American forests.* McGraw-Hill Book Co., Inc., New York.

MATTHEWS, D. M. *Manual of timber management.* Ontario Dept. of Land and Forests, Toronto, Canada, Part V.

NATIONAL LUMBER MANUFACTURERS' ASSOC. 1947. *Lumber industry facts, 1947.* Washington, D. C.

U. S. BUREAU OF LABOR STATISTICS. *Average wholesale prices and index numbers of individual commodities.* Monthly. Washington, D. C.

U. S. FOREST SERV., DIVISION OF FOREST ECONOMICS. 1945. *State forest tax law digest of 1945.* Washington, D. C.

U. S. TIMBER CONSERVATION BOARD. National survey of lumber supply and demand. *Report of the Lumber Survey Committee.* Quarterly. Washington, D. C.

# LOGGING

---

## CONTENTS

## CONTENTS (*Continued*)

### Water Transport and Storage of Wood

# LOGGING

## Planning and Cost Control

Logging has been called the key to forestry. Even in forests managed primarily for purposes other than wood production, some cutting is often inevitable. The best silvicultural plan can be wrecked by poorly planned or careless logging. Moreover, because logging costs are usually the major item in the total cost of forest products, and are rising, efficient and economical logging is essential to sustained yield forest management. Such logging must be **planned.**

Successful planning of a logging operation requires simultaneous consideration of the forest itself, and of men and machines. In extensive logging operations, if each area is clearcut with the help of temporary roads and other improvements, and then is abandoned for a rotation period while camps as well as the labor force are moved to another site, intensive forestry is an obvious impossibility. Only a labor force permanently maintained within the area will permit the required frequency and timing of logging, of silvicultural, and protective operations. Conversely, only such operations will provide jobs for a permanent labor force.

Even in northern operations the traditionally seasonal conduct of logging may often be overcome by permanent, all-season roads, and by mechanization of operations. Successful mechanization requires not only machines but also good techniques for their use, capable, trained labor, and thoughtful supervision. Logging being a continuous chain of successive operations, its mechanization must be soundly organized on the assembly-line principle so as to prevent bottlenecks, or the overloading of individual units.

A number of problems in logging are often so intimately related that an over-all plan is necessary for their solution. For example, where efficiency of woods operations suffers from the lack of continuity in labor and forest use (nomadic practice), the required change may best be achieved by means of a set of integrated measures, introduced gradually but concurrently, such as (1) deseasonalization of logging, (2) logging mechanization, (3) building up a permanent labor force (steady workers usually want a real home, however modest, within reach of their work), (4) a change to sustained yield operating with permanent improvements, and (5) the integration of logging with silviculture and protection.

An analysis of an "annual logging cycle"—a pattern that a given logging operation tends to follow with regard to kinds and quantities of work being done at certain times of the year—can often be of help in considering the improvements that may be required in the "framework" of that operation. Fig. 1 shows, respectively, the annual logging cycles of a highly seasonal pulpwood operation in eastern Canada (with high labor turnover) and of a continuous (year-round), better stabilized operation. Some improvements can frequently be made by a study and manipulation of the curves for the individual steps of logging, aiming at having each kind of work done when it would be most efficient, but avoiding excessive peaks and troughs in the total labor curve.

When starting his logging work, the inexperienced forester may have little or no opportunity to plan operations. He will, however, have unlimited opportunities

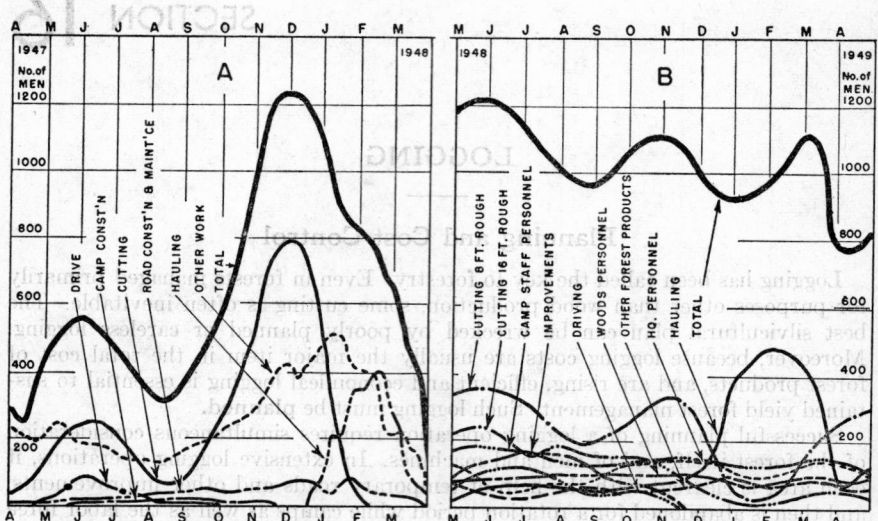

**Fig. 1. Annual employment in the pulpwood industry in eastern Canada.**

A, a highly seasonal operation; B, a year-round, more stabilized operation. (Stability as a factor in efficient forest management, by A. Koroleff, Pulp and Paper Research Institute of Canada, 1951.)

for carefully observing how various kinds of work are done. A fund of sound information absolutely essential to effective planning can be acquired by the careful assembling of miscellaneous experiences. Thanks to his professional education, he will think of tomorrow as well as today—not only of silviculture (in which logging is his principal tool) but of labor and management. The simplest job can give him an insight into all three of these elements of every logging operation.

In order to be properly integrated with the over-all planning of an enterprise, planning of woods operations should start at the very beginning. To find a "best" solution in a given case, the planning of logging operations should be done boldly and imaginatively, but it should be based on adequate knowledge from personal experience, observation, and a study of different operations. If risks must be taken, they must be "calculated" risks.

The general plan should be made first, and with due care; the details come later. This long-term plan should cover the period to the completion of the cut on the area to be operated, or to a perpetual, sustained yield operation. The plan involves cost estimates of every part of the proposed operation, divided into capital, maintenance, and production; and also estimates of the profits expected on the investments.

If the project is to proceed, the major plan should be broken down into shorter periods and into the main components of the operation. This planning falls into two phases—getting the physical work done, and controlling the costs. The manager first makes a general budget estimate for a period no longer than a year, based on the few major divisions of the operation and depending on estimated unit cost of work such as road construction, felling and bucking, skidding, loading, hauling, etc. By accumulating cost accounting data for each appropriate phase of the operation, a basis is obtained for setting up standards of operating practices and costs. After a period of study and trial, major parts of the operation can be broken down into further subdivisions and the accounting periods can be shortened, so that the operating reports may be received more frequently. As experience accumulates, such records will promptly show which parts of the operation proceed normally and which call for immediate attention on account of inadequate action or high cost.

## Logging Production

Data shown on the following charts (Figs. 2–8) represent a composite from many sources, including answers to questionnaires sent to S.A.F. members, publications of state and federal agencies, articles in trade journals, and field investigations. Maximum values are rarely attained, although there may be exceptions where even the highest production shown has been exceeded. In most instances, operation averages will fall in the average range indicated by cross hatching on the charts. A single numerical average value is not shown because of the many variable factors that differ between operations. In some regions operations are seasonal, but in others where operations are year-long, there are seasonal variations in production. Some of the most important factors causing variations are as follows:

1. Type of labor, i.e., full-time skilled, part-time (farmers, etc.).
2. Method of payment, i.e., contract or per hour.
3. Logs per M bd. ft., i.e., large diameter, long vs. small, short logs.
4. Logs per tree, i.e., tall vs. short timber.
5. Season of the year, i.e., summer vs. winter, dry vs. wet.
6. Basis of computation, i.e., lumber tally; International, Scribner, Doyle log scales, etc.
7. Percent of defect, i.e., sound vs. defective timber.
8. Volume of timber per acre, i.e., dense vs. scattered timber.
9. Percent of slope, i.e., mountains vs. flat lands.
10. Utilization standards and value, i.e., walnut vs. Douglas-fir, etc.

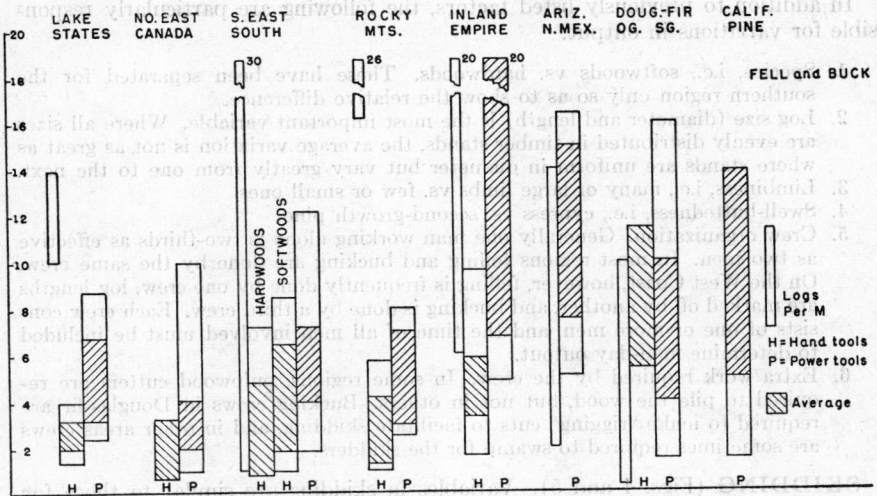

Fig. 2. Felling and bucking—production of M bd. ft. per man-day.

**FELLING AND BUCKING** (Figs. 2 and 3). Saw-log output in the Central States is approximately the same as that in the Northeast. Hardwood pulpwood averages 0.8 to 3.5 cords per man-day for hand tools, and 1.6 to 5.2 for power tools. In the East, chain saws are considered equivalent to one man, or a chain saw increases man-day output by one-third to one-half. Highest outputs are obtained on pulpwood operations with slasher saws. On small trees, such as those in the Lake States, hand bow saws are the most productive.

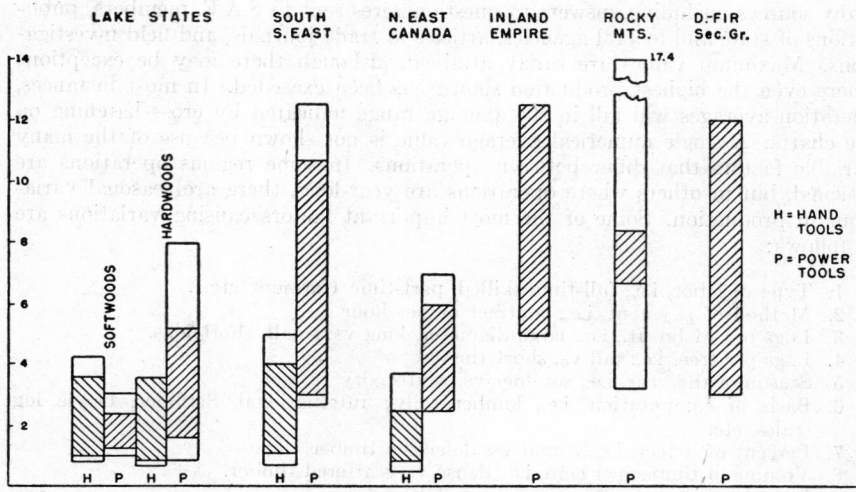

Fig. 3. Felling and bucking—production of cords per man-day.

In addition to previously listed factors, the following are particularly responsible for variations in output.

1. Species, i.e., softwoods vs. hardwoods. These have been separated for the southern region only so as to show the relative difference.
2. Log size (diameter and length) is the most important variable. Where all sizes are evenly distributed in timber stands, the average variation is not as great as where stands are uniform in diameter but vary greatly from one to the next.
3. Limbiness, i.e., many or large limbs vs. few or small ones.
4. Swell-buttedness, i.e., cypress vs. second-growth pine.
5. Crew organization. Generally one man working alone is two-thirds as effective as two men. In most regions felling and bucking are done by the same crew. On the West Coast, however, felling is frequently done by one crew, log lengths are marked off by another, and bucking is done by a third crew. Each crew consists of one or more men, and the time of all men involved must be included to determine man-day output.
6. Extra work required by the crew. In some regions, pulpwood cutters are required to pile the wood, but not in others. Bucking crews in Douglas-fir are required to make "rigging" cuts to facilitate skidding, and in other areas crews are sometimes required to swamp for the skidders.

**SKIDDING** (Figs. 4 and 5). Variables in skidding are similar to those for felling and bucking, but they can be reduced to three main factors: weight, distance, and noneffective time.

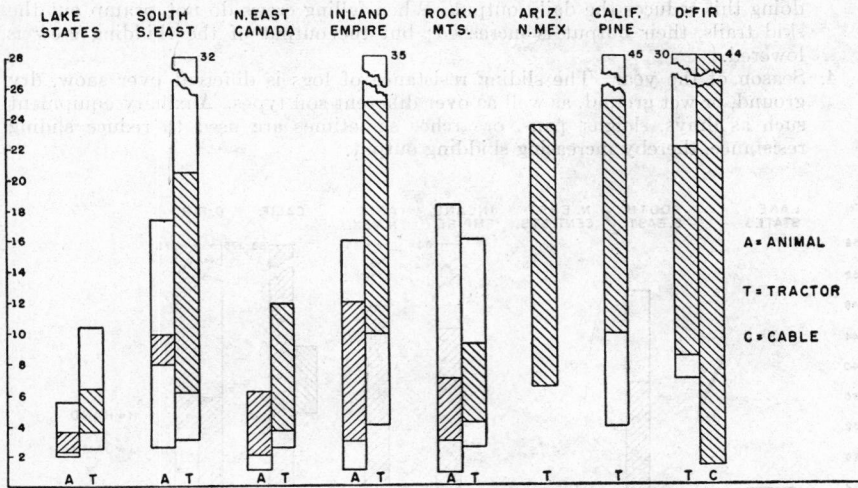

Fig. 4. Skidding—production in M bd. ft. per man-day.

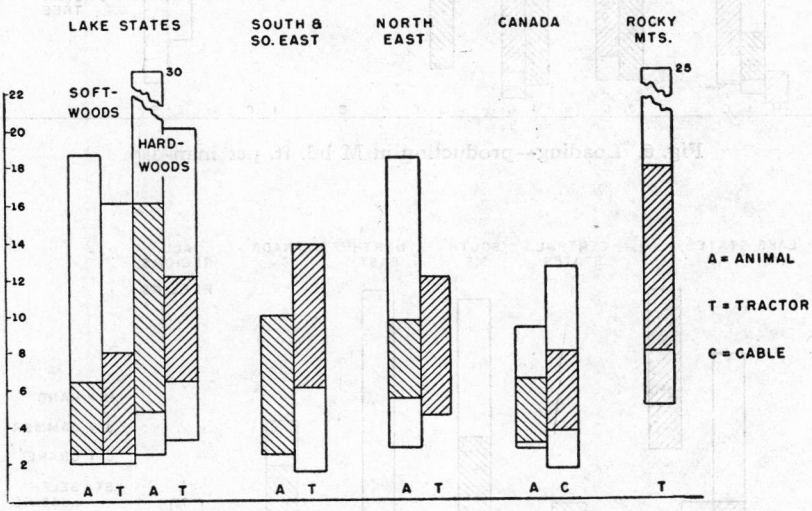

Fig. 5. Skidding—production in cords per man-day.

1. Weight. Hardwoods weigh approximately twice as much as softwoods, and require more power to skid. Skidding downhill requires less power than on the level; degree of slope thus affects output.
2. Distance. In general, the shorter the skidding distance, the greater the number of trips and output per day. A general rule of thumb is that 400 to 600 ft. is the maximum efficient distance for horse skidding, yet in the Appalachian regions distances up to 1½ mi. are not uncommon.
3. Noneffective time. When more than one log is required for an efficient load for the skidding unit, bunching of logs is required. The amount of time spent

doing this reduces the daily output. When felling crews do not swamp out the skid trails, their output is increased; but the output of the skidding crew is lowered.

4. Season of the year. The sliding resistance of logs is different over snow, dry ground, or wet ground, as well as over different soil types. Auxiliary equipment such as drays, sleighs, pans, or arches sometimes are used to reduce sliding resistance, thereby increasing skidding output.

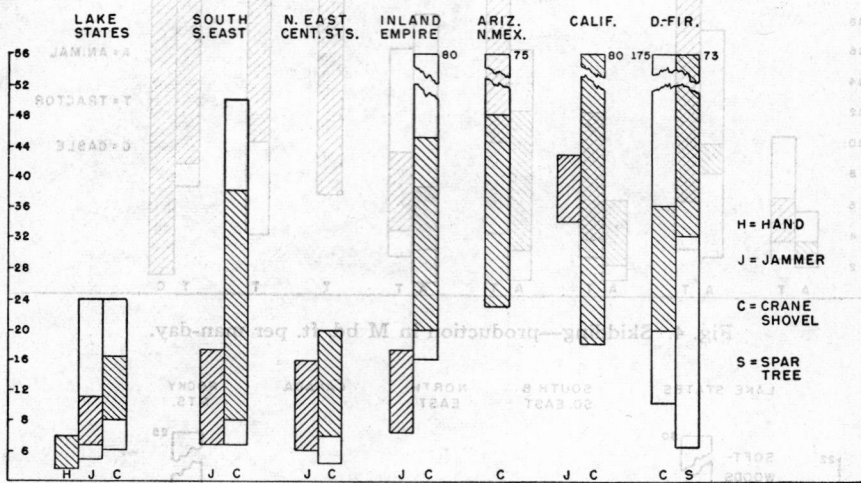

Fig. 6. Loading—production in M bd. ft. per man-day.

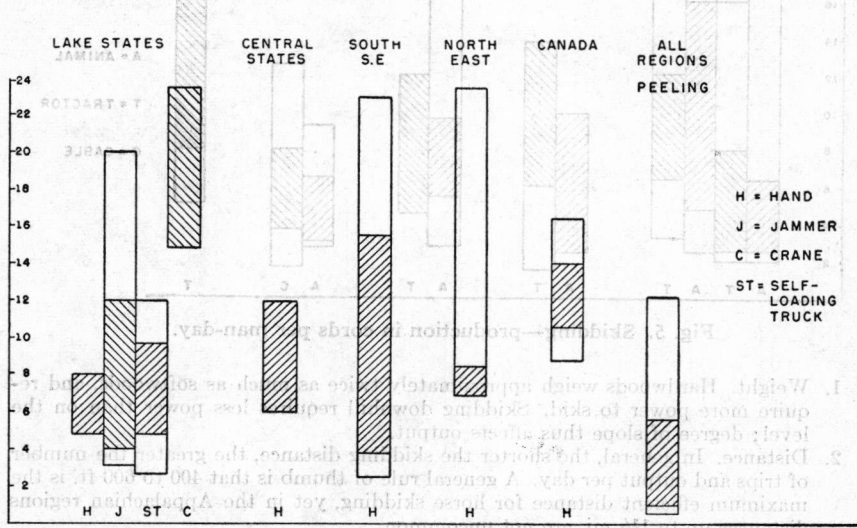

Fig. 7. Loading and peeling—production of cords per man-day.

**LOADING** (Figs. 6 and 7). Loading output is affected by weight, number of pieces, effective time, and the variables influencing these three items.

1. Weight. There is a limit to the weight that man power or animal power can hoist in a day, and the height of lift is important. Men can load more pulpwood onto pallets or sleds than they can onto trucks. They can load more cords of softwood per day than of hardwood.

2. Machine loaders generally have enough power to handle the largest log encountered on the operation, and therefore weight is not as important as the number of pieces or logs per M bd. ft. It takes as long to load a log scaling 100 bd. ft. as one scaling 500 bd. ft.

3. Effective crew loading time varies considerably. Loaded trucks must be moved out and empties spotted. Sometimes loaded trucks are moved and then chained while in other cases the load is chained before moving, thus reducing effective time. Poor scheduling of trucks is perhaps the greatest factor affecting loading crew output.

**HAULING** (Fig. 8). Hauling output is affected by size of load, length of haul, quality of road, and effective time.

1. Size of load is influenced principally by size of logs, size of trucks, and weight restrictions on public roads.

2. Length of haul is the main reason why there is not a greater variation in output between eastern and western operations. Eastern loads are small while western hauling distances are long.

3. Quality of roads determines truck speeds and is affected by surfacing, curvatures, grades, and widths.

4. Effective time is influenced primarily by loading and unloading time. Often trucks on short hauls have an effective time of 50 percent or less. In some cases, the truck driver also serves as a member of the loading crew, thus increasing his effective output although not that of the trucks.

**PEELING** (Fig. 7). Pulpwood peeling output per man-day is approximately the same for all regions. Variation is largely due to seasonal influence. Output is lowest at the beginning and ending of the growing season.

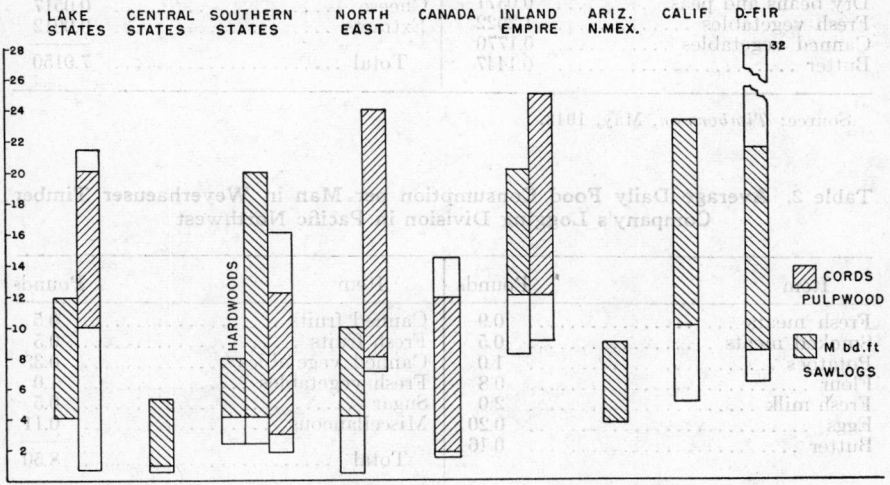

Fig. 8. Hauling—production per man-day.

# Labor

**LABOR LAWS.** Foresters of Canada and the United States who employ labor for any kind of logging or forestry work or are responsible for such employment should first inform themselves in detail on the latest federal, state, or provincial laws governing wages, hours, minimum age of employment, compensation for industrial injuries and unemployment, housing, sanitation, safety, and related matters. Information as to federal laws in Canada may be obtained from the Department of Labor, and from the Unemployment Insurance Commission, Ottawa, and in the United States from the U. S. Department of Labor, Washington, D. C. In the provinces and states, information on similar laws and regulations can be obtained from departments of labor at their respective capitals. Within these laws, local customs may vary widely, or details may be governed by agreements with labor unions. Satisfactory labor relations will depend on an intimate knowledge of these matters.

**FEEDING MEN IN CAMPS.** Tables 1 and 2 show the average amount of food consumed per man at two different logging camps.

**Table 1. Total Food Consumption per Man in Logging Camps of Anaconda Copper Mining Company, Woodworth, Montana, in 1942**

| Item | Pounds per man-day | Item | Pounds per man-day |
|---|---|---|---|
| Flour | 0.6351 | Sugar | 0.1954 |
| Meats and fish | 1.6410 | Tea and coffee | 0.0901 |
| Canned milk | 0.0763 | Eggs | 0.2942 |
| Fresh milk | 1.1699 | Cereals | 0.0805 |
| Canned fruit | 0.3033 | Syrup and molasses | 0.1653 |
| Fresh fruit | 0.4476 | Spices and condiments | 0.0906 |
| Dry fruit | 0.0438 | Lard | 0.0880 |
| Dry beans and peas | 0.0371 | Cheese | 0.0517 |
| Fresh vegetables | 1.2622 | Extracts | 0.0012 |
| Canned vegetables | 0.1770 | | |
| Butter | 0.1447 | Total | 7.0150 |

Source: *Timberman*, May, 1943.

**Table 2. Average Daily Food Consumption per Man in Weyerhaeuser Timber Company's Logging Division in Pacific Northwest**

| Item | Pounds | Item | Pounds |
|---|---|---|---|
| Fresh meats | 0.9 | Canned fruits | 0.5 |
| Smoked meats | 0.5 | Fresh fruits | 0.5 |
| Potatoes | 1.0 | Canned vegetables | 0.33 |
| Flour | 0.8 | Fresh vegetables | 1.0 |
| Fresh milk | 2.0 | Sugar | 0.5 |
| Eggs | 0.20 | Miscellaneous | 0.11 |
| Butter | 0.16 | Total | 8.50 |

Source: *West Coast Lumberman*, July, 1938.

## FEEDING OF ANIMALS.

### Table 3. Suggested Schedule for the Proper Feeding and Watering of Horses

About 2 hr. before work—All the water the horse will drink; ¼ of daily hay ration; a little water; ⅓ of daily oats ration.

Middle of morning—A pail of water.

At noon meal—(Water at least ¼ hr. before feeding.) About ¼ or ⅕ of daily hay ration; a little water; ⅓ of oats ration.

Mid-afternoon—A pail of water.

After work—½ pail of water; a little hay.

At evening meal—All the water horse will drink; remainder of oats ration.

Half an hour to 1 hr. later—Remainder of hay ration.

Source: A. Koroleff, *Skidding teamster's handbook, efficiency in skidding of wood and handling of horses,* Canadian Pulp and Paper Assn., Montreal, 1942.

## Hand Tools

**AXES.** Axe patterns are of a great variety, largely to suit individual preference. The double-bit axe, favored by northern and western lumberjacks, has one keen blade for chopping; the other blade is sharpened to a less acute angle for grubbing around roots or cutting knots and other exceptionally hard wood. A single-bit axe (the poll is used to drive **wooden** wedges) is preferred in the South, and generally in farming regions.

Axe weights average 3 to 4½ lb., occasionally up to 6 lb. French-Canadian pulpwood cutters of the Northeast prefer 2½ to 3 lb. single-bit axes.

Handles are usually 28 to 36 in. long, including the eye, straight for double-bit, more or less curved for single-bit; preferably of hickory (wide-ringed wood is strongest; brown heartwood has no defect).

To "hang" an axe (Fig. 9), if the old handle was broken, drive it out of the head backwards with a steel bar and hammer. Have both the new handle and the wedge dry. For a wedge, use wood heavily impregnated with resin.

**How to Sharpen an Axe.** Correct grinding is important; do not use a high-speed, dry, grinding wheel—the temper of the cutting edge will be destroyed.

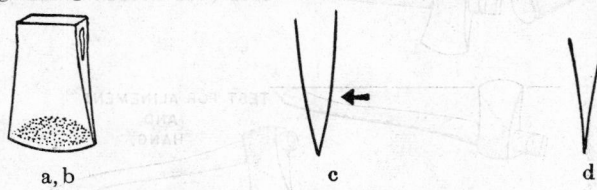

a, b                    c                    d

   a. Grind slowly on a wheel kept very wet.

   b. Start to grind from 2 to 3 in. back from the cutting edge and work to about ½ in. from the edge. Work for a fan-shaped effect, leaving reinforcement at corners for adequate strength.

   c. Then "roll off" a convex bevel, as shown in the illustration, which is the exact gauge and shape of a properly ground cutting edge.

   d. Avoid a concave edge which leaves insufficient support. This illustration shows an axe ground the wrong way; it will break very easily.

### Care of an Axe.

   1. Do not use an axe as a maul or as a wedge. Axe heads are not made for such use and will split or break at the eye if abused in this way.

   2. Do not strike with the flat of the axe; it will crack under sidewise blows.

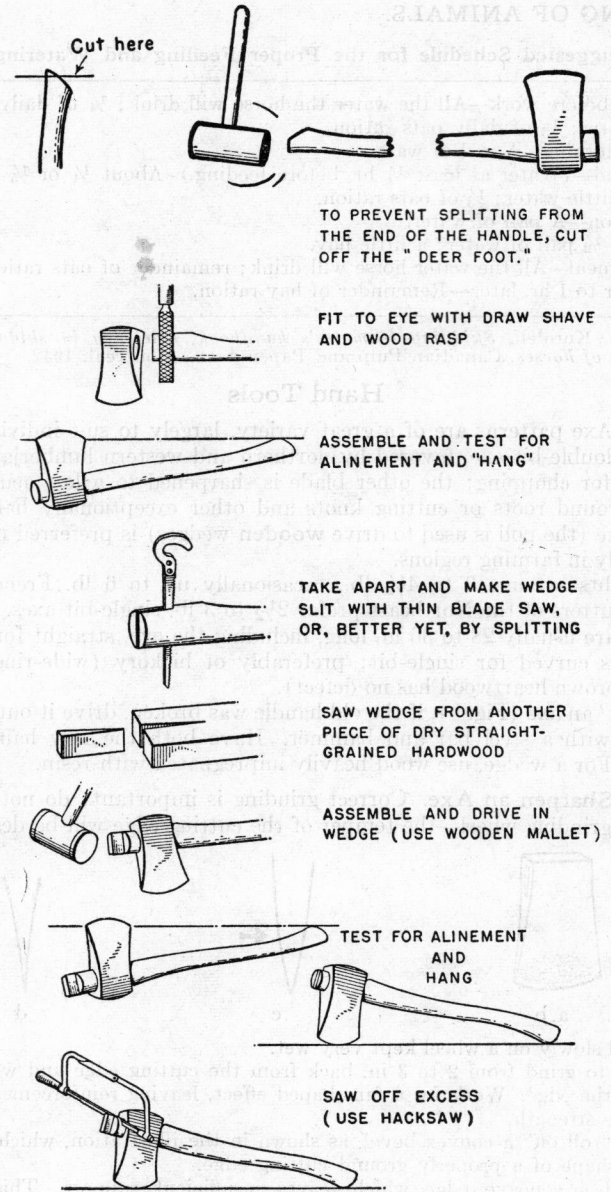

Cut here

TO PREVENT SPLITTING FROM
THE END OF THE HANDLE, CUT
OFF THE " DEER FOOT."

FIT TO EYE WITH DRAW SHAVE
AND WOOD RASP

ASSEMBLE AND TEST FOR
ALINEMENT AND "HANG"

TAKE APART AND MAKE WEDGE
SLIT WITH THIN BLADE SAW,
OR, BETTER YET, BY SPLITTING

SAW WEDGE FROM ANOTHER
PIECE OF DRY STRAIGHT-
GRAINED HARDWOOD

ASSEMBLE AND DRIVE IN
WEDGE (USE WOODEN MALLET)

TEST FOR ALINEMENT
AND
HANG

SAW OFF EXCESS
( USE HACKSAW )

**Fig. 9. Hanging an axe.**

3. Do not let the axe get rusty. Rust eats away the metal and destroys the value
   of a cutting tool.
4. Keep the axe dry, but not next to the stove. Rust dulls it, and too much heat
   dries out the handle.

Source: Figs. 9 through 25 are from *Northeastern loggers' handbook*. U. S. Forest
Serv. Northeast. Forest Exp. Sta.

5. If the head works loose due to shrinkage of the handle, soak overnight in linseed oil (preferably); in an emergency, water will do a temporary job.

**CROSSCUT SAWS.** Most crosscut saws have two types of teeth: (1) cutting teeth, which sever the fibers on each side of the cut, and (2) raker teeth, which act like a plane, so that the shaving-like chips are raked into the gullets (between cutting teeth and rakers), and are carried out of the cut (see Fig. 10).

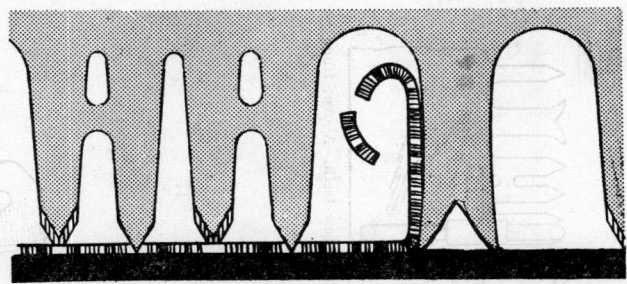

**Fig. 10. Action of a well-sharpened saw; it makes shavings—not sawdust.**

The arrangement and shape of teeth vary widely. In Fig. 11, A illustrates lance teeth. There are four perforated lance teeth to each raker. This is generally the most satisfactory design for all log cutting except in extra hard or frozen timber. The Pacific Coast pattern does not have perforations, and the gullets are larger to allow plenty of room for shavings in large-diameter timber.

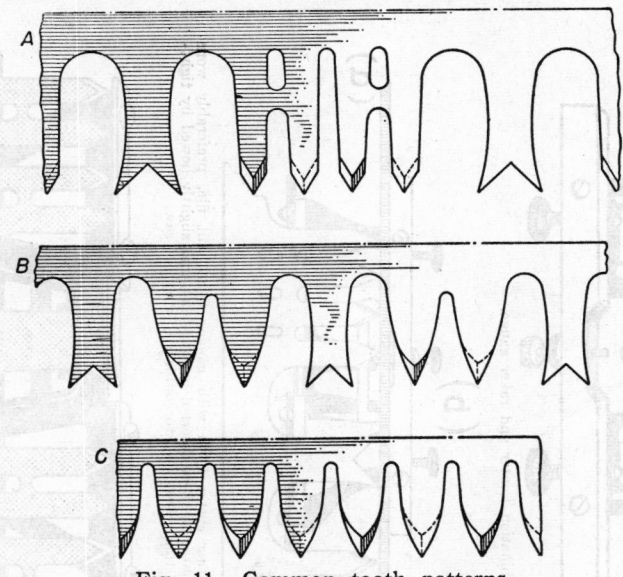

**Fig. 11.  Common tooth patterns.**
A, for softwoods; B, for hardwoods; C, for dry wood only.

Fig. 11 B illustrates the Champion tooth. There are two of these to each raker. This design is suited for cutting extra hard or frozen timber.

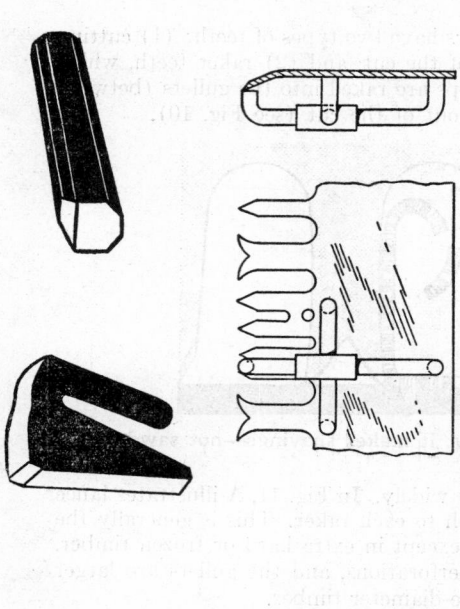

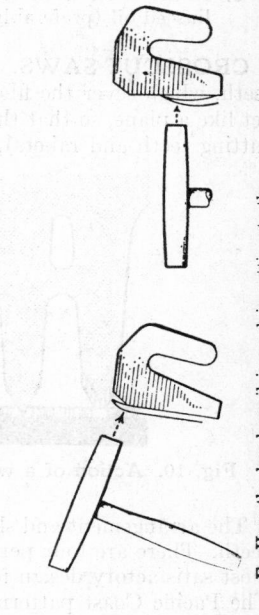

D. Tools for setting saw teeth. Above: Hand anvils; below: set gauge, or "spider."

E. How the hand anvil is used in setting teeth.

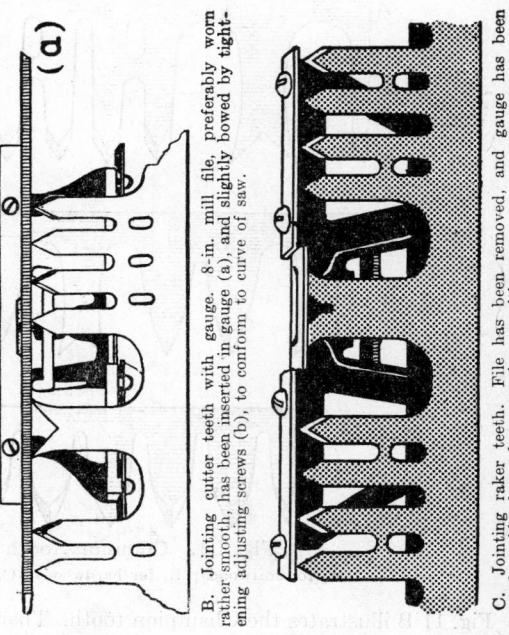

A. Combination jointer and raker gauge.

B. Jointing cutter teeth with gauge. 8-in. mill file, preferably worn rather smooth, has been inserted in gauge (a), and slightly bowed by tightening adjusting screws (b), to conform to curve of saw.

C. Jointing raker teeth. File has been removed, and gauge has been turned upside down from previous position.

Fig. 11 C is for dry wood only. A variation of this, the peg tooth, has straight sides and is used in saws cutting wood of small diameter and for topping spar trees.

**Saw Patterns.** Many kinds are manufactured, for various uses. One-man crosscuts have a fixed hand-saw grip and a detachable handle which can be attached to the other end of the saw for use by a second man. Lengths of one-man saws are usually from 3½ to 5 ft. Two-man crosscuts have detachable handles at both ends and are usually 5 to 8 ft. long (lengths to 10 ft. or more are used in the Pacific Northwest, and to 16 ft. or longer in redwoods). Most patterns are made several gauges thinner at the back than at the cutting edge for freer cutting.

Bow saws, used both for felling trees and bucking logs up to about 16 in. in diameter, commonly have blades 36, 42, or 48 in. long. The thin blade minimizes wedging. Adjustable frames, to maintain needed tension on the blade (200 lb. or more), are available in the more expensive models.

**Care of Saws.** For best results, a saw should be sharpened after each day of regular use. Sharpening should be done on a specially built filing rack which can be home-made from a 3 by 10 in. plank, beveled on one side and curved to the same convexity as the cutting edge of the saw. The tools needed are flat files, a combination jointer and raker gauge, a setting hammer, a hand anvil, and a set gauge or spider (Fig. 12, A and D). The steps in saw filing are:

1. Jointing should be done after about every three filings. Place the saw-jointing tool over the teeth and file off any teeth that are too long (B).
2. Fitting raker teeth (C). The traditional straight type of raker teeth are first swaged or hammered to spread the points slightly so that they act like a plane in removing the shavings. Many modern saws have swage-ground rakers, making this step unnecessary. Next the edges are filed to a sharp cutting edge. When finished, the raker teeth should be about 1/64 in. shorter than the cutting teeth.
3. Filing the cutting teeth. This is done on a bevel and with a slight roll, leaving the edge of the tooth slightly rounded rather than straight. Care should be taken to have a keen edge, but needle points are not necessary and the saw will retain its edge longer if the points are not too thin.
4. Set the cutting teeth (E). Bend alternate teeth outward by placing the set block against the tooth not lower than ¼ in. from the point and hitting the opposite side firmly with a set hammer.

The amount of set for a modern taper-ground crosscut should be about 0.016 in. for softwoods and about 0.008 in. for hardwoods. For flat-ground saw blades, it should be about twice as much.

Pliers-like setting tools are commonly used in setting the teeth on bow saw blades. They are also available for setting crosscut saw teeth, but they are not recommended since they place the set too far down on the tooth.

Further and more detailed instructions for filing various types of crosscut saws are available from the manufacturers of these saws. Frequently these booklets are available at local hardware stores.

**PEELING TOOLS. Peeling Season.** Wood is peeled most easily in the spring and early summer, during a period of 6 to 12 weeks, depending on the region and species. Some species, if felled when frozen, will peel easily in the following spring for periods of 2 to 3 weeks (for use of chemicals, see Section 6).

**The Spud.** The spud is the most commonly used tool for sap peeling during the peeling season. Many good spuds have been made from old automobile or buggy springs, with wooden plates riveted together on one end for a handle, or from a garden spade (Fig. 13).

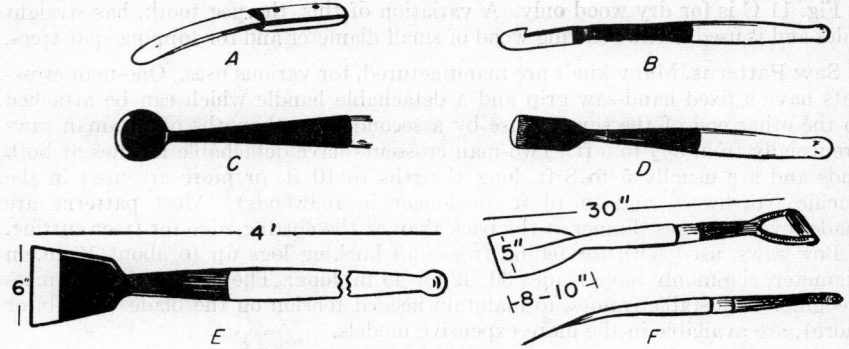

**Fig. 13. Types of spuds.**

A, made from auto spring; B, spud for hemlock; C, saucer-shaped; D, narrow spud, favored for use on hardwoods; E, spud for cedar; F, made from spade.

For small timbers and thin bark, such as northeastern spruce and fir pulpwood, a spud only 10 to 15 in. long is frequently used. For heavier barked species and bigger logs, such as hemlock, chestnut oak, and most hardwood pulpwood, the spud may be 24 to 30 in. long, and for really hard-barked species such as hickory and cedar, 4 ft. long.

The spud is usually used around the log, instead of lengthwise of it. For the harder barked species an axe cut through the bark is made lengthways of the log and on top of it; the spud is inserted into this cut and the bark stripped off. If it is desired to save the bark, axe cuts around the log at about 4-ft. intervals are also made, so that the bark comes off in plates.

**Drawshaves.** For debarking outside the peeling season, broad-bladed spuds such as the cedar spud and the spud made from a spade (Fig. 13 F) are sometimes used, but the most popular method is to use the drawshave or timber shave. The drawshave (Fig. 14) used for debarking is a larger, sturdier model of the familiar carpenter's drawshave. Frequently the handles are bent outward as shown to give a firmer grip and stronger pull. The timbershave (Fig. 15) has a curved knife so that more of the surface of a round timber is contacted at a time.

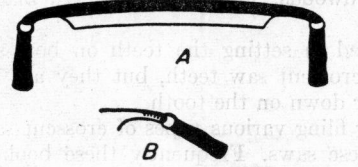

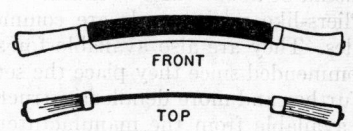

FRONT

TOP

**Fig. 14. A, the drawshave; B, handle bent outward for better grip.**

**Fig. 15. The timbershave.**

It is easier to use the drawshave on a slightly uphill pull. Make shaving horses, for use with short bolts, with one pair of legs longer than the other. When a long timber is to be shaved, one end of it is placed on a log or other support and the man doing the shaving straddles it.

**WEDGES. Felling and Bucking Wedges.** For use with crosscut saws, felling and bucking wedges (Fig. 16) are made of either wood or steel. Hardwood wedges are generally used by crews cutting softwoods and steel wedges by those cutting hardwoods. These wedges are usually no more than 6 or 8 in. long, 2 or 3 in. wide, and taper from an edge about 1/16 in. thick to a shank about 1 in. thick.

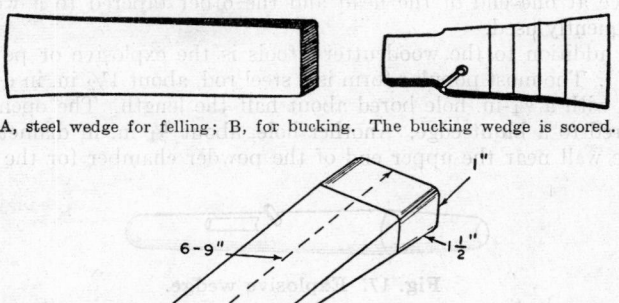

A, steel wedge for felling; B, for bucking. The bucking wedge is scored.

C. A hardwood wedge.

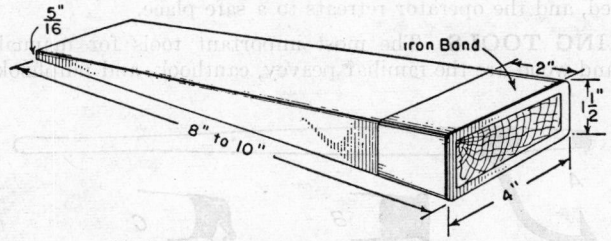

D. A wooden wedge for use with chain saws.

**Fig. 16. Wedges.**

Steel wedges are often "creased" on the two faces to make them hold better in the cut. Smooth wedges can be "ragged" on the faces with a cold chisel to accomplish the same purpose. Steel wedges should be left untempered so that they will not chip when hit with a tempered sledge. Flying fragments from such chipping (spalling) have resulted in many serious injuries.

Wooden wedges are of approximately the same size and pattern. Dense, close-grained hardwoods such as dogwood, persimmon, sugar maple, and beech are preferred for making these wedges, but they can be made from almost any **dry** hardwood. One advantage of the wooden wedge is that it can safely be pounded with the poll of a single-bit axe; it is therefore not necessary for the crew to carry an extra tool for wedging.

Steel wedges should never be used behind chain saws. Wooden wedges, or wedges of some soft metal such as magnesium or aluminum, are used instead. They are considerably bigger than those used with hand saws. The chain saw cuts a wider kerf, so the entering edge of the wedge is made $5/16$ to $3/8$ in. wide, and it tapers to about $1\frac{1}{2}$ in. at the shank. Special mallets with rawhide faces should be used in pounding magnesium wedges.

**Splitting Wedges.** Wedges are also used to split wood. Splitting wedges are considerably bigger than felling and bucking wedges. Some are shaped like a huge cold chisel, others like an oversized single-bit axe head. Splitting wedges are pounded in with a sledge hammer, usually a considerably bigger one than that used by the felling and bucking crews. A special wood splitters' maul, with a sledge-hammer face at one end of the head and the other tapered to a wedge-shaped edge, is frequently used.

A recent addition to the woodcutters' tools is the explosive or powder wedge (see Fig. 17). The most popular form is a steel rod, about 1½ in. in diameter and 18 in. long, with a ¾-in. hole bored about half the length. The open end of the rod is tapered to a blunt edge. Another hole, about ¼ in. in diameter, is bored through the wall near the upper end of the powder chamber for the fuse.

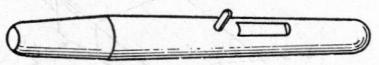

Fig. 17. Explosive wedge.

In use, a charge of black powder is placed inside the wedge, and some dry wadding is shoved in to cover it. Then the wedge is pounded into a sound place in the end of the chunk to be split. The fuse is next inserted. A heavy chunk may be placed against the outside end of the wedge to keep it from kicking back, the fuse is lighted, and the operator retreats to a safe place.

**HANDLING TOOLS.** The most important tools for manually handling round logs and wood are the familiar peavey, canthook, and pulphook. (Figs. 18, 19.)

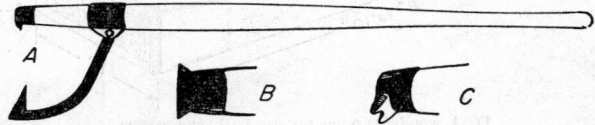

Fig. 18. A, the canthook; B, hog-nose toe ring; C, crowfoot, for handling square timbers.

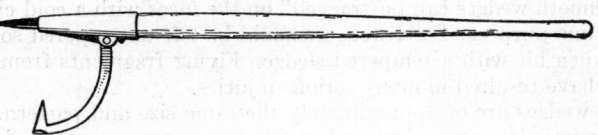

Fig. 19. The peavey, or cant dog.

Canthooks are used largely around log decks and at the mill for rolling logs from one place to another. Peaveys are more commonly used in the woods. The steel spike at the end can be stuck into the ground or into wood for use as a pry in getting down lodged trees, in guiding a rolling log, or in tightening a chain on a log sled. Logs can be rolled out from behind stumps or other obstructions for skidding, or away from each other for bucking or scaling.

A variation of the canthook, for use in the woods, is the log jack. This is an ordinary canthook, with a wooden or steel rocker installed at the lower end of the handle, opposite the lip. With this tool a small pole, even a tree length, can be grasped and rolled up on the rocker for bucking. This raises the stick off the ground, thus keeping the saw out of the dirt. It also eliminates pinching troubles (see Fig. 20).

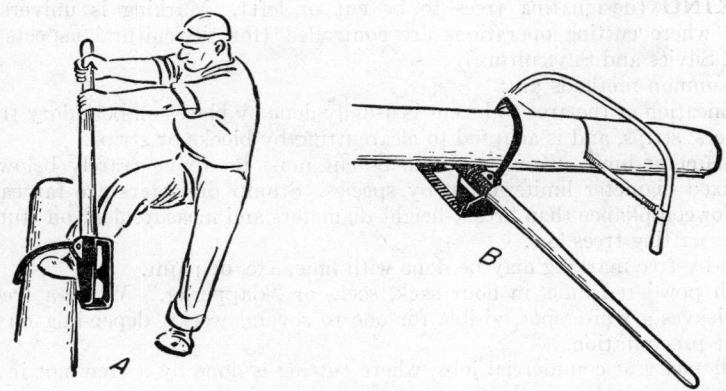

Fig. 20. **Use of a log jack. A, first position; B, second position.**

For handling short bolts (2 to 6 ft. in length) the most generally used tool is the pulphook. This is a more sturdily built form of the hay or cargo hook so commonly used by farmers, stevedores, and warehousemen.

The essential features are that the proper grade and weight of steel be used in the frame and point of the hook. A frame constructed of one piece of steel is generally considered stronger than one welded from two or three pieces. Because a flat, square, triangular, or oblong tip gives greater holding power, by shearing through some of the wood fibers instead of cleaving between them as it enters the wood, it is preferred to a round point.

The pulphook (Fig. 21) is used as an extension of the arm to reduce bending in lifting and carrying bolts of wood and to give a firmer grip on them. The point is embedded in either the side or end of the bolt, and the bolt is then pulled or lifted so that it can be cradled in the other arm. When the carry has been made, the bolt is propelled to its position on the new pile by means of the hook.

Fig. 21. **The pulphook is useful in handling frozen wood.**

# Cutting

**MARKING** (designating trees to be cut or left). Marking is universally employed where cutting operations are controlled (for silvicultural aspects see Section **6**, Silvics and Silviculture).

Some common methods are:

1. Delineation of the area to be cut is usually done by blazes on boundary trees, as for fellers' strips, and is adapted to clearcutting by blocks or strips.

2. In diameter limit cutting, trees to be cut must be above (rarely below or within) fixed diameter limits, often by species. Stump diameters are far easier to check for compliance than breast-height diameters and measurement on stumps encourages cutting trees low.

3. Tree-by-tree marking may be done with lime, axe, or paint.

   a. With powdered lime, in flour sack, sock, or "klapperlet." When a tree is struck it leaves a white spot, visible for one to several weeks, depending on the amount of precipitation.

   b. With axe. For commercial jobs, where cutting is done by a crew not in the landowner's employ, this is the most satisfactory method of marking trees to be cut. Blazes are made at eye height, all in one compass direction (on the south side, or on the downhill side if slope is considerable), or below stump height and stamped with an identifying mark on the pole of the marking hatchet. Strips are generally marked east and west, or on the contour, in widths of about 125 ft. in average saw-timber stands, but narrower in dense woods or heavy underbrush. Placing stump blazes on the side toward which the marker is proceeding facilitates liaison on the return strip. Even a light marking hatchet often permits "sounding" the tree to detect hopelessly defective butts. Well-made blazes are recognizable up to 2 yr. in fast-growing timber and 5 yr. or more in slow-growing timber.

   c. With paint. Paint can be applied with a brush direct from the can; for ease in carrying the can, open with a can-opener, bend back the top, and tack the top to the head of a walking stick. Oil stream guns, such as Alemite or De Vilbiss, of one-quart capacity are also used. These are trigger-operated, high-pressure oil guns. Enlarge the spray hole slightly. Dilute the paint to the thinnest consistency that will leave an opaque mark on the tree. (Recommended mixture: 1 gal. of oil-base paint to 1 or 1½ gal. kerosene or equal, depending on brand and quality of paint. Mix well and strain to prevent clogging the gun. Water-base paint tends to clog the gun.) About 200 trees can be properly marked, both above and below stump height, with 1 qt. of the mixture; such paint marks are discernible up to 2 yr. Recommended paint colors are orange, yellow, blue, white, or red, whichever contrasts best with bark color of the tree species. In cases where it is more economical or otherwise desirable to mark the "leave" trees, paint does not injure them as an axe would.

**SCALING PRACTICES.** (For a discussion of log rules and deduction for defects, see Section **1**, Forest Measurements.) Because scaling practices differ both between and within regions, local practice should be determined in advance of any scaling job. Check on the following:

1. Place of scaling. In woods at stump, landing, or log deck; on truck or railroad car; in water at mill.

2. Log rule used. Doyle (East, South, on commercial operations generally); Scribner Decimal C (U. S. Forest Service, other federal agencies); International (Lake States, and increasingly in the South); Spaulding (New Brunswick); Maine (British Columbia).

3. Log lengths scaled as one log. These vary from 6 ft. in some hardwoods (such as walnut) to 40 ft. in softwoods in Alaska, British Columbia, and the Pacific Northwest. Commonest softwood length is 16 ft.; hardwoods generally less. Two-foot intervals are usual in the West, 1-ft. in the East; special products (basket veneer logs, for example) measured to shorter intervals. Lengths longer than maximum are scaled as two or more logs.

4. Taper allowance, long logs. This may be actual, or a stipulated amount per length of log, as 1 in. to 8 ft.

5. Trimming allowance. This varies from 2 in. for short logs up to 8 in. for 40-ft. logs, plus 2 in. for each additional 10 ft.

6. Measurement of diameter. (a) Where. Commonly at small end, but may be middle; rarely large end. Many exclude sapwood (rare). (b) How. By scale or stick, or calipers and rule book. Average diameter (U. S. Forest Service). Sometimes smallest diameter, or largest; horizontal diameter, or vertical. Small logs sometimes credited, by agreement, with a fixed minimum diameter, such as 8 in. (c) Fractional inches. Average to closest inch (U. S. Forest Service); or drop all fractions. (d) Bark thickness. Generally exclude both thicknesses; occasionally include one or both thicknesses.

7. Log identification. Number or brand, after scaling. Feller's or bucker's identification. Designation of culls.

8. Merchantability standards: size limits, deductible and permissible defects, species acceptable, grades and grading rules. These vary greatly with species, locality, and ultimate product. Scale is usually net, but typically gross for payment of woods work or transportation; best to record both scales in case of dispute or to accumulate data on culls.

9. Penalty scale or check. How and when applied; contract provisions. Limits of error. Stump scaling.

10. Records. Forms to be used. Purposes and breakdown of scale desired (i.e., for payment of fellers, transportation, stumpage, or by owners). To whom and where delivered.

11. Other duties, if any, of scaler. Supervision of cutting standards. Time keeper. Other.

Scribner's Lumber and Log Book gives the scale of logs 8 to 60 in. in diameter, and 8 to 40 ft. long, by "Doyle's Log Rule." This pocket booklet is in wide use by lumbermen in the Northeast. Where logs are cut and scaled tree-length (often up to 50 ft. or longer, depending on state laws governing maximum lengths allowed on public highways), the usual practice is to measure the diameter with a caliper at mid-point, after chipping off the bark, and scale as two logs of that diameter and as nearly as possible half the length; a 65-ft. log measuring 14 in. at midpoint would be scaled as the sum of 33-ft. and 32-ft. logs, both of that diameter.

**FELLING AND BUCKING** (see also "Hand Tools" used in these operations, pages **16 · 9**–17).

**Power Saws.** The development of power saws has increased production per man-day by 20 to 100 percent over that with hand tools, depending on the terrain, the volume and number of stems cut per acre, and the class of labor employed.

**Power chain saws.** These are powered by gasoline, electricity, or compressed air. Innovations and improvements are constantly being made in both the saws and the cutting chains. These include a removable tailstock for two-man saws, facilitating withdrawal of the saw if the tree pinches in felling; one-man saws for felling and bucking small timber, or limbing; bow saws having the advantages and limitations of hand saws of the same design; and some greatly simplified cutting chains.

**Drag saws.** A drag saw is a heavy crosscut saw powered by a pitman arm attached to a small motor. Drag saws have been commonly used in this country in permanent installations on mill decks and as semiportable tools to cut short blocks of fuelwood at logging camps and on farms. The ordinary models weigh up to 300 lb., so they are equipped with wheels and handles like a wheelbarrow to make movement from one job to another possible.

There are also lighter weight drag saws that can be carried by tree fellers. These are commonly used in felling and bucking in redwood stands. Maintenance of a drag-saw blade is the same as maintenance of the standard crosscut saw.

**Wheeled circular saws.** The wheeled circular saw is confined, for the most part, to use in the level, open, pine woods of the South. It is a circular saw, 30 to 36 in. in diameter, mounted on a mandrel on the front of a frame with wheels and handles something like an oversize garden cultivator. The saw can be set to cut either horizontally for felling or vertically for bucking. Power is transmitted to it by means of a flexible shaft or V-belt from a motor mounted over the axle and between the shafts of the frame.

Both wheeled circular saws and drag saws are driven by simpler, sturdier motors than chain saws because the weight of the motor is less important.

Sharpening the circular saw is similar to that for comparable saws used for crosscutting in sawmills and elsewhere. Simple jointing and set gauges are available from saw manufacturers.

**PEELING. Mechanical Peeling Devices.** No completely satisfactory device for bark removal has been developed. Various peeling machines work reasonably well under limited conditions or with specific kinds of products. Few have been developed with the necessary mobility or portability to meet varying field conditions. Mechanical peelers include the following types.

| Type | Operation |
|---|---|
| 1. Machines that rupture cambium | Predominantly crushing action; loosens the cambium and permits direct removal of bark. |
|   a. Hammer peelers | Hammers strike log or bolt as it is fed beneath them; the log may or may not be rotated. |
|   b. Chain peelers | Either slack or tight chains which beat the bark off, or crush and squeeze the bark off. |
|   c. Drums | Material is tumbled in cylinders; friction and pounding erode away bark; may have internal projections to increase efficiency; drum may rotate or be stationary. |
|   d. Semidrums | Material is rolled in cylinders with top open; seldom portable. |
| 2. Knife cutting machines | Operated as jointers or planers, or cutting heads are lowered to the log or bolt, which is rotated; some are of the lathe type, but generally the log is rotated; they may remove an appreciable volume of wood in the process; individual pieces are processed, so quality and size of raw material are important. |
| 3. Hydraulic machines | A late development (West Coast). |

## Land Transport

For the construction and maintenance of logging roads, see Section **18**, Forest Road Engineering.

**MANUAL.** Except for very short distances, such as are involved in loading or unloading, manual transportation of forest products is seldom used in North America. The hand tools (pulphooks, canthooks, and peaveys) used in these operations are described earlier in this section under "Hand Tools."

**ANIMAL.** For several years internal combustion engines have been replacing horse, mule, and ox on logging jobs all over the country. Now it seems that this trend has been partly reversed. Even in the Pacific Northwest, as loggers begin selective cutting in second-growth stands and as they get into the smaller timber on rugged upper slopes, there is increased interest in animal logging.

An intelligent, woods-wise horse or mule often works without reins or words of command, bringing single sticks or two or three small sticks to the landing, stopping with the load in position to be unhooked, and after being unhooked going back to the woods by himself to have another load attached. Where relatively small timber is being selectively cut, and skidding distances do not exceed about 400 ft., the single skidding horse is usually about the most efficient and economical method of removing forest products from the woods.

Over such short distances it is generally not worth while to use a scoot or sled because the loss of maneuverability will offset the larger loads possible with such antifriction devices. For ground skidding, a log chain is used, consisting of links $\frac{3}{8}$ in. to $\frac{1}{2}$ in. in diameter, 10 to 16 ft. long, with a slip hook at one end and a grab hook at the other. The singletree (whiffletree) used in back of the horse is also equipped with a grab hook at the center so that the chain can be gripped at any point (Fig. 22).

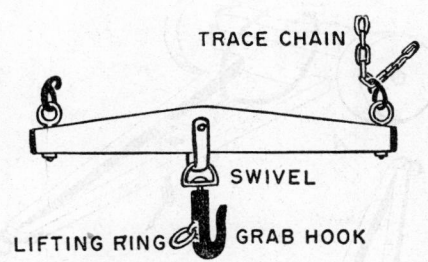

TRACE CHAIN

SWIVEL

LIFTING RING    GRAB HOOK

Fig. 22. Singletree (whiffletree) for logging.

For bigger logs there are several antifriction devices used with a single skidding animal. The simplest is the crotch or lizard; others are the go-devil, a simple, loosely articulated sled without thills (shafts) or tongue; and the more elaborate yarding sled, dray, and scoot (Fig. 23).

Logging teams are more directly in competition with the tractor and truck, and their use will probably continue to decline. Antifriction devices used with teams include the yarding sled, dray, and scoot, in larger, sturdier models with a tongue instead of thills. In more level open woods, typical of the South, bummers (Fig. 24) and log carts are also used.

Ground skidding with a team is done with a skidding chain or sometimes with a pair of skidding tongs. In the Appalachians long trains of logs, connected with

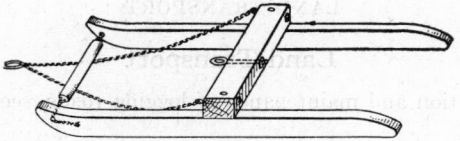

The go-devil.

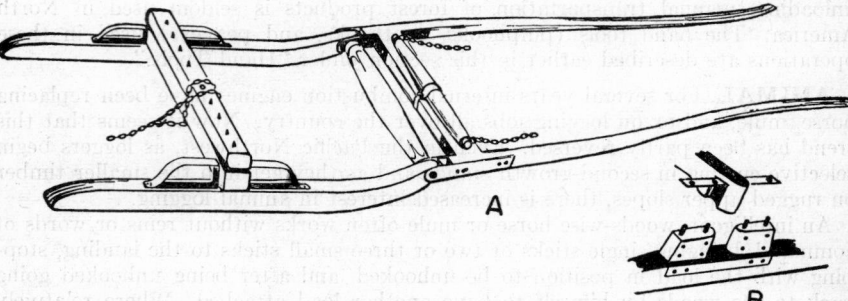

A, details of the yarding sled; B, another method of attaching bunks.

The travois, or dray.

**Fig. 23. Sleds for use with a single horse.**

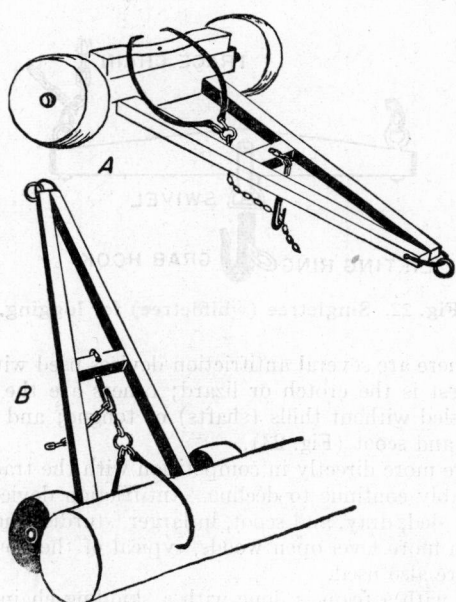

**Fig. 24. A, bummer; B, method of loading the bummer.**

**16 · 22**

log dogs or grabs, are frequently brought down the slopes. These dogs are connected in pairs by a short length of chain, with a swivel link at the center. They are driven into the logs with a grab maul, which is a sturdy wooden handle encased at the lower end with about a 1-in.-thick ring of soft iron (Fig. 25). At the landing they are removed with a grab skipper, which is a sledge with one face extended to a long point (Fig. 25).

A. Grab maul.

B. Grab skipper.

### Fig. 25. Tools for driving or removing grabs.

In considering whether an animal or tractor will be more economical for a given job, many factors must be taken into account. Productivity of animals will vary under different conditions more than that of tractors because animals tire and must be rested during or after extreme efforts. The heavier the loads, and the steeper the grades, the more rest time they will need. Costs of feed vary more than that of diesel and lubricating oil. Animals have to be fed and cared for during the periods when they are not working. On the other hand, tractors call for a higher initial investment, tractor operators usually command higher wages than teamsters, and tractor maintenance and repairs are much more costly than treatment of sick or injured stock. The results of one comparison of team and tractor costs are given in Table 4.

### Table 4. Cost of Skidding Compared for Team and Tractor

| Team and driver | | | | Tractor and operator | | | |
|---|---|---|---|---|---|---|---|
| Skidding distance (feet) | Cost per day | Bd. ft. skidded per day | Cost per M bd. ft | Skidding distance (feet) | Cost per day | Bd. ft. skidded per day | Cost per M bd. ft. |
| 200 | $12 | 6,250 | $1.92 | 300 | $26.88 | 11,900 | $2.26 |
| 400 | 12 | 4,425 | 2.71 | 500 | 26.88 | 10,340 | 2.60 |
| 600 | 12 | 3,425 | 3.50 | 1,000 | 26.88 | 7,680 | 3.50 |

Source: Northeastern Forest Exp. Sta., Comparison of skidding costs per thousand board feet, team and tractor, at various distances, *Sta. Paper No. 18*, 1948.

**CHUTES (DRY).** The use of chutes in North American logging has been declining. Long chutes are expensive, and their design calls for considerable engineering ability. Chutes are best adapted to moving wood or logs down steep slopes from a plateau or series of benches, where at least 1 cord of wood is available per foot of chute length. On the slope itself this quantity of wood is rarely available for direct delivery to the chute.

**Pole Chutes.** These, made from local material, are by far the most common. Peeled hardwood poles, unless too crooked, are better than softwood poles. Chutes must be substantially built, and the smoother their contour, both vertical and horizontal, the less the wood skips and bounces in them. Good construction of cross-sections at varying heights above the ground is shown in Fig. 26.

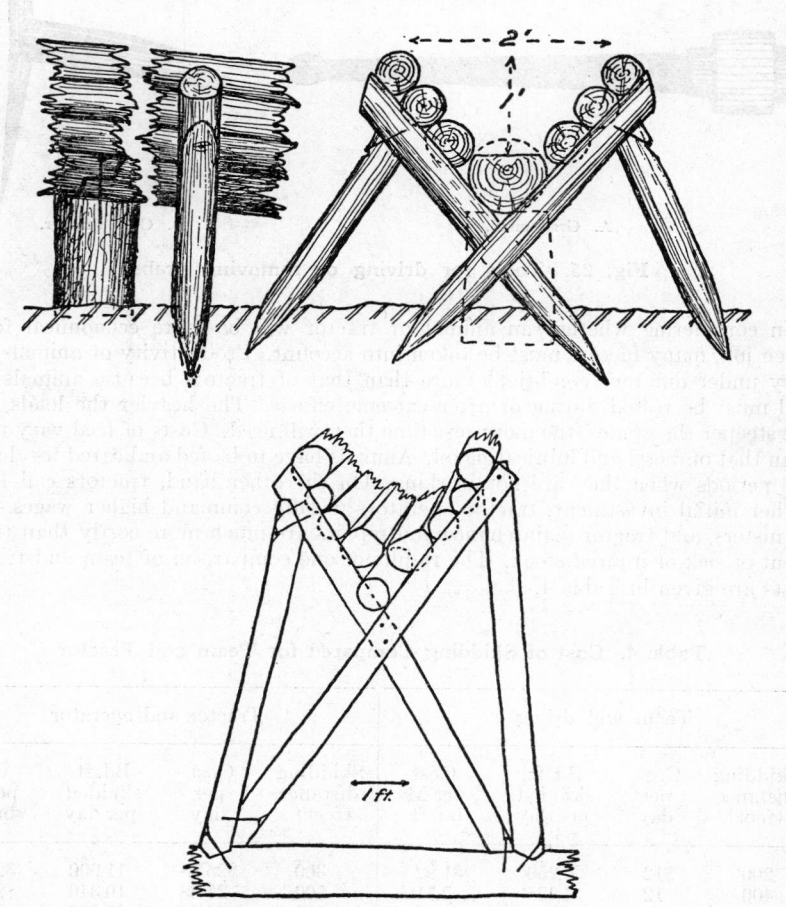

**Fig. 26. Types of pole chutes (eastern Canada).**

Above: supports are those used when trough is 5 ft. or less above the ground. Below: a good type of trough and trestle bent for a V-shaped chute. (Alexander M. Koroleff and R. C. Bryant, The transportation of wood in chutes, *Yale School of Forestry Bull. No. 34,* 1932.)

**Grades.** Minimum vertical angles (average angle of repose), in degrees, are shown below for chutes transporting different classes of material:

### Table 5. Minimum Vertical Angles for Chutes

|  | Dry chutes | Wet chutes | Snow chutes |
|---|---|---|---|
| Boles (27–100 ft. long).............. | 19 | 8.5 | 7.0 |
| Logs (10–26 ft. long)................ | 21 | 10.0 | 7.5 |
| Bolts (6–7 ft. long)................. | 22 | 12.0 | 8.5 |
| Firewood, split, hardwood........... | 22 | 14.0 | 8.5 |
| Firewood, split, softwood........... | 24 | 17.0 | 12.0 |

On unavoidably steep pitches or long sustained grades, brakes are essential. The most generally successful devices are "bear traps," or "wolf brakes"—one or more poles with one end suspended above the chute and the other lying in it— illustrated in Figs. 27 and 28.

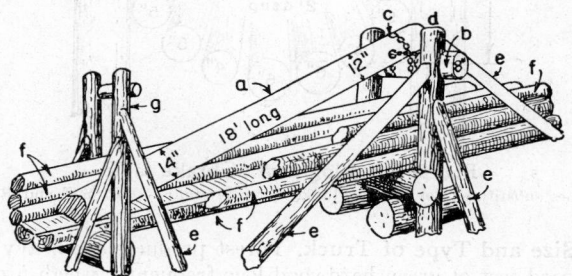

### Fig. 27. Side view of a typical rigid-axis wolf brake.

(a) Brake arm; (b) cross support on which the brake arm rests and to which it is chained; (c) chain used to fasten the arm to the cross support; (d) and (e) supporting posts and braces; (f) logs comprising the chute channel; (g) framework to hold arm in position and to prevent it from being thrown too high in the air. (Koroleff and Bryant, *op. cit.*)

**Curves.** Lateral, as well as vertical curves, should ordinarily be avoided. Where lateral curves are used as a braking device, the convex side of the chute must be built higher to prevent wood from jumping out. The radius of a successful lateral curve must be increased with the length of the wood being chuted, and with variation **in either direction** from its optimum velocity. Generally a radius of about 100 ft. is the minimum for 4-ft. bolts, and 300 ft. for standard length logs. The most successful lateral curves are those which are in the form of a spiral rather than a true segment of a circle, with more gentle curvatures leading into, and if possible out of, the more abrupt curve.

**Metal Chutes.** Metal chutes, both of steel and of hard aluminum alloys, have been the subject of considerable experimentation but of only limited practical application. Theoretically, the first cost of a metal chute would be higher than that of a pole chute, but it could be used again and again. However, when it is mounted on trestles of material obtained locally, installation costs of metal chutes have been found to be about as high as those of pole chutes.

**TRUCKS.** Motor trucks have become by far the most common means of transport of forest products from the landing in the woods to the mill. They are particularly adapted to scattered stands and to integrated logging.

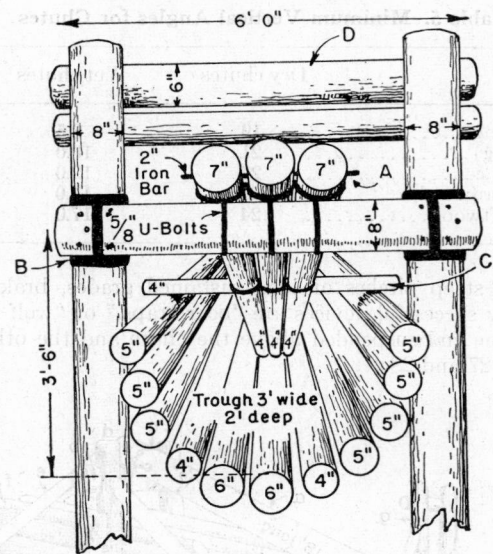

**Fig. 28. A 3-log arm or brake table.**
This is sometimes substituted for a 1-log brake on wide chutes. (Koroleff and Bryant, *op. cit.*)

**Choice of Size and Type of Truck.** Forest products are heavy commodities. A thousand board feet of green hardwood logs frequently weigh 5 or more tons; of green softwood logs, about 3.5 tons. Consequently, there has been a tendency among logging operators to overload their trucks, and to use heavier and heavier trucks. Overloading usually results in excessive truck maintenance costs, high depreciation, serious accidents, or fines for exceeding state limits on truck weights.

On private logging roads, state limits do not apply. They frequently are exceeded, particularly in the West. On the other hand, on many logging jobs in the East and South they cannot be approached because of the lower weight limitations of rural roads and bridges.

Table 6 reviews comparative specifications for representative trucks used in logging.

**Small vs. large trucks.** Large trucks have a high per-minute cost when not working; small trucks have a high volume-unit-mile cost when traveling. Therefore any factor which increases loading or nonworking time, either absolutely or relative to time at the stump plus that from stump to mill, favors the small truck. Scattered stands and smaller logs increase loading time; good roads decrease travel time. Their combined effect on cost of truck transportation is illustrated below:

**Assume** the following conditions:

|                               | 3-ton truck | 10-ton truck |
| ----------------------------- | ----------- | ------------ |
| Average load ................................ | 2,000 bd. ft. | 6,000 bd. ft. |
| Fixed cost per minute..................... | $0.04       | $0.12        |
| Operating cost per hour .................. | $6.00       | $14.00       |

Table 6. Comparative Specifications for Representative Trucks Used in Logging in the United States, 1950

| Size class [a] | Make | Model | Type [j] | Fuel | Max. net brake hp. | Wheelbase (in.) | Net vehicle weight: chassis and cab (lbs.) | Recommended max. gross vehicle weight (lb.) | Approx. price (chassis and cab) F.O.B. factory |
|---|---|---|---|---|---|---|---|---|---|
| (c) | Chevrolet, Detroit, Mich. | 6503 | 4×2 | Gas | 98 | 179 | 5,150 | 16,000 | $2,200 |
| (d) | Ford, Dearborn, Mich. | 9E8Q-8 | 4×2 | Gas | 145 | 178 | 6,130 | 19,000 | 3,135 |
| (e) | Gen. Motors, Pontiac, Mich. | HF-620 | 4×2 | Gas | 155 | 165, 183, 201 | 8,600 | 23,000 | 4,763 |
| | Int. Harv., Chicago, Ill. | HDCR-640 | 4×2 | Diesel | 133 | 141, 153, 165 | 9,305 | 22,000 | 7,389 |
| (f) | Int. Harv., Chicago, Ill. | L-210 | 4×2 | Gas or Diesel | 162 | 175 | 11,000 | 30,000 | (b) |
| | Autocar, Ardmore, Pa. | C-7064S | 6×4 | Gas | 165 | 200-248 | 13,800 | 38,000 | 10,635 |
| | Autocar, Ardmore, Pa. | DC-10064 | 6×4 | Diesel | 165 | 204-252 | 17,800 | 40,000 | 14,050 |
| (g) | Sterling, Milwaukee, Wis. | HB-2755 | 6×4 | Gas | 172 | Variable | 15,900 | 57,500 | 15,700 |
| | Sterling, Milwaukee, Wis. | HA-2755D | 6×4 | Diesel | 150 | Variable | 17,300 | 57,500 | 18,400 |
| | Four-Wheel Drive, Clintonville, Wis. | M-6×6-6 | 6×6 | Gas | 186 | 243 | 21,000 | 60,000 | 20,930 |
| | Four-Wheel Drive, Clintonville, Wis. | M-6×6-D | 6×6 | Diesel | 180 | 243 | 21,600 | 60,000 | 22,330 |
| (h) | Sterling, Milwaukee, Wis. | SF-6506D | 6×4 | Diesel | 266 | Variable | 44,500 | 130,000 | 51,000 |
| | Kenworth, Seattle, Wash. | 584 | 6×4 | Gas or Diesel | 150-300 | 211 + or − | 30,000 | 180,000 [i] | (b) |

[a] Size classes used are (recommended gross vehicle weight):
4 — 14,001-16,000 lb.
5 — 16,001-19,500 lb.
6 — 19,501-26,000 lb.
7 — 26,001-50,000 lb.
8 — 50,001-100,000 lb.
9 — Over 100,000 lb.

[b] Information not supplied by manufacturer.
[c] Trucks of this size also built by Chevrolet, Dodge, Duplex, FWD, and Studebaker.
[d] Trucks of this size also built by Chevrolet, Dodge, Duplex, FWD, General Motors, International Harvester, Studebaker, and Brock-way.

[e] Trucks of this size also built by Dodge, Duplex, Ford, FWD, International Harvester, Mack, Oshkosh, and Sterling.
[f] Trucks of this size also built by Dodge, Duplex, Federal, Diamond T, FWD, General Motors, Mack, Oshkosh, Reo, Sterling, Walter, Sicard, Euclid, Corbitt, and International Harvester.
[g] Trucks of this size also built by Federal, FWD, General Motors, International Harvester, Mack, Oshkosh, Sterling, Walter, Hayes, Euclid, Peterbilt, and Kenworth.
[h] Trucks of this size also built by Knuckey, Walter, Hayes, and Peterbilt; because of their size, they cannot be used on public highways.
[i] Gross combination weight (truck and trailer).
[j] Number of wheel hubs by number of hubs powered.

Then:

CASE 1. LOADING TIME 5 MIN. PER M BD. FT.; 30-MI. ROUND TRIP AT 15 MPH AVERAGE

| | 3-ton truck | | 10-ton truck | |
|---|---|---|---|---|
| | Total | Per M | Total | Per M |
| Loading cost .................... | $ 0.40 | $0.20 | $ 3.60 | $0.60 |
| Trip cost ....................... | 12.00 | 6.00 | 28.00 | 4.66 |
| Totals ...................... | $12.40 | $6.20 | $31.60 | $5.22 |

CASE 2. LOADING TIME 15 MIN. PER M BD. FT.; 30-MI. ROUND TRIP AT 30 MPH AVERAGE

| | 3-ton truck | | 10-ton truck | |
|---|---|---|---|---|
| | Total | Per M | Total | Per M |
| Loading cost .................... | $1.20 | $0.60 | $10.80 | $1.80 |
| Trip cost ....................... | 6.00 | 3.00 | 14.00 | 2.66 |
| Totals ...................... | $7.20 | $3.60 | $24.80 | $4.46 |

Source: *Northeastern loggers' handbook,* U. S. Dept. Agr., Handbook No. 6, 1951.

A method for computing fixed cost and operating cost for a truck is given in Table 7.

### Table 7. Sample Calculation of Truck Cost per Hour *

Special 6-cord, 6-by-4, Pulpwood Truck:

| | |
|---|---|
| Cost, complete with pulpwood rack............................ | $8,000 |
| Tire replacement cost (charged against mileage)............... | 1,000 |
| Net investment .............................................. | 7,000 |
| Average round trip .......................................... | 40 mi. |
| Working day ................................................. | 7.0 hr. |
| Working days per year ....................................... | 300 days |
| Depreciation period ........................................ | 5 yr. |
| Average fixed investment (60% of net investment)............. | $4,200 |

#### FIXED COST PER HOUR

| | Yearly | Daily | Hourly |
|---|---|---|---|
| Interest @ 6% on average fixed investment... | $ 252.00 | $ 0.84 | $0.120 |
| Depreciation (total net investment, 5 yr.).... | 1,400.00 | 4.67 | .667 |
| Insurance (estimated) ...................... | 350.00 | 1.17 | .167 |
| License fees (average) ..................... | 300.00 | 1.00 | .143 |
| Garage, storage, light, heat, water.......... | 300.00 | 1.00 | .143 |
| Repainting every 2 yr....................... | 50.00 | 0.17 | .024 |
| Driver's wages @ $1.50 per hr............... | 3,150.00 | 10.50 | 1.500 |
| Total fixed charges whether traveling or not.. | $5,802.00 | $19.35 | $2.76 |

Total fixed cost per minute: $0.046

#### OPERATING COST PER HOUR

| | |
|---|---|
| Tires, 5,000 hr. @ $1,000 per set ......................................... | $0.500 |
| Chassis repair (excluding accidents) ...................................... | .457 |
| Body and equipment maintenance ......................................... | .080 |
| Lubrication, inspection, adjustment ....................................... | .094 |
| Fuel, 3.8 gal. per hr. @ 20¢ ............................................. | .760 |
| Engine oil, 1 qt. every 5 hr. @ 25¢ ...................................... | .050 |
| Total operating cost per hour ............................................ | $1.941 |
| Total cost while traveling (fixed plus operating) ......................... | $4.70 |

* These cost figures are illustrative only. They were adapted from average cost figures provided by Mack–International Motor Truck Co. For any specific case the appropriate figures would have to be obtained and worked out as above.

Source: Northeast. Forest Exp. Sta., Choosing methods and equipment for logging, *Sta. Paper No. 18.*

Table 8. Comparison of Loading Costs for Skidway and Mechanical Loader Methods

| Method of loading | Volume loaded per day (M bd. ft.) | Loading time per M bd. ft. (min.) | Truck stand-by costs | | Skidway costs per M bd. ft. | Mechanical loader costs | | | | | | Total loading cost per M bd. ft. |
|---|---|---|---|---|---|---|---|---|---|---|---|---|
| | | | | | | Operating | | | Stand-by | | Cost per M | |
| | | | Per hour | Per M bd. ft. | | Cost per hour | Cost per M | Total time (hr.) | Cost per hour | Total cost | | |
| Rolling from skidways | 50 | 15 | $2.88 | $0.72 | $1 | ... | ... | ... | ... | ... | ... | $1.72 |
| Rolling from skidways | 10 | 15 | $2.88 | $0.72 | $1 | ... | ... | ... | ... | ... | ... | $1.72 |
| Mechanical loading crane | 50 | 5 | $2.88 | $0.24 | ... | $5 | $0.42 | 3.8[a] | $3 | $11.49 | $0.23 | $0.89 |
| Mechanical loading crane | 10 | 5 | $2.88 | $0.24 | ... | $5 | $0.42 | 7.2[b] | $3 | $21.51 | $2.15 | $2.81 |

[a] 480 min. (8-hr. day) minus 250 min. (loading 50 M bd. ft. @ 5 min. per M) = 230 min. or 3.8 hr.

[b] 480 min. minus 50 min. (loading 10 M bd. ft. @ 5 min. per M) = 430 min., or 7.2 hr.

### Table 9. Crawler Tractor

| Manufacturer | Model | Price F.O.B. factory October, 1950 Standard model [a] | Max. drawbar (hp.) | Fuel | Tread (in.) Standard | Hillside | Shipping weight standard [b] (lbs.) |
|---|---|---|---|---|---|---|---|
| Cletrac | HG | $1,860 | 21.85 | Gas | 42 | 68 | 3,163 |
| Deere | MC | 2,080 | 20.0 | Gas | | | 3,769 |
| Ustrac | 10–A | 2,595 | 20.4 | Gas | 29.5 | | 3,425 |
| Cletrac | AG | 3,350 | 30.60 | Gas | 42 | 50 | 7,086 |
| Cletrac | AD | 3,775 | 30.50 | Diesel | 42 | 50 | 7,662 |
| Caterpillar | D–2 | 3,625 | 32.00 | Diesel | 40 | 50 | 6,710 |
| International | T–6 | 3,235 | 32.92 | Gas | 40 | 50 | 6,750 |
| International | TD–6 | 3,610 | 31.30 | Diesel | 40 | 50 | 7,035 |
| Allis-Chalmers [c] | HD–5 | 5,605 | 40.26 | Diesel | 44 | 60 | 10,500 |
| Caterpillar | D–4 | 4,780 | 43.00 | Diesel | 44 | 60 | 10,065 |
| Cletrac | BG | 4,200 | 38.00 | Gas | 44 | 52 | 8,514 |
| Cletrac | BD | 4,880 | 38.05 | Diesel | 44 | 52 | 9,374 |
| International | T–9 | 4,255 | 42.98 | Gas | 44 | 60 | 9,300 |
| International | TD–9 | 4,863 | 40.50 | Diesel | 44 | 60 | 9,540 |
| Allis-Chalmers [c] | HD–9 | 9,705 | 70.00 | Diesel | 74 | | 18,800 |
| Caterpillar | D–6 | 7,605 | 65.00 | Diesel | 60 | 74 | 16,725 |
| Cletrac | DG | 5,975 | 60.67 | Gas | 48 | 61 | 12,472 |
| Cletrac | DD | 7,375 | 60.47 | Diesel | 48 | 61 | 13,233 |
| International | TD–14A | 7,462 | 65.90 | Diesel | 56 | 74 | 15,520 |
| Allis-Chalmers [c] | HD–15 | 13,915 | 102.00 | Diesel | 74 | | 27,850 |
| Caterpillar | D–7 | 10,385 | 80.44 | Diesel | 74 | 74 | 25,130 |
| International | TD–18A | 10,030 | 89.29 | Diesel | 62 | 74 | 22,570 |
| Allis-Chalmers [c] | HD–20 | 20,360 | Torque converter | Diesel | 84 | | 41,000 |
| Caterpillar | D–8 | 14,150 | 130.00 | Diesel | 78 | 78 | 35,570 |
| Cletrac | FDE | 13,800 | 110.00 | Diesel | 69 | | 29,760 |
| International | TD–24 | 17,750 | 148.43 | Diesel | 80 | | 37,500 |

[a] Hillside models slightly higher in cost.
[b] Hillside models slightly heavier in weight.
[c] Data as of September, 1951.

**Loading.** Hand-loading forest products on trucks and trailers has been one of the most costly and back-breaking phases of the logging operation. On operations where men are not employed exclusively on any one task, such as loading, the substitution of a power-loader does not always reduce costs. Table 8 shows why.

Obviously, the operator cutting only 10 M bd. ft. per day could not afford this type of mechanical loader.

## Comparison Chart

| Max. speed (mph) | Max. drawbar pull (lb.) | Recommended winch | Recommended arch/sulky |
|---|---|---|---|
| 5.25 | 3,060 | Carco SG winch | Carco junior logging sulky |
| 6.00 | 3,500 | | |
| 5.87 | 3,960 | | |
| | | | |
| 3.74 | 6,020 | Carco E winch | |
| 3.74 | 6,500 | Carco E winch | Carco standard logging sulky or arch |
| 5.10 | 6,250 | Hyster D–2–N towing winch; Hyster D–2 tractor donkey | Hyster logging sulky/ pneumatic tires or crawler tracks |
| 5.40 | 7,652 | Carco E winch; Isaacson WO–6A and WO–69 winch | |
| 5.40 | 7,710 | Carco E winch; Isaacson WO–6A and WO–69 winch | |
| | | | |
| 5.47 | 10,080 | Carco E winch | |
| 5.30 | 9,450 | Hyster D–4–N towing winch; Hyster D–4–N tractor donkey | Carco standard logging sulky or arch |
| 5.40 | 7,600 | Carco E winch | Hyster logging sulky/ pneumatic tires or crawler tracks |
| 5.41 | 8,012 | Carco E winch | Isaacson Karry–Kart– KK50 |
| 5.30 | 9,868 | Carco E winch; Isaacson WO–9A and WO–69 winch | |
| 5.30 | 9,900 | Carco E winch; Isaacson WO–9A and WO–69 winch | |
| | | | |
| 5.68 | 16,920 | Carco F winch; Carco R donkey | |
| 5.80 | 15,500 | Carco F winch; Hyster D–6–N towing winch; Hyster D–6–N tractor donkey | Carco junior arch Hyster 67 logging arch |
| 5.30 | 11,000 | Carco F winch | |
| | | | |
| 4.88 | 11,816 | Carco F winch | Isaacson Karry arch– KA60 |
| 5.70 | 14,652 | Carco F winch; Carco R donkey; Isaacson WO–14 winch | |
| | | | |
| 5.80 | 25,060 | Carco G winch; Carco T–donkey | Carco small or medium arch |
| 6.00 | 21,350 | Carco F winch; Carco T–donkey, Hyster D–7–N tow winch, Hyster D–7–L tractor donkey | Hyster 67 or 78 logging arch |
| 5.70 | 20,234 | Carco G winch; Carco T–donkey; Isaacson WO–18 winch | Isaacson Karry arch– KA80 |
| | | | |
| 7.00 | 36,900 | Carco J winch; Carco K–donkey | Carco redwood arch |
| 4.80 | 28,700 | Carco J winch, Carco K–donkey, Hyster D–8–N towing winch; Hyster D–8 tractor yarder | Hyster 78 or 80 logging arch |
| 4.95 | 26,800 | Carco J; Carco T; Carco K–8 | Isaacson Karry arch KA–140 |
| 7.80 | 33,714 | Isaacson WO–24 winch; Carco J winch | |

Recently several types of self-loaders for trucks have been developed which are relatively inexpensive and particularly efficient for loading scattered logs. One type has a winch mounted in back of the truck cab, powered by a power takeoff on the truck transmission. The winch cable is carried up a mast behind the truck cab and out to a sheave on the end of a swinging jib boom over the truck bed. These loaders are being successfully used throughout the country, not only to load but also to skid small logs for short distances. Several types are now commercially manufactured.

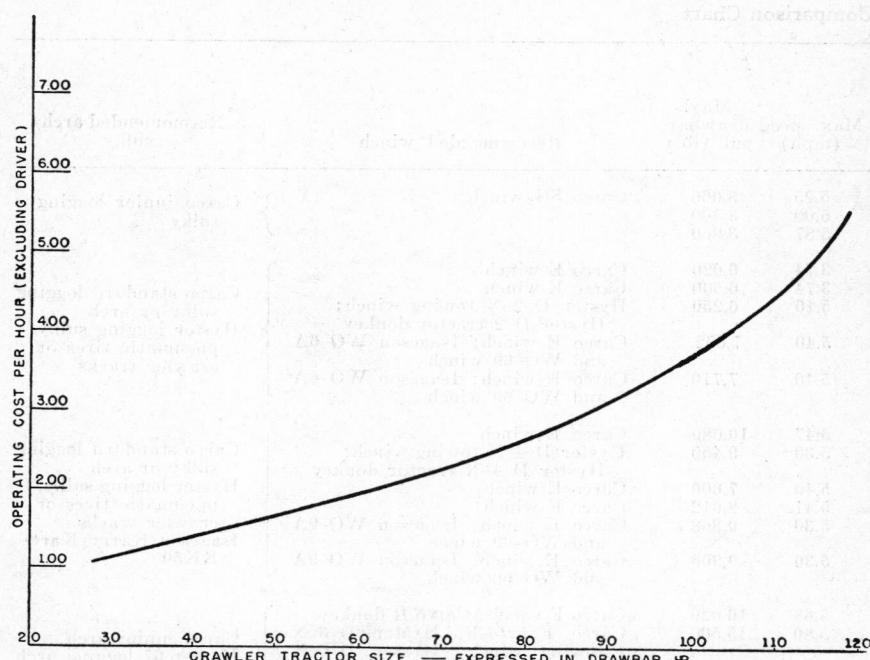

**Fig. 29. Estimated cost of owning and operating crawler tractors (cost data October, 1950).**

(International and Allis-Chalmers Tractor Companies.)

Another type uses a similarly mounted winch, but the cable is carried out under the truck bed to a pair of sheaves under the middle of the bed. From there the cable is carried out to one side of the bed, over another sheave and up a stake at the top of which there is another sheave. This provides the truck with its own crosshaul. A similar arrangement is being used to load bundles of pulpwood.

For short wood the most successful inexpensive loaders have been of the conveyor type. Some of these have been mounted on old automobile or wheel tractor chassis, but recently highly portable models have been developed that can be hung on the side of a pulp truck.

**TRACTORS.** By reason of their maneuverability, adaptability to a wide range of topographic conditions, and over-all economy, tractors have opened new possibilities in logging on every scale. They may also be used to build roads and fire lines, plow snow, and do many other forest jobs.

In some areas, notably the South, farm-type wheel tractors have been used successfully in skidding such small material as pulpwood, poles, small logs, and veneer blocks. A relatively new development is the half-track attachment available for Ford tractors. This innovation, which is easily attached to the standard tractor, is a great aid in boggy or swampy soil.

For heavy logging, however, the crawler tractor is required. Effectiveness and economy depend on the selection of a type, with suitable auxiliary equipment such as winches and arches, adapted to the particular job. Some of those in common use in the United States and Canada are described in Table 9.

**Estimated Cost of Owning and Operating Crawler Tractors.** Fig. 29 illustrates the estimated cost of owning and operating crawler tractors of various horsepowers. These data were furnished by the International and Allis-Chalmers Tractor Companies. It should be recognized that the figures do not include the operator's wages; also, they are only estimates, which will vary with changing economic conditions.

For an Allis-Chalmers HD5B tractor, with a maximum drawbar horsepower of 40.26, a total operating cost of $1.418 per hour (without operator's wage) is typical. It was computed as follows:

**Assume:**

| | |
|---|---|
| Delivery price (price F.O.B. factory plus shipping cost) | $4,966.25 |
| Depreciation period—years | 5 |
| Depreciation period—hours | 10,000 |
| Average investment [a] | $2,980.00 |

**Computation:**

| | | |
|---|---|---|
| Fixed cost per hour | | $1.121 |
| Interest, taxes, insurance [b] | $0.149 | |
| Depreciation [c] | 0.496 | |
| Repairs and labor [d] | 0.476 | |
| Operating cost per hour | | 0.297 |
| Fuel, diesel, 1.8 gal. @ 13¢ [e] | $0.224 | |
| Trans. and final drive oil, 0.2 gal. @ 80¢ | .016 | |
| Engine oil, 0.05 gal. @ 80¢ | .040 | |
| Replaceable filter element | .005 | |
| Track roller grease, 0.01 lb. @ 20¢ | .002 | |
| Miscellaneous grease, 0.05 lb. @ 20¢ | .010 | |
| Total cost per hour [f] | | $1.418 |

[a] Figured at 60% of the delivered cost with 5-yr. depreciation; 58.3% with 6-yr., 62.5% with 4-yr.
[b] In absence of specific figures, generally estimated at 10% of "average investment," yearly (interest 6%, taxes 2%, insurance and storage 2%).
[c] Delivered price divided by hours of life.
[d] Variable, but average 96% of delivered price.
[e] Consumption of fuel, oil, and grease varies with age of tractor and operating conditions; unit price varies with locality, quality, and quantity contracted at one time.
[f] Does not include operator's wage, which is highly variable. Other tabular data based on field operations in August, 1950.

**Production Potentials.** Some of the factors affecting production of tractor skidding are:

1. Tractive effort available. Traction is a function of weight, and varies from 85 percent of equipped tractor weight in excellent soil conditions to 35 percent in poorly cohesive soils.
2. Grade resistance. Adverse grade increases the pull required for each ton of payload and tractor at the rate of 20 lb. per ton for each 1 percent of grade.
3. Sliding resistance of logs per ton. This varies from about 1,100 lb. per ton on wet black soil to about 1,800 lb. per ton on dry clay soil. Large logs have less sliding resistance per ton of weight than small logs.
4. Rolling resistance of tractor, arches, and sulkies. This varies with ground surface conditions and the type of equipment used (see Table 10).
5. Skidding method. Whether logs are ground-skidded or with arch or sulky.

**Table 10. Pounds Required to Haul a Ton of Gross Load Over Different Types of Surface, on Level Ground**

| Type of surface | Steel tires, plain bearings | High-pressure rubber tires, antifriction bearings | Nontrussed crawler-track type of wheels | Low-pressure rubber tires, antifriction bearings |
|---|---|---|---|---|
| Smooth concrete ......... | 40 | 35 | 55 | 45 |
| Macadam, good .......... | 70 | 65 | 65 | 55 |
| Earth roads, dusty ....... | 120 | 110 | 80 | 70 |
| Unplowed earth .......... | 190 | 150 | 110 | 80 |
| Plowed earth ............. | 225 | 190 | 130 | 90 |
| Earth road, uneven or muddy surface ......... | 250 | 210 | 160 | 180 |
| Loose sand or gravel ..... | 300 | 275 | 180 | 240 |
| Very muddy, sticky soil ... | 400 | 350 | 225 | 320 |

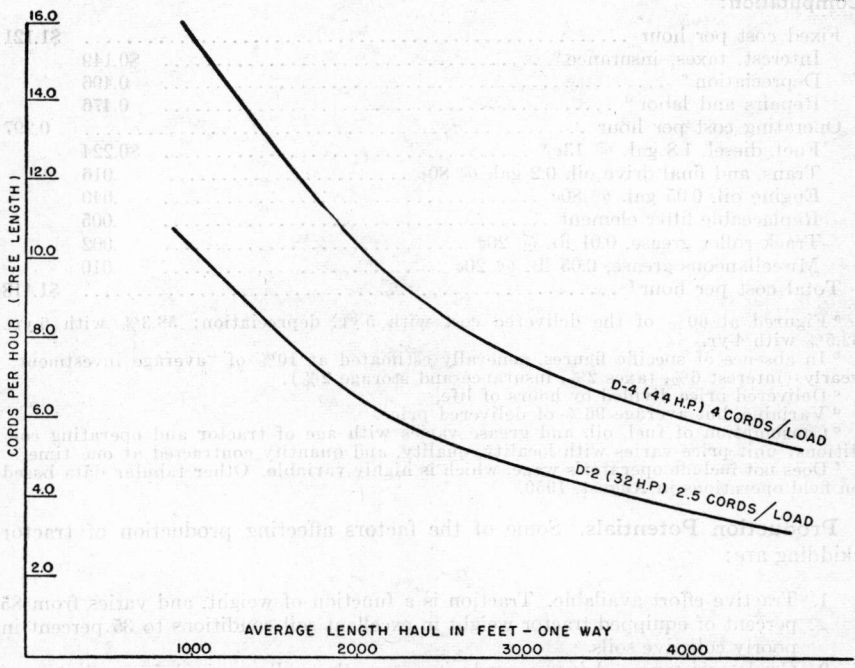

**Fig. 30. Estimated hourly production with Caterpillar tractors equipped with winch and Hyster logging sulky with pneumatic tires.**

(Caterpillar Tractor Co.)

**Pulpwood.** Fig. 30 gives an approximate indication of the pulpwood production potentials of a crawler tractor equipped with winch and sulky, under specified conditions; it was prepared from data furnished by the Caterpillar Tractor Company. Assume ideal conditions of level ground, balanced operation, 100 percent operating efficiency, and logs weighing approximately 43 lb. per cu. ft.; 50-min. hours, 6 min. per load for hooking and unhooking, with loads prebunched; average travel speed: loaded (second gear) 220 ft. per min. and unloaded (fifth gear), 449 ft. per min.

About 60 percent of the figures indicated on this graph should be used for a fairly good pulpwood operation, with no adverse grades. For difficult operations as little as 35 percent of the amount indicated should be used. Factors to be considered in using these data are: (1) difficulty in maintaining average cords per load, (2) topography and soils, (3) undergrowth, (4) weather, (5) altitude, (6) mechanical condition of equipment, (7) density of stands, (8) variable weight of logs in mixed stands of timber, and (9) efficiency of over-all operation.

**Saw logs.** The estimated hourly production of saw logs by various size Caterpillar tractors, equipped with Hyster winches and sulky or arch, and under the conditions described in the first footnote, is shown in Table 11.

To determine the theoretical log-carrying and grade-negotiating capacity of any tractor or tractor-arch combination, the tractor drawbar pull, rolling resistance, grade resistance, and sliding resistance of load must be known.

**Example 1.** Ground skidding method. Given:
1. 100 lb. per ton is an average tractor rolling resistance, which is already deducted in the drawbar pull figures published by the tractor manufacturer.
2. Ground conditions are such, however, that the rolling resistance is 150 lb. per ton.
3. Equipped tractor weight approximately 9½ tons.
4. Drawbar pull in second gear is 14,000 lb.
5. The log sliding resistance per ton of log weight for 16 ft. logs on dry clay is 1,700 lb. per ton.
6. Logs weigh 12,000 lb. per M bd. ft.

Find: Load carrying capacity.
1. 9½-ton tractor × 50 lb. per ton of extra rolling resistance effort (on account of ground conditions) = 475 lb.
2. 14,000-lb. drawbar pull − 475 lb. = 13,525 lb.
3. 13,525/1,700 = 8 tons of payload.
4. At 12,000 lb. per M bd. ft. = 6 tons.
5. 8/6 = 1.3 M bd. ft.

Answer: 1.3 M bd. ft. load carrying capacity on level or slight downgrade.

**Example 2.** Arch logging. Given:
1. Same data as in above example.
2. Combined weight of winch and arch 4.6 tons.

Find: Load carrying capacity.
1. 9½-ton tractor × 50 lb. per ton of extra rolling resistance effort on account of ground conditions = 475 lb.
2. Rolling resistance winch and arch = 4.6 × 150 = 690 lb. Total extra rolling resistance = 1,165 lb.
3. 14,000-lb. drawbar pull − 1,165 = net drawbar pounds pull available = 12,835 lb.
4. Assume 50 percent of weight of log is carried on arch and 50 percent is dragging on ground. Then log sliding resistance = 50% × 1,700 lb. per ton = 850 lb. per ton, plus rolling resistance = 50% × 150 = 75 lb. per ton; total = 925 lb.
5. 12,835/925 = 13.9 tons payload.

**Table 11. Hourly Volume in Board Feet of Logs Skidded Various Distances by Crawler Tractors, Logs in 32 Ft. Lengths.**

| Tractor | Average diameter of logs | Average No. of logs per load | Average bd. ft. per load | Average length of haul in feet—one way | | | | | |
|---|---|---|---|---|---|---|---|---|---|
| | | | | 500 | 1,000 | 1,500 | 2,500 | 3,500 | 4,500 |
| **Caterpillar D-2, D2N towing winch and Hyster logging sulky with pneumatic tires** | 8 | 15.0 | 480 | 2,570 | 1,890 | 1,650 | 1,056 | 816 | 662 |
| Average travel speeds | 12 | 7.0 | 896 | 4,800 | 3,520 | 3,090 | 1,960 | 1,520 | 1,240 |
| Loaded, 2d gear—220 f.p.m. | 16 | 4.0 | 1,120 | 6,000 | 4,400 | 3,850 | 2,460 | 1,900 | 1,545 |
| Unloaded, 5th gear—449 f.p.m. | 28 | 1.0 | 1,152 | 6,170 | 4,530 | 3,960 | 2,530 | 1,960 | 1,580 |
| **Caterpillar D-4, D4N towing winch and Hyster logging sulky with pneumatic tires** | 8 | 20.0 | 640 | 3,400 | 2,500 | 2,100 | 1,380 | 1,050 | 885 |
| Average travel speeds | 12 | 9.0 | 1,152 | 6,100 | 4,500 | 3,780 | 2,490 | 1,885 | 1,570 |
| Loaded, 2d gear—211 f.p.m. | 16 | 5.0 | 1,440 | 7,630 | 5,600 | 4,720 | 3,110 | 2,360 | 1,960 |
| Unloaded, 4th gear—475 f.p.m. | 28 | 1.3 | 1,498 | 7,940 | 5,840 | 4,900 | 3,230 | 2,460 | 2,040 |
| **Caterpillar D-6, D6N towing winch and D6N logging arch** | 16 | 9.0 | 2,880 | | 10,600 | 8,320 | 5,790 | 4,430 | 3,600 |
| Average travel speeds | 20 | 5.3 | 2,970 | | 10,950 | 8,600 | 5,970 | 4,570 | 3,710 |
| Loaded, 2d gear—202 f.p.m. | 32 | 2.0 | 2,940 | | 10,850 | 8,500 | 5,900 | 4,530 | 3,680 |
| Unloaded, 4th gear—387 f.p.m. | 44 | 1.0 | 2,960 | | 10,900 | 8,560 | 5,950 | 4,550 | 3,700 |
| **Caterpillar D-7, D7N towing winch and D7N logging arch** | 16 | 9.0 | 2,880 | | 10,300 | 8,500 | 5,750 | 4,370 | 3,570 |
| Average travel speeds | 20 | 8.0 | 4,480 | | 15,900 | 12,800 | 8,900 | 6,860 | 5,560 |
| Loaded, 2d gear—194 f.p.m. | 32 | 3.0 | 4,400 | | 15,600 | 12,600 | 8,750 | 6,750 | 5,460 |
| Unloaded, 4th gear—405 f.p.m. | 44 | 1.5 | 4,440 | | 15,500 | 12,650 | 8,800 | 6,740 | 5,500 |
| **Caterpillar D-8, D8N towing winch and D8N logging arch** | 16 | 12.0 | 3,840 | | 13,300 | 10,300 | 7,200 | 5,400 | 4,400 |
| Average travel speeds: | 20 | 10.0 | 5,600 | | 19,400 | 15,000 | 10,300 | 7,900 | 6,400 |
| Loaded, 2d gear—194 f.p.m. | 32 | 4.0 | 5,900 | | 20,500 | 15,900 | 10,900 | 8,300 | 6,700 |
| Unloaded, 4th gear—317 f.p.m. | 44 | 2.0 | 5,900 | | 20,500 | 15,900 | 10,900 | 8,300 | 6,700 |

These estimated production figures are calculated and are based entirely upon ideal conditions of level ground, a balanced operation, 100% operating efficiency, and logs weighing 13 lb. per bd. ft. Doyle Scale and 11 lb. per bd. ft. Scribner Scale. Fifty-min. hours are used; 6 min. per load for hooking and unhooking; and loads of more than three trees to be bunched for the sulky tractor (D-2, D-4), and loads of more than four trees to be bunched for the arch tractor (D-6, D-7, D-8).

For fairly good logging operations with no adverse grades for the loaded haul, 70% of the above figures should be used; for difficult operations, 40% of the above figures may be used.

Loads skidded by the D-2 and D-4 tractors were computed by using the Scribner Rule; those skidded by the D-6, D-7, and D-8 were computed by using the Doyle Rule.

Source: Caterpillar Tractor Co.

6. At 12,000 lb. per M bd. ft. = 6 tons.
7. 13.9/6 = 2.3 M bd. ft.

Answer: 2.3 M bd. ft. carrying capacity on level or slight downgrade.

The above example indicates that it is possible almost to double the payload by using a winch and arch with the tractor. While this is not always true, it is safe to say that tractor-sulky or tractor-arch logging will generally increase production by 50 percent. Fig. 31 shows the relatively greater efficiency of arch logging over drawbar skidding (data furnished by the Pacific Car and Foundry Co.). About 25 percent general saving in maintenance and repairs is obtained by this method. The log load can be dropped when the tractor reaches boggy or rocky ground, and the tractor is then moved up to better footing, where the load is winched up to the tractor for further transportation; the arch delivers cleaner logs, thereby saving mill saws.

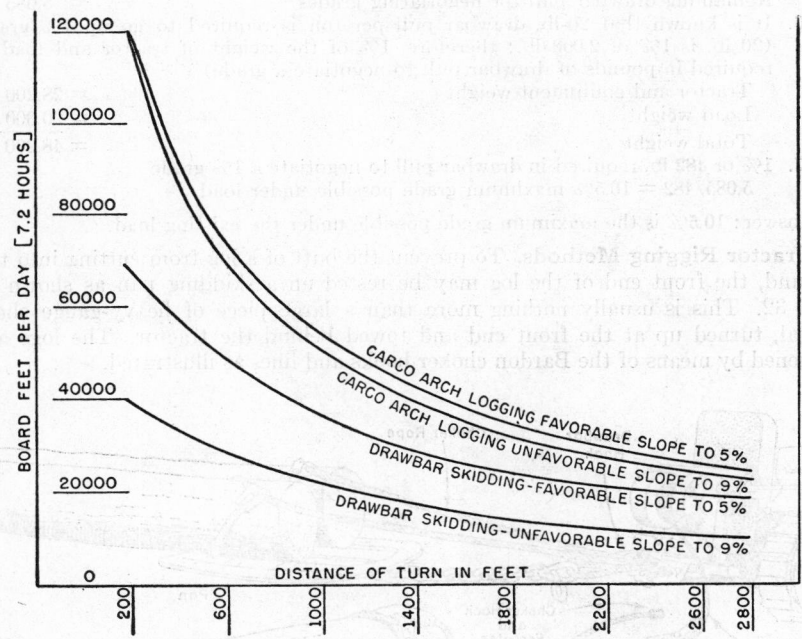

Fig. 31. **Arch logging vs. drawbar skidding.**

Average stand 17,500 bd. ft. per acre, 5 logs per M, 32-ft. log lengths; tractor gross weight 21,000 lb., approximately 75 horsepower. (Pacific Car and Foundry Co.)

A loaded uphill grade up to 5 percent is generally considered acceptable; the maximum uphill grade should not exceed 10 percent, except under special conditions. The maximum empty uphill grade should not exceed 15 percent, although grades up to 30 percent can be negotiated. A predominance of steep grades may dictate the use of other logging methods, such as the high lead system, or the construction of arch logging roads that the tractor can economically negotiate.

**Example 3.** Grade negotiating determinations. Given:
1. Same data as in Example 1 except
   a. Tractor drawbar pull, first gear = 15,500 lb.
   b. Weight of log load 10 tons.

Find: Maximum grade under load.

| | | |
|---|---|---|
| 1. 9½-ton tractor × 50 lb. per ton of extra rolling resistance effort on account of ground conditions | = | 475 lb. |
| 2. Rolling resistance, empty winch and arch 4.6 × 150 | = | 690 lb. |
| 3. Assume ½ of log load (10 tons) is carried by arch 10/2 × 150 | = | 750 lb. |
| 4. Assume ½ of log load dragged on ground 10/2 × 1,700 | = | 8,500 lb. |
| Total | = | 10,415 lb. |

Therefore, 10,415 lb. of drawbar pull will be required to overcome rolling and sliding resistance on level ground.

5. Total drawbar pull available in first gear       15,500 lb.
   Drawbar pull required to overcome rolling and sliding resistance     10,415 lb.
   Remaining drawbar pull for negotiating grades   =   5,085 lb.
6. It is known that 20-lb. drawbar pull per ton is required to go up 1% grade (20 lb. is 1% of 2,000 lb.); therefore, 1% of the weight of tractor and load is required in pounds of drawbar pull to negotiate a grade)
   Tractor and equipment weight       = 28,200 lb.
   Load weight       = 20,000 lb.
   Total weight       = 48,200 lb.
7. 1% or 482 lb. required in drawbar pull to negotiate a 1% grade
   5,085/482 = 10.5% maximum grade possible under load.

Answer: 10.5% is the maximum grade possible under the existing load.

**Tractor Rigging Methods.** To prevent the butt of a log from cutting into the ground, the front end of the log may be rested on a skidding pan as shown in Fig. 32. This is usually nothing more than a large piece of heavy-gauge sheet metal, turned up at the front end and towed behind the tractor. The logs are fastened by means of the Bardon choker hooks and lines as illustrated.

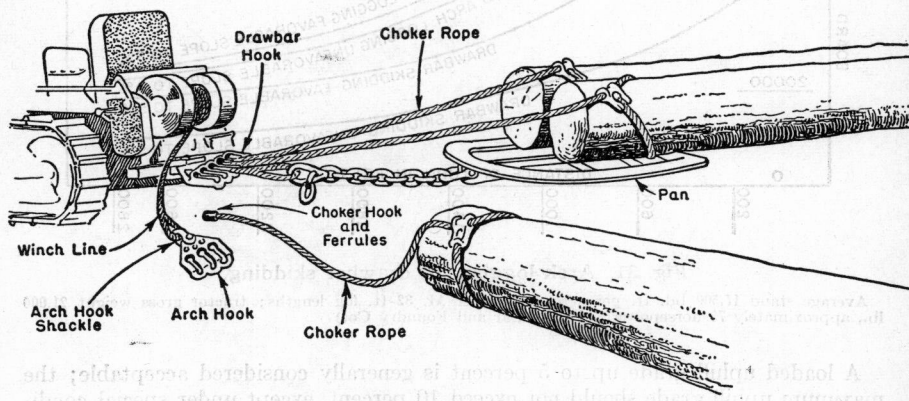

**Fig. 32. Tractor logging with skidding pan.**

To increase the capacity further, the tractor may be equipped with a winch. A capacity load can be made up by reaching for each log with the winch line and using the winch line as the drawbar when hauling. This method, also using

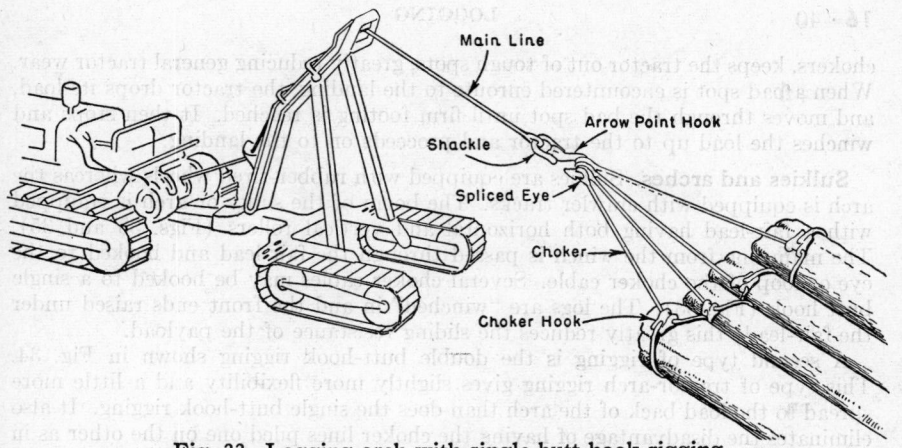

Main Line

Arrow Point Hook

Shackle

Spliced Eye

Choker

Choker Hook

Fig. 33. Logging arch with single butt-hook rigging.

A. Double butt-hook rigging.

Main Line

Spliced Eye

Shackle

Tag Line

Swivel

Choker Hook

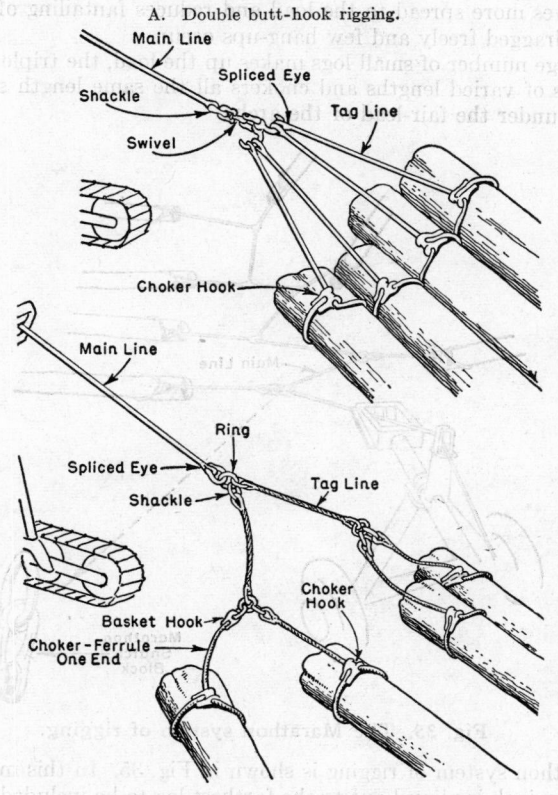

Main Line

Ring

Spliced Eye

Shackle

Tag Line

Choker Hook

Basket Hook

Choker — Ferrule One End

B. Double tag-line rigging.

Fig. 34. Methods of rigging, tractor-arch logging.

chokers, keeps the tractor out of tough spots, greatly reducing general tractor wear. When a bad spot is encountered enroute to the landing, the tractor drops its load, and moves through the bad spot until firm footing is reached. It then stops and winches the load up to the tractor and proceeds on to the landing.

**Sulkies and arches.** Sulkies are equipped with rubber-tired wheels whereas the arch is equipped with crawler tracks. The boom of the sulky or arch is equipped with a fair-lead having both horizontal and vertical rollers (Figs. 33 and 35). The main line from the winch is passed through the fair-lead and hooked to the eye or loop of the choker cable. Several choker cables may be hooked to a single butt hook (Fig. 33). The logs are "winched" in and the front ends raised under the fair-lead; this greatly reduces the sliding resistance of the payload.

A second type of rigging is the double butt-hook rigging shown in Fig. 34. This type of tractor-arch rigging gives slightly more flexibility and a little more spread to the load back of the arch than does the single butt-hook rigging. It also eliminates the disadvantage of having the choker lines piled one on the other as in a single butt-hook rigging.

Another type of rigging is the double tag-line rigging (Fig. 34). This rigging is often used in tractor-arch units when a large number of logs make up a load, because it gives more spread to the load and reduces fantailing of the free ends; the logs are dragged freely and few hang-ups occur.

When a large number of small logs makes up the load, the triple tag-line rigging with tag lines of varied lengths and chokers all the same length serves to spread the logs well under the fair-lead of the arch.

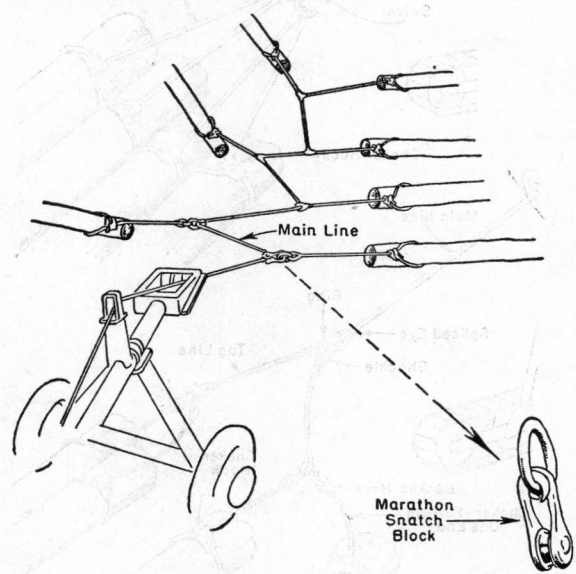

Fig. 35. The Marathon system of rigging.

The Marathon system of rigging is shown in Fig. 35. In this method, the main line from the winch is played out to the farthest log to be included in a given load. Additional logs, located between the end log and the fair-lead, are hooked to the

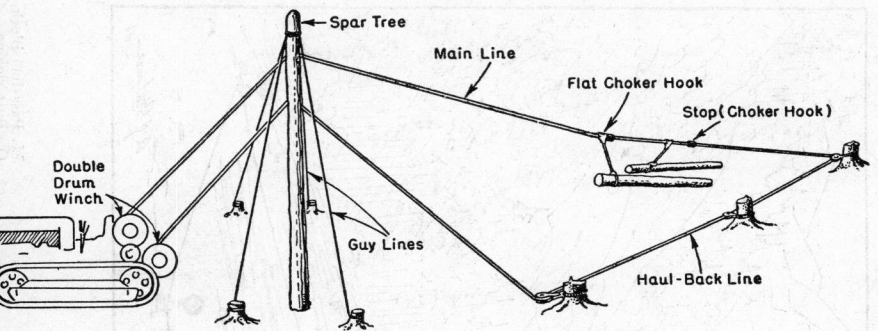

Fig. 36. Tractor equipped with double-drum winch used in high-lead logging.

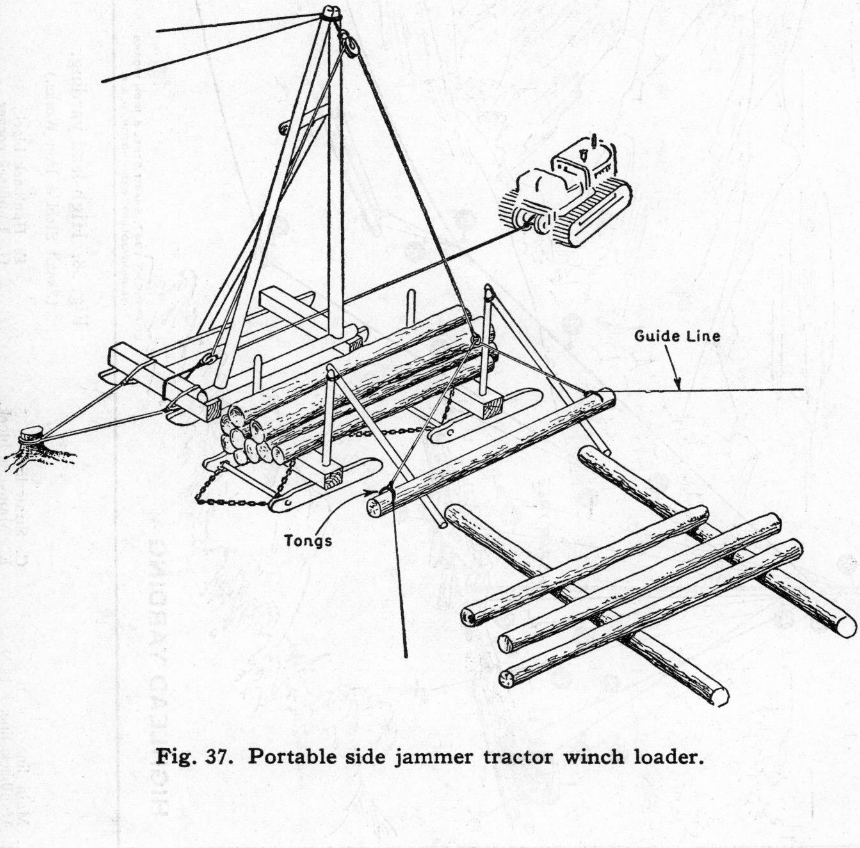

Fig. 37. Portable side jammer tractor winch loader.

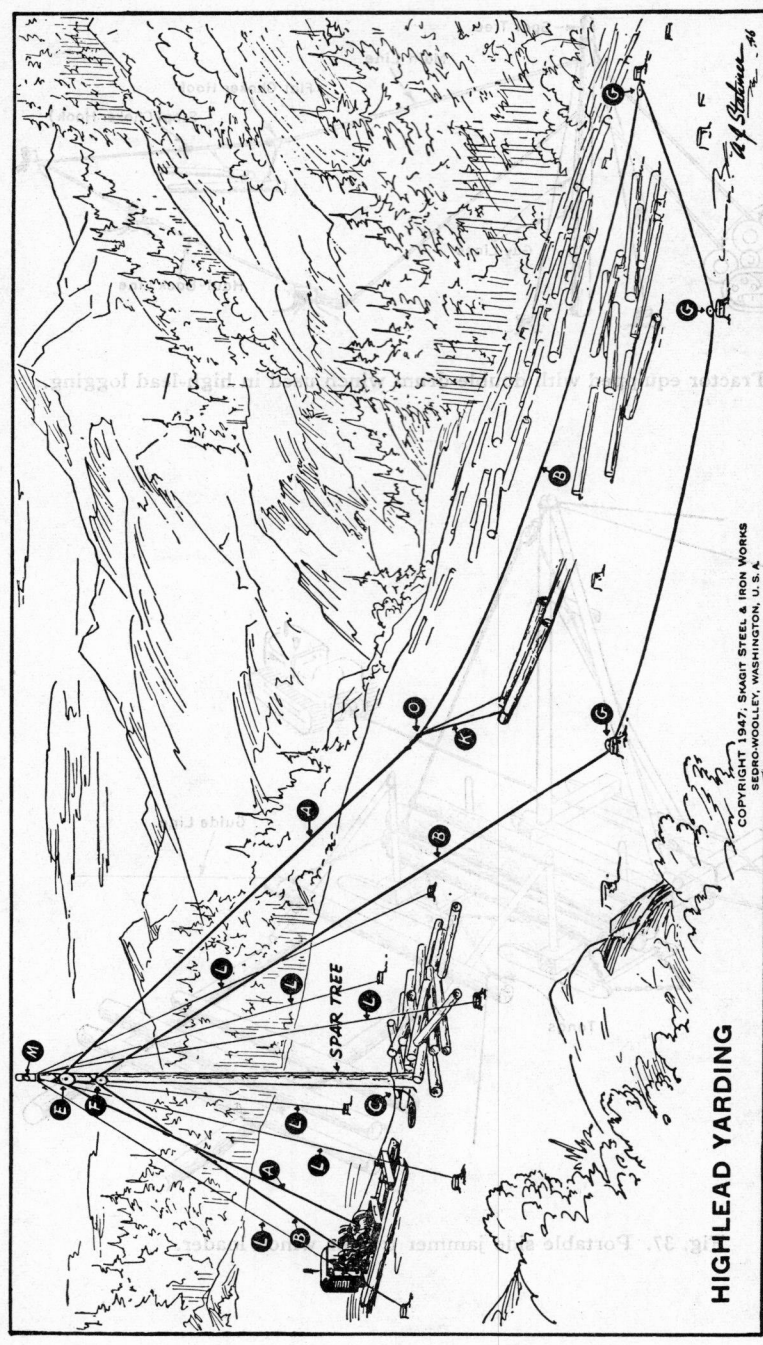

**HIGHLEAD YARDING**

COPYRIGHT 1947, SKAGIT STEEL & IRON WORKS
SEDRO-WOOLLEY, WASHINGTON, U.S.A.

## Fig. 38. High-lead yarding.
(Skagit Steel & Iron Works.)

A. Main line.
B. Haulback line.
C. Straw line.
E. Main-line block.
F. Haulback block.
G. Haulback corner
K. Chokers
L. Guy line.
M. Pass-line block.
O. Butt rigging.

main line by means of the Marathon snatch block (Fig. 35). Bunching under the fair-lead becomes automatic because the snatch blocks ride the main line when hauled in.

**Tractors in High-Lead Logging.** Tractors equipped with double- or triple-drum winches are often used in high-lead logging (Fig. 36). The tractor is securely anchored to a stump and one winch line is used as the main line and the other as the haulback line. Logs are cold-decked at the spar tree. There are, of course, many variations of this type of rigging, depending on local custom and conditions.

**Winch Loading.** Tractors equipped with winches are often used to load logs on trucks, sleighs, or drays. Again, there are numerous ways in which the tractors can be utilized as power units for loading; these may include simple A-frames (Fig. 37), A-frames with booms, gin poles, McLean or double-ton boom, etc.

**CABLE LOGGING SYSTEMS.** The essential equipment for a cable hauling system consists of:

1. A hoist, termed a "donkey" or "yarder," with two or more winches or drums, powered by an internal combustion engine through a multispeed transmission or a torque converter. A drum is required for each line used in the system rigged. Donkeys are commonly mounted on heavy timber sleds, and are also mounted on steel wheels, or truck chassis, and on barges or rafts. Two- and three-drum "tractor donkeys" are made for mounting on the rear end of crawler tractors (Fig. 36).

2. Wire rope and attachments: a main line for pulling in logs, a haulback

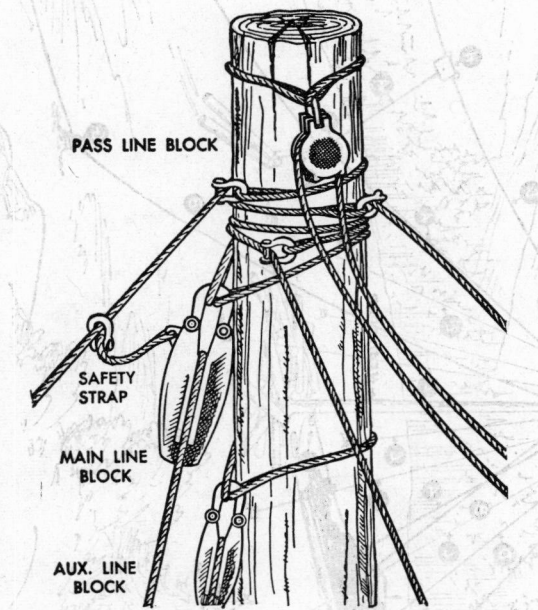

PASS LINE BLOCK

SAFETY
STRAP

MAIN LINE
BLOCK

AUX. LINE
BLOCK

**Fig. 39. Method of rigging a spar tree for high-lead logging.**
(Allis-Chalmers Mfg. Co.)

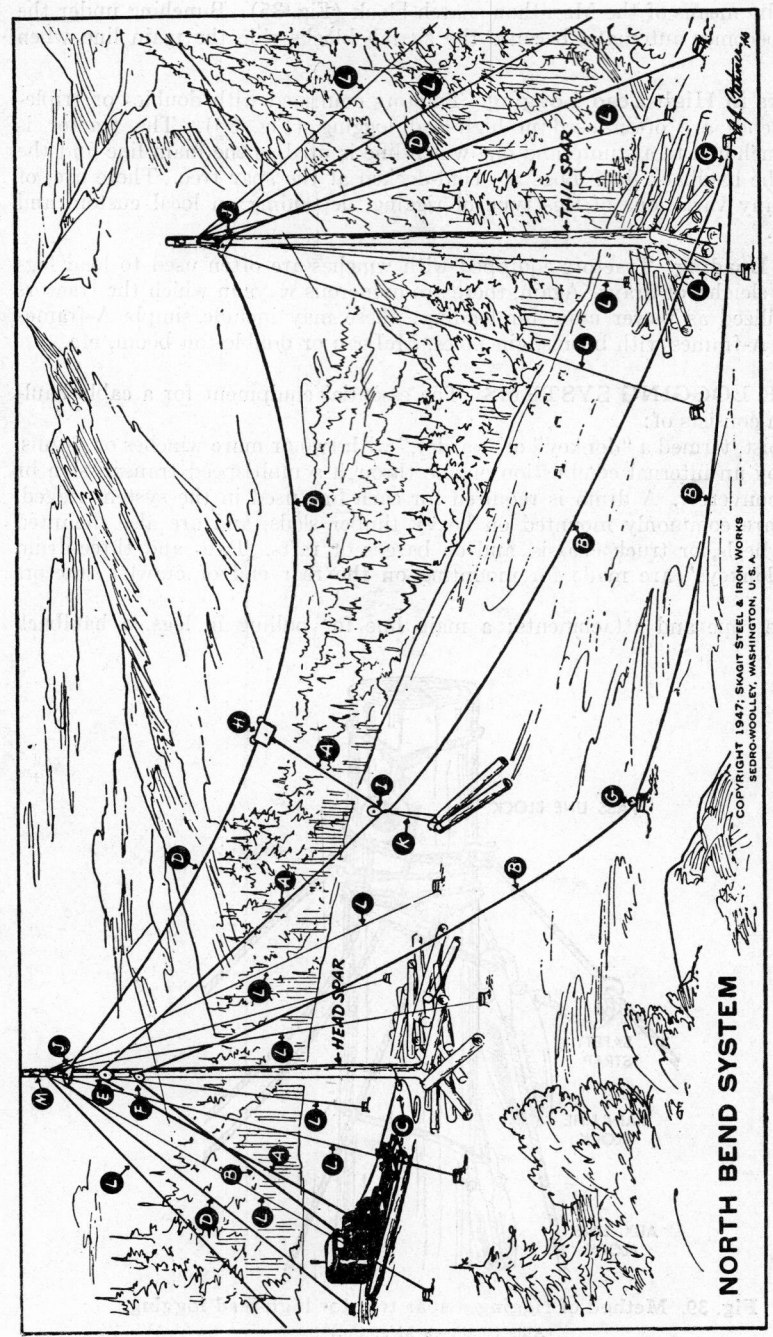

**NORTH BEND SYSTEM**

COPYRIGHT 1947; SKAGIT STEEL & IRON WORKS
SEDRO-WOOLLEY, WASHINGTON, U.S.A.

Fig. 40. North Bend system.
(Skagit Steel & Iron Works.)

A. Main line.
B. Haulback line.
D. Skyline.
E. Main-line block.
G. Haulback corner or tail block.
I. Fall block.
J. Tree shoe.
L. Guy line.
M. Pass-line block.

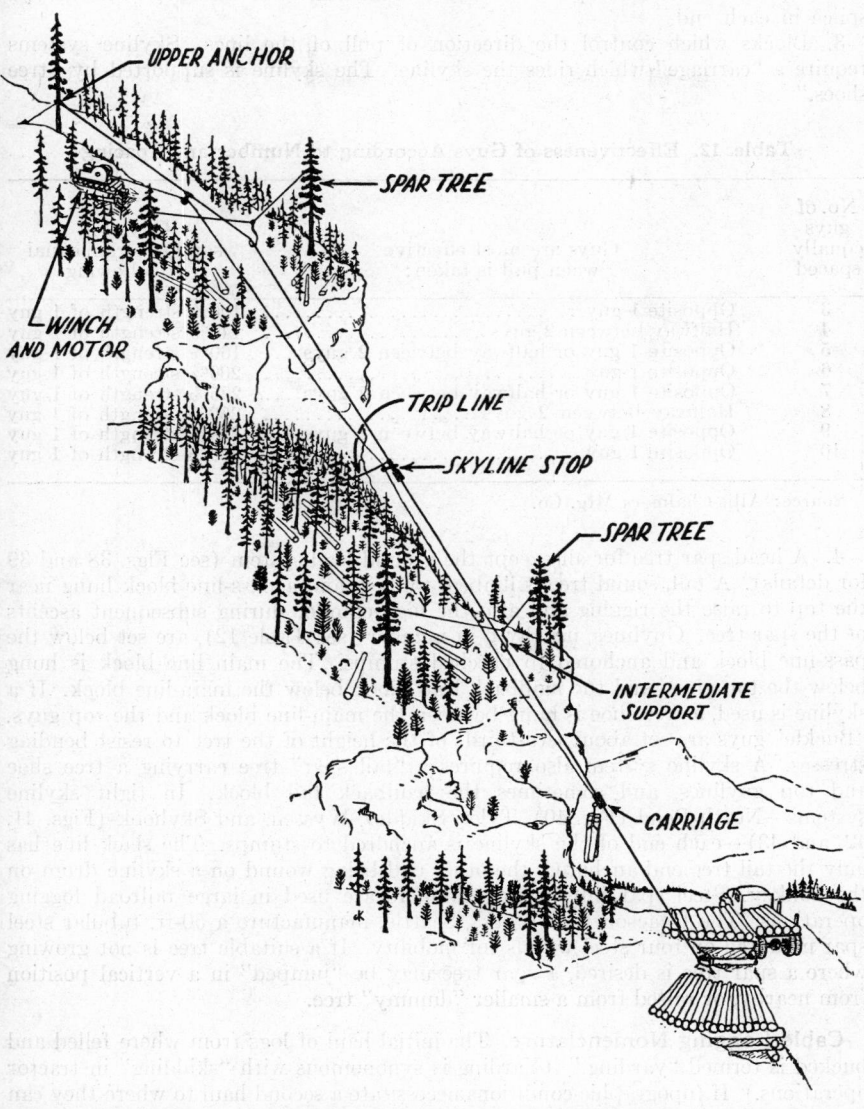

**Fig. 41. Wyssen system. General layout, showing use of intermediate supports to clear obstacles and support long spans.**

(U. S. Forest Service, Forest Products Lab., Wyssen cable system, 1948.)

for pulling the main line out, and a straw line for rigging up and pulling the haulback out through the blocks and back to the spar tree. The main line and haulback are joined through "butt rigging" of clevises, links, and swivels carrying the "butt hooks" to which the chokers which are placed around the logs are hooked.

Blocks are hung with "straps" made up of short lengths of wire rope with an eye splice in each end.

3. Blocks which control the direction of pull of the lines. Skyline systems require a "carriage" which rides the skyline. The skyline is supported by "tree shoes."

**Table. 12.  Effectiveness of Guys According to Number and Spacing**

| No. of guys equally spaced | Guys are most effective when pull is taken: | Guys will support strain equal to following |
|---|---|---|
| 3 | Opposite 1 guy | 100% strength of 1 guy |
| 4 | Halfway between 2 guys | 140% strength of 1 guy |
| 5 | Opposite 1 guy or halfway between 2 guys.... | 160% strength of 1 guy |
| 6 | Opposite 1 guy | 200% strength of 1 guy |
| 7 | Opposite 1 guy or halfway between 2 guys.... | 225% strength of 1 guy |
| 8 | Halfway between 2 guys | 260% strength of 1 guy |
| 9 | Opposite 1 guy or halfway between 2 guys.... | 290% strength of 1 guy |
| 10 | Opposite 1 guy | 323% strength of 1 guy |

Source: Allis-Chalmers Mfg. Co.

4. A head spar tree for all except the ground lead system (see Figs. 38 and 39 for details). A tall, sound tree is limbed, topped, and a pass-line block hung near the top to raise the rigging and also the high-climber during subsequent ascents of the spar tree. Guylines, usually 6 in number (see Table 12), are set below the pass-line block and anchored to notched stumps. The main line block is hung below the top guys, and the haulback lead block below the main-line block. If a skyline is used, a tree shoe is hung between the main-line block and the top guys. "Buckle" guys are set about two-thirds of the height of the tree to resist bending stresses. A skyline system also requires a "tail spar" tree carrying a tree shoe and top guylines, and sometimes the haulback tail block. In tight skyline systems—North Bend (Fig. 40), Tyler, Skidder, Wyssen, and Skyhook (Figs. 41, 42, and 43)—each end of the skyline is anchored to stumps. The slack line has only the tail tree end anchored, the other end being wound on a skyline drum on the donkey. Steel spar interlocking skidders are used in large railroad logging operations. The Isaacson Iron Works, Seattle, manufacture a 50-ft. tubular steel spar mounted on four steel wheels for mobility. If a suitable tree is not growing where a spar tree is desired, a spar tree may be "jumped" in a vertical position from nearby, or raised from a smaller "dummy" tree.

**Cable Logging Nomenclature.** The initial haul of logs from where felled and bucked is termed "yarding." (Yarding is synonomous with "skidding" in tractor operations.) If topographic conditions necessitate a second haul to where they can be loaded on wheeled vehicles, this is termed "swinging." Logs may be "cold-decked" if the yarding is to be completed before swinging, or "hot-decked" if the two operations are conducted concurrently.

The crew of a moving cable system usually consists, at a minimum, of a "hook-tender" or working foreman; a "rigging slinger" who supervises two or more "choker setters" and gives signals to a signalman, who transmits them through an electric horn to the donkey engineer who operates the yarder; and a "chaser" to unhook the chokers from the logs at the landing. A high-climber or head rigger corners of 1,000 ft. or more. The average "setting" of area logged to a given spar tree is 30 to 40 acres. The high lead is more efficient yarding uphill because there is always a lift on the log. With downhill yarding there is no lift on the log above the elevation of the main-line block.

Sky-line yarding or swinging distance depends mainly on the terrain, but is obtainable, as determined by the customary engine power, depending on to the ground profile. Customary sky-line distances are twice the high-lead yarding distance, or 1,400 to 1,600 ft.

Cable systems as equipment is adapted to elevations, although ground loads and "low-lead" and "high-lead" have been used for yarding in tractor selection areas where tractors is desirable. The topographic and operating conditions to which each system is adapted, and the comparative advantages and disadvantages, are given in Table 13.

Loading or tree loading systems used with cable hauling systems require:

1. Loader, usually smaller than the yarder, or any drums as the mast.
2. Winding lines, boom swinging lines, and guy lines.
3. Blocks along the lines.
4. Tools, hooks, or straps for changing the block.
5. Loading drums of any line and the jacks.
6. The mast, spar tree used for the swinging system, or a boom tree or "gin pole" for loading or hauling loadings.

There is a trend toward the use of shovel loaders with cable yarding and swinging because of the mobile, saving in rig-up time of the yarder, and its operating efficiency. However, the shovel loader involves a much higher capital investment than the cable loading systems.

RAILROAD. Two classes are recognized: main line and spur. Many functions are performed in a logging operation. They are designed not-connected ("rod") steam locomotive to the load. Main lines approach the standards of common principles of common-carrier railroad engineering covered, reference books are applicable to main lines.

Spurs are temporary and short, and short hauls at slow speeds from logging landings to "make-up" sidings on the main line, where trains are made up for the main-line haul. Geared locomotives or saddle-tank rod locomotives are usually used on spurs. Three types of geared locomotives are used. The Shay has two or three cylinders mounted vertically on the right-hand side near the cab, two or three cylinders mounted vertically on the left to the cab. The Heisler shaft. The Climax has a cylinder on each side at an angle to the horizontal. On the geared types, all wheels of both locomotive and tender are driven.

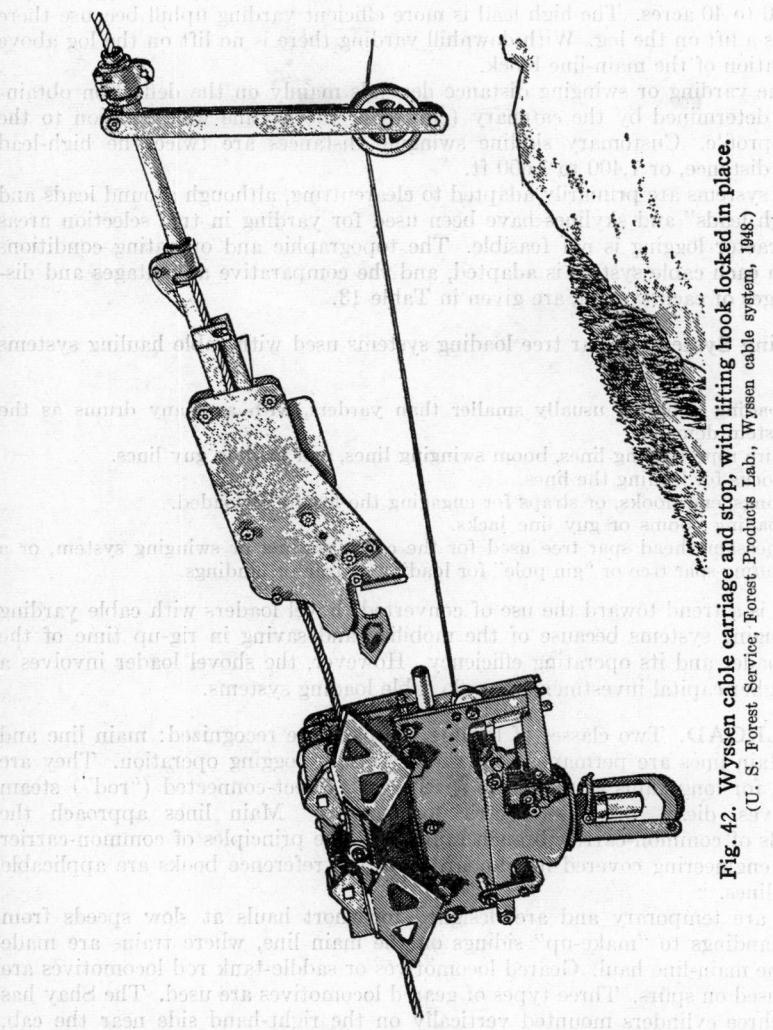

**Fig. 42. Wyssen cable carriage and stop, with lifting hook locked in place.**
(U. S. Forest Service, Forest Products Lab., Wyssen cable system, 1948.)

tops and rigs the spar tree. The loading crew consists of a head loader, one or more second loaders, and a loading engineer.

**Output and Yarding Distance.** The output of cable yarding systems, and consequently the cost, varies with size of logs, density of stand per acre, topography, yarding distance, power and speed of the donkey, and labor efficiency. Swinging costs and output vary with the same factors.

The efficient high-lead yarding distance depends upon the height to which the main-line block is elevated to give a lift on the log to overcome obstacles. In the Douglas-fir region the average external yarding distance is 700 to 800 ft. with long corners of 1,000 ft. or more. The average "setting" or area logged to a given spar tree is 30 to 40 acres. The high lead is more efficient yarding uphill because there is always a lift on the log. With downhill yarding there is no lift on the log above the elevation of the main-line block.

Skyline yarding or swinging distance depends mainly on the deflection obtainable, as determined by the catenary (curve) of the skyline with relation to the ground profile. Customary skyline swinging distances are twice the high-lead yarding distance, or 1,400 to 1,600 ft.

Cable systems are primarily adapted to clearcutting, although ground leads and "low-high leads" and skylines have been used for yarding in tree selection areas where tractor logging is not feasible. The topographic and operating conditions to which each cable system is adapted, and the comparative advantages and disadvantages of each system, are given in Table 13.

**Loading Systems.** Spar tree loading systems used with cable hauling systems require:

1. Loading donkeys, usually smaller than yarders, with as many drums as the system demands.
2. Wire rope loading lines, boom swinging lines, and loading guy lines.
3. Blocks for leading the lines.
4. Tongs, end hooks, or straps for engaging the log to be loaded.
5. Loading booms or guy line jacks.
6. The same head spar tree used for the cable yarding or swinging system, or a loading spar tree or "gin pole" for loading at tractor landings.

There is a trend toward the use of converted shovel loaders with cable yarding and swinging systems because of the mobility and saving in rig-up time of the shovel loader and its operating efficiency. However, the shovel loader involves a much higher capital investment than do cable loading systems.

**RAILROAD.** Two classes of logging railroads are recognized: main line and spur. Main lines are permanent for the life of the logging operation. They are designed for long hauls at moderate speeds with direct-connected ("rod") steam locomotives, diesel, or diesel-electric locomotives. Main lines approach the standards of common-carrier branch railroads. The principles of common-carrier railroad engineering covered in standard text and reference books are applicable to main lines.

Spurs are temporary and are designed for short hauls at slow speeds from logging landings to "make-up" sidings on the main line, where trains are made up for the main-line haul. Geared locomotives or saddle-tank rod locomotives are usually used on spurs. Three types of geared locomotives are used. The Shay has two or three cylinders mounted vertically on the right-hand side near the cab, with the drive shaft outside the wheels. The boiler is offset to the left. The Heisler has two cylinders opposed at a 90° angle (like a V-8 motor) with a central drive shaft. The Climax has a cylinder on each side like the conventional rod engine, but the cylinders are set at about a 20° angle with the horizontal. On the geared locomotives all wheels are drivers and are driven through bevel pinions and gears. The power is doubled to trebled through the gearing, with consequent reduction in speed. Grades on spurs are usually limited to 6 percent and curves to 24° to 30°. When the timber along a spur has been logged, the rails and ties are taken up and re-laid on a new spur.

In recent years the trend in railroad logging operations has been to substitute motor truck feeders to main lines for railroad spurs, and to transfer the entire

Fig. 43. Wyssen winch and motor unit being moved up a steep slope by winding up the cable.

(U. S. Forest Service, Forest Products Lab., Wyssen cable system, 1948.)

truckload to the railroad car instead of dumping and reloading. The transfer is usually rigged in a manner similar to the tight-line loading system previously described under "Cable Logging Systems," with multiple-block purchase to increase the lifting power of the donkey.

Large railroad logging operations use a third class of "branch lines" which are intermediate between main lines and spurs in standards and operating life.

Skeleton log cars are most popular for long (32 to 40 ft.) logs. Various patent bunks and chock-blocks are used. Short (16-ft.) logs are usually carried on flatcars with bunks and stake pockets for wood stakes. For extra-long (60 to 80 ft. or longer) logs, disconnected trucks are used.

The rising labor cost of track maintenance may be reduced by the use of modern power tools such as pneumatic tampers, power bolt-tighteners, drills, tie-pullers, etc. It pays to use metal tie plates under the rail on every tie. "Creeping

## Table 13. Comparison of Cable Systems

| Name of Cable System | Conditions to which adapted | Advantages | Disadvantages |
|---|---|---|---|
| Ground lead | Yarding small timber on smooth topography, low stumps, short distance (obsolete in the West). | Simple rig-up (hang mainline block on stump); no spar tree to rig; slower, less destructive. | Low output due to hang-ups and changing choker holds to free; least efficient of cable systems. |
| High lead | Yarding, mainly uphill, in any size and density of timber (most used yarding system on West Coast); swinging uphill short distances on fairly smooth topography. | Simplicity of rigging compared to skyline systems; lower capital investment; any donkey can be used. | Less control of logs than skyline systems; more destructive; inefficient down steep slopes—equivalent to ground lead above elevation of main-line block. |
| Grabinski modification of high lead | Yarding downhill or across gullies where hang-ups would occur with high lead. | Holding brake on haulback line gives lift on log to clear obstacles. | Reports differ as to whether haulback line life decreased; larger haulback desirable. |
| North Bend | Swinging from cold decks, uphill or level (most used swinging system on West Coast). | Simplest rigging of skyline systems; yarding donkey can be used; more control of log than high lead and more lift to overcome obstacles. | Less lift and control of log than other skyline systems; length of time to rig up precludes use for yarding. |
| Modified North Bend | Swinging downhill. | More lift on log to clear obstacles. | More stress on skyline. |
| Tyler | Swinging across canyons, over cliffs, or where conditions require lifting log clear of ground. | Frees log from ground conditions; saves breakage in cedar. | Requires special donkey with extra drum for lifting line; high stress on skyline and wear on lifting line. |
| Slackline | Yarding or swinging downhill or across canyons, or over broken topography. | Skyline can be quickly raised or lowered while hauling in logs to suit ground conditions; faster rig-up and road changing; longer yarding distance than high lead. | Requires special donkey with large skyline drum; greater capital investment. |
| Interlocking skidder | Yarding or swinging under any topographic conditions where skyline deflection can be obtained; best in dense stands of medium-sized timber. | Excellent control of logs; interlocking skidding and reeding lines hold logs at any desired height; fast road changing using two skylines, one being rigged ahead. | Highest capital investment, largest crew, most complicated rigging; steel spar skidder limited to railway operations. |
| Wyssen cable | Yarding pulpwood or small logs on slopes steep enough to operate by gravity. | Permits logging steep slopes inoperable by conventional eastern pulpwood logging methods. | Winch must be moved to top of slope; practical operating load limit about 3,000 lb. |
| Skyhook | Swinging from cold decks or tractor-yarded hot decks where deflection is unobtainable for other skyline systems (intermediate supports may be used). | Lifts logs clear of ground; highest speed (30 mph); logs can be loaded directly from skyhook; can change direction at supports. | Two skylines needed; length of time required to rig up; requires considerable volume of timber coming to one "skyroad" to amortize rig-up cost. |
| **Name of Spar Tree Loading System** | | | |
| Guyline—single line | Small, short logs; low volume to be loaded at a landing and relatively low production. | Simplest rigging, lowest investment; can be operated from extra drum on yarding donkey. | More manhandling of log to position; slower loading than with other systems; more hazard to vehicle being loaded. |
| Duplex | Used more for loading railway cars than trucks; high-lead or cable swing landings. | Fast, better control of log, high production. | Requires special Duplex donkey, two men on tongs; heavy tongs must be carried out to where logs lie; somewhat rough on ears. |
| McLean boom | Any spar tree loading, cable or tractor landings. | Better control of log, safer, than guyline systems; easier work for tong men; good output. | Requires two men to set tongs; more time to rig up. |
| Heel boom | Same as McLean boom. | Only one tong man needed; best control of log; high output. | Time to rig up; heavier boom (shod with steel rails on under side where log is heeled). |
| Tight line | Tractor landing, storage yard. | Can take logs from wide tractor landing, leaving more room for tractors to drop logs. | Slower than boom systems unless a powerful donkey is used; small donkeys require block purchase, reducing speed. |

**16 · 50**

switches" should be provided on steep grades, for the rails will gradually move down the grade and otherwise kink the track. Super-elevation of the outer rail on curves should be precisely calculated for the operating speed of the train.

Grades and curves on spurs in mountainous terrain are largely dictated by topography, but for economy of operation the maxima should be calculated before location in order that the desired number of cars can be hauled per trip. The following formulas are applicable to logging railroad spurs. Formulas applicable to main lines will be found in standard reference books.

**Locomotive Tractive Effort.** The tractive power developed by a rod locomotive is:

$$T = \frac{b^2 s P}{D} \tag{1}$$

where $T$ is pounds, $b$ is bore of cylinder in inches, $s$ is length of piston stroke in inches, and $P$ is the mean effective pressure in pounds, which is a percentage of the boiler pressure that in turn varies with the piston speed. $D$ is the diameter of the drive wheels in inches. Piston speed is calculated from locomotive speed in miles per hour, piston stroke ($s$), and diameter of the drive wheels ($D$), by the following formula, and mean effective boiler pressure for various piston speeds is given in the following table:

$$\text{Piston speed} = \frac{56 \, s \, \text{(miles per hour)}}{D} \tag{2}$$

| Piston speed | Mean effective pressure |
|---|---|
| Up to 178 | 85% |
| 350 | 66 |
| 540 | 50 |
| 960 | 30 |

The tractive effort for a given locomotive at various speeds may also be obtained from the manufacturer. Compound engines increase T as calculated above by 20 percent.

The usable tractive effort $T$ depends upon the weight on the drive wheels and the factor of adhesion between the drivers and the rails.

$$T = f \text{ (lb. weight on drivers)} \tag{3}$$

$f$ for wet rail 20 percent, $f$ for dry rail 22.5 percent, $f$ for sanded rail, starting, 25 percent.

Usually the $T$ in formula (3) is the one used in determining performance, as locomotives are designed with a surplus of cylinder power at low speeds. For geared locomotives, use formula (3) if the manufacturers' data are not available. With old locomotives in which boiler pressure has been reduced, use the lesser $T$ of formulas (1) and (3).

**Train Resistances.** In order to pull a train of cars the tractive effort of the locomotive must overcome the resistances offered by gradient, curvature, rolling (friction in the journals and wheels on the track), and, at higher speeds, the atmosphere. All resistances are expressed in pounds per ton of weight of train.

Grade resistance = 20 lb. per ton per % of grade (G)  $\qquad$ (4)

Curve resistance (C):  $\qquad$ (5)

| Degree of curve | Curve resistance per degree | Equivalent grade % |
|---|---|---|
| 1 to 8 | 0.8 lb. per ton | 0.04% per degree |
| 9 to 15 | 0.6 lb. per ton | 0.03% per degree |
| 16 and up | 0.4 lb. per ton | 0.02% per degree |

Rolling resistance ($R$) depends on how well the track is ballasted and maintained, and on the condition of the car wheels and journals.

Loaded cars, good logging railroad, 10 lb. per ton.   (6)
Empty cars, good logging railroad, 12 lb. per ton.
Loaded cars, fair logging railroad, 15 lb. per ton.
Empty cars, fair logging railroad, 18 lb. per ton.
Loaded cars, poor logging railroad, 20 lb. per ton.
Empty cars, poor logging railroad, 30 lb. per ton.

For starting from rest, increase rolling resistance 50 percent.

Atmospheric resistance = 0.002 (mph)$^2$ × (head end area in sq. ft.)   (7)

This is usually neglected at the slow speeds operated on logging spurs.

Equating the above formulas, and using $W$ for weight of train of cars in tons, and $L$ for weight of locomotive in tons,

$$T = (W + L) \times (R + 20G + C)$$   (8)

To find the weight of train in tons which a locomotive will pull on a given grade and curve:

$$W = \frac{T - L\,(R + 20\,G + C)}{R + 20\,G + C}$$   (9)

To find the grade up which a locomotive can pull a train of given weight on a given maximum curve:

$$G = \frac{T - (R + C) \times (W + L)}{20\,(W + L)}$$   (10)

If the profile grades of the railroad are compensated for curvature by reducing the grades on the curves by the equivalent grade percent given in (5), the $C$ may be eliminated from formulas (8), (9), and (10) above.

**Examples.** What is the tractive effort of a 63-ton saddle-tank rod locomotive, engines 17-in. bore × 24-in. stroke, boiler pressure 160 lb., diameter of drivers 44 in., weight on drivers 98,000 lb.? Assume slow speed at which mean effective pressure is 85 percent.

From formula (1) the tractive power developed is:

$$T = \frac{17^2 \times 24 \times (160 \times 0.85)}{44} = 21{,}438 \text{ lb.}$$

From formula (3), with $f$ for wet rail, the usable tractive effort developed is:

$$T = 0.20 \times 98{,}000 = 19{,}600 \text{ lb.}$$

A spur is to be located to a landing where anticipated production of 11 cars a day is to be switched once a day by the above locomotive. Cars weigh 10 tons empty, 40 tons loaded. Under fair logging railroad conditions, to what maximum adverse and favorable compensated grades should the spur be located?

$$\text{Adverse } G = \frac{19{,}600 - 15\,[(11 \times 40) + 63]}{20\,[(11 \times 40) + 63]} = \frac{19{,}600 - 7{,}545}{10{,}060} = 1.2\%$$

$$\text{Favorable } G = \frac{19{,}600 - (15 \times 63) - [(18 \times 11) \times 10]}{20\,[(11 \times 10) + 63]}$$

$$= \frac{19{,}600 - 945 - 1{,}980}{3{,}460} = \frac{16{,}675}{3{,}460} = 4.8\%$$

Note that the rolling resistance for loaded cars is used for the locomotive and that curve resistance has been ignored. Should there be a 5° curve, say, the adverse grade on the curve should be reduced by formula (5) to 1.0% : 1.2 − 5(0.04).

### Rail Super-elevation.

$$e = 0.00044DV^2$$

where $e$ is the super-elevation in inches of the outer rail over the inner rail
$D$ is the degree of curve
$V$ is the speed in miles per hour.

## Water Transport and Storage of Wood

**FLUMES.** The 90° flume (V-shape) is the most satisfactory for wood transport. A "backbone" is required in the vertex of the flume and a square timber (about 4½ by 4½ in.) can be sawed diagonally in two, to fit. An advantage of the V-shape flume, when fluming small logs, is that if a jam forms, the water will back up, rise, and tend to lift the jam and disperse it.

**Water Requirements.** Tables 14–17 contain data on the depth of water required to float logs, volume of flow, and velocity of water.

**Table 14. Depth of Water in V-Flume, in Inches, Required to Float Logs of Various Diameters and Weight per Cubic Foot**

| Large-end diameter of logs (in.) | Weight of logs (lb. per cu. ft.) | | | | | |
|---|---|---|---|---|---|---|
| | 30 | 35 | 40 | 45 | 50 | 55 |
| 6 | 2.6 | 3.0 | 3.4 | 3.8 | 4.2 | 4.6 |
| 8 | 4.0 | 4.4 | 5.0 | 5.5 | 6.1 | 6.6 |
| 10 | 5.4 | 5.9 | 6.6 | 7.3 | 8.0 | 8.7 |
| 12 | 6.7 | 7.5 | 8.3 | 9.0 | 9.9 | 10.7 |
| 14 | 8.2 | 9.0 | 9.8 | 10.8 | 11.8 | 12.7 |
| 16 | 9.5 | 10.5 | 11.5 | 12.5 | 13.6 | 14.8 |
| 18 | 11.0 | 12.0 | 13.1 | 14.4 | 15.6 | 16.8 |
| 20 | 12.3 | 13.5 | 14.8 | 16.1 | 17.5 | 19.0 |
| 22 | 13.6 | 15.0 | 16.4 | 17.8 | 19.4 | 21.0 |
| 24 | 15.0 | 16.5 | 18.0 | 19.6 | 21.3 | 23.0 |
| 26 | 16.5 | 18.0 | 19.7 | 21.4 | 23.2 | 25.1 |
| 28 | 17.8 | 19.6 | 21.3 | 23.2 | 25.2 | 27.2 |
| 30 | 19.2 | 21.0 | 22.9 | 24.9 | 27.0 | 29.2 |

Source: Woodlands Section, Canadian Pulp and Paper Assn., The design of log flumes, Index No. 509.

**Capacity of Flume.** Logs in a flume (or river) travel faster than the water in which they float. Their velocity is the total of (a) this excess velocity + (b) mean velocity of water in flume. The capacity of flumes in Table 17 is based on 1 log per 100 ft. of flume. If there should be 3 logs per 100 ft., multiply the figures given by 3.

**Table 15. Volume of Flow of Water in V-Flumes, in Cubic Feet per Second, for Various Depths of Water and Gradients of Flume**

| Depth of water in flume (in.) | Grade of flume (percent) | | | | | | | | | | |
|---|---|---|---|---|---|---|---|---|---|---|---|
| | 0.2 | 0.5 | 1.0 | 2.0 | 3.0 | 4.0 | 5.0 | 6.0 | 8.0 | 10.0 | 12.0 |
| 8 | 2 | 3 | 5 | 6 | 7 | 9 | 10 | 11 | 12 | 15 | 16 |
| 10 | 3 | 5 | 7 | 10 | 12 | 15 | 16 | 18 | 20 | 23 | 26 |
| 12 | 4 | 7 | 11 | 15 | 18 | 22 | 24 | 27 | 31 | 35 | 39 |
| 14 | 6 | 11 | 15 | 22 | 26 | 32 | 35 | 38 | 44 | 50 | 55 |
| 16 | 9 | 15 | 21 | 29 | 36 | 42 | 46 | 52 | 59 | 66 | 73 |
| 18 | 12 | 19 | 27 | 38 | 47 | 55 | 62 | 68 | 78 | 86 | 95 |
| 20 | 15 | 25 | 35 | 49 | 61 | 71 | 79 | 87 | 99 | 110 | 122 |
| 22 | 19 | 32 | 44 | 62 | 76 | 88 | 99 | 108 | 124 | 128 | 152 |
| 24 | 24 | 38 | 55 | 75 | 93 | 108 | 121 | 132 | 152 | 170 | 185 |
| 26 | 29 | 46 | 65 | 92 | 103 | 131 | 147 | 160 | 185 | 205 | 224 |
| 28 | 35 | 55 | 77 | 109 | 134 | 155 | 175 | 191 | 220 | 243 | 266 |
| 30 | 41 | 65 | 92 | 129 | 158 | 184 | 206 | 225 | 260 | 290 | 320 |

Source: Woodlands Section, Canadian Pulp and Paper Assn., The design of log flumes, Index No. 509.

**Construction. Substructure.** Flume boxes are usually supported by trestles or bents constructed of round timbers. Depending upon terrain, trestles are often anchored in rock-filled cribs. One flume in eastern Canada is supported on single poles with two side guys. This has proved to be very practical. Because flume foundations generally heave in the spring with frost action, part of the annual maintenance will be realignment of the grade.

**Table 16. Mean Velocity of Water in V-Flumes, in Feet per Second**

| Depth of water in flume (in.) | Grade of flume (percent) | | | | | | | | | | |
|---|---|---|---|---|---|---|---|---|---|---|---|
| | 0.2 | 0.5 | 1.0 | 2.0 | 3.0 | 4.0 | 5.0 | 6.0 | 8.0 | 10.0 | 12.0 |
| 2 | 1.0 | 1.8 | 2.4 | 3.0 | 4.0 | 5.0 | 5.5 | 6.0 | 7.0 | 7.5 | 8.5 |
| 4 | 1.5 | 2.6 | 3.7 | 5.5 | 6.5 | 7.9 | 8.5 | 9.5 | 11.0 | 12.5 | 13.5 |
| 6 | 2.0 | 3.3 | 5.0 | 7.0 | 8.5 | 10.0 | 11.2 | 12.3 | 13.9 | 15.9 | 17.0 |
| 8 | 2.6 | 4.0 | 5.9 | 8.2 | 10.0 | 11.5 | 13.0 | 14.3 | 16.5 | 18.2 | 20.0 |
| 10 | 2.9 | 4.6 | 6.6 | 9.2 | 11.4 | 13.0 | 14.9 | 16.1 | 18.2 | 20.9 | 22.6 |
| 12 | 3.3 | 5.2 | 7.2 | 10.4 | 12.6 | 14.6 | 16.3 | 17.9 | 20.5 | 23.0 | 25.0 |
| 14 | 3.6 | 5.7 | 7.9 | 11.1 | 13.7 | 15.9 | 17.7 | 19.3 | 22.3 | 25.0 | 27.2 |
| 16 | 3.9 | 6.1 | 8.5 | 12.0 | 14.5 | 17.0 | 19.0 | 20.9 | 24.0 | 26.9 | 29.0 |
| 18 | 4.2 | 6.5 | 9.0 | 13.0 | 15.8 | 18.0 | 20.3 | 22.1 | 25.8 | 28.5 | 31.5 |
| 20 | 4.5 | 7.0 | 9.7 | 13.6 | 16.9 | 19.0 | 21.7 | 23.5 | 27.4 | 30.6 | 33.5 |
| 22 | 4.7 | 7.3 | 10.3 | 14.3 | 17.7 | 20.2 | 22.8 | 25.0 | 28.8 | 32.2 | 35.5 |
| 24 | 4.9 | 7.6 | 11.0 | 15.2 | 18.5 | 21.5 | 23.8 | 26.5 | 30.5 | 34.0 | 37.0 |
| 26 | 5.0 | 8.0 | 11.5 | 16.0 | 19.5 | 22.5 | 25.4 | 27.7 | 32.0 | 35.8 | 39.0 |
| 28 | 5.3 | 8.2 | 11.9 | 16.5 | 20.5 | 23.5 | 26.5 | 28.7 | 33.2 | 37.2 | 41.0 |
| 30 | 5.5 | 8.5 | 12.0 | 17.2 | 21.5 | 24.5 | 27.5 | 30.0 | 34.6 | 38.5 | 42.6 |

Source: Woodlands Section, Canadian Pulp and Paper Assn., The design of log flumes, Index No. 509.

**Box.** The sides of the flume box usually consist of two layers of 1-in. board with the joints staggered to reduce leakage. Boards are nailed from the outside, the nails being clinched in the direction of water flow.

When grades are steep, logs tend to slide rather than float and the sides of the flume box are generally reinforced with strips of ¼-in. steel to prevent wear and

## Table 17. Capacity of V-Flume

| Velocity of logs in feet per second | Number of logs per hour |
|---|---|
| 5 | 170 |
| 10 | 360 |
| 15 | 550 |
| 20 | 720 |

tear. Strips of aluminum are sometimes placed along the waterline and have been found to reduce friction and jamming of short wood.

**General principles.** When building long flumes, it is customary to start at the upper or intake end. Lumber is cut to size and floated down the flume as construction progresses.

Some of the cardinal principles to be observed in flume construction have been laid down by N. C. Brown.

1. Keep the flume as close to the ground as possible.
2. Except in steep grades, water should be maintained within 8 in. of the top of the flume.
3. The flume should be located as near as possible to the center of the timber supply of the region to be served. This does not apply where flumes are used for special purposes such as transporting wood from one watershed to another, from river to mill, etc.
4. The right-of-way should be cut wide enough to prevent damage to the flume by windfalls.
5. Easy and quick loading and emptying are essential to low-cost operation.

Under average conditions, flumes are considered to be a very economical method of log transportation. Maintenance is not very high if the flume timbers are treated with preservatives. Flume operating generally requires a patrolman every two to four miles to prevent jams and to repair leaks.

**RIVER DRIVE.** Advantages of river driving:

1. Where streams are abundant and precipitation in the form of snow and spring rains is adequate, the relative cheapness of river improvements permits the operation of light stands of timber per acre.
2. In extremely rough country the high cost of land improvements may make water transportation the only economic means of extracting wood.

Disadvantages of river driving:

1. Delivery to the processing plant is seasonal, resulting in the need for large and expensive storage facilities.
2. Wood stored for any considerable period is subject to deterioration and presents a distinct fire hazard.
3. Invested capital and logging costs are tied up for long periods and liquidation is usually slow.
4. Sinkage losses may amount to a considerable item of cost.
5. Most hardwoods do not float easily.
6. Damaged ends of logs tend to reduce their value.
7. Companies driving logs or pulpwood are usually liable for any damage to properties adjacent to the streams upon which they are operating.

A knowledge of precipitation and runoff in any watershed where river driving is being considered is essential in planning operations. Snow surveys are of great help in establishing what water will be available during the spring freshet. Knowledge of maximum and minimum flow during the period of the drive is almost a necessity. When calculating the water which must be available to drive a given quantity of wood safely, use the minimum values recorded for precipitation and runoff; when calculating gate openings for driving dams, use maximum values.

Low altitude, rolling country, and watersheds with lakes usually have a low runoff and also low maximum flows. Flat creeks will require more water to drive than steep ones.

Precipitous country and high altitudes present the reverse of the above. During the driving season, due to high precipitation and runoff, these rivers are generally, contrary to the impression of many, the most economical to drive.

A discharge of 1 sec.-ft. per sq. mi. is the equivalent of a runoff of 0.03719 in. in one day. Runoffs corresponding to greater discharges or longer periods are obtainable by multiplication. One sec.-ft. is equivalent to 1.983 acre-feet of runoff in one day.

**Driving (Splash) Dams.** The use of small driving dams will improve the efficiency of stream driving, particularly where the watersheds are small. They serve to create a reservoir, to regulate the runoff, and to raise the water level of difficult sections of the stream. When locating a dam, strive to find a site that will give the most water for the smallest dam. However, the narrowest site may not always be the best because there must be room to pass the freshet water. As driving dams generally have a low head, site requirements are not as stringent as for more permanent hydroelectric developments.

**Foundations and percolation factors.** If the dam is placed on solid rock, there is little likelihood of trouble. Where the site is of silt, sand, or gravel and boulders, steps must be taken to keep percolation through the foundation to a minimum. This percolation follows the watertight toe fill (horizontal) and the sheet piling, or other watertight vertical construction, which joins it (Fig. 44). Clay, or other impervious material, is used in the toe of the dam, and sheet piling or other watertight construction extends vertically downward from it. If the dam is to be safe, the combined length of these members, or path of seepage, must

**Table 18. Percolation Factors for Earth Dams**

| Material | Lane [a] | Bligh [b] |
|---|---|---|
| Very fine sand or silt | 8.5 | 18 |
| Fine sand | 7.0 | 15 |
| Medium sand | 6.0 | |
| Coarse sand | 5.0 | 12 |
| Fine gravel | 4.0 | |
| Medium gravel | 3.5 | |
| Gravel and sand | | 9 |
| Coarse gravel and cobbles | 3.0 | |
| Boulders, cobbles, and gravel | 2.5 | |
| Boulders, gravel, and sand | | 4–6 |
| Soft clay | 3.0 | |
| Medium clay | 2.0 | |
| Hard clay | 1.8 | |
| Very hard clay (hardpan) | 1.6 | |

[a] $\dfrac{BC + CD + \frac{1}{3}AB}{x}$ (See Fig. 44.)

[b] $\dfrac{AB + BC + CD}{r}$ (See Fig. 44.)

Source: National Resources Committee, *Low dams*, 1938.

exceed the head (or depth of water at the dam) by the ratios shown in Table 18. The ratios, or percolation factors, as calculated by Bligh will be seen to be considerably more conservative than those by Lane.

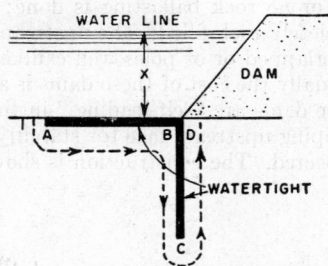

**Fig. 44. Earth dam, showing path of percolating water.**

**Types of driving dams.** Three general types of dams are in use:

1. The crib or pier dam. This is the most permanent type of dam and the safest; it is also the most expensive. If used when the foundation is good, it will retain a large head of water. Care must be taken in preparing the foundation. Sills are often fastened in place with rock bolts to rock, or trenches are dug for the sills on hardpan or gravel sites. Large timbers should be used, drifted together at every point of contact with ½- to ⅝-in. pins. When the crib work reaches the level of the streambed (best checked by an Abney level), sluiceways to pass logs and surplus water must be allowed for. These will vary in width and number, depending on the size of the stream and the volume of wood and water. Sluiceways are usually placed in the center of the natural stream channel, especially if only one is required.

When sluicing wood, the wider the gate openings, the greater will be the amount of wood which can be sluiced through them in a given time. Considering a gate with the stop logs in to function as a weir and full-gate opening as a gate (orifice), Table 19 may be used as a guide to discharge.

**Table 19. Discharge Through Sluices**

| Head (ft.) | Weir discharge (c.f.s.) for 1 ft. of spillway | Gate discharge (c.f.s.) for 1 ft. of width |
|---|---|---|
| 1.0 | 3.33 | 2.64 |
| 1.5 | 6.12 | 4.85 |
| 2.0 | 9.42 | 7.48 |
| 2.5 | 13.16 | 10.49 |
| 3.0 | 17.30 | 13.83 |
| 3.5 | 21.80 | 17.52 |
| 4.0 | 26.64 | 21.48 |
| 5.0 | 37.23 | 30.07 |
| 6.0 | 48.94 | 40.05 |
| 7.0 | 61.67 | 50.50 |
| 8.0 | 75.34 | 62.49 |
| 9.0 | 89.91 | 75.48 |
| 10.0 | 105.30 | 89.44 |

**Example.** Assume a dam on a creek where it is estimated that 100 c.f.s. is normal driving water; that the wood is small, requiring only about 1.5 ft. of water over the stop logs. One 15-ft. gate with that depth of water will require about 92 c.f.s. (15 × 6.12 c.f.s.).

The face of crib dams may be vertical or sloping. The sloping face (45°) is usually used where little or no rock ballasting is done; the vertical face is used where the dams are completely rock filled. The upstream face of the dam may be either of sawn boards overlapped or of poles well caulked with moss or oakum.

2. The rafter dam. Usually the cost of these dams is about half that of the crib dam of similar size. These dams are "self-loading," in that they depend upon the weight of water on the sloping upstream face for stability. They are ideal where a relatively low head is expected. The construction is shown in Fig. 45.

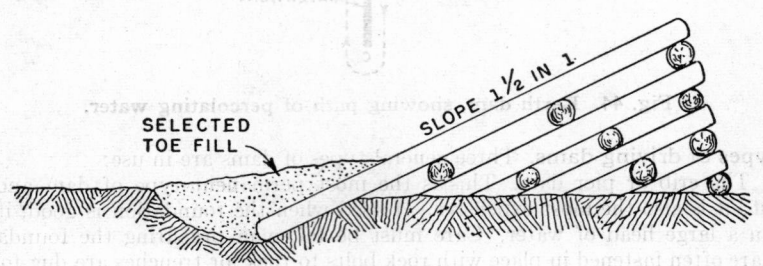

**Fig. 45. Rafter dam.**

3. Post dams. This is the cheapest type of temporary dam and is used where the life expectancy is 2 or 3 yr. It is "self-loading." Its framework consists of one or two rows of mud sills which stretch clear across the site (Fig. 46). Upright posts are located at intervals along these sills and horizontal stringers across the tops of the posts. Sheathing is then placed, supported by these stringers and sunk into the ground in the toe fill trench. Well caulked and with toe fill placed, the dam is complete. The gates and sluices are the same as in the other types of dam.

There are many types of gates: solid one piece, vertical stop log, half moon, or taintor, but the horizontal stop-log type of closure remains the most widely used.

**STORAGE OF WOOD IN WATER.** "In storing 4-ft. bolts of wood with diameters of 4 to 30 in. (8-in. average), with all wood on the surface of the water and not tightly packed, the average is about 160 cords per acre. Wood tightly packed averages 240 cords, and wood very tightly packed, as by a river current, averages 250 cords." This estimate is by a Nova Scotia paper company. Another authority gives 308 sq. ft. as the area required by a cord of floating pulpwood.

### BIBLIOGRAPHY

ALLIS CHALMERS MFG. Co., 1948. *Fundamentals of logging.*

AMERICAN PULPWOOD ASSN. 1949—to date. Equipment handbook. Looseleaf. New York.

AMERICAN PULPWOOD ASSN. 1949—to date. Training manual. Looseleaf. New York.

BRANDSTROM, A. J. F. 1933. *Analysis of logging costs and operating methods in the Douglas fir region.* Charles Lathrop Pack Forestry Foundation, Washington, D. C.

BROWN, N. C. 1949. *Logging.* John Wiley & Sons, Inc., New York.

CANADIAN PULP AND PAPER ASSN. 1951. Woodcutters' handbook—how to cut more pulpwood safely without greater effort.

CANADIAN PULP AND PAPER ASSN. 1953. Development of mechanical pulpwood logging methods for eastern Canada.

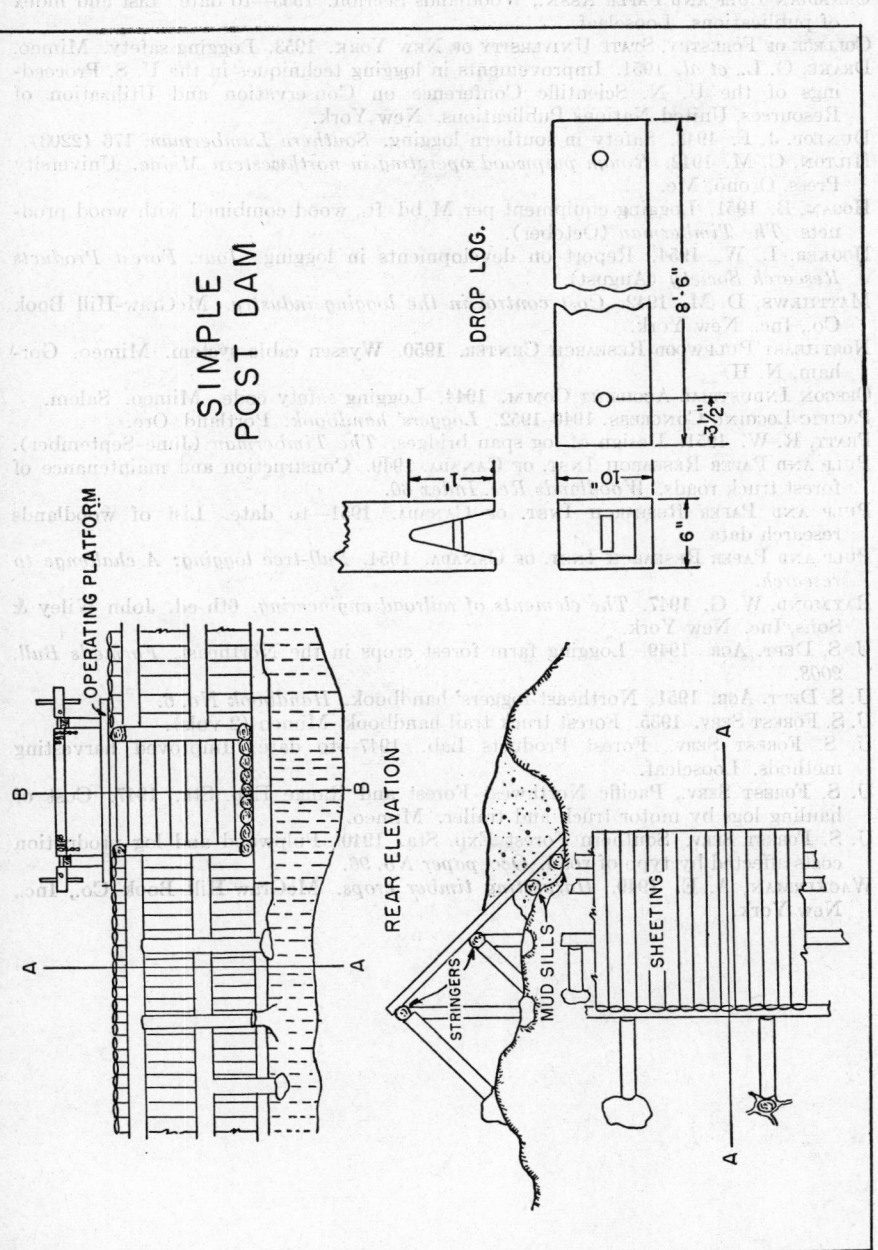

Fig. 46. Simple post dam.

CANADIAN PULP AND PAPER ASSN., Woodlands Section. 1953—to date. List and index of publications. Looseleaf.

COLLEGE OF FORESTRY, STATE UNIVERSITY OF NEW YORK. 1953. Logging safety. Mimeo.

DRAKE, G. L., *et al.* 1951. Improvements in logging techniques in the U. S. Proceedings of the U. N. Scientific Conference on Conservation and Utilization of Resources, United Nations Publications. New York.

DUNLOP, J. F. 1948. Safety in southern logging. *Southern Lumberman,* 176 (2203).

HILTON, C. M. 1942. *Rough pulpwood operating in northwestern Maine.* University Press, Orono, Me.

HOGAN, B. 1951. Logging equipment per M bd. ft., wood combined with wood products. *The Timberman* (October).

HOOKER, L. W. 1954. Report on developments in logging. *Jour. Forest Products Research Society* (August).

MATTHEWS, D. M. 1942. *Cost control in the logging industry.* McGraw-Hill Book Co., Inc., New York.

NORTHEAST PULPWOOD RESEARCH CENTER. 1950. Wyssen cable system. Mimeo. Gorham, N. H.

OREGON INDUSTRIAL ACCIDENT COMM. 1944. Logging safety code. Mimeo. Salem.

PACIFIC LOGGING CONGRESS. 1940–1952. *Loggers' handbook.* Portland, Ore.

PRATT, R. W. 1951. Design of log span bridges. *The Timberman* (June–September).

PULP AND PAPER RESEARCH INST. OF CANADA. 1949. Construction and maintenance of forest truck roads. *Woodlands Res. Index 60.*

PULP AND PAPER RESEARCH INST. OF CANADA. 1951—to date. List of woodlands research data.

PULP AND PAPER RESEARCH INST. OF CANADA. 1954. *Full-tree logging: A challenge to research.*

RAYMOND, W. G. 1947. *The elements of railroad engineering.* 6th ed. John Wiley & Sons, Inc., New York.

U. S. DEPT. AGR. 1949. Logging farm forest crops in the Northeast. *Farmer's Bull. 2008.*

U. S. DEPT. AGR. 1951. Northeast loggers' handbook. *Handbook No. 6.*

U. S. FOREST SERV. 1935. Forest truck trail handbook Mimeo (2 vols).

U. S. FOREST SERV., Forest Products Lab. 1947—to date. Improved harvesting methods. Looseleaf.

U. S. FOREST SERV., Pacific Northwest Forest and Range Exp. Sta. 1947. Cost of hauling logs by motor truck and trailer. Mimeo.

U. S. FOREST SERV., Southern Forest Exp. Sta. 1940. Pulpwood and log production costs affected by type of road. *Occ. paper No. 96.*

WACKERMAN, A. E. 1949. *Harvesting timber crops.* McGraw-Hill Book Co., Inc., New York.

# SURVEYING

## CONTENTS

# CONTENTS (*Continued*)

# SURVEYING

## Measurement of Horizontal Distance

**PACING.** Pacing is the least accurate of the means of measurement. As in all measurements between points on the earth's surface, distances are recorded in terms of the horizontal distance. Pacing is indispensable in timber cruising, and in land surveying it may be a very valuable supplement to the more accurate methods. A few simple rules will help.

1. Be systematic. Because the method is crude, it should not be rendered valueless by careless recording of paces, ignoring changes of slope and cover, or by failing to check paced measurements against measured (chained or taped) distances at every opportunity.
2. Count double steps only. As used here, a pace means 2 steps.
3. Adopt a short pace that can be held all day. A convenient pace on open, level ground is 5.28 ft., or 1,000 to the mile. Pace repeatedly over a measured course on such ground, until a variation of less than 3 paces in every 100 is attained.
4. After attaining this degree of accuracy on level, open ground, one should test his pace against measured distances on slopes, in brush, and on marshy ground. In difficult terrain no attempt should be made to maintain a standard pace. Instead, allow for its inevitable shortening (downhill as well as uphill) by repeating the count at intervals. For example, on moderate slopes count every tenth pace twice: 1, 2, 3, 4, 5, 6, 7, 8, 9, 10, 10, 11, etc. On steeper slopes it may be found necessary to repeat every fifth count: 1, 2, 3, 4, 5, 5, 6, 7, 8, 9, 10, 10, 11, etc. On the steepest slopes in very heavy brush, in swamps, or among boulders, every count may have to be repeated. Consistent accuracy in pacing under such conditions is attained only by practice and is maintained only by constant checking. Errors of 2 to 4 chains per mile are to be expected of the average pacer; of the experienced pacer, 2 chains or less.
5. On precipitous ground, or in impenetrable brush, estimate by eye the number of paces ahead to some recognizable point, such as a tree or rock, and detour around the obstacle without pacing.
6. A Jacob's staff, or ordinary walking stick, will promote more accurate pacing in brush or rocks.
7. It is suggested that pacing results be regularly recorded and checked against known distances, under various conditions. If possible, a pacer should check every day and preferably both morning and afternoon because of fluctuation as the day wears on.

**MEASUREMENT BY CHAIN OR TAPE. Gunter's Chain.** The original tool for measuring distances in the woods of the United States and Canada was commonly the Gunter's chain. It is 66 ft. long and is composed of 100 links of stout wire, each 7.92 in. long. Because nearly all woodland areas are expressed in acres, and 10 square chains equals 1 acre, chains and links are more convenient units than feet in area surveys. Its ruggedness makes the Gunter's chain a still-valuable tool for use in rough or brushy country. For retracing old surveys made with the same tool it is sufficiently accurate. In use it must of course be kept horizontal. On slopes where the difference between the ends of the chain exceeds about 5 ft. (shoulder height for the man down the slope), it becomes necessary to "break chain," that is, to measure no more than ½ chain of horizontal distance, or even less, at a time. A plumb bob is rarely used with a chain, which is read only to the nearest link or half-link; verticals over points of measurement are judged by eye.

Before measuring any distances with a Gunter's chain all links must be straight. The significance of the brass tabs that take the place of numerical graduations must be kept in mind. Adjustable handles make it possible to allow somewhat for inevitable wear. If a badly worn chain is the only tool available for a survey, its length should be compared with a more accurate chain or tape at the first opportunity; and if the discrepancy is sufficient, all important distances measured should be corrected in accordance with the paragraph dealing with the correction of nonstandard tapes (see page **17·3**).

**Engineers' Tapes.** These tapes come in lengths of 100, 200, or 300 ft. They are better adapted to highway and similar work than to measurements of forest areas. They are graduated in even feet, with the first and/or last foot graduated in tenths or hundredths of a foot to measure fractional distances. Two methods of graduating the fractional foot are used, as shown in Fig. 1; before using an unfamiliar tape, make sure where zero is located, and in which direction from it the fractions of a foot are numbered.

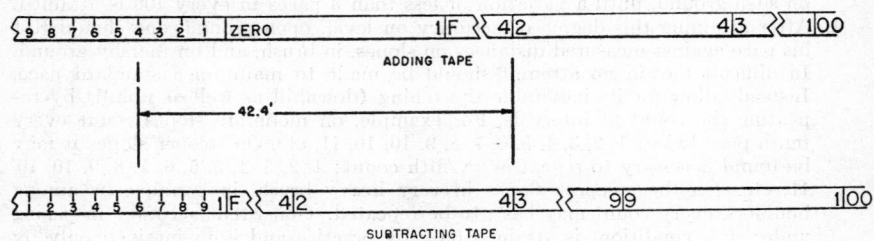

**Fig. 1. Engineers' tapes.**

In measuring the distance between two points with the adding tape, simply add the tenths at the first point to the even foot mark held at the second point. The distance indicated on the adding tape in Fig. 1 is 42.4 ft. With the subtracting tape the tenths at the first point are subtracted from the even number of feet at the second point. The distance indicated on the subtracting tape in Fig. 1 is again 42.4 ft. The adding tape is the more desirable, since errors in measurement are less likely to occur.

**Surveyors' Tapes.** These are usually 2 chains, or 132 ft. in length but are obtainable in 3- and 5-chain lengths. They are graduated in links. Slope tapes are 2-chain surveyors' tapes, supplemented by correction graduations for use in slope chaining with the topographic Abney level, as described under "The Abney Hand Level," page **17·30**. The correction graduations are placed on two "trailers." One trailer, for measuring distances of 1 chain, is found on the **under** side of the second chain, beyond the brass tab marking the end of the first chain. Care must be taken not to confuse its graduations with the standard graduations on the opposite side of the tape. The second trailer, for measuring distances of 2 chains, is an actual addition to the tape, beyond the end of the second chain. Its graduations are likewise on the **under** side.

The error to be expected even in careful work with an Abney level and slope tape is 1 ft. in 500. This assumes that where the slope changes sharply within 2 chains, only 1 chain-length will be measured at a time, and the Abney will be read again for the second chain-length.

**Common Sources of Error in Taping.** The principal mechanical errors are careless use of the plumb bob, and bad alignment and sag of the tape. Adequate tension—generally a pull of 20 to 30 lb.—on the tape will reduce sag sufficiently for ordinary work. Because errors due to sag are cumulative, corrections can be made mathematically in very accurate work. Human errors in taping are unpredictable; they include adding or dropping a full tape-length; adding or dropping a foot (43.4 instead of 42.4 in Fig. 1) when measuring fractional feet; transposing or reading wrong numbers (37.81 for 37.18, or 89 for 68); careless calling of numbers to the notekeeper (53.0 for 50.3); taking the wrong point on the tape for 0 or 100 ft.; and so on. Eternal vigilance is necessary to avoid such blunders. Never fail to check the simplest measurement; for example, a glance at the graduation 70, two feet from 68, would prevent anyone from inverting 68 to read 89.

**Correction for Nonstandard Tapes.** It is not uncommon to find a steel tape of nonstandard length, particularly those which long use has stretched slightly. To determine the correction, let $S$ equal the standard length of the tape; $T$ equal its true (actual) length; $L$ equal the true length of the line; and $M$ equal the measured length of the line. Then $T/S$ is the length of the tape in terms of standard, and $L = (T/S)M$. Variations in tape length due to temperature are negligible. Tapes are usually made of standard length at 68° F., and a change of 15° F. will produce an error of only 0.001 ft. in 100.0 ft.

The error to be expected in taping horizontal distances is about 1 ft. in 5,000. This will require a standard tape, plus ordinary care in plumbing, aligning, and in preventing sag.

**Special Problems in the Use of a Tape.**

**1. Laying out a right angle.** If a line being surveyed through woods runs into a large tree or boulder, it is often necessary to offset around the obstacle. To make an accurate right-angle offset from a given point on such a line, without setting up the

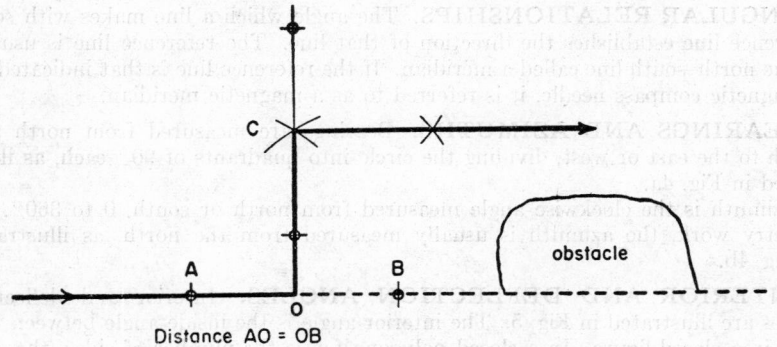

Distance AO = OB

Fig. 2. **Measuring around an obstacle.**

compass or transit at that point, measure any convenient distance beyond the point and the same distance back of it. From two points thus established (*A* and *B* in Fig. 2) swing equal arcs in the direction of the offset. Their intersection, point *C*, will be on a perpendicular to the survey line from the original point.

If for any reason it is impossible to measure beyond the original point, measure back from it a distance of 4 ft. From this point swing an arc of 5 ft., and from the original point an arc of 3 ft. in the direction of the offset; their intersection will be on the perpendicular from the original point (see left-hand diagram, Fig. 3). Increased accuracy should result from doubling or tripling all of these distances.

**2. Measuring inaccessible lines.** Occasionally it may be necessary to measure the distance to an inaccessible point, such as the far bank of a stream, with tape only (see right-hand diagram, Fig. 3). To measure *VW*, make *UV* any convenient length in range with *VW*; make *VO* any convenient length and *OY* equal to and in range with *VO*; measure *UO* and make *OX* equal to and in range with *UO*; place a stake at *Z* in range with both *XY* and *OW*. Line *XYZ* will be parallel to line *UVW* and line *YZ* will be equal in length to line *VW*.

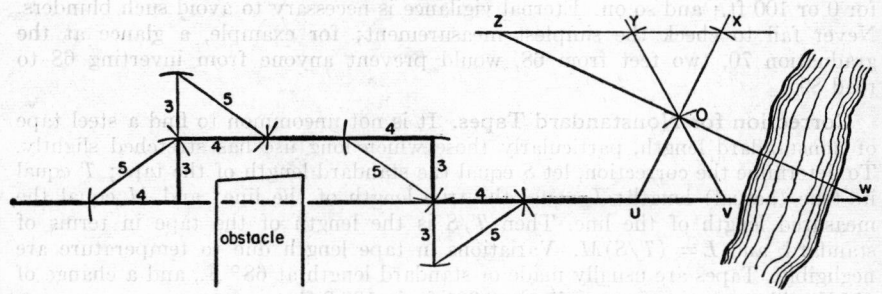

**Fig. 3. Measuring inaccessible lines.**

**STADIA.** Stadia measurement of distance, by a transit or telescopic alidade in first-class adjustment, is infrequently used in forest surveying because of poor visibility even in very open woods. It is described in "The Engineer's Transit," page 17·38.

## Measurement of Direction

**ANGULAR RELATIONSHIPS.** The angle which a line makes with some reference line establishes the direction of that line. The reference line is usually a true north–south line called a meridian. If the reference line is that indicated by a magnetic compass needle, it is referred to as a magnetic meridian.

**BEARINGS AND AZIMUTHS.** Bearings are measured from north and south to the east or west, dividing the circle into quadrants of 90° each, as illustrated in Fig. 4a.

Azimuth is the clockwise angle measured from north or south, 0 to 360°. In forestry work, the azimuth is usually measured from the north, as illustrated in Fig. 4b.

**INTERIOR AND DEFLECTION ANGLES.** Interior and deflection angles are illustrated in Fig. 5. The interior angle is the inside angle between two lines in a closed figure. In a closed polygon, if *n* is the number of sides, the sum of the interior angles is $(2n - 4) \times 90$.

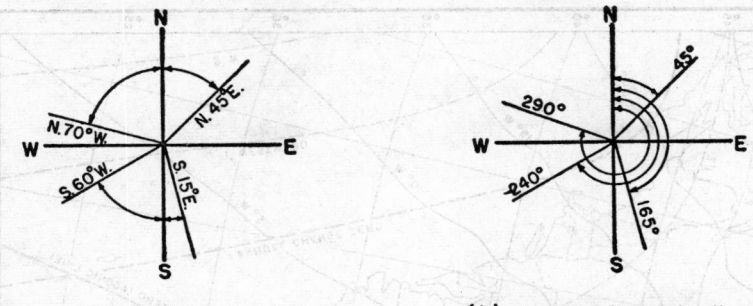

*(a)* Bearings                    *(b)* Corresponding Azimuths

**Fig. 4.  Bearing and azimuth.**

The deflection angle is that angle which is deflected from a straight line prolonged through the occupied station from the previous station. When the interior angle is less than 180°, the deflection angle is 180° minus the interior angle. If the interior angle is more than 180°, the deflection angle is the interior angle minus 180°. Deflection angles must be designated "R" or "L" to indicate whether they were turned right or left from the prolonged line.

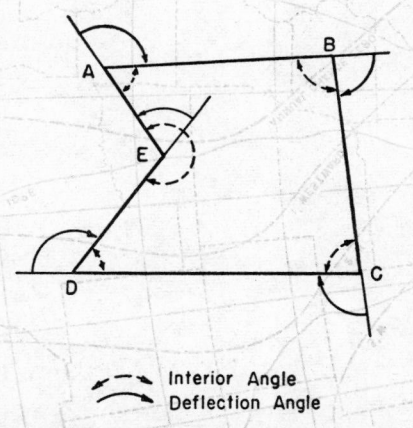

⌐ ‑ ‑ ⌐  Interior Angle
‑‑‑‑‑‑‑  Deflection Angle

**Fig. 5.  Interior and deflection angles.**

**MAGNETIC DECLINATION.** Magnetic declination is the angular variation of the magnetic meridian from the true meridian. This variation is due in part to the fact that the magnetic and true north poles are some 1,300 mi. apart. If the north end of the compass needle points to the east of the true meridian, the declination is said to be east; if it points to the west, the declination is said to be west.

Along a line which passes roughly through eastern Manitoba, western Ontario, Lake Michigan, northeastern Indiana, southwestern Ohio, eastern Kentucky and Tennessee, and western North and South Carolina, the compass needle points directly to true north as well as to magnetic north. This is known as the agonic

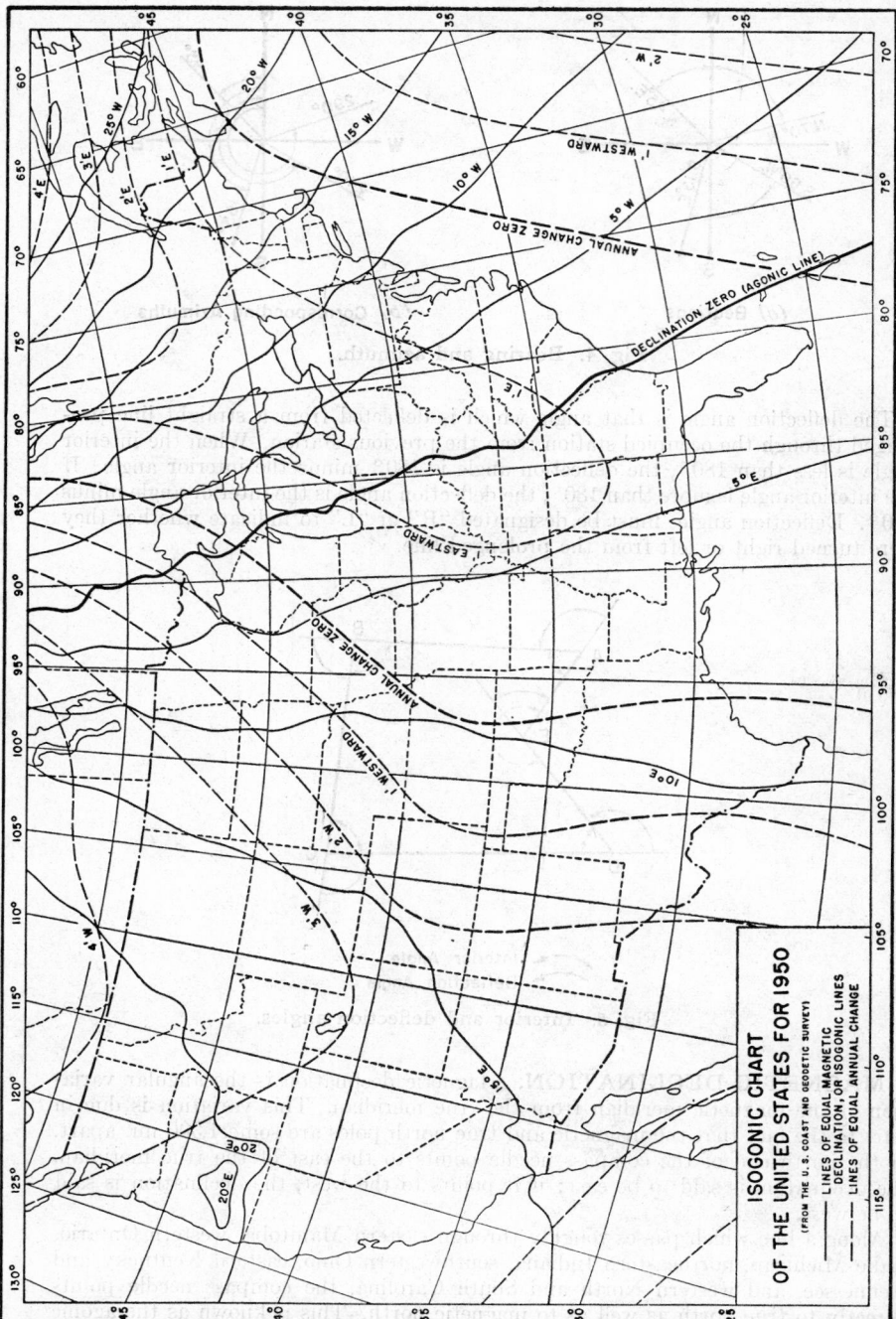

Fig. 6. Simplified isogonic chart for the United States.

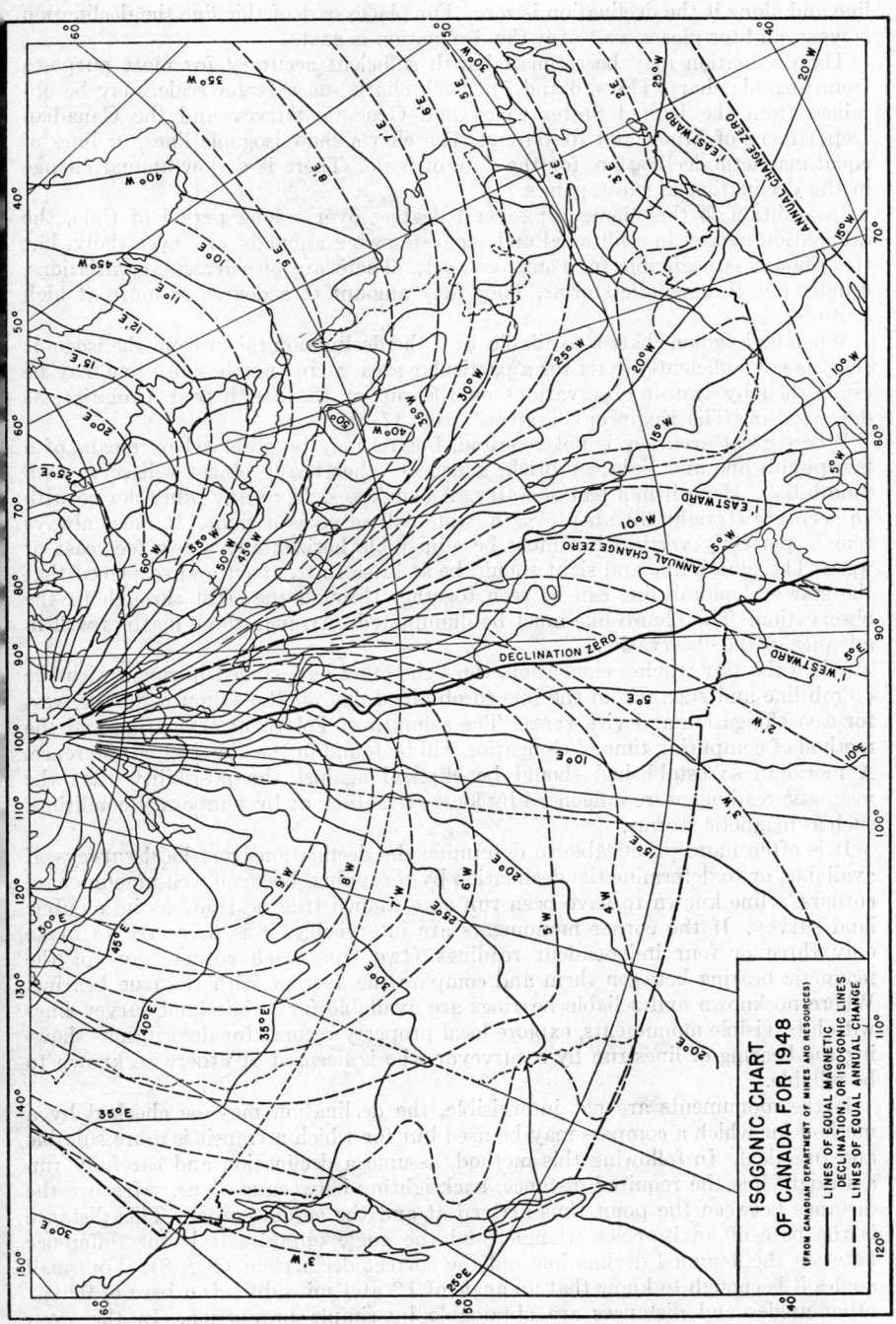

Fig. 7. Simplified isogonic chart for Canada.

ISOGONIC CHART
OF CANADA FOR 1948
(FROM CANADIAN DEPARTMENT OF MINES AND RESOURCES)

—— LINES OF EQUAL MAGNETIC
DECLINATION, OR ISOGONIC LINES
---- LINES OF EQUAL ANNUAL CHANGE

line and along it the declination is zero. For places east of this line the declination is **west**, and for places west of it the declination is **east**.

The declination may be estimated with sufficient accuracy for most purposes from isogonic charts (Figs. 6 and 7). Such charts, on a larger scale, may be obtained from the United States Coast and Geodetic Survey and the Canadian Department of Mines and Resources. The charts show isogonic lines, or lines of equal magnetic declination, for the date of issue. There is a slow annual change in the declination at most points.

In addition to this change of several degrees over a long period of time, the declination makes an additional and separate swing annually and even daily, but the amount is negligible for compass work. There are also irregular variations, usually due to magnetic storms. They may amount to a degree or more at high latitudes.

When no isogonic chart is available, or if the declination taken from the isogonic chart is not sufficiently exact for a particular area, a true north–south line may be established by transit observations on the sun or the North Star (Polaris), as described in "The Engineer's Transit," page 17·38.

Where great accuracy is not required, Polaris may be observed by means of a fine plumb line and sight. A brick, stone, or other heavy object will serve as a plumb bob. Hang it in a pail of water. A compass sight or any other device with an accurate straight slit about 1/16 in. wide will serve as a sight. It must always remain perfectly vertical but must be adjustable horizontally a few feet east or west. The plumb line and sight should be at least 15 ft. apart and so placed that the star and plumb line can be seen together through the sight throughout the observation. The plumb line must be illuminated. Arrange these matters well in advance of the observation.

When the star reaches elongation, the sight must be fastened in range with the plumb line and star. From the line so obtained, lay off the azimuth, to the west for east elongation and vice versa. The azimuth of Polaris at elongation and the method of computing time of elongation will be found in the above-cited reference. A meridian so established should be checked against the possibility that the magnetic readings were influenced by local attraction, or by temporary conditions such as magnetic storms.

It is often more practicable to determine the declination from local surveys, if available, or to determine the declination by rerunning, between well-monumented corners, a line known to have been run on a known true bearing—as in a public land survey. If the corner monuments are intervisible, it is necessary to make only three or four independent readings (two from each corner, say) of the magnetic bearing between them and compare the average with the true bearing. Where no known and reliable bearings are available for public land survey lines with intervisible monuments, explore local property records for descriptions showing the bearing of lines run by a surveyor who is licensed or otherwise known to be reliable.

If the monuments are not intervisible, the declination may be checked by a method for which a compass may be used but for which a transit is more suitable and practical. In following this method, assume a declination and carefully run a straight line the required distance, backsighting between stations. Measure the distance between the point thus arrived at and the actual corner. This distance is the base of an isosceles triangle, and the angle opposite it is the difference between the assumed declination and the correct declination (Fig. 8). For small angles it is enough to know that an angle of 1° at 1 mi. subtends a base of 92 ft.; other angles and distances are obtainable by simple proportion. In the west,

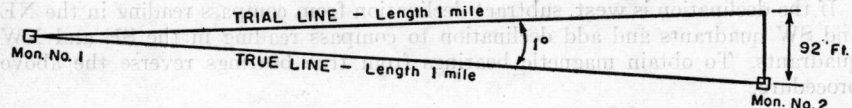

**Fig. 8. Checking magnetic declination.**

assume that too much declination will throw the trial line to the left of the original line, too little will throw it to the right. In the east, the reverse is true.

   **Example.** The magnetic declination is to be obtained by rerunning a township line with a true bearing of N89°W. An assumed declination of 15°E is set off by compass, and the line is rerun on this bearing. (If for any reason the declination cannot be set off, the line may be run on a calculated bearing.)

   A point set on the rerun line at a distance of 1 mi. from the starting monument is found to be 70 ft. to the *left* of the section corner monument, which also is 1 mi. from the starting monument. The error in declination is then 70/92 × 60 min., or approximately 45 min. too much. The correct declination is then 14°15′E.

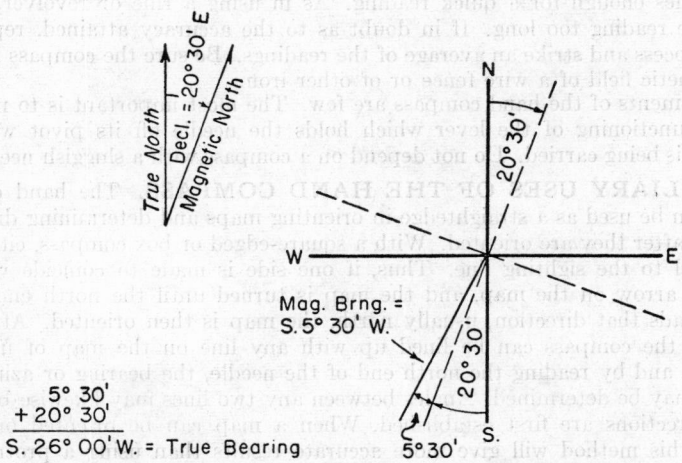

**Fig. 9. Magnetic and true direction.**

   **Conversion of Magnetic to True Bearing.** The conversion of magnetic to true bearing, or vice versa, will be simplified and checked by preparing a sketch to portray the situation, as in Fig. 9. The declination as shown in Fig. 9 is 20°30′E. The magnetic bearing is S5°30′W, and the true bearing of the line is desired. Set up the quadrant representing the true cardinal directions and superimpose in correct relationship the magnetic quadrant. The true bearing by inspection is S26°00′W. By using the same approach, true directions may be converted to magnetic directions. Note that correction for declination often changes the quadrant of bearings close to the cardinal directions.

   A rule of thumb for the conversion of magnetic to true bearings is suggested. To obtain true bearings, if the declination is **east,** add declination to compass reading in the NE and SW quadrants and subtract declination from compass reading in the SE and NW quadrants.

If the declination is **west,** subtract declination from compass reading in the NE and SW quadrants and add declination to compass reading in the SE and NW quadrants. To obtain magnetic bearings from true bearings reverse the above procedure.

## The Hand Compass

Hand compasses vary widely in construction. To use any make successfully requires simultaneous sighting, leveling, and reading of the bearing or azimuth. Peep sights and level bubbles are rarely usable. Graduations on the compass circle of 5°, which permit reading to 2 or 3°, are as good as finer graduations, which cannot be read unless the compass is set on a stump or other level surface. A useful refinement is a mechanism for setting off the magnetic declination.

To use a hand compass, it is held in both hands, with elbows supported against the body—far enough from the body to avoid the magnetism of jackknife, keys, etc., in clothing pockets. If, after sighting, the needle still swings widely, time can be saved by tilting the box of the compass to stop the needle just as it reaches the approximate midpoint of its swing; when the box is again leveled, the needle soon settles enough for a quick reading. As in using a rifle or revolver, do not delay the reading too long. If in doubt as to the accuracy attained, repeat the whole process and strike an average of the readings. Be sure the compass is not in the magnetic field of a wire fence or of other iron.

Adjustments of the hand compass are few. The most important is to maintain proper functioning of the lever which holds the needle off its pivot while the compass is being carried. Do not depend on a compass with a sluggish needle.

**AUXILIARY USES OF THE HAND COMPASS.** The hand compass may often be used as a straightedge in orienting maps and determining directions on maps after they are oriented. With a square-edged or box compass, either side is parallel to the sighting line. Thus, if one side is made to coincide with the direction arrow on the map, and the map is turned until the north end of the needle reads that direction, usually north, the map is then oriented. After it is oriented, the compass can be lined up with any line on the map of unknown direction, and by reading the north end of the needle, the bearing or azimuth of the line may be determined. Angles between any two lines may likewise be found if the directions are first established. When a map can be oriented on a flat surface, this method will give more accurate results than using a protractor—unless a large, finely graduated one is at hand.

## The Staff Compass

The staff compass box is fastened rigidly to a vertical spindle which is free to revolve in a conical socket in the leveling head of the Jacob's staff. The staff is a wooden leg with the leveling head screwed on one end and a pointed steel shoe fastened on the other end. A staff may be made from an ordinary hoe handle by straightening and sharpening the shank, cutting off the opposite end of the handle for a suitable length, and attaching the leveling head. Makeshift Jacob's staffs are often cut from a straight sapling. The staff makes it possible to steady the compass in a level position. This feature, combined with the well-defined sighting line on the compass and a comparatively sensitive needle, makes the staff compass sufficiently precise for angular measurements connected with most forest surveying

Staff compass circles are usually graduated in degrees. Half degrees and quarter degrees may be estimated. Readings to half degrees, or even to quarter degrees when found practical, are recommended for traverse work. It is seldom practical to read a surveyor's compass closer than 15 min.

Most staff compasses have the degree divisions etched upon a movable ring which can be moved either way by means of an adjusting pin to set off the known declination. Once this is done the compass readings will be true bearings. Using this procedure will eliminate later office calculations. To adjust the compass for this purpose (with **west** declination), turn the declination arc toward the west the amount of declination to get vanes to point to true north. CAUTION: because letters are reversed on face of compass, turn arc toward the letter E. With **east** declination reverse the process.

Staff compass survey distances are ordinarily taped. If reasonable care is used in reading bearings and taping distances, the error of closure for staff compass surveys will be about 1/300.

**ADJUSTMENT.** The needle lever must be kept functioning, as described for the hand compass. The plane of the bubbles must be parallel to the compass plate. Level the compass, rotate it 180°. If the bubbles are then out of level, correct each tube by one-half the movement and relevel. Repeat the process until the levels remain constant when the compass is rotated.

After making the level bubbles parallel to the compass plate, check to see that the plane of the sights is perpendicular to the plane of the bubbles. To do this, level the instrument and sight to a plumb line hung a short distance away. If the plumb line coincides with the sighting line throughout the length of the latter, the instrument is in adjustment. If not, remove the sighting leaf and grind off at the base so that it sets level. Before doing this, check to see that the sighting vane itself is not bent, in which case straightening of the vane may be sufficient to correct the error.

Should the wire in the sighting vane become bent or broken, a horsehair or fine thread can be inserted; either one will serve as a satisfactory temporary substitute for the sighting wire.

**AVOIDING ERRORS.** Errors may be avoided if one will:

1. Keep the staff vertical when occupying a station, and keep the needle and level bubbles properly adjusted.
2. Make sure that the needle is not sticking.
3. See that the sighting vane or vertical hair is vertical and not bent out of line.
4. Let the needle settle before reading the direction.
5. Be sure to read the right end of the needle.
6. Be sure to read the graduations correctly.
7. Be careful to move forward to the same object on which the foresight was taken.
8. Take a backsight and record the backsight bearing from each station in order to reduce the opportunities for mistakes in reading angles and errors introduced by local attraction.
9. Keep as far as possible from wire fences and other objects containing iron.

Possible errors in running a compass traverse are of three kinds: mistakes, systematic errors, and accidental errors. Mistakes can be avoided or at least kept to a minimum by taking backsights as well as foresights at each station occupied, by intermediate ties to established corners and land net markers, and by pacing between compass stations as a check against dropped chain lengths in taping. Systematic errors may be due to nonstandard tapes, poor adjustment of the compass, and refraction. They can be eliminated by noting and correcting them. Accidental errors are those which remain after removal of mistakes and correction for systematic errors. Meticulous attention to angle and distance measurements is the best protection against a significant amount of accidental error.

**LOCAL ATTRACTION.** Local attraction is a common phenomenon in many mountainous areas, where the lines of magnetic force are altered by iron ore deposits. Everywhere, objects of iron or steel and electric lines may cause local attraction. Usually it is possible to correct for this condition.

The foresight and backsight bearings of a line between two stations will disagree numerically if local attraction exists at one station in a traverse and not at an adjacent station, or is greater at one than at the other. However, **all** bearings

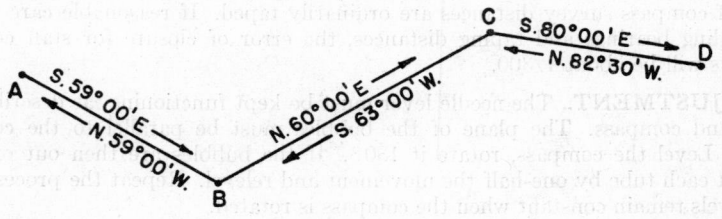

Arrows indicate back and forward bearings. Both bearings agree on line AB. Therefore bearing BC is assumed to be correct, N. 60°00' E.

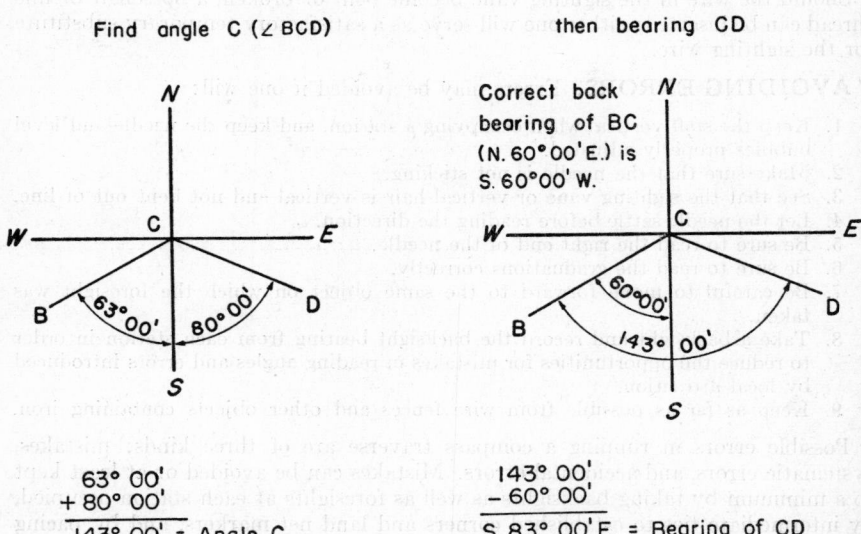

Find angle C (∠ BCD)

then bearing CD

Correct back bearing of BC (N. 60°00' E.) is S. 60°00' W.

$$\begin{array}{r} 63°\ 00' \\ +\ 80°\ 00' \\ \hline 143°\ 00' = \text{Angle C} \end{array}$$

$$\begin{array}{r} 143°\ 00' \\ -\ 60°\ 00' \\ \hline \text{S. } 83°\ 00'\text{ E.} = \text{Bearing of CD} \end{array}$$

Fig. 10. **Adjusting for local attraction.**

taken from any one station will be affected equally. Therefore, at that station the angle between any pair of lines is the true angle, regardless of the amount of local attraction. It follows, then, that all the angles in the traverse may be computed; and by using these angles, the bearings may be calculated through the affected area from the closest unaffected line showing agreement in back and forward bearings. Fig. 10 illustrates this method of adjusting for local attraction.

All personal error must obviously be eliminated before attempting to correct for local attraction. If there is a discrepancy between foresight and backsight bearings after compass adjustments and readings have been checked meticulously, it is reasonable to assume that local attraction has affected the needle, and it is necessary to make an adjustment accordingly. However, it should be remembered that bearings and angles may fail to close completely because of accumulated errors due to natural minute accumulations and other causes unrelated to local attraction.

Local attraction may be avoided when prolonging a straight line across a section of land for strip mapping or cruising by using the compass as a sighting device only, disregarding needle readings after the initial setup and prolonging the line by backsights and foresights on natural objects or "butterflies," i.e., a set stake with a piece of paper fastened near the top to identify the sight stake line.

## Surveying Old Property Lines

Deeds are intended to convey property within boundaries which will form a closed traverse. Artificial or natural features where mentioned as boundaries take precedence over lines determined by recorded measurements and bearings. The features must, generally, be specifically mentioned in the deed in order to have the force or authority of monuments. In the event of a discrepancy between the area mentioned in a deed and that existing within the described boundaries, the latter control. Distances given in deeds are assumed to be measured on a straight line unless given as so many feet along a meandering feature such as a highway, stream, or wall.

Procedure is as follows:

1. Be sure the bearings and distances from the deed or other source of information have been accurately copied. Record the date of survey and any information available as to magnetic or true reference.
2. If the area is a closed polygon, map it with protractor and scale to detect any serious error of closure; if one exists, check copying; if necessary, examine earlier deeds or maps, usually to be found recorded at local county courthouses, to locate errors in copying.
3. From date of survey and available information on rates of change in declination, compute declination to lay off on compass in the field.
4. On the ground begin at the corner most authentically known, and run to a similar corner to check declination.
5. Do not blaze a trial line (bark nicks are permissible), but if the final line must eventually be blazed, set stakes on the trial line at standard intervals, and reset them, by proportion, when the declination error has been determined.
6. Search out old residents who may be able to assist in locating corners.

Do not assume that a corner marker is missing because it is not visible. Stone monuments are often buried 2 or 3 ft. deep. By digging deep, it may be possible to locate a few remaining fibers or other subsurface evidence that will establish the position of a corner stake that has long since decayed above ground.

It must be remembered that a resurvey of an established line is for re-establishing **original** boundaries and corners. These must not be moved because they fail to conform with the description of the property or the original survey notes.

## Field Notes

Field notes should be so made that the only one reasonable interpretation is the correct one. However, there is no standard method of keeping field notes. Careful planning is well worth while. Fig. 11 illustrates a serviceable form, with accompanying sketch map, for a closed traverse.

*(Left-hand page )*      *(Right-hand page )*

| Sta. | Hor. Dist. | F.S. Bearing | B.S. Bearing | Int. Angle | Correct Bearing | Boundary Survey of Camp Blank Primitive National Forest |
|---|---|---|---|---|---|---|
| | | | Due N. | | | on N. W. Cor. Sec. 2 |
| A | | | | | | ¾" steel pipe 1100.0' due South of Sec. Corner |
| | 1614.2 | S.59°30'E. | N.59°30'W. | | S.59°30'E. | N |
| B | | | | 115°30' | | |
| | 1210.0 | N.56°00'E. | S.58°30'W. | | N.56°00'E. | N. W. Cor. Sec. 2   E   Road   D · 810' |
| C | | | | 111°00'  110°30' | | |
| | 900.5 | N.11°00'W. | S.13°00'E. | | N.13°00'W. | |
| D | | | | 116°00' | | A |
| | 1340.0 | N.77°00W. | S.77°00'E. | | N.77°00'W. | C |
| E | | | | 118°00' | | Creek |
| | 1348.0 | S.41°00'W. | N.41°00'E. | | S.41°00'W. | B+80' |
| A | | | | 79°30' | | |
| | | | | 539°30' | | B |
| | | | | 540°00' | | |
| 2 n-4 (90) = | 10-4 (90) = 540° | | | check | | February 29, 19— |
| | | | | | | John Doe, chief of party |
| | | | | | | Richard Doe, compassman |
| | | | | | | Edward White, head chainman |
| | | | | | | Robert Black, rear chainman |
| | | | | | | Equipment: Staff compass # 1505 |
| | | | | | | 200 foot steel tape |
| | | | | | | Ax, plumb bobs |
| | | | | | | Weather: Cloudy & cold |
| | | | | | | Visibility poor |

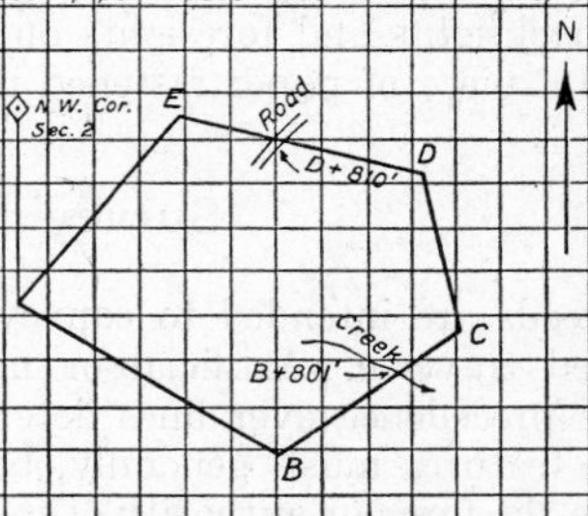

**Fig. 11. Field notes.**

**EXPLANATORY NOTES.** Explanatory notes should show, as a minimum, when, by whom, and with what major equipment the survey was made; the tie to a known point; and major topographic and cultural features, recorded on the map part of the notes. Streams, roads, ridges, etc., are often of great help in retracing forest surveys where corner monuments have been destroyed; where surveyed lines cross such features, the distance to the previous corner should be carefully recorded. CAUTION: Field note entries may be crossed out and corrected but must never be erased.

**ABBREVIATIONS AND SYMBOLS.** Some of the more common abbreviations and symbols used in field notes are:

| | | | |
|---|---|---|---|
| Sta. | Station | B.S. | Backsight |
| B.M. | Bench mark | Tp. | Township |
| T.P. | Turning point | Rn. | Range |
| P.I. | Point of intersection | Sec. | Section |
| P.C. | Point of curvature | ₵ | Center line |
| P.T. | Point of tangency | ∠ | Angle |
| Elev. | Elevation | Az. | Azimuth |
| Dist. | Horizontal distance | Br. | Bearing |
| H.I. | Height of instrument | Cor. | Corner |
| △ | Triangulation station | D.E. | Difference in elevation |
| ⊙ | Traverse station | Int. | Interior |
| ↑ | Transit or level | Defl. | Deflection |
| F.S. | Foresight | Mag. | Magnetic |

**CORRECTING FIELD NOTES.** Correcting of field notes should, if at all possible, be done while still in the field.

1. Balance the interior angles, as shown in Fig. 11. Their sum should be equal to 90° multiplied by 4 less than twice the number of sides. When the error in five setups is greater than 1° (if cumulative, an average error of at least 12 min.; if compensating, one or more errors much greater than that), the angles should be measured. The error in Fig. 11 is 30 min. This may reasonably be thrown to one angle. Because even the figure of a man may be covered by the vertical hair in the front sight of a compass, angular errors are more likely on short shots than on long ones. It is therefore reasonable to correct by 30 min. the interior angle at Station *C*, preceding the shortest side of the polygon.

2. Correct for local attraction. In Fig. 11 the bearing of line *BA* (recorded as backsight in line following Station *A*) coincides numerically with *AB*, indicating no local attraction at *B*. Hence the bearing of *BC* may be taken as correct. But *CB* differs by 2° from *BC*, showing that there is local attraction at *C*. The correct bearing of *CD* is therefore computed from *BC* and the interior angle (now corrected; see previous paragraph) at *C*. The correctness of this process is confirmed by the bearing of *DC*, and no numerical discrepancy between foresight and backsight is found in subsequent courses.

3. Correct recorded distances for nonstandard lengths of tape, as explained on page 17·3.

**ERRORS OF CLOSURE.** A traverse which on the ground returned to its starting point rarely closes exactly when calculated or plotted because all linear and angular measurements are subject to error, either actual or in plotting. The error of closure is usually expressed as the ratio of the calculated or plotted linear error to the measured and recorded perimeter. In the following table two degrees of performance are recognized: allowable—under average physical conditions, and with ordinary care; and attainable—without adverse physical conditions, and with refined measurements.

**Table 1. Errors of Closure: Degrees of Performance**

| Equipment | Allowable | Attainable |
|---|---|---|
| Hand compass and pacing.................. | 1:20 | 1:40 |
| Staff compass and tape.................... | 1:300 | 1:800 [a] |
| Transit and tape........................ | 1:2,000 [b] | 1:5,000 [c] |

[a] Assumes refinement in measurement not justified in many forest surveys.
[b] Angles measured to nearest minute and distances to nearest 1/10 ft.
[c] Angles measured to 15 sec. and distances to nearest 1/100 ft.

**TRAVERSE BY LATITUDES AND DEPARTURES.** For determining the bearing and distance between any two points on an open traverse (a tie-line, for example), plotting a road or trail, calculating the area of a closed traverse (as described earlier), and for other purposes, latitudes and departures are conveniently used. The latitude of a course is its measured length multiplied by the natural cosine of its bearing. The latitude for a northerly bearing is considered plus; for a southerly bearing, minus. The departure of a course is its measured length multiplied by the natural sine of its bearings. Easterly bearings are considered plus; and westerly bearings, minus.

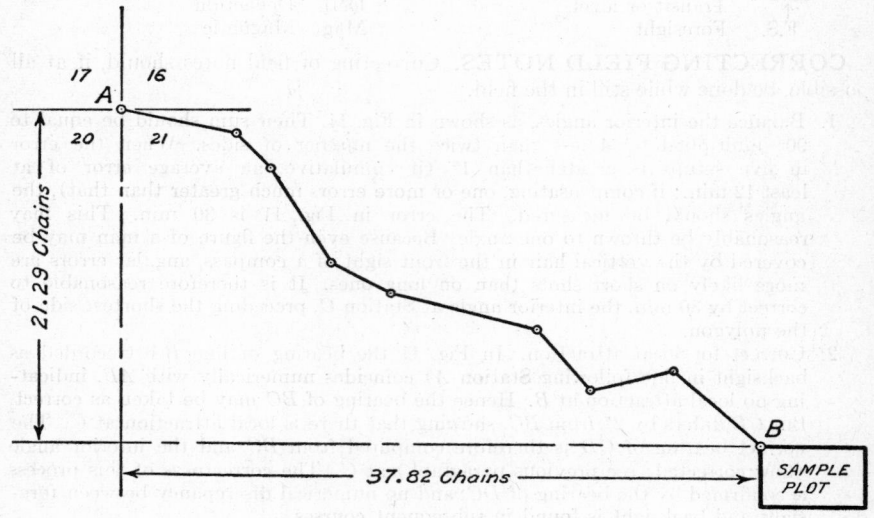

Fig. 12a. Sample traverse.

**COMPUTING A TRAVERSE.** Fig. 12a shows a traverse connecting the SE corner of section 17 (point $A$) and the NW corner of a sample plot (point $B$). Bearings and distances are shown (in chains) on the left side of Fig. 12b. Find the distances north or south and east or west from starting point $A$ to point $B$ at the corner of the sample plot.

From the table of natural sines and cosines (see Section **23**) find the cosine (latitude) for 78°; this is 0.2079. Multiply by the distance 7 (chains); $7 \times 0.2079 = 1.46$. Call it minus $(-)1.46$ since the bearing is south; $-1.46$ is the latitude for the first course beyond starting point $A$. Find the sine (departure) for 78°; this is 0.9781; $7 \times 0.9781 = +6.85$. This is the departure for the first course beyond starting point $A$, and is plus since the bearing is east.

Latitude and departures for the other courses are similarly computed. For the courses in Fig. 12b the latitudes are $-1.46$, $-2.19$, $-6.00$, $-2.00$, $-2.33$, $-3.83$, $+1.29$, and $-4.77$. The sum of the minus latitudes is 22.58, and of the plus latitudes, 1.29. $(-)22.58 - (+) 1.29 = (-)21.29$. Traverse point $B$ is 21.29 chains south of starting point $A$. Departures for the courses in Fig. 12b are $+6.85$, $+2.05$, $+3.61$, $+3.46$, $+8.69$, $+3.21$, $+4.83$, and $+5.12$. They total $(+)37.82$; thus, traverse point $B$ is 37.82 chains east of starting point $A$.

| | | N or S | | E or W | |
|---|---|---|---|---|---|
| Starting Point | A | 40.00 | N | 0.00 | |
| Traverse Point | B | 18.71 | N | 37.82 | E |
| Distance to | B | 21.29 | S | 37.82 | E |

## TRAVERSE

| BEARING | DIST. | Latitude N or S | | Departure E or W | |
|---|---|---|---|---|---|
| Starting Point | | 40.00 | N | 0.00 | |
| S 78 E | 7 | 1.46 | S | 6.85 | E |
| Traverse Point | | 38.54 | N | 6.85 | E |
| S 43 E | 3 | 2.19 | S | 2.05 | E |
| Traverse Point | | 36.35 | N | 8.90 | E |
| S 31 E | 7 | 6.00 | S | 3.61 | E |
| Traverse Point | | 30.35 | N | 12.51 | E |
| S 60 E | 4 | 2.00 | S | 3.46 | E |
| Traverse Point | | 28.35 | N | 15.97 | E |
| S 75 E | 9 | 2.33 | S | 8.69 | E |
| Traverse Point | | 26.02 | N | 24.66 | E |
| S 40 E | 5 | 3.83 | S | 3.21 | E |
| Traverse Point | | 22.19 | N | 27.87 | E |
| N 75 E | 5 | 1.29 | N | 4.83 | E |
| Traverse Point | | 23.48 | N | 32.70 | E |
| S 47 E | 7 | 4.77 | S | 5.12 | E |
| Traverse Point | | 18.71 | N | 37.82 | E |
| Traverse Point | | | | | |
| Traverse Point | | | | | |
| Traverse Point | | | | | |

Fig. 12b. Traverse form.

**USE OF TRAVERSE COMPUTATION FORM.** Fig. 12b illustrates a convenient form for computing a traverse. On the top line below "bearing" in the extreme left column, enter the bearing of the first course of the traverse; on the top line of the next column to the right, enter the distance for the first course; on the second line below, enter the bearing and distance for the second course. Enter bearings and distances for subsequent courses in the sequence in which they are measured.

Unless working with standard coordinates (used on military and some state maps), assume starting point coordinates about equal to the sum of the distances. This will eliminate the possibility of minus coordinates in the latitude and departure columns opposite the "Traverse Point." In Fig. 12b the sum of the distances is 37 (chains). Assume 40.0 for a north coordinate. Enter opposite "Starting point" in the block at the top of Fig. 12b and on the top line of the latitude column. Since inspection shows that all departures are plus (east), the starting point coordinate for the departure column can be 0.00.

Latitudes and departures are obtained as previously explained and entered opposite the bearing and distance in the appropriate column to the right in Fig. 12b. The direction of the bearing is also entered, N or S for latitudes and E or W for departures. Latitudes are subtracted if south, or added if north. Departures are subtracted if west, added if east. The coordinates for traverse point $B$ are found to be 18.71N and 37.82E. Enter these in the blocks at the top of Fig. 12b and subtract the smaller coordinate. If the coordinates for the final traverse point are less than for the starting point, the end of the traverse is south (or west) of the starting point; if greater, the traverse ends north (or east) of the starting point. In Fig. 12a point $B$ is 21.29 chains south and 37.82 chains east of point $A$. The straight line distance from $A$ to $B$ is $\sqrt{21.29^2 + 37.82^2} = 43.40$ chains.

**TRAVERSE TABLES.** Computation of latitudes and departures is often facilitated by traverse tables, in which the natural sines and cosines have been multiplied by distances of 1 to 10 units. Fig. 13 is a condensed traverse table for whole degrees. Latitudes appear in the NS columns and departures in the EW columns.

To find the latitude for a bearing of S78E and distance of 7 chains, find 78° in the extreme right column; at the left of 78° and in the column designated (at the bottom) 7NS, read 146. This is the latitude for 700 chains. For 7 chains this becomes 146/100, or 1.46. Because the bearing is south, the latitude is −1.46. Opposite 78° in the column designated (at the bottom) 7EW, find 685. For 7 chains and E bearing, the departure is +6.85. If the distance is 7.7 chains, add 0.146 to 1.46 to obtain the latitude, which becomes −1.61, to the nearest link; to obtain the departure −7.53, add 0.68 to 6.85. Carefully check by inspection the pointing-off of values taken from the table, as errors are easily made in the addition of decimal values.

## Methods of Plotting and Determination of Areas

Nearly every forest survey, whether it encloses an area or not, is sooner or later plotted. There are several methods. Areas may be determined either by plotting or by strictly mathematical methods.

### PLOTTING THE SURVEY.

1. Examine the field notes for completeness and correct them as described under "Field Notes" if this was not done in the field.
2. Choose a method appropriate to the survey methods used in the field and the precision desired. A compass survey, in which angles were measured no closer than ¼° and distances to the nearest link, can be plotted with the ordinary 6-in. protractor and an engineer's scale to give areas accurately to 1/100 of an acre. However, if such a traverse is to serve as the control for the entire survey of an extensive area, it should be plotted by more exact methods.
3. Unless the field sketch can be relied on for the purpose, plot the survey very roughly on scratch paper (a) to determine over-all dimensions, which control

| READ DOWN | CHAINS OR HUNDREDS OF FEET — LINKS OR FEET | | | | | | | | | | | | | | | | | | | | DEGREES |
|---|---|---|---|---|---|---|---|---|---|---|---|---|---|---|---|---|---|---|---|---|---|
| | 1 | | 2 | | 3 | | 4 | | 5 | | 6 | | 7 | | 8 | | 9 | | 10 | | |
| | N/S | E/W | N/S | E/W | N/S | E/W | N/S | E/W | N/S | E/W | N/S | E/W | N/S | E/W | N/S | E/W | N/S | E/W | N/S | E/W | |
| 1 | 100 | 2 | 200 | 4 | 300 | 5 | 400 | 7 | 500 | 9 | 600 | 10 | 700 | 12 | 800 | 14 | 900 | 16 | 1000 | 18 | 89 |
| 2 | 100 | 3 | 200 | 7 | 300 | 10 | 400 | 14 | 500 | 17 | 600 | 21 | 700 | 24 | 800 | 28 | 899 | 31 | 999 | 35 | 88 |
| 3 | 100 | 5 | 200 | 10 | 300 | 16 | 399 | 21 | 499 | 26 | 599 | 31 | 699 | 37 | 799 | 42 | 899 | 47 | 999 | 52 | 87 |
| 4 | 100 | 7 | 200 | 14 | 299 | 21 | 399 | 28 | 499 | 35 | 599 | 42 | 698 | 49 | 798 | 56 | 898 | 63 | 998 | 70 | 86 |
| 5 | 100 | 9 | 199 | 17 | 299 | 26 | 398 | 35 | 498 | 44 | 598 | 52 | 697 | 61 | 798 | 70 | 897 | 78 | 996 | 87 | 85 |
| 6 | 99 | 10 | 199 | 21 | 298 | 31 | 398 | 42 | 497 | 52 | 597 | 63 | 696 | 73 | 796 | 84 | 895 | 94 | 994 | 104 | 84 |
| 7 | 99 | 12 | 198 | 24 | 298 | 37 | 397 | 49 | 496 | 61 | 596 | 73 | 695 | 85 | 794 | 98 | 893 | 110 | 992 | 122 | 83 |
| 8 | 99 | 14 | 198 | 28 | 297 | 42 | 396 | 56 | 495 | 70 | 594 | 84 | 693 | 97 | 792 | 111 | 891 | 125 | 990 | 139 | 82 |
| 9 | 99 | 16 | 198 | 31 | 296 | 47 | 395 | 63 | 494 | 78 | 593 | 94 | 691 | 109 | 790 | 125 | 889 | 141 | 988 | 156 | 81 |
| 10 | 98 | 17 | 197 | 35 | 295 | 52 | 394 | 69 | 492 | 87 | 591 | 104 | 689 | 122 | 788 | 139 | 886 | 156 | 985 | 174 | 80 |
| 11 | 98 | 19 | 196 | 38 | 294 | 57 | 393 | 76 | 491 | 95 | 589 | 114 | 687 | 134 | 785 | 153 | 883 | 172 | 982 | 191 | 79 |
| 12 | 98 | 21 | 196 | 42 | 293 | 62 | 391 | 83 | 489 | 104 | 587 | 125 | 685 | 146 | 782 | 166 | 880 | 187 | 978 | 208 | 78 |
| 13 | 97 | 22 | 195 | 45 | 292 | 68 | 390 | 90 | 487 | 112 | 585 | 135 | 682 | 158 | 780 | 180 | 877 | 202 | 974 | 225 | 77 |
| 14 | 97 | 24 | 194 | 48 | 291 | 73 | 388 | 97 | 485 | 121 | 582 | 145 | 679 | 169 | 776 | 194 | 873 | 218 | 970 | 242 | 76 |
| 15 | 97 | 26 | 193 | 52 | 290 | 78 | 386 | 104 | 483 | 129 | 580 | 155 | 676 | 181 | 773 | 207 | 869 | 233 | 966 | 259 | 75 |
| 16 | 96 | 28 | 192 | 55 | 288 | 83 | 385 | 110 | 481 | 138 | 577 | 165 | 673 | 193 | 769 | 220 | 865 | 248 | 961 | 276 | 74 |
| 17 | 96 | 29 | 191 | 58 | 287 | 88 | 383 | 117 | 478 | 146 | 574 | 175 | 669 | 205 | 765 | 234 | 861 | 263 | 956 | 292 | 73 |
| 18 | 95 | 31 | 190 | 62 | 285 | 93 | 380 | 124 | 476 | 154 | 571 | 185 | 666 | 216 | 761 | 247 | 856 | 278 | 951 | 309 | 72 |
| 19 | 95 | 33 | 189 | 65 | 284 | 98 | 378 | 130 | 473 | 163 | 567 | 195 | 662 | 228 | 756 | 260 | 851 | 293 | 946 | 326 | 71 |
| 20 | 94 | 34 | 188 | 68 | 282 | 103 | 376 | 137 | 470 | 171 | 564 | 205 | 658 | 239 | 752 | 274 | 849 | 308 | 940 | 342 | 70 |
| 21 | 93 | 36 | 187 | 72 | 280 | 108 | 373 | 143 | 467 | 179 | 560 | 215 | 654 | 251 | 747 | 287 | 840 | 323 | 934 | 358 | 69 |
| 22 | 93 | 37 | 185 | 75 | 278 | 112 | 371 | 150 | 464 | 187 | 556 | 225 | 649 | 262 | 742 | 300 | 834 | 337 | 927 | 375 | 68 |
| 23 | 92 | 39 | 184 | 78 | 276 | 117 | 368 | 156 | 460 | 195 | 552 | 234 | 644 | 273 | 736 | 313 | 828 | 352 | 920 | 391 | 67 |
| 24 | 91 | 41 | 183 | 81 | 274 | 122 | 365 | 163 | 457 | 203 | 548 | 244 | 639 | 285 | 731 | 325 | 822 | 366 | 914 | 407 | 66 |
| 25 | 91 | 42 | 181 | 85 | 272 | 127 | 363 | 169 | 453 | 211 | 544 | 254 | 634 | 296 | 725 | 338 | 816 | 380 | 906 | 423 | 65 |
| 26 | 90 | 44 | 180 | 88 | 270 | 132 | 360 | 175 | 449 | 219 | 539 | 263 | 629 | 307 | 719 | 351 | 809 | 395 | 899 | 438 | 64 |
| 27 | 89 | 45 | 178 | 91 | 267 | 136 | 356 | 182 | 446 | 227 | 535 | 272 | 624 | 318 | 713 | 363 | 802 | 409 | 891 | 454 | 63 |
| 28 | 88 | 47 | 177 | 94 | 265 | 141 | 353 | 188 | 441 | 235 | 530 | 282 | 618 | 329 | 706 | 376 | 795 | 423 | 883 | 470 | 62 |
| 29 | 87 | 48 | 175 | 97 | 262 | 145 | 350 | 194 | 437 | 242 | 525 | 291 | 612 | 339 | 700 | 388 | 787 | 436 | 875 | 485 | 61 |
| 30 | 87 | 50 | 173 | 100 | 260 | 150 | 346 | 200 | 433 | 250 | 520 | 300 | 606 | 350 | 693 | 400 | 779 | 450 | 866 | 500 | 60 |
| 31 | 86 | 52 | 171 | 103 | 257 | 154 | 343 | 206 | 429 | 258 | 514 | 309 | 600 | 361 | 686 | 412 | 771 | 464 | 857 | 515 | 59 |
| 32 | 85 | 53 | 170 | 106 | 254 | 159 | 339 | 212 | 424 | 265 | 509 | 318 | 594 | 371 | 678 | 424 | 763 | 477 | 848 | 530 | 58 |
| 33 | 84 | 54 | 168 | 109 | 252 | 163 | 335 | 218 | 419 | 272 | 503 | 327 | 587 | 381 | 671 | 436 | 755 | 490 | 839 | 545 | 57 |
| 34 | 83 | 56 | 166 | 112 | 249 | 168 | 332 | 224 | 414 | 280 | 497 | 336 | 580 | 391 | 663 | 447 | 746 | 503 | 829 | 559 | 56 |
| 35 | 82 | 57 | 164 | 115 | 246 | 172 | 328 | 229 | 410 | 287 | 492 | 344 | 573 | 402 | 655 | 459 | 737 | 516 | 819 | 574 | 55 |
| 36 | 81 | 59 | 162 | 118 | 243 | 176 | 324 | 235 | 404 | 294 | 485 | 353 | 566 | 411 | 647 | 470 | 728 | 529 | 809 | 588 | 54 |
| 37 | 80 | 60 | 160 | 120 | 240 | 181 | 319 | 241 | 399 | 301 | 479 | 361 | 559 | 421 | 639 | 481 | 719 | 542 | 799 | 602 | 53 |
| 38 | 79 | 62 | 158 | 123 | 236 | 185 | 315 | 246 | 394 | 308 | 473 | 369 | 552 | 431 | 630 | 493 | 709 | 556 | 788 | 616 | 52 |
| 39 | 78 | 63 | 155 | 126 | 233 | 189 | 311 | 252 | 389 | 315 | 466 | 378 | 544 | 441 | 622 | 503 | 699 | 566 | 777 | 629 | 51 |
| 40 | 77 | 64 | 153 | 129 | 230 | 193 | 306 | 257 | 383 | 321 | 460 | 386 | 536 | 450 | 613 | 514 | 689 | 579 | 766 | 643 | 50 |
| 41 | 75 | 66 | 151 | 131 | 226 | 197 | 302 | 262 | 377 | 328 | 453 | 394 | 528 | 459 | 604 | 525 | 679 | 590 | 755 | 656 | 49 |
| 42 | 74 | 67 | 149 | 134 | 223 | 201 | 297 | 268 | 372 | 335 | 446 | 401 | 520 | 468 | 594 | 535 | 669 | 602 | 743 | 669 | 48 |
| 43 | 73 | 68 | 146 | 136 | 219 | 205 | 293 | 273 | 366 | 341 | 439 | 409 | 512 | 477 | 585 | 546 | 658 | 614 | 731 | 682 | 47 |
| 44 | 72 | 69 | 144 | 139 | 216 | 208 | 288 | 278 | 360 | 347 | 432 | 417 | 504 | 485 | 575 | 556 | 647 | 625 | 719 | 695 | 46 |
| 45 | 71 | 71 | 141 | 141 | 212 | 212 | 283 | 283 | 354 | 354 | 424 | 424 | 495 | 495 | 566 | 566 | 636 | 636 | 707 | 707 | 45 |

| DEGREES | E/W | N/S | E/W | N/S | E/W | N/S | E/W | N/S | E/W | N/S | E/W | N/S | E/W | N/S | E/W | N/S | E/W | N/S | E/W | N/S | READ UP |
|---|---|---|---|---|---|---|---|---|---|---|---|---|---|---|---|---|---|---|---|---|---|
| | 1 | | 2 | | 3 | | 4 | | 5 | | 6 | | 7 | | 8 | | 9 | | 10 | | |
| | LINKS OR FEET — CHAINS OR HUNDREDS OF FEET | | | | | | | | | | | | | | | | | | | | |

Fig. 13. Traverse table.

selection of a scale for the final map; (b) to enable centering it on the sheet available for drafting so that the N–S lines are parallel to the sides of the sheet (the N at the top of the sheet) and to provide room for an adequate legend; and (c) to locate the best starting point for plotting.

**Protractor Plotting.** Protractor plotting should be done on cross-section paper, if at all possible, so that each bearing may be independently plotted. If plain paper must be used, draw a reference meridian through the first station, and at the second and all subsequent stations lay off the **interior angles** (see Fig. 11). Through about every fourth station draw a meridian and plot the next course from its bearing; should the course so plotted vary by more than ¼° from the direction established from the interior angle, preceding courses should be checked for angular error.

Theoretically, a closed traverse in the field should close on paper; in practice it rarely does. If remeasurement of plotted angles and distances reveals no error, measure the distance between the final corner as plotted and the starting corner, and divide this by the perimeter. If this ratio is greater than the allowable error tabulated on page **17·15**, a resurvey in the field is the only satisfactory procedure.

An error of less magnitude may be corrected graphically. If the courses of the survey are roughly equal, divide the error equally. If some courses are much longer than others, the amount each corner is moved may be proportional to the length of the course preceding it. No change in the recorded bearings and distances should be made to conform to the plotted counterparts. However, any feature referenced to corners or courses in the field should be plotted to conform to their adjusted positions.

**The Tangent Method.** The tangent method is one of several methods which are more exact than the protractor method for plotting traverses. Protractor plotting is usually satisfactory for rough compass surveys, but occasionally the surveyor may wish to plot careful compass or transit traverses with more precision than is possible with the protractor. The tangent method consists in laying off the angles by constructing at each vertex a right triangle whose base is 10 in. (or any other unit) and whose other leg is the natural tangent of the angle laid off, using the same unit as the base.

In Fig. 14 lay off on the meridian line a length $Ao$ of at least 10 in. and erect a perpendicular at $o$ on the right-hand side of the meridian if the bearing of the

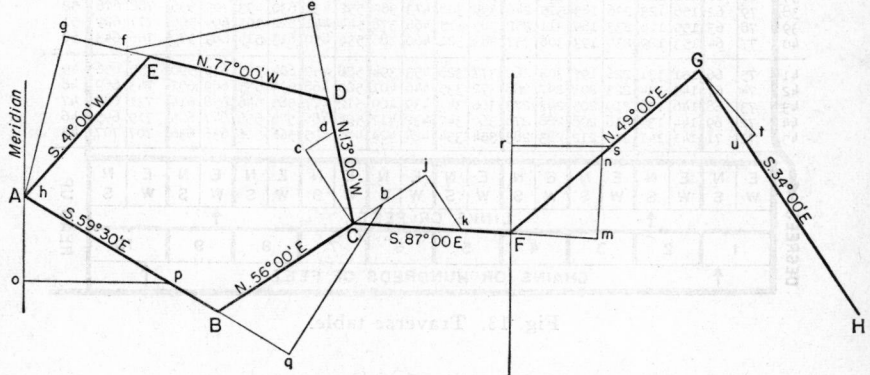

**Fig. 14. Tangent method of plotting traverses.**

first course is east, and on the left-hand side if it is west. From a table of natural functions obtain the tangent of the bearing of the first course, multiply the tangent by 10, and scale off this distance (*op*). Draw *Ap*, which is the direction of the first course. On *Ap* scale off *AB*, the length of the first course. Extend *AB* and lay off *Bq* equal to 10 in.; again erect a perpendicular and on the perpendicular scale off the length *qb* equal to 10 times the tangent of the deflection angle at *B*. This determines the direction of *BC* from the first course. The remaining lines of the traverse are plotted in the same manner, each time using the deflection angle. Sometimes it is more convenient to plot the complement of an angle rather than the angle itself. The complement of the angle was used in plotting the lines determining *CD*.

Where the survey is not a closed traverse, as *A, B, C, F, G, H* in Fig. 14, every third or fourth course should be checked by finding the angle between it and the meridian line. In checking the course *FG*, for example, draw a meridian through *F* parallel to *Ao*, scale off *Fr* = 10 in., and erect perpendicular *rs*. Scale the distance *rs* and obtain the angle *rFs* from a table of tangents. If the angle that the course makes with the meridian line disagrees with the calculated bearing of that course by any considerable amount, say 10 min., the previous courses should be replotted. If the error is very small, the direction of the course being checked should be altered so that the small error is carried no further.

**Graphical Methods of Determining Areas.** Graphical methods of determining areas give results within the allowable limits of accuracy for most compass and tape surveys. The commonest requires the use of cross-section paper in plotting.

**Example.** Assume that the traverse has been plotted and adjusted for closure on cross-section paper divided into squares 1 in. on a side and subdivided into squares ¹⁄₁₀ in. on a side. A scale of 1 in. equals 400 ft. was used; then each large square represents 3.67 acres and each small square, 0.037 acre. Row by row, or column by column, tally each large square falling wholly within the boundaries of the survey and mark it in some way to avoid duplication. Examine separately each large square only partly within the boundary, counting (again row by row, or column by column) the small squares wholly or partly within the boundary. With practice, it will be accurate enough to make this count cumulative, estimating ocularly and adding mentally the fractional squares. Before recording the count of small squares, check it by inspection against the entire area of the large square. Appropriate summations should give the total plotted area to within a few small squares. For acreage, multiply by the factors given earlier.

Another rapid method of determining area graphically is to plot and scale the survey in terms of chains. Knowing that 10 square chains equal 1 acre, scale off horizontal parallel lines 10 chains apart. The total length of two adjacent lines in chains divided by 2 equals the number of acres between the two lines. Repeat this process for the other segments and total.

By a variation of this second method, approximate areas may be determined directly from notes in the field. Run a straight line through the center of the tract, and at every 10 chains measure out in each direction to the edge of the area. The sum of all the lateral distances, in chains, will give the approximate acreage of the area. This method works particularly well on long, narrow tracts, such as a burn along a ridge. The larger the area, the greater is the accuracy in all these cases.

Another method used by the Forest Service employs the overlay grid. This is a variation of the use of cross-section paper but has the advantage of use on maps, plotted notes, or aerial photographs. The grid is made of a transparent medium upon which are etched 25 one-inch squares. Each of the large squares is subdivided into 64 smaller squares. When the grid is superimposed:

On 1 in. = 1 mi. photo-index sheets, each small square equals 10 acres.
On 2 in. = 1 mi. photo-index sheets, each small square equals 2.5 acres.
On 1:20,000 photographs, each square equals 0.996 acre.
On 1:62,500 maps, each square equals 9.73 acres.

Other scales commonly used in plotting forest maps are:

1 in. = 660 ft. (10 chains), where 1 large square = 10 acres.
1 in. = 330 ft. ( 5 chains), where 1 large square = 2½ acres.

**Area by Polar Planimeter.** A planimeter is the most accurate means of measuring areas, whether enclosed by straight or curved lines, directly from maps. Carefully used, planimeters measure small areas within 1.0 percent of error, larger areas to within 0.1 percent. Planimeters vary greatly in complexity, cost, and portability, but the operation of all is the same:

1. If the bar is not adjustable, test the scale of the instrument by tracing a square or circle of known area; most planimeters measure square inches. Tables pasted in the case of adjustable instruments indicate how to set the bar for other scales. (Slight adjustments may be made to allow for map shrinkage.)
2. Before starting to measure an area, locate the fixed pole of the planimeter (generally a needle point) so that the entire perimeter can be easily reached with the tracing-point. It is better to divide an area for measurement into two or more parts than to operate the instrument fully extended.
3. Having the fixed pole firmly located, hold the tracing-point accurately with one hand on some well-marked point of the perimeter, and with the other hand turn the graduated movable wheel, in slight contact with the paper, until it reads zero against the vernier (the needle on the horizontal dial should also point to zero). A hand lens may be necessary for accuracy in reading the vernier. Another method is to read the scale before and after tracing the boundary and then subtract the second reading from the first. This eliminates the need for setting all scales at zero but also allows opportunity for error in reading the scale and subtracting.
4. Trace the perimeter clockwise (counterclockwise gives negative readings) back to the starting point. Do this by hand, *not* with a straightedge.
5. Record the reading on (a) the horizontal dial, (b) the movable wheel, and (c) the vernier.
6. Without resetting the instrument retrace the perimeter, and record the double reading; divide by 2. If the result differs appreciably from the first reading, check for errors.
7. If the fixed pole was *within* the area being measured, *add the constant* engraved on the back of the instrument to the final reading.

**Double Meridian Distance Method (Latitude and Double Departure).** Fig. 15 is a tabular arrangement for computing the area enclosed by the traverse in Fig. 11 by the double meridian distance method. Entries in Columns 1, 2, and 3 in Fig. 15 are courses, corrected bearings, and distances copied from Fig. 11. Latitudes and departures (Columns 4, 5, 6, and 7) are obtained as previously explained under "Field Notes" and balanced as described below.

Double meridian distances (DMD) are obtained as follows:

DMD of the first course of a traverse equals its departure; DMD of subsequent courses is the algebraic sum of (a) the DMD of the preceding course, (b) the departure of the preceding course, and (c) the departure of the course itself; DMD of the last course should equal its departure but have the opposite algebraic sign.

*Boundary Survey of Camp Blank - Primitive N. F.*

John Doe

Feb. 29, 19-

*Area Computation*

| (1) | (2) | (3) | (4) | (5) | (6) | (7) | (8) | (9) | (10) | (11) | (12) |
|---|---|---|---|---|---|---|---|---|---|---|---|
| | | | Latitude | | Departure | | Balanced | | | Double Area | |
| Sta. | Bearings | Dist. (feet) | N.+ | S.– | E.+ | W.– | Lat. | Dep. | D.M.D. | + | – |
| A-B | S. 59½° E. | 1614.2 | | 819.2 | 1390.8 | | –824.0 | +1390.5 | 1390.5 | | 1,145,772 |
| B-C | N. 56° E. | 1210.0 | 676.6 | | 1003.1 | | +673.0 | +1002.9 | 3783.9 | 2,546,565 | |
| C-D | N. 13° W. | 900.5 | 877.4 | | | 202.6 | +874.8 | –202.8 | 4584.0 | 4,010,083 | |
| D-E | N. 77° W. | 1340.0 | 301.5 | | | 1305.7 | +297.5 | –1305.9 | 3075.3 | 914,902 | |
| E-A | S. 41° W. | 1348.0 | | 1017.3 | | 884.4 | –1021.3 | –884.7 | 884.7 | | 903,544 |
| | | 6412.7 | 1855.5 | 1836.5 | 2393.9 | 2392.7 | | | | 7,471,550 | 2,049,316 |
| | | | 1836.5 | | 2392.7 | | | | | 2,049,316 | |
| | | | 19.0 | | 1.2 | | | | | 5,422,234 | |

Closing Linear Error $= \sqrt{19.0^2 + 1.2^2}$

$\qquad = 19.04$

Error of Closure $= 19.04/6412.7 = 1$ in $337$

$2\underline{|5,422,234}$

2,711,117 sq. ft.

$= 62.24$ acres

*Note: These Lat. & Dep. were computed using 4 place tables.*

**Fig. 15. Area computation by double meridian distance method.**

To compute the area within a closed traverse (polygon) by the DMD method, multiply the DMD for each course by the latitude of the course, carefully observing the algebraic signs. This is called the "double area" (Columns 11 and 12 in Fig. 15). Next obtain the algebraic sum of the double areas and divide by 2. The result will be the area enclosed by the traverse in the units of measurements used in the survey. In Fig. 15 the distances (Column 3) are in feet. The final result in Column 11 is in square feet therefore, and (after division by 2) is divided by 43,560 in order to obtain the acreage.

**Example.** From Fig. 13, or from the table of trigonometric functions (see Section 23) cos (latitude) 59½° is 0.5075; and for course A–B it is 0.5075 times the distance (1,614.2) = 819.2. Since bearing is south, enter 819.2 in Column 5. Sin 59½° (departure) is $0.8616 \times 1,614.2 = 1,390.8$ and is entered in Column 6 because it is east. Similarly, obtain and enter latitudes and departures for B–C, C–D, and subsequent courses.

Next balance the latitudes and departures. Plus and minus latitudes and plus and minus departures theoretically add algebraically to zero, but in practice they seldom do. In a compass and tape survey (Fig. 11) the errors are more likely to be due to the rough results obtained at the angles rather than to the taped distances. The rule for balancing latitudes and departures in these surveys is therefore as follows: The correction to be applied to the latitude or departure of any course is to the total error in latitude or departure, without regard to algebraic signs, as the length of the course is to the perimeter of the polygon. The rule for balancing latitudes and departures in a transit and tape survey is: The correction applied to the latitude of any course is to the total error in latitude as the latitude of that course is to the sum of all latitudes, without regard to algebraic signs; similarly for the departures.

Assuming that Fig. 15 computations are for a compass survey, the latitude adjustment for course $A$–$B$ is obtained from: Adjustment:$19.00 = 1{,}614.2{:}6{,}412.7$; Adjustment $= 4.8$. The correction is added since the Column 5 total is the smaller. $819.2 + 4.8 = 824.0$. Enter 824.0 in Column 8, being careful to preserve the minus sign. Similarly, balance the remaining latitudes and departures, entering the latter in Column 9. Note that plus latitudes in Column 8 have been decreased in the balancing process since the total for Column 4 was greater than for Column 5. Plus and minus corrections (Columns 8 and 9) should be equal. Thus, while departure corrections

| COURSE | BEARING | DISTANCE | LATITUDE | | DEPARTURE | |
|---|---|---|---|---|---|---|
| | | | N + | S − | E + | W − |
| A - B | S 59½° E | 1614.2 | | 819.2 | 1390.8 | |
| B - C | N 56° E | 1210.0 | 676.6 | | 1003.1 | |
| C - D | N 13° W | 900.5 | 877.4 | | | 202.6 |
| D - E | N 77° W | 1340.0 | 301.5 | | | 1305.7 |
| E - A | —— | —— | | | —— | —— |
| | | | 1855.5 | 819.2 | 2393.9 | 1508.3 |
| | | | −819.2 | | −1508.3 | |
| | | | 1036.3 | | 885.6 | |

Tan. Bearing $E$–$A$ = $\dfrac{885.6}{1036.3}$ = 0.8545. From table of

Natural Tangents 0.8545 is tan. for 40°-31'. Bearing is S 40°-31' W

Distance $E$–$A$ = $\dfrac{Departure}{Sin.\ of\ Bearing}$ = $\dfrac{885.6}{Sin.\ 40\text{-}31}$ = 1363.2

**Fig. 16. Computation for closing bearing and distance.**

carried to the nearest 100th are equal (0.25) for both courses $D-E$ and $E-A$, the correction is called 0.2 for $D-E$ and 0.3 for $E-A$ in order to balance the corrections. DMD for $A-B$ equals departure as stated above; enter 1,390.5 in Column 10 on line with $A-B$. DMD for $B-C$ as explained above is DMD for $(A-B)$ + (Departure for $A-B$) + (Departure for $B-C$) = 1,390.5 + 1,390.5 + 1,002.9 = 3,783.9 (Column 10). Compute DMD for $C-D$, $D-E$, and $E-A$ in like manner.

Compute double area (Column 12) for $A-B$. As explained above, $DA$ = DMD × Lat. = 1,390.5 × $(-824.0)$ = 1,145,772. Compute $DA$ for $B-C$ = 3,783.9 × 673.0 = 2,546,565, entered in Column 11 since it is plus (+). Obtain the algebraic sum of the double areas and divide by 2 to obtain the area enclosed by the traverse in square feet, since distances (Column 3) are in feet. If distances are in chains, the area will be in square chains.

**To compute a closing bearing and distance** for a traverse which was not completed in the field. In Fig. 16, find the bearing and distance $E-A$ in order to close a traverse which ended at $E$. The computation is shown in Fig. 16. The computation for distance may be checked by repeating the above procedure, using the latitude instead of the departure and the cosine of the bearing instead of the sine. The above-computed bearing and distance for course $E-A$ will differ from that shown in Fig. 11, since the entire closing error is concentrated in the computed bearing and distance.

**AREA COMPUTATION FROM TRAVERSE FORM.** Where rough results are acceptable it is sometimes convenient to compute the area enclosed by a traverse on the traverse form shown in Fig. 12b. To compute the area for the closed traverse in Fig. 15, enter the courses and distances as in Fig. 17. Obtain the latitudes and departures as previously described and compute the coordinates

| BEARING | DISTANCE | LATITUDE | N S | | | DEPARTURE | E W | |
|---|---|---|---|---|---|---|---|---|
| Starting Point A | | 1000.0 | N | | | 00 0 | | |
| S 59½ E | 1614.2 | 819.2 | S | +1180.8 X | +1390.8 | | E | = +1,642,257 |
| Traverse Sta. B | | 180.8 | N | | 1390.8 | | E | |
| N 56 E | 1210.0 | 676.6 | N | +1038.2 X | +1003.1 | | E | = +1,041,418 |
| Traverse Sta. C | | 857.4 | N | | 2393.9 | | E | +2,683,675 |
| N 13 W | 900.5 | 877.4 | N | +2592.2 X | −202.6 | | W | = − 525,180 |
| Traverse Sta. D | | 1734.8 | N | | 2191.3 | | E | |
| N 77 W | 1340.0 | 301.5 | N | +3771.1 X | −1305.7 | | W | = −4,923,925 |
| Traverse Sta. E | | 2036.3 | N | | 885.6 | | E | |
| S 41 W | 1348.0 | 1017.3 | S | + 3055.3 X | −884.4 | | W | = −2,702,107 |
| Traverse Sta. A | | 1019.0 | N | | 1.2 | | E | − 8,151,212 |
| | | | | | | | | 2,683,675 |
| | | | | 87,120)5,467,537 | | | | 5,467,537 |
| | | | | | 62.76 acres | | | |

Fig. 17. Area computation from traverse form.

of latitude for each traverse point. Multiply the algebraic sum of the coordinates of latitude by the departure for each course. Divide the algebraic sum of these products by 87,120 (twice 43,560) if the distances are in feet, or by 20 if the distances are in chains, to obtain the area. In Fig. 17 no adjustment was made in coordinates of latitude or in the departures to compensate for the accumulated errors in latitude (+19.0 ft.) and departure (+1.2 ft.); hence, the acreage (62.7) in Fig. 17 is larger than the 62.24 acres in Fig. 11 and approximate only.

**THE TRAVERSE BOARD.** The traverse board is a flat board usually 24 × 30 in. (some are 15 in. square), mounted on a tripod and designed for plotting traverses in the field by graphical methods. The board is oriented by a self-contained magnetic needle built into one edge and is leveled by a bubble on the alidade or with a pocket level. The alidade is a steel straightedge having a raised peep sight at the rear and a raised sighting notch at the front.

Survey lines are projected by setting the table over one end of the line, sighting in the next station with the alidade, measuring the distance by pacing or with a tape, scaling that distance along the straightedge, and plotting the point thus determined. The accuracy attained will depend upon the care used in keeping the board properly oriented, and in measuring and plotting the distances. When using the needle for orientation, care must be taken to avoid error due to local attraction. It is, therefore, wise to check the orientation by backsights and to keep stations close enough together to make this feasible. In dense timber or rough country the length of plotted lines should be kept within the length of the needle. Points off the traverse which are clearly visible from any two stations may be mapped by intersection from them, without measuring distances on the ground.

A closed traverse, such as that shown in Fig. 11, will obviously close when plotted by means of a traverse board survey. On the other hand, owing to the rough methods used, a board traverse between two points of known origin may

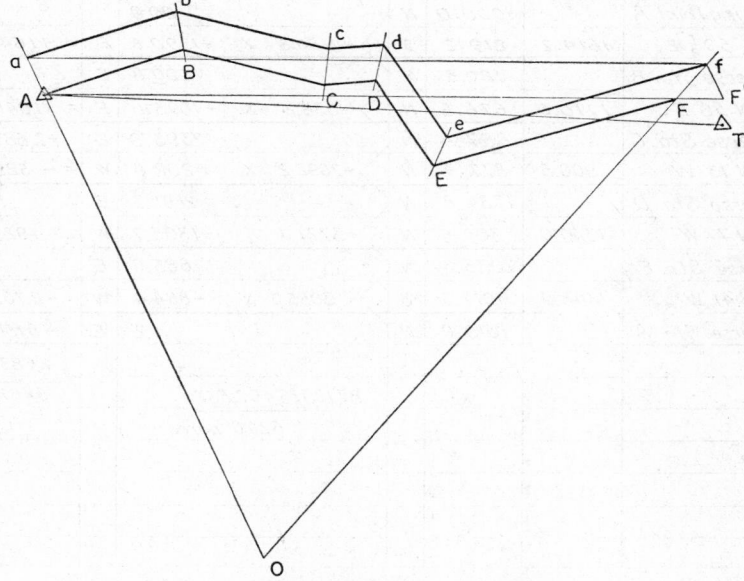

Fig. 18. Traverse adjustment (graphical).

fail to close on those points when superimposed or transferred to a map. In this case the plotted traverse may be adjusted by the method of similar triangles.

**Example.** In Fig. 18 let *A–B–C–D–E–F* represent the unadjusted traverse between two known points *A* and *T*. Station *F* is presumably point *T*. However, when the plotted traverse is transferred to a map and originated at point *A*, point *F* is found to fall NW of and short of point *T*. To adjust the traverse: (1) Draw *AF*; (2) project *AF* to *F'*, making *AF' = AT*; (3) select any point *O* and draw *OA* and *OF*; (4) draw *F'f* parallel to *OA*; (5) draw *af* parallel to *AF*; (6) draw radials *ob, oc, od,* and *oe*; (7) draw *ab* parallel to *AB, bc* parallel to *BC,* etc., through to *f*. (8) Traverse *a* to *f* then represents the adjustment of *A* to *F*. To transfer it to the map on which *A* and *T* are accurately located, it may be reproduced on tracing paper and superimposed on the map; the corners are then pricked through.

## Aneroid Barometer

The aneroid barometer is a convenient instrument for determining differences in elevation where a low order of accuracy will suffice. It is adapted to use for road reconnaissance, type, and timber-cruiser maps where distances are paced and 50-ft. or greater contour intervals are used. Because barometer readings are affected by constantly changing atmospheric pressures (maximum changes in atmospheric pressure result in apparent differences in elevation up to 1,800 ft.), the best results are obtained when it is possible to tie into points of known elevation every 2 hr. or oftener. Avoid using the aneroid barometer on days of changing weather conditions.

**ADJUSTMENT.** To check the barometer for adjustment, first tap the glass lightly with the forefinger. The needle should move slightly, each time returning to its original position, otherwise it is out of order. Next, read the instrument, within a matter of minutes, at points having a known difference of 50 to 100 ft. in elevation, such as the top and bottom of a fire-lookout tower, or of a building. Several repetitions of this process should establish whether the instrument is reasonably sensitive, or how consistently it is in error.

**USE.** On the movable foot-scale, set the known or assumed elevation of the starting point opposite the needle, then read and record successive elevations at subsequent stations, together with the time of each reading. (See Fig. 19.) Concurrently observe the following precautions:

1. Handle the barometer carefully. At the time the movable scale is set, note and record some reading on it opposite a graduation of the immovable scale (inches of pressure) as a means of detecting accidental movement of the foot-scale.
2. Before reading, tap the instrument gently on the glass.
3. Because of the lag of the needle in adjusting to pressure change, it is advisable to wait a few minutes to allow the needle to "catch up" after arrival at a point where a reading is to be taken.
4. Always hold the barometer in the same position to read. Some instruments vary as much as 50 ft. between the horizontal and vertical position.
5. Take advantage of every opportunity to check with points of known elevation. As soon as a check point is reached, note the total change in apparent elevation caused by weather conditions, and the interval of time during which it took place. Distribute the error between the stations in proportion to the time spent in reaching them. (In Fig. 19, Station *B* was reached in $\frac{1}{7}$ of the total time between leaving Station *A* and returning to it; therefore $\frac{1}{7}$ of the 140-ft. **drop** in reading at *A* was **added** to the elevation recorded at *B*. Watch the plus and minus signs.)

| Station | Distance (feet) | Time | Obs. Elev. | Elev. Correction | Corrected Elev. |
|---------|------|------|------|------|------|
| A |  | 8:00 | 500(B.M) | – | – |
|  | 1000 |  |  |  |  |
| B |  | 8:15 | 600 | +20 | 620 |
|  | 1000 |  |  |  |  |
| C |  | 8:45 | 1300 | +60 | 1360 |
|  | 1000 |  |  |  |  |
| D |  | 9:15 | 1200 | +100 | 1300 |
|  | 3000 |  |  |  |  |
| A |  | 9:45 | 360 | +140 | 500 |

Fig. 19. Field notes—barometric readings.

6. Before using the aneroid barometer for mapping extensive areas, or laying out a logging job, establish adequate control. On tractor or high lead jobs one large timber operator in the Northwest establishes control points with a transit every 2 mi., and with the double Abney method every ½ mi. He maps 50-ft. contours between these points with the aneroid barometer, enabling him satisfactorily to locate truck roads and logging settings. On railroad jobs this method cannot be used because logging railroad layouts require a map of much greater accuracy.
7. In the absence of adequate control elevations, a barometer may be read regularly at a centrally located camp and its readings used to correct those taken in the field. A barograph so located is rarely a practical substitute.

## The Abney Hand Level

An Abney level (Fig. 22) measures the angle between the horizontal plane and the line of sight along a slope. Next to the compass, the Abney is probably the most essential and useful instrument for the forest surveyor.

Three types of graduated limbs may be obtained for the Abney. The percent limb is based on an angular unit represented by the ratio of 1 unit vertically to 100 units horizontally. The degree limb is based on an angular unit of 1° or 1/360 of a circle. The topographic limb is based on an angular unit represented by the ratio of 1 unit vertically to 66 units horizontally. Choice of Abney depends largely on personal preference. Many Abneys are constructed with a reversible scale, reading percents on one side and degrees or topographic units on the other.

The accuracy of the Abney is comparable to that of the staff compass. Accidental errors which accumulate in slope chaining where the Abney is used to measure the slope angle should not exceed 10 ft. per mi. in elevation or 30 ft. in distance.

**ADJUSTMENT.** Three field adjustments must be made on the Abney level:

1. To make the horizontal cross hair (wire) correspond with the etched line on the prism when the instrument reads zero: (a) set the index arm at zero; (b) loosen the small screw on the top of the telescope tube at the end farthest from the eye, to the right of center; (c) move the slide containing the prism

and cross-hair slide, held in place by this screw, until the cross hair and etched line coincide; and (d) tighten the screw.

2. To adjust the height of the level vial above the telescope tube so that the cross hair and etched line coincide at steep angles (at such angles the bubble appears crescent-shaped, in which case the etched line should appear near the concave side of the bubble): (a) loosen the four tiny anchor screws on the side of the vial; (b) turn the two capstan screws, locked by the anchor screws, until the vial is at the proper height; and (c) tighten the anchor screws.

3. To make the level vial parallel to the line of sight by the "two-peg" method (Fig. 20): (a) set and **keep** the index arm at zero; (b) sight from a point *A* at a convenient height on a pole or tree, and have an assistant mark point *B* on another tree about 100 ft. distant; (c) from *B* sight back to the original tree at *C,* directly above or below *A;* (d) establish *D* halfway between *A* and *C* (*BD* is then a horizontal line); (e) sighting from *B* to *D,* adjust the capstan screws holding the level vial (see adjustment 2) until the level bubble is exactly centered in its tube.

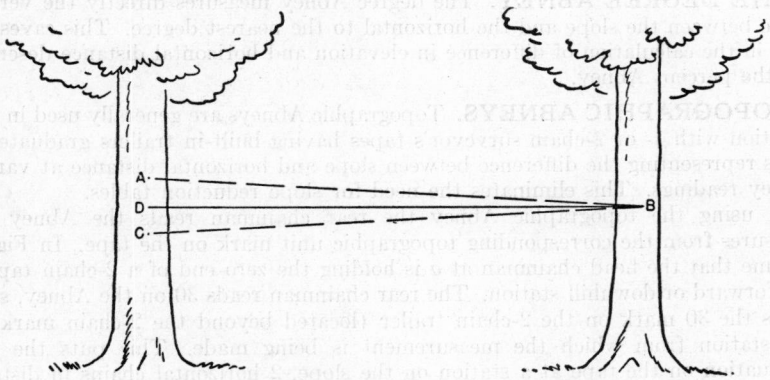

Fig. 20. Abney adjustment—"two-peg" method.

**USE OF ABNEY FOR SLOPE CHAINING.** The use of the Abney for slope chaining requires that the instrument be held steady and that a previous level line (height of instrument or H.I.) be determined so that the line of sight is always parallel to the tape. Efficient organization of a two-man crew usually finds the head chainman as the compassman, prolonging his line of sight by natural landmarks and his own backsights independent of the other man. The rear chainman operates the Abney and keeps notes. If double Abney work is desired, the head chainman also has an Abney.

**THE PERCENT ABNEY.** The percent Abney measures the number of feet rise per 100 ft. of horizontal distance. The percent reading expressed as a decimal is also the tangent of the slope angle. Thus, in slope chaining, difference in elevation and horizontal distance are obtained by multiplying the measured slope distance by the sine and cosine respectively of the slope angle whose tangent is equal to the Abney reading expressed as a decimal.

**Example.** In Fig. 21, assume the reading on a percent Abney is 40 percent and the slope distance measured between *A* and *C* is 200 ft.

To obtain the horizontal distance and difference in elevation, find in a table of trigonometric functions the angle whose tangent is 0.40; this is 21°48′ (φ in Fig. 21). The sine and cosine of the slope angle in this example are 0.3714 and 0.9285, respectively. The difference in elevation *BC* is therefore 200 × 0.3714, or 74.3 ft., and the

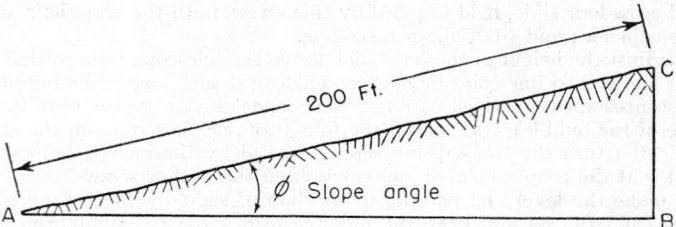

**Fig. 21. Use of percent Abney.**

horizontal distance $AB$ is $200 \times 0.9285$, or 185.7 ft. If no trigonometric tables are available, $AB$ and $BC$ (which is 40 percent of $AB$) may be calculated geometrically. $ABC$ is a right triangle; therefore $(AC)^2 = (AB)^2 + (0.4AB)^2$.

**THE DEGREE ABNEY.** The degree Abney measures directly the vertical angle between the slope and the horizontal to the nearest degree. This saves one step in the calculation of difference in elevation and horizontal distance described for the percent Abney.

**TOPOGRAPHIC ABNEYS.** Topographic Abneys are generally used in conjunction with 1- or 2-chain surveyor's tapes having built-in trailers graduated in units representing the difference between slope and horizontal distance at various Abney readings. This eliminates the need for slope reduction tables.

In using the topographic Abney the rear chainman reads the Abney and measures from the corresponding topographic unit mark on the tape. In Fig. 22 assume that the head chainman at $a$ is holding the zero end of a 2-chain tape at the forward or downhill station. The rear chainman reads 30 on the Abney, so he holds the 30 mark on the 2-chain trailer (located beyond the 2-chain mark) at the station from which the measurement is being made. This puts the zero graduation on the tape at a station on the slope, 2 horizontal chains in distance from the rear station. For measuring a distance of 1 chain, the rear chainman would hold the 30 mark on the trailer (under side of tape, beyond the 1-chain mark). The slope distance need not be known. The horizontal distance in chains times the Abney reading gives the difference in elevation in feet.

Care must be taken in reading the Abney to make the final reading after the head chainman is in position and applying the proper tension on the chain. When the head chainman moves up or downhill from his initial stopping place to the actual station, there may be a change in the slope from the preliminary trial reading taken by the rear chainman.

The topographic Abney and tape permit fast, cheap work where it is possible to take all distances to the nearest full chain length. Where it becomes necessary to make frequent measurements in fractional chains, it is easiest to tape the horizontal distances directly, although tables are available for computing these distances from the Abney readings. The formula is:

$$\text{Horizontal distance} = \frac{\text{Measured slope distance}}{\text{Slope distance for 1 chain horizontal}}$$

To use the formula, take the Abney reading for the particular slope and find that reading on the 1-chain trailer (under side of tape). Turn the tape over and observe the actual distance from the zero mark on the tape to the Abney reading beyond the 1-chain mark. This gives the slope distance for one horizontal chain.

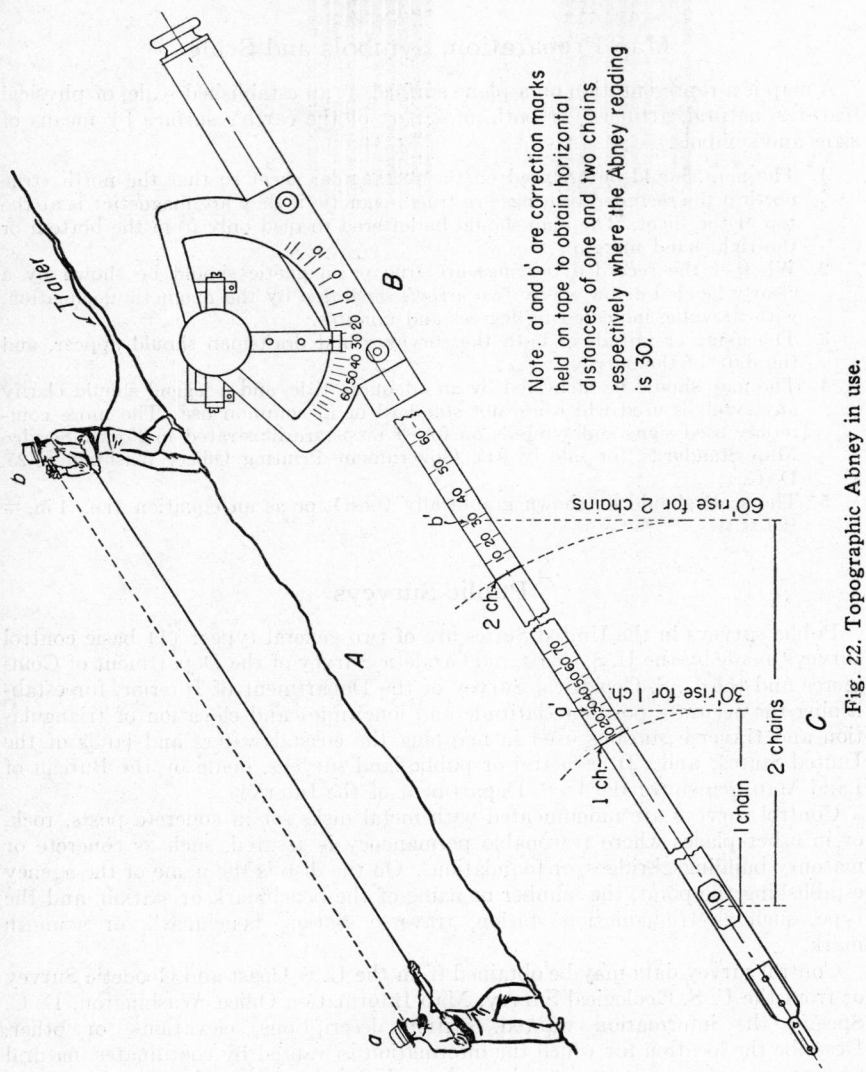

Fig. 22. Topographic Abney in use.

Note: a' and b' are correction marks held on tape to obtain horizontal distances of one and two chains respectively where the Abney reading is 30.

**Example.** Suppose the Abney reading is 50 and the taped slope distance is 84 links, or 0.84 chain. Find 50 on the 1-chain trailer, turn the tape over and read 125.5 links, interpolating for the tenths of a link. This is 1.255 chains. Substituting in the formula: Horizontal distance = 0.84/1.255 = 0.67 chain. Difference in elevation = 0.67 × 50 (Abney reading) = 33.5 ft.

**AUXILIARY EQUIPMENT.** Auxiliary equipment sometimes used with an Abney in addition to chain and compass is a flashlight and staff. A flashlight to sight on is helpful in taking shots through foliage or brush. A staff with which to steady the Abney is also helpful to an inexperienced operator.

## Map Preparation, Symbols and Scale

A map is a representation on a plane surface, at an established scale, of physical features, natural, artificial, or both, of a part of the earth's surface by means of signs and symbols.

1. The map should be oriented on the rectangular sheet so that the north (true north if the recorded bearings are true, magnetic if they are magnetic) is at the top of the sheet. The map should be lettered to read only from the bottom or the right-hand margin.
2. Whether the recorded bearings are true or magnetic should be shown by a clearly labeled arrow, or by two arrows separated by the magnetic declination, with its value indicated in degrees and minutes.
3. The name or initials of both the surveyor and draftsman should appear, and the date of the survey.
4. The map should be identified by an adequate title, and a legend should clarify any symbols used which are not standard or in common use. The more commonly used signs and symbols on forest maps are illustrated in Forest Service Map Standards, for sale by the Government Printing Office, Washington 25, D. C.
5. The scale should be shown graphically (best), or as an equation (i.e., 1 in. = 100 ft.).

## Public Surveys

Public surveys in the United States are of two general types: (1) basic control surveys, made by the U. S. Coast and Geodetic Survey of the Department of Commerce and the U. S. Geological Survey of the Department of Interior, for establishing the accurate position (latitude and longitude) and elevation of triangulation and traverse stations used in mapping the coastal waters and lands of the United States; and (2) cadastral or public land surveys, made by the Bureau of Land Management of the U. S. Department of the Interior.

Control surveys are monumented with metal disks set in concrete posts, rock, or in other places where reasonable permanency is assured, such as concrete or masonry buildings, bridges, or foundations. On the disk is the name of the agency establishing the point, the number or name of the benchmark or station, and the type, such as triangulation station, traverse station, benchmark, or azimuth mark.

Control survey data may be obtained from the U. S. Coast and Geodetic Survey or from the U. S. Geological Survey, Map Information Office, Washington, D. C. Specify the information wanted, station descriptions, elevations, or other. Describe the location for which the information is wanted by coordinates, natural features, or reference to points shown by a U.S.G.S. quadrangle. Give the name of the station, if known, or describe identifying marks.

**U. S. PUBLIC LAND SURVEYS.** The rectangular system for the survey of public lands owned by the national government was inaugurated under the old Articles of Confederation in 1785. The federal system for rectangular surveys was followed generally throughout the western United States, but other systems were followed in many eastern states. The thirteen original states retained ownership of their public lands when the Constitution was adopted, hence many of the old surveys in those states are described by metes and bounds, and are exceedingly difficult to retrace. (See "Surveying Old Property Lines," page **17·13**.)

Grants of lands made to private individuals or companies by the British Crown were usually described by metes and bounds, with distances in poles (¼ chain) or chains. Lands granted by the French Crown were usually expressed as so many arpents in area, so many arpents frontage, and so many arpents on each side. As a unit of area an arpent approximates 0.85 acre, the linear term refers to the length of the side of one square arpent and equals 2.91667 chains (192.5 ft.). Grants by the Spanish Crown and the Mexican Government often gave distances in varas. The value of the vara differs in several localities. In Texas, 36 varas equals 100 ft. Texas, at the time it was admitted to the Union, was exempted from the rectangular surveys system as executed by the federal government.

The first rectangular surveys by the federal government were made in Ohio and were experimental in character at first. Several base lines and meridians were employed in making the earliest surveys, numbers of sections per township varied, and different systems were tried for numbering the sections. Consequently difficulty may be expected in determining the relative location of townships and sections in Ohio.

A forester surveying land in a district now or formerly a part of the United States public lands should procure from the Government Printing Office a copy of the Manual of Instructions for the Survey of the Public Lands of the United States. In this will be found all general and specific instructions regarding the system. The manual has been prepared by the Bureau of Land Management,

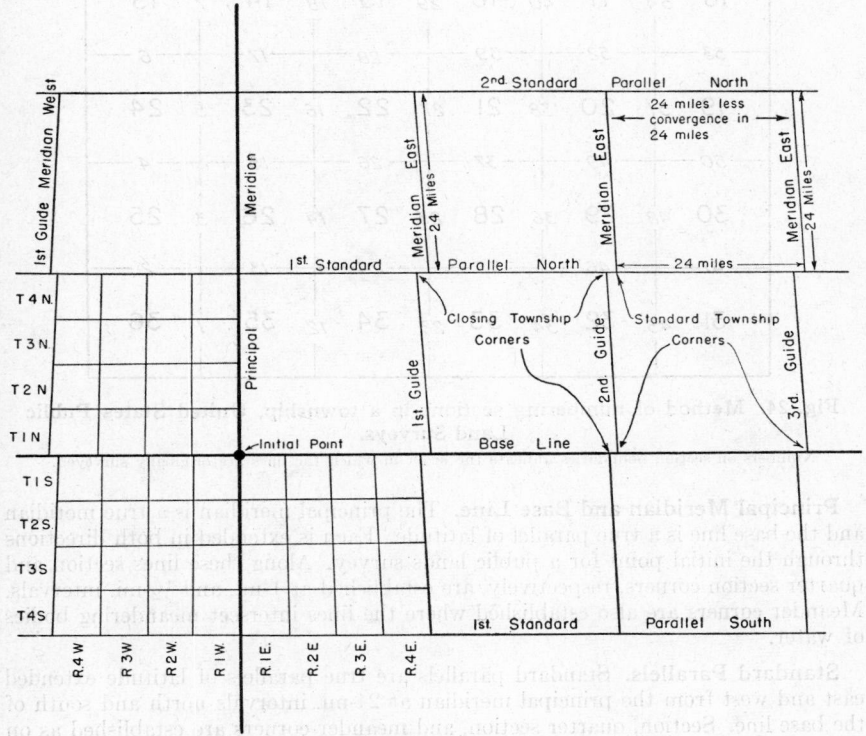

Fig. 23. System of public land surveys.

U. S. Department of the Interior, and contains rules based upon acts of Congress establishing the system for the survey of public lands in the United States.

The rules provide that the public lands shall be divided by north and south lines run according to the true meridian and by others crossing them at right angles, so as to form tiers of townships, the latter 6 mi. square. (See Fig. 23.) Townships are numbered progressively east, west, north, and south from the initial point. Thus the township in the extreme southwest of Fig. 23 is designated Township 4 South, Range 4 West. Townships are subdivided into 36 sections, each approximately 1 mi. square and containing 640 acres, as near as may be. Sections are numbered as shown in Fig. 24.

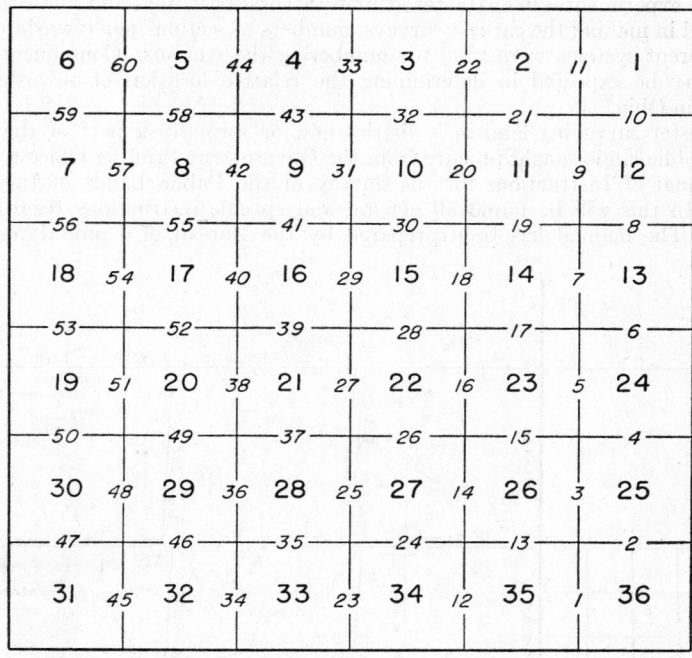

**Fig. 24. Method of numbering sections in a township, United States Public Land Surveys.**

Numbers on section boundaries indicate the order in which the lines are originally surveyed.

**Principal Meridian and Base Line.** The principal meridian is a true meridian and the base line is a true parallel of latitude. Each is extended in both directions through the initial point for a public lands survey. Along these lines section and quarter section corners, respectively, are established at 1-mi. and ½-mi. intervals. Meander corners are also established where the lines intersect meandering bodies of water.

**Standard Parallels.** Standard parallels are true parallels of latitude extended east and west from the principal meridian at 24-mi. intervals north and south of the base line. Section, quarter section, and meander corners are established as on the base line.

**Guide Meridians.** Guide meridians are true meridians extended north from the base line or standard parallels at intervals of 24 mi. east and west from the principal meridian. Guide meridians terminate invariably at the point of intersection with standard parallels. Owing to the convergence of the meridians, the intersection will not coincide with the township corner previously established on the standard parallel. The intersection is therefore called a "closing township corner."

Because the meridians converge, it is evident that the requirement that the lines conform to true meridians and that townships be 6 mi. square is mathematically impossible. The general procedure in making U. S. Public Land Surveys is, therefore, as illustrated in Fig. 23: (1) to establish independent initial points in a state or geographical region to be surveyed, as the origin for surveys; (2) to survey principal meridians and base lines originating at the initial point; (3) to establish guide meridians, initiated at base lines, and standard parallels initiated at principal meridians, at suitable intervals to maintain a workable adherence to a township 6 mi. square; and (4) to subdivide the township into 36 sections by running parallel lines through the township from south to north and from east to west at intervals of 1 mi.

By law the corners thus established (even if later surveys show them to be erroneously located) remain the proper markers of any subdivision for which they were intended, the boundary lines **actually run and marked** remain the proper boundaries, and the length of lines as returned are held to be the true length.

**Resurvey.** Preliminary to making new surveys, a resurvey or retracement of contiguous surveyed land is made, if there is any reason to question the accuracy of any portion of the old survey. Missing corners are re-established and delapidated corners are remonumented. It is from this practice that closing corners so commonly result. Because the original monuments and the intervening distances and course hold, irrespective of whether the retracement disagrees, and because it is usually the intent to establish adjoining new tracts that are normal as nearly as possible, closing corners are set that define such new tracts. This results in a double set of corners separated by varying distances, depending on the inaccuracy of the earlier surveys. These are invariably shown on official plats and field notes.

**The Township.** The regular township, illustrated in Fig. 24, is normally subdivided into 36 sections, each theoretically containing 640 acres. Greater or lesser areas, as determined by the survey, are confined to the 11 sections on the north and west boundaries.

**Meander Lines.** Meander lines are traverses of the margin of a permanent natural body of water. In original surveys, meander lines are not run as boundary lines but for the purpose of defining the sinuosities of the bank or shore line and for ascertaining the quantity of land remaining after segregation of the water area. All lakes of 25 acres or more are meandered. Likewise, all islands above mean high water are meandered. Navigable rivers and bayous as well as all rivers not embraced in the class denominated "navigable," the right-angle width of which is 3 chains and upward, are meandered on both banks at the ordinary high-water mark by taking the general courses and distances of their sinuosities.

**Error of Closure.** The error of closure is the ratio of the length of line representing the equivalent of the errors in latitude and departure, to the length of the perimeter of the figure constituting the survey. The limit of closure for U. S. rectangular surveys is expressed by the fraction 1/452, provided the limit of closure in neither latitude nor departure exceeds 1/640; where a survey qualifies under the latter limit, the former is bound to be satisfied. Thus an accumulative error of 12½ links (99 in.) per mi. of perimeter, either in latitude or departure, will not be exceeded in an acceptable survey. The closure around a normal section must therefore be within 50 links; around a normal tier of sections, 175 links; and around a normal township, 300 links.

**Standard Corner Markers.** Standard corner markers are now wrought-iron posts, zinc coated, 2-in. inside diameter, cut in 30-in. lengths surmounted by a brass cap on which the section and township are indicated in abbreviated form. The pipe is filled with concrete. Brass tablets are used in rock outcrop.

The earliest surveys were marked by pits and mounds, blazed trees, stones with scribings to indicate the number of miles to the next township corner in cardinal directions, or by other improvisations.

**Witness Corners.** Witness corners are monumented points, usually on a line of a survey near a corner, employed in situations where it is impracticable to occupy the site of the corner itself.

**Reference Corners.** Reference corners are employed when a permanent monument cannot be established at the site of the corner, for example where the corner falls within a roadway. A tablet or marked stone is buried at the true corner point and reference monuments set at suitable places outside the roadway.

**System of Corner Markings.** The marking on corners follows a system using capital letters and Arabic figures, relating to the township, range, and section to which the corner belongs. The ordinary markings common to all classes of corners are given in Table 2.

**Table 2. Common System of Marking Survey Monuments**

| Marks | To indicate | Marks | To indicate |
|---|---|---|---|
| AM | Amended | R | Range |
| AMC | Auxiliary meander corner | RM | Reference monument |
| AP | Angle point | S | Section |
| BO | Bearing object | S | South |
| BT | Bearing tree | SC | Standard corner |
| C | Center | SE | Southeast |
| CC | Closing corner | SMC | Special meander corner |
| E | East | SW | Southwest |
| LM | Location monument | T | Township |
| M | Miles | TR | Tract |
| MC | Meander corner | W | West |
| N | North | WC | Witness corner |
| NE | Northeast | WP | Witness point |
| NW | Northwest | ¼ | Quarter section |
| PL | Public land | 1/16 | Sixteenth section |

**Corner Accessories.** Corner accessories are for the purpose of indicating the position of a corner monument so that the latter may be relocated in case of destruction or obliteration. They consist of (1) bearing trees or other natural objects, (2) mounds of stones, or (3) pits and memorials. In general, one bearing object in each section is located and marked. Bearing trees are usually within a distance not exceeding three chains. Memorials, consisting of glassware, stoneware, a marked stone, a charred stake, or pieces of metal, are deposited where bearing objects are not available. Pits are 18 in. square and 12 in. deep, with the side 3 ft. distant from the corner monument. In arid climate and in some cover types, pits are often discernible after 50 yr. or longer.

**STATE COORDINATE SYSTEMS.** Several states have adopted systems of plane coordinates which are shown on the topographical quadrangles published for areas in those states. The coordinates of prominent and identifiable points on these systems may be obtained, usually from the State Engineer Offices or from the U. S. Coast and Geodetic Survey at Washington, D. C. Coordinate systems have been developed by the U. S. Coast and Geodetic Survey for all states.

Several states have more than one zone, or projection. The dividing line between zones is always a county boundary. The extent of these zones is limited in order to keep errors to about 1 to 10,000. Such a limit is better than transit traverse closures. All first and second order triangulation published in the future will have state coordinates furnished. The coordinate system is a more permanent or more recoverable base than the public land net for referencing forest data on large areas in a single ownership where section lines are unimportant.

**RECTANGULAR SURVEY SYSTEM OF CANADA.** Surveys in Canada east of the Prairie Provinces are generally comparable to those made in the original thirteen states, have about the same degree of accuracy, and are similarly difficult to relocate or retrace. The Dominion Land Surveys Act, as amended March 17, 1908, provides that the Dominion lands in the provinces of Manitoba, Saskatchewan, Alberta, British Columbia, and the Northwest Territories be laid out into quadrilateral townships of 6 mi. square. Each township contains 36 sections as nearly 1 mi. square as the convergence of the meridians permits. Sections are numbered as in Fig. 25.

| | | | | | |
|---|---|---|---|---|---|
| 31 | 32 | 33 | 34 | 35 | 36 |
| 30 | 29 | 28 | 27 | 26 | 25 |
| 19 | 20 | 21 | 22 | 23 | 24 |
| 18 | 17 | 16 | 15 | 14 | 13 |
| 7 | 8 | 9 | 10 | 11 | 12 |
| 6 | 5 | 4 | 3 | 2 | 1 |

Fig. 25. Method of numbering sections in township, Dominion Land Survey of Canada.

The Canada Act provides that there shall be a road allowance along all range lines and alternate township lines, and at 2-mi. intervals across townships. These allowances are exclusive of the sections and no part thereof is taken from the area of the section. The allowance for road width is generally 66 ft., but it varies along correction lines. In some systems the allowance is 99 ft.

The Act provides that the lines bounding townships on the east and west sides shall be meridians and those on the north and south shall be chords to parallels of latitude. Townships are numbered northerly from the first base line, which coincides with the International Boundary or 49th parallel of latitude. The ranges in Manitoba are numbered east and west from a principal meridian about ten miles west of Pembina. Other meridians, designated 2d, 3d, 4th, 5th, etc., have been established in other provinces.

The Canadian Surveys of base lines differ materially from those in the United States. Correction lines are established between townships two and three, six and seven, etc. Corners are placed on all lines 40 chains apart. The east and west deficiency or surplus in a township is thrown into the range of quarter sections adjoining the west boundary of the township. A single row of monuments to indicate township, section, and quarter-section corners is placed on all survey lines. On north and south lines the monuments are placed on the west limits of the road allowance. On east and west lines they are placed on south limits of the road allowance. Corners on correction lines are placed and marked independently for the township on each side.

## The Engineer's Transit

The transit is used where required accuracy is greater than the accuracy ordinarily attained with the compass and Abney, as for example, in running the exterior boundary control for the mapping of an extensive area, or establishing the geodetic position of the control points.

**ADJUSTMENT.** As with all instruments, it is important to keep the transit in adjustment. An instrument which has been dropped, severely shaken, or knocked about, or which for some other reason will not remain in adjustment with ordinary handling, should be returned to the manufacturer for repair. Adjustments which can be checked are as a rule made by the surveyor and should be made in the order described below.

**Plate Bubble.** To adjust the plate bubble, set up the instrument, bring each plate bubble to the center of its tube, turn the instrument through 180°. The apparent error is twice the real error, so the bubble is brought back half the distance. Relevel the instrument and repeat the test. Each bubble must be adjusted independently.

**Cross Hairs.** To adjust the cross hairs, level the instrument, sight on some well-defined object with the lower or upper portion of the vertical hair, and rotate the telescope on the horizontal axis to see if the cross hair remains on the object. If it does not, rotate the cross-hair ring until the point does remain on the vertical hair throughout the rotation on the horizontal arm. After the vertical hair is adjusted, sight the instrument on some clearly defined object 200 to 300 ft. away from the instrument. Reverse the telescope and set a point in line of sight. With the telescope in the reversed position, sight again on the original point. Reverse the telescope. If the point previously set is in the line of sight, then the line of sight is perpendicular to the horizontal axis. If not, one-fourth of the error is removed by shifting the cross-hair ring in the proper direction horizontally. Only one-fourth of the error is adjusted in this case since a double reversal is involved. Repeat the operation until the point remains in the line of sight.

**Stadia Wires.** Stadia wires are sometimes adjustable with respect to the space between them. When so, they are not in the same plane with the vertical and horizontal cross hairs and hence are not seen with the same focusing of the eyepiece. Adjustable stadia hairs should be tested daily and set so that 100 shall be the coefficient of the rod intercept. This may be done by laying off $100 + (F + c)$ ft. (see Fig. 27) from the center of the instrument and adjusting the wires to intercept 1 ft. on a rod held at the further end of the line.

**Standards.** To adjust the standards (to make the horizontal axis perpendicular to the vertical axis of the instrument), set up the instrument, sight on some point $A$ such as a church steeple, rotate the telescope on the horizontal axis and set a point $B$ in line of sight at approximately the height of the instrument. Reverse the telescope, sight on point $B$, raise the telescope and, if the instrument is in adjustment, point $A$ will be in the line of sight. If not, raise or lower the adjustable end of the horizontal arm to correct for one-half the error.

**Bubble.** To adjust the telescope bubble, use the two-peg adjustment method described under adjustments of the Abney level.

**Vernier.** To adjust the vernier of the vertical circle, level the telescope and read the vertical circle vernier. If the index does not read zero, loosen the screws holding the vernier and make the zeros on the vernier and circle coincide.

**Objective Slide.** To adjust the objective slide be sure that the cross hairs are in adjustment by using very distant points. This will require the objective to be drawn in nearly as far as possible. Next repeat the test by using two points very near the instrument. This will require that the objective be run out; any error in adjustment will change the direction of the line of sight so that it will no longer be perpendicular to the horizontal axis of the instrument. If the instrument fails to stand this test, the objective does not move parallel to the line of sight. The adjustment is made by moving the adjustment screws of the objective so as apparently to increase the error, by estimation, one-fourth of the correction required. The adjustments of the objective slide (centering the eyepiece tube and centering the circles) are usually made by the instrument maker.

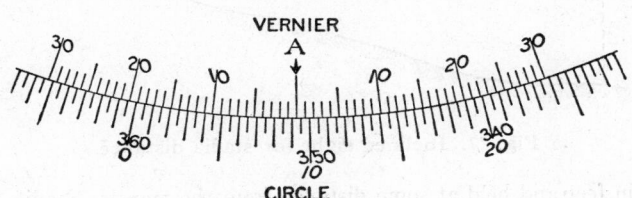

Fig. 26.  Transit vernier.

**VERNIER READINGS.** A vernier is a device for subdividing the smallest graduations on an instrument, such as the limb or circle of a transit. Its use is illustrated in Fig. 26. Here the circle is divided into degrees and half-degrees and every tenth whole degree is numbered, clockwise on an inner row of figures and counterclockwise on an outer row. It is read from a movable vernier having an arrow at zero and 30 graduations on each side of it, every tenth of which is numbered, clockwise to the left of the arrow and counterclockwise to the right.

Thirty graduations on the vernier are exactly equal to 29 of the smallest graduations (½ degree, or 30 minutes) of the circle. To read the clockwise transit angle to 1/30 of ½ degree, i.e., to 1 min., note that the arrow of the vernier points about half-way between 350°30′ and 351°00′ (inner row of numerals) on the circle. The reading is roughly 350°45′. But if one runs his eye along the vernier graduations to the left of the arrow, he will come to a graduation that is **exactly** opposite a graduation on the circle. The vernier graduation is 14 (the circle graduation has no significance). The correct bearing is then 350°30′ plus 14′, or 350°44′.

Similarly, to read the counterclockwise angle to 1 min., first note that the arrow on the vernier points about halfway between 9°00′ and 9°30′ on the outer row of circle numerals. The angle is roughly 9°15′. But by running the eye along the vernier graduations to the right of the arrow one comes to a graduation **exactly** opposite a graduation on the circle. This is graduation 16 on the vernier. The correct angle is then 9°16′.

**USE OF TRANSIT FOR STADIA MEASUREMENTS.** In addition to vertical and horizontal cross hairs, practically all transits are equipped with two additional horizontal hairs known as stadia wires. By observing them, horizontal distances and differences in elevation may be determined from a vertical rod

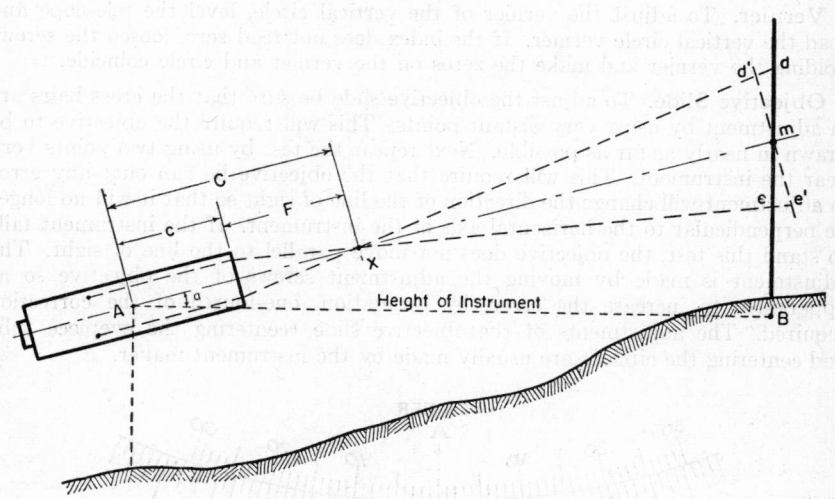

**Fig. 27. Inclined sight for stadia distance.**

graduated in feet and held at some distance from the transit. Stadia furnishes a rapid means of measuring distances or differences in elevation for filling in details of topographic surveys in open country.

The formula for distance, $S$, is: $S = (F/i)s + (F + c)$, where $F$ is the focal length of the objective lens, $s$ the rod intercept, $i$ the distance between the stadia hairs, and $c$ the distance from the center of the instrument to the objective. The stadia hairs in most transits are set so that $F$ divided by $i = 100$. To obtain the horizontal distance when the telescope is level, multiply the rod interval by 100 and add the constant $(F + c)$. The manufacturer furnishes the value of the constant $(F + c)$ with each instrument; ordinarily it is 1.

When stadia distances are measured with the telescope in other than a level position, the rod interval represents a slope distance. To reduce slope distance to horizontal distance, the vertical angle must be known. Set the middle horizontal hair of the transit, located at $A$ in Fig. 27, on the rod graduation mark equal to the H.I. (the height of the horizontal axis of the telescope above the ground). This is point $m$. From the vertical circle on the transit read the angle $mAB = a$ in Fig. 27. The error introduced by holding the rod vertical while making an inclined sight is negligible and is disregarded ($de$ is assumed equal to $d'e'$). In Fig. 27 the line of sight is along line $Am$, and the vertex of the triangle made by the stadia hairs is at point $x$ between the instrument and the rod.

To find the horizontal distance $AB$, and the vertical distance $Bm$, first calculate the distance $Am$ from the formula just given for a horizontal distance, $S$:

$$S = \left(\frac{F}{i}\right) s + (F + c)$$

Assuming $F/i = 100$, and $(F + c) = 1$, $Am = 100s + 1$. Then use the following formulas to determine $AB$ and $Bm$:

$$AB = (Am) \,(\cos mAB)^2$$
$$Bm = (Am) \,(\tfrac{1}{2} \sin [2\, mAB])$$

**Example.** In Fig. 27 assume a transit with an $F + c$ of 1.0, and H.I. 4.8 at point $A$; that the intercept on the rod held at point $m$ is 3.82 ft., and that when the middle cross hair of the transit is set on the 4.8 mark on the rod, the vertical arc reads $22°30'$. Then distance $AB = 383 \times \cos^2 22°30' = 326.9'$, and the difference in elevation of the ground at $A$ and at $m$ is $383 \times \frac{1}{2} \sin 45° = 135.4'$. $Am$ may also be found from $AB \times \tan 22°30'$. Tables found in most engineering handbooks, or obtainable from transit manufacturers, can be used to avoid these computations. The correction for a vertical rod on inclined sights is included in such tables.

Discrepancies between stadia and taped distance measurements should not exceed 1 part in 300 where ordinary care is used in the survey. Differences in elevation should be within $\pm 1$ ft. for distances up to 300 ft. where the vertical angle is $20°$; it should be more accurate where the angle is smaller. Errors of measurement are compensating rather than cumulative, therefore stadia traverses may be expected to close within the error allowed for compass and tape surveys, from 1/300 to 1/500.

**ESTABLISHING A TRUE BEARING FROM OBSERVATIONS ON THE NORTH STAR (POLARIS).** As indicated in Fig. 28, Polaris revolves counterclockwise about the pole. At its highest point, U.C., it is said to be in upper culmination; when it reaches the lowest point, L.C., it is at lower culmination. In either position it is on the true meridian. When Polaris reaches the most easterly point of its orbit, it is at eastern elongation, E.E.; likewise at the most westerly point it is at western elongation, W.E. Eastern elongation precedes and western elongation follows upper culmination (see Table 3). Lower culmination precedes or follows upper culmination by 11 hr., 58 min.

**Observation at Elongation.** The time of elongation is computed in the example on page 17·42. About half an hour before the computed time of elongation, set the transit up over one end of the line for which the true bearing is desired. Illuminate the cross hairs by means of a flashlight or a lantern, preferably held by an assistant. Set the vertical hair on the star and clamp the plates. It will be observed that the star moves very slowly in azimuth. If the transit has an erecting telescope, this movement will be to the left when the star is approaching western elongation; it will be to the right if it is approaching eastern elongation.

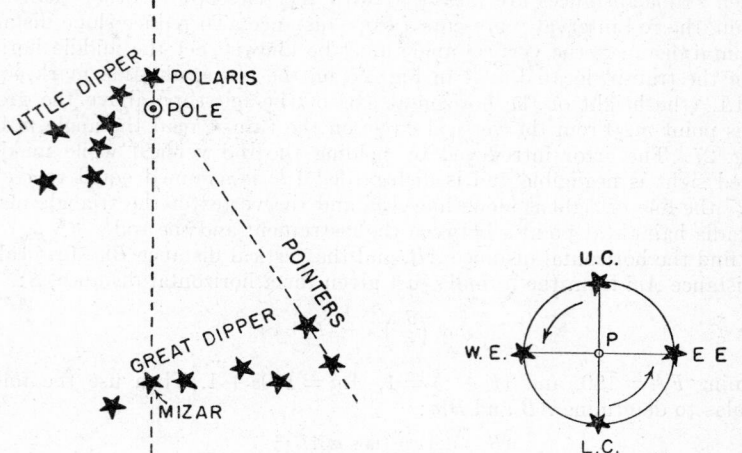

**Fig. 28. Positions of Polaris.**

With an inverting telescope the reverse will be true. As the star nears its elongation it no longer moves in azimuth but will move vertically, downward if in western elongation, upward if at eastern elongation. This shows that the position of elongation has been reached. Now lower the telescope without disturbing its azimuth and set a point on a stake some 300 or 400 ft. north of the transit, in line with the vertical hair. To set the point bring a lantern into line by sighting across the top of the telescope. Set the point a few inches in front of the lantern. A handkerchief held behind the point marker and in front of the lantern will make the marker easier to see. Next, quickly reverse the telescope, relevel the plate levels if necessary, point again at the star and set another point. If the two points do not agree, take a point midway between.

To obtain a meridian lay off from this last point the azimuth of Polaris at elongation, computing the azimuth as shown below. The azimuth or true bearing of the survey line can be found by measuring from this north point to the line in question.

### Computation for time of elongation.

**Example.** To find the time of eastern elongation for May 5, 1955, assume that an observation is to be made at a point in the vicinity of the National Airport at Washington, D. C. From a government map of the area the longitude is found to be 77°02′45″W and the latitude 38°51′00″N. Express the longitude as a decimal 77.0458° and convert to hours. One hour is equal to 15 degrees of longitude from the Prime Meridian through Greenwich. Whence:

$$\frac{77.0458}{15} = 5.1364 \text{ hr.} = 5 \text{ hr. } 8.2 \text{ min.}$$

Greenwich civil time of eastern elongation on May 1, 1954 (Table 3) = 5 hr. 19.2 min.
Corrections:

| | |
|---|---:|
| 4 days to May 5: 4 × 3.93 (footnote b, Table 3) minus | 15.7 min. |
| For year 1955 (Table 3) plus | 1.8 min. |
| For latitude 39° (footnote a, Table 3) | 0.0 min. |

## Table 3. Time of Upper Culmination, Western and Eastern Elongations, of Polaris, for Meridian of Greenwich, Latitude 40°N [a]

Civil dates and civil times, 1954*

| Date [b] | Upper culmination (hr. min.) | Western elongation (hr. min.) | Eastern elongation (hr. min.) |
|---|---|---|---|
| Jan. 1 | 19 08.3 | 1 18.2 | 13 12.4 |
| Jan. 11 | 18 28.8 | 0 28.7 | 12 32.9 |
| Jan. 21 | 17 49.3 | 23 45.2 | 11 53.4 |
| Jan. 31 | 17 09.8 | 23 05.7 | 11 13.9 |
| Feb. 10 | 16 30.2 | 22 26.1 | 10 34.3 |
| Feb. 20 | 15 50.7 | 21 46.6 | 9 54.8 |
| Mar. 2 | 15 11.2 | 21 07.1 | 9 15.3 |
| Mar. 12 | 14 31.8 | 20 27.7 | 8 35.9 |
| Mar. 22 | 13 52.4 | 19 48.3 | 7 56.5 |
| April 1 | 13 13.0 | 19 08.9 | 7 17.1 |
| April 11 | 12 33.6 | 18 29.5 | 6 37.7 |
| April 21 | 11 54.3 | 17 50.2 | 5 58.4 |
| May 1 | 11 15.1 | 17 11.0 | 5 19.2 |
| May 11 | 10 35.8 | 16 31.7 | 4 39.9 |
| May 21 | 9 56.6 | 15 52.5 | 4 00.8 |
| May 31 | 9 17.5 | 15 13.4 | 3 21.6 |
| June 10 | 8 38.4 | 14 34.3 | 2 42.5 |
| June 20 | 7 59.2 | 13 55.1 | 2 03.3 |
| June 30 | 7 20.1 | 13 16.0 | 1 24.2 |

| Date | Upper culmination (hr. min.) | Western elongation (hr. min.) | Eastern elongation (hr. min.) |
|---|---|---|---|
| July 10 | 6 41.0 | 12 36.9 | 0 45.1 |
| July 20 | 6 02.0 | 11 57.9 | 0 06.1 |
| July 30 | 5 22.9 | 11 18.8 | 23 23.0 |
| Aug. 9 | 4 43.8 | 10 39.7 | 22 44.0 |
| Aug. 19 | 4 04.7 | 10 00.6 | 22 04.8 |
| Aug. 29 | 3 25.5 | 9 21.4 | 21 25.7 |
| Sept. 8 | 2 46.4 | 8 42.3 | 20 46.6 |
| Sept. 18 | 2 07.2 | 8 03.1 | 20 07.4 |
| Sept. 28 | 1 28.0 | 7 23.9 | 19 28.2 |
| Oct. 8 | 0 48.8 | 6 44.7 | 18 49.0 [c] |
| Oct. 18 | 0 09.6 | 6 05.5 | 18 09.8 |
| Oct. 28 | 23 26.4 | 5 26.2 | 17 30.5 |
| Nov. 7 | 22 47.0 | 4 46.9 | 16 51.1 |
| Nov. 17 | 22 07.7 | 4 07.5 | 16 11.8 |
| Nov. 27 | 21 28.3 | 3 28.1 | 15 32.4 |
| Dec. 7 | 20 48.9 | 2 48.7 | 14 53.0 |
| Dec. 17 | 20 09.4 | 2 09.3 | 14 13.5 |
| Dec. 27 | 19 29.9 | 1 29.8 | 13 34.0 |

Correction for subsequent years

| Year | Min. |
|---|---|
| 1955 | + 1.8 |
| 1956 | − 0.3 [c] |
| 1957 | + 1.4 |
| 1958 | + 3.2 |
| 1959 | + 4.8 |
| 1960 | + 2.5 [c] |
| 1961 | + 4.0 |
| 1962 | + 5.5 |
| 1963 | + 7.0 |
| 1964 | + 4.6 [c] |
| 1965 | + 6.1 |
| 1966 | + 7.6 |
| 1967 | + 9.3 |
| 1968 | + 7.1 [c] |
| 1969 | + 8.9 |
| 1970 | +10.8 |
| 1971 | +12.7 |
| 1972 | +10.8 [c] |
| 1973 | +12.7 |

[a] For latitude correction, western elongation, add 2.5 min. for 10°; 1.7 min. for 20°; 0.9 min. for 30°; subtract 0.6 min. for 45°; 1.4 min. for 50°; and 3.4 min. for 60°. Reverse signs for eastern elongation.

[b] Reduce times shown in this table by 3.93 min. for each day to any one day in the 10-day intervals.

[c] Apply an additional +3.9 min. for dates preceding Feb. 29.

* Source: The *Ephemeris*—1954; Bureau of Land Management, Department of Interior.

| Local meridian time, eastern elongation | = 5 hr.  5.3 min. |
|---|---|
| Longitude correction to E.S.T. (see above) plus | 8.2 min. |
| Civil time if computed from midnight, hence | 5 hr. 13.5 min. |
| Eastern elongation for May 5, 1955 then occurs at | 5:13.5 A.M. E.S.T. |

## Computation of the azimuth of Polaris at elongation.

| Polar distance for 1955 from Table 4 | 56.8 min. |
|---|---|
| Correction from Table 4 | 0 |
|  | 56.8 min. |

$$\text{Azimuth of Polaris} = \frac{\text{Polar distance}}{\text{Cos of latitude}} = \text{Polar distance} \times \text{Secant of latitude}$$

From Table 5, secant of latitude 38°51′ = 1.2840
Azimuth = 1.2840 × 56.8 = 73 min.; then bearing of Polaris is N1°13′E and the meridian is 1°13′ to the left of the line established at elongation.

### Table 4.  Polaris: Polar Distance

| Year | Min. | Year | Min. | Year | Min. |
|---|---|---|---|---|---|
| 1950 | 58.3 | 1960 | 55.3 | 1970 | 52.4 |
| 1951 | 58.0 | 1961 | 55.0 | 1971 | 52.1 |
| 1952 | 57.7 | 1962 | 54.7 | 1972 | 51.9 |
| 1953 | 57.4 | 1963 | 54.5 | 1973 | 51.6 |
| 1954 | 57.1 | 1964 | 54.2 | 1974 | 51.3 |
| 1955 | 56.8 | 1965 | 53.9 | 1975 | 51.0 |
| 1956 | 56.5 | 1966 | 53.6 | 1976 | 50.7 |
| 1957 | 56.2 | 1967 | 53.3 | 1977 | 50.4 |
| 1958 | 55.9 | 1968 | 53.0 | 1978 | 50.2 |
| 1959 | 55.6 | 1969 | 52.7 | 1979 | 49.9 |

Corrections to polar distance for month of year (minutes):

| | | | |
|---|---|---|---|
| Jan. 1 −0.3 min. | Apr. 1 −0.2 min. | July 1 +0.2 min. | Oct. 1 −0.1 min. |
| Feb. 1 −0.4 min. | May 1  0.0 min. | Aug. 1 +0.2 min. | Nov. 1 −0.3 min. |
| Mar. 1 −0.3 min. | June 1 +0.1 min. | Sept. 1  0.0 min. | Dec. 1 −0.5 min. |

### Table 5.  Secants of Latitudes, Natural Functions

| Latitude | Secant | Latitude | Secant | Latitude | Secant | Latitude | Secant |
|---|---|---|---|---|---|---|---|
| 10 | 1.0154 | 25 | 1.1034 | 40 | 1.3054 | 55 | 1.7434 |
| 11 | 1.0187 | 26 | 1.1126 | 41 | 1.3250 | 56 | 1.7883 |
| 12 | 1.0223 | 27 | 1.1223 | 42 | 1.3456 | 57 | 1.8361 |
| 13 | 1.0263 | 28 | 1.1326 | 43 | 1.3673 | 58 | 1.8871 |
| 14 | 1.0306 | 29 | 1.1433 | 44 | 1.3902 | 59 | 1.9416 |
| 15 | 1.0353 | 30 | 1.1547 | 45 | 1.4142 | 60 | 2.0000 |
| 16 | 1.0403 | 31 | 1.1666 | 46 | 1.4395 | 61 | 2.0627 |
| 17 | 1.0457 | 32 | 1.1792 | 47 | 1.4663 | 62 | 2.1300 |
| 18 | 1.0515 | 33 | 1.1924 | 48 | 1.4945 | 63 | 2.2027 |
| 19 | 1.0576 | 34 | 1.2062 | 49 | 1.5242 | 64 | 2.2812 |
| 20 | 1.0642 | 35 | 1.2208 | 50 | 1.5557 | 65 | 2.3662 |
| 21 | 1.0711 | 36 | 1.2361 | 51 | 1.5890 | 66 | 2.4586 |
| 22 | 1.0785 | 37 | 1.2521 | 52 | 1.6243 | 67 | 2.5593 |
| 23 | 1.0864 | 38 | 1.2690 | 53 | 1.6616 | 68 | 2.6695 |
| 24 | 1.0946 | 39 | 1.2867 | 54 | 1.7013 | 69 | 2.7904 |

If local adjustments to time are in effect, such as "daylight saving," the necessary correction must be allowed in computing the time of elongation.

**Observation at Culmination.** The time of culmination of Polaris having been found from Table 3, a rough determination of the meridian can be made by pointing the telescope upon Polaris at that exact instant, and producing the line on the ground as previously described.

The time of upper culmination may also be determined by observing when Polaris and the star Mizar, the second star from the end of the handle of the great dipper (see Fig. 28), are in the same vertical plane and following Polaris for the proper interval afterward. In 1952 Polaris reached upper culmination 27 min. and 48 sec. after Polaris and Mizar were in the same vertical plane. The interval increases about 37 sec. for each year. Thus the increase for 1954 was 2 × 37 = 74 sec., and the interval in 1954 was about 29 min. and 0.02 sec. If the exact interval is desired for a particular year, look in the Nautical Almanac for that year.

For rough work, an observation made on Polaris with either transit or a plumb line an hour before or after upper culmination (or eastern or western elongation) should give a line within one degree east or west of the true meridian. In projecting the direction of Polaris on the ground with a plumb line, suspend the plumb bob from a tripod set over a pail of water. This will keep the line steady. Project the direction of Polaris on the ground by setting a point as previously described. Make three or four settings and take the average for the meridian. With a compass, obtain the angle between this meridian and the survey line. This will be the true bearing of the survey line within 1° if the work has been carefully done.

## BIBLIOGRAPHY

The Bibliography for this section on Surveying is combined with that of the following section on Forest Road Engineering because of the integration of the subject matter involved in the two sections. (See page 18·61.)

# FOREST ROAD ENGINEERING

## CONTENTS

# FOREST ROAD ENGINEERING

## Simple Curves

A simple curve is a circular arc joining two tangents (Fig. 1). The first tangent point, or point where the curve begins, is called the point of curvature (P.C.). The point where the curve ends, and the next tangent begins, is called the point of tangency (P.T.). The point where the tangents intersect is designated the point of intersection (P.I.).

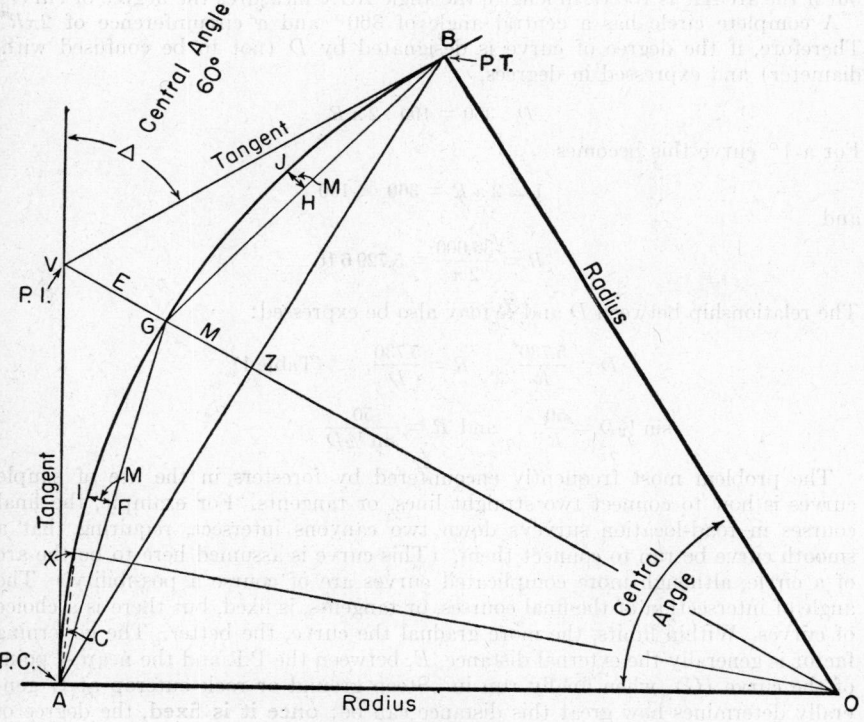

Fig. 1. Curve diagram.

## NOMENCLATURE AND RELATIONSHIPS. (Fig. 1.)

$$R = \text{Radius} = OA = OB = OG$$
$$L = \text{Length of curve} = AGB$$
$$L = 100\frac{\triangle}{D}$$
$$L = 0.0174533\triangle R$$

$Lc$ = Long chord = $AZB$
$\qquad Lc = 2R \sin \frac{1}{2}\triangle$
$T$ = Tangent distance = $AV = BV$
$T = R \tan \frac{1}{2}\triangle$
$D$ = Degree of curve, in degrees and decimals of degree
$E$ = External distance = $GV$
$E = \dfrac{R}{\cos \frac{1}{2}\triangle} - R$ or $E = R \operatorname{exsec} \frac{1}{2}\triangle$

$M$ = Middle ordinate = $GZ$
$M = R\,(1 - \cos\frac{1}{2}\triangle)$ or
$M = R\,(\operatorname{vers}\frac{1}{2}\triangle)$
$\triangle$ = delta = Central angle = P.I. angle
$VAB$ = Total deflection angle = $\frac{1}{2}AOB = \frac{1}{2}\triangle$
$\qquad \sin \frac{1}{2}\triangle = \dfrac{AB}{2R}\left(\text{or } \dfrac{AZ}{AO}\right)$
$C$ = Any short chord, as $AX$
$VAX = \frac{1}{2}AOX$ = Deflection angle for $C$

## RADII OF CURVES AND DEGREES OF CURVATURE.
Curves are designated either by radius or by the degree of curve. The mathematical relationships between these quantities are shown on page 18 · 3. In railroad and highway work, curves are usually designated by degrees. A 1° curve is defined as a curve having such a radius that 100 ft. of arc will subtend a 1° central angle. On a 2° curve a 100-ft. arc subtends a 2° central angle, and so on. In Fig. 1, if arc $AGB$ equals 100 ft., the degree of curve will have the same measure as the angle $AOB$; but if the arc $AX$ is 100 ft. in length, the angle $AOX$ measures the degree of curve.

A complete circle has a central angle of 360° and a circumference of $2\pi R$. Therefore, if the degree of curve is designated by $D$ (not to be confused with diameter) and expressed in degrees,

$$D : 360 = 100 : 2\pi R$$

For a 1° curve this becomes

$$1 \times 2\pi R = 360 \times 100$$

and

$$R = \frac{36,000}{2\pi} = 5,729.6 \text{ ft.}$$

The relationship between $D$ and $R$ may also be expressed:

$$D = \frac{5.730}{R}, \qquad R = \frac{5.730}{D}, \qquad \text{(Table 1)}$$

$$\sin \frac{1}{2}D = \frac{50}{R}, \quad \text{and } R = \frac{50}{\sin \frac{1}{2}D}$$

The problem most frequently encountered by foresters in the use of simple curves is how to connect two straight lines, or tangents. For example, the final courses in road-location surveys down two canyons intersect, requiring that a smooth curve be run to connect them. (This curve is assumed here to be the arc of a circle, although more complicated curves are of course a possibility.) The angle of intersection of the final courses, or tangents, is fixed, but there is a choice of curves. Within limits, the more gradual the curve, the better. The governing factor is generally the external distance, $E$, between the P.I. and the nearest point of the curve ($G$), when finally run in. Steep ground or rock outcrop at $G$ generally determines how great this distance can be; **once it is fixed,** the degree of curve, its radius, and the distance from P.I. at which the curve begins and ends (Tables 1 and 2), are also fixed. Several methods of laying out simple curves may be employed, depending on the equipment available.

## LAYING OUT A CURVE BY EXTERNALS.
To connect the two tangents in Fig. 1 with a curve:

At P.I. measure the angle between the tangents, which is equal to the central angle; call it 60°. Stand at P.I. and estimate the distance to where the road should

### Table 1. Radii for Various Degrees of Curve

(Figured on the basis of $R = 5,730$ ft. for a 1° curve)

| Degree of curve | Radius of curve in feet | Degree of curve | Radius of curve in feet | Degree of curve | Radius of curve in feet |
|---|---|---|---|---|---|
| 0°30′ | 11,460.0 | 9°30′ | 603.2 | 23°30′ | 243.8 |
| 0°40′ | 8,595.0 | 10°00′ | 573.0 | 24°00′ | 238.8 |
| 0°50′ | 6,876.0 | 10°30′ | 545.7 | 24°30′ | 233.9 |
| 1°00′ | 5,730.0 | 11°00′ | 520.9 | 25°00′ | 229.2 |
| 1°20′ | 4,297.5 | 11°30′ | 498.3 | 26°00′ | 220.4 |
| 1°30′ | 3,820.0 | 12°00′ | 477.5 | 27°00′ | 212.2 |
| 1°40′ | 3,438.0 | 12°30′ | 458.4 | 28°00′ | 204.6 |
| 2°00′ | 2,865.0 | 13°00′ | 440.8 | 29°00′ | 197.6 |
| 2°20′ | 2,455.7 | 13°30′ | 424.4 | 30°00′ | 191.0 |
| 2°30′ | 2,292.0 | 14°00′ | 409.3 | 31°00′ | 184.8 |
| 2°40′ | 2,148.8 | 14°30′ | 395.2 | 32°00′ | 179.1 |
| 3°00′ | 1,910.0 | 15°00′ | 382.0 | 33°00′ | 173.6 |
| 3°20′ | 1,719.0 | 15°30′ | 369.6 | 34°00′ | 168.5 |
| 3°30′ | 1,637.1 | 16°00′ | 358.1 | 35°00′ | 163.7 |
| 3°40′ | 1,562.7 | 16°30′ | 347.3 | 36°00′ | 159.2 |
| 4°00′ | 1,432.5 | 17°00′ | 337.0 | 37°00′ | 154.9 |
| 4°20′ | 1,322.3 | 17°30′ | 327.4 | 38°00′ | 150.8 |
| 4°30′ | 1,273.3 | 18°00′ | 318.3 | 39°00′ | 146.9 |
| 4°40′ | 1,227.9 | 18°30′ | 309.7 | 40°00′ | 143.2 |
| 5°00′ | 1,146.0 | 19°00′ | 301.6 | 42°00′ | 136.4 |
| 5°30′ | 1,041.8 | 19°30′ | 293.8 | 44°00′ | 130.2 |
| 6°00′ | 955.0 | 20°00′ | 286.5 | 46°00′ | 124.6 |
| 6°30′ | 881.5 | 20°30′ | 279.5 | 48°00′ | 119.4 |
| 7°00′ | 818.6 | 21°00′ | 272.9 | 50°00′ | 114.6 |
| 7°30′ | 764.0 | 21°30′ | 266.5 | 52°00′ | 110.2 |
| 8°00′ | 716.3 | 22°00′ | 260.5 | 54°00′ | 106.1 |
| 8°30′ | 674.1 | 22°30′ | 254.7 | 56°00′ | 102.3 |
| 9°00′ | 636.6 | 23°00′ | 249.1 | | |

be; say it is 15 ft. (This is the external distance; P.I. to $G = E$.) From Table 2, calculate the radius for a 60° central angle and 15-ft. external distance; it is approximately 100 ft. (External for 60° = 0.1547; and 15.0/0.15 = 100.) From Table 2, calculate the tangent distance for a 100-ft. radius and 60° central angle: 0.57735 × 100 = 57.7. ( For this purpose 58 ft. is close enough.) Measure 58 ft. from P.I. toward $A$ and set P.C. Measure 58 ft. from P.I. toward $B$ and set P.T. Measure 15 ft. from P.I. toward $G$ and set stake at $G$. Three points on the curve are now located; the P.C., middle, and P.T.—a sufficient number for a short curve.

When a curve is too long to construct from the three points P.C., $G$, and P.T., intermediate points should be staked such as at $I$ and $J$ in Fig. 1. This can be done by laying off middle ordinates at $F$ and $H$, which are midpoints on chords P.C.$G$ and P.T.$G$, respectively. The formula for finding the middle ordinate is $M = R$ $(1-\cos \Delta/2)$. $\Delta$ for chords P.C.$G$ and P.T.$G$ is 30°, and $\Delta/2$ is 15°. If $R = 100$, find middle ordinate for $FI = HJ = 100(1-\cos 15°) = 100 - 96.593 = 3.41$ ft. Middle ordinates for chords 20 ft. to 100 ft. and various radii may be found from Table 3.

Ordinarily chord lengths such as P.C.$G$ and P.T.$G$ will be obtained by measurements on the ground. They may also be calculated from the formula: chord length $= 2R \sin \frac{1}{2} \Delta$ where $\Delta$ is the central angle for the subchord whose length

## Table 2. Tangents and Externals for Curves of Radius 1

| Central angle | Tangent distance | External distance | Central angle | Tangent distance | External distance | Central angle | Tangent distance | External distance |
|---|---|---|---|---|---|---|---|---|
| 1 | 0.00873 | 0.00004 | 55 | 0.52057 | 0.12738 | 109 | 1.40195 | 0.72205 |
| 2 | .01746 | .00015 | 56 | .53171 | .13257 | 110 | 1.42815 | .74345 |
| 3 | .02619 | .00034 | 57 | .54296 | .13789 | 111 | 1.45501 | .76552 |
| 4 | .03492 | .00061 | 58 | .55431 | .14335 | 112 | 1.48256 | .78829 |
| 5 | .04366 | .00095 | 59 | .56577 | .14896 | 113 | 1.51084 | .81180 |
| 6 | .05241 | .00137 | 60 | .57735 | .15470 | 114 | 1.53986 | .83608 |
| 7 | .06116 | .00187 | 61 | .58905 | .16059 | 115 | 1.56696 | .86116 |
| 8 | .06993 | .00244 | 62 | .60086 | .16663 | 116 | 1.60033 | .88708 |
| 9 | .07870 | .00309 | 63 | .61280 | .17283 | 117 | 1.63185 | .91388 |
| 10 | .08749 | .00382 | 64 | .62487 | .17918 | 118 | 1.66428 | .94160 |
| 11 | .09629 | .00463 | 65 | .63707 | .18569 | 119 | 1.69766 | .97029 |
| 12 | .10510 | .00551 | 66 | .64941 | .19236 | 120 | 1.73205 | 1.00000 |
| 13 | .11394 | .00647 | 67 | .66189 | .19920 | 121 | 1.76749 | 1.03077 |
| 14 | .12278 | .00751 | 68 | .67451 | .20622 | 122 | 1.80405 | 1.06267 |
| 15 | .13165 | .00863 | 69 | .68728 | .21341 | 123 | 1.84177 | 1.09574 |
| 16 | .14054 | .00983 | 70 | .70021 | .22077 | 124 | 1.88073 | 1.13005 |
| 17 | .14945 | .01111 | 71 | .71329 | .22833 | 125 | 1.92098 | 1.16568 |
| 18 | .15838 | .01247 | 72 | .72654 | .23607 | 126 | 1.96261 | 1.20269 |
| 19 | .16734 | .01391 | 73 | .73996 | .24400 | 127 | 2.00569 | 1.24116 |
| 20 | .17633 | .01543 | 74 | .75355 | .25214 | 128 | 2.05030 | 1.28117 |
| 21 | .18534 | .01703 | 75 | .76733 | .26047 | 129 | 2.09654 | 1.32282 |
| 22 | .19438 | .01872 | 76 | .78129 | .26902 | 130 | 2.14451 | 1.36620 |
| 23 | .20345 | .02049 | 77 | .79544 | .27778 | 131 | 2.19430 | 1.41142 |
| 24 | .21256 | .02234 | 78 | .80978 | .28676 | 132 | 2.24604 | 1.45859 |
| 25 | .22169 | .02428 | 79 | .82434 | .29579 | 133 | 2.29984 | 1.50784 |
| 26 | .23087 | .02630 | 80 | .83910 | .30541 | 134 | 2.35585 | 1.55930 |
| 27 | .24008 | .02842 | 81 | .85408 | .31509 | 135 | 2.41421 | 1.61313 |
| 28 | .24933 | .03061 | 82 | .86929 | .32501 | 136 | 2.47509 | 1.66947 |
| 29 | .25862 | .03290 | 83 | .88473 | .33519 | 137 | 2.53865 | 1.72850 |
| 30 | .26795 | .03528 | 84 | .90040 | .34563 | 138 | 2.60509 | 1.79043 |
| 31 | .27732 | .03774 | 85 | .91633 | .35635 | 139 | 2.67462 | 1.85545 |
| 32 | .28675 | .04030 | 86 | .93252 | .36733 | 140 | 2.74748 | 1.92380 |
| 33 | .29621 | .04295 | 87 | .94896 | .37860 | 141 | 2.82391 | 1.99574 |
| 34 | .30573 | .04569 | 88 | .96569 | .39016 | 142 | 2.90421 | 2.07155 |
| 35 | .31530 | .04853 | 89 | .98270 | .40203 | 143 | 2.98868 | 2.15155 |
| 36 | .32492 | .05146 | 90 | 1.00000 | .41421 | 144 | 3.07768 | 2.23607 |
| 37 | .33460 | .05449 | 91 | 1.01761 | .42672 | 145 | 3.17159 | 2.32551 |
| 38 | .34433 | .05762 | 92 | 1.03553 | .43956 | 146 | 3.27085 | 2.42030 |
| 39 | .35412 | .06085 | 93 | 1.05378 | .45274 | 147 | 3.37594 | 2.52094 |
| 40 | .36397 | .06418 | 94 | 1.07237 | .46628 | 148 | 3.48741 | 2.62796 |
| 41 | .37388 | .06761 | 95 | 1.09131 | .48019 | 149 | 3.60588 | 2.74198 |
| 42 | .38386 | .07115 | 96 | 1.11061 | .49448 | 150 | 3.73205 | 2.86370 |
| 43 | .39391 | .07479 | 97 | 1.13029 | .50916 | 151 | 3.86671 | 2.99393 |
| 44 | .40403 | .07853 | 98 | 1.15037 | .52425 | 152 | 4.01078 | 3.13357 |
| 45 | .41421 | .08239 | 99 | 1.17085 | .53977 | 153 | 4.16530 | 3.28366 |
| 46 | .42447 | .08636 | 100 | 1.19175 | .55572 | 154 | 4.33148 | 3.44541 |
| 47 | .43481 | .09044 | 101 | 1.21310 | .57213 | 155 | 4.51071 | 3.62023 |
| 48 | .44523 | .09464 | 102 | 1.23490 | .58902 | 156 | 4.70463 | 3.80973 |
| 49 | .45573 | .09895 | 103 | 1.25717 | .60639 | 157 | 4.91516 | 4.01585 |
| 50 | .46631 | .10338 | 104 | 1.27994 | .62427 | 158 | 5.14455 | 4.24084 |
| 51 | .47698 | .10793 | 105 | 1.30323 | .64268 | 159 | 5.39552 | 4.48740 |
| 52 | .48773 | .11260 | 106 | 1.32704 | .66164 | 160 | 5.67128 | 4.75877 |
| 53 | .49858 | .11740 | 107 | 1.35142 | .68117 | 161 | 5.97576 | 5.05886 |
| 54 | .50953 | .12233 | 108 | 1.37638 | .70130 | 162 | 6.31375 | 5.39245 |

is to be calculated. In Fig. 1, $G$ is midway between the P.C. and the P.T., thus $\Delta$ for chord P.C.$G$ in the above example is $60/2 = 30°$ and the length of chord P.C.$G$ is $2 \times 100$ (sin $30°/2$) $= 51.76$. Length of chord P.C.$I$ (assuming point $I$ is the midpoint of arc P.C.$IG$) is $2 \times 100$ (sin $15°/2$), etc.

## Table 3. Middle Ordinates

$$\text{(In feet)}\quad M = R - \sqrt{R^2 - \left(\frac{C}{2}\right)^2} = R \text{ vers}\, \frac{\Delta}{2}$$

| Radius (ft.) | Chord length in feet | | | | | | | | | |
|---|---|---|---|---|---|---|---|---|---|---|
| | 20 | 25 | 30 | 40 | 50 | 60 | 70 | 80 | 90 | 100 |
| 40....... | 1.27 | 2.01 | 2.92 | 5.36 | 8.77 | 13.54 | 20.64 | | | |
| 45....... | 1.13 | 1.77 | 2.57 | 4.69 | 7.58 | 11.46 | 16.72 | 24.38 | | |
| 50....... | 1.01 | 1.59 | 2.30 | 4.17 | 6.70 | 10.00 | 14.29 | 20.00 | 28.21 | |
| 55....... | 0.92 | 1.44 | 2.08 | 3.77 | 6.01 | 8.90 | 12.57 | 17.25 | 23.38 | 32.09 |
| 60....... | .84 | 1.32 | 1.91 | 3.43 | 5.46 | 8.04 | 11.27 | 15.28 | 20.31 | 26.83 |
| 65....... | .77 | 1.21 | 1.75 | 3.15 | 5.00 | 7.34 | 10.23 | 13.77 | 18.10 | 23.47 |
| 70....... | .72 | 1.13 | 1.63 | 2.92 | 4.62 | 6.75 | 9.38 | 12.55 | 16.38 | 21.01 |
| 75....... | .67 | 1.05 | 1.51 | 2.72 | 4.29 | 6.26 | 8.67 | 11.56 | 15.00 | 19.10 |
| 80....... | .63 | 0.98 | 1.42 | 2.54 | 4.01 | 5.84 | 8.06 | 10.72 | 13.86 | 17.55 |
| 85....... | .59 | .93 | 1.33 | 2.39 | 3.76 | 5.47 | 7.54 | 10.00 | 12.89 | 16.26 |
| 90....... | .56 | .87 | 1.26 | 2.25 | 3.54 | 5.15 | 7.08 | 9.38 | 12.06 | 15.17 |
| 100....... | .50 | .78 | 1.13 | 2.02 | 3.18 | 4.61 | 6.33 | 8.35 | 10.70 | 13.40 |
| 110....... | .45 | .71 | 1.03 | 1.83 | 2.88 | 4.17 | 5.72 | 7.53 | 9.63 | 12.02 |
| 120....... | .42 | .65 | 0.94 | 1.68 | 2.63 | 3.81 | 5.21 | 6.86 | 8.76 | 10.91 |
| 130....... | .38 | .60 | .87 | 1.55 | 2.43 | 3.51 | 4.79 | 6.31 | 8.05 | 10.00 |
| 140....... | .36 | .56 | .81 | 1.44 | 2.25 | 3.25 | 4.45 | 5.84 | 7.43 | 9.23 |
| 150....... | .33 | .52 | .75 | 1.34 | 2.10 | 3.03 | 4.14 | 5.43 | 6.91 | 8.58 |
| 160....... | .31 | .49 | .71 | 1.25 | 1.96 | 2.84 | 3.87 | 5.08 | 6.46 | 8.01 |
| 170....... | .29 | .46 | .66 | 1.18 | 1.85 | 2.67 | 3.64 | 4.77 | 6.06 | 7.52 |
| 180....... | .28 | .44 | .63 | 1.11 | 1.74 | 2.52 | 3.44 | 4.50 | 5.72 | 7.08 |
| 190....... | .26 | .41 | .59 | 1.06 | 1.65 | 2.38 | 3.25 | 4.26 | 5.41 | 6.70 |
| 200....... | .25 | .39 | .56 | 1.00 | 1.57 | 2.26 | 3.09 | 4.04 | 5.13 | 6.35 |
| 210....... | .24 | .37 | .54 | 0.95 | 1.49 | 2.15 | 2.94 | 3.84 | 4.88 | 6.04 |
| 220....... | .23 | .36 | .51 | .91 | 1.43 | 2.05 | 2.80 | 3.67 | 4.65 | 5.76 |
| 230....... | .22 | .34 | .49 | .87 | 1.36 | 1.96 | 2.68 | 3.50 | 4.45 | 5.50 |
| 240....... | .21 | .33 | .47 | .83 | 1.31 | 1.88 | 2.57 | 3.36 | 4.26 | 5.27 |
| 250....... | .20 | .31 | .45 | .80 | 1.25 | 1.81 | 2.46 | 3.22 | 4.08 | 5.05 |
| 275....... | .18 | .28 | .41 | .73 | 1.14 | 1.64 | 2.24 | 2.93 | 3.71 | 4.58 |
| 300....... | .17 | .26 | .38 | .67 | 1.05 | 1.52 | 2.05 | 2.68 | 3.40 | 4.20 |
| 325....... | .15 | .24 | .35 | .62 | 0.96 | 1.39 | 1.89 | 2.47 | 3.13 | 3.87 |
| 350....... | .14 | .22 | .33 | .57 | .90 | 1.29 | 1.75 | 2.29 | 2.90 | 3.59 |
| 375....... | .13 | .21 | .30 | .53 | .83 | 1.20 | 1.64 | 2.14 | 2.71 | 3.35 |
| 400....... | .12 | .20 | .28 | .50 | .78 | 1.13 | 1.54 | 2.00 | 2.54 | 3.14 |
| 425....... | .11 | .18 | .26 | .47 | .74 | 1 06 | 1.44 | 1.83 | 2.39 | 2.89 |
| 450....... | .11 | .17 | .25 | .44 | .69 | 1.00 | 1.36 | 1.78 | 2.25 | 2.79 |
| 475....... | .10 | .17 | .24 | .42 | .66 | 0.95 | 1.29 | 1.69 | 2.14 | 2.64 |
| 500....... | .10 | .16 | .22 | .40 | .62 | .90 | 1.23 | 1.60 | 2.03 | 2.49 |
| 550....... | .09 | .14 | .20 | .36 | .57 | .82 | 1.12 | 1.46 | 1.84 | 2.28 |
| 600....... | .08 | .13 | .19 | .33 | .52 | .75 | 1.03 | 1.33 | 1.75 | 2.09 |
| 650....... | .08 | .12 | .17 | .31 | .48 | .69 | 0.94 | 1.23 | 1.56 | 1.93 |
| 700....... | .07 | .11 | .16 | .29 | .45 | .64 | .87 | 1.14 | 1.45 | 1.79 |
| 750....... | .07 | .10 | .15 | .27 | .42 | .60 | .81 | 1.07 | 1.34 | 1.67 |
| 800....... | .06 | .10 | .14 | .25 | .39 | .56 | .76 | 1.00 | 1.26 | 1.56 |
| 850....... | .06 | .09 | .13 | .24 | .37 | .53 | .72 | 0.94 | 1.19 | 1.47 |
| 900....... | .05 | .09 | .13 | .22 | .35 | .50 | .68 | .89 | 1.12 | 1.39 |
| 950....... | .05 | .08 | .12 | .21 | .33 | .47 | .64 | .84 | 1.07 | 1.32 |
| 1,000....... | .05 | .08 | .11 | .20 | .31 | .45 | .61 | .80 | 1.02 | 1.25 |
| 1,100....... | .04 | .07 | .10 | .18 | .28 | .41 | .55 | .73 | 0.93 | 1.14 |
| 1,200....... | .04 | .06 | .09 | .17 | .26 | .37 | .50 | .67 | .84 | 1.04 |
| 1,300....... | .04 | .06 | .09 | .15 | .24 | .35 | .47 | .62 | .78 | 0.96 |
| 1,400....... | .04 | .06 | .08 | .14 | .22 | .32 | .43 | .57 | .73 | .89 |
| 1,500....... | .03 | .05 | .08 | .13 | .21 | .30 | .40 | .53 | .67 | .83 |
| 1,600....... | .03 | .05 | .07 | .13 | .19 | .28 | .38 | .50 | .64 | .78 |
| 1,700....... | .03 | .05 | .06 | .12 | .19 | .26 | .36 | .47 | .60 | .74 |
| 1,800....... | .03 | .04 | .06 | .11 | .18 | .25 | .34 | .44 | .56 | .70 |

## LAYING OUT A CURVE BY TANGENT OFFSETS (Fig. 2). Formula:

$$\text{Tangent offset} = \text{Radius} - \sqrt{\text{Radius}^2 - \text{Tangent distance}^2}$$
$$= OT - \sqrt{OT^2 - TD^2}$$

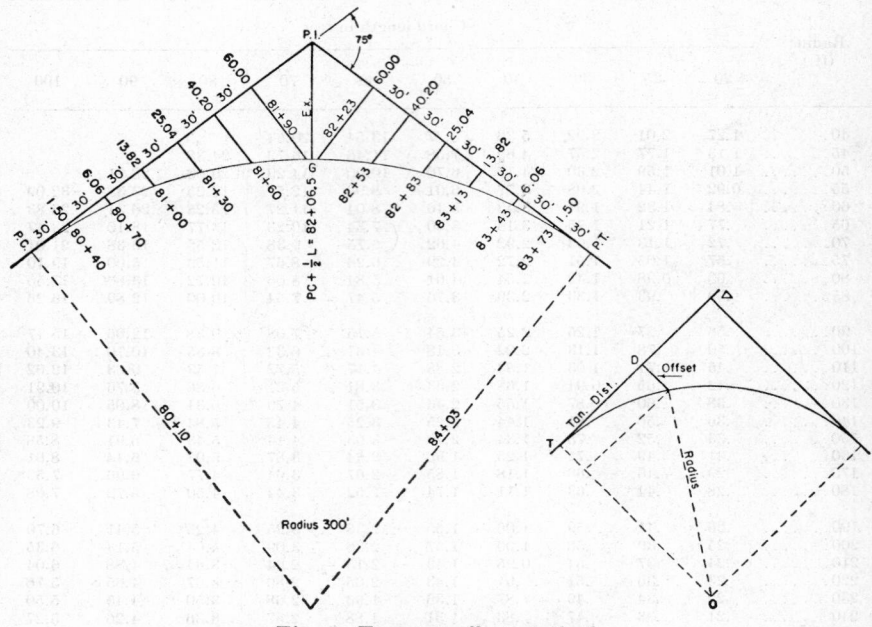

Fig. 2. Tangent offset method.

To lay out a curve by use of tangent offsets, computed from Table 4:

1. Set stakes on tangents at distances from the P.C. and P.T. equal to tenths of the curve radius.
2. Offset these stakes at right angles to the tangent by the amount obtained in multiplying the radius by the appropriate factor from this table.

**Table 4. Tangent Offset Factors for Tangent Distances Expressed in Decimals of the Radius**

| Tenths and twentieths of radius distance | Factor | Tenths and twentieths of radius distance | Factor |
|---|---|---|---|
| 0.05 | 0.00125 | 0.50 | 0.13397 |
| .10 | .00500 | .55 | .16484 |
| .15 | .01131 | .60 | .20000 |
| .20 | .02021 | .65 | .24007 |
| .25 | .03175 | .70 | .28586 |
| .30 | .04606 | .75 | .33856 |
| .35 | .06325 | .80 | .40000 |
| .40 | .08348 | .85 | .47322 |
| .45 | .10697 | .90 | .56411 |
| | | .95 | .68775 |

**Example.** Assume that the P.I. angle between the tangents to be joined by a curve is 75° (Fig. 2) and that the topography permits an external (P.I. to $G$) of about 79 ft. From Table 2—for curves with a radius of 1 ft.—it is evident that a curve with a radius of 300 ft. may be used: 79/0.26047 = 303.

1. From Table 2 calculate the tangent distance 230 ft., 0.76733 × 300, and measure it back from P.I. to establish P.C. and P.T. For purposes of illustration, assume that P.C. is at Station 80 + 10.
2. Set stakes every 30 ft. (¹⁄₁₀ of the radius) on the tangents from P.C. and P.T. toward P.I.
3. Read in Table 4, opposite 0.10 in the left-hand column, the tangent offset factor 0.00500 in the right-hand column, and multiply it by the radius. The result is 1.5 ft., the tangent offset at the first station beyond P.C., or 80 + 40. Measure this offset at right angles to the tangent and drive a stake; it is on the curve.
4. Calculate similarly from Table 4 the offsets at Stations 80 + 70 (0.02021 × 300), 81 + 00, etc., and continue to stake out the curve toward point $G$.
5. Establish $G$ itself by bisecting the internal angle at P.I., and measuring off from P.I. the external, calculated from Table 2. The distance of $G$ from P.C. is ½ the length of the curve from P.C. to P.T., which is in turn calculated from the formula: $L = 0.0174533 \triangle R$.
6. Beginning at P.T., set stakes on the curve in similar fashion toward $G$.

**LAYING OUT A CURVE BY DEFLECTION ANGLES.** Assume that a curve is to be laid out between tangents intersecting with a P.I. angle of 37° 10′ so that the external distance from the P.I. to the curve will be approximately 30 ft., as in Fig. 3. From Table 2 find opposite a central angle of 37°, and inter-

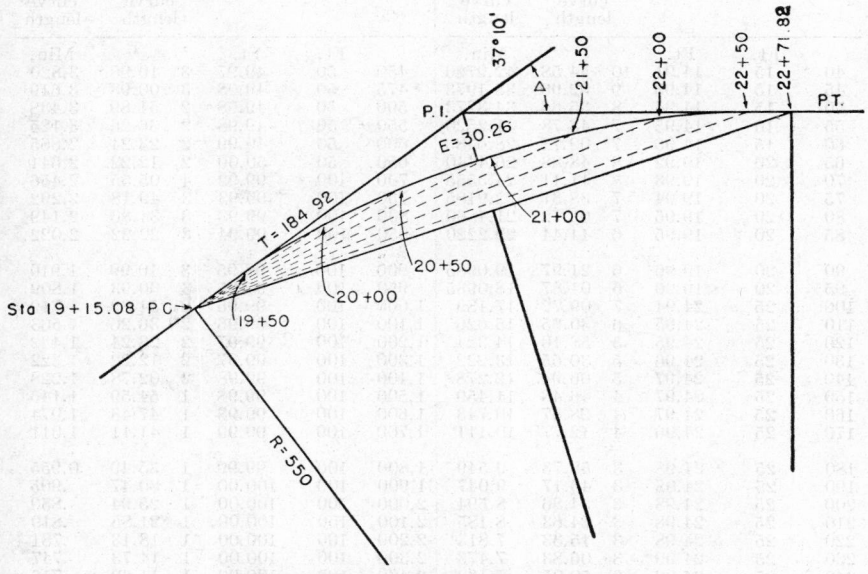

**Fig. 3. Curve layout by deflection angles.**

polating for the 10′, the external distance 0.05501 for a radius = 1. Dividing this into the chosen external distance of 30 ft., we get 545. A 550-ft. radius is therefore adopted. The external distance is 30.26 ft. From Table 2 the tangent distance for a P.I. angle of 37°10′ (37.17°) and radius = 1 is 0.33621. Multiplying by 550 ft. gives 184.92 ft. as the length of the tangents for the curve in Fig. 3. Find the length of curve from the formula on page **18 · 2**.

$$L = 0.0174533 \triangle R = 0.01745 \times 37.17 \times 550 = 356.74$$
Assume that P.I. station $= 21 + 00$

| | |
|---|---|
| Subtract tangent distance | $= \quad 1 + 84.92$ |
| Then P.C. station | $= \overline{19 + 15.08}$ |
| Add length of curve | $= \quad 3 + 56.74$ |
| Then P.T. station | $= \overline{22 + 71.82}$ |

Table 5 shows the deflection angle to be turned off at any station on a curve of specified radius to establish subsequent stations at appropriate intervals. From this it will be seen that on a curve of 550-ft. radius the deflection angle for stations 50 ft. apart is 2°36.26′ (for 1 ft. the angle is 3.125 min.).

As the first even 50-ft. station beyond P.C. is only 34.92 ft. beyond it, the deflection angle at P.C. is 34.92 × 3.125 min., or 1°49′. The first stake on the curve is then set at this angle clockwise from the tangent, at a distance of 34.90 ft. (chord length: curve length = 49.98:50, from Table 5). This is Station 19 + 50. Subsequent deflection angles are cumulative, as long as the transit remains at P.C. Thus the angle to

### Table 5. Deflection Angles for Curves of Various Radii and Chord Lengths

| Radius | Curve length | Chord length | Total curve length (°) | Total curve length (′) | 1-ft. curve length (Min.) | Radius | Curve length | Chord length | Total curve length (°) | Total curve length (′) | 1-ft. curve length (Min.) |
|---|---|---|---|---|---|---|---|---|---|---|---|
| | Ft. | Ft. | | | | | Ft. | Ft. | | | |
| 40 | 15 | 14.91 | 10 | 44.58 | 42.9720 | 450 | 50 | 49.97 | 3 | 10.98 | 3.820 |
| 45 | 15 | 14.93 | 9 | 32.96 | 38.1973 | 475 | 50 | 49.98 | 3 | 00.93 | 3.619 |
| 50 | 15 | 14.94 | 8 | 35.66 | 34.3773 | 500 | 50 | 49.98 | 2 | 51.89 | 3.438 |
| 55 | 15 | 14.95 | 7 | 48.78 | 31.2520 | 550 | 50 | 49.98 | 2 | 36.26 | 3.125 |
| 60 | 15 | 14.96 | 7 | 09.72 | 28.6480 | 600 | 50 | 49.99 | 2 | 23.24 | 2.865 |
| 65 | 20 | 19.92 | 8 | 48.88 | 26.4440 | 650 | 50 | 50.00 | 2 | 12.22 | 2.644 |
| 70 | 20 | 19.93 | 8 | 11.11 | 24.5555 | 700 | 100 | 99.92 | 4 | 05.55 | 2.456 |
| 75 | 20 | 19.94 | 7 | 38.37 | 22.9185 | 750 | 100 | 99.93 | 3 | 49.18 | 2.292 |
| 80 | 20 | 19.95 | 7 | 09.72 | 21.4860 | 800 | 100 | 99.93 | 3 | 34.86 | 2.149 |
| 85 | 20 | 19.95 | 6 | 44.44 | 20.2220 | 850 | 100 | 99.94 | 3 | 22.22 | 2.022 |
| 90 | 20 | 19.96 | 6 | 21.97 | 19.0985 | 900 | 100 | 99.95 | 3 | 10.99 | 1.910 |
| 95 | 20 | 19.96 | 6 | 01.87 | 18.0935 | 950 | 100 | 99.95 | 3 | 00.93 | 1.809 |
| 100 | 25 | 24.94 | 7 | 09.72 | 17.189 | 1,000 | 100 | 99.96 | 2 | 51.89 | 1.719 |
| 110 | 25 | 24.95 | 6 | 30.65 | 15.626 | 1,100 | 100 | 99.96 | 2 | 36.26 | 1.563 |
| 120 | 25 | 24.95 | 5 | 58.10 | 14.324 | 1,200 | 100 | 99.97 | 2 | 23.24 | 1.432 |
| 130 | 25 | 24.96 | 5 | 30.55 | 13.222 | 1,300 | 100 | 99.97 | 2 | 12.22 | 1.322 |
| 140 | 25 | 24.97 | 5 | 06.94 | 12.278 | 1,400 | 100 | 99.98 | 2 | 02.78 | 1.228 |
| 150 | 25 | 24.97 | 4 | 46.48 | 11.459 | 1,500 | 100 | 99.98 | 1 | 54.59 | 1.146 |
| 160 | 25 | 24.97 | 4 | 28.57 | 10.743 | 1,600 | 100 | 99.98 | 1 | 47.43 | 1.074 |
| 170 | 25 | 24.96 | 4 | 12.77 | 10.111 | 1,700 | 100 | 99.99 | 1 | 41.11 | 1.011 |
| 180 | 25 | 24.98 | 3 | 58.73 | 9.549 | 1,800 | 100 | 99.99 | 1 | 35.49 | 0.955 |
| 190 | 25 | 24.98 | 3 | 46.17 | 9.047 | 1,900 | 100 | 100.00 | 1 | 30.47 | .905 |
| 200 | 25 | 24.98 | 3 | 34.86 | 8.594 | 2,000 | 100 | 100.00 | 1 | 25.94 | .859 |
| 210 | 25 | 24.98 | 3 | 24.63 | 8.185 | 2,100 | 100 | 100.00 | 1 | 21.85 | .819 |
| 220 | 25 | 24.98 | 3 | 15.33 | 7.813 | 2,200 | 100 | 100.00 | 1 | 18.13 | .781 |
| 230 | 25 | 24.99 | 3 | 06.83 | 7.473 | 2,300 | 100 | 100.00 | 1 | 14.73 | .747 |
| 240 | 25 | 24.99 | 2 | 59.05 | 7.162 | 2,400 | 100 | 100.00 | 1 | 11.62 | .716 |
| 250 | 25 | 24.99 | 2 | 51.89 | 6.876 | 2,500 | 100 | 100.00 | 1 | 08.75 | .688 |
| 275 | 25 | 24.99 | 2 | 36.26 | 6.250 | 3,000 | 100 | 100.00 | | 57.30 | .573 |
| 300 | 50 | 49.94 | 4 | 46.48 | 5.730 | 3,500 | 100 | 100.00 | | 49.11 | .491 |
| 325 | 50 | 49.95 | 4 | 24.44 | 5.289 | 4,000 | 100 | 100.00 | | 42.97 | .430 |
| 350 | 50 | 49.96 | 4 | 05.55 | 4.911 | 4,500 | 100 | 100.00 | | 38.20 | .382 |
| 375 | 50 | 49.96 | 3 | 49.18 | 4.584 | 5,000 | 100 | 100.00 | | 34.38 | .344 |
| 400 | 50 | 49.97 | 3 | 34.86 | 4.297 | 6,000 | 100 | 100.00 | | 28.65 | .287 |
| 425 | 50 | 49.97 | 3 | 22.22 | 4.044 | 7,000 | 100 | 100.00 | | 24.56 | .246 |

### Table 6. Minutes in Decimals of a Degree

| | | | | | | | | | |
|---|---|---|---|---|---|---|---|---|---|
| 1 | 0.0167 | 11 | 0.1833 | 21 | 0.3500 | 31 | 0.5167 | 41 | 0.6833 | 51 | 0.8500 |
| 2 | .0333 | 12 | .2000 | 22 | .3667 | 32 | .5333 | 42 | .7000 | 52 | .8667 |
| 3 | .0500 | 13 | .2167 | 23 | .3833 | 33 | .5500 | 43 | .7167 | 53 | .8833 |
| 4 | .0667 | 14 | .2333 | 24 | .4000 | 34 | .5667 | 44 | .7333 | 54 | .9000 |
| 5 | .0833 | 15 | .2500 | 25 | .4167 | 35 | .5833 | 45 | .7500 | 55 | .9167 |
| 6 | .1000 | 16 | .2667 | 26 | .4333 | 36 | .6000 | 46 | .7667 | 56 | .9333 |
| 7 | .1167 | 17 | .2833 | 27 | .4500 | 37 | .6167 | 47 | .7833 | 57 | .9500 |
| 8 | .1333 | 18 | .3000 | 28 | .4667 | 38 | .6333 | 48 | .8000 | 58 | .9667 |
| 9 | .1500 | 19 | .3167 | 29 | .4833 | 39 | .6500 | 49 | .8167 | 59 | .9833 |
| 10 | .1667 | 20 | .3333 | 30 | .5000 | 40 | .6667 | 50 | .8333 | 60 | 1.0000 |

Station 20 + 00 is 1°49' + 2°36', or 4°25'. To Station 22 + 50 it is 1°49' + 6 (2°36.26') = 17°27'. Chord lengths are each 49.98 ft.

From Station 22 + 50 to the P.T. at 22 + 71.82 the deflection is 21.82 × 3.125 = 68' or 1°08', making a total deflection to 22 + 71.82 of 17°27' + 1°08' = 18°35'. This corresponds to half the central angle of 37°10', thereby checking the deflection angles. (The total deflection angle for a curve is equal to half the central angle.) If all stations on the curve are not visible from the P.C., the transit may be moved to a new station and the deflection turned from a backsight on any preceding station.

For illustrating the procedure, the angular and distance measurements given in this example are more precise than necessary for staking curves on forest roads. It is advisable to carry the computations through to the minute and to hundredths of a foot, but angles read with a compass, and distances measured to the nearest half-foot, are exact enough for unpaved roads.

**LAYING OUT A VERTICAL CURVE (PARABOLA).** In Fig. 4, $AC$ is an upgrade to be connected by a parabolic curve with a downgrade, $CB$. Extend $AC$ to $D$ so that $AD$ is approximately equal to $AB$. Let $d$ be the vertical distance at a specific point from $AC$, or its extension $CD$, to the curve. Values for $d$ are obtained from the formula:

$$d = \frac{(g - g^1)}{2N} a^2$$

where $g$ = rise per 100 ft. of upgrade ($A$ to $C$)
$g'$ = fall per 100 ft. of downgrade ($C$ to $B$)
$N$ = number of 100-ft. stations on the curve $AB$
$a$ = serial number of the station (1st, 2d, etc.) from $A$

**Example.** In Fig. 4,

$A$ is Station 20 + 00, for which the assumed elevation is 100 ft.
$C$ is 300 ft. from $A$ at elevation 116.50; thus $g = +5.50$
$B$ is 300 ft. from $C$ at elevation 101.50, making $g' = -5.00$
$N$ is 6

Then, for the first station from $A$ on $ACD$,

$$d = \frac{5.50 - (-5.00)}{2 \times 6} \times (1)^2 = \frac{10.50}{12} = 0.875$$

For the second station

$$d = \frac{10.50}{12} \times (2)^2 = 3.50$$

$d$ is similarly computed for each station on $ACD$. The elevation of the curve at each station is then obtained as shown by the following tabulation:

| Station | Elevation on $AD$ | $d$ | Elevation on curve |
|---------|-------------------|-----|--------------------|
| 20 + 00 | 100.00 | 00 | 100.00 |
| 21 + 00 | 105.50 | 0.875 | 104.625 |
| 22 + 00 | 111.00 | 3.50 | 107.50 |
| 23 + 00 | 116.50 | 7.875 | 108.625 |
| 24 + 00 | 122.00 | 14.0 | 108.00 |
| 25 + 00 | 127.50 | 21.875 | 105.625 |
| 26 + 00 | 133.00 | 31.50 | 101.50 |

Discrepancies between stationing on $AD$ and on the curve itself are insignificant. It is safe to assume the distance $AD = AB$ in laying out vertical curves on forest roads.

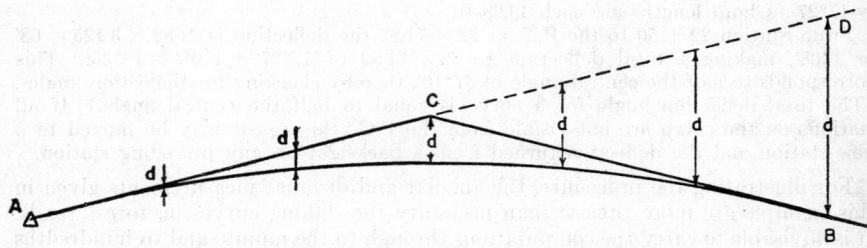

**Fig. 4. Laying out a vertical curve (parabola).**

## Forest Truck Roads

Permanent transportation facilities through the forest are prerequisites to intensive forest management. They are needed for forest protection, for economic logging, and the utilization of by-products. Sometimes supplementing railroads and navigable or at least drivable streams, a network of forest roads may make it possible to change from clearcutting at long intervals to light cutting at short intervals, with all the advantages familiar to foresters.

**SELECTION OF ROAD STANDARD.** Transportation costs are the economic basis for the selection of forest road construction standards. Assuming that the necessary capital is available, the choice of a forest road standard rests on reaching a sensible balance between the total cost of cheap transportation of forest products (and personnel) over an expensive road with that of expensive transportation over cheap roads. Because of their superior speed, trucks usually represent cheap transportation as compared with animals and crawler-tractors. The discussion below is largely confined to truck roads.

The standard should be chosen only after a study of the over-all picture and after checking with the forest management plan. Too high a standard will result in high construction costs, not warranted by the use to which the road will be put; too low a standard will result in high operating and maintenance costs. It must be kept in mind that the rougher the topography, the lower the standard of construction of the road that can be built for a fixed sum. However, an appropriate road will result in greater operating savings as the country becomes rougher.

There are two standards by which to describe roads:

1. **Physical standards.** Grade, curves, width, surface, etc., which will render a specified service at the least annual cost.
2. **Service standards.** Speed of travel or elapsed time; or total cost of transportation per ton-mile, which equals

$$\frac{\text{(Hourly truck cost, including wages of driver)} \times 2}{\text{(Miles per hour)} \times \text{(Load in tons)}} + \frac{\text{Cost of construction (and maintenance) per mile}}{\text{Total tonnage hauled}}$$

The cost of construction per mile is often expressed as average annual cost by amortizing the cost of construction over a predetermined number of years and adding the estimated average annual maintenance cost. In such cases the "total tonnage" would be the total tonnage hauled annually.

The U. S. Forest Service recognizes three service standards for National Forest timber haul roads: (1) main haul roads into the major drainages, or main arteries of travel through the principal forest area, designed for speeds over 25 mph; (2) laterals or branches from main roads into the principal tributary drainages, designed for speeds up to 25 mph; and (3) spurs or minor branch roads adequate for hauling to reload landings, and for forest fire protection, permitting traffic up to 15 mph. The physical standards corresponding to the above service standards for standard trucks (8½ ft. wide over all), assuming adequate surfacing for all, are given in Table 7.

### Table 7. Road Standards by Forest Service Class of Road

| Item | Class of road | | |
|------|:---:|:---:|:---:|
| | I | II | III |
| Minimum right-of-way .......................... | 45 ft. | 25 ft. | 20 ft. |
| Minimum width, ditch to ditch ................ | 22 ft. | 16 ft.* | 10 ft.* |
| Minimum width, wheeling surface .............. | 16 ft. | 12 ft. | 8 ft. |
| Minimum radius of curvature † ................. | 100 ft. | 50 ft. | 40 ft |
| Maximum grades .............................. | 8% | 10% | 15% |
| Maximum sustained grade ..................... | 6% | 7% | 10% |
| Horizontal sight distance ..................... | 350 ft. | 200 ft. | 100 ft. |

\* Plus intervisible turnouts where there is uncontrolled two-way traffic.
† In general, minimum curvature by Forest Service standards is twice tabulated values.

No set of physical standards applies universally. Each item will be influenced by local conditions, such as topography, climate, available road-surfacing materials, and use, such as class of trucks. Steeper grades, for example, are often allowed in very rough country to prevent prohibitive construction costs. Sustained grades up to 17 percent have been observed on main forest truck roads under extremely difficult conditions. Short steep grades of 14 to 17 percent are easily traversed if they are straight and are preceded by a level stretch or slight downgrade. But a short, steep grade of as little as 10 percent, especially if on a curve, may cause difficulty at the top of a long, gradual upgrade. Maintenance may be more expensive on a steep grade than on a flatter grade of much greater length.

Proper sight distance is a factor often neglected in the construction of forest roads. Brush and obstructions alongside the road present hazards. The following minima are prescribed by the American Association of State Highway Officials: for travel at 30 mph, 200 ft.; 40 mph, 275 ft.; 50 mph, 350 ft.; 60 mph, 475 ft.

The influence of the various factors in the first term of the above formula, "Service Standards," for total cost per ton-mile is illustrated by the following: a 2-ton truck costing $4.00 per hour, including the wages of the driver, has a hauling cost of $0.267 per ton-mile with an average round-trip speed of 15 mph, and a cost of $0.40 when the round trip averages only 10 mph.

To compute round-trip speeds per hour, average the time required to run 1 mi. loaded with the time required to run 1 mi. light, and divide the average into 60 min. Thus, for a loaded speed of 25 mph, and a speed when light of 35 mi.:

$$\text{Time for 1 mi. at 25 mph} = \frac{60}{25} = 2.400 \text{ min.}$$

$$\text{Time for 1 mi. at 35 mph} = \frac{60}{35} = 1.714 \text{ min.}$$

$$\text{Total, round-trip mile} = 4.114 \text{ min.}$$

$$\text{Average time per mile} = \frac{4.114}{2} = 2.057 \text{ min.}$$

$$\text{Average round-trip speed} = \frac{60}{2.057} = 29.2 \text{ mph.}$$

(Averaging the 25 and 35 mph gives 30 mi.—too high a rate.)

To determine how much may justifiably be spent in improving a mile of temporary road so that average round-trip speed for trucks is increased from 10 to 15 mph, with hauling costs as just given, subtract $0.267 from $0.40 and multiply by the tonnage to be hauled. If several years are required to remove the total tonnage, discount to the present each annual saving, at an appropriate rate of interest, and add. If the road is permanent, serving a sustained-yield operation, figure the annual saving and capitalize. Road maintenance costs may be ignored in calculating benefits of improvement if they are materially the same for the road whether improved or not; otherwise average annual maintenance cost should be considered in evaluating the improvement.

**ROAD LOCATION.** The importance of adequate surveys and careful planning for road construction justifies engineering costs up to 5 percent of total costs for low standard roads, while 10 or 15 percent is reasonable for engineering permanent heavy-duty hauling roads in rough country. Surveys, investigation, and planning are worth what they will save in construction costs.

**Selection of Route.** Very little road location is done without the use of aerial photographs. Topography, as expressed by drainage and contour, is readily determined from air photographs. In actual practice, tentative road locations are usually drawn on a large base map, and photographs of the area are studied from start to finish of the road; both the preferred and the alternate road locations are marked on the photographs. The proposed routes are then checked on the ground to assess properly the ground surface conditions because soft, wet spots or hidden rock ledges seldom show up on the photographs. A thorough investigation should be made of all the possible routes before deciding upon the final location.

Avoid uphill hauls for the load if at all practicable. If the load is destined for some point at a higher elevation, if it must be hauled over a summit to reach its destination, or must be hauled uphill because economy dictates going over rather than around rocky points, hold to uniformly sustained grades as far as possible. Frequent changes in grade increase differential wear on trucks, and shifting of gears slows the rate of travel. Adjust the uphill grade to the maximum which the local trucks pull under full load when traveling at speeds appropriate for the gear that must be used on the grade. Step grade changes up to the maximum of the next lower gear. When stepping up the grade, slack off 1 or 2 percent from the preceding ruling grade for a short distance. This will facilitate shifting gears under load and make the shift easier on both driver and truck. When ground conditions permit a choice in uphill grades for a reasonable expenditure, calculate the effect of different grades on truck haul speeds and the combined effect of these and extra construction cost on total hauling cost.

**Location Survey.** The next step is to go into the field and locate the proposed road line on the ground. If the marked aerial photographs are taken into the field, it is usually a simple matter to follow the proposed road line on the ground and tie it to topographical features and type boundaries. Where necessary, the line is swung to one side or the other to avoid obstacles which were not apparent from the photographs.

If aerial photographs of the area are not available, considerably more work is entailed in the location survey. In hardwood regions location work should be carried out in the spring or fall when the foliage is off the trees. The road location crew of two or three men blazes the line roughly. The line is then usually carefully chained and mapped. Complete notes should be taken on the conditions both above and below ground. These notes will serve as a basis for estimating the cost of road construction.

The most effective means by which the road locator can keep construction costs to a minimum is through the proper use of gradient. By ascending and descending (within the limits allowed by the road specifications), the locator can (1) avoid rock or heavy clearing, (2) eliminate curves, (3) place location on desirable soil, and (4) improve natural drainage.

Frequent closely spaced grade changes should be avoided, however, on roads intended for trucks loaded with 4,000 bd. ft. of logs or more. On heavy-duty roads it usually pays to keep adverse grades below 6 percent. On these roads material savings may be made in maintaining more uniform grades by cutting through the summits and filling across depressions, if care is taken to balance the quantities in adjacent cut and fill sections.

Curvature is also important on logging roads. Where practicable, keep the curves flat enough to allow trucks to round them without reducing average speed. Avoid short radius curves and restricted sight distance at points where trucks will ordinarily accelerate to overcome a change in grade. A guide to light truck speeds which may be expected on roads with rolling grades and reasonably good road surface is shown in Table 8.

**Table 8. Light Truck Speeds, Rolling Grades, Fair Road Surface**

|  | Speeds when curvature is the control | |
| --- | --- | --- |
|  | Open curve | Blind curve |
| 50 ft. radius ................................ | 16 mph | 15 mph |
| 70 ft. radius ................................ | 18 mph | 17 mph |
| 100 ft. radius ................................ | 20 mph | 18 mph |
|  | Speeds when grade is the control | |
|  | Uphill * | Downhill |
| 3% ................................................ | 30 mph | 30 mph |
| 5% ................................................ | 29 mph | 29 mph |
| 5½% ............................................... | 29 mph | 28 mph |
| 7½% ............................................... | 28 mph | 25 mph |
| 8% ................................................ | 28 mph | 25 mph |
| 10% ............................................... | 24 mph | 22 mph |

* For heavy logging trucks, reduce tabulated values by rates ranging from 50% on 3% grades to 75% on 10% grades.

Stream crossings are ruling points, and the road line is made subordinate to them. When a bridge site is chosen, the road line is blazed back to tie in with the road location line.

**Staking for Construction.** First blaze the center line for the road and then spot-blaze the boundaries of the road allowance. The right-of-way between the outer boundaries is then cleared. Because changes are often made in road location during the survey, however, the center line is sometimes not blazed. Instead, a narrow line is established and pickets are driven at regular intervals. If it is decided to move the road line to one side or the other, the pickets can readily be moved; blazes cannot be erased, and blazed lines diverging from the final road line tend to confuse the tractor operators.

As the clearing progresses, the center line of the road is staked out, usually at 100-ft. stations, and ditch-line stakes are placed as a guide for ditching and grading. If grading is heavy, slope stakes should be set to mark the toe of the slope for fills and the top of the slope for cuts. These stakes should be set back a uniform distance from the actual slope limits in order to protect them against disturbance by construction operations.

If the outside ditch lines are clearly staked for the grader or dragline operator, center-line stakes may be omitted. Working from the ditch-line pickets, the operator ditches and works the spoil up onto the roadway. Pickets, either center line or ditch, are necessary to prevent the operators from weaving down the right-of-way, choosing the line of least resistance. It is essential that the stakes be followed and the road built to the grade established if the standard of road construction is to be maintained.

**Location of Road-Building Materials.** The usual procedure for locating gravel deposits for truck road construction is for the survey crew to try to locate them while locating the road. As such deposits, in wooded country, will be covered with overburden and vegetation, a valuable tool is a small spade or trenching tool. A sufficient number of test pits should be dug to disclose the nature and extent of the gravel deposit.

The use of aerial photographs for locating granular deposits has proved practical and relatively accurate, although the nature of the deposit (coarse gravel, fine gravel, sand, etc.) must be determined on the ground. The average pattern produced by granular materials is easy to identify. Granular deposition follows natural laws and may be expected only under certain conditions, and not under others. Granular deposits are usually closely associated with the different methods of deposition by running water. Identification of soils from aerial photographs is based upon an evaluation of land form, vegetation, gully shapes, drainage system, color tones, etc. The main characteristics of a gravel pattern are a light soil-color tone, a well-drained appearance with an absence of surface drainage, and no evidence of water or ice deposition.

To assess a deposit of gravel properly, test pits should be dug. Pointed steel rods, ¾ to 1 in. in diameter, in lengths of 5 ft., are sometimes driven into the ground and will prove effective up to 12–15 ft. As the limit of one rod is reached, it is withdrawn and a longer rod is inserted in the hole. Differences in type and consolidation of soils can be judged by the sound and speed of driving. To withdraw a sounding rod, a light chain is wound around the rod and around a stout pole so that the pole acting as a lever raises the rod. The rod may be withdrawn more readily if it is first turned with a pipe wrench thereby loosening it somewhat.

A rough estimate of the amount of clay present in a gravel deposit can be made by shaking up a sample of the gravel in water, in an ordinary fruit jar, and allowing it to settle. The clay and silt will settle in a thin layer on top of the gravel, and the thickness of the clay layer in relation to that of the whole sample can be taken as the proportion of clay present.

**ROAD CONSTRUCTION. Clearing the Right-of-Way.** After the road line has been blazed or staked out, the next step is to clear the right-of-way. The cost and method employed will differ with the type of terrain. In swamp areas it is usually cheapest to contract clearing by hand labor. Trees and brush are felled flush with the ground and care is taken not to disturb the mat of roots and moss which tends to float the road. In regions where frost occurs, clearing the right-of-way is often done when frost is in the ground to make for better working conditions. The use of bulldozers is often possible.

When clearing the right-of-way through upland types, bulldozers are almost universally used to push over trees and stumps and to move aside the felled timber. Trees are often cut with high stumps before bulldozing, even when the merchantable timber is to be removed from the area. It is best to leave large, deep-rooted hardwoods uncut before bulldozing, as the additional leverage resulting from the weight of the tree as it leans aids greatly in forcing the tree over. With very large trees, roots are cut with the bulldozer blade on the pushing side; then, pushing high up on the tree for greater leverage, the tree is rocked a few times to loosen it. It may be practicable to push up a dirt ramp with the bulldozer blade and then place the blade higher on the tree to obtain even greater leverage.

In practice it is often found preferable to operate two machines together when clearing. A winch on at least one will be a great help. When "bulling" large trees, or where there are boulders, one tractor is often used to help the other. Most of the time, however, one tractor is used ahead of the other; the first "pioneers" the road, while the second puts the finishing touches on the clearing. The tractor with a winch is often used to pull out stumps which the bulldozer cannot push out.

**Table 9. Performance Standards in Clearing and Grubbing**

| Equipment | Time rates | | Unit | Conditions |
|---|---|---|---|---|
| Hand tools .......... | 1½ | man-hr./unit | Tree | 3-man blasting team, good conditions |
| | 125 | man-hr./unit | Acre | Light clearing |
| | 350 | man-hr./unit | Acre | Medium clearing |
| | 25 | man-hr./unit | 100 lin. yd. | Light clearing, 30 ft. wide |
| | 70 | man-hr./unit | 100 lin. yd. | Medium clearing, 30 ft. wide |
| Tractor—66–90 dbhp with bulldozer....... | 1.0 | units/hr. | Acre | Light stripping or clearing |
| | 0.25 | units/hr. | Acre | Medium clearing |
| | 20–50 | units/hr. | Trees | 4 to 10 in. diam. |
| | 3–12 | units/hr. | Trees | 12 to 30 in. diam. |

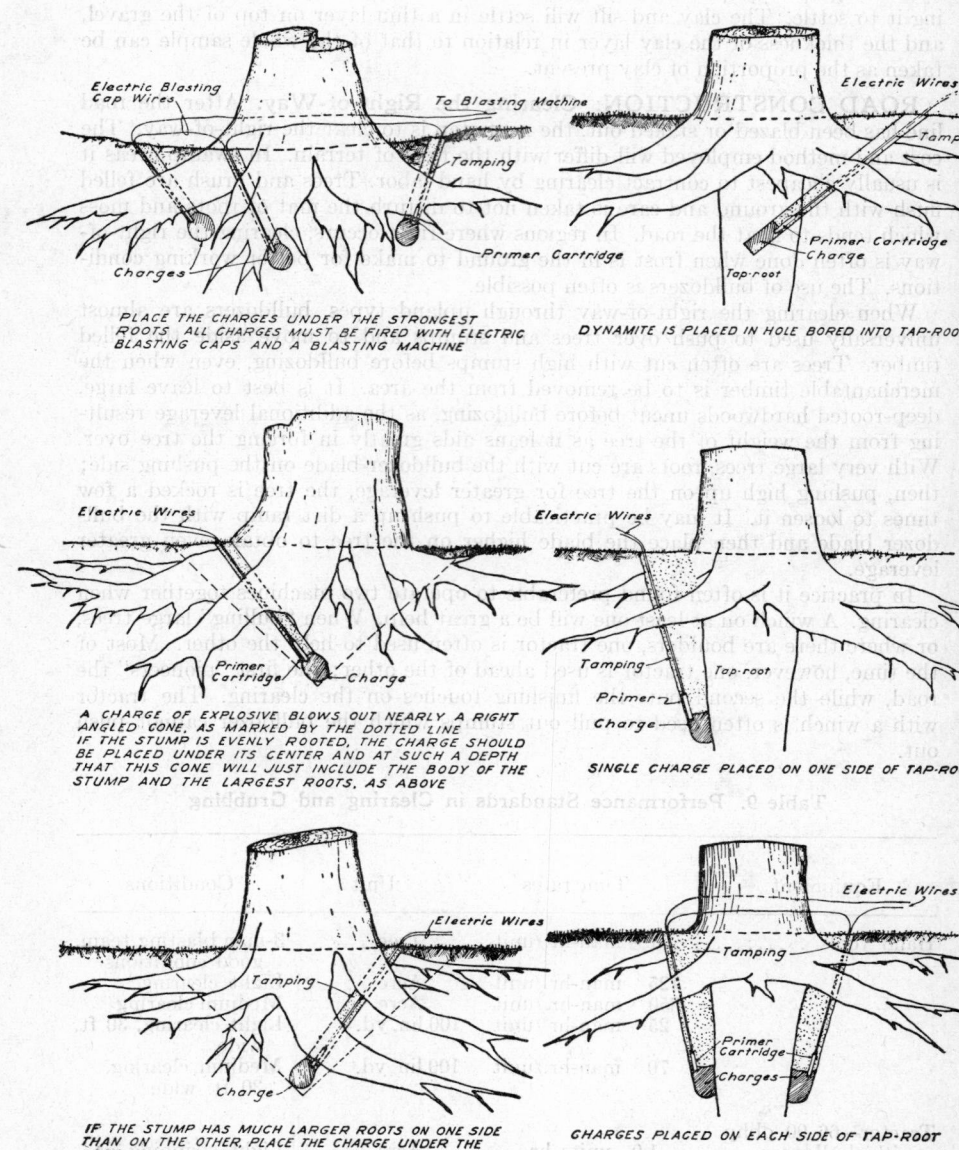

PLACE THE CHARGES UNDER THE STRONGEST ROOTS. ALL CHARGES MUST BE FIRED WITH ELECTRIC BLASTING CAPS AND A BLASTING MACHINE

DYNAMITE IS PLACED IN HOLE BORED INTO TAP-ROOT

A CHARGE OF EXPLOSIVE BLOWS OUT NEARLY A RIGHT ANGLED CONE, AS MARKED BY THE DOTTED LINE. IF THE STUMP IS EVENLY ROOTED, THE CHARGE SHOULD BE PLACED UNDER ITS CENTER AND AT SUCH A DEPTH THAT THIS CONE WILL JUST INCLUDE THE BODY OF THE STUMP AND THE LARGEST ROOTS, AS ABOVE

SINGLE CHARGE PLACED ON ONE SIDE OF TAP-ROOT

IF THE STUMP HAS MUCH LARGER ROOTS ON ONE SIDE THAN ON THE OTHER, PLACE THE CHARGE UNDER THE STRONGER SIDE.

CHARGES PLACED ON EACH SIDE OF TAP-ROOT

Fig. 5. Loading and blasting stumps.

**Clearing and Grubbing.** Fig. 5 shows methods commonly used for removing stumps with explosives. Methods of drilling, loading, and blasting rock and boulders which cannot be excavated with the bulldozer are illustrated in Figs. 6 and 7.

**Air Compressors.** The capacity rating of portable air compressors is based on the number of cubic feet of "free air" delivered per minute at sea level. Standard-production compressors when new can be expected to exceed the rated capacity by about 5 percent. "Free air" is defined as air at normal temperatures and barometric pressures. The amount of air delivered by a compressor decreases with altitude above sea level, as shown in Table 10.

The horsepower developed by gasoline and diesel engines decreases about 3 percent for each 1,000-ft. rise in elevation. Although engines furnished with portable compressors usually have sufficient reserve to maintain air output at higher elevations, the supplier should always be advised of the range in elevations at which the compressors will be used. Air-operated tools consume about $3\frac{1}{3}$ percent more air for each 1,000 ft. above sea level.

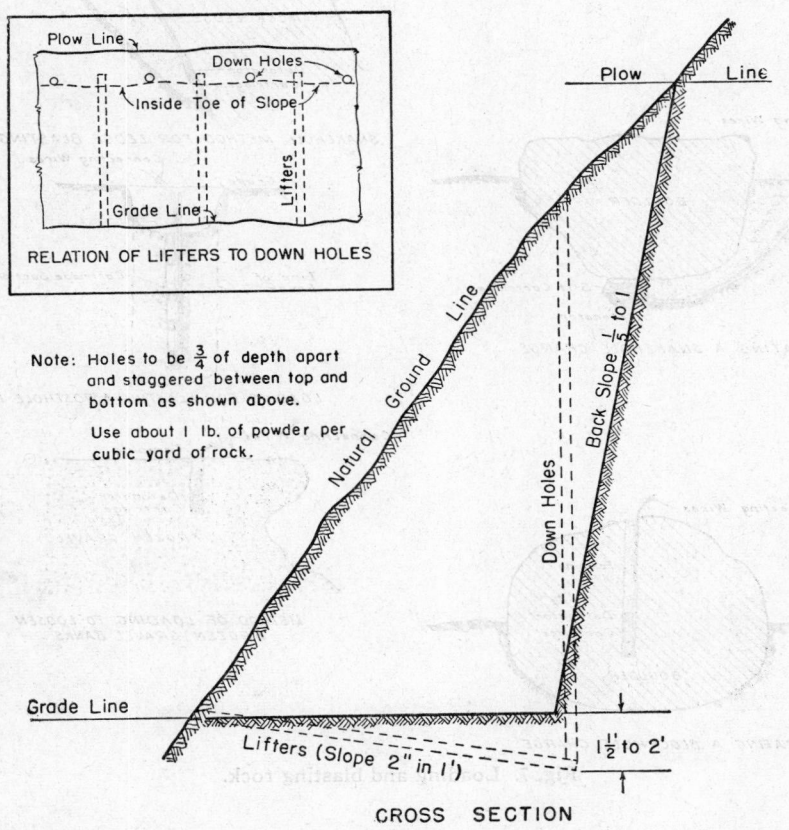

RELATION OF LIFTERS TO DOWN HOLES

Note: Holes to be $\frac{3}{4}$ of depth apart and staggered between top and bottom as shown above.

Use about 1 lb. of powder per cubic yard of rock.

CROSS SECTION

Fig. 6. Drilling diagram.

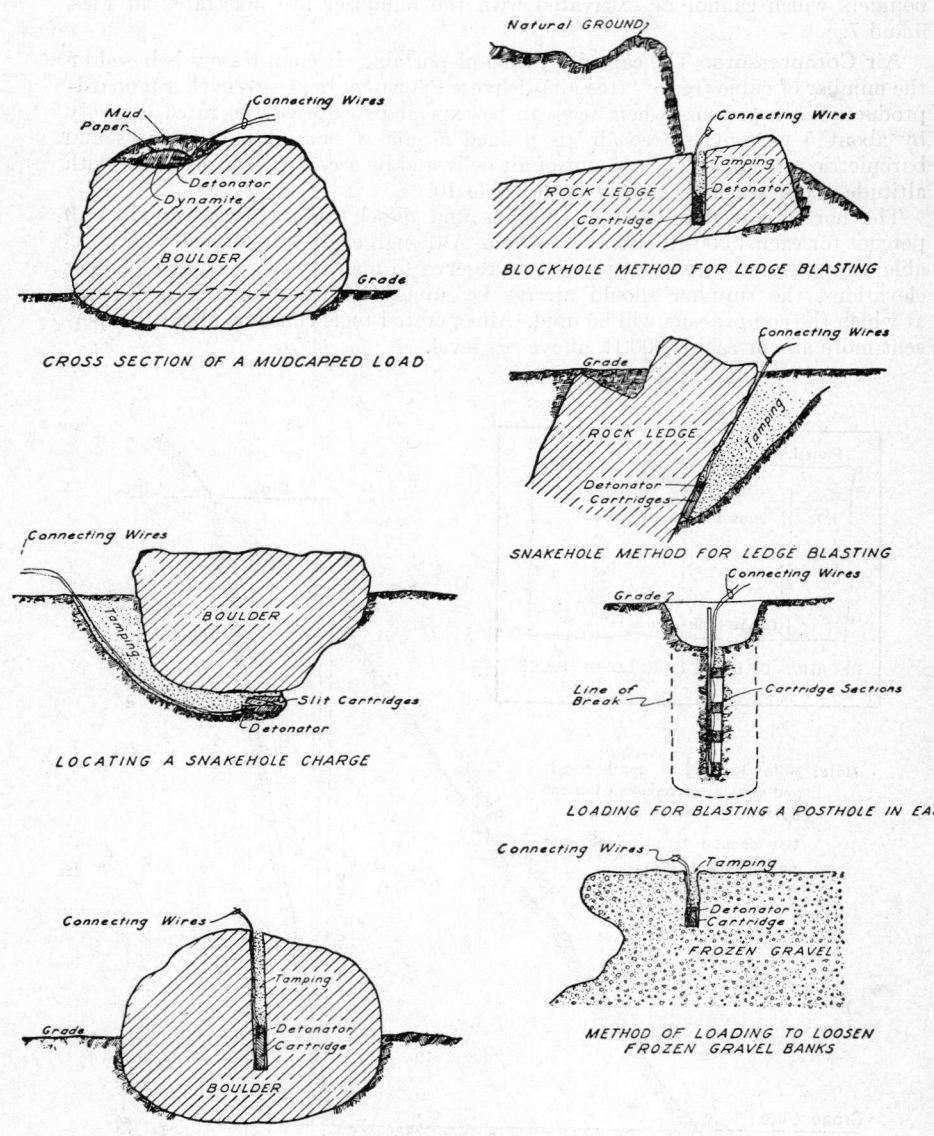

Fig. 7. Loading and blasting rock.

**Compressed air transmission.** The loss of pressure when air is delivered through 100 ft. of pipe of various diameters is shown in Table 11; for longer lengths the drop is proportional, i.e., for 500 ft. of pipe it is five times the tabular values. Globe valves, tees, and elbows further reduce the pressure, and their use should be confined to a minimum. All low points on the air line should have a valve or trap to catch and release the water that condenses along the line; it should be drained daily. In operating a battery of two or more compressors, over-all economy will be improved if the regulators of the individual units are step adjusted so that the units unload successively, beginning with the smaller. When air requirements have diminished so that the demand can be met by a lesser number of units, the larger base load units should be removed from service first.

**Table 10. Free Air Delivery in Cubic Feet per Minute of Compressors Operating At a Gauge Pressure of 100 Lb. at Various Elevations**

| Sea level rating of compressors | Feet above sea level | | | | |
|---|---|---|---|---|---|
| | 2,000 | 4,000 | 6,000 | 8,000 | 10,000 |
| | Two-stage compressors | | | | |
| 105 | 102.6 | 98.9 | 95.3 | 91.7 | 88.2 |
| 160 | 155.5 | 150.7 | 105.3 | 139.7 | 134.4 |
| 210 | 204.1 | 197.8 | 190.7 | 183.3 | 176.4 |
| 315 | 306.2 | 296.7 | 286.0 | 275.0 | 264.6 |
| | Single-stage compressors | | | | |
| 105 | 104.5 | 103.9 | 103.4 | 102.8 | 102.3 |
| 160 | 158.9 | 157.8 | 156.7 | 155.6 | 154.5 |
| 210 | 208.5 | 207.1 | 205.6 | 204.2 | 202.8 |
| 315 | 312.9 | 310.7 | 308.6 | 306.5 | 304.4 |

**Table 11. Compressed Air Transmission at 100 Lb. Gauge Pressure**

| Delivery of free air (Cu. ft. per min.) | Pressure drop in pounds per 100 ft. for pipes of various sizes | | | | | |
|---|---|---|---|---|---|---|
| | 1″ | 1¼″ | 1½″ | 2″ | 2½″ | 3″ |
| 70 | 1.4 | 0.3 | 0.1 | | | |
| 80 | 1.8 | .4 | .2 | 0.05 | | |
| 90 | | .5 | .2 | .06 | | |
| 100 | | .6 | .3 | .07 | | |
| 150 | | 1.5 | .6 | .2 | 0.06 | |
| 200 | | | 1.1 | .3 | .1 | |
| 250 | | | | .5 | .2 | 0.06 |
| 300 | | | | .7 | .3 | .08 |
| 350 | | | | .9 | .4 | .11 |

**Grading.** The term "grading" includes clearing right-of-way, cut and fill, corduroying, and shaping the roadbed. The preparation of the roadbed is one of the most important operations in gravel road construction. The road surface is only as good as the subgrade on which it is placed. Grading, in Table 12, refers to the rough shaping of the roadbed after the right-of-way has been cleared.

**Table 12. Performance Standards in Grading**

| Equipment | Rate in units per hour | Unit | Conditions |
|---|---|---|---|
| Tractor—66 to 90 dbhp with bulldozer......... | 400 | Lin. ft. | Sidehill cut, medium soil, 10° slope |
| | 190 | Lin. ft. | Sidehill cut, medium soil, 20° slope |
| | 110 | Lin. ft. | Sidehill cut, medium soil, 30° slope |
| | 120 | Cu. yd. | Sidehill cut, medium soil |
| | 90 | Cu. yd. | Sidehill cut, heavy soil |
| | 130 | Cu. yd. | 50-ft. level haul, medium soil |
| | 80 | Cu. yd. | 100-ft. level haul, medium soil |
| Scraper, 8 cu. yd. towed with tractor 66 to 90 dbhp ................. | 95 | Cu. yd. | 500-ft. level haul, medium soil |
| | 60 | Cu. yd. | 800-ft. level haul, medium soil |
| Shovel, power, ¾ yd..... | 45 | Cu. yd. | Hard digging |
| | 75 | Cu. yd. | Easy digging |
| Grader motorized....... | 0.2 | Mile | Digging side ditches and shaping crown, 4 round trips |
| Hand tools ...........1.2–2.4 | | Cu. yd. | Loading loose material into truck, one man with shovel |
| | 1.5 | Cu. yd. | Excavation with pick and shovel, to 5 ft., easy digging |

**Methods of computation for end areas.** Formulas for level, three-level, and five-level sections are shown in Fig. 8. A general method of computing volumes for road cuts where surface is irregular is an application of the double meridian distance method of computing field areas (see page 17·22). The cross-section notes should show a distance and a cut (or fill) for every angle point in the section.

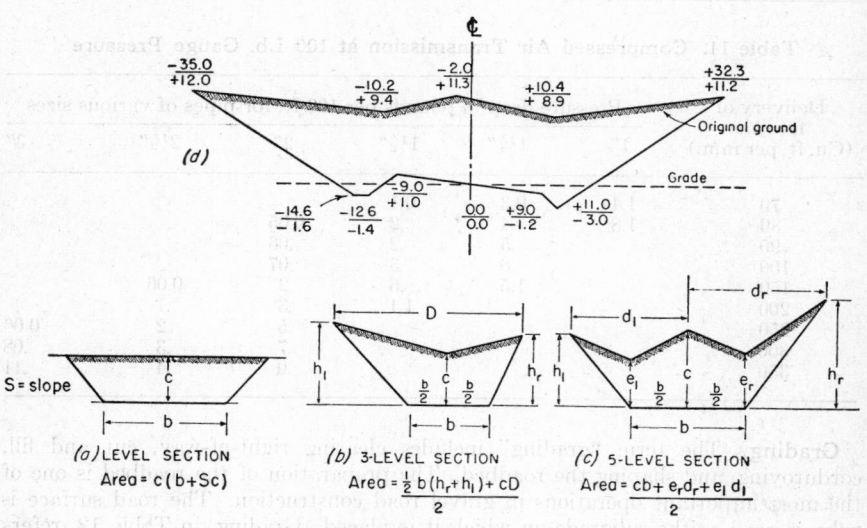

Fig. 8. End area computation.

Write the cuts above grade as plus (+) and those below as minus (−). Write the distances to right of center as plus (+) and those to left as minus (−). Refer to the extreme left point in Fig. 8; here the cut is 12 ft. at a distance of 35 ft. left of the center line.

Start at any cut and proceed clockwise around the figure, multiplying every cut by the distance for point next in advance, minus distance for point next back, always using algebraic signs. The algebraic values of these quotients divided by 2 is the area.

**Example.** Starting at the extreme left:

$$
\begin{array}{rl}
& + \qquad - \\
+12\ [-10.2 - (-14.6)] = & 52.8 \\
+\ 9.4\ [-\ 2.0 - (-35.0)] = & 310.2 \\
+11.3\ [+10.4 - (-10.2)] = & 232.8 \\
+\ 8.9\ [+32.3 - (-\ 2.0)] = & 305.3 \\
+11.2\ [+11.0 - (+10.4)] = & 6.7 \\
-\ 3.0\ [+\ 9.0 - (+32.3)] = & 69.9 \\
-\ 1.2\ [\quad 0.0 - (+11.0)] = & 13.2 \\
+\ 1.0\ [-12.6 - (\quad 0.0)] = & \qquad 12.6 \\
-\ 1.4\ [-14.6 - (-\ 9.0)] = & 7.8 \\
-\ 1.6\ [-35.0 - (-12.6)] = & \underline{35.8} \\
\end{array}
$$

$$
\begin{array}{r}
1,034.5 \quad 12.6 \\
-12.6 \\
\hline
2\ )\overline{1,021.9} \\
\hline
510.9\ \text{sq. ft.}
\end{array}
$$

To obtain cubic yards per 100 ft., multiply the average end areas by **3.7.** Thus if the end area in the above example holds uniform for 100 ft., the volume for that station is 510.9 × 3.7 = 1,890.3 cu. yd.

**Corduroy.** Corduroy consists of logs or poles, usually 4 in. in diameter and larger, laid tightly together. It is used on temporary light-duty roads, under the following conditions.

1. On rough, rocky terrain, generally dry, the corduroy is laid on stringers to even off the road. Uniformity of size of the sticks is desirable. They should be placed as tightly together as possible and nailed or spiked at every stick or every second stick. Tracks can be adzed flat to reduce bumping, or plank tracks may be laid. Under some circumstances the corduroy may be overlaid with earth or gravel.

2. Over wet, swampy ground the corduroy is seldom laid on stringers. If stringers are used, they are generally laid on top of the corduroy, at the sides, to act as guard rails or to contain the fill material placed over the corduroy. This type of corduroy is often poles 16–24 ft. in length. Usually the brush and limbs from the trees used are placed beneath the corduroy as a mat. Often whole trees, with the tops on, are used as corduroy. They may be placed crosswise, or lengthwise in very soft, wet swamps, to give an added bridging effect. The useful life of a corduroy road will be extended considerably if covered with earth.

3. Corduroy is used as a roadway on bridges and trestles. This type of corduroy is similar to that on rough terrain. The main difference is that it is off the ground and gets better air circulation than the other types. Vibration from wheels will result in a need for constant repairs. Plank tracks should be laid on the corduroy wherever possible.

**Fill.** When a roadbed must be raised to insure proper grade or drainage, or corduroy must be covered, earth fill is used. Often the material taken from roadside ditches is sufficient to provide the subgrade. In hilly country the material removed from cuts provides the fill. In swampy or level ground or among boulders, however, material from the roadway is insufficient and fill must be obtained from borrow pits.

When placing fill, keep in mind that both shrinkage and settlement will occur, and the settled fill will be considerably lower than when placed. Care should be taken that sod, stumps, and other organic matter are excluded. The amount of "borrow" required for a cubic yard of embankment is as follows: gravel, 1.12 cu. yd.; gravel and sand, 1.13; clay and clayey earth, 1.15; light sandy earth, 1.20; vegetable surface soil, 1.24; ledge rock, 0.70. These empirical values are applicable where actual densities are not ascertainable. They are based on power equipment wheel compaction.

Where possible, earth fill should be placed in layers from 6 to 18 in. thick, preferably not more than 12 in. thick. Each layer should be compacted before another layer is added. Pneumatic-tired or sheepsfoot rollers may be used to obtain this compaction. Often compaction can be accomplished by the passage of wheeled and crawler-tread equipment if care is taken to stagger the tracks over all of the fill.

Settlement may continue over a period of years, although most of it will occur during the first year. If fill is placed over swamp sections, the weight of the fill may compress or displace the unstable material underlying it and cause the whole section of fill to subside.

**Turnpiking or use of side borrow as fill.** Where side borrow is used when grading a road, soil conditions are usually such that drainage does not present a real problem. Usually the inside face of the ditch is fairly flat while the outside is inclined so that the bank will not crumble or the ditch fill in as rapidly as when the ditch has a vertical back face. In grading, a shallow cut is made first with the point of the grader blade just within the outer ditch line. With each pass of the blade the ditch is cut deeper and nearer the center of the road. After ditching is completed, the loose earth is spread over the road and graded to finish the road surface.

In grading, the most satisfactory results are obtained when the grader carries about two-thirds of a bladeful of earth ahead of the blade and delivers a small ridge of loose earth at the heel. In this way, successive rounds roll the material back and forth across the road, break up the lumps, compact the loose earth, and shape the subgrade. If one side of a road is higher than the other, it is necessary to transfer earth from one side to the other. On the low side, the grader blade should just scrape the top of the spoil and leave most of the earth on the low shoulder. On the high side the grader is set so that practically all the spoil is carried to the center and very little is left on the high shoulder. With several passes of the grader, the lack of balance can be eliminated.

**Use of cut material as fill.** Bulldozers are used where earth is to be moved short distances and where turn-around space is limited. The best effect is obtained if material can be moved downhill, and the bulldozer is kept in the same path each trip. The material which is wasted off the ends in the first few trips forms windrows which serve to hold the material in front of the blade and thus increase the yardage moved. Table 13 gives estimated bulldozer production in cubic yards per hour, bank measure, and is based on 60-min.-hr. efficiency, no grades, single dozer, no trench, and a dig-and-travel speed of 1.5 mph.

### Table 13. Bulldozer Performance in Cut-and-Fill Work

| Tractor model | Distance (ft.) | Sand | Common earth | Clay | Broken rock |
|---|---|---|---|---|---|
| | | Typical excavation production in cubic yards per hour, return speed 2.5 mph | | | |
| D–8........ | 50 | 186 | 166 | 145 | 124 |
| | 100 | 112 | 100 | 88 | 74 |
| | 150 | 80 | 72 | 62 | 54 |
| | 200 | 64 | 56 | 49 | 42 |
| D–7........ | 50 | 169 | 150 | 132 | 113 |
| | 100 | 102 | 90 | 79 | 67 |
| | 150 | 73 | 65 | 56 | 48 |
| | 200 | 56 | 50 | 44 | 38 |
| D–6........ | 50 | 110 | 98 | 86 | 73 |
| | 100 | 67 | 59 | 52 | 44 |
| | 150 | 48 | 42 | 37 | 31 |
| | 200 | 37 | 34 | 29 | 25 |
| D–4........ | 50 | 94 | 83 | 72 | 62 |
| | 100 | 56 | 50 | 44 | 37 |
| | 150 | 41 | 36 | 31 | 26 |
| | 200 | 31 | 28 | 24 | 20 |
| | | Typical excavation production in cubic yards per hour, return speed 5 mph | | | |
| D–7........ | 50 | 193 | 172 | 150 | 128 |
| | 100 | 119 | 107 | 94 | 80 |
| | 150 | 86 | 77 | 67 | 58 |
| | 200 | 68 | 61 | 54 | 46 |
| D–6........ | 50 | 127 | 113 | 98 | 85 |
| | 100 | 78 | 70 | 61 | 53 |
| | 150 | 56 | 50 | 44 | 38 |
| | 200 | 44 | 40 | 35 | 30 |

### Table. 14. Slope of Repose for Embankments

| Material | Slope of repose |
|---|---|
| Clean sand .............................. | 1 on 1.5 |
| Sand and clay ........................... | 1 on 1.33 |
| Clay, dry ............................... | 1 on 1.75 |
| Clay, damp, plastic ..................... | 1 on 3 |
| Gravel, clean ........................... | 1 on 1.33 |
| Gravel and clay ......................... | 1 on 1.33 |
| Gravel, sand, and clay.................. | 1 on 1.5 |
| Soil .................................... | 1 on 1.33 |
| Rotten rock ............................. | 1 on 1 |

## Table 15. Volume of Cuts and Fills in Cubic Yards per 100 Ft. of Length

| Average depth of cut or height of fill (ft.) | Width of base of cut or crown of fill (ft.) Side slope 1 to 1 | | | | Add for each additional 2 ft. of width | Add where slope is 1 to 1½ | Add where slope is 1 to 2 |
|---|---|---|---|---|---|---|---|
| | 20 | 30 | 32 | 42 | | | |
| 1 | 78 | 115 | 122 | 159 | 7 | 2 | 4 |
| 2 | 163 | 237 | 252 | 326 | 15 | 7 | 15 |
| 3 | 256 | 367 | 389 | 500 | 22 | 16 | 33 |
| 4 | 356 | 504 | 534 | 682 | 30 | 30 | 59 |
| 5 | 463 | 648 | 686 | 870 | 37 | 46 | 93 |
| 6 | 578 | 800 | 845 | 1,065 | 45 | 67 | 133 |
| 7 | 700 | 959 | 1,011 | 1,271 | 52 | 91 | 181 |
| 8 | 830 | 1,126 | 1,185 | 1,483 | 59 | 118 | 237 |
| 9 | 967 | 1,300 | 1,367 | 1,700 | 67 | 150 | 300 |
| 10 | 1,111 | 1,481 | 1,557 | 1,928 | 74 | 185 | 370 |

**Use of fill material from borrow pits.** Whenever extensive fill is required, it is usually necessary to open up borrow pits as a source of material.

**Scrapers.** Scrapers are used for earth work extending over a considerable area involving cuts and fills. In hard ground a pusher tractor or rooter will help increase speed of loading and will result in higher output. Output of scrapers is difficult to estimate on narrow roads in rough country, typical of most construction in extensive forests. Under more favorable conditions an 8-cu.-yd. scraper with a D-7 tractor moves about 80 cu. yd. of medium soil in an hour on one-way hauls of 500 ft.; 55 cu. yd. on 1,000-ft. hauls; and 45 cu yd. on 1,500-ft. hauls. Downgrades of 10 percent increase these yardages by about 12 percent. Outputs of 12-cu.-yd. scrapers exceed that of 8-cu.-yd. scrapers by about 15 percent on level hauls, and up to 25 percent on long, uphill hauls.

**Road Surface.** The surface of a road has little capacity to sustain loads but is of great importance in protecting the road base against wear resulting from the traffic imposed upon it. A surface of loose floating gravel does not fill the function of a road surface, nor does a surface where the gravel has become displaced or worn thin by traffic. The condition of the surface will depend to a large extent upon the condition of the subgrade and the drainage of both surface and subgrade.

A properly surfaced road should present a compacted surface with sufficient crown or side slope, usually ½ to ¾ in. per ft. of width for one-lane roads, to permit any rain falling on it to drain off rapidly to the side. The center of the road should be at least 18 in. above the probable high-water line in the ditches. However, care should be taken not to have so high a crown that the inside of the rear dual wheels of trucks will take the load, resulting in uneven tire wear. The type of soil in the subgrade will govern the amount of crown required. Light sandy soils which drain quickly require less crown than heavy clays which retain the water and become muddy and rutted even if drained.

**Stabilization of Road Surfaces.** The principles of soil stabilization should be understood by all forest engineers. A stabilized road has a smooth, hard-wearing surface that will not wash or blow away. Soil stabilization is the process of giving natural soils enough abrasive resistance and shear strength to carry normal traffic, even under severe weather conditions, without breaking up. Not all roads require stabilization, but on every forest road there are usually stretches which should have this special treatment. Without it such stretches may block traffic even when the remainder of the road system is in good condition.

The commoner soils, or soil components, encountered in road building are defined as follows:

1. **Gravel.** A mass of detached rock particles, generally water-worn, ranging in size from ¼ to 6 in. "Bank run" or "pit run" gravel are terms generally applied to a mixture of sand and gravel, often with an appreciable clay or silt content.

2. **Sand.** Granular material composed of rock particles ranging in diameter from 0.25 to 0.002 in. Grains are loose and may be readily seen and felt. Lacks plasticity and cohesion, although it may show considerable stability when wet owing to the film phenomenon of moisture.

3. **Silt.** Fine granular material (rock flour) ranging in diameter from 0.002 to 0.0002 in. Lacks plasticity and has little dry strength. Feels smooth in the hand in contrast to the grittiness of fine sand. If mixed with water, the particles will settle in from 30 min. to 1 hr.

4. **Clay.** Extremely fine-grained material less than 0.0002 in. in diameter. Cohesive and plastic so that if moist it can be rolled into a long thread (this cannot be done with silt). Forms hard lumps when dry, often impossible to crush with the hands. Does not feel gritty between the teeth as does silt.

5. **Muck.** Decomposed organic material mixed with inorganic soil. Usually black in color. Has strong odor when dried and burned.

6. **Peat.** Consists of partly decayed plant material. It is fibrous in texture and plant remains are visible.

7. **Marl.** Clay with calcium carbonate.

Stabilization may be accomplished by increasing the density of a soil—adding fine soil particles to the mixture—and by maintaining a suitable moisture content. A stabilized soil mixture has three major constituents: (1) a well-graded coarse aggregate, which may be pit-run gravel or crushed rock, with a maximum size of about 1 in.; (2) a fine aggregate, such as sand, used to fill the large voids between the coarse stone, and containing sufficient material of small size to insure plasticity of the mix; and (3) a clay binder to provide cohesion. The binding agent is not clay alone; it consists in part of the moisture film on the finer clay particles. Good drainage is therefore important for stabilized roads, because if the soil becomes saturated the moisture film on the particles may lose surface tension. The desirable percentage of clay as a binder in a gravel surface is usually 8 to 10 percent. It should be remembered that where clay is abundant in the subsurface or base of the road, it tends to work up in time and increase the clay content of the surface, particularly on low ground; conversely, on high ground, wind and water constantly reduce the proportion of clay. Resurfacing should be planned with these facts in mind.

**Graveling.** Gravel should have good wearing qualities. Angular gravel or crushed rock will require less binding material than will round or smooth gravel. River gravel will not usually compact unless clay or other binders are added.

Gravel is usually loaded by shovel, dragline, or bulldozer and chute. Under good conditions, with bulldozer and a trough of poles, 100 cu. yd. per hr. can be loaded. A trough for loading gravel can be constructed where the bed of gravel overhangs a road, or even in flat "thin" pits. The platform is built so there is about 10 ft. from the bottom to the top of the trough. It is high enough to allow trucks to pass beneath the lip of it. Sill logs are embedded in the ground and the floor logs are set at an incline. They should project enough past the sill logs to place the load in the center of the truck box but not so far that the tractor has to ride on the projecting platform. The remainder of the platform should be sufficiently long and embedded in the gravel to ensure stability. The side walls of the chute should be about 2½ ft. high to confine the gravel being pushed by the bulldozer. The bulldozer pushes a bladeful of gravel up the platform and into the truck; often one bladeful is a truckload.

Tables 16 and 17 show hourly production for loading gravel and fill material for draglines and power shovels. The yardages are calculated on a basis of 60-min. hr. and assume that the working radius is within the manufacturers' recommendation for machine stability.

**Table 16.  Short Boom Dragline Performance—Cubic Yards per Hour**

| Class of material | Bucket capacity in cubic yards | | | | | | | | |
|---|---|---|---|---|---|---|---|---|---|
| | ⅜ | ½ | ¾ | 1 | 1¼ | 1½ | 1¾ | 2 | 2½ |
| Light, moist clay or loam | 70 | 95 | 130 | 160 | 195 | 220 | 245 | 265 | 305 |
| Sand or gravel........ | 65 | 90 | 125 | 155 | 185 | 210 | 235 | 255 | 295 |
| Good common clay..... | 55 | 75 | 105 | 135 | 165 | 190 | 210 | 230 | 265 |
| Clay, tough, hard...... | 35 | 55 | 90 | 110 | 135 | 160 | 180 | 195 | 230 |
| Clay, wet, sticky....... | 20 | 30 | 55 | 75 | 95 | 110 | 130 | 145 | 175 |

**Table 17.  Shovel Performance—Cubic Yards per Hour**

| Class of material | Dipper capacity in cubic yards | | | | | | | | |
|---|---|---|---|---|---|---|---|---|---|
| | ⅜ | ½ | ¾ | 1 | 1¼ | 1½ | 1¾ | 2 | 2½ |
| Moist loam or light sandy clay ......... | 85 | 115 | 165 | 205 | 250 | 285 | 320 | 355 | 405 |
| Sand and gravel...... | 80 | 110 | 155 | 200 | 230 | 270 | 300 | 330 | 390 |
| Good common earth... | 70 | 95 | 135 | 175 | 210 | 240 | 270 | 300 | 350 |
| Clay, hard, tough..... | 50 | 75 | 110 | 145 | 180 | 210 | 235 | 265 | 310 |
| Rock, well blasted.... | 40 | 60 | 95 | 125 | 155 | 180 | 205 | 230 | 275 |
| Common, with rocks and roots.......... | 30 | 50 | 80 | 105 | 130 | 155 | 180 | 200 | 245 |
| Clay, wet and sticky.. | 25 | 40 | 70 | 95 | 120 | 145 | 165 | 185 | 230 |
| Rock, poorly blasted.. | 15 | 25 | 50 | 75 | 95 | 115 | 140 | 160 | 195 |

**Use of Clay and Sand in Stabilization.** Clay is often used to stabilize sand roads, and vice versa. On sand roads, clay is spread over the grade deep enough to provide sufficient binder for the full depth of the stabilized layer. It is then dried and pulverized. It is mixed with sand by repeated bladings, and shaped with a grader. On clay roads, the procedure is to scarify the surface to loosen the required amount of clay binder for the mixture. The clay is dried and pulverized on the grade and then bladed into windrows on each side of the road. The sand is spread uniformly over the grade and the clay is bladed back on the sand and the whole is dry-mixed. After the first heavy rain, the road may be shaped to final cross section.

**Use of Chemicals in Stabilization.** Chemicals are sometimes used in soil stabilization. Deliquescent salts help prevent too great a fluctuation in the soil moisture content. Of these, calcium chloride may be applied at the rate of ½ to 2½ lb. per sq. yd., or 1.76 to 8.80 tons per mi. of 12-ft. road. In regions where summer humidity is favorable, as along the Eastern Seaboard and in the Lake States, it is used to lay dust; it cannot be used for this purpose in dry portions of the West. Salt-treated roads may be overly popular with animals where game population is high.

Hydrated lime has been used to treat gumbo clays to increase their stability and reduce their stickiness. The clay is scarified and pulverized to a depth of 6 in. Hydrated lime at 3½ lb. per sq. yd. is added, and the whole thoroughly mixed before grading to shape.

**Ditching and Drainage.** Proper drainage is essential to the stability of gravel roads. The crown of the road is shaped so as to shed water into side ditches. Ditches parallel to the road carry water through culverts away from the road. Minimum grades should be from 1 to 3 percent for sodded ditches and from 2 to 5 percent for ditches with irregularities and checks in them. A ditch that does not drain becomes a catch basin for water, which tends to saturate the subgrade. Frequent offtake ditches will reduce the volume of water carried and will reduce erosion.

**Table 18. Mean Velocities Permissible in Unlined Ditches**

| Material | Mean velocity (ft. per sec.) |
|---|---|
| Uniformly graded sand and cohesionless silts............ | 0.75–1.50 |
| Well-graded sands ..................................... | 1.50–2.50 |
| Silty sand ............................................. | 2.50–3.00 |
| Clays .................................................. | 3.00–5.00 |
| Coarse gravel ......................................... | 5.00–8.00 |

**Table 19. Drainage Ditch Construction Rates**

| Equipment | Rate in units per hour | Unit | Conditions |
|---|---|---|---|
| Motor grader ................. | 450 | Cu. yd. | V-ditch, light soil |
| | 300 | Cu. yd. | V-ditch, medium soil |
| Hand tools .................. | 3 man-hr. | 100 ft. | V-ditch, 3 ft. wide, 1 ft. deep, light soil |
| | 10 man-hr. | 100 ft. | V-ditch, 3 ft. wide, 1 ft. deep, medium soil |
| Dynamite, 2-man crew......... | 20 | Lin. ft. | Ditching in swamp, 2-man crew |
| Dragline, ⅝ yd. bucket........ | 100 | Lin. ft. | |

**Ditching in Swamps.** Ditching in wet swamps with dynamite is possible by means of the sympathetic detonation method. By this method only the explosive at one end is primed and the concussion of this explosion is sufficient to propagate the detonation through the wet earth and set off the whole line of charges. Proper loading will lift the soil to 200 ft. in the air and leave a clean ditch. In swamp soils a good, sharp crowbar is effective for making holes; if the soil is soft and mucky, a heavy stick will serve the purpose.

As with all jobs employing explosives, this work should be done only under experienced direction. A blaster's license is required in many states. Some authorities recommend spacings of 18 to 28 in. between holes, using one half-pound cartridge per hole for long ditches. For short distances ("single-column loads") the recommended charges are heavier, as shown in Table 20.

### Table 20.  Ditching by Dynamite—Single-Column Loads

| Cartridges per hole | Depth to top of charge (in.) | Depth of ditch (ft.) | Top width of ditch (ft.) | Distance between holes (in.) | Pounds per 100 ft. |
|---|---|---|---|---|---|
| ½ | 6–8 | 1½–2 | 4–5 | 12 | 25 |
| 1 | 6–12 | 2½–3 | 6 | 15 | 40 |
| 2 | 6–12 | 3–3½ | 8 | 18 | 67 |
| 3 | 6–12 | 4–4½ | 10 | 21 | 86 |
| 4 | 6–12 | 5–5½ | 13 | 24 | 100 |
| 5 | 6–12 | 6–6½ | 16 | 24 | 125 |

**Culverts.** The determination of culvert size does not ordinarily lend itself to mathematical precision. Table 21 is based on an empirical formula given on page 10 · 25.

### Table 21.  Culvert Openings Required for Various Drainage Areas

| Drainage area | | Waterway openings required (sq. ft.) | | | |
|---|---|---|---|---|---|
| Acres | Sq. mi. | Mountainous land | Hilly land | Rolling land | Flat land |
| 1 | 0.0016 | 0.9–2.0 | 0.8–1.7 | 0.8–1.5 | 0.8–1.1 |
| 2 | .0031 | 1.5–3.1 | 1.0–2.7 | 0.8–2.3 | 0.8–1.7 |
| 4 | .0062 | 2.5–4.7 | 1.7–4.1 | 1.1–3.4 | 0.8–2.6 |
| 8 | .0125 | 4.3–7.2 | 2.9–6.2 | 1.9–5.2 | 1.0–3.9 |
| 10 | .016 | 5.1–8.2 | 3.4–7.1 | 2.2–6.0 | 1.2–4.5 |
| 15 | .023 | 6.8–10 | 4.6–9.0 | 3.0–7.6 | 1.5–5.8 |
| 20 | .031 | 8.3–13 | 5.7–11 | 3.8–9.1 | 1.9–6.8 |
| 30 | .047 | 12–16 | 7.7–14 | 5.1–12 | 2.6–8.8 |
| 40 | .062 | 14–19 | 9.5–17 | 6.4–14 | 3.2–10 |
| 60 | .094 | 19–25 | 13–21 | 8.8–18 | 5.4–16 |
| 100 | .156 | 28–35 | 19–29 | 13–24 | 6.4–18 |
| 150 | .234 | 38–47 | 26–37 | 17–31 | 8.6–23 |
| 200 | .312 | 48–59 | 32–44 | 21–37 | 11–28 |
| 250 | .39 | 56–59 | 38–50 | 29–47 | 14–35 |
| 300 | .47 | 64–79 | 43–58 | 29–47 | 14–35 |
| 400 | .62 | 80–98 | 53–71 | 36–56 | 18–42 |
| 500 | .78 | 95–116 | 64–85 | 42–64 | 21–48 |
| 600 | .94 | | 73–97 | 48–72 | 24–54 |
| 800 | 1.25 | | 90–120 | 60–85 | 30–64 |
| 1000 | 1.56 | | | 71–98 | 36–73 |
| 1500 | 2.34 | | | 96–125 | 48–94 |
| 2000 | 3.12 | | | | 60–112 |
| 2500 | 3.91 | | | | 71–128 |
| 3000 | 4.70 | | | | 81–142 |

Note: Within size ranges given above, use larger openings for factors contributing to rapid runoff of surface water such as high rainfall intensity, impervious soil, lack of ground cover. Use smaller openings for low rainfall intensity, open country, porous soil, sodded or wooded areas.

Culverts accommodating a stream should have the same alignment as that of the stream, as direct entrance to the culvert is desirable. A common mistake is to place culverts too low, with no allowance made for sedimentation. Culverts must be placed on a firm foundation to prevent transverse breaking due to uneven settlement or clogging as a result of the weight of the fill, which pushes the center section of the culvert below the grade of the ends.

Open culverts are often effective on uncrowned side-hill roads for draining the inside ditch, but they tend to clog under blading, weathering, and traffic. The surface drains are placed obliquely across the road at the same grade as the ditch it is draining. A common design is a trough 3 in. wide and 4 in. deep, inside measurements, made of 6×4 or 8×4 white oak, or similar hard, durable wood. The boards are spiked together at the bottom and must be reinforced at the top by three iron straps, using any available scrap stock. On high-crowned roads two short culverts, laid staggered in herringbone fashion, are better than one culvert of full road width. V-shaped open culverts tend to work loose and rise out of the holding trench. Two pieces of salvage rail steel placed side by side will often make an effective open drain.

The length of a culvert depends upon a number of factors, among which are the width of roadway, slope of embankment, and height of fill. The best method of determining the required length is by a sketch of an embankment showing a plan and profile. Another method of determining the length of culvert ($L$) is shown in Fig. 9 and the formula below it.

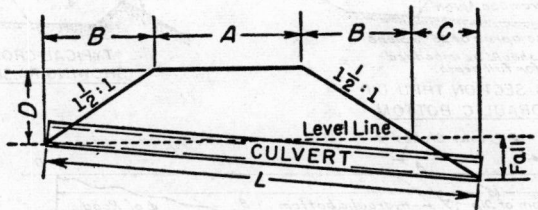

Fig. 9. Method of determining length of culvert.

$$L = A + 2B + C$$

in which $A$ = width of roadway; $B$ = sideslope ratio to $D$;
$D$ = depth of fill at inlet; $C = 1\frac{1}{2}$ fall
$$\text{Fall} = \% \text{ fall} \times (A + 2B) \text{ (approx.)}$$

Assume $A = 20$ ft.; $D = 10$ ft.; fall of culvert = 10%

Then $B = 1\frac{1}{2}D = 1\frac{1}{2} \times 10 = 15$ ft.
$C = 1\frac{1}{2}$ fall $= 1\frac{1}{2}$ (10% × 50 ft.) = 7$\frac{1}{2}$ ft. (approx.)

Then required length of culvert is
20 + 2 (15) + 7$\frac{1}{2}$ = 57$\frac{1}{2}$ ft.

Allowing for approximation of $C$ and ordering culvert to nearest 2-ft. section, order a culvert 60 ft. long.

**Dips.** Dips are devices for draining light-duty roads on grades not over 10 percent. As the name implies, they are depressions, with center lines at angles of 45° to 60° from the center line of the road. They are illustrated in Fig. 10 and are installed below outcurves, above incurves, through fills, and elsewhere as needed on outsloped or insloped sections of the road. A raised shoulder should be constructed the full length of the dip. Where the dip is outsloped, a spillway opening 2 ft. wide at the bottom is left through the raised shoulder. When insloped, dips discharge into a culvert.

Crossgrade of dip $AC$, (c) in Fig. 10, must be 1 or 2 percent greater than the grade of the original road; the success of the dip depends upon this relationship. The bottom of the dip is 15 ft. wide for all grades. Distance $AD$ should be 50 ft. on grades up to 5 percent and should be increased 5 ft. for each percent of grade over 5. Outslope should increase gradually from $D$ to $C$, so that water from $D$ follows the course indicated by wavy line $B$, which ends at the hydraulic bottom, 2 ft. uphill from the bottom of the dip. Here a drainage apron must be securely placed in the raised shoulder at the hydraulic center line, at a 25 percent slope, with its upper end slightly below the bottom of the dip; its face should make a 15° angle with the center line of the road. It leads into a downspout placed in the fill slope with its top flush with the natural ground line. This in turn discharges into a spillway flume, at right angles to the center of the road, embedded in the slope for its full depth. The final discharge should be upon rock or some kind of protective work to prevent erosion.

**Miscellaneous.** Figs. 11, 12, and 13 illustrate log cribbing and guard rail construction on forest roads.

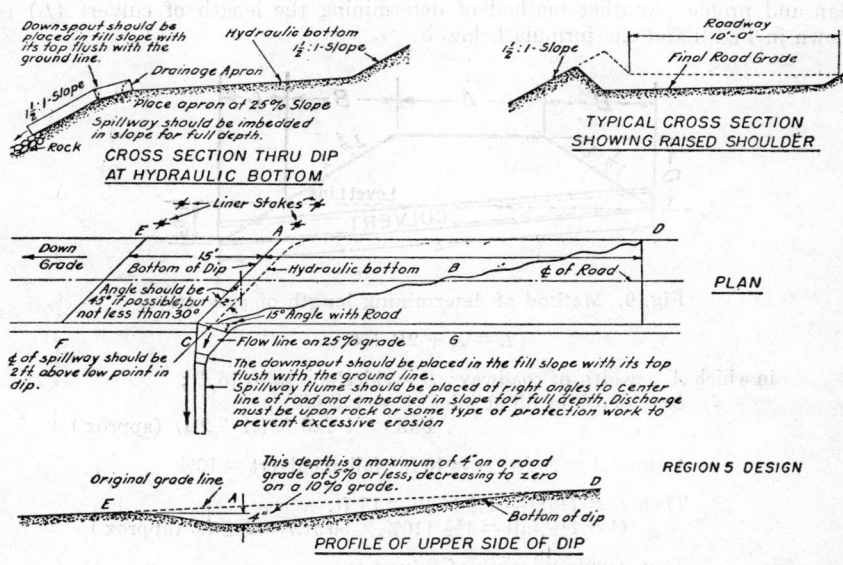

**Fig. 10. Intercepting dip.**

**ROAD MAINTENANCE.** Maintenance includes reditching, redistribution of surface material, elimination of mudholes, prevention of frost heaving, etc. Proper maintenance requires planning so that the activities entailed may be correlated with other operations to permit proper scheduling of work and equipment. Blading or dragging the road surface should not be overdone, but it is false economy to let a road deteriorate to a point where the deferred repairs are more costly than routine maintenance would have been.

Rails free of bark and approximately same diameter as posts (at least 12"). Select rail lengths according to material available. Make post spacing uniform for any one continous guard. Use posts of durable species or treated for resistance to decay. Use $\frac{3}{4}$" diam. drift pins about twice as long as diam. of rail. Drive flush with top of rail but avoid bruising.

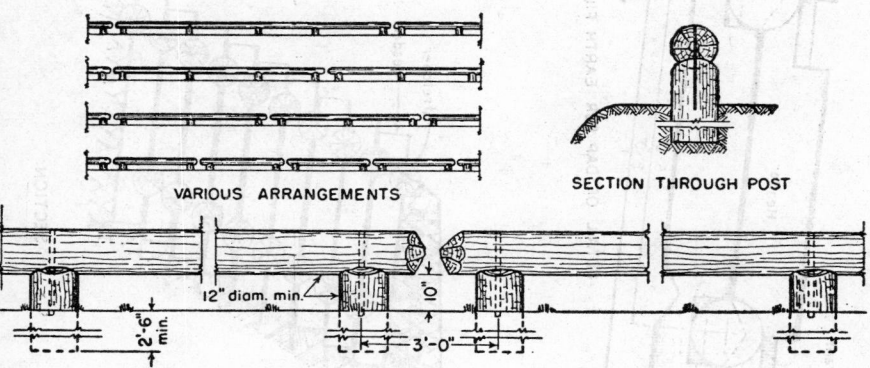

VARIOUS ARRANGEMENTS            SECTION THROUGH POST

12" diam. min.        10"

2'-6" min.        3'-0"

Fig. 11. Log guard rail, open sections, vertical posts.

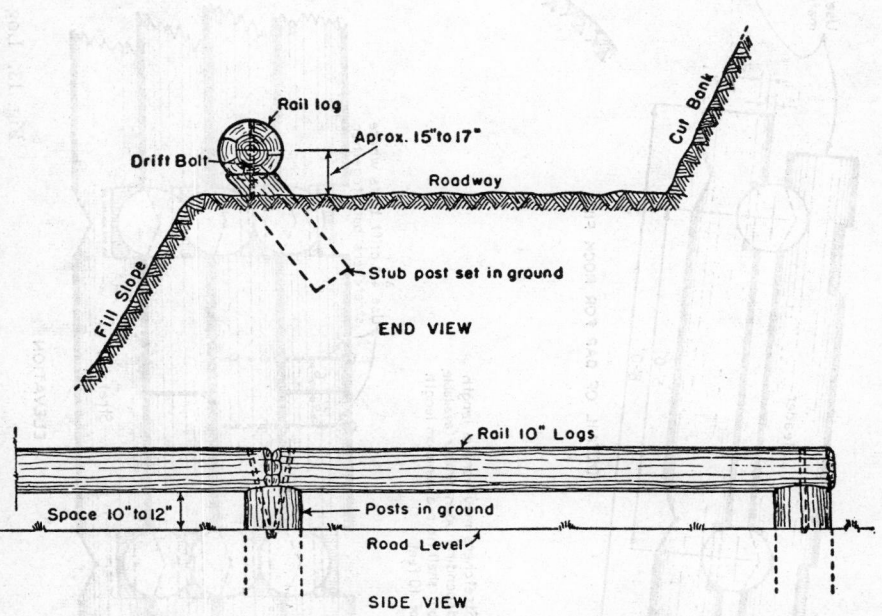

Rail log

Aprox. 15" to 17"

Drift Bolt

Roadway

Cut Bank

Stub post set in ground

Fill Slope

END VIEW

Rail 10" Logs

Space 10" to 12"        Posts in ground

Road Level

SIDE VIEW

Fig. 12. Log guard rail, closed sections, slanted posts.

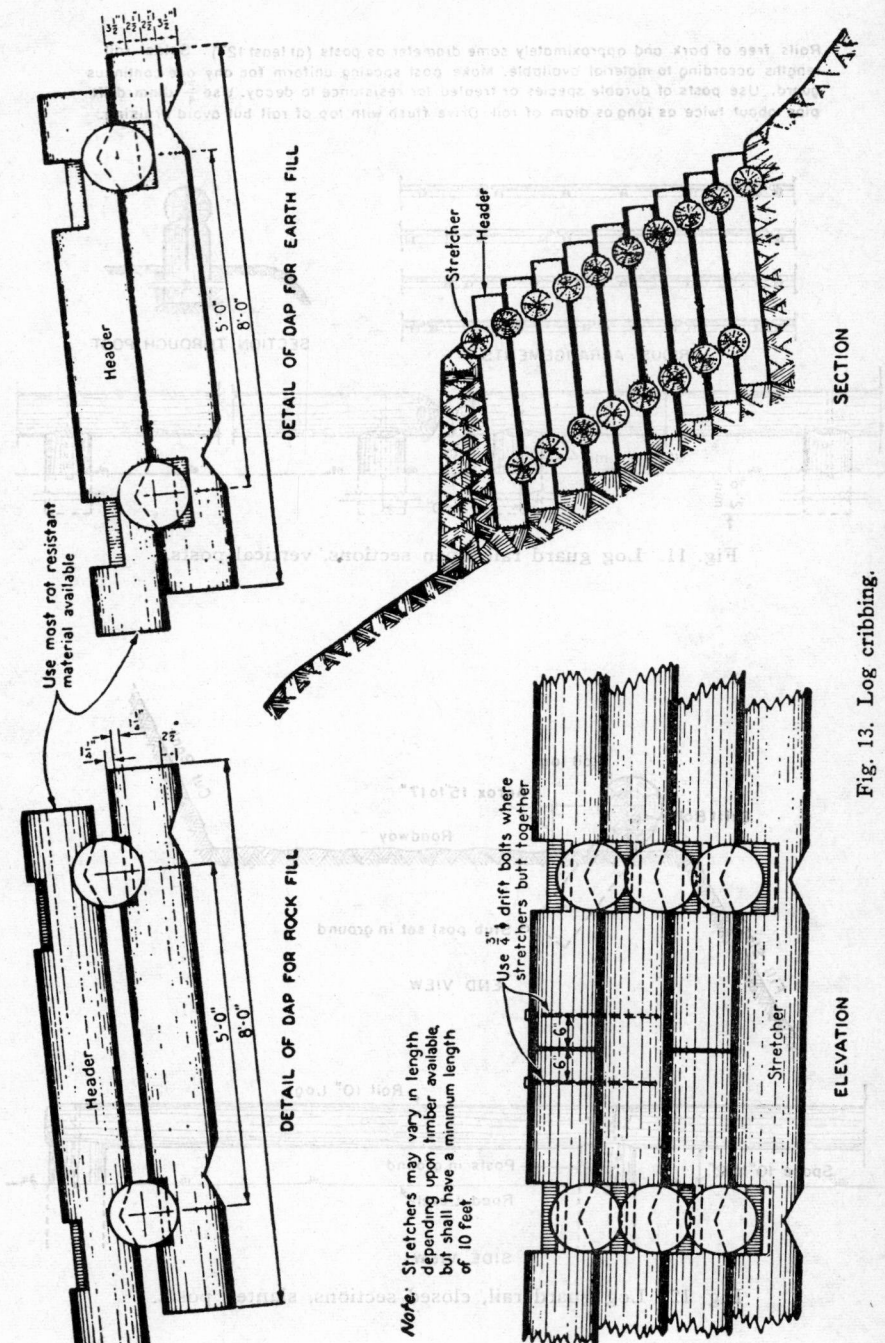

Use most rot resistant material available

Header

DETAIL OF DAP FOR EARTH FILL

Header

DETAIL OF DAP FOR ROCK FILL

5'-0"
8'-0"

Stretcher
Header

SECTION

*Note*: Stretchers may vary in length depending upon timber available, but shall have a minimum length of 10 feet.

Use $\frac{3}{4}$" drift bolts where stretchers butt together

Stretcher

ELEVATION

Fig. 13. Log cribbing.

**Reditching.** This will entail repairing washouts and cleaning debris from the ditch. Often a road grader is used to obtain the proper slope to the ditch and to re-establish the back slope of the ditch.

**Surface Maintenance.** To maintain a smooth road surface on earth or gravel requires a smoothing operation at frequent intervals. The interval will depend upon the type of surface and the amount of traffic. The following outline for such maintenance is adapted from the U. S. Forest Service Truck Trail Construction Handbook (out of print).

1. Work the surface after a rain, when the soil pulverizes readily. Do not drag when the soil is too sticky, but do not wait to blade or drag until the soil is completely dry.
2. Work the surface early in the spring, as soon as the frost is out of the ground. Dragging a muddy stretch of road will aid in drying it out, because the sun and wind will have free access to the thin layer of saturated soil which the drag spreads over the road surface.
3. Smooth the surface before freeze-up. If a road is bladed or dragged in the fall, it will usually freeze smoothly and remain in this condition during most of the winter.
4. Work a gravel road when wet. Gravel can be worked better in a wet condition as long as it is not saturated.
5. If a grader is available, blading is preferable to dragging and is less likely to result ultimately in a corrugated surface.
6. If only a drag is available, load it as heavily as the motive power will permit.

**Frost Action in Roads.** Surface soil consists of soil particles, moisture, and air. When frozen, it becomes a material which may be compared with concrete. This material loses its hardness as soon as it thaws. Completely dry sands will not freeze and in snowless countries, in cold weather, there is dust on earth and gravel roads.

There are two phases to frost action on roads: (1) heaving in certain places in the winter and early spring, and (2) back-settling and softening of these places in the late spring. The amount of frost action in a soil is closely related to its water properties, particularly to its permeability. Frost heave may occur in any soil, provided there is an excess of moisture either within the earth mass itself or coming from without. Only in the latter case will the heave be of considerable size. Water from without reaches the heave area if there is a shallow water table, if the soil contains a high percentage of fine particles, and if it has good permeability. Silty soils suffer much from frost action, while coarse sands or heavy clays suffer very little.

Insulating the road tends to reduce frost action. Sometimes a considerable depth of snow is permitted to build up on the road surface to act as a natural insulation. Sand is widely used to prevent frost action; a layer of coarse sand up to 10 in. thick, placed between the road surface and the subsoil, breaks the capillary movement of water between them. Frost heaving results from the upward capillary action of water, so it is important to keep the free water level well below the sand layer. If ditches are not deep enough, the sand layer will act as a conduit for the water and will greatly increase frost action in the covering soil.

Measures taken each spring can only be makeshifts. The road surface and grade are full of water and are soft so that traffic damages them. The weight of the loads permitted on the road should be sharply reduced during this period. As soon as ruts appear, they should be bladed full and the roadbed restored to a shape that will insure surface runoff.

**Washboarding.** The primary cause of washboarding is the tangential force transmitted to the soil surface by the wheel of any vehicle. Both nonpneumatic tires and high vehicle speeds increase washboarding; stiff springs on vehicles reduce it. Washboarding of sand and gravel roads is possible only where free surface materials rest on a resistant base. If the base becomes softened, so that the free particles are embedded instead of displaced, corrugations are not found. Washboarding becomes sharply defined where the loose particles are ½ in. or more in diameter and becomes less as the particle size decreases. Temporarily, washboarding may be removed or considerably reduced by blading or scarifying. The only permanent cure is stabilization of the road base and removal of the loose surface material.

**Mudholes.** Rocks should not be thrown into mudholes. The holes should be drained, the mud cleaned out, and the hole filled with the best material available. Mudholes occur primarily as a result of poor drainage; when this is corrected, they should no longer offer a problem.

**Maintenance of Right-of-Way.** Keep brush from encroaching on the roadway, where it will present a hazard to safe driving and may retard the drying out of the roadbed after winter storms.

Chemical control is now widely used. Chemicals such as 2, 4-D, Isopropyl ester, and alkanolomine salt have proved successful. In eradicating alder along roads in Washington and Oregon, experiments (Morrison) show that:

1. Spraying should be carried out just after the growing season has begun, when the leaves have reached normal development. A pumper capable of pressures from 200 to 600 lb. can be used and a nozzle that will produce a fine spray is desirable. For roadside work, a tank of 500 gal. capacity, equipped with an agitator, appears most practical.
2. A relatively weak application, repeated in a couple of weeks, is better than one heavy application.
3. The shorter and smaller the plants, the easier they are to kill, and the less trouble it is to get proper application. A height of 10 ft. should probably be the maximum.
4. Not more than 2 gal. of 2, 4-D should be required for 1 mi. of roadside work.
5. Fire hazard tends to be low because alder decays rapidly and breaks off in wind or under snow.

For control of other species, consult the U. S. Forest Service branch of research. Successful control for some species depends on the season of treatment as well as on the chemical used.

**Snow Fences.** The function of a snow fence parallel to a truck road is to intercept drifting snow and prevent its deposit in the road. To accommodate the intercepted snow the distance between the fence and the road should be 16 ft. for every foot of effective height of the fence. There should be a space of 6 in. between the bottom of the fence and the ground.

A widely used type of snow fence is made of wooden slats 4 ft. long, ¼ in. thick, and 2 in. wide, spaced about 2 in. apart. They are held upright by three double strands of No. 10 or No. 12 wire, and for convenience in handling and summer storage are manufactured in lengths of about 24 ft. The supporting posts, 4 × 4 in., are set 2 ft. deep in the ground, about 12 ft. apart.

Where drifting snow is a serious problem, the grade line of a truck road should, wherever possible, be slightly above the average elevation of the anticipated snow level so that the road will receive the full benefit of the sweeping action of winds. Snow fences may often be improvised from branches and tops of spruce or fir, or even grain sacks, suspended from or woven into wire strands.

**Natural Windbreaks.** Strips of timber left along main roads often make effective windbreaks. Four rows of planted trees, with low shrubbery on the windward side, are of considerable value, the snow being deposited in front of and within the windbreak. Coniferous trees make the most effective windbreaks.

**Snow Removal from Roads.** The equipment used for snow removal is varied. Truck-mounted snowplows, either V- or one-way type, are designed to discharge snow rapidly. The faster the truck is driven, the farther the snow will be thrown and the more evenly it will be scattered. Such equipment works best in dry snow of a depth not greater than half the height of the blade. Truck plows can handle recently drifted snow, not packed or crusted, to a depth of 36 in. The main function of a truck plow is not to move snow back off the road but to keep roads open to traffic. Displacement plows are generally tractor mounted. This type of plow discharges the snow to the side in a mass and builds up side banks. These plows are of the V-type. Rotary plows or snow blowers are used when conditions have exceeded the capacity of the V-plows. Their use prevents banks from getting too high and permits the removal of snow back from the shoulders of the road. Road patrol graders are often adaptable to snowplowing. Although slower than a truck, such equipment has proved very effective and economical because it can be used the year round. Care should be taken not to remove road-surfacing material in snowplow operations.

# Bridges

**STANDARD HIGHWAY BRIDGE CAPACITIES.** The two principal loads considered in bridge design are: (1) the dead load, consisting of the weight of the structure; and (2) the live load. Specifications for live loads have been established by the American Association of State Highway Officials (A.A.S.H.O.); these specifications have been generally adopted by designing agencies in the United States as satisfactorily representing the usual type of legal highway loads. The A.A.S.H.O. establishes five loading classifications: H10, H15, H20, H15–S12, and H20–S16.

Engineered bridges on public highways may range in capacity from those designed for H10 loading to bridges designed for H20–S16. Many bridges are posted for load limits. It will pay to consult with highway authorities before hauling large loads of logs or lumber over unposted bridges.

The H loadings consist of a two-axle truck in which the number following the H indicates the gross weight of the truck in tons. The HS loadings consist of a two-axle truck and single-axle semitrailer in which the number following the S indicates axle load of the semitrailer in tons. For design purposes the weight of the truck plus its load is presumed to be distributed as shown in Fig. 14. The graphs show H20 and H20–S16 maximum moments and end reactions for different spans.

Moment determination is the measure of the effect of a load which will tend to cause bending in a beam. The end reaction is the measure of the downward pressure exerted by the load at each end of the span, i.e., over the abutments or piers. Where the spans are the same, the moment and end reactions respectively for an H15 load are 75 percent of those for the H20 load, and for an H10 load they are 50 percent of those for the H20 load. Similarly, moments and reactions for

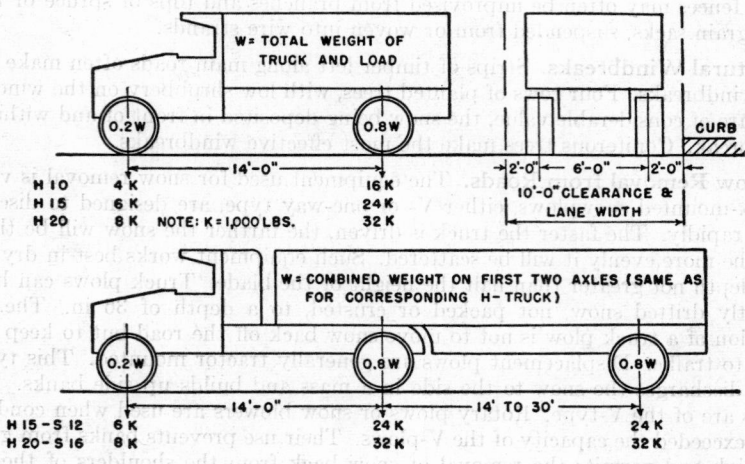

| | 4 K | 16 K |
|---|---|---|
| H 10 | 4 K | 16 K |
| H 15 | 6 K | 24 K |
| H 20 | 8 K | 32 K |

NOTE: K = 1,000 LBS.

| | | | |
|---|---|---|---|
| H 15 - S 12 | 6 K | 24 K | 24 K |
| H 20 - S 16 | 8 K | 32 K | 32 K |

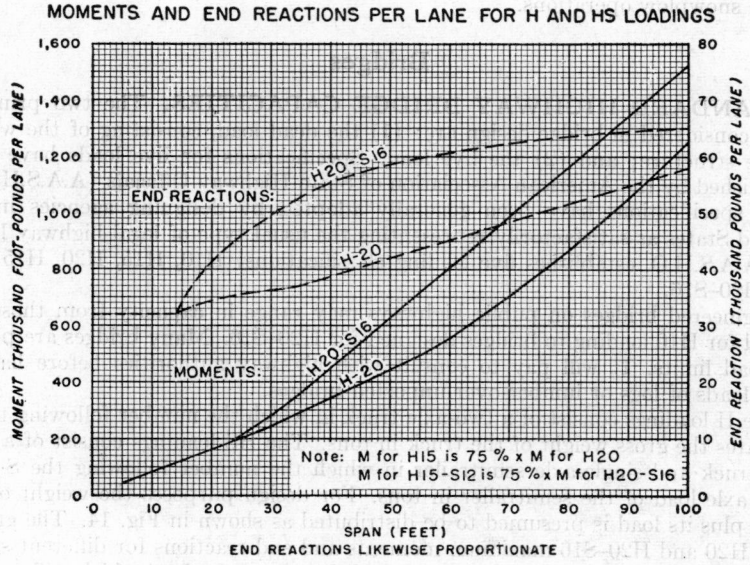

MOMENTS AND END REACTIONS PER LANE FOR H AND HS LOADINGS

Note: M for H15 is 75 % x M for H20
M for H15-S12 is 75 % x M for H20-S16

SPAN (FEET)
END REACTIONS LIKEWISE PROPORTIONATE

Fig. 14. Standard H and HS trucks; moments and end reactions per lane for H and HS loadings.

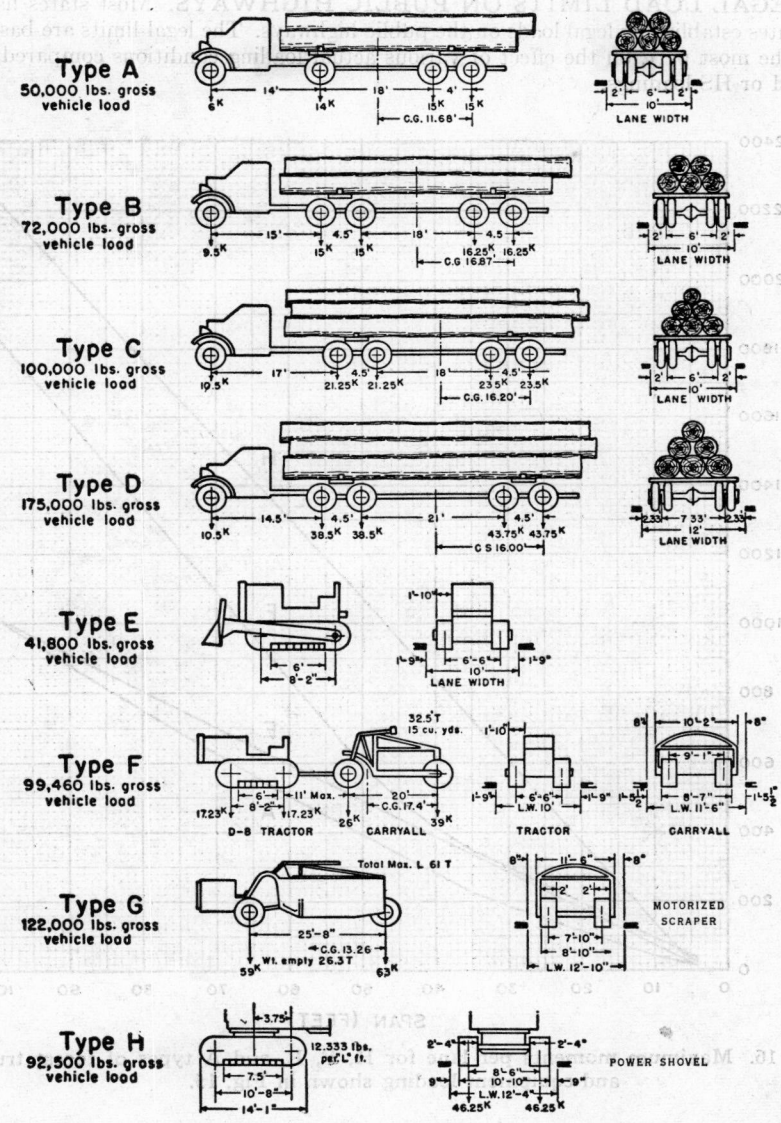

**Type A**
50,000 lbs. gross
vehicle load

**Type B**
72,000 lbs. gross
vehicle load

**Type C**
100,000 lbs. gross
vehicle load

**Type D**
175,000 lbs. gross
vehicle load

**Type E**
41,800 lbs. gross
vehicle load

**Type F**
99,460 lbs. gross
vehicle load

**Type G**
122,000 lbs. gross
vehicle load

**Type H**
92,500 lbs. gross
vehicle load

**Fig. 15. Typical forest truck and equipment loads by types of loading.**

three-axle loads are proportionate; for H15–S12, they are 75 percent of H20–S16.

**LEGAL LOAD LIMITS ON PUBLIC HIGHWAYS.** Most states have statutes establishing legal loads on the public highways. The legal limits are based, for the most part, on the effect of various actual loading conditions compared to the H or HS loadings.

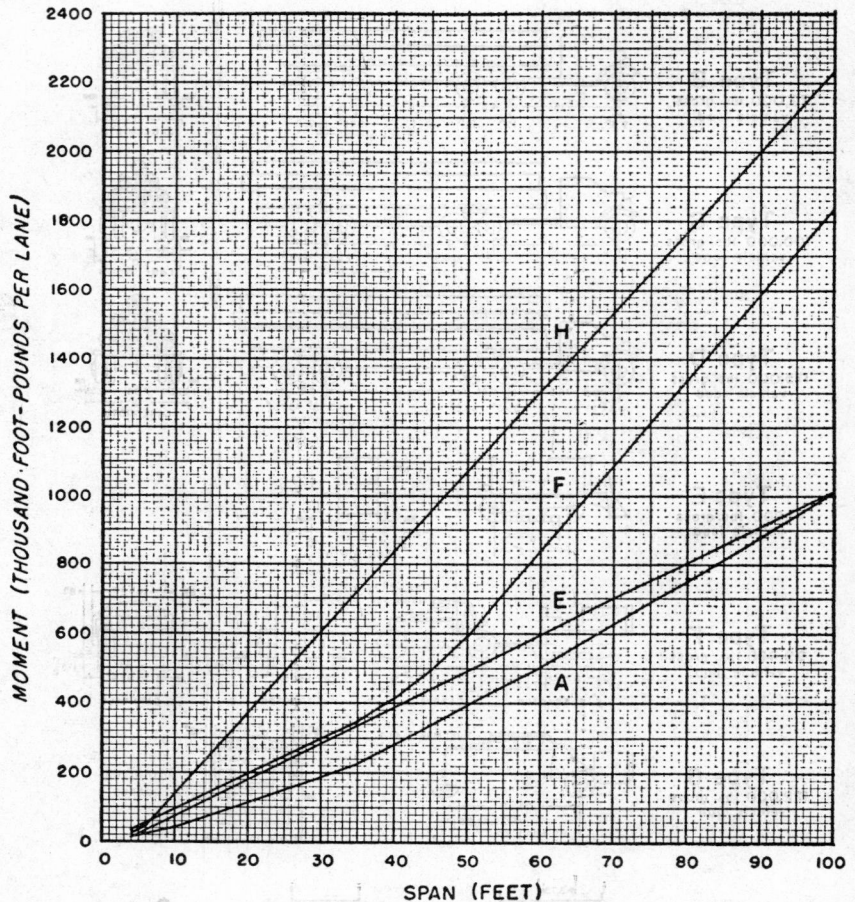

Fig. 16. Maximum moments per lane for H, F, E, and A types of forest truck and equipment loading shown in Fig. 15.

**SPECIAL DESIGN LOADINGS.** Heavy construction equipment and the log truck and trailer loads common in some forest areas will cause effects exceeding those of H and HS loadings. Where these conditions exist, the bridge should be checked for the effect of the actual load.

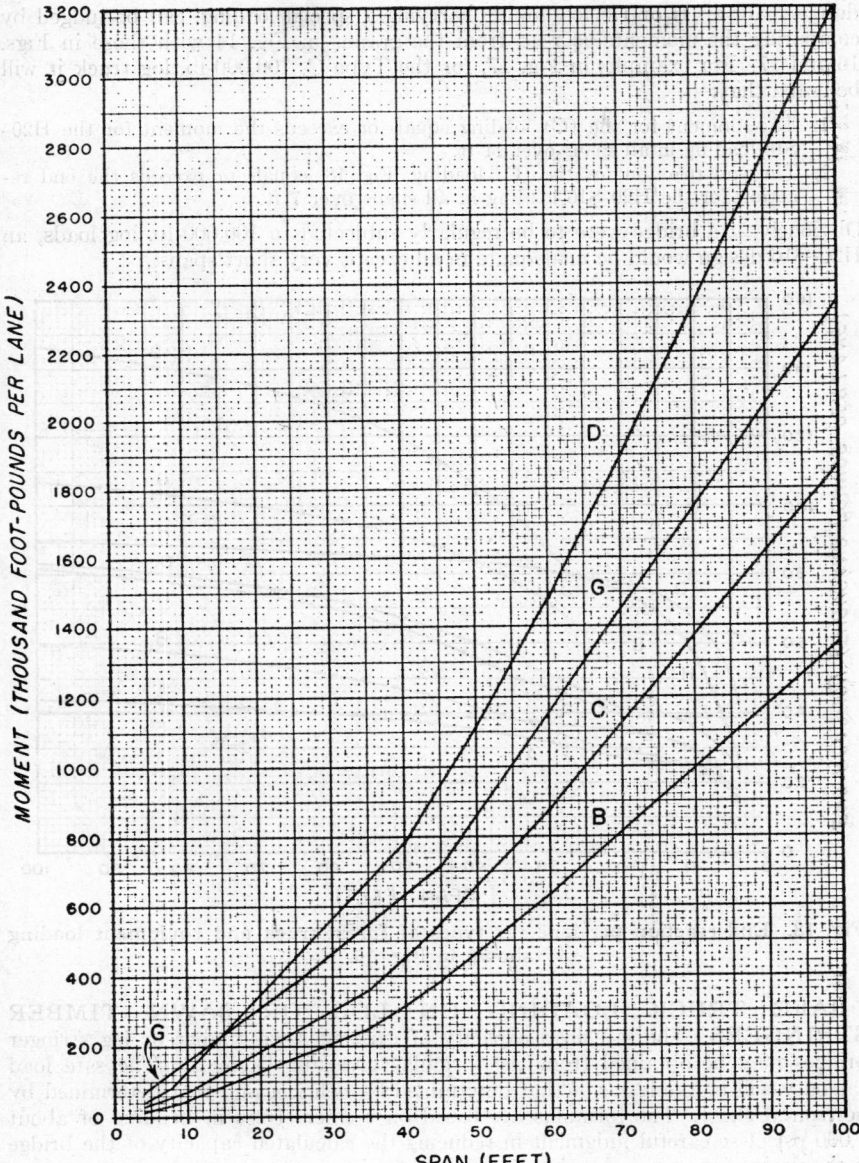

Fig. 17. Maximum moments per lane for D, G, C, and B types of forest truck and equipment loading shown in Fig. 15.

Fig. 15 shows various types of loads for which the moments may be found for different spans from the graphs in Figs. 16 and 17. The relative safety of a bridge designed for an H or HS loading, in carrying a special loading, can be judged by comparing the moments as read from the graphs in Fig. 14 with those in Figs. 16 and 17. For example, in Fig. 17, for the Type C, 100,000-lb. log truck it will be noted that:

1. The moment for the (C) loading equals or exceeds the moment for the H20-S16 loading in all spans over 11 ft.
2. The end reaction for the (C) loading, Fig. 18, equals or exceeds the end reaction for the H20-S16 loading in all spans over 7 ft.

Obviously, if a bridge were to be regularly subjected to 100,000-lb. log loads, an H20-S16 design would be inadequate in all except very short spans.

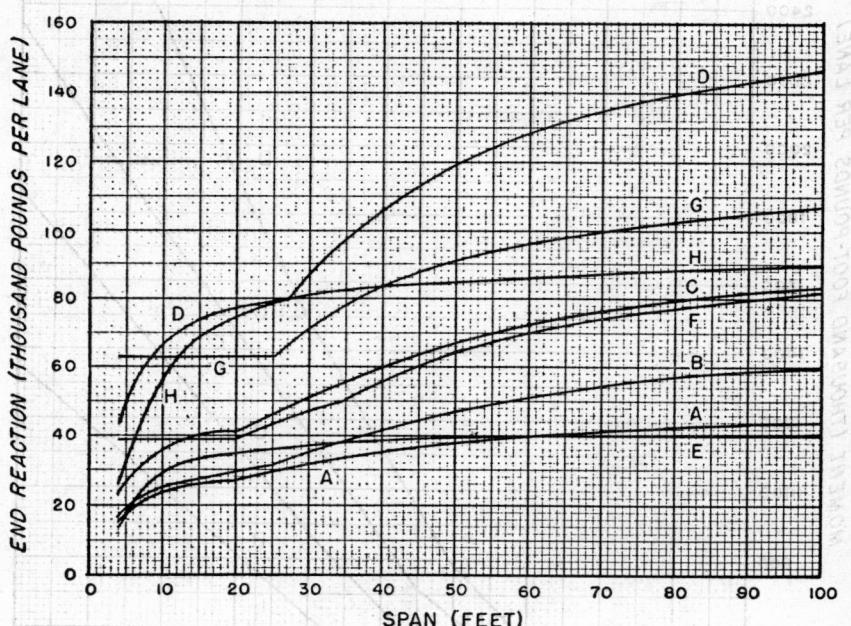

**Fig. 18. End reaction per lane for types of forest truck and equipment loading shown in Fig. 15.**

**SAFE TRUCK LOADING ON LOG OR SAWN TIMBER STRINGERS.** The safe load capacity of existing sawn timber or log stringer bridges may be obtained from the formulas given in Table 22. The safe load capacity will be the lesser of that determined by bending and that determined by horizontal shear. The formulas are based on a fiber stress in bending of about 1,000 psi. Use careful judgment in reducing the calculated capacity of the bridge if the timber is not sound or is of a weaker species.

**Example A.** What is the maximum safe truck loading in tons on a log stringer bridge of 29'0" span where 18-in. log stringers are spaced 2'6" center to center and the allowable fiber stress is 900 psi? The bridge has 3" × 12" floor plank with 3" run planks.

Table 22

```
┌─────────────────────────────────────────────────────────────┐
│         FORMULAE FOR COMPUTING MAXIMUM                       │
│         SAFE TRUCK LOADING ON TIMBER                         │
│                STRINGER BRIDGES                             │
│                                                              │
│    For log stringer bridges with 3"x 12" floor planks       │
│   and 3"run planks in good condition, or 2"x 4" laminated   │
│   deck without run planks.                                   │
│                                                              │
│     T =  .20 D³      For 8'-12' Spans                        │
│          ───────                                            │
│           L S                                               │
│                                               For           │
│     T =  .19 D³      For 13'-18' Spans        Bending       │
│          ───────                                            │
│           L S                                 Also investigate│
│                                               for shear as   │
│     T =  .18 D³      For 19'-24' Spans        shown in formula│
│          ───────                              below.        │
│           L S                                               │
│                                                              │
│     T =  .17 D³      For 25'-30' Spans                       │
│          ───────                                            │
│           L S                                               │
└─────────────────────────────────────────────────────────────┘
```

$$T = \frac{.20\,D^3}{LS} \quad \text{For } 8'\text{-}12' \text{ Spans}$$

$$T = \frac{.19\,D^3}{LS} \quad \text{For } 13'\text{-}18' \text{ Spans}$$

$$T = \frac{.18\,D^3}{LS} \quad \text{For } 19'\text{-}24' \text{ Spans}$$

$$T = \frac{.17\,D^3}{LS} \quad \text{For } 25'\text{-}30' \text{ Spans}$$

For Bending — Also investigate for shear as shown in formula below.

Where:

T = Safe truck loading of bridges in tons.
D = Diameter of logs at center in inches.
L = Span center to center of bearing in feet.
S = Average stringer spacing in feet.
For plank floor bridges without run planks use 80 % of above capacity.

FOR HORIZONTAL SHEAR:

$$T = \frac{A}{3S} \quad \text{For } 8'\text{-}14' \text{ Spans} \qquad T = \frac{A}{4S} \quad \text{For } 15'\text{-}30' \text{ Spans}$$

Where A = Cross-sectional area of stringer in square inches at support and T and S are the same as above.

To compute capacity of sawed timber stringer bridges in bending change stringer to equivalent size log as shown below and use log stringer formula.

For computing shear use area of sawed stringer.

| | | | |
|---|---|---|---|
| 4"x12" =10" Log | 4"x14" =11" Log | 6"x16" =14" Log | 8"x18" =16" Log |
| 6"x12" =11"  " | 6"x14" =13"  " | 8"x16" =15"  " | 10"x18" =18"  " |
| 8"x12" =12"  " | 8"x14" =14"  " | 10"x16" =16"  " | 12"x18" =19"  " |
| 10"x12" =13"  " | 10"x14" =15"  " | 12"x16" =17"  " | 14"x18" =20"  " |
| 12"x12" =14"  " | 12"x14" =16"  " | 14"x16" =18"  " | 16"x18" =21"  " |

Stringers with a depth of more than twice the width should have adequate bracing between them

The above formulae are based on sound Douglas Fir or Tamarack. If timber is not sound a reduction in capacity must be made in accordance with best judgment of investigator.

Use 80 % of above values for sound pine, cedar or spruce.

Computed By: H.H.D                    U.S. Forest Service, R-4

In bending: $T = \dfrac{0.17 D^3}{LS} = \dfrac{0.17 \times 18 \times 18 \times 18}{29 \times 2.5} \times \dfrac{900}{1,000} = 12.3 \text{ tons}$

In shear:  $T = \dfrac{A}{4S} = \dfrac{\pi \times 9 \times 9}{4 \times 2.5} = 25.4 \text{ tons}$

Maximum safe truck loading is 12.3 tons.

## Table 23. Standard Stress Grades and Working Stresses—Soft Woods

| Species | Extreme fiber in bending or tension parallel to grain (psi) | Maximum horizontal shear (psi) | Compression perpendicular to grain (psi) | Compression parallel to grain (psi) ($L/d = 11$ or less) | Modulus of elasticity in bending (psi) |
|---|---|---|---|---|---|
| 1 | 2 | 3 | 4 | 5 | 6 |
| Bald Cypress (southern) | | | | | |
| 1700f structural ..... | 1,700 | 145 | 360 | 1,425 | 1,200,000 |
| 1300f structural..... | 1,300 | 120 | 360 | 1,125 | 1,200,000 |
| Cedars:* | | | | | |
| Red, western 1000f... | 1,000 | 100 | 200 | 800 | 1,000,000 |
| White, Port Orford | | | | | |
| 1200f ............. | 1,200 | 100 | 250 | 1,100 | 1,500,000 |
| Douglas-Fir, coast region | | | | | |
| Dense select structural | 2,150 | 145 | 455 | 1,550 | 1,600,000 |
| Select structural .... | 1,900 | 120 | 415 | 1,450 | 1,600,000 |
| 1700f—Dense No. 1.. | 1,700 | 145 | 455 | 1,325 | 1,600,000 |
| 1450f—No. 1 ........ | 1,450 | 120 | 390 | 1,200 | 1,600,000 |
| Douglas-Fir, inland reg. | | | | | |
| Select structural .... | 2,150 | 145 | 455 | 1,750 | 1,600,000 |
| Structural .......... | 1,900 | 100 | 400 | 1,400 | 1,500,000 |
| Common structural .. | 1,450 | 95 | 380 | 1,250 | 1,500,000 |
| Hemlock, eastern | | | | | |
| Select structural..... | 1,300 | 85 | 360 | 850 | 1,100,000 |
| Prime structural .... | 1,200 | 60 | 360 | 775 | 1,100,000 |
| Common structural .. | 1,100 | 60 | 360 | 650 | 1,100,000 |
| Hemlock, western (West coast) | | | | | |
| 1600f—Select structural ........ | 1,600 | 100 | 360 | 1,100 | 1,400,000 |
| 1450f—No. 1 ........ | 1,450 | 100 | 360 | 1,075 | 1,400,000 |
| 1100f—No. 2 ........ | 1,100 | 90 | 360 | 850 | 1,400,000 |
| Larch, western | | | | | |
| Select structural .... | 2,150 | 145 | 455 | 1,750 | 1,500,000 |
| Structural .......... | 1,900 | 120 | 415 | 1,450 | 1,500,000 |
| Common structural .. | 1,450 | 120 | 390 | 1,325 | 1,500,000 |
| Pine, red (Norway) | | | | | |
| Prime structural .... | 1,200 | 75 | 360 | 900 | 1,200,000 |
| Common structural .. | 1,100 | 75 | 360 | 775 | 1,200,000 |
| Utility structural ... | 950 | 75 | 360 | 650 | 1,200,000 |
| Pine, southern | | | | | |
| Dense select structural ............. | 2,400 | 120 | 455 | 1,750 | 1,600,000 |
| Dense structural .... | 2,000 | 120 | 455 | 1,400 | 1,600,000 |
| Dense struc. S.E. & S. | 1,800 | 120 | 455 | 1,300 | 1,600,000 |
| Dense No. 1 structural | 1,600 | 120 | 455 | 1,150 | 1,600,000 |
| Pine, south, longleaf | | | | | |
| Select structural .... | 2,400 | 120 | 455 | 1,750 | 1,600,000 |
| Prime structural .... | 2,000 | 120 | 455 | 1,400 | 1,600,000 |
| Struc. S.E. & S. .... | 1,800 | 120 | 455 | 1,300 | 1,600,000 |
| No. 1 structural ..... | 1,600 | 120 | 455 | 1,150 | 1,600,000 |
| Redwood | | | | | |
| Dense structural .... | 1,700 | 110 | 320 | 1,450 | 1,200,000 |
| Heart structural .... | 1,300 | 95 | 320 | 1,100 | 1,200,000 |
| Spruce, eastern | | | | | |
| 1450f structural .... | 1,450 | 110 | 300 | 1,050 | 1,200,000 |
| 1300f structural .... | 1,300 | 95 | 300 | 975 | 1,200,000 |
| 1200f structural .... | 1,200 | 95 | 300 | 900 | 1,200,000 |

* From A.A.S.H.O. Standard Specifications for Highway Bridges, 1949 edition. All other data abridged from N.L.M.A. National Design Specifications for Stress Grade Lumber and Its Fastenings, revised 1948.

## Table 24. Standard Stress Grades and Working Stresses—Hard Woods

| Species | Extreme fiber in bending or tension parallel to grain (psi) | Maximum horizontal shear (psi) | Compression perpendicular to grain (psi) | Compression parallel to grain (psi) ($L/d = 11$ or less) | Modulus of elasticity in bending (psi) |
|---|---|---|---|---|---|
| 1 | 2 | 3 | 4 | 5 | 6 |
| **Ash, white** | | | | | |
| 2150f Grade ........ | 2,150 | 145 | 600 | 1,700 | 1,500,000 |
| 1900f Grade ........ | 1,900 | 145 | 600 | 1,500 | 1,500,000 |
| 1700f Grade ........ | 1,700 | 145 | 600 | 1,325 | 1,500,000 |
| 1450f Grade ........ | 1,450 | 120 | 600 | 1,150 | 1,500,000 |
| **Beech, birch, hard maple** | | | | | |
| 2150f Grade ........ | 2,150 | 145 | 600 | 1,750 | 1,600,000 |
| 1900f Grade ........ | 1,900 | 145 | 600 | 1,525 | 1,600,000 |
| 1700f Grade ........ | 1,700 | 145 | 600 | 1,350 | 1,600,000 |
| 1450f Grade ........ | 1,450 | 120 | 600 | 1,150 | 1,600,000 |
| **Elm, rock** | | | | | |
| 2150f Grade ........ | 2,150 | 145 | 600 | 1,750 | 1,300,000 |
| 1900f Grade ........ | 1,900 | 145 | 600 | 1,525 | 1,300,000 |
| 1700f Grade ........ | 1,700 | 145 | 600 | 1,350 | 1,300,000 |
| 1450f Grade ........ | 1,450 | 120 | 600 | 1,150 | 1,300,000 |
| **Elm, soft** | | | | | |
| 1700f Grade ........ | 1,700 | 120 | 300 | 1,225 | 1,200,000 |
| 1450f Grade ........ | 1,450 | 120 | 300 | 1,050 | 1,200,000 |
| 1200f Grade ........ | 1,200 | 120 | 300 | 875 | 1,200,000 |
| **Gum, black and red** | | | | | |
| 1700f Grade ........ | 1,700 | 120 | 360 | 1,225 | 1,200,000 |
| 1450f Grade ........ | 1,450 | 120 | 360 | 1,050 | 1,200,000 |
| 1200f Grade ........ | 1,200 | 120 | 360 | 875 | 1,200,000 |
| **Hickory** | | | | | |
| 2150f Grade ........ | 2,150 | 145 | 720 | 1,725 | 1,800,000 |
| 1900f Grade ........ | 1,900 | 145 | 720 | 1,550 | 1,800,000 |
| 1700f Grade ........ | 1,700 | 145 | 720 | 1,350 | 1,800,000 |
| **Oak, red and white** | | | | | |
| 2150f Grade ........ | 2,150 | 145 | 600 | 1,550 | 1,500,000 |
| 1900f Grade ........ | 1,900 | 145 | 600 | 1,375 | 1,500,000 |
| 1700f Grade ........ | 1,700 | 145 | 600 | 1,200 | 1,500,000 |
| 1450f Grade ........ | 1,450 | 120 | 600 | 1,050 | 1,500,000 |
| **Poplar, yellow** | | | | | |
| 1500f Grade ........ | 1,500 | 110 | 300 | 1,200 | 1,100,000 |
| 1250f Grade ........ | 1,250 | 110 | 300 | 950 | 1,100,000 |
| **Tupelo** | | | | | |
| 1700f Grade ........ | 1,700 | 120 | 360 | 1,225 | 1,200,000 |
| 1450f Grade ........ | 1,450 | 120 | 360 | 1,050 | 1,200,000 |
| 1200f Grade ........ | 1,200 | 120 | 360 | 875 | 1,200,000 |

The formula may be used for determining the safe capacity of bridges for loads equivalent to conventional truck loading by a comparison of moment values shown by graphs in Figs. 14 and 17.

**Example B.** Is a bridge of 23-ft. span safe for the Type B load shown in Fig. 15 if the stringers are $8 \times 18$-in. timbers on 19-in. centers and allowable fiber stress is 1,000 psi? Eight by 18-in. rectangular timbers are equal to similarly spaced log stringers 16 in. in diameter.

$$\text{Bending: } T = \frac{0.18 D^3}{LS} = \frac{0.18 \times 16 \times 16 \times 16}{23 \times 1.6} \times \frac{1,000}{1,000} = 20.0 \text{ tons}$$

$$\text{Shear: } T = \frac{A}{4S} = \frac{\pi \times 9 \times 9}{4 \times 2.5} = 31.4 \text{ tons}$$

From Fig. 14, bending moment for a 20-ton truck (using the smaller of the allowable tonnages just computed), on a 23-ft. span is read as 180,000 ft.-lb. From Fig. 17, bending moment for Type B load is read as 150,000 ft.-lb. The bridge is therefore safe for the Type B load.

**PLANNING NEW BRIDGES.** Bridges of most concern to the forester will ordinarily consist of either log or sawn timber stringers for relatively short spans, or timber trusses for longer spans. Where a major bridge is required or construction with permanent materials is contemplated, a bridge engineer should be consulted in planning the project. Regardless of the size or type of construction, care is needed in planning the waterway capacity, foundations, and stringers or other span members.

**Investigation of Site and Required Waterway. Alignment.** Other things being equal, choose a site where curvature on and off the bridge is at a minimum. If necessary, to reduce undesirable curvature, stringer bridges may be skewed with respect to the stream channel, provided the piers and abutments are located parallel to the direction of the stream. Skews with truss bridges should be avoided because of the longer span required and the structural complications which are incurred.

**Channel.** The channel adjacent to the site should be straight, with uniform profile and unobstructed flow. Look for stable banks and avoid locations where drift may lodge, forcing the stream to one side, with resultant channel or bank scour.

**Waterway.** For bridges of untreated timber (temporary) construction, the waterway beneath the bridge should at least be adequate to pass a volume of runoff which might be expected to occur an average of once in 25 yr. Bridges built of treated timber or other permanent materials should have a waterway adequate for at least a 50-yr. flood. If no runoff records are available for the particular stream, use those for similar adjacent watersheds. Confirm the high-water elevation thus determined by an intensive search for high-water marks up and downstream from the bridge, by questioning local residents, and by investigation of the performance of any other bridges in the vicinity.

**Site survey and bridge layout.** As a minimum, the bridge survey should consist of determining the profile along the center line of the roadway, including the channel bottom, and extended at least 200 ft. beyond the ends of the bridge. Plot the profile to a natural scale of 10 ft. per in. and draw on it the high-water elevation.

Giving full consideration to the clearance between high water and the underside of the structure for free passage of drift or ice, establish the bridge grade line on the profile for satisfactory continuity with the approach roads. Place the bottom of the stringers at least 3 ft. above maximum high water. Generally the bridge deck should be on a level grade. Inclined grades complicate construction, reduce stream clearance at one end or the other, and, with wood decks, are hazardous to traffic.

Determine the layout for the bridge and indicate on the profile the location of the piers and abutments. If drift in the stream is a factor, locate the piers, respective to the main high-water current, for free passage of full-length trees. Avoid pockets between the banks and piers where drift may lodge and threaten the stability of the pier. In establishing the over-all length of the bridge, do not crowd the channel to the point where velocity of the stream will be increased, inducing scour. Consider the effect of channel piers in obstructing the waterway area and the resultant increased velocity between them.

**Foundations. Subsurface investigation.** Comparative stability, permanence, and lower maintenance should be weighed in deciding whether concrete, treated or untreated timber, or logs will be used for the piers and abutments of the bridge. Regardless of type, subsurface investigation should precede the design. Rod soundings or auger borings in earth that is relatively free of boulders and open test pits are common methods. The investigation will give information for determining the bearing capacity of the foundation material, the required depth of excavation for scour protection, the firmness of the soil, its water content, and the extent of sheathing and bracing that may be required in excavation for the footings.

Table 25 gives allowable bearing pressure which may safely be used for footings on various types of soils.

**Table 25. Allowable Bearing Pressure for Footings**

| Soil: General description | Condition | Safe allowable pressure (psf) |
|---|---|---|
| **Fine-grained soils:** Clays, silts, very fine sands, or mixtures of these containing few coarse particles of sand or gravel | Soft, unconsolidated, having high moisture content (mud) ...... | 1,000 |
| | Stiff, partly consolidated, medium moisture content ........... | 4,000 |
| | Hard, well-consolidated, low moisture content (slightly damp to dry) ............... | 8,000 |
| Sands and well-graded sandy soils containing some silt and clay... | Loose, not confined ........... | 3,000 |
| | Loose, confined ............... | 5,000 |
| | Compact ..................... | 10,000 |
| Gravel and well-graded gravelly soils containing some sand, silt, and clay ..................... | Loose, not confined ........... | 4,000 |
| | Loose, confined ............... | 6,000 |
| | Compact ..................... | 12,000 |
| | Cemented sand and gravel ...... | 16,000 |
| Rock ......................... | Poor quality rock, soft and fractured; also hardpan .......... | 10,000 |
| | Good quality; hard and solid.... | 20,000* |

\* Minimum.

**Abutments and Piers.** Abutment is the term applied to the supports at the ends of the bridge. Piers are intermediate supports between abutments. Each abutment is designed and constructed to support its own weight, its share of the dead load of the bridge, the live load, and the horizontal pressure of earth backfill behind the abutment. The combination of horizontal and vertical loads can tend to produce uplift at the heel (bank face) of the abutment and consequent instability. The horizontal pressure should therefore be counteracted with anchor rods or cables attached near the top of the abutment, anchor logs in the case of log crib abutments, spread footings or batter in the case of concrete abutments.

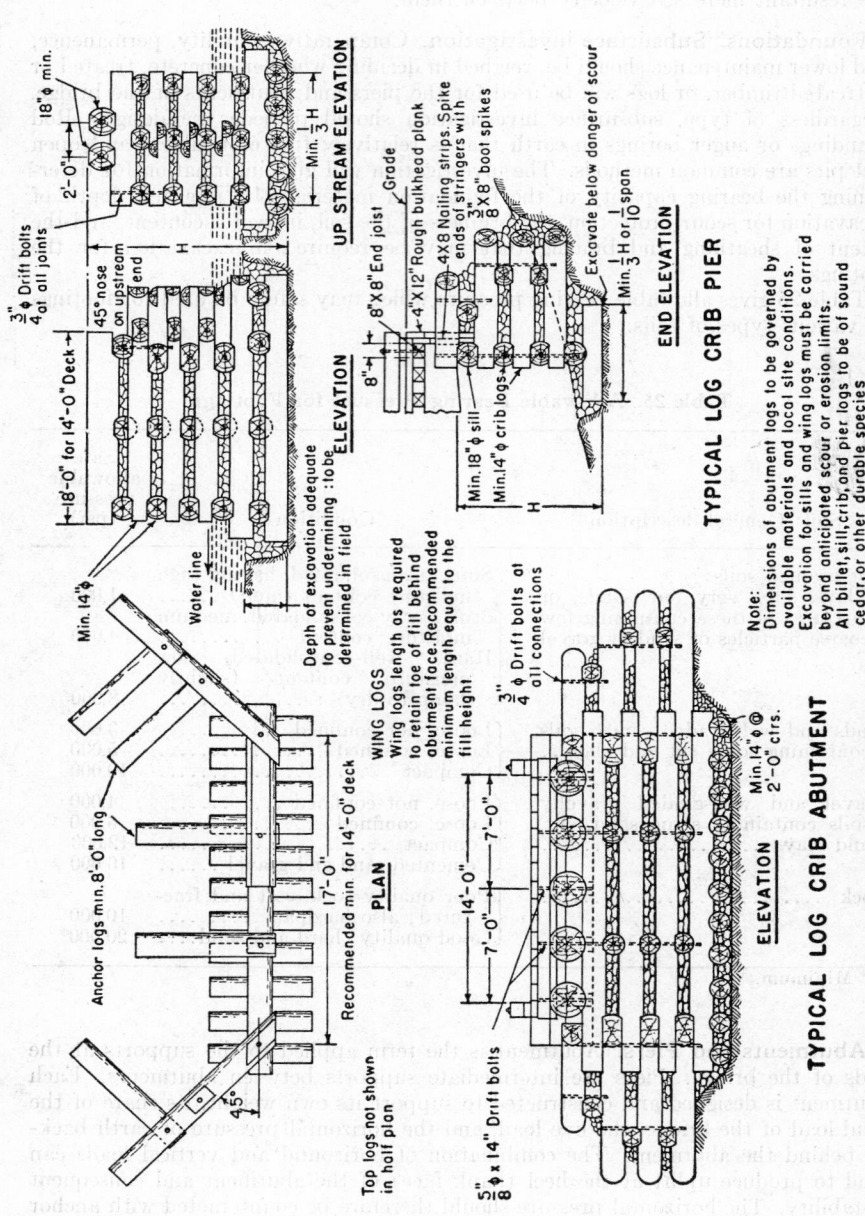

**Fig. 19.** Typical log crib abutment and pier for log stringer bridge.

Reference should be made to engineering handbooks for the design of concrete abutments.

Fig. 19 illustrates a typical log crib abutment.

Bridge piers may be (1) a single row or bent of piles; or (2) double bents (by end elevation), as shown in Fig. 20, where two rows of piling are braced together for greater lateral and longitudinal stability, often needed to support the ends of adjoining log stringer spans; or (3) concrete construction. Double-bent construction is simple, causes least waterway obstruction, and is generally most satisfactory except where impact from drift or the pressure and abrasion of ice is probable. If adequate protection cannot be obtained by sheathing on the outside faces of the double bent or by fender piles, log crib or concrete construction may be necessary.

Cribs are built up log-cabin fashion with notched and doweled joints. The width at the base is not less than one-third the height. The interior of the crib is filled with rock larger than the openings between the logs to give the pier weight and stability. Concrete piers should be used for important structures or where permanence is desirable from the standpoint of avoiding future replacement costs. For any type of pier construction be sure that the footing is sufficiently imbedded for safety against undermining and that the soil bearing pressure is within the allowable limit.

The average pressure from the vertical load on the ground underlying a pier is obtained by dividing the total vertical load on the pier by its total footing area. The footing is then proportioned so as to keep the pressure within the allowable bearing pressure for the soil.

**Example C.** Required—footing area for the pier of a 17-ft. span where the dead load weight of bridge is 600 lb. per running ft.; live load H20-S16 (from Fig. 14), maximum end reaction pressure is 37,700 lb.; weight of pier is 25 tons; and the pier will be supported by loose but well-graded gravel having an allowable bearing pressure of 4,000 lb. per sq. ft. (see Table 25). Call the length of the bridge 19 ft. in order to allow for the end of the stringer which rests on the pier. Half of the bridge will rest on each pier, whence

$$\frac{(9.5 \times 600) + 37.700 + 50.000}{4,000} = 23.4 \text{ sq. ft.} = \text{required area of footing}$$

**Excavation for footings.** In order to obtain satisfactory imbedment safe from scour, most pier construction will require excavation through water. The excavation will have to be unwatered for inspection of the foundation material, leveling the footing areas, seating the footing sills, or pouring the footing concrete. Cofferdam construction will normally be required to control infiltration of water and caving of sides of excavation. Give careful thought to the construction of the cofferdam for structural adequacy, ease of excavation through its braces, and subsequent placement of sills or construction of concrete forms.

For timber pier or abutment sills founded on bedrock, whether near the ground line or under water, a sloping surface should be leveled by cutting the rock into steps and pouring a concrete base to a uniform elevation. Footings for concrete piers or abutments on rock will likewise be excavated and stepped, when required, to key the structure into the rock for resistance to movement.

**Piles.** In soft material with low bearing pressure and susceptibility to scour, or in deep water where it is difficult and expensive to excavate for and found spread footings, pile foundations may be necessary. Piles develop their load capacity by skin friction, by column action, or by a combination of the two. The

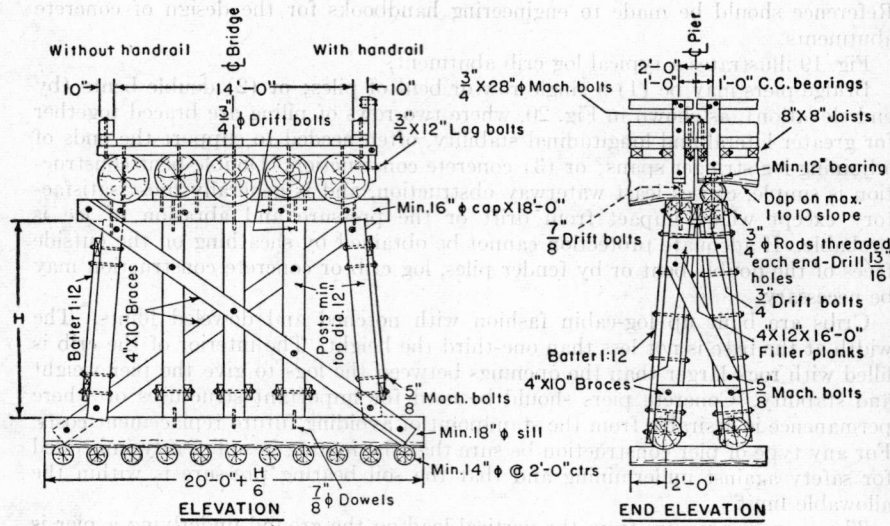

**TYPICAL DOUBLE BENT PIER**

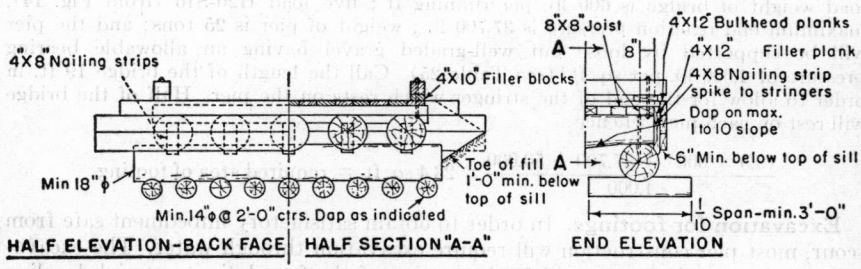

**TYPICAL MUD SILL ABUTMENT**

**Note:**
All billet, sill, crib and pier logs to be
of sound cedar, or other durable species

**Fig. 20. Typical double-bent pier and abutment for log stringer bridge.**

required load capacity of the pile determines how deep it is to be driven. However, to assure adequate lateral support for the pile, the penetration should never be less than 8 ft. For this reason avoid the use of piles in boulder streambeds where adequate penetration is impracticable, or where hardpan or bedrock is relatively close to the surface.

Table 26 will help in determining the estimated length of timber pile required to develop the required load capacity in various types of soils. The estimated capacity of timber piles which derive their support principally from skin friction

## Table 26. Timber Pile Load Capacity

| | Range of safe load, in tons per foot of penetration for pile of mean diameter * | | |
|---|---|---|---|
| Soil type | 9" | 12" | 15" |
| **Fine-grained soils:** Clays, silts, very fine sands or mixtures containing few coarse sand and gravel particles | | | |
| Condition 1: Soft, unconsolidated, high moisture content (mud) ...................... | 0.1 –0.15 | 0.13–0.2 | 0.16–0.25 |
| Condition 2: Stiff, partly consolidated, medium moisture content ........................ | 0.15–0.4 | 0.2 –0.6 | 0.25–0.8 |
| Condition 3: Hard, well consolidated, low moisture content (slightly damp or dry).... | 0.4 –0.9 | 0.6 –1.2 | 0.8 –1.5 |
| Sands and well-graded sandy soils containing some silt and clay ........................... | 0.6 –1.2 | 0.8 –1.6 | 1.0 –2.0 |
| Gravel, well-graded sandy soils containing some sand, silt, and clay ......................... | 0.7 –2.0 | 1.0 –2.5 | 1.2 –3.0 |

* For other pile diameters, safe load varies in proportion to diameter. Pile must be driven at least 8 ft. in firm ground and 15 to 20 ft. in soft ground. Piles resting on a hard stratum act as columns and the above tabulation does not apply.

should be confirmed by application of the following formulas, using data obtained during driving:

1. Piles driven by drop hammers.

$$\text{Wood piles } P = \frac{2w_d h}{s + 1.0}$$

2. Piles driven by single-acting steam or pneumatic hammer.

$$\text{Wood piles } P = \frac{2W_r H}{s + 0.1}$$

3. Piles driven by double-acting steam or pneumatic hammer.

$$\text{Wood piles } P = \frac{3H(W_r + Am)}{s + 0.1}$$

where $h$ = average height in feet of fall of drop hammer for last six blows
$H$ = stroke of ram in inches
$P$ = estimated safe load capacity in pounds per pile
$s$ = average pile penetration in inches per blow for the last six blows of drop hammer or last twenty blows of pneumatic or steam hammer (For small values of $s$, the formula does not give consistent results. In that case, an average may be taken for several adjacent piles driven to approximately the same penetration.)
$w_d$ = weight of drop hammer in pounds
$W_r$ = weight of ram of steam or pneumatic hammer in pounds
$A$ = area of piston in square inches
$m$ = air or steam pressure in pounds per square inch

Unless the full length of the pile will be below ground water line, select the most durable species available for use as piles. The piles should be cut from straight, sound trees having a uniform taper from butt to tip. A straight line from the center of the butt to the center of the tip should be within the body of the pile. If possible, piles should be cut in the winter or late fall and the bark should be peeled soon after cutting. Pressure-creosoted piling is recommended for permanent bridges.

Sharpen the tips of all piles, and, in hard driving, protect the points with steel shoes. Expedient shoes made of two pieces of ¼-in. strap iron welded together in the form of a cross, bent up and nailed to the sharpened point of the pile, are effective. Wire wrap or ring the head of the pile to control crushing and prevent splitting under impact from the hammer. For best efficiency and least damage to the pile, use a drop hammer weighing twice as much as the pile (see Table 27). Use care in positioning the piles and in holding them to their correct position during driving. If the pile persists in drifting out of line, pull it and start over.

**Table 27. Drop Hammer Weights for Pile Driving**

| Weight of hammer in pounds (for maximum fall of 10 ft.) | Recommended maximum length of wood pile (ft.) | Recommended maximum weight of pile (lb.) |
| --- | --- | --- |
| 1,200 drop hammer ................. | 25 | 600 |
| 1,800 drop hammer ................. | 30 | 900 |
| 2,500 drop hammer ................. | 40 | 1,250 |
| 3,000 drop hammer or steam or pneumatic hammer ............. | 50 | 1,500 |

A pile is driven to its limiting strength when driven to refusal; that is, when the last six blows will not drive it more than ⅛ in. per blow. If the amount of penetration at refusal is inadequate, use jets or light charges of dynamite at the bottom of the hole to pass obstruction. Avoid overdriving, which may break, broom, or crush the pile.

**Stringer Sizes.** When using local materials, the choice of stringer types will be controlled by the availability of materials to meet the strength requirements for the span. Sawn timber stringers, inasmuch as they are cut from the heart of the tree, thereby removing the faster decaying sapwood, are preferred over log stringers. However, the limitations on commercially available sizes of sawn timber may require the use of log stringers for spans over 25 or 30 ft. Except in the best old growth areas, limitations on diameters will prohibit consideration of log stringer spans of more than 60 or 70 ft.

**Formulas used in determining stringer sizes for resistance to bending.**

1. $\dfrac{Wl^2}{8}$ = Maximum bending moment for uniformly distributed load, in foot-pounds

2. $bh^2 = \dfrac{6M}{f}$ for rectangular timbers

3. $D^3 = \dfrac{10M}{f}$ for round timbers and logs

where $M$ = moment of dead load plus live load, in inch-pounds
$l$ = length of span, in feet
$W$ = weight of floor and stringers in pounds per foot of span
$b$ = width of stringer, in inches
$h$ = depth of stringer, in inches
$D$ = diameter of round timber, inside bark, at small end of log, in inches
$f$ = extreme fiber stress in bending, in pounds per square inch (obtainable from tables of allowable unit stresses for the species of timber available)

Unit work stress values found in most tables of allowable stresses apply to lumber which will be used under continuously dry conditions, to pressure-treated lumber for open exposure, and to the heartwood of a durable species under dry conditions of use. A 10 percent reduction of such values is recommended for untreated sawn timber subjected to alternate wet and dry conditions.

For the allowable stress in log stringers, considering the sapwood present, the exposure to which the stringer will be subjected, and the unknown defects which may be present in the interior of the log, it is recommended that no more than 67 percent of tabular values be used. The basic grade of the log as compared to the grade of lumber for which the allowable stress is given in tables must depend on the judgment of the bridge designer. Full consideration should be given to ring count, density, knots, shake, spiral grain, or other defects.

**Shear Stresses.** Shear stresses are approximately the same for a given load, regardless of length of span. Generally no shear calculations are required for long spans because the bending stress determines the size of beam required. In the field, shear calculations are seldom necessary. No calculations need be made for round timbers. For rectangular timber no shear calculation need be made for spans which are twelve or more times the depth of a beam under a distributed load, or seven or more times the depth of a beam under a concentrated load.

**Flooring.** Bridge floors must be rigid enough to distribute the weight of the vehicle and its load to all stringers. Minima are as follows for

1. General utility bridges:
    a. Either lay plank at least 3 in. thick solidly across stringers, with three 3 × 12-in. run planks in each wheel track, lengthwise of the bridge, or
    b. Lay 2 × 4's, on edge, or 6-in. poles flattened to 4 in., to form a solidly laminated floor.

2. Heavy-duty bridges (or on light bridges, where center-to-center spacing of log stringers exceeds 30 in.): Lay timbers or logs across the stringers to serve as floor joists, and lay flooring, 3 in. or thicker, solidly on the joists lengthwise of the bridge. Spike or drift-bolt all flooring and joists securely to the stringers.

**Determining Size of Stringers Required for Specified Conditions.** Fig. 22 suggests the number and size of sawed stringers of Douglas-fir or larch for bridges with spans 11 to 39 ft.

**Example.** The following calculation shows how to use Formula 1, page **18·50**, in checking tabular values under specific conditions:
Assume a one-lane bridge to carry H20-S16 loads; span between abutments of 25 ft.; 3-in. plank floor; run planks 3 in. thick (ignore the fact that they are laid only in wheel tracks); $f = 1,000$ lb. per sq. in.; all wood weighing 40 lb. per cu. ft. Assume also that ten stringers will be used, spaced 18 in., center to center. How large should the stringers be?

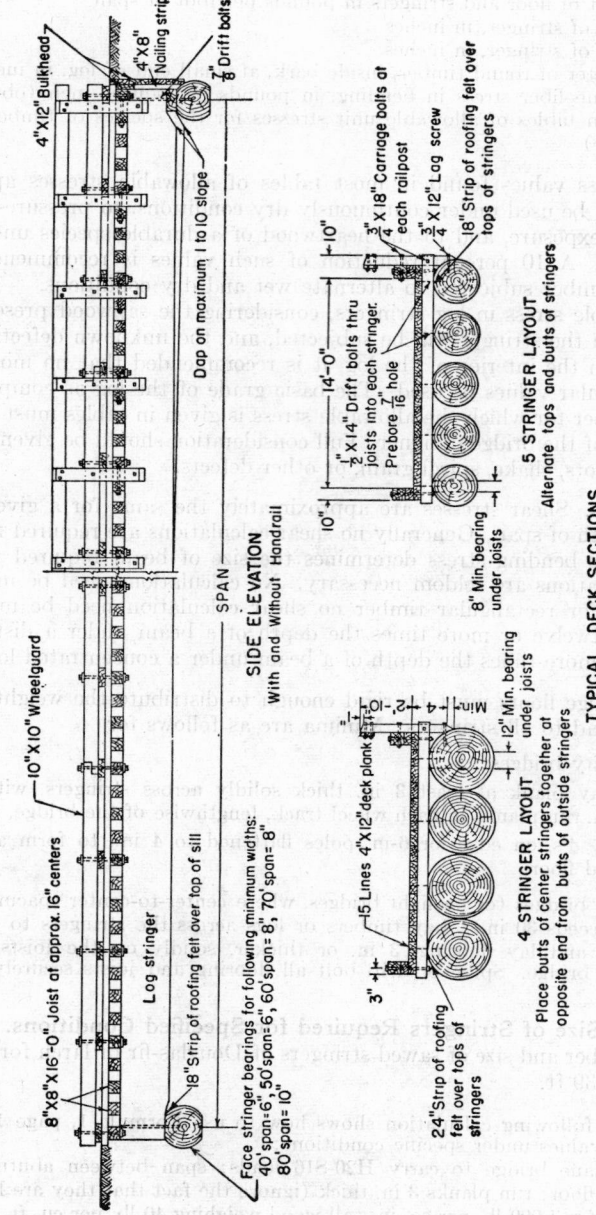

**SIDE ELEVATION**
With and Without Handrail

**TYPICAL DECK SECTIONS**
With and Without Handrail

**5 STRINGER LAYOUT**
Alternate tops and butts of stringers

**4 STRINGER LAYOUT**
Place butts of center stringers together at
opposite end from butts of outside stringers

**Fig. 21. U. S. Forest Service, Region 6, log stringer bridge.**

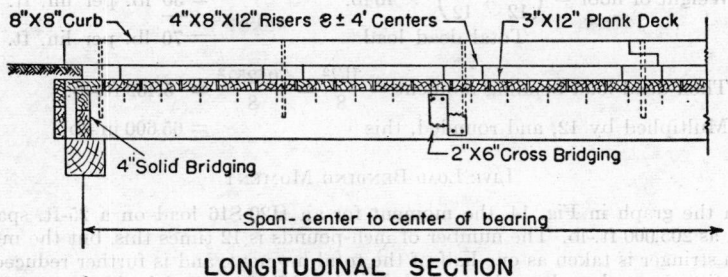

8"X8"Curb — 4"X8"X12"Risers 8±4' Centers — 3"X12" Plank Deck

4"Solid Bridging — 2"X6"Cross Bridging

Span- center to center of bearing

## LONGITUDINAL SECTION

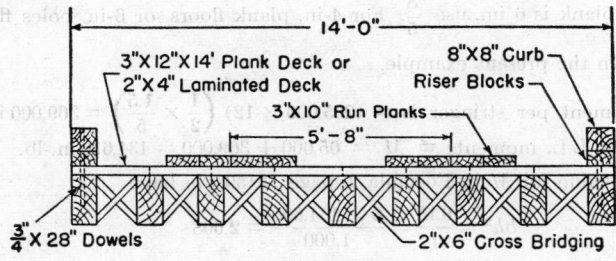

14'-0"

3"X12"X14' Plank Deck or 2"X4" Laminated Deck — 8"X8" Curb / Riser Blocks

3"X10" Run Planks

5'-8"

¾"X 28" Dowels — 2"X6"Cross Bridging

## CROSS SECTION

## STRINGER TABLE*

| SPAN | STRINGERS |
|------|-----------|
| 11 | 7 – 8" X 14" X 12' |
| 13 | 8 – 8" X 14" X 14' |
| 15 | 9 – 8" X 14" X 16' |
| 17 | 8 – 8" X 16" X 18' |
| 19 | 9 – 8" X 16" X 20' |
| 21 | 10 – 8" X 16" X 22' |
| 23 | 9 – 8" X 18" X 24' |
| 25 | 10 – 8" X 18" X 26' |
| 27 | 9 – 10" X 18" X 28' |
| 29 | 10 – 10" X 18" X 30' |
| 31 | 11 – 10" X 18" X 32' |
| 33 | 12 – 10" X 18" X 34' |
| 35 | 11 – 10" X 20" X 36' |
| 37 | 12 – 10" X 20" X 38' |
| 39 | 12 – 12" X 20" X 40' |

*For H20–S16 loading use No. 1 Common Rocky Mountain Douglas Fir or Larch. Design fiber stress 1000 lbs. per sq. in., horizontal shear 100 lbs. per sq. in.

For H30–S24 loading use size and number of stringers as shown for 4' longer span or use 1450f stress grade No.1 Douglas Fir Beams and Stringers of the number and size as shown in table.

Decking Notes: Fasten floor plank to stringers with 60d nails. Fasten run plank to floor with ½"x 5"lag screws and cut washers. Space at 2' alternate centers and place 2 lag screws at each end of each plank. Countersink lag screws flush with top of plank. Stagger joints in plank.

Fig. 22. U. S. Forest Service, Region 4, timber stringer bridge.

### DEAD LOAD BENDING MOMENT

Assume weight for each stringer will be        40 lb. per lin. ft.

Weight of floor $= \left( \dfrac{18}{12} \times \dfrac{6}{12} \right) \times 40$ lb.      $= 30$ lb. per lin. ft.

           Total dead load           $= 70$ lb. per lin. ft.

Then dead load bending moment $= \dfrac{Wl^2}{8} = \dfrac{70(25)^2}{8} = 5{,}469$ ft.-lb.

Multiplied by 12, and rounded, this        $= 65{,}600$ in.-lb.

### LIVE LOAD BENDING MOMENT

From the graph in Fig. 14, the moment for an H20-S16 load on a 25-ft. span can be read as 205,000 ft.-lb. The number of inch-pounds is 12 times this, but the moment on each stringer is taken as one-half of the total moment, and is further reduced by a distribution factor based on the stringer spacing ($S$) expressed in feet.

For load distribution per stringer when $S$ is 4 ft. or less, and combined thickness of floor and run plank is 6 in., use $\dfrac{S}{5}$. For 4-in. plank floors, or 6-in. poles flattened to 4 in., use $\dfrac{S}{4}$. In the present example,

Live load moment per stringer is $= (205{,}000 \times 12) \left( \dfrac{1}{2} \times \dfrac{1.5}{5} \right) = 369{,}000$ in.-lb.

Total D.L. and L.L. moments $= M = 65{,}600 + 369{,}000 = 434{,}600$ in.-lb.

Substituting this value for $M$ in Formula 2, page **18·50**, we have

$$bh^2 = \frac{6M}{f} = \frac{6 \times 434{,}600}{1{,}000} = 2{,}608$$

A stringer $8 \times 18$ inches ($8 \times 18 \times 18 = 2{,}592$ in this formula) satisfies the requirement within 1 percent. A stringer $10 \times 16$ in. does nearly as well, and one $12 \times 16$ in. is even better. But at 40 lb. to the cu. ft., the $8 \times 18$-in. stringer weighs only 40 lb. per lin. ft. (the assumed weight), whereas the other dimensions weigh 11 to 25 percent more. The $8 \times 18$-in. stringer is obviously the best choice. If its weight were materially higher than the assumed 40 lb., the D.L. moment should be recalculated.

The stringer table in Fig. 22 shows ten $8 \times 18$ stringers for an H20-S16 load on a 25-ft. span, which agrees with the above calculation.

**Log stringers.** For log stringers the procedure is the same as above except that the formula for bending stress is $D^3 = 10M/f$.

**Example.** Assume 6 logs, spaced 30 in. center to center, for H15 loading on a 21-ft. span; roadway width 14 ft.; 3-in. plank floor, with 3-in run plank; $f = 900$; and wood weighing 36 lb. per cu. ft.

### DEAD LOAD BENDING MOMENT

Assume weight for each stringer $= 64$ lb. per lin. ft.
Weight of floor per stringer

$$\frac{1}{6} \left( 14 \times \frac{6}{12} \right) \times 36 \text{ lb.} = 42 \text{ lb. per lin. ft.}$$

       Total dead load          $= 106$ lb. per lin. ft.

Dead load bending moment $= \dfrac{Wl^2}{8} = \dfrac{106(21)^2 \times 12}{8} = 70{,}100$ in.-lb.

LIVE LOAD BENDING MOMENT

is 75 percent of moment for H20 load in Fig. 14

$$(128{,}000 \times 12)\left(\frac{1}{2} \times \frac{2.5}{5}\right) = 384{,}000 \text{ in.-lb.}$$

Total D.L. + L.L. bending moment = $M = 454{,}100$ in.-lb.

Then $D^3 = \dfrac{10(454{,}100)}{900}$, and $D = 17$, or the diameter of the log (small end) in inches. Such a log, averaging about 18 in. in diameter throughout its length, approximates the assumed weight per linear foot.

Table 28, for use in the West, gives the specifications for log stringers required in bridges with spans of 40 to 80 ft.

**Sample Bridge Plans.** Figs. 21 to 25 are bridge plans in use by the U. S. Forest Service.

Table 28. Log Stringer Sizes for Bridge Shown in Fig. 21

H15 - S12 LOADING

| CLASS | 40 FT. SPAN | | | 50 FT. SPAN | | | 60 FT. SPAN | | | 70 FT. SPAN | | | 80 FT. SPAN | | |
|---|---|---|---|---|---|---|---|---|---|---|---|---|---|---|---|
| | NO. | DIA. | LENGTH | NO. | DIA. | LENGTH | NO. | DIA. | LENGTH | NO. | DIA. | LENGTH | NO. | DIA. | LENGTH |
| Close-grained Douglas-fir, 1200 f. | 5 | 22" | 42'-0" | 5 | 26" | 52'-0" | 5 | 29" | 62'-0" | 5 | 33" | 72'-0" | 4 | 41" | 82'-0" |
| Common Douglas-fir, 900 f. | 5 | 24" | 42'-0" | 5 | 28" | 52'-0" | 5 | 32" | 62'-0" | 4 | 39" | 72'-0" | 4 | 45" | 82'-0" |
| Pine, Cedar, 700 f. | 5 | 26" | 42'-0" | 5 | 31" | 52'-0" | 5 | 35" | 62'-0" | 4 | 43" | 72'-0" | | | |

H20 - S16 LOADING

| CLASS | 40 FT. SPAN | | | 50 FT. SPAN | | | 60 FT. SPAN | | | 70 FT. SPAN | | | 80 FT. SPAN | | |
|---|---|---|---|---|---|---|---|---|---|---|---|---|---|---|---|
| Close-grained Douglas-fir, 1200 f. | 5 | 24" | 42'-0" | 5 | 27" | 52'-0" | 5 | 31" | 62'-0" | 4 | 38" | 72'-0" | 4 | 43" | 82'-0" |
| Common Douglas-fir, 900 f. | 5 | 26" | 42'-0" | 5 | 30" | 52'-0" | 5 | 34" | 62'-0" | 4 | 42" | 72'-0" | 4 | 47" | 82'-0" |
| Pine, Cedar, 700 f | 5 | 28" | 42'-0" | 5 | 33" | 52'-0" | 4 | 41" | 62'-0" | 4 | 46" | 72'-0" | | | |

One-half of the sapwood is to be deducted in measuring the diameter. In so far as practical, the stringers shall be straight, sound, out of wind, and free of defects of all kinds that impair their strength enough to make them unsuitable for the use intended. No large knots are to be allowed in the middle third of the span. They should be cut from live trees not less than 30 days before use and shall be seasoned with the bark on. Immediately before use in the work, all bark shall be peeled and the logs shall be trimmed smooth of all knots and projections.

**Selection, Preparation, and Fabrication of Logs.** Logs to be used as stringers for bridges should be carefully selected. All stringer logs for any one span should match so far as diameter, taper, and inherent stiffness are concerned. They should be straight, sound, free of scars, cat faces, wind shake, splits, or other defects which might impair their use. The ring count and density should correspond to that specified for structural grade saw timber of the species.

High standard workmanship in the selection, fabrication, and fitting of logs can mean the difference between a short-lived and a long-lived bridge. Cut the logs as far in advance as possible. In order to reduce checks, season them with the bark on and peel them immediately before use. During the seasoning period set them on skids, away from contact with the ground. Have adequate equipment on hand for moving and handling the logs and other timbers. Insist on careful fabrication. Allow no misfit joints and uneven bearing surfaces; these will detract materially from the life of the bridge.

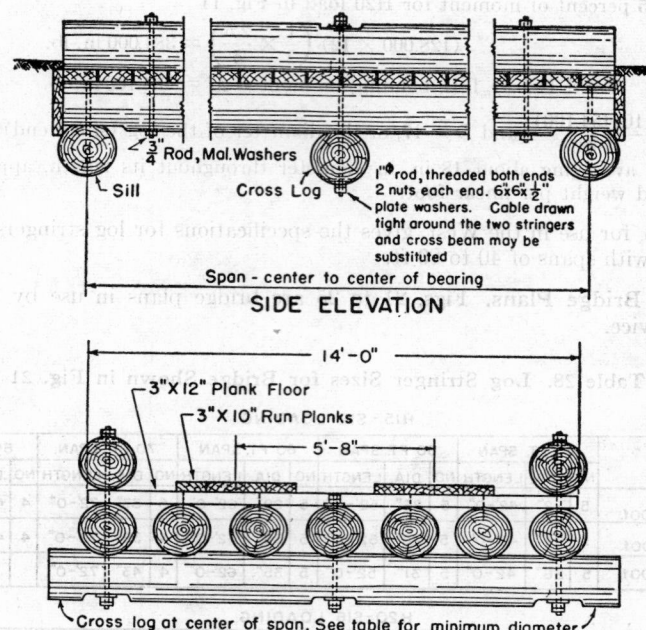

**SIDE ELEVATION**

- $\frac{3}{4}$" Rod, Mal. Washers
- Sill
- Cross Log
- 1" rod, threaded both ends 2 nuts each end. 6"x6"x$\frac{1}{2}$" plate washers. Cable drawn tight around the two stringers and cross beam may be substituted
- Span - center to center of bearing

**CROSS SECTION**

- 14'-0"
- 3"X12" Plank Floor
- 3"X10" Run Planks
- 5'-8"
- Cross log at center of span. See table for minimum diameter

Hew bottom of stringer and notches to shape of three sides of an octagon to prevent excessive hewing of stringer for bearing.

- $\frac{3}{4}$" Dowel
- Stringer

**DETAIL AT BEARING**

\* For H30-S24 loading use 2" larger diameter stringers and 1" larger diameter cross logs
\*\* Including curb logs

## STRINGER TABLE - H2O-S16 LOADING *

### 9 STRINGERS ** REQUIRED IN ALL SPANS

| SPAN | DIAMETER AT CENTER | LENGTH REQUIRED | DIAMETER OF CROSS LOG |
|------|--------------------|-----------------|-----------------------|
| 15'  | 13"                | 17'             | 12"                   |
| 20'  | 14"                | 22'             | 13"                   |
| 25'  | 16"                | 27'             | 14"                   |
| 30'  | 18"                | 32'             | 15"                   |
| 35'  | 20"                | 37'             | 16"                   |
| 40'  | 22"                | 42'             | 17"                   |
| 45'  | 24"                | 47'             | 18"                   |
| 50'  | 26"                | 52'             | 18"                   |

Notes: This table based on use of Rocky Mountain Douglas-Fir or Tamarack. If Spruce, Pine or Cedar is used increase diameter 2".

Decking Notes: Fasten floor plank to stringers with 60d nails. Fasten run planks to floor with $\frac{1}{2}$" x 5" log screws and cut washers. Space at 2' alternate centers and place 2 log screws at each end of each plank. Countersink log screws flush with top of plank. Stagger joints in run plank.

**Fig. 23. U. S. Forest Service, Region 4, log stringer bridge.**

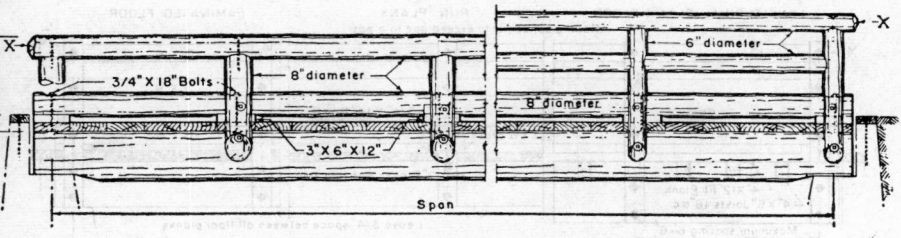

## SIDE ELEVATION

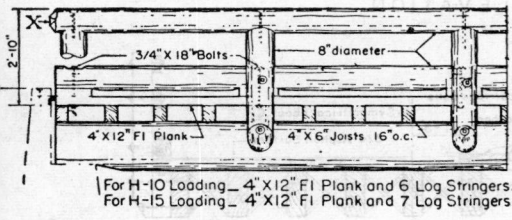

For H-10 Loading— 4"X 12" Fl Plank and 6 Log Stringers.
For H-15 Loading— 4"X 12" Fl Plank and 7 Log Stringers

### PART ELEVATION

7 Log Stringers for H-15 Loading.

### HALF SECTION

## ALTERNATE FLOOR SYSTEM SHOWING PLANK LAID LONGITUDINALLY
### NO RUN PLANK REQUIRED

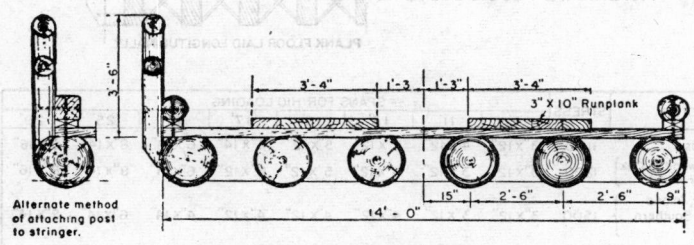

Alternate method
of attaching post
to stringer.

### SECTION

| Span |  | STRINGERS | | | |
|---|---|---|---|---|---|
|  |  | 6 Logs 10 Ton Load | | 7 Logs 15 Ton Load | |
|  |  | Diameter | | Diameter | |
| ft. | Length ft. | A | B | A | B |
| 9 | 10 | 12 | 11 | 13 | 12 |
| 11 | 12 | 13 | 12 | 14 | 13 |
| 13 | 14 | 14 | 12 | 15 | 14 |
| 15 | 16 | 14 | 13 | 16 | 14 |
| 17 | 18 | 15 | 13 | 17 | 15 |
| 21 | 22 | 16 | 14 | 18 | 16 |
| 25 | 26 | 17 | 15 | 19 | 17 |
| 29 | 30 | 18 | 16 | 20 | 18 |

A- Spruce (red or white), Douglas-Fir (Rocky Mt.), Hemlock (Eastern), Larch, Tamarack, Redwood, Yellow Poplar, Southern Cypress and Chestnut.

B- Yellow Birch, Douglas-Fir (Wash. & Oreg), Oak (red or white), Pine (Southern Yellow), Black Locust, and Sugar Maple.

Notes:
Place stringers so knots or defects are on top.
Allow no large knots in the middle third of span.
Run planks to be fastened to floor with two 1/2 X 5 1/2 lag screws in each board every 4 feet.
In measuring round timber, deduct 1/2 the depth of sap wood on each side of the heart.
Bending Stress 900 lbs. per sq. in. for A, 1300 for B.
Measure diameter at center line of span.
Alternate large and small ends.
Leave 3/4" space between all floor planks.
X- One cluster of six 1/2 in. buttons; or reflector of equal visibility both sides of each end of bridge.

## Fig. 24. Log stringer bridge.
Loading H10 and H15 spans, 9 to 29 ft.

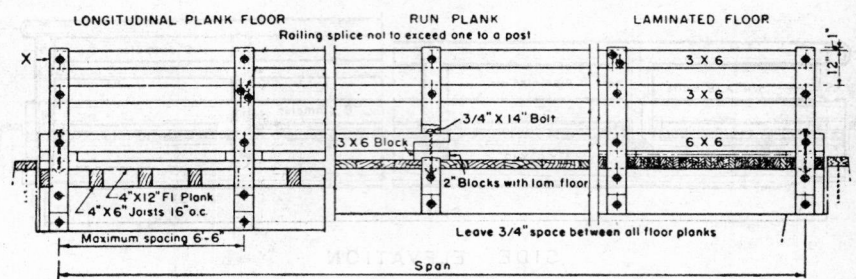

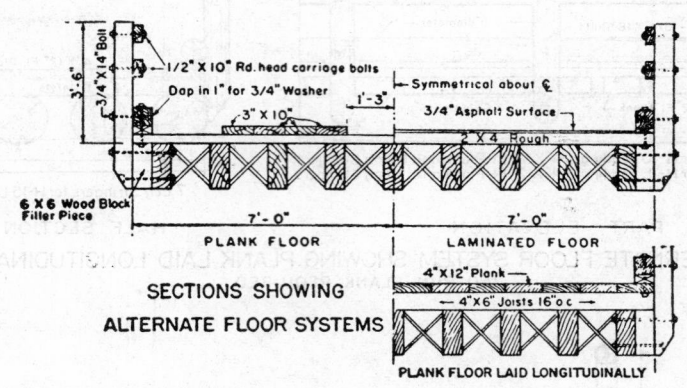

ELEVATION

SECTIONS SHOWING
ALTERNATE FLOOR SYSTEMS

PLANK FLOOR LAID LONGITUDINALLY

| SPECIES | STRESS | SPANS FOR H10 LOADING | | | | | | | |
|---|---|---|---|---|---|---|---|---|---|
| | | 9' | 11' | 13' | 15' | 17' | 21' | 25' | 29' |
| Sou Cypress | 1100 | 3"x12" | 4"x12" | 5"x12" | 5"x12" | 6"x14" | 6"x14" | 8"x14" | 8"x16" |
| Larch, Redwood & Oak (Red or White) | 1200 | 3"x12" | 3"x12" | 4"x12" | 5"x12" | 6"x12" | 6"x14" | 8"x14 | 8"x16" |
| Douglas-Fir, Inland Empire Fir, Southern Yellow Pine | 1500 | 3"x12" | 3"x12" | 4"x12" | 4"x12" | 4"x12" | 4"x14" | 6"x14" | 8"x14" |

| SPECIES | STRESS | SPANS FOR H15 LOADING | | | | | | | |
|---|---|---|---|---|---|---|---|---|---|
| | | 9' | 11' | 13' | 15' | 17' | 21' | 25' | 29' |
| Sou. Cypress | 1100 | 5"x12" | 4"x14" | 6"x14" | 6"x14" | 8"x14" | 8"x16" | 8"x16" | 10"x16" |
| Larch, Redwood & Oak (Red or White) | 1200 | 4"x12" | 5"x12" | 6"x12" | 6"x14" | 6"x14" | 8"x14" | 8"x16" | 10"x16" |
| Douglas-Fir, Inland Empire Fir, Southern Yellow Pine | 1500 | 4"x12" | 4"x12" | 5"x12" | 6"x12" | 6"x14" | 8"x14" | 8"x14" | 8"x16" |

**Notes:**

Run planks to be fastened to floor with two 5 1/2" lag screws in each board every four (4) feet.

Laminated Floor: 30d nails 24" ctrs. in each 2 X 4, staggered 8" with nails in adjacent strip. Toe nail each strip to every third stringer, staggered so that spacing of nails along stringer is 6 inches.

Bolt holes to be drilled with bit 1/16" smaller than diameter of bolt.

All joints and contact surfaces should be treated with creosote or asphaltum paint before assembling.

For multiple spans, use sill for bent cap. Butt outside stringers, lap inside stringers.

X — One cluster of six 1/2 in. buttons; or reflector of equal visibility both sides of each end of bridge.

Fig. 25. Timber beam bridge.

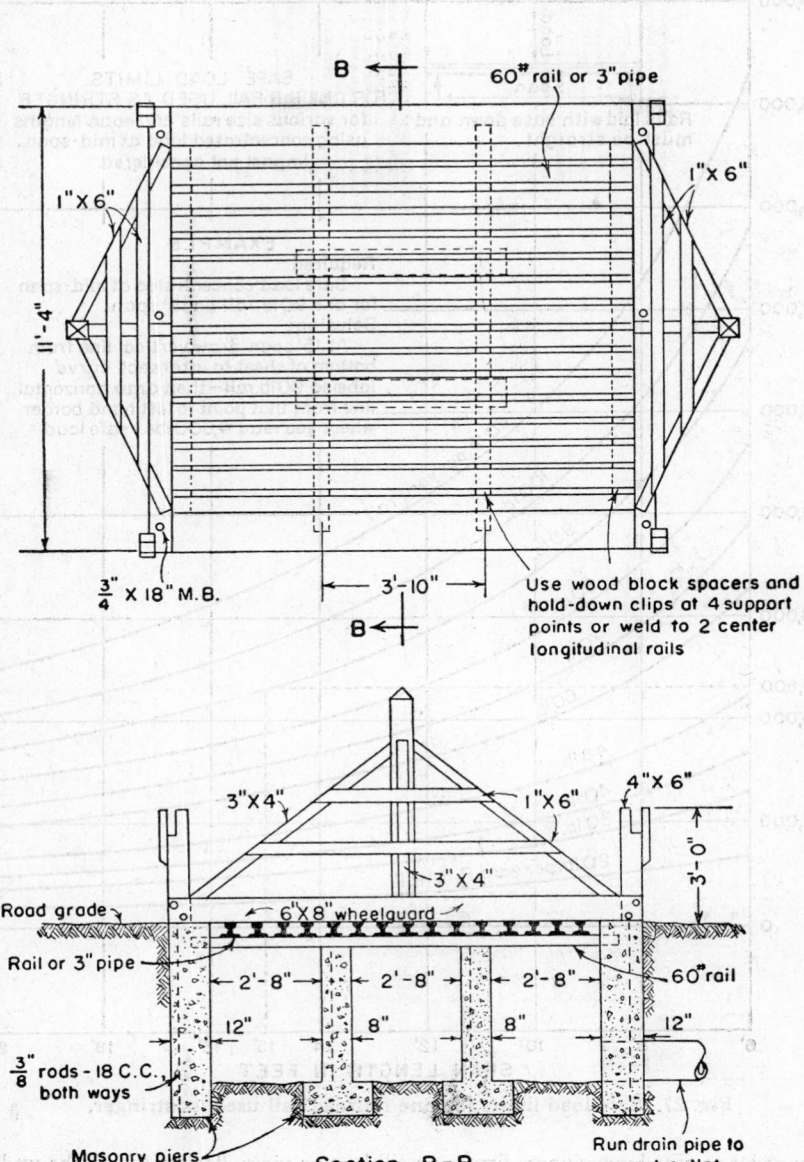

**Fig. 26.** Cattle guard of 60-lb. railroad rails for H15 loading.
(3″ pipe may be used for all except longitudinal members)

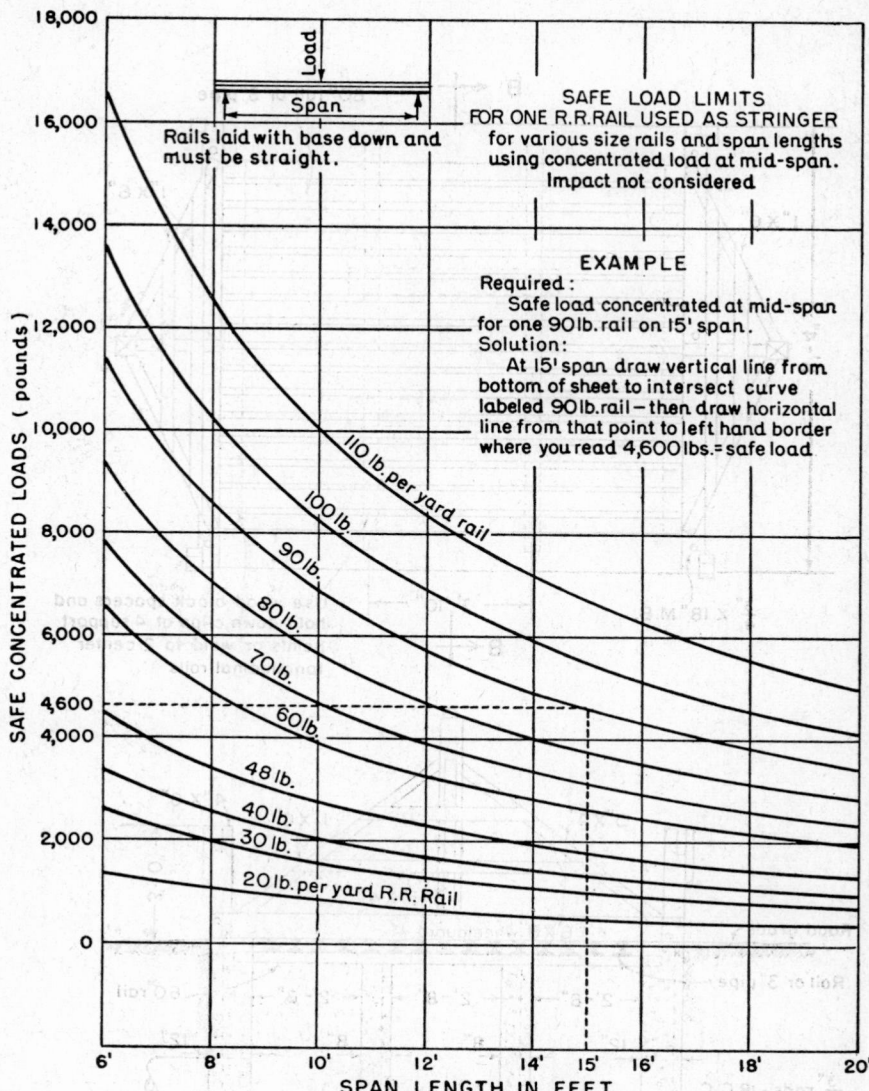

Fig. 27. Safe load limits for one railroad rail used as stringer.

In order to seat log stringers firmly on sill logs or piers, flatten (dap) the under side of the stringer where it rests on the sill or pier cap (Fig. 21). Avoid excessive daps. The better method of leveling the top of a log stringer is shown by the side elevation in Fig. 21. The log sill at the left has been set so as to bring the top of the butt end of the stringer to the desired elevation. The bottom of the stringer has been dapped just enough to provide a firm seat. The opposite (right) end of the stringer has been brought to level by inserting a block between the sill and the stringer.

Dap stringers only as required by the width of bearing on the sill log or pier cap and taper the dap on a 1:10 or flatter slope from the inside edge of the dap out to the bottom of the log, as in Fig. 21. A flatter slope, say 1:12, would be preferable in reducing the tendency for shear concentration. Notching the sill is another device for avoiding excessive dapping in the stringers, but this introduces a water-holding pocket in the sill at the end of the stringer. The pocket is sure to accelerate decay at a critical point on the stringer.

**Protection Against Decay.** To retard the effects of decay in the untreated timber construction, ventilate the sills and stringer ends as much as practicable. Use rock rather than earth for backfill at the ends of the bridge because of the superior drainage and ventilation it will give. Do not permit untreated timber stringers or other structural members to come in contact with earth.

Use roofing felt over the upper surfaces of horizontal logs such as sills and stringers in order to shed water. Handle the felt carefully to avoid punctures or tears. In log crib construction avoid notches on the upper surfaces which will hold water and encourage decay; do the necessary notching on the under side of the logs.

**Railroad Rails: Cattle Guard Construction; Load Limits for Stringers.** Fig. 26 gives the specifications and requirements for cattle guards built with 60-lb. railroad rails. Fig. 27 shows the safe load limits for railroad rails used as stringers in bridges and similar structures.

### BIBLIOGRAPHY
(For Sections 17 and 18)

ALLEN, C. FRANK. 1920. *Field and office tables.* 3d ed. McGraw-Hill Book Co., Inc., New York.

BREED, C. B., and G. L. HOSMER. 1945. *The principles and practice of surveying.* 8th ed. John Wiley & Sons, Inc., New York.

BROWN, N. C. 1949. *Logging.* John Wiley & Sons, Inc., New York.

CANADIAN INDUSTRIES, LTD. 1940. *Blaster's handbook.* 2d ed. Montreal, Canada.

CODDINGTON, E. F. 1944. *Azimuth determinations.* Engineering Exp. Sta., Ohio State University, Columbus.

DEMOISY, RALPH G. 1949. *Forest surveying.* Oregon State College Cooperative Assn., Corvallis.

HARGER, WILSON G., and EDMUND A. BONNEY. 1927. *Handbook for highway engineers.* 4th ed. McGraw-Hill Book Co., Inc., New York.

IVES, H. C. 1941. *Highway curves.* 3d ed. John Wiley & Sons, Inc., New York.

MERRIMAN, T., and T. H. WIGGIN. 1930. *American civil engineers handbook.* 5th ed. John Wiley & Sons, Inc., New York.

MORRISON, V. L. 1948. Keeping roads alder-free by use of chemical sprays. Oregon State Board of Forestry, Salem, Ore. Typewritten report.

PENCE, W. D., and M. S. KETCHUM. 1932. *Surveying manual.* 5th ed. John Wiley & Sons, Inc., New York.

POWER CRANE & SHOVEL ASSN. 1947. *Technical Bull. No. 1.* New York.

RITTER, L. J., JR., and R. J. PAQUETTE. 1951. *Highway engineering.* The Ronald Press Co., New York.

SILVERSIDES, C. R., and A. KOROLEFF. 1949. *Construction and maintenance—forest truck roads.* Pulp & Paper Research Institute of Canada, Montreal.

TRAUTWINE, JOHN C. 1929. *The civil engineer's reference book.* Trautwine Co., Ithaca, N. Y.

TRACY, JOHN C. 1907. *Plane surveying.* John Wiley & Sons, Inc., **New York.**
U. S. DEPT. OF INTERIOR. 1931. *Manual of instructions for the survey of the public lands of the United States.* Washington, D. C.
U. S. FOREST SERV. 1935. *The Abney level handbook.* 2d ed.
U. S. FOREST SERV. 1935. *Engineering field tables.*
U. S. FOREST SERV. 1940. *Truck trail handbook.*
U. S. WAR DEPT. 1944. *Field manual.* Government Printing Office, Washington, D. C.
U. S. WAR DEPT. 1947. *Field manual.* Government Printing Office, Washington, D. C.

SECTION **19**

# AERIAL PHOTOGRAPHY

## CONTENTS

# CONTENTS (*Continued*)

# AERIAL PHOTOGRAPHY

## Uses of Aerial Photographs in Forestry

Much of the United States and southern Canada has been photographed from the air. If they are intelligently used, with full knowledge of their limitations as well as their advantages, aerial photographs can provide the forester with quick, accurate, and usable information of many kinds. Air photographs are not maps, but by simple methods here described, distances, directions, and areas may be obtained from them in a small fraction of the time required for ground surveys. By more intensive methods, very accurate maps can be prepared from them.

The forester's ability to obtain from air photographs information of value in his work is in proportion not only to the quality of the photographs and the intensiveness of his methods, but also to his familiarity with conditions on the ground. If all he needs to know is the approximate boundaries and area of forest, as distinct from other cover types, he can obtain the information from the enlarged prints of single photographs, such as are on file in many field offices of the Soil Conservation Service and other units of the U. S. Department of Agriculture. He may even make rough distinctions on such photographs between saw timber and cordwood, or between hardwood and softwood stands.

But from a full set (not simply the alternate prints just referred to) of contact prints of photographs taken according to well-considered specifications, the forester can obtain with a stereoscope and other special apparatus a great deal of additional information. This may range from the location of topographic features and the determination of "blind spots" (areas not directly visible from a system of fire towers) to estimates of stand volumes by species. Incipient outbreaks of insects or disease can sometimes be recognized; burns may be recorded; logging conditions evaluated; sites for improvements located; forest, range, and recreational potentials differentiated; and so on through the whole range of forest problems.

## Obtaining and Handling Aerial Photographs

**INFORMATION CONCERNING EXISTING PHOTOGRAPHY.** A map of existing photography in the United States together with other pertinent information is published at intervals by the Map Information Office, U. S. Geological Survey, Washington, D. C. Prints of photographs taken for governmental agencies should be ordered from the agency concerned.

The U. S. Department of Agriculture photography includes work contracted by the Forest Service, Soil Conservation Service, and Commodity Stabilization Service (formerly P.M.A.). C.S.S. prints should be ordered from Eastern Laboratory, Performance and Aerial Photographic Division, C.S.S., U. S. Department of Agriculture, Washington, D. C., for all eastern states (including South Dakota, Nebraska, Oklahoma, and Texas); and from the Western Laboratory of the same organization, Salt Lake City, Utah, for western states (including North

**19·1**

Dakota and Kansas). Private photography should be ordered from the aerial survey companies. For listings, see Photogrammetric Engineering, published by the American Society of Photogrammetry, Washington, D. C.

**MARKING PHOTOGRAPHS.** Permanent markings should be made with India or other permanent ink. In the field, ink can be carried in an Ink-O-Graph stylus-type fountain pen. Temporary markings are best made with a grease-type colored pencil, advertised for use with glazed surfaces. Marks can be removed with cotton swabs saturated in standard organic solvents such as benzene or acetone. Care should be taken not to dent photographs by pencil pressure. Water-soluble poster inks can also be used.

**PROTECTING PHOTOGRAPHS IN THE FIELD.** Map cases, war surplus or homemade, should be used. Cellulose acetate sheeting, with adhesive on the under side and a matte surface on the upper side for ease in writing with soft pencils, protects individual photographs. This can be obtained from suppliers of engineering and drafting equipment.

**STORING PHOTOGRAPHS.** Photographs must be kept flat to prevent curling. They can be tightly packed (under pressure) in original boxes or in standard filing drawers.

**HOW PHOTOGRAPHS ARE NUMBERED.** Each photograph is marked with the date of photography, code designation indicating project, and number. The time of photography is usually indicated on the first and last photograph of each strip. If the flight strips run east and west, the information always appears along the west edge; if the strips run north and south, the information appears along the north edge. If the number of the photograph has two parts, the first part will usually refer to the number of the roll of film. The last part refers to the number of the exposure.

## Photograph Specifications

**COMMON TYPES OF PHOTOGRAPHS.** **Vertical.** The camera axis is vertical or nearly so. The photograph therefore closely resembles a map and may be used with a minimum of correction. This type of photograph is commonly used in forestry work.

**Oblique.** The optical axis of the camera is at an angle to the vertical. Photographs showing the horizon are termed **high obliques**; those not showing the horizon are **low obliques**. Obliques cover a greater area than verticals taken under the same conditions but require far more correcting for map making and measuring purposes. High lands tend to mask the detail beyond.

**Tricamera Photography.** Three cameras are used in this type of photography, one pointed vertically, one pointed obliquely to the left of the plane axis, and one pointed obliquely to the right. The geometric relations among the three photographs simplify corrections for the obliques. Tricamera photography is chiefly used in high altitude reconnaissance (trimetrogon photography) but is also recommended by some for winter forest photography in eastern Canada.

**Mosaics.** Several photographs are assembled into a single picture and used as a map substitute. The accuracy of this type of photograph depends upon the method of assembling (controlled or uncontrolled), roughness of topography, and specifications of the original photography.

**FOCAL LENGTH OF CAMERA. Short focal length** (wide-angle lens, i.e., the 6-in. Metrogon lens) permits wide coverage from low altitude. It exaggerates the third-dimensional effect but also increases image displacement due to relief on photographs. This type of camera is best for forest photography over flat land.

**Medium focal length** (standard is 8.25 in.) is best for all-round photography at common forestry scales.

**Long focal length** (telephoto lens) minimizes both stereoscopic effect and image displacement. It is best for very mountainous country and for large-scale photography.

**SCALE.** Scale is determined by flying height and focal length. It is not constant on any given photograph but varies according to ground elevation and tilt of the camera (see page **19 · 7**). Scale is usually given in terms of **representative fraction** (*RF*). Divide by 12 for scale in feet per inch, etc.

**Example.** *RF* of 1:15,840 equals 1,320 ft. per in., 20 chains per in., or 4 in. per mi.

**Small Scales.** Practical minimum scales for forest analysis are 1:20,000 to 1:25,000. Much U. S. Department of Agriculture photography is at these scales, which are relatively inexpensive. They are usable for broad forest classification but not for detailed forest information.

**Medium Scales.** The most widely used forestry scales are 1:15,000 and 1:15,-840. They are moderate in cost and provide much forestry information.

**Large Scales.** Optimum scales for forest analysis are 1:8,000 to 1:12,000, but they are too expensive for most projects.

**SEASON OF PHOTOGRAPHY.** The proper time for photography frequently depends upon the local climatic cycle. The percentage of clear days is a very important item in aerial photography costs.

**Winter photography** is best for engineering and cartographic purposes, for locating points on the ground, and when there is no interest in deciduous trees. Too heavy a snow cover, however, will cloak detail (especially the nature of lakes, streams, and open swamps), and provide too much contrast for high quality photographs. It is generally unsatisfactory for mountainous country because of the loss of detail in long shadows resulting from the low altitude of the sun (frequently, all north slopes are in shadow).

**Summer photography** is best for forest stand classification. Deciduous trees must be in leaf to form sharp resolvable images.

**Spring and fall photography** frequently provides excellent species contrast but is apt to be variable and risky.

**TYPE OF EMULSION.** The primary goal is high quality photography providing detailed and sharp tree images. The degree of contrast is of secondary importance.

**Panchromatic Photography.** This is definitely best for winter and fall photography and is most apt to provide high quality photography in summer. It is generally recommended for pure hardwood and pure softwood regions. Best tone contrasts on panchromatic can be obtained by overexposure (by normal standards) of the negative, together with compensating underexposure of the printing paper.

**Infrared.** This is an emulsion used primarily for summer photography of mixed wood regions where hardwood-softwood distinction is important. It can be of high quality but, if not properly taken and printed, may show too much photographic contrast and poorer image resolution than panchromatic. A red filter gives maximum contrast; minus blue (yellow) gives less contrast.

**Color.** Color photography is still expensive and of somewhat poorer resolution than black and white. However, it is valuable for special purposes such as the detection of insect-killed trees.

**PRINTING PAPER.** Glossy paper is best for office use, semimatte for field use. Double-weight paper has much less dimensional change and is much more durable than single-weight. Paper contrast should be carefully matched to negative quality to provide maximum tone contrast in the grays between forest types while still avoiding pure blacks and whites where the detail is lost.

**SAMPLE SPECIFICATIONS.** Important points in private contract negotiations should be covered by specifications. For standard approved contract forms, see Manual of Photogrammetry. The following items should be defined:

1. Area covered. Shown on attached maps.
2. Confidential nature of survey. No information regarding the survey will be divulged except by permission of the ordering company.
3. Ownership of photographic negatives. These are the property of the purchasing company regardless of where they are kept or stored. No sales of reproductions will be made without approval of the purchasing company.
4. Responsibility for damages. The survey company will be fully responsible for the safety and liability of its own personnel and equipment.
5. Scale. A stated scale calculated for a stated ground elevation will be maintained. Permissible variation, 5 percent.
6. Overlap. Along the line of flight this shall average 60 percent and shall be between 55 and 65 percent. Between flights, it shall average 30 percent and be between 15 and 45 percent.
7. Broken flight lines. Two exposures of the new photography shall overlap the last two exposures of the old photography.
8. Tilt. This should average less than 2° and should not exceed 5°. It should not interfere with the use of the photographs in radial line triangulation.
9. Crab (deviation of photograph alignment from the line of flight). This should not affect more than 10 percent of the width of the photograph.
10. The make, model, and serial number of camera and lens. These should be specified.
11. Film and filter combination. These should be specified.
12. Photograph quality. This must conform to the submitted samples. All photographs shall be free from blemishes or cloud shadows.
13. Season of photography. This should be specified. The desired date of completion of photography and delivery of materials should also be given.
14. Flight log. This should be supplied to purchaser and should give time, dates, etc., for each strip of photography.
15. Delivery. Standard delivery consists of two sets of contact prints and one set of index mosaics. Both sets of prints should be free from staple holes or other blemishes, unless the purchaser wishes to save money by accepting one set of prints (used in making index mosaics) with staple holes. Additional materials desired should be listed in detail.
16. Radial line plots and mosaics. If ordered, it should be clearly stated who will furnish ground control (i.e., survey data), and what control points will be used. The purchaser should list points such as fire towers that he would like to have correctly located. Good ground control is essential if satisfactory radial line plots or mosaics are to be constructed.
17. Business arrangements. These include prices, delivery schedule, payments, cost of additional materials (extra prints, etc.), and cancellation provisions.

## Stereoscopy

Stereoscopy is the science of viewing objects in three dimensions. As applied to photogrammetry, it pertains to the depth of perception which one achieves by simultaneously viewing with his left and right eyes the photographic images of an object as recorded from left and right camera stations. Unless both eyes of the observer are sufficiently strong to perceive the image clearly, he will be unable to study the photographs stereoscopically. If the photographs are properly oriented, stereoscopic study does not involve eyestrain. Careful orientation is particularly important when parallax and other measurements are to be made with the aid of the stereoscope.

Two overlapping photographs which can be viewed stereoscopically are termed a **stereo pair.** In aerial photogrammetry the stereo pair usually consists of any two vertical aerial photographs which were taken from successive camera stations along a single line of flight.

**PREPARATION OF THE PHOTOGRAPHS.** To prepare photographs for stereoscopy the following procedure should be used:

1. On each photograph, mark the **principal point,** defined by the intersection of perpendicular lines connecting opposite **fiducial marks.** The fiducial marks are of various designs and usually appear in the middle of each edge of the photographs. The principal point may be temporarily located with a pencil or permanently circled with India ink, best done with a drop-center pen.
2. Also place a dot on each photograph at the position where the principal point of the adjacent photograph appears. This is called the **conjugate principal point.** Because the principal point rarely coincides with a recognizable topographic or cultural feature (as where a road crosses a stream), its location as the conjugate principal point on an adjacent photograph often requires very careful scrutiny of both prints.
3. On each photograph draw a line connecting the principal and the conjugate principal point. This is called the **flight line.**
4. Place the photographs so that the corresponding photographic images (topographic, cultural, or vegetative) in the overlap area are roughly superimposed and the two flight line segments fall in a continuous straight line.
5. Observe the direction in which the shadows on the photographs fall with respect to the observer. If they would fall more nearly toward him by rotating the photographs **as a unit** through an arc of 180°, do so; otherwise, leave them as they are.

**USE OF THE STEREOSCOPE.** To use the lens stereoscope, a portable model of which is shown in Fig. 1, slide the lenses apart, about the distance between your eyes. Then separate the photographs, either by moving the left photograph to the left or the right one to the right, until the distance between corresponding photograph images is approximately 2¼ in. Take care that during this process the two flight line segments remain perfectly aligned (Fig. 1). For the mirror stereoscope, the separation is considerably greater, the exact amount depending upon the design of the particular instrument.

Place the stereoscope over the photographs so that the common flight line of the photographs is parallel to an imaginary line passing through the centers of the stereoscope lenses or mirrors. The two images should fuse into one when observed through the stereoscope. If they do not, the separation distance between the two photographs may be changed until a single image appears. The separation of the two lenses in the lens stereoscope should remain so that each eye is

**Fig. 1. Orientation of the stereo pair for stereoscopic study, showing method of manipulation for seeing center of overlap.**

centered over its respective lens. In scanning the photographs, care should be taken to see that the two flight line segments always form a continuous line and that the axis of the stereoscope remains parallel with this line.

In order to observe with the lens stereoscope the entire area common to the two photographs, it will be necessary to have the left photograph on top when viewing the right half of the overlap area, and vice versa. If an area in the middle of the overlap remains obscured by either of these orientations, the edge of the top photograph should be lifted and rolled back sufficiently to disclose it (Fig. 1). This difficulty does not arise with the mirror stereoscope, but the stereoscopic image seen by use of this instrument is of a smaller size than that obtained with the lens stereoscope. Binocular attachments are sometimes available for use with a mirror stereoscope to help overcome this difficulty.

## HINTS TO AID STEREOSCOPIC VISION.

1. Practice fusing two black dots on separate sheets of white paper. The best separation under a lens stereoscope will prove to be somewhere between 1½ to 2½ in. Use this separation with the photographs.
2. On the photographs, practice fusing distinct objects such as houses, clearings, or single trees. Once fusion is accomplished, the rest of the photograph can also be seen three-dimensionally.
3. Place a vertical cardboard partition between the two photographs so that the eyes cannot stray to the wrong photograph.
4. Increase the illumination of the image seen by the weaker eye, or shade the image seen by the stronger eye.
5. If eyeglasses are worn for *distant* vision, wear them while using the stereoscope.

**NAKED EYE STEREOSCOPIC VISION.** With practice, the stereoscope may be eliminated, especially in the field. Orient the photographs as for stereoscopic study but begin with a separation of the images of about 1 in. One convenient method is to stare at a distant object and interpose photographs about 12 in. from the eye; another, use a cardboard partition (or extra photograph) to keep the eyes parallel.

## Measuring Aerial Photographs

**GEOMETRY.** A photograph is not a map. Images are displaced with relation to their true map position because of (1) topographic relief, (2) camera tilt, (3) lens and camera errors, and (4) dimensional changes in film and printing paper. The most important geometric relationships are shown in Fig. 2.

**Principal Point.** The principal point ($A$ and $B$, Fig. 2) is found by the intersection of lines connecting the fiducial marks. It is the point where the optical axis of the camera intersects the photograph.

**Nadir.** The nadir ($N$) is the point where a perpendicular to the ground through the lens center intersects the photograph. In a truly vertical photograph (Photograph A), the principal point and the nadir coincide. Most so-called vertical photographs have a small amount of tilt (Photograph B). The separation between the nadir and the principal point is a measure of tilt. It is time consuming to locate the nadir, however, and it is therefore customary to assume that the photograph is truly vertical and that all measurements can be made from the principal point. If the tilt is less than 2° or 3°, no substantial error will be introduced by this assumption, which is made throughout the discussion below.

**Conjugate Principal Points.** The 60 percent overlap, along the line of flight, of adjacent photographs makes it possible to locate the principal point of Photograph A on Photograph B, and vice versa. They are then known as conjugate principal points ($A'$ and $B'$, Fig. 2).

**Flight Line.** The flight line is located for the overlap area by connecting the principal point and the conjugate point on either of the overlapping photographs.

**Displacement.** Any high object (example, the flagpole in Fig. 2) will appear to lean outward away from the nadir (or principal point for vertical photographs) because of displacement. Although the top of the pole ($X$) is directly above the bottom ($Y$), it appears farther away from the photograph center. Generalizing, any high elevation will appear on the photograph farther away from the principal point (or more correctly, the nadir) than its true map position, while any depression will appear closer to the center than its true map position. This displacement is the basis of the stereoscopic image obtained when two overlapping photographs are viewed together with a stereoscope, and it constitutes the chief source of error that must be overcome in making maps from aerial photographs.

When both the top and bottom of objects such as flagpoles and large trees can be clearly seen on the aerial photograph, height can be determined by measurement of this displacement on a **single** photograph.

$$h = \frac{dH}{r}$$

Where $h$ is the height of the object or distance between $X$ and $Y$ in Fig. 2; $d$ is the displacement of this object on the photograph ($xy$); $H$ is the height of the aircraft above the base of the object; and $r$ is the radial distance from the top of the object to the center of the photograph ($xA$ or $xB$, depending upon the photograph). In practice, application of this formula is limited because of the difficulty

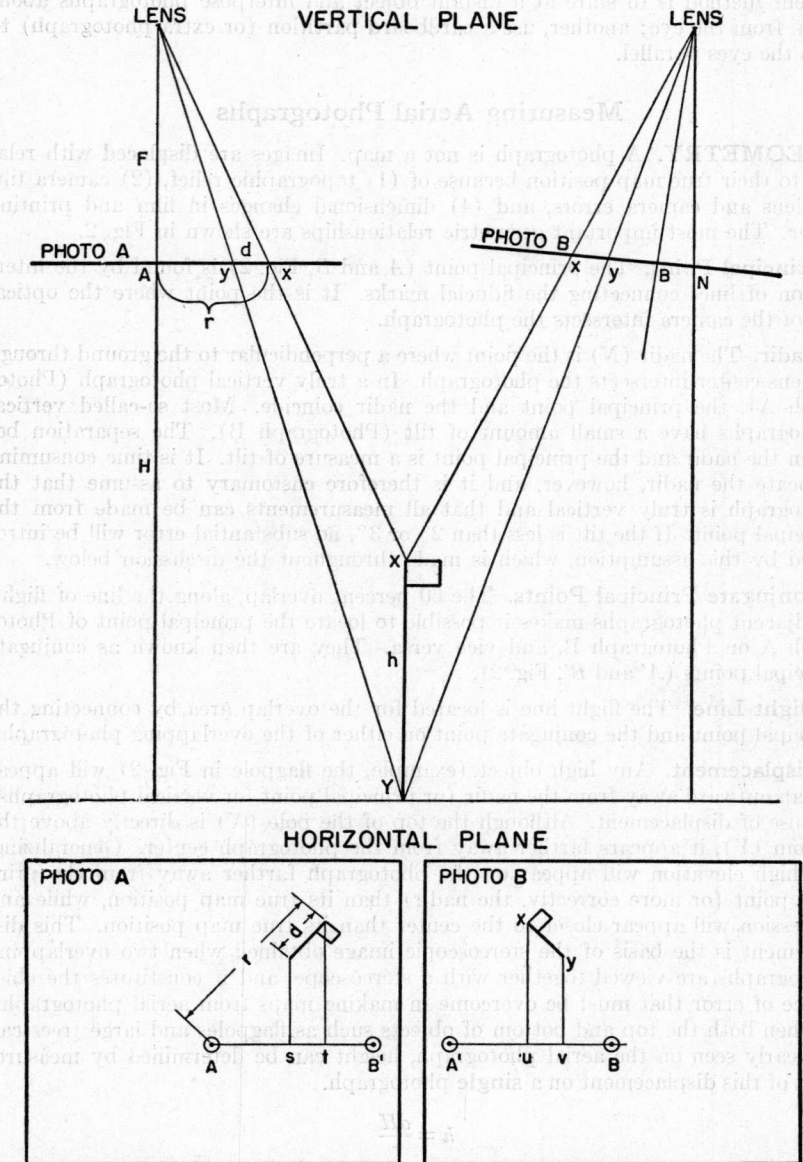

Fig. 2. Geometric relationships of the stereo pair.

of seeing both top and bottom of the displaced image clearly on a single photograph.

**Parallax.** The combined displacement of two images of the same object on two overlapping photographs may be used generally for the determination of elevations or object height. This is termed the **parallax** method. The combined displacement parallel to the line of flight of a given point measured from the photograph center is the **absolute parallax** (*P*). The absolute parallax of the base of the flagpole (Fig. 2) is the sum of distances *sA* and *vB*; that of the top of the flagpole is the sum of *tA* and *uB*. If there is no tilt, the absolute parallax is the same for all objects having the same elevation above sea level. The difference between two absolute parallax values is called the **parallax difference** (*dp*). The parallax difference between the top and bottom of the flagpole is the sum of *tA* and *uB* minus the sum of *sA* and *vB*; or more simply, the sum of *sT* and *uV*. The height of any object can thus be found by the **parallax formula,** which is the basis of tree height measurement and of topographic mapping (page **19 · 12**).

**SCALE.** (See "Scale," page **19·3**.) For vertical photographs, the basic formula is:

$$RF \text{ (representative fraction)} = \frac{f \text{ (focal length)}}{H \text{ (flying height above datum)}}$$

*f* and *H* should be in the same units of measure. The focal length is usually 6, 8¼, or 12 in. (0.5, 0.6875, or 1.0 ft.). The formula is solved graphically in Fig. 3.

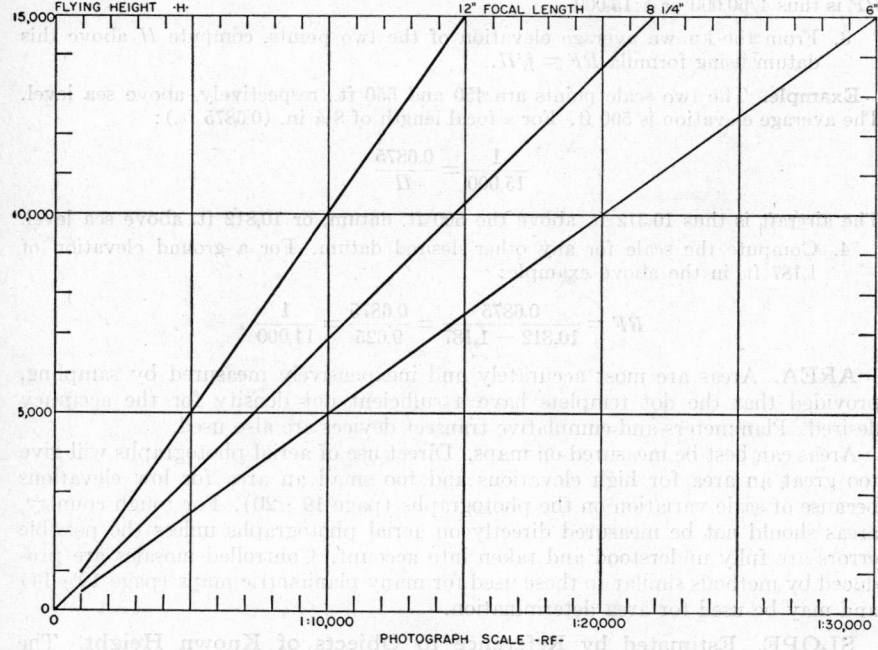

**Fig. 3. Relationship between scale (RF) and flying height for standard focal lengths.**

A vertical photograph has a different scale for each elevation on the ground because $H$ varies with ground elevation. Therefore, a photograph has a specific scale only with reference to a specified ground elevation or datum. If a distance on the ground is known, the scale can be computed by:

$$RF = \frac{\text{Photograph distance between two points}}{\text{Ground distance between same two points}}$$

Both measures should be in the same units (feet or inches). If a good map is available, the photograph scale can be computed by:

$$RF = \frac{\text{Photograph distance}}{\text{Map distance}} \times \text{Map } RF$$

**Example.** Photograph distance between two points is 3.6 in., map distance is 1.2 in., map scale is 1:62,500. $RF$ then equals

$$\frac{3.6}{1.2} \times \frac{1}{62,500} = \frac{1}{20,833}, \text{ or } 1:20,833.$$

For rough country, employ the following procedure:

1. Select two points that are accurately located both on a base map and on the photographs. To minimize the possible effect of photograph tilt, they should preferably be located approximately equidistant from and on opposite sides of the principal point.
2. Compute the scale from the formula above (ground distance known).

**Example.** Photograph distance is 4.0 in.; ground distance is 5,000 ft. or 60,000 in.; $RF$ is thus 4/60,000 or 1:15,000.

3. From the known average elevation of the two points, compute $H$ above this datum using formula $RF = f/H$.

**Example.** The two scale points are 450 and 550 ft., respectively, above sea level. The average elevation is 500 ft. For a focal length of 8¼ in. (0.6875 ft.):

$$\frac{1}{15,000} = \frac{0.6875}{H}$$

The aircraft is thus 10,312 ft. above the 500 ft. datum, or 10,812 ft. above sea level.

4. Compute the scale for any other desired datum. For a ground elevation of 1,187 ft. in the above example:

$$RF = \frac{0.6875}{10,812 - 1,187} = \frac{0.6875}{9,625} = \frac{1}{14,000}$$

**AREA.** Areas are most accurately and inexpensively measured by sampling, provided that the dot templets have a sufficient dot density for the accuracy desired. Planimeters and cumulative transect devices are also used.

Areas can best be measured on maps. Direct use of aerial photographs will give too great an area for high elevations and too small an area for low elevations because of scale variation on the photographs (page **19 · 20**). For rough country, areas should not be measured directly on aerial photographs unless the possible errors are fully understood and taken into account. Controlled mosaics are produced by methods similar to those used for many planimetric maps (page **19 · 14**) and may be used for area determination.

**SLOPE. Estimated by Reference to Objects of Known Height.** The photo-interpreter is frequently able to recognize mature dominant trees which he knows from field experience to have an average height of, say, roughly 90 ft.

Using these trees as a vertical measuring stick while viewing the area stereoscopically, he estimates that $A$ is higher than $B$ by approximately three such tree heights, or 270 ft. If the ground distance between $A$ and $B$ scales 1,500 ft., an 18 percent slope is indicated.

**Estimated by Reference to Slopes of Known Steepness.** Pick two points for which elevations are known or which are otherwise obtainable. Connect these points with a straight line on both photographs. The apparent slope of this line, as seen stereoscopically, can be compared with the apparent slope between $A$ and $B$ for which an estimate is desired. Since the first slope can be directly calculated, the second can be estimated from the comparison.

Use a slope parallax wedge, which, when placed over the stereoscopic model and viewed stereoscopically, reveals three lines having slopes of 10, 20, and 30 percent respectively. Since the wedge is printed on transparent material, the actual ground slope can be simultaneously compared with the three known slopes and the degree of ground slope can be estimated.

**Accurate Photograph Measurement of Slope.** For an accurate measurement of slope, proceed as follows:

1. Orient the stereo pair carefully. Tack or tape the photographs to prevent even slight movement.
2. Compute ground distance between the two points in feet. (See "Scale," page **19·9**.)
3. Measure the absolute parallax for both top and bottom of the slope. The simplest method is to use an engineer's rule and measure the distance from an image point on one photograph to the same image point on the other to the nearest 0.01 in. Subtracting this figure from the distance between the respective principal points will give the absolute parallax directly. More accurate measurements can be made with a parallax wedge or parallax bar device, either with or without the stereoscope.
4. From the parallax formula (see "Geometry," page **19·7**), compute the difference in elevation between two points.
5. The percent slope is obtained by dividing this difference in elevation by the horizontal distance between the two points and multiplying by 100.

**TEST FOR INTERVISIBILITY OF TWO POINTS.** From a stereoscopic study of aerial photographs it is possible to determine whether two points on the ground are intervisible, providing that (1) both points are in the area common to a stereo pair of photographs, and (2) the two points are at different perpendicular distances from the flight line. Simply draw a fine but sharp line between the two points on each of the photographs. If they are intervisible, this line will appear to float above the ground; if not, this line will appear to intersect the ground at one or more points as evidenced by its splitting where intervening terrain obscures the intervisibility.

**TREE HEIGHTS. Single Displacement Method.** This method can be used on single photographs (see page **19·7**), but is limited to trees located near the border of vertical large-scale photographs. Both top and bottom of the tree must be clearly visible. It is of limited value for verticals but is usable on large-scale obliques, providing the tilt angle or position of nadir is known.

**Shadow Length Measurement.** Measurement of shadow length is easy but low in accuracy because of the large number of variables affecting the result. The angle of elevation of the sun at the instant of photography must be known. This must be computed from latitude, time, and date of photography.

**Parallax Method.** This is the most satisfactory method, but it requires considerable training and practice. It is based upon the parallax formula:

$$h = \frac{H \times dP}{p + dP}$$

where object height $(h)$ and aircraft height above the base of the object $(H)$ are in feet, and absolute parallax $(P)$ and parallax difference $(dP)$ are in inches. A graphical solution of the formula is shown in Fig. 4.

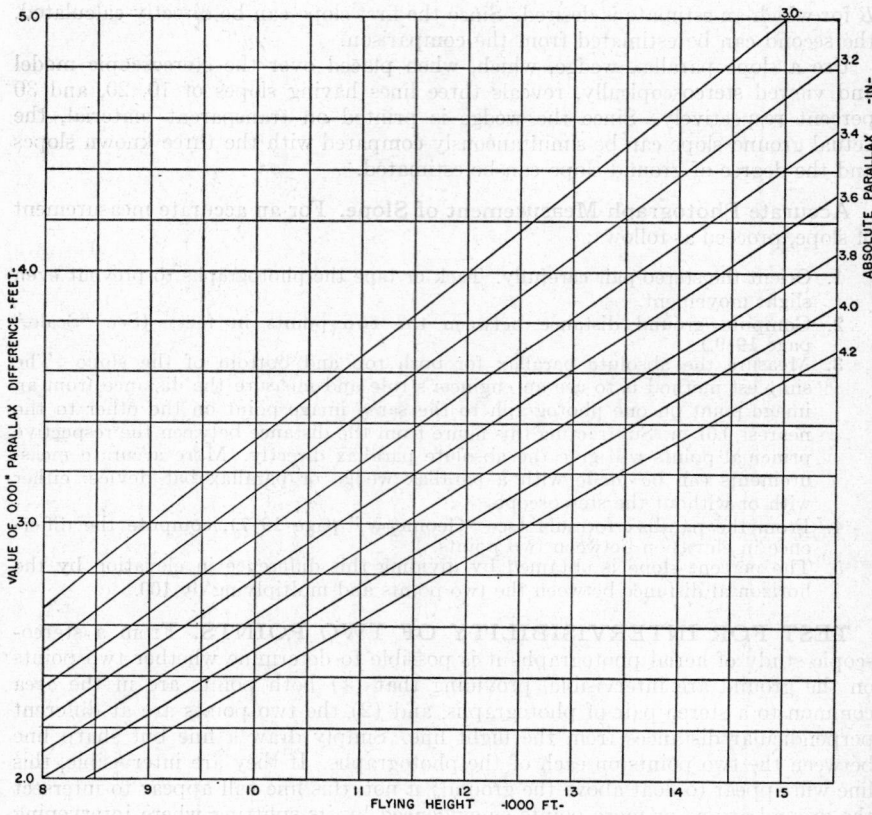

**Fig. 4. Graphic solution of the parallax formula.**

**Base Length.** Base length (the average distance between principal and the appropriate conjugate principal points on the two photographs of the stereo pair—the average of $AB'$ and $A'B$ in Fig. 2) may be substituted for absolute parallax in most cases. Where the ground elevation of the base of the tree differs by more than a few hundred feet from that of the principal points, however, use the following general method:

1. Carefully orient the stereo pair so that the common flight lines form a single continuous line and the images are separated the correct distance for stereoscopic vision. Fasten the photographs down.

2. Measure the distance between the two principal points to the nearest 0.01 in.
3. Measure the distance between corresponding images on the two photographs at or near the base of the tree.
4. Subtract (3) from (2) to obtain the absolute parallax of the tree base.
5. To obtain the parallax difference, measure with a parallax wedge or other floating mark device. Several techniques are available. The simplest but least accurate is to use the parallax wedge or parallax bar as a precise rule without the aid of the stereoscope. Measure first the absolute parallax for the base of the tree by the techniques (2) to (4) above, and then repeat the process to obtain the absolute parallax at the top of the tree. The difference between the readings is $dP$. The best method is to use the parallax wedge under a stereoscope. Look for the single fused line of dots sloping down through the stereoscopic image and splitting apart both at the ground level and high in the air. The parallax difference is obtained directly by counting the number of dots between the dot at the same height as the tree top and the dot at the ground level where the dots split into two lines.
6. Obtain the tree height from the formula or from Fig. 4.

**Example.** Flying height is 13,400 ft., the ground is level and the base length (which is equal to absolute parallax for the base of the tree in this case) is 3.50 in. The parallax difference is 0.015 in. The chart shows a tree height of 3.8 ft. for each 0.001 in. $dP$, so the tree height is 57 ft. By formula:

$$h = \frac{13,400 \times 0.015}{3.50 + 0.015} = 57.2 \text{ ft.}$$

The parallax method will normally give tree height within 5 to 10 ft., provided the photographs are of moderate to large scale, the tree image is sharp, and both the ground elevation and the tree top can be clearly seen. Best results are obtained by measuring only those trees that meet these conditions and then using these measurements as a basis for the ocular estimate of other tree heights in the same stereoscopic image.

**CROWN DIAMETERS.** The diameter of tree crowns is measured directly under magnification (as, for instance, the lens stereoscope) by any micrometer measuring device. Micrometer wedges (two diverging lines on a transparency, permitting measurements of small distances to the nearest 0.001 in.) and dot wedges (a series of dots of different sizes for comparison with the crown size) are commonly used. To convert photographic measurements in fractions of an inch to feet of crown width, first divide the denominator of the natural scale ($RF$) of the photograph by 12, then multiply by the measured diameters.

**STAND DENSITY. Crown Counts.** Crown counts are usable only for stands where individual crowns are sharp and distinct in the stereoscopic image. Count the number of crowns on an inscribed area of $\frac{1}{5}$ acre or similar circle. Make allowance for scale variation of the photograph in rough country.

**Crown Closure.** This is the most commonly used aerial photographic estimate of stand density. It is usually estimated ocularly to the nearest 10 percent. Valuable photo-interpretive aids include various types of crown-density scales for comparison.

## Map Making from Aerial Photographs

**GENERAL PRINCIPLES.** A photograph is not a map. Images are displaced because of topographic relief, tilt, and other factors. Furthermore, a single photograph covers a relatively small area so that photographs must ordinarily be assembled to make a map. Map making thus consists of two steps: (1) preparation of a control network, usually by radial line triangulation, by which the various photographs can be assembled into a single system, and (2) transfer of detail from the photographs to this control network.

**RADIAL LINE TRIANGULATION.** In a truly vertical photograph, all image displacement is either directly away from or toward the principal point. That is, the true location of the point pictured will be somewhere along a radial line drawn from the principal point through the image. By photographic triangulation methods directly analogous to those used in surveying triangulation, it is possible to prepare a control network or even a complete map from the intersections of these radial lines. Certain simple applications of this principle are of convenience in field use.

**Assembling a Series (Strip) of Photographs.** Assemble a strip as follows:

1. Locate the principal and conjugate principal points on all photographs of the flight strip. The end photographs will have one conjugate point while the others will have two each.
2. Draw flight line segments connecting the principal and conjugate points.
3. Fasten one photograph on a flat surface.
4. Overlay the overlapping photograph so that common principal points are superimposed, and fasten down.
5. Repeat this process until the whole strip is fastened down.

The result will be a strip of photographs laid down in a single assembly to the approximate average scale computed at the elevation of the principal points.

**Mapping by Resection from a Stereo Pair.** Radial triangulation from a single stereo pair, for farm woodlots, logging areas, or other tracts covered by a single overlap area (Fig. 5), can be undertaken as follows:

1. Fasten both photographs down so that the flight lines are perfectly aligned and the distance between the two conjugate points ($A'B'$) is equal to the average distance between the principal and conjugate points on both photographs (average of $AB'$ and $A'B$).
2. Overlay with a large sheet of tracing paper.
3. For photograph $A$, draw radial lines from the principal point through images of corners and other landmarks of the tract for which a map is desired.
4. Repeat this process for corresponding images on photograph $B$.
5. The intersection of corresponding lines gives the map location of that point. Sketch in the details connecting each two points thus located.

The resulting map is relatively free from the displacement errors of the photographs and will be at three times the scale of the average scale of the photographs computed at the principal points (since $AB$ is three times as long as the average of $AB'$ and $A'B$). The scale can be varied by changing the separation of the two photographs, but the above procedure is suitable only for making maps at two or more times the scale of the photographs.

**PLANIMETRIC DETAIL.** Detail must be transferred from photographs to an outline base map or network of points of known location. This may be constructed either from a ground survey or by radial line triangulation from aerial photographs.

Single print transfer devices are inexpensive, rapid, and simple to operate, but incorporate into the map all displacement errors of the photograph being used. Errors are localized, however, by the radial line control network. Two general types of instruments are in use: (1) reflecting projectors similar to a camera

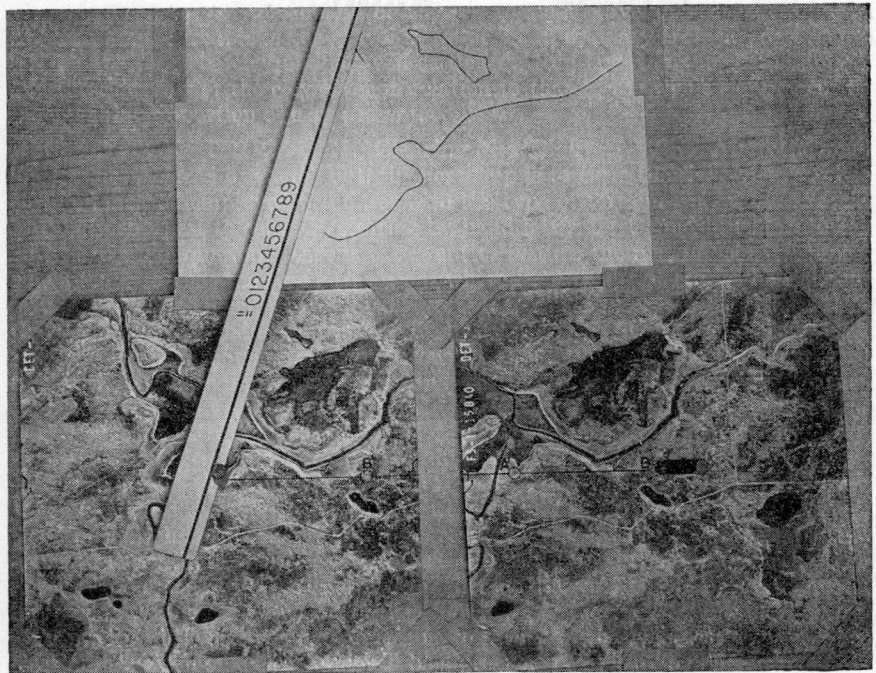

**Fig. 5. Mapping a small tract by radial line triangulation.**

enlarger but permitting the use of opaque photographs, and (2) camera lucida instruments such as Sketchmaster and Rectoplanigraph, utilizing semitransparent mirrors.

Stereoscopic mapping devices are more expensive and more difficult to operate. They do, however, permit the elimination of many or all of the image displacement errors and are recommended for the mapping of rough country. Simple types include (1) mechanical radial line plotters such as the Kail plotter, and (2) stereoscopic camera lucida instruments such as the Multiscope.

Without instruments, photographic detail can be transferred by (1) tracing over a light table, (2) sketching, (3) pantograph, or by (4) secondary radial line resection as detailed in "Radial Line Triangulation," page **19 · 14**. Method 4 is the most accurate.

**TOPOGRAPHIC DETAIL.** Refer to standard photogrammetry texts for precise methods capable of yielding contour intervals from 1 to 20 ft. For approximate form line sketching, with form line or contour intervals of 50 to 100 ft., proceed as follows:

1. Orient the photographs for study with a lens stereoscope and fasten down.
2. Overlay transparent paper or sheeting over the right-hand photograph.
3. Write the known elevations on the tracing paper over the actual points.
4. Sketch in the form lines by stereoscopic observation.

Remember that the tilt of the photographs may tilt the whole stereoscopic image. Check for this by remembering that lake shores and sluggish meandering streams are really or nearly level regardless of any apparent slope in the stereoscopic model.

**LOCATING GROUND POINTS ON THE PHOTOGRAPH.** Frequently, in preparing a map by photogrammetric means, it is desired to show the correct map position of property boundaries, trails, small buildings, and other features not identifiable on the photographs. For example, if a section corner falls in dense timber, there may be no possibility of determining its exact position on the photographs even if the interpreter has the photographs with him in the field at the time he is occupying the corner. However, there usually is a point in the general vicinity of the section corner which can be definitely recognized in the photographs. While the interpreter occupies the section corner in the field, he should accurately mark this identifiable point on the photograph and determine its bearing and distance from the corner. In the office, the map position of this identifiable point is plotted by standard photogrammetric procedures, and the true map position of the section corner or other desired point is found by plotting the bearing and distances obtained in the field.

## Stand Classification from Aerial Photographs

**GENERAL PRINCIPLES.** The classification of stands according to forest types, size classes, density classes, and site classes is basic to forest mapping and the use of aerial photographs in controlling forest inventory. The photo-interpreter must be a forester experienced in local forest conditions. Preferably, he should check his photo-interpretation in the field at frequent intervals. Stereograms (mounted stereoscopic pictures of known forest conditions) and other aids are useful but will not replace professional training and field experience.

Stand classification should be carried out under the stereoscope, preferably under magnification (provided by a lens stereoscope or by a binocular attachment to the mirror stereoscope). The degree of stand classification possible from aerial photographs should be determined by local forest conditions and the nature of existing photographs. If the degree required is beyond the ability of the photo-interpreter, the resulting errors of classification will largely negate the value of the photographs. If, on the other hand, the degree of classification is too broad, costs are increased because expensive field work will be required to do what might have been accomplished by inexpensive photo-interpretation.

With poor quality and small-scale photographs, classification into forest and nonforest land may be all that is justified. More elaborate classifications might recognize three broad forest types (softwood, hardwood, mixed wood), and three broad size classes (saw timber, pole timber, small growth).

Intermediate scales and qualities of photographs may permit classification of forest land into type classes, height classes, and density classes. Definitions and ranges will depend upon local conditions and requirements. Code designations for the various categories simplify mapping; if at all possible, prepare a comprehensive code in advance instead of improvising as the work progresses.

Detailed photographic classification is restricted to high-quality, large-scale photographs. More forest types, height classes, and density classes can be recognized. Stand classification in terms of height and density is preferable to volume classes for photo-interpretive purposes because volume is dependent upon many factors not directly assessable in the stereoscopic image. Many foresters, however, find it preferable to base the photographic classification on volume classes because of practical considerations.

Before classification is begun, decision should be made on the minimum area of forest class which will be recognized. Thus detailed surveys in country with variable timber may dictate the need for use of 10- or even 5-acre minima for stand or type units. For extensive surveys, particularly where timber is uniform over large areas, a minimum area of 40 or more acres may suffice. Standard minima should be used for each project so that area statistics will be comparable for all forest classes. This applies whether stands are actually delineated and mapped in place or are merely classified by photographic sampling described below (page 19 · 20). In photographic sampling, any dot samples falling upon minor stand details will be classified according to the major stand details in the vicinity surrounding the dot pin point. Thus, if minimum areas to be recognized are 10 acres and a dot falls on a 1-acre opening in a saw timber stand that is 10 acres or more in size, the dot would be classified as saw timber.

**SPECIES AND TYPE IDENTIFICATION.** Many species and types can be identified by stereoscopic study of good quality photographs of a satisfactory scale. Few other distinctions, however, can be made on aerial photographs.

No single key for species and type identification can be devised which would be satisfactory under all conditions. Identification must be based upon local knowledge as applied to a specific set of photographs. Photo-interpretive knowledge may be brought together in the form of keys (see below) or stereograms (mounted stereoscopic photographs of known forest types). The following excerpt from an unpublished study by Chase and Korotev indicates the kind of guide recommended:

**Example of Forest Type Key.**
I. Upland sand soils (generally flat or as dunes)
   A. Oak—Crowns light to very light, fairly solid, generally round-topped and billowy. Often open grown or in clumps. Very dark shadows. On driest sites. Defoliated oak appears furry.
   B. Aspen—Crowns very light to light, small, and indefinite in appearance, crowded appearance in patches. Not squat-looking although short. Often fuzzy.
   C. Jack pine—Crowns dark to very dark, generally pointed. Medium to very dark shadows. Often patchy or scattered. Crowns small except for open grown trees. Height relatively good in comparison with crown diameter.
II. Upland rich soil (generally hilly and well drained)
   A. Northern hardwoods—Individual crowns vary from light to medium tone, giving mottled effect over wide area. Crowns large and definite, rounded to irregular, appearing curdled or billowy. Openings (shadows very dark) are sharply irregular. Crowns wide and height good.

Careful observation and the thoughtful preparation of such a key at the beginning of a photo-interpretation job brings out many slight differences which later provide for more accurate classification. Obviously most of these observations are made as the pictures are studied under a stereoscope in the field.

**Criteria Used in Identification.** The basic criteria in species or type identification in the order of their usual importance to the forester are: background information, physiography, tone, texture, shape, size, crown closure, and shadow.

**Background information.** In beginning to classify species or forest cover types on a pair of photographs, bear in mind characteristics of the photographs and observe first the general features of the terrain and forest. Type of photography, scale, scale differences, focal length of camera, time of year, imperfections due to photographing, developing, or printing, and flight variations should be known. Mentally relate the stereoscopic image to the image seen from the ground. This brings everything to scale and provides for a check on many classifications.

**Physiography.** Under a stereoscope, the topography and drainage features are relatively easily identified and provide a handy criterion for the separation of species and types on the basis of moisture requirements or elevation limits (see "Site Classification" below).

**Tone.** Tone is variable in most sets of pictures and even on individual prints. It refers to the degree of darkness of the lighted portion of the tree crowns as distinguished stereoscopically from shaded portions and shadows. Sand and grass are usually light grays, hardwoods generally medium grays, and conifers tend toward dark grays or black, although many exceptions occur. The south, southeast, and southwest sides of vertical photographs generally have somewhat lighter tones than the sides away from the sun because of the larger amount of light reflected toward the camera. More light is reflected and the resulting tones are therefore lighter for trees in the upper canopy, trees with large, smooth leaves, and trees or stands with dense, compact crowns.

**Texture.** Texture of the crown canopy varies widely with species, size class, and density. Small-topped species such as the pines and aspen in uniform even-aged stands present a fine-grained, even texture. Well-stocked northern hardwoods tend to present an uneven texture pattern because of the large rounded crowns and the uneven-aged structure of the stand.

**Shape.** When crowns are not too small or crowded, the shape of the crowns of the more mature trees becomes a valuable criterion. The shape of the shadow cast in clearings is also useful. Large open-topped trees show great spreading limbs. Eastern white pine shows an irregular rosette of limbs; spruce and fir, a close symmetrical rosette; northern white-cedar with its solid symmetrical shape often appears as two concentric circles.

**Size.** Size includes total height and crown diameter. Some species may be recognized by their position above or below the general canopy level. The ratio of crown size to total height is also frequently indicative.

**Crown closure.** Density of the crown affects tone, texture, size, and shadow. The reaction of individual species to density provides characteristics by which they may be recognized. Density of the individual tree crown is sometimes characteristic. For example, certain thin-leaved species appear in the stereoscopic image to have their crowns floating above the ground, a feature which may also be associated with early dropping of leaves.

**Shadow.** The deeper and more rounded the crowns, the larger and blacker will be the shadow fragments. Shadows are a major factor contributing to tone and texture.

**SITE CLASSIFICATION.** The degree to which site can be classified from aerial photographs varies widely. The most information can be obtained from photographs in regions where site quality is closely correlated with topographic location and also in areas where old-growth timber is still prevalent. In cut-over regions and areas of low relief, site classification from aerial photographs should be restricted to relatively broad strata.

**General Approach.** Basically, site quality is a reflection of soils, topography, and local climate; hence, it is desirable at the outset to collect all available data relative to these factors and to work out correlations among them which are indicative of site quality. Study the photographs stereoscopically in the field to find out which of the factors that are indicative of site are consistently identifiable in the photographs. Restrict this procedure to representative areas in each site class. Look particularly for relative topographic position and the appearance of the vegetative cover.

**Drainage.** In typical forested areas, where ridges and valleys alternate, factors related to water runoff or drainage tend to produce an orderly arrangement of sites as related to position on the slope. At the lower levels the water table tends to lie close to or even above the soil surface. The soils tend to be deep, finely divided, and rich in the mineral nutrients essential for plant growth, but they are often poorly drained and poorly aerated. Along ridge lines, the water table may be low and the soils shallow and infertile. Ridge tops are often subjected to greater climatic extremes than the lower slopes. North- and east-facing slopes tend to be cooler and more moist than south- and west-facing slopes.

Site classifications made from a stereoscopic study of aerial photographs often consist basically of the following categories: ridge top, upper slope, middle slope, lower slope, and flat. Exaggeration of the apparent height of objects in the stereoscopic image facilitates this classification. Many local exceptions to the general rule occur, as for instance the occurrence of dry sandy outwash plains at low elevations in glaciated regions.

**Appearance of Vegetation.** The appearance of the vegetative cover, particularly where old-growth forest types predominate, is a valuable guide to site classification. The height attained by dominant trees at **maturity** usually is directly proportional to site quality. Judgment concerning relative height based upon stereoscopic study is usually sufficient.

**Indicator Species.** In some instances there are indicator species which tend to be specific for certain sites and which are identifiable on the photographs. Still another guide is the ratio of tree height to crown diameter which, for a given species, is apt to be higher for better sites than for poorer sites. The poorest sites are often the most easily detected on aerial photographs. Among the factors which frequently indicate low site quality are low timber density, low density of total woody vegetation, short height, rounded tips and sparse foliage of even the dominant trees, rock outcrops, indicating shallow soil, and the presence of species characteristic of poor sites.

**Training Aids.** Valuable training aids include keys in which the diagnostic features discernible on the photographs are systematically set forth for each site class and mounted stereo pairs (stereograms) picturing examples of each site class on photographs of the same specifications as those to be used in mapping.

**Office Mapping.** In site class mapping in the office, boundaries are delineated directly on the photographs. Judgment is based upon stereoscopic study involving frequent reference to the keys, stereograms, and occasional field checking.

**Final Field Checking.** Spot checks at random are necessary to determine the accuracy of photographic site classification. Often, the degree of site classification desired is beyond that provided by the photo-interpretation and final refinements must be made in the field.

## Combining Aerial Survey and Ground Survey

**GENERAL PRINCIPLES.** To correlate the aerial and ground survey, proceed as follows:

1. Classify stands into classes on aerial photographs.
2. Determine the area of each class either from stand maps constructed from aerial photographs (below), or by direct sampling on the photographs (below).

Photo-classification of these areas is verified by random field checks and the aerial photographic estimates are adjusted accordingly (page 19·22).

3. From the above information, the number of plots that must be taken on the ground within each class is computed (page 19·23).

4. The points where these field plots should be taken are located by random methods on the aerial photographs (page 19·23).

5. The field plots are then measured by standard procedures to determine the average per acre volume of each class recognized in the aerial photographic classification (page 19·24).

**AREA DETERMINATION BY MAPPING.** In all cases of rough topography and in special cases where a forest map is required, areas of forest classes may best be determined as follows:

1. Select photographs on which boundaries of forest classes will be delineated. These may be alternate photographs in a stereo coverage.

2. Mark effective or central areas of all selected photographs, drawing corresponding lines for this bisection through detail common to overlapping photographs. Approximate rectangles are thus drawn on all selected photographs which provide ties for mapping from one photograph to another over the project area without duplication in detail.

3. Classify, code, and delineate boundaries of all forest classes on the selected photographs, using any adjacent photographs for stereoscopic study as needed in the preliminary photo-interpretation.

4. Check the photo-interpretation in the field as needed to get all details required for the survey, noting this information on the photographs. These check should be made whenever possible by the photo-interpreters themselves, thus tending to make their future work more accurate.

5. Transfer forest class data (boundaries and symbols) from the photographs to a base map using for control features such as field references, roads, streams, and other topographic features which are common both to the photographs and to the map.

6. Compute areas of various forest classes.

**AREA DETERMINATION BY PHOTOGRAPH SAMPLING.** Photograph sampling is a rapid method for obtaining area statistics when (1) a forest map is not required, (2) the gross acreage in a survey unit is known, and (3) topography is gentle so that variations in photograph scale do not introduce bias in area estimates. The procedure is as follows:

1. The minimum number of items of sample (dots) to be taken within the survey unit is predetermined by the formula:

$$N = \frac{P(1 - P)t^2}{(AE)^2}$$

where $P$ is an estimate of the proportion of the area in forest or the particular class
$AE$ is the allowable error expressed as a decimal
$t$ is a constant that reflects the reliability to be placed in the estimate

(See Section 23, Mathematical Formulas and Definitions, page 26.)

**Example.** Assume that the main item of interest is the acreage of saw-timber stands. A reasonable estimate of the percentage of area in this class is 25 percent. It is desired to determine the proportion of the area in saw timber with an allowable error $(AE)$ of 0.005, and this should be correct in 19 out of 20 times. So $t = 1.96$. Then

$$N = \frac{0.25(1.00 - 0.25)(1.96)^2}{(0.005)^2} = 28,812$$

Repeat this calculation for any other highly important forest classes, using the best estimate of the proportion, $P$. The total number of dots to use is the largest number for any class.

2. If area sampling is done on a photo-index or mosaic, a transparent templet is made that has a pattern of dots spaced at the proper interval to give at least the required number falling within the survey unit when the templet is overlaid on the photo-index or mosaic. Generally, unless sampling is merely for a simple item such as total forest area, it is preferable or necessary to use the individual photographs in a stereoscopic coverage. The approximate number of photographs with centers falling within the boundaries of the survey unit is determined by reference to the photo- or line-index of the photographic project.

3. An appropriate dot pattern (systematic or random) is chosen and is marked on transparent material (clear cellulose acetate is suggested) to form a templet. The total number of required dots divided by the number of photographs to be sampled indicates the number of dots to be located on the templet. This figure is rounded up to the nearest whole number. The templet should be slightly larger than the photograph size. The dot pattern, however, should be centered over the central portion of the templet within a rectangular area of approximately 4½ by 2½ in. When such a pattern (smaller than the average effective photograph area) is centered over a photograph so the long axis of the pattern is perpendicular to the flight line, there will be no possibility of duplicating sampling of the same photographic details when adjacent overlapping photographs (9 in. square) are used, even with probably maximum overlap.

**Example.** Assume that where 28,800 total dots are required for a sample of a survey unit, there are approximately 1,100 photographs in the stereoscopic coverage with centers falling within the unit. This requires 28,800 divided by 1,100, or 26.2 dots per photograph. Rounding upward, 27 dots per photograph are required. Thus dots could be spaced in a systematic pattern in three rows 1 in. apart, each row having 9 dots ½ in. apart.

4. The dot templet is laid over each photograph in turn. For ease in orientation in the same manner over each photograph, the position of the fiducial marks should be marked on the templet and these marks used for orientation.

5. A tally is kept of dots falling over photographic details of any forest or land class for which area estimates are desired and which are being interpreted.

6. The ratio of total dots tallied in any one class to the total of all dots falling within the survey project, multiplied by 100, gives the percent of land in that class.

**Example.** The final total tally of dots within the gross project area proves to be 29,400 (not identical with the number calculated as needed or with the number expected if 27 dots were tallied for all 1,100 photographs, because a few dots fell outside the project boundary indicated on the photographs that straddled the boundary).

Assume the examination of 29,400 points or plots on the aerial photographs gave 6,520 plots in saw timber, 18,440 plots in pole timber, and 4,440 plots in other timber, and that the gross area ($A$) was 835,400 acres. The area of each of these photo classes is:

$$\text{Saw timber:} \quad 835,400 \left( \frac{6,520}{29,400} \right) = 185,459 \text{ acres}$$

$$\text{Pole timber:} \quad 835,400 \left( \frac{18,440}{29,400} \right) = 523,796 \text{ acres}$$

$$\text{Other timber:} \quad 835,400 \left( \frac{4,440}{29,400} \right) = 126,145 \text{ acres}$$

If these determinations are assumed to be correct, their sampling errors ($E$) can be calculated from the equation:

$$E = \sqrt{\frac{P(1 - P)}{N}}$$

For the saw-timber class the error is

$$E = \sqrt{\frac{(0.222)(1.0 - 0.222)}{29,400}} = \sqrt{0.000,005,875} = 0.00242$$

or 1.1 percent of $P(0.222)$.

## ADJUSTMENTS OF PHOTOGRAPH AREA ESTIMATES FOLLOWING GROUND CHECKS.

In all but reconnaissance surveys, a definite percentage of the photographic plots should be checked on the ground. This is automatically provided for where the average volume per acre of each class is determined from ground plots, but it involves an extra operation if only area estimates are desired. Usually, every $n$th (**example:** every 100th or other multiple) dot is checked in the field for correctness of photo-interpretation. At least 20 to 30, and preferably more, dots should be checked for each class. This ground check provides the basis for adjusting photograph area estimates.

If only a few plots are checked in the field and many changes are noted, the adjusted area will have a much larger sampling error. The following example illustrates the calculation of the adjusted area and its error:

**Example.** Assume that in the second example on page **19·21**, 50 plots in the saw-timber class, 100 plots in the pole-timber class, and 40 plots in the other timber class were checked in the field. Also assume that the ground check indicated 90 percent (45 out of 50) of the saw-timber plots were saw timber, 20 percent (20 out of 100) of the pole-timber plots were saw timber, and 10 percent (4 out of 40) of the other timber plots were saw timber. These data would indicate that an adjustment was needed in the estimation of the saw-timber area. The procedure for doing this is shown below.

| Photo-class or strata | No. of photo-plots $N_i$ | Proportion $P_i$ | No. plots In field sample $n_i$ | No. plots In saw timber $n_{si}$ | Proportion saw timber $P_{si}$ | $P_iP_{si}$ |
|---|---|---|---|---|---|---|
| Saw timber .... | 6,520 | 0.222 | 50 | 45 | 0.90 | 0.1998 |
| Pole timber ... | 18,440 | .627 | 100 | 20 | .20 | .1254 |
| Other timber .. | 4,440 | .151 | 40 | 4 | .10 | .0151 |
| Total ........ | 29,400 | 1.000 | | | | 0.3403 |

The adjusted proportion of the area in saw timber $(_aP_s)$ is 0.3403 and is obtained from the equation

$$_aP_s = \Sigma P_iP_{si}$$

($\Sigma$ means "sum of.")

The area of saw timber is

$$A_S = A\Sigma P_iP_{si} = (835,400)(0.3403) = 284,287$$

The error of the adjusted area is obtained from the equation

$$E_{A_S} = A\sqrt{\Sigma P_i{}^2\frac{P_{si}(1-P_{si})}{n_i} + \frac{\Sigma P_iP_{si}{}^2 - (\Sigma P_iP_{si})^2}{N}}$$

The calculation of the error is shown below.

| Photo-class or strata | $P_i$ | $P_{s_i}$ | $n_i$ | $P_i{}^2\dfrac{P_{s_i}(1-P_{s_i})}{n_i}$ | $P_iP_{s_i}$ | $P_iP_{s_i}{}^2$ |
|---|---|---|---|---|---|---|
| Saw timber ... | 0.222 | 0.9 | 50 | 0.000,088,711 | 0.1998 | 0.179,82 |
| Pole timber ... | .627 | .2 | 100 | .000,629,006 | .1254 | .025,08 |
| Other timber .. | .151 | .1 | 40 | .000,051,302 | .0151 | .001,51 |
| Total ......... | 1.000 | — | — | 0.000,769,019 | 0.3403 | 0.206,41 |

$$E_{A_s} = (835,400) \sqrt{0.000,769,019 + \frac{[0.206,41 - (0.3403)^2]}{29,400}}$$

$$= (835,400)\sqrt{0.000,769,019 + 0.000,003,082} = 23,213$$

which is 8.2 percent of the adjusted area of saw timber.

## NUMBER OF PLOTS NEEDED FOR GROUND VOLUME SAMPLING.

The use of aerial photographs in forest inventory not only permits the low-cost computation of acreage of each forest class but also permits the allocation of ground plots to each class so that a reduced number of plots can be taken in order to obtain a desired degree of accuracy. This technique of stratification frequently results in reducing the number of ground plots that might otherwise be taken from one-half to two-thirds without sacrificing the desired over-all accuracy.

If a large number of classes have been recognized in the photo-classification, it is advisable to group these according to the approximate average volume per acre for the purpose of computing the number of field plots needed.

All saw-timber classes might be grouped as high volume, medium volume, or low volume. If the number of plots that can be taken in a stratum is not fixed, and if a sampling error can be specified, then

$$N = \frac{(CV)^2}{(AE)^2}$$

where $N$ is the number of plots, $CV$ is the coefficient of variation (standard deviation of plot volume within the class, expressed as a percent of the average plot volume), and $AE$ is the allowable error, also expressed as a percent.

**Example.** For high-volume saw-timber types, the estimated average volume is 30 M bd. ft. per acre and the estimated standard deviation of plot volume is 12 M bd. ft. per acre, thus giving a $CV$ of 40 percent. If the allowable error is 2 percent, the number of plots needed in this type is $40^2$ divided by $2^2$, or 400 plots. The sampling error is always much less than the actual total cruising error from all sources (see the subject matter in Section 1, Forest Measurements, for more detailed information).

If the error for the total volume in all classes is specified, the sample size can be determined by optimum allocation procedures. (See Section 23 on mathematics for the case when the area is determined from a map. When the area is determined by photograph sampling, with a very large sample, the area estimates are often assumed to be free of error for practical purposes.)

## USING THE PHOTOGRAPHS TO LOCATE GROUND PLOTS.

Once the number of ground plots needed in each class has been determined, these plots can be located by use of the aerial photographs. For each class, compute the proportion of field plots to the number of dots tallied in this class on the photographs or stand map. Thus, if 16,600 photograph plots fell in large volume saw-timber types, and 415 ground plots are desired in these types, every 40th dot should be located on the ground and used as the plot center for a ground plot.

If these plots are located on the base map, plot locations are then transferred to the individual photographs by pin prick, judging location by eye or finding it by use of a plotting device. The photographs are then taken into the field and used to find the desired spot on the ground. Any landmark visible on photographs or map near the plot location can be used to locate the field position of the plot, thus expediting field work as compared to the alternative of running long traverses from land lines or other control.

**VOLUME COMPUTATIONS.** The total volume in a photo-class is the product of the area of the class and the average volume per acre. If the volume of a class—say, the saw-timber class—is desired and the adjusted area is used, then the adjusted average volume per acre must be used. The adjusted average volume for the saw timber is calculated as shown below, where $x_i$ is the average volume of those plots in a photo-class that were called saw timber on ground check.

| Photo-class or strata | $P_i$ | $P_{s_i}$ | $\bar{x}_i$ | $P_i P_{s_i} \bar{x}_i$ |
|---|---|---|---|---|
| Saw timber | 0.222 | 0.9 | 30 M | 5.9940 M |
| Pole timber | .627 | .2 | 5 M | 0.6270 M |
| Other timber | .151 | .1 | 1 M | .0151 M |
| | | | | 6.6361 M |

In the calculation of the adjusted average volume, the averages are weighted by $P_i P_{s_i}$.

The total volume ($T_s$) on the saw-timber area is obtained from the equation $T_s = A_s (P_i P_{s_i} \bar{x}_i)$,

$$T_s = (284{,}287)\ (6.6361\ M) = 1{,}886{,}557\ M$$

# Direct Volume Estimates from Aerial Photographs

**GENERAL PRINCIPLES.** Gross volume per acre (but not net volume excluding defect) can be estimated directly from aerial photographs. Individual estimates are not particularly accurate, but the errors tend to average out so that the average of a number of estimates for the same class of timber can be used for reconnaissance purposes or for determining the number of ground plots to be established in that class. The three general methods, as described below, include the stereogram method, the aerial volume table method, and conversion tables for use with standard volume tables. Whenever possible, aerial photographic estimates of stand volume should be checked by ground plots.

**STEREOGRAM METHOD.** This method is based upon ocular comparison of the stereoscopic image of the stand with stereograms of similar stands. The procedure is as follows:

1. Sample plots are established in various sizes of stands on the ground in places where they can be specifically located on the aerial photographs.
2. Portions of the aerial photographs (usually 1-in. square) having these plots in the center are cut out and mounted for stereoscopic study on a card or sheet containing the plot data.
3. Volumes of various stands on a per acre basis are estimated by stereoscopic comparison with the various stereograms of the plots of known volume. Photographs of the same specifications must be used for both the stereograms and the unknown stands.

**AERIAL VOLUME TABLES.** These may be constructed from tree and stand measurements obtained on the ground either on a per acre or on a per tree basis. **Stand aerial volume tables** usually give the per acre volumes for various height classes and crown closure classes. Average crown diameter is another variable used. Stand volume tables based upon total height and basal area per acre are statistically of a high order of accuracy, but they require an estimate of basal area in terms of crown closure and other variables discernible on the photographs.

**Tree aerial volume tables** usually give the volume per tree for various height and crown diameter classes. They are generally less satisfactory than the stand type because of the difficulty of counting accurately the number of crowns per acre on aerial photographs. Existing aerial volume tables are summarized on page 19 · 27.

**CONVERSION TABLES.** Conversion tables give the estimated d.b.h. of trees for various crown diameters or combinations of crown diameters and height, thus permitting the use of conventional volume tables in aerial photographs. Although statistically unsound (d.b.h. is treated first as a dependent and then as an independent variable), they are frequently satisfactory for providing rough estimates of volume per tree. An approximate rule of thumb for the East and South is that the d.b.h. in inches is equal to three-quarters of the crown diameter in feet if the crown diameter is 30 ft. or less. In the Pacific Northwest, the d.b.h. in inches may be assumed to equal the crown diameter in feet.

**ADJUSTMENTS OF PHOTOGRAPHIC VOLUME ESTIMATES BY FIELD PLOTS.** The procedure for adjusting photographic volume estimates by field plots is as follows:

1. Estimate the plot volume on a large number of plots established on the photographs. These may be located by dot templets.
2. Mark every $n$th photograph plot (enough to get a total of at least several dozen marked plots) in the population being sampled.
3. Obtain both a photograph volume estimate and a field volume measurement of these marked plots.
4. Compute the average volume of the marked plots from field data $(\overline{Y}_s)$.
5. Compute the average volume of the same marked plots as estimated on the photographs $(\overline{X}_s)$.
6. Compute the average volume as determined from photographs of all plots estimated on the photographs (including those marked) $(\overline{X}_L)$.
7. Using data from the marked plots only, plot individual field plot volumes over corresponding photograph plot volumes in a scatter diagram (Fig. 6).
8. Draw a regression line from the diagram and determine its slope or regression coefficient $(b)$ from the diagram or by computation.
9. Compute the adjusted average volume $(\overline{Y}_a)$ for the large photograph volume sample by the following formula (based on unpublished office memorandum by F. A. Johnson, U. S. Forest Service, Pacific Northwest Forest and Range Exp. Sta., 1950) or by reading vertically to the regression line from the value of $\overline{X}_L$ on the $x$-axis and horizontally to find the value of $\overline{Y}_a$ on the $y$-axis.

$$\overline{Y}_a = \overline{Y}_s + b \, (\overline{X}_L - \overline{X}_s)$$

**Example** (Fig. 6). An inventory was made using stand aerial volume tables in heavy volume saw timber; 340 photograph volume plots were taken, and every tenth plot (total of 34) was marked and measured also on the ground. The average photograph volume estimate for all plots was 10.2 M cu. ft. gross per acre $(\overline{X}_L)$. The average estimated by photographs for the marked plots was 9.41 M cu. ft. gross per

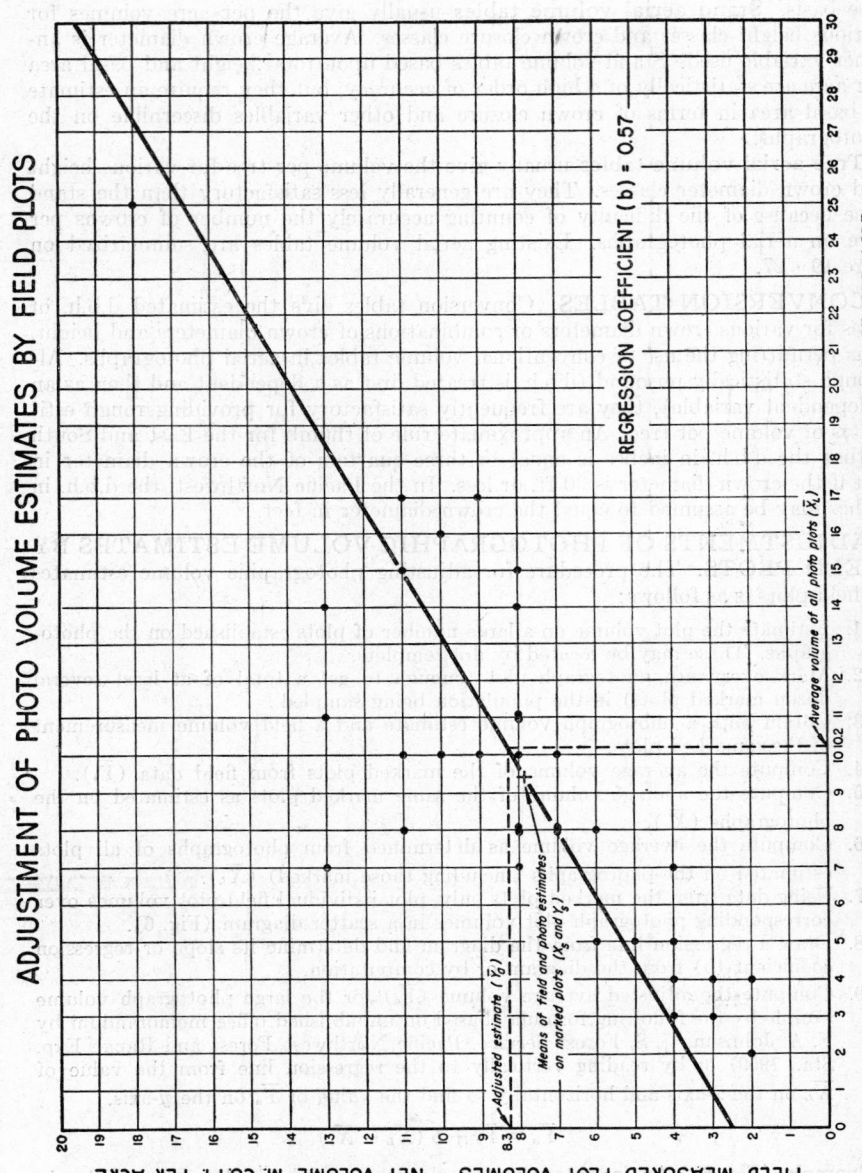

Fig. 1. Adjustment of photo volume estimates by field plots

acre ($\overline{X}_s$). The average field volume on these same marked plots was 7.9 M cu. ft. net per acre ($\overline{Y}_s$). The regression coefficient ($b$) (as indicated on the scatter diagram of the net field over gross photograph volume for the 34 marked plots) was 0.57. The adjusted average net volume per acre of the saw-timber sample is:

$$\overline{Y}_a = 7.9 + 0.57\ (10.2 - 9.41) = 8.35\ \text{M cu. ft.}$$

Computation from the diagram is made by reading vertically from $\overline{X}_L$ the value of 10.2 to the regression line, then horizontally to find the $\overline{Y}_a$ value of 8.3.

### Sources of Mensurational Data for Direct Volume Estimates from Aerial Photographs

1. Conversion to d.b.h. for eastern white pine, white spruce: Nash, A. J. (Canadian Institute of Forestry, Toronto, Canada), Some volume tables for use in air survey, *Forestry Chronicle*, 24(1):4–14. 1948.
2. Stand aerial volume tables for typical hardwood stands in Indiana, Illinois, Kentucky, and Missouri: Central States Forest Experiment Station, Columbus, Ohio.
3. Tree aerial volume tables for red spruce, balsam fir, eastern hemlock, yellow birch, beech, sugar maple, paper birch, red maple: Northeastern Forest Experiment Station, Upper Darby, Pa.
4. Stand aerial volume tables, tree aerial volume tables, and conversion to d.b.h. tables for Douglas-fir: Pacific Northwest Forest Experiment Station, Portland, Ore.
5. Stand aerial volume tables for eastern white pine and loblolly pine; tree aerial volume tables for eastern white pine, red spruce, balsam fir, and eastern hemlock; conversion to d.b.h. graphs for eastern white pine, white spruce, balsam fir, yellow birch, beech, paper birch, sugar maple, red maple, pitch pine, and longleaf pine: Spurr, Stephen H., *Aerial photographs in forestry* (see Bibliography).
6. Stand volume formulas (height and basal area basis) for Douglas-fir, longleaf pine, loblolly pine, eastern white pine, red pine, Norway spruce, white spruce, black spruce, red spruce, balsam fir, and northeastern hardwoods; tree aerial volume tables for red spruce, black spruce, white spruce, and balsam fir: Spurr, Stephen H., *Forest inventory* (see Bibliography).

## BIBLIOGRAPHY

AMERICAN SOCIETY OF PHOTOGRAMMETRY. 1952. *Manual of photogrammetry.* 2d ed. Washington, D. C.
AMERICAN SOCIETY OF PHOTOGRAMMETRY. *Photogrammetric Engineering.* (Quarterly.)
LORENZ, GILBERT G., JOHN T. PENNINGTON, and IRWIN K. ROTH (compilers). 1949. Symposium: New developments in photogrammetric equipment. *Photogram. Engineer.* 15:333–450.
SISAM, J. W. B. 1947. *The use of aerial survey in forestry and agriculture.* Commonwealth Agricultural Bureaus, Oxford, Eng.
SPURR, STEPHEN H. 1948. *Aerial photographs in forestry.* The Ronald Press Co., New York.
SPURR, STEPHEN H. 1952. *Forest inventory.* The Ronald Press Co., New York.
SPURR, STEPHEN H. 1954. History of forest photogrammetry and aerial mapping. *Photogram. Engineer.* 20:551–560.
SPURR, STEPHEN H. 1954. Forest photogrammetry and aerial mapping. A bibliography, 1887–1953. School of Natural Resources, University of Michigan. 49 pp.
U. S. FOREST SERV., Central States Forest Exp. Sta. 1948. Dot-type scale for measuring tree-crown diameters on aerial photographs. *Sta. Note 48.*
U. S. FOREST SERV., Lake States Forest Exp. Sta. 1955. Photo-interpretation aids.
U. S. FOREST SERV., Northeastern Forest Exp. Sta. 1947. Estimating tree heights from shadows on vertical air photographs. *Sta. Paper No. 12.*
WOOD, EDWARD S., JR. 1949. Photogrammetry for the non-photogrammetrist. *Photogram. Engineer.* 15:249–275.

# COMMUNICATIONS

## CONTENTS

## CONTENTS (*Continued*)

# COMMUNICATIONS

Communication facilities are today essential to forest activities. The telephone has long been indispensable in fire protection. Detection systems, no matter how complete and well manned, will not function efficiently unless there is a rapid and dependable means of relaying messages between the eyes of the forest and the administrative centers. Use of the radio has introduced a flexibility to communications hitherto unknown on forest lands. Foresters and the forest industries now use both telephone and radio, not for protection work alone but for operational purposes and as an aid in case of emergency. Communication facilities are the means by which men, machines, and materials are tied together over wide areas while employed on diversified activities.

It takes planning to make a communications system function. Three steps in establishing a system are equally essential: (1) engineering survey, (2) construction, and (3) operation.

## Radio Communications in the United States

Radio communications are now widely employed in private, state, and federal forest management. They are dependable and versatile. Space on the air is divided into air lanes called channels. Each channel is assigned a fixed number, called the midfrequency. Different groups of channels are assigned to each type of eligible service. Thus the private forest enterprises will have exclusive space on the air separate from either the state conservation departments or the federal Forest Service. Individuals or forests within a given service are assigned specific channels to prevent interference between systems or networks. A service or an individual company will not be able to talk to another service or company. To cross-tie two systems necessitates each operator's having a receiver on the other's frequency.

**CHANNEL ASSIGNMENTS.** In the United States the Federal Communications Commission is the agency ultimately responsible for the allocation of channels to the federal, state, and private agencies requesting a system. The Interdepartment Radio Advisory Committee (I.R.A.C.) allocates the channels assigned by the F.C.C. to federal agencies. The Forestry-Conservation Communications Association, acting through the chairman of subject committees in each of four regions, recommends frequencies to the states in each area. Current names and addresses of association officers may be secured from the nearest office of the Federal Communications Commission (see pages 20·4–6) or the nearest state agency that is a member of the association.

The agency which coordinates channels to private operators is the Forest Industries Radio Communications, Eugene, Oregon. It receives its authority under Subpart H—Forest Products Radio Service, Part II, "Rules Governing Industrial Radio Services" (revised to April 27, 1949; effective July 1, 1949), listed in the Federal Register of May 6, 1949, and quoted as follows:

**Fig. 1. Frequency administrative divisions of Forest Industries Radio Communications.**

SUBPART H—FOREST PRODUCTS RADIO SERVICE

**§ 11.351. Eligibility.** (a) The following persons are eligible to hold authorizations to operate radio stations in the Forest Products Radio Service:

(1) A person who is engaged in tree logging, tree farming, or related woods operations.

(2) A non-profit corporation or association, organized for the purpose of furnishing a radio communication service solely to persons who are actually engaged in one or more of the activities set forth in subparagraph (1) of this paragraph. Such a corporation or association shall render service only on a non-profit cost-sharing basis, said costs to be prorated on an equitable basis among all persons to whom service is rendered. Records which reflect this cost-sharing, non-profit basis shall be maintained and held available for inspection by Commission representatives.

(b) Each application for authority to operate in the Forest Products Radio Service shall be accompanied by a statement in detail sufficient to indicate clearly the applicant's eligibility under paragraph (a) of this section. In addition, each person licensed under the provisions of paragraph (a)(2) of this section shall obtain prior approval from the Commission for each person who proposes to participate in the licensee's service.

**§ 11.352. Frequencies available for base and mobile stations.** (a) The following frequencies are available for assignment to base and mobile stations in the Forest Products Radio Service only:

| Mc. | Mc. | Mc. | Mc. |
|-----|-----|-----|-----|
| 29.73 | 49.26 | 49.38 | 49.50 |
| 29.77 | 49.30 | 49.42 | |
| 49.22 | 49.34 | 49.46 | |

(b) The following frequencies are available for assignment to base and mobile stations in the Forest Products Radio Service on a shared basis with other services:

| Kc. | Mc. | Mc. | Mc. |
|---|---|---|---|
| 1676 * | 49.54 | 153.11 | 153.35 |
| 1700 * | 49.58 | 153.17 | 158.31 |
| 2398 | 49.62 | 153.23 | 158.37 |
|  | 49.66 | 153.29 | 158.43 |
|  | 153.05 |  |  |

(c) The following frequencies are available for assignment to base and mobile stations in the Forest Products Radio Service on a shared basis with other services, under the terms of a developmental grant only:

| Mc. | Mc. | Mc. | Mc. |
|---|---|---|---|
| 456.05 | 456.55 | 451.05 | 451.55 |
| 456.15 | 456.65 | 451.15 | 451.65 |
| 456.25 | 456.75 | 451.25 | 451.75 |
| 456.35 | 456.85 | 451.35 | 451.85 |
| 456.45 | 456.95 | 451.45 | 451.95 |

(d) Frequencies in the bands listed below are available for assignment to base and mobile stations in the Forest Products Radio Service on a shared basis with other services, under the terms of a developmental grant only; the exact frequency and the authorized bandwidth will be specified in the authorization:

| Mc. | Mc. |
|---|---|
| 2450–2500 | 6425– 6575 |
| 3500–3700 | 11700–12200 |

§ 11.353. **Frequencies available for fixed stations.** (a) Subject to the condition that no harmful interference will be caused to reception of television channel number 4 or 5, the following frequencies are available for assignment to fixed stations in the Forest Products Radio Service on a shared basis with other services:

| Mc. | Mc. | Mc. | Mc. |
|---|---|---|---|
| 72.02 | 72.82 | 73.62 | 74.42 |
| 72.06 | 72.86 | 73.66 | 74.46 |
| 72.10 | 72.90 | 73.70 | 74.50 |
| 72.14 | 72.94 | 73.74 | 74.54 |
| 72.18 | 72.98 | 73.78 | 74.58 |
| 72.22 | 73.02 | 73.82 | 75.42 |
| 72.26 | 73.06 | 73.86 | 75.46 |
| 72.30 | 73.10 | 73.90 | 75.50 |
| 72.34 | 73.14 | 73.94 | 75.54 |
| 72.38 | 73.18 | 73.98 | 75.58 |
| 72.42 | 73.22 | 74.02 | 75.62 |
| 72.46 | 73.26 | 74.06 | 75.66 |
| 72.50 | 73.30 | 74.10 | 75.70 |
| 72.54 | 73.34 | 74.14 | 75.74 |
| 72.58 | 73.38 | 74.18 | 75.78 |
| 72.62 | 73.42 | 74.22 | 75.82 |
| 72.66 | 73.46 | 74.26 | 75.86 |
| 72.70 | 73.50 | 74.30 | 75.90 |
| 72.74 | 73.54 | 74.34 | 75.94 |
| 72.78 | 73.58 | 74.38 | 75.98 |

(b) Frequencies in the bands listed below are available for assignment to fixed stations in the Forest Products Radio Service on a shared basis with other services, under the terms of a developmental grant only; the exact frequency and the authorized bandwidth will be specified in the authorization:

| Mc. | Mc. |
|---|---|
| 952– 960 | 6575– 6875 |
| 1850–1990 | 12200–12700 |
| 2110–2200 | 16000–18000* |
| 2450–2500* | 26000–30000 |
| 2500–2700 | |

* Use of frequencies in the bands 2450–2500, and 17850–18000 Mc. is subject to no protection from interference due to the operation of industrial, scientific, and medical devices on the frequencies 2450 and 18000 Mc.

A current list of the frequencies of privately operated radios is given in the Directory of Forest Industries Radio Communications. It may be obtained from Forest Industries Radio Communications (page 20·1) or by directing an inquiry to the nearest office of the F.C.C. (below). Also available are alphabetic lists of licensees and corresponding call signs, arranged both alphabetically and numerically. Similar current listings of state organization radios by agencies and frequencies may be obtained from the Forestry-Conservation Communications Association (page 20·1).

**FEDERAL COMMUNICATIONS COMMISSION.** Radio users encountering interference on channels assigned to them can obtain assistance in locating and eliminating it from the engineer-in-charge of the Commission in their local radio district. The Commission has divided the United States and its outlying possessions into 24 districts, with headquarters as listed below.

### Location of Field Offices, Radio Districts, F.C.C.

UNITED STATES RADIO DISTRICTS

Address the District F.C.C. Engineer-in-Charge

District No. 1, Boston, Mass. The states of CONNECTICUT, MAINE, MASSACHUSETTS, NEW HAMPSHIRE, RHODE ISLAND and VERMONT.

District No. 2, New York, N. Y. In the state of NEW YORK, the counties of Albany, Bronx, Columbia, Delaware, Dutchess, Greene, Kings, Nassau, New York, Orange, Putnam, Queens, Rensselaer, Richmond, Rockland, Schenectady, Suffolk, Sullivan, Ulster and Westchester; in the state of NEW JERSEY, the counties of Bergen, Essex, Hudson, Hunterdon, Mercer, Middlesex, Monmouth, Morris, Passaic, Somerset, Sussex, Union and Warren.

District No. 3, Philadelphia, Pa. In the state of PENNSYLVANIA, the counties of Adams, Berks, Bucks, Carbon, Chester, Cumberland, Dauphin, Delaware, Lancaster, Lebanon, Lehigh, Monroe, Montgomery, Northampton, Perry, Philadelphia, Schuylkill and York; in the state of NEW JERSEY, the counties of Atlantic, Burlington, Camden, Cape May, Cumberland, Gloucester, Ocean and Salem; and the county of Newcastle in the state of DELAWARE.

District No. 4, Baltimore, Md. The state of MARYLAND; in the state of VIRGINIA, the counties of Arlington, Clark, Fairfax, Fauquier, Frederick, Loudoun, Page, Prince William, Rappahannock, Shenandoah and Warren; the counties of Kent and Sussex in the state of DELAWARE; in the state of WEST VIRGINIA, the counties of Barbour, Berkeley, Grant, Hampshire, Hardy, Harrison, Jefferson, Lewis, Marion, Mineral, Monongalia, Morgan, Pendleton, Preston, Randolph, Taylor, Tucker and Upshur.

District No. 5, Norfolk, Va. The state of VIRGINIA except that part lying in District 4, and the state of NORTH CAROLINA except that part lying in District 6.

District No. 6, Atlanta, Ga. The states of GEORGIA, SOUTH CAROLINA and TENNESSEE; the state of ALABAMA except that part lying in District 8; in the state of NORTH CAROLINA, the counties of Ashe, Avery, Buncombe, Burke, Caldwell, Cherokee,

Clay, Cleveland, Graham, Haywood, Henderson, Jackson, McDowell, Macon, Madison, Mitchell, Polk, Rutherford, Swain, Transylvania, Watauga and Yancey.

District No. 7, Miami, Fla. The state of FLORIDA except that part lying in District 8.

District No. 8, New Orleans, La. The states of ARKANSAS, LOUISIANA and MISSISSIPPI; in the state of TEXAS, the city of Texarkana; in the state of FLORIDA, the county of Escambia; in the state of ALABAMA, the counties of Mobile and Baldwin.

District No. 9, Houston, Tex. In the state of TEXAS, the counties of Angelina, Aransas, Atascosa, Austin, Bandera, Bastrop, Bee, Brooks, Bexar, Blanco, Brazoria, Brazos, Burleson, Caldwell, Calhoun, Cameron, Chambers, Colorado, Comal, DeWitt, Duval, Dimmit, Edwards, Fayette, Fort Bend, Frio, Galveston, Gillespie, Goliad, Gonzales, Grimes, Guadalupe, Hardon, Hays, Harris, Hidalgo, Jackson, Jasper, Jefferson, Jim Hogg, Jim Wells, Karnes, Kennedy, Kendall, Kerr, Kinney, Kleberg, LaSalle, Lavaca, Lee, Liberty, Live Oak, Matagorda, Madison, Maverick, McMullen, Medina, Montgomery, Nacogdoches, Newton, Nueces, Orange, Polk, Real, Refugio, San Augustine, San Jacinto, San Patricio, Sabine, Starr, Travis, Trinity, Tyler, Uvalde, Val Verde, Victoria, Walker, Waller, Washington, Webb, Wharten, Willacy, Williamson, Wilson, Zapata and Zavala.

District No. 10, Dallas, Tex. The state of TEXAS except that part lying in District 9 and in the city of Texarkana; the states of OKLAHOMA and NEW MEXICO.

District No. 11, Los Angeles, Calif. The state of ARIZONA; in the state of NEVADA, the county of Clarke; in the state of CALIFORNIA, the counties of Imperial, Inyo, Kern, Los Angeles, Orange, Riverside, San Bernardino, San Diego, San Luis Obispo, Santa Barbara and Ventura.

District No. 12, San Francisco, Calif. The state of CALIFORNIA except that part lying in District 11; the state of NEVADA except the county of Clarke.

District No. 13, Portland, Ore. The state of OREGON; the state of IDAHO except that part lying in District 14; in the state of WASHINGTON, the counties of Wahkiakum, Cowlitz, Clark, Skamania and Klickitat.

District No. 14, Seattle, Wash. The state of MONTANA; the state of WASHINGTON except that part lying in District 13; in the state of IDAHO, the counties of Benewah, Bonner, Boundary, Clearwater, Idaho, Kootenai, Latah, Lewis, Nez Perce and Shoshone.

District No. 15, Denver, Colo. The states of COLORADO, UTAH and WYOMING; in the state of NEBRASKA, the counties of Banner, Box Butte, Cheyenne, Dawes, Deuel, Garden, Kimball, Morrill, Scottsbluff, Sheridan and Sioux; in the state of SOUTH DAKOTA, the counties of Butte, Custer, Fall River, Lawrence, Meade, Pennington, Shannon and Washington.

District No. 16, St. Paul, Minn. The states of MINNESOTA and NORTH DAKOTA; the state of SOUTH DAKOTA except that part lying in District 15; the state of WISCONSIN except that part lying in District 18; in the state of MICHIGAN, the counties of Alger, Baraga, Chippewa, Delta, Dickinson, Gogebic, Houghton, Iron, Keweenaw, Luce, Mackinac, Marquette, Menominee, Ontonagon and Schoolcraft.

District No. 17, Kansas City, Mo. The states of KANSAS and MISSOURI; the state of IOWA except that part lying in District 18; the state of NEBRASKA except that part lying in District 15.

District No. 18, Chicago, Ill. The states of ILLINOIS and INDIANA; in the state of IOWA, the counties of Allamakee, Buchanan, Cedar, Clayton, Clinton, Delaware, Des Moines, Dubuque, Fayette, Henry, Jackson, Johnson, Jones, Lee, Linn, Louisa, Muscatine, Scott, Washington and Winneshiek; in the state of WISCONSIN, the counties of Brown, Columbia, Calumet, Crawford, Dane, Dodge, Door, Fond du Lac, Grant, Green, Iowa, Jefferson, Keewanee, Kenosha, Lafayette, Manitowoc, Marinette, Milwaukee, Ozaukee, Oconto, Outgamie, Racine, Richland, Rock, Sauk, Sheboygan, Walworth, Washington, Waukesha and Winnebago; the state of KENTUCKY except that part lying in District 19.

District No. 19, Detroit, Mich. The state of OHIO; the state of MICHIGAN except that part lying in District 16; the state of WEST VIRGINIA except that part lying in District 4; in the state of KENTUCKY, the counties of Bath, Bell, Boone, Bourbon, Boyd, Bracken, Breathitt, Campbell, Carter, Clark, Clay, Elliott, Estill, Fayette, Fleming, Floyd, Franklin, Gallatin, Garrard, Grant, Greenup, Kenton, Harlan, Harrison, Jackson, Jessamine, Johnson, Knott, Knox, Laurel, Lawrence, Lee, Leslie, Letcher, Lewis, Lincoln, Madison, Magoffin, Martin, Mason, McCreary, Menifee, Montgomery, Morgan, Nicholas, Owen, Owsley, Pendleton, Perry, Pike, Powell, Pulaski, Robertson, Rockcastle, Rowan, Scott, Wayne, Whitely, Wolfe and Woodford.

District No. 20, Buffalo, N. Y. The state of NEW YORK except that part lying in District 2; the state of PENNSYLVANIA except that part lying in District 3.

District No. 21, Honolulu, T.H. The Territory of HAWAII and outlying Pacific possessions except Alaska and adjacent islands.

District No. 22, San Juan, P.R. PUERTO RICO and the VIRGIN ISLANDS.

District No. 23, Juneau, Alaska. The territory of ALASKA and adjacent islands.

District No. 24, Washington, D. C.

| A - ABLE | ● — | K - KING | — ● — |
|---|---|---|---|
| B - BAKER | — ● ● ● | L - LOVE | ● — ● ● |
| C - CHARLIE | — ● — ● | M - MIKE | — — |
| D - DOG | — ● ● | N - NAN | — ● |
| E - EASY | ● | O - OBOE | — — — |
| F - FOX | ● ● — ● | P - PETER | ● — — ● |
| G - GEORGE | — — ● | Q - QUEEN | — — ● — |
| H - HOW | ● ● ● ● | R - ROGER | ● — ● |
| I - ITEM | ● ● | S - SUGAR | ● ● ● |
| J - JIG | ● — — — | T - TARE | — |

| U - UNCLE | ● ● — |
|---|---|
| V - VICTOR | ● ● ● — |
| W - WILLIAM | ● — — |
| X - XRAY | — ● ● — |
| Y - YOKE | — ● — — |
| Z - ZEBRA | — — ● ● |

Fig. 2. Radiotelegraph or Morse code.

**Geographic Assignment of Call Signs.** The following geographic allocation of call signs (Federal Register, vol. 14) will be used for all fixed, land, and radio-navigation land stations, except coast stations (other than coastal telephone stations in Alaska):

| Call sign area | Call sequence |
|---|---|
| Colorado, Iowa, Kansas, Minnesota, Missouri, Nebraska, North Dakota, South Dakota | KAA–KBZ WAA–WBZ |
| Connecticut, Maine, Massachusetts, New Hampshire, Rhode Island, Vermont | KCA–KDZ WCA–WDZ |
| New Jersey, New York | KEA–KFZ WEA–WFZ |
| Delaware, District of Columbia, Maryland, Pennsylvania | KGA–KHZ WGA–WHZ |
| Alabama, Georgia, Florida, Kentucky, North Carolina, South Carolina, Tennessee, Virginia | KIA–KJZ WIA–WJZ |
| Arkansas, Louisiana, Mississippi, New Mexico, Oklahoma, Texas | KKA–KLZ WKA–WLZ |

| | |
|---|---|
| California ...................................................... | KMA–KNZ<br>WMA–WNZ |
| Arizona, Idaho, Montana, Nevada, Oregon, Utah, Washington,<br>  Wyoming .................................................... | KOA–KPZ<br>WOA–WPZ |
| Michigan, Ohio, West Virginia .................................... | KQA–KRZ<br>WQA–WRZ |
| Illinois, Indiana, Wisconsin ..................................... | KSA–KTZ<br>WSA–WTZ |

## EMERGENCY COMMUNICATIONS (C.A.A.). Search and Rescue.

U. S. Air Force Air Rescue groups and squadrons within continental United States are as follows:

48th Air Rescue Sqdn.
Eglin AFB
Fla.

4th Air Rescue Gp.
Hamilton AFB
San Rafael, Calif.

42d Air Rescue Sqdn.
March AFB
Riverside, Calif.

43d Air Rescue Sqdn.
McChord AFB
Tacoma, Wash.

44th Air Rescue Sqdn.
Lowry AFB
Denver, Colo.

47th Air Rescue Sqdn.
Ellington AFB
Houston, Texas

49th Air Rescue Sqdn.
Selfridge AFB
Mt. Clemens, Mich.

5th Air Rescue Gp.
Westover AFB
Chicopee, Mass.

| NO. | MESSAGE | CODE SYMBOL |
|---|---|---|
| 1 | Operation completed. | L L L |
| 2 | We have found all personnel. | L L |
| 3 | We have found only some personnel. | ⊢⊢ |
| 4 | We are not able to continue.  Returning to base. | X X |
| 5 | Have divided into two groups.  Each proceeding in direction indicated. | 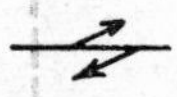 ⇗ |
| 6 | Information received that aircraft is in this direction. | → → |
| 7 | Nothing found.  Will continue to search. | N N |

Fig. 3. Ground-air visual code for use by ground search parties.

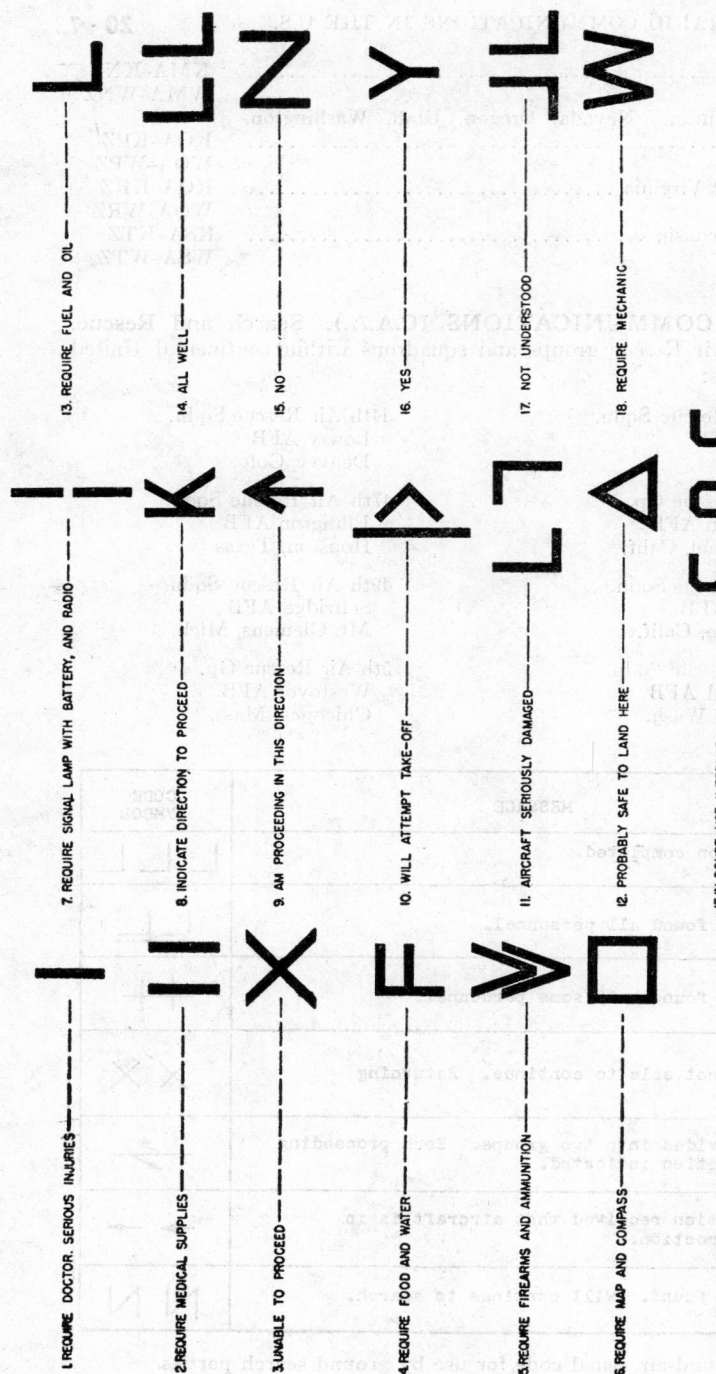

| 1. REQUIRE DOCTOR. SERIOUS INJURIES | 7. REQUIRE SIGNAL LAMP WITH BATTERY, AND RADIO | 13. REQUIRE FUEL AND OIL |
| 2. REQUIRE MEDICAL SUPPLIES | 8. INDICATE DIRECTION TO PROCEED | 14. ALL WELL |
| 3. UNABLE TO PROCEED | 9. AM PROCEEDING IN THIS DIRECTION | 15. NO |
| 4. REQUIRE FOOD AND WATER | 10. WILL ATTEMPT TAKE-OFF | 16. YES |
| 5. REQUIRE FIREARMS AND AMMUNITION | 11. AIRCRAFT SERIOUSLY DAMAGED | 17. NOT UNDERSTOOD |
| 6. REQUIRE MAP AND COMPASS | 12. PROBABLY SAFE TO LAND HERE | 18. REQUIRE MECHANIC |
| | IF IN DOUBT, USE INTERNATIONAL SYMBOL | |

INSTRUCTIONS:
1. Lay out symbols by using strips of fabric or parachutes, pieces of wood, stones, or any available material.
2. Provide as much color contrast as possible between material used for symbols and background against which symbols are exposed.
3. Symbols should be at least 10 ft. high or larger, if possible. Care should be taken to lay out symbols exactly as shown to avoid confusion with other symbols.
4. In addition to using symbols, every effort is to be made to attract attention by means of radio, flares, smoke, or other available means.
5. When ground is covered with snow, signals can be made by dragging, shoveling or tramping the snow. The depressed areas forming the symbols will appear to be black from the air.
6. Pilot should acknowledge message by rocking wings from side to side.

Fig. 4. Ground to air emergency code for use as distress signals as recommended by the Civil Aeronautics Administration.

**HOW TO USE THEM**

If you are forced down and are able to attract the attention of the pilot of a rescue airplane, the body signals illustrated on this page can be used to transmit messages to him as he circles over your location. Stand in the open when you make the signals. Be sure that the background, as seen from the air, is not confusing. Go through the motions slowly and repeat each signal until you are positive that the pilot understands you.

Fig. 5. Visual emergency signals recommended by the Civil Aeronautics Administration.

**FIELD COMPUTATIONS.** Two-way radio as applied to the field of forestry means radio-telephone voice communications either between fixed land stations or between moving units, or both. Radio waves travel through space at a rate of 300,000,000 meters per second. This equals the speed of light, which is 186,000 miles per second. Frequency is expressed in cycles per second. To compute the frequency in cycles per second, use the formula:

$$\text{Frequency} = \frac{300,000,000}{\text{wave length (meters)}}$$

**Example.**

$$\frac{300,000,000}{6} = 50,000 \text{ kc.} = 50 \text{ mc. per sec.}$$

**Computing Probable Range of Signal for a Given Power.** Propagation of radio waves for radio communication in the very high frequency range is based upon line-of-sight characteristics. For an effective radiated signal the radio horizon may be calculated from the following equation:

$$D = 1.42 \left(\sqrt{HT} + \sqrt{HR}\right)$$

where $D$ = line-of-sight (distance in miles)

$HT$ = height of transmitter antenna, in feet, above average elevation of terrain

$HR$ = height of receiving antenna, in feet, above average elevation of terrain

**Example.**

Let height of transmitter antenna and pole = 86 ft.

Height of rise in ground above average elevation of area = 58 ft.

Then $HT$ = Total height = 144 ft.

Let height of receiving antenna and pole (level ground) = $HR$ = 64 ft.

Then, provided no high mountains intervene, $D = 1.42(\sqrt{144} + \sqrt{64}) = 28.4$ miles = total radio horizon between top of transmitting antenna and top of receiving antenna.

**OPERATING HINTS AND CARE OF EQUIPMENT. General Instructions for Radio Operators in Charge of a Radio System.**

1. No one without a radio operator's license is permitted to operate a base station (an operator's license is obtainable free of charge at any F.C.C. field office).
2. No adjustments or repairs to a set except receiver tuning are permitted except by a first- or second-class licensed radio technician. This applies to private and state units but not to federal installations.
3. In any given service all channels are shared. This requires that communications be confined to business and emergency transmissions.
4. No profane or obscene language is permitted over the air.
5. Emergency calls take precedence over all other types of communications.
6. Always identify your station by giving its call letters. This may be done at the beginning of a call or following the message.
7. Each service has a set of rules for operating procedure. Be sure you know these before using your two-way radio set.
8. Always consult Radio Service Rules and Regulations, Federal Communications Commission.

### General Hints on Care of Radio Equipment.

1. Mobile radio units are for field use. Like portables and handie-talkies, they operate from a battery source. Wet batteries must be kept charged and dry batteries replaced. A weak battery will not operate the transmitter.
2. Handle your radio set with care. Try to protect it from dampness and dust.
3. Always test a set before you leave for the field.
4. Do not attempt repairs unless you are a licensed technician.
5. Ungrounded antennas are not safe during an electric storm.

**Lightning Protection for Radio Equipment.** The degree of protection against lightning required for radio equipment varies so widely with local conditions that generalized instructions are impossible. Some antennas now manufactured have built-in spark gaps. In their absence, the standards set by local power and telephone companies on this very important subject should be studied and followed.

## Radio Communications in Canada

All radio frequency assignments in Canada are made by the Department of Transport, Ottawa. The department endeavors "to consolidate forestry operations in specific sections of the 152/174 mc/s band; however, each requirement is dealt with on its merits and the order of frequency (that is to say, very high frequency or medium frequency) is determined by the distances, type of operation, terrain, etc., involved." (Quoted from a letter to the editor from the Controller of Telecommunications, Jan. 9, 1953.) The Canadian Ground Air Visual Signal Code is identical with that of the United States (see Fig. 4). Field offices of departmental radio inspectors are given below.

| | |
|---|---|
| Radio Inspector in Charge | Radio Inspector |
| Victoria, B. C. | Calgary, Alta. |
| District Superintendent of Radio | Edmonton, Alta. |
| Halifax, N. S. | Fort William, Ont. |
| Montreal, Que. | Hamilton, Ont. |
| Regina, Sask. | Kelowna, B. C. |
| St. John's, Nfld. | Kingston, Ont. |
| Toronto, Ont. | Kitchener, Ont. |
| Vancouver, B. C. | London, Ont. |
| Winnipeg, Man. | Moose Jaw, Sask. |
| Senior Radio Inspector | Quebec, Que. |
| St. John, N. B. | Saskatoon, Sask. |
| Radio Division | Sherbrooke, Que. |
| Ottawa, Ont. | Sydney, N. S. |
| | Windsor, Ont. |

## Telephone Systems *

**TELEPHONE VERSUS RADIO.** Wire lines should be used where practical. A combination of telephone and radio is the ideal system in forest industries and in the protection field. Telephone communications to outside centers of population from a headquarters is the accepted system, while radio from headquarters to the field or to the operating areas is now taking over. Although radio

* Nearly all of this material on telephone systems is adapted, or quoted verbatim, from the Telephone Handbook of the U. S. Forest Service, dated April, 1947.

communication, even for a short distance, is cheaper to establish than telephone service, first costs alone must not decide the choice between telephones and radios. There are not enough air lanes to accommodate all who wish radio facilities. Radio communications should be engineered for mobile purposes, with telephone systems employed in fixed point-to-point service. While this is the general intent and purpose of the Federal Communications Commission (in the United States), it stands to reason that for safety and emergency purposes the two systems may often parallel each other in geographical location and functional design.

A telephone system may be a single-wire line (ground-return) or a two-wire system (metallic circuit). The single line is hung between the transmitter and the receiver, principally on trees, and is grounded at each instrument. In a metallic system two wires are used, hung on poles; the current is returned from the receiver to the transmitter through the second wire and not by way of the ground as in a single-line system.

**POLE LINES (METALLIC CIRCUITS). Spans.** Because the poles, their setting, and their replacement constitute the major items of construction cost, the longest spans consistent with loading and topographic conditions should be used (Table 1). (This is loading by ice and snow in severe storms; for a map showing regions of light, medium, and heavy loading in the United States, see

**Table 1. Telephone Line Span by Loading and Topographic Requirements**

| Span, feet | | No. of poles per mile | Use or terrain |
|---|---|---|---|
| 50–132 | ...................... | 105–40 | Exceptionally heavy loading areas |
| 150–212 | ...................... | 35–25 | Heavy loading areas |
| 175–251 | ...................... | 30–21 | Medium loading, average terrain |
| 250–500 | ...................... | 21–10.5 | Light loading, flat or rolling country |

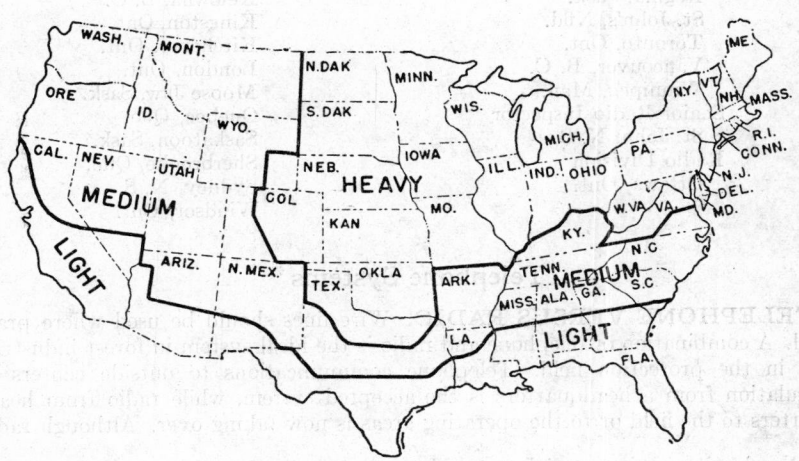

**Fig. 6. General storm loading areas in the United States.**

Fig. 6. Do not confuse such loading with "overloading"—too many telephones on a single line.)

**Exceptional Spans.** Where loading will permit, spans up to 1,000 or 1,200 ft. may be practical, when crossing a ravine or canyon. Short spans, on the other hand, should be used over ridges or through mountain passes where ice and snow may weight the wires. Holes should be dug at the spots selected by the locator; where rock is encountered, it is permissible to move not to exceed 10 ft. in either direction.

**Pole Depth.** The stability of the line is dependent to a large degree upon the depth at which the poles are set. Shallow setting will result in costly maintenance and will reduce the dependability of the line. Holes should be dug perpendicularly to the depths shown in Table 2.

### Table 2. Pole Depths by Footing Character

| Length of pole (ft.) | | Depth of setting in feet (unguyed) | | |
| --- | --- | --- | --- | --- |
| | | Firm soil | Sand or loose soil | Rock |
| 20 | ...................... | 4 | 5 | 3 |
| 25 | ...................... | 5 | 5½ | 3 |
| 30 | ...................... | 5½ | 6 | 3½ |
| 35 | ...................... | 6 | 6½ | 4 |
| 40 | ...................... | 6 | 7 | 4 |
| 45 | ...................... | 6½ | 7½ | 4½ |

Hole depths are measured from the lower side of the ground slope. After the hole has been dug, the survey stake should be reset close to the hole for the reference of the pole-setting crew. Unguyed corner poles should be set 6 in. deeper than shown. For long spans, 600 ft. or over, an additional depth of 12 in. should be provided. In very swampy or wet soils additional depth of setting will not necessarily give the desired stability; in such cases use swamp footings and underground braces.

Owing to topographic conditions, the holes will usually have to be dug by hand. In a few instances it may be advantageous and economical to use a machine borer. In clay or adobe soils, which are extremely difficult to dig with crowbars and shovels, blasting is often most effective.

**Pole Dimensions and Specifications.** See "Poles" in Section **14**, Utilization and Wood Technology, pages **14**·14–52, for a discussion of dimensions and specifications. Also see "Round Timbers," page **14**·53.

**Wire.** Like all equipment used in the communications field, the wire used in the construction of telephone lines must meet exacting specifications. It has been the repeated experience of the forest industries that material of dubious origin, such as alleged war surplus, rarely produces a workable and trouble-free telephone system. Saving in first costs is all too often offset by heavy repair bills. On any one section of a metallic circuit it is essential that both wires be of the same material, gauge, and age. Any difference will cause noise on the line.

A list of the physical and electrical characteristics of line wire is given in Table 3.

## Table 3. Physical and Electrical Characteristics of Line Wire

| Size and kind of wire | Diameter (in.) | Rated breaking load (lb.) | Weight per mile (lb.) | Standard package length [a] (mi.) | Resistance at 68° F. | | Transmission loss [c] per loop mile, 1,000 cycles (decibels) |
|---|---|---|---|---|---|---|---|
| | | | | | Per 1000 ft. (ohms) | Per loop mile [b] (ohms) | |
| No. 9 BWG galvanized iron EBB | 0.148 | 785 | 314 | 0.25 | 2.92 | 30.9 | 0.25 |
| AWG, high strength, 40% conductivity, copper-covered steel wire | | | | | | | |
| No. 12 | .081 | 785 | 96 | 1.0 [d] | 4.05 | 42.8 | .21 |
| No. 10 | .102 | 1,130 | 152 | 1.0 [d] | 2.53 | 26.7 | .15 |
| No. 8 | .128 | 1,660 | 242 | 1.0 [d] | 1.60 | 16.9 | .11 |
| No. 6 | .162 | 2,433 | 385 | 1.0 [d] | 1.01 | 10.7 | .07 |
| B & S HD copper | | | | | | | |
| No. 10 | .102 | 529 | 166 | 1.0 [d] | 1.04 | 11.0 | .07 |
| No. 8 | .128 | 826 | 264 | 1.5 | 0.65 | 6.9 | .05 |

[a] Mill length coils.
[b] 2 mi. of wire.
[c] Varies with age and condition of wire.
[d] Approximate.

**Long spans.** Table 4 gives specifications for number, size, and spacing of wires on long spans. For type of dead-end fixture on long spans see Fig. 7.

**Table 4. Minimum Spacing, Number and Size of Wires, Vertical One-Pole Construction, Two to Four Wires**

| Length of span (ft.) | Kind and size of wire | Minimum spacing between wires |
|---|---|---|
| 300 to 500 ................... | Copper-covered steel No. 10 | 22 in. |
| 500 to 1,000 ................... | Copper-covered steel No. 8 | 22 in. |
| Over 1,000 ................... | Copper-covered steel No. 6* | 28 in. |

* For heavy loading areas increase wire size to No. 4.

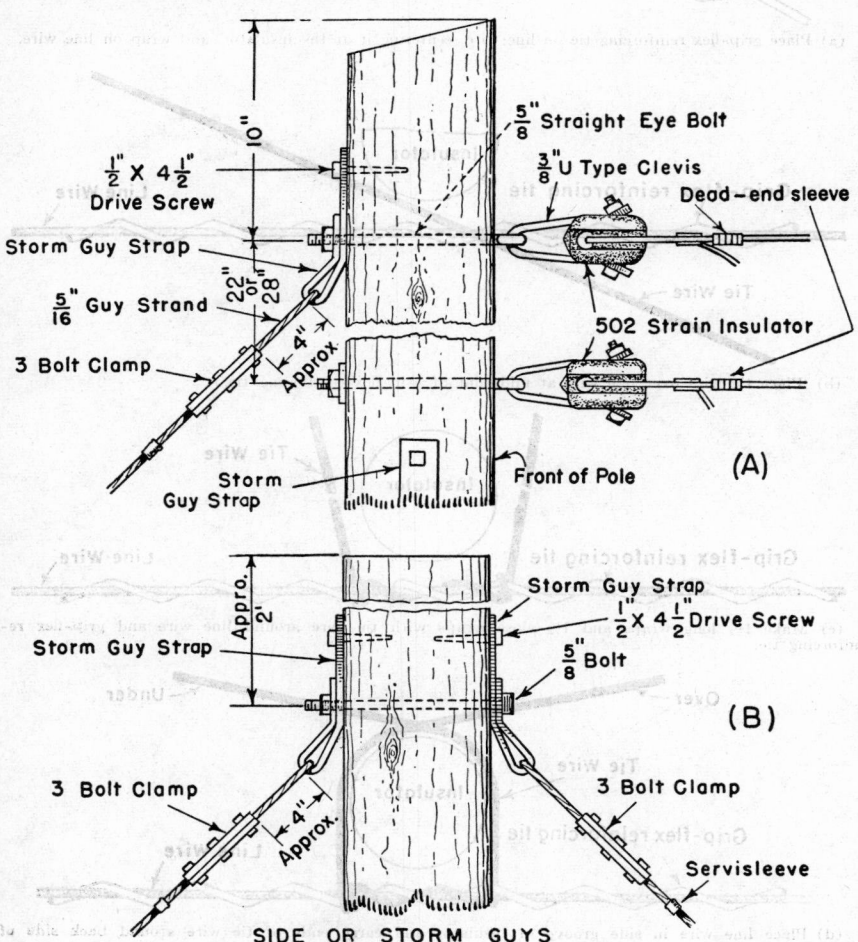

Fig. 7. Attaching insulators and guys to dead-end poles, for long spans.

**Fig. 8.** Modified "horseshoe tie" for tying iron line wire in side-groove insulators.

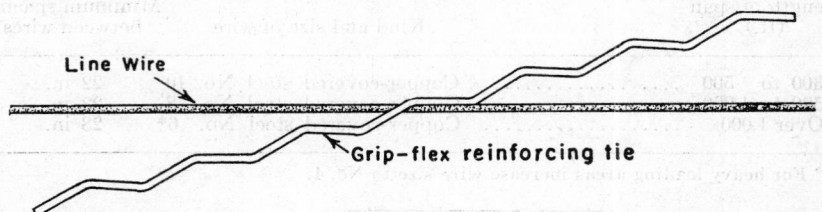

(a) Place grip-flex reinforcing tie on line wire, centering it at the insulator, and wrap on line wire.

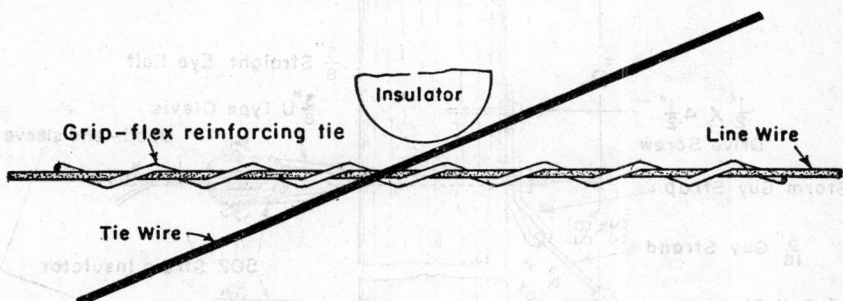

(b) Place tie wire over line wire at midpoint of grip-flex reinforcing tie.

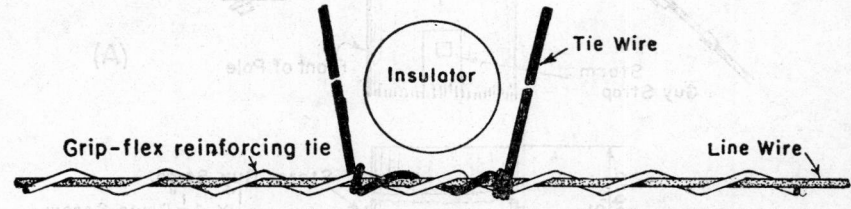

(c) Make 1½ long wraps and 1½ close wraps with tie wire around line wire and grip-flex reinforcing tie.

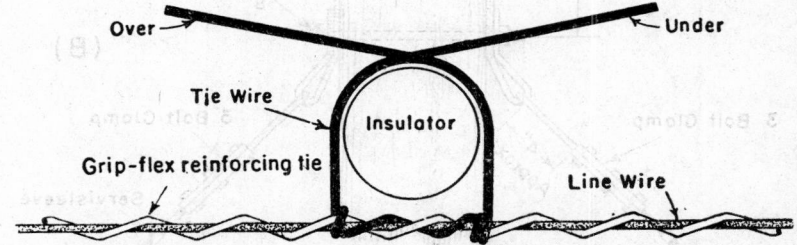

(d) Place line wire in side groove of insulator and carry ends of tie wire around back side of insulator.

**Fig. 9.** Tying copper or copper-covered steel wire in side-groove insulator.

**Tie wires.** For tight tie observe the specifications given in Table 5.

**Table 5. Reinforcing Wire, and Binding or Tie Wire, Used in Tying Line Wires, of Various Types, to Insulators**

| Type of line wire | Reinforcing wire, size and length (in.) | Binding or tie wire,* size and length (in.) | Approximate weight, per 100 complete ties |
|---|---|---|---|
| Copper-covered steel | | | |
| No. 12 AWG ........ | No. 10 AWG × 10 | No. 12 AWG × 24 | 6 lb. |
| No. 10 AWG ........ | No. 9 AWG × 12 | No. 12 AWG × 24 | 7 lb. |
| No. 8 AWG ........ | No. 7 AWG × 15 | No. 10 AWG × 24 | 14 lb. |
| No. 6 AWG ........ | No. 5 AWG × 17 | No. 9 AWG × 28 | 25 lb. |
| Solid hard-drawn copper | | | |
| No. 10 AWG ........ | No. 9 AWG × 12 | No. 12 AWG × 24 | 7 lb. |
| No. 8 AWG ........ | No. 7 AWG × 15 | No. 10 AWG × 24 | 14 lb. |
| Galvanized iron | | | |
| No. 9 EBB ........ | None | No. 12 galvanized iron | Cut as needed |

\* Factory annealed copper-covered steel wire.

**Tying wires to insulators.** For tying copper or copper-covered steel wire in side-groove insulators, see Fig. 9. For tying iron wire in side-groove insulators, use the modified "horseshoe" tie, as shown in Fig. 8.

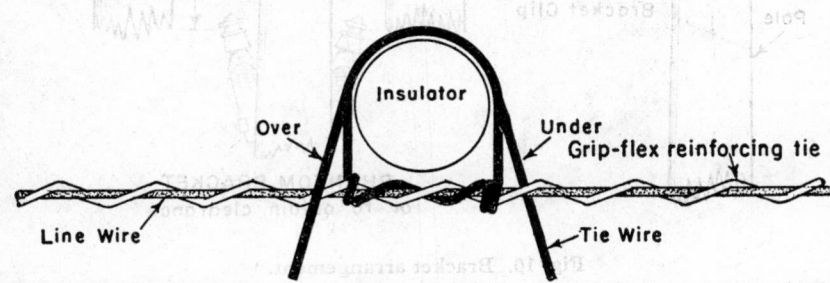

(e) Bring ends of tie wire to front of insulator with one under and one over line wire and complete tie as in (f).

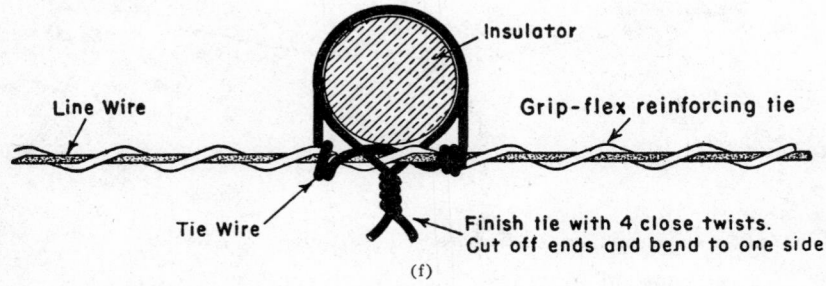

**Fig. 9. Tying copper or copper-covered steel wire in side-groove insulator.**
(Continued)

**BRACKETS.** For proper bracket installation, see Figs. 10 and 11.

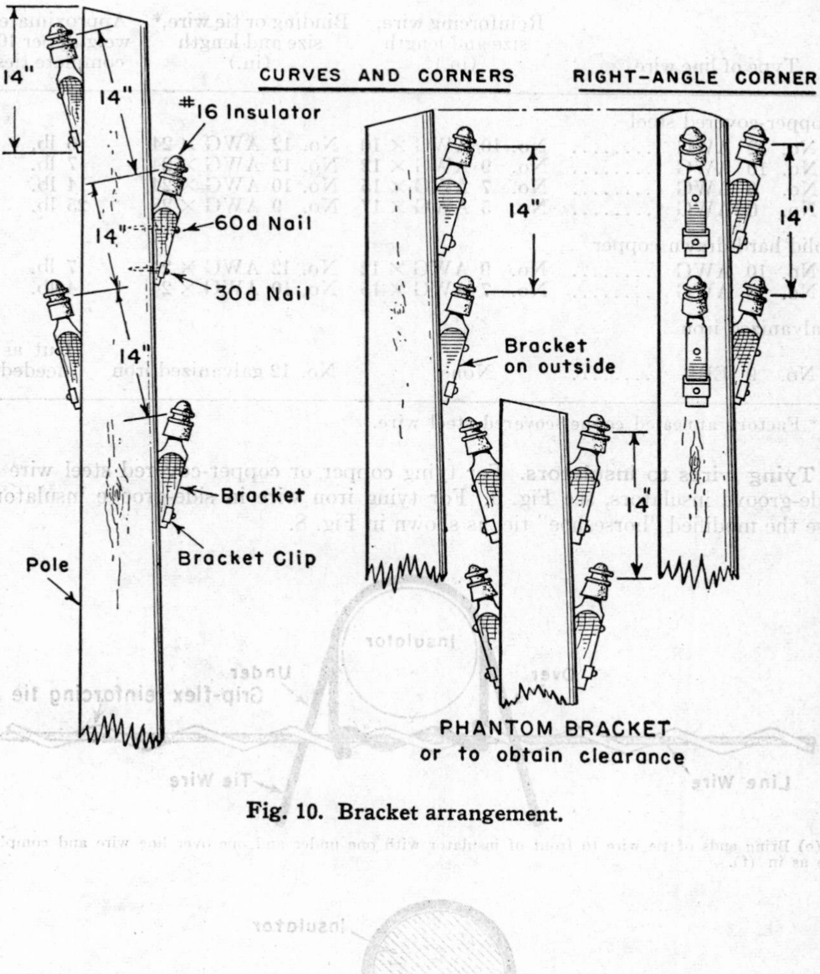

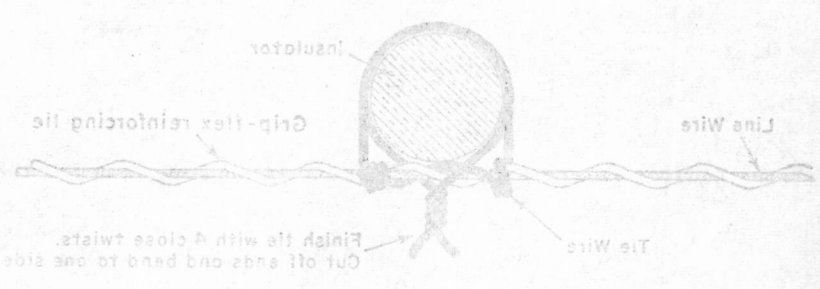

CURVES AND CORNERS      RIGHT—ANGLE CORNER

14"

14"

#16 Insulator

14"

60d Nail

30d Nail

14"

14"

Bracket
on outside

14"

Bracket

Bracket Clip

Pole

14"

PHANTOM BRACKET
or to obtain clearance

**Fig. 10. Bracket arrangement.**

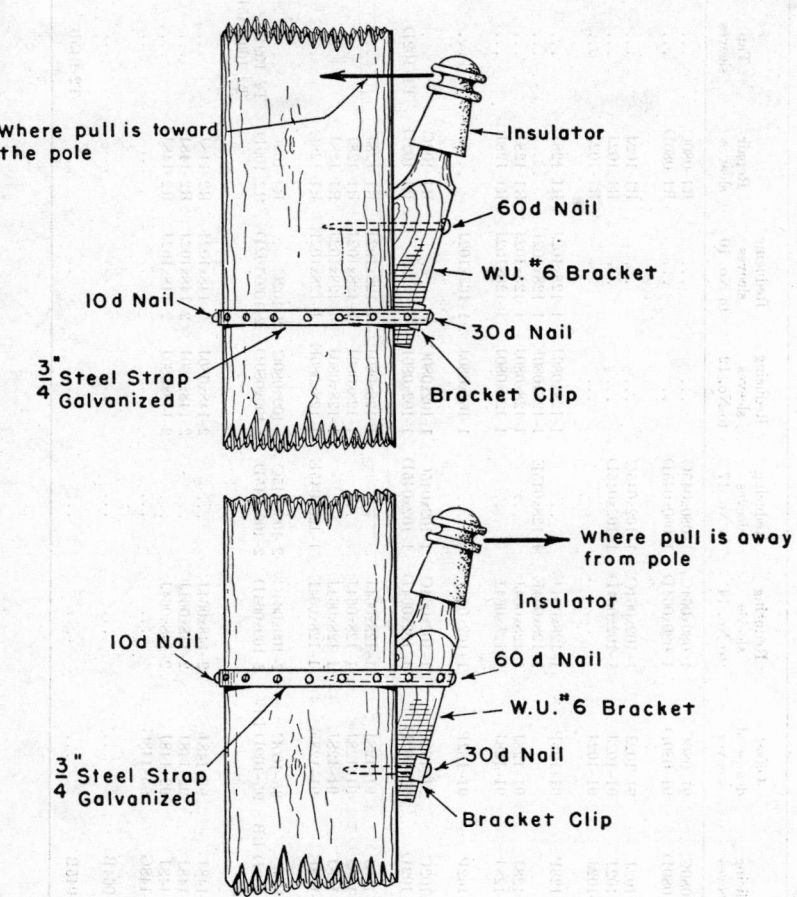

Fig. 11. Bracket installation where pull is toward or away from pole.

## Table 6. Manufacturer's Catalog Numbers for Splicing Tools and Sleeves

| Wire size and kind | Type of tool | Splicing sleeves | Offset dead-end sleeves | Reducing sleeves to No. 14 | Reducing sleeves to No. 17 | Reducing sleeves to No. 12 | Reducing sleeves to No. 10 | Repair sleeves | Tap sleeves |
|---|---|---|---|---|---|---|---|---|---|
| No. 12 AWG copperweld | 31–CJ | 1–080C | 91–080C | 1–080x064C | 1–080x045C | ... | ... | R1–080C | ... |
|  | 31–DJ | 1–080D | 91–080D | 1–080x064D | 1–080x045D | ... | ... | R1–080D | ... |
| No. 10 AWG copperweld | 31–CJ | 1–102J | 91–102J | 1–102x064C | 1–102x045C | ... | ... | R1–102J | ... |
|  | 31–DJ | 1–102J | 91–102J | 1–102x064D | 1–102x045D | ... | ... | R1–102J | ... |
|  | 51–PJ | 1–102J | 91–102J | ... | ... | ... | ... | R1–102J | ... |
| No. 8 AWG copperweld | 51–PJ | 1–128P | 91–128P | 1–128x064J | ... | 1–128x080J | 1–128x102J | R1–128J | ... |
|  | 31–E | ... | ... | 1–128x064E | 1–128x045E | 1–128x080E | 1–128x102E | ... | ... |
|  | 31–DJ | 1–128J | 91–128J | 1–128x064J | ... | 1–128x080J | 1–128x102J | R1–128J | ... |
|  | 31–CJ | 1–128J | 91–128J | 1–128x064J | ... | 1–128x080J | 1–128x102J | R1–128J | ... |
| No. 6 AWG copperweld | 51–PJ | 1–162P | 91–162P | 1–162x064J | ... | 1–162x080J | 1–162x102J | ... | ... |
| No. 10 B&S hard-drawn copper | 31–CJ | 1–102C | 91–102C | 1–102x064C | 1–102x045C | 1–102x080C | ... | R1–102C | ... |
|  | 31–DJ | 1–102D | 91–102D | 1–102x064D | 1–102x045D | 1–102x080D | ... | R1–102D | T1–102D |
| No. 8 B&S hard-drawn copper | 31–CJ | 1–128J | 91–128J | 1–128x064J | ... | 1–128x080J | 1–128x102J | R1–128J | ... |
|  | 31–DJ | 1–128J | 91–128J | 1–128x064J | ... | 1–128x080J | 1–128x102J | R1–128J | ... |
|  | 51–PJ | 1–128J | 91–128J | 1–128x064J | ... | 1–128x080J | 1–128x102J | R1–128J | ... |
|  | 31–E | 1–128E | 91–128E | 1–128x064E | 1–128x045E | 1–128x080E | 1–128x102E | R1–128E | ... |
| No. 12 BWG iron | 31–CJ | 5–109C | 95–109C | 2–109x064C | 2–109x045C | 4–109x080C | 2–102C | R4–109C | T2–109D |
|  | 31–DJ | 5–109D BB | 95–109D BB | 2–109x064D | 2–109x045D | 2–109x080D | 2–109x102D | R2–109D | T2–109x045D |
| No. 9 BWG iron | 31–CJ | 2–148J | 92–148J | 2–148x064J | ... | 2–148x080J | 2–148x102J | R2–148J | ... |
|  | 31–DJ | 2–148J | 92–148J | 2–148x064J | ... | 2–148x080J | 2–148x102J | R2–148J | ... |
|  | 51–PJ | 2–148J | 92–148J | 2–148x064J | ... | 2–148x080J | 2–148x102J | R2–148J | ... |
|  | 31–GC | 5–148G | 95–148G | ... | ... | ... | ... | ... | ... |
| No. 14 B&S copper .064 | 17–2 | 3–064B | ... | ... | ... | ... | ... | ... | ... |
| No. 17 B&S bronze .045 | 17–2 | 3–045B | ... | ... | ... | ... | ... | ... | T2–045B |

Source: Western Electric Co.

**Line Sag.** Table 7 gives the sag for different kinds and sizes of wire for various temperatures, spans, and loading. In selecting the proper sag for given spans, use the value in the sag table for the span length within the nearest 10 ft. Obtain the **shade** temperature of the air along the route of each span which is being measured.

**Using the sag gauge.** (See Figs. 12 and 13.) For bracket-line construction, the hook part of the gauge should be placed in a position relative to that on the crossarm. This can be effected either by holding or by a spike driven slightly into the pole at the proper height.

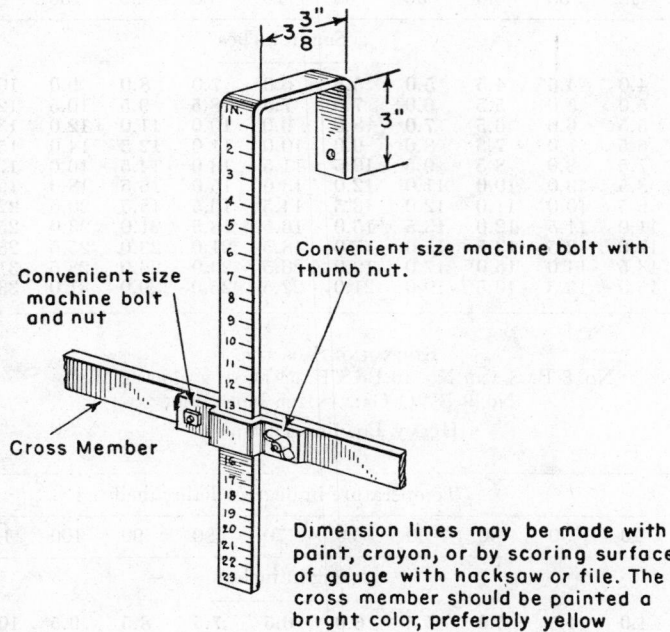

Fig. 12. Sag gauge.

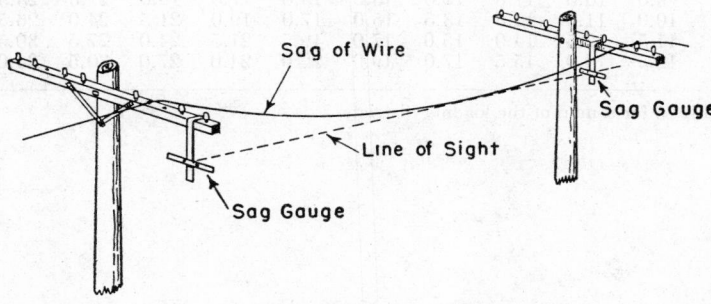

Fig. 13. Method of using the sag gauge.

## Table 7. Recommended Sag in Line Wires, Pole Lines

STRINGING SAGS FOR
No. 8 B&S AND No. 10 B&S HARD-DRAWN COPPER WIRE
No. 9 BWG GALVANIZED IRON WIRE
Medium and Light Loading Districts *

| Span length (ft.) | Temperature in degrees Fahrenheit | | | | | | | | | | |
|---|---|---|---|---|---|---|---|---|---|---|---|
| | 20 | 30 | 40 | 50 | 60 | 70 | 80 | 90 | 100 | 110 | 120 |
| | Sag in inches | | | | | | | | | | |
| 100 | 4.0 | 4.5 | 4.5 | 5.0 | 5.5 | 6.0 | 7.0 | 8.0 | 9.0 | 10.0 | 11.0 |
| 110 | 5.0 | 5.0 | 5.5 | 6.0 | 7.0 | 7.5 | 8.5 | 9.5 | 10.5 | 12.0 | 13.0 |
| 120 | 5.5 | 6.0 | 6.5 | 7.0 | 8.0 | 9.0 | 10.0 | 11.0 | 12.0 | 13.0 | 14.0 |
| 130 | 6.5 | 7.0 | 7.5 | 8.0 | 9.0 | 10.0 | 11.0 | 12.5 | 14.0 | 15.5 | 17.0 |
| 140 | 7.5 | 8.0 | 8.5 | 9.5 | 10.5 | 11.5 | 13.0 | 14.5 | 16.0 | 17.5 | 19.0 |
| 150 | 8.5 | 9.0 | 10.0 | 11.0 | 12.0 | 13.0 | 15.0 | 16.5 | 18.0 | 19.5 | 21.0 |
| 160 | 9.5 | 10.0 | 11.0 | 12.0 | 13.5 | 14.5 | 16.5 | 18.5 | 20.5 | 22.0 | 23.0 |
| 170 | 11.0 | 11.5 | 12.0 | 13.5 | 15.0 | 16.5 | 18.5 | 21.0 | 23.0 | 25.0 | 27.0 |
| 180 | 12.0 | 12.5 | 13.5 | 15.0 | 17.0 | 18.5 | 21.0 | 23.0 | 25.5 | 28.0 | 31.0 |
| 190 | 13.5 | 14.0 | 15.0 | 17.0 | 19.0 | 20.5 | 23.0 | 26.0 | 28.5 | 31.0 | 34.0 |
| 200 | 15.0 | 15.5 | 16.5 | 19.0 | 21.0 | 22.5 | 25.0 | 29.0 | 31.0 | 33.0 | 36.0 |

STRINGING SAGS FOR
No. 8 B&S AND No. 10 B&S HARD-DRAWN COPPER WIRE
No. 9 BWG GALVANIZED IRON WIRE
Heavy Loading District

| Span length (ft.) | Temperature in degrees Fahrenheit | | | | | | | | | | |
|---|---|---|---|---|---|---|---|---|---|---|---|
| | 20 | 30 | 40 | 50 | 60 | 70 | 80 | 90 | 100 | 110 | 120 |
| | Sag in inches | | | | | | | | | | |
| 100 | 4.0 | 4.5 | 5.0 | 5.5 | 6.0 | 6.5 | 7.5 | 8.5 | 9.5 | 10.5 | 11.5 |
| 110 | 5.0 | 5.0 | 6.0 | 6.5 | 7.0 | 8.0 | 9.0 | 10.0 | 11.5 | 13.0 | 14.5 |
| 120 | 5.5 | 6.0 | 7.0 | 7.5 | 8.5 | 9.5 | 10.5 | 12.0 | 13.5 | 15.0 | 16.5 |
| 130 | 6.5 | 7.0 | 8.5 | 9.0 | 10.0 | 11.5 | 12.5 | 14.0 | 16.0 | 18.0 | 20.0 |
| 140 | 7.5 | 8.5 | 9.5 | 10.5 | 11.5 | 13.0 | 14.5 | 16.5 | 18.5 | 20.5 | 22.5 |
| 150 | 9.0 | 10.0 | 11.0 | 12.0 | 13.0 | 15.0 | 17.0 | 19.0 | 21.5 | 23.5 | 26.0 |
| 160 | 10.0 | 11.0 | 12.5 | 13.5 | 15.0 | 17.0 | 19.0 | 21.5 | 24.0 | 26.5 | 30.0 |
| 170 | 11.5 | 12.5 | 14.0 | 15.0 | 17.0 | 19.5 | 21.5 | 24.0 | 27.5 | 30.5 | 34.0 |
| 180 | 12.5 | 14.0 | 15.5 | 17.0 | 19.0 | 22.0 | 24.0 | 27.0 | 30.5 | 34.0 | 38.0 |

* See Fig. 6 for a map of the loading districts.

**Table 7. Recommended Sag in Line Wires, Pole Lines** (Continued)

STRINGING SAGS FOR
No. 12 AWG AND No. 10 AWG, HIGH-STRENGTH, 40% CONDUCTIVITY
COPPER-COVERED STEEL WIRE
Medium and Light Loading Districts—Short Spans

| Span length (ft.) | Temperature in degrees Fahrenheit | | | | | | | | | | |
|---|---|---|---|---|---|---|---|---|---|---|---|
| | 20 | 30 | 40 | 50 | 60 | 70 | 80 | 90 | 100 | 110 | 120 |
| | Sag in inches | | | | | | | | | | |
| 100 | 2.8 | 3.0 | 3.3 | 3.6 | 4.0 | 4.5 | 5.1 | 5.7 | 6.4 | 7.5 | 8.6 |
| 110 | 3.3 | 3.5 | 3.9 | 4.3 | 5.0 | 5.5 | 6.1 | 6.9 | 7.7 | 8.8 | 10.0 |
| 120 | 3.9 | 4.2 | 4.7 | 5.1 | 6.0 | 6.5 | 7.3 | 8.1 | 9.0 | 10.2 | 11.5 |
| 130 | 4.6 | 5.0 | 5.6 | 6.1 | 7.0 | 7.6 | 8.5 | 9.4 | 10.4 | 11.6 | 13.1 |
| 140 | 5.5 | 5.9 | 6.5 | 7.1 | 8.0 | 8.8 | 9.7 | 10.8 | 11.8 | 13.2 | 14.8 |
| 150 | 6.4 | 6.8 | 7.5 | 8.2 | 9.0 | 10.0 | 11.0 | 12.1 | 13.4 | 14.9 | 16.4 |
| 160 | 7.3 | 7.8 | 8.6 | 9.4 | 10.5 | 11.3 | 12.4 | 13.7 | 15.0 | 16.5 | 18.2 |
| 170 | 8.3 | 8.9 | 9.8 | 10.7 | 11.5 | 12.7 | 13.9 | 15.3 | 16.7 | 18.3 | 20.0 |
| 180 | 9.4 | 10.0 | 11.0 | 12.0 | 13.0 | 14.2 | 15.4 | 17.0 | 18.5 | 20.1 | 22.0 |
| 190 | 10.5 | 11.3 | 12.4 | 13.4 | 14.5 | 15.8 | 17.0 | 18.7 | 20.3 | 22.0 | 24.0 |
| 200 | 11.6 | 12.6 | 13.7 | 14.8 | 16.0 | 17.4 | 18.9 | 20.6 | 22.1 | 24.0 | 26.0 |
| 210 | 12.9 | 13.8 | 15.1 | 16.2 | 17.5 | 19.2 | 20.6 | 22.4 | 24.1 | 26.1 | 28.0 |
| 220 | 14.2 | 15.2 | 16.6 | 17.9 | 19.5 | 21.0 | 22.4 | 24.4 | 26.2 | 28.2 | 30.2 |
| 230 | 15.6 | 16.7 | 18.2 | 19.5 | 21.0 | 22.8 | 23.4 | 26.4 | 28.4 | 30.4 | 32.5 |
| 240 | 17.0 | 18.3 | 19.9 | 21.3 | 23.0 | 24.8 | 26.5 | 28.5 | 30.6 | 32.7 | 34.9 |
| 250 | 18.6 | 19.9 | 21.6 | 23.1 | 25.0 | 26.9 | 28.8 | 30.7 | 32.8 | 35.1 | 37.3 |
| 260 | 20.2 | 21.6 | 23.4 | 25.1 | 27.0 | 29.0 | 31.0 | 33.0 | 35.0 | 37.5 | 39.8 |
| 270 | 22.0 | 23.4 | 25.4 | 27.2 | 29.0 | 31.1 | 33.2 | 35.2 | 37.4 | 40.0 | 42.4 |
| 280 | 23.8 | 25.4 | 27.3 | 29.4 | 31.5 | 33.4 | 35.6 | 37.7 | 40.0 | 42.6 | 45.1 |
| 290 | 25.6 | 27.3 | 29.4 | 31.6 | 33.5 | 35.8 | 38.2 | 40.2 | 42.4 | 45.3 | 47.8 |
| 300 | 27.6 | 29.4 | 31.6 | 34.0 | 36.0 | 38.4 | 40.7 | 42.9 | 45.0 | 48.0 | 50.5 |
| 310 | 29.6 | 31.6 | 33.8 | 36.2 | 38.5 | 40.8 | 43.3 | 45.5 | 47.8 | 50.7 | 53.3 |
| 320 | 31.8 | 34.0 | 36.2 | 38.6 | 41.0 | 43.4 | 46.0 | 48.4 | 50.6 | 53.6 | 56.1 |
| 330 | 34.0 | 36.2 | 38.6 | 41.2 | 43.5 | 46.0 | 48.8 | 51.1 | 53.4 | 56.4 | 59.2 |
| 340 | 36.4 | 38.8 | 41.2 | 43.8 | 46.5 | 48.8 | 51.6 | 54.0 | 56.2 | 59.4 | 62.0 |
| 350 | 39.0 | 41.3 | 43.8 | 46.4 | 49.0 | 51.4 | 54.4 | 57.1 | 59.2 | 62.4 | 65.2 |

STRINGING SAGS FOR
No. 10 AWG HIGH-STRENGTH, 40% CONDUCTIVITY
COPPER-COVERED STEEL WIRE
Medium and Light Loading Districts—Medium Spans

| Span length (ft.) | Temperature in degrees Fahrenheit | | | | | | | | | | |
|---|---|---|---|---|---|---|---|---|---|---|---|
| | 20 | 30 | 40 | 50 | 60 | 70 | 80 | 90 | 100 | 110 | 120 |
| | Sag in inches | | | | | | | | | | |
| 350 | 39.0 | 41.3 | 43.8 | 46.4 | 49.0 | 51.4 | 54.4 | 57.1 | 59.2 | 62.4 | 65.2 |
| 375 | 45.4 | 48.0 | 50.7 | 53.5 | 56.2 | 59.0 | 61.9 | 64.4 | 66.8 | 69.8 | 73.0 |
| 400 | 52.6 | 55.2 | 58.3 | 61.2 | 64.0 | 67.0 | 70.1 | 72.7 | 76.0 | 78.5 | 81.6 |
| 425 | 60.1 | 63.1 | 66.5 | 69.4 | 72.5 | 75.5 | 78.8 | 81.3 | 84.3 | 87.5 | 90.7 |
| 450 | 68.4 | 71.8 | 75.4 | 78.5 | 81.6 | 84.8 | 88.0 | 91.0 | 94.1 | 97.0 | 100.0 |
| 475 | 77.3 | 81.0 | 84.6 | 88.0 | 91.0 | 94.5 | 97.6 | 100.6 | 104.0 | 106.5 | 110.0 |
| 500 | 86.4 | 90.2 | 94.0 | 97.3 | 100.0 | 104.0 | 107.4 | 110.6 | 114.4 | 117.1 | 120.4 |

**Table 7. Recommended Sag in Line Wires, Pole Lines** (Continued)

STRINGING SAGS FOR
No. 8 AWG, HIGH-STRENGTH, 40% CONDUCTIVITY
COPPER-COVERED STEEL WIRE
Medium and Light Loading Districts—Long Spans

| Span length (ft.) | Temperature in degrees Fahrenheit | | | | | | | | | | |
|---|---|---|---|---|---|---|---|---|---|---|---|
| | 20 | 30 | 40 | 50 | 60 | 70 | 80 | 90 | 100 | 110 | 120 |
| | Sag in feet | | | | | | | | | | |
| 500 | 3.8 | 3.9 | 4.1 | 4.3 | 4.6 | 4.8 | 5.0 | 5.2 | 5.5 | 5.7 | 6.0 |
| 550 | 4.9 | 5.1 | 5.3 | 5.5 | 5.8 | 6.1 | 6.3 | 6.6 | 6.9 | 7.2 | 7.5 |
| 600 | 7.6 | 7.9 | 8.2 | 8.5 | 8.8 | 9.1 | 9.5 | 9.8 | 10.1 | 10.5 | 10.8 |
| 650 | 11.2 | 11.5 | 11.9 | 12.2 | 12.6 | 12.9 | 13.2 | 13.6 | 13.9 | 14.2 | 14.5 |
| 700 | 15.3 | 15.7 | 16.0 | 16.4 | 16.7 | 17.0 | 17.3 | 17.6 | 18.0 | 18.3 | 18.6 |
| 750 | 19.8 | 20.1 | 20.4 | 20.8 | 21.1 | 21.4 | 21.7 | 22.0 | 22.4 | 22.7 | 23.0 |
| 800 | 24.6 | 24.9 | 25.2 | 25.5 | 25.9 | 26.2 | 26.5 | 26.8 | 27.1 | 27.4 | 27.6 |
| 850 | 29.6 | 29.9 | 30.2 | 30.5 | 30.8 | 31.1 | 31.4 | 31.7 | 32.0 | 32.3 | 32.6 |
| 900 | 35.0 | 35.3 | 35.6 | 35.9 | 36.2 | 36.5 | 36.8 | 37.1 | 37.3 | 37.6 | 37.9 |
| 950 | 40.7 | 41.0 | 41.3 | 41.6 | 41.9 | 42.2 | 42.5 | 42.7 | 43.0 | 43.3 | 43.6 |
| 1,000 | 46.7 | 47.0 | 47.2 | 47.5 | 47.8 | 48.1 | 48.3 | 48.6 | 48.9 | 49.2 | 49.4 |
| 1,100 | 59.6 | 59.9 | 60.1 | 60.4 | 60.7 | 60.9 | 61.2 | 61.5 | 61.7 | 62.0 | 62.3 |
| 1,200 | 74.0 | 74.2 | 74.5 | 74.8 | 75.0 | 75.3 | 75.5 | 75.8 | 76.0 | 76.3 | 76.6 |
| 1,300 | 89.8 | 90.0 | 90.3 | 90.6 | 90.8 | 91.1 | 91.3 | 91.6 | 91.8 | 92.1 | 92.3 |
| 1,400 | 107.2 | 107.4 | 107.7 | 107.9 | 108.2 | 108.4 | 108.7 | 108.9 | 109.2 | 109.4 | 109.6 |
| 1,500 | 126.2 | 126.5 | 126.7 | 127.0 | 127.2 | 127.4 | 127.7 | 127.9 | 128.2 | 128.4 | 128.6 |

STRINGING SAGS FOR
No. 12 AND No. 10 AWG, HIGH-STRENGTH, 40% CONDUCTIVITY
COPPER-COVERED STEEL WIRE
Heavy Loading District—Short Spans

| Span length (ft.) | Temperature in degrees Fahrenheit | | | | | | | | | | |
|---|---|---|---|---|---|---|---|---|---|---|---|
| | 20 | 30 | 40 | 50 | 60 | 70 | 80 | 90 | 100 | 110 | 120 |
| | Sag in inches | | | | | | | | | | |
| 80 | 2.3 | 2.5 | 2.8 | 3.2 | 3.7 | 4.3 | 5.0 | 5.9 | 6.8 | 7.8 | 8.9 |
| 90 | 2.8 | 3.2 | 3.6 | 4.0 | 4.7 | 5.3 | 6.2 | 7.2 | 8.2 | 9.4 | 10.5 |
| 100 | 3.6 | 4.0 | 4.5 | 5.1 | 5.8 | 6.6 | 7.6 | 8.7 | 9.9 | 11.1 | 12.3 |
| 110 | 4.4 | 4.9 | 5.5 | 6.2 | 7.0 | 7.9 | 9.0 | 10.2 | 11.3 | 12.7 | 14.0 |
| 120 | 5.2 | 5.9 | 6.6 | 7.4 | 8.2 | 9.3 | 10.6 | 11.8 | 13.1 | 14.5 | 15.8 |
| 130 | 6.3 | 7.0 | 7.8 | 8.8 | 9.8 | 10.8 | 12.2 | 13.6 | 15.0 | 16.4 | 17.8 |
| 140 | 7.4 | 8.2 | 9.1 | 10.2 | 11.2 | 12.5 | 14.0 | 15.5 | 16.9 | 18.3 | 19.9 |
| 150 | 8.7 | 9.5 | 10.6 | 11.7 | 13.0 | 14.4 | 16.0 | 17.4 | 19.0 | 20.5 | 21.9 |
| 160 | 10.0 | 11.0 | 12.0 | 13.4 | 14.6 | 16.2 | 17.8 | 19.4 | 21.0 | 22.6 | 24.4 |
| 170 | 11.5 | 12.5 | 13.7 | 15.2 | 16.7 | 18.2 | 20.0 | 21.6 | 23.3 | 25.0 | 26.6 |
| 180 | 13.0 | 14.2 | 15.5 | 17.1 | 18.7 | 20.3 | 22.0 | 23.8 | 25.6 | 27.3 | 29.2 |
| 190 | 14.6 | 16.0 | 17.4 | 19.2 | 20.8 | 22.5 | 24.4 | 26.2 | 28.1 | 29.8 | 31.8 |
| 200 | 16.4 | 18.0 | 19.4 | 21.3 | 23.0 | 24.9 | 26.8 | 28.6 | 30.6 | 32.4 | 34.5 |

## Table 7.  Recommended Sag in Line Wires, Pole Lines (Continued)

STRINGING SAGS FOR
No. 10 AND No. 8 AWG, HIGH-STRENGTH, 40% CONDUCTIVITY
COPPER-COVERED STEEL WIRE
Heavy Loading District—Short Spans

| Span length (ft.) | Temperature in degrees Fahrenheit | | | | | | | | | | |
|---|---|---|---|---|---|---|---|---|---|---|---|
| | 20 | 30 | 40 | 50 | 60 | 70 | 80 | 90 | 100 | 110 | 120 |
| | Sag in inches | | | | | | | | | | |
| 200 | 16.4 | 18.0 | 19.4 | 21.3 | 23.0 | 24.9 | 26.8 | 28.6 | 30.6 | 32.4 | 34.5 |
| 210 | 18.6 | 20.2 | 21.8 | 23.5 | 25.4 | 27.3 | 29.3 | 31.3 | 33.2 | 35.2 | 37.0 |
| 220 | 20.7 | 22.4 | 24.0 | 25.9 | 27.8 | 29.8 | 32.0 | 34.0 | 36.0 | 38.0 | 39.8 |
| 230 | 23.0 | 24.7 | 26.5 | 28.4 | 30.4 | 32.6 | 34.7 | 36.9 | 38.8 | 41.0 | 42.8 |
| 240 | 25.4 | 27.2 | 29.0 | 31.0 | 33.0 | 35.4 | 37.6 | 39.8 | 41.8 | 44.0 | 46.0 |
| 250 | 27.8 | 29.7 | 31.6 | 33.8 | 36.0 | 38.2 | 40.6 | 42.8 | 44.9 | 47.0 | 49.0 |
| 260 | 30.4 | 32.5 | 34.5 | 36.7 | 38.8 | 41.2 | 43.6 | 45.8 | 48.1 | 50.2 | 52.4 |
| 270 | 33.2 | 35.4 | 37.4 | 39.8 | 42.0 | 44.4 | 46.8 | 49.1 | 51.3 | 53.6 | 55.8 |
| 280 | 36.0 | 38.3 | 40.5 | 42.8 | 45.1 | 47.6 | 50.0 | 52.4 | 54.6 | 56.8 | 59.4 |
| 290 | 39.0 | 41.4 | 43.7 | 46.0 | 48.4 | 50.9 | 53.2 | 55.6 | 58.0 | 60.3 | 63.0 |

STRINGING SAGS FOR
No. 8 AWG, HIGH-STRENGTH, 40% CONDUCTIVITY
COPPER-COVERED STEEL WIRE
Heavy Loading District—Medium Spans

| Span length (ft.) | Temperature in degrees Fahrenheit | | | | | | | | | | |
|---|---|---|---|---|---|---|---|---|---|---|---|
| | 20 | 30 | 40 | 50 | 60 | 70 | 80 | 90 | 100 | 110 | 120 |
| | Sag in inches | | | | | | | | | | |
| 300 | 42.0 | 44.6 | 47.1 | 49.5 | 51.9 | 54.2 | 56.7 | 59.1 | 61.5 | 63.9 | 66.1 |
| 310 | 45.5 | 48.0 | 50.3 | 53.0 | 55.5 | 57.7 | 60.3 | 62.7 | 65.1 | 67.5 | 69.6 |
| 320 | 48.8 | 51.4 | 53.8 | 56.5 | 59.0 | 61.4 | 64.0 | 66.4 | 68.9 | 71.3 | 73.0 |
| 330 | 52.4 | 55.0 | 57.5 | 60.2 | 62.7 | 65.2 | 67.7 | 70.3 | 72.8 | 75.1 | 77.4 |
| 340 | 56.0 | 58.7 | 61.3 | 64.0 | 66.6 | 69.1 | 71.6 | 74.3 | 76.8 | 79.3 | 81.5 |
| 350 | 59.9 | 62.6 | 65.2 | 68.0 | 70.8 | 73.4 | 75.9 | 78.5 | 81.0 | 83.5 | 85.7 |

STRINGING SAGS FOR
No. 8 AWG, HIGH-STRENGTH, 40% CONDUCTIVITY
COPPER-COVERED STEEL WIRE
Heavy Loading District—Long Spans

| Span length (ft.) | Temperature in degrees Fahrenheit | | | | | | | | | | |
|---|---|---|---|---|---|---|---|---|---|---|---|
| | 20 | 30 | 40 | 50 | 60 | 70 | 80 | 90 | 100 | 110 | 120 |
| | Sag in feet | | | | | | | | | | |
| 350 | 5.0 | 5.2 | 5.4 | 5.7 | 5.9 | 6.1 | 6.3 | 6.5 | 6.7 | 7.0 | 7.2 |
| 400 | 11.0 | 11.2 | 11.4 | 11.5 | 11.7 | 11.9 | 12.0 | 12.2 | 12.3 | 12.5 | 12.7 |
| 500 | 21.8 | 22.0 | 22.1 | 22.2 | 22.4 | 22.5 | 22.7 | 22.9 | 23.1 | 23.3 | 23.5 |
| 600 | 35.1 | 35.3 | 35.4 | 35.5 | 35.6 | 35.7 | 35.8 | 36.0 | 36.1 | 36.2 | 36.4 |
| 700 | 51.0 | 51.1 | 51.2 | 51.3 | 51.5 | 51.6 | 51.8 | 51.9 | 52.0 | 52.1 | 52.3 |
| 800 | 70.1 | 70.2 | 70.3 | 70.4 | 70.6 | 70.7 | 70.9 | 71.0 | 71.1 | 71.2 | 71.4 |

### Table 7. Recommended Sag in Line Wires, Pole Lines (Continued)

STRINGING SAGS FOR

No. 6 AWG, HIGH-STRENGTH, 40% CONDUCTIVITY
COPPER-COVERED STEEL WIRE

Heavy Loading District—Long Spans

| Span length (ft.) | Temperature in degrees Fahrenheit | | | | | | | | | | |
|---|---|---|---|---|---|---|---|---|---|---|---|
| | 20 | 30 | 40 | 50 | 60 | 70 | 80 | 90 | 100 | 110 | 120 |
| | Sag in feet | | | | | | | | | | |
| 800 | 44.6 | 44.8 | 44.9 | 45.1 | 45.3 | 45.5 | 45.7 | 45.9 | 46.1 | 46.3 | 46.5 |
| 900 | 59.3 | 59.5 | 59.7 | 59.8 | 60.0 | 60.2 | 60.4 | 60.6 | 60.8 | 60.9 | 61.1 |
| 1,000 | 76.1 | 76.3 | 76.5 | 76.7 | 76.8 | 77.0 | 77.2 | 77.4 | 77.6 | 77.7 | 77.9 |
| 1,100 | 95.3 | 95.4 | 95.6 | 95.8 | 96.0 | 96.1 | 96.3 | 96.5 | 96.6 | 96.8 | 97.0 |
| 1,200 | 116.9 | 117.1 | 117.3 | 117.4 | 117.6 | 117.8 | 117.9 | 118.1 | 118.3 | 118.5 | 118.6 |
| 1,300 | 141.4 | 141.6 | 141.8 | 141.9 | 142.1 | 142.3 | 142.4 | 142.6 | 142.8 | 142.9 | 143.1 |
| 1,400 | 169.2 | 169.3 | 169.5 | 169.7 | 169.8 | 170.0 | 170.2 | 170.3 | 170.5 | 170.6 | 170.8 |
| 1,500 | 200.7 | 200.9 | 201.1 | 201.2 | 201.4 | 201.5 | 201.7 | 201.9 | 202.0 | 202.1 | 202.3 |

**Line Loading.** The efficiency of any telephone circuit, ground return or metallic, is largely determined by its loading (not to be confused with "loading" by ice and snow). Each mile of wire, each instrument, each repeating coil, and other auxiliary equipment attached to a telephone circuit adds to the line load. In addition, any contact the wires make with any object not properly insulated, like brush, trees, buildings, cracked insulators or no insulators, power line induction, etc., increases this same load. It has been determined that the top load a circuit can carry is 31 db. (a unit for the measurement of sound). However, if the circuit is loaded to this extent by length and instruments, it will invariably be overloaded by foreign objects—poor splices, leaks, and insulators. Therefore it is best to plan the circuit for an instrument and wire load not to exceed 20 db. Then the load that is accidentally placed on the circuit can be carried usually without impairment of the transmission and receiving levels. Where it is necessary to load a line more than 20 db., tests should be made to locate any foreign load on the circuit and in no case should the load, both foreign and instrument, exceed 31 db. The following decibel ratings should be used for determining loads of both wire and instruments.

| Parts of the telephone circuit | | Average db. load | |
|---|---|---|---|
| Wire No. 9 EBB | Ground return system | 0.15 | |
| Wire No. 9 EBB | Metallic system | .25 | |
| Wire No. 12 AWG copper-covered 40 percent | Ground return system | .14 | |
| Wire No. 12 AWG copper-covered 40 percent | Metallic system | .22 | (Per loop mile) |
| Wire No. 10 AWG copper-covered 40 percent | Metallic system | .15 | |
| Wire No. 8 AWG copper-covered 40 percent | Metallic system | .11 | |
| Wire No. 6 AWG copper-covered 40 percent | Metallic system | .08 | |
| Wire No. 10 B&S copper | Metallic system | .08 | |
| Wire No. 8 B&S copper | Metallic system | .06 | |
| Ringer 2500 ohm | | 1.00 | |
| Repeating coils | | 0.50 | |
| Howlers | | 0.65 | |
| Spur lines | | 1.00 plus wire length load | |

**Transposition of Wires.** Transposition of line wires in a metallic circuit is necessary for its proper functioning. In addition, transposition of wires is necessary where they parallel other telephone circuits, power transmission wires, or other wires. Transposing prevents the accumulation on the circuit of noise inducted from these other wires. Where other wires are parallel with the circuit wires, not necessarily close, the circuit wires are regarded as an exposed circuit or wire system. For such a line or circuit, transposition systems have been designed to overcome this inducted interference and at the same time provide the necessary transposing of metallic circuit wires regardless of exposure.

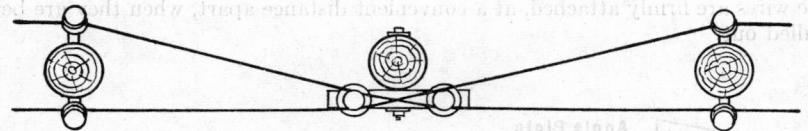

Fig. 14A. Transposition, R1 system.

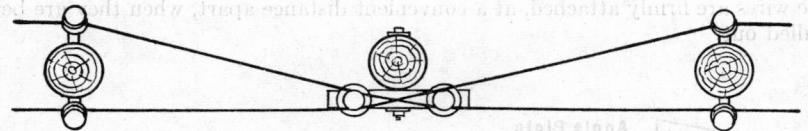

This design can be used on either 2·4·6·8 or 10·pin crossarms.

◯ **Indicates transposition omitted.**

Fig. 14B. R1 transposition design.

The R1 transposition system provides the necessary transposing of the circuit wires and adequately handles the exposure factor. In addition, it provides, without cutting and dead-ending conductor wires, point-type transposition; it is simple, readily understandable, and requires no great experience in replacing if conductor wires are broken.

The most practical method of transposing wires is to "throw" the transpositions at the time the wire is reeled out. This step requires attention to the details of the transposition plan for the circuit. Each transposition point and type should be designated on the ground in advance of the wire stringing. A "transposition running board" should be used in stringing the wires. It is a short board to which the wires are firmly attached, at a convenient distance apart, when they are being pulled out.

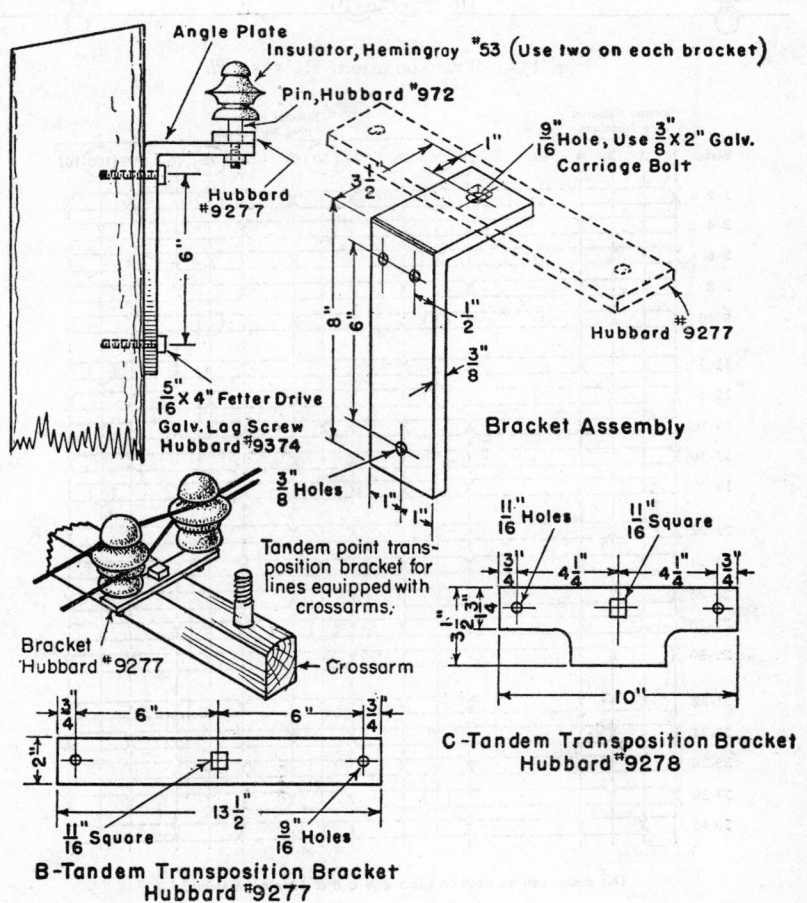

Fig. 14C. R1 transposition bracket and angle plate.

The R1 system provides that every other pole be a transposition pole, except where two or more circuits are carried on the same pole. In that case, the transpositions should be staggered on any two adjacent circuits, thus making every pole a transposition pole for at least one of the circuits, whether of bracket or crossarm construction (Figs. 14A and 14B). The length of the span has no appreciable effect on the transpositions as long as the every-other-pole scheme is followed. The transpositions should be made on Whitall Tatum No. 15 or Hemingray No. 53 or similar double-groove glass insulators mounted on a tandem transposition bracket assembly or crossarm (Fig. 14C).

In bracket construction the top pair of wires will be transposed as 5 and 6 and the bottom pair as 15 and 16. This method is advantageous to later replacement of the bracket construction with crossarms. On a two-wire bracket line in which spans average over 150 ft., transpose on the B transposition bracket in straight sections and at corners of 15 ft. pull or less. At corners where the pull exceeds 15 ft., use a C tandem transposition bracket. Both B and C brackets will be mounted on an angle plate. For R1 bracket assembly, see Fig. 14C.

**Lightning Protection.** This is absolutely essential for all telephone lines, whether on poles or trees. It is included in the general discussion of grounding systems, page **20·34**.

## TREE LINES (GROUND RETURN).

Economy in construction—little clearing of the right-of-way, avoidance of the cost of poles and their setting, and the use of a single wire—recommends the use of ground-return tree lines in forested country. Noise (static) caused by electric storms is greater on ground-return lines than on metallic circuits. The number of telephone instruments effectively operated on such lines is only 9. Grounded lines are not satisfactory if they parallel other grounded lines or are near power systems. In spite of these drawbacks, the average national forest in the United States is largely dependent for telephone service on ground-return tree lines.

A tree line is constantly subject to falling limbs and trees, but the use of split insulators and slack enough in the wire so that a weight of from 75 to 90 lb. will pull the wire to the ground between hangers of standard height permits the line to render continued service unless the accumulated windfall is too great.

**Location.** Some of the factors affecting location will be apparent from a study of Fig. 15. The line should be located adjacent to, or at least in plain view of, a road or trail to facilitate maintenance. Short cuts which totally obscure the line from view should be avoided. Where there is danger that a broken wire may fall into the travelway, place the wire on the opposite side of the trees. Where road crossings are unavoidable, they should be as nearly as possible at right angles. Consider the possibility of sheltering the line against high winds, falling timber, deep snow, floods, and landslides. Make full use of long spans where adequate clearance above ground and freedom from overhanging timber are assured. Except in long-span construction, avoid using poles in tree lines, even if this necessitates a detour. In rolling country take full advantage of rises on which to locate tie trees without raising the insulators above normal heights.

Two men should do the locating, equipped with a piece of light wire, 140 ft. in length, with a grip hold on each end. The foreman should be on the head end of the wire; as he selects the tie trees (usually 140 ft. apart), the line is pulled tight. He then sights along it and selects the side of each tree for the rear man, when the latter comes up, to designate as the line wire side.

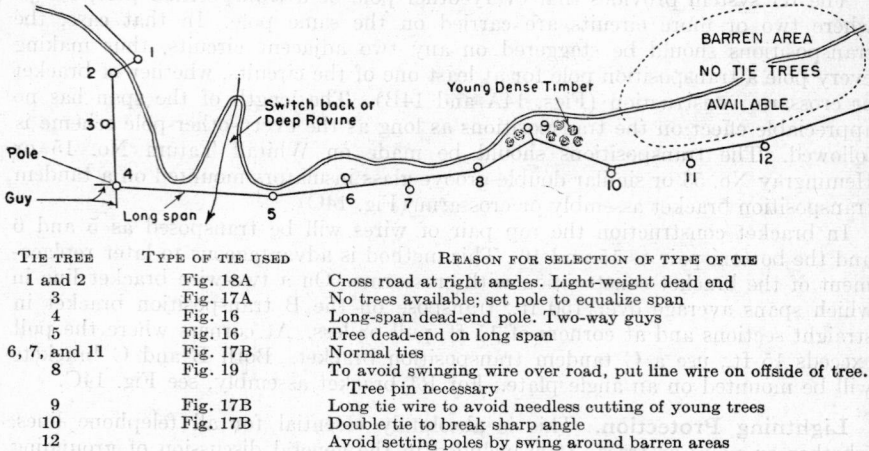

| TIE TREE | TYPE OF TIE USED | REASON FOR SELECTION OF TYPE OF TIE |
|---|---|---|
| 1 and 2 | Fig. 18A | Cross road at right angles. Light-weight dead end |
| 3 | Fig. 17A | No trees available; set pole to equalize span |
| 4 | Fig. 16 | Long-span dead-end pole. Two-way guys |
| 5 | Fig. 16 | Tree dead-end on long span |
| 6, 7, and 11 | Fig. 17B | Normal ties |
| 8 | Fig. 19 | To avoid swinging wire over road, put line wire on offside of tree. Tree pin necessary |
| 9 | Fig. 17B | Long tie wire to avoid needless cutting of young trees |
| 10 | Fig. 17B | Double tie to break sharp angle |
| 12 | | Avoid setting poles by swing around barren areas |

**Fig. 15. Suggestions for selection of tree ties for line along a trail or road.**

**Line Wire.** Copper-covered steel wire should be used, except for extensions of existing lines of galvanized iron wire. The copper-covered wire should be No. 12, except in long spans, where it should be No. 8 or even heavier. The galvanized iron wire should be No. 9 EBB where the line to be extended is of that gauge.

**Tie Trees.** Trees about 8 in. d.o.b. at line-wire height are best. Large trees are difficult to climb. Slow-growing trees, if healthy, are preferred.

**Spans.** Too much emphasis cannot be put on the uniformity of span, which produces uniformity of slack. The most satisfactory span is 140 ft.; a 10-ft. variation either way, but preferably toward shortening, is permissible. On steep slopes the span should not exceed 100 ft. Where a span up to 200 ft. is necessary to avoid setting a pole, adjust three spans on each side to 185, 170, and 155 ft. Use poles, uniformly spaced (see Table 1 for spacing), to avoid spans over 200 ft.

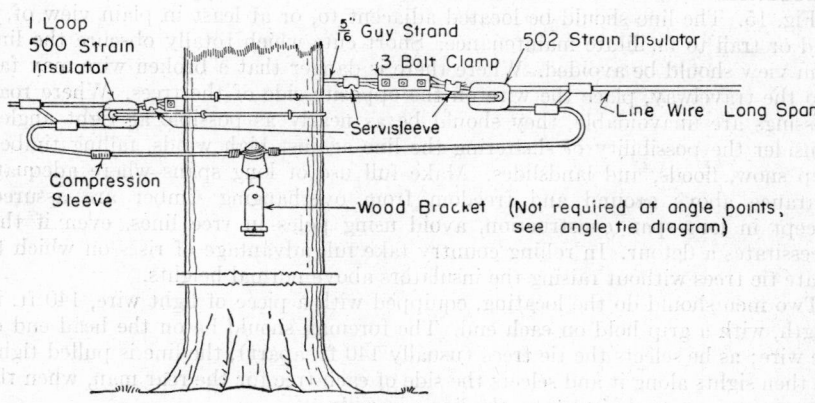

**Fig. 16. Long-span tree dead end.**

**Long Spans.** Spans of 1,000 ft. or more are both good practice and economical under certain physical conditions. Heavier construction is used throughout. Use long spans only across canyons or ravines where ground clearance is sufficient to permit proper sag. For supporting long spans use large trees, rock bluffs, or poles that are strong enough to carry loads due to sleet or ice storms. Be sure the line is clear of overhanging limbs or trees. Dead ends, fittings, and anchorage should be adequate to withstand maximum expected tensions on the line (see Fig. 16).

**Ties.** Tie the tie wire solidly around the split insulator, and attach it to the tree staple with a twist which will pull out under 200 lb. pressure (Fig. 17B); use No. 9 EBB iron wire or No. 10 copper-covered hard-drawn steel, the length dependent on alignment and other conditions. For the use of iron tree pins, see Fig. 19.

**Stringing and Hanging Wire.** Pay out wire from a "barrow reel" carried by two men, or in rough terrain on a horse. Never drag it over rocks, barbed-wire fences or other sharp objects, or pull it with an animal or by mechanical means. In clearing (limbing) trees and in hanging wire, use a light but rugged ladder (not an extension ladder) rather than climbers, but have climbers on hand to meet unusual situations. Smooth off bark before driving a staple in the tie tree, but do not cut through the bark; drive staples—3- or 4-in., depending on bark thickness—no deeper than is necessary for good support. The staple should be high enough above the ground to give, with the tie wire, a clearance at the middle of the span of 12 to 15 ft. normally, and not less than 18 ft. where the line crosses travelways. Compression sleeves should always be used in splicing line wire. Slack or sag is essential—3 to 4 ft. for spans of 100 to 140 ft. Too much slack is better than too little, always provided that proper clearances are maintained.

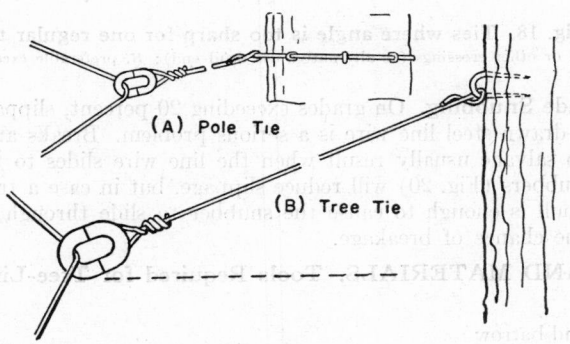

**Fig. 17. Tie (tree line).**

**Use of Poles in Tree Lines.** Where not over ten consecutive poles with 160-ft. spacing are needed, use tree-line construction methods, except that the split insulator is fastened to the pole, not with a staple, but by wrapping the tie wire around the pole. When more than ten consecutive poles are needed, dead-end the tree line on the second pole from each end and use brackets on the intermediate poles.

**Dead-Ending. Sharp angles.** See Figs. 16 and 18. Strain insulators are specially constructed insulators of extra strength.

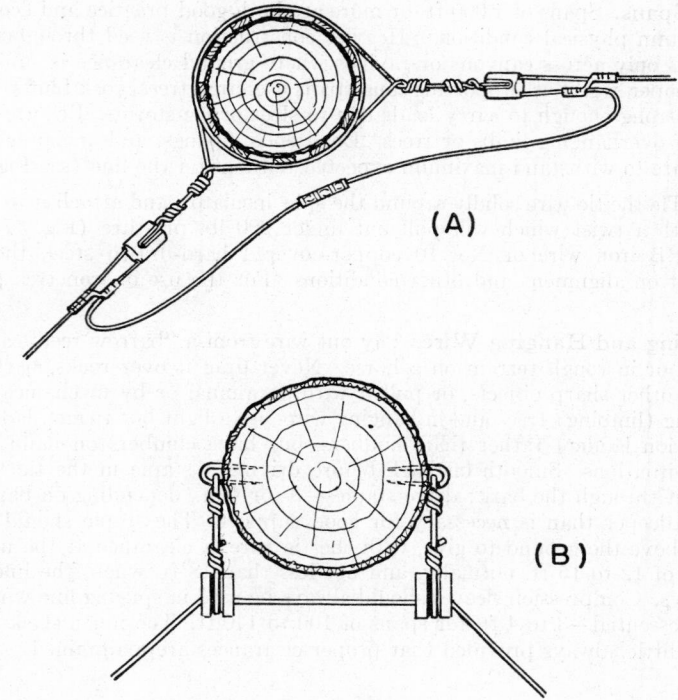

**Fig. 18. Ties where angle is too sharp for one regular tie.**

*A*, best at road or other crossings (as alternative use dead end); *B*, preferable except at crossings.

**Down-Grade Snubbing.** On grades exceeding 20 percent, slippage of copper-covered hard-drawn steel line wire is a serious problem. Breaks and tangles not practicable to salvage usually result when the line wire slides to the bottom of the slope. Snubbers (Fig. 20) will reduce slippage, but in case a tree falls across the line the pull is enough to cause the snubber to slide through the insulator, minimizing the chance of breakage.

**TOOLS AND MATERIALS. Tools Required for Tree-Line Construction.**

```
1  reel, hand barrow
2  ladders, light, 16-ft.; extension ladders not recommended
2  axes, double bit
1  saw, crosscut, adequate length
2  climbers, tree, pairs; 3-in. gaffs for hardwoods and thin-barked conifers, 5-in. for
      thick-barked trees
2  belts, tool
2  straps, safety, rope with steel core preferred
3  pliers, pairs, 8-in., side-cutting
1  tool, splicing
1  axe, hand
1  saw, pruner's
1  saw, pruning, long handle
2  ropes, 25-ft., ⅜ in., for hand lines
```

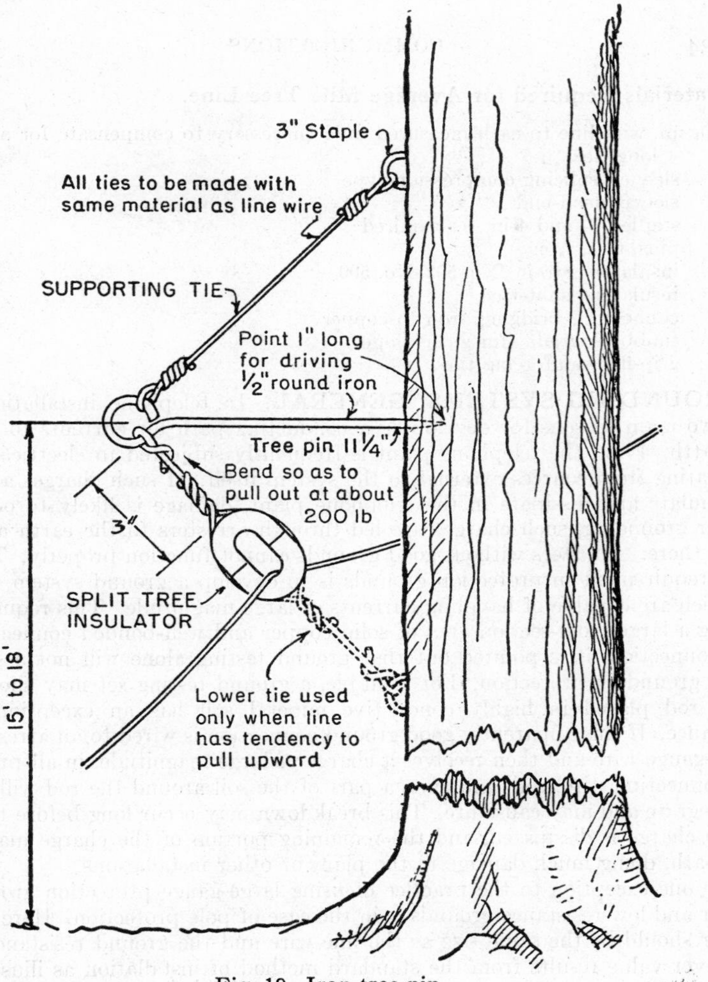

3" Staple

All ties to be made with
same material as line wire

SUPPORTING TIE

Point 1" long
for driving
½" round iron

Tree pin 11¼"
Bend so as to
pull out at about
200 lb

3"

SPLIT TREE
INSULATOR

Lower tie used
only when line
has tendency to
pull upward

15' to 18'

Fig. 19. Iron tree pin.

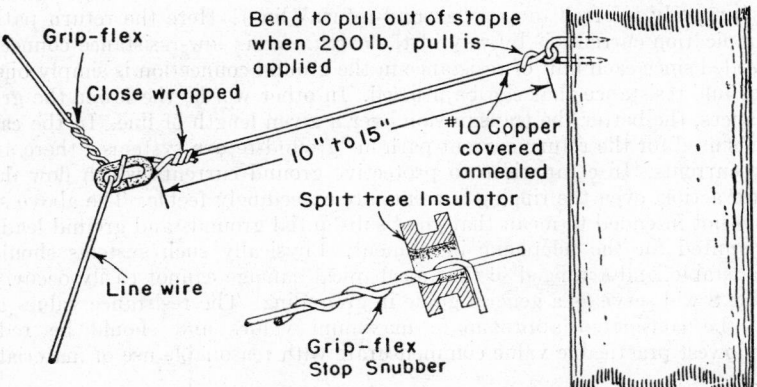

Grip-flex

Close wrapped

Bend to pull out of staple
when 200 lb. pull is
applied

10" to 15"

#10 Copper
covered
annealed

Split tree Insulator

Line wire

Grip-flex
Stop Snubber

Fig. 20. Grip-flex stop for steep slopes.

20 · 33

### Materials Required for Average Mile Tree Line.

1½₁₀ mi. wire line to each measured mile (necessary to compensate for angles and long ties)

| | |
|---|---|
| 3 | sleeves, splicing compression-type |
| 1 | sleeve, dead-end |
| 38 | staples, 3- and 4-in., as required |
| 4 | pins, tree, iron |
| 4 | insulators, strain, No. 502–No. 500 |
| 38 | insulators, split-tree |
| 4 | connectors, bridging, iron to copper |
| 3 | snubbers, grade (for steep slopes) |
| 38 | grip-flex reinforcing ties |

**GROUNDING SYSTEMS, GENERAL.** In telephone installations there are two main reasons for developing a conducting path for currents to flow into the earth. First, the telephone plant is frequently subjected to electrical charges originating from sources external to the system itself. If such charges are left to accumulate and dissipate in the telephone plant, damage is likely to occur. By proper grounding, such charges are led through arresters to the earth and dissipated there. Arresters without good grounds cannot function properly. The principal requirement in protection grounds is to develop a ground system, all parts of which are capable of handling currents of large magnitude. This requires leads having a large cross-section area of solid copper and well-bonded connections. In this connection, it is pointed out that ground testing alone will not assure adequate grounding protection. For example, a ground testing set may show that a small rod placed in highly conductive mineral soil has an exceptionally low resistance. If this apparently good ground connection is wired to an arrester using small-gauge wire and then receives a charge of large magnitude, in all probability the connecting wire, rod, and even a part of the soil around the rod will actually disintegrate and may cause fire. This breakdown may occur long before the whole of the charge is dissipated, and the remaining portion of the charge may seek a new path, doing much damage to the plant or other installations.

The one exception to the practice of using large-gauge protection ground conductor and low-resistance grounds is in the case of pole protection. Here the conductor should be the same size as the line wire and the ground resistance left at whatever value results from the standard method of installation as illustrated in Fig. 22.

The second reason for grounding is in connection with the so-called "grounded line" (properly referred to as a "ground-return" line). Here the return path for communication currents is by way of the earth. Again low-resistance connections are needed since each unit of resistance in the ground connection is simply one less unit of line resistance that can be utilized. In other words, the lower the ground resistances, the better the transmission over a given length of line. In the case of grounds used for the return current path in "ground-return systems," there are no heavy currents. In comparison to protective ground currents which flow during arrester action, even the ringing currents are exceedingly feeble. The above statement is not intended to mean that good substantial grounds and ground leads are not required for the telephone instrument. Physically such systems should be strong, stable, and arranged so that mechanical damage cannot easily occur.

Table 8 will serve as a general guide in grounding. The resistance values given are to be considered approximate maximum values and should be reduced to the lowest practicable value commensurate with reasonable use of material and labor.

**Table 8. Ground Resistance Values**

| Purpose of the ground | Maximum resistance in ohms | Ground lead |
|---|---|---|
| Pole protection grounds..................... | Measurement not necessary | Line wire |
| Gap arresters protecting entrance cables, underground construction [a]..................... | 10 | No. 2 copper |
| Gap arresters at lookouts—guard station (instrument protection)..................... | Tie to lookout, protection 25-50 | |
| Gap arrester at repeat coils [a]................. | 20–50 | No. 10 copper weatherproof |
| Carbon block or vac. arresters. Power Protector No. 99A [a].............................. | Less than 100 | No. 10 copper weatherproof |
| Telephone grounds for local service [a].......... | 10–200 | No. 10 copper |
| Ground common to 2 or more circuits where crosstalk must be avoided [a]................ | 20 | No. 10 copper weatherproof |
| Telephone ground for average service [a]........ | 50 | No. 10 copper weatherproof |

[a] Measurement of ground resistance required.

**Testing Grounds.** There are several types of direct reading, easy-to-operate ground-testing instruments available which give ground resistance in ohms. Approved ground-testing sets are made by the following manufacturers, among others: "Vibro Ground Test Set," Linn O. Morrow, Philadelphia, Pa. "Megger Ground Tester Set," Jas. G. Biddle Co., Philadelphia, Pa. Models adapted to field use weigh, with the necessary ground rods and test wires, about 20 lb. and cost about $150. Essentially, the principle of operation is the same for most types. Two auxiliary rods on other ground connections are used, spaced about 50 to 100 ft. away from the ground being measured, and leads connect all three grounds to the instrument. (See Fig. 21.) Briefly, operation is as follows: The test set

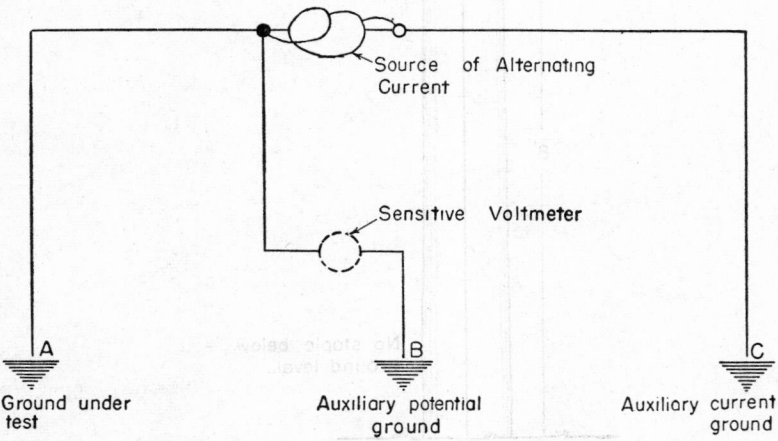

Fig. 21. Ground testing method (direct reading instruments).

causes current to flow through the ground under test $(A)$ and auxiliary ground $(C)$. If there is resistance to the flow of this current at $(A)$, then a voltage will exist between it and other points on the earth, as at $(B)$. The sensitive voltmeter measures this voltage and indicates it in terms of ohms of resistance. The resistance of the auxiliary ground has essentially no effect upon the accuracy of the measurements.

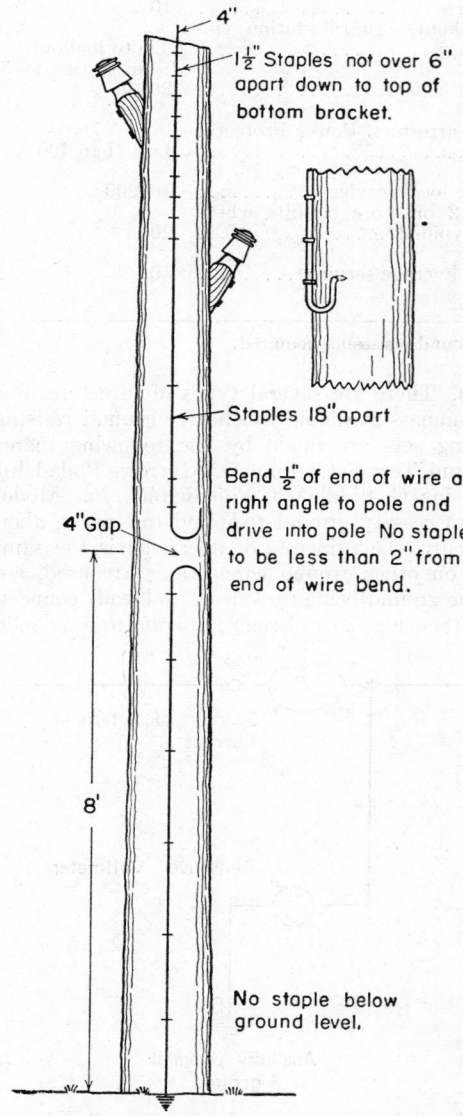

4"

$1\frac{1}{2}$" Staples not over 6" apart down to top of bottom bracket.

Staples 18"apart

Bend $\frac{1}{2}$" of end of wire at right angle to pole and drive into pole No staple to be less than 2" from end of wire bend.

4"Gap

8'

No staple below ground level.

Fig. 22.  Ground conductors for pole protection.

Ohmmeters are not recommended for measuring ground resistance since the value of the auxiliary ground is not known and to determine this value involves a procedure too lengthy to be practicable. Furthermore, earth currents frequently upset these measurements. Experience has shown that ground resistance does not remain constant and that tests should be made frequently enough to insure satisfactory service. Such tests should be made during the dry season.

Ground rods are commonly used when developing a ground system. However, other buried metallic objects, such as water systems, are also good grounds under certain conditions. The resistance of a ground usually depends upon the type of soil in contact with the surface of the ground rod or other buried metal. Clay soils are usually excellent grounds; sandy or gravelly soils, even when damp, are seldom good; volcanic ash is almost invariably poor. The more moisture permanently in the soil, the better.

**Pole Protection.** Fig. 22 shows the standard method of installing lightning arresters on poles. In heavy lightning zones, install arresters on every pole; in medium and light zones, install arresters on every fifth or tenth pole (local commercial telephone companies can advise as to such zones). Pole protection should not be installed on telephone lines passing through timber where the height of the trees exceeds pole height and the distance between pole and tree does not exceed the difference between pole and tree height.

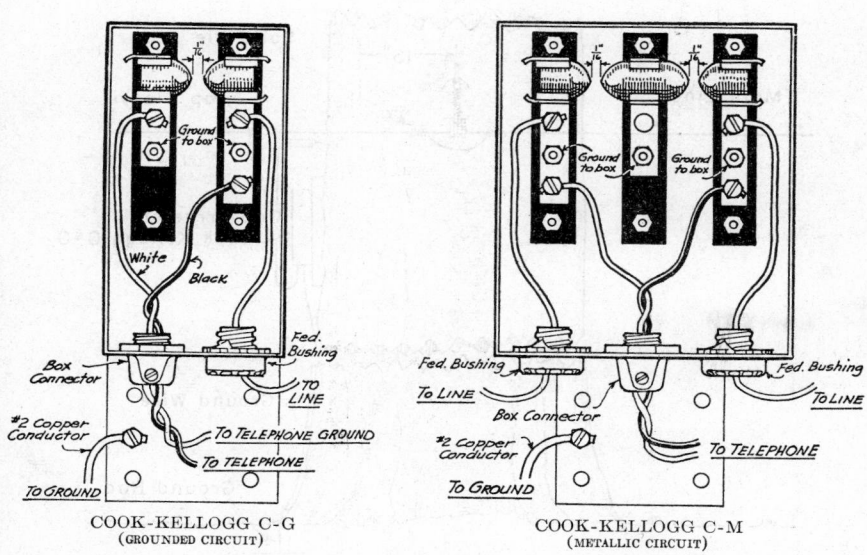

COOK-KELLOGG C-G
(GROUNDED CIRCUIT)

COOK-KELLOGG C-M
(METALLIC CIRCUIT)

Fig. 23. Ball-gap lightning arresters.

Note that the conductor wire is the same as the line wire. It is most easily attached to the pole before erection. The portion from the apparent ground level to the bottom of the pole should be left loose and buried with the pole as it is set, with as much earth as possible between it and the pole.

**Line and Instrument Protection.** The ball-gap type arrester with a $\frac{1}{16}$-in. gap (Fig. 23) is the standard set by the U. S. Forest Service for the primary protection system, with a carbon-block arrester located within a few feet of the telephone instrument. Ball-gap arresters should be installed at the termination of open-wire telephone lines where such lines join with telephone installations. The arrester should be installed on the last pole, never on the building housing the telephone. In heavy lightning zones an additional arrester should be installed on the next to the last pole and on a pole 1 or 2 mi. away, wherever a thoroughly satisfactory ground (of lower resistance than the grounds at the terminal poles, and in no case over 25 ohms) is available.

Gap arresters, unlike the ground conductor shown in Fig. 22, require No. 2 soft copper conductor wire extending 4 in. above the top of the pole and standard 5-ft. copper-covered ground rods driven full length into solid soil (not the freshly-tamped soil around the pole). Where soils are shallow and remain unfrozen, the conductors can be laid horizontally. Where connection is made with a water system or other buried metal pipe, do not use solder; use a tinned copper strip clamp. The connecting wire between the conductor and a ground rod should be copper or copper-covered steel wire not less than No. 10 gauge, and a ground rod clamp should be used. Attachment to the line wire is the same as for tree lines (Fig. 24). On lines along or leading to a ridge, additional gap-arresters should be used. If such lines are spurs to main lines in the valley, arresters should be used on the first poles on each side of the junction.

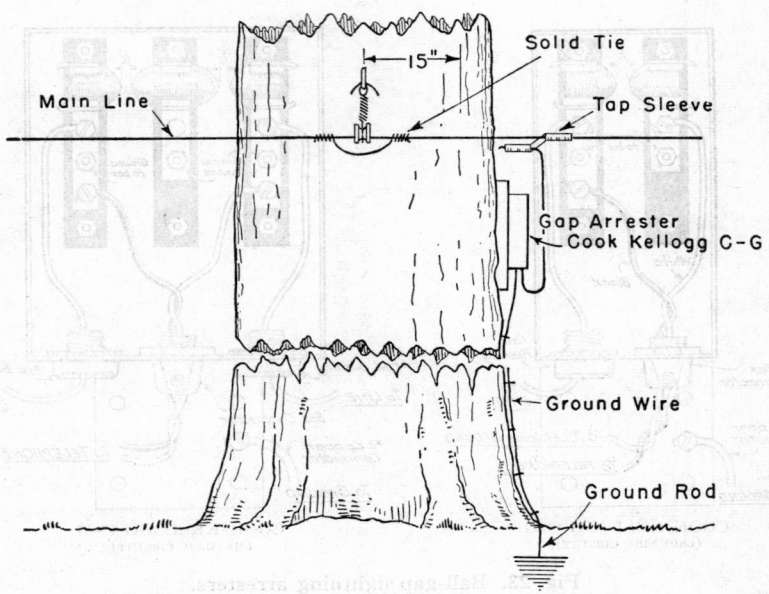

Fig. 24. Gap arrester installation (tree line).

**Multiple Rods.** Where a single rod is unsatisfactory owing to high resistance and where for reasons of shallow soil a longer rod is not practicable, the addition of one or more rods driven in the same area and connected together will often reduce the ground resistance to a satisfactory level. As will be noted from Fig. 25, the use of two ground rods connected in multiple and with a separation of 6 ft. will lower the resistance from approximately 72 percent for one rod to 60 percent for the two. Often a third rod, connected in multiple with the same separation (6 ft.), will reduce the resistance another 12 percent, or to 48 percent. Wires connecting multiple rods should be underneath the surface out of reach of pawing or digging animals. The connecting wire should be copper or copper-covered steel not less than No. 10 gauge. The wire connections to the ground rod should be made by a ground rod clamp.

Experience has shown that with few exceptions the 5-ft. copper-covered ground rod is sufficient to obtain a good ground. The slight decrease obtained in the resistance by spreading the multiple grounds more than 6 ft. does not appear to be justified.

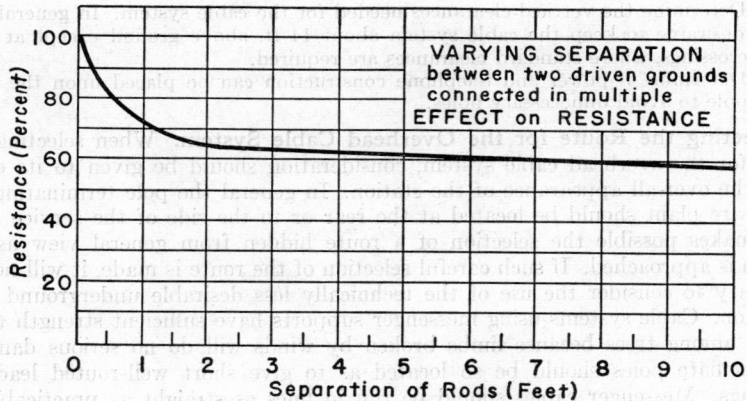

Fig. 25. Effect on resistance of varying separation between two driven grounds connected in multiple.

**Chemical Treatment.** In soils where the mineral content is low, a better ground can be secured by applying salt in the proper manner. This is applied as shown in Fig. 26. Use about 50 lb. of rock salt to treat each rod. As salt is readily soluble in water, the salt content of a treated soil will change as the salt is carried away by leaching. On an average, the resistance of a ground can be reduced by 75 to 80 percent and will remain effective for about 12 to 18 months, at which time the salt should be replenished. The salt should not come directly in contact with the rod, as excessive corrosion may occur. Multiple rods, without salt, may be necessary to secure a satisfactory ground in areas where deer and other game are plentiful if protection to the ground connections from animals cannot be assured.

## PLANNING AND LAYOUT OF ENTRANCE AND DISTRIBUTION
**LINES.** Careful planning of aerial construction at terminal points, especially at ranger and guard stations, will greatly lessen the many objections to this type of construction. From a communication service feature, this type of construction is far more reliable and is not subjected to so many hazards as is underground construction. Planning should take full advantage of any screening possibilities and utilize the traveled and seen route. The open wire plant is assumed to be terminated on a pole at the side or rear of the building area.

1. Determine the number of buildings to be served by all of the lines, such as buildings having switchboards.
2. Determine what other buildings need only one line, as when a single instrument is to be installed.
3. Determine if more than one local circuit is needed to connect the local telephones, basing this determination upon the number of phones and the anticipated division of traffic.
4. Lay out pole and messenger line on a site plan in an arrangement that will give the best appearance, avoid turns, and occupy the most direct route consistent with other details. Junction poles where branch leads are to be attached should be placed so that the drop wires will lead to the right point on the building being served. Locate intermediate poles one-half the diameter of the pole to one side of the cable line. Junction poles should be located one-half the diameter of the pole to the side opposite the direction in which the branch line leads. A typical layout is shown in Fig. 27.
5. Determine the vertical clearances needed for the cable system. In general it is desirable to keep the cable system about 14 ft. above ground except at road crossings, where standard clearances are required.
6. Determine if power and telephone construction can be placed upon the same pole to avoid unnecessary poles.

**Selecting the Route for the Overhead Cable System.** When selecting the route for the overhead cable system, consideration should be given to its effect upon the over-all appearance of the station. In general the pole terminating the open wire plant should be located at the rear or to the side of the service area. This makes possible the selection of a route hidden from general view as the station is approached. If such careful selection of the route is made, it will not be necessary to consider the use of the technically less desirable underground construction. Cable systems using messenger supports have sufficient strength to be placed among trees because limbs broken by winds will do no serious damage. Intermediate poles should be so located as to give short well-routed leads to buildings. Messenger cables should be run in lines as straight as practicable to avoid excessive guying.

**Overhead Construction.** The use of drop wire in overhead construction will be the primary standard for all leads extending from the open wire plant to the various buildings requiring service. A messenger cable with cable rings will be used to support the drop wire when the number of lines exceeds three and when the length of the run is in excess of 75 ft. Local ice loading may require that unsupported span lengths be reduced or even eliminated, regardless of the number of drop wires.

Messenger cables under tension should not be terminated on frame buildings or other structures of light construction in lieu of poles. In some instances buildings may be used to support the vertical weight of the cable at an intermediate point. Use a pole to terminate the messenger cable near the building. If ice loading is a problem, a slack messenger may be required to give additional support to the drop wires. In most instances, the messenger from pole to building will not be required, regardless of the number of wires, if the distance does not exceed 20 ft.

**MAINTENANCE OF TELEPHONE LINES. Mapping.** For efficient maintenance of any telephone line, a detailed map of the line is necessary. Symbols for use on such a map are shown in Fig. 28.

**Circuit Noise.** Any electrical interference with the desired communication on a line is termed "noise." The four principal types are power hum, cross talk from

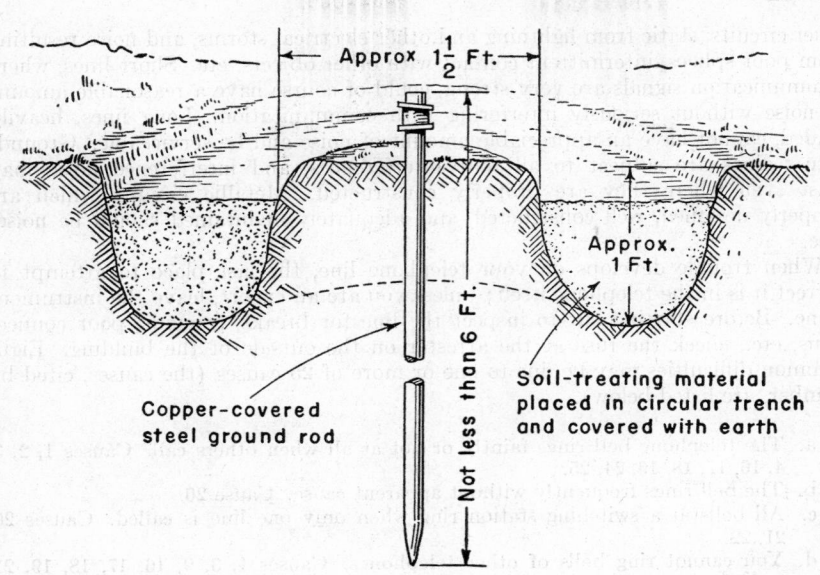

Fig. 26.  Chemical treatment of ground.

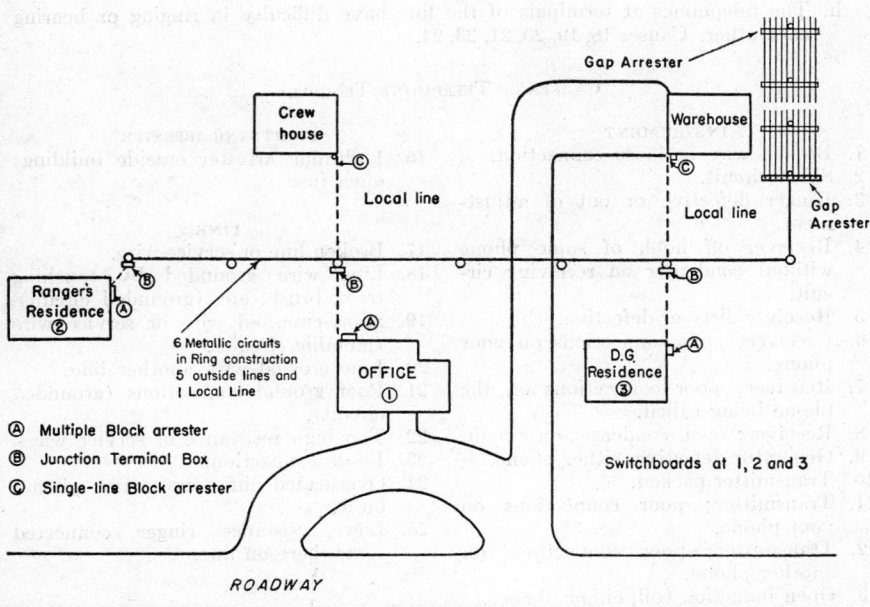

Fig. 27.  Typical overhead telephone layout at ranger or guard station.

other circuits, static from lightning and other electrical storms, and noise resulting from poor splices, intermittent contact with other objects, etc. Short lines, where communication signals are very strong, could of course have a reasonable amount of noise without seriously interfering with communication. Long lines, heavily loaded, cannot have an appreciable amount of noise and be serviceable. Ground-return lines are subject to all four interferences, and interference noise may exist even where they are properly constructed. Metallic circuits which are properly designed, well constructed, and adequately maintained should be noise-free.

When trouble develops on your telephone line, the last place to attempt to correct it is in the telephone itself; unless you are an expert, leave the instrument alone. Before starting out to inspect the line for breaks, grounds, poor connections, etc., check the fuse at the arrester on the outside of the building. Eight common difficulties may be due to one or more of 25 causes (the causes, cited by number, are listed below).

a. The telephone bell rings faintly or not at all when others call. Causes 1, 2, 3, 4, 16, 17, 18, 19, 24, 25.
b. The bell rings frequently without apparent cause. Cause 20.
c. All bells at a switching station ring when only one line is called. Causes 20, 21, 22.
d. You cannot ring bells of other telephones. Causes 1, 3, 9, 16, 17, 18, 19, 21, 24, 25.
e. Others cannot hear you talk. Causes 7, 10, 11, 13, 14, 15.
f. You cannot hear others talk. Causes 5, 6, 8, 12, 13, 14.
g. Your conversation is interrupted so that at times you hear only parts of words or sentences. Causes 5, 18, 19, 20, 21, 23.
h. The telephones at terminals of the line have difficulty in ringing or hearing each other. Causes 18, 19, 20, 21, 23, 24.

### CAUSES OF TELEPHONE TROUBLE

#### INSTRUMENT

1. Broken wire or loose connection.
2. Short circuit.
3. Ringer defective or out of adjustment.
4. Receiver off hook of some phone without condenser on receiving circuit.
5. Receiver dirty or defective.
6. Receiver; poor connections on your phone.
7. Receiver; poor connections on the phone being called.
8. Receiver; open condenser on circuit.
9. Generator defective, either phone.
10. Transmitter packed.
11. Transmitter; poor connections on your phone.
12. Transmitter; poor connections on another phone.
13. Open induction coil, either phone.
14. Hook switch out of adjustment, either phone.
15. Battery defective, either phone.

#### LIGHTNING ARRESTER

16. Lightning arrester outside building: open fuse.

#### LINE

17. Broken line or service wire.
18. Line wire grounded by touching trees, brush, etc. (grounded circuit).
19. Short-circuited wire or service wire (metallic circuit).
20. Line crossed with another line.
21. Poor ground connections (grounded circuit).
22. Too high resistance of service wires.
23. Loose connection.
24. Overloaded line—too many phones on it.
25. Low resistance ringer connected somewhere on line.

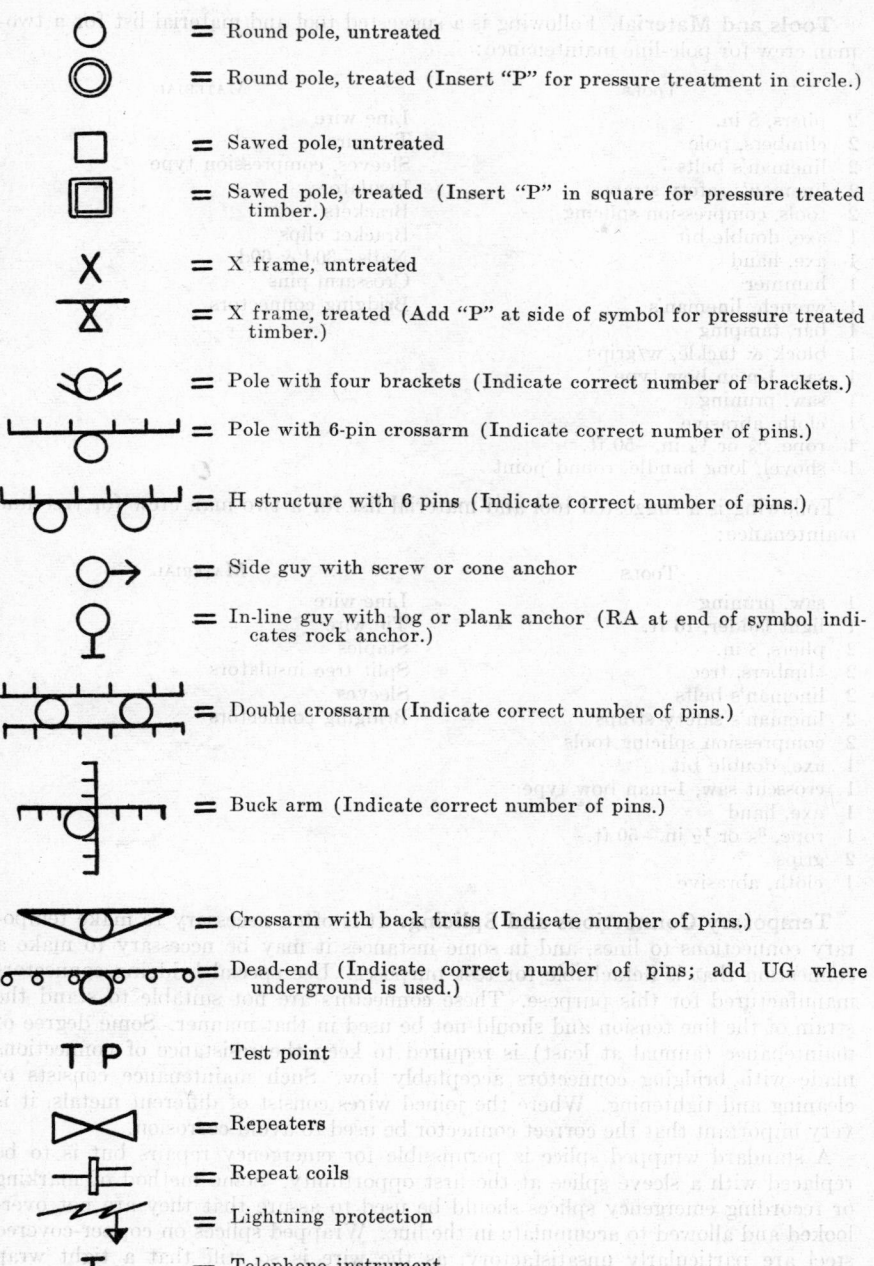

| | |
|---|---|
| ○ | = Round pole, untreated |
| ◎ | = Round pole, treated (Insert "P" for pressure treatment in circle.) |
| □ | = Sawed pole, untreated |
| ▣ | = Sawed pole, treated (Insert "P" in square for pressure treated timber.) |
| X | = X frame, untreated |
| X̅ | = X frame, treated (Add "P" at side of symbol for pressure treated timber.) |
| | = Pole with four brackets (Indicate correct number of brackets.) |
| | = Pole with 6-pin crossarm (Indicate correct number of pins.) |
| | = H structure with 6 pins (Indicate correct number of pins.) |
| O→ | = Side guy with screw or cone anchor |
| φ | = In-line guy with log or plank anchor (RA at end of symbol indicates rock anchor.) |
| | = Double crossarm (Indicate correct number of pins.) |
| | = Buck arm (Indicate correct number of pins.) |
| | = Crossarm with back truss (Indicate number of pins.) |
| | = Dead-end (Indicate correct number of pins; add UG where underground is used.) |
| T P | Test point |
| | = Repeaters |
| | = Repeat coils |
| | = Lightning protection |
| T | = Telephone instrument |

**Fig. 28. Symbols for mapping telephone lines.**

**Tools and Material.** Following is a suggested tool and material list for a two-man crew for pole-line maintenance:

| Tools | Material |
|---|---|
| 2 pliers, 8 in. | Line wire |
| 2 climbers, pole | Tie wire |
| 2 lineman's belts | Sleeves, compression type |
| 2 lineman's safety straps | Insulators |
| 2 tools, compression splicing | Brackets |
| 1 axe, double bit | Bracket clips |
| 1 axe, hand | Nails—30d & 60d |
| 1 hammer | Crossarm pins |
| 1 wrench, lineman's | Bridging connectors |
| 1 bar, tamping | |
| 1 block & tackle, w/grips | |
| 1 saw, 1-man bow type | |
| 1 saw, pruning | |
| 1 cloth, abrasive | |
| 1 rope, ⅜ or ½ in.—50 ft. | |
| 1 shovel, long handle, round point | |

Following is a suggested tool and material list for a two-man crew for tree-line maintenance:

| Tools | Material |
|---|---|
| 1 saw, pruning | Line wire |
| 1 light ladder, 16 ft. | Tie wire |
| 2 pliers, 8 in. | Staples |
| 2 climbers, tree | Split tree insulators |
| 2 lineman's belts | Sleeves |
| 2 lineman's safety straps | Bridging connectors |
| 2 compression splicing tools | |
| 1 axe, double bit | |
| 1 crosscut saw, 1-man bow type | |
| 1 axe, hand | |
| 1 rope, ⅜ or ½ in.—50 ft. | |
| 2 grips | |
| 1 cloth, abrasive | |

**Temporary Connections and Splicing.** It is often necessary to make temporary connections to lines, and in some instances it may be necessary to make a connection that is detachable for test purposes. Use special bridging connectors manufactured for this purpose. These connectors are not suitable to stand the strain of the line tension and should not be used in that manner. Some degree of maintenance (annual at least) is required to keep the resistance of connections made with bridging connectors acceptably low. Such maintenance consists of cleaning and tightening. Where the joined wires consist of different metals, it is very important that the correct connector be used to avoid corrosion.

A standard wrapped splice is permissible for emergency repairs but is to be replaced with a sleeve splice at the first opportunity. Some method of marking or recording emergency splices should be used to assure that they are not overlooked and allowed to accumulate in the line. Wrapped splices on copper-covered steel are particularly unsatisfactory, as the wire is so stiff that a tight wrap cannot be made without damaging the wire.

The following instructions are for the use of the compression tools listed in Table 6. Manufacturers of other tools and materials issue instructions for the use of their products. All sleeves and tools are stamped with identifying numbers and letters. The sleeve, in addition to a stock number, is stamped with the groove letter, the tool by number and letter (as "51 PJ"), and the tool groove by letter (as "P"). The groove letter is found on one side of the jaw, close to the corresponding groove. The groove letter on the jaw should always correspond with the letter on the sleeve. Always be sure the letters are identified before applying compression.

Compression-type splices require that the ends of both wires be clean for slightly more than half the length of the sleeve. This is necessary regardless of whether the wire is old or new. Use abrasive paper made especially for this purpose, No. 00 emery cloth, or a fine grade of steel wool. Do not scrape with a knife or wear through the galvanizing or copper coating.

## SAFETY RULES. Construction and Repairs.

### Climbing

1. Examine poles (especially at the ground line for rot) for safe condition before climbing. Test them by vigorous pushing.
2. Make sure that spurs are properly fitted to the leg.
3. Check before using to be sure lineman's equipment is in good condition.
   a. Gaffs properly sharpened and of correct length.
   b. Climbers and straps dependable and properly fitted to climber.
   c. Safety strap and belt checked for cuts, cracks, sticking, riveting, and pliability.
4. When climbing poles or trees, take short steps, place spur and gaff forcefully where they will not slip. As each step in climbing is made, make a deliberate and forceable step with knee bowed out. Avoid cracks, knots, nails, signs, or other objects which will cause slipping. (Signs or nails should not be placed on poles.)
5. Lineman's safety tool belt with safety strap properly adjusted to pole or tree to be climbed will be worn while off the ground. The strap should be adjusted by the lineman after he has started his climb by having both climber spurs firmly imbedded in the tree or pole.
   The safety strap should not be around pole or tree while lineman is moving up or down.
6. Do not jump from trees or poles when wearing spurs. Horseplay has no place in climbing or other line work.
7. Use extreme caution when climbing icy, frozen, cracked, knotty, rotten, crooked, case-hardened, or especially soft poles or trees.
8. Never climb a pole which has a metal or wooden sign on it until the sign has been removed.
9. It is advisable to wear serviceable work gloves while climbing.

### Working aloft

1. Safety straps should be fastened at all times when working aloft.
2. Crossarms, braces, pins, and small limbs should not be used for support. Use a safety strap around that portion of the pole above the top crossarm only when the pole is 15 in. or more higher than the crossarm.
3. Use hand lines to pass tools, equipment, and materials to and from lineman or to rehand wire in insulators.
4. Ground workers shall keep out from underneath tree or pole workers.

### Inspection

1. Inspect lineman's belt for worn, hard, or dry leather, worn or broken sewing, loose rivets, worn buckles, rollers, and tongues. Replace when in doubt as to its serviceability.

2. See that gaffs are kept sharp and pole spurs are replaced when gaffs are less than 1⅛ in. long (measured on the under side). Discard tree spurs when less than 3 in. long.

### Equipment

1. It is generally safer to use pole spurs on small, thin-barked trees. Tree spurs should be used for rough, thick-barked trees.
2. Use of steel core safety rope is optional.
3. Do not use substitute material, such as ropes, wire, etc., for temporary repairs. Obtain new parts.
4. Safety belts and straps shall not be spliced.

### Maintenance

1. Guard against "flip" when wire is cut or released from overhanging trees, branches, stumps, etc.
2. Guard the eyes from loose wire ends.

## Poles.

### Loading and transporting

1. Provide substantial, nonslipping, and well-braced skids where hand loading is necessary. Eliminate heavy lifting.
2. When hauling poles, except after distribution has started along pole right-of-way, see that they are securely chained while the vehicle is in motion. Attach a red flag to the rear end of the longest pole. Prohibit riders on pole loads and anyone walking alongside the load while the poles are being distributed.

   a. No one should ride on top of a load of poles and no one whose presence is not required should stand on the load when unloading and distributing poles.

   b. Do not wear climbers when working on stepped poles.

### Raising

1. Inspect pike poles and arches (hook ladders) for serviceable condition.
2. When raising long poles, extend holding lines from near their tops in order to steady them.
3. Hold poles with two peaveys to prevent roll when being raised with pike poles.
4. If there is danger of a pole falling, line wires from a pole should not be cut without first guying or bracing.
5. Do not stand on butt of pole to force it into the hole when pole is being raised.
6. Keep in the clear when a man is working on the pole.

## Tree Lines.

1. Do not work or loiter under trees which are being limbed.
2. Exercise great care when limbing a tree to avoid cutting your safety belt line.
3. Examine all hand lines frequently to insure their soundness.
4. Use pruning saws wherever possible. Extensions are a valuable aid.

## Wire.

### Hanging wire

1. In working on lines paralleling high voltage lines, wear rubber gloves and use insulated tools, as these lines often become charged with static electricity.
2. When repairing breaks on such lines, ground the line on both sides of the break before starting work.
3. Line workers should not contact wire during overhead or nearby lightning storms.
4. Use chains to ground a line by throwing a chain over the wire on each side of the break and securing it to the ground by a bar pick or similar tool.

**Stringing wire**

1. In using come-alongs, be sure to keep in the clear so that in case of a slip or breakage the ends of the wire will not whip against you.
2. Do not wear climbers while working on the ground, or when using a ladder.

## BIBLIOGRAPHY

CIVIL AERONAUTICS ADMINISTRATION. 1950. *Flight information manual.* Vol. 4, No. 2. U. S. Dept. Commerce, Washington, D. C.

FEDERAL COMMUNICATIONS COMMISSION. 1953. *Radio service rules and regulations* (revised). U. S. Dept. Commerce, Washington, D. C.

*Federal Register.* May 6, 1949. General Services Administration, Washington, D. C.

*Federal Register.* November 6, 1949.

U. S. FOREST SERV. 1947. *Telephone handbook.*

WESTERN ELECTRIC Co. Catalogue numbers.

# CHEMISTRY AND PHYSICS OF WOOD

## CONTENTS

# CHEMISTRY AND PHYSICS OF WOOD

## Chemistry of Wood

A wood cell is a cavity surrounded by a rigid wall. The outside of this wall is called the primary wall; the inside, the secondary wall. A common layer between cells, called the intercellular substance, cements them together.

The cell wall and the intercellular layer consist principally of cellulose, lignin, and hemicellulose. The bulk of the cellulose is found in the secondary wall; lignin occurs largely in the primary wall and the intercellular layer, but to a limited extent also in the secondary wall. Hemicelluloses are thought to be associated with submicroscopic units of cellulose, called fibrils, found mainly in the secondary walls.

A number of extraneous substances may be present in wood, residing largely in the cell cavities and varying widely among species. These include tannins, acids, fats, oils, sugars, proteins, and others. These substances may be removed with suitable solvents without affecting the residual wall.

A small amount of mineral residue results from the burning of wood. This is called ash.

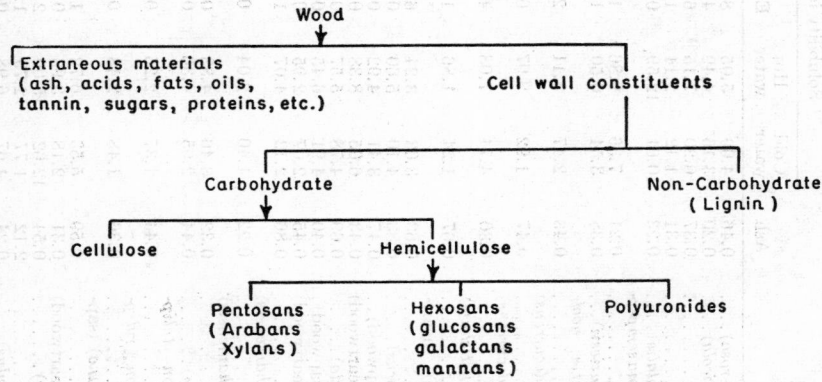

**Fig. 1. Chart of the chemical components of wood.**

It should not be inferred from the chart that the groups listed necessarily exist as separate entities. Some of the groups may be in co-existence, since it is not always possible to separate easily the constituents into clear chemical entities.

## COLOR REACTIONS WITH CHEMICALS AND COLORIMETRIC IDENTIFICATION. Phloroglucinol Reagent.

The reagent most frequently used in the test for lignified or woody tissue is phloroglucinol reagent (Wiesner reagent), which gives a reddish-purple coloration with lignin-containing materials. The reaction is carried out by first moistening the plant material with dilute hydrochloric acid (dil. HCl) and then applying to it an aqueous solution of the

**Table 1. Chemical Analyses of Some Common Woods** (Expressed in percentages)

| Species | Ash | Solubility in | | | | Acetic acid | Methoxyl | Pentosan | Cellulose | Lignin | In cellulose | |
|---|---|---|---|---|---|---|---|---|---|---|---|---|
| | | Cold water | Hot water | Ether | 1% NaOH | | | | | | Pentosan | Alpha cellulose |
| Ponderosa pine (*Pinus ponderosa*) | 0.46 | 4.09 | 5.05 | 8.52 | 20.30 | 1.09 | 4.49 | 7.35 | 57.41 | 26.65 | 6.82 | 62.10 |
| Western white pine (*P. monticola*) | 0.20 | 3.16 | 4.49 | 4.26 | 14.78 | 1.30 | 4.56 | 6.97 | 59.71 | 26.44 | 5.33 | 64.61 |
| Longleaf pine (*P. palustris*) | 0.37 | 6.20 | 7.15 | 6.32 | 22.36 | 0.76 | 5.05 | 7.46 | 58.48 | | 7.71 | |
| White spruce (*Picea glauca*) | 0.31 | 1.12 | 2.14 | 1.36 | 11.57 | 1.59 | 5.30 | 10.39 | 61.85 | | 9.63 | |
| Western larch (*Larix occidentalis*) | 0.23 | 10.61 | 12.59 | 0.81 | 22.14 | 0.71 | 5.03 | 10.80 | 57.80 | | 8.94 | |
| Redwood (heartwood) (*Sequoia sempervirens*) | 0.21 | 7.36 | 9.86 | 1.07 | 20.00 | 1.08 | 5.21 | 7.80 | 48.45 | 34.21 | 7.40 | 78.81 |
| Douglas-fir (*Pseudotsuga menziesii*) | 0.38 | 3.54 | 6.50 | 1.02 | 16.11 | 1.04 | 4.95 | 6.02 | 61.47 | | 5.34 | |
| Alaska-cedar (*Chamaecyparis nootkatensis*) | 0.43 | 2.47 | 3.11 | 2.55 | 13.41 | 1.59 | 5.25 | 7.87 | 53.86 | 31.32 | 7.30 | 62.68 |
| Incense-cedar (*Libocedrus decurrens*) (sapwood) | 0.47 | 1.92 | 2.97 | 0.67 | 11.16 | 1.33 | 5.95 | 12.08 | 49.09 | 34.73 | 10.14 | 50.69 |
| Incense-cedar (*Libocedrus decurrens*) (heartwood) | 0.30 | 4.74 | 7.08 | 4.78 | 19.99 | 0.68 | 6.21 | 12.04 | 44.53 | 33.67 | 11.88 | 66.62 |
| Baldcypress (*Taxodium distichum*) (sapwood) | 0.67 | 1.24 | 1.86 | 1.52 | 9.59 | 0.71 | 4.67 | 8.63 | 52.90 | 35.16 | 6.07 | 67.14 |
| Baldcypress (*T. distichum*) (heartwood) | 0.63 | 3.03 | 3.24 | 6.40 | 12.08 | 0.34 | 4.01 | 7.28 | 51.14 | 32.67 | 6.09 | 67.11 |
| Tanoak (*Lithocarpus densiflorus*) | 0.83 | 4.10 | 5.60 | 0.80 | 23.96 | 5.23 | 5.74 | 19.59 | 58.03 | 24.85 | 22.82 | 56.77 |
| White oak (*Quercus alba*) (sapwood) | 0.47 | 3.41 | 4.92 | 0.56 | 21.44 | 2.96 | 5.99 | 22.49 | 51.36 | 31.74 | 24.78 | 60.94 |
| White oak (*Quercus alba*) (heartwood) | 0.43 | 6.05 | 8.38 | 0.67 | 24.24 | 2.78 | 5.91 | 21.95 | 50.40 | 32.02 | 24.38 | 60.15 |
| Shagbark hickory (*Carya ovata*) | 0.69 | 4.78 | 5.57 | 0.63 | 19.04 | 2.51 | 5.63 | 18.82 | 56.22 | 23.44 | 21.89 | 76.32 |
| Pignut hickory (*C. glabra*) (sapwood) | 0.40 | 4.91 | 6.45 | 0.29 | 19.11 | 3.58 | 5.56 | 18.18 | 56.08 | 21.87 | 16.90 | 51.55 |
| Pignut hickory (*C. glabra*) (heartwood) | 0.45 | 2.07 | 2.95 | 0.36 | 15.10 | 3.08 | 5.79 | 18.64 | 58.81 | 22.85 | 16.20 | 59.44 |
| Basswood (*Tilia americana*) | 0.86 | 2.12 | 4.07 | 1.96 | 23.76 | 5.79 | 6.00 | 19.93 | 61.24 | | 24.28 | |
| Yellow birch (*Betula alleghaniensis*) (sapwood) | 0.22 | 1.40 | 2.04 | 0.68 | 18.28 | 3.05 | 5.57 | 21.83 | 57.74 | 26.23 | 21.46 | 52.28 |
| Yellow birch (*Betula alleghaniensis*) (heartwood) | 0.32 | 3.46 | 4.83 | 0.90 | 20.83 | 2.31 | 5.37 | 21.79 | 55.91 | 26.38 | 21.84 | 57.37 |
| Sugar maple (*Acer saccharum*) | 0.44 | 2.65 | 4.36 | 0.25 | 17.64 | 4.46 | 7.25 | 21.71 | 60.78 | | 24.48 | |
| Yellow-poplar (*Liriodendron tulipifera*) (sapwood) | 0.44 | 1.37 | 2.25 | 0.20 | 16.83 | 3.23 | 5.85 | 18.60 | 58.08 | 23.47 | 17.27 | 42.23 |
| Yellow-poplar (*Liriodendron tulipifera*) (heartwood) | 0.36 | 1.48 | 2.48 | 0.51 | 17.64 | 2.81 | 5.95 | 18.78 | 59.52 | 22.94 | 16.40 | 48.99 |
| White ash (*Fraxinus americana*) (sapwood) | 0.59 | 5.53 | 6.72 | 1.03 | 21.85 | 3.47 | 5.18 | 20.01 | 50.05 | 27.17 | 19.25 | 64.89 |
| White ash (*F. americana*) (heartwood) | 0.31 | 2.18 | 3.93 | 0.45 | 19.28 | 2.49 | 5.28 | 19.89 | 53.43 | 27.89 | 17.05 | 53.57 |
| Mesquite (*Prosopis juliflora*) | 0.54 | 12.62 | 15.09 | 2.30 | 28.52 | 2.03 | 5.55 | 13.96 | 45.58 | 30.47 | 17.75 | 76.48 |
| Balsa (*Ochroma lagopus*) | 2.12 | 1.77 | 2.79 | 1.23 | 20.37 | 5.80 | 5.68 | 17.65 | 54.15 | 26.50 | 19.99 | 75.64 |
| Eucalyptus (*Eucalyptus globulus*) | 0.24 | 4.67 | 6.98 | 0.56 | 18.57 | 1.85 | 6.73 | 20.09 | 57.62 | 25.07 | 20.96 | 68.86 |

phenol. If desired, 1 gm. of phloroglucinol can be dissolved in 25 ml. of water and 25 ml. conc. HCl and used when freshly prepared (smaller amounts in proportion can be prepared).

**Mäule Reaction.** The Mäule reaction can be used to separate gymnosperms from angiosperms. Lignified material when left in 1 percent $KMnO_4$ solution for 5 min., washed, treated with dil. HCl, washed, and then immersed in an ammonia solution acquires a deep red color with angiospermous woods but only an indefinite yellowish or brownish color with gymnosperms. Chlorine water can be used in place of $KMnO_4$ and HCl, and any alkali or organic base can replace ammonia, but usually not with advantage.

**Methanol-Hydrochloric Acid.** A reagent which may prove of considerable value in the separation of anatomically similar species is methanol-hydrochloric acid, which is made with 25 ml. conc. HCl in 1,000 ml. MeOH. The test is made in a test tube on a small amount of shavings with 5–10 ml. of the reagent.

In certain species purple color appears in 10–15 min., but in other cases it is not evident until several hours have elapsed. For comparison it is best to wait a standard (and sufficient) length of time before describing the color. The intensity of coloration may be of aid in delimiting the usefulness of the test.

In the genus *Acer*, all the species examined, except boxelder (*Acer negundo*) and its varieties, gave an intense purple color in a short period. The pith of young twigs of box elder, as well as wood which had inner bark attached, gave the purple color.

**Color Tests for Differentiating Heartwood and Sapwood of Certain Oaks, Pines, and Douglas-Fir.** (U. S. Forest Service, Forest Products Lab., 1948.) Three chemical color tests have been developed by which sapwood and heartwood of certain oaks, pines, and Douglas-fir can be readily differentiated. They consist of the application of a small amount of chemical solution across the grain of the wood. The chemical used depends upon the kind of wood to be tested.

**Test for oaks.** The chemical solution used to distinguish heartwood from sapwood in oak is Taylor's concentrated Benzo Yellow pH indicator, a chemical used for making acidity tests. Its reaction to the more acid heartwood and to the less acid sapwood produces the characteristic color differentiation. The heartwood stains red and the sapwood yellow. A minute or longer may be required for the full development of color. Occasionally the red heartwood color occurs mainly in the wood rays, and in such cases a hand lens will aid in observing it.

The chemical has been found to give generally good results with Oregon white oak, white oak, chestnut oak, swamp chestnut oak, northern red oak, black oak, scarlet oak, and roble (*Quercus copeyensis*), a Costa Rican species of oak. It apparently is about equally effective on green and on seasoned wood. Indefinite or erratic results may be obtained, however, when it is applied to wood treated with preservative chemicals, to wood exposed to long weathering, or to wood infected by stain or decay fungi, molds, or the organisms present in "sour" logs. Consequently, the test is not recommended for use under any of these conditions.

**Test for pines.** In the pines, the boundary between heartwood and sapwood is frequently difficult to recognize with certainty. A chemical solution found to be effective in distinguishing between southern yellow pine, lodgepole pine, and red pine, and which gives fairly good results with western white pine, sugar pine, and ponderosa pine as well, can be made as follows:

Dissolve 5 gm. of benzidine in 23 cc. of 25 percent hydrochloric acid and 970 cc. of water. (Note: concentrated c.p. hydrochloric acid contains about 38 percent of the acid; to make a 25 percent solution, pour out 25 cc. of chemically pure concentrated acid and add to it enough water to make 38 cc. of liquid.) Next, prepare a 10 percent solution of sodium nitrite.

When ready to make tests on wood, mix the two prepared solutions in equal amounts. When the mixture is applied to the wood, color reaction takes place in a few moments, the sapwood appearing yellowish brown and the heartwood red. The mixture, as tested so far, does not produce useful colorations on beech, oak, larch, the spruces, Douglas-fir, or the true firs.

**Test for Douglas-fir.** The heartwood and sapwood of Douglas-fir can usually be differentiated with a 0.75 percent water solution of sodium alizarine-sulfate (Alizarine Red S; Alizarine carmine). This indicator, which changes color in the pH range of about 3.7 to 5.2, stains heartwood yellow and the sapwood pink, or some other shade of red. The indicator works on both dry and green wood, and the colors are comparatively permanent. There is some evidence that the test works best on a freshly exposed surface. A little alcohol added to the solution will make it wet dry wood more rapidly.

**Table 2. Composition of Wood Ash ***

| | Ash, % | CaO | K₂O | Na₂O | MgO | Fe₂O₃ | SiO₂ | P₂O₅ | SO₃ | Cl |
|---|---|---|---|---|---|---|---|---|---|---|
| *Acer platanoides*.... | 0.3–0.4 | 21.0–44.0 | 20.0–30.0 | | 14.0–15.0 | | | 14.0–20.0 | | |
| *Fraxinus americana*. | 0.43 | 17.7 | 34.7 | 0.94 | 0.45 | 2.9 | 7.05 | 2.7 | 8.6 | 0.26 |
| *Larix europaea*..... | 0.2 | 33–62 | 18–30 | 1.0–2.7 | 12.0–17.0 | | 2.0–3.0 | 5.0–10.0 | 1.5–3.3 | |
| *Pinus palustris*..... | 0.49 | 37.2 | 10.3 | 2.3 | 4.2 | 2.7 | 3.4 | 2.65 | 4.3 | 0.2 |
| *Pinus sylvestris*..... | 0.3–0.6 | 50 | 15 | | 9 | | 2 | 9 | 4 | |
| *Quercus alba*....... | 0.37 | 21.2 | 29.9 | 1.94 | 2.43 | 0.5 | 3.2 | 6.7 | 4.1 | 1.0 |

* The composition of wood ash is variable even within species. The principal metallic constituents are calcium, magnesium, and potassium, and the acid radicals are usually carbonate, silicate, and phosphate. Small amounts of sodium, iron, manganese, and aluminum are always present, and trace amounts of many other elements may be present. As many as 27 different elements have been found in the ash of both *Pinus strobus* and *Pinus monticola*.

# Chemical Products of Wood

**TANNINS.** Vegetable tannins are used for the manufacture of heavy leathers, such as sole leather, in the drilling of oil wells to control the viscosity and water loss of drilling fluids, in water treatment, in flotation of certain ores, as antioxidants in edible fats, and in iron gallotannate ink. The tannin consumption in the United States averages about 150,000 tons annually. Domestic sources provide a little more than half of this, but imports are increasing steadily.

The chief domestic source of tannin was the wood of chestnut (*Castanea dentata*) from the Appalachian area. This constituted about 25 percent of our consumption. This source is now practically exhausted owing to the chestnut blight.

The bark of eastern hemlock (*Tsuga canadensis*) is an important source of tannin. The bark is stripped into pieces 4-ft. long and in various widths up to 18 in.

Well-seasoned bark should have a moisture content of 20 percent or less, oven-dry basis; wetter bark cannot be stored in bulk without deterioration. Bark from water-driven logs is not acceptable owing to loss of tannin by leaching. A cord of dry bark weighs slightly more than a ton. The two general methods of extracting tannin from bark are the open tank diffusion and the percolation methods.

Barks of various oaks are also important sources of tannin. The principal species used are chestnut oak (*Quercus prinus*) and tanoak (*Lithocarpus densiflora*). The bark is stripped into 4-ft. pieces. Possible future domestic sources include western hemlock bark, second-growth Douglas-fir bark, mangrove bark (*Rhizophora mangle*) from Florida, sumac leaves, canaigre root (*Rumex hymenosepalus*), and redwood.

**CHARCOAL.** A certain amount of the charcoal made in the United States is produced in pit kilns and portable ovens. Most of the charcoal, however, results from destructive distillation of wood. The species used in pit kilns and portable ovens are lodgepole, shortleaf, and Virginia pine, beech, birch, hickory, maple, and oaks. Billets of wood 3 to 4 ft. long and 2 to 6 in. in diameter are at least partially air-seasoned for best results.

The carbonization time depends on the size of kiln, the moisture content of the wood, the species, and weather conditions. It may take 2 to 5 days for a few cords to 2 weeks for a 30- to 50-cord pile. The yield is about 30 to 40 bushels of charcoal per cord, where 20 lb. is considered a bushel. Charcoal weighs about ¼ the original dry weight of wood and occupies ½ the space.

**Hardwood Destructive Distillation Products.** The principal species used for hardwood distillation are maple, beech, birch, oak, hickory, black cherry, ash, elm. Minor species that are used include poplar, willow, basswood, hophornbeam, sourwood, black walnut, dogwood.

Two processes are used: (1) the usual batch process, in which cordwood is the raw material, and (2) the Badger-Stafford continuous process, which uses chips or hogged wood. The cordwood is cut to lengths of 4 to 5 ft. and pieces exceeding 6 to 7 inches in diameter are split; bark is not removed and unsound wood is rejected. The wood is seasoned, preferably for 1 yr. unless predryers heated with flue gases are available.

The process consists essentially of heating the dried or partially dried wood in a retort with a limited amount of air. The products, besides water, are noncondensable gases, pyroligneous acid, tars, and charcoal. About 900 lb. of charcoal are obtained per cord of wood. Principal uses are for fuel, briquets, and activated carbon.

**SOFTWOOD DESTRUCTIVE DISTILLATION PRODUCTS.** The species used are longleaf and slash pines. The material used is principally resinous heartwood from fallen trees, logs, and stumps that are so old that the sapwood has rotted away. Slabs from trees tapped for naval stores are also used. This material is cut into 4-ft. lengths and seasoned if not already dry. Destructive distillation yields charcoal (900 lb./cd.), turpentine (7–12 gal./cd.), pine oil (1½–4 gal./cd.), dipentene, pine tar (50 gal./cd.), tar oils (12 gal./cd.), and pitch, but little methanol or acetic acid.

**MAPLE SYRUP AND SUGAR.** Practically all commercial production of these products is from sugar maple and black maple. Sap flow begins from the middle of February in the southern part of the commercial range and the middle of March toward its northern limits. Ideal weather has daytime temperatures of 40 to 50° F. and cold nights with temperatures below freezing. During a season, which lasts an average of 4 to 6 weeks, there are usually several runs of a few days duration each.

Trees to be tapped should be more than 8 in. in diameter. Trees more than 12 in. in diameter may have two tap holes and those exceeding 20 in., three tap holes. The ideal mature stand of sugar maple should contain 50 to 60 trees per acre, but the average number of trees is usually 30 or less.

Maple sap at flow is 90 to 98 percent water and 0.5 to 10 percent solids, of which 90 percent is sucrose. The average sucrose in sap is 2 to 3 percent. The average yield of sap per tree per season is 10 to 20 gal. but may go as high as 40 gal. It has been found that the yield of sap is in direct relation to the size of the crown of the tree.

Maple syrup must contain not less than 65 percent total solids (of which about 95 percent is sucrose) and weigh not less than 11 lb. per gal. Syrup of standard density, when cooled to 60° F., should have a Baumé reading of 35.6°. The color varies from light straw to a very dark reddish-brown. The best grade has the lightest color. Normally 40 to 50 gal. of sap are required to make 1 gal. of syrup.

Maple sugar is produced by further concentration of the syrup. Soft sugar is produced by boiling until a temperature of 238° to 240° F. is reached and then stirring continuously during cooling. Hard sugar comes from boiling at temperatures of 242° to 245° F. and stirring rapidly while cooling. One gallon of syrup gives 6½ to 9 lb. of sugar.

**MEDICINALS AND PHARMACEUTICALS. 1. Cascara.** Cascara sagrada, a powerful drug used primarily as a laxative, is prepared from the bark of cascara (*Rhamnus purshiana*). The usual practice is to peel the trees in the late spring and early summer when the cambium is active. Good practice is to remove only one-fouth to one-third of the bark and not to have the incised portions too close. The peeled bark is dried, broken into small pieces, and sacked for shipment to drug houses.

**2. Creosote (wood).** Wood creosote, an oily antiseptic liquid obtained by the distillation of wood tar, especially that of beechwood, is a complex mixture of various phenols, principally guaiacol and cresol, and their ethers. The fraction used begins to boil at approximately 203° C. and at least 90 percent by volume distills between 203° and 220° C. Specific gravity should not be less than $1.076^{25/25}$.

**3. Tar oil.** Tar oil is the volatile oil from pine tar rectified by steam distillation. It is a thin, dark reddish-brown liquid whose chief active constituents are phenolic substances. It has a strong empyreumatic odor and taste. It is insoluble in water but miscible with alcohol; sp. gr. $0.960-0.990^{25/25}$.

**4. Sassafras oil.** Oil of sassafras is obtained from the roots and stumps (primarily the root bark, 6 to 9 percent oil) of sassafras (*Sassafras albidum*) by steam distillation. The stumps are cut into small chips, which are placed in large retorts with a capacity of as much as 10 tons. The average yield is 20 lb. per ton of chips.

**5. Birch oil.** Birch oil is identical with wintergreen oil and is now the chief source of the natural oil. The bark of sweet birch (*Betula lenta*) contains the glucoside which is hydrolyzed to the oil. A ton of bark produces 5 lb. of birch oil and a cord of branches and stems about 4 lb.

6. **Black cherry bark.** Wild black cherry bark is collected in the autumn from *Prunus serotina.* It contains prunasin. It is used chiefly in the form of syrup as a vehicle for cough medicine.

7. **White pine bark.** The dried inner bark of eastern white pine (*Pinus strobus*) is used in small amounts. It must not contain more than 1.5 percent outer bark, 0.2 percent other foreign organic matter, and 0.5 percent acid-insoluble ash.

8. **Witch hazel.** The bark of witch hazel (*Hamamelis virginiana*) contains a volatile oil which can be prepared by steam distillation.

9. **Populi gemmi.** Populi gemmi is obtained from the buds of balsam poplar (*Populus balsamifera*) and its variety, balm of Gilead. The resinous exudation has a peculiar, agreeable, balsamic odor and a bitter, balsamic, somewhat pungent taste.

10. **Storax.** Storax is a yellowish, fragrant, balsamic liquid or gum obtained in this country from sweetgum (*Liquidambar styraciflua*). The tree is ringed part way around about 2 ft. from the ground in early spring and the bark peeled off. The gum is scraped from the surface every 2 to 3 weeks and a new ring cut. The exudate is heated over a slow fire in a trench, strained, and put in a can where it solidifies like beeswax. About ½ to 1 lb. of storax can be obtained per tree.

11. **Canada balsam.** Canada balsam (or turpentine) is obtained from the bark blisters on balsam fir (*Abies balsamea*). The oleoresin is collected by puncturing the blisters in dry weather from June to snowfall. About 150 blisters yield 1 pint. The yellowish viscous liquid ultimately dries to a transparent resinous substance. Its main use is for cementing in optical equipment and as a mounting medium in microscopy. Sp. gr. 0.987–0.994. $n^{20/4}$ 1.52–1.54.

12. **Oregon balsam.** Oregon balsam is obtained from bole cavities of wind-shaken Douglas-fir trees (*Pseudotsuga menziesii*). As much as 1 to 3 gal. comes from a single pocket. The trees can be spotted from one-sided crowns and bent trunks. This oleoresin cannot be used in microscopic work because of its low index of refraction.

13. **Conifer leaf oils.** Conifer leaf oils are prepared from species such as black and white spruce, eastern hemlock, arborvitae, and redcedar. The leaves and young twigs are cut to ½ to 1 in. lengths in a chopper and steam distilled for 5 to 8 hr. to obtain the oil.

14. **Cedar leaf oil.** Cedar leaf oil is steam distilled from arborvitae leaves and twigs. About 30 lb. of oil are obtained per ton of leaves. Sp. gr. 0.910–0.920. $n^{20}$ 1.4560–1.4590. The action of fenchone and thujone, the important constituents of this oil, is similar to that of camphor oil.

**DYES.** 1. **Extracts of Osage-orange** (*Maclura pomifera*) contain dyeing principals giving yellow shades with mordants, and could very well be used in the textile and leather industries.

2. **Quercitrin** is obtained from the inner bark of black oak (*Quercus velutina*). The bark is removed from the tree, dried, and ground. The fine powder of a yellow or buff color contains the dyeing principal. The hot extract should be prepared for immediate use. A mordant is used. It is used in cotton and woolen printing. A very fine buff or brown powder called quercetin is prepared from quercitron bark by acid hydrolysis. Its coloring property greatly exceeds that of the bark.

**WOOD OILS AND GUMS.** 1. **Cedarwood oil.** Cedarwood oil is obtained by steam distillation of the heartwood of eastern, southern, and Mexican red-cedars. The yield is 2.5 to 4.5 percent oil. A volatile oil can also be obtained from Port-Orford-cedar.

2. **Spruce gum.** Spruce gum is an exudation resulting from injuries to the sapwood of various eastern spruces (*Picea* ssp.). It takes about 5 yr. to form a hard, brittle, amberlike gum, but it darkens if left too long on the tree. The territory can be reworked every 5 to 7 yr. Spruce gum is sold in lump and chip grades based on clearness and weight. It is cleaned by steaming and straining. Small amounts go into a spruce chewing gum and medicinals.

3. **Turpentine and pine oil.** Longleaf pine and slash pine stumps are pulled and hogged to make chips which are steam distilled to give turpentine and some pine oil. They may also be extracted with a solvent such as gasoline. This process gives about 400 lb. rosin, 8 gal. turpentine, 3.5 gal. pine oil, and 1.5 gal. monocyclic hydrocarbons per ton of chips. Pine oil is not obtained in gum oleoresin.

4. **Sulfate turpentine.** In the kraft pulping of hard pines sulfate turpentine is obtained in yield of 0.5 to 2 gal./cd.

5. **Tall oil.** Tall oil, a by-product from the pine kraft pulp industry, is largely a mixture of resin and fatty acids. It is obtained as skimmings from the spent liquor and may be redistilled to give purer fatty acids and resin acids and phytosterols.

6. **Cymene.** Sulfite turpentine or crude cymene is recovered from the condensed relief gases of the sulfite digester in yields ranging from ⅓ to 1 gal. per ton of pulp. The principal source is spruce and balsam fir, but it may be obtained from pine sapwood if it is pulped.

7. **Mucic acid and galactan.** The wood of western larch (*Larix occidentalis*) contains variable amounts (up to about 15 percent) of a water-soluble polysaccharide known as arabogalactan. This substance tends to be concentrated in the butt logs. The logs are chipped and extracted with water, the arabogalactan is then hydrolyzed and oxidized to mucic acid, which may be substituted for tartaric acid in certain cases.

## Physics of Wood

The physical properties of wood are such that it has been used by man since the beginning of time. Because of those properties, it is suited to a wide variety of uses, and by those same properties unsuited to certain other uses. Wood is strong for its weight, it is little affected by temperature changes, it is easily worked into various shapes, and easily fastened together by nail or screw. It does not rust and it absorbs shock and vibration. Some woods are ornamental without finish, while all woods are readily painted or varnished. On the other hand, wood is limited in hardness and strength and varies in its strength properties. It decays, burns, swells, and shrinks with moisture changes, splits easily, and is susceptible to insect damage and rot.

The anatomical structure of wood is extremely complex, and its physical properties vary, not only between different species, but within species and even within the parts of an individual tree.

**SPECIFIC GRAVITY OF WOOD. Definition:** The ratio of the weight of the oven-dry wood to the weight of a volume of water equivalent to the overall volume of the wood. It is numerically the same as the density when the latter is expressed in metric units. Three different specific gravities are used:

1. Dry-volume specific gravity.
2. Current-volume specific gravity.
3. Green (or swollen) volume specific gravity.

Except when used in a qualitative sense, "specific gravity" should always have the proper prefix.

## Approximate Conversion of Green-Volume to Dry-Volume Specific Gravity.

$$\rho_o = \frac{\rho_g}{1 - 0.28\rho_g}$$

where $\rho_o$ is the dry-volume specific gravity
$\rho_g$ is the green-volume specific gravity of the wood

**Common Methods of Determination.** 1. Dry-volume specific gravity: Oven dry, weigh, and measure volume.

2. Current-volume specific gravity: Measure volume, oven dry, and weigh.

3. Green-volume specific gravity: Soak in water until completely swollen, measure volume, oven dry, and weigh.

Material: Rectangular blocks, irregular blocks, sticks, splinters, or borings from a hole.

Oven drying: In oven at 105° C. or 220° F. to constant weight (about 2 hr. for material less than 0.5 in. long in fiber direction, overnight for specimens up to 3 in. long).

Weighing: Weigh to about 0.5 percent accuracy in grams or convert to grams (1 oz. = 28.4 gm.; 1 lb. = 454 gm.).

Measuring dimensions: If the specimens are large rectangles 2 to 3 in. in each direction, the measurements can be made with a rule to about $\frac{1}{64}$-in. accuracy; if smaller, the rectangles should be measured with vernier or micrometer calipers or a dial gauge. The measurements can also be made by collecting the borings from a drilled hole in a board. The volume of the borings can be obtained from the diameter of the drill and the thickness of the board. This method is suitable only for determining the specific gravity at current volume. The measurements should be converted to centimeters if not made in centimeters (1 in. = 2.54 cm.; 1 cu. in. = 16.4 cc.).

Measuring volume directly: By immersion of the wood in stick or splinter form in water in a graduated cylinder and determining the rise in level of the liquid surface, or by immersion of the wood in block form in a pan of water on a balance scale with a sharp rod without the block touching the sides of the container. The added weight to restore balance is the weight of the water displaced and, if in grams, is equal to the volume of the specimen in cubic centimeters.

In the case of green wood, the measurement can be made directly on the sticks, splinters, or blocks, followed by oven drying to determine the weight.

When the oven-dry-volume specific gravity is sought, the wood in stick or block form is first dried and weighed. It is then dipped in molten paraffin to seal the capillaries, scraped to remove any excess of paraffin, and then the volume is measured as just described. Coating with paraffin is not suitable for splinters, as the volume of wax is no longer negligible. In this case soak the oven-dry weighed splinters in kerosene until saturated. Wipe or shake off the excess. Measure the increase in kerosene surface level in a graduated cylinder when the specimens are immersed. The paraffin-coating methods are not suitable for determining the specific gravity at current volume.

Rapid approximate method for directly determining the specific gravity at current volume (Forest Products Lab. Rep. No. 1358): Cut rectangular specimens 0.5 in. square by 5 or 10 in. long, mark length into 10 equal divisions, float upright in cylinder of water. The proportion of the length submerged gives the specific gravity directly. The measurements should be made as rapidly as possible to avoid changes in specific gravity due to absorption of water.

**SPECIFIC GRAVITY OF WOOD SUBSTANCE. Definition:** The ratio of the oven-dry weight of the wood to the weight of a volume of water equivalent to the volume of the solid substance making up the wood. The volume is less than the over-all volume by the volume of the contained air and water.

**Value:** Approximately 1.46 for all woods. The apparent specific gravity of wood substance determined in water (average value about 1.53) is, however, valuable for calculations of void volumes of swollen wood.

**SPECIFIC GRAVITY–VOID VOLUME RELATIONSHIPS.** Fractional Void Volume of Dry Wood: $V_o$.

$$V_o = 1 - \frac{\rho_o}{\rho_s}$$

where $\rho_o$ is the dry-volume specific gravity of the wood
$\rho_s$ is the specific gravity of wood substance, 1.46.

**Fractional Void Volume of Wood at or Above the Fiber-Saturation Point:** $V_g$.

$$V_g = 1 - \rho_g \left( \frac{1}{\rho_a} + m \right)$$

where $\rho_g$ is the green-volume specific gravity of the wood
$\rho_a$ is the apparent specific gravity of the wood substance, 1.53
$m$ is the moisture content of the wood expressed as a fraction of the oven-dry weight.

**SPECIFIC HEAT OF WOOD. Definition:** The ratio of the amount of heat required to raise the temperature of the material by 1° C., and the amount required to raise the temperature of an equal mass of water by 1° C.

**Value:** Approximately 0.266 at 0° C. for all species of wood; independent of specific gravity; increases with increasing temperature.

$$H_s = 0.266 + 0.00116t$$

where $t$ is the average temperature in ° C.

**Comparison with Other Materials.** The specific heat of cellulose is practically the same as that of wood. The specific heat of cement and aluminum are about two-thirds of the value for wood. The values for charcoal and glass are about half the value for wood, and those for the other common metals vary from one-quarter to one-half of the value for wood.

**HEAT CONDUCTIVITY OF WOOD. Definition:** The quantity of heat, $Q$, that flows across unit thickness, $X$, of material with a unit cross section, $A$, under unit temperature differences between faces $(t_2 - t_1)$ in unit time $\theta$, thus

$$K = \frac{QX}{A\theta(t_2 - t_1)}$$

$K$ is in English units when $Q$ is in Btu, $\theta$ in hours, $X$ in feet or inches, $A$ in square feet, and $(t_2 - t_1)$ in ° F. $K$ is in cgs units when $Q$ is in calories, $\theta$ in seconds, $X$ in centimeters, $A$ in square centimeters, and $(t_2 - t_1)$ in °C. To convert English units per inch thickness to cgs units, multiply by 0.000345.

**Values:** These vary with direction. They are slightly greater in the tangential direction than in the radial direction and are 2.25 to 2.75 times greater in the ongitudinal than in the tangential direction. They increase with an increase in the dry-volume specific gravity of the wood, $\rho_o$, and with an increase in the moisture content, $m$. For dry wood in the tangential direction the thermal conductivity in English units, $K$, per inch of thickness is

$$K = \rho_o(1.39 + 0.028m) \quad 0.165$$

where $m$ is the moisture content in percentage below about 40 percent. Above 40 percent moisture content, the moisture content correction factor should be changed from $0.028m$ to $0.038m$.

The thermal conductivity of wood and wood products is compared with other building materials in Table 3. The table shows that wood and its fibrous products are excellent insulators.

**Table 3. Thermal Conductivity of Common Building Materials at Ordinary Temperatures** [a]

| Material | Thermal conductivity [b] |
|---|---|
| Copper | 2,700 |
| Aluminum | 1,400 |
| Steel | 315 |
| Granite | 12–28 |
| Marble | 14–20 |
| Concrete, sand, and stone aggregates | 11–16 |
| Slate | 10 |
| Concrete, cinder aggregates | 4.9 |
| Brick, common building | 4.8 |
| Window glass | 3.6–7.2 |
| Plaster, common building | 3.0 |
| Compressed cement-asbestos board | 2.7 |
| Wood, parallel to grain (sp. gr. 0.35–0.70) | 1.6–2.9 |
| Concrete, blast-furnace aggregate | 1.6 |
| Gypsum board, between layers of paper | 1.4 |
| Composition shingles, felt-bitumen-gravel | 1.33 |
| Asbestos board | 0.8 |
| Wood, across the grain (sp. gr. 0.35–0.70) | 0.65–1.15 |
| Insulating boards, wood and agricultural-waste fibers (sp. gr. 0.15–0.30) | 0.27–0.32 |
| Cork board | 0.27–0.32 |
| Glass wool | 0.27 |
| Fibrous slag | 0.27 |
| Redwood bark | 0.26–0.31 |
| Wood-fiber insulation blankets, between sheets of paper | 0.25–0.27 |
| Hair-fiber insulation blankets, between sheets of paper | 0.25 |
| Cotton-fiber insulation blankets, between sheets of paper | 0.25 |
| Kapok-fiber insulation blankets, between sheets of paper | 0.24 |

[a] In the increasing order of their value as insulators.
[b] Units: Btu/(hr.) (sq. ft.) (°F. per inch).

## COEFFICIENT OF LINEAR THERMAL EXPANSION. Definition:
The increase in length per unit of length for a temperature rise of 1° F.

**Values:** These vary in the three structural directions. In the longitudinal direction they are independent of the specific gravity of the wood and range from $1.7 \times 10^{-6}$ to $2.5 \times 10^{-6}$ per ° F. for different species. Older data do not take into account the effect of specific gravity. Most of them, however, are qualitatively comparable with the more recent values.

Values for normal laminates, plywood, impreg, and compreg can be calculated from the values for normal wood, together with the values for the resin and the modulus of elasticity in compression of the wood. Values in the fiber direction for normal wood are from one-tenth to one-half of the values for common metals, concrete, and glass, but the transverse values for wood are, in general, somewhat greater. Values for wood can, in general, be neglected for uses where swelling and shrinking occur, as swelling and shrinking are considerably greater.

**EXOTHERMIC REACTION AND SPONTANEOUS COMBUSTION TEMPERATURES. Definition:** The temperature of the heating medium above which the temperature of the contained wood rises spontaneously above that of the heating medium as a result of chemical decomposition of the wood.

**Value:** 273° C., or 523° F.

**Spontaneous Combustion Temperature. Definition:** The temperature at which the material ignites spontaneously.

**Values:** These vary with the size, shape, manner of piling of material, air circulation, method and rate of heating, the control of radiation, and the place within the wood at which the temperature is measured. Estimated values vary from 273° to 500° C., or 523° to 932° F.

**EFFECT OF CHEMICALS UPON THE STRENGTH OF WOOD. Types of Effect.**

1. Reversible swelling and temporary loss in strength caused by such nonreacting chemicals as water in breaking secondary structural bonds that can be reformed on shrinking.
2. Nonreversible degradation of the wood due to hydrolysis, as with acids.
3. Nonreversible degradation of the wood due to solution and softening of hemicelluloses and lignin, as with alkalies.
4. Nonreversible degradation of the wood due to oxidation, as with concentrated nitric acid.

**Extent of Action.** In spite of the fact that wood swells in water and may temporarily lose up to half of its strength relative to the air-dry values, and that a number of chemicals degrade the wood permanently, these actions are in many cases so slow as to make wood an ideal material for tanks and certain chemical equipment. Alcohols and other wood-swelling organic liquids reduce the compressive strength of wood to about the same extent as when the wood is swollen to the same degree in water. Nonswelling liquids, such as petroleum oils and creosote, have a negligible effect upon the strength of wood.

Wood is much more resistant to dilute acids and acid salts than is cast iron or ordinary steel, but it is less resistant to alkalies. Table 4 gives the relative strength values for wood specimens after soaking in acid and alkalies for 4 weeks. Softwoods are, in general, more acid-resistant than hardwoods. It appears that acids with pH values above about 2, or bases with pH values below 10, will have little weakening effect upon wood at room temperature over reasonable periods of time.

In high concentrations, zinc salts and iron salts show some weakening effect upon wood. The weakening shows up first as a loss in toughness. Zinc chloride preservatives are commonly used in such low concentrations that the weakening effect can, in general, be neglected.

**Treatments to Increase Acid Resistance.** Treatments with heavy coal tars have been shown to increase the acid resistance of wood. They have been successfully applied to wood used for filter plates and frames, acid-storage tanks,

Table 4. Deterioration Due to 4-Week Soaking in Acids and Bases at Room Temperature, Measured by Modulus of Rupture Relative to Water-Soaked Specimens

| Species | HCl | | H₂SO₄ | | HNO₃ | | Lactic | | Acetic | | NaOH | | NH₄OH | |
|---|---|---|---|---|---|---|---|---|---|---|---|---|---|---|
| | Concentration in percent | | | | | | | | | | | | | |
| | 2 | 10 | 2 | 10 | 2 | 10 | 2 | 10 | 2 | 10 | 2 | 10 | 2 | 10 |
| Larch | *1.09 | 0.81 | 1.11 | 1.00 | 1.07 | 0.95 | 1.21 | 1.10 | 1.07 | 1.04 | 0.96 | 0.52 | 1.06 | 0.92 |
| Pine | 1.08 | 0.84 | 1.13 | 0.84 | 1.07 | 0.93 | 1.25 | 1.11 | 1.11 | 0.88 | 0.96 | 0.51 | 1.00 | 0.79 |
| Spruce | 1.00 | 0.82 | 1.02 | 0.94 | 0.98 | 0.96 | 1.00 | 1.04 | 1.09 | 0.99 | 0.93 | 0.44 | 0.98 | 0.75 |
| Beech | 0.96 | 0.55 | 0.97 | 0.87 | 0.83 | 0.71 | 1.13 | 1.02 | 0.97 | 0.93 | 0.59 | 0.31 | 0.67 | 0.43 |
| Oak | 0.93 | 0.52 | 0.97 | 0.82 | 0.82 | 0.65 | 0.99 | 1.05 | 0.96 | 0.87 | 0.58 | 0.29 | 0.65 | 0.36 |
| Basswood | 0.88 | 0.48 | 0.87 | 0.81 | 0.76 | 0.57 | 1.08 | 0.96 | 1.09 | 1.00 | 0.55 | 0.21 | 0.61 | 0.33 |

* Values greater than 1.0 are caused by less swelling in water than in the solution during the soaking period.

Source: Kollmann.

walks and platforms around chemical equipment subject to acid spillage or drip, ducts for acid vapors, drainage boxes, and lumber in general use near operations involving acids.

**PERMANENT EFFECT OF HEAT UPON THE STRENGTH OF WOOD.** Heating wood at moderate temperatures for prolonged periods of time or at high temperatures for short periods of time decreases the strength. Dry heat reduces the hygroscopicity of the wood as well as the strength. Moist heat is more deleterious to its strength than dry heat.

**ELECTRICAL PROPERTIES OF WOOD. Direct-Current Electrical Resistivity of Wood. Definition:** The electromotive force in volts between two ends of a conductor of unit cross section per unit of length (in centimeters) required to cause the flow of a direct current of 1 ampere. Units: ohm centimeters.

**Values:** These vary with the grain direction, specific gravity, and moisture content of the wood. Resin treatment increases the electrical resistivity of wood. In general, the resistivity of oven-dry wood is from $3 \times 10^{17}$ to $3 \times 10^{18}$ ohm centimeters.

**High-Frequency Alternating-Current Resistivity of Wood. Definition:** The high-frequency alternating-current electromotive force in volts between two ends of a conductor of unit cross section per unit of length (in centimeters) required to cause the flow of an alternating current of 1 ampere. Units: ohm centimeters.

**Values:** These vary with the frequency and the grain direction, specific gravity, and moisture content of the wood.

**Oven-dry wood:**

Longitudinal $6 \times 10^6$ ohm centimeters at 2 mc. per sec.
Transverse $18 \times 10^6$ ohm centimeters at 2 mc. per sec.
Transverse $2 \times 10^6$ ohm centimeters at 15 mc. per sec.

**Specific Inductive Capacity of Wood. Definition:** The ratio of the capacity of a condenser with the substance under consideration as dielectric to the capacity of the same condenser with air or a vacuum as the dielectric. It is the dielectric constant of a material relative to the dielectric constant of a vacuum. The values, in general, vary from 1.0 for air to 81 for water. Good conductors cannot sustain a charge and hence do not exhibit dielectric properties.

**Values:** These vary with the frequency, the grain direction, specific gravity, and the moisture content of the wood.

**Power Factor of Wood. Definition:** The cosine of the phase angle by which the current leads the voltage when a normal alternating voltage is applied to the electrodes of a condenser containing the dielectric material under consideration. In simpler terms, it is the ratio of the power absorbed in the material per cycle of oscillation to the total apparent power stored in the material during that cycle.

**Values:** These vary with the frequency, with the grain direction, the specific gravity, and the moisture content of the wood.

**FIBER-SATURATION POINT OF WOOD. Definition:** The moisture content at which the cell wall substance is saturated with water, but no free water exists in the permanent capillary structure. Units: weight per unit weight.

**Values:** These vary but slightly among species. The spread of values determined by different methods is 27 to 32 percent. For most purposes, an average value of 30 percent of the dry weight of the wood at room temperature can be used. The fiber-saturation point decreases about 0.1 percent for each degree increase in temperature from 0° to 100° C. (32° to 212° F.).

Methods for determining: (1) Extrapolating moisture content–relative humidity curves for predried wood to 100 percent relative humidity; (2) extrapolating moisture content–volumetric shrinkage curves determined on thin cross sections of wood to zero shrinkage; (3) determining the moisture content above which the linear moisture content strength relationship no longer holds; (4) determining the moisture content above which the approximately linear moisture content logarithm of the electrical resistivity relationship no longer holds; (5) extrapolating the moisture-content, differential heat-of-swelling relationship to zero heat of swelling.

## MOISTURE CONTENT AND SPECIFIC GRAVITY–SHRINKAGE RELATIONSHIPS. Moisture Content–Shrinkage Relationship.
When shrinkage measurements are made on thin cross sections of wood, stresses due to moisture gradients are practically eliminated. Under these conditions the shrinkage is almost directly proportional to the moisture lost from the fiber-saturation point to the oven-dry condition. Although there is some deviation from this simple relationship in the case of commercial sizes of wood, the relationship may be used to estimate the shrinkage that will occur to any given moisture content.

$$S_m = \frac{30 - m}{30} S$$

where $S$ is the total shrinkage (either volumetric, radial, or tangential) from the fiber-saturation point to the oven-dry condition, $S_m$ is the corresponding shrinkage to the moisture content $m$ in percent.

**Specific Gravity-Shrinkage Relationship.** The volumetric shrinkage, $S$, of wood under stress-free conditions and in the absence of collapse is directly proportional to the specific gravity of the wood $\rho$. The proportionality constant is equal to the fiber-saturation point of wood on a volume of water per unit weight of woods low in extractives. This is slightly less than the normal fiber-saturation point expressed as a fraction because of absorption compression of the water on the wood, thus

$$S = 0.28\rho$$

The relationship holds very well for thin cross sections of wood that are low in extractives. In the case of wood containing high concentrations of water-soluble extractives such as redwood, the shrinkage may be lower than the relationship calls for by as much as 25 percent because of bulking of the fiber by the extractives. For woods that are low in extractives and relatively free from a tendency to collapse, the relationship holds reasonably well for wood of commercial sizes. Collapse when it occurs increases the shrinkage. Woods that tend to collapse appreciably on drying are basswood, willow, cottonwood, and blue gum (*Eucalyptus globulus*).

## SWELLING OF WOOD IN VARIOUS LIQUIDS.
Wood swells in water and various water-soluble liquids but not in hydrocarbon oils. Recent research indicates that swelling is related with the tendency of the liquid to form hydrogen bonds. Table 5 gives the external volumetric swelling relative to that in water for oven-dry softwood cross sections in various water-free organic liquids. The presence of small amounts of water greatly increases swelling of wood in such liquids as ether and aniline.

**Table 5. External Volumetric Swelling Relative to That in Water for Oven-Dry White Pine [a] and Sitka Spruce [b] Sections in Various Water-Free Organic Liquids**

| Swelling media | Relative swelling (percent) | Dielectric constant | Reference |
|---|---|---|---|
| Carbon tetrachloride | 1.7 | 2.24 | |
| Chloroform | 3.2 | 5.05 | [a] |
| Ethyl ether | 3.0 | 4.33 | |
| Dioxane | 62 | 2.2 | [b] |
| Benzol | 0 | 2.28 | |
| Toluol | 1.6 | 2.39 | |
| Aniline | 4.8 | 7.25 | |
| Chlorbenzene | 5.2 | 5.94 | [a] |
| Brombenzene | 5.8 | 5.40 | |
| Benzaldehyde | 6.0 | 18.0 | |
| Nitrobenzene | 13.7 | 36.1 | |
| Amyl alcohol | 4.9 | 15.8 | |
| N-butyl alcohol | 13.5 | 17.8 | |
| Propyl alcohol | 45 | 21.8 | [a] |
| Ethyl alcohol | 83 | 25.7 | |
| Methyl alcohol | 95 | 31.2 | |
| Ethyleneglycol monoethyl ether | 87 | ... | [b] |
| Acetone | 63 | 21.4 | |
| Methyl acetate | 80 | 7.3 | [a] |
| Ethyl acetate | 54 | 6.4 | |
| Oleic acid | 39 | 2.45 | |
| Valeric acid | 57 | 2.68 | |
| Propionic acid | 67 | 3.19 | [a] |
| Acetic acid | 75 | 7.1 | |
| Formic acid | 120 | 62.0 | |
| Formamide | 123 | 84.0 | |
| Tri-n-butylamine | 8.2 | ... | |
| Di-n-butylamine | 9.4 | ... | |
| Triethylamine | 14.6 | 3.2 | |
| Diethylamine | 108 | 3.7 | |
| N-butylamine | 139 | 5.4 | |
| N-diethylaniline | 3.7 | ... | |
| N-dimethylaniline | 4.5 | 4.5 | [b] |
| N-methylaniline | 5.4 | 6.0 | |
| N-ethylaniline | 6.2 | 5.9 | |
| Quinoline | 0 | 8.9 | |
| 2-picoline | 111 | 10.2 | |
| Pyridine | 118 | 12.5 | |
| Morpholine | 129 | ... | |
| Piperidine | 131 | 5.9 | |
| Water | 100 | 81 | [a] [b] |

[a] A. J. Stamm. U. S. Dept. Agr. Misc. Publ. 240. 1936.
[b] A. N. Nayer. Ph. D. Thesis, Univ. Minnesota. 1948.

## EQUILIBRIUM MOISTURE CONTENTS OF WOOD AT VARIOUS HUMIDITIES AND TEMPERATURES.

The moisture content of wood increases with an increase in the relative humidity to which it is subjected according to the sigmoid type of curves given in Figs. 2 and 3.

**Effect of Conditions Under Which Equilibrium Is Attained.** The equilibrium moisture content at any relative humidity (relative vapor pressure × 100) is higher if attained under desorption (drying) conditions than when attained under adsorption conditions, as is shown in Fig. 2. This figure represents adsorption followed by desorption. The first desorption curve starting with green wood will be somewhat above the subsequent desorption curve shown in the figure at the higher relative humidities. Between relative humidities of 10 percent and 95 percent the ratio of the adsorption to the subsequent desorption values is about 0.83. With the use of this factor adsorption data can be transposed to desorption data or vice versa.

When wood is only partially dried and then allowed again to adsorb moisture, the equilibrium moisture content values at various relative humidities cross over from the desorption curve to the adsorption area. Any point within the hysteresis loop may thus represent the equilibrium conditions, depending on how they were attained.

**Effect of Temperature.** An increase in temperature causes a decrease in the equilibrium moisture content, as is shown in Fig. 3 for a series of desorption

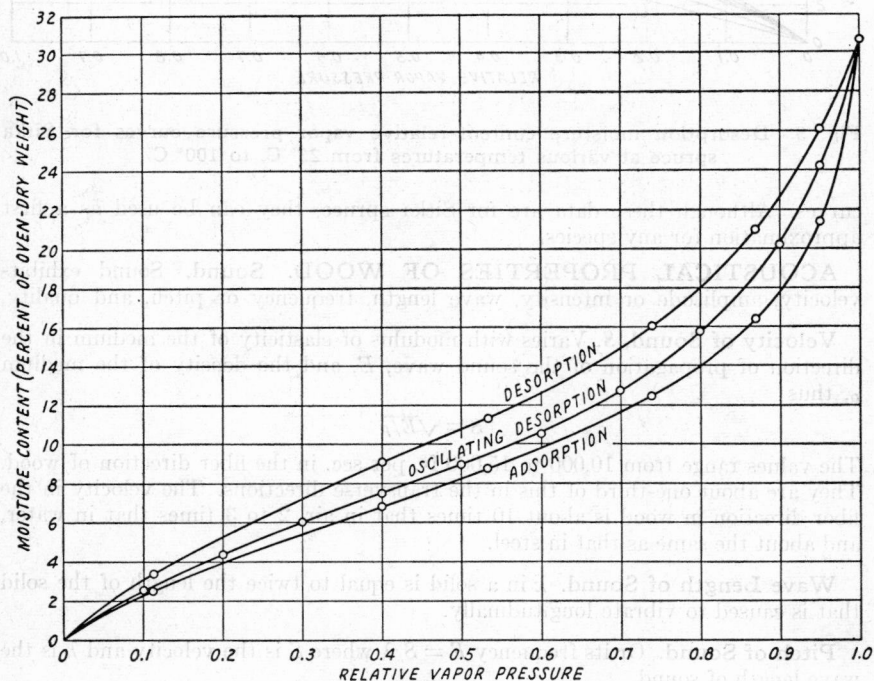

**Fig. 2.** Adsorption–desorption, moisture content–relative vapor pressure curves for Sitka spruce at 25° C.

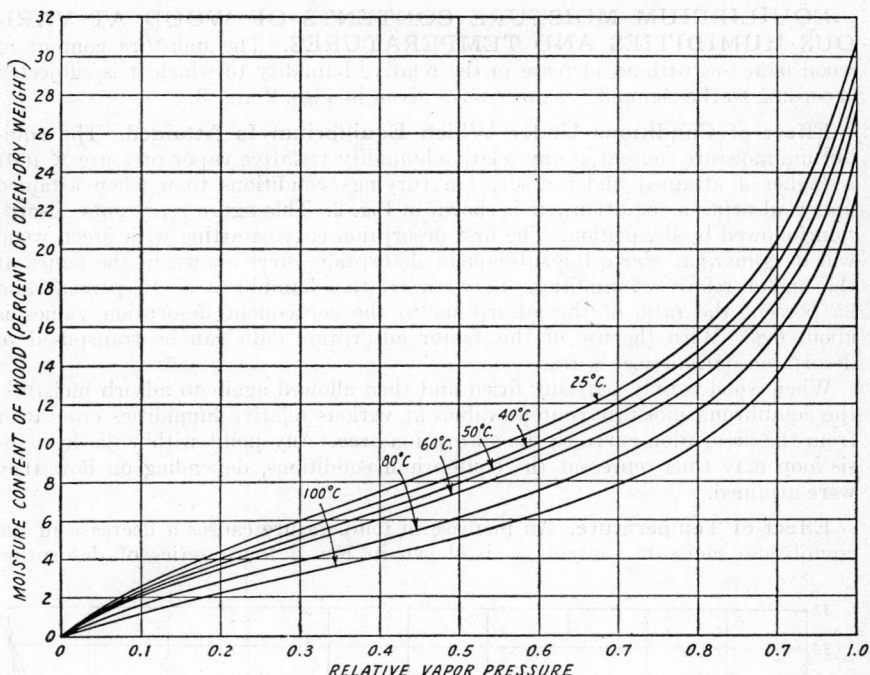

**Fig. 3. Desorption moisture content–relative vapor pressure curves for Sitka spruce at various temperatures from 25° C. to 100° C.**

curves. Although these data are for Sitka spruce, they can be used as a first approximation for any species.

**ACOUSTICAL PROPERTIES OF WOOD. Sound.** Sound exhibits velocity, amplitude or intensity, wave length, frequency or pitch, and quality.

**Velocity of Sound, S.** Varies with modulus of elasticity of the medium in the direction of propagation of the sound wave, $E$, and the density of the medium $\rho$, thus

$$S = \sqrt{E/\rho}$$

The values range from 10,000 to 15,000 ft. per sec. in the fiber direction of wood. They are about one-third of this in the transverse directions. The velocity in the fiber direction in wood is about 10 times that in air, 2 to 3 times that in water, and about the same as that in steel.

**Wave Length of Sound.** $\lambda$ in a solid is equal to twice the length of the solid that is caused to vibrate longitudinally.

**Pitch of Sound.** Or its frequency $F = S/\lambda$ where $S$ is the velocity and $\lambda$ is the wave length of sound.

**Quality of Sound.** Uniform texture, specific gravity, and absence of stresses have been shown important for all musical instrument applications.

## BIBLIOGRAPHY

BESCHER, R. H. 1947. Acid-proofing of wood. *Forest Prod. Res. Soc. Proc.* 1:120–123.

BROWN, N. C. 1950. *Forest products.* John Wiley & Sons, Inc., New York.

CLARK, J. D., and J. WILLIAMS. 1933. The electrical conductivity of commercial dielectrics and its variation with temperature. *Jour. Phys. Chem.* 37:119–131.

COLLINS, T. T., JR. 1945. Sulfite turpentine—a review of the literature. *Paper Ind.* 27:537–541; 719–722.

ERICKSON, H. D., and L. W. REES. 1940. The effect of several chemicals on the swelling and the crushing strength of wood. *Jour. Agr. Research* 60:593.

GOOS, A. W., and A. A. REITER. 1946. New products from wood carbonization. *Indus. & Eng. Chem.* 38:132–135.

HAWLEY, L. F. 1926. *Wood chemistry,* ACS Monograph No. 28. Reinhold Publ. Corp., New York.

HENDERSHOT, O. P. 1924. Thermal expansion of wood. *Science* 60:456.

ISENBERG, I. H., and M. A. BUCHANAN. 1945. A color reaction of wood with methanol—hydrochloric acid. *Jour. Forestry* 43:888–890.

KOBE, K. A., and F. L. GOIN. 1939. Exothermal decomposition temperature of wood impregnated with flammable organic liquids. *Indus. & Eng. Chem.* 31:1171–1172.

KOEHLER, A., and R. THELEN. 1926. *The kiln drying of lumber.* McGraw-Hill Book Co., Inc., New York.

KOLLMANN, F. 1936. *Technologie des holzes.* Julius Springer, Berlin.

KNIGHT, A. C., and G. H. PRATT. 1935. The humidity–moisture content relations of wood. *Engineering* 139:472–473.

MACLEAN, J. S. 1941. Thermal conductivity of wood. *Heating, Piping and Air Conditioning* 13:380.

MARKS, L. S. (ed.) 1941. *Mechanical engineers handbook.* McGraw-Hill Book Co., Inc., New York.

NAYER, A. N. 1948. Swelling of wood in various organic liquids. Ph. D. thesis, Univ. of Minnesota.

OREGON STATE COLLEGE. 1949. Dielectric properties of Douglas-fir at high frequencies. Ore. Eng. Exp. Sta. *Bull. No. 28.*

PANSHIN, A. J., et al. 1950. *Forest products—their sources, production, and utilization.* McGraw-Hill Book Co., Inc., New York.

STAMM, A. J. 1927. The electrical resistance of wood as a measure of its moisture content. *Indus. & Eng. Chem.* 19:1021–1025.

STAMM, A. J. 1929. The fiber saturation point of wood as obtained from electric conductivity measurements. *Indus. & Eng. Chem.* (Anal. Ed.) 1:94–97.

STAMM, A. J., and W. K. LOUGHBOROUGH. 1942. Variation in shrinking and swelling of wood. *Soc. Mech. Eng. Trans.* 64:379–386.

STAMM, A. J., and H. TARKOW. 1950. Penetration of cellulose fibers. *Jour. Phys. Colloid Chem.* 54:745.

STATE UNIV. OF N. Y., COLLEGE OF FORESTRY. 1948. The dielectrical properties of wood at several radio frequencies. *Tech. Publ. No. 69.*

TECHNICAL ASSN. OF THE PULP AND PAPER INDUSTRY. 1948. Nature of the chemical components of woods. *Monograph Series No. 6.*

U. S. FOREST SERV., FOREST PRODUCTS LAB.:
1943. *Report No. 1358.* Unpublished.
1945. Effects of heat on the properties and serviceability of wood. *Report No. R1471.*
1946. Heat-stabilized wood (staywood). *Report No. R1621.*
1948. Color tests for differentiating heartwood and sapwood of certain oaks, pines, and Douglas-fir. *Tech. Note 253.*

WEATHERWAX, R. C., and A. J. STAMM. 1945. The electrical resistivity of resin-treated wood and laminated hydrolyzed-wood and paper base plastics. *Elec. Eng. Trans.* 64:833.

WEATHERWAX, R. C., and A. J. STAMM. 1947. The coefficients of thermal expansion of wood and wood products. *Am. Soc. Mech. Eng. Trans.* 69:421.

WISE, L. E., and E. C. JAHN (eds.). 1952. *Wood chemistry*, 2d. ed., ACS Monograph No. 97. Reinhold Publ. Co., New York.

# CHEMICAL AND PHYSICAL TABLES
# AND DEFINITIONS

## CONTENTS

# CHEMICAL AND PHYSICAL TABLES AND DEFINITIONS

## Chemical Tables and Definitions

### Table 1. Symbols for Chemical Elements

| Element | Symbol | Element | Symbol | Element | Symbol |
|---------|--------|---------|--------|---------|--------|
| Actinium | Ac | Holmium | Ho | Radium | Ra |
| Aluminum | Al | Hydrogen | H | Radon | Rn |
| Americium | Am | Indium | In | Rhenium | Re |
| Antimony | Sb | Iodine | I | Rhodium | Rh |
| Argon | A | Iridium | Ir | Rubidium | Rb |
| Arsenic | As | Iron | Fe | Ruthenium | Ru |
| Astatine | At | Krypton | Kr | Samarium | Sm |
| Barium | Ba | Lanthanum | La | Scandium | Sc |
| Beryllium | Be | Lead | Pb | Selenium | Se |
| Bismuth | Bi | Lithium | Li | Silicon | Si |
| Boron | B | Lutetium | Lu | Silver | Ag |
| Bromine | Br | Magnesium | Mg | Sodium | Na |
| Cadmium | Cd | Manganese | Mn | Strontium | Sr |
| Calcium | Ca | Mercury | Hg | Sulfur | S |
| Carbon | C | Molybdenum | Mo | Tantalum | Ta |
| Cerium | Ce | Neodymium | Nd | Technetium | Tc |
| Cesium | Cs | Neptunium | Np | Tellurium | Te |
| Chlorine | Cl | Neon | Ne | Terbium | Tb |
| Chromium | Cr | Nickel | Ni | Thallium | Tl |
| Cobalt | Co | Niobium | | Thorium | Th |
| Copper | Cu | (Columbium) | Nb | Thulium | Tm |
| Curium | Cm | Nitrogen | N | Tin | Sn |
| Dysprosium | Dy | Osmium | Os | Titanium | Ti |
| Erbium | Er | Oxygen | O | Uranium | U |
| Europium | Eu | Palladium | Pd | Vanadium | V |
| Fluorine | F | Phosphorus | P | Wolfram | |
| Francium | Fr | Platinum | Pt | (Tungsten) | W |
| Gadolinium | Gd | Plutonium | Pu | Xenon | Xe |
| Gallium | Ga | Polonium | Po | Ytterbium | Yb |
| Germanium | Ge | Potassium | K | Yttrium | Y |
| Gold | Au | Praseodymium | Pr | Zinc | Zn |
| Hafnium | Hf | Promethium | Pm | Zirconium | Zr |
| Helium | He | Protactinium | Pa | | |

### Table 2. Common Names and Formulas for Some Chemicals

| Common name | Chemical name | Formula |
|---|---|---|
| Absolute alcohol | Ethyl alcohol, anhydrous | $C_2H_5OH$ |
| Acetate of lime | Calcium acetate | $Ca(C_2H_3O_2)_2$ |
| Acetone | Dimethylketone | $CH_3COCH_3$ |
| Acetone alcohol | Methyl alcohol | $CH_3OH$ |
| Alum | Generally refers to potassium aluminum sulfate, potash alum. | $K_2SO_4 \cdot Al_2(SO_4)_3 \cdot 24 H_2O$ |
| Alum, papermakers (also known as alum) | Aluminum sulfate | $Al_2(SO_4)_3 \cdot 18H_2O$ |
| Ammate | Ammonium sulfamate | $NH_4OSO_2NH_2$ |
| Aqua regia | Nitric acid and hydrochloric acid | $HNO_3 + 3\ HCl$ |
| Baking soda | Sodium bicarbonate | $NaHCO_3$ |
| Bauxite | Hydrated alumina | $Al_2O_3 \cdot 2H_2O$ |
| Benzine | Gasoline, petrol | |
| Benzol | Benzene | $C_6H_6$ |
| Bleaching powder | Calcium hypochlorite | $CaOCl_2$ |
| Blue vitriol | Copper sulfate | $CuSO_4 \cdot 5H_2O$ |
| Borax | Sodium tetraborate | $Na_2B_4O_7 \cdot 10H_2O$ |
| Burnt lime | Calcium oxide | $CaO$ |
| Calomel | Mercurous chloride | $HgCl$ |
| Camphor, artificial | Pinene hydrochloride | $C_{10}H_{17}Cl$ |
| Camphor, gum | Camphor (natural) | $C_{10}H_{16}O$ |
| Cane sugar | Sucrose | $C_{12}H_{22}O_{11}$ |
| Carbolic acid | Phenol | $C_6H_5OH$ |
| Caustic potash | Potassium hydroxide | $KOH$ |
| Caustic soda | Sodium hydroxide | $NaOH$ |
| Chalk | Calcium carbonate | $CaCO_3$ |
| Corn sugar | Glucose | $C_6H_{12}O_6 \cdot H_2O$ |
| Corrosive sublimate | Mercuric chloride | $HgCl_2$ |
| Cream of tartar | Potassium hydrogen tartrate, potassium bitartrate | $KHC_4H_4O_6$ |
| 2,4-D | 2,4 Dichlorophenoxyacetic acid | $C_6H_3Cl_2OCH_2COOH$ |
| DDT | Dichlorodiphenyltrichloroethane | $(C_6H_4Cl)_2CH\ CCl_3$ |
| Dextrose | Glucose | $C_6H_{12}O_6 \cdot H_2O$ |
| Epsom salts | Magnesium sulfate | $MgSO_4 \cdot 7H_2O$ |
| Ethanol | Ethyl alcohol | $C_2H_5OH$ |
| Formalin | Formaldehyde, 40% in water | $HCHO$ |
| Furfural | Furfuraldehyde | $C_4H_3O \cdot CHO$ |
| Fusel oil | Mixed amyl alcohols | $C_5H_{11}OH$ |
| Galena | Lead sulfide (natural) | $PbS$ |
| Glauber's salt | Sodium sulfate | $Na_2SO_4 \cdot 10H_2O$ |
| Glucose | Dextrose | $C_6H_{12}O_6 \cdot H_2O$ |
| Glycerin | Glycerol | $C_3H_5(OH)_3$ |
| Grain alcohol | Ethyl alcohol | $C_2H_5OH$ |
| Grape sugar | Glucose | $C_6H_{12}O_6 \cdot H_2O$ |
| Green vitriol | Ferrous sulfate | $FeSO_4 \cdot 7H_2O$ |
| Gypsum | Calcium sulfate | $CaSO_4 \cdot 2H_2O$ |
| Hypo | Sodium thiosulfate | $Na_2S_2O_3 \cdot 5H_2O$ |
| Kaolin | Aluminum silicate | $Al_2O_3 \cdot 2SiO_2 \cdot 2H_2O$ |
| Kieselguhr | Siliceous earth | $SiO_2$ |
| Lampblack | Impure carbon | $C$ |
| Levulose | Fructose | $C_6H_{12}O_6$ |
| Lime | Calcium oxide | $CaO$ |
| Litharge | Lead monoxide | $PbO$ |
| Magnesia | Magnesium oxide | $MgO$ |
| Magnesite | Magnesium carbonate | $MgCO_3$ |
| Marble | Calcium carbonate | $CaCO_3$ |
| Marsh gas | Methane | $CH_4$ |
| Methanol | Methyl alcohol | $CH_3OH$ |
| Milk of lime | Calcium hydroxide | $Ca(OH)_2$ |

**Table 2. Common Names and Formulas for Some Chemicals (Continued)**

| Common name | Chemical name | Formula |
|---|---|---|
| Milk of magnesia | Magnesium hydroxide | $Mg(OH)_2$ |
| Milk sugar | Lactose | $C_{12}H_{22}O_{11}\cdot H_2O$ |
| Muriatic acid | Hydrochloric acid | $HCl$ |
| Oil of vitriol | Concentrated sulfuric acid | $H_2SO_4$ |
| Oil of wintergreen | Methyl salicylate | $O—HOC_6H_4CO_2CH_3$ |
| Papermakers' alum | Aluminum sulfate | $Al_2(SO_4)_3\cdot 18H_2O$ |
| Paris green | Copper aceto-arsenite | $Cu(C_2H_3O_2)_2\cdot 3CuAs_2O_4$ |
| Picric acid | Trinitrophenol, symmetrical | $C_6H_2(NO_2)_3OH$ |
| Plaster of Paris | Calcium sulfate | $CaSO_4\cdot \frac{1}{2}H_2O$ |
| Potash | Potassium carbonate | $K_2CO_3$ |
| Prussian blue | Ferric ferrocyanide | $Fe_4[Fe(CN)_6]_3$ |
| Prussic acid | Hydrocyanic acid | $HCN$ |
| Pyrites | Ferrous disulfide | $FeS_2$ |
| Pyroligneous acid | Crude acetic acid | $CH_3COOH$ |
| Pyroligneous spirit | Methyl alcohol | $CH_3OH$ |
| Quick lime | Calcium oxide | $CaO$ |
| Quicksilver | Mercury | $Hg$ |
| Rectified spirit | Ethyl alcohol, 90–95% | $C_2H_5OH$ |
| Red lead | Lead tetraoxide | $Pb_3O_4$ |
| Rochelle salt | Potassium sodium tartrate | $KNaC_4H_6O_6\cdot 4H_2O$ |
| Rock salt | Sodium chloride | $NaCl$ |
| Rouge | Ferric oxide | $Fe_2O_3$ |
| Saccharin | o-Benzoic sulfimide | $C_6H_4\cdot COSO_2NH$ |
| Sal ammoniac | Ammonium chloride | $NH_4Cl$ |
| Salt | Sodium chloride | $NaCl$ |
| Salt cake | Impure sodium sulfate | $Na_2SO_4$ |
| Salt of tartar | Potassium carbonate | $K_2CO_3$ |
| Saltpeter | Potassium nitrate | $KNO_3$ |
| Silica | Silicon dioxide | $SiO_2$ |
| Slaked lime | Calcium hydroxide | $Ca(OH)_2$ |
| Soda | Sodium carbonate | $Na_2CO_3\cdot 10H_2O$ |
| Soda ash | Crude sodium carbonate | $Na_2CO_3$ |
| Soda lime | Mixture of calcium oxide and sodium hydroxide | $CaO + NaOH$ |
| Soft soap | Potash soap | |
| Superphosphate | Impure calcium acid phosphate | $CaH_4(PO_4)_2$ |
| 2,4,5-T | 2,4,5 Trichlorophenoxyacetic acid | $C_6H_2Cl_3OCH_2COOH$ |
| Table salt | Sodium chloride | $NaCl$ |
| Talc | Hydrated magnesium silicate | $Mg_3Si_4O_{11}\cdot H_2O$ |
| Tartar | Crude potassium bitartrate | $KHC_4H_4O_6$ |
| Tartar emetic | Antimony potassium tartrate | $K(SbO)C_4H_4O_6\cdot \frac{1}{2}H_2O$ |
| TNT | Trinitrotoluene | $C_6H_2(CH_3)(NO_2)_3$ (1,2,4,6) |
| Toluol | Toluene | $C_6H_5CH_3$ |
| Unslaked lime | Calcium oxide | $CaO$ |
| Vanillin | Methyl protocatechuic aldehyde | $C_6H_3(OH)(OCH_3)CHO$ (1,2,4) |
| Vinegar acid | Acetic acid | $CH_3COOH$ |
| Vinegar salts | Calcium acetate | $(CH_3COO)_2Ca$ |
| Vitriol | Sulfuric acid | $H_2SO_4$ |
| Washing soda | Sodium carbonate | $Na_2CO_3\cdot 10H_2O$ |
| Water glass | Sodium silicates in water | |
| White lead | Basic lead carbonate | $2PbCO_3 + Pb(OH)$ |
| Wood alcohol | Methyl alcohol | $CH_3OH$ |
| Wood spirit | Methyl alcohol | $CH_3OH$ |
| Wood vinegar | Crude acetic acid (pyroligneous acid) | $CH_3COOH$ |
| Xylol | Xylene | $C_6H_4(CH_3)_2$ |
| Zinc white | Zinc oxide | $ZnO$ |

**DEFINITIONS OF CHEMICAL AND PHYSICAL TERMS.** (Many of the following terms are from the *Handbook of chemistry and physics*, The Chemical Rubber Co.)

**Absolute humidity.** See Humidity, absolute.

**Absolute pressure.** See Pressure, absolute.

**Absolute temperature.** Temperature reckoned from absolute zero. See Temperature.

**Absolute zero.** The temperature at which a gas would show no pressure if the general law for gases would hold for all temperatures. It is equal to $-273.18°C$. or $-459.72°F$.

**Acceleration.** The time rate of change of velocity in either speed or direction, measured by the change in unit time. Cgs unit, one centimer per second per second.

**Acceleration due to gravity.** The acceleration of a body freely falling in a vacuum. The International Committee on Weights and Measures has adopted as a standard, or accepted value, 980.665 cm./sec.$^2$ or 32.174 ft./sec.$^2$.

**Achromatic.** A term applied to lenses signifying their more or less complete correction for chromatic aberration.

**Acids.** Acids are substances whose molecules ionize in water solution to give the hydrogen ion from their constituent elements. The strength of an acid is proportional to the concentration of hydrogen ions present.

**Acid, strong.** Acid which ionizes highly and has many hydrogen ions in dilute solution; an ionic compound or one which reacts with water, yielding a high effective concentration, or activity of hydrogen ions.

**Acid, weak.** Covalent compound which ionizes little and yields but few hydrogen ions in aqueous solution, e.g., acetic acid.

**Acoustic absorptivity.** Ratio of sound energy absorbed by a surface to that which reaches it.

**Adiabatic.** A body is said to undergo an adiabatic change when its condition is altered without gain or loss of heat. The line on the pressure volume diagram representing the above change is called an adiabatic line.

**Adsorption.** The condensation of gases, liquids, or dissolved substances on the surfaces of solids is called adsorption.

**Aerobic.** Bacteria or organisms which can use only free atmospheric oxygen.

**Aerosols.** Series of esters of sulfonated maleic anhydride, used as wetting agents.

**Alidade.** Instrument for plane table surveying.

**Alignment chart.** Nomograph in which all the axes are vertical.

**Aliquot.** A definite proportion of a given quantity.

**Alkaloid.** Nitrogen base, usually of vegetable origin which exhibits marked physiological (often toxic) effect on humans and animals; has a bitter taste.

**Amorphous.** Without definite form, not crystallized.

**Amphoteric.** Possessing both pronounced basic and acid properties.

**Anaerobic.** Class of bacteria or organisms which are inhibited or killed by free atmospheric oxygen.

**Anion.** A negatively charged ion.

**Anode.** Positive pole of an electrolytic system; that pole at which oxidation or loss of electrons takes place. In a secondary cell it is positive, and in a primary cell it is negative.

**Atom.** The smallest part of an element which can participate in ordinary chemical changes. The atoms of a given element are unvarying in average mass, but are different in such mass from atoms of all other elements.

**Atomic number.** The number of excess positive charges on the atomic nucleus. This charge of the nucleus is the essential feature which distinguishes one element from another and determines the position of the element in the periodic table.

**Atomic weight.** Atomic weight is the relative weight of the atom, on the basis of oxygen as 16. If these weights are expressed in grams, they are called gram atomic weights.

**Avogadro's Law.** Equal volumes of different gases at the same pressure and temperature contain the same number of molecules.

**Azeotropic.** A constant boiling mixture when the distillate has the same composition as the substance being distilled.

**Bagasse.** The fibrous residue which is left after the juice has been expressed from sugar cane.

**Bakelite.** A plastic produced by polymerization of phenol and formaldehyde. It is thermosetting and infusible, burns slowly, and can be incorporated in varnishes and lacquers.

**Barkometer.** Density scale for tanning extracts.

**Base.** Bases are substances which ionize in water to give the hydroxyl ion from their constituent elements. The strength of a base is proportional to the concentration of hydroxyl ions.

**Base exchange.** See Cation exchange.

**Base, weak.** A base which ionizes slightly in dilute aqueous solution yielding relatively few hydroxyl ions; generally a covalent compound.

**Bemberg yarn.** Trade name for cellulose silk made by the cuprammonium process.

**Blushing.** Clouding or whitening of lacquer coating because of too rapid drying or high humidity.

**Brake horsepower (bhp).** Available power developed by motors, engines, and the like.

**British thermal unit (Btu).** Mechanical equivalent of heat; amount of heat necessary to raise 1 lb. of water 1° F.; equal to 778.3 ft.–lb.

**Carbon, active.** Also called activated charcoal. A more or less pure form of carbon characterized by a high adsorptive capacity for foreign molecules.

**Catalytic agent.** A substance which by its mere presence alters the velocity of a reaction, and may be recovered unaltered in nature or amount at the end of the reaction.

**Cathode.** Negative pole of an electrolytic system.

**Cation.** A positively charged ion.

**Cation exchange.** The property of replacement of one metallic ion of a solid by another from solution in water. These exchanges are reversible and are used in water softening processes, such as the permutit process. Also called base exchange.

**Celanese.** An artificial silk made from cellulose acetate.

**Cellulase.** Enzyme by means of which bacteria hydrolyze cellulose.

**Celluloid.** A cellulose nitrate, thermoplastic, of good molding properties. It burns rapidly and is resistant to oils and hydrocarbons.

**Charcoal, activated.** See Carbon, active.

**Chromatic aberration.** Due to the difference in the index of refraction for different wave lengths, light of various wave lengths from the same source cannot be focused at a point by a simple lens. This is called chromatic aberration.

**Conductance.** Conductance, the reciprocal of resistance, is measured by the ratio of the current flowing through a conductor to the difference of potential between its ends. The practical unit of conductance, the mho, the conductance of a body through which 1 ampere of current flows when the potential difference is 1 volt. The conductance of a body in mho is the reciprocal of the value of its resistance in ohms.

**Conductivity, electrical.** Measured by the quantity of electricity transferred across unit area, per unit potential gradient per unit time.

**Conductivity, thermal.** Time rate of transfer of heat by conduction, through unit thickness, across unit area for unit difference of temperature. It is measured as calories per second per square centimeter for a thickness of 1 cm. and a difference of temperature of 1° C.

**Covalency.** The formation of a compound by means of a sharing of electrons between the combining atoms.

**Declination.** The angle between the vertical plane containing the direction of the earth's field at any point and a plane containing the geographic north and south meridian.

**Dew point.** The temperature at which condensation of water vapor in the air takes place.

**Dialysis.** Process of separating colloids from crystalloids by diffusion through a semipermeable membrane.

**Dielectric constant.** For a given medium, the reciprocal of the force of attraction between two electric charges of unit value separated by a distance of 1 cm.

**Dip.** The angle measured in a vertical plane between the direction of the earth's magnetic field and the horizontal.

**Doppler effect (light).** The apparent change in the wave length of light produced by the motion in the line of sight of either the observer or the source of light.

**Elasticity.** The property by virtue of which a body resists and recovers from deformation produced by force.

**Elastic limit.** The smallest value of the stress producing permanent alteration.

**Electromotive series.** A list of the metals arranged in the decreasing order of their tendencies to pass into ionic form by losing electrons.

**Electron.** A very small negatively charged particle. Electrons appear to be uniform in mass and charge and to be one of the basic elements of which atoms are made.

**Elements.** Substances which cannot be decomposed by the ordinary types of chemical change, or made by chemical union.

**Equivalent weight** or **Combining weight.** Equivalent weight or combining weight of an element or ion is its atomic or formula weight divided by its valence. Elements entering into combination always do so in quantities proportional to their equivalent weights.

**Fatigue strength (limit).** Range of stress that an elastic material will stand a number of successive times without failure.

**Fluidity.** The reciprocal of viscosity.

**Friction, coefficient of.** The coefficient of friction between two surfaces is the ratio of the force required to move one over the other to the total force pressing the two together.

**Guncotton.** Cellulose trinitrate, a fully or nearly fully nitrated cellulose used for explosives.

**Hardness.** Property of substances determined by their ability to abrade or indent one another. An arbitrary scale of hardness is based upon 10 selected minerals. For metals the diameter of the indentation made by a hardened steel sphere (Brinnell) or the height of rebound of a small drop hammer (Shore Scleroscope) serve to measure hardness. The load, in pounds, required to imbed a 0.444-in. ball to ½ its diameter measures the hardness of wood.

**Heat of combustion.** Heat of combustion of a substance is the amount of heat evolved by the combustion of 1 gm. molecular weight of the substance.

**Hooke's Law.** Within the elastic limit of any body, the ratio of the stress to the strain produced is constant.

**Humidity, absolute.** Mass of water vapor present in unit volume of the atmosphere, usually measured as grams per cubic meter. It may also be expressed in terms of the actual pressure of the water vapor present.

**Hydrogen equivalent.** Hydrogen equivalent of a substance is the number of replaceable hydrogen atoms in 1 molecule or the number of atoms of hydrogen with which 1 molecule could react.

**Hydrogen ion concentration.** The concentration of hydrogen ions in solution when the concentration is expressed as gram-ionic weights per liter. A convenient form of expressing hydrogen ion concentration is in terms of the negative logarithm of this concentration. The negative logarithm of the hydrogen ion concentration is called pH. The significance of pH is still in dispute (*J. Am. chem. soc.* 60: 1094, 1938).

Water at 25° C has a concentration of H ion of $10^{-7}$ and of OH ion of $10^{-7}$ moles per liter. Thus the pH of water is 7 at 24° C.

**Hydrolysis.** Hydrolysis is a double decomposition reaction involving the splitting of water into its ions and the formation of a weak base or both.

**Index of refraction.** Index of refraction for any substance is the ratio of the velocity of light in a vacuum to its velocity in the substance. It is also the ratio of the sine of the angle of incidence to the sine of the angle of refraction. In general, the index of refraction for any substance varies with the wave length of the refracted light.

**Induction.** Any change in the intensity or direction of a magnetic field causes an electromotive force in any conductor in the field. The induced electromotive force generates an induced current if the conductor forms a closed circuit.

**Ion.** Atom or group of atoms (formed from acids, bases, or salts dissolved in water and certain other solvents) which has gained or lost electrons and carries an electrical charge.

**Isotopes.** Isotopes are elements occupying the same place in the periodic system, having the same nuclear charge, but differing somewhat in atomic weight. Most of the ordinary inactive elements have been shown to consist of a mixture of isotopes.

**Isotropic.** Having its properties the same in all directions, e.g., carefully annealed copper in contrast to drawn copper wire.

**Latent heat of vaporization.** The quantity of heat which is necessary to change 1 gm. of liquid to vapor without change of temperature, measured as calories per gram.

**Modulus of elasticity.** The stress required to produce unit strain, which may be a change of length (Young's modulus); a twist or shear (modulus of rigidity or modulus of torsion); or a change of volume (bulk modulus), expressed in dynes per square centimeter.

**Molal solution.** A molal solution contains 1 mole per 1,000 gm. of solvent.

**Molar solution.** A molar solution contains 1 mole or gram molecular weight of the solute in 1 liter of solution.

**Mole.** A mass numerically equal to the molecular weight. For example, 1 mole of sulfuric acid (mol. wt. 98.08) contains 98.08 gm. of the acid.

**Molecular volume.** Volume occupied by 1 mole. Numerically equal to the molecular weight divided by the density.

**Molecular weight.** The sum of the atomic weights of all the atoms present in a molecule.

**Molecule.** The smallest unit quantity of matter which can exist by itself and retain all the properties of the original substance.

**Normal solution.** A normal solution contains 1 gm. molecular weight of the dissolved substance divided by the hydrogen equivalent of the substance (that is, 1 gm. equivalent) per liter of solution.

**Ohm's Law.** Current in terms of electromotive force $E$ and resistance $R$.

**Oxidation.** Oxidation is any process which increases the proportion of oxygen or acid-forming element or radical in a compound.

**Periodic Law.** Elements when arranged in the order of their atomic weights or atomic numbers show regular variations in most of their physical and chemical properties.

**pH.** See Hydrogen ion concentration.

**Phenol coefficient.** Minimal concentration of phenol that kills a microorganism in a definite time, divided by the concentration of the other disinfectant required to destroy the same organism in the same length of time; a numerical expression of disinfecting value.

**Polarized light.** Light which exhibits different properties in different directions at right angles to the line of propagation is said to be polarized. Specific rotation is the power of liquids to rotate the plane of polarization. It is stated in terms of specific rotation or the rotation in degrees per decimeter per unit density.

**Polymorphism.** The ability to exist in two or more crystalline forms.

**Power.** The time rate at which work is done. Units of power: the watt, 1 joule (ten million ergs) per second; the kilowatt is equal to 1,000 watts; the horsepower, 33,000 ft.-lb. per minute, is equal to 746 watts.

**Pressure.** Force applied to, or distributed over, a surface; measured as force per unit area. The pressure due to a force $F$ distributed over an area $A$,

$$P = \frac{F}{A}$$

**Absolute pressure.** Pressure measured with respect to zero pressure. **Gauge pressure.** Pressure measured with respect to that of the atmosphere.

**Proton.** An elementary particle having a positive charge equivalent to the negative charge of the electron but possessing a mass approximately 1,845 times as great. The proton is in effect the positive nucleus of the hydrogen atom.

**Rayon.** A generic term for filaments made from various solutions of modified cellulose, such as viscose rayon from cellulose xanthate, acetate rayon from cellulose acetate, and Bemberg rayon from a cuprammonium solution of cellulose.

**Reduction.** Reduction is any process which increases the proportion of hydrogen or base-forming elements or radicals in a compound.

**Refluxing.** The continuous return of condensed vapor to the boiling liquid by the use of a cooled column.

**Relative humidity.** The ratio of the quantity of water vapor present in the atmosphere to the quantity which would saturate at the existing temperature. It is also the ratio of the pressure of water vapor present to the pressure of saturated water vapor at the same temperature.

**Resistance.** A constant property of a given conductor, depending on the material, its dimensions and temperature, and which determines current flow for a given potential difference. Resistance is expressed in ohms, a conductor having 1 ohm resistance when unit potential difference produces a flow of unit current.

**Resolving power.** Resolving power of a telescope or microscope is indicated by the minimum separation of two objects for which they appear distinct and separate when viewed through the instrument.

**Saccharification.** Process of hydrolyzing polysaccharides to simpler sugars, such as starch by the enzyme diastase or cellulose by mineral acids, etc.

**Salt.** Any substance which yields ions, other than hydrogen or hydroxyl ions. A salt is obtained by displacing the hydrogen of an acid by a metal.

**Salt cake.** A commercial sodium sulfate.

**Saponification.** Hydrolysis of an oil or fat with an alkali to form a soap, e.g., treatment of glycerol oleate with sodium hydroxide to form sodium oleate (a soap) and glycerine.

**Saponification number.** The number of milligrams of potassium hydroxide necessary to saponify completely 1 gram of a fat or oil.

**Solute.** That constituent of a solution which is considered to be dissolved in the other, the solvent. The solvent is usually present in larger amount than the solute.

**Solvent.** That constituent of a solution which is present in larger amount; or, the constituent which is liquid in the pure state, in the case of solutions of solids or gases in liquids.

**Specific gravity.** The ratio of the mass of a body to the mass of an equal volume of water at 4° C. or other specified temperature.

**Specific heat.** The ratio of the thermal capacity of a substance to that of water at 15°C.

**Strain.** The deformation resulting from a stress measured by the ratio of the change to the total value of the dimension in which the change occurred.

**Stress.** The force producing or tending to produce deformation in a body measured by the force applied per unit area.

**Temperature.** Temperature may be defined as the condition of a body which determines the transfer of heat to or from other bodies. The customary unit of temperature is the Centigrade degree, 1/100 the difference between the temperature of melting ice and that of water boiling under standard atmospheric pressure. The degree Fahrenheit is 1/180, and the degree Reaumur 1/80, the same difference of temperature. The fundamental temperature scale is the absolute, thermodynamic, or Kelvin scale in which the temperature measure is based on the average kinetic energy per molecule of a perfect gas. The zero of the Kelvin scale is $-273.18°$ C. The temperature scale adopted by the International Bureau of Weights and Measures is that of the constant volume hydrogen gas thermometer. The magnitude of the degree in both these scales is defined as 1/100, which is the difference between the temperature of melting ice and that of boiling water at 760 mm. pressure.

**Urea resin.** A thermosetting condensation product of urea and formaldehyde, widely used as a plastic material.

**Valence.** Valence of an atom of an element is that property which is measured by the number of atoms of hydrogen (or its equivalent) one atom of that element can hold in combination if negative, or which it can displace in a reaction if it is positive.

**Viscose process.** Process for making rayon from a syrupy, highly viscous solution of cellulose xanthate in dilute caustic soda.

**Viscosity.** All fluids possess a definite resistance to change of form and many solids show a gradual yielding to forces tending to change their form. This property, a sort of internal friction, is called viscosity; it is expressed in dyne-seconds per $cm^2$ or poises.

**Vulcanized fiber.** A product made by the action of zinc chloride on cellulose (paper) which is very resistant to chemical action (except prolonged treatment with strong acids).

**QUALITATIVE ANALYSIS OF COMMON ELEMENTS AND IONS.** For the systematic scheme of analysis for qualitative recognition of the common elements and ions, including both the basic and acidic constituents, reference should be made to one of the standard volumes on qualitative chemical analysis.

**COLOR INDICATORS FOR pH DETERMINATION.** Fig. 1 shows that the indicators change color at different concentrations of H ion. Therefore, the H-ion concentration of a sample can be determined by adding to it a measured amount of indicator and comparing the color developed with the color obtained when the same amount of indicator is added to a standard buffer solution of known H-ion concentration. In practice a series of buffer solutions differing from each other in steps of 0.2 pH for the effective range of the indicator are prepared, a definite amount of indicator is added to each, and the color standard thus formed is sealed in an ampule. These standards, if protected from direct light, are stable for a considerable time.

**ARTS, FORMULAS, AND RECIPES** (*Hand. chem. and physics*). **Bluing Steel and Iron.** The metal is cleaned with a potassium bichromate-sulfuric acid mixture, then washed with ammonium hydroxide and rubbed dry. Apply ammonium polysulfide until the desired depth of color is obtained, allowing the object to dry after each application and rubbing briskly with a soft clean cloth. The result

ph Units  0  1  2  3  4  5  6  7  8  9  10  11  12  13  14

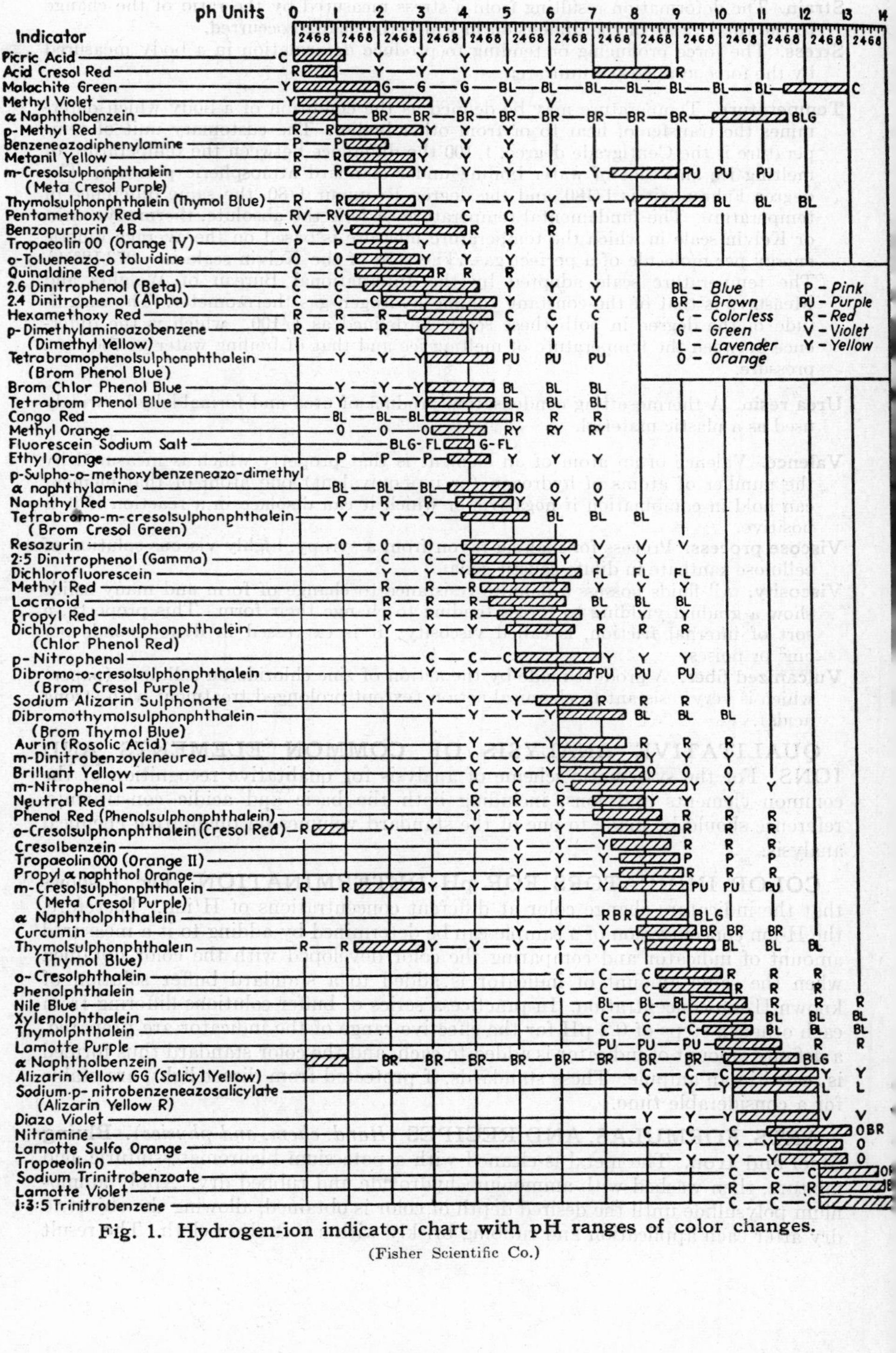

Indicator

Picric Acid
Acid Cresol Red
Malachite Green
Methyl Violet
α Naphtholbenzein
p-Methyl Red
Benzeneazodiphenylamine
Metanil Yellow
m-Cresolsulphonphthalein
  (Meta Cresol Purple)
Thymolsulphonphthalein (Thymol Blue)
Pentamethoxy Red
Benzopurpurin 4 B
Tropaeolin 00 (Orange IV)
o-Tolueneazo-o toluidine
Quinaldine Red
2,6 Dinitrophenol (Beta)
2,4 Dinitrophenol (Alpha)
Hexamethoxy Red
p-Dimethylaminoazobenzene
  (Dimethyl Yellow)
Tetrabromophenolsulphonphthalein
  (Brom Phenol Blue)
Brom Chlor Phenol Blue
Tetrabrom Phenol Blue
Congo Red
Methyl Orange
Fluorescein Sodium Salt
Ethyl Orange
p-Sulpho-o-methoxy benzeneazo-dimethyl
  α naphthylamine
Naphthyl Red
Tetrabromo-m-cresolsulphonphthalein
  (Brom Cresol Green)
Resazurin
2,5 Dinitrophenol (Gamma)
Dichlorofluorescein
Methyl Red
Lacmoid
Propyl Red
Dichlorophenolsulphonphthalein
  (Chlor Phenol Red)
p-Nitrophenol
Dibromo-o-cresolsulphonphthalein
  (Brom Cresol Purple)
Sodium Alizarin Sulphonate
Dibromothymolsulphonphthalein
  (Brom Thymol Blue)
Aurin (Rosolic Acid)
m-Dinitrobenzoyleneurea
Brilliant Yellow
m-Nitrophenol
Neutral Red
Phenol Red (Phenolsulphonphthalein)
o-Cresolsulphonphthalein (Cresol Red)
Cresolbenzein
Tropaeolin 000 (Orange II)
Propyl α naphthol Orange
m-Cresolsulphonphthalein
  (Meta Cresol Purple)
α Naphtholphthalein
Curcumin
Thymolsulphonphthalein
  (Thymol Blue)
o-Cresolphthalein
Phenolphthalein
Nile Blue
Xylenolphthalein
Thymolphthalein
Lamotte Purple
α Naphtholbenzein
Alizarin Yellow GG (Salicyl Yellow)
Sodium-p-nitrobenzeneazosalicylate
  (Alizarin Yellow R)
Diazo Violet
Nitramine
Lamotte Sulfo Orange
Tropaeolin 0
Sodium Trinitrobenzoate
Lamotte Violet
1:3:5 Trinitrobenzene

Legend:

| | |
|---|---|
| BL – Blue | P – Pink |
| BR – Brown | PU – Purple |
| C – Colorless | R – Red |
| FL – Green | V – Violet |
| L – Lavender | Y – Yellow |
| O – Orange | |

Fig. 1. Hydrogen-ion indicator chart with pH ranges of color changes.

(Fisher Scientific Co.)

is a deep blue which may be made very nearly black by repeated applications. Rubbing with boiled linseed oil will deepen this color more. The finish thus obtained is very resistant to oxidation.

### Table 3.  Approximate pH Values for Acids and Bases

(All values are based on measurements at 25° C. and rounded to the nearest tenth)

#### ACIDS

| | | | |
|---|---|---|---|
| Hydrochloric, N | 0.1 | Formic, 0.1N | 2.3 |
| Hydrochloric, 0.1N | 1.1 | Lactic, 0.1N | 2.4 |
| Hydrochloric, 0.01N | 2.0 | Acetic, N | 2.4 |
| Sulfuric, N | 0.3 | Acetic, 0.1N | 2.9 |
| Sulfuric, 0.1N | 1.2 | Acetic, 0.01N | 3.4 |
| Sulfuric, 0.01N | 2.1 | Benzoic, 0.01N | 3.1 |
| Orthophosphoric, 0.1N | 1.5 | Alum, 0.1N | 3.2 |
| Sulfurous, 0.1N | 1.5 | Carbonic (saturated) | 3.8 |
| Oxalic, 0.1N | 1.6 | Hydrogen sulfide, 0.1N | 4.1 |
| Tartaric, 0.1N | 2.2 | Arsenious (saturated) | 5.0 |
| Malic, 0.1N | 2.2 | Hydrocyanic, 0.1N | 5.1 |
| Citric, 0.1N | 2.2 | Boric, 0.1N | 5.2 |

#### BASES

| | | | |
|---|---|---|---|
| Sodium hydroxide, N | 14.0 | Ammonia, N | 11.6 |
| Sodium hydroxide, 0.1N | 13.0 | Ammonia, 0.1N | 11.1 |
| Sodium hydroxide, 0.01N | 12.0 | Ammonia, 0.01N | 10.6 |
| Potassium hydroxide, N | 14.0 | Potassium cyanide, 0.1N | 11.0 |
| Potassium hydroxide, 0.1N | 13.0 | Magnesia (saturated) | 10.5 |
| Potassium hydroxide, 0.01N | 12.0 | Sodium sesquicarbonate, 0.1M | 10.1 |
| Sodium metasilicate, 0.1N | 12.6 | Ferrous hydroxide (saturated) | 9.5 |
| Lime (saturated) | 12.4 | Calcium carbonate (saturated) | 9.4 |
| Trisodium phosphate, 0.1N | 12.0 | Borax, 0.1N | 9.2 |
| Sodium carbonate, 0.1N | 11.6 | Sodium bicarbonate, 0.1N | 8.4 |

#### APPROXIMATE pH VALUES FOR BUFFER SYSTEMS

For concentrations of approximately 0.1 molar, the general average variation will be ±1.0 pH from the value given.

| | |
|---|---|
| Glycocoll-sodium chloride-hydrochloric acid | 2.0 |
| Potassium acid phthalate-hydrochloric acid | 2.8 |
| Primary potassium citrate | 3.7 |
| Acetic acid-sodium acetate | 4.6 |
| Potassium acid phthalate-sodium hydroxide | 5.0 |
| Secondary sodium citrate | 5.0 |
| Potassium acid phosphate-disodium phosphate | 6.8 |
| Potassium acid phosphate-sodium hydroxide | 6.8 |
| Boric acid-borax | 8.5 |
| Borax | 9.2 |
| Boric acid-sodium hydroxide | 9.2 |
| Sodium bicarbonate-sodium carbonate | 10.2 |
| Disodium phosphate-sodium hydroxide | 11.5 |

**Cements and Adhesives. Acidproof cement. 1.** A handy acid-resisting cement can be made by mixing sodium silicate and asbestos powder to the consistency of a thin paste. If allowed to dry for a day, the resulting cement will resist the strongest acids.

2. Barium sulfate 4 parts, waterglass 3 parts, asbestos 1 part. Sodium fluosilicate or sodium fluoborate is advised in addition when the cement is used on glass.

### Aquarium cement.

1. Glazier's putty..................................... 10 lb.
   Litharge ........................................ 1 lb.
   Red lead ........................................ 1 lb.
   Asphaltum ....................................... 4 oz. fl.

Mix with boiled linseed oil to the proper consistency. Lamp black may be added to give a gray color.

2. Red lead ....................................... 3 parts
   Litharge (PbO) ................................. 7 parts
   Fine sand ...................................... 10 parts
   Powdered rosin ................................. 1 part

Add sufficient spar varnish to give the proper consistency.

**Cupric oxide cement.** For a strong adhesive cement for attaching metal articles to each other or for cementing glass, a paste of cupric oxide and phosphoric acid is very satisfactory. The cement is adhesive, strong, and sets quite rapidly.

**Litharge cement for joining metal to glass.** In the preparation of tanks with glass sides or bottom, it is desired to make these watertight by cementing the glass to the iron frame or to repair the leaks that may occur.

Litharge ........................... 260 grams
Glycerin solution (glycerin 2 parts, water
   1 part) ........................... 100 milliliters (cc.)

Place the litharge in a mortar, add the diluted glycerin slowly while grinding. Mix thoroughly by grinding a short time. Heat will be evolved and the mixture will begin to set. While still soft, pour it into place and by means of a spatula work it into position as in the case of putty. Allow to stand for a day when it will be thoroughly hard.

If desired, it may be covered with a layer of white lead or aluminum paint.

**Cleaning Compounds and Methods. Cleaning fluid.** An excellent solution for cleaning grease stains from cloth or leather consists of the following:

$CCl_4$ .............................................. 80%
Ligroin ............................................ 16%
Amyl alcohol (ter.) ................................ 4%

### Cleaning solution for glass.

400 cc. saturated solution sodium dichromate (Technical).
600 cc. conc. sulfuric acid poured slowly with stirring into the dichromate solution.

Avoid contact with flesh or clothing.

**Iodine stains.** Iodine stains can readily be removed from clothing by washing the stain with a 10 percent solution of sodium thiosulfate ("hypo") in water.

### Paintbrush cleaner.

1. Kerosene ........................................ 2 pt.
   Oleic acid ...................................... 1 pt.
2. Aqueous ammonia (conc.)......................... ¼ pt.
   Denatured alcohol ............................... ¼ pt.

Stir (2) into (1) until uniform. To clean brushes, place in the mixture over night. Wash thoroughly with warm water.

**Removal of carbonaceous matter.** A 10 to 15 percent solution of NaOH (caustic soda) removes carbon, etc., quickly. Rinse well with acid and $H_2O$.

**Removing carbon residue from glassware.**

| | |
|---|---|
| Trisodium phosphate ($Na_3PO_4$) | 2 tbs. |
| Sodium oleate | 1 tbs. |
| Soft water | 1 qt. |

Allow to stand in the solution for several minutes, brush off the incrustation, and rinse with water.

**Glass-grinding fluid.**

| | |
|---|---|
| Turpentine | 45 cc. |
| Ether (ethyl oxide) | 22.5 cc. |
| Camphor gum | 31 gm. |

To be used with powdered emery for grinding glass. For smoothing edges, a sheet of emery cloth moistened with the above solution may be used. Plane surfaces should be ground on thick plate glass. For grinding glass stoppers, use coarse emery; turn in one direction, finish with fine emery.

**Glass-Grinding Medium.** Glycerin may be used instead of a camphor-turpentine mixture for a medium in which to suspend emery powder for grinding glass. Glycerin has body enough and is sufficiently viscous to carry the emery well, and besides this it is water-soluble, thus making it very easy to wash away the excess grinding agent when the job is done or when it is desirable to make a close inspection of the work done.

**Heating Baths.** For uniform heating of reactions, the following materials have proved satisfactory:

| | |
|---|---|
| For temperatures up to 100° C. | Steam |
| For temperatures from 100°–250° C. | Crisco or Nujol |
| For temperatures from 200°–300° C. | o-tolyl phosphate |
| For temperatures above 250° C. | Wood's metal |

**Ink for Glass Marking.**

| | |
|---|---|
| Barium sulfate | 15 parts by weight |
| Ammonium bifluoride | 15 parts by weight |
| Ammonium sulfate | 10 parts by weight |
| Oxalic acid | 8 parts by weight |
| Glycerin | 40 parts by weight |
| Water | 12 parts by weight |

If too thick, add more water. If the action is too slow, up to 5 percent of sodium fluoride may be added. Use in a hood or well ventilated room.

**Label Protection. Collodion for labels on bottles.** Dissolve 3–4 gm. pyroxylin in 100 cc. 1:3 mixture of alcohol and ether (25 cc. absolute alcohol, 75 cc. dry ether). First soak the pyroxylin in the alcohol, then add the ether.

**Labels for bottles.** Labels should be written in India ink. They can be made waterproof and durable by coating with a saturated solution of paraffin in benzene.

**Lacquer for protecting labels.** An excellent lacquer for protecting labels can be made by dissolving 20 gm. of vinyl acetate polymer (Vinylite A) in 100 cc. of a mixture of 3 parts of toluene and 1 part of 95 percent alcohol. This lacquer forms a colorless, transparent film which resists most reagents very well.

**Protecting varnish for labels.** Typed labels may be protected by several coats of a varnish made by dissolving ordinary toothbrush handles in acetone. The quantity of solvent should be adjusted to give a convenient viscosity. The varnish is water and acid resistant.

**Lubricant, Dry.** Melt a quantity of paraffin and add as much fine flake or powdered graphite as is readily moistened by the melted wax. Cool and cut while soft into convenient sticks. This lubricant, when rubbed on the surfaces involved, adheres and greatly reduces friction. It is particularly useful when one or both of the surfaces are of wood or other nonmetallic substance.

**Mildew Prevention on Leather Book Bindings.** Make a 2 to 5 percent solution—not more than 5 percent—of copper sulfate. Immerse a soft towel or cloth in this solution. Remove the cloth and thoroughly wring out. Then hang out to dry. When thoroughly dried, it can be used to rub leather-bound books. One treatment of the cloth will easily take care of scores or a hundred volumes, and the leather will not be marked by the chemical.

**Phenol (Carbolic Acid) Burns.** To chemically pure glycerin add bromine until slightly colored or saturated. Keep in a glass-stoppered bottle and apply quickly to phenol burns. The bromide reacts instantly with the phenol to form phenyl bromides.

**Polarity Test Paper.** Dissolve 1 gram of phenolphthalein in a small quantity of alcohol. Add the solution of phenolphthalein to 100 cc. of a 10 percent solution of potassium chloride in distilled water. Filter paper should be soaked in the solution and dried. When a strip of such paper is moistened with water and then placed in contact with the two terminals, it will show a bright red stain at the negative terminal.

**Resistant Paints and Varnishes. Acidproof wood stain.**

SOLUTION No. 1
125 gm. of copper sulfate
125 gm. of potassium chlorate
1,000 gm. of water

SOLUTION No. 2
150 gm. of good fresh anilin oil
180 gm. of concentrated hydrochloric acid
1,000 gm. of water

Wood must be free from paint, varnish, grease, or chemicals. Apply two coats of solution No. 1 boiling hot with a paint brush, allowing each coat to dry thoroughly before the next coat is applied. Then apply two coats of solution No. 2 in the same way. When the wood is completely dried, wash off excess chemicals with hot soapsuds. Finish with raw linseed oil. Polish comes from rubbing the oil down well with a cloth or sponge. Whenever the finish gets dingy again go over it with a coat of linseed oil and rub smooth.

**Resistant paint.** The following paint, when used on galvanized iron, has been found to hold up well, without cracking or peeling in a 3-yr. test. It can also be used on black iron, tin, copper, or stone such as is used for laboratory desk tops. It withstands dilute acids.

Formula: Stir in 10 parts by weight of benzol into 30 parts by weight of ordinary thin coal tar. Then add with vigorous stirring 10 parts by weight of Silica Black (a new product patented under U. S. No. 1,940,352).

**Scale Polish.** To brighten up refractometer and polarimeter scales without injury to the metal, rub with bone black or clarifying charcoal. A dry cloth with a little of the bone black is rubbed on the scale until a bright polish is produced. The divisions then stand out clearly and are easily read. The great advantage is that the fine lines are not worn away and no corrosive material is left to cause discolorations.

## Physical Tables and Definitions

Definitions of physical terms are combined with those of chemical terms, pages 22·4 to 22·9.

### Table 4. Weights and Specific Gravity of Some Common Substances

| Substance | Weight (lb. per cu. ft.) | Specific gravity or density (grams per cc.) |
|---|---|---|
| Air | 0.075 | 0.0012 |
| Water | 62.4 | 1.00 |
| Wood (depending on kind) | 2.5–87 | 0.04–1.40 |
| Paper | 44–72 | 0.7–1.15 |
| **Metals and alloys** | | |
| Magnesium | 106 | 1.7 |
| Aluminum | 168 | 2.7 |
| Zinc | 443 | 7.1 |
| Iron, cast | 437–493 | 7.0–7.9 |
| Steel | 474–487 | 7.6–7.8 |
| Copper | 530 | 8.5 |
| Nickel | 555 | 8.9 |
| Silver | 655 | 10.5 |
| Lead | 705 | 11.3 |
| Mercury | 849 | 13.6 |
| **Building materials** | | |
| Asphalt | 69–94 | 1.1–1.5 |
| Brick | 87–137 | 1.4–2.2 |
| Glass, common | 150–175 | 2.4–2.8 |
| **Fuels** | | |
| Charcoal, pine | 18–28 | 0.28–0.44 |
| Charcoal, oak | 35 | 0.57 |
| Coal, bituminous | 75–94 | 1.2–1.5 |
| Coal, anthracite | 87–112 | 1.4–1.8 |

## EQUATIONS FOR CONVERTING DEGREES CENTIGRADE TO DEGREES FAHRENHEIT, AND VICE-VERSA.

$$°F. = 9/5° \ C. + 32 \tag{1}$$

$$°C. = 5/9(°F. - 32) \tag{2}$$

where °F. = degrees Fahrenheit

and °C. = degrees Centigrade

### Table 5. Boiling Point of Water at Various Pressures

| Pressure in millimeters of mercury | Degrees Centigrade | Degrees Fahrenheit | Pressure in millimeters of mercury | Degrees Centigrade | Degrees Fahrenheit |
|---|---|---|---|---|---|
| 690 | 97.3 | 207.2 | 750 | 99.6 | 211.3 |
| 695 | 97.5 | 207.5 | 755 | 99.8 | 211.7 |
| 700 | 97.7 | 207.9 | 760 | 100.0 | 212.0 |
| 705 | 97.9 | 208.2 | 765 | 100.2 | 212.3 |
| 710 | 98.1 | 208.6 | 770 | 100.4 | 212.7 |
| 715 | 98.3 | 208.9 | 775 | 100.5 | 213.0 |
| 720 | 98.5 | 209.3 | 780 | 100.7 | 213.3 |
| 725 | 98.7 | 209.6 | 785 | 100.9 | 213.6 |
| 730 | 98.9 | 210.0 | 790 | 101.1 | 214.0 |
| 735 | 99.1 | 210.3 | 795 | 101.3 | 214.3 |
| 740 | 99.3 | 210.6 | 800 | 101.4 | 214.6 |
| 745 | 99.4 | 211.0 | | | |

### Table 6. Freezing and Boiling Points of Common Materials; Calibration of Thermometers; Antifreezes

| Substance | Point | Degrees Centigrade | Degrees Fahrenheit |
|---|---|---|---|
| Carbon dioxide (solid) ................ | Vapor pressure | −78.5 | −109.3 |
| Mercury ........................... | Freezing | −38.9 | −38.0 |
| Carbon tetrachloride .................. | Freezing | −22.9 | −9.2 |
| Ice ............................... | Melting | 0.0 | 32 |
| Chloroform ........................ | Boiling | 61.3 | 142.3 |
| Ethyl alcohol ....................... | Boiling | 78.3 | 172.9 |
| Benzene ........................... | Boiling | 80.0 | 176 |
| Steam ............................. | Condensing | 100.0 | 212 |
| Antifreezes (water mixtures): | | | |
| a. 20.2% alcohol by volume ......... | Freezing | −7.5 | 18.5 |
| 40.5% alcohol by volume ......... | Freezing | −23.6 | −10.5 |
| 78.2% alcohol by volume ......... | Freezing | −51.3 | −60.3 |
| b. 20% glycerol by weight .......... | Freezing | −4.8 | 23.4 |
| 40% glycerol by weight .......... | Freezing | −15.4 | 4.3 |
| 70% glycerol by weight .......... | Freezing | −37.8 | −36.0 |
| c. 20% Prestone by weight ......... | Freezing | −7.9 | 17.8 |
| 40% Prestone by weight ......... | Freezing | −22.3 | −8.2 |
| 60% Prestone by weight ......... | Freezing | −49.3 | −56.7 |

Source: Lange and Forker.

**THE RELATION BETWEEN SPECIFIC GRAVITY AND THE BAUMÉ SCALES.** The following equations give the relation between specific gravity and the Baumé scales commonly used in the United States:

For liquids heavier than water,

$$\text{Bé} = 145 - \frac{145}{\text{Specific gravity}} \tag{1}$$

Table 7.  Baumé and Specific Gravity of Some Common Liquids and
Solutions

| Liquids | Specific gravity or density (grams per cc.) | Baumé (Bé) |
|---|---|---|
| Water | 1.00 | 0.0 |
| Acetone | 0.79 | 47.2 |
| Acids | | |
|   Acetic (100%) | 1.05 | 6.9 |
|   Hydrochloric (40.1%) | 1.20 | 24.2 |
|   Nitric (95.1%) | 1.50 | 48.3 |
|   Sulfuric (93.2%) | 1.84 | 66 |
| Alcohol | | |
|   Ethyl | 0.79 | 47.2 |
|   Methyl | 0.81 | 42.8 |
| Benzene | 0.90 | 17.4 |
| Carbon tetrachloride | 1.60 | 54.4 |
| Chloroform | 1.49 | 47.7 |
| Ether | 0.74 | 59.2 |
| Gasoline | 0.66–0.69 | 82.1–72.9 |
| Glycerol | 1.26 | 30.0 |
| Kerosene | 0.82 | 40.7 |
| Milk | 1.028–1.035 | 3.95–3.90 |
| Naphtha | | |
|   Petroleum ether | 0.67 | 79.0 |
|   Wood | 0.81–0.85 | 42.8–34.7 |
| Oils | | |
|   Castor | 0.97 | 14.3 |
|   Cottonseed | 0.93 | 20.5 |
|   Creosote | 1.04–1.10 | 5.58 |
|   Linseed, boiled | 0.94 | 18.9 |
| Turpentine (spirits) | 0.87 | 30.9 |

For liquids lighter than water,

$$B\acute{e} = \frac{140}{\text{Specific gravity}} - 130 \tag{2}$$

where Bé represents the Baumé units (adopted by the United States Bureau of
Standards).

Table 8.  Howe Scale of Colors for Estimating the Temperature of Heated Metals

| Color | Degrees Centigrade | Degrees Fahrenheit |
|---|---|---|
| Lowest visible red | 475 | 887 |
| Dull red | 550–625 | 1,022–1,157 |
| Full cherry red | 700 | 1,292 |
| Light red | 850 | 1,562 |
| Orange | 900 | 1,652 |
| Full yellow | 950–1,000 | 1,742–1,832 |
| White | 1,150 and up | 2,102 and up |

### Table 9. Heat Value of Fuels

| Fuel | Btu per pound |
|---|---|
| Wood | |
| Beech (13% water) | 7,500 |
| Birch (11.8% water) | 7,570 |
| Oak (13.3% water) | 7,180 |
| Pine (12.2% water) | 7,960 |
| Charcoal (to $CO_2$) | 14,500–14,700 |
| Pitch | 15,100 |
| Coal | |
| Anthracite | 8,200–14,100 |
| Semianthracite | 10,400–13,700 |
| Bituminous | 10,200–14,700 |
| Semibituminous | 12,600–14,900 |
| Subbituminous | 8,700–10,600 |
| Lignite | 5,990– 7,350 |
| Peat | 510– 4,100 |
| Petroleum | 18,500–18,590 |

For approximate weight and heating values per cord of different woods, see Section **14**, Utilization and Wood Technology.

**PHOTOGRAPHIC DATA. Film Speed Rating Systems.** The data in Table 11 are presented as a general guide. There is no mathematical relationship between the different film ratings because there is no common basis for them. However, in practice it is possible to compare the systems so that it will be pos-

### Table 10. Filter Factor for Various Films
D = Daylight.   T = Tungsten.

| Film type | Yellow | | | | Orange | | Red | | Green | | | |
| | K–1 | | K–2 | | G–1 | | A–1 | | X–1 | | X–2 | |
| | D | T | D | T | D | T | D | T | D | T | D | T |
|---|---|---|---|---|---|---|---|---|---|---|---|---|
| Eastman I [a] | 2 | 1.5 | 2.5 | 2 | 5 | 3 | .. | .. | .. | .. | .. | .. |
| Eastman II [b] | 1.5 | 1.5 | 2 | 1.5 | 3.5 | 2.5 | 4.5 | 3 | 4 | 3 | 6 | 5 |
| Eastman III [c] | 1.5 | 1.5 | 2 | 1.5 | 3 | 2.5 | 3.5 | 2.7 | 4.5 | 3 | 6 | 5 |
| Agfa IV [d] | 2 | 1.8 | 4 | 3 | 12 | 8 | .. | .. | .. | .. | .. | .. |
| Agfa V [e] | 1.6 | 1.4 | 2 | 1.6 | 3 | 2 | 6 | 3 | 4 | 3 | 6 | 4 |
| Agfa VI [f] | 1.4 | 1.2 | 1.8 | 1.4 | 3 | 1.8 | 4 | 2 | 4 | 3 | 6 | 3 |
| DuPont VII [g] | 1.7 | 1.5 | 4 | 2 | 5 | 3 | .. | .. | 4.5 | 3 | .. | .. |
| DuPont VIII [h] | 1.4 | 1.2 | 1.6 | 1.5 | 2.5 | 2 | 8 | 4 | 4 | 3 | .. | .. |
| Gevaert IX [i] | 1.4 | 1.3 | 2.3 | 1.5 | 3 | 2.5 | 10 | 6 | .. | .. | .. | .. |

[a] Regular N.C., Verichrome, Super Speed Ortho Portrait, Super Ortho Press.
[b] Panatomic X, Plus X, Micro File, Super XX (35 mm.).
[c] Super XX (rolls and packs), Super Panchro Press, Tri X-Pan, Cine Super X, Cine Super XX.
[d] All Plenachrome, Commercial ortho.
[e] Supreme, Hypan, Isopan.
[f] Superpan Press, Triple S pan.
[g] Ortho-7, X-F Ortho.
[h] Arrow Pan, X-F Pan, High Speed Pan, Fine Grain Pan.
[i] Panchromosa, Microgran.

## Table 11. Film Speed Ratings

| ASA exposure index | General Electric | Weston numbers | American Scheiner degrees | European Scheiner degrees | Relative exposure required |
|---|---|---|---|---|---|
| 0.6 | 0.6 | 0.5 | 6 | 12 | 106.7 |
| 0.8 | — | 0.6 | 7 | 13 | 80.0 |
| 1.0 | 1.0 | 0.7 | 8 | 14 | 64.0 |
| 1.2 | 1.5 | 1.0 | 9 | 15 | 53.3 |
| 1.6 | 2.0 | 1.2 | 10 | 16 | 40.0 |
| 2.0 | — | 1.5 | 11 | 17 | 32.0 |
| 2.5 | 3 | 2 | 12 | 18 | 25.6 |
| 3 | 4 | 2.5 | 13 | 19 | 21 33 |
| 4 | — | 3 | 14 | 20 | 16.00 |
| 5 | 6 | 4 | 15 | 21 | 12.80 |
| 6 | 8 | 5 | 16 | 22 | 10.67 |
| 8 | 10 | 6 | 17 | 23 | 8.00 |
| 10 | 12 | 8 | 18 | 24 | 6.40 |
| 12 | 16 | 10 | 19 | 25 | 5.33 |
| 16 | 20 | 12 | 20 | 26 | 4.00 |
| 20 | 24 | 16 | 21 | 27 | 3.20 |
| 25 | 32 | 20 | 22 | 28 | 2.56 |
| 32 | 40 | 24 | 23 | 29 | 2.00 |
| 40 | 48 | 32 | 24 | 30 | 1.60 |
| 50 | 64 | 40 | 25 | 31 | 1.28 |
| 64 | 80 | 50 | 26 | 32 | 1.00 |
| 80 | 100 | 64 | 27 | 33 | 0.80 |
| 100 | 125 | 80 | 28 | 34 | .64 |
| 125 | 150 | 100 | 29 | 35 | .50 |
| 160 | 200 | 125 | 30 | 36 | .40 |
| 200 | 250 | 160 | 31 | 37 | .32 |
| 250 | 300 | 200 | 32 | 38 | .25 |
| 320 | 400 | 250 | 33 | 39 | .20 |
| 400 | 500 | 320 | 34 | 40 | .16 |
| 500 | 600 | 400 | 35 | 41 | .13 |
| 650 | 800 | 500 | 36 | 42 | .10 |
| 800 | 900 | 650 | 37 | 43 | .08 |
| 1,000 | 1,000 | 800 | 38 | 44 | .06 |

sible to use a film with one type of rating with an exposure meter using a different system. In spite of the fact that these data have been compiled from different sources which diverge slightly, the figures may be used with reasonable confidence.

**Approximate Filter Factors.** For convenience, films have been arranged in Table 10 in groups having approximately the same color response. In some cases the filter factors differ slightly from the values suggested by film manufacturers, but in no case is the difference sufficient to impair the use of the film. For more exact values, consult the film manufacturer.

## BIBLIOGRAPHY

FURMAN, N. H. (ed.). 1939. *Scott's standard methods of chemical analysis.* D. Van Nostrand Co., Inc., New York.

HODGMAN, C. S. (ed.). 1949. *Handbook of chemistry and physics.* 31st ed. Chemical Rubber Publ. Co., Cleveland, Ohio.

KEHL, GEORGE L. 1939. *The principles of metallographic laboratory practice.* Mc-Graw-Hill Book Co., Inc., New York.

LANGE, N. A., and G. M. FORKER. 1944. *Handbook of chemistry.* Handbook Publishers, Inc., Sandusky, Ohio.

# MATHEMATICAL FORMULAS AND DEFINITIONS

## CONTENTS

# MATHEMATICAL FORMULAS AND DEFINITIONS

## Arithmetic

**LOGARITHMS.** Any number, whether greater or less than unity, can be expressed as a power of another number. Common logarithms, expressing the numbers from 1 to 999 as powers of 10, are given in Table 4 (page 23 · 37). In this form numbers may be multiplied or divided, or their roots extracted, with very much less labor than by ordinary arithmetic. The processes depend upon the laws of exponents, which with 10 as a base may be illustrated as follows:

$$10^x \times 10^y = 10^{x + y}$$

$$\frac{10^x}{10^y} = 10^x \times 10^{-y} = 10^{x - y}$$

$$\sqrt[x]{10} = 10^{1/x}$$

The tabular figures are decimals, although the decimal point is omitted to save space; thus, log 4 is 0.6021. They are called mantissae, and are the only part of the logarithms appearing in the table. Every logarithm, however, has in addition a characteristic, or one or more digits or zeros to the left of the decimal point. For whole numbers the characteristic of the logarithm is always one less than the number of digits in the original number (called the antilogarithm). Thus the log of 4 is 0.6021; of 40 it is 1.6021; and of 400, 2.6021. For numbers smaller than 1 the characteristic is always negative, and is one more than the number of zeros immediately following the decimal point: log 0.4 = $\bar{1}$.6021; log 0.04 = $\bar{2}$.6021; etc. The negative sign is written above the characteristic only, because the mantissa is always positive. When, as shown later, logarithms are added or subtracted, it is convenient to write negative characteristics as a positive number minus 10; thus log 0.04 = $\bar{2}$.6021 = 8.6021 − 10. The logarithm of a number larger than 999 can be obtained from the table by interpolation. The log of 4,672, for example, lies proportionately between 3.6693 and 3.6702, the logs for 4,670 and 4,680. Interpolation is also necessary with decimals to a greater number of places than 0.999.

To find a number (antilogarithm) which corresponds to a given logarithm, the procedure is reversed. Logarithmic computation is illustrated as follows:

1. To multiply any numbers, write them in log form and add algebraically, that is, observing the signs of the characteristics.

**Example.** 542 × 0.278 × 8.135.

> log (542) (0.278) (8.135) = log (542) + log (0.278) + log (8.135)
> log (542) = 2.7340 or 2.7340
> log (0.278) = $\bar{1}$.4440 or 9.4440 − 10
> log (8.135) = 0.9103 or 0.9103
> Adding: 3.0883 or 13.0883 − 10

The number in the log table corresponding to the mantissa (.0883) is 1,226. Pointing off 3 + 1 places, the product of the three numbers is 1,226, if calculated from Table 4.

2. To divide one number by another, write them in log form and subtract the latter number.

**Example.** 3.26 divided by 0.0482.

$$\log \left( \frac{3.26}{0.0482} \right) = \log (3.26 - \log (0.0482)$$

$$\begin{aligned}
\log (3.26) &= 0.5132 \text{ or } 10.5132 - 10 \\
\log (0.0482) &= \overline{2}.6830 \text{ or } 8.6830 - 10 \\
\text{Subtracting:} & \qquad\qquad\quad 1.8302
\end{aligned}$$

The number in the log table corresponding to the mantissa (.8302) is **6,764.** Pointing off 1 + 1 places, the quotient is **67.64.**

3. To raise a number to a given power, multiply the log of the number by the desired power.

**Example.** $(2.73)^3$

$$\log (2.73)^3 = 3 \log (2.73)$$
$$\log (2.73) = 0.4362$$
$$\log (2.73)^3 = 3(0.4362) = 1.3086$$

The number in the log table corresponding to the mantissa (.3086) is **2,035.** Pointing off 1 + 1 places, the cube is **20.35.**

4. To extract the root of a number, divide the log of the number by the desired root.

**Example.** $\sqrt[3]{376}$

$$\log \sqrt[3]{376} = \tfrac{1}{3} \log (376)$$
$$\log (376) = 2.5752$$
$$\log \sqrt[3]{376} = \tfrac{1}{3}(2.5752) = 0.8584$$

The number in the log table corresponding to the mantissa (.8584) is **7,218.** Pointing off 0 + 1 places, the cube root is **7.218.**

**SLIDE-RULE CALCULATIONS.** The section on logarithms has made it clear that converting numbers into their logarithms can shorten the laborious processes of multiplying, dividing, and extracting roots. The slide rule is simply a mechanical device for doing these jobs. A glance will show that the graduations on 6 of the 7 scales of the common type of 10-in. rule are not arithmetic but logarithmic (one- or two-cycle). Moving one scale relative to those adjacent therefore adds or subtracts logarithms, which is the equivalent of multiplying or dividing the original numbers (antilogs). This is equally true whether the quantities involved are ordinary numbers (Scales A, B, C, and D on most rules), or trigonometric functions (Scales S and T). Squares or square roots are read from two fixed scales (A and D), by means of the hairline on the glass indicator.

The manual which is sold with most slide rules gives detailed directions for their use. Some common operations, assuming the use of a 10-in. rule, are illustrated below. A good light and care in reading the scales are always necessary; a magnifier on the indicator is very helpful.

**Multiplication.** Use identical Scales C and D. Note that (1) the graduations, designated by large numerals 1, on the extreme right and left of each scale, are called the right and left indexes; (2) the small numerals at the left are not 1, 2, 3, etc., but 11, 12, 13, up to 20; (3) on the remainder of the scales, 2 is therefore actually 20, 3 is 30, etc.; (4) between 20 and 30, and between 30 and 40, the smallest graduations are 0.2; and (5) above 40, 0.5. To multiply 18 by 45, set the hairline of the indicator on 18 on Scale D, and move the slide to the right until the left-hand index (large, not small 1) is also aligned under the hairline of the indicator. Being careful not to disturb this alignment, move the indicator to the 45 graduation on Scale C. The corresponding reading on Scale D is 81, to which it is evident from inspection that a 0 should be added, making it 810.

If $25 \times 45$ is desired, the above procedure puts 45 on Scale C off the slide rule, to the right; it is then necessary to set the right-hand index of Scale C opposite 25 on Scale D, and to move the indicator to the left until its hairline is over 45 on Scale C. The corresponding reading on Scale D is about halfway between 112 and 113, or 112.5, or by inspection 1,125.

**Division.** To divide 18 by 45, place the indicator over 18 on Scale D, move the slide until 45 on Scale C is also aligned under the indicator hair. Without disturbing this alignment, move the indicator until its cross-hair is over the right-hand index of Scale C; the corresponding reading on Scale D is 40, or by inspection 0.40.

If the above process puts the right-hand index of Scale C off the rule, as in dividing 72 by 45, read the value (in this case, 16) on Scale D opposite the left-hand index of Scale C, and point off by inspection, as before: 1.6. Confusion may result in division because the alignment of the two numbers to be divided places the index on Scale D opposite a number on Scale C; this number is the reciprocal of the quotient. The quotient must be read on the same scale as the denominator of the fraction, or Scale D. The final reading in both multiplication and division is on the fixed scale, D.

**Square Root.** Square roots are obtained from readings on the fixed scales A and D, with the help of the indicator. Note that on Scale A there are two cycles of numbers, identically graduated. To find the square root of 9, place the hairline of the indicator over this number on the left cycle of Scale A, and read the corresponding number on Scale D: 3. But to obtain the square root of 90, place the indicator over 90 on the right cycle of Scale A, and read 9.48 on Scale D. The somewhat complicated rule for determining which cycle to use is: from the decimal point, group the digits in 2's, adding any necessary zeros; if the group farthest to the left is 1 to 9, use the left-hand cycle; if it is 10 to 99, use the right-hand cycle. Thus:

| | | | | | | |
|---|---|---|---|---|---|---|
| 3 | 00 | 00., | 3 00., | 03., | .03 , | and | .00 03 | left-hand cycle |
| 30 | 00 | 00; | 30 00., | 30., | .30 , | .00 30 | right-hand cycle |

**Proportions.** To solve a proportion in the form $x : 24 = 11 : 18$, use Scales C and D; consider this as $C:D = C:D$. Set 11 on Scale C opposite 18 on Scale D. Move the indicator to 24 on D, and read $x = 147$ (or, by inspection, 14.7) on Scale C. The $x$ corresponding to any figure other than 24 can be read on C if the slide is left undisturbed.

**Solution of Triangles.** The foregoing procedure, substituting Scale S for Scale B, is useful in such solutions of right and oblique triangles as depend on the sine in the formula:

$$\frac{a}{\sin A} = \frac{b}{\sin B} = \frac{c}{\sin C}$$

To solve this formula, select any term, such as $a/\sin A$, for which both quantities are known, and align the numerator on Scale A with the denominator on Scale S. The unknowns in the other terms can then be read opposite the known values.

**Sines.** To obtain natural sines, align Scales A and S precisely. For any angle on Scale S the sine may be read opposite on Scale A. Note that angles smaller than 0°34.4′ do not appear on Scale S. For such angles sines are nearly proportional to angles; to obtain them, divide the number of minutes by 3,440, using Scales C and D (in pointing off the result, remember that sin 0°1′ is approximately 0.0003).

**Latitudes and Departures.** (See page 17·16, Surveying.) These are obtained from sines by the formulas:

Latitude = Distance × Sine of (90° minus the bearing)
Departure = Distance × Sine of bearing

Where closed traverses are made by rough methods (as the boundary of a burn, traced by hand compass and pacing) latitudes and departures may be accurately enough computed on the slide rule: align the index on Scale S with the distance on Scale A, and read the result on A, opposite the angle on S.

**Tangents.** Scale T may be used to obtain natural tangents of all angles between 5° 43′ and 84°17′, in the same manner as Scale S. But for other angles the process is complicated, and the slide rule is therefore unlikely to be of practical use in problems involving tangents.

**Logarithms.** These may be obtained, to 3 decimal places, from Scales C, D, and L. For example, find log 50. With Scales C and D uppermost on the slide, set 5 on C opposite the right index of D. Set the hairline on the indicator over the left-hand index of C, and carefully reverse the slide, so that the zero on Scale L is under the hairline on the indicator. Shift the indicator to coincide with the right-hand index of Scale D, and on Scale L read 0.699, the mantissa of the required logarithm. Because 50 has two digits, complete the logarithm as 1.699. The process of calculating logarithms is obviously too laborious for extensive use.

**Accuracy of the Slide Rule.** A 10-in. slide rule gives results correct to within about 1 part in 1,000, or 1/10 of 1 percent.

**POSITION OF DECIMAL POINT IN MULTIPLYING AND DIVIDING. Multiplication.** To multiply decimals, multiply as with whole numbers. Point off from the right of the product as many decimal places as there are in the sum of the decimal places of the numbers multiplied. Prefix zeros to the product, if necessary, to fill out the number of places.

**Example.**

$$0.542 \times 5.162 = 2.797804$$

**Division.** To divide a decimal by a whole number, divide as with whole numbers, placing the decimal point in the quotient directly above or below the decimal point in the dividend.

**Example.**

$$25\overline{)478.25} \quad 19.13$$

To divide a decimal by a decimal, move the decimal point of the divisor to the right until the divisor becomes a whole number; then move the decimal point of the dividend to the right the same number of places as it was moved in the divisor, adding zeros if necessary. Then divide as shown in the preceding example.

**Example.**

$$35.32 \div 0.4$$

$$8\ 8.3$$

$$0.4.\overline{)35.3.2}$$

**ROUNDING OFF.** In order to express a quotient to a desired accuracy, division should be carried to one more decimal place than is needed. If this extra figure is 5 or more, drop it and add 1 to the figure in the preceding place. Put a minus sign after the quotient. If the figure is less than 5, drop it entirely and put a plus sign after the quotient.

**RECIPROCALS.** The reciprocal of a whole number is obtained by expressing the number as a fraction and inverting the fraction. Thus the reciprocal of 2 (2/1) is ½. The reciprocal of a fraction is obtained by inverting the fraction. Thus the reciprocal of ¾ is 4/3, and of 3½ (7/2) it is 2/7. In dividing fractions, the dividend is multiplied by the reciprocal of the divisor. Thus ¾ ÷ 3 = ¾ × ⅓ = ¼. When a group of numbers is to be divided by the same divisor the operation is greatly simplified by multiplying each number by a decimal reciprocal of the divisor.

# Algebra

**POWERS AND ROOTS (EXPONENTS).** A power $a^n$ with a positive integral exponent $n$ is defined as the repeated product of $n$ factors each equal to $a$.

$$a^n = a \cdot a \cdot a \cdot \ \ldots \text{ to } n \text{ factors}$$

$$a^{-n} = \frac{1}{a^n}$$

$$a^m \cdot a^n = a^{m+n}$$

$$\frac{a^m}{a^n} = a^{m-n}$$

$$(ab)^n = a^n b^n$$

$$\left(\frac{a}{b}\right)^n = \frac{a^n}{b^n}$$

$$(a^m)^n = (a^n)^m = a^{mn}$$

An $n$th root of a given number $a$ is defined as a number whose $n$th power is equal to $a$.

$$(\sqrt[n]{a})^n = a$$

$$a^{\frac{1}{n}} = \sqrt[n]{a}$$

$$a^{\left(\frac{m}{n}\right)} = \sqrt[n]{a^m}$$

$$\sqrt[n]{ab} = \sqrt[n]{a}\,\sqrt[n]{b}$$

$$\sqrt[n]{\frac{a}{b}} = \frac{\sqrt[n]{a}}{\sqrt[n]{b}}$$

$$\sqrt[n]{\sqrt[m]{a}} = \sqrt[mn]{a}$$

If $f(x) = (x + a)^2$, then $\sqrt{f(x)} = x + a$.

**Extract the Square Root of a Number.** Problem: $\sqrt{5317636}$. Divide this number into pairs of digits starting from the decimal, 5, 31, 76, 36. Then proceed as outlined below.

**Example.**

| Trial divisor | Number | Square root |
|---|---|---|
| | 5 31 76 36 | 2306 |
| | 4 | |
| 4⌀3 | 1 31 | |
| | 1 29 | |
| 460 | 2 76 | |
| | | |
| 460⌀6 | 2 76 36 | |
| | 2 76 36 | |

Step 1. Find the largest whole number the square of which is equal to or less than the first number (or pair of numbers) on the left, i.e., 5. It is obviously 2. Place 2 in the square root column and $2^2$ or 4 under the number 5. Subtract 4 from 5 and bring down the next pair of digits, i.e., 31, giving 131.

Step 2. Double the square root so far obtained, i.e., 2, and multiply by 10, giving 40. Place in the trial divisor column. 40 is contained in 131 three times. Replace the zero by 3, giving 43. Multiply the adjusted divisor, 43, by 3, giving 129, and place under the 131. Put 3 in the square root column to the right of the 2. Subtract 129 from 131 and bring down the next pair of numbers, i.e., 76, giving 276. If the first difference had been 128 instead of 131, then the adjusted divisor would have had to be lowered to 42. 42 would then be multiplied by 2 and the 2 placed in the square root.

Step 3. Double the square root, 23, and multiply by 10, giving 460, and place in the trial divisor column. Adding even the lowest unit, 1, makes the adjusted divisor larger than 276. So 0 is added to the square root and the next pair of numbers is brought down.

Step 4. Double the square root 230 and multiply by 10 giving 4,600, and place in the trial divisor column. 4,600 is contained in 27,636 six times, so change the last 0 to 6, giving 4,606, and multiply by 6, giving 27,636. Place under the 27,636 and put 6 in the square root column; since the difference is zero, the answer is exact. If the difference were not zero or the number had decimals in it, another pair of numbers would have had to be brought down, proceeding as before until enough places were obtained. The numbers being brought down are sometimes zeros.

**MULTIPLICATION OF POLYNOMIALS.** Multiply each term in the multiplicand by each term in the multiplier. Collect and combine the terms containing identical powers of identical variables.

**Example.**

$$(3x^4 + 2x - 1)(2x^3 + 3x^2 + 1)$$

$$= 3x^4(2x^3 + 3x^2 + 1) + 2x(2x^3 + 3x^2 + 1) - 1(2x^3 + 3x^2 + 1)$$

$$= \begin{cases} 6x^7 + 9x^6 + 0x^5 + 3x^4 \\ \qquad\qquad\quad + 4x^4 + 6x^3 + 0x^2 + 2x \\ \qquad\qquad\qquad\qquad - 2x^3 - 3x^2 + 0x - 1 \end{cases}$$

$$= 6x^7 + 9x^6 \qquad\quad + 7x^4 + 4x^3 - 3x^2 + 2x - 1$$

**DIVISION OF POLYNOMIALS.** Arrange the terms of the dividend in descending powers of $x$, supplying a zero coefficient whenever a power of $x$ is missing; arrange the terms of the divisor similarly. Divide the highest power term in the dividend by the highest power term in the divisor. Record the quotient, multiply each term in the divisor by it, and place the products underneath the corresponding powers in the dividend. Subtract, and then repeat the division processes until the remainder is of a lower degree than the divisor. The fraction $\left(\dfrac{\text{remainder}}{\text{divisor}}\right)$, if not zero, should be appended to the quotient as a remainder term

**Example.**

$$
\begin{array}{l}
\text{Divisor} \qquad\qquad 3x^4 \qquad\quad\; + 2x - 1 \;\leftarrow\text{Quotient}\\
2x^3 + 3x^2 + 0 + 1\,\overline{\smash{)}\,6x^7 + 9x^6 + 0 + 7x^4 + 4x^3 - 3x^2 + 2x - 1}\;\leftarrow\text{Dividend}\\
\qquad\qquad\qquad\; 6x^7 + 9x^6 + 0 + 3x^4\\
\qquad\qquad\qquad\; \overline{\phantom{6x^7 + 9x^6 + 0 + 3x^4}}\\
\qquad\qquad\qquad\qquad\qquad\quad 4x^4 + 4x^3 - 3x^2 + 2x\\
\qquad\qquad\qquad\qquad\qquad\quad 4x^4 + 6x^3 + 0 \;\;\; + 2x\\
\qquad\qquad\qquad\qquad\qquad\quad \overline{\phantom{4x^4 + 6x^3 + 0 + 2x}}\\
\qquad\qquad\qquad\qquad\qquad\qquad\; -2x^3 - 3x^2 + 0 \;\; -1\\
\qquad\qquad\qquad\qquad\qquad\qquad\; -2x^3 - 3x^2 + 0 \;\; -1\\
\qquad\qquad\qquad\qquad\qquad\qquad\; \overline{\phantom{-2x^3 - 3x^2 + 0 - 1}}\\
\qquad\qquad\qquad\qquad\qquad\qquad\qquad\qquad\qquad\; 0 \;\;\leftarrow\text{Remainder}
\end{array}
$$

**FACTORING OF POLYNOMIALS.** Let $a$, $b$, $c$, be constants or functions of one or more variables.

$a^K - b^K = \left(a^{\frac{K}{2}} - b^{\frac{K}{2}}\right)\left(a^{\frac{K}{2}} + b^{\frac{K}{2}}\right)$ when $K$ is an even integer.

$a^K - b^K = (a - b)\,(a^{K-1} + a^{K-2}b^1 + a^{K-3}b^2 + \ldots + b^{K-1})$ when $K$ is an odd integer.

$a^K + b^K = (a + b)\,(a^{K-1} - a^{K-2}b^1 + a^{K-3}b^2 - \ldots + b^{K-1})$ when $K$ is an odd integer.

$$a^2 + 2ab + b^2 \qquad\qquad\qquad\qquad\qquad\qquad = (a + b)^2$$

$$a^3 + 3a^2b + 3ab^2 + b^3 \qquad\qquad\qquad\qquad\; = (a + b)^3$$

$$a^4 + 4a^3b + 6a^2b^2 + 4ab^3 + b^4 \qquad\qquad\quad = (a + b)^4$$

$$a^2 + b^2 + c^2 + 2(ab + ac + bc) \qquad\qquad\quad = (a + b + c)^2$$

$$a^3 + b^3 + c^3 + 3(a^2b + a^2c + ab^2 + b^2c + ac^2 + bc^2) + 6abc \qquad = (a + b + c)^3$$

$$a^4 + b^4 + c^4 + 4(a^3b + a^3c + ab^3 + b^3c + ac^3 + bc^3) +$$
$$6(a^2b^2 + a^2c^2 + b^2c^2) + 12(a^2bc + ab^2c + abc^2) \qquad = (a + b + c)^4$$

In the absence of recognizable factorable patterns, a factorable pattern can sometimes be secured by regrouping, by substituting $a$, $b$, $c$, for more complicated functions, or by adding and subtracting quantities needed to complete perfect polynomial expansions. Failing this, trial and error division can be tried, using likely low degree divisors. A zero remainder will indicate that the divisor is a root of the equation.

To factor the polynomial,

$$ax^2 + bx + c = 0$$

find the factors of $a$. Let these factors be $m$ and $n$, so $a = mn$. Find the factors of $c$. Let these factors be $p$ and $q$, so $c = pq$. The coefficient $b$ is then $mq + np$. Thus

$$ax^2 + bx + c = mnx^2 + (mq + np)x + pq = (mx + p)(nx + q) = 0$$

Knowing $m$, $n$, and $p$ and $q$, then the particular combination of $m$ with $p$ and $q$ can be obtained by inspection or by trial division.

**EXPANSION OF POLYNOMIALS TO INTEGRAL POWERS.** Let $a$ and $b$ be constants or functions of one or more variables. Let $K$ be a constant integer and $R$ be a variable integer.

Binomial (2-term polynomial) expanded to $K$th power:

$$(a+b)^K = a^K + \frac{(K)}{(1)}a^{K-1}b + \frac{(K)(K-1)}{1\cdot2}a^{K-2}b^2 + $$
$$\frac{K(K-1)(K-2)}{1\cdot2\cdot3}a^{K-3}b^3 + \cdots + b^K \qquad (1)$$

Note that $a^0$ (or any quantity to the zero power) $= 1$.

$$(a+b)^K = a^K\binom{K}{0} + \binom{K}{1}a^{K-1}b + \binom{K}{2}a^{K-2}b^2 + \cdots + \binom{K}{R}a^{K-R}b^R$$
$$+ \binom{K}{K-1}ab^{K-1} + \binom{K}{K}b^K \qquad (2)$$

where $\binom{K}{R} =$ combination of $K$ things taken $R$ at a time.

$$\binom{K}{R} = \frac{K!}{(K-R)!R!}$$

where $K! = 1\cdot2\cdot3 \cdots (K-1)\cdot(K)$ or factorial $K$, and

$$(K-R)! = 1\cdot2\cdot3 \cdots (K-R-1)\cdot(K-R) \text{ or factorial } (K-R).$$

Note factorial zero equals one, i.e., $0! = 1$.

$$(a+b)^5 = a^5 + 5a^4b + 10a^3b^2 + 10a^2b^3 + 5ab^4 + b^5$$

**SOLUTION OF POLYNOMIAL EQUATIONS WITH INTEGRAL POWERS OF ONE UNKNOWN.** Arrange the terms in descending powers of the unknown $x$, supplying a zero coefficient where a consecutive power of $x$ is missing. Let $a$, $b$, $c$, $d$, $e$, be real numbers, and let $x_1$, $x_2$, etc., denote a set of solutions, all of which satisfy the equation.

Linear or first-degree equation:

$$ax + b = 0$$

There is only one solution, and it is real:

$$x = -\frac{b}{a}$$

Quadratic or second-degree equation:

$$ax^2 + bx + c = 0$$

To solve such an equation, rearrange it, and add a term to both sides which completes the square containing the unknown:

$$ax^2 + bx + c = 0 \qquad x^2 + \left(\frac{b}{a}\right)x = -\frac{c}{a} \qquad x^2 + \left(\frac{b}{a}\right)x + \frac{b^2}{4a^2} = \frac{b^2}{4a^2} - \frac{c}{a}$$

Extract the square roots:

$$x + \frac{b}{2a} = \pm\sqrt{\frac{ab^2 - 4a^2c}{4a^3}} = \pm\sqrt{\frac{b^2 - 4ac}{4a^2}} = \pm\frac{\sqrt{b^2 - 4ac}}{2a}$$

$$x = \frac{-b \pm \sqrt{b^2 - 4ac}}{2a}$$

## SOLUTION OF SETS OF POLYNOMIAL EQUATIONS WITH MORE THAN ONE UNKNOWN.

Arrange one equation so that terms involving unknowns ($x, y, \ldots$ etc.) are aligned with terms involving the same unknown in another equation, and so that the constants are on the extreme right-hand side of the equations:

$$ax + by = c$$
$$dx + ey = f$$

Multiply each equation by an appropriate factor so that each equation contains an unknown term common to the other. Subtract:

$$dax + dby = dc$$
$$\underline{adx + aey = af}$$
$$(bd - ae)y = cd - af$$

In order for solution to be possible, the original equations must be as numerous as the unknowns. The above process is repeated when there are more than two unknowns, until all but one unknown have been eliminated, as above. Then the constant is divided by the coefficient of the last unknown, thus:

$$y = \frac{cd - af}{bd - ae}$$

## PROGRESSIONS.

An array of numbers proceeding according to a definite law is called a series or a progression.

**Arithmetical Progressions.** If the successive terms are found by adding or subtracting a constant amount, the common difference, the progression is arithmetical. The terms of an arithmetical progression are

$$a, a + d, a + 2d, a + 3d, \text{ etc.}$$

The $n$th term being $a + (n - 1)d$.

The sum of an arithmetical progression of $n$ terms is

$$a + (a + d) + (a + 2d) + (a + 3d) + \cdots + [a + (n - 1)d]$$
$$= \frac{n}{2}[2a + (n - 1)d] = na + \frac{n(n - 1)}{2}d$$

**Geometrical Progressions.** A geometrical progression is one in which the successive terms are found by multiplying by a constant number or multiplier; the latter is referred to as the ratio of the series and is found by dividing any term by the preceding term. The terms of a geometrical progression are

$$a, ar, ar^2, ar^3, \text{ etc.}$$
The $n$th term is $ar^{n-1}$.

The sum of the $n$ terms of a geometrical progression is

$$a + ar + ar^2 + ar^3 + \cdots + ar^{n-1} = \frac{a - ar^n}{1 - r} = \frac{a(1 - r^n)}{(1 - r)}$$

**PERMUTATIONS (ELEMENTAL SETS DISTINGUISHABLE AS TO COMPONENTS OR ARRANGEMENT).** Each different arrangement or selection in a definite order which can be made from a given number of things is called a permutation of those things. The number of permutations obtainable by using $K$ out of $K$ distinguishable elements is factorial $K$. Note that the symbols $K!$ and $/K$ denote factorials:

$$/K = K! = (K)\ (K-1)\ (K-2)\ \cdots\ (3)\ (2)\ (1)$$

The number of permutations of 4 things taken 4 at a time is 24. As $K = 4$, then

$$K! = 4\cdot3\cdot2\cdot1 = 24$$

The number of permutations obtainable by using $K$ out of $K$ elements where $M_1$ elements are all alike, $M_2$ are alike, $M_3$ are alike, etc., and where

$$M_1 + M_2 + M_3 + \cdots = K$$

is

$$\frac{K!}{M_1! M_2! \cdots}$$

i.e., the number of permutations of five letters, $A,A,B,B,B$, is

$$\frac{5!}{2!3!} = \frac{5\cdot4\cdot3\cdot2\cdot1}{1\cdot2\cdot1\cdot2\cdot3} = 10$$

The number of permutations obtainable by using $R$ out of $K$ distinguishable elements is

$$\frac{K!}{(K-R)!}$$

i.e., the number of permutations of two of the three letters, $a$, $b$, and $c$, taken two at a time is

$$\frac{3!}{(3-2)!} = \frac{1\cdot2\cdot3}{1} = 6$$

**COMBINATIONS (ELEMENTAL SETS DISTINGUISHABLE AS TO COMPONENTS, DISREGARDING ARRANGEMENT).** Each different selection without regard to order which can be made from a given number of things is called a combination of those things. The number of combinations obtainable by using $R$ out of $K$ distinguishable elements is

$$\frac{K!}{(K-R)!R!} = \frac{(K)\ (K-1)\ (K-2)\ \cdots\ (R+1)}{1\cdot2\cdot3\ \cdots\ (K-R)!}$$

This ratio is often denoted as follows:

$$\frac{K!}{(K-R)!R!} = \binom{K}{R} = \binom{K}{K-R} = C^K_R$$

The number of combinations of two of the four letters, $a$, $b$, $c$, and $d$, is

$$\frac{4!}{(4-2)!2!} = \frac{1 \cdot 2 \cdot 3 \cdot 4}{1 \cdot 2 \cdot 1 \cdot 2} = 6$$

The number of combinations obtainable by using $0, 1, 2, \cdots (K-1), (K)$ out of $K$ distinguishable elements is

$$\binom{K}{0} + \binom{K}{1} + \cdots + \binom{K}{K-1} + \binom{K}{K} = \sum_{R=0}^{R=K} \binom{K}{R} = 2^K$$

Each of these coefficients is the coefficient of the $p$ or $q$ in the binomial expansion

$$(p+q)^K$$

**BINOMIAL PROBABILITY.** Let $P$ denote the probability of an event occurring and $Q$ the probability of an event not occurring.

$$P = \frac{\text{Number of occurrences of the event}}{\text{Number of opportunities of the event}}$$

$$Q = 1 - P$$

The probability of a successive occurrence of individual events is the product of the probability of the events. If $P_1$ is the probability of event 1 and $P_2$ is the probability of event 2, then the probability of $P_{12}$ of the simultaneous occurrence of events 1 and 2 is

$$P_{12} = (P_1)(P_2)$$

If there are $K$ opportunities, then the probability of getting $0, 1, 2, 3, \ldots K$ of these events is given by the terms of the binomial distribution, i.e.,

$$(P+Q)^K =$$

$$P^K + C_1^K P^{K-1} Q + C_2^K P^{K-2} Q^2 + \cdots + C_R^K P^{K-R} Q^R + \cdots + C_{K-1}^K PQ^{K-1} + Q^K$$

or

$$(P+Q)^K = \sum_{R=0}^{K} C_R^K P^{K-R} Q^R$$

**Example.** If a seed dealer specifies that the seed viability is .9, then $P = .9$ and $Q = .1$. If five randomly selected seeds are planted, the probability that all will germinate is

$$P_{1,2,3,4,5} = (.9)(.9)(.9)(.9)(.9) = 0.59049$$

The expansion of the binomial

$$(.9 + .1)^5 = (.9)^5 + (5)(.9)^4(.1) + \frac{(5)(4)}{2}(.9)^3(.1)^2$$

$$+ \frac{(5)(4)(3)}{3!}(.9)^2(.1)^3 + \frac{(5)(4)(3)(2)}{4!}(.9)(1)^4 + (.1)^5$$

gives the probability of getting five successes or seed germinations, four successes and one failure, three successes and two failures, two successes and three failures, one success and four failures, and zero successes and five failures.

## Geometry

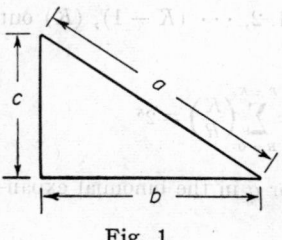

**Fig. 1.**

In a right triangle the square of the hypotenuse (the side opposite the right angle) is equal to the sum of the squares of the other two sides. (Fig. 1)

$$a^2 = b^2 + c^2$$

If a triangle is inscribed in a semicircle, the angle opposite the diameter is a right (90°) angle. All angles at the periphery of a circle, subtended by the diameter, are right angles. (Fig. 2)

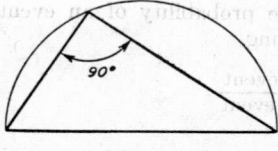

**Fig. 2.**

To bisect a line $AB$: With the ends $A$ and $B$ as centers and a radius greater than one-half the line, draw circular arcs. Through the intersections $C$ and $D$, draw line $CD$. This line divides $AB$ into two equal parts and is perpendicular to $AB$. (Fig. 3)

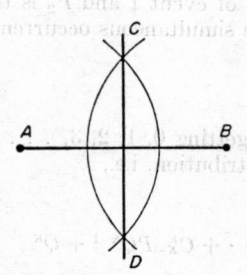

**Fig. 3.**

To erect a perpendicular to a straight line at a point $A$ on that line: With $A$ as a center and with any radius, draw circular arcs intersecting the given line at $B$ and $C$. Then, with $B$ and $C$ as centers and a radius longer than $AB$, draw circular arcs intersecting at $D$. Line $DA$ is perpendicular to $BC$ at $A$.

To draw a perpendicular to $BC$ from an external point $D$: From $D$ draw a circular arc intersecting the line at $B$ and $C$; from $B$ and $C$ draw equal arcs intersecting on the opposite side of $BC$ from $D$; the line from $D$ through their intersection will be perpendicular to $BC$. (Fig. 4)

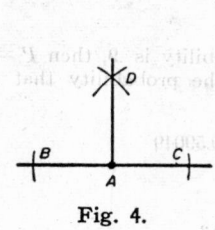

**Fig. 4.**

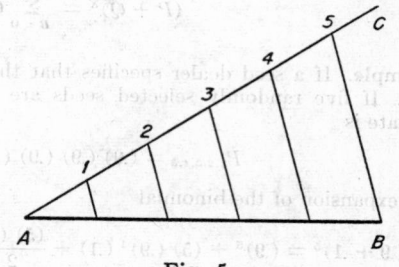

**Fig. 5.**

To divide a straight line $AB$ into a number of equal parts: Let it be required to divide $AB$ into five equal parts. Draw line $AC$ at any angle with $AB$. Set off on $AC$ five equal parts of any convenient length. Draw $B5$ and then draw lines parallel with $B5$ through the other division points on $AC$. The points where these lines intersect $AB$ are the required division points. (Fig. 5)

To bisect an angle *BAC*: With *A* as a center and any radius, draw arc *DE*. With *D* and *E* as centers and a radius greater than one-half *DE*, draw circular arcs intersecting at *F*. Line *AF* divides the angle into two equal parts. (Fig. 6)

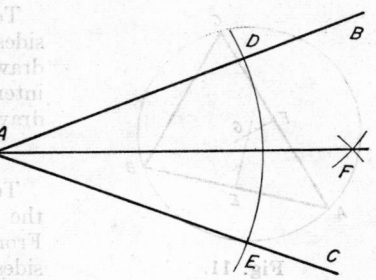

Fig. 6.

To lay out a 60° angle: With *A* as center and any radius, draw an arc *BC*. With point *B* as center and *AB* as radius, draw an arc intersecting at *E* the arc just drawn. *EAB* is a 60° angle.

A 30° angle can be obtained either by dividing a 60° angle into two equal parts or by drawing a line *EG* perpendicular to *AB*. Angle *AEG* is then 30°. (Fig. 7)

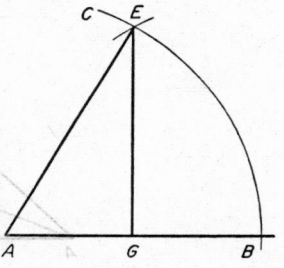

Fig. 7.

To lay out a 45° angle: From point *A* on line *AB* set off a distance *AC*. Draw the perpendicular *DC* and set off a distance *CE* equal to *AC*. Draw *AE*. Angle *EAC* is a 45° angle. (Fig. 8)

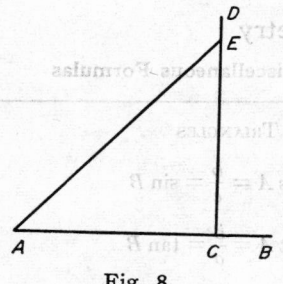

Fig. 8.

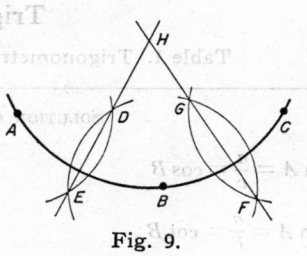

Fig. 9.

To find the center of a circle, or of an arc of a circle: Select three points on the periphery of the circle, as *A*, *B*, and *C*. With each of these points as center and the same radius, describe intersecting arcs. Through the points of intersection draw lines *DE* and *FG*. Point *H*, where these lines intersect, is the center of the circle. (Fig. 9)

To bisect a circular arc *AB*: With *A* and *B* as centers, and a radius larger than half the distance between *A* and *B*, draw circular arcs intersecting at *C* and *D*. Line *CD* divides arc *AB* into two equal parts at *E*. (Fig. 10)

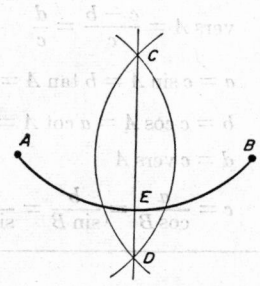

Fig. 10.

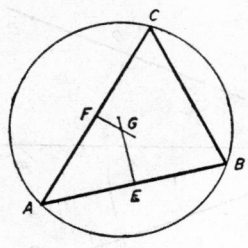

To describe a circle about a triangle: Bisect the sides $AB$ and $AC$, and from the midpoints $E$ and $F$ draw lines at right angles to the sides. These lines intersect at $G$. With $G$ as center and $GA$ as radius draw circle $ABC$. (Fig. 11)

**Fig. 11.**

To inscribe a circle in a triangle: Bisect two of the angles, $A$ and $B$, by lines intersecting at $D$. From $D$ draw a line $DE$ perpendicular to one of the sides, and with $DE$ as a radius draw circle $EFG$. (Fig. 12)

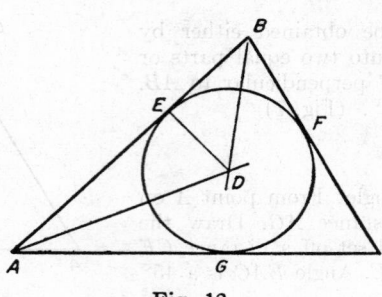

**Fig. 12.**

# Trigonometry

## Table 1. Trigonometric and Miscellaneous Formulas

---

SOLUTION OF RIGHT TRIANGLES

$$\sin A = \frac{a}{c} = \cos B \qquad\qquad \cos A = \frac{b}{c} = \sin B$$

$$\tan A = \frac{a}{b} = \cot B \qquad\qquad \cot A = \frac{b}{a} = \tan B$$

$$\sec A = \frac{c}{b} = \operatorname{cosec} B \qquad\qquad \operatorname{cosec} A = \frac{c}{a} = \sec B$$

$$\operatorname{vers} A = \frac{c - b}{c} = \frac{d}{c} \qquad\qquad \operatorname{exsec} A = \frac{e}{c}$$

$$a = c \sin A = b \tan A = c \cos B = b \cot B = \sqrt{(c + b)(c - b)}$$

$$b = c \cos A = a \cot A = c \sin B = a \tan B = \sqrt{(c + a)(c - a)} = c - c \operatorname{vers} A$$

$$d = c \operatorname{vers} A \qquad\qquad e = c \operatorname{exsec} A$$

$$c = \frac{a}{\cos B} = \frac{b}{\sin B} = \frac{a}{\sin A} = \frac{b}{\cos A} = \frac{d}{\operatorname{vers} A} = \frac{e}{\operatorname{exsec} A} = b + b \operatorname{exsec} A$$

---

### Table 1. Trigonometric and Miscellaneous Formulas (Continued)

SOLUTION OF OBLIQUE TRIANGLES

| Given | Sought | Formulas |
|---|---|---|
| $A, B, a$ | $b, c$ | $b = \dfrac{a}{\sin A} \cdot \sin B, \qquad c = \dfrac{a}{\sin A} \sin (A + B)$ |
| $A, a, b$ | $B, c$ | $\sin B = \dfrac{\sin A}{a} \cdot b, \qquad c = \dfrac{a}{\sin A} \cdot \sin C$ |
| $C, a, b$ | $A - B$ | $\tan \tfrac{1}{2} (A - B) = \dfrac{a - b}{a + b} \tan \tfrac{1}{2} (A + B)$ |
| $a, b, c$ | $A$ | If $s = \tfrac{1}{2}(a + b + c), \sin \tfrac{1}{2} A = \sqrt{\dfrac{(s - b)(s - c)}{bc}}$ |
| | | $\cos \tfrac{1}{2} A = \sqrt{\dfrac{s(s - a)}{bc}}; \tan \tfrac{1}{2} A = \sqrt{\dfrac{(s - b)(s - c)}{s(s - a)}}$ |
| | | $\sin A = \dfrac{2\sqrt{s(s - a)(s - b)(s - c)}}{bc}$ |
| | | $\text{vers } A = \dfrac{2(s - b)(s - c)}{bc}$ |
| | area | $\text{area} = \sqrt{s(s - a)(s - b)(s - c)}$ |
| $A, B, C, a$ | area | $\text{area} = \dfrac{a^2 \sin B \cdot \sin C}{2 \sin A}$ |
| $C, a, b$ | area | $\text{area} = \tfrac{1}{2} ab \sin C$ |

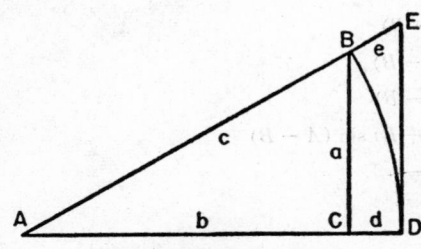

Fig. 13. Right triangle.

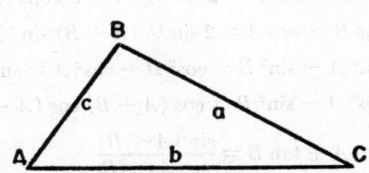

Fig. 14. Oblique triangle.

**Table 1. Trigonometric and Miscellaneous Formulas** (Continued)

GENERAL TRIGONOMETRIC FORMULAS

$$\sin A = 2 \sin \tfrac{1}{2} A \cos \tfrac{1}{2} A = \sqrt{1 - \cos^2 A} = \tan A \cos A = \sqrt{\tfrac{1}{2}(1 - \cos 2A)}$$

$$\cos A = 2 \cos^2 \tfrac{1}{2}A - 1 = 1 - 2 \sin^2 \tfrac{1}{2} A = \cos^2 \tfrac{1}{2}A - \sin^2 \tfrac{1}{2} A = 1 - \text{vers } A$$

$$\tan A = \frac{\sin A}{\cos A} = \frac{\sqrt{1 - \cos^2 A}}{\cos A} = \frac{\sin 2A}{1 + \cos 2A}$$

$$\cot A = \frac{\cos A}{\sin A} = \frac{\sin 2A}{1 - \cos 2A} = \frac{\sin 2A}{\text{vers } 2A}$$

$$\text{vers } A = 1 - \cos A = \sin A \tan \tfrac{1}{2}A = 2 \sin^2 \tfrac{1}{2} A$$

$$\text{exsec } A = \sec A - 1 = \tan A \tan \tfrac{1}{2} A = \frac{\text{vers } A}{\cos A}$$

$$\sin 2A = 2 \sin A \cos A$$

$$\cos 2A = 2 \cos^2 A - 1 = \cos^2 A - \sin^2 A = 1 - 2 \sin^2 A$$

$$\tan 2A = \frac{2 \tan A}{1 - \tan^2 A}$$

$$\cot 2A = \frac{\cot^2 A - 1}{2 \cot A}$$

$$\text{vers } 2A = 2 \sin^2 A = 2 \sin A \cos A \tan A$$

$$\text{exsec } 2A = \frac{2 \tan^2 A}{1 - \tan^2 A}$$

$$\sin^2 A + \cos^2 A = 1$$

$$\sin (A \pm B) = \sin A \cos B \pm \sin B \cos A$$

$$\cos (A \pm B) = \cos A \cos B \mp \sin A \sin B$$

$$\sin A + \sin B = 2 \sin \tfrac{1}{2} (A + B) \cos \tfrac{1}{2} (A - B)$$

$$\sin A - \sin B = 2 \cos \tfrac{1}{2} (A + B) \sin \tfrac{1}{2} (A - B)$$

$$\cos A + \cos B = 2 \cos \tfrac{1}{2} (A + B) \cos \tfrac{1}{2} (A - B)$$

$$\cos B - \cos A = 2 \sin \tfrac{1}{2} (A + B) \sin \tfrac{1}{2} (A - B)$$

$$\sin^2 A - \sin^2 B = \cos^2 B - \cos^2 A = \sin (A + B) \sin (A - B)$$

$$\cos^2 A - \sin^2 B = \cos (A + B) \cos (A - B)$$

$$\tan A + \tan B = \frac{\sin (A + B)}{\cos A \cos B}$$

$$\tan A - \tan B = \frac{\sin (A - B)}{\cos A \cos B}$$

## Areas and Volumes

Notation: $a, b, c, d, s$ denote lengths, $A$ denotes area, $C$ denotes circumference, $D$ denotes diameter, $R$ denotes radius, and $V$ denotes volume.

### Right Triangle. (Fig. 15)

$A = \frac{1}{2} ab$

$c = \sqrt{a^2 + b^2}; \quad a = \sqrt{c^2 - b^2}; \quad b = \sqrt{c^2 - a^2}$

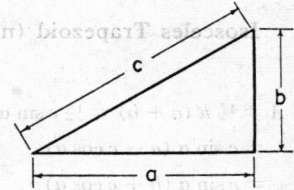

Fig. 15.

### Oblique Triangle. (Fig. 16)

$A = \frac{1}{2} bh$

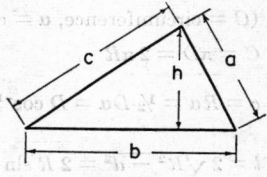

Fig. 16.

### Equilateral Triangle. (Fig. 17)

$A = \frac{1}{2} ah = \frac{1}{4} a^2 \sqrt{3}$

$h = \frac{1}{2} a \sqrt{3}$

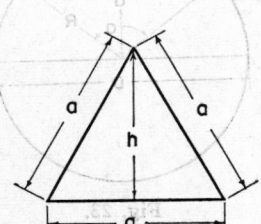

Fig. 17.

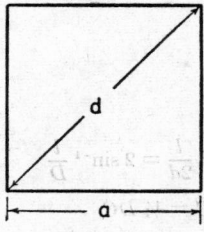

Fig. 18.

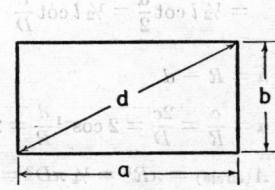

Fig. 19.

### Square. (Fig. 18)

$A = a^2; \quad d = a\sqrt{2}$

### Rectangle. (Fig. 19)

$A = ab; \quad d = \sqrt{a^2 + b^2}$

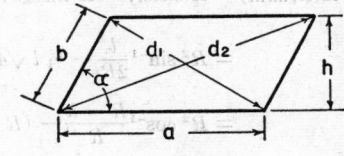

Fig. 20.

### Parallelogram (opposite sides parallel). (Fig. 20)

$$A = ah = ab \sin \alpha$$

$$d_1 = \sqrt{a^2 + b^2 - 2ab \cos \alpha}$$

$$d_2 = \sqrt{a^2 + b^2 + 2ab \cos \alpha}$$

**Trapezoid (one pair of opposite sides parallel).**

(Fig. 21)

$$A = \tfrac{1}{2}\, h\, (a + b)$$

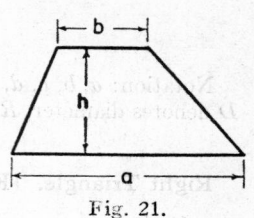

Fig. 21.

**Isosceles Trapezoid (nonparallel sides equal).**

(Fig. 22)

$$A = \tfrac{1}{2}\, h\, (a + b) = \tfrac{1}{2}\, c \sin \alpha\, (a + b)$$
$$= c \sin \alpha\, (a - c \cos \alpha)$$
$$= c \sin \alpha\, (b + c \cos \alpha)$$

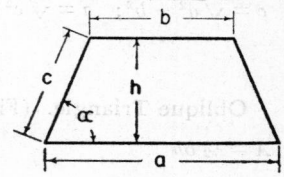

Fig. 22.

**Circle.** (Fig. 23)

($C$ = circumference, $\alpha$ = central angle in radians)

$$C = \pi D = 2\,\pi R$$

$$c = R\alpha = \tfrac{1}{2}\, D\alpha = D \cos^{-1} \frac{d}{R} = D \tan^{-1} \frac{l}{2d}$$

$$l = 2\sqrt{R^2 - d^2} = 2\,R \sin \frac{\alpha}{2} = 2\,d \tan \frac{\alpha}{2} = 2\,d \tan \frac{c}{D}$$

$$d = \tfrac{1}{2}\sqrt{4R^2 - l^2} = \tfrac{1}{2}\sqrt{D^2 - l^2} = R \cos \frac{\alpha}{2}$$

$$= \tfrac{1}{2}\, l \cot \frac{\alpha}{2} = \tfrac{1}{2}\, l \cot \frac{c}{D}$$

$$h = R - d$$

$$\alpha = \frac{c}{R} = \frac{2c}{D} = 2 \cos^{-1} \frac{d}{R} = 2 \tan^{-1} \frac{l}{2d} = 2 \sin^{-1} \frac{l}{D}$$

$$A_{(\text{circle})} = \pi R^2 = \tfrac{1}{4}\, \pi D^2 = \tfrac{1}{2}\, RC = \tfrac{1}{4}\, DC$$

$$A_{(\text{sector})} = \tfrac{1}{2}\, Rc = \tfrac{1}{2}\, R^2\alpha = \tfrac{1}{8}\, D^2\alpha$$

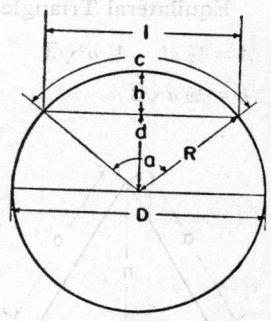

Fig. 23.

$$A_{(\text{segment})} = A_{(\text{sector})} - A_{(\text{triangle})} = \tfrac{1}{2}\, R^2\, (\alpha - \sin \alpha) = \tfrac{1}{2}\, R \left( c - R \sin \frac{c}{R} \right)$$

$$= R^2 \sin^{-1} \frac{l}{2R} - \tfrac{1}{4}\, l \sqrt{4R^2 - l^2} = R^2 \cos^{-1} \frac{d}{R} - d \sqrt{R^2 - d^2}$$

$$= R^2 \cos^{-1} \frac{R - h}{R} - (R - h) \sqrt{2\,Rh - h^2}$$

$$\pi = 3.1416 \qquad D = C\, \frac{l}{\pi} = C \times 0.3183 \qquad R = C\, \frac{l}{2\pi} = C \times 0.15915$$

$$D = \sqrt{A}\, \sqrt{\frac{4}{\pi}} = \sqrt{A} \times 1.12838 \qquad A = C^2\, \frac{l}{4\pi} = C^2 \times 0.07958$$

The side of a square that shall equal the area of a circle =

$$D\sqrt{\frac{\pi}{4}} = D \times 0.8862 \qquad \text{or} \qquad C\sqrt{\frac{l}{4\pi}} = C \times 0.2821$$

Doubling the diameter of a circle quadruples its area.

The diameter of a circle that shall contain the area of a given square = the side of the square × 1.1284.

The side of an inscribed equilateral triangle = $D \times 0.866$.

The side of an inscribed square = $D \times 0.7072$, or $C \times 0.225$.

A radian is a central angle which intercepts a circular arc equal to its radius. Because the circumference of a circle = $2\pi R$, one radian = $360/2\pi = 57.2958$ degrees, and one degree = $0.01745$ radians.

**Ellipse.** (Fig. 24)

$A = \pi ab$

Perimeter $(s) =$

$$\pi(a+b)\left[1 + \tfrac{1}{4}\left(\frac{a-b}{a+b}\right)^2 + \frac{1}{64}\left(\frac{a-b}{a+b}\right)^4 \right.$$
$$\left. + \frac{1}{256}\left(\frac{a-b}{a+b}\right)^6 + \cdots\right]$$

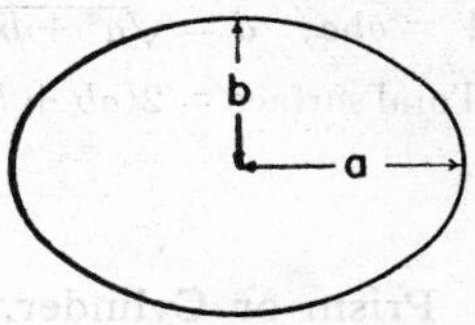

Fig. 24.

**Parabola.** (Fig. 25)

$A = \tfrac{2}{3} ld$

Length of arc $(s) = \tfrac{1}{2}\sqrt{16\,d^2 + l^2} + \frac{l^2}{8\,d}\,ln\left(\frac{4\,d + \sqrt{16\,d^2 + l^2}}{l}\right)$

$= l\left[1 + \tfrac{2}{3}\left(\frac{2\,d}{l}\right)^2 - \tfrac{2}{5}\left(\frac{2\,d}{l}\right)^4 + \cdots\right]$

Height of segment $(d_1) = \dfrac{d}{l^2}(l^2 - l_1{}^2)$

Width of segment $(l_1) = l\sqrt{\dfrac{d-d_1}{d}}$

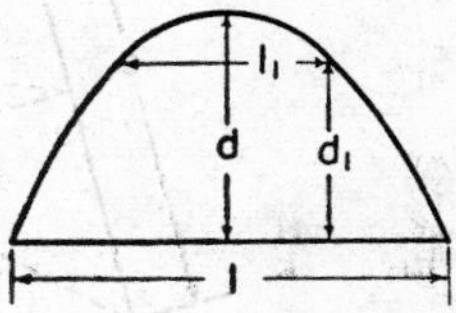

Fig. 25.

**Area by Approximation.** Let $y_0$, $y_1$, $y_2$, $\cdots$, $y_n$ be the measured lengths of a series of equidistant parallel chords, and let $h$ be their distance apart, then the area enclosed by any boundary is given approximately by one of the following rules. (Fig. 26)

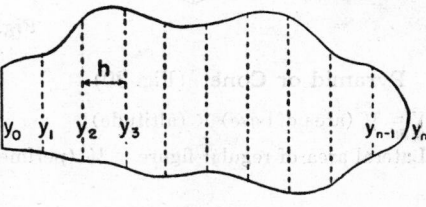

Fig. 26.

$A_T = h\left[\tfrac{1}{2}(y_0 + y_n) + y_1 + y_2 + \cdots + y_{n-1}\right]$

(Trapezoidal Rule)

$A_D = h\left[0.4(y_0 + y_n) + 1.1(y_1 + y_{n-1}) + y_2 + y_3 + \cdots + y_{n-2}\right]$

(Durand's Rule)

$A_S = \tfrac{1}{3}h\left[(y_0 + y_n) + 4(y_1 + y_3 + \cdots + y_{n-1}) + 2(y_2 + y_4 + \cdots + y_{n-2})\right]$

(Simpson's Rule, where $n$ is even)

The larger the value of $n$, the greater is the accuracy of approximation. In general, for the same number of chords, $A_S$ gives the most accurate, $A_T$, the least accurate approximation.

### Cube. (Fig. 27)

$V = a^3$; $\quad d = a\sqrt{3}$

Total surface $= 6\,a^2$

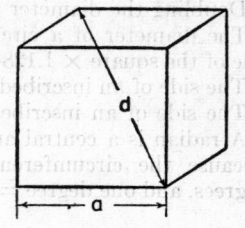

### Rectangular Parallelepiped. (Fig. 28)

$V = abc$; $\quad d = \sqrt{a^2 + b^2 + c^2}$

Total surface $= 2(ab + bc + ca)$

**Fig. 27.**

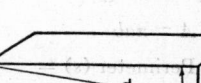
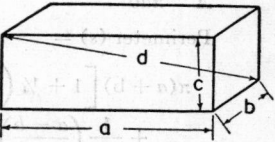

**Fig. 28.**

### Prism or Cylinder. (Fig. 29)

$V =$ (area of base) $\times$ (altitude)

Lateral area $=$ (perimeter of right section) $\times$ (lateral edge)

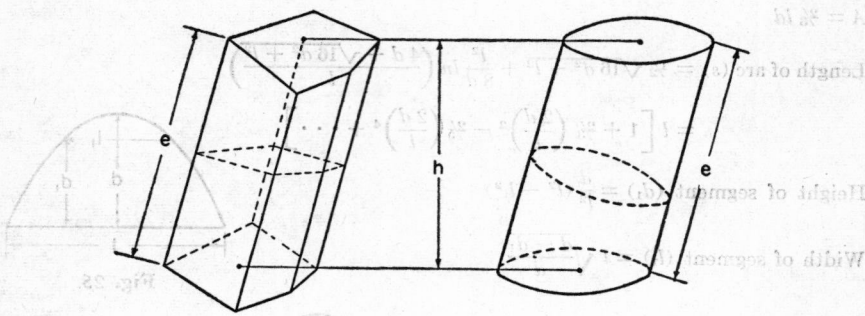

**Fig. 29.**

### Pyramid or Cone. (Fig. 30)

$V = \frac{1}{3}$ (area of base) $\times$ (altitude)

Lateral area of regular figure $= \frac{1}{2}$ (perimeter of base) $\times$ (slant height)

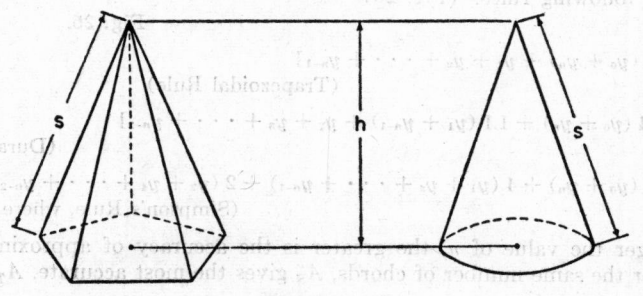

**Fig. 30.**

## Frustum of Pyramid or Cone. (Fig. 31)

$V = \frac{1}{3} (A_1 + A_2 + \sqrt{A_1 \times A_2})\, h$, where $A_1$ and $A_2$ are areas of bases, and $h$ is altitude.

Lateral area of regular figure = ½ (sum of perimeters of bases) × (slant height)

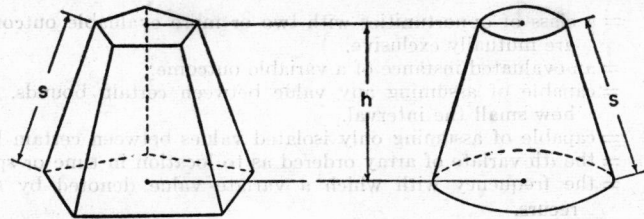

**Fig. 31.**

## Sphere. (Fig. 32)

$A_{(\text{sphere})} = 4\pi R^2 = \pi D^2$

$A_{(\text{zone})} = 2\pi R h = \pi D h$

$V_{(\text{sphere})} = \frac{4}{3}\pi R^3 = \frac{1}{6}\pi D^3$

$V_{(\text{spherical sector})} = \frac{2}{3}\pi R^2 h = \frac{1}{6}\pi D^2 h$

$V_{(\text{spherical segment of one base})}$

$= \frac{1}{6}\pi h_1 (3\, r_1^2 + h_1^2) = \frac{1}{3}\pi h_1^2 (3\, R - h_1)$

$V_{(\text{spherical segment of two bases})}$

$= \frac{1}{6}\pi h (3\, r_1^2 + 3\, r_2^2 + h^2)$

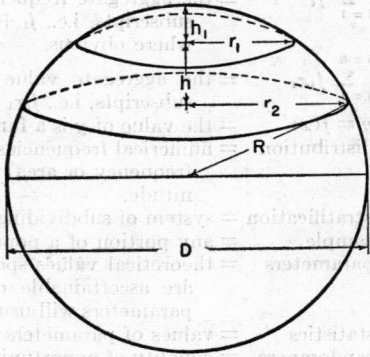

**Fig. 32.**

$A_{(\text{sphere})} = D \times C; \quad V_{(\text{sphere})} = A \times \frac{1}{6} D$

$\quad\quad$ or $C^3 \times 0.016887$

$D_{(\text{sphere})} = \sqrt[3]{V} \times 1.2407$ or $\sqrt{A} \times 0.56419$

$C_{(\text{sphere})} = \sqrt{A} \times 1.7725$ or $\sqrt[3]{V} \times 3.8978$

## Paraboloidal Segment. (Fig. 33)

$V_{(\text{segment of one base})} = \frac{1}{2}\pi r_1^2 h$

$V_{(\text{segment of two bases})} = \frac{1}{2}\pi (r_1^2 + r_2^2) d$

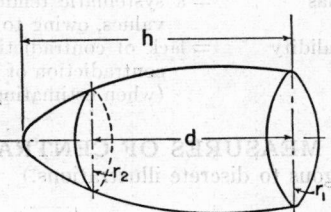

**Fig. 33.**

## Neiloidal Segment. (Fig. 34)

$V_{(\text{segment of one base})} = \pi/6 (r_1^2 + 4r_3^2) h$

$V_{(\text{segment of two bases})} = \pi/6 (r_1^2 + 4r_3^2 + r_2^2) d$

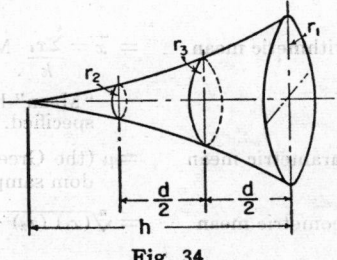

**Fig. 34.**

## Statistical Terminology

### POPULATION.

| | |
|---|---|
| variable | = a class of opportunities with two or more evaluable outcomes which are mutually exclusive. |
| variate | = an evaluated instance of a variable outcome. |
| continuous | = capable of assuming any value between certain bounds, no matter how small the interval. |
| discrete | = capable of assuming only isolated values between certain bounds. |
| $x_i$ | = the $i$th variate of array ordered as to location in time or space. |
| $f_i$ | = the frequency with which a variate value denoted by subscript $i$ recurs. |
| $\Sigma$ | = sum of. |
| $\sum\limits_{i=1}^{i=k} f_i$ | = the aggregate frequency of variates, including the indicated range of subscripts, i.e., $f_1 + f_2 + \cdots + f_k$. Limit symbols may be omitted where obvious. |
| $\sum\limits_{i=1}^{i=k} f_i x_i$ | = the aggregate value of variates, including the indicated range of subscripts, i.e., $f_1 x_1 + f_2 x_2 + \cdots + f_k x_k$. |
| $y = f(x)$ | = the value of $y$ is a function of (or depends on) the value of $x$. |
| distribution | = numerical frequencies or areas under a curve (usually relative to total frequency or area) associated with specified ranges of variate magnitude. |
| stratification | = system of subdividing a population into groups. |
| sample | = any portion of a population. |
| parameters | = theoretical values specifying an entire population distribution. They are ascertainable only for theoretical models. Symbols denoting parameters will usually be shown as Greek letters. |
| statistics | = values of parameters calculated from sample observations. |
| randomness | = equality of opportunity without regard to arrangement, association, or attributes. |
| bias | = a systematic tendency of sample values to deviate from population values, owing to erroneous assumptions in sampling or calculations. |
| validity | = lack of contradiction of premise by conclusion (deduction); lack of contradiction of observation by hypothesis (induction); lack of bias (when estimating parameters by means of statistics). |

### MEASURES OF CENTRAL TENDENCY. (Continuous cases are analogous to discrete illustrations.)

quadratic mean $\quad = \sqrt{\dfrac{\sum\limits^{k} x_i^2}{k}}$ Useful in averaging diameters, etc.

arithmetic mean $\quad = \bar{x} = \dfrac{\sum\limits^{k} x_i}{k}$ Most useful of all means.

"Mean" hereafter implies arithmetic mean unless otherwise specified.

parametric mean $\quad = \mu$ (the Greek letter mu) = population mean, and $\bar{x}$ from random sample is the unbiased estimate of $\mu$.

geometric mean $\quad = \sqrt[n]{(x_1)(x_2)\cdots(x_n)}$ Antilog of arithmetic mean log.

| | | |
|---|---|---|
| harmonic mean | $=\dfrac{n}{\dfrac{1}{x_1}+\dfrac{1}{x_2}\cdots+\dfrac{1}{x_n}}$ | Useful in averaging rates when equal amounts of work are performed at different rates. |

comparison of means = quadratic mean $\geqq$ arithmetic mean $\geqq$ geometric mean $\geqq$ harmonic mean.

mode = variate value recurring with greatest frequency, or abscissa at which curve peaks.

median = variate value having equal frequency of greater and lesser variates, or abscissa whose ordinate divides area under curve into 2 equal portions.

## MEASURES OF DISPERSION.

range = largest variate minus smallest variate.

parentile = sets of variate values dividing variates arrayed by magnitude into $N$ equal parts, or abscissas whose ordinates divide area under curve into $N$ equal parts (median, tertiles, quartiles, . . . deciles, percentiles, etc.).

mean deviation $=\dfrac{\overset{n}{\Sigma}\,|\,x_i-\overline{x}\,|}{n}$ where $|\,x_i-\overline{x}\,|$ means absolute value, disregarding sign.

variance $=s^2=\left[\dfrac{n}{n-1}\right]\left[\dfrac{\overset{n}{\Sigma}(x_i-\overline{x})^2}{n}\right]$

$=\left[\dfrac{n}{n-1}\right]\left[\dfrac{\overset{n}{\Sigma}x_i{}^2}{n}-\left(\dfrac{\overset{n}{\Sigma}x_i}{n}\right)^2\right]$

with $n$ elements determining $\overline{x}$. Note that since $\mu$ is estimated by $\dfrac{\overset{n}{\Sigma}x_i}{n}$, only $(n-1)$ elements can vary from it independently. The factor $\dfrac{n}{n-1}$ corrects for this bias, and $s^2$ is an unbiased estimate of $\sigma^2$ if the sample is random.

degrees of freedom $= df =$ the number of independent opportunities for deviating from parameters, appropriate to a measure of dispersion. One $df$ is lost each time a parameter implicit in the measure of dispersion is derived from sample data.

standard deviation $= \sigma$ or its unbiased estimate of $s$.

coefficient of variation $=\dfrac{\sigma}{\mu}$ or its unbiased estimate $\dfrac{s}{\overline{x}}$.

chi square $=\chi^2=\dfrac{\overset{n}{\Sigma}\,(x_i-\mu)^2}{\sigma^2}$ with $(n-1)$ $df$'s if $\mu$ is estimated from the sample.

student's $t$ $=t=\dfrac{x-\mu}{s_x}$ with $df$'s appropriate to $s_x$.

variance ratio $=F=\dfrac{s_1^2}{s_2^2}$ with $\dfrac{df_1}{df_2}$, where $s_1^2$ is independent of $s_2^2$.

## Statistical Formulas and Sampling

**SYMBOLS.** In statistical writing, certain symbols are used as shorthand to simplify the writing. In most statistical writing the Greek symbols are used to represent the population parameters or constants which are not known. The sample supplies estimates of these parameters. The sample parameters are usually expressed by ordinary letters of the alphabet, i.e., $a$, $b$, $c$, . . . . The only exception to the use of Greek symbols for population constants is the Greek $\Sigma$, which is used to indicate "the sum of" the variable that follows the summation sign.

**Mean Value.** Let $x_i$ denote one of a group of $k$ observations of some set of data. The most commonly used expression of the central or average value is the arithmetic mean. In symbolic form the equation for the arithmetic mean is

$$\bar{x} = \frac{x_1 + x_2 + \cdots + x_i + \ldots + x_k}{k} = \frac{\sum\limits_{i=1}^{k} x_i}{k}$$

where $\bar{x}$ equals the arithmetic mean. The symbol $\sum\limits_{i=1}^{k}$ means the sum of the $k$ values of $x_i$.

**Standard Deviation.** The dispersion or scatter of observations around the arithmetic mean is usually measured by the statistical constant, standard deviation. The sample estimate of this statistic is defined as follows:

$$s = \sqrt{\frac{\sum\limits_{i=1}^{k} (x_i - \bar{x})^2}{k-1}} = \sqrt{\frac{\sum\limits_{i=1}^{k} x_i^2 - \frac{\left(\sum\limits_{i=1}^{k} x_i\right)^2}{k}}{k-1}}$$

The second form of the equation is more convenient for computational use.

**Example.** Five plots taken to estimate cordwood volume of a wood lot had the following volumes of 3, 4, 5, 7, and 11 cords. To calculate the arithmetic mean and standard deviation, we note that $x_i$ has the values 3, 4, 5, 7, and 11. Then substituting in the equations above, we have

$$\bar{x} = \frac{3 + 4 + 5 + 7 + 11}{5} = \frac{30}{5} = 6$$

$$\text{and } s = \sqrt{\frac{3^2 + 4^2 + 5^2 + 7^2 + 11^2 - \frac{(30)^2}{5}}{5-1}} = \sqrt{\frac{220 - 180}{4}}$$

$$= \sqrt{10} = 3.16$$

If the sample of five observations has been selected in a random manner, the mean, $\bar{x}$, is then an unbiased estimate of the mean of the population of data.

**Standard Error of the Mean.** In a random sample the statistic $s$ is an estimate of the population standard deviation and as such can be used to estimate the reliability of the sample mean. For random sampling the standard error of the mean (denoted as $s_{\bar{x}}$) is given by the equation

$$s_{\bar{x}} = \frac{s}{\sqrt{k}}\sqrt{1 - \frac{k}{K}}$$

where $K$ denotes the number of observations in the population being sampled and $k$ is the number of observations in the sample. If $K$ is large in comparison with the sample size $k$, the fraction $k/K$ is approximately zero and therefore can be neglected. If a sample of five plots out of a possible 500 are selected, giving $\bar{x} = 6$ and $s = 3.16$, then the standard error of the mean would be

$$s_x = \frac{3.16}{\sqrt{5}}\sqrt{1 - \frac{5}{500}} = \frac{3.16}{2.236}\sqrt{1 - 0.01} = 1.415(0.995) = 1.408$$

This statistic, the standard error of the mean, and the probability distribution associated with the statistic $t$ are useful in placing confidence bands around the sample mean.

The statistic $t$ is defined as

$$t = \frac{\bar{x} - \mu}{s_{\bar{x}}}$$

where $\mu$ is the population mean which is unknown and $\bar{x}$ and $s_{\bar{x}}$ are as given above. The value of $\mu$ will lie in the range

$$\bar{x} - (t)s_{\bar{x}} < \mu < \bar{x} + (t)s_{\bar{x}}$$

or

$$6 - 1.408(t) < \mu < 6 + 1.408(t)$$

The value of $t$ is obtained from a $t$ table (Table 2) after the probability distribution level ($P$) has been chosen. Using the probability level for $P = 0.05$ and for 4 degrees of freedom, $t$ is found to be equal to 2.78. (The degrees of freedom are equal to the number of observations less the number of statistical constants computed from the data. In this case, $df = n - 1$.) The confidence band becomes

$$6 - 1.408(2.78) < \mu < 6 + 1.408(2.78)$$
$$6 - 3.914 < \mu < 6 + 3.914$$
$$2.086 < \mu < \qquad 9.914$$

Thus, in 19 out of 20 times this range would be expected to include the population mean.

The level of significance can be set at any level; however, the common levels are $P = 0.3$, 0.05, or 0.01. For samples with 30 or more degrees of freedom, these probabilities correspond approximately to an error of 1, 2, or 2.58 times the standard error; thus $t$ would be 1.0, 2.0, or 2.58.

**Sample Size.** To determine sample size, use is made of the equation for $t$.

$$t = \frac{\bar{x} - \mu}{s_{\bar{x}}} = \frac{\bar{x} - \mu}{\frac{s_x}{\sqrt{k}}\sqrt{1 - \frac{k}{K}}}$$

which, when solved for $k$, gives

$$k = \frac{(ts_x)^2}{(\bar{x} - \mu)^2 + \frac{(ts_x)^2}{K}}$$

## Table 2. Five Percent Probability Values of $F$, $t$, and $\chi^2$

(Values of $t$ are those that give an area of 2.5 percent in each tail, the sum of the two tails being 5 percent; values of $F$ and $\chi^2$ are those that give an area in the upper tail of 5 percent.)

| $n_2$ | $t$ | $n_1$=1 | 2 | 3 | 4 | 5 | 6 | 7 | 8 | 9 | 10 | 12 | 15 | 20 | 24 | 30 | 40 | 60 | 120 | ∞ | $\chi^2$ | $n_2$ |
|---|---|---|---|---|---|---|---|---|---|---|---|---|---|---|---|---|---|---|---|---|---|---|
| 1 | 12.71 | 161.45 | 199.50 | 215.71 | 224.58 | 230.16 | 233.99 | 236.77 | 238.88 | 240.54 | 241.88 | 243.91 | 245.95 | 248.01 | 249.05 | 250.09 | 251.14 | 252.20 | 253.25 | 254.32 | 3.84 | 1 |
| 2 | 4.30 | 18.51 | 19.00 | 19.16 | 19.25 | 19.30 | 19.33 | 19.35 | 19.37 | 19.38 | 19.40 | 19.41 | 19.43 | 19.45 | 19.45 | 19.46 | 19.47 | 19.48 | 19.49 | 19.50 | 5.99 | 2 |
| 3 | 3.18 | 10.13 | 9.55 | 9.28 | 9.12 | 9.01 | 8.94 | 8.89 | 8.85 | 8.81 | 8.79 | 8.74 | 8.70 | 8.66 | 8.64 | 8.62 | 8.59 | 8.57 | 8.55 | 8.53 | 7.81 | 3 |
| 4 | 2.78 | 7.71 | 6.94 | 6.59 | 6.39 | 6.26 | 6.16 | 6.09 | 6.04 | 6.00 | 5.96 | 5.91 | 5.86 | 5.80 | 5.77 | 5.75 | 5.72 | 5.69 | 5.66 | 5.63 | 9.49 | 4 |
| 5 | 2.57 | 6.61 | 5.79 | 5.41 | 5.19 | 5.05 | 4.95 | 4.88 | 4.82 | 4.77 | 4.74 | 4.68 | 4.62 | 4.56 | 4.53 | 4.50 | 4.46 | 4.43 | 4.40 | 4.36 | 11.07 | 5 |
| 6 | 2.45 | 5.99 | 5.14 | 4.76 | 4.53 | 4.39 | 4.28 | 4.21 | 4.15 | 4.10 | 4.06 | 4.00 | 3.94 | 3.87 | 3.84 | 3.81 | 3.77 | 3.74 | 3.70 | 3.67 | 12.59 | 6 |
| 7 | 2.36 | 5.59 | 4.74 | 4.35 | 4.12 | 3.97 | 3.87 | 3.79 | 3.73 | 3.68 | 3.64 | 3.57 | 3.51 | 3.44 | 3.41 | 3.38 | 3.34 | 3.30 | 3.27 | 3.23 | 14.07 | 7 |
| 8 | 2.31 | 5.32 | 4.46 | 4.07 | 3.84 | 3.69 | 3.58 | 3.50 | 3.44 | 3.39 | 3.35 | 3.28 | 3.22 | 3.15 | 3.12 | 3.08 | 3.04 | 3.01 | 2.97 | 2.93 | 15.51 | 8 |
| 9 | 2.26 | 5.12 | 4.26 | 3.86 | 3.63 | 3.48 | 3.37 | 3.29 | 3.23 | 3.18 | 3.14 | 3.07 | 3.01 | 2.94 | 2.90 | 2.86 | 2.83 | 2.79 | 2.75 | 2.71 | 16.92 | 9 |
| 10 | 2.23 | 4.96 | 4.10 | 3.71 | 3.48 | 3.33 | 3.22 | 3.14 | 3.07 | 3.02 | 2.98 | 2.91 | 2.84 | 2.77 | 2.74 | 2.70 | 2.66 | 2.62 | 2.58 | 2.54 | 18.31 | 10 |
| 11 | 2.20 | 4.84 | 3.98 | 3.59 | 3.36 | 3.20 | 3.09 | 3.01 | 2.95 | 2.90 | 2.85 | 2.79 | 2.72 | 2.65 | 2.61 | 2.57 | 2.53 | 2.49 | 2.45 | 2.40 | 19.68 | 11 |
| 12 | 2.18 | 4.75 | 3.89 | 3.49 | 3.26 | 3.11 | 3.00 | 2.91 | 2.85 | 2.80 | 2.75 | 2.69 | 2.62 | 2.54 | 2.51 | 2.47 | 2.43 | 2.38 | 2.34 | 2.30 | 21.03 | 12 |
| 13 | 2.16 | 4.67 | 3.81 | 3.41 | 3.18 | 3.03 | 2.92 | 2.83 | 2.77 | 2.71 | 2.67 | 2.60 | 2.53 | 2.46 | 2.42 | 2.38 | 2.34 | 2.30 | 2.25 | 2.21 | 22.36 | 13 |
| 14 | 2.14 | 4.60 | 3.74 | 3.34 | 3.11 | 2.96 | 2.85 | 2.76 | 2.70 | 2.65 | 2.60 | 2.53 | 2.46 | 2.39 | 2.35 | 2.31 | 2.27 | 2.22 | 2.18 | 2.13 | 23.68 | 14 |
| 15 | 2.13 | 4.54 | 3.68 | 3.29 | 3.06 | 2.90 | 2.79 | 2.71 | 2.64 | 2.59 | 2.54 | 2.48 | 2.40 | 2.33 | 2.29 | 2.25 | 2.20 | 2.16 | 2.11 | 2.07 | 25.00 | 15 |
| 16 | 2.12 | 4.49 | 3.63 | 3.24 | 3.01 | 2.85 | 2.74 | 2.66 | 2.59 | 2.54 | 2.49 | 2.42 | 2.35 | 2.28 | 2.24 | 2.19 | 2.15 | 2.11 | 2.06 | 2.01 | 26.30 | 16 |
| 17 | 2.11 | 4.45 | 3.59 | 3.20 | 2.96 | 2.81 | 2.70 | 2.61 | 2.55 | 2.49 | 2.45 | 2.38 | 2.31 | 2.23 | 2.19 | 2.15 | 2.10 | 2.06 | 2.01 | 1.96 | 27.59 | 17 |
| 18 | 2.10 | 4.41 | 3.55 | 3.16 | 2.93 | 2.77 | 2.66 | 2.58 | 2.51 | 2.46 | 2.41 | 2.34 | 2.27 | 2.19 | 2.15 | 2.11 | 2.06 | 2.02 | 1.97 | 1.92 | 28.87 | 18 |
| 19 | 2.09 | 4.38 | 3.52 | 3.13 | 2.90 | 2.74 | 2.63 | 2.54 | 2.48 | 2.42 | 2.38 | 2.31 | 2.23 | 2.16 | 2.11 | 2.07 | 2.03 | 1.98 | 1.93 | 1.88 | 30.14 | 19 |
| 20 | 2.09 | 4.35 | 3.49 | 3.10 | 2.87 | 2.71 | 2.60 | 2.51 | 2.45 | 2.39 | 2.35 | 2.28 | 2.20 | 2.12 | 2.08 | 2.04 | 1.99 | 1.95 | 1.90 | 1.84 | 31.41 | 20 |
| 21 | 2.08 | 4.32 | 3.47 | 3.07 | 2.84 | 2.68 | 2.57 | 2.49 | 2.42 | 2.37 | 2.32 | 2.25 | 2.18 | 2.10 | 2.05 | 2.01 | 1.96 | 1.92 | 1.87 | 1.81 | 32.67 | 21 |
| 22 | 2.07 | 4.30 | 3.44 | 3.05 | 2.82 | 2.66 | 2.55 | 2.46 | 2.40 | 2.34 | 2.30 | 2.23 | 2.15 | 2.07 | 2.03 | 1.98 | 1.94 | 1.89 | 1.84 | 1.78 | 33.92 | 22 |
| 23 | 2.07 | 4.28 | 3.42 | 3.03 | 2.80 | 2.64 | 2.53 | 2.44 | 2.37 | 2.32 | 2.27 | 2.20 | 2.13 | 2.05 | 2.00 | 1.96 | 1.91 | 1.86 | 1.81 | 1.76 | 35.17 | 23 |
| 24 | 2.06 | 4.26 | 3.40 | 3.01 | 2.78 | 2.62 | 2.51 | 2.42 | 2.36 | 2.30 | 2.25 | 2.18 | 2.11 | 2.03 | 1.98 | 1.94 | 1.89 | 1.84 | 1.79 | 1.73 | 36.42 | 24 |
| 25 | 2.06 | 4.24 | 3.39 | 2.99 | 2.76 | 2.60 | 2.49 | 2.40 | 2.34 | 2.28 | 2.24 | 2.16 | 2.09 | 2.01 | 1.96 | 1.92 | 1.87 | 1.82 | 1.77 | 1.71 | 37.65 | 25 |
| 26 | 2.06 | 4.23 | 3.37 | 2.98 | 2.74 | 2.59 | 2.47 | 2.39 | 2.32 | 2.27 | 2.22 | 2.15 | 2.07 | 1.99 | 1.95 | 1.90 | 1.85 | 1.80 | 1.75 | 1.69 | 38.89 | 26 |
| 27 | 2.05 | 4.21 | 3.35 | 2.96 | 2.73 | 2.57 | 2.46 | 2.37 | 2.31 | 2.25 | 2.20 | 2.13 | 2.06 | 1.97 | 1.93 | 1.88 | 1.84 | 1.79 | 1.73 | 1.67 | 40.11 | 27 |
| 28 | 2.05 | 4.20 | 3.34 | 2.95 | 2.71 | 2.56 | 2.45 | 2.36 | 2.29 | 2.24 | 2.19 | 2.12 | 2.04 | 1.96 | 1.91 | 1.87 | 1.82 | 1.77 | 1.71 | 1.65 | 41.34 | 28 |
| 29 | 2.05 | 4.18 | 3.33 | 2.93 | 2.70 | 2.55 | 2.43 | 2.35 | 2.28 | 2.22 | 2.18 | 2.10 | 2.03 | 1.94 | 1.90 | 1.85 | 1.81 | 1.75 | 1.70 | 1.64 | 42.56 | 29 |
| 30 | 2.04 | 4.17 | 3.32 | 2.92 | 2.69 | 2.53 | 2.42 | 2.33 | 2.27 | 2.21 | 2.16 | 2.09 | 2.01 | 1.93 | 1.89 | 1.84 | 1.79 | 1.74 | 1.68 | 1.62 | 43.77 | 30 |
| 40 | 2.02 | 4.08 | 3.23 | 2.84 | 2.61 | 2.45 | 2.34 | 2.25 | 2.18 | 2.12 | 2.08 | 2.00 | 1.92 | 1.84 | 1.79 | 1.74 | 1.69 | 1.64 | 1.58 | 1.51 | 55.76 | 40 |
| 60 | 2.00 | 4.00 | 3.15 | 2.76 | 2.53 | 2.37 | 2.25 | 2.17 | 2.10 | 2.04 | 1.99 | 1.92 | 1.84 | 1.75 | 1.70 | 1.65 | 1.59 | 1.53 | 1.47 | 1.39 | 79.08 | 60 |
| 120 | 1.98 | 3.92 | 3.07 | 2.68 | 2.45 | 2.29 | 2.17 | 2.09 | 2.02 | 1.96 | 1.91 | 1.83 | 1.75 | 1.66 | 1.61 | 1.55 | 1.50 | 1.43 | 1.35 | 1.25 | 146.57 | 120 |
| ∞ | 1.96 | 3.84 | 3.00 | 2.60 | 2.37 | 2.21 | 2.10 | 2.01 | 1.94 | 1.88 | 1.83 | 1.75 | 1.67 | 1.57 | 1.52 | 1.46 | 1.39 | 1.32 | 1.22 | 1.00 | | ∞ |
| $\chi^2$ | | 3.84 | 5.99 | 7.81 | 9.49 | 11.07 | 12.59 | 14.07 | 15.51 | 16.92 | 18.31 | 21.03 | 25.00 | 31.41 | 36.42 | 43.77 | 55.76 | 79.08 | 146.57 | | | $\chi^2$ |

For large values of $n$ ($n_1$ in this table) $\chi^2$ is approximately $n\left(1 - \dfrac{2}{9n} + 1.645\sqrt{\dfrac{2}{9n}}\right)^3$. For a normal curve, 5 percent of the observations are larger than $\mu + 1.645\sigma$.

Note that when $n_1 = 1$, $F = t^2$; and when $n_2 = \infty$, $F = \dfrac{\chi^2}{n}$.

Source: Cowden, Dudley J., and Mercedes S. Cowden, *Practical problems in business statistics*, Prentice-Hall, Inc., 1948 (by permission).

Now $(\bar{x} - \mu)$ is the allowable error. In this example, it will be assumed that $(x - \mu) = 0.5$, $s_x = 3.16$ and $K = 500$. The value chosen for $t$ determines the reliability to be placed in the allowable error. If it is desired to choose the sample size so that there is only one chance in 20 $(P = 0.05)$ that an error of size 0.5 would occur, then $t$ would equal approximately 2.0. So

$$k = \frac{(2.0 \times 3.16)^2}{(0.5)^2 + \dfrac{(2.0 \times 3.16)^2}{500}} = \frac{39.9424}{(0.25) + 0.0799} = \frac{39.9424}{0.3299} = 121$$

**Stratified Sampling.** Completely random sampling is often not the most efficient type of sampling. In many cases, the practising forester is sufficiently familiar with the population he is to sample to know the important factors that are causing variation. This knowledge of variation in the population can be used to reduce the sample size or to reduce the error for a given sample size, provided enough information is available to permit this knowledge of population variation to be used. A forester knows that stand volume varies with stand density and stand size class. If a map showing timber density and size class is available, then this information can be used. If a map is not available, then the knowledge cannot be used. The following, however, illustrates how the information can be used when it is available:

Let $K_i$ = the total number of plots in the $i$th stratum or mapped class
  $\bar{x}_i$ = the average volume on the sample of plots in the $i$th stratum
  $n$ = the number of strata
  $k_i$ = the number of sample plots taken in the $i$th stratum
  $T$ = the total volume of all strata

Then total volume in all strata is

$$T = \sum_{i=1}^{n} K_i \bar{x}_i$$

The variance of $T$ is

$$s^2{}_T = \sum_{i=1}^{n} K_i^2 s_{\bar{x}_i}^2 = \sum_{i=1}^{n} K_i^2 \frac{s_i^2}{k_i} \left(1 - \frac{k_i}{K_i}\right)$$

**Example.** Consider the following example consisting of three mapped classes. In this example, $T = 13,800,000$ and $s_T = \sqrt{4,987,983,200,000} = 2,233,379$. Thus $T = 13,800,000 \pm 2,233,379$ or $T = 13,800,000 \pm 16.2$ percent.

The determination of sample size for any particular class is as has been outlined previously. If, however, the accuracy is placed on the total volume for all classes, then the value of $k'$ that will make the total error a minimum is obtained from the equation. Where $k' = \sum_{i=1}^{n} k_i$

$$k' = \frac{t^2 \left( \sum_{i=1}^{n} K_i s_i \right)^2}{(\bar{x} - \mu)^2 + t^2 \sum_{i=1}^{n} K_i s_i^2}$$

Most of the computations needed are tabulated on page **23·29**.

$(\bar{x} - \mu)$ is the allowable error which is set. If we assume it to be **5 percent** of $T$. then

$$(\overline{x} - \mu) = (0.05) \ (13{,}800{,}000) = 690{,}000$$

The value for $t$ determines the confidence to be placed in the estimate of error $(\overline{x} - \mu)$, which for this example is put at 2.0. This means that in one time out of 20 an error larger than $(\overline{x} - \mu)$ would be expected. Substituting in the equation for $k'$ gives

$$k' = \frac{(2.0)^2 \ (8{,}680{,}000)^2}{(690{,}000)^2 + (2.0)^2 \ (22{,}724{,}000{,}000)}$$

$$= \frac{301{,}369{,}600{,}000{,}000}{476{,}100{,}000{,}000 + 90{,}896{,}000{,}000}$$

$$= \frac{301{,}369{,}600{,}000{,}000}{566{,}996{,}000{,}000}$$

$$= 532$$

The distribution of $k' = 532$ among the three classes is shown in the last column. It is based on the proportion that $K_i s_i$ makes of the total

$$\sum_{i=1}^{n} K_i s_i$$

**Proportions and Their Errors.** In case the variate being considered is one that can be present or absent, then a sample of $N$ random observations will give $n$ observations with the variate present and $(N - n)$ with the variate absent. The proportion $n/N = P$ is the sample estimate of the population proportion, $\mu$.

The expected number of observations with the variate present is $NP$. The error of $NP$ and of $P$ can be readily calculated:

$$S_{NP} = \sqrt{NP(1 - P)}$$

and

$$S_P = \sqrt{\frac{P(1 - P)}{N}}$$

**Example.** Assume that it is desired to estimate the proportion of an area that is timber, and this is to be done from aerial photographs. Assume also that the photos are of a quality that it is possible to state whether an area is or is not forested. Then a sample of 2,000 points is classified and 1,600 are called forest. The sample estimate of the proportion is:

$$P = \frac{1{,}600}{2{,}000} = 0.80$$

The error of $P$ is:

$$S_P = \sqrt{\frac{(0.8) \ (0.2)}{2{,}000}} = \sqrt{0.00008} = 0.0089$$

Using a $t$ of 2.0, the fiducial band would be

$$0.8 - 0.0089 \ (2.0) \text{ and } 0.8 + 0.0089 \ (2.0)$$

or

$$0.7822 \text{ to } 0.8178$$

There is thus a probability of 0.95 that the true preportion is in the range 0 7822 to 0.8178.

| Class | Area (acres) | Number ¼-acre plots = $K_i$ | Mean volume $\bar{x}_i$ | $K_i\bar{x}_i$ | $s_i$ | $s_i^2$ | $k_i$ | $s_i^2/k_i$ | $\left(1-\dfrac{k_i}{K_i}\right)$ | $s_{\bar{x}_i}^2 = \dfrac{s_i^2}{k_i}\left(1-\dfrac{k_i}{K_i}\right)$ | $K_i^2 s_{\bar{x}_i}^2$ |
|---|---|---|---|---|---|---|---|---|---|---|---|
| Saw timber | 600 | 2,400 | 5,000 | 12,000,000 | 3,000 | 9,000,000 | 100 | 900,000 | 0.9583 | 862,470 | 4,967,827,200,000 |
| Pole | 400 | 1,600 | 1,000 | 1,600,000 | 800 | 640,000 | 80 | 8,000 | 0.9500 | 7,600 | 19,456,000,000 |
| Cut-over | 100 | 400 | 500 | 200,000 | 500 | 250,000 | 50 | 5,000 | 0.8750 | 4,375 | 700,000,000 |
| Total | | | | 13,800,000 | | | | | | | 4,987,983,200,000 |

| Class | Area (acres) | Number ¼-acre plots = $K_i$ | Mean volume $\bar{x}_i$ | $K_i\bar{x}_i$ | $s_i$ | $K_{i}s_i$ | $s_i^2$ | $k_i$ | $s_i^2/k_i$ | $p_i$ | $k'_i$ | $K_{i}s_i^2$ |
|---|---|---|---|---|---|---|---|---|---|---|---|---|
| Saw timber | 600 | 2,400 | 5,000 | 12,000,000 | 3,000 | 7,200,000 | 9,000,000 | 100 | 900,000 | 0.830 | 442 | 21,600,000,000 |
| Pole | 400 | 1,600 | 1,000 | 1,600,000 | 800 | 1,280,000 | 640,000 | 80 | 8,000 | 0.147 | 78 | 1,024,000,000 |
| Cut-over | 100 | 400 | 500 | 200,000 | 500 | 200,000 | 250,000 | 50 | 5,000 | 0.023 | 12 | 100,000,000 |
| Total | | | | 13,800,000 | | 8,680,000 | | | | 1.000 | 532 | 22,724,000,000 |

The error of the total number of points in forest is

$$\sqrt{(2,000)\ (0.8)\ (0.2)} = \sqrt{320} = 17.89$$

To determine sample size, the procedure is the same as for an arithmetic average.

1. The allowable error and its probability of occurrence has to be specified.
2. Estimate of the population proportion has to be made.

Thus

$$t = \frac{P - \mu}{S_p}$$

$$tS_p = (P - \mu)$$

$$t\sqrt{\frac{P(1 - P)}{n}} = (P - \mu)$$

$$\frac{t\sqrt{P(1 - P)}}{P - \mu} = \sqrt{n}$$

As an example, let $P - \mu$ be an allowable error of 0.01 and $t = 2.0$ so that the probability of exceeding this error is 0.05. If the best estimate of the population proportion is 0.8, then

$$\sqrt{n} = \frac{2\sqrt{(0.8)\ (0.2)}}{0.01} = \frac{2(0.4)}{0.01} = \frac{0.80}{0.01} = 80$$

$$n = 6,400$$

A sample of size 6,400 should be used to get the accuracy desired. That is, if the sample mean was 0.8, then in 19 out of 20 times the correct proportion should be within the range of $0.8 \pm 0.01$.

**CURVE FITTING.** Many problems in forestry require the determination of the relation between variables. Many of these relationships involve only two variables, such as the relation between tree volume and tree diameter. Others involve several variables. However, this short presentation is not an attempt to cover the entire field because it deals only with procedures for getting the curves. No attempt is made to present the standard tests of significance of the equation coefficient since entire books are written on this one subject. The importance or significance of the relationship must be based on the judgment of the worker. For a complete coverage, reference should be made to a standard text on correlation or curve-fitting procedure.

Curves can be fitted in two ways: (a) by the solution of a set of normal equations which were derived by the mathematical procedure known as least squares, and (b) by inspection and freehand drawing of curves. To use the first procedure, a mathematical equation must be assumed. With the other approach, the data accompanied by rationalization determine the form of the curves.

**Example.** Consider the data shown below. These data are measurements of diameter and board-foot volume of 10 trees.

| Tree No. | 1 | 2 | 3 | 4 | 5 | 6 | 7 | 8 | 9 | 10 |
|---|---|---|---|---|---|---|---|---|---|---|
| D.b.h. (in.) | 10 | 11 | 12 | 14 | 14 | 15 | 15 | 15 | 17 | 19 |
| Volume (bd. ft.) | 45 | 40 | 50 | 100 | 70 | 90 | 100 | 110 | 150 | 230 |

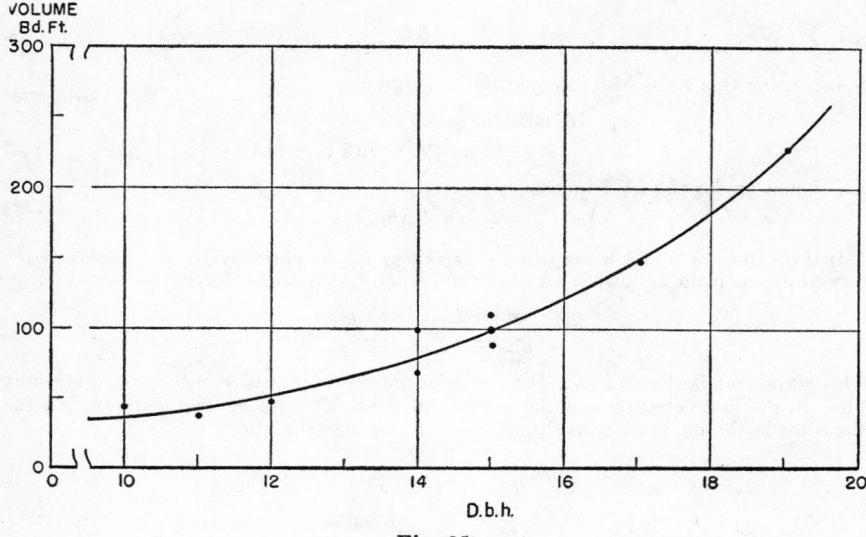

**Fig. 35.**

A plot of the data is shown in Fig. 35. The trend in these data is a curve with a slight upward swing. As stated before, it is necessary to decide on a curve form before a curve can be fitted to these data. We know that tree volume varies as the square of d.b.h. Since this is true, a plot of volume over the square of d.b.h. should be approximately a straight line. The plot of volume over the square of d.b.h. is shown in Fig. 36 (p. **23**·24). Fig. 36 would indicate that there is a straight-line relation between volume and the square of the diameter. From analytical geometry it is found that a straight line can be represented by an equation of the form:

$$y = a + b(x)$$

where $a$ is the $y$-intercept, or the value of $y$ when $x = 0$ and $b$ is the slope of the line, i.e., the change in $y$ for a unit change in $x$.

In this example $y$ is the volume and $x$ is the squared diameter. If the line is to be fitted to the data in Fig. 36 by freehand procedure, then for a straight line certain guides are available to locate the line.

1. A straight line passes through the point, $\overline{x}$ and $\overline{y}$, the arithmetic averages of $x$ and $y$.
2. The algebraic sum of the deviations from the line should be zero. The deviations are usually figured in number of squares on graph paper. The deviation for $x = 100$ is $+25$.

If the line goes through the point $(\overline{x}, \overline{y})$ and also represents the general trend, the line will be very close to that obtained by the least squares procedure if the sums of the deviations are zero. If an equation is needed after the line is drawn, it can be obtained by reading two pairs of values of $x$ and $y$ on the line and solving the two equations for the constants, $a$ and $b$. For $x = 100$, $y = 21$ and for $x = 400$, $y = 233$ The two equations are:

| | |
|---|---|
| (1) | $a + b(100) = \phantom{0}21$ |
| (2) | $a + b(400) = 233$ |
| (2) − (1) | $b(300) = 212$ |

$$b = \frac{212}{300} = 0.703$$

Substituting this value of $b$ in equation No. 1 gives

$$a + (0.703)(100) = 21$$
$$a = 21 - 70.3 = -49.3$$

The equation for the freehand curve is

$$y = -49.3 + 0.703(x)$$

If the values of $a$ and $b$ are to be determined mathematically by the least squares procedure, then the following set of normal equations must be solved for $a$ and $b$:

$$an + b\Sigma x = \Sigma y$$
$$a\Sigma x + b\Sigma x^2 = \Sigma xy$$

This is the standard set of equations to solve for obtaining the constants of a straight line. In the first equation $n$ is the number of pairs of $x$ and $y$. The computation for the sums in these equations is shown in the following tabulation:

| $x$ | $y$ | $x^2$ | $xy$ |
|---|---|---|---|
| 100 | 45 | 10,000 | 4,500 |
| 121 | 40 | 14,641 | 4,840 |
| 144 | 50 | 20,736 | 7,200 |
| 196 | 100 | 38,416 | 19,600 |
| 196 | 70 | 38,416 | 13,720 |
| 225 | 90 | 50,625 | 20,250 |
| 225 | 100 | 50,625 | 22,500 |
| 225 | 110 | 50,625 | 24,750 |
| 289 | 150 | 83,521 | 43,350 |
| 361 | 230 | 130,321 | 83,030 |
| 2,082 | 985 | 487,926 | 243,740 |

Substituting the sums in the normal equations gives

$$
\begin{array}{ll}
10(a) + \phantom{00}2{,}082(b) = \phantom{000}985 & (1) \\
2{,}082(a) + 487{,}926(b) = 243{,}740 & (2) \\
\hline
a + \phantom{00}208.2(b) = \phantom{0}98.5 & (3) = (1) \div 10 \\
a + \phantom{00}234.4(b) = 117.1 & (4) = (2) \div 2{,}082 \\
\hline
\phantom{a + 000}26.2(b) = \phantom{0}18.6 & (5) = (4) - (3)
\end{array}
$$

$$b = \frac{18.6}{26.2} = 0.7099 \qquad (6)$$

$$
\begin{array}{l}
a + (208.2)(0.7099) = \phantom{0}98.5 \qquad \text{Substitute } b \text{ in (3)} \\
a + 147.8 = \phantom{0}98.5 \\
\phantom{a + 147.8} a = -147.8 + 98.5 = -49.3
\end{array}
$$

The equation then becomes

$$y = -49.3 + 0.71(x)$$

The transformation was suggested to make the relationship linear because straight-line relations are easier to handle. If the original variable, d.b.h., had been used, then the relation would be curved, as indicated in Fig. 35. When fitting a freehand curve to such data, the basis for judging the fit is:

1. The curve follows the general trend of the data.
2. The algebraic sum of the deviations is zero and this sum should hold approximately for each third of the curve.

To fit the curve by mathematical methods requires, as before, the assuming of an equation form. The most common equation form is that of a polynomial—a first-degree polynomial being that of a straight line and a second-degree polynomial having an upward or downward swing. A second-degree polynomial is of the form:

$$y = a + b(x) + c(x^2)$$

The normal equations for a second-degree polynomial are

$$(a)n + (b)\,\Sigma x + (c)\Sigma x^2 = \Sigma y$$
$$(a)\Sigma x + (b)\,\Sigma x^2 + (c)\Sigma x^3 = \Sigma xy$$
$$(a)\Sigma x^2 + (b)\,\Sigma x^3 + (c)\Sigma x^4 = \Sigma x^2 y$$

The computation of these sums is shown in the tabulation below.

| $x$ | $y$ | $x^2$ | $x^3$ | $x^4$ | $xy$ | $x^2 y$ |
|---|---|---|---|---|---|---|
| 10 | 45 | 100 | 1,000 | 10,000 | 450 | 4,500 |
| 11 | 40 | 121 | 1,331 | 14,641 | 440 | 4,840 |
| 12 | 50 | 144 | 1,728 | 20,736 | 600 | 7,200 |
| 14 | 100 | 196 | 2,744 | 38,416 | 1,400 | 19,600 |
| 14 | 70 | 196 | 2,744 | 38,416 | 980 | 13,720 |
| 15 | 90 | 225 | 3,375 | 50,625 | 1,350 | 20,250 |
| 15 | 100 | 225 | 3,375 | 50,625 | 1,500 | 22,500 |
| 15 | 110 | 225 | 3,375 | 50,625 | 1,650 | 24,750 |
| 17 | 150 | 289 | 4,913 | 83,521 | 2,550 | 43,350 |
| 19 | 230 | 361 | 6,859 | 130,321 | 4,370 | 83,030 |
| 142 | 985 | 2,082 | 31,444 | 487,926 | 15,290 | 243,740 |

The solution of these normal equations is shown below.

$$10(a) + \quad 142(b) + \quad 2,082(c) = \quad 985 \qquad (1)$$
$$142(a) + \quad 2,082(b) + \quad 31,444(c) = \quad 15,290 \qquad (2)$$
$$2,082(a) + 31,444(b) + 487,926(c) = 243,740 \qquad (3)$$

$$a + 14.2 \quad (b) + 208.2 \quad (c) = \quad 98.5 \qquad (4) = (1) \div 10$$
$$a + 14.6620(b) + 221.4366(c) = 107.6761 \qquad (5) = (2) \div 142$$
$$a + 15.1028(b) + 234.3545(c) = 117.0701 \qquad (6) = (3) \div 2,082$$

$$0.4620(b) + \quad 13.2366(c) = \quad 9.1761 \qquad (7) = (5) - (4)$$
$$0.9028(b) + \quad 26.1545(c) = \quad 18.5701 \qquad (8) = (6) - (4)$$

$$b + \quad 28.6506(c) = \quad 19.8617 \qquad (9) = (7) \div 0.4620$$
$$b + \quad 28.9704(c) = \quad 20.5695 \qquad (10) = (8) \div 0.9028$$

$$0.3198(c) = \quad 0.7078 \qquad (11) = (10) - (9)$$

$$c = \quad 2.21326 \qquad (12) = (11) \div 0.3198$$

Substitute this value of $c$ in (10) and solve for $b$.

$$b + (2.21326)\,(28.9704) = 20.5695$$
$$b + 64.1190 = 20.5695$$
$$b = -43.5495$$

Substitute the values of $b$ and $c$ in (4) and solve for $a$.

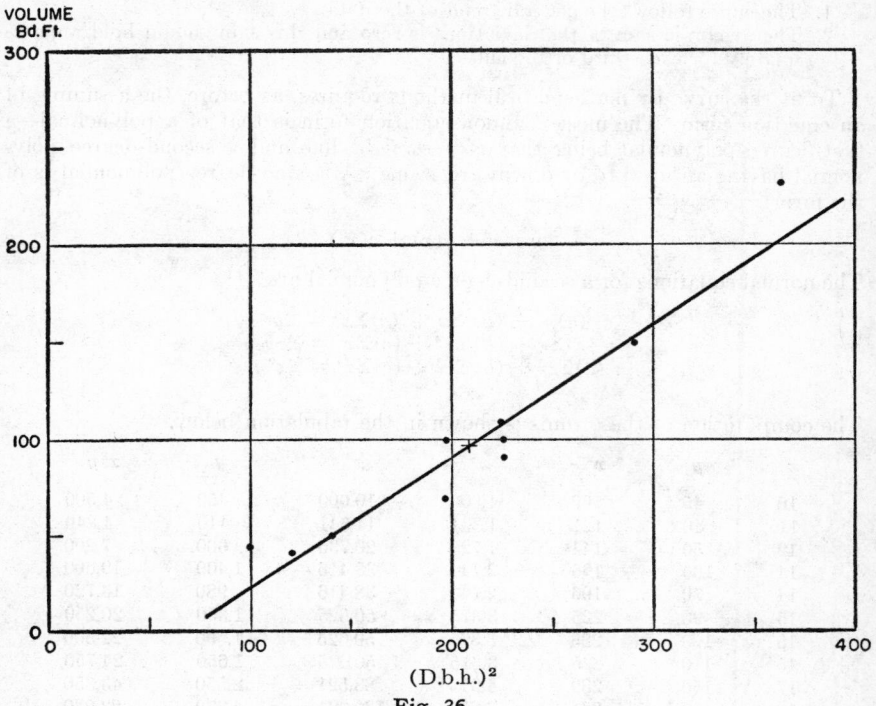

VOLUME
Bd. Ft.

(D.b.h.)²

Fig. 36.

$$a + (-43.5495)(14.2) + 2.21326(208.2) = 98.5$$
$$a - 618.4029 + 460.8007 = 98.5$$
$$a = 256.1022$$

The final equation is

$$y = 256.1022 - 43.5495(x) + 2.21326(x^2)$$

A word of caution should be noted: Unless the form of the relationship can be based on a rationalization of the relationship, it is dangerous to extend the curve beyond the range of the data. This caution should be exercised on both mathematical and freehand curves.

If an equation is of the form

$$y = a + b\left(\frac{1}{x}\right)$$

then, if the reciprocal of $x$ is used instead of $x$, the relation will be linear.

If an equation is of the form

$$y = ab^{(cx)}$$

then, if the logarithm of $y$ is plotted over $x$, the relationship will be linear.

If an equation is of the form

$$y = ax^b$$

then plotting the logarithm of $y$ over the logarithm of $x$ will give a straight line.

# Mathematical Tables

Table 3. Squares, Cubes, Square and Cube Roots, Circumferences and
Areas of Circles *

| No. | Square | Cube | Square root | Cube root | Reciprocal | Circumference | Area |
|---|---|---|---|---|---|---|---|
| 1 | 1 | 1 | 1.0000 | 1.0000 | 1.00000 | 3.1416 | 0.7854 |
| 2 | 4 | 8 | 1.4142 | 1.2599 | .50000 | 6.2832 | 3.1416 |
| 3 | 9 | 27 | 1.7321 | 1.4422 | .33333 | 9.4248 | 7.0686 |
| 4 | 16 | 64 | 2.0000 | 1.5874 | .25000 | 12.5664 | 12.5664 |
| 5 | 25 | 125 | 2.2361 | 1.7100 | .20000 | 15.708 | 19.635 |
| 6 | 36 | 216 | 2.4495 | 1.8171 | .16667 | 18.850 | 28.274 |
| 7 | 49 | 343 | 2.6458 | 1.9129 | .14286 | 21.991 | 38.485 |
| 8 | 64 | 512 | 2.8284 | 2.0000 | .12500 | 25.133 | 50.266 |
| 9 | 81 | 729 | 3.0000 | 2.0801 | .11111 | 28.274 | 63.617 |
| 10 | 100 | 1,000 | 3.1623 | 2.1544 | .10000 | 31.416 | 78.540 |
| 11 | 121 | 1,331 | 3.3166 | 2.2240 | .09091 | 34.558 | 95.033 |
| 12 | 144 | 1,728 | 3.4641 | 2.2894 | .08333 | 37.699 | 113.10 |
| 13 | 169 | 2,197 | 3.6056 | 2.3513 | .07692 | 40.841 | 132.73 |
| 14 | 196 | 2,744 | 3.7417 | 2.4101 | .07143 | 43.982 | 153.94 |
| 15 | 225 | 3,375 | 3.8730 | 2.4662 | .06667 | 47.124 | 176.71 |
| 16 | 256 | 4,096 | 4.0000 | 2.5198 | .06250 | 50.625 | 201.06 |
| 17 | 289 | 4,913 | 4.1231 | 2.5713 | .05882 | 53.407 | 226.98 |
| 18 | 324 | 5,832 | 4.2426 | 2.6207 | .05556 | 56.549 | 254.47 |
| 19 | 361 | 6,859 | 4.3589 | 2.6684 | .05263 | 59.690 | 283.53 |
| 20 | 400 | 8,000 | 4.4721 | 2.7144 | .05000 | 62.832 | 314.16 |
| 21 | 441 | 9,261 | 4.5826 | 2.7589 | .04762 | 65.973 | 346.36 |
| 22 | 484 | 10,648 | 4.6904 | 2.8020 | .04545 | 69.115 | 380.13 |
| 23 | 529 | 12,167 | 4.7958 | 2.8439 | .04348 | 72.257 | 415.48 |
| 24 | 576 | 13,824 | 4.8990 | 2.8845 | .04167 | 75.398 | 452.39 |
| 25 | 625 | 15,625 | 5.0000 | 2.9240 | .04000 | 78.540 | 490.87 |
| 26 | 676 | 17,576 | 5.0990 | 2.9625 | .03846 | 81.681 | 530.93 |
| 27 | 729 | 19,683 | 5.1962 | 3.0000 | .03704 | 84.823 | 572.56 |
| 28 | 784 | 21,952 | 5.2915 | 3.0366 | .03571 | 87.965 | 615.75 |
| 29 | 841 | 24,389 | 5.3852 | 3.0723 | .03448 | 91.106 | 660.52 |
| 30 | 900 | 27,000 | 5.4772 | 3.1072 | .03333 | 94.248 | 706.86 |
| 31 | 961 | 29,791 | 5.5678 | 3.1414 | .03226 | 97.389 | 754.77 |
| 32 | 1,024 | 32,768 | 5.6569 | 3.1748 | .03125 | 100.53 | 804.25 |
| 33 | 1,089 | 35,937 | 5.7446 | 3.2075 | .03030 | 103.67 | 855.30 |
| 34 | 1,156 | 39,304 | 5.8310 | 3.2396 | .02941 | 106.81 | 907.92 |
| 35 | 1,225 | 42,875 | 5.9161 | 3.2711 | .02857 | 109.96 | 962.11 |
| 36 | 1,296 | 46,656 | 6.0000 | 3.3019 | .02778 | 113.10 | 1,017.88 |
| 37 | 1,369 | 50,653 | 6.0828 | 3.3322 | .02703 | 116.24 | 1,075.21 |
| 38 | 1,444 | 54,872 | 6.1644 | 3.3620 | .02632 | 119.38 | 1,134.11 |
| 39 | 1,521 | 59,319 | 6.2450 | 3.3912 | .02564 | 122.52 | 1,194.59 |
| 40 | 1,600 | 64,000 | 6.3246 | 3.4200 | .02500 | 125.66 | 1,256.64 |
| 41 | 1,681 | 68,921 | 6.4031 | 3.4482 | .02439 | 128.81 | 1,320.25 |
| 42 | 1,764 | 74.088 | 6.4807 | 3.4760 | .02381 | 131.95 | 1,385.44 |
| 43 | 1,849 | 79,507 | 6.5574 | 3.5034 | .02326 | 135.09 | 1,452.20 |
| 44 | 1,936 | 85,184 | 6.6332 | 3.5303 | .02273 | 138.23 | 1,520.53 |
| 45 | 2,025 | 91,125 | 6.7082 | 3.5569 | .02222 | 141.37 | 1,590.43 |
| 46 | 2,116 | 97,336 | 6.7823 | 3.5830 | .02174 | 144.51 | 1,661.90 |
| 47 | 2,209 | 103,823 | 6.8557 | 3.6088 | .02128 | 147.65 | 1,734.94 |
| 48 | 2,304 | 110,592 | 6.9282 | 3.6342 | .02083 | 150.80 | 1,809.56 |
| 49 | 2,401 | 117,649 | 7.0000 | 3.6593 | .02041 | 153.94 | 1,885.74 |
| 50 | 2,500 | 125,000 | 7.0711 | 3.6840 | .02000 | 157.08 | 1,963.50 |

Table 3.  Squares, Cubes, Square and Cube Roots, Circumferences and
Areas of Circles * (Continued)

| No. | Square | Cube | Square root | Cube root | Recip- rocal | Circum- ference | Area |
|---|---|---|---|---|---|---|---|
| 51 | 2,601 | 132,651 | 7.1414 | 3.7084 | .01961 | 160.22 | 2,042.82 |
| 52 | 2,704 | 140,608 | 7.2111 | 3.7325 | .01923 | 163.36 | 2,123.72 |
| 53 | 2,809 | 148,877 | 7.2801 | 3.7563 | .01887 | 166.50 | 2,206.18 |
| 54 | 2,916 | 157,464 | 7.3485 | 3.7798 | .01852 | 169.65 | 2,290.22 |
| 55 | 3,025 | 166,375 | 7.4162 | 3.8030 | .01818 | 172.79 | 2,375.83 |
| 56 | 3,136 | 175,616 | 7.4833 | 3.8259 | .01786 | 175.93 | 2,463.01 |
| 57 | 3,249 | 185,193 | 7.5498 | 3.8485 | .01754 | 179.07 | 2,551.76 |
| 58 | 3,364 | 195.112 | 7.6158 | 3.8709 | .01724 | 182.21 | 2,642.08 |
| 59 | 3,481 | 205,379 | 7.6811 | 3.8930 | .01695 | 185.35 | 2,733.97 |
| 60 | 3,600 | 216,000 | 7.7460 | 3.9149 | .01667 | 188.50 | 2,827.43 |
| 61 | 3,721 | 226,981 | 7.8102 | 3.9365 | .01639 | 191.64 | 2,922.47 |
| 62 | 3,844 | 238,328 | 7.8740 | 3.9579 | .01613 | 194.78 | 3,019.07 |
| 63 | 3,969 | 250,047 | 7.9373 | 3.9791 | .01587 | 197.92 | 3,117.25 |
| 64 | 4,096 | 262,144 | 8.0000 | 4.0000 | .01562 | 201.06 | 3,216.99 |
| 65 | 4,225 | 274,625 | 8.0623 | 4.0207 | .01538 | 204.20 | 3,318.31 |
| 66 | 4,356 | 287,496 | 8.1240 | 4.0412 | .01515 | 207.34 | 3,421.19 |
| 67 | 4,489 | 300,763 | 8.1854 | 4.0615 | .01493 | 210.49 | 3,525.65 |
| 68 | 4,624 | 314,432 | 8.2462 | 4.0817 | .01471 | 213.63 | 3,631.68 |
| 69 | 4,761 | 328,509 | 8.3066 | 4.1016 | .01449 | 216.77 | 3,739.28 |
| 70 | 4,900 | 343,000 | 8.3666 | 4.1213 | .01429 | 219.91 | 3,848.45 |
| 71 | 5,041 | 357,911 | 8.4261 | 4.1408 | .01408 | 223.05 | 3,959.19 |
| 72 | 5,184 | 373,248 | 8.4853 | 4.1602 | .01389 | 226.19 | 4,071.50 |
| 73 | 5,329 | 389,017 | 8.5440 | 4.1793 | .01370 | 229.34 | 4,185.39 |
| 74 | 5,476 | 405,224 | 8.6023 | 4.1983 | .01351 | 232.48 | 4,300.84 |
| 75 | 5,625 | 421,875 | 8.6603 | 4.2172 | .01333 | 235.62 | 4,417.86 |
| 76 | 5,776 | 438,976 | 8.7178 | 4.2358 | .01316 | 238.76 | 4,536.46 |
| 77 | 5,929 | 456,533 | 8.7750 | 4.2543 | .01299 | 241.90 | 4,656.63 |
| 78 | 6,084 | 474,552 | 8.8318 | 4.2727 | .01282 | 245.04 | 4,778.36 |
| 79 | 6,241 | 493,039 | 8.8882 | 4.2908 | .01266 | 248.19 | 4,901.67 |
| 80 | 6,400 | 512,000 | 8.9443 | 4.3089 | .01250 | 251.33 | 5,026.55 |
| 81 | 6,561 | 531,441 | 9.0000 | 4.3267 | .01235 | 254.47 | 5,153.00 |
| 82 | 6,724 | 551,368 | 9.0554 | 4.3445 | .01220 | 257.61 | 5,281.02 |
| 83 | 6,889 | 571,787 | 9.1104 | 4.3621 | .01205 | 260.75 | 5,410.61 |
| 84 | 7,056 | 592,704 | 9.1652 | 4.3795 | .01190 | 263.89 | 5,541.77 |
| 85 | 7,225 | 614,125 | 9.2195 | 4.3968 | .01176 | 267.04 | 5,674.50 |
| 86 | 7,396 | 636,056 | 9.2736 | 4.4140 | .01163 | 270.18 | 5,808.80 |
| 87 | 7,569 | 658,503 | 9.3274 | 4.4310 | .01149 | 273.32 | 5,944.68 |
| 88 | 7,744 | 681,472 | 9.3808 | 4.4480 | .01136 | 276.46 | 6,082.12 |
| 89 | 7,921 | 704,969 | 9.4340 | 4.4647 | .01124 | 279.60 | 6,221.14 |
| 90 | 8,100 | 729,000 | 9.4868 | 4.4814 | .01111 | 282.74 | 6,361.73 |
| 91 | 8,281 | 753,571 | 9.5394 | 4.4979 | .01099 | 285.88 | 6,503.88 |
| 92 | 8,464 | 778,688 | 9.5917 | 4.5144 | .01087 | 289.03 | 6,647.61 |
| 93 | 8,649 | 804,357 | 9.6437 | 4.5307 | .01075 | 292.17 | 6,792.91 |
| 94 | 8,836 | 830,584 | 9.6954 | 4.5468 | .01064 | 295.31 | 6,939.78 |
| 95 | 9,025 | 857,375 | 9.7468 | 4.5629 | .01053 | 298.45 | 7,088.22 |
| 96 | 9,216 | 884,736 | 9.7980 | 4.5789 | .01042 | 301.59 | 7,238.23 |
| 97 | 9,409 | 912,673 | 9.8489 | 4.5947 | .01031 | 304.73 | 7,389.81 |
| 98 | 9,604 | 941,192 | 9.8995 | 4.6104 | .01020 | 307.88 | 7,542.96 |
| 99 | 9,801 | 970,299 | 9.9499 | 4.6261 | .01010 | 311.02 | 7,697.69 |
| 100 | 10,000 | 1,000,000 | 10.0000 | 4.6416 | .01000 | 314.16 | 7,853.98 |

* When values in first columns are diameters.
Source: Adapted from Hudson and Lipka.

## Table 4. Logarithms of Numbers

| 1 | 0 | 1 | 2 | 3 | 4 | 5 | 6 | 7 | 8 | 9 |
|---|---|---|---|---|---|---|---|---|---|---|
| 0 | 0000 | 0000 | 3010 | 4771 | 6021 | 6990 | 7782 | 8451 | 9031 | 9542 |
| 1 | 0000 | 0414 | 0792 | 1139 | 1461 | 1761 | 2041 | 2304 | 2553 | 2788 |
| 2 | 3010 | 3222 | 3424 | 3617 | 3802 | 3979 | 4150 | 4314 | 4472 | 4624 |
| 3 | 4771 | 4914 | 5051 | 5185 | 5315 | 5441 | 5563 | 5682 | 5798 | 5911 |
| 4 | 6021 | 6128 | 6232 | 6335 | 6435 | 6532 | 6628 | 6721 | 6812 | 6902 |
| 5 | 6990 | 7076 | 7160 | 7243 | 7324 | 7404 | 7482 | 7559 | 7634 | 7709 |
| 6 | 7782 | 7853 | 7924 | 7993 | 8062 | 8129 | 8195 | 8261 | 8325 | 8388 |
| 7 | 8451 | 8513 | 8573 | 8633 | 8692 | 8751 | 8808 | 8865 | 8921 | 8976 |
| 8 | 9031 | 9085 | 9138 | 9191 | 9243 | 9294 | 9345 | 9395 | 9445 | 9494 |
| 9 | 9542 | 9590 | 9638 | 9685 | 9731 | 9777 | 9823 | 9868 | 9912 | 9956 |
| 10 | 0000 | 0043 | 0086 | 0128 | 0170 | 0212 | 0253 | 0294 | 0334 | 0374 |
| 11 | 0414 | 0453 | 0492 | 0531 | 0569 | 0607 | 0645 | 0682 | 0719 | 0755 |
| 12 | 0792 | 0828 | 0864 | 0899 | 0934 | 0969 | 1004 | 1038 | 1072 | 1106 |
| 13 | 1139 | 1173 | 1206 | 1239 | 1271 | 1303 | 1335 | 1367 | 1399 | 1430 |
| 14 | 1461 | 1492 | 1523 | 1553 | 1584 | 1614 | 1644 | 1673 | 1703 | 1732 |
| 15 | 1761 | 1790 | 1818 | 1847 | 1875 | 1903 | 1931 | 1959 | 1987 | 2014 |
| 16 | 2041 | 2068 | 2095 | 2122 | 2148 | 2175 | 2201 | 2227 | 2253 | 2279 |
| 17 | 2304 | 2330 | 2355 | 2380 | 2405 | 2430 | 2455 | 2480 | 2504 | 2529 |
| 18 | 2553 | 2577 | 2601 | 2625 | 2648 | 2672 | 2695 | 2718 | 2742 | 2765 |
| 19 | 2788 | 2810 | 2833 | 2856 | 2878 | 2900 | 2923 | 2945 | 2967 | 2989 |
| 20 | 3010 | 3032 | 3054 | 3075 | 3096 | 3118 | 3139 | 3160 | 3181 | 3201 |
| 21 | 3222 | 3243 | 3263 | 3284 | 3304 | 3324 | 3345 | 3365 | 3385 | 3404 |
| 22 | 3424 | 3444 | 3464 | 3483 | 3502 | 3522 | 3541 | 3560 | 3570 | 3598 |
| 23 | 3617 | 3636 | 3655 | 3674 | 3692 | 3711 | 3729 | 3747 | 3766 | 3784 |
| 24 | 3802 | 3820 | 3838 | 3856 | 3874 | 3892 | 3909 | 3927 | 3945 | 3962 |
| 25 | 3979 | 3997 | 4014 | 4031 | 4048 | 4065 | 4082 | 4099 | 4116 | 4133 |
| 26 | 4150 | 4166 | 4183 | 4200 | 4216 | 4232 | 4249 | 4265 | 4281 | 4298 |
| 27 | 4314 | 4330 | 4346 | 4362 | 4378 | 4393 | 4409 | 4425 | 4440 | 4456 |
| 28 | 4472 | 4487 | 4502 | 4518 | 4533 | 4548 | 4564 | 4579 | 4594 | 4609 |
| 29 | 4624 | 4639 | 4654 | 4669 | 4683 | 4698 | 4713 | 4728 | 4742 | 4757 |
| 30 | 4771 | 4786 | 4800 | 4814 | 4829 | 4843 | 4857 | 4871 | 4886 | 4900 |
| 31 | 4914 | 4928 | 4942 | 4955 | 4969 | 4983 | 4997 | 5011 | 5024 | 5038 |
| 32 | 5051 | 5065 | 5079 | 5092 | 5105 | 5119 | 5132 | 5145 | 5159 | 5172 |
| 33 | 5185 | 5198 | 5211 | 5224 | 5237 | 5250 | 5263 | 5276 | 5289 | 5302 |
| 34 | 5315 | 5328 | 5340 | 5353 | 5366 | 5378 | 5391 | 5403 | 5416 | 5428 |
| 35 | 5441 | 5453 | 5465 | 5478 | 5490 | 5502 | 5514 | 5527 | 5539 | 5551 |
| 36 | 5563 | 5575 | 5587 | 5599 | 5611 | 5623 | 5635 | 5647 | 5658 | 5670 |
| 37 | 5682 | 5694 | 5705 | 5717 | 5729 | 5740 | 5752 | 5763 | 5775 | 5786 |
| 38 | 5798 | 5809 | 5821 | 5832 | 5843 | 5855 | 5866 | 5877 | 5888 | 5899 |
| 39 | 5911 | 5922 | 5933 | 5944 | 5955 | 5966 | 5977 | 5988 | 5999 | 6010 |
| 40 | 6021 | 6031 | 6042 | 6053 | 6064 | 6075 | 6085 | 6096 | 6107 | 6117 |
| 41 | 6128 | 6138 | 6149 | 6160 | 6170 | 6180 | 6191 | 6201 | 6212 | 6222 |
| 42 | 6232 | 6243 | 6253 | 6263 | 6274 | 6284 | 6294 | 6304 | 6314 | 6325 |
| 43 | 6335 | 6345 | 6355 | 6365 | 6375 | 6385 | 6395 | 6405 | 6415 | 6425 |
| 44 | 6435 | 6444 | 6454 | 6464 | 6474 | 6484 | 6493 | 6503 | 6513 | 6522 |
| 45 | 6532 | 6542 | 6551 | 6561 | 6571 | 6580 | 6590 | 6599 | 6609 | 6618 |
| 46 | 6628 | 6637 | 6646 | 6656 | 6665 | 6675 | 6684 | 6693 | 6702 | 6712 |
| 47 | 6721 | 6730 | 6739 | 6749 | 6758 | 6767 | 6776 | 6785 | 6794 | 6803 |
| 48 | 6812 | 6821 | 6830 | 6839 | 6848 | 6857 | 6866 | 6875 | 6884 | 6893 |
| 49 | 6902 | 6911 | 6920 | 6928 | 6937 | 6946 | 6955 | 6964 | 6972 | 6981 |

Table 4. Logarithms of Numbers (Continued)

| 50 | 0 | 1 | 2 | 3 | 4 | 5 | 6 | 7 | 8 | 9 |
|---|---|---|---|---|---|---|---|---|---|---|
| 50 | 6990 | 6998 | 7007 | 7016 | 7024 | 7033 | 7042 | 7050 | 7059 | 7067 |
| 51 | 7076 | 7084 | 7093 | 7101 | 7110 | 7118 | 7126 | 7135 | 7143 | 7152 |
| 52 | 7160 | 7168 | 7177 | 7185 | 7193 | 7202 | 7210 | 7218 | 7226 | 7235 |
| 53 | 7243 | 7251 | 7259 | 7267 | 7275 | 7284 | 7292 | 7300 | 7308 | 7316 |
| 54 | 7324 | 7332 | 7340 | 7348 | 7356 | 7364 | 7372 | 7380 | 7388 | 7396 |
| 55 | 7404 | 7412 | 7419 | 7427 | 7435 | 7443 | 7451 | 7459 | 7466 | 7474 |
| 56 | 7482 | 7490 | 7497 | 7505 | 7513 | 7520 | 7528 | 7536 | 7543 | 7551 |
| 57 | 7559 | 7566 | 7574 | 7582 | 7589 | 7597 | 7604 | 7612 | 7619 | 7627 |
| 58 | 7634 | 7642 | 7649 | 7657 | 7664 | 7672 | 7679 | 7686 | 7694 | 7701 |
| 59 | 7709 | 7716 | 7723 | 7731 | 7738 | 7745 | 7752 | 7760 | 7767 | 7774 |
| 60 | 7782 | 7789 | 7796 | 7803 | 7810 | 7818 | 7825 | 7832 | 7839 | 7846 |
| 61 | 7853 | 7860 | 7868 | 7875 | 7882 | 7889 | 7896 | 7903 | 7910 | 7917 |
| 62 | 7924 | 7931 | 7938 | 7945 | 7952 | 7959 | 7966 | 7973 | 7980 | 7987 |
| 63 | 7993 | 8000 | 8007 | 8014 | 8021 | 8028 | 8035 | 8041 | 8048 | 8055 |
| 64 | 8062 | 8069 | 8075 | 8082 | 8089 | 8096 | 8102 | 8109 | 8116 | 8122 |
| 65 | 8129 | 8136 | 8142 | 8149 | 8156 | 8162 | 8169 | 8176 | 8182 | 8189 |
| 66 | 8195 | 8202 | 8209 | 8215 | 8222 | 8228 | 8235 | 8241 | 8248 | 8254 |
| 67 | 8261 | 8267 | 8274 | 8280 | 8287 | 8293 | 8299 | 8306 | 8312 | 8319 |
| 68 | 8325 | 8331 | 8338 | 8344 | 8351 | 8357 | 8363 | 8370 | 8376 | 8382 |
| 69 | 8388 | 8395 | 8401 | 8407 | 8414 | 8420 | 8426 | 8432 | 8439 | 8445 |
| 70 | 8451 | 8457 | 8463 | 8470 | 8476 | 8482 | 8488 | 8494 | 8500 | 8506 |
| 71 | 8513 | 8519 | 8525 | 8531 | 8537 | 8543 | 8549 | 8555 | 8561 | 8567 |
| 72 | 8573 | 8579 | 8585 | 8591 | 8597 | 8603 | 8609 | 8615 | 8621 | 8627 |
| 73 | 8633 | 8639 | 8645 | 8651 | 8657 | 8663 | 8669 | 8675 | 8680 | 8686 |
| 74 | 8692 | 8698 | 8704 | 8710 | 8716 | 8722 | 8727 | 8733 | 8739 | 8745 |
| 75 | 8751 | 8756 | 8762 | 8768 | 8774 | 8779 | 8785 | 8791 | 8797 | 8802 |
| 76 | 8808 | 8814 | 8820 | 8825 | 8831 | 8837 | 8842 | 8848 | 8854 | 8859 |
| 77 | 8865 | 8871 | 8876 | 8882 | 8887 | 8893 | 8899 | 8904 | 8910 | 8915 |
| 78 | 8921 | 8927 | 8932 | 8938 | 8943 | 8949 | 8954 | 8960 | 8965 | 8971 |
| 79 | 8976 | 8982 | 8987 | 8993 | 8998 | 9004 | 9009 | 9015 | 9020 | 9025 |
| 80 | 9031 | 9036 | 9042 | 9047 | 9053 | 9058 | 9063 | 9069 | 9074 | 9079 |
| 81 | 9085 | 9090 | 9096 | 9101 | 9106 | 9112 | 9117 | 9122 | 9128 | 9133 |
| 82 | 9138 | 9143 | 9149 | 9154 | 9159 | 9165 | 9170 | 9175 | 9180 | 9186 |
| 83 | 9191 | 9196 | 9201 | 9206 | 9212 | 9217 | 9222 | 9227 | 9232 | 9238 |
| 84 | 9243 | 9248 | 9253 | 9258 | 9263 | 9269 | 9274 | 9279 | 9284 | 9289 |
| 85 | 9294 | 9299 | 9304 | 9309 | 9315 | 9320 | 9325 | 9330 | 9335 | 9340 |
| 86 | 9345 | 9350 | 9355 | 9360 | 9365 | 9370 | 9375 | 9380 | 9385 | 9390 |
| 87 | 9395 | 9400 | 9405 | 9410 | 9415 | 9420 | 9425 | 9430 | 9435 | 9440 |
| 88 | 9445 | 9450 | 9455 | 9460 | 9465 | 9469 | 9474 | 9479 | 9484 | 9489 |
| 89 | 9494 | 9499 | 9504 | 9509 | 9513 | 9518 | 9523 | 9528 | 9533 | 9538 |
| 90 | 9542 | 9547 | 9552 | 9557 | 9562 | 9566 | 9571 | 9576 | 9581 | 9586 |
| 91 | 9590 | 9595 | 9600 | 9605 | 9609 | 9614 | 9619 | 9624 | 9628 | 9633 |
| 92 | 9638 | 9643 | 9647 | 9652 | 9657 | 9661 | 9666 | 9671 | 9675 | 9680 |
| 93 | 9685 | 9689 | 9694 | 9699 | 9703 | 9708 | 9713 | 9717 | 9722 | 9727 |
| 94 | 9731 | 9736 | 9741 | 9745 | 9750 | 9754 | 9759 | 9763 | 9768 | 9773 |
| 95 | 9777 | 9782 | 9786 | 9791 | 9795 | 9800 | 9805 | 9809 | 9814 | 9818 |
| 96 | 9823 | 9827 | 9832 | 9836 | 9841 | 9845 | 9850 | 9854 | 9859 | 9863 |
| 97 | 9868 | 9872 | 9877 | 9881 | 9886 | 9890 | 9894 | 9899 | 9903 | 9908 |
| 98 | 9912 | 9917 | 9921 | 9926 | 9930 | 9934 | 9939 | 9943 | 9948 | 9952 |
| 99 | 9956 | 9961 | 9965 | 9969 | 9974 | 9978 | 9983 | 9987 | 9991 | 9996 |

## Table 5. Natural Functions of Angles

| Angle | Sine | Cosine | Tangent | Cotangent | Angle* |
|---|---|---|---|---|---|
| 0°00′ | .0000 | 1.0000 | .0000 | ∞ | 90°00′ |
| 10 | .0029 | 1.0000 | .0029 | 343.77 | 50 |
| 20 | .0058 | 1.0000 | .0058 | 171.89 | 40 |
| 30 | .0087 | 1.0000 | .0087 | 114.59 | 30 |
| 40 | .0116 | .9999 | .0116 | 85.940 | 20 |
| 50 | .0145 | .9999 | .0145 | 68.750 | 10 |
| 1°00′ | .0175 | .9998 | .0175 | 57.290 | 89°00′ |
| 10 | .0204 | .9998 | .0204 | 49.104 | 50 |
| 20 | .0233 | .9997 | .0233 | 42.964 | 40 |
| 30 | .0262 | .9997 | .0262 | 38.188 | 30 |
| 40 | .0291 | .9996 | .0291 | 34.368 | 20 |
| 50 | .0320 | .9995 | .0320 | 31.242 | 10 |
| 2°00′ | .0349 | .9994 | .0349 | 28.636 | 88°00′ |
| 10 | .0378 | .9993 | .0378 | 26.432 | 50 |
| 20 | .0407 | .9992 | .0407 | 24.542 | 40 |
| 30 | .0436 | .9990 | .0437 | 22.904 | 30 |
| 40 | .0465 | .9989 | .0466 | 21.470 | 20 |
| 50 | .0494 | .9988 | .0495 | 20.206 | 10 |
| 3°00′ | .0523 | .9986 | .0524 | 19.081 | 87°00′ |
| 10 | .0552 | .9985 | .0553 | 18.075 | 50 |
| 20 | .0581 | .9983 | .0582 | 17.169 | 40 |
| 30 | .0610 | .9981 | .0612 | 16.350 | 30 |
| 40 | .0640 | .9980 | .0641 | 15.605 | 20 |
| 50 | .0669 | .9978 | .0670 | 14.924 | 10 |
| 4°00′ | .0698 | .9976 | .0699 | 14.301 | 86°00′ |
| 10 | .0727 | .9974 | .0729 | 13.727 | 50 |
| 20 | .0756 | .9971 | .0758 | 13.197 | 40 |
| 30 | .0785 | .9969 | .0787 | 12.706 | 30 |
| 40 | .0814 | .9967 | .0816 | 12.251 | 20 |
| 50 | .0843 | .9964 | .0846 | 11.826 | 10 |
| 5°00′ | .0872 | .9962 | .0875 | 11.430 | 85°00′ |
| 10 | .0901 | .9959 | .0904 | 11.059 | 50 |
| 20 | .0929 | .9957 | .0934 | 10.712 | 40 |
| 30 | .0958 | .9954 | .0963 | 10.385 | 30 |
| 40 | .0987 | .9951 | .0992 | 10.078 | 20 |
| 50 | .1016 | .9948 | .1022 | 9.7882 | 10 |
| 6°00′ | .1045 | .9945 | .1051 | 9.5144 | 84°00′ |
| 10 | .1074 | .9942 | .1080 | 9.2553 | 50 |
| 20 | .1103 | .9939 | .1110 | 9.0098 | 40 |
| 30 | .1132 | .9936 | .1139 | 8.7769 | 30 |
| 40 | .1161 | .9932 | .1169 | 8.5555 | 20 |
| 50 | .1190 | .9929 | .1198 | 8.3450 | 10 |
| 7°00′ | .1219 | .9925 | .1228 | 8.1443 | 83°00′ |
| 10 | .1248 | .9922 | .1257 | 7.9530 | 50 |
| 20 | .1276 | .9918 | .1287 | 7.7704 | 40 |
| 30 | .1305 | .9914 | .1317 | 7.5958 | 30 |
| 40 | .1334 | .9911 | .1346 | 7.4287 | 20 |
| 50 | .1363 | .9907 | .1376 | 7.2687 | 10 |
| 8°00′ | .1392 | .9903 | .1405 | 7.1154 | 82°00′ |
| 10 | .1421 | .9899 | .1435 | 6.9682 | 50 |
| 20 | .1449 | .9894 | .1465 | 6.8269 | 40 |
| 30 | .1478 | .9890 | .1495 | 6.6912 | 30 |
| 40 | .1507 | .9886 | .1524 | 6.5606 | 20 |
| 50 | .1536 | .9881 | .1554 | 6.4348 | 10 |
| Angle | Cosine | Sine | Cotangent | Tangent | Angle |

For reading angles 45° to 90° refer to headings at bottom of facing page.
Source: New York State College of Forestry.

## Table 5. Natural Functions of Angles (Continued)

| Angle | Sine | Cosine | Tangent | Cotangent | Angle |
|---|---|---|---|---|---|
| 9°00′ | .1564 | .9877 | .1584 | 6.3138 | 81°00′ |
| 10 | .1593 | .9872 | .1614 | 6.1970 | 50 |
| 20 | .1622 | .9868 | .1644 | 6.0844 | 40 |
| 30 | .1650 | .9863 | .1673 | 5.9758 | 30 |
| 40 | .1679 | .9858 | .1703 | 5.8708 | 20 |
| 50 | .1708 | .9853 | .1733 | 5.7694 | 10 |
| 10°00′ | .1736 | .9848 | .1763 | 5.6713 | 80°00′ |
| 10 | .1765 | .9843 | .1793 | 5.5764 | 50 |
| 20 | .1794 | .9838 | .1823 | 5.4845 | 40 |
| 30 | .1822 | .9833 | .1853 | 5.3955 | 30 |
| 40 | .1851 | .9827 | .1883 | 5.3093 | 20 |
| 50 | .1880 | .9822 | .1914 | 5.2257 | 10 |
| 11°00′ | .1908 | .9816 | .1944 | 5.1446 | 79°00′ |
| 10 | .1937 | .9811 | .1974 | 5.0658 | 50 |
| 20 | .1965 | .9805 | .2004 | 4.9894 | 40 |
| 30 | .1994 | .9799 | .2035 | 4.9152 | 30 |
| 40 | .2022 | .9793 | .2065 | 4.8430 | 20 |
| 50 | .2051 | .9787 | .2095 | 4.7729 | 10 |
| 12°00′ | .2079 | .9781 | .2126 | 4.7046 | 78°00′ |
| 10 | .2108 | .9775 | .2156 | 4.6382 | 50 |
| 20 | .2136 | .9769 | .2186 | 4.5736 | 40 |
| 30 | .2164 | .9763 | .2217 | 4.5107 | 30 |
| 40 | .2193 | .9757 | .2247 | 4.4494 | 20 |
| 50 | .2221 | .9750 | .2278 | 4.3897 | 10 |
| 13°00′ | .2250 | .9744 | .2309 | 4.3315 | 77°00′ |
| 10 | .2278 | .9737 | .2339 | 4.2747 | 50 |
| 20 | .2306 | .9730 | .2370 | 4.2193 | 40 |
| 30 | .2334 | .9724 | .2401 | 4.1653 | 30 |
| 40 | .2363 | .9717 | .2432 | 4.1126 | 20 |
| 50 | .2391 | .9710 | .2462 | 4.0611 | 10 |
| 14°00′ | .2419 | .9703 | .2493 | 4.0108 | 76°00′ |
| 10 | .2447 | .9696 | .2524 | 3.9617 | 50 |
| 20 | .2476 | .9689 | .2555 | 3.9136 | 40 |
| 30 | .2504 | .9681 | .2586 | 3.8667 | 30 |
| 40 | .2532 | .9674 | .2617 | 3.8208 | 20 |
| 50 | .2560 | .9667 | .2648 | 3.7760 | 10 |
| 15°00′ | .2588 | .9659 | .2679 | 3.7321 | 75°00′ |
| 10 | .2616 | .9652 | .2711 | 3.6891 | 50 |
| 20 | .2644 | .9644 | .2742 | 3.6470 | 40 |
| 30 | .2672 | .9636 | .2773 | 3.6059 | 30 |
| 40 | .2700 | .9628 | .2805 | 3.5656 | 20 |
| 50 | .2728 | .9621 | .2836 | 3.5261 | 10 |
| 16°00′ | .2756 | .9613 | .2867 | 3.4874 | 74°00′ |
| 10 | .2784 | .9605 | .2899 | 3.4495 | 50 |
| 20 | .2812 | .9596 | .2931 | 3.4124 | 40 |
| 30 | .2840 | .9588 | .2962 | 3.3759 | 30 |
| 40 | .2868 | .9580 | .2994 | 3.3402 | 20 |
| 50 | .2896 | .9572 | .3026 | 3.3052 | 10 |
| 17°00 | .2924 | .9563 | .3057 | 3.2709 | 73°00′ |
| 10 | .2952 | .9555 | .3089 | 3.2371 | 50 |
| 20 | .2979 | .9546 | .3121 | 3.2041 | 40 |
| 30 | .3007 | .9537 | .3153 | 3.1716 | 30 |
| 40 | .3035 | .9528 | .3185 | 3.1397 | 20 |
| 50 | .3062 | .9520 | .3217 | 3.1084 | 10 |
| 18°00′ | .3090 | .9511 | .3249 | 3.0777 | 72°00′ |

| Angle | Cosine | Sine | Cotangent | Tangent | Angle |
|---|---|---|---|---|---|

## Table 5. Natural Functions of Angles (Continued)

| Angle | Sine | Cosine | Tangent | Cotangent | Angle |
|---|---|---|---|---|---|
| 18°00′ | .3090 | .9511 | .3249 | 3.0777 | 72°00′ |
| 10 | .3118 | .9502 | .3281 | 3.0475 | 50 |
| 20 | .3145 | .9492 | .3314 | 3.0178 | 40 |
| 30 | .3173 | .9483 | .3346 | 2.9887 | 30 |
| 40 | .3201 | .9474 | .3378 | 2.9600 | 20 |
| 50 | .3228 | .9465 | .3411 | 2.9319 | 10 |
| 19°00′ | .3256 | .9455 | .3443 | 2.9042 | 71°00′ |
| 10 | .3283 | .9446 | .3476 | 2.8770 | 50 |
| 20 | .3311 | .9436 | .3508 | 2.8502 | 40 |
| 30 | .3338 | .9426 | .3541 | 2.8239 | 30 |
| 40 | .3365 | .9417 | .3574 | 2.7980 | 20 |
| 50 | .3393 | .9407 | .3607 | 2.7725 | 10 |
| 20°00′ | .3420 | .9397 | .3640 | 2.7475 | 70°00′ |
| 10 | .3448 | .9387 | .3673 | 2.7228 | 50 |
| 20 | .3475 | .9377 | .3706 | 2.6985 | 40 |
| 30 | .3502 | .9367 | .3739 | 2.6746 | 30 |
| 40 | .3529 | .9356 | .3772 | 2.6511 | 20 |
| 50 | .3557 | .9346 | .3805 | 2.6279 | 10 |
| 21°00′ | .3584 | .9336 | .3839 | 2.6051 | 69°00′ |
| 10 | .3611 | .9325 | .3872 | 2.5826 | 50 |
| 20 | .3638 | .9315 | .3906 | 2.5605 | 40 |
| 30 | .3665 | .9304 | .3939 | 2.5386 | 30 |
| 40 | .3692 | .9293 | .3973 | 2.5172 | 20 |
| 50 | .3719 | .9283 | .4006 | 2.4960 | 10 |
| 22°00′ | .3746 | .9272 | .4040 | 2.4751 | 68°00′ |
| 10 | .3773 | .9261 | .4074 | 2.4545 | 50 |
| 20 | .3800 | .9250 | .4108 | 2.4342 | 40 |
| 30 | .3827 | .9239 | .4142 | 2.4142 | 30 |
| 40 | .3854 | .9228 | .4176 | 2.3945 | 20 |
| 50 | .3881 | .9216 | .4210 | 2.3750 | 10 |
| 23°00′ | .3907 | .9205 | .4245 | 2.3559 | 67°00′ |
| 10 | .3934 | .9194 | .4279 | 2.3369 | 50 |
| 20 | .3961 | .9182 | .4314 | 2.3183 | 40 |
| 30 | .3987 | .9171 | .4348 | 2.2998 | 30 |
| 40 | .4014 | .9159 | .4383 | 2.2817 | 20 |
| 50 | .4041 | .9147 | .4417 | 2.2637 | 10 |
| 24°00′ | .4067 | .9135 | .4452 | 2.2460 | 66°00′ |
| 10 | .4094 | .9124 | .4487 | 2.2286 | 50 |
| 20 | .4120 | .9112 | .4522 | 2.2113 | 40 |
| 30 | .4147 | .9100 | .4557 | 2.1943 | 30 |
| 40 | .4173 | .9088 | .4592 | 2.1775 | 20 |
| 50 | .4200 | .9075 | .4628 | 2.1609 | 10 |
| 25°00′ | .4226 | .9063 | .4663 | 2.1445 | 65°00′ |
| 10 | .4253 | .9051 | .4699 | 2.1283 | 50 |
| 20 | .4279 | .9038 | .4734 | 2.1123 | 40 |
| 30 | .4305 | .9026 | .4770 | 2.0965 | 30 |
| 40 | .4331 | .9013 | .4806 | 2.0809 | 20 |
| 50 | .4358 | .9001 | .4841 | 2.0655 | 10 |
| 26°00′ | .4384 | .8988 | .4877 | 2.0503 | 64°00′ |
| 10 | .4410 | .8975 | .4913 | 2.0353 | 50 |
| 20 | .4436 | .8962 | .4950 | 2.0204 | 40 |
| 30 | .4462 | .8949 | .4986 | 2.0057 | 30 |
| 40 | .4483 | .8936 | .5022 | 1.9912 | 20 |
| 50 | .4514 | .8923 | .5059 | 1.9768 | 10 |
| 27°00′ | .4540 | .8910 | .5095 | 1.9626 | 63°00′ |

| Angle | Cosine | Sine | Cotangent | Tangent | Angle |
|---|---|---|---|---|---|

## Table 5. Natural Functions of Angles (Continued)

| Angle | Sine | Cosine | Tangent | Cotangent | Angle |
|---|---|---|---|---|---|
| 27°00′ | .4540 | .8910 | .5095 | 1.9626 | 63°00′ |
| 10 | .4566 | .8897 | .5132 | 1.9486 | 50 |
| 20 | .4592 | .8884 | .5169 | 1.9347 | 40 |
| 30 | .4617 | .8870 | .5206 | 1.9210 | 30 |
| 40 | .4643 | .8857 | .5243 | 1.9074 | 20 |
| 50 | .4669 | .8843 | .5280 | 1.8940 | 10 |
| 28°00′ | .4695 | .8829 | .5317 | 1.8807 | 62°00′ |
| 10 | .4720 | .8816 | .5354 | 1.8676 | 50 |
| 20 | .4746 | .8802 | .5392 | 1.8546 | 40 |
| 30 | .4772 | .8788 | .5430 | 1.8418 | 30 |
| 40 | .4797 | .8774 | .5467 | 1.8291 | 20 |
| 50 | .4823 | .8760 | .5505 | 1.8165 | 10 |
| 29°00′ | .4848 | .8746 | .5543 | 1.8040 | 61°00′ |
| 10 | .4874 | .8732 | .5581 | 1.7917 | 50 |
| 20 | .4899 | .8718 | .5619 | 1.7796 | 40 |
| 30 | .4924 | .8704 | .5658 | 1.7675 | 30 |
| 40 | .4950 | .8689 | .5696 | 1.7556 | 20 |
| 50 | .4975 | .8675 | .5735 | 1.7437 | 10 |
| 30°00′ | .5000 | .8660 | .5774 | 1.7321 | 60°00′ |
| 10 | .5025 | .8646 | .5812 | 1.7205 | 50 |
| 20 | .5050 | .8631 | .5851 | 1.7090 | 40 |
| 30 | .5075 | .8616 | .5890 | 1.6977 | 30 |
| 40 | .5100 | .8601 | .5930 | 1.6864 | 20 |
| 50 | .5125 | .8587 | .5969 | 1.6753 | 10 |
| 31°00′ | .5150 | .8572 | .6009 | 1.6643 | 59°00′ |
| 10 | .5175 | .8557 | .6048 | 1.6534 | 50 |
| 20 | .5200 | .8542 | .6088 | 1.6426 | 40 |
| 30 | .5225 | .8526 | .6128 | 1.6319 | 30 |
| 40 | .5250 | .8511 | .6168 | 1.6212 | 20 |
| 50 | .5275 | .8496 | .6208 | 1.6107 | 10 |
| 32°00′ | .5299 | .8480 | .6249 | 1.6003 | 58°00′ |
| 10 | .5324 | .8465 | .6289 | 1.5900 | 50 |
| 20 | .5348 | .8450 | .6330 | 1.5798 | 40 |
| 30 | .5373 | .8434 | .6371 | 1.5697 | 30 |
| 40 | .5398 | .8418 | .6412 | 1.5597 | 20 |
| 50 | .5422 | .8403 | .6453 | 1.5497 | 10 |
| 33°00′ | .5446 | .8387 | .6494 | 1.5399 | 57°00′ |
| 10 | .5471 | .8371 | .6536 | 1.5301 | 50 |
| 20 | .5495 | .8355 | .6577 | 1.5204 | 40 |
| 30 | .5519 | .8339 | .6619 | 1.5108 | 30 |
| 40 | .5544 | .8323 | .6661 | 1.5013 | 20 |
| 50 | .5568 | .8307 | .6703 | 1.4919 | 10 |
| 34°00′ | .5592 | .8290 | .6745 | 1.4826 | 56°00′ |
| 10 | .5616 | .8274 | .6787 | 1.4733 | 50 |
| 20 | .5640 | .8258 | .6830 | 1.4641 | 40 |
| 30 | .5664 | .8241 | .6873 | 1.4550 | 30 |
| 40 | .5688 | .8225 | .6916 | 1.4460 | 20 |
| 50 | .5712 | .8208 | .6959 | 1.4370 | 10 |
| 35°00′ | .5736 | .8192 | .7002 | 1.4281 | 55°00′ |
| 10 | .5760 | .8175 | .7046 | 1.4193 | 50 |
| 20 | .5783 | .8158 | .7089 | 1.4106 | 40 |
| 30 | .5807 | .8141 | .7133 | 1.4019 | 30 |
| 40 | .5831 | .8124 | .7177 | 1.3934 | 20 |
| 50 | .5854 | .8107 | .7221 | 1.3848 | 10 |
| 36°00′ | .5878 | .8090 | .7265 | 1.3764 | 54°00′ |
| Angle | Cosine | Sine | Cotangent | Tangent | Angle |

## Table 5. Natural Functions of Angles (Continued)

| Angle | Sine | Cosine | Tangent | Cotangent | Angle |
|---|---|---|---|---|---|
| 36°00′ | .5878 | .8090 | .7265 | 1.3764 | 54°00′ |
| 10 | .5901 | .8073 | .7310 | 1.3680 | 50 |
| 20 | .5925 | .8056 | .7355 | 1.3597 | 40 |
| 30 | .5948 | .8039 | .7400 | 1.3514 | 30 |
| 40 | .5972 | .8021 | .7445 | 1.3432 | 20 |
| 50 | .5995 | .8004 | .7490 | 1.3351 | 10 |
| 37°00′ | .6018 | .7986 | .7536 | 1.3270 | 53°00′ |
| 10 | .6041 | .7969 | .7581 | 1.3190 | 50 |
| 20 | .6065 | .7951 | .7627 | 1.3111 | 40 |
| 30 | .6088 | .7934 | .7673 | 1.3032 | 30 |
| 40 | .6111 | .7916 | .7720 | 1.2954 | 20 |
| 50 | .6134 | .7898 | .7766 | 1.2876 | 10 |
| 38°00′ | .6157 | .7880 | .7813 | 1.2799 | 52°00′ |
| 10 | .6180 | .7862 | .7860 | 1.2723 | 50 |
| 20 | .6202 | .7844 | .7907 | 1.2647 | 40 |
| 30 | .6225 | .7826 | .7954 | 1.2572 | 30 |
| 40 | .6248 | .7808 | .8002 | 1.2497 | 20 |
| 50 | .6271 | .7790 | .8050 | 1.2423 | 10 |
| 39°00′ | .6293 | .7771 | .8098 | 1.2349 | 51°00′ |
| 10 | .6316 | .7753 | .8146 | 1.2276 | 50 |
| 20 | .6338 | .7735 | .8195 | 1.2203 | 40 |
| 30 | .6361 | .7716 | .8243 | 1.2131 | 30 |
| 40 | .6383 | .7698 | .8292 | 1.2059 | 20 |
| 50 | .6406 | .7679 | .8342 | 1.1988 | 10 |
| 40°00′ | .6428 | .7660 | .8391 | 1.1918 | 50°00′ |
| 10 | .6450 | .7642 | .8441 | 1.1847 | 50 |
| 20 | .6472 | .7623 | .8491 | 1.1778 | 40 |
| 30 | .6494 | .7604 | .8541 | 1.1708 | 30 |
| 40 | .6517 | .7585 | .8591 | 1.1640 | 20 |
| 50 | .6539 | .7566 | .8642 | 1.1571 | 10 |
| 41°00′ | .6561 | .7547 | .8693 | 1.1504 | 49°00′ |
| 10 | .6583 | .7528 | .8744 | 1.1436 | 50 |
| 20 | .6604 | .7509 | .8796 | 1.1369 | 40 |
| 30 | .6626 | .7490 | .8847 | 1.1303 | 30 |
| 40 | .6648 | .7470 | .8899 | 1.1237 | 20 |
| 50 | .6670 | .7451 | .8952 | 1.1171 | 10 |
| 42°00′ | .6691 | .7431 | .9004 | 1.1106 | 48°00′ |
| 10 | .6713 | .7412 | .9057 | 1.1041 | 50 |
| 20 | .6734 | .7392 | .9110 | 1.0977 | 40 |
| 30 | .6756 | .7373 | .9163 | 1.0913 | 30 |
| 40 | .6777 | .7353 | .9217 | 1.0850 | 20 |
| 50 | .6799 | .7333 | .9271 | 1.0786 | 10 |
| 43°00′ | .6820 | .7314 | .9325 | 1.0724 | 47°00′ |
| 10 | .6841 | .7294 | .9380 | 1.0661 | 50 |
| 20 | .6862 | .7274 | .9435 | 1.0599 | 40 |
| 30 | .6884 | .7254 | .9490 | 1.0538 | 30 |
| 40 | .6905 | .7234 | .9545 | 1.0477 | 20 |
| 50 | .6926 | .7214 | .9601 | 1.0416 | 10 |
| 44°00′ | .6947 | .7193 | .9657 | 1.0355 | 46°00′ |
| 10 | .6967 | .7173 | .9713 | 1.0295 | 50 |
| 20 | .6988 | .7153 | .9770 | 1.0235 | 40 |
| 30 | .7009 | .7133 | .9827 | 1.0176 | 30 |
| 40 | .7030 | .7112 | .9884 | 1.0117 | 20 |
| 50 | .7050 | .7092 | .9942 | 1.0058 | 10 |
| 45°00′ | .7071 | .7071 | 1.0000 | 1.0000 | 45°00′ |
| Angle | Cosine | Sine | Cotangent | Tangent | Angle |

## Table 6. Lengths of Degrees and Minutes of Parallels [a]

(Degrees in statute miles; minutes in feet)

| Along parallel at | 1 degree in statute miles | 1 minute in feet [b] | Along parallel at | 1 degree in statute miles | 1 minute in feet [b] |
|---|---|---|---|---|---|
| Equator | 69.172 | 6086.9 | 46° | 48.136 | 4235.8 |
| 1° | 69.162 | 6086.2 | 47 | 47.261 | 4158.7 |
| 2 | 69.130 | 6083.3 | 48 | 46.372 | 4080.7 |
| 3 | 69.078 | 6078.7 | 49 | 45.469 | 4001.3 |
| 4 | 69.005 | 6072.4 | 50 | 44.552 | 3920.6 |
| 5 | 68.911 | 6063.9 | | | |
| 6 | 68.795 | 6054.1 | 51° | 43.621 | 3838.6 |
| 7 | 68.660 | 6041.9 | 52 | 42.676 | 3755.6 |
| 8 | 68.504 | 6028.1 | 53 | 41.719 | 3671.2 |
| 9 | 68.326 | 6012.4 | 54 | 40.749 | 3585.9 |
| 10 | 68.129 | 5995.0 | 55 | 39.766 | 3499.3 |
| | | | 56 | 38.771 | 3411.7 |
| 11° | 67.910 | 5976.0 | 57 | 37.764 | 3323.1 |
| 12 | 67.670 | 5955.0 | 58 | 36.745 | 3233.6 |
| 13 | 67.410 | 5932.0 | 59 | 35.716 | 3143.0 |
| 14 | 67.131 | 5907.4 | 60 | 34.674 | 3051.1 |
| 15 | 66.830 | 5880.8 | | | |
| 16 | 66.510 | 5852.6 | 61° | 33.623 | 2958.6 |
| 17 | 66.169 | 5822.8 | 62 | 32.560 | 2865.1 |
| 18 | 65.808 | 5790.9 | 63 | 31.488 | 2771.0 |
| 19 | 65.427 | 5757.5 | 64 | 30.406 | 2675.8 |
| 20 | 65.026 | 5722.0 | 65 | 29.315 | 2579.7 |
| | | | 66 | 28.215 | 2482.9 |
| 21° | 64.606 | 5685.3 | 67 | 27.106 | 2385.5 |
| 22 | 64.166 | 5646.6 | 68 | 25.988 | 2287.0 |
| 23 | 63.706 | 5605.9 | 69 | 24.862 | 2180.0 |
| 24 | 63.228 | 5563.9 | 70 | 23.729 | 2088.2 |
| 25 | 62.729 | 5519.9 | | | |
| 26 | 62.212 | 5474.7 | 71° | 22.589 | 1987.8 |
| 27 | 61.676 | 5427.4 | 72 | 21.441 | 1886.8 |
| 28 | 61.122 | 5378.5 | 73 | 20.287 | 1785.1 |
| 29 | 60.548 | 5328.0 | 74 | 19.127 | 1683.1 |
| 30 | 59.956 | 5275.9 | 75 | 17.960 | 1580.4 |
| | | | 76 | 16.788 | 1477.3 |
| 31° | 59.345 | 5222.4 | 77 | 15.611 | 1373.7 |
| 32 | 58.716 | 5166.9 | 78 | 14.428 | 1269.7 |
| 33 | 58.071 | 5110.2 | 79 | 13.242 | 1165.3 |
| 34 | 57.407 | 5051.8 | 80 | 12.051 | 1060.4 |
| 35 | 56.725 | 4991.7 | | | |
| 36 | 56.027 | 4930.4 | 81° | 10.857 | 955.4 |
| 37 | 55.311 | 4867.4 | 82 | 9.659 | 850.1 |
| 38 | 54.579 | 4802.8 | 83 | 8.458 | 744.4 |
| 39 | 53.829 | 4736.8 | 84 | 7.255 | 638.4 |
| 40 | 53.063 | 4669.6 | 85 | 6.049 | 532.1 |
| | | | 86 | 4.842 | 426.2 |
| 41° | 52.281 | 4600.7 | 87 | 3.632 | 319.5 |
| 42 | 51.483 | 4530.5 | 88 | 2.422 | 213.3 |
| 43 | 50.669 | 4458.9 | 89 | 1.211 | 106.6 |
| 44 | 49.840 | 4385.8 | 90 | 0 | 0 |
| 45 | 48.995 | 4311.6 | | | |

[a] From the equator to either pole a degree of latitude increases from 68.703 to 69.407 statute miles, and a minute from 6045.9 to 6107.9 ft.
[b] Meters converted to feet on the basis of 1 meter = 3.28083 ft.
Source: U. S. Coast and Geodetic Survey.

## Equivalents and Converting Factors

In the following tables (7 to 12) the unit value on which the conversion is based is indicated as 1. Conversion units are not carried beyond six decimal places. When the final digit is not exact but represents a rounding to the nearest value, it is italicized. Figures in parentheses () below the decimal figure are approximate values for use in rough calculations where a high degree of accuracy is unnecessary. Figures in brackets [] below the decimal figure are exact values.

### Table 7. Length; Unit Conversion Factors, with Approximate Values

| Inches | Links | Feet | Yards | Rods | Chains [1] | Miles [2] | Centimeters | Meters | Kilometers |
|---|---|---|---|---|---|---|---|---|---|
| [3]1 | 0.126263 (⅛) | 0.083333 [1/12] | 0.027778 [1/36] | 0.00505 (1/200) | ---- | ---- | 2.540005 (2½) | 0.0254 (1/40) | ---- |
| 7.92 | 1 | 0.66 (⅔) | 0.22 | 0.04 [1/25] | 0.01 [1/100] | ---- | 20.11684 (20) | 0.201168 (⅕) | ---- |
| 12 | 1.515152 (1½) | [4]1 | 0.333333 [⅓] | 0.060606 (1/16) | 0.015152 [1/66] | 0.000189 | 30.48006 (30) | 0.304801 (3/10) | 0.000305 |
| 36 | 4.545455 (4½) | 3 | 1 | 0.181818 (⅕) | 0.045455 (1/22) | 0.000568 | 91.44018 | 0.914402 (9/10) | 0.000914 |
| 0.3937 (⅖) | 0.04971 (1/20) | 0.032808 (1/30) | 0.010936 (1/90) | ---- | ---- | ---- | [5]1 | 0.01 | ---- |
| 39.37 (40) | 4.97096 (5) | 3.280833 | 1.09361 | 0.198838 (⅕) | 0.04971 (1/20) | 0.000621 (1/1600) | 100 | 1 | 0.001 |
| | | | | | | | | | |
| 198 | 25 | 16.5 | 5.5 | 1 | 0.25 [¼] | 0.003125 [1/320] | | 5.02921 (5) | 0.005029 (1/200) |
| 792 | 100 | 66 | 22 | 4 | 1 | 0.0125 [1/80] | | 20.1168 (20) | 0.020117 (1/50) |
| ---- | ---- | 5,280 | 1,760 | 320 | 80 | 1 | | 1,609.347 (1,600) | 1.609347 (1⅗) |
| ---- | ---- | 660 | 220 | 40 | [6]10 | 0.125 [⅛] | | 201.168 | 0.201168 (⅕) |
| ---- | ---- | 3,280.83 | 1,093.61 | 198.838 (200) | 49.7096 (50) | 0.62137 (⅝) | | 1,000 | 1 |

[1] Surveyor's chain; the engineer's chain = 100 links of 1 ft. each is not used.
[2] 1 nautical mile (termed "knot" as unit of velocity) = 1.516 statute miles = 1.85325 km. = 1 minute of arc on earth's surface at the equator.
[3] British units: 1 yard = 0.9144 m.; 1 foot = 30.48 cm.; 1 inch = 2.54 cm.; 1 hand = 4 in. or 10.16 cm.; 1 span = 9 in. = 22.86 cm.; 1 cubit = 18 in. = 45.72 cm.
[4] 1 vara (Spanish measure) = 2.78 ft.
[5] 1 millimeter = 0.1 cm. = 0.0394 in. = 0.0033 ft.
[6] 10 chains = 1 furlong.

Source: U. S. Dept. Agr.

### Table 8. Area or Surface; Unit Conversion Factors, with Approximate Values

| Square inches | Square links | Square feet | Square yards | Square chains | Acres [1] | Square centimeters | Square meters | Hectares | Square kilometers |
|---|---|---|---|---|---|---|---|---|---|
| 1 | 0.015942 (1/63a) | 0.006944 | ---- | ---- | ---- | 6.451626 (6½) | 0.000645 | ---- | ---- |
| 62.7264 (63) | 1 | 0.4356 (3/7) | ---- | 0.0001 | 0.00001 | 404.6873 | 0.040469 (1/25) | ---- | ---- |
| 144 | 2.295684 | 1 | 0.111111 [1/9] | 0.00023 | 0.000023 | 929.034 | 0.092903 (1/11) | ---- | ---- |
| 1,296 | 20.6612 (20) | 9 | 1 | 0.002066 (1/500) | 0.000207 | 8,361.31 | 0.836131 (5/6) | ---- | ---- |
| 0.155 (1/7) | ---- | 0.001076 (1/1000) | ---- | ---- | ---- | ²1 | 0.0001 | ---- | ---- |
| 1,549.997 | 24.7104 | 10.76387 (11) | 1.19599 (1 1/5) | 0.002471 (1/400) | 0.000247 | 10,000 | 1 | 0.0001 | ---- |
|  | 10,000 | 4,356 | 484 | ³1 | 0.1 |  | 404.687 | 0.040469 (1/25) | 0.000405 (1/2500) |
|  |  | 43,560 | 4,840 | 10 | ⁴1 |  | 4,046.87 | 0.404687 (2/5) | 0.004047 (1/250) |
|  |  | 27,878,400 | 3,097,600 | 6,400 | ⁵640 |  | 2,589,998 | 258.9998 (260) | 2.589998 (2 3/5) |
|  |  | 107,638.7 | 11,959.9 (12,000) | 24.7104 (25) | 2.471044 (2½) |  | 10,000 | 1 | 0.01 |
|  |  | 10,763,867 | 1,195,985 | 2,471.04 (250) | 247.104 |  | 1,000,000 | 100 | 1 |

[1] 1 arpent (de Paris), a French measure = about 0.846 acre (in common use in Canada).
[2] 1 mm.² = 0.01 cm.² = 0.0016 sq. in.
[3] 1 square chain = 16 sq. rd.
[4] 1 acre = area 208.71 (210) feet square = 3.16 chains square.
[5] 1 square mile = 640 acres = 1 section. 36 sections = 1 township (6 miles square). 1 square league = 5,760 acres (English land league), or 4,439 acres (old Spanish land league) or 4,428.4 acres (used in Texas).

Source: U. S. Dept. Agr.

## Table 9. Volume and Capacity; Unit Conversion Factors, with Approximate Values

| United States measure of volume [1] | | United States dry measure, quarts | United States apothecaries' and liquid measure [2] | | | | Metric system | | |
|---|---|---|---|---|---|---|---|---|---|
| Cubic inches | Cubic feet | | Fluid ounces | Pints | Quarts | Gallons | Cubic centimeters [3] | Liters [4] | Cubic meters (steres) |
| 1 | 0.0005799 | 0.014881 | 0.554113 (½) | 0.034632 (1/30) | 0.017316 (1/60) | 0.004329 | 16.3872 (16) | 0.016387 (1/60) | ---------- |
| 1,728 | [5] 1 | 25.714 (26) | 957.5 | 59.8442 (60) | 29.9221 (30) | 7.48052 (7½) | 28,317 | 28.316 (28) | 0.028317 (1/35) |
| 1.80469 (1⅘) | ---------- | ---------- | 1 | 0.0625 [1/16] | 0.03125 [1/32] | ---------- | 29.5737 (30) | 0.029573 (1/34) | ---------- |
| 28.875 (30) | ---------- | 0.429684 (⅖) | 16 | 1 | 0.5 [½] | 0.125 [⅛] | 473.179 (475) | 0.473167 (½) | ---------- |
| 57.75 (58) | 0.033420 (1/30) | 0.859367 (⅚) | 32 | 2 | 1 | 0.25 [¼] | 946.359 (950) | 0.946333 (1) | 0.000946 |
| 231 | 0.133681 (⅛) | 3.43747 | 128 | 8 | 4 | [6] 1 | 3785.43 (4,000) | 3.785332 (4) | 0.003785 (1/265) |
| 0.061023 (1/16) | ---------- | 0.000908 | 0.033814 (1/30) | 0.002113 | 0.001057 (1/1000) | ---------- | 1 | 0.0010 (1/1000) | 0.000001 |
| 61.0250 (61) | 0.035315 | 0.908102 | 33.8147 (34) | 2.11342 (2) | 1.05671 (1) | 0.264178 (¼) | 1,000.027 (1,000) | 1 | 0.001 (1/1000) |
| | | | Bushels | | | | | | |
| 67.200625 (67) | 0.038889 (1/25) | 1 | 0.03125 [1/32] | ---------- | 1.163647 (1⅙) | 0.290912 | 1,101.23 | 1.101198 | 0.001 (1/1000) |
| 2,150.42 | 1.24446 (1¼) | [7] 32 | 1 | ---------- | 37.2367 (37) | 9.309177 (9) | 35,239.28 | 35.23833 (35) | 0.035239 (1/30) |
| | 35.3145 (35) | 908.078 (910) | 28.3774 | ---------- | 1,056.68 (1,000) | 264.170 (265) | 1,000,000 | 999.973 (1,000) | [8] 1 |

[1] 1 cubic yard = 27 cu. ft. = 21.696 bu. = 0.7646 $m.^3$ (stere).

[2] 1 gill = 7.2187 cu. in. = 4 fluid oz. = 0.25 (¼) liquid pt. = 0.125 (⅛) liquid qt. = 0.0312 (1/32) gal. = 0.1183 l.

[3] 1 cubic millimeter = 0.001 $cm.^3$

[4] 1 liter = volume pure water at 4° C. and 760 mm. pressure weighing 1 kg. = 0.0284 bu. = 0.0013 cu. yd.

[5] 1 cubic foot = 0.8036 bu. = 0.037 cu. yd.

[6] 1 British Imperial gallon = 10 lb. distilled water at 62° F. (and barometer at 30 in.) = 277.418 cu. in. = 1.2009 U. S. gal. = 0.1605 cu. ft. = 4.546 l.

[7] 32 quarts = 1 bu. The British Imperial bushel = 8 British gal. = 2219.34 cu. in. = 1.032 U.S. bu. = 36.37 l.

[8] 1 $m.^3$ = 1.308 cu. yd.

Source: U. S. Dept. Agr.

## Table 10. Weight; Unit Conversion Factors, with Approximate Values

| Grains [1] | Avoirdupois weight [2] | | | Troy and apothecaries' weight | | | Metric system | | |
|---|---|---|---|---|---|---|---|---|---|
| | Drams | Ounces | Pounds | Drams | Ounces | Pounds | Milligrams | Grams | Kilograms |
| 1 | 0.03657 (1/27) | 0.002286 | 0.000143 [1/7000] | 0.016667 [1/60] | 0.002083 (1/500) | 0.000174 | 64.7989 (65) | 0.064799 (1/15) | ---------- |
| 27.34375 | 1 | 0.0625 [1/16] | 0.003906 (1/250) | 0.45573 (1/2) | 0.056966 | 0.004747 (1/210) | ---------- | 1.771845 | ---------- |
| 437.5 (440) | 16 | [3] 1 | 0.0625 [1/16] | 7.292 | 0.9115 | 0.075955 (1/13) | ---------- | 28.34953 (28) | ---------- |
| 7,000 | 256 | 16 | 1 | 116.667 | 14.5833 (14½) | 1.21528 (1⅕) | ---------- | 453.592 (450) | 0.453592 (½) |
| 60 | 2.194286 (2) | 0.137143 (1/7) | 0.008571 | 1 | 0.125 [1/8] | 0.010417 [1/96] | ---------- | 3.887935 (4) | ---------- |
| 480 | 17.55429 | 1.09714 (1) | 0.06857 (1/15) | 8 | 1 | 0.083333 [1/12] | ---------- | 31.10348 (31) | ---------- |
| 5,760 | 210.651 | 13.1657 (13) | 0.822857 (⅘) | 96 | 12 | 1 | ---------- | 373.2418 (375) | 0.373242 (⅖) |
| 0.015432 (1/65) | 0.000564 | ---------- | ---------- | 0.000257 | ---------- | ---------- | [4] 1 | 0.001 | ---------- |
| 15.43236 (15) | 0.564383 | 0.035274 (1/28) | 0.002205 | 0.257206 | 0.032151 (1/30) | 0.002679 | 1,000 | 1 | 0.001 |
| | Hundredweight | | | Short tons | Long tons | | Milliers, tonnes, or metric tons | | |
| | 1 | ---------- | 100 | 0.05 [1/20] | 0.045 (1/20) | ---------- | 0.045359 (1/20) | ---------- | 45.35924 (45) |
| | 20 | ---------- | 2,000 | 1 | 0.89286 (9/10) | ---------- | 0.90718 (9/10) | ---------- | 907.1849 (900) |
| | 22.4 | ---------- | 2,240 | 1.12 (1 1/10) | 1 | ---------- | 1.01605 (1) | ---------- | 1,016.05 (1,000) |
| | 22.05 | ---------- | 2,204.62 | 1.102311 (1 1/10) | 0.984206 | ---------- | [5] 1 | ---------- | 1,000 |
| 15,432.4 | 0.022046 | 35.27396 (35) | 2.204622 (2⅕) | 0.001102 | 0.000984 | 2.679228 (2½) | 0.001 | 1,000 | 1 |

[1] The grain is common to avoirdupois, troy, and apothecaries' systems.
[2] British units include 1 hundredweight (long or one-twentieth long ton) = 4 quarters = 8 stone = 112 lb. = 50.8 kg: 1 stone = 14 lb. = 6.35 kg.
[3] 1 ounce (avoirdupois) = 0.001 cu. ft. of water at 16.7° C., or 62.06° F.
[4] 1 metric carat = 200 mg. = 3.086471 grains.
[5] 1 tonne = 10 quintals = 100 myriagrams.

Source: U. S. Dept. Agr.

## Table 11. Weight as Applied to Volume; Unit Conversion Factors, with Approximate Values

| Grains per cubic inch | Pounds per cubic yard | Pounds per bushel | Pounds per cubic foot | Pounds per gallon | Kilograms per cubic meter | Grams per cubic centimeter |
|---|---|---|---|---|---|---|
| 1 | ---------- | 0.307203 | 0.246857 (¼) | 0.0330 (1/30) | 3.95425 (4) | 0.003954 (1/250) |
| | 1 | ---------- | 0.037037 [1/27] | ---------- | 0.593273 (⅗) | 0.000593 |
| 3.25518 (3¼) | ---------- | 1 | 0.803564 (⅘) | 0.107421 (1/10) | 12.8718 (13) | 0.012872 |
| 4.05093 (4) | 27 | 1.24446 (1¼) | [1] 1 | 0.133681 (1/7) | 16.0184 (16) | 0.016018 (1/60) |
| 30.3030 (30) | ---------- | 9.3092 (9⅓) | 7.48052 (7½) | [2] 1 | 119.826 (120) | 0.119826 (⅛) |
| | 1.68556 (1⅔) | 0.077689 | 0.062428 (1/16) | 0.008345 (1/120) | 1 | 0.001 |
| 252.893 (250) | 1,685.56 (1,700) | 77.6893 (80) | 62.4283 (62½) | 8.34545 (8) | 1,000 | [3] 1 |

[1] 1 pound per cubic foot = 1.6019 kg. per hectoliter = 0.0135 ton per cu. yd.
[2] 1 pound per gallon = 0.1198 kg. per l.
[3] 1 gram per cubic centimeter = 1 tonne (metric ton) per m.$^3$ = (approximately) 1 kg. per l.

Source: U. S. Dept. Agr.

Table 12. Weight or Pressure as Applied to Area;[1] Unit Conversion Factors, with Approximate Values

| Pounds per square foot | Pounds per square inch | Feet of water column or head [2] | Kilograms per square meter | Grams per square centimeter | Milli-meters of mercury column [3] | Atmos-pheres |
|---|---|---|---|---|---|---|
| 1 | 0.006944 [1/144] | 0.016018 (1/60) | 4.88241 (5) | 0.488241 (1/2) | ---------- | 0.000473 |
| 144 | [4]1 | 2.306645 | 703.067 | 70.3067 (70) | 51.7134 | 0.068044 (1/15) |
| 62.4283 | 0.433530 | [5]1 | 304.801 | 30.4801 | 22.4193 (22 1/2) | 0.029499 (1/35) |
| 0.204817 (1/5) | 0.001422 | 0.003281 | 1 | 0.1 | ---------- | 0.0000968 (1/10000) |
| 2.04817 (2) | 0.01422 (1/70) | 0.03281 | 10 | 1 | ---------- | 0.000968 |
| 2.784578 (2 3/4) | 0.019337 (1/50) | 0.044604 | [6]13.59545 | 1.359545 (1 1/3) | [7]1 | 0.001316 |
| 2,116.28 | 14.6964 (14 7/10) | 33.8993 | 10,332.54 | 1,033.254 | 760 | [8]1 |

[1] Pressure unit = 1 barye = 1 dyne per cm.[2] = 0.001 gm. per cm.[2] = 0.0102 kg. per m.[2] = (approximately) 0.000001 atmosphere. 1 megadyne = 1 million or $10^6$ dynes per cm.[2] = 0.9869 atmosphere.

[2] At 4° C., or 39.2° F.

[3] At 0° C., or 32° F. 1 in. of mercury column = 70.728 lb. per sq. ft. = 1.133 ft. of water = 345.325 kg. per m.[2] = 25.4 mm. of mercury = 0.0334 atmosphere.

[4] 1 lb. per sq. in. = 0.072 ton per sq. ft.

[5] 1 foot of water = 0.8826 in. of mercury = 0.3048 m. of water.

[6] The specific gravity of mercury at 0° C.

[7] 1 millimeter of mercury = 0.03937 in. of mercury = 0.0136 m. of water.

[8] 1 atmosphere = 29.9212 in. of mercury = 10.3325 m. of water.

Source: U. S. Dept. Agr.

# BIBLIOGRAPHY

ALLEN, EDWARD S. 1947. *Six place tables.* 7th ed. McGraw-Hill Book Co., Inc., New York.

BREED, C. B., and G. L. HOSMER. 1945. *The principles and practice of surveying:* Vol. 1, *Elementary surveying.* 8th ed. John Wiley & Sons, Inc., New York.

COWDEN, DUDLEY J., and MERCEDES S. COWDEN. 1948. *Practical problems in business statistics.* Prentice-Hall, Inc., New York.

HUDSON, R. G., and J. LIPKA. 1940. *Manual of mathematics.* Rev. ed. John Wiley & Sons, Inc., New York.

NEW YORK STATE COLLEGE OF FORESTRY. 1933. Foresters' tables for New York State. *Bull. No. 14,* Syracuse, N. Y.

U. S. COAST AND GEODETIC SURVEY. 1946. Tables for a polyclinic projection of maps and lengths of terrestrial arcs of meridians and parallels. 6th ed. U. S. Dept. Commerce, Washington, D. C.

U. S. DEPT. AGR. 1949. Converting factors and tables of equivalents used in forestry. *Misc. Publ. No. 225.*

# GENERAL INDEX

(Boldface numbers, followed by a dot, refer to sections; lightface numbers following are the pages of the section.)

**Seed** (*Continued*)
  Seeding rate, 11·74, 11·76–77
  Source of, 6·34–35
**Seedbeds**
  Humus for, 5·14
  Methods of improving, 6·40
**Seeding** (See also "Planting Trees")
  Erosion-control, 10·21
  Precipitation and, 11·74
  Range reseeding, 11·73–75
    Seeding rate, 11·74, 11·76–77
    Species, 11·74, 11·76–77
  Techniques, 6·38–39
  Tree planting vs., 6·38
**Seedlings**
  Chemical injury to, 5·19
  Diseases, 8·28–30
  Insect damage
    Roots, 8·5–6
    Shoots, terminal, 8·7–9
    Stems, 8·6–7
  Liquid fertilizers for, 5·24–25
  Planting, 6·36–37
  Protection of, on ranges, 11·46, 11·75
  Root-top ratio, 5·26
**Seeps,** Water development and, 11·58–59
**Selenium-Bearing Plants,** 11·44
**Shade Trees**
  Diseases of, 8·30–39
  List of, 12·31–36
**Shake,** Definition of, 14·23
**Shales,** Calcareous, soil-forming rock, 5·4
**Shavings,** Wood, 14·73
**Shear Plates,** 14·36
**Shearing,** Christmas trees, 6·59–61
**Shears,** Rigging equipment, 13·24
**Sheep**
  Breeds of range, 11·35–37
  Forage, 11·43 (See also "Forage")
  Insects and diseases, 11·44
  Nutrient allowances, recommended, 11·41
  Water requirements, 11·44, 11·58
    Water troughs, 11·63–64
**Shelterbelts**
  Selecting right trees for, 6·66
  Windbreaks and, 6·63–66
**Shingles,** 14·69–70
  Exposure to weather, 14·69
  Specifications, 14·69
**Shoots of Seedlings,** Insect injuries to, 8·7–9
**Shorthorn Cattle,** 11·35
**Shovels, Power,** 18·26
**Shrinkage of Wood**
  Moisture content and, 21·15
  Specific gravity and, 21·15
**Shrubs** (See also "Woody Plants")
  List of woody plants for game food and cover, 9·28–31
  Native and exotic, for special conditions and use, 12·25–30
  Utilization standards, 11·32
  With yellow foliage, 12·24
**Signs,** Recreational areas, 12·19
**Silica,** Natural forms of, 5·2
**Silviculture,** 6·1–67
  Artificial reforestation, 6·32–39
  Bulldozing, 6·40
  Christmas trees, 6·57–63
  Common hand planting tools, 6·32–33
  Disking, 6·40
  Harvest cuttings, 6·40, 6·43–52
  Humus, effects of, on, 5·14
  Insect and disease control, 8·1–40
  Natural regeneration by seed, 6·31–32

**Silviculture** (*Continued*)
  Planting machines, 6·34–35
  Policy for seed source, 6·34–35
  Prescribed burning, 6·40, 11·65–67
  Pruning, 6·55
  Shearing, 6·59–61
  Shelterbelts and windbreaks, 6·63–66
  Site classifications, 6·40, 6·43–52
  Vigor classifications, 6·41–42
**Singletree,** For logging, 16·21
**Sinking Funds,** Computation of payments, 15·16–17
**Sites**
  Classification, 6·40, 6·43–52
    Aerial photography, 19·18–19
    Aspens, 6·43
    Balsam fir, 6·43
    Black spruce, 6·46
    Conifers, mixed old-growth forests, 6·52
    Douglas-fir, 6·43
    Eastern white pine, 6·51
    Jack pine, 6·47
    Loblolly pine, 6·48
    Lodgepole pine, 6·48
    Longleaf pine, 6·49
    Ponderosa pine, 6·49
    Red pine, 6·50
    Red spruce, 6·47
    Redwood, 6·46
    Shortleaf pine, 6·50
    Slash pine, 6·51
    Sweetgum, 6·44
    Upland oaks, 6·45
    Western hemlock, 6·44
    Western larch, 6·45
    Western white pine, 6·52
    White spruce, 6·47
    Yellow-poplar, 6·46
  For direct seeding, 6·38–39
  Forest types, 6·24–30
  Low-quality, 8·1
  Nursery, 5·21
  Selection of tree-planting, 5·26–27
**Skidding,** 16·4–6
  Arch logging vs. drawbar, 16·37
  Saw logs, 16·35–38
  Tractors for, 16·30–43 (See also "Tractors")
  Trucks for, 16·29, 16·30–32
**Slash Disposal,** Christmas trees, 6·63
**Slate,** Soil-forming rocks, 5·4
**Slide-Rule Calculations,** 23·2–4
**Sling Psychrometer,** Obtaining relative humidity by means of, 7·6–8
**Slings,** Barrel, 13·15
**Slopes**
  Geological features of, 5·6
  Grading, slope of repose for embankments, 18·23
  Influence stability of soils, 11·30
  Measuring (See also "Surveying")
    Abney used for slope chaining, 17·29–30
    Aerial photographs, 19·10–11
    Aneroid barometer, 17·27–28
    Gunter's chains, 17·1–2
    Surveyor's tapes, 17·2–3
  Scarp or strike, 5·6
  Soils on, 11·3
**Smalian's Formula,** For measuring cubic-foot volume of logs, 1·51–52
**Smoke,** Trees resistant to, 12·31–36
**Snakeroot, White** (*Eupatorium rugosum*), 11·72
**Snakes,** 11·75
**Sneezeweed** (*Helenium hoopesii*), 11·72